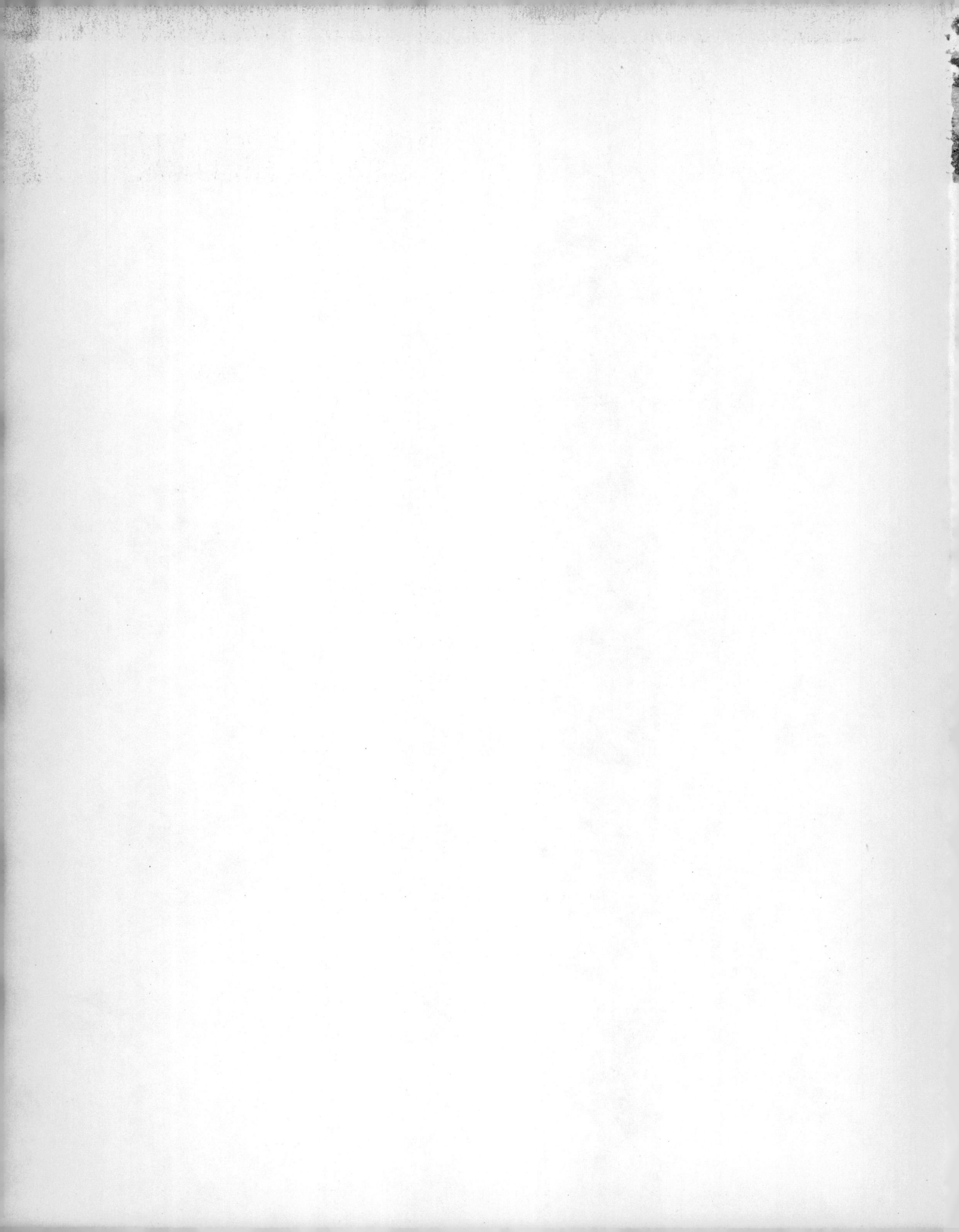

## PROCEEDINGS OF CONFERENCE

## FUNDAMENTAL ASPECTS OF STRESS CORROSION CRACKING

September 11-15, 1967
The Ohio State University
Department of Metallurgical Engineering

### Sponsors

Air Force Materials Laboratory
Atomic Energy Commission
Office of Naval Research

### General Chairman

Professor R. W. Staehle
The Ohio State University

### Co-Chairmen

Professor A. J. Forty
University of Warwick, England

Dr. D. van Rooyen
The International Nickel Company

### Members of the Organizing Committee

R. C. Carlston
D. L. Douglass
J. F. Eckel
E. H. Phelps
L. R. Scharfstein
A. Van Echo
A. R. C. Westwood

Published by
**National Association of Corrosion Engineers**
2400 West Loop South
Houston, Texas

Library of Congress Catalog Card No. 68–26493

# PREFACE

The purpose of this conference was to identify those elements which underlie a quantitative approach to predicting the incidence of stress corrosion cracking. Present applications of materials require more than generalities to describe the useful life of equipment. To obtain the required predictive capability for stress corrosion failures as a function of the variables in metal-environment systems requires a much higher order of fundamental knowledge than heretofore and presently available. To this end the conference was arranged according to the following format.

1. Attendance was by invitation in order to obtain a balance among: those working in the various alloy systems; those in the relevant disciplines such as electrochemistry, physical metallurgy, corrosion science, fracture mechanics, fundamental interests, and applied interests.

2. Each day's session was devoted to a single different alloy system: Copper and Noble Metal Alloys; Homogeneous Fe-Cr-Ni Austenitic Alloys; Iron Base Alloys and Carbon Steels; Aluminum Base Alloys; and Titanium Base Alloys.

3. Each session was introduced by a review paper which was followed by a series of research papers. The review papers are intended to give comprehensive and evaluated interpretations of the literature up to the date of the meeting. The research papers were given by those actively involved in conducting significant work. These papers were intended to give the newest results as well as the author's current best opinion on the subject of stress corrosion cracking as shown by his own work.

4. Several general papers were given which consider current problems of general interest to all areas of stress corrosion cracking.

5. All verbal discussion on the papers was recorded by tape and court reporter. These discussions were subsequently sent to their originators for revisions and additions. The revised discussions on each paper were then sent to each author for rebuttal and comment.

6. Subsequent to the conference the chairman and co-chairman of each session prepared an evaluation of the day's activities for inclusion in this volume.

In brief the above approach yielded a very high quality of attack on the problem of stress corrosion cracking. While it proved to be very difficult to come up with many quantitative conclusions, nonetheless, most of the critical issues were clearly defined. Taken together the papers, reviews, discussions and evaluations in this volume should provide those already conducting research, as well as those who are newly entering the field, a useful as well as accessible basis.

The arrangement of papers in this proceedings deviates slightly from the order in the meeting. The papers of general interest are grouped together at the beginning. The slight rearrangements are based on considering alloy systems in terms of their relative heterogeneity or complexity. The most complex system (titanium) is last and the simplest (noble alloys) is first.

The editors have exercised their prerogatives extensively in view of the length of these proceedings. Much of the original floor discussion is omitted and only those items of direct significance to the *mechanism* of cracking remain. Several of the papers submitted by non-American scientists were edited (with the author's approval) to adopt the American vernacular. Micron markers have been added to almost all photomicrographs (optical as well as electron).

On Tuesday evening of the Conference a number of movies showing stress corrosion cracking were exhibited. These were: Stress Corrosion Cracking of a Magnesium Alloy by D. K. Priest, F. H. Beck and M. G. Fontana; Stress Corrosion Cracking of Stainless Steel at 205 C by W. W. Kirk, F. H. Beck and M. G. Fontana; Stress Corrosion Cracking of Stainless Steel in Boiling $MgCl_2$ by N. A. Nielsen from du Pont; Stress Corrosion Cracking of a 8-1-1 Titanium Alloy in Hot Salt by S. R. Rideout of Savannah River, du Pont; Crack Propagation in an 8-1-1 Titanium Alloy by Douglas Aircraft; Stress Corrosion Cracking of an Aluminum Alloy by Alcoa; and Cracking of Armco Iron in $CaNO_3$ by K. Bohnenkamp. The Proceedings contain no direct comment on these movies.

# PREFACE

This meeting would not have been possible without the encouragement and support of several sponsoring agencies. We wish to thank most heartily the following agencies and individuals: Air Force Materials Laboratory in Dayton, Ohio (A. M. Lovelace, H. M. Burte, C. T. Lynch, and H. L. Gegel); Atomic Energy Commission, Nuclear Technology Branch (J. M. Simmons, A. Van Echo); Office of Naval Research (W. G. Rauch, R. C. Carlston).

Special thanks are also extended to members of the organizing committee who contributed greatly of their time and skills to arrange various aspects of the meeting: A. J. Forty, D. van Rooyen, R. Carlston, D. L. Douglass, J. Eckel, E. N. Pugh, E. H. Phelps, L. R. Scharfstein, A Van Echo, A. R. C. Westwood.

The session chairmen were: Copper, Gold, Silver Alloys—A. J. Forty and E. N. Pugh; Iron, Nickel, Chromium Alloys—D. L. Douglass and D. van Rooyen; Movies of Stress Corrosion—D. van Rooyen; Iron Base Alloys—E. H. Phelps and R. N. Parkins; Aluminum Base Alloys—M. J. Pryor and M. R. Bothwell; Special Topics—A. R. C. Westwood and W. Rostoker; Panel Discussion—W. D. Robertson; Titanium Base Alloys—S. P. Rideout and J. C. Scully. The adroitness exercised by the chairmen in the conduct of the meetings permitted vigorous and extensive floor discussions.

The sessions were opened on the first day by addresses from: N. G. Fawcett, President of The Ohio State University; H. A. Bolz, Dean of The College of Engineering, The Ohio State University; M. G. Fontana, Chairman of the Department of Metallurgical Engineering, The Ohio State University; A. M. Lovelace, Director, Air Force Materials Laboratory.

The assistance of T. J. Hull, Executive Secretary of the National Association of Corrosion Engineers, his staff, and especially Mrs. Daughdrill who carefully set all the type are especially appreciated for their efforts in preparing this volume. We should like to pay special tribute also to Professor M. G. Fontana who has contributed significantly to the resolution of industrial corrosion problems through his support of education and research in all areas of corrosion engineering and science and who made the facilities of the Department of Metallurgical Engineering available for this Conference.

An unusual product of this meeting was a poem prepared during the week of the meeting by S. P. Rideout. While such efforts are usually of a lightheartedness not becoming a serious technical volume, this so well epitomized the nature of the problem and the spirit of the Conference that it is included on page iii.

It would be inappropriate to conclude without acknowledging that the success of this meeting, and the enthusiasm generated thereby, was due in large part to the attendees themselves who participated exuberantly during the technical sessions as well as far into the night. To quote a personal letter from J. C. Scully: ".....I have arrived home a thoroughly exhausted human being....."

R. W. Staehle
Editor and Chairman of the Meeting

A. J. Forty
D. van Rooyen
Co-editors and Co-chairmen of the Meeting

## On Stress Corrosion

The image of stress corrosion I see
Is that of a huge unwanted tree,
Against whose trunk we chop and chop,
But which outgrows the chips that drop;

And from each gash made in its bark
A new branch grows to make more dark
The shade of ignorance around its base,
Where scientists toil with puzzled face.

Chemists and metallographers,
Technicians and philosophers,
Though struggling individually,
Their common goal: to fell the tree.

At intervals researchers gather,
And on mechanisms all palaver;
Each to his own work will refer,
Ignoring those who don't concur.

But as we speculate and ponder,
Those who run the mills out yonder
To us with anxious voices wail,
"Please help us lengthen 'time to fail!'

For us to pay your research bills
By sale of products from our mills,
Wheels must turn and planes must fly,
And on high-strength alloys we rely."

Thus, as we argue with each other,
Let us not forget our brother,
Our Siamese twin, the engineer,
Whose working profits sent us here.

The Conference ended, let us pledge
To go again with sharpened edge,
And with redoubled energy
To pit ourselves against this tree.

S. P. Rideout
Savannah River Laboratory

# ATTENDANCE LIST

### International Conference on
### Fundamental Aspects of Stress Corrosion Cracking
### The Ohio State University
### September 11-15, 1967

Mr. R. E. Adams
Titanium Metals Corporation
of America

Mr. J. S. Armijo
Stanford Research Institute

Dr. R. Ashbrook
NASA – Lewis Research Center

Dr. J. F. Bates
Applied Research Laboratory
U. S. Steel Corporation

Dr. T. R. Beck
Boeing Scientific Research
Laboratory

Mr. W. D. Benjamin
TRW Equipment Laboratories

Dr. L. R. Bidwell
Wright-Patterson Air
Force Base

Dr. M. J. Blackburn
Boeing Scientific Research
Laboratory

Mr. A. W. Blackwood
American Smelting and Refining
Company

Dr. K. Bohnenkamp
Max-Planck Institut fur
Eisenforschung, West Germany

Dr. A. P. Bond
Climax Molybdenum Company
of Michigan

Dr. C. J. L. Booker
Sir John Cass College
England

Dr. M. R. Bothwell
Dow Chemical Company

Dr. J. D. Boyd
Battelle Memorial Institute

Mr. W. K. Boyd
Battelle Memorial Institute

Dr. S. B. Brummer
Tyco Laboratories, Inc.

Dr. H. M. Burte
Wright-Patterson Air Force Base

Dr. R. C. Carlston
Naval Postgraduate School

Dr. C. F. Cheng
Argonne National Laboratory

Dr. F. H. Cocks
Tyco Laboratories, Inc.

Dr. H. R. Copson
International Nickel Co., Inc.

Dr. H. L. Craig, Jr.
Reynolds Metals Company

Mr. G. J. Danek
Naval Ship Research & Development
Anapolis Division

Dr. H. M. Davis
Army Research Office

Mr. E. E. Denhard, Jr.
Armco Steel Corporation

Dr. R. A. Dodd
University of Wisconsin

Dr. D. L. Douglass
Stanford Research Institute

Dr. J. E. Draley
Argonne National Laboratory

Dr. F. Endtinger
Swiss Aluminum Ltd.
Switzerland

Dr. M. G. Fontana
The Ohio State University

Prof. A. J. Forty
University of Warwick
England

Mr. M. Garfinkle
NASA – Lewis Research Center

Dr. H. L. Gegel
Wright-Patterson Air Force Base

Dr. M. A. Genshaw
University of Pennsylvania

Dr. W. W. Gerberich
University of California

Dr. G. M. Gordon
General Electric

Prof. L. Graf
Max-Planck Institut fur
Metallforschung, West Germany

Mr. L. Grall
Service d'Etude de La Corrosion
Aqueuse et d'Electrochimie
France

Dr. J. A. S. Green
Martin Company

Dr. E. G. Haney
Mellon Institute

Dr. J. T. Harrison
Gas Council Engineering
Research Station
England

Dr. E. W. Haycock
Shell Development Company

Mr. F. Haynie
Battelle Memorial Institute

Dr. R. F. Hehemann
Case Institute of Technology

Dr. W. J. Helfrich
Kaiser Aluminum & Chemical Corp.

Dr. M. Henthorne
The Carpenter Steel Company

Dr. T. P. Hoar
University of Cambridge
England

Dr. W. P. Hubner
AB Atomenergi
Sweden

Dr. M. J. Humphries
University of Newcastle
England

Dr. D. Iyengar
Lehigh University

Dr. Alvin J. Jacobs
Rocketdyne

Mr. S. Tudor
U. S. Naval Applied Science Lab.

Prof. H. H. Uhlig
Massachusetts Institute of
 Technology

Mr. D. A. Vaughan
Battelle Memorial Institute

Dr. D. van Rooyen
The International Nickel Company

Dr. D. A. Vermilyea
General Electric Company

Prof. K. Vetter
Freie Universitat Berlin
 West Germany

Dr. E. von Tiesenhausen
Titanium Metals Corporation
 of America

Dr. J. R. Weeks
Brookhaven National Laboratory

Dr. R. Wei
Lehigh University

Mr. I. H. Welinsky
Westinghouse Bettis Atomic
 Power Laboratory

Dr. A. R. C. Westwood
Martin Company

Dr. B. E. Wilde
General Electric Company

Mr. J. C. Williams
Boeing Scientific Research Lab.

Row 10: J. F. Bates, G. M. Gordon, W. D. Benjamin, W. P. Hubner, M. Bothwell, J. C. Williams, M. J. Blackburn, H. G. Nelson, C. F. Cheng. Row 9: B. E. Wilde, D. Sprowls, E. E. Denhard, G. J. Danek, E. G. Haney, H. L. Craig, D. Thompson, J. E. LeSurf. Row 8: L. Grall, A. P. Bond, R. Sprague, R. P. Procter, C. Sargent, H. Gegel, T. Beck, H. P. Leckie. Row 7: Beginning three from left: J. T. Harrison, H. Kirkpatrick, C. T. Lynch, H. H. Burte, A. Ronnquist, R. A. Oriani. Row 6: N. Nielsen, M. Henthorne, R. N. Parkins, M. J. Humphries, F. H. Cocks, A. W. Blackwood, R. D. Iyengar, E. Phillips, L. R. Bidwell, H. Rosenthal. Row 5: S. P. Rideout, E. H. Phelps, C. J. Booker, H. M. Davis, G. Sandoz, D. van Rooyen, J. S. Armijo, M. O. Speidel, L. Graf, H. Mazille. Row 4: E. W. Haycock, D. Douglass, J. Kruger, P. R. Swann, M. A. Genshaw, D. E. Piper, A. R. Westwood, A. J. Sedriks, J. A. Green, J. Leja. Row 3: K. Bohnenkamp, S. Ketcham, R. A. Dodd, W. J. Helfrich, S. Tudor, R. F. Hehemann, H. Kohl, H. Spahn, M. A. Streicher, A. J. Forty, W. D. Sylwestrowicz, R. W. Staehle. Row 2: A. Jacobs, R. Carlston, K. Vetter, H. Uhlig, H. R. Copson, G. Martin, M. Levy, E. N. Pugh, M. Prazak, M. Smialowski. Row 1: H. H. Johnson, W. D. Robertson, F. W. Pement, L. Raymond, D. A. Vermilyea, H. Pickering, J. C. Scully, L. Scharfstein, N. Tiner, S. Shimodaira.

# TABLE OF CONTENTS

# EVALUATION OF CURRENT STATE OF
# STRESS CORROSION CRACKING

## R. W. Staehle

The aim of the conference was to develop a basis for quantitative prediction of the incidence of stress corrosion cracking. This objective was far too ambitious and unrealistic in terms of available knowledge. It must be said honestly and can be said without contradiction that there presently is no reliable fundamental theory of stress corrosion cracking in any alloy-environment system which can be used to predict the performance of equipment even in environments where conditions are readily defined.

Despite this presently discouraging state of affairs, the meeting did achieve an important secondary objective. Each of the major theories was laid bare in the discussions with respect to important deficiencies. There was actually considerable agreement on the nature and reality of these deficiencies. This is not to say that the particular theory is necessarily wrong but that the objections raised are legitimate and critical. Negative results in evaluating the various objections would certainly tend to invalidate the respective theory.

Another important accomplishment of this conference was the assembly of virtually the entire story in one place. The reviews in this volume are of the same vintage. Further, every major theory had a thorough airing and criticism from the viewpoint of all major scientific disciplines involved.

A final significant accomplishment of the meeting and its proceedings is the assembly of the important experimental techniques being used for mechanistic studies.

Thus, while the current understanding of the mechanism of stress corrosion cracking is still meager, workers in the field have for the first time a thorough collection of literature and evaluated opinion upon which to base subsequent work which, hopefully, may eventually attain the desired capability of predicting the incidence of stress corrosion cracking.

In view of the seriousness and insidious nature of the stress corrosion cracking problem in all areas of industry it is surprising that progress has been so slow. The fact that progress has been slow is probably attributable to some combination of the following:

1. Stress corrosion cracking is an extremely complex phenomenon involving as it does environmental, metallurgical, interfacial, and continuum considerations. Few workers have even a minimally adequate knowledge of the areas outside their respective specialties. Thus, balanced research programs cannot easily be arranged. Such "channeled interests" lead to experiments which are highly defined in one area but poorly defined in others. For example, those using the fracture mechanics approach are notably lax in specifying environmental conditions; those conducting corrosion tests where specimens are simply immersed to determine time to cracking are also lax in monitoring or specifying electrochemical conditions; those conducting electrochemically controlled experiments are often lax in specifying conditions of stress and metallurgy.

2. Metal producers, industrial users, and government agencies have been lax in support of research leading to a resolution of the problem. Real progress cannot be made on the basis of "one man part time" or "two graduate students—three year" programs. It is necessary to initiate programs which include a balanced approach, are adequately funded, and extend for committed times to ten years. An indication of the kind of effort necessary would be three professional workers full time for ten years on a problem as narrow as the titanium-methanol system.

3. The utopian dream exists that there is a single mechanism responsible for cracking. This has led many workers astray. There is now abundant evidence that a variety of critical mechanistic processes exist depending on the metal-environment system.

4. Metal producers and some industries have not contributed to the open technical literature from their great store of privately developed information. There is a generally mistaken concept that showing susceptibility to cracking of particular alloys is bad for business.

5. The fundamental information required for interpreting experiments does not exist. For example, the mechanism of dissolution and passivation are very poorly understood in simple metal-environment systems. The perturbation of adding chloride ions or nitrate creates a still further complication. The whole area of adsorption phenomena as affecting cleavage, electrode kinetics, and plastic flow enjoys at this time only precariously based speculation.

6. Research workers have been too content to ascribe the mechanism to such tenuous processes as "electro-chemical-mechanical," "film rupture," "stacking faults," "hydrogen embrittlement," etc.

7. The technical public has not been well-educated. It certainly is inconceivable to most engineers (even in

metallurgy) that a few ppm of chloride can crack stainless steel or a few ppm of ammonia can crack brass. Engineers, both design and material, must be alerted and made sensitive to the problem.

One of the striking facts which emerged was that stress corrosion cracking is more epidemic than previously thought. Several years ago the serious stress corrosion problems were the chloride cracking of stainless steel, ammonia cracking of brass, caustic cracking of iron base alloys, and hydrogen embrittlement of high strength steels. The extent of this proliferation is adequately discussed in the reviews and research papers. The obvious question is raised then of "What other environment-metal systems are susceptible?" Present theories give us no reliable clues to be used in predicting cracking in as yet untested systems.

Further evaluation here would only repeat the information in the evaluations of the separate sessions which were prepared by the respective session chairmen. However, the following items are mentioned as being especially significant:

1. H. H. Johnson showed that stress corrosion cracks can propagate in high strength steel at one atmosphere of hydrogen gas. This cracking is stifled when about 0.5 v/o of oxygen is added. These data raise at least two important issues. First, the internal pressure theory of hydrogen embrittlement may be very questionable since the activity of hydrogen within the metal cannot exceed that outside the metal even under non-equilibrium conditions. Second, if an adsorption process is controlling, why is the crack stifled when oxygen is added? If it adsorbs to prevent hydrogen entering into the metal, then its tendency to weaken metal-metal bonds would be greater than that for hydrogen.

2. In the discussion following his paper N. A. Nielsen shows a fractograph of the region exactly at the base of the advancing crack for a stainless steel specimen exposed to a boiling $MgCl_2$ solution. This fractograph indicates strongly that the morphology of this region is characteristic primarily of cleavage and not of dissolution. If this conclusion is correct, it raises serious questions concerning the tunneling and slip step dissolution models of crack propagation. It also raises the question as to how such a cleavage is possible in a ductile material.

3. The paper by Sandoz demonstrated that prior fatigue cracks will propagate in such diverse environments as gaseous butane, ethylene glycol, decane, isopropyl alcohol, as well as others with the fractographs showing identical morphology. This behavior is similar to that observed in salt water. Subsequent work by Sandoz in the same vein has shown cracking in carbon disulfide. Self initiating (no prior fatigue crack) stress corrosion cracks

have been observed in methanol, $N_2O_4$, and salt water solutions by other authors. This great diversity raises serious questions concerning the types of mechanisms involved—is there a unifying concept or are there many different types?

4. The significance of ordering and stacking fault energies as being controlling considerations in cracking is waning. There is abundant evidence that slip processes are important but it would appear that (a) there may be a wider range of processes which produce dislocation co-planarity (e.g., precipitate structure) and (b) the degree of coplanarity may not be significant. It would appear that chemical reaction processes are much more critical.

5. The observation by Graf that prior active pitting on nonstressed specimens will suppress cracking when the stress is applied suggests strongly that the initiation process on the metal surface is strongly affected by local currents.

6. The work of Beck on electrochemical factors involved in advancing cracks provides an important tool in analyzing possible processes which can operate. Using his model he can rationalize crack velocity, concludes that an electrochemical mechanism is critical, and excludes hydrogen embrittlement as significant. Whether these trends are eventually proven to be critical has yet to be demonstrated; but his analysis offers a great improvement for approaching the environmental problem inside cracks.

7. The chemical reactivity of static dislocations, either solute enriched or not, appears no longer to be a significant consideration.

8. In consideration of the film rupture model for the cracking of brasses and possibly of titanium in $N_2O_4$ much more attention should be given to whether film rupture is a cause or an observed after-effect. Perhaps the film forms by precipitation of rapidly dissolved material at highly active slip steps.

9. There was an almost uniform conclusion that no unifying mechanism of stress corrosion cracking exists.

Finally, the papers and discussion of this conference do not give a magic key to predicting the incidence of cracking; however, they do delineate the major issues. Hopefully, subsequent work will benefit from this foundation. Experimentally, the key to major improvements in understanding will come from work which considers as equally important the information and techniques of several of the relevant scientific disciplines. Before additional understanding will come to stress corrosion much more fundamental information is necessary in areas of dissolution, passivity, heterogeneous electrodes, slip behavior, and cleavage.

# PART I

# GENERAL ASPECTS OF
# STRESS CORROSION CRACKING

# COMMENTS ON THE HISTORY, ENGINEERING
# AND SCIENCE OF STRESS CORROSION CRACKING

R. W. Staehle
The Ohio State University

## Abstract

Historical aspects in the study of stress corrosion cracking are reviewed. Some of the critical issues in the engineering implications of stress corrosion cracking are discussed and these include: Incorporation of stress corrosion data in mechanical design, terminology and nomenclature, correlations with liquid metal embrittlement, testing, and general education. Important concepts in mechanistic considerations are reviewed. The possibility of evolving a general mechanism is discounted.

This is the fourth major conference on the general mechanistic aspects of stress corrosion cracking. The first was held in 1944, the second in 1956, and the third in 1959. Proceedings of each of these conferences were published.[1-2] In addition to these proceedings, a number of texts and symposia dealing with stress corrosion cracking have been published.[4-12] General mechanistic aspects of stress corrosion cracking have been treated by a number of authors[13-20] and will not be treated here, except for a few comments.

In 1940 an article was written, "Stress Corrosion Cracking of Austenitic Chromium-Nickel Steels and Its Industrial Limitations," by James Hodge and John Miller.[21] This article identified clearly the general significance and ramifications of the problem. Previously, most of the cracking problems in stainless steels were attributed to fatigue or weld cracking. It was inconceivable, for example, that a few ppm of chloride would be sufficient to produce such debilitating consequences as were observed. A number of written discussions were prepared and some of the comments are interesting in view of present knowledge:

M. A. Scheil, A. O. Smith Corporation
While this paper is interesting, it may be misinterpreted and is therefore liable to create a negative reaction to austenitic steels in any form, unless it is realized that the tests, as carried out in the experiments, relate to a selected media which may not be duplicated in many types of service or even in the service described by the authors when moisture is eliminated from the ethyl chloride.

W. B. Brooks, Carnegie-Illinois Steel
The suggestion is made that these failures may be closely allied to the season cracking of brass and other face-centered cubic metals and alloys. Season cracking, as it is commonly understood, is a purely intercrystalline phenomenon whereas here we are dealing with transcrystalline as well as intercrystalline cracks. It is believed that the data may be clearly explained and that no direct relationship between this type of cracking and season cracking may be established.

...It would not seem, therefore, that we may anticipate failures of this type occurring in unsuspected places, so the industrial implications of this phenomenon do not loom large. Failures are rare and will become more so as understanding spreads...

Contrary to the expectations above, the problem of stress corrosion cracking has become widespread not only with respect to environments which cause cracking but also with respect to alloy systems which crack. Even the often stated maxim that pure metals do not crack is in doubt.[22] Titanium alloys, at one time thought to be immune to stress corrosion cracking, are now found to be susceptible to intergranular and transgranular cracking in such diverse environments as liquid nitrogen tetroxide ($N_2O_4$), methanol, and salt water. Likewise, Inconel-600, an often used alternative for stainless steels in chloride environments, has been shown to be susceptible to both modes of cracking in such unpretentious environments as high purity water in the 300 C range with a few ppm of oxygen or lead contamination.[23] Figure 1 is a montage of a failure of a Ti-6Al-4V tank used to contain $N_2O_4$. Normally such cracking will not occur if impurities such as $O_2$, NO, $H_2O$, Cl are properly controlled. Figure 2 shows intergranular cracking of Inconel-600 in high purity water at 315 C.[24]

It is not possible here to provide a critical review of mechanistic aspects of cracking; the problems are too extensive and various mechanisms too complicated for critical discussion in a single paper. Such considerations are included in the various review papers of this Conference. Instead, specific aspects concerned with research (technique and interpretation), terminology, engineering, and education in connection with stress corrosion cracking are emphasized.

## Seriousness and Unexpected Nature of Stress Corrosion Cracking

Stress corrosion cracking is one of the truly insidious phenomena of metallurgical pathology because the failure usually cannot be detected prior to use of the article. The most insidious features of conditions associated with cracking are the following:

(1) Alloys subject to cracking are normally considered the passive and non-corroding alloys which, in many environments, corrode uniformly at rates of less than five mils per year. Figure 3 compares the deterioration due to stress corrosion cracking and that due to general metal oxidation. The latter would

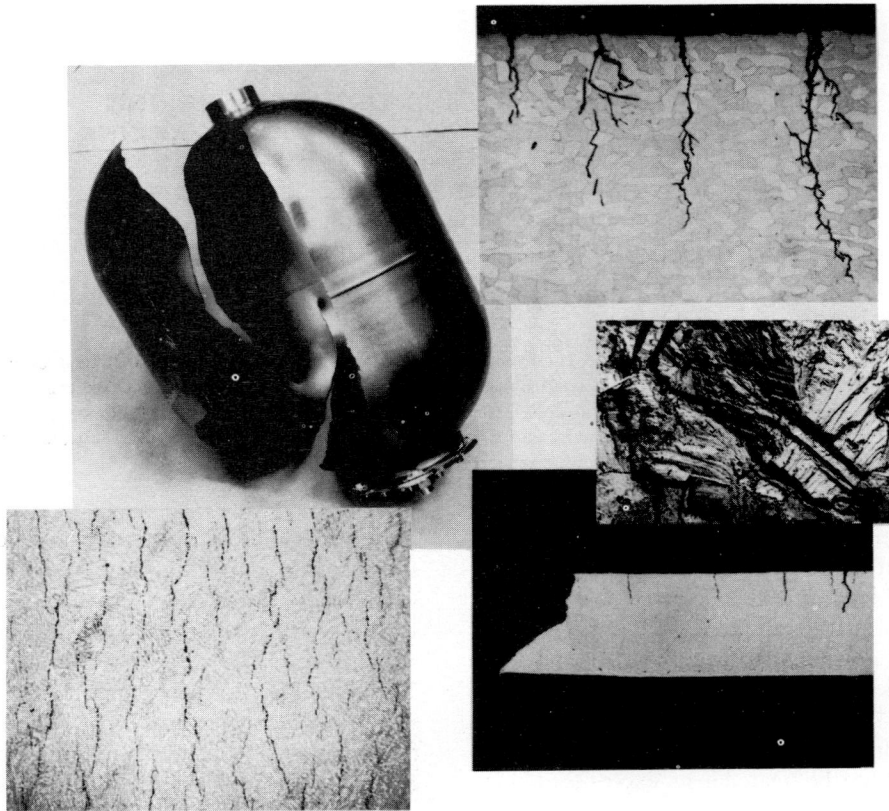

FIGURE 1 — Stress corrosion cracking of a Ti-6Al-4V pressure vessel stressed at about 80% of yield stress and exposed to $N_2O_4$. Photographs starting at top right are: cross sectional photomicrograph, fractograph, macrograph of cross section, photomicrograph of inside surface. (Courtesy of G. Kappelt, Bell Aerosystems)

require years to reduce the cross section to unusable dimensions whereas the same environment might cause cracking of a stressed specimen in a few hours or days. The loss of cross section is the same but the metal loss differs greatly. Figure 3c shows the effect of stress corrosion cracking on the tensile curve.

(2) Environmental species which cause stress corrosion cracks are often those which appear innocuous either as regards identity or quantity. It seems a ridiculous result that the amount of chloride in drinking water can cause the cracking of a thick stainless steel section in a few hours. The idea that a slight amount of ammonia in the air would cause cracking of copper alloys likewise seems intuitively unreasonable.

(3) Stress corrosion cracks can propagate with no externally applied stress. Those from welding, forming, or machining are sufficient. Further, once a crack starts, it is possible for it to continue with no applied or residual stress but simply to be driven by pressures from the corrosion products.[25] Pressures due to corrosion products of the order of 4000-7000 psi have been determined.

(4) Alloys which can be developed to have extremely high strength often have a small fraction of that strength available if exposed to environments as innocuous as pure water (e.g., Type 4340 steel at high strength levels).

FIGURE 2 — Incoloy-600 exposed in 350 C high purity water for six months at 50,000 psi. (Courtesy H. Coriou)

4

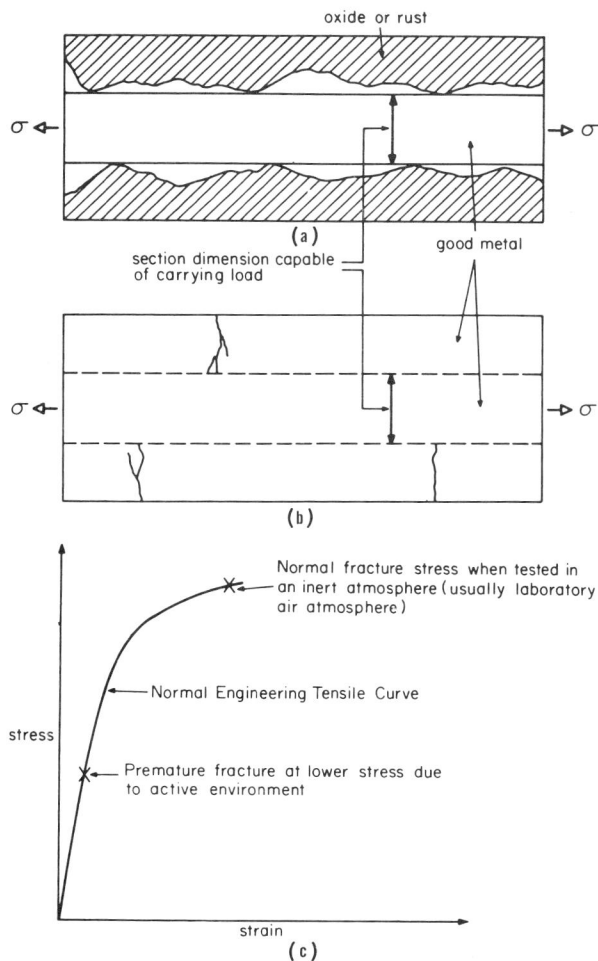

FIGURE 3 — Reduction in load-carrying cross section due to (a) general corrosion, (b) environmentally induced cracks, and (c) effects of stress corrosion cracking on tensile curve.

## Incorporation of Stress Corrosion Data in Mechanical Design

It is no longer adequate for design manuals to list simply information on tensile properties or fatigue properties. A serious effort should be undertaken to specify the environments in which these mechanical properties were determined and to extend the information to the effect of various environments which are known to reduce usable maximum strengths. The argument that the environmental effects are varied and impossible to specify is a presently unacceptable answer to the problem — too many major equipment failures have occurred as a result of stress corrosion cracking. The professional societies, industry, and governments need to initiate an undertaking to codify environmentally affected variations on usable strengths. Such information should be as available and as accessible to designers as present mechanical property data.

## Terminology

Various attempts have been made to refine the termi-

nology associated with stress corrosion cracking by using such terms as "stress environment cracking," "corrosion cracking," and "stress cracking." It has generally been conceded that "season cracking" and "caustic embrittlement" should be combined with the term, "stress corrosion cracking." Presently persisting is the trend to distinguish "stress corrosion cracking" as a process involving anodic dissolution and "hydrogen embrittlement" as a term involving the absorption cathodically produced hydrogen. A final set of distinctions involves the phenomena of "intergranular corrosion" and "stress assisted intergranular corrosion." Distinguishing among these phenomena is often complicated by shifts in the mode of cracking between intergranular and transgranular cracking as affected either by metallurgical or environmental changes.

It is proposed here that "stress corrosion cracking" be used as the generic term for all of the above phenomena in which stress plays a part. Such a proposal is made for the following reasons:

(1) The real distinction between phenomena controlled by hydrogen embrittlement and dissolution processes is not clear. In our laboratories as well as others we find that slow crack growth (starting with a fatigue crack) in high strength steels as well as high strength titanium alloys can occur in the range of potentials from about -1.0 to +1.0 volts (SHE). At the upper part of this range hydrogen reduction is impossible; and at the lower part metal oxidation is impossible (in the case of iron).

(2) The distinction between "stress assisted intergranular corrosion" and intergranular "stress corrosion cracking" is many times difficult to make and often somewhat artificial. The extent to which alloys corrode intergranularly in the absence of stress is often a matter of degree and can differ widely.

(3) "Season cracking" and "caustic embrittlement" have been absorbed into stress corrosion cracking.

(4) The term, "stress environment cracking" while being somewhat more general, appears to be stilted and usually requires apology or explanation.

Thus, for use in textbooks, as a label for a general field of research, and for other categorization, the term "stress corrosion cracking" appears to be the most generally applicable and least confusing.

Many of the other terms such as "hydrogen embrittlement" and "stress enhanced intergranular corrosion" are in fact descriptions of detailed processes or specific aspects of the general problem. Note that there never has been such a term as "anodic dissolution stress corrosion cracking" to parallel "hydrogen embrittlement."

Another important aspect of terminology involves the description of mechanisms. It is common for authors to report a series of experimental results and then to reach the conclusion that: "This supports the 'electrochemical mechanical' theory" or "This supports the 'film rupture' theory." In view of the proliferation of identified operating processes, such general descriptions of mechanisms are no longer adequate. It is less confusing to readers if much more specific descriptions are used or if authors would simply refrain from making statements not warranted by their data.

## Correlations with Liquid Metal Embrittlement

Correlations and analogies between liquid metal embrittlement and stress corrosion cracking have been proposed by some authors.[26] Such comparisons are probably reasonable from the very broad sense in which exterior phenomena alter the load carrying capacity and ductility of alloys. Analogies regarding temperature dependence, grain size, crack velocity, stress, alloy chemistry and other parameters are deceptive since these variables affect numerous metallurgical processes according to the same algebraic sign of the dependence. Mechanistically, such analogies may be very dangerous and lead well intentioned workers astray. To point out a few of the differences between liquid metal embrittlement and stress corrosion cracking:

(1) The species involved in aqueous processes are charged and as such they undergo interactions with surfaces and with each other which do not occur in the realm of solid metal-liquid metal interfaces.

(2) Transgranular cracking is not common in liquid metal environments but is common in all major alloy systems (iron, nickel, titanium, magnesium, and copper) except perhaps aluminum. Shifts from transgranular to intergranular cracking in aqueous systems can be accomplished either by alteration of the environment or of the alloy.

(3) The solution step in aqueous systems includes a process involving higher energy than in liquid metals. For example, using standard heats of formation, the removal of a mole of silver atoms from the lattice and placing them in the solution as silver ions involves the energy cycle:[27]

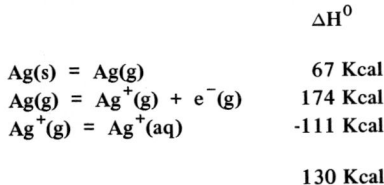

$$\Delta H^0$$

$$Ag(s) = Ag(g) \qquad 67 \text{ Kcal}$$
$$Ag(g) = Ag^+(g) + e^-(g) \qquad 174 \text{ Kcal}$$
$$Ag^+(g) = Ag^+(aq) \qquad -111 \text{ Kcal}$$

$$130 \text{ Kcal}$$

For comparison $\Delta H^0$ for fusion of silver would be 1-4 Kcal/mole. The energies involved in the liquid metal and aqueous dissolutions are clearly much different. Further, the strain energy contributions, say of a dislocation, which is about 1/20 of the total free energy change for the aqueous corrosion reaction now becomes of the same order as the energy in the liquid metal solution reaction.

(4) For every dissolution step, a reduction or cathodic step must occur. The reduction rate may control, in many cases, the anodic process (e.g., the rate of stress corrosion cracking of austenitic stainless steel in neutral pH chloride solutions is controlled by the availability of a reducible species—oxygen).

Mechanistic studies of stress corrosion cracking must avoid being conducted by analogy but should attend to the basic nature of the environmental as well as metallurgical processes. These need to be characterized, quantified, and synthesized to obtain reliable mechanistic models.

## A General Mechanism

A general mechanism for stress corrosion cracking by now seems to be an unreasonable and unattainable goal. Specific processes appear to operate under specific sets of metallurgical and environmental conditions. From a rather broad point of view it can be said that there is a general mechanism in the sense that slip processes do operate, dissolution does occur, electrochemical reduction does occur, etc. A montage showing many of the common processes is given in Figure 4. However, it is the degree to which each of these component processes operates which controls the cracking. Thus, in a given cracking process only three or four component processes operating together may be necessary to specify the sufficient conditions for cracking. It is this critical combination of processes which comprises "the mechanism."

## The Restricted Lateral Dissolution Criterion and Specificity of the Environment

In certain alloy systems the advance of cracks appears clearly to involve continuing dissolution processes. If this dissolution is incited by slip step emergence or lattice disarray as suggested by Hoar, a simple question is raised as to why the exposed ledges do not continue to dissolve laterally until a structural feature such as a grain boundary is reached. On the other hand, in a film forming system, one might ask why dissolution occurs at all — why isn't the slip step immediately passivated. The fact that a rather limited lateral extension occurs is somewhat surprising, especially in view of the relatively broad extent of dissolution often observed in pitting. Presumably, the alleged acidic condition at the base of a crack should cause considerable dissolution. Sometimes this, in fact, happens as shown in Figure 5. Extended dissolution and relatively narrow cracks were found in the same specimen. Thus, it would appear that there are chemical conditions in which conditions for cracking change to conditions which favor a more extended dissolution pattern. Therefore, a criterion for obtaining the narrow crack-like geometry would involve a certain set of environmental-metallurgical features which conspire to limit the lateral extent of dissolution.

The necessity for explaining restricted lateral dissolution provides a useful boundary condition for considering possible mechanisms. For example, with reference to the impending transition from crack-like dissolution geometries to broad dissolution suggested by Figure 5, the question is raised as to just what is it that can permit extended dissolution in some cases and not in others. Using this concept as a boundary condition and, in view of the narrowness of cracks, normally observed, it would be unreasonable to suggest that cracking progresses because of a low pH at the crack tip. If the pH were too low, extended lateral dissolution would occur. The restricted extent of lateral progress could also be explained if the crack were progressing in a partially brittle manner such as by successive rupture of a thick brittle layer as suggested by numerous workers in connection with the cracking of brass.

Dissolution of freshly formed hydrides (presuming they were the only reactive material) would provide another possibility. Thus dissolution would stop when the hydride was dissolved, the hydrogen produced in dissolution would be absorbed, reform a hydride and the process would repeat itself. In the case of the iron-nickel-chromium alloys, the rationalization for restricted lateral dissolution could be furnished by passive oxide formation, adsorption of a special species (stress-sorption?) or by step poisons.

While the environment-metal systems in which stress corrosion cracking occurs are often characterized as being specific, such a specificity should not be taken to be an unreasonable state of affairs in view of what must be accomplished by the environment. For example, for cracks which proceed by dissolution the environment must function in the following way:

(1) The environment-metal chemistry must produce a stifling reaction which meets the "restricted lateral dissolution criterion." However, enough dissolution must occur at each slip step event for incremental crack advance to occur.

(2) If the crack indeed progresses by a dissolution process, the environment must assure that the oxidized species is soluble for some minimum period of time and does not precipitate or otherwise form a film which would inhibit the small but necessary dissolution which occurs at each slip step event.

(3) The environmental reduction half cell controls the maximum noble potential at the metal surface. Thus a hydrogen ion reduction would not be expected to oxidize copper in a copper-gold alloy and therefore neither hydrochloric nor sulfuric acids (and much less neutral chloride solutions—no matter how concentrated) could be expected to cause stress corrosion cracking of Cu-Au alloys. However, the $Fe^{+++}/Fe^{++}$ redox potential is intermediate between those of the copper and gold dissolution half cells, and ferric chloride therefore would be expected to cause cracking in Cu-Au alloys (it does).

(4) Environmental species must not adsorb to block either necessary reduction or oxidation processes involved with the transient dissolution at emergent slip steps. Otherwise crack progress would stop or not begin in the first place.

Environments which meet the above specifications are not so common and this result no doubt accounts for the fact that stress corrosion cracking occurs only in specific environment-alloy systems.

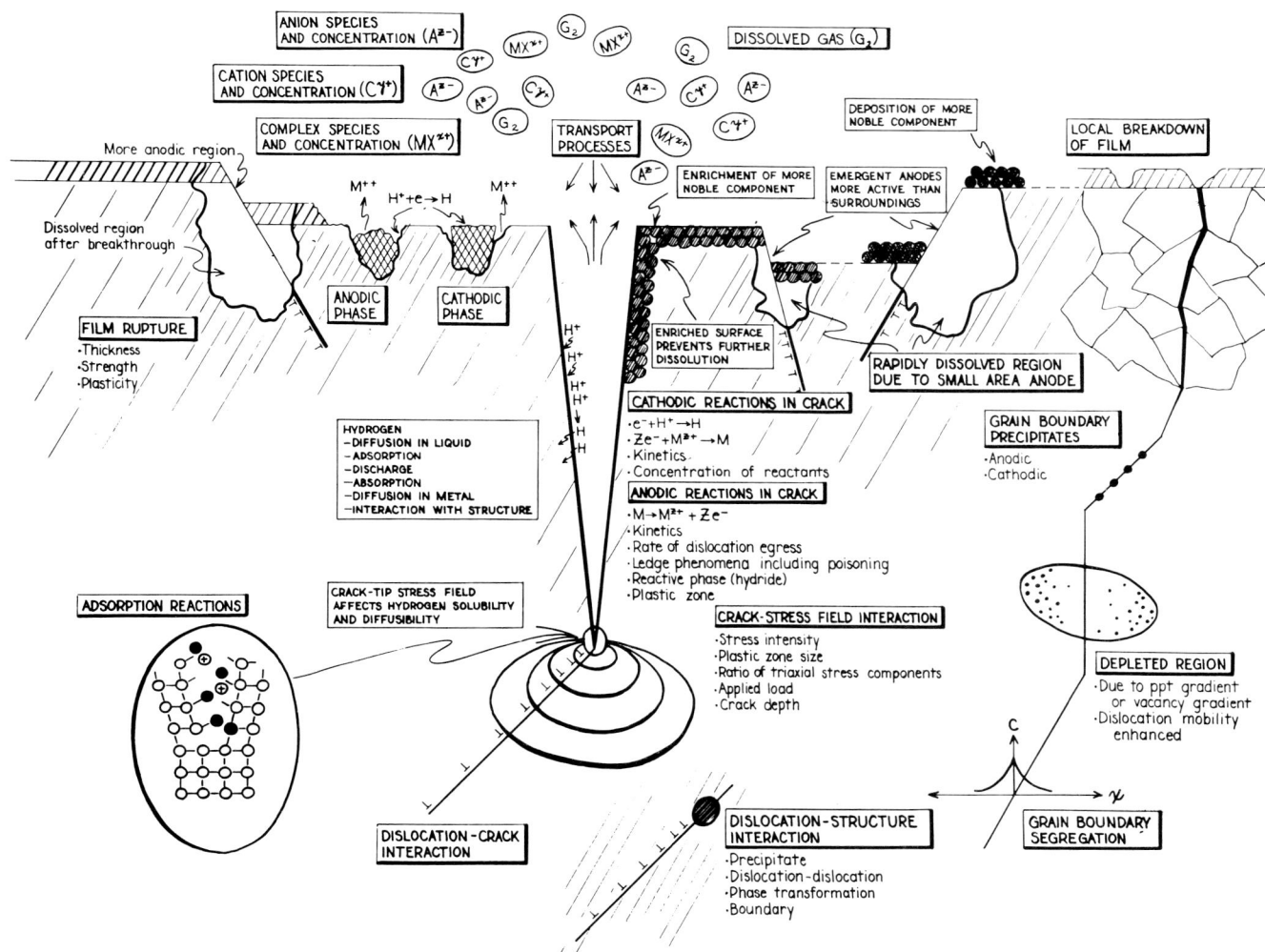

FIGURE 4 — Montage showing important processes operating which affect stress corrosion cracking.

## Initiation and Propagation Stages

Erroneous conclusions from an engineering and mechanistic point of view can result from not considering the specific nature of initiation and propagation stages of cracking. For example, consider the case of Type 4340 steel. Green and Haney[28] presented a curve showing time-to-failure vs pH which is reproduced in Figure 6. Between pH 0 and pH 2.5 there is an order of magnitude increase in time to failure; and at pH 6 failure does not occur in at least 2.5 orders of magnitude more. Specimens used were relatively thin foils several mils thick. Johnson and Staehle[29] in studying crack propagation in specimens having initial fatigue cracks and being approximately an inch thick found that the crack velocity was relatively insensitive to pH or to continuous cathodic charging. This is illustrated in Figure 7. In fact, holding the specimen at relatively cathodic potentials actually slowed the cracks rather than accelerating them. The studies of Green and Haney and of Johnson and Staehle are thus complementary with the former considering essentially the pH dependence on initiation and the latter considering pH dependence on

propagation. If one were only to consider the trend of Figure 6, it would be concluded that high strength steel is acceptable in neutral solutions. However, if a weld crack or other fabrication crack were present, the alloy would surely crack providing the stress intensity exceeded the applicable $K_{I_{scc}}$. Mechanistically, the use of Figure 6 would lead to concluding that the rate of hydrogen ion reduction is significant in the propagation stage while, according to Figure 7, it is not.

In a similar vein, Hoar and Hines in numerous studies with stainless steel alloys demonstrated that the initiation and propagation stages could be defined by monitoring open circuit electrochemical potentials. Thus, when only the total time-to-failure is given as a parameter to test, say the effect of alloy addition, it would be extremely important to isolate whether the resulting effect acted during the initiation or propagation stage.

Separate and special attention should be given to the detailed nature of initiation and propagation stages of cracking. Simply measuring the time to failure is not an adequate definition of even a phenomenological experiment.

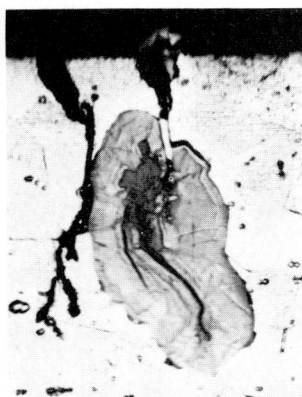

Fe-15Ni-20Cr-0.1O
260 C, 0.1 w/o NaCl, O$_2$

Fe-16Ni-20Cr
260 C, 0.1 w/o NaCl, O$_2$

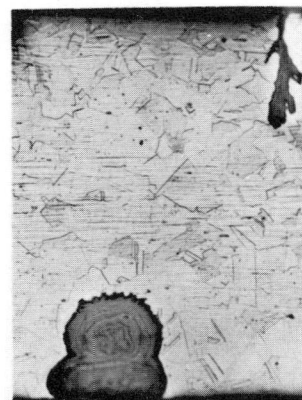

Type 316
260 C, 0.1 w/o NaCl, O$_2$

Fe-15Ni-20Cr-0.1S
260 C, 0.1 w/o NaCl, O$_2$

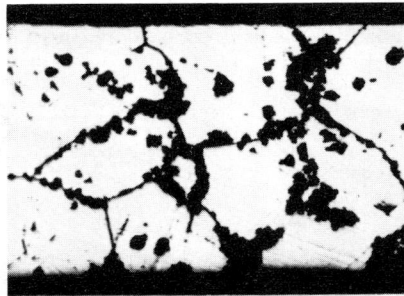

Type 310
MgCl$_2$

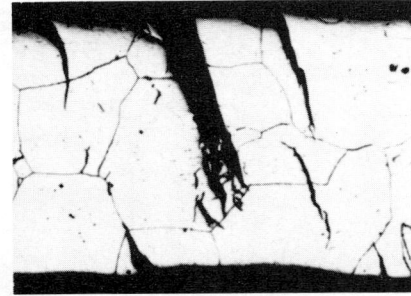

Type 310
MgCl$_2$

FIGURE 5 — Cross sectional photomicrographs of Fe-Ni-Cr alloys exposed at 260 C to 1000 ppm NaCl plus 500 ppm oxygen, or to boiling MgCl$_2$ at 154 C.

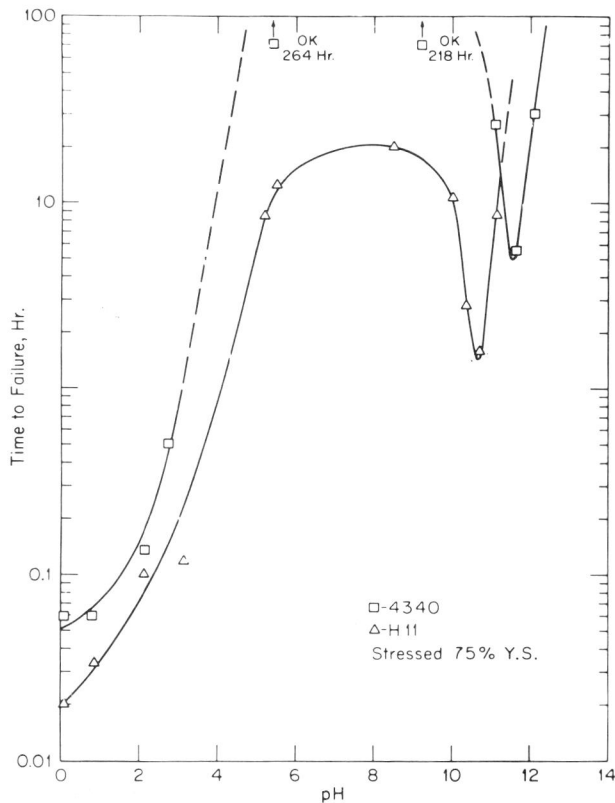

FIGURE 6 — Time to failure for Type 4340 and H-11 steels vs pH in 0.6 N NaCl solutions for foil specimens. (Green and Haney. Reference 28)

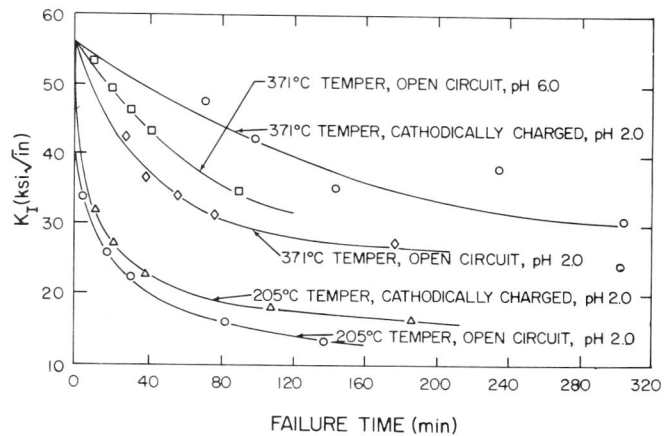

FIGURE 7 — Stress intensity at failure vs time for Type 4340 steels for two heat treatments exposed at two pH's and at open circuit and at continuous cathodic charging conditions. Specimens are cantilever loaded bars with prior fatigue crack. (Johnson. Reference 29)

## Control and Identification of Experiment, Special Precautions

It is often possible to reach erroneous conclusions regarding mechanisms as a result of testing technique and a few examples will be discussed here.

In studying crack propagation in high strength materials it is often useful to determine the effect of applied potentials, both anodic and cathodic, on crack velocity in the slow growth regime. In the study by Johnson and Staehle[29] it was found that crack velocity was affected by the location of entry of what is probably hydrogen. The specimens were the usual pre-cracked and cantilever beam and were exposed bare. Upon examining the fracture face, the slow growth regime was found to follow an inverted "U" pattern as shown in Figure 8a. When the specimen was coated on the sides, the crack propagation front was straight and cracking proceeded more slowly. The straight crack front is shown in Figure 8b. This has special implication in studying crack propagation mechanisms of thin sheet. In such a thin geometry, the entire thickness would be affected by the premature embrittlement before the crack front arrived.

Another area of concern is the method of stressing. In his study of the cracking of Inconel-600 in high tempera-ture water, Coriou[24] originally used specimens stressed by a three point loading jig. In contrast to the extensive cracking shown in Figure 2, which was done at constant load in tension, the cracking from the constant strain test was minimal and barely visible after five months of testing. While such a large difference is not always observed between the results of constant strain and constant load tests, clearly the mechanistic conclusions as well as the engineering significance are greatly altered depending on which testing technique is used.

A further concern with respect to stressing specimens is the magnitude of applied stress. The three primary alternatives are: (1) establish the complete $t_f$ vs $\sigma$ curve for each alloy, (2) test all at a constant stress, or (3) test at a constant fraction of the yield. While the first alternative is the most desirable, it is not always the most expedient. In that case, the third alternative is probably the best approach if one wishes to be concerned particularly with effects of chemical interactions. The use of plastically strained U-bends as a tool for comparison of effects of alloy chemistry is also considered to be very crude and probably very poor for defining trends.

Control and analysis of environmental variables is critical to establishing good phenomenological information both for engineering use and for boundary conditions on mechanistic studies. The extensively publicized curve of Williams[31] showing a critical relationship for chloride and oxygen concentration in cracking of stainless steel was obtained in a wetting and drying situation. Thus, the chloride concentration on the specimen surface was undefinable and the access of oxygen varied greatly in the liquid and vapor phases. Despite these inadequacies, this experimental relationship has served widely (and in many cases erroneously) as a basis for design of industrial equipment.

FIGURE 8 — Fracture faces of Type 4340 steel specimens from cantilever beam specimens. (a) Slow crack region progressing in from sides as well as from prior fatigue crack. (b) Slow crack front parallel with prior fatigue crack. (Johnson. Reference 29)

## Heterogeneous Materials and Heterogeneous Dissolution

Most engineering materials are heterogeneous — some more than others. Those heterogeneities may or may not affect the stress corrosion processes; but it appears to be common practice to ascribe very important roles to features such as dislocation or precipitates. In many cases these suppositions are easily checked.

For example, consider the case of dislocations. Numerous authors have suggested that dislocations are in fact sites for preferential dissolution. Thus a coplanar pile up after dissolving should lead to the formation of an incipient crack. However, dislocations do not necessarily dissolve, even where solute segregation is suspected. Figure 9 shows thin foils of Fe-Ni-Cr alloys from material clearly known to be susceptible to cracking in boiling $MgCl_2$. The areas, which appear parallel, are the result of dissolution along slip traces where dislocations moved while the foil was stressed and simultaneously immersed in boiling $MgCl_2$. As the dissolution proceeded away from the site of the original slip trace, the advancing dissolution encounters numerous prior dislocations already present. It is noteworthy that not a single observation was made in these studies of preferential dissolution along static dislocations.

While dislocations, probably solute enhanced, have definitely been observed to dissolve, such a process is certainly not common in Fe-Ni-Cr alloys in boiling $MgCl_2$. Certainly, where dissolution of dislocations — be they solute enriched or not — is a critical factor in a mechanism, the likelihood of such a process should be checked at least by a process such as the one used above. Attesting to the fact that solute enriched dislocations do, in fact, dissolve under certain circumstances is the excellent study by Pickering on aged Fe-Si alloys which obtained the micrograph in Figure 10 showing a dissolved dislocation.[33] This particular foil had been strained and aged and then strained again so that there were two populations of dislocations: some with solute segregation and some without. Dislocations with the solute segregations were shown to dissolve.

Local heterogeneities of dissolution in high strength steels is presently being studied in our laboratory. Figure 11a shows a typical dissolution pattern on Type 4340 steel exposed to boiling $MgCl_2$. The carbon-rich precipitates have not dissolved but the region immediately adjacent has. On the other hand, exposing the same steel to high pH solution resulted in the reverse dissolution pattern in which the carbide itself dissolved preferentially. The linking up of such heterogeneous dissolution would be likely to form or

10

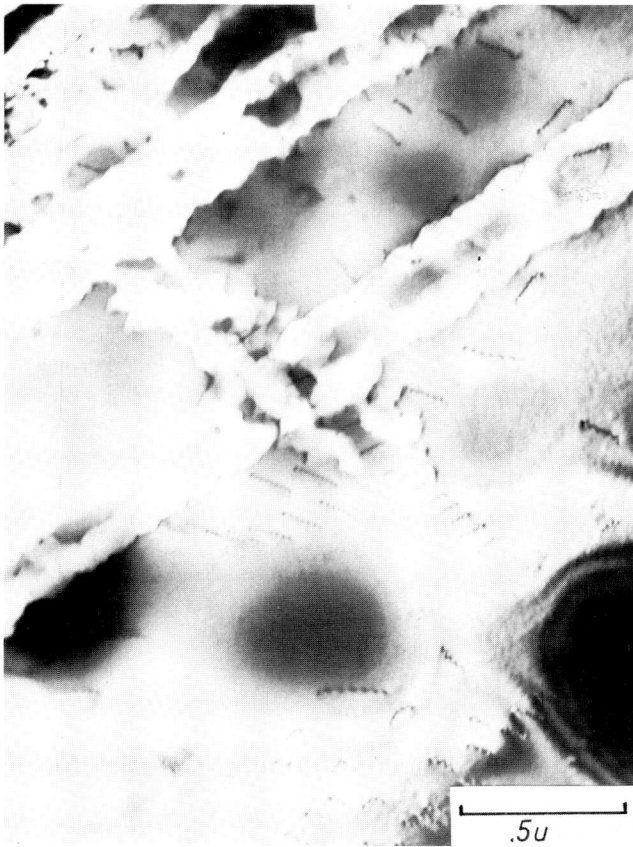

FIGURE 9 — Transmission electron micrograph of Fe-15Ni-20Cr-1.5Be alloy after exposure to boiling MgCl₂. Note that static dislocations are not preferentially attacked at dissolution interface. (J. Davis. Reference 35)

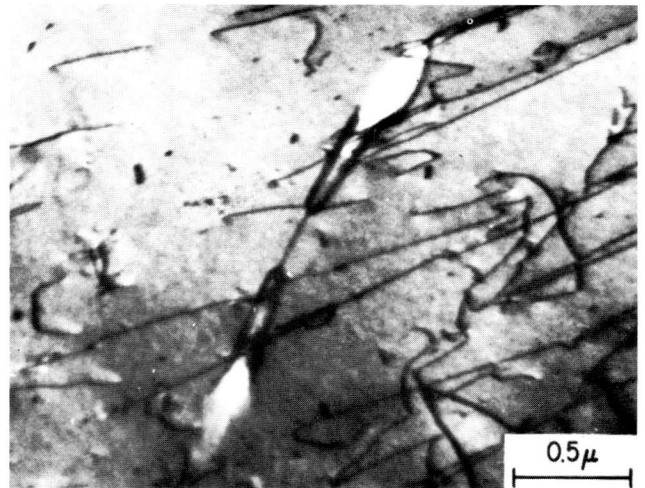

FIGURE 10 — Transmission electron micrograph of preferential dissolution at dislocation in Fe-3% Si alloy etched in HCl-methanol solution. Dissolution occurs at aged dislocation. Other dislocations resulted from straining after aging. (Pickering. Reference 33)

at least aid in forming the necessary crack to bring the stress intensity to the required value of $K_{I_{scc}}$ for the initiation of slow crack growth. Another trend is clear from the results expressed in Figure 9. Relatively anodic and cathodic areas may shift depending on the nature of the heterogeneity and the environmental chemistry. Thus, suggestions concerning the supposed role of metallurgical heterogeneities must be made with considerable caution.

Figure 12a shows an instance of heterogeneous dissolution in a homogeneous material. This alloy, a Fe-15Ni-20Cr-0.1P alloy, was examined in the electron microscope before and after exposure to boiling MgCl₂. The peculiarly geometric dissolution sites are associated neither with dislocations nor with precipitates for there were none. The same base alloy without phosphorous is shown in Figure 12b to sustain random pits of generally non-descript geometries.

Finally, Figure 13 compares slip step dissolution trenches on pure iron, pure nickel and on an Fe-Ni-Cr alloy susceptible to stress corrosion cracking in chloride environments (the former two materials are not susceptible to stress corrosion cracking). When such dissolution traces were first observed it was popular to suggest that there was

a direct correlation between their occurrence and susceptibility. The fact that the dissolution trenches occur in a variety of susceptible and non-susceptible alloys suggests that the phenomenon is somewhat more general and not limited to alloys which are susceptible to stress corrosion cracking. Thus, the occurrence of such traces and slip step dissolution may be a condition, but not the only one, for cracking.

**Education**

It is probably safe to say that fully three quarters of all stress corrosion failures could have been prevented if the persons responsible for design, construction, and maintenance of equipment had been sufficiently aware of the problem. Thus, it would be beneficial for the industrial society to emphasize educational ventures as well as those in research. Many alloys are presently available which could be used in place of susceptible ones; construction and maintenance procedures based on a consciousness of the problem would prevent many failures. Properly planned corrosion tests in anticipated environments would forecast otherwise immanent difficulties. The cartoon in Figure 14 illustrates the simplicity of the educational problem. Lubricants, used to prevent adjacent stainless parts from galling, often contain chlorides. The chloride in these lubricants is often sufficient to cause stress corrosion cracking failures which can have disastrous results.

These comments are not intended to stem the flow of research funds but to emphasize that many industrial failures could easily be prevented through educational programs sponsored by government, industry, and professional societies.

(a)

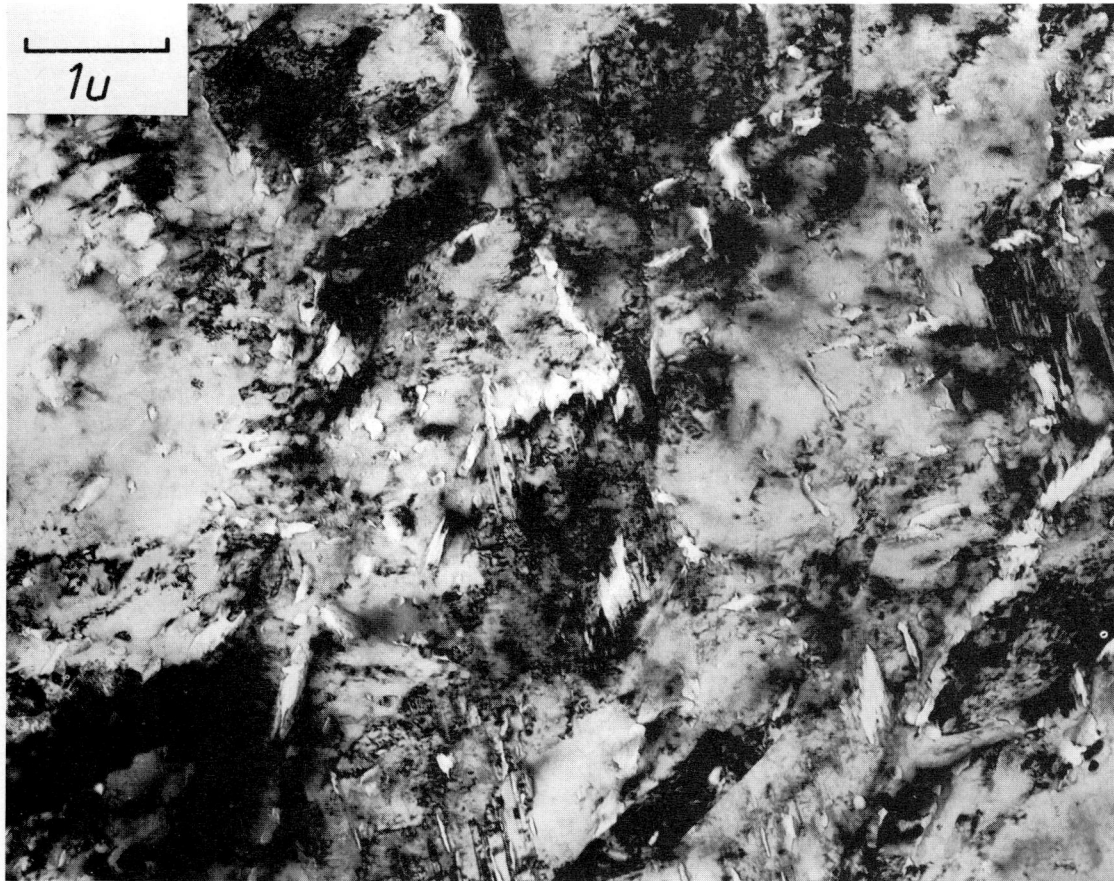

(b)

FIGURE 11 — Transmission electron micrographs of thin foils of 4340 steel heat treated at 425 C. (a) Top: exposed to boiling MgCl$_2$. (b) Bottom: exposed to boiling NaOH at pH 14. 50,000X. (Cron and Staehle. Reference 32)

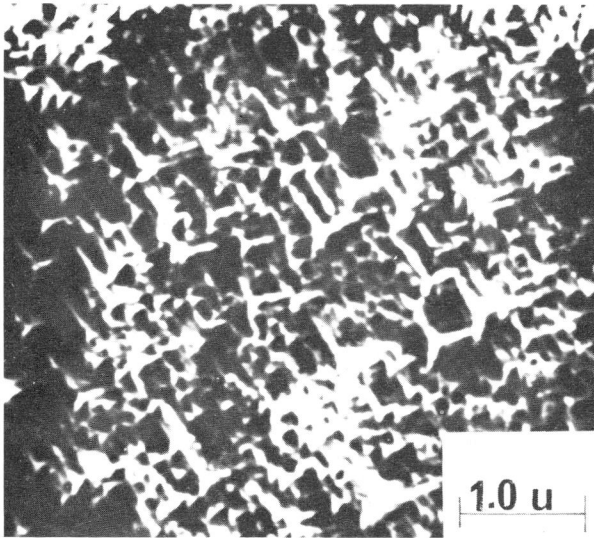

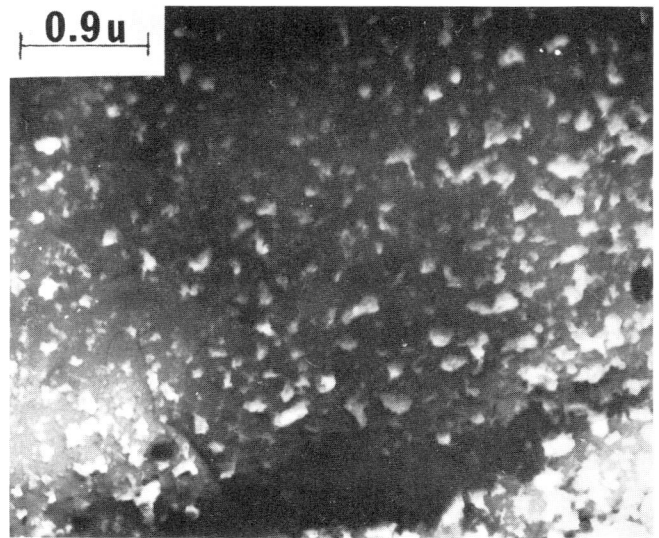

(a)

(b)

FIGURE 12 — Transmission electron micrographs of thin foils of Fe-15Ni-20Cr base alloy exposed to boiling MgCl$_2$ (a) containing phosphorous (b) without phosphorous.

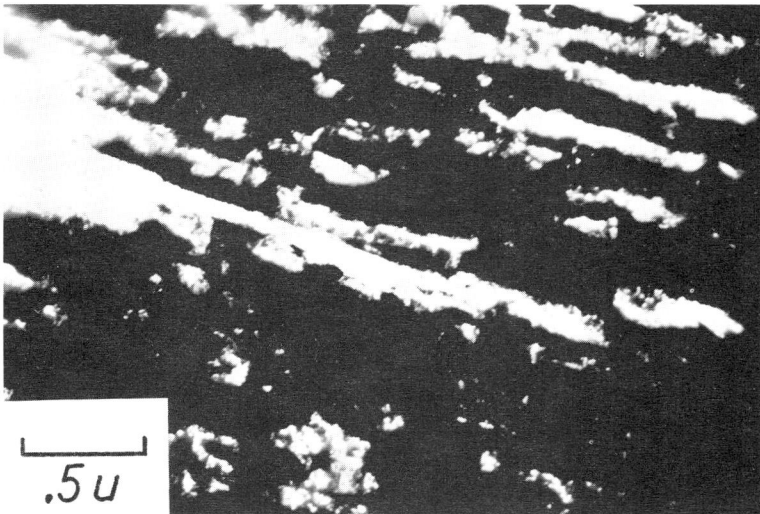

(a)

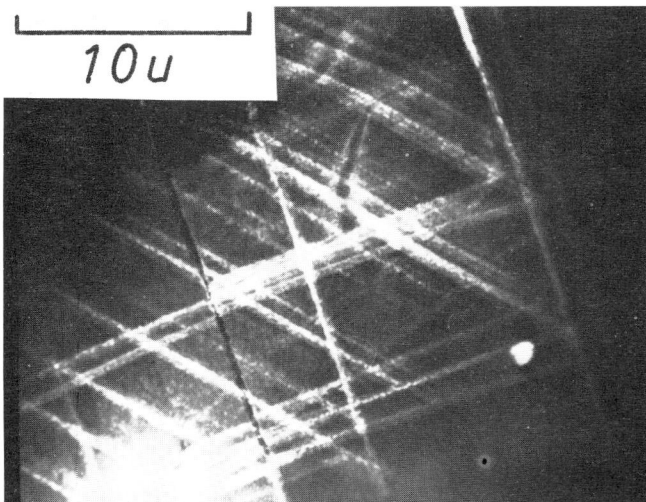

(b)

(c)

FIGURE 13 — Transmission electron micrographs of stressed thin foils exposed to boiling MgCl$_2$ solution (a) pure iron, (b) pure nickel, (c) Fe-75Ni-15Cr.

13

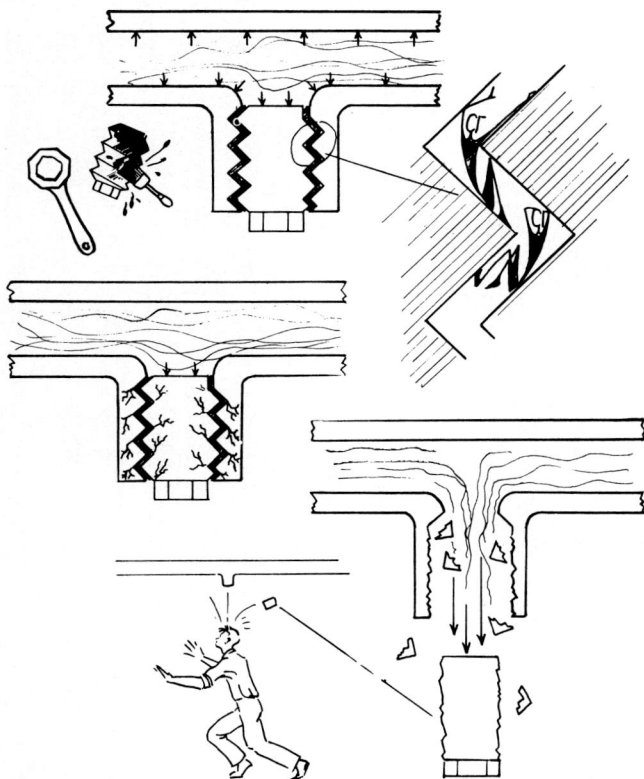

FIGURE 14 — Cartoon illustrating problem of using chloride containing lubricant for joining stainless steel parts. The chloride in the lubricant and the aqueous environment combine to cause cracking at regions of high stress.

## Aims of Research in Stress Corrosion Cracking

The problem of stress corrosion cracking is one of the most serious problems in development of reliable equipment in numerous major industries. Its significance increases as the trend to higher strength/weight ratios and thin sections increases, for example, in the transportation industry. Research in stress corrosion cracking should be directed along lines which define clearly the expected lifetime of structures and the limitations of environment and performance within which these structures can operate reliably. Thus, there is a great incentive to develop reliable mechanistic bases for stress corrosion cracking which will permit quantitative predictions of equipment lifetimes in their anticipated environmental conditions.

## References

1. Physical Metallurgy of Stress Corrosion Fracture. *Interscience*, New York, 1959, AIME.
2. W. D. Robertson, ed. *Stress Corrosion Cracking and Embrittlement*, Wiley, New York, 1956.
3. *Stress Corrosion Cracking of Metals*, ASTM-AIME, 1945.
4. H. L. Logan. *The Stress Corrosion of Metals*, Wiley, Electrochemical Society, 1966, New York.
5. A. R. C. Westwood and N. S. Stoloff, eds. *Environment Sensitive Mechanical Behavior*, Gordon and Breach (1966) New York, AIME.
6. I. A. Levin. *Intercrystalline Corrosion and Corrosion of Metals Under Stress*, 1962, Consultants Bureau.
7. *Stress Corrosion Cracking of Titanium*, STP 397, ASTM, 1966.
8. V. I. Likhtman, P. A. Rebinder and G. V. Karpenko. *Effect of Surface-Active Media on Deformation of Metals*, Chemical Publishing Co.
9. Ake Bresle, ed. *Recent Advances in Stress Corrosion*, Almquist and Wiksell, Stockholm, 1961.
10. M. Smialowski. *Hydrogen in Steel*, Pergamon Press, 1962, New York.
11. V. V. Romanov. Stress Corrosion Cracking of Metals, Jerusalem: Israel Program for Scientific Translations, 1961.
12. *Report on Stress Corrosion Cracking of Austenitic Chromium-Nickel-Stainless Steels.* ASTM-STP 264, 1960.
13. R. N. Parkins. Stress Corrosion Cracking, *Metallurgical Review*, 9, 1964, 201.
14. W. D. Robertson and A. S. Tetelman. A Unified Structural Mechanism for Intergranular and Transgranular Corrosion Cracking, *Strengthening Mechanisms in Solids* (Cleveland, Ohio, ASM).
15. J. J. Harwood from Ref. 2, p. 11.
16. T. P. Hoar. *Corrosion, 19*, 1963, 331t.
17. J. G. Hines. *Corrosion Science, 1*, 1961, 21.
18. R. B. Mears, R. H. Brown and E. H. Dix from Ref. 3, p. 323.
19. S. Barnartt. *Corrosion, 18*, 1962, 322t.
20. H. H. Uhlig. Ref. 1, p. 1.
21. J. C. Hodge and J. L. Miller. *Trans ASM, 28*, 1940, 25.
22. E. N. Pugh, W. G. Montague and A. R. C. Westwood. *Corrosion Science, 6*, 1966, 345.
23. H. R. Copson and S. W. Dean. *Corrosion, 21*, 1965, 1.
24. H. Coriou, L. Grall, C. Mathieu and M. Peles. *Corrosion, 22*, 1966, 280.
25. H. W. Pickering, F. H. Beck and M. G. Fontana. *Corrosion, 18*, 1962, 230t.
26. W. Rostoker and W. Nichols. *Trans ASM, 63*, (1956).
27. W. Latimer. *Oxidation Potentials*, Prentice Hall, New York, 1952.
28. J. A. S. Green and E. G. Haney. Sixty-Ninth Annual Meeting of ASTM, June 27, 1966.
29. K. C. Johnson. M. S. Thesis, The Ohio State University, 1967.
30. T. P. Hoar and J. G. Hines. *JISI, 182*, 1956, 124.
31. W. L. Williams. *Corrosion, 13*, 1957, 539t.
32. C. N. Cron and R. W. Staehle. Ohio State University, unpublished results.
33. H. W. Pickering. *Acta Met., 13*, 1965, 437.
34. T. P. Hoar. This Conference.
35. J. A. Davis. Ph.D. Thesis, The Ohio State University, 1969.

# REACTION FILMS, METAL DISSOLUTION
# AND STRESS CORROSION CRACKING

D. A. Vermilyea
General Electric

## Abstract

This paper reviews knowledge about the physical and chemical nature of solid-aqueous solution interfaces, dissolution of metals, and formation, structure, and properties of reaction films. A critique is given of the various theories of stress corrosion cracking in the light of the knowledge concerning surface phenomena.

## Introduction

In nearly all exposure conditions, engineering metals are protected against corrosion by some kind of reaction film, often an oxide or hydroxide. Such films are thought to play an essential role in stress corrosion cracking. This report discusses the nature of such films, their formation, their surfaces and the surfaces on which they grow, and their properties. A critique of theories of stress corrosion cracking and the role of reaction films also is included.

## Solid Surfaces

### Inhomogeneities in Solids

Since surfaces occur where a solid terminates, the starting point for our discussion concerns the inside of solids. Most important for our purposes are the various inhomogeneities, both chemical and structural, within the solid. The structural defects include lattice vacancies, interstitial atoms, dislocations, and grain boundaries. (For reviews, see Lomer[1] and Weinberg.[2]) A good discussion of point defects can be found in the book by Friedel.[7] Studies during the past decade, recently reviewed by Amelinckx,[3] have revealed the tremendous variety of types and arrangements of dislocations that may be found in crystals. A very carefully prepared single crystal may contain few or no dislocations, but all metals of interest for stress corrosion cracking contain more than $10^6$ dislocation lines per square centimeter, and in most cases the dislocation density may be more nearly $10^{10}$ to $10^{12}$ $cm^{-2}$. These dislocations may be in the form of small and large loops, geometrical arrays, irregular tangles, or pile-ups at barriers. Grain boundaries range from regular dislocation arrays for small-angle boundaries to poorly understood more complex regions probably one or two atom distances wide for high-angle boundaries.

It is important to realize that most of these defects represent departures from equilibrium, especially at ambient temperatures. The energy to form a lattice vacancy ($\sim 0.5$ to $1.5$ ev[1]) is low enough for a small concentration to be stable, but for interstitials, dislocations, and grain boundaries the free energies of formation of a single defect in a cubic centimeter are positive and large, and the crystal at equilibrium would not contain any such defects. Consequently the chemical potential of atoms at such defects is greater than that in the bulk of the material, and such atoms are therefore more reactive.

Chemical inhomogeneities include particles of different composition than the matrix, often formed during material production or by deliberate heat treatment to produce desirable mechanical properties, but more often present inadvertently, and segregation at dislocations and grain boundaries. Since segregation may be one of the most important factors involved in stress corrosion cracking, it is desirable to give a brief review.

In a perfectly pure metal there can be no chemical segregation, but there can be a very nonuniform distribution of lattice vacancies, as pointed out by Aust, Peat, and Westbrook.[4] From a microhardness study of high-purity lead, these investigators found that there was a soft region around grain boundaries and at the surface; Figure 1 shows their data for hardness near a grain boundary. The hardness is higher within the bulk of the sample because an excess of vacancies was retained by quenching from 300 C; these vacancies probably agglomerated to form some kind of larger defect which impedes dislocation motion.

In alloys, in addition to nonuniform vacancy distributions, there is the additional possibility that the different components of the alloy have different energies of interaction with the structural defects so that the composition becomes nonuniform. First of all there may be an association with lattice vacancies as a result of electrical or elastic forces. While both the theoretical and experimental information concerning such interaction leaves much to be desired,[5] it is widely believed that such associations do occur and that interaction energies can be substantial. A most important consequence of such interaction is that the diffusion of both solute and solvent atoms is enhanced, partly because of an increased vacancy concentration and partly because of a greater exchange rate near the vacancy (for reviews, see Reference 5 and Lazarus[6]).

Dislocations and grain boundaries also interact differently with the alloy components, so that segregation is expected. For dislocations, calculated and observed interaction energies vary from 0.01 to 0.5 ev,[7] so that very large concentrations can occur if equilibrium is reached. The interaction energies for carbon and nitrogen with dislocations are especially large, about 0.55 ev, and extensive segregation of these elements has been observed. Friedel (Reference 7, p. 407) quotes a value given by Pitsch of 40 carbon atoms per atom distance of dislocation. Evidently major composition changes can be expected in the vicinity of dislocations.

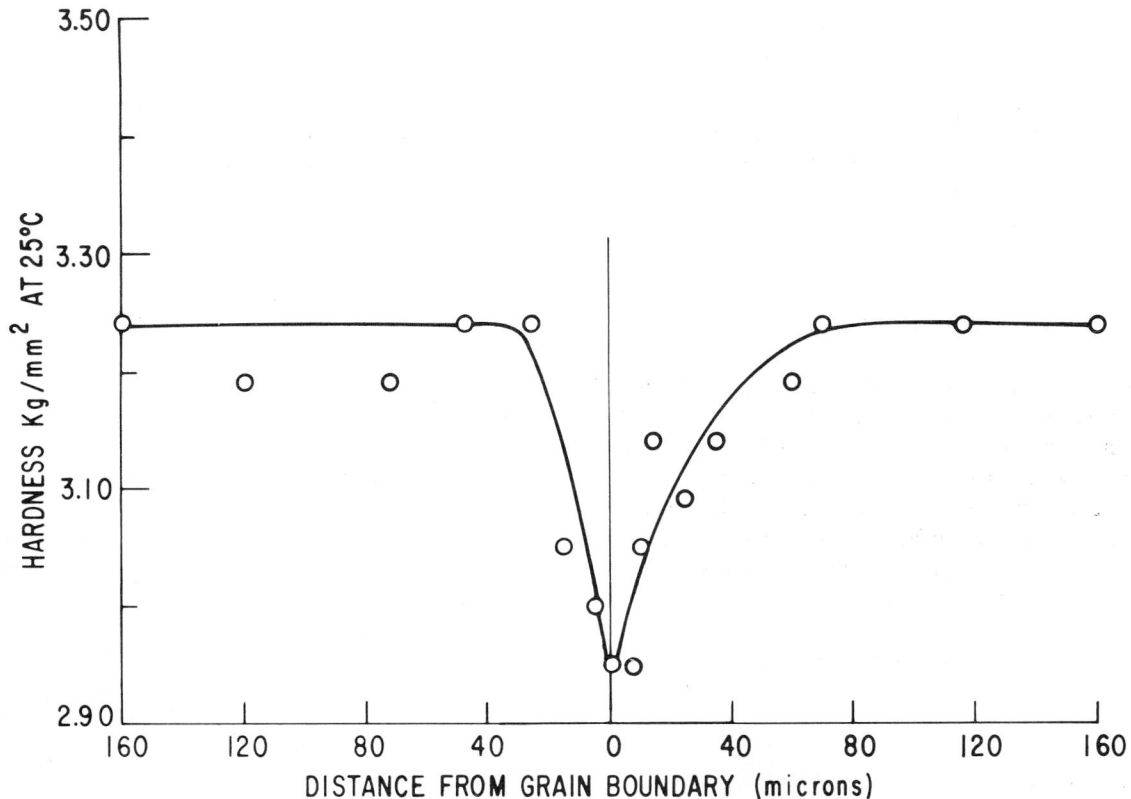

FIGURE 1 — Hardness-distance profile at the grain boundary of a quenched lead bi-crystal. (After Aust et al.[4]).

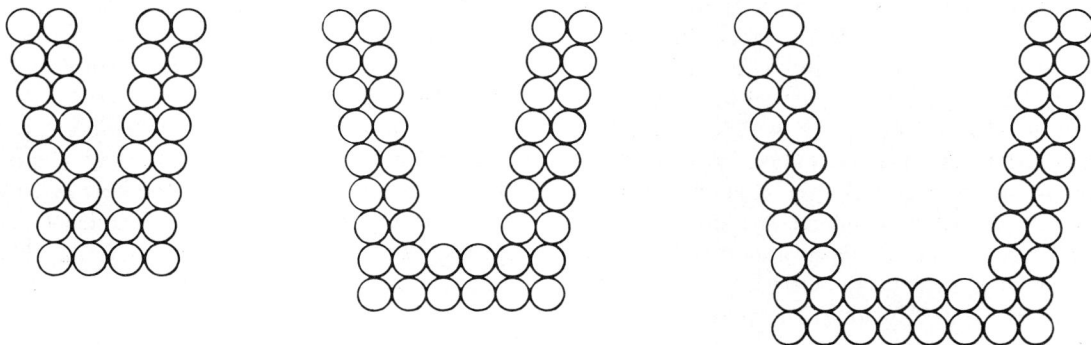

FIGURE 2 — Corrosion of material in a crack, showing the development of a low-index face at the bottom.

While there is less detailed knowledge about grain boundary segregation (Reference 5, p. 539, Cahn,[8] Westbrook[9]) similar extensive composition changes may occur near grain boundaries. Evidence obtained from microhardness studies indicates that the distance over which segregation occurs may be of the order of several microns.[9] Such segregation is probably not caused by direct atom-boundary interaction, but by a kinetic process. An explanation[10,11] is that rapid cooling from an annealing temperature results in a supersaturation of vacancies, which migrate to boundary sinks where they are annihilated. Solute is transported toward the boundary along with the vacancies because of the vacancy solute interaction, so that solute segregation over a considerable distance can occur.

*Surface Structure and Composition*

During the past decade the geometrical character of surfaces has been discussed extensively, and familiarity may now be assumed with the concepts of incomplete surface layers (called "steps" or "ledges") and with irregularities (called "jogs" or "kinks") in the steps. The role of screw dislocations and crystal edges in acting as sources of steps is also well known. It is perhaps worth noting that the spacing of surface steps is given approximately by

$$d = Ar*  \qquad (1)$$

where A is a constant with a value of about 13 to 19 and r* is the radius of a critical nucleus for two-dimensional nucleation.[12] Even the modest overvoltage of 150 mv would produce a step spacing on copper of about 100 Å, assuming a surface energy of 2000 ergs/cm$^2$. In most corrosion situations, with rather large driving forces, surfaces will contain large numbers of steps and jogs for the exchange of ions with the environment. The occurrence of multiatomic steps is also very probable.[13]

There is one special situation of interest in stress corrosion cracking, however, in which step generation is not guaranteed and which is worth a slight digression. At the tip of a very narrow crack there is no way to develop new steps unless a screw dislocation intersects the crack. Figure 2 shows schematically the blunting of the crack which is expected if there are no dislocations intersecting the bottom of the crack. (Steps are presumably generated on the sides of the crack where dislocations intersect the surface.) Thus, because of the finite spacing between dislocations, the bottom of a stress corrosion crack may approach an ideal surface.

In addition to the steps, the surface will also contain regions of different composition at the sites where dislocations, grain boundaries, and second phase particles or nonmetallic inclusions such as oxides, nitrides, or carbides intersect the surface. Since corrosion generally, and stress corrosion in particular, results in continued removal of an old surface and regeneration of a new surface farther into the bulk, some discussion of the kinetics of segregation is essential. A first approximation would consider that all segregation is controlled by bulk solute diffusion, in which

case no appreciable change in segregation could occur at room temperature for most systems. However, in real metals diffusion can be much faster because an excess of vacancies may be present as a result of rapid cooling or cold-work. In addition, diffusion along defects such as dislocations and grain boundaries is known to occur in many systems with an activation energy only about half that for bulk diffusion. Finally, strain fields near dislocations and grain boundaries may result in accelerated diffusion.

We may consider for illustrative purposes nickel, for which the activation energy, Q, for diffusion is about 2.8 ev. Calculating the diffusion coefficient, D, from

$$D = D_0 \exp - (Q/kT)  \qquad (2)$$

assuming $D_0 = 1$ we find $D \cong 10^{-49}$ at 25 C. The time for diffusion over a 10 Å distance is then astronomical. For vacancy motion, on the other hand, the activation energy is about 1.0 ev,[7] $D = 10^{-17}$, and the time is $10^3$ seconds. At 100 C, where $D = 10^{-14}$, the time would be only 1 second. In a nickel alloy with more than about 6 percent solute the activation energies would probably be substantially less than the values used in these calculations.[6] It is therefore quite reasonable to expect diffusion of substitutional constituents even in alloys having high melting points over distances of 10 Å to 100 Å in the vicinity of lattice defects at room temperature. The diffusion of interstitial components is usually faster, and segregation over greater distances can be expected.

One special influence on diffusion is pertinent to stress corrosion, namely, the influence of stress. At the tip of a crack there may be a small region under locally very high stress because of an absence of any glissile dislocations. It is conceivable that such stresses could approach the theoretical tensile strength for the material (about 10 percent of the elastic modulus). Activation volumes for substitutional diffusion are about half the atomic volume,[7] or about 5 cm$^3$/mole. At a stress of $10^6$ psi the activation energy would be changed by 0.35 ev, and the diffusion rate at room temperature could be increased by about $10^6$. While stresses of such magnitude may be unlikely, some such accelerating effect cannot be entirely discounted.

*Electrical Double Layers*

Of great importance in kinetic phenomena at interfaces are the surface energy and the distribution of electrically charged particles, both of which depend in an essential way on the electrical potential distribution. Extensive studies on mercury have resulted in extensive understanding, while for solid metals our knowledge is meager. Thus the point of zero charge for solid metals is not known with accuracy, although from the rather meager information available[14] it appears to be nearly linearly related to the work function. A very rough empirical equation describing the data is

$$E_z = -4.4 + \varphi  \qquad (3)$$

in which $E_z$ is the point of zero charge on the standard

hydrogen electrode scale and $\varphi$ is the work function in volts.

There is even less information available about the surface energies of solid metal electrodes. For mercury the lowering of surface energy in the presence of water at the point of zero charge is small, about 40 ergs/cm$^2$, and the decrease produced by a potential difference of 1 volt across the double layer is only about 100 ergs/cm$^2$. Since the double-layer capacities of solid metal electrodes are of the same order as the mercury double-layer capacity, it is expected that similar changes in surface energy would occur on solid metal electrodes.

Adsorption by chemical forces other than electrostatic attraction will also lower the surface energy. On mercury such adsorption has been observed to lower the surface energy by amounts up to about 50 to 100 ergs/cm$^2$. A very rough calculation can be made to establish the order of magnitude of this effect for solid metals, for which experimental data are almost nonexistent. Imagine that adsorption of an uncharged organic substance occurs with a constant heat of adsorption of 10 kcal/mole (a rather high adsorption energy) and that the saturation density is $10^{14}$ molecules per square centimeter or about $10^{-10}$ moles/cm$^2$. Then if saturation occurs the change in surface energy resulting from adsorption is about $10^{-6}$ cal/cm$^2$ or about 40 ergs/cm$^2$. Adsorption of uncharged organic molecules is unlikely except at potentials near the point of zero charge, as shown by studies on mercury.

It is concluded that for solid metals the surface energy is not likely to be reduced very far below the value for the metal-vacuum interface, unless some especially strong adsorption occurs. Metal-vacuum surface energies are usually of the order of $10^3$ ergs/cm$^2$.[15] The Handbook of Chemistry and Physics gives information on liquid metal-vacuum interfaces and the corresponding values for solid metals should be only slightly greater. For metals such as zinc, aluminum, chromium, cobalt, nickel, iron, silver, gold, and copper the metal-aqueous solution surface energy is expected on this basis to be between $10^3$ and $2 \times 10^3$ ergs/cm$^2$.

Double layers at ionic compound solution interfaces are much better understood than those at solid metals. An excellent review has been given by Hayden[16] of information on silver halide-solution interfaces, while information on oxides and other systems can be found in papers by Parks,[17] Parks and deBruyn,[18] and Tamamushi.[19] It can generally be said that double-layer capacities are of similar magnitude to those at mercury, about 10 to 50 $\mu$f/cm$^2$. Surface energies for oxides are generally lower than for metals. Empirical rules given by Eberhart[20] lead to values of 250 ergs/cm$^2$ for PbO, 400 for SiO$_2$, 850 for Al$_2$O$_3$, 400 for BeO and 700 for FeO; other data are given in Reference 15. Water is known to interact strongly with oxide surfaces, and it is expected that adsorption of water will result in substantial lowering of the surface energies of oxides. From information on heat of immersion given by Healy and Fuerstenau[21] it is estimated that interaction with water could lower the surface energy by as much as several hundred ergs/cm$^2$. Variations of oxide surface

tension with double-layer potential are expected to be of the same order as on mercury.

The double-layer potential difference on oxides and hydroxides is determined by the exchange of protons or hydroxyl ions, and is therefore a function of pH.[17,18] Parks gives Table 1 concerning points of zero charge of oxides.

**TABLE 1 – Points of Zero Charge of Oxides**

| Class | pH of Zero Charge |
|---|---|
| M$_2$O | >11.5 |
| MO | 8.5 to 12.5 |
| M$_2$O$_3$ | 6.5 to 10.4 |
| MO$_2$ | 0 to 7.5 |
| M$_2$O$_5$, MO$_3$ | < 0.5 |

It may be seen that for many of the most useful materials such as zinc, aluminum, stainless steel, and magnesium the point of zero charge of the oxide film will be between pH 6 and pH 12. Since the variation of double-layer potential with pH is not likely to be larger than 0.06 volt per pH unit,[22] very large double-layer potential differences are not likely. Double-layer capacities appropriate to externally applied potential changes are of the order of $10^3$ to $10^4$ $\mu$F/cm$^2$,[22,23] so it is not likely that any change of double-layer potential can be caused by changing the potential of the metal electrode on which a film has formed. It is therefore not likely that the surface energies of oxides will change significantly with changes of solution composition or of externally applied potentials.

There is also some information available on adsorption of surface active agents on ionic solids[16] and on oxides.[24] Heats of adsorption up to 7000 to 9000 cal/mole at the isoelectric point have been observed.

## Dissolution of Metals

The general nature of crystal growth and dissolution involving ion exchanges at jogs on surface steps is now well known. In addition to steps provided by dislocations, growth can also result on steps provided by impurity particles which contact the growing surface and which satisfy obvious conditions of catalyzing deposition. The observation of electroplating on nonmetallic fibers which contact an electrode is an interesting example.[25] It should be noted that electrolytic *dissolution* is a relatively rapid process since for most metals an overvoltage of a few tenths of a volt suffices to give dissolution currents of 10 to 100 ma/cm$^2$. Step generation during dissolution of most metals is easy because of the presence of many dislocations and grain boundaries or crystal edges.

Of special importance to stress corrosion cracking is dissolution near defects. Consider first dissolution at defects in a pure metal. Because of the excess energy associated with dislocations and grain boundaries it is possible to have localized corrosion of materials near such defects. Several investigators have applied nucleation theory[26,27] and the dislocation theory of crystal growth[28-30] to this problem; Johnston[31] and Amelinckx[3] have given excellent reviews of this work. As an example to illustrate the methods used, consider dissolution of a grain boundary. The surface energies of metals are considerably higher than grain boundary energies, and dissolution of the boundary creates two surfaces so that the process will not occur without a considerable driving force, and we must consider the kinetic process. (Note that if the surface energy was very low the metal should spontaneously fall apart at grain boundaries!) The most favorable case for nucleation of a surface step at a grain boundary would be for the nucleus to be one atom wide. Then the change in free energy, $\Delta G$, accompanying the formation of a nucleus (assumed rectangular and one atom deep) is

$$\Delta G = a^2 \ell \Delta G_V + 2a\ell\sigma_S - a\ell\sigma_B + 2a^2\sigma_S \qquad (4)$$

in which a is the atomic dimension, $\ell$ is the length of the nucleus, $\Delta G_V$ is the free energy decrease per unit volume accompanying dissolution, $\sigma_S$ is the surface energy, and $\sigma_B$ is the boundary energy. Evidently nucleation consists of removing just one atom, for $\Delta G$ is linear in $\ell$ and either increases or decreases as $\ell$ increases; only the situation for which $\Delta G_V$ is large enough so that $\Delta G$ decreases with $\ell$ can result in nucleation. Therefore, taking $\ell = a = 3 \cdot 10^{-8}$, $\sigma_S = 10^3$ ergs/cm$^2$, $\sigma_B = 500$ ergs/cm$^2$, we find

$$\Delta G = 2.7 \cdot 10^{-23} \Delta G_V + 3.2 \cdot 10^{-12} \qquad (5)$$

Now the rate of nucleation will be given by

$$R = \frac{\nu}{a} e^{-\Delta H/kT} \quad e^{-\Delta G/kT} \qquad (6)$$

in which $\nu$ is a vibration frequency and $\Delta H$ is the activation energy for removing an atom from a kink site in a step. Assuming that a large driving force is applied so that $\Delta H \sim 0$, taking $\nu = 10^{13}$ sec$^{-1}$ and noting that in order to be noticeable R should be at least 1/sec/cm of grain boundary we find that $\Delta G$ should be no larger than about $1.9 \cdot 10^{12}$ ergs. From Equation (5) we find that $\Delta G_V$ should be at least $-5 \cdot 10^{10}$ ergs/cm$^2$. In terms of an overvoltage, $\eta$, for dissolution,

$$\Delta G_V = \frac{-4.2 \cdot 10^7 \, zF\rho\eta}{M} \qquad (7)$$

in which z is the valence, F Faraday's constant, $\rho$ the density, and M the molecular weight. If $z = 2$ and $\rho/M = 0.1$ we find that $\eta$ should be about 0.25 volt. Once nucleation has occurred the rest of the atoms along the boundary would be removed rapidly, so the boundary corrosion rate would be about 1 atom layer per second; a small increase of overvoltage would increase the rate greatly.

The similar calculations for dislocations all agree that for metals, and for Burgers vectors of one atom distance, rather large overvoltages are required to nucleate steps at dislocations. All of these treatments are doubtless substantially in error because of the use of macroscopic quantities such as surface energy for nuclei only a few atoms in size, but the order of magnitude of the energy required is certainly correct. The treatment of Schaarwachter[27] is especially interesting, because he takes the core energy of dislocations into account explicitly. He finds that the nucleation free energy at a dislocation, $\Delta G_d^*$ is related to the nucleation free energy elsewhere on the surface, $\Delta G_S^*$, by the equation

$$\Delta G_d^* = P \, \Delta G_S^* \qquad (8)$$

$$P = \left(\frac{1 - aq\mu b}{4\pi\sigma_S}\right)^2 \qquad (9)$$

in which $a$ is a constant with a value of 1.5 to 2.0, q is another constant equal to about 0.1, $\mu$ is the shear modulus, and b the Burgers vector. For the typical values for metals, $\mu = 3 \times 10^{11}$ erg cm$^{-3}$, b = $3 \times 10^{-8}$ cm, $\sigma_S = 10^3$ erg cm$^{-2}$ and taking $a = 2$, q = 0.1 we find P $\cong 0.75$. Thus the free energy for nucleation at a dislocation, while less than for nucleation at any point on the surface, is still very large and therefore a large driving force or overvoltage will be required for nucleation.

Because of the fact, mentioned above, that most metals dissolve very rapidly at overvoltages of a few tenths of a volt, the formation of observable etch pits at clean dislocations requires a very special set of conditions, and does not often occur. Adsorption of some poison at steps seems to be universally required; the poison is often highly specific, and rules for predicting useful poisons are not known. Oxide film formation also seems to be helpful.[32] Adsorption helps by slowing step motion so that the pit (or trench) sides become steeper and more visible and also makes it easier to achieve a large driving force at the surface without hindrance from transport phenomena in the environment. Adsorption at steps may also lower the step energy (without necessarily lowering the energy of the surface itself noticeably) and make nucleation more probable. It is interesting that the poison does not reduce the rate of nucleation but only the rate of step motion. According to classical concepts, step motion is involved in nucleation and an influence on the rate of step motion should also influence the nucleation rate. Perhaps when the nucleus contains only a few atoms adsorption does not take place on the subcritical nucleus, which can therefore form rapidly, but only on larger steps, which are therefore slowed down. Such a mechanism might be thought most likely for a rather large step poison. Another necessary condition for etch pitting is that the rate of nucleation on the surface at points removed from dislocations not be too high; this condition imposes an upper limit on the driving force, and may make pit observation impossible under some circumstances.[26,27] It is also found experimentally, and predicted by the theories, that etch-pit formation at clean dislocations should only occur on surfaces having an orientation close to that of a low index crystal face.

Summarizing the discussion of corrosion near defects in pure metals, we may say that local corrosion is possible on close packed surfaces at high overvoltages when specific poisons or oxide films are present. The pits or trenches produced are normally rather shallow. The conditions in a stress corrosion crack are probably not conducive to such attack. It is true that the driving force is often high, specific environments are necessary, and films are often present. However, the presence of close packed faces is doubtful, and the complications of transport in the solution and resistance of the solution in the pore may make difficult the attainment of a large driving force at the tip of the crack.

When the metal is not pure and there is segregation at the dislocation it is much easier to form etch pits, and most dislocation etchants for metals require decoration of the dislocation. Segregation lowers the strain energy of a dislocation and tends to decrease the rate of nucleation of steps, and hence it might be thought that etch pits would be less visible; such an effect has been observed in LiF.[31] The reason that segregation often increases the corrosion rate at dislocations in metals is probably associated with a change in the film present on the metal.[3,32] If a more readily soluble film is formed, then attack will be more rapid at the dislocation. An alternative explanation[31] is that the surface energy is lower at a dislocation at which segregation has occurred; this seems unlikely in metal systems. When segregation has occurred it is even possible to form etch grooves at dislocations lying just below the surface[31] (see also Reference 7, page 13, for examples). The etching of decorated dislocations, in contrast to that of dislocations in pure metals, may produce tunnels several times as long as wide.[31,33] Furthermore, the orientation of the surface exposed to the solution does not seem critical for decorated dislocations.

It seems likely that suitable conditions for etching decorated dislocations may well occur in stress corrosion cracking. Severe local deformation should produce many dislocations and point defects, and segregation at a distance of the order of protective film thicknesses is likely. Favorable environmental conditions in corrosion cracks (concentration of acid and specific anions) may readily be imagined.

Corrosion tunnels that are not necessarily associated with dislocations have also been observed in LiF by Westwood and Rubin.[34] It is believed that those tunnels formed because dissolution poisons (organic molecules or ferric ions) were not able to reach the bottom of the tunnel because of the long diffusion path. Such tunnels would not be likely when an oxide film affords protection, since water is always readily available to reform a film.

## Formation and Characterization of Reaction Films

Film formation has been reviewed in some detail in several recent publications,[35-37] and a brief discussion of the relevance of films in corrosion phenomena was given recently.[38] Consequently only those aspects of special interest to stress corrosion will be discussed. When the potential of a metal electrode is raised to the point where a reaction film of some kind is stable, or just slightly beyond, it is nearly always observed that the film does form. There seems to be no evidence that any great amount of overvoltage is required to nucleate film growth, typical values being 10 to 100 mv. It is supposed[35] that the reason for easy nucleation is that the metal acts as a good catalyst because of the low surface energy of the film and high surface energy of the metal. It is invariably observed for fairly soluble compounds normally regarded as "ionic," like halides and sulfates, that film formation occurs by a process of nucleation and growth of discrete crystals. Growth to complete coverage occurs by solution and reprecipitation, and the complete film may be quite thick — as much as several microns. Less is known about the initial formation of films usually considered to be responsible for passivity, for example, $Al_2O_3$, $Fe_2O_3$, $Cr_2O_3$, NiO, MgO, $TiO_2$, $ZrO_2$, $Ta_2O_5$, etc. For many of these metals it is not possible to start with a bare surface in contact with an aqueous solution because the standard potential for film formation is very negative. The initial condition thus plays a major role, and obscures phenomena occurring during film formation, so that the initial stages of growth are not understood. Such films are usually very thin ($\sim 10^{-7}$ cm) at complete coverage.

Once coverage is complete the film may thicken by ion transport. Such transport is rather complicated,[36] showing a strong dependence on the history of the film. It seems to be generally true that both ions are mobile to some extent, at least in thick anodic films; if only one ion moves it seems to be the anion.[43] The following argument suggests that film thicknesses reached by ion transport should generally be very small. The activation energies for diffusion in most oxides and other ionic compounds are 1.0 ev or greater. If $D_0 = 1$ then according to Equation (2) at room temperature $D = 10^{-17}$ and the mean diffusion distance in one day is about 100 Å. When the activation energy is substantially higher than 1.0 ev negligible growth would occur by diffusion alone, but in such cases high field ion transport will cause growth to 20 Å to 50 Å. These thicknesses are in the range reported for passive films. Thicker films can only be expected for some other growth mechanism, usually involving solution transport. For instance, the initial growth of a fairly soluble film from a few nuclei can yield a thick film, as can the development of porosity as in thick porous aluminum oxide films. Finally, one of the many possible causes of stress in reaction films (change of hydration state or crystal structure, recrystallization, etc.) may result in continued reaction by preventing complete and permanent coverage.

It is important to emphasize the role of the dissolution rate of the film in determining the behavior of the metal electrode. Consider the passivation of iron by the process described years ago by Mueller,[39] in which an initial film of iron sulfate is replaced at high enough potentials by an oxide. If the dissolution rate of such a primary film is very high, then the current density will be large and resistance and concentration polarization will make difficult the attainment of a high potential and conversion to the oxide will not occur. Since high dissolution rates are usually the rule for halides, it is likely that the deleterious effect of such ions is a result of rapid solution of the primary film. Once the passive film is formed its dissolution rate controls the overall corrosion rate. The extremely slow chemical attack of acids on $Cr_2O_3$ and $Fe_2O_3$ correlates well with the protection afforded by these compounds. When film dissolution is slow it is even possible to achieve stable passivity when the thermodynamic solubility of the oxide is high. Examples are passivity of iron and stainless steel in acid solutions and anodic oxidation of tantalum in 37 percent HCl.

It may perhaps be useful to discuss the formation of $Ta_2O_5$ on tantalum in 37 percent HCl in slightly more detail. In such a solution the film is highly soluble because of the formation of chloride complexes of tantalum; molar solutions of tantalum chloride can readily be prepared. However, the attack of such a solution on anodic $Ta_2O_5$ is extremely slow; less than one monolayer of oxide is removed in 4 months at room temperature. Thus if any film ever forms it will remain to protect the surface. Now imagine a bare tantalum surface exposed to such a solution, and imagine that the potential is slowly raised above the standard potential for forming the oxide. The probability that enough chloride ions would exist in the proper configuration to form a complex ion with a tantalum ion leaving a kink site must be very small. For film formation, on the other hand, a tantalum ion need only react with one or a few water molecules which are readily available. Hence, film formation may occur more readily than complex ion formation, and all the film formed may reasonably be expected to stay permanently on the surface.

The dissolution of ionic compounds has been discussed recently[38,45] from a theoretical point of view. It was shown that the dependence of dissolution rate on externally applied potentials should be small and that the dependence on proton concentration should be a power between 1/2 and 4/3 depending on the oxide or hydroxide. Little experimental information is available, especially about the role of solution composition in determining the dissolution rate. It may be expected that highly imperfect reaction films can have rather different solubilities and solution rates than the same well-crystallized phase.

Our knowledge of the structure and composition of surface films is meager. In the first place we can expect variations on different regions of the surface where the metal is inhomogeneous, as at dislocations, grain boundaries, and inclusions. Secondly, there is abundant evidence for incorporation of material from the solution. Such incorporation is expected because of the heterogeneous nature of deposition; as crystals grow together material is trapped in boundaries. Water has been reported present in large amounts.[40,41] We know little of the distribution of such trapped materials.

Films generally are at least finely polycrystalline, and some may be truly amorphous.[41] Thick anodic barrier films on tantalum and aluminum are amorphous in the sense of giving only very diffuse x-ray and electron diffraction patterns, while passive films on stainless steel are also reported to be amorphous or "gel-like."[41] The passive

film on iron in neutral borate solutions, on the other hand, is reported to be crystalline with a rather small particle size.[42]

In summary, reaction films tend to be very inhomogeneous, imperfect, and of variable composition. An example of a recent careful characterization[44] of films formed on cadmium in KOH may suffice to illustrate the complexity which may occur. Breiter and Vedder used several techniques including x-ray diffraction, electron microscopy, infrared analysis, and electrochemical measurements in order to study the films on cadmium. They found that films formed at high potentials (above about 70 mv vs a hydrogen electrode in the same solution) comprised two well crystallized hydroxide phases, the stable $\beta$-Cd(OH)$_2$ and metastable $\gamma$-Cd(OH)$_2$, plus a very large amount of a phase which yielded no x-ray pattern and, since it showed no OH$^-$ absorption in the infrared was presumed to be an oxide. The $\beta$ and $\gamma$ Cd(OH)$_2$ probably formed by precipitation from solution, since such precipitation does produce well-crystallized hydroxides. The mechanism of oxide formation is unknown. The oxide thickness was about 1000 Å; and hence, since the oxidation of cadmium in laboratory air yields films about 100 Å thick it is clear that the mechanism of oxide formation must differ substantially from that for air oxidation. Porosity is one possible explanation; no evidence for or against such a hypothesis was found. The overall reaction was found to proceed at different rates on different crystal faces, yielding very different film thicknesses on different grains.

### Deformation and Fracture of Reaction Films

Perhaps the most important properties of a film from the stress corrosion point of view are mechanical: what stresses exist in the film and how it deforms or fractures. There is only fragmentary knowledge of the stresses in very thin reaction films. There is information on anodic films,[46-48] which shows that tensile stresses are present in most very thin anodic films. As film growth to about 1000 Å occurs there may sometimes be a reversal and compressive stresses may develop. Presumably passive films would usually be thin enough for stresses to remain tensile. Bradhurst and Leach[47] found that the stress tended to be more compressive at low current densities, and interpreted the change with current density in terms of a changing ratio of cationic to anionic flux. The same authors showed that stresses in films could be relieved if ionic motion under the influence of a field occurred; a minimum ionic flux was required to accomplish the stress relief. It should be noted that such stress relief in a passive film would tend to prevent the occurrence of fracture in such films on a deforming metal.

The deformation of reaction films has also been little studied. Early results on aluminum oxide[46,49] indicated brittle fracture, although the elastic strain at fracture was reported to be about 2 percent.[46] Recent results for $Ta_2O_5$, $Al_2O_3$, and $ZrO_2$[50] confirmed the brittle behavior of $Al_2O_3$ but showed that $ZrO_2$ had some ductility while $Ta_2O_5$ films up to 1000 Å thick could be deformed substantially without fracture. In fact, the results for $Ta_2O_5$ suggested that films could sometimes be deformed as much as 50 percent without fracture.

We have recently used a different technique to study deformation of thin reaction films on a number of metals. Briefly, the specimen in wire form was covered with an oxide film at one potential and then stretched at a constant rate (28.5 percent/min) at a less positive potential. The current required to reform any film at areas exposed by cracking was recorded and taken as a measure of ductility. The initial film was thicker than the stable film produced at the second potential, so a perfectly ductile film should give no current until its thickness was reduced sufficiently by the deformation. A brittle film, on the other hand, would generate currents of the order of 10 $\mu a/cm^2$ (for our conditions) as soon as cracking occurred.

Figures 3, 4, and 5 show typical current-extension plots for films on tantalum, 18-8 stainless steel, and 80Ni-20Cr. The upper curve in each figure is for a specimen anodized and pulled at the same potential; a brittle film should give approximately the same curve. Films on all specimens have some ductility, as shown by the fact that current-extension curves for thicker films were always lower. A rough quantitative measure of the plasticity is obtained from

$$\% C = \frac{i_t - i}{i_t} \times 100 \qquad (10)$$

in which % C is roughly the percentage of the area covered, i is the current for a wire anodized at a potential higher than that at which it was stretched, and $i_t$ the current at the same wire elongation when anodizing and stretching potentials were the same. A high % C indicates a ductile film. Some results for several materials and films about 30 Å to 50 Å thick, stretched at room temperature, are given in

Table 2. Only minor differences resulted from the use of different electrolytic solutions, including chloride solutions.

There are at least three reasons why the results correspond to a *minimum* film ductility. First, specimen deformation is nonuniform, and local deformation may thin even a perfectly ductile film so that current can flow. Second, we have observed that cracking occurs most readily at flaws in the films, and none of the materials was free of inclusions. Third, in the second technique $Ta_2O_5$ films showed much less ductility than was found in the earlier tests[50] which are felt to be far more accurate for detecting very small amounts of cracking. A likely explanation of this discrepancy is that ionic current can flow through the intact film while it is being deformed; this idea is in some respects similar to that of Bradhurst and Leach[47] on stress relief resulting from ionic flow. The field applied during deformation of most films was a fairly large fraction of the forming field, and while deformation occurs and ions are being moved mechanically a drift in the field is likely. Only $10^{13}$ ions/$cm^2$ sec would need to move through the film to

**TABLE 2 - Results for Several Materials and Films**

| Metal | % C Wire Elongation | |
|---|---|---|
| | 5% | 10% |
| Tantalum | 92 | 89 |
| 16Cr, 14Ni, bal Fe | 87 | 84 |
| 304 Stainless | 86 | 77 |
| Iron | 81 | 56 |
| Aluminum | 75 | 50 |
| Nichrome (59Ni, 15Cr, 24Fe + minor elements) | 56 | 54 |
| Zirconium | 52 | 38 |
| 80 Cr-20 Ni | 16 | 18 |

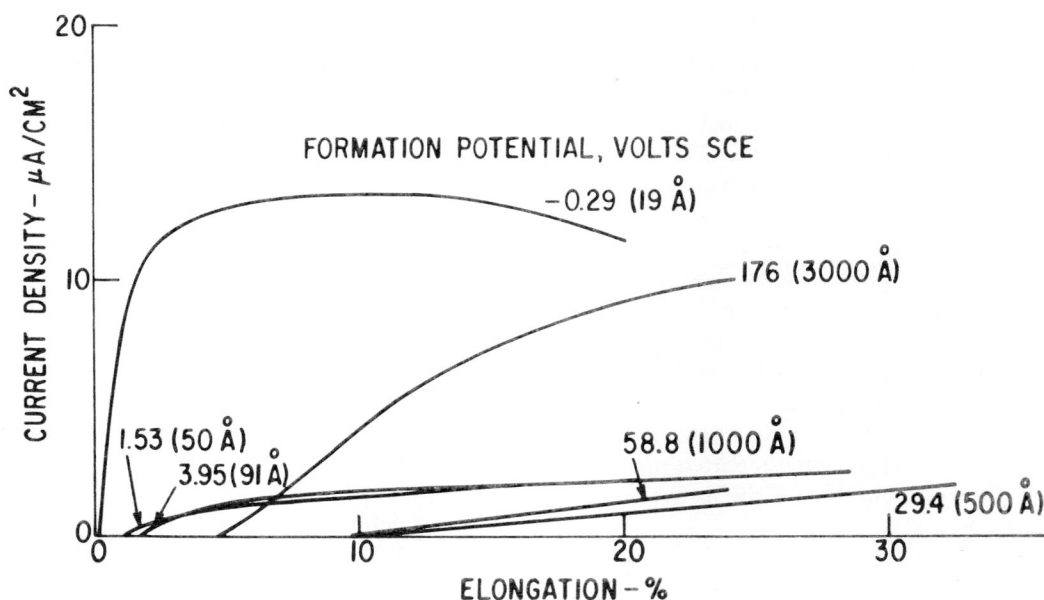

FIGURE 3 — Current density-extension curves for zone-refined tantalum wire covered with oxide films of different thickness. Deformation potential -0.29 volt SCE; 1 percent ammonium borate solution.

give the observed currents. In the first techniques we measured only electronic currents flowing through the film after any ionic transient had died away, and hence did not record such currents.

Of course, these three reasons why a minimum ductility was measured make quantitative discussion difficult. Perhaps a better procedure would be to regard the very thin $Ta_2O_5$ films as completely ductile, and compare current time curves for another material with those for $Ta_2O_5$. On that basis, films on 18-8 stainless steel would also be regarded as almost completely ductile.

Such large ductilities were not expected from the behavior of oxides in bulk. Two possibilities present themselves by way of rationalization. First, Westbrook and Jorgensen[52,53] have noted the profound effect of the presence of water on the hardness and other properties of bulk crystals, and attribute the influence to an increase in the ease of deformation at wet surfaces. Thin films in solutions are very wet indeed, and may perhaps have increased ductility as a result. Water is known from other studies to be a plasticizer of rocks[54] and of silica.[55] The second possibility is that the structure of the reaction films

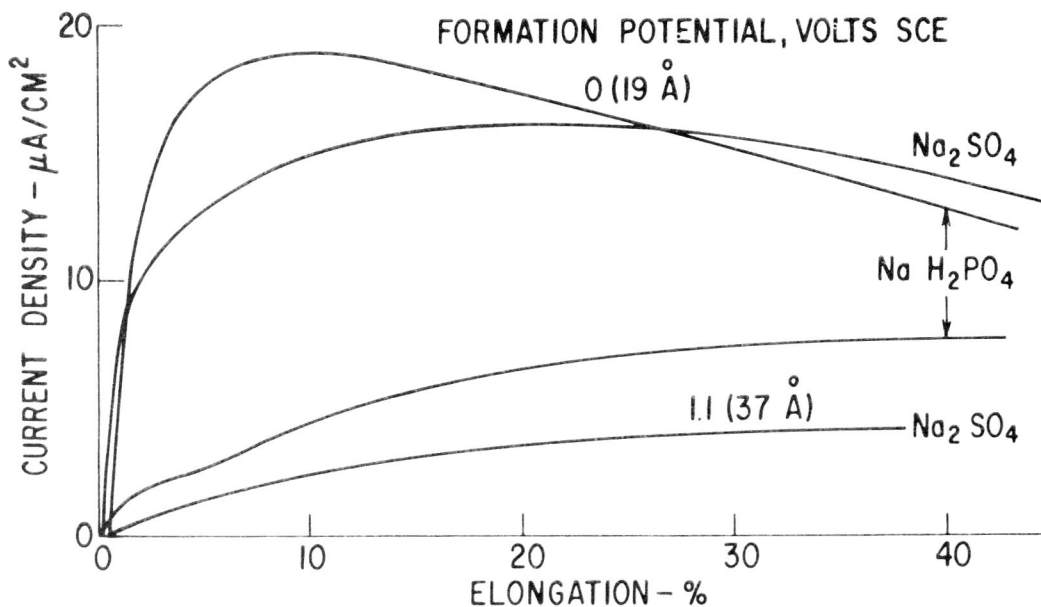

FIGURE 4 — Current density-extension curves for film-covered Type 304 stainless steel wire. Deformation potential 0.0 volt SCE.

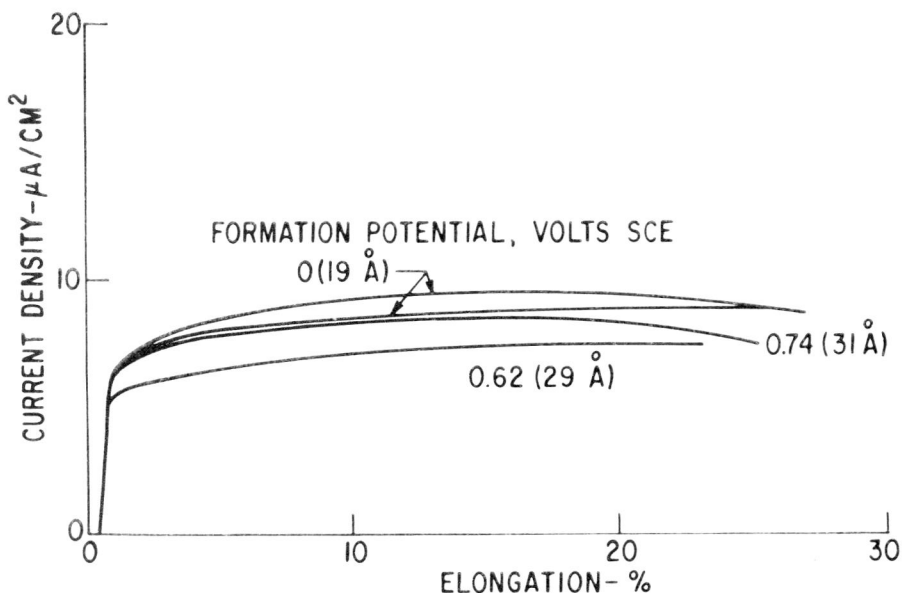

FIGURE 5 — Current density-extension curves for film-covered specially prepared 80Ni-20Cr wire. Deformation potential 0.0 volt SCE in 1 M $Na_2SO_4$.

is far different from that of bulk crystals, and such a structure may be much more ductile. It is easier to imagine liquid-like behavior in a gel than in a crystal. Further studies of the ductility of films and the relation to film structure would be highly desirable.

## Critique of Theories of Stress Corrosion Cracking

In this section the role that reaction films may play in stress corrosion cracking will be discussed. The discussion will be confined mostly to metals and to situations in which some kind of electrochemical process is involved. There are, according to the theories, three fundamentally different conceptual conditions which may cause stress corrosion cracking. First, the surface tension may be lowered enough to produce brittle failure. Second, the material may be rendered thermodynamically unstable by the stress in a very local region. Third, all of the material is continuously maintained in a thermodynamically unstable regime but does not corrode because of a kinetic limitation; stress corrosion cracking occurs when the protection fails locally.

### Reduction of Surface Tension

The problem is to understand how the surface tension can be reduced from the metal-vacuum value, typically 1000 to 2000 ergs/cm$^2$ to the values required to fit the data. Coleman, Weinstein, and Rostoker[56] deduced surface energies of 157 ergs/cm$^2$ for stainless steel and 93 ergs/cm$^2$ for a magnesium-aluminum alloy. The arguments already presented indicate that extremely large adsorption energies, perhaps 100 kcal/mole, would be required to cause such a reduction of surface energy. Such large energies have not been reported for metal-aqueous solution interfaces, and in particular there is no indication that the chloride ion, responsible for stress corrosion cracking in several ferrous and nickel base alloys, has any tendency for such strong adsorption. It is conceivable that the large reduction in surface energy could result from reaction film formation, although visualization of an atomic fracture mechanism is difficult. It would also be difficult to see, if reaction films are responsible for the reduction in surface tension, why pure metals would not be susceptible and why a specific environment is necessary. A further problem, previously discussed by others, is that plastic work accompanying fracture of a ductile metal would contribute to the effective surface energy.

### Local Thermodynamic Instability

Charles and Hillig[57] have proposed that very high stresses may exist in a material at the crack tip, and that such stresses may change the kinetics as well as the thermodynamic driving force. There is no reason why the material in bulk could not be at equilibrium with its surroundings with only the highly stressed material at the crack tip unstable. If a uniform strain of 3 percent of the volume is thought to occur under a hydrostatic tension of 10$^6$ psi, then the work done is about 2 x 10$^9$ ergs, or (if the molecular weight divided by the density is 10) roughly 500 cal/mole, corresponding to an overvoltage of 20 mv. Such a low driving force is not likely to result in rapid cracking of most metals, even if a stress of 10$^6$ psi could be imagined to occur, because metals are usually polarized anodically to much greater potentials by the corrosion process. The mechanism may have some applicability in other systems, for instance, in the stress corrosion cracking of AgCl in solutions forming complexes.[58,59] The addition of a strong complexer greatly increases the dissolution rate of ionic crystals by changing the double-layer potential.[48] It is known[60] that silver halides can dissolve rapidly at small driving forces in complex forming solutions. If a sufficient stress concentration can occur then a crack could be produced by rapid local dissolution. Pre-saturation may be required to prevent blunting of incipient cracks by general dissolution. According to this view the observed correlation with the charge of the complex results from the fact that more highly charged complexes occur in general when the complex stability is high, a condition which also increases the dissolution rate. An alternative explanation for this type of stress corrosion cracking[76] appears questionable because the interpretation requires a very long time for relaxation of the double layer in the AgCl.

### Local Breakdown of Protection

The remaining theories (film rupture, attack at areas of chemical segregation, hydrogen embrittlement, stress assisted dissolution, and strain assisted dissolution) belong to the category in which the metal is unstable but is protected by a passive film which is locally destroyed in some fashion. It is believed that this is the usual situation for metals. Under these conditions an electrochemical cell is set up between the crack tip and the rest of the surface, and local current densities as high as amperes/cm$^2$ can be imagined. Thus passivity, while essential to use of the material, establishes a condition of instability which is conducive to stress corrosion cracking.

Cracking evidently may proceed rapidly once an incubation period has been passed. It is possible that the development of some locally favorable situation is required. For instance, corrosion near an inclusion or other flaw in the film may result in a local concentration of anions or pH change which can trigger attack. Or a pit may simply be a stress concentrator. Little is known about this induction period or of the nature of the initial attack.

There are some ideas which have been generated which probably apply equally to all theories, and which will be discussed first. Wedging by corrosion products can increase the applied stress to a critical level. There is evidence for such an effect but that is not by itself sufficient to understand stress corrosion cracking. The influence of the deformation mode of the material, whether by localized slip on a few planes or by more general dislocation motion, has been shown to be important.[73] However, while localized deformation probably accentuates any of the effects to be discussed it is not the fundamental mechanism of attack.

*Stress assisted dissolution* was proposed by Charles and Hillig[57] to explain static fatigue of glass and other types of stress corrosion. According to this theory, the activated process of the rate determining step is accelerated by stress at the crack tip. The process is autocatalytic, for stress accelerates the reaction, sharpens the crack tip, and the stress is thereby further concentrated. A stable crack is formed when blunting because of surface tension balances sharpening by stress assisted corrosion. The theory is in good agreement with the phenomena of static fatigue.

For metals, it is questionable whether this theory is useful. In glasses, corrosion involves migration of sodium ions within the glass to the surface, and an atomic process with a large activation volume can be imagined. For metals no similar phenomenon is thought to occur. It is hard to see how stress would have a great deal of influence on removal of atoms from surface kinks. Stress might accelerate diffusion to defects near the surface, but then it is simply a contributory factor to another mechanism. It is also harder to imagine very high stresses in a metal. Conceivably the theory could apply to the reaction film, which would be thinned locally at a high rate. However, the corrosion rate of the passive films seems always exceedingly slow, and even a considerable acceleration would still give a low overall cracking rate.

*Strain assisted dissolution* has been proposed to account for high local corrosion rates. According to this theory, rapidly yielding metal dissolves faster than static metal. Some evidence of such an effect has been given (Scully and Hoar;[61] see the paper for references to earlier work). The experiments by Hoar and co-workers involved straining various alloys exposed to boiling 42 percent $MgCl_2$ solution and measuring currents or change in potential. The experiments are therefore similar to those described above,[51] in which the ductility of oxide films was measured. It should be noted that in the $MgCl_2$ the specimen is passive, and that when straining occurs the passive layer is thinned and must be regrown. The currents observed by Scully and Hoar for iron nickel alloys at a strain rate of 107 percent/min and zero solution flow rate range from 50 to 170 $\mu a/cm^2$. Bubar and Vermilyea,[51] at 25 C and a strain rate of 28.5 percent/min observed currents for various metals of 10 to 20 $\mu a/cm^2$. Considering the higher temperature (which probably produces a thicker film) and the higher strain rate used by Scully and Hoar, it is not hard to imagine that the currents were simply those required to reform the passive film. When Scully and Hoar used a high solution flow rate they observed currents which were higher by about a factor of 100. It is likely that the effect of solution flow rate is on the process of reforming the passive film. Suppose that the original film cracks. Then in the crack a layer of some chloride might be expected initially, and a Mueller-type process of passivation[39] can be anticipated. Vigorous agitation can be expected to change substantially the total current flow required to establish the chloride film and then replace it with the final passive film. Evidence that a nonmetallic passive film is formed on stainless steel in boiling 42 percent $MgCl_2$ is presented by Swann and Embury.[73]

Van Rooyen[62] performed experiments on strain induced polarization in boiling 42 percent $MgCl_2$. He found that there were depolarizations up to about 85 mv at small total current densities, but did not observe depolarization at very high current densities, even at strain rates as high as 100 percent/sec. The result at low-current density can be interpreted in terms of disruption of the passive film, while at the high-current densities (to 0.7 amp/$cm^2$) the metal was obviously not passive.

It is concluded that strain induced changes in polarization current are associated with passivity and are caused by disruption of passive films; Windfeldt[64] made a similar suggestion. In agreement with this hypothesis results by Windfeldt for copper[63] and for iron and nickel[64] show small changes in polarization under conditions in which passivity is likely to be absent. For copper, Windfeldt found changes of only a few millivolts (maximum 0.5 to 6 mv) at strain rates of a few percent/sec and very low current densities. In agreement with Van Rooyen, he found no potential change at high strain rates. The small changes observed are probably associated with production on the surface of impurity free regions; at high current densities the surface is cleaned by continuous dissolution. For iron and nickel, potential shifts to 40 mv were observed, again probably because of disruption of impurity layers on the surface.

Straining can introduce some extra atomic steps on the surface, and hence in the case of an ideal crystal surface might be expected to influence the dissolution. However, on the usual rough surface these additional steps are probably of importance mainly because they are not contaminated.

*Rupture of a brittle surface* layer is the fundamental mechanism involved in explanations based on hydrogen embrittlement and on rupture of surface films. It is a proven mechanism; experiments conducted mostly on brass in ammonia solutions leave little doubt that repeated cracking of a brittle tarnish layer can cause a crack to propagate through the metal.[65,66] The rate of propagation of a crack by this mechanism can be calculated as follows. It is assumed that the film grows rapidly to a thickness X on any bare area, and that the crack has a width at the tip equal to X. At a critical strain $\epsilon_c$ the film cracks exposing bare metal which is immediately recovered. Figure 6 shows the process envisaged. The time, $t_c$, necessary to produce a crack is given by

$$t_c = \epsilon_c / \dot{\epsilon} \qquad (11)$$

where $\dot{\epsilon}$ is the strain rate in the film at the crack tip. The crack propagation rate, dl/dt, is then

$$\frac{dl}{dt} = \frac{X}{t_c} = \frac{X\dot{\epsilon}}{\epsilon_c} \qquad (12)$$

To give dl/dt = 0.03 cm/hr, with $X = 3 \cdot 10^{-4}$ cm, and taking $\epsilon_c = 10^{-3}$ the required strain rate is about $3 \cdot 10^{-5}$ per second. If there are $10^3$ active slip bands per centimeter, the strain rate times the number of slip systems, or $10^3 \cdot 3 \cdot 10^{-5} \cdot 3 \cdot 10^{-4} \cong 10^{-5}$ $sec^{-1}$. The specimen

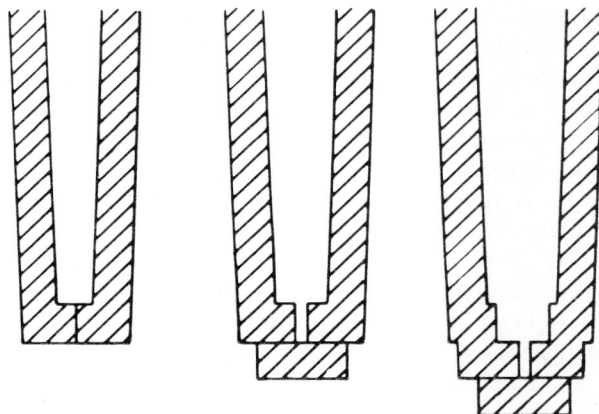

FIGURE 6 — Crack propagation film rupture.

strain rate is independent of film thickness for a given dl/dt and $\epsilon_c$, but the strain rate at the crack tip is much greater for very thin reaction films. If the crack width is large compared to the film thickness, then more than one fracture would be required to advance the crack by a distance X, so a higher strain rate is required.

It is interesting to compare this result with that obtained on the assumption that the film thickness is uniformly reduced by the deformation. In that case, since the strain rate of the film is

$$\dot{\epsilon} = \frac{1}{X} \frac{dX}{dt} \tag{13}$$

we have immediately

$$\frac{dl}{dt} = X\dot{\epsilon} \tag{14}$$

which differs from Equation (12) by the factor $\epsilon_c$, so that a given strain rate gives a smaller crack propagation rate. For a brittle film and a crack width very much larger than the film thickness, the crack propagation rate would be given by Equation (14).

The strain rate deduced above, $10^{-5}$ sec$^{-1}$ is rather large, for presumably if no cracks were present the same creep rate would be observed. In addition, the crack rate assumed was moderate; rates higher by a factor of $10^2$ have been reported. Also, the assumed critical strain for fracture was rather low. In order to have a crack rate of 1 cm/hr, with $\epsilon_c = 10^{-2}$ and other conditions the same the specimen strain rate would have to be about $10^{-2}$ sec$^{-1}$, which seems excessive. Strain rates calculated from Equation (14) for a uniformly thinned film would be even greater. Perhaps in the absence of corrosion creep is blocked, a function of corrosion being to remove work-hardened material or eliminate surface pinning of dislocations.[67,74] Alternatively, such large strain rates would not be necessary if there were some way to magnify the length change produced by each crack. For example, if a very large amount of corrosion was required to produce the passive film, then the crack propagation rate for a given strain rate would increase. Hydrogen embrittlement could be considered such a phenomenon, as could tunnel corrosion

along defects.

The applicability of the film rupture theory to stress corrosion cracking of iron-chromium-nickel alloys, and in general to materials producing very thin passive layers, can be debated. Our results, given in Table 2, show that the films formed are fairly ductile, and that the films formed on high nickel alloys are less ductile than those on 18-8 stainless, while the susceptibility to stress corrosion cracking is higher for 18-8. The fact that ion motion in a film on a metal can relieve stresses in the film has already been mentioned. A further problem for very thin films and narrow cracks is that the only effective deformation is the one which occurs on slip systems which intersect the crack. For thin narrow cracks the total area of crack tip is very small, so that exceedingly restricted slip is required; very small cross slip would take the deformation elsewhere and stop the crack. It should also be pointed out that creep deformation, which presumably is responsible for the rupture of the reaction film, increases with increasing stacking fault energy,[75] while susceptibility to stress corrosion cracking tends to decrease with increasing stacking fault energy. A final problem with the film rupture theory is to understand why pure metals are immune to stress corrosion cracking. It could be postulated that films on pure metals are more ductile; we know of little information on that point except that in our tests[50,51] we observed cracking sooner on alloys containing inclusions.

*Attack at areas of chemical segregation* should also be regarded as a proven mechanism. There is little doubt that stress corrosion cracking in some precipitation hardenable aluminum alloys occurs in a region of altered composition along grain boundaries. There is also no doubt that corrosion will occur more rapidly at defects where segregation has occurred, as shown by studies of pitting at dislocations and by grain boundary attack. In addition, direct observations of attack at defects under stress corrosion conditions have recently been reported.[68] This mechanism gives a ready interpretation of the tunnels observed by Nielsen,[69] which are hard to understand on the basis of the film rupture theory.

A hypothetical example may suffice to clarify the type of mechanism considered. An alloy is exposed in a solution under conditions such that a passive film is formed. Passivity is caused by an oxide film containing mostly metal B, which is present in the matrix A at a concentration of about 10 percent. Local corrosion at an inclusion in the surface generates a small crevice in which a large acid concentration develops. Now local deformation occurs in the region of stress concentration at the crevice, and segregation occurs so that the dislocations present have insufficient metal B over some region around the dislocations. The film formed over the dislocations is not able to resist the solution in the crevice, passivity is destroyed and cannot be reformed on the dislocations, which are rapidly corroded by electrochemical action. The weakened material along the slip plane is then torn apart by the stress, and the process repeats. The process can be nearly continuous or occur in a series of rapid fractures followed by slow attack. Note that corrosion along the dislocations results in a fairly large crack extension for little slip, in contrast to the film rupture theory.

Some investigators[70,71] have found local corrosion at slip planes, but not at dislocations. Such observations have led to suggestions that regions of disorder in short-range ordered alloys are sites of attack, or that tunnel corrosion occurs at ruptures in surface films. It is difficult to see for metals how tunnel corrosion can occur in the absence of a continuous susceptible path, since water is the passivating agent and there is no difficulty transporting water to repassivate the tunnel. Pure metals would also be susceptible to such tunnel corrosion, but do not stress corrosion crack. It is even doubtful if a single plane of altered composition is sufficient, for the composition of the passive film would be averaged over a distance about equal to the film thickness. It is therefore felt that segregation at defects is the most likely cause of tunnel corrosion. The fact that local corrosion is not seen at dislocations may mean that the dislocations moved after the corrosion, or that the observed dislocations are aged differently than those present during stress corrosion cracking, or that the environment is not the same.

is physically and chemically inhomogeneous. Physical defects include steps and kinks, dislocations, and grain boundaries. Even the purest metals available will have composition variations around the structural defects. Such composition changes may occur over distances of a few angstroms to microns, depending on the metal and on the thermal and mechanical history of the specimen. Most engineering metals will in addition have inclusions of various kinds, representing major composition variations. The surface energy of metal-aqueous solution interfaces is probably not much different from the metal-vacuum surface energy.

Corrosion occurs by ion removal from kinks and resulting step motion, and simple dissolution is a relatively unhindered process for most metals. Enhanced corrosion at defects in pure metals is relatively uncommon, and requires special conditions such as adsorption of some specific poison to slow step motion and a surface orientation close to some low index plane. Enhanced corrosion at decorated defects is rather common, and can occur with any surface orientation, although adsorption of a specific ion or film formation is required.

Reaction film formation is also a relatively unhindered process, probably because the metal surface is a good catalyst for film formation. Nucleation and growth overvoltages are low for oxide films. The rate of dissolution of the film substance plays a major role in determining the morphology of the final film and the extent of protection afforded by the film; films with very low dissolution rates make complete coverage easier and yield the best protection. With regard to the properties of reaction films, recent studies have indicated that some of these may be considerably more ductile than has been supposed.

A critique of theories of stress corrosion indicates that for metals the phenomenon usually involves either the rupture of surface reaction layers or hydrogen embrittled layers, or selective electrochemical dissolution along defects at which segregation has occurred.

## Acknowledgment

Conversations with E. W. Hart were of considerable help in formulating some of the ideas in the report.

## Summary

The metal surface in contact with an aqueous solution

## References

1. W. M. Lomer. *Progr. Metal Phys.*, 8, 255 (1959).
2. F. Weinberg. *ibid.*, p. 105.
3. S. Amelinckx. Solid State Phys., Suppl. No. 6 (1964).
4. K. T. Aust, A. J. Peat and J. H. Westbrook. *Acta Met.*, 14, 1469 (1966).
5. *Perspectives in Materials Research*, U. S. Govt. Printing Off. (1963), p. 253.
6. D. Lazarus. *Solid State Phys.*, 10, 71 (1960).
7. J. Friedel. *Dislocations*, Addison-Wesley, Reading, Mass. (1964), p. 356.
8. R. W. Cahn. *Impurities and Imperfections*, Am. Soc. Metals, Cleveland, Ohio (1955), p. 41.
9. J. H. Westbrook. *Met. Rev.*, 9, 415 (1964).
10. A. U. Seybolt, J. H. Westbrook and D. Turnbull. *Acta Met.*, 12, 1456 (1964).
11. J. H. Westbrook. *Analysis of the Nature of Grain Boundaries in Ceramics*, Third Intern. Matls. Symp., Ceramic Microstructures (1966).
12. D. A. Vermilyea. *Proc. First Intern. Conf. on Metallic Corrosion*, Butterworths, London (1962), p. 62.
13. N. Cabrera and D. A. Vermilyea. *Growth and Perfection of Crystals*, John Wiley and Sons, Inc., New York (1958), p. 393.
14. P. Delahay. *Double Layer and Electrode Kinetics.* Interscience, New York (1965).
15. D. A. Vermilyea. *Advances in Electrochemistry and Electrochemical Engineering*, Vol. 3, Interscience, New York (1963), p. 211.
16. D. A. Hayden. *Recent Progr. Surface Sci.*, 1, 94 (1964).
17. G. A. Parks. *Chem. Rev.*, 65, 177 (1965).
18. G. A. Parks and P. L. deBruyn. *J. Phys. Chem.*, 66, 967 (1962).

19. B. Tamamushi. *Colloidal Surfactants,* Academic Press, New York (1963), p. 179.
20. J. G. Eberhart. *Trans. AIME,* **236,** 1362 (1966).
21. T. W. Healy and D. W. Fuerstenau. *J. Colloid Sci.,* **20,** 376 (1965).
22. D. A. Vermilyea. *Surface Sci.,* **2,** 444 (1964).
23. D. A. Vermilyea. *J. Electrochem. Soc.,* **113,** 1067 (1966).
24. H. C. Li and P. L. deBruyn. *Surface Sci.,* **5,** 203 (1966).
25. T. C. J. Ovenston, C. A. Parker and A. E. Robinson. *J. Electrochem. Soc.,* **103,** 390 (1956).
26. N. Cabrera. *Conference on Semiconductor Surface Physics,* Univ. of Pa. Press, Philadelphia, Pa. (1957), p. 327.
27. W. Schaarwächter. *Phys. Stat. Sol.,* **12,** 375, 865 (1965).
28. N. Cabrera, M. M. Levine and J. S. Plaskett. *Phys. Rev.,* **96,** 1153 (1954).
29. N. Cabrera and M. M. Levine. *Phil. Mag.,* **1,** 450 (1956).
30. F. C. Frank. *Acta Cryst.,* **4,** 497 (1951).
31. W. G. Johnston. *Progress in Ceramic Science,* Vol. 2, Pergamon Press, New York (1962), p. 3.
32. D. A. Vermilyea. *Acta Met.,* **6,** 381 (1958).
33. J. C. Suits and J. R. Low. *Acta Met.,* **5,** 285 (1957).
34. A. R. C. Westwood and H. Rubin. *J. Appl. Phys.,* **33,** 2001 (1962).
35. D. A. Vermilyea. *Advances in Electrochemistry and Electrochemical Engineering,* **3,** Interscience, New York (1963), p. 211.
36. L. Young. *Anodic Oxide Films,* Academic Press, London (1961).
37. M. Fleischmann and H. R. Thirsk. *Advances in Electrochemistry and Electrochemical Engineering,* **3,** Interscience, London (1963), p. 123.
38. D. A. Vermilyea. "The Formation and Dissolution of Reaction Films," presented at Washington Corrosion Dialogue, March 1966.
39. H. J. Mueller. *Die Bedeckungstheorie der Passivitat der Metalle,* Verlag, Chemie, Berlin (1933).
40. G. Okamoto, M. Nagayama, T. Ishikawa and T. Shibata. *Second International Conference on Metallic Corrosion,* National Association of Corrosion Engineers, Houston, Texas (1966), p. 558.
41. T. N. Rhodin. *Ann. N. Y. Acad. Sci.,* **58,** 855 (1954).
42. M. Nagayama and M. Cohen. *J. Electrochem. Soc.,* **109,** 781 (1962).
43. J. A. Davies, B. Domeij, J. P. S. Pringle and F. Brown. *J. Electrochem. Soc.,* **112,** 675 (1965).
44. M. W. Breiter and W. Vedder. submitted to Trans. Faraday Soc.
45. D. A. Vermilyea. *J. Electrochem. Soc.,* **113,** 1067 (1966).
46. D. H. Bradhurst and J. S. Ll. Leach. *Trans. Brit. Ceram. Soc.,* **62,** 793 (1963).
47. D. H. Bradhurst and J. S. Ll. Leach. *J. Electrochem. Soc.,* **113,** 1245 (1966).

48. D. A. Vermilyea. *J. Electrochem. Soc.,* **110,** 345 (1963).
49. C. Edeleanu and T. J. Law. *Phil. Mag.,* **7,** 573 (1962).
50. S. F. Bubar and D. A. Vermilyea. *J. Electrochem. Soc.,* **113,** 892 (1966).
51. S. F. Bubar and D. A. Vermilyea. *J. Electrochem. Soc.,* **114,** 882 (1967).
52. J. H. Westbrook and P. J. Jorgensen. *Trans. AIME,* **233,** 425 (1965).
53. J. H. Westbrook. *Environment Sensitive Mechanical Properties,* Gordon and Breach, New York (1967).
54. E. Orowan. *Sci.,* **146,** 1003 (1964).
55. D. T. Griggs and J. D. Blacic. *Sci.,* **147,** 292 (1965).
56. E. G. Coleman, D. Weinstein and W. Rostoker. *Acta Met.,* **9,** 491 (1961).
57. R. J. Charles and W. B. Hillig. *High Strength Materials,* John Wiley and Sons, Inc., New York (1965), p. 682.
58. A. R C. Westwood, D. L. Goldheim and E. N. Pugh. *Disc. Faraday Soc.,* No. 38, 147 (1964).
59. A. R. C. Westwood, D. L. Goldheim and E. N. Pugh. *Materials Science Research,* **3,** Plenum Press, New York (1966), p. 553.
60. W. Jaenicke and M. Haase. *Ber. Bunsenges.,* **63,** 521 (1959).
61. J. C. Scully and T. P. Hoar. *Proc. Second Intern. Conf. on Metallic Corrosion,* National Association of Corrosion Engineers, Houston, Texas (1966), p. 184.
62. D. Van Rooyen. *Proc. First Intern. Conf. on Metallic Corrosion,* Butterworths, London (1962), p. 309.
63. A. Windfeldt. *Electrochem. Acta.,* **9,** 1295 (1964).
64. A. Windfeldt. *ibid.,* p. 1139.
65. A. J. Forty and P. H. Humble. *Proc. Second Intern. Conf. on Metallic Corrosion,* National Association of Corrosion Engineers, Houston, Texas (1966) p. 80.
66. A. J. McEvily, Jr. and A. P. Bond. *J. Electrochem. Soc.,* **112,** 131 (1966).
67. E. W. Hart, private communication.
68. D. Tromans and J. Nutting. *Corrosion,* **21,** 288 (1965).
69. N. A. Nielsen. *Proc. Second Intern. Conf. on Metallic Corrosion,* National Association of Corrosion Engineers, Houston, Texas (1966), p. 116.
70. M. R. Louthan, Jr. *Corrosion,* **21,** 288 (1965).
71. H. W. Pickering and P. R. Swann. *Corrosion,* **19,** 373 (1963).
72. J. S. Armijo and B. E. Wilde. submitted to *Corrosion,* September 1966.
73. P. R. Swann and J. D. Embury. *High Strength Materials,* John Wiley and Sons, Inc., New York (1965), p. 327.
74. J. C. Scully. *Brit. Corrosion J.,* **1,** 355 (1966).
75. D. McLean. Rept. *Progr. Phys.,* **29,** 1 (1966).
76. A. R. C. Westwood, D. L. Goldheim and E. N. Pugh. *Phil. Mag.,* **15,** 105 (1967).

## Discussion

**P. R. Swann, Imperial College:**

It seems that film repair is the only reaction you consider in your experiments on deformed specimens. In practice it is observed that a certain amount of dissolution takes place at active slip steps in addition to film repair and this would presumably contribute to the current that you measure. Would such a contribution affect the interpretation of your results?

**D. A. Vermilyea:**

In our experiments Bubar and I compare the current flowing during extension of a wire anodized at a high potential with that of a similar wire anodized at the same potential at which it is extended. If there is dissolution at active slip steps it should be the same in both experiments.

Such dissolution, if present, should result in a current which is larger than that required to repassivate the surface and might, therefore, make the estimated ductility too low. There are several other reasons why the observed currents are too large and estimated ductility too low; these reasons are given in the paper. We know of no evidence to suggest any large amount of dissolution at active slip steps under our conditions, and we do observe currents of the order of magnitude expected if all current flow causes film repair.

**D. L. Douglass, Stanford Research:**

I would like to comment on Dave Vermilyea's paper. The results are very interesting, but I don't think they apply to stress corrosion fracture. Most of the films he studied, I believe, are amorphous, and we don't really know what the films are that form during stress corrosion of the various materials. I think it is also a little risky to say there is a certain amount of deformation. In the case of Bradhurst and Leach's work, elastic deformation of two to three percent was found. The aluminum oxide was amorphous, having a much lower elastic modulus than one would expect for crystalline material. Actually, the deformation was strictly elastic up the point at which fracture occurred.

It appears questionable to compare your results to the films actually formed under stress corrosion conditions.

### D. A. Vermilyea:

**I agree that there is no proof in our experiments that films present during stress corrosion cracking are ductile. I believe we can legitimately raise the question of ductility, however, and ask of those who assume the films to be brittle "How do you know?" With regard to elastic deformation, our wires were extended as much as thirty percent and I doubt if such elastic extension could be expected.**

### A. R. C. Westwood, RIAS:

Dr. Vermilyea has commented on the possible influence of adsorbed water on the ductility of surface oxide films. In support of this possibility, recent work at RIAS[1] has shown that adsorbed complex ions of high charge, or polar molecules of high dipole moment, can significantly influence the mobility of surficial[2] (near-surface) dislocations in MgO. Such phenomena, which are

[1] A. R. C. Westwood, D. L. Goldheim and R. G. Lye. *Phil. Mag.*, **16**, 505 (1967); *Phil. Mag.*, **17**, 951 (1968).
[2] This term, taken from geology and used to denote the region at and just below the surface, was suggested by Dr. H. M. Davis, of ARO-Durham.

examples of the Rebinder effect, are considered to result from chemisorption-induced changes in the state of ionization of surficial impurity atoms and other point defects. This leads to variations in the nature of the interactions between these defects and moving dislocations, altering dislocation mobility and hence oxide hardness. Since the mobility of dislocations can be influenced to depths of at least $10\mu$ into solid MgO crystals, it may be concluded that the deformation behavior of the normally much thinner surface oxide films should be extremely environment-sensitive.

### H. Spahn, BASF:

Dr. Vermilyea concludes that, in the mechanism of stress corrosion cracking, strain-induced changes in polarization current are of importance—these changes being associated with passivity and caused by disruption of passive films.

In support of this are observations we made in potentiostatic corrosion fatigue work with 18/8 stainless steels and 13 percent chromium steels in sulfuric acid. Keeping the potential in the passive region (e.g., at $\epsilon_h$ = + 750 mV) the anodic current remains for a large number of load cycles at the very low values typical for passivity (see Figure 1). After a certain fraction of the specimen lifetime (e.g., 90 percent) the current starts to increase considerably.

The mechanistic aspect of this corrosion fatigue work can be summarized as follows: at normal air fatigue loads a certain number of cycles elapses until at some site surface gliding occurs. It is only at this site that the passive layer is disrupted and thereafter repassivated. In the repassivation process a certain amount of electricity (supplied by the potentiostat or a redox system) has to flow which in turn means that in the region of a glide step some metal is

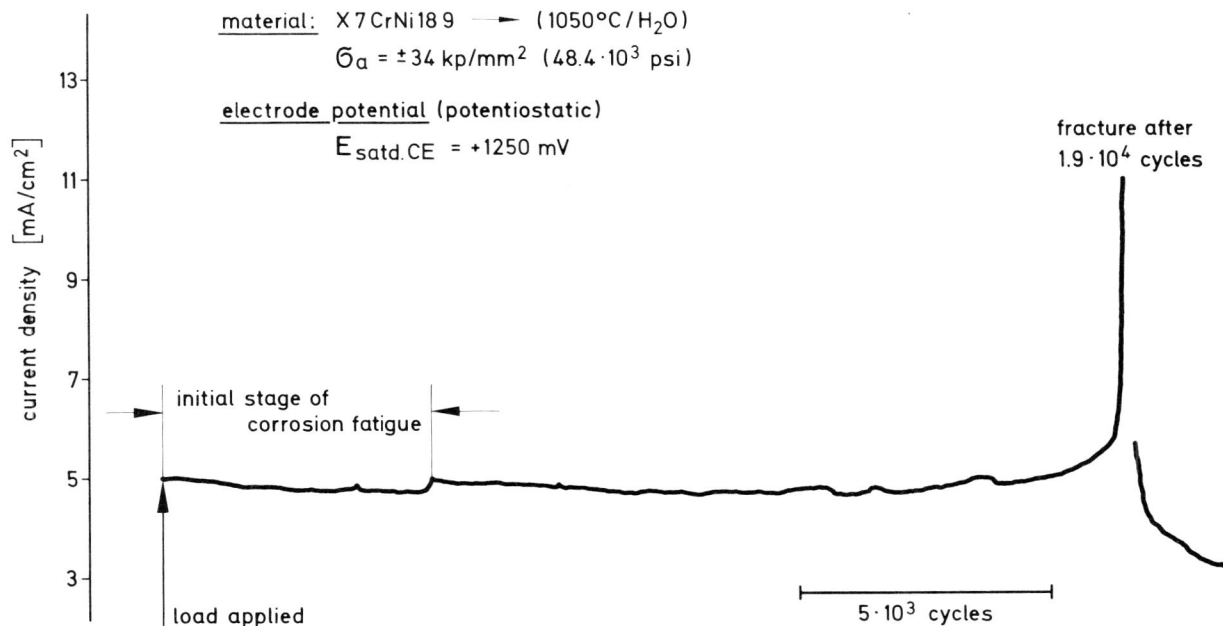

material: X 7 CrNi 18 9 ⟶ (1050°C / H$_2$O)
$6_a$ = ±34 kp/mm$^2$ (48.4·10$^3$ psi)

electrode potential (potentiostatic)
$E_{satd.CE}$ = +1250 mV

fracture after 1.9·10$^4$ cycles

initial stage of corrosion fatigue

load applied

5·10$^3$ cycles

**FIGURE 1a — Current density vs number of cycles for a Fe-18Cr-8Ni alloy.**

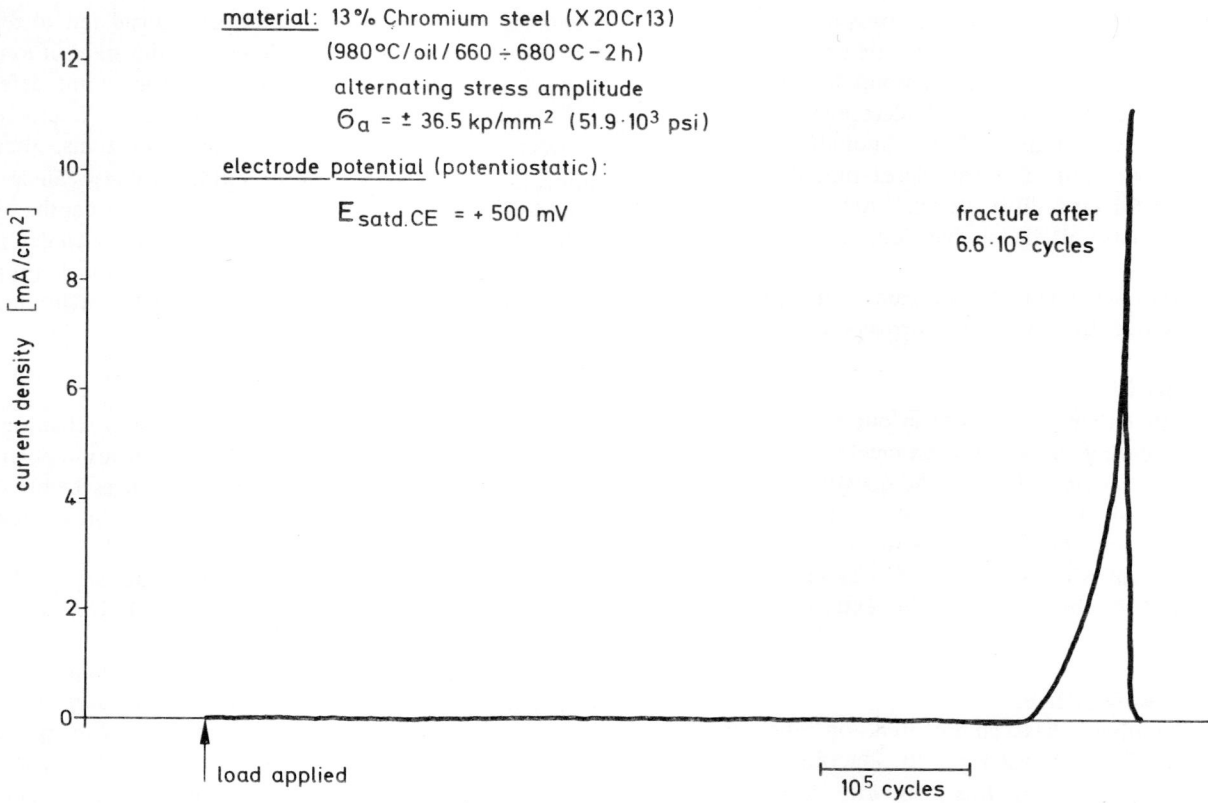

FIGURE 1b — Current density vs number of cycles for a Fe-13Cr alloy.

material: 13% Chromium steel (X 20 Cr 13)
(980°C/oil/ 660 ÷ 680°C − 2 h)
alternating stress amplitude
$\sigma_a = \pm 36.5 \, kp/mm^2 \; (51.9 \cdot 10^3 \, psi)$
electrode potential (potentiostatic):

$E_{satd.CE} = +500 \, mV$

fracture after
$6.6 \cdot 10^5$ cycles

load applied

$10^5$ cycles

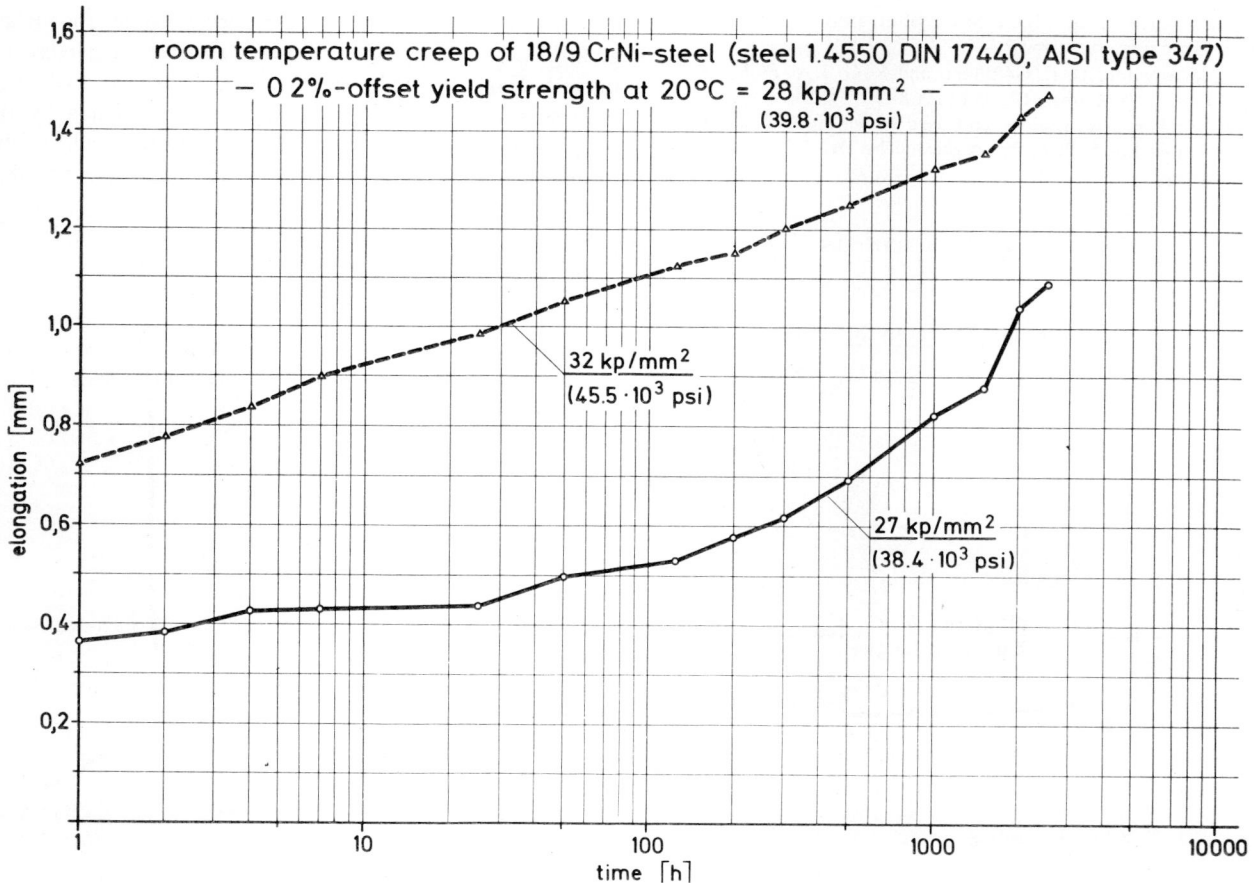

FIGURE 2 — Room temperature creep of a Fe-18Cr-9Ni steel at two applied stresses

room temperature creep of 18/9 CrNi-steel (steel 1.4550 DIN 17440, AISI type 347)
— 0 2%-offset yield strength at 20°C = 28 kp/mm² —
$(39.8 \cdot 10^3 \, psi)$

32 kp/mm²
$(45.5 \cdot 10^3 \, psi)$

27 kp/mm²
$(38.4 \cdot 10^3 \, psi)$

30

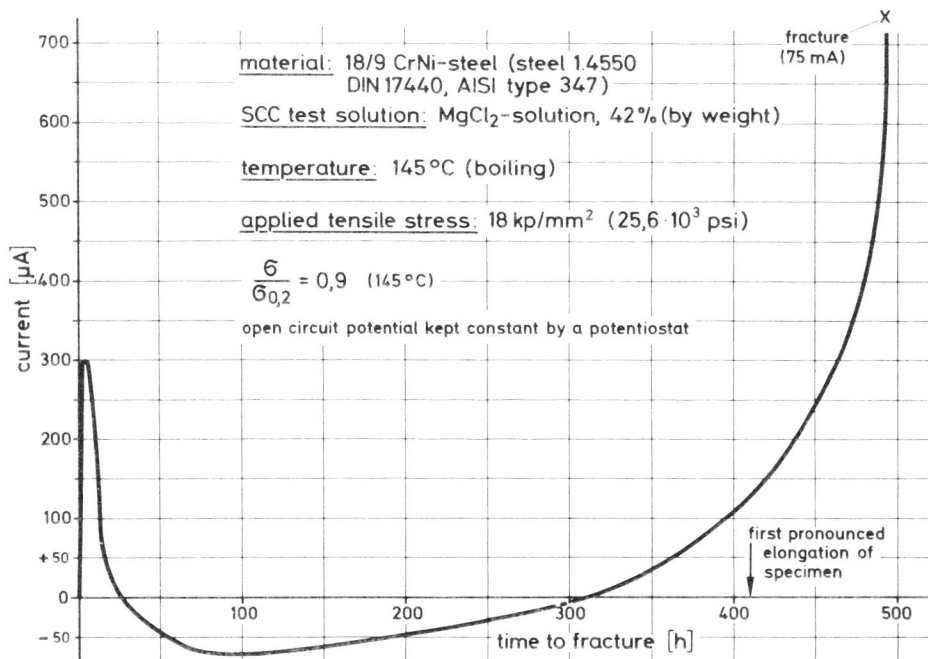

FIGURE 3 – Current vs time to fracture for Type 347 stainless steel exposed to boiling $MgCl_2$.

The figure contains the following labels:

material: 18/9 CrNi-steel (steel 1.4550 DIN 17440, AISI type 347)

SCC test solution: $MgCl_2$-solution, 42% (by weight)

temperature: 145°C (boiling)

applied tensile stress: 18 kp/mm² (25,6·10³ psi)

$\frac{6}{6_{0,2}} = 0,9$ (145°C)

open circuit potential kept constant by a potentiostat

fracture (75 mA)

first pronounced elongation of specimen

dissolved forming a micro-notch, at the tip of which the stress intensity is increased. For obvious reasons this situation leads to further gliding, repassivation (with metal dissolution) and so forth. These processes enhance each other and cause an increase in current density that can be observed in Figure 1. At high repassivating current densities (e.g., when using a potentiostat) only one crack can be observed which leads to fracture. This clearly indicates that the rupture of the passive film is an elementary step in the corrosion fatigue mechanism under passive conditions. The site at which a glide step first protrudes through the passive layer is both the crack and the fracture initiation point (cf. Spahn, H.: Zeitschr. phys. Chem. 234 (1967) 1-25).

Whereas in corrosion fatigue the mechanistic aspects of film rupture can be understood by the formation of glide bands (T- or F-bands) extrusions, intrusions and related phenomena this is more difficult for the static load in stress corrosion cracking.

Experiments with constant strain rates do provide for the plastic deformation necessary for film rupture. They resemble the conditions during the final portion of corrosion fatigue (cf. the steep rise before fracture in Figure 1). However, we observed stress corrosion failures of stainless steel specimens in boiling 10 percent $MgCl_2$-solution after some 10,000 hours. Any mechanism must account for this and can so by assuming some sort of creep.

Surprisingly we found that austenitic stainless steels do show creep even at room temperature, as Figure 2 demonstrates. It seems possible to assume that even in diluted chloride solutions this type of long-time creep could rupture the passive film and lead to sites of preferential attack that intensify the stress so far as to trigger further

plastic deformations over long periods of time.

A long-time potentiostatic SCC experiment shown in Figure 3 supports this assumption. After a steady state open circuit potential had been attained, this potential was kept constant and the current was recorded. Though the specimen was loaded below its yield point, sufficient gliding must have occurred after applying the load to rupture the film as can be concluded from the current peak at the onset. In contrast to electrolytes that do not cause stress corrosion (e.g., $H_2SO_4$) it takes considerable time to repassivate the austenitic steel in 42 percent $MgCl_2$-solution. This repassivation process lowers the anodic current leading in this experiment to a cathodic current after some 25 hours. The increase of current is believed to be due to the aforementioned creep processes. They disturb or rupture the passive film at sites where slip occurs. In the repassivation process metal is dissolved whereby the stress increases, new gliding takes place and so forth. This part of the mechanism seems to be closely related to the corrosion fatigue mechanism of stainless steels in the passive state. Again in close correlation to corrosion fatigue (cf. Figure 1) the slip processes become more and more intensive and the tip of the micro-notches may then remain active most of the time as would be true when any film formed by repassivation is ruptured by the slip processes.

**D. A. Vermilyea:**

**Dr. Spahn has incorrectly interpreted my conclusions concerning the role of rupture of passive films. Rather than conclude that such rupture is important I hope that I have cast some doubt on the importance of film rupture.**

31

# HYDROGEN IN METALS

R. A. Oriani
United States Steel Corporation

## Abstract

This is a critical review of the theoretical concepts and the experimental situation relating to hydrogen dissolved in transition metals, with particular attention to iron. Consideration of the thermodynamic and electronic data leads to the picture of dissolved hydrogen existing upon an interstitial site as an ion screened by conduction electrons, vibrating as an Einstein oscillator, and interacting strongly with other hydrogens, other solute species, and with a variety of structural features. The mobility of dissolved hydrogen in normal lattice regions is very high, reaching the highest value in $\alpha$-iron at an activation energy of 1900 cal/g.atom. The large spread in apparent diffusivities measured in alloyed or cold-deformed metals, particularly iron, is due to the trapping of the hydrogen caused by the attractive interactions with chemical and structural singularities, chiefly internal interfaces. The interaction with elastic stress fields, and the diffusion motivated by gradients of stress, of electrical potential, and of temperature are discussed. The effects arising from the charging of metals with hydrogen of high fugacity are briefly presented.

## I. Introduction

The question of hydrogen in metals—its state, inter-actions, mobility, and influence on mechanical properties—is a complicated one and much has been written on it. The only justification for the present review is that there seems to be a need to consider these questions carefully, in the light of recent work, in order to furnish relevant background for the consideration of the phenomenology and the theories of hydrogen embrittlement and of stress-corrosion cracking with which the present symposium is concerned.

This review has as its goal, therefore, the critical evaluation of information and of concepts that may be of relevance to the understanding of hydrogen embrittlement and of stress-corrosion cracking. It does not attempt to be comprehensive, but will be selective in dealing mostly with the transition metals of interest in these two areas, and chiefly, though not exclusively, with the metal-hydrogen phases which have the pure metal as the limiting composition. The discussion begins with the statics of hydrogen in metals, that is, the thermodynamics and electronic interactions of dissolved hydrogen with the lattice atoms, with other solutes, with structural defects and with stress fields. It then proceeds to the dynamic aspects such as vibration, diffusion, and response to thermal and electrical gradients. The review concludes with some information on the effects of charging with hydrogen.

## II. The Dissolved State of Hydrogen

### The Nature of Dissolved Hydrogen

#### The Dissociated State of Hydrogen

In the main, we wish to restrict our attention to the primary metallic solutions of hydrogen, i.e., those which are contiguous to the pure metallic component and include it as a limiting case. For such systems one finds that there is in general a temperature and concentration range in which Sievert's law[1] is obeyed, namely

$$c = sp^{1/2} \qquad (1)$$

where c is the concentration of dissolved hydrogen in equilibrium with gaseous hydrogen at pressure p, and s is a constant of proportionality. This empirical expression is consistent with the equation for chemical equilibrium

$$K = \frac{a_H}{p^{1/2}} \qquad (2)$$

written for

$$\tfrac{1}{2}H_2 \, (g) = \underline{H} \qquad (3)$$

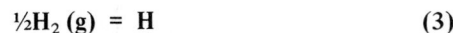

where $a_H$ is the activity of the dissolved, dissociated hydrogen, which can be regarded as proportional to c at sufficiently low hydrogen concentrations. Agreement of the empirical expression with that derived on the assumption of dissociation of the diatomic molecule leads one to assert that dissolved hydrogen exists in the metal in its dissociated form; we may call this atomic hydrogen, subject to further discussion. Deviations from (1) are observed, particularly at low temperatures and at high hydrogen fugacities (or effective pressures) and these will be discussed subsequently.

Comparison of Equations (1) and (2) shows that Sievert's law constant is really the chemical equilibrium constant divided by an activity coefficient, f. Hence one can derive

$$\ln s = \ln \frac{c}{p^{1/2}} = -\frac{\Delta \overline{H}}{RT} + \frac{\Delta \overline{S}}{R} - \ln f, \quad (4)$$

in which $\Delta \overline{H}$ and $\Delta \overline{S}$ are respectively, the relative partial molal enthalpy and the relative partial molal entropy of the dissolved hydrogen. Thus, the slope of a curve of concentration against reciprocal temperature, at constant gas pressure, yields $\Delta \overline{H}$ divided by the gas constant, R. Because of confusion in the literature, it seems necessary to remark that $\Delta \overline{H}$ as related to process (3) is obtainable only from an isobaric plot, not from the temperature dependence of the terminal solubility in the usual phase diagram. In addition, the classification of metals into exothermic and endothermic occluders (of hydrogen) according to whether $\Delta \overline{H}$ is negative or positive has no fundamental significance beyond fixing the sign of the variation of concentration with temperature at constant gas pressure. In particular, the separation into these two classes is of no significance as to the mechanism of electronic interaction, but simply categorizes the systems into the class for which the energy of electronic interaction is a smaller, but negative, quantity than the energy of dissociation of molecular hydrogen, and into the class for which the opposite is the case.

*The Interstitial Position of Dissolved Hydrogen*

In addition to knowing that dissolved hydrogen exists in the dissociated form in solid or liquid metals, one would like to know its position in the lattice (in the case of the solid state) and the nature of the electronic interactions. With respect to the first point, the partial molal volumes of hydrogen given in Table 1 provide a reason for the inference that the dissolved hydrogen is interstitial in the various lattices. Remembering that the diameter of a hydrogen atom is 1.06 Å, much smaller than that of any of the metal atoms, it does not seem likely that the expansion of the lattice could reach near equality with the molal volume of the host atom by the incorporation of the hydrogen atom upon a substitutional lattice position. One would infer, then that the hydrogen atoms occupy interstitial positions, and we note in passing that the dissolved hydrogen atom is not small, as has often been thought; in fact the perturbation of the lattice is quite significant, and in α-iron it is about 1/3 of that caused by dissolved carbon.

Another indication that hydrogen occupies interstitial positions in lattices of transition metals is obtained from

the consideration of the measured $\Delta \overline{S}$. Lieser and Witte[2] measured the relative partial molal entropy for hydrogen in solution in Cu, Ni, Ag, and Co and found values ranging from -16.6 to -18.8 cal/deg g atom. Writing down the statistical mechanical expression for $\Delta \overline{S}$ by representing the dissolved hydrogen as Einstein oscillators randomly distributed over the tetrahedral interstitial sites in the f.c.c. lattices (four octahedral sites at ½, 0, 0 and twelve tetrahedral sites at ± ¼ ¼ ¼, per unit cell), they obtain vibration frequencies of about $3 \times 10^{13}$ sec$^{-1}$, considerably higher than the Debye frequency of the lattice. Eichenauer, Löser, and Witte[3] performed more precise solubility measurements for hydrogen and deuterium in nickel and copper and analyzed the results more carefully in terms of occupation of only the octahedral site as well as the alternative, occupation of both kinds of sites. They concluded that greater internal consistency is obtained on the assumption of occupation only of the octahedral interstitial sites and obtained vibration frequencies of about $1.7 \times 10^{13}$ sec$^{-1}$, and a ratio of vibration frequencies of the two isotopes, $\nu_H/\nu_D$, of about 1.4. McQuillan et al[4] similarly analyzed their measured values of $\Delta \overline{S}_H$ in βTi and βZr, in terms of Einstein oscillators on the tetrahedral sites (of which there are six per metal atom in the b.c.c. lattice, at ¼, ½, 0), and found concentration-dependent frequencies of vibration of between 1 and $3.5 \times 10^{13}$ sec$^{-1}$, and $\nu_H/\nu_D \approx 1.4$.

These results cannot in themselves be considered a proof for the interstitial nature of dissolved hydrogen in these metals; they are only consistent with the concept of interstitial site occupation. However, this interpretation gains considerable strength when coupled with the neutron diffraction analysis of Bergsma and Goedkoep[5] for f.c.c. β-Pd(H). They found that the hydrogen atoms (at 90 C) have an Einstein frequency of $1.4 \times 10^{13}$ sec$^{-1}$ and a root-mean-square amplitude of vibration of 0.24 ± .02 Å, whereas the Pd lattice has a Debye frequency of $0.63 \times 10^{13}$ sec$^{-1}$ and a r.m.s. amplitude of 0.10 ± .01 Å. These

**TABLE 1 – Partial Molal Volume of Hydrogen in Various Metals**

| Host Lattice | $\overline{V}_H$ cm$^3$/g atom | Reference |
|---|---|---|
| Pd | 1.73 | (1) |
| β-Ti | 4.1 | (2) |
| β-Zr | 5.3 | (2) |
| Ta | 9.4 | (3) |
| α-Fe | 2.0 | (4) |
| Nb | 4.5 | (5) |

(1)Calculated from data in R. P. Elliott, *Constitution of Binary Alloys,* McGraw-Hill Co., New York, 1965, p. 502; W. T. Lindsay, Jr. *Abstracts of Amer.* Chem. Soc., National Mtg., Pgh., March 1966.
(2)Calculated from data in Reference 4.
(3)Calculated from data in M. Hansen, *Constitution of Binary Alloys,* 2nd Ed., McGraw-Hill Book Co., New York, 1958.
(4)See Reference 74, end of chapter.
(5)See Reference 37, end of chapter.

results can in themselves be taken as strong indication of the interstitial nature of the hydrogen dissolved in Pd. In addition they,[5] as well as Worsham, Wilkinson, and Shull,[6] were able to locate by neutron diffraction the hydrogen atoms in $\beta$Pd(H); these were found to occupy the octahedral positions.

Other systems for which the dissolved hydrogen has been located by neutron diffraction are the b.c.c. $Ta_2D$, for which Wallace[7] finds tetrahedral site occupation, and the f.c.c. $NiH_{.6}$ for which Wollan, Cable, and Koehler[8] locate the hydrogens on the octahedral holes. This substance is considered in this survey, even though it is separated from the terminal solid solution by a two-phase field[9] because of the simple structure of the lattice. For a similar reason we may here point out that Rundle, Shull, and Wollan[10] found that the hydrogens are on the tetrahedral sites in f.c.t. $ZrH_2$, and that the same result was found by Sidhu, Heston, and Zauberis[11] for f.c.t. $HfH_2$. The neutron diffraction results of Roberts[12] are interesting in showing that below 207 K the deuterium atoms in $VD_{0.75}$ develop an ordered arrangement in which the deuteriums occupy a primitive cubic lattice having twice the lattice parameter of the vanadium unit cell. Wallace[13] also found that the hydrogens in $Ta_2H$ order at low temperatures.

Neutron diffraction can locate the hydrogen atoms only when these are at a relatively large concentration. For the very low concentration range, one may make inferences from the magnitude of the diffusivity of a solute as well as from that of the pre-exponential term, $D_O$ in the diffusivity compared with the magnitude calculated by some model for the diffusion of interstitials. The latter has been done by several authors using Zener's[14] model, which can be written as

$$D_O = \alpha \, a^2 \, n \, \nu e^{\Delta S^*/R}$$

$$\nu = (\Delta E^*/2m \, \lambda^2)^{1/2} \tag{5}$$

$$\Delta S^* \approx -[d(G/G_O)/dT] \quad \Delta E^* \equiv \beta(\Delta E^*/T_m).$$

In these expressions, a is the lattice parameter, $\alpha$ is a geometric factor equal to 1/24 for a b.c.c. and to 1/12 for a f.c.c. lattice, n is the number of interstitial positions per unit cell (n = 6 octahedral sites in the b.c.c. lattice, n = 4 octahedral sites in the f.c.c. lattice), $\nu$ is the frequency of vibration at the equilibrium position, and $\Delta S^*$ is the entropy of activation for the change of place. This last has been approximated by Zener by the temperature dependence of the elastic shear modulus, G, and on the harmonic oscillator approximation $\nu$ may be calculated in terms of the activation energy, $\Delta E^*$, for the atom of mass m to jump a distance $\lambda$. R and $T_m$ are, respectively, the gas constant and the melting point of the metal. Table 2 collects the results of new calculations on the basis of occupancy of octahedral interstitial sites. Agreement within a factor of ten with the experimental values of $D_O$ may be taken as indicative of the correctness of the hypothesis of the interstitial nature of the dissolved hydrogen.

Finally, the observation[15,16] of Snoek relaxation peaks for hydrogen in b.c.c. iron is convincing evidence that hydrogen is interstitially dissolved in a-iron. The general similarity between the characteristics of the Snoek peaks of hydrogen and of carbon in a-iron suggest that both solutes occupy the same type of interstitial site, and this is generally agreed to be the octahedral for carbon. However, it should be pointed out that the similarity argument is not a strong one, and in any case there are still reasonable doubts[17] about the identification of the sites for carbon in a-iron.

The net result of our considerations thus far is that dissolved hydrogen exists in the dissociated (atomic form) in metals, very probably upon interstitial lattice sites in all transition metals. There is certainty that the location is interstitial in a-iron, $NiH_{.6}$, $Ta_2D$, $\beta$Pd(H), $ZrH_2$, and $HfH_2$, and except for H in a-Fe, certainty also as to the type of interstitial site occupied.

TABLE 2

Values of the Pre-Exponential Term, $D_O$, Calculated from Zener's Model for Interstitial Diffusion of Hydrogen Compared with Experimental Values

| Metal | $\Delta E^*$ | Reference | $\beta^{(1)}$ | $10^4 \, D_O$, calc'd | $10^4 \, D_O$, expl. | Reference |
|---|---|---|---|---|---|---|
| a-Fe | 1920 cal/g at. | 86 | 0.43 | 51 cm$^2$/sec | 6.4 cm$^2$/sec | 86 |
| $\gamma$-Fe | 10,700 | 86 | 0.43$^{(2)}$ | 420 | 66 | 86 |
| Ni | 9,470 | 3 | 0.43$^{(2)}$ | 340 | 67 | 3 |
| Pd | 5,600 | 96 | 0.18 | 90 | 43 | 96 |
| Cu | 9,750 | 3 | 0.35 | 380 | 115 | 3 |
| Au | 5,640 | (3) | 0.31 | 180 | 5.6 | (3) |
| Ba | 4,540 | (4) | 0.90 | 270 | 40 | (4) |

(1) Values of $\beta$ taken from Reference 14.
(2) Assumed equal to $\beta$ for a-Fe.
(3) W. Eichenauer and D. Liebscher, Z. Naturforsch, 17a, 355 (1962).
(4) C. C. Hammerberg, M. S. Thesis, Iowa State University, November, 1965.

We now turn to the question of the electronic state of the dissolved hydrogen. The energy contributions in the process of dissolution of gaseous hydrogen into a metal must include first of all the dissociation of the hydrogen molecule (which is of course independent of the nature of the metal), and secondly the energy of interaction of the dissolved hydrogen at its site in the lattice. The latter will depend in detail upon the degree of approach of the dissolved hydrogen to one of the following limiting cases: (1) the hydrogen atom loses its electron to the electronic bands of the metal, (2) the atomic hydrogen retains its identity as an atom, or (3) the atomic hydrogen acquires another electron to become an anion. It must be emphasized that these states are the conceptual extremes and that there is no reason why reality should not lie somewhere between them.

The salt-like hydrides of the alkali metals and alkaline earth metals seem to be of Type (3), in which the interactions are simply coulombic. Inasmuch as these are never terminal solutions, we will not discuss them further. For transition metal-hydrogen solutions, the evidence definitely indicates that Type (1) obtains since one finds that the electronic properties which are sensitive to the characteristics of the band electrons are strongly affected by the dissolution of hydrogen, whereas if Type (2) prevailed only small changes due to volume expansion would be expected. Hence, one would expect that the dissolution of hydrogen would be facilitated by whatever factors favor the removal (ionization) of the electron into the conduction band, and would be made more difficult by increasing ion-core repulsions between the proton and the metal ions. The interplay of these factors is very difficult to unravel by comparing various metal-hydrogen systems because the property changes are too abrupt. More can be learned by considering the more gradual changes within one metal-hydrogen system, or within one binary metal-hydrogen system.

The classical example is the linear decrease of magnetic susceptibility ($\chi$) of Pd(H) alloys with increasing content,[18] which has been interpreted as showing that the electron from the hydrogen enters the d-band of Pd, thereby decreasing the number of holes in the d-band and hence, decreasing the susceptibility. It should be mentioned in passing that the linearity of $\chi(c_H)$ in Pd should not be given a subtle electronic interpretation since it is due to the not always recognized fact that this alloy system has a large two-phase field. The magnetic susceptibilities of the Ti(H), Ta(H), and V(H) systems have been measured by Trzebiatowski and Stalinski,[19] Stalinski,[20] and Zanowick and Wallace,[21] respectively. Except for V(H), $\chi$ varies in a complex manner with increasing hydrogen concentration, but at this stage the only point we wish to make is that the dissolved hydrogen clearly disturbs the electronic structure of the metal. If one can extract the temperature-independent portion (the Pauli paramagnetic susceptibility, $\chi_p$) of the overall paramagnetic susceptibility, then from its variation with composition one may make some definite

statements about the composition dependence of the electronic density of states at the Fermi surface, $N(E_F)$, since $N(E_F)$ and $\chi_p$ are linearly related.

If the electrons from the hydrogen indeed enter the conduction bands of the metal, one would expect to find a change in the Knight shift of the metallic host atom as the hydrogen concentration is increased. A large variation of the Knight shift of vanadium with hydrogen content has been observed by Oriani et al,[22] Betsuyaku et al,[23] and Schreiber and Graham,[24] and a smaller variation for Nb in Nb(H) by Zamir and Cotts.[25] In alkali metals and in the noble metals, the Knight shift, K, is chiefly a function of the density of the s-electrons at the nucleus times their spin susceptibility. Hence, in such metals one would be able to deduce from the Knight shift variation with alloying how the density of states at the Fermi surface varies with composition and one would also expect simple correlations between $K(c_H)$ and $\chi(c_H)$. However, in transition metals the interrelations are not straight-forward[26] because K has contributions from contact interaction with the s-electrons, from core polarization by d-electrons (which may be a positive or a negative contribution), and from an orbital contribution from the electrons in filled states in the d-band. Nevertheless, one can make the qualitative statement that the variations observed[22-25] in Knight shift show that in these two systems the electron from the hydrogen joins the electron bands of the host lattice. Although the work of Schreiber[27] on La-H, Y-H, and Sc-H is somewhat beyond the scope of this paper in that it does not involve terminal solid solutions, it is relevant in that he is able to interpret the decrease of the Knight shift of the metallic atom with increasing hydrogen concentration as showing a lowering of the density of states as the electron from the hydrogen enters the conduction band. Of significance also is that Rohy and Cotts[28] found that the Knight shift of vanadium in alloys of V-Cr-H is a unique function of the electron/atom ratio, independent of the Cr/H ratio, upon assignment of 5, 6, and 1 to V, Cr, and H, respectively, as the number of electrons per atom that enter the conduction bands.

In view of the foregoing information we conclude that the hydrogen dissolves in transition metals by ionizing, that is, by giving up its electron to the collective electron gas of the metal just as an ordinary metallic solute would be expected to do. Clearly a large $N(E_F)$ should favor the dissolution of hydrogen because the larger is the $N(E_F)$ the less is the energy of the system raised by the entry of the electron into the conduction band. Figure 1 presents some of the available data[29-31] that bears on this question. Remembering that $N(E_F) \propto \chi_p$, and that for these systems $\chi_p \approx \chi$, we see that in the range of electron/atom ratio of 5 to 6.4 there is indeed the expected qualitative correlation between the enthalpy of solution of hydrogen and the $N(E_F)$ for the various alloys. The fact that the qualitative correlation is not observed in Figure 1 for the range of e/a from 4 to 5, nor is it observed in Figure 2 taken from Ebisuzaki and O'Keeffe[32] for alloys of nickel (the electronic specific heat is also proportional to $N(E_F)$) shows that other effects must also be considered.

The fact that hydrogen is ionized as dissolved in the transition metals necessitates a strong perturbation of the conduction electron distribution in the immediate neighborhood of the solute[33] in such a way that the positive charge is shielded by a local excess electron density. Friedel[34] has shown that this shielding, or screening, has a radius of about 1 Å, and is tighter the larger is the density of states at the Fermi surface. Because electrical neutrality is achieved within a very small radius one might in some contexts refer to the dissolved hydrogen as atomic in nature, but it seems best to use the term screened ion to describe the state of hydrogen in solution in a metal.

It should be mentioned here that the response of dissolved hydrogen in metals to an applied electric field (electromigration or solid-state "electrolysis") cannot be interpreted at the present time to give information on the state of ionization of the hydrogen. This will be discussed in a subsequent section.

## Interactions of Dissolved Hydrogen

### Interactions With Solutes

It is appropriate to begin this section with an account of the interactions between the dissolved hydrogen ions themselves. Any deviation from Equation (1) immediately signals the existence of an interaction, either short-range or long-range, between the hydrogens; deviations from Sievert's law are invariably found whenever a metal-hydrogen system is carefully examined at even modest concentrations. Indeed, Sievert's law should be regarded as a law strictly valid only in the limit of vanishing solute concentration, of just the same character as Henry's law.[35]

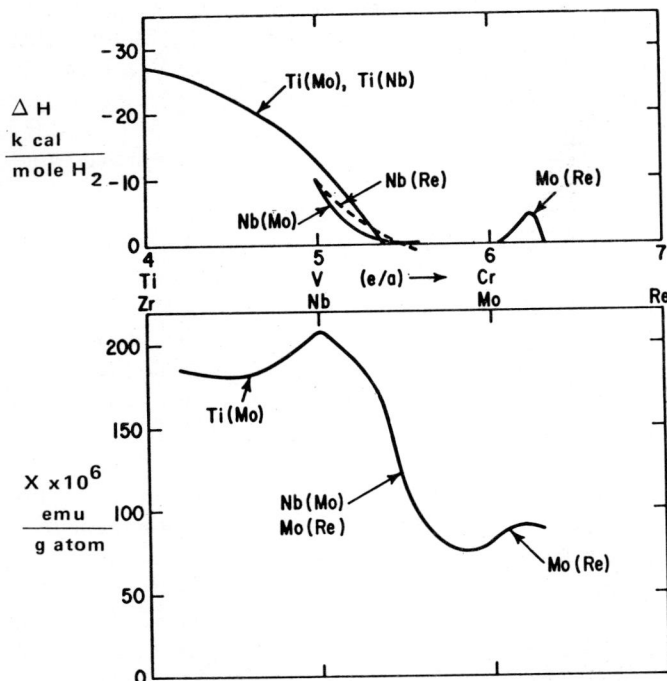

FIGURE 1 — Enthalpy of solution of hydrogen and magnetic susceptibility as functions of the electron-to-atom ratio in binary alloys of transition metals. From References 29-31.

From the point of view that the dissolving hydrogen gives up its electron to the conduction bands of the metal, one would expect to find a negative deviation from Sievert's law (i.e., at a given concentration a smaller equilibrium pressure than that extrapolated from the Sievert's relation valid at lower concentrations) whenever the $N(E_F)$ rises with increasing hydrogen concentration, and conversely, a positive deviation when $N(E_F)$ decreases. Figure 1 has already presented some data bearing on this expectation, and to these may be added the case of $\beta$-Ti(H) and $\beta$-Zr(H), for which the density of states increases,[4] and for which the enthalpy of solution of hydrogen increases negatively[4] (therefore a negative deviation from Sievert's law), with increasing hydrogen concentration. The change in electronic environment produced by the dissolved hydrogen affects additional incoming hydrogen even at considerable inter-hydrogen distances, and hence may be called a long-range interaction. The behavior of hafnium alloyed with about 10% Zr shows that other interactions must also be considered. Katz and Berger[36] find that in this alloy in the $\alpha$-phase the deviations from Sievert's law are towards higher gas pressures, and in keeping with this, the enthalpy of solution of hydrogen becomes less negative with increasing hydrogen concentration. In view of the behavior of the $\beta$-Zr(H) system this is surprising since one would expect the same relation in Hf as in Zr between $N(E_F)$ and $c_H$.

The Nb(H) system displays negative deviations[37] from Sievert's law and increasingly negative[37] enthalpy of solution of hydrogen with increasing $c_H$, which are not in keeping with the decreasing $N(E_F)$ with increasing $c_H$.[4] The problem presented by the Nb(H) system has been discussed frequently for the Pd(H) system, for which Lacher[38] found it necessary to postulate an attractive interaction between the hydrogens in order to obtain a consistent statistical mechanical rationalization of the miscibility gap. The attractive interaction cannot arise through the effect of $c_H$ on $N(E_F)$, since the opposite effect is to be expected on that basis in view of the $N(E_F)$ vs $c_{Ag}$ derived from the measurements of electronic specific heat[39] and of magnetic susceptibility[40] of Pd(Ag) alloys. Lacher did not specify the nature of the attractive interaction, but Stackelberg and Ludwig[41] have argued, as did Fisher[42] for oxygen and nitrogen in tantalum, that the attraction is due to the interaction of elastic strain fields. Makrides[43] on the other hand has suggested a moderately long-range attractive interaction arising from the oscillating electronic charge density about a solute atom in a metal (the "Friedel wiggles"), the amplitude of which decreases as the cube of the distance from the solute.[44]

Simons and Flanagan[45] have given the most comprehensive account of the situation in the Pd(H) system. The miscibility gap arises because of the attractive interactions (of unspecified origin) between the hydrogens which in the $\alpha$-phase (i.e., the low-hydrogen side of the miscibility gap) produce negative deviations from Sievert's law.[46] The attractive interaction is overcome at high hydrogen concentrations by repulsive interactions due to the decreasing $N(E_F)$ associated with the filling up of the

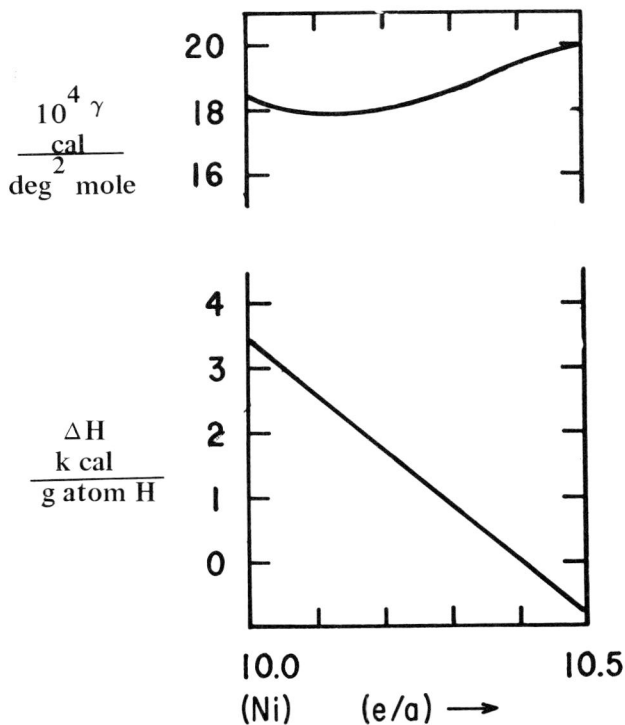

**FIGURE 2** — Electronic specific heat and enthalpy of solution of hydrogen as functions of the electron-to-atom ratio in binary alloys of nickel. From Reference 32.

4d-band in Pd. This is shown by the decreasing values of $-\Delta \bar{H}$ with increasing $c_H$ in the $\beta$-phase.[47] The $a$-field in Pd(H) alloys may be increased by adding Ag or Au, and it has been found that the enthalpy of solution of hydrogen increases negatively as the silver[43,48] or the gold content[49] is increased. This is thought to be due to strong attractive interactions between the hydrogens and the dissolved Ag or Au which more than compensate for the decrease of the density of states in the d-band caused by the dissolution of Ag or of Au.

We see that the understanding of the variation of solubility of hydrogen with alloying elements is tentative even in the most intensively studied systems. It seems best therefore not to try to rationalize the empirical solubility relations, but simply to indicate some significant points. In solid metals in which hydrogen at moderately low temperatures has a solubility in the range of parts per million, it is very probable that adventitious impurities, internal interfaces, and structural imperfections will make a significant contribution to the amount of hydrogen retained in the metal, and this will be discussed in some detail later. This is particularly true for iron, for which much work on hydrogen solubilities has been done on complex alloys. The work of Armbruster[50] (see Table 3) is typical of the best work on solid iron alloys; it shows a small variation of hydrogen solubility and a larger variation of heat of solution with alloying, and it is extremely difficult to assign responsibility to any one solute addition.

The elucidation of the effect of a specific component on the solubility of hydrogen in iron is facilitated by consideration of the data on liquid alloys. Figure 3, modified from Weinstein and Elliott,[51] shows how the hydrogen solubility is affected by the addition of single components to liquid iron, and Figure 4 indicates the variation of the heat of solution of hydrogen with alloying addition (also in liquid alloys). In the opinion of this writer, the interactions between solutes in metallic solution are approximately the same in the liquid as in the solid state, and that at the present time the data on the liquid state are to be preferred for the purpose of evaluating hydrogen-second component interactions in the dissolved state in iron. That problems exist in the liquid state, however, is shown by the discrepancy in the heat of solution of hydrogen into "pure" liquid iron at 1600 C. Weinstein and Elliott[51] obtain 8715 ± 150 cal/g atom H, whereas Schenck and Lange[52] obtain 7605. These authors[52] give very good data on the variation of hydrogen solubility (under 1 atm $H_2$) and of the $\Delta \bar{H}_H$ with composition for the liquid binary alloys of nickel with Fe, Co, and Cu.

**TABLE 3**

Effect of Alloying on Solubility and on Heat of Solution
of Hydrogen in b.c.c. Iron (Reference 50)

| Composition, wt.% | | | | | Hydrogen Solubility at 600 C Under 1 Torr Hydrogen Pressure | Heat of Solution of Hydrogen kcal/mole $H_2$ |
|------|------|------|------|------|------|------|
| C | Mn | Si | Cr | Ni | p.p.m. | |
| .011 | - | - | - | - | 0.0193 | 13.3 |
| .39 | .73 | .19 | .048 | .012 | .0158 | 14.2 |
| .30 | .70 | .128 | - | - | .0218 | 13.6 |
| .12 | .47 | .003 | - | - | .0215 | 13.1 |
| .10 | .39 | .007 | - | - | .0179 | 16.2 |
| .20 | 1.46 | .205 | - | - | .0207 | 14.8 |
| .05 | .23 | 3.17 | - | - | .0242 | 18.6 |
| .32 | .64 | .245 | - | 3.64 | .0202 | 16.2 |
| .32 | .47 | .28 | 12.78 | - | .0146 | 16.4 |
| .09 | .46 | .395 | 15.60 | .33 | .0156 | 15.9 |

Bagshaw and Mitchell[53] also give data for the hydrogen solubility in liquid alloys of Fe and of Ni. Himmler[54] has measured the hydrogen solubility in solid alloys of copper with Ni, Pt, Sn, Al, and Zn. Lieser and Witte[2] summarize the work of the Darmstadt school on the hydrogen solubility and on the $\Delta \bar{H}_H$ in various solid alloys.

Many papers report the variation of hydrogen content with alloying additions where the hydrogen has been charged in by acid attack or by electrochemical means. It is appropriate to warn that the data generated by this means are very probably worthless from the point of view of lattice solubility of hydrogen; this will be discussed at length in a later section.

*Interaction of Hydrogen With*
*Structural Features*

Since dissolved hydrogen expands the host lattice and since it exists as a screened ion, one would expect interactions with dislocations, vacancies, stacking faults, interfaces, etc., either through their elastic fields, through their electrostatic fields, or both. Internal friction peaks ascribed to an attractive hydrogen-dislocation interaction have often been observed.[15,55-58] Recently, Gibala[16,59-61],(1) carried out an extensive investigation, using Ferrovac-E iron cold-worked to various degrees and charged electrolytically with hydrogen. He was able to show that the cold-work peak is caused by the relaxation of dislocations in their associated hydrogen atmospheres, as per the theory of Schoeck.[62] He has derived an interaction free energy of 6400 ± 1600 cal/g atom of hydrogen. It is interesting that one may calculate a number of about this magnitude (actually 9600 cal/g atom H) by taking the interaction free energy as $\bar{V}_H \sigma_h$ from the thermodynamic theory of Li, Oriani and Darken,[63] and calculating $\sigma_h$, the hydrostatic component of the stress system with the

---

(1)The writer appreciates the kindness of Professor Gibala in sending him these manuscripts prior to publication.

equations for the stresses given by Li.[64] This calculation is for a point on the tensile side of an edge dislocation two Burgers vectors distant from the core.

Arons et al[65] have observed a cold-work internal friction peak in palladium with various concentrations of hydrogen. They have identified it as due to a hydrogen-dislocation interaction, but insufficient information is given for an evaluation of the interaction energy. Internal friction peaks have also been observed[66] in hydrogen-charged austenitic stainless steel.

There seems not to exist any definite information on the interaction of dissolved hydrogen with substitutional vacancies or with grain boundaries. In the latter case, the presumption is strong that there would be an attractive interaction in view of the interaction with dislocations discussed above. There does exist some information with respect to stacking faults, however. Rudee and Higgins[67] saturated pure copper with hydrogen by equilibrating with the gas at temperatures between 900 and 1050 C. Upon examining the subsequently prepared filings at room temperature they found a stacking fault probability that increased with hydrogen content. The interpretation of this finding must be equivocal however, since the precipitation of hydrogen upon cooling may be responsible for production of the stacking faults.

More definite is the work of Whiteman and Troiano[68] who found that electrolytic charging of 25 Cr-20 Ni stainless steel to about one at.% H increased the fault density from essentially zero to one faulted plane in ninety. But more significantly, application of the extended-node technique[69] gave a stacking-fault energy of 16 erg/cm² as compared with a typical value of 30 erg/cm² for a hydrogen-free alloy. Thus, we have definite evidence for an attractive interaction between dissolved hydrogen and stacking faults. This is attributed by the authors to the effect of electron/atom ratio on the stacking fault energy proposed by Sivertsen and Nicholson,[70] but in view of the extremely small concentration of lattice-dissolved hydrogen this writer would argue that Whiteman and Troiano have observed a short-range interaction that may aptly be called adsorption.

Stacking faults represent one type of two-dimensional structural features of which internal interfaces are perhaps more obvious. In addition to grain boundaries, about which

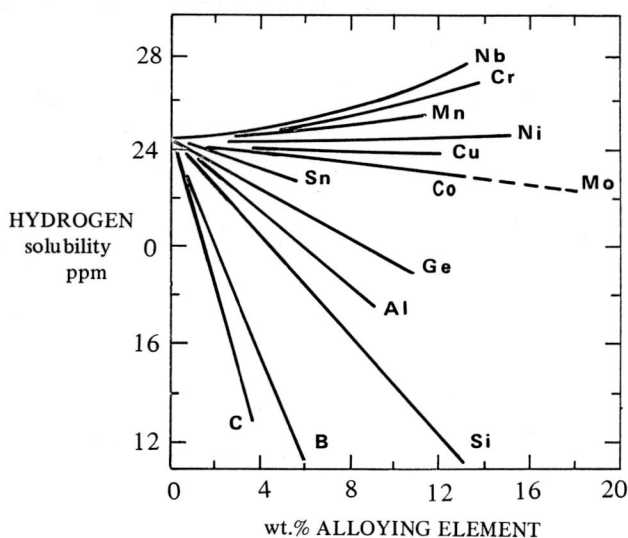

FIGURE 3 — Solubility of hydrogen gas at 1 atm in binary alloys of iron at about 1600 C. From References 51 and 53.

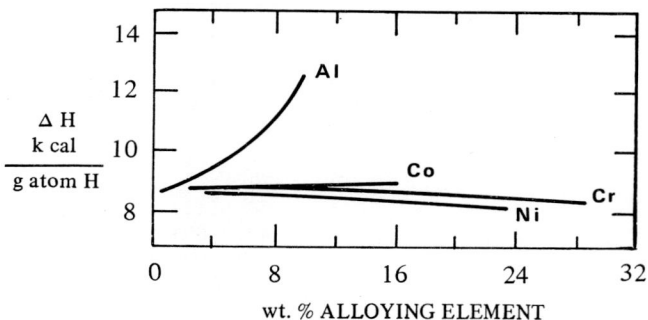

FIGURE 4 — Enthalpy of solution of hydrogen from the gas at 1 atm into binary alloys of iron. From Reference 51.

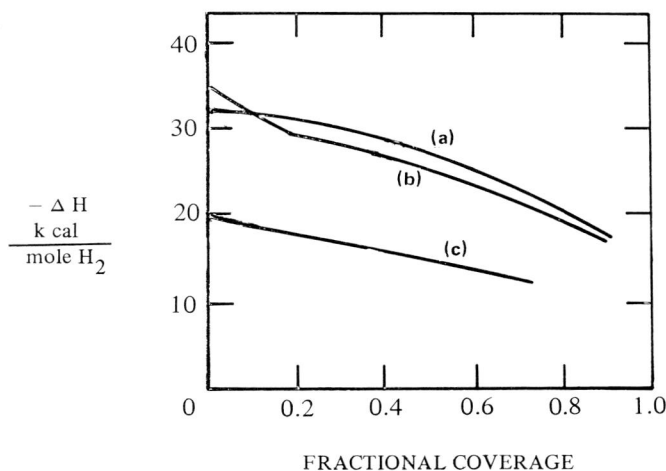

FIGURE 5 — Heats of chemisorption of $H_2$ on iron films as functions of coverage. References: (a) O. Beeck, *Adv. in Catalysis,* 2, 177 (1950); (b) J. Bagg and F. C. Tompkins, *Trans. Faraday Soc.,* 51, 1071 (1955); and (c) A. S. Porter and F. C. Tompkins, *Proc. Roy. Soc.,* A217, 529 (1953).

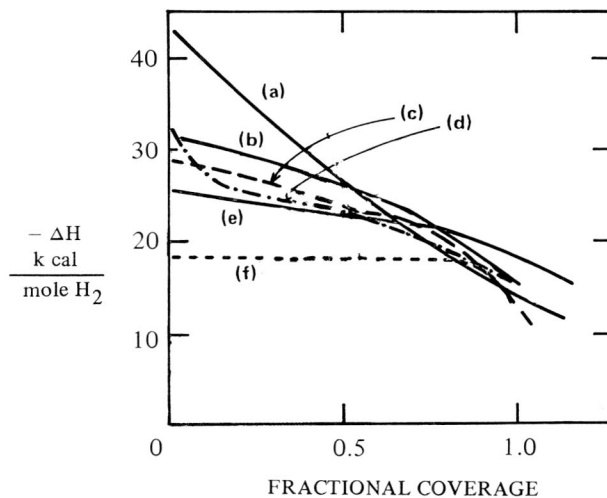

FIGURE 6 — Heat of chemisorption of $H_2$ on nickel films as functions of coverage. References: (a) D. F. Klemperer and F. S. Stone, *Proc. Roy. Soc.,* A243, 375 (1957); (b) O. Beeck, W. A. Cole and A. Wheeler, *Disc. Faraday Soc.,* 8, 314 (1950); (c) M. Wahba and C. Kemball, *Trans. Faraday Soc.,* 49, 1351 (1953); (d) E. Rideal and F. Sweett, *Proc. Roy. Soc.,* A257, 291 (1960); (e) D. Brennan and F. H. Hayes, *Trans. Faraday Soc.,* 60, 589 (1964); and (f) F. J. Brocker and G. Wedler, *Disc. Faraday Soc.,* 41, 87 (1966).

a few words have already been written, we may inquire about the interfaces between solid phases, as well as those between the solid metal and voids. With respect to solid-solid interfaces nothing seems to be known relative to adsorption of dissolved hydrogen. The adsorption of hydrogen upon the metal-gas interface has been frequently studied, but the experiments do not show as much quantitative agreement as one might wish.

We are interested in the adsorption of hydrogen on the internal surfaces of microcavities produced by plastic deformation. Such surfaces are probably fairly clean when initially formed, and the composition of the surface probably represents the average bulk composition, if the temperature does not rise much above room temperature, since only hydrogen is sufficiently mobile. Only recently have experimental techniques in the field of adsorption been sufficiently developed to permit evaluation of adsorption on clean metal surfaces and there still remains some uncertainty on the details, as Figures 5 and 6 show. For the present purpose the significant point is that the magnitude of the heat of adsorption of hydrogen on either iron or nickel is such that at room temperature one will have essentially full monolayer coverage with atomic hydrogen even under a gas pressure of only 0.1 torr. Other transition metals have similarly large enthalpies of adsorption, as Table 4 shows. The variation of the enthalpy of adsorption is usually found to decrease with increasing coverage.

It may be remarked here that it seems likely to this writer that the process of producing an adsorbed layer of hydrogen at a metal-vacuum interface from dissolved hydrogen does not need to overcome any kinetic barrier other than that of hydrogen diffusion in the bulk. There are no experimental data bearing on this point. However, if the surface already has upon it material characterized by a greater heat of adsorption, then one can expect a surface barrier to the transfer of hydrogen from the dissolved state

to the gaseous phase.[2] This is argued by analogy with the results of Podgurski[71] on the effect of carbon monoxide on the evolution of dissolved nitrogen from iron.

*Interaction With Stress Fields*

It is now well recognized[63,72] that an elastic tensile stress decreases, and an elastic compressive stress increases, the chemical potential of an interstitial solute. This is true whether the elastic stress is externally applied or is residual as, for example, about a dislocation or about a precipitate particle.

Dissolved hydrogen, being a particularly mobile interstitial solute, is very apt to achieve the necessary inhomogeneous distribution for uniform chemical potential in an inhomogeneous elastic stress field. If the stress field has a non-vanishing hydrostatic component, $\sigma_h = 1/3 (\sigma_{xx} + \sigma_{yy} + \sigma_{zz})$, where the $\sigma_{ii}$ are the three principal stresses, and if the lattice is elastically isotropic and the dissolved hydrogens expand the lattice equally in all directions the complete equation[63] for chemical equilibrium may be simplified to

$$RT \ln \frac{c_r}{c_\infty} = \bar{V}_H \, \sigma_h \qquad (6)$$

where $c_r$ is the hydrogen concentration of point r at which

[2] Subsequent to the writing of this paragraph, Professor H. H. Johnson informed the writer of the existence of direct experimental evidence on the strong blocking action exerted by oxygen adsorbed on iron upon the transfer of hydrogen from the dissolved state to the gaseous phase. (See V. C. Ewing and A. R. Ubbelohde, *Proc. Roy. Soc.* (London) A230, 301 (1955).)

**TABLE 4 – Initial Heats of Hydrogen Chemisorption**

| Metal | $-\Delta H$, kcal/mole $H_2$ | Reference |
|-------|------|-----------|
| Fe | 32 | (1) |
| Ni | 31 | (1) |
| Ta | 45 | (1) |
| W | 45 | (1) |
| Cr | 45 | (1) |
| Rh | 28 | (1) |
| Ti | 28 | (2) |
| Pt | 25 | (3) |
| Pd | 28 | (1) |

(1)O. Beeck, *Disc. Faraday Soc.*, 8, 118 (1950).
(2)G. Wedler and H. Strothenk, *Berg. Bunsenges. Physik. Chem.*, 70, 214 (1966).
(3)J. G. Aston, *J. Phys. Chem.*, 67, 2042 (1963).

the stress system has the hydrostatic component $\sigma_h$, and $c_\infty$ is the hydrogen concentration under conditions of $\sigma_h = 0$.

As an example of the magnitude of this effect, consider the stresses at point $(r, \theta)$ due to an edge dislocation:[64]

$$\sigma_{xx} = -\sin \theta \,(2 + \cos 2\theta)/r$$

$$\sigma_{yy} = (\sin \theta \,\cos 2\theta)/r \qquad (7)$$

$$\sigma_{zz} = -2\nu (\sin \theta)/r$$

The dislocation is taken as situated on the z-axis with the extra half-plane of atoms along the positive y-axis. The unit of stress is $Gb/2\pi(1-\nu)$ with $G$ and $\nu$ being the shear modulus and Poisson's ratio of the matrix and b the Burgers vector of the dislocation. Li[73] has worked out Equation (6) for the interstitial solute concentration in the field of an edge dislocation and the results are shown in Figure 7. Applying this to hydrogen dissolved in ferrite for which $\overline{V}_H \approx 2$ cm$^3$/g. atom,[74] and taking T = 300 K, we see that the inner iso-concentration contour at which $c/c_\infty = 50$ has a diameter of about 10 Å, while the next contour line for which $c/c_\infty = 5$ has a diameter of about 25 Å. While we have not yet numerically integrated these relations to evaluate the total excess hydrogen, approximate calculations show that the excess hydrogen held by the stress field of an edge dislocation (beyond, say, r = 2b) can easily be larger than the amount held at the core of the dislocation.

Similar excess concentrations of dissolved hydrogen will obtain at equilibrium in the stress field of a microcrack produced by an externally applied force, or that of an aspherical inclusion, or that of a screw dislocation. In the last case, since a screw dislocation has zero dilatation, the full equation[63] for the concentration distribution must be used.

It must be emphasized that the dissolved hydrogen thus concentrated at a region in a lattice where $\sigma_h$ is positive (i.e., of tensile character) has exactly the same chemical potential as everywhere else. Consequently, there is no greater tendency at that point than elsewhere to precipitate, to adsorb, or to enter into any chemical reaction. It is clear, however, that should the elastic stress situation

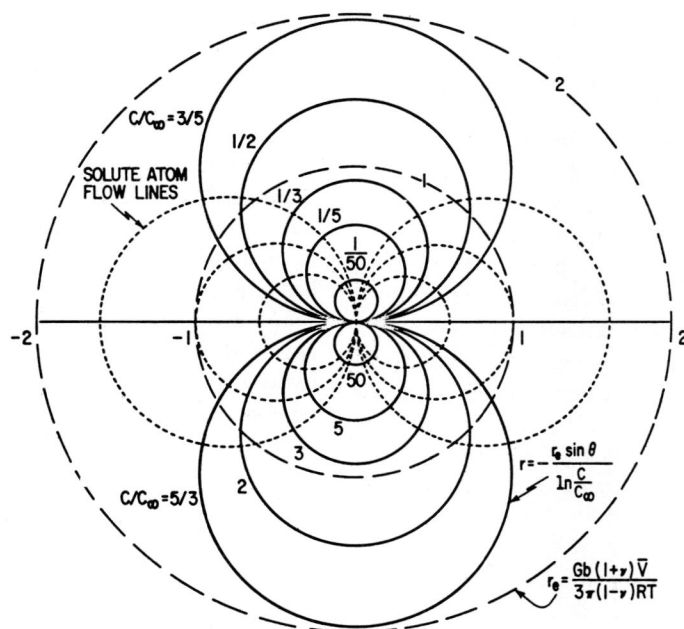

FIGURE 7 – Equilibrium isoconcentration contours of interstitial solute in the stress field of an edge dislocation (after Li[73]). The scale of distance is given by the numerical values on the dashed circles, the unit of which is $Gb(1+\nu)V/3\pi(1-\nu)RT$. See text for definitions of the symbols. Also shown are the paths that the solute atoms would follow in order to re-establish equilibrium after a small departure from the equilibrium distribution. The dislocation is to be thought of as at the center of the figure, with the extra half-plane of atoms in the upper half of the diagram.

suddenly change at a region which had accumulated dissolved hydrogen because of the then existing stress, the dissolved hydrogen would find itself temporarily at a higher chemical potential than elsewhere and may then precipitate or enter into a chemical reaction. A sudden change of stress condition may result from the motion of a dislocation or of a microcrack.

## III. Dynamics of Hydrogen in the Dissolved State

### Thermal Vibrations

The vibrational state of dissolved hydrogen in transition metals has been discussed in a previous section. Analysis of the entropy of solution and direct neutron diffraction determinations characterizé the dissolved hydrogen as an Einstein oscillator.

### Isothermal Permeation and Diffusion

*General Remarks on the Experimental Data*

Even a brief inspection of the literature on the diffusion of hydrogen through metals, particularly iron, impresses one with the large amount of scatter in the data. Figure 8 gives a representative sampling of data from the literature, and shows that the scatter increases considerably as the temperature is decreased.

There are two broad categories of methods by which the diffusivity has been evaluated. The first is a transient technique, in which one measures the time required for hydrogen permeation through a metal sheet to build up to a given fraction of the steady-state value. The second general category is that of measuring separately the steady-state permeation and of determining the hydrogen content just

under the input surface; the diffusivity is then obtained by dividing the permeation rate by the concentration. Each of these has many variants depending on whether the hydrogen is supplied via a gas phase, by acid pickling, or by electrolytic deposition, how the surfaces are prepared, how the permeating hydrogen is detected, and the state of purity and of cold-work of the metal.

*Trapping Theory*

A variation such as that shown in Figure 8 at once suggests that one is dealing with a structure-sensitive property. One recognizes, furthermore, that interactions of dissolved hydrogen with structural and chemical singularities will increase in importance as the value of the enthalpy of solution increases positively (and hence the lattice-dissolved hydrogen concentration decreases) and as the diffusion temperature decreases.

In order to make sense of the diversity of data in this field, we shall adopt the point of view first espoused by Darken and Smith[75] and subsequently by other writers[76-78] that the diffusing hydrogen can be trapped at a variety of special positions within the metal. Such trapped hydrogen will not be as mobile as hydrogen in normal lattice sites. Darken and Smith[75] applied the theory of subscale formation kinetics[79] to the concept of hydrogen trapping and showed that if one were naively to calculate a diffusivity from the time required for hydrogen to appear at the output side of a metal diaphragm, one would calculate too small a diffusivity by the factor $c_\ell^o/\bar{c}_t$ where $\bar{c}_t$ is the mean total concentration of hydrogen in the hydrogen-penetrated region, and $c_\ell^o$ is the concentration of lattice-dissolved (hence mobile) hydrogen at the input side of the diaphragm. They also showed that the presence of traps causes the hydrogen absorption rate to be larger than

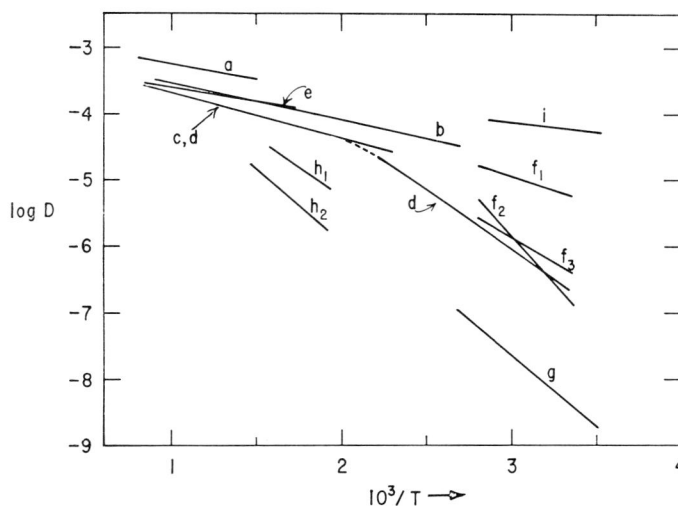

FIGURE 8 — Representative data for the apparent diffusivity of hydrogen in a-iron and in ferritic steels. D in cm$^2$/sec; T in $^0$K. References: (a) Reference 87; (b) C. Sykes, H. H. Burton, and C. C. Gegg, *J. Iron Steel Inst.*, 156, 155 (1947); (c) T. M. Stross and F. C. Tompkins, *J. Chem. Soc.*, p. 230 (1956); (d) Reference 76; (e) Reference 86; (f) R. C. Frank, D. E. Swets and D. L. Fry, *J. Appl. Phys.*, 29, 892 (1958). Curve 1: by build-up method, with annealed mild steel. Curve 2: by decay method with cold-worked mild steel. Curve 3: by decay method with annealed mild steel; (g) R. M. Barrer, *Trans. Faraday Soc.*, 36, 1242 (1940); (h) M. L. Hill and E. W. Johnson, *Trans. Met. Soc. AIME*, 215, 717 (1959). Curve 1: mild steel, 30% reduction in area. Curve 2: mild steel, 60% reduction in area; and (i) Reference 89.

the desorption rate by the factor $(\bar{c}_t/c_\ell^0)^{1/2}$. This effect was experimentally observed for cold-worked mild steel by these investigators.

McNabb and Foster[80] have worked out a somewhat more realistic trapping model, in that the trapped hydrogen is taken to be in local equilibrium with normal, lattice-dissolved hydrogen. We can render their equations more physically meaningful by using a reduced form of the bi-molecular reaction theory of Waite.[81] The resulting model assumes that upon diffusing to within a small distance $r_0$ from an empty trap the dissolved hydrogen is captured, that the trap may hold only one hydrogen, and that the activation energy for release of a trapped hydrogen is the sum of the trap depth, $E_t$, and the activation energy for normal diffusion of hydrogen, $E_a$. We can transcribe some of McNabb and Foster's equations, as follows.

Consider a slab of metal of thickness a; let the concentration of lattice-dissolved hydrogen be maintained at the concentration $c_0$ just below one face and at zero at the other. The flux through the latter face will be zero initially, then will rise gradually to a constant value. The total throughput plotted against time will have a linear asymptote which intersects the time axis at $\tau_i$, the determination of which is a common way of evaluating the diffusivity in the absence of surface control. The relationship between $\tau_i$, the true lattice diffusivity, D, and the number of traps per unit volume, $N_t$, is (for small degree of filling of the trap population).

$$\tau_i = \frac{a^2}{6D}\,(1 + N_t\,S_t)\,\left[1 - \frac{c_0 N_t\,S_t^2}{2(1 + N_t S_t)} + \ldots\right] \quad (8)$$

where

$$S_t = 4\pi r_0\,\lambda^2\,\exp(E_t/kT). \quad (9)$$

$\lambda$ is the diffusive jump distance and k and T are the Boltzmann constant and the absolute temperature respectively. (It may be mentioned that in terms of McNabb and Foster's kinetic parameters k and p, $S_t = k/p$.)

One sees from Equation (8) that a naive interpretation of a measurement of $\tau_i$ would lead to a calculated apparent diffusivity smaller than the true diffusivity by a factor equal to the reciprocal of the coefficients of $(a^2/6D)$. Similarly, the temperature dependence of the measured intercept leads to too large an activation energy:

$$k\,\frac{\partial \ln\tau_i}{\partial(1/T)} = E_a + \frac{N_t S_t}{1 + N_t S_t}\,E_t \quad (10)$$

Thus, at high temperatures, and/or when the trap depth and density are small, the apparent activation energy $\to E_a$. Conversely, when the temperature is low, and/or $N_t$ and $E_t$ are large, E(apparent) $\to (E_a + E_t)$.

Another way of seeing the effect of traps is to form the ratio of the amount of hydrogen evolved after time $\tau$ from one side of a slab of metal in which the initial lattice concentration throughout is $c_0$, to the amount absorbed in

the same time into initially hydrogen-free metal when the surface concentration is maintained at $c_0$. This ratio is

$$\frac{Q_{ev}(\tau)}{Q_{ab}(\tau)} = (1 + c_0 S_t)\left(1 - \frac{2}{\pi}\,c_0 S_t\right) \quad (11)$$

which is valid for small $c_0 S_t$ and large $N_t S_t$. In addition, the equilibrium total hydrogen content per unit volume when the lattice concentration is $c_0$ everywhere may be compared to the steady-state mean total hydrogen content per unit volume when one side of a metal slab is maintained at a lattice concentration $c_0$ and the other side at zero concentration. This ratio is

$$\frac{\overline{C}_{tot,eq.}}{\overline{C}_{tot,st.}} = \frac{c_0^2 S_t^2\,[1 + (N_t + c_0)\,S_t]}{(1 + c_0 S_t)\left\{c_0^2 S_t^2/2 + N_t S_t\,[c_0 S_t - \ln(1 + c_0 S_t)]\right\}} \quad (12)$$

*Applications of Trapping Theory*

It is interesting to evaluate these equations for some assumed, typical values of the parameters. To evaluate $S_t$, we may take $r_0 = \lambda = 3$ Å, and $E_t = 6400$ cal/g atom, assuming that the traps are sites at dislocation cores and using Gibala's value.[59,60] This yields $S_t = 1.4 \times 10^{-17}$ cm$^3$ at room temperature. At $10^{10}$ dislocation lines per cm$^2$, $N_t \approx 9 \times 10^{17}$ sites/cm$^3$, taking one site per dislocation intersecting one atomic plane in iron. We will assume $c_0 = 8.6 \times 10^{16}$ H atoms per cm$^3$, corresponding to 1 ppm. Under these conditions, Equation (8) yields $\tau_i = 7.3$ $(a^2/6D)$. Similarly, Equation (10) gives $E_a + 0.93\,E_t$ for the apparent activation energy, or $(E_a + 5.9)$ k cal/g atom.

This calculation for the assumed parameters may be compared with the apparent activation energy of 7.9 k cal/g.atom calculated from the results of Foster, McNabb, and Payne[82] for evolution of hydrogen from a mild steel charged by reaction with aqueous hydrogen sulfide. Johnson and Hill[76] also obtained 7.8 k cal/g atom as the apparent activation energy near room temperature for the evolution of hydrogen from gas-phase-charged electrolytic or Ferrovac iron. At temperatures higher than about 225 C they obtained 3.2 k cal/g atom as the activation energy for hydrogen evolution. It is significant that the trapping model with the above values of the parameters gives $(E_a + 0.3)$ k cal/g atom as the apparent activation energy at 227 C; at even higher temperatures, $E_{app} \to E_a$. For the same parameters, the ratio of amount of hydrogen evolved to that absorbed is 0.52 from Equation (11) evaluated at room temperature. Equation (12) yields 1.8, whereas in the absence of traps the ratio would be two. The specific numbers obtained in the above calculations are not to be considered significant, except as indications of reasonable magnitudes and of similarities with some experimental results. In addition, it seems probable that all of the spread shown in Figure 8 may be understood since there is the possibility of larger dislocation densities put in by cold work and of the existence of more energetic sites for trapping hydrogen such as upon the metal-vacuum interfaces of microcavities.

## The True Diffusivity of Hydrogen in α-Iron

Because of the many possibilities for trapping hydrogen at chemical and structural singularities in α-iron, it seems best to deduce the intrinsic diffusion characteristics of dissolved hydrogen by analyzing steady-state permeabilities. The reason for this is that at steady state all the traps are filled to fixed levels, so that their effect vanishes. The concentration of freely diffusing hydrogen is obtainable by extrapolation from high-temperature determinations on purified iron.

Gonzalez[83] has carefully considered most existing determinations of steady-state permeability for systematic errors, purity of iron, and general technique. Figure 9 gives his choice of best data for steady-state permeability of hydrogen in α-iron. An equation that represents the permeability between 130 and 900 C within 90% confidence level is

$$P = 2.9 \times 10^{-3} \exp(-8400/RT)$$

where the P is expressed in $cm^3$ ($H_2$ NTP) $cm^{-1}$ $sec^{-1}$ $atm^{-1/2}$. The enthalpy of permeability is 8400 ± 400 cal/g atom at 95% confidence level. The best equation[83] for the lattice concentration of hydrogen in α-iron in equilibrium with gaseous hydrogen at pressure p is

$$c = 3.7\, p^{1/2} \exp(-6500/RT)$$

with the heat of solution as 6500 ± 300 cal/g. atom. This equation (with p in atm and c in $cm^3$ ($H_2$,NTP)/$cm^3$ Fe) results from consideration of the data of Armbruster,[50]

Maas,[84] Blake, Jordan and Pumphrey,[85] and Heumann and Primas,[86] and of the evaluation of Geller and Sun.[87] The diffusion activation energy is the difference between these two enthalpies, or 1900 ± 500 cal/g.atom. It is the remarkable smallness of the activation energy that makes the problem of trapping so significant for this system.

Three sets of experiments using the transient method have given diffusion activation energies in the same range as the above value. Fedorov[88] obtained 1800 cal/g atom in the temperature range 300 to 1000 C. Beck et al[89] obtained 1300 cal/g atom by an electrolytic technique in the temperature range 10 to 75 C. Heumann and Primas[86] obtained 1920 cal/g atom in the range 300 to 900 C. There have also been isolated determinations of D at 15 C for H in pure iron which have yielded values of the order of $10^{-5}$ $cm^2$/sec: Raczynski[90] 1 x $10^{-5}$ $cm^2$/sec, Devanathan et al[91] 8.3 x $10^{-5}$, and Beck et al 6.3 x $10^{-5}$. In addition, Gibala[16] obtained 2000 cal/g atom from the temperature dependence of the Snoek peak in hydrogen-charged α-iron. This correspondence between the high-temperature activation and that determined at very low temperatures by internal friction makes it unnecessary to consider, as Heller did,[15] whether or not quantum-mechanical tunnelling is the mechanism for the motion of hydrogen in αiron at low temperatures.

We must surmise that measurements by transient techniques that yield diffusivities at 25 C smaller than the $10^{-5}$ $cm^2$/sec range, or activation energies larger than about 2000 cal/g atom are vitiated either by trapping phenomena, partial surface control, or both, even for reasonably pure iron not subjected to intentional deformation. The effective traps need not be dislocations; they could be internal surfaces. For example, $E_t$ at a clean iron-vacuum internal surface would be about 20 kcal/g atom, and that at an inclusion-iron interface could well be nearly as large. It is also conceivable that solute

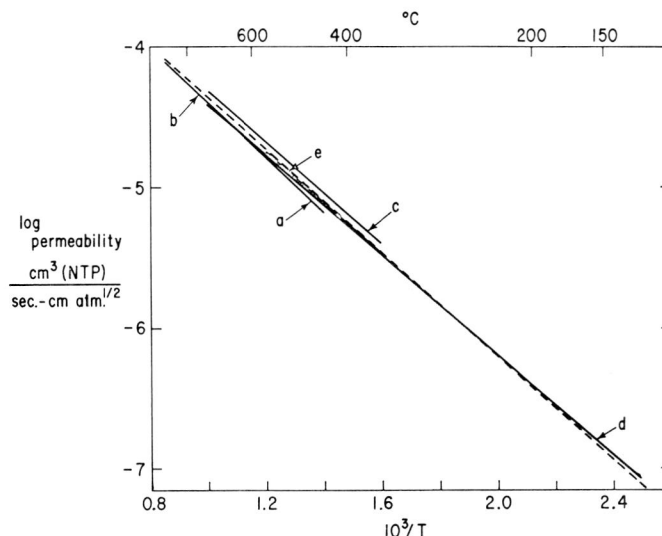

FIGURE 9 — Selected data for steady-state permeability of hydrogen in α-iron (after Gonzalez[83]). References: (a) P. L. Chang and W. D. G. Bennett, *J. Iron Steel Inst.*, 170, 205 (1952); (b) H. Schenck and H. Taxhet, *Arch Eisenhuttenw.*, 30, 220 (1963); (c) J. K. Gorman and W. R. Nardella, *Vacuum*, 12, 19 (1962); (d) W. L. Bryan and D. F. Dodge, *A. I. Chem. Eng. J.*, 9, 223 (1963); and (e) O. D. Gonzalez, *Trans. Met. Soc. AIME*, 239, 929 (1967). Dashed line: plot of equation P = 2.9 x 10⁻³ exp (-8400/RT).

atoms, singly or in clusters, could act as traps though their overall contribution can only be minor. In addition, dissolved impurities may produce a permeation barrier at the specimen surface, which only partially controls the observed permeation. As Ash and Barrer[92] have shown, it is possible for the permeation rate to vary inversely with specimen thickness, within the usual accuracy of measurement, and still have a contribution from the surface impedance.

Because of the works described above which have yielded a high hydrogen diffusivity and low activation energy at room temperature, we cannot accept the recent suggestion by Rosales and Ono[93] that the low-temperature anomalous behavior of hydrogen in iron is due to the formation of di-interstitials which increase in number as the temperature decreases and which are immobile. This would be an intrinsic property of dissolved hydrogen in iron, so that it would be impossible ever to observe a high, room-temperature diffusivity.

### Variation of Diffusivity With Composition

Because of sensitivity to traps, it is very difficult to ascertain whether or not any investigator has succeeded in demonstrating the composition dependence of the intrinsic, or true, diffusivity of hydrogen in b.c.c. iron. The experimental results should be analyzed as per Equations 8 and 10, for example, with independent evaluation of $c_0$ at various environmental gas pressures. In the absence of such tests, one should restrict an examination of the literature to experiments at high temperature and with moderately large alloying additions. For example, Schwarz and Zitter[94] find that at 650 C, the diffusivity of H in $a$-iron binaries is stationary with alloying additions up to 1.4 wt.% C (two-phase alloy), 1.8 wt.% Si, 28 wt.% Cr or 11 wt.% Ni; (with Mn the $D_H$ decreases by about 1/10 at 14 wt.% Mn probably because of the change of phase to f.c.c.). At room temperature, nevertheless, all of these systems evince a large variation in apparent diffusivity of hydrogen. However, even at the higher temperature there is some disagreement with other investigators. For example, Geller and Sun[87] have recorded almost a three-fold decrease in $D_H$ at about 650 C in giving from zero to 1.85 wt.% Si. We conclude therefore that except for the marked effect of change of phase from b.c.c. to f.c.c. we know very little indeed about the change of $D_H$ in iron with alloying additions.

The situation is about the same for H in metals other than iron. Hill and Johnson[95] give a tabulation showing $E_a$ for H in nickel ranging from 5.5 to 14.8 kcal/g.atom, with considerable clustering about the value of 9 kcal/g.atom; however, this is less scatter than shown by the many attempts to determine $E_a$ for H in $a$-iron. Some fairly definite remarks can be made on the composition dependence of $D_H$ in palladium. Von Stackelberg and Ludwig[41] agree with Jewett and Makrides[96] that $D_H$ in $\beta$-Pd(H) at 27 C is larger than $D_H$ in $a$-Pd(H) by almost a factor of 10. Remembering that these differ only in the hydrogen content, and consequently in the lattice parameter, it would seem that $D_H$ increases as the lattice parameter increases. Indeed, Gubanov[97] has postulated that $D_H$ is governed by the difference between the size of the interstitial site in a metal and the radius of the screening charge about the dissolved proton. However, Gubanov's attempted correlation breaks down in comparing $D_H$ in various metals, and also in individual binaries. For example, Jewett and Makrides[96] found that $D_H$ decreases as the silver content of Pd-Ag alloys is increased, although the lattice parameter is thereby increased. Contrariwise, addition of Cu to Pd decreases the lattice parameter, but Piper[98] found $D_H$ to be independent of Cu content in f.c.c. Pd-Cu alloys.

### Surface Diffusion of Hydrogen

The mobility of hydrogen adsorbed on metal surfaces can be measured experimentally principally by the technique of field emission microscopy. Gomer, Wortman, and Lundy[99] found by this means that chemisorbed hydrogen on tungsten exhibits a mobility that depends markedly on the degree of coverage of the surface. At coverages larger than one-half monolayer, the migration occurs with an activation energy of about 6 kcal/g.atom, and corresponds to a spreading, with a sharp boundary, over the close-packed surface planes and trapping on the atomically rough regions of the field-emitter specimen. The trapping strength of such locations becomes manifest when migration at low coverages is studied. Under these circumstances, the trapping sites at the rough regions cannot all be saturated, so that the untrapping process becomes rate controlling for the migration over the surface. Then the surface diffusion proceeds without a sharp boundary and with an activation energy of 9.5 k cal/g atom and, at very low coverages, of 16 k cal/g atom.

On the other hand, on nickel[100] chemisorbed hydrogen diffuses without a sharp boundary at all degrees of surface coverage. This is interpreted[100] as showing that there are no, or very few, traps on the surface of the nickel field emitter; this is reasonable because the field-emitter tip of this f.c.c. metal consists of terraces and steps of only close-packed surfaces. In this case, the activation energy for surface migration was measured[100] at 7 k cal/g atom. One can calculate from the data of Wortman et al[100] that at 37 C, $(D_H)_{Ni}$ surface $\approx 4 \times 10^{-8}$ cm$^2$ sec$^{-1}$. This is in excellent agreement with $(D_H)_{Ni}$ surface $\leqslant 5 \times 10^{-8}$ cm$^2$ sec$^{-1}$ at 37 C obtained by Iino[101] by porous-plug technique under hydrogen gas pressures in the micron range. For comparison, at 37 C Hill and Johnsons' equation for the $D_H$ in the lattice of nickel gives $4.5 \times 10^{-9}$ cm$^2$ sec$^{-1}$

Although data are too scarce to generalize with confidence, we may point out that the ratio of activation energy for H diffusion on atomically smooth surfaces to the initial heat of adsorption (per ½ H$_2$) is 1/4 for tungsten and 1/2 for nickel. On this basis, the activation energy for hydrogen diffusion on atomically smooth surfaces of $a$-iron may lie between 4 and 8 k cal/g atom, and hence may well be slower than bulk diffusion.

Rideal and Sweett[102] have compared the experimental

entropies of adsorption with those calculated by statistical mechanics for mobile adsorbed H atoms on nickel. The surface diffusivities they calculate are several orders of magnitude larger than those experimentally determined, and the activation energy for diffusion calculated by them[102] ranges from 3.5 to less than 1 k cal/g atom, depending on coverage.

### Diffusion in Gradients of Other Than Composition

*Gradient of Elastic Stress*

For the same assumptions used to derive Equation (6) from the general equation[63] for the chemical potential, $\mu$, of hydrogen in an elastic stress field the hydrostatic component of which is $\sigma_h$, one can write

$$\mu = \mu^o - \bar{V}_H \sigma_h \qquad (13)$$

where $\mu^o$ is the chemical potential of dissolved hydrogen at zero stress. Both $\mu$ and $\mu^o$ refer to the same hydrogen concentration. Since grad $\mu$ is the fundamental driving force for diffusion, the flux of solute is

$$\mathbf{J} = - Bc \; grad \; \mu$$
$$= -D \; grad \; c + \frac{Dc \; \bar{V}_H}{kT} \; grad \; \sigma_h \qquad (14)$$

where B and D are the normal mobility and diffusivity, respectively, and where we have assumed that $\mu^o$ and c are related through a composition-independent activity coefficient.

Thus, a diffusive flux of hydrogen will be established in an iso-concentration field from positions in the lattice where $\sigma_h < 0$ to points where $\sigma_h > 0$. Troiano[103] has long hypothesized that dissolved hydrogen will diffuse to points of "maximum triaxiality", and if one interprets this to mean maximum, positive $\sigma_h$ then we are saying the same thing and have given a theoretical justification of it. It must be emphasized, however, that the increased hydrogen concentration at such points does not imply a higher supersaturation there.

Stress-induced diffusive flux of hydrogen will occur in the stress fields due to inclusions, dislocations, or cracks. Figure 7 indicates the flux path in the stress field of an edge dislocation. It is interesting to compare the magnitude of a stress-induced flux to that induced by a concentration gradient. We may ask what stress situation is necessary so that a stress-induced flux equals a concentration-induced flux of hydrogen. From Equation (14), for equality of fluxes,

$$D \; grad \; c = \frac{Dc \; \bar{V}_H}{kT} \; grad \; \sigma_h$$

from which

$$\frac{\Delta \sigma_h}{\Delta c} = \frac{kT}{c \bar{V}_H}$$

Now, maximum $\Delta c = c - 0$, so that $\Delta \sigma_h = \sigma_h - 0 = kT/\bar{V}_H =$

$1.25 \times 10^{10}$ dyne cm$^{-2}$ at room temperature and for $\bar{V}_H = 2$ cm$^3$/g atom in $\alpha$-iron.[74] Hence, over the same distance in the lattice, $\Delta \sigma_h \cong 1.3 \times 10^{10}$ dyne cm$^{-2}$ will produce the same flux as a $\Delta c = c$. Note that $\sigma_h = 1.3 \times 10^{10}$ is smaller than the $2 \times 10^{11}$ dyne/cm$^2$ calculated to obtain at a point two Burgers vectors away from the core on the tensile side of an edge dislocation.

*Gradient of Electrical Potential or of Temperature*

Whereas stress-induced diffusion is a classical diffusion process in the sense that the random jumping of an interstitial solute atom is biased by a thermodynamic driving force, the diffusion produced by an electrical potential gradient or by a temperature gradient is really the result of an interaction of the atom with another flux. In the case of the electrical potential gradient the solute as it jumps collides with charge carriers of the metal conduction bands which are themselves moving because of the externally applied electric field. The observed drift of the interstitial solute is therefore dependent on the details of the momentum exchange between the two moving entities.[104] At the present state of the theory one cannot deduce anything about the ionic state of the solute in the metallic matrix, although one might be deluded in this direction by the terminology ("effective charge") by which the experimentally observed relation between flux and applied field is usually expressed.

The diffusion in a temperature gradient is even more complex. In this case, the externally applied temperature gradient produces fluxes of charge carriers and also of phonons (lattice vibrations). Both can interact with the solute as it jumps, though one expects the electron collision to be the more important in a metal.[105]

The behavior of dissolved hydrogen in such fields has been studied in several metals.[104,105] Depending on the metal, hydrogen may drift to the positive or to the negative side or to the hotter or to the colder side of the specimen. The important point in the context of this review is that, unlike stress-induced diffusion, diffusion induced by either a temperature or electrical potential gradient can produce a supersaturation and hence induce a precipitation or a reaction. In addition, the forces produced by an electrical or thermal gradient can be quite large in comparison to that generated by a concentration gradient. This force is expressible as

$$F_c = \frac{kT \; grad \; c}{c}$$

The force due to a temperature gradient is

$$F_T = \frac{Q^* \; grad \; T}{T}$$

and that due to an electrical potential gradient, grad $\phi$, is

$$F_\phi = Z^* |e| \; grad \; \phi$$

In these equations, $Q^*$ is the phenomenological heat of

45

transport, $Z^*$ the effective charge in electromigration, and $|e|$ the absolute charge of the electron. Carrying out calculations for hydrogen in a-iron at room temperature, one finds

$$F_c = 4.2 \times 10^{-14} \text{ dyne/atom}$$

$$F_T = 2.3 \times 10^{-12} \text{ dyne/atom}$$

$$F_\phi = 3.8 \times 10^{-13} \text{ dyne/atom}$$

The parameters employed are $(1/c)$ grad $c = 1$ cm$^{-1}$, $Q^* = -10,000$ cal/g atom (extrapolated from Reference 105) and grad $T = 10^3$ deg/cm, $Z^* = 0.24$[104] and grad $\phi = 1$ volt/cm. Clearly, there are ample ranges of accessible grad $\phi$ and of grad $T$ for which the forces generated thereby are larger than that produced by a gradient of concentration of dissolved hydrogen.

## IV. Brief Remarks on the Charging of Metals With Hydrogen

Up to this point in this review two characteristics of dissolved hydrogen have been stressed which are of great importance in understanding the singular effect of hydrogen on static and dynamic mechanical properties. These properties are the great intrinsic mobility of dissolved hydrogen, and the attractive interactions with structural irregularities. These are particularly significant in b.c.c. iron and its alloys.

Another characteristic of hydrogen, singular among the possible solutes in metals, is the relative ease with which, purposefully or unwittingly, hydrogen at extremely high fugacities can be made available at the surface of a metal. This may happen, for example, by attack of acid upon a metal, by corrosion of iron, or by electrolytic charging. During the active reaction between iron and acid, the effective fugacity of hydrogen at the surface will be a function of kinetic factors. Darken and Smith[75] took as a measure of the effective fugacity the e.m.f. developed between the dissolving steel and a hydrogen electrode, and calculated fugacities of the order of $10^8$ atm. Although the assumption underlying this measurement can only be a gross approximation, the effective fugacity in that work must have been within two or three powers of ten from the order indicated.

The input fugacity of hydrogen can be nicely controlled, though not measured, by adjusting the conditions for acid attack or for cathodic deposition of hydrogen. The pH of the electrolyte, the presence of organic or inorganic adsorbates, the chemical composition of the metal and the cathodic current density can affect the effective fugacity of hydrogen. The measurement of the fugacity is very difficult, and it has not been the subject of experimental investigation. It is however a very important question which will be discussed further below.

In this connection it is interesting to consider Gibala's[16] work on the Snoek peak in a-iron. He cathodically charged cold-rolled Ferrovac E iron in a solution of 4% $H_2SO_4$ with a small amount of $NaAsO_2$ as an inhibitor for the recombination reaction (i.e., that of forming $H_2$ (g)). Using charging current densities in the range from 0.002 to 0.2 amp/cm$^2$ and times between a few minutes to one day, he obtained total hydrogen concentrations in the range from 7 to 30 ppm. Gibala[60] attempts to estimate the concentration of lattice-dissolved hydrogen from considerations depending in large part on the assumption that hydrogen produces essentially no lattice expansion in a-iron and upon the observed intensity of the Snoek peak for hydrogen in comparison with that for carbon. He obtains 0.1 to 1.0 ppm as the probable range of lattice solubility produced by his charging conditions. However, the partial molal volume of hydrogen in a-Fe is not vanishingly small,[74] and we may re-estimate the lattice solubility by making the likely assumption that $\delta\lambda$, the difference in local strain in different crystallographic directions about an interstitial, is proportional to the cube root of the partial molal volume. Then, one can compare the relaxation strength, $\bar{a}$, per unit concentration of interstitial, of hydrogen to that of carbon as follows:

$$\frac{\bar{a}_H}{\bar{a}_c} = \left(\frac{\delta\lambda_H}{\delta\lambda_c}\right)^2 = \left(\frac{\bar{V}_H}{\bar{V}_c}\right)^{2/3} \approx (2/6)^{2/3} \approx 0.5$$

This revises Gibala's estimate for the concentration of lattice-dissolved hydrogen to 0.01 to 0.1 ppm.

We may now compare this to the lattice concentration under 1 atm. $H_2$ gas at room temperature of about $10^{-3}$ ppm, obtained from Gonzalez' equation. Thus, Gibala's cathodic charging produced a supersaturation of 10 to 100, or a fugacity of from 100 to $10^4$ atm. There are at least two points to be noted here. One is that the ratio of total hydrogen in the iron to the lattice-dissolved hydrogen is about (7 to 30)/($10^{-2}$ to $10^{-1}$) and the other point is that a finite supersaturation may be maintained in the lattice (with respect to 1 atm of gaseous $H_2$) presumably in equilibrium with trapped hydrogen. In addition, Gibala[60] has estimated that the strength of the cold-work internal friction peaks corresponds to 0.01 to 0.4 ppm of hydrogen. Thus, the hydrogen dissolved in the lattice plus that on the cores of dislocations able to contribute to the Koster peak, plus probably also the hydrogen held in the stress fields of the dislocations make up only a minor portion of the total hydrogen charged in by Gibala.

At the present time one can only speculate that grain boundaries, and dislocation tangles and microcavities created by cold-working this pure iron are the traps responsible for holding the bulk of the hydrogen. Naeser and Dautzenberg[106] have shown that the hydrogen content taken up by cold-worked Armco iron from gaseous hydrogen at 1 atm. increases with increasing amount of cold work. Furthermore, they found that for a given degree of cold work, the hydrogen uptake increased as the carbon content was increased from 0.002 to 0.18% in parallel with the measured density decrement caused by the cold work. These experimenters were of the opinion that the hydrogen in excess of lattice solubility was upon the internal surfaces of microcracks and microcavities produced by the cold work. One may add that one can show that for samples equilibrated with gaseous hydrogen at one atmosphere pressure, the amount of hydrogen held as gas within the micropores makes a minor contribution as long as the micropores have radii below 1000 Å. For a spherical cavity holding gaseous hydrogen at 1 atm and room temperature, the ratio of mass of hydrogen held as gas in the volume to that held as adsorbed species on the internal surface is about $1.5 \times 10^4$ r, where r is the cavity radius in cm. Harhai et al[107] also reached the conclusion that occluded hydrogen is held mainly on the internal surfaces of cold-worked iron-carbon alloys equilibrated with gaseous hydrogen. The main reason for this conclusion is that by means of concurrent density measurements they were able to show that the void volume was virtually unchanged by annealing the cold-worked alloy although this treatment drastically reduced the occlusion of hydrogen. This would indicate that the annealing markedly changes the adsorption characteristics of the void surfaces.

It is unlikely that in the experiments in which the means of charging was gaseous hydrogen at 1 atm. the act of hydrogen charging itself produced new traps or a greater number of them. However, charging under high fugacities will certainly have this result, as attested by the work of Flis[108] with mild steel and iron, of van Ooijen[109] with iron and nickel, and particularly that of Tetelman and Robertson[110] who observed plastic deformation and cracking as a result of cathodic charging iron-silicon alloys.

One other possible result of hydrogen charging should be mentioned briefly, that of forming a chemical compound. Podgurski[111] found that hydrogen charging cold-worked steel above 200 C produced methane, the volume of which agreed well with the volume of microcavities as calculated from the measured density decrement due to the cold deformation. This reaction would not occur significantly at temperatures below 200 C because of slow kinetics, and at temperatures above 600 C the relative amount of methane quickly decreases because of the variation of the equilibrium constant with temperature. Hydrogen charging may also produce hydrides. Szummer[112] produced a surface hydride phase by cathodic charging of nickel. Vaughan et al[113] have suggested the formation of an iron-nickel-chromium hydride in austenitic stainless steel.

## V. Conclusions

Hydrogen dissolves in transition metals as discrete ions which are screened by the conduction electrons, causing important changes in the electron energy bands, and which are located in interstitial sites in the lattice. Whereas the factors controlling solubility are not fully understood, two important considerations are the magnitude of the density of electronic states at the Fermi surface and of its derivative with electron density, and the short-range interactions of hydrogen ions with hydrogen ions or with other metallic solutes. Dissolved hydrogen interacts strongly with structural singularities of various kinds, as well as with stress fields. These strong interactions, coupled with the relatively low temperatures for significant mobility of hydrogen in the normal lattice, lead to many apparently anomalous phenomena in permeation and diffusion of hydrogen. These can be rationalized in terms of trapping theory. Intrinsic solubilities are also difficult to determine because of such interactions.

It would seem that the most important experimental problems to do in the future in order to understand the multifarious phenomena associated with hydrogen charging of metals are the carrying out of a variety of transient and steady-state experiments of the sort described in the section on trapping theory. These should be done conjointly at a variety of known, externally applied fugacities of hydrogen, using extremely pure metals and alloys to which has been applied a variety of carefully specified cold-deformation treatments. The use of a range of measured hydrogen fugacities should be particularly important, as this would enable the characterization of the number and types of the various traps in the lattice, much as was done by Wriedt and Darken[114] for nitrogen in steel. Certainly, other techniques such as density measurement, internal friction and electron microscopy should be concurrently applied.

## Acknowledgments

The author is grateful for several discussions with his colleagues Drs. O. D. Gonzalez and R. P. Frankenthal.

## References

1. A. Sieverts. *Z. Metallkunde,* **21,** 37 (1929).
2. K. H. Lieser and H. Witte. *Z. fur Elektrochemie,* **61,** 367 (1957).
3. W. Eichenauer, W. Löser and H. Witte. *Z. Metallkunde,* **56,** 287 (1965).
4. A. D. McQuillan, C. E. Ells, N. Pessall, A. P. Bennett, J. Basterfield, and A. D. Wallbank. Report from the University of Birmingham, "The Solution of Hydrogen in Body-Centered-Cubic Metals" (1964).
5. J. Bergsma and J. A. Goedkoep. *Physica,* **26,** 744 (1960).
6. J. E. Worsham, Jr., M. K. Wilkinson, and C. G. Shull. *J. Phys. Chem. Solids,* **3,** 303 (1957).
7. W. E. Wallace. *J. Chem. Phys.,* **35,** 2156 (1961).
8. E. O. Wollan, J. W. Cable, and W. C. Koehler. *J. Phys. Chem. Solids,* **24,** 1141 (1963).
9. T. Bonesewski and G. C. Smith. *J. Phys. Chem. Solids,* **21,** 115 (1961).
10. R. E. Rundle, C. G. Shull, and E. O. Wollan. *Acta Cryst.,* **5,** 22 (1952).
11. S. S. Sidhu, L. Heston, and D. D. Zauberis. *Acta Cryst.,* **9,** 607 (1956).
12. B. W. Roberts. *Phys. Rev.,* **100,** 1257 (1955).
13. Reported in Battelle Colloquium on Phase Stability in Metals and Alloys, (1966); Agenda Discussion edited by R. A. Oriani and A. L. Bement, p. 431.
14. C. Zener. *Imperfections in Nearly Perfect Crystals.* Wiley and Sons, New York, 1952, p. 289.
15. W. R. Heller. *Acta Met.,* **9,** 600 (1961).
16. R. Gibala. "Internal Friction in Hydrogen-Charged Iron". Report from Case Institute of Technology, Cleveland (1967).
17. D. N. Beshers. *J. Appl. Phys.,* **36,** 290 (1965).
18. B. Svensson. *Ann. der Physik.,* **5F,** 299 (1933).

19. W. Trzebiatowski and B. Stalinski. *Bull. Acad. Polonaise des Sciences,* **1,** 131 (1953).
20. B. Stalinski. *Bull. Acad. Polonaise des Sciences,* **2,** 245 (1954).
21. R. L. Zanowick and W. E. Wallace. *J. Chem. Phys.,* **36,** 2059 (1962).
22. R. A. Oriani, E. McCliment, and J. F. Youngblood. *J. Chem. Phys.,* **27,** 330 (1957).
23. H. Betsuyaku, Y. Takagi, and Y. Betsuyaku. *J. Phys. Soc. Japan,* **19,** 1089 (1964).
24. D. S. Schreiber and L. D. Graham. *J. Chem. Phys.,* **43,** 2573 (1965).
25. D. Zamir and R. M. Cotts. *Phys. Rev.,* **134,** A666 (1964).
26. J. Butterworth. *Proc. Phys. Soc.,* **83,** 71 (1964).
27. D. S. Schreiber. *Phys. Rev.,* **137,** A860 (1965).
28. D. Rohy and R. M. Cotts. *Bull. Amer. Phys. Soc.,* (Ser. II) **12,** 315 (1967).
29. D. W. Jones and A. D. McQuillan. *J. Phys. Chem. Solids,* **23,** 1441 (1962).
30. D. W. Jones, N. Pessall, and A. D. McQuillan. *Phil. Mag.,* **6,** 455 (1961).
31. D. W. Jones. *Phil. Mag.,* **9,** 709 (1964).
32. Y. Ebisuzaki and M. O'Keeffe. *Phil. Mag.,* **14,** 867 (1966).
33. I. Isenberg. *Phys. Rev.,* **79,** 736 (1950).
34. J. Friedel. *Adv. in Physics,* **3,** 446 (1954).
35. R. A. Oriani and C. B. Alcock. *Trans. Met. Soc. AIME,* **224,** 1104 (1962).
36. O. M. Katz and J. A. Berger. *Trans. Met. Soc. AIME,* **233,** 1005 (1965).
37. W. M. Albrecht, W. D. Goode, and M. W. Mallett. *J. Electrochem. Soc.,* **106,** 981 (1959).
38. J. R. Lacher. *Proc. Roy. Soc., London,* **A161,** 525 (1937).
39. F. E. Hoare and B. Yates. *Proc. Roy. Soc.* **(London) A240,** 42 (1957).
40. F. E. Hoare, J. C. Matthews and J. C. Walling. *Proc. Roy. Soc.* (London) **A216,** 502 (1953).
41. M. von Stackelberg and P. Ludwig. *z. Naturforsch.,* **19a,** 93 (1964).
42. J. C. Fisher. *Acta Met.,* **6,** 13 (1958).
43. A. C. Makrides. *J. Phys. Chem.,* **68,** 2160 (1964).
44. A. Blandin, E. Daniel, and J. Friedel. *Phil. Mag.,* **4,** 180 (1959).
45. J. W. Simons and Ted B. Flanagan. *Can. J. Chem.,* **43,** 1665 (1965); *J. Phys. Chem.,* **70,** 3750 (1966).
46. J. W. Simons and Ted B. Flanagan. *J. Phys. Chem.,* **69,** 3773 (1965).
47. P. L. Levine and K. E. Weale. *Trans. Faraday Soc.,* **56,** 357 (1960); E. Wicke and G. H. Nernst. *Z. Elektrochem.,* **68,** 224 (1964).
48. H. Brodowsky. *Z. Physik. Chem.* (N.F.) **44,** 129 (1965).
49. A. Maeland and Ted B. Flanagan. *J. Phys. Chem.,* **69,** 3575 (1965).
50. M. H. Armbruster. *J. Am. Chem. Soc.,* **65,** 1043 (1943).
51. M. Weinstein and J. F. Elliott. *Trans. Met. Soc. AIME,* **227,** 382 (1963).
52. H. Schenck and K. W. Lange. *Arch. Eisenhuttenw.,* **37,** 739 (1966).
53. T. Bagshaw and A. Mitchell. *J. Iron Steel Inst.,* **204,** 87 (1966); T. Bagshaw, D. Engledow, and A. Mitchell. *ibid.,* **203,** 160 (1965).
54. W. Himmler. *Z. Physik. Chem.,* **195,** 244, 253 (1950).
55. L. C. Chang and M. Gensamer. *Acta Met.,* **1,** 483 (1953).
56. L. C. Weiner and M. Gensamer. *Acta Met.,* **5,** 692 (1953).
57. J. Hewitt. BISRA, Harrogate Conference, Oct. 1961; *Proceedings,* p. 83 (1962).
58. R. E. Maringer, E. B. Swetman, L. L. Marsh, and G. K. Manning. NACA TN4328 (1958).
59. R. Gibala. *AIME Abstract Bull.* (Inst. of Metals Div.) **1,** 36 (1966).
60. R. Gibala. "Hydrogen-Dislocation Interaction in Iron", Report from Dept. of Metallurgy, Case Institute of Technology, 1967. *Trans. Met. Soc. AIME,* **239,** 1574 (1967).
61. R. Gibala. "On the Mechanism of the Köster Relaxation Peak", Report from the Dept. of Metallurgy, Case Institute of Technology, 1967.
62. G. Schoeck. *Acta Met.,* **11,** 617 (1963).
63. J. C. M. Li, R. A. Oriani and L. S. Darken. *Z. Physik. Chem.,* **(N.F.) 49,** 271 (1966).
64. J. C. M. Li. "Electron Microscopy and the Strength of Crystals", ed. by G. Thomas and J. Washburn, p. 713 (1963).
65. R. R. Arons, J. Bouman, M. Wijzenbeek, P. T. A. Klaase, C. Tuyn, G. Leferink, and G. DeVries. *Acta Met.,* **15,** 144 (1967).
66. J. A. Peterson, R. Gibala, and A. R. Troiano. To be published, *J. Appl. Phys.*
67. M. L. Rudee and R. A. Higgins. *Phys. Stat. Sol.,* **4,** K101 (1964).
68. M. B. Whiteman and A. R. Troiano. *Phys. Stat. Sol.,* **7,** K109 (1964).
69. A. Howie and P. R. Swann. *Phil. Mag.,* **6,** 1215 (1961).
70. J. M. Sivertsen and M. E. Nicholson. *Prog. Matl. Sci.,* **9,** 305 (1961).
71. H. H. Podgurski, F. N. Davis and R. P. Smith. *J. Vacuum Sci. Tech.,* **4,** 186 (1967).
72. Ling Yang, G. T. Horne and G. M. Pound. *Proceedings of a Symposium, Physical Metallurgy of Stress Corrosion Cracking, Pittsburgh, 1959.* Interscience Publishers, Inc., New York, 1959, p. 29.
73. J. C. M. Li. Unpublished calculation.
74. R. A. Oriani. *Trans. Met. Soc. AIME,* **236,** 1368 (1966).
75. L. S. Darken and R. P. Smith. *Corrosion,* **5,** 1 (1949).
76. E. W. Johnson and M. L. Hill. *Trans. Met. Soc. AIME,* **218,** 1104 (1960).
77. G. Naeser and N. Dautzenberg. *Arch. Eisenhuttenw.,* **36,** 175 (1965).
78. V. A. Gol'tsov, P. V. Gel'd and M. M. Shteynberg. *Metalloved Term Obrabotka Metall.,* No. 4, 14 (1965).
79. L. S. Darken. *Trans. AIME,* **150,** 157 (1942).
80. A. McNabb and P. K. Foster. *Trans. Met. Soc. AIME,* **227,** 618 (1963).
81. T. R. Waite. *Phys. Rev.,* **107,** 463 (1957).
82. P. K. Foster, A. McNabb, and C. M. Payne. *Trans. Met. Soc. AIME,* **233,** 1022 (1965).
83. O. D. Gonzalez. Personal communication; submitted to *J. Metals.*
84. H. Maas. Dissertation, Munster, 1958.
85. P. D. Blake, M. F. Jordan, and W. I. Pumphrey. Hydrogen in Steel, Special Report 73, *Iron and Steel Inst.* (London), p. 76-82 (1962).
86. Th. Heumann and D. Primas. *Z. Naturforsch,* **21A,** 260 (1966).
87. W. Geller and T. K. Sun. *Arch. Eisenhuttenw.,* **21,** 423 (1950).
88. S. N. Fedorov. "Mekhanizm Vzaimodeistviya Met s Gaz," Nauka (Moscow) p. 186-190 (1964).
89. W. Beck, J. O'M. Bockris, J. McBreen, and L. Nanis. *Proc. Roy. Soc.,* **A290,** 220 (1966).
90. W. Raczynski. *Archwm. Hutn.,* **3,** 59 (1958).
91. M. A. Devanathan, Z. Stachurski, and W. Beck. *J. Electrochem. Soc.,* **110,** 886 (1963).
92. R. Ash and R. M. Barrer. *Phil. Mag.* (8th Ser.) **4,** 1197 (1959).
93. L. Rosales and K. Ono. Abstract Bull., Inst. Met. Div. AIME, *Met. Soc.,* **2,** 54 (1967).
94. W. Schwarz and H. Zitter. *Arch. Eisenhuttenw.,* **36,** 343 (1965).
95. M. L. Hill and E. W. Johnson. *Acta Met.,* **3,** 566 (1955).
96. D. N. Jewett and A. C. Makrides. *Trans. Faraday Soc.,* **61,** 932 (1965).
97. A. I. Gubanov. *Soviet Phys. Solid State,* **6,** 790 (1964).
98. J. Piper. *J. Appl. Phys.,* **37,** 715 (1966).
99. R. Gomer, R. Wortman, and R. Lundy. *J. Chem. Phys.,* **26,** 1147 (1957).
100. R. Wortman, R. Gomer, and R. Lundy. *J. Chem. Phys.,* **27,** 1099 (1957).

101. H. Iino. Dissertation, Massachusetts Institute of Technology, Dept. of Chemical Engineering (1966).
102. E. K. Rideal and F. Sweett. *Proc. Roy. Soc.*, A257, 291 (1960).
103. A. R. Troiano. *Trans. ASM*, 52, 54 (1960).
104. R. A. Oriani and O. D. Gonzalez. *Trans. Met. Soc. AIME*, 239, 1041 (1967).
105. O. D. Gonzalez and R. A. Oriani. *Trans. Met. Soc. AIME*, 233, 1878 (1965).
106. G. Naeser and N. Dautzenberg. *Arch. Eisenhuttenw.*, 36, 175 (1965).
107. J. G. Harhai, T. S. Viswanathan, and H. M. Davis. *ASM Trans. Quart.*, 58, 210 (1965).
108. J. Flis. *Bull. Acad. Polon. Sci. Ser. Sci. Chem.*, 12, 809 (1964).
109. D. J. van Ooijen. *J. Phys. Chem. Solids*, 23, 1173 (1962); D. J. van Ooijen and J. D. Fast. *Acta Met.*, 11, 211 (1963).
110. A. S. Tetelman and W. D. Robertson. *Trans. Met. Soc. AIME*, 224, 775 (1962).
111. H. H. Podgurski. *Trans. Met. Soc. AIME*, 221, 389 (1961).
112. A. Szummer. *Bull. Acad. Polon. Sci. Ser. Sci. Chem.*, 12, 651 (1964).
113. D. A. Vaughan, D. I. Phalen, C. L. Peterson, and W. K. Boyd. *Corrosion*, 19, 315t (1963).
114. H. A. Wriedt and L. S. Darken. *Trans. Met. Soc. AIME*, 233, 11, 122 (1965).

## General References

J. D. Fast. "Interaction of Metals and Gases", Academic Press (New York) 1965.

M. Smialowski, "Hydrogen in Steel", Pergamon Press (New York) 1962.

G. G. Libowitz, "The Nature and Properties of Transition Metal Hydrides", *J. Nuclear Mat.*, 2, 1 (1960).

P. Cotterill, "The Hydrogen Embrittlement of Metals", *Progr. Mat. Sci.*, 9, No. 4, 205 (1961).

E. E. Fletcher and A. R. Elsea, "Hydrogen Movement in Steel-Entry, Diffusion and Elimination", DMIC Report 219, June 30, 1965, Battelle Memorial Institute.

## Discussion

**H. G. Nelson, NASA, Ames Research Center:**

I found your paper very interesting, but I have a few comments I wish to make with respect to our recent studies on hydrogen permeation of normalized SAE 4130 steel.

We have conducted permeation tests under *steady-state* conditions on steel membranes over a range of temperature from 80 to 600 C. We observed a constant activation energy and pressure dependence of hydrogen permeation equal to 9.6 kcal/mole and pressure to the one half power. The most interesting observation, however, was that the absolute rate of steady-state permeation was found to be independent of membrane thickness over the range tested from 0.010 to 0.250 inch. This latter observation implies that the controlling step in the hydrogen permeation process is a surface reaction involving atomic hydrogen. Furthermore, we observed that if we added one percent oxygen to our hydrogen, the same thickness independence occurred by the activation energy increased slightly and the pressure dependence of steady-state permeation changed from pressure to the one half power to pressure to the first power.

The specimen configuration was a hollow cylinder and as we thinned the membrane, we reduced the exit surface area. Our results of steady-state permeation were found to be independent of these two variables so we must conclude that it is the entering surface which is controlling permeation.

**R. A. Oriani:**

These observations of Dr. Nelson are very interesting and obviously bear on complicated phenomena. If I may venture a tentative interpretation, I would first of all agree with Dr. Nelson that the thickness independence of the steady-state permeation certainly indicates surface control by a process of activation energy of 9.6 kcal/mole. Addition of oxygen further occludes the surface making access of the hydrogen into the metal more difficult, since now the iron surface is undoubtedly covered by FeO. If one postulates that the access to the underlying metal can proceed only through sites on the surface not blocked by FeO, one can say that the permeation rate is proportional to $\theta_{Fe}$, or the fraction of the surface which is unoxidized. However, $\theta_{Fe}$ is proportional to the activity of iron on the surface layer, and by the relation

$$H_2 + FeO_{(s)} = Fe_{(s)} + H_2O$$

we see that the activity of iron on the surface is proportional to the first power of the pressure of $H_2$. This may be the explanation of Dr. Nelson's results.

**M. Smialowski, Institute of Physical Chemistry:**

As shown by recent calculations and determinations done by Dr. Raczysnki[1] in our laboratory, the highest attainable pressure of gaseous hydrogen in voids is of the order of 13,000 atmospheres, and not of 100,000 atm., as it was formerly admitted.[2] The pressure of approximately 13,000 atm. may be attained by intense electrolytic charging of iron samples in sulfuric acid solution with arsenic.

1. W. Raczysnki. *Bull. Acad. Pol. Sci., Ser. Sci. Chim.*, 15, 15 (1966).
2. M. Smialowski. *Hydrogen in Steel*. Edited by Pergamon Press, Oxford, 1962, p. 175.

**R. A. Oriani:**

One must distinguish carefully between fugacity and pressure, since at the high pressures involved hydrogen departs widely from ideal behavior. Carney, Chipman, and Grant[1] have considered this and have calculated that at room temperature a lattice content of 10 ppm corresponds to almost $31 \times 10^6$ atm fugacity, the corresponding pressure being only 14,500 atm.

In addition, one must distinguish between the theoretically attainable fugacity and that actually attainable because of kinetic limitations. For example, Darken and Smith[2] calculate a limiting fugacity of $10^{14}$ atm developable by reaction of iron with acid which is normal both with respect to $H^+$ and to $Fe^{++}$. However, such a fugacity would not in practice be attainable because, among other reasons, the pressures corresponding to lower fugacities would have caused loss of hydrogen by yielding and blister formation.

1. D. J. Carney, J. Chipman, and N. Grant. *AIME Elec. Furn. Steel Proc.*, **6**, 34 (1948).
2. L. S. Darken and R. P. Smith. *Corrosion*, **5**, 1 (1949).

### M. A. Genshaw, University of Pennsylvania:

We are studying hydrogen entry and diffusion in metals by the method of cathodic charging. How can we detect trapping in these measurements at essentially room temperature without resorting to making measurements at high temperatures?

### R. A. Oriani:

To detect trapping of hydrogen during cathodic charging at room temperature without recourse to any measurements at higher temperatures, I would compare the apparent diffusivity calculated from the observed lag time for the throughput of hydrogen to the value of diffusivity extrapolated from high-temperature measurements. If the former is much smaller than the latter I would conclude that trapping is occurring.

If Dr. Genshaw is not averse to measurements by hot-extraction techniques of the actual hydrogen contents of cathodically charged specimens, then a more direct way of detecting trapping becomes available to him. He should then compare the amount of hydrogen evolved in a certain time from one side of a specimen in which the initial lattice concentration is $c_0$ to the amount absorbed in the same time interval into initially hydrogen-free metal when the surface concentration is maintained at $c_0$. Deviation of this ratio from unity (see Equation (11) of my paper) is symptomatic of trapping.

### H. H. Uhlig, MIT:

One of the questions which often arises when considering hydrogen entry into the metal is the maximum possible hydrogen pressure. This is defined by thermodynamics for the reaction between hydrogen ions and an iron surface to form hydrogen gas. The hydrogen pressure calculated for a situation which produces ferrous hydroxide (of known solubility product fixing $Fe^{++}$ activity) is about forty atmospheres. This is the *maximum* pressure one can obtain.

If one applies a greater $H_2$ pressure, iron would plate out instead of corroding. At lower pH values at which ferrous hydroxide is soluble the calculated fugacity of $H_2$ is orders of magnitude higher.

It is only in the acid region that one observes extremely high pressures. If anyone chooses to disbelieve that such high pressures exist, he has only to try to contain the hydrogen produced by the corrosion reaction. The resultant pressure will deform or crack any material either on the iron surface or employed as container.

# THE ELECTROCHEMICAL INTRODUCTION
# OF HYDROGEN INTO METALS

J. McBreen
Yardney Electric Corporation
and

M. A. Genshaw
University of Pennsylvania

## Abstract

The kinetics of the entry of electrolytic hydrogen into metals is discussed in terms of the mechanism of hydrogen evolution. The most important parameter involved in the entry of hydrogen into metals is the coverage of adsorbed hydrogen on the metal surface. The dependence of the hydrogen coverage on potential and current is discussed in terms of both Langmuir and Temkin adsorption of hydrogen for the various possible mechanisms for hydrogen evolution. The amount of hydrogen which enters a metal depends on the hydrogen coverage, the energetics of transfer of adsorbed hydrogen to the metal bulk, and the energetics of the desorption step which leads to hydrogen evolution. The extent to which adsorbed impurities on the metal surface can affect the energetics of these various processes is discussed. In investigating the entry of electrolytic hydrogen into metals, a number of factors such as supersaturation of the metal with hydrogen can vitiate any results obtained. Guidelines to obviate such difficulties are given.

## I. Introduction

Cailletet,[1] in 1864, found that some of the hydrogen evolved when an iron vessel was immersed in dilute sulfuric acid was absorbed by the iron. In 1922 Bodenstein[2] found that the amount of hydrogen entering iron could be increased by application of a cathodic current. His results showed that the amount of hydrogen permeating an iron membrane was directly proportional to the square root of the applied current density. These two simple observations show that some of the hydrogen produced during corrosion of iron can enter the metal, and that the quantity of hydrogen entering the metal can be increased by applying a cathodic current. Thus it is apparent that the entry of electrolytic hydrogen into a metal is related to the hydrogen evolution reaction.

## II. The Hydrogen Evolution Reaction

### A. Electrochemical Kinetics

The reaction which produces hydrogen electrolytically is as follows.

$$2H_3O^+ + 2e^- \rightarrow H_2 + 2H_2O \quad \text{(in acid solutions)}$$

$$2H_2O + 2e^- \rightarrow H_2 + 2OH^- \quad \text{(in alkaline solutions)}$$

Although the reaction has long been known and at first glance looks rather simple, nevertheless a thorough understanding of the mechanism was not achieved until after 1950.

Before going into the kinetics of hydrogen evolution, a brief discussion of the equations of electrochemical kinetics is in order. The rate expression for a chemical reaction has the following form:

$$\text{Rate} = K \prod^n C_n^{x_n} \quad (1)$$

where k is a rate constant and the remainder of the expression is a product of powers of concentrations. The rate constant varies with temperature as follows:

$$K = ke^{-\frac{W}{RT}} \quad (2)$$

where k and R are constants, and W is the energy of activation for the reaction.

Combining Equation (1) and Equation (2) we have

$$\text{Rate} = ke^{-\frac{W}{RT}} \prod C_n^{x_n} \quad (3)$$

The rate expression for an electrochemical reaction combines all the terms in Equation (3) along with a potential term. This can best be illustrated by taking the concrete example of the reaction

$$H_3O^+ + e^- + M \rightarrow M...H + H_2O$$

where M represents a metal surface and M...H represents hydrogen adsorbed on the metal surface. The rate of this reaction, in terms of current, can be expressed as follows:

$$i = 2Fka_{H_3O^+}(1 - \theta)e^{-\frac{W}{RT}} e^{-\beta(V_E - V_{rev})F/RT} \quad (4)$$

where $a_{H_3O^+}$ is the activity of the hydronium ions at the electrode surface, $\theta$ = the hydrogen coverage of the metal, $\beta$ = a constant $\approx 0.5$ (this represents the portion of the potential which affects the reaction), $V_E$ = the potential of the electrode, $V_{rev}$ = the reversible hydrogen potential, $V_E - V_{rev} = V$ = overpotential, and F = the Faraday.

When the potential of an electrode is sufficiently close to the reversible potential, we have to take into account the reverse reaction

$$M...H + H_2O \rightarrow H_3O^+ + e^- + M .$$

The rate of the overall reaction is then

$$i = 2F[k_1 \, a_{H_3O^+}(1 - \theta)e^{-\beta VF/RT} \qquad (5)$$
$$-k_{-1}\theta e^{(1 - \beta) VF/RT}]$$

where $k_1$ is the rate constant for the forward reaction and $k_{-1}$ is the rate constant for the reverse reaction. At the reversible potential the rate of the forward reaction is equal to the rate of the reverse reaction. When we are more than 50 mV more negative to the reversible potential, the reaction becomes irreversible and the expression for the reverse reaction can be dropped from the rate equation. In the case of an electrochemical reaction at the reversible potential, there is no net current flow. However, both the forward and reverse reactions occur at equal rates, i.e.,

$$\overrightarrow{i} = \overleftarrow{i} = i_0 \qquad (6)$$

The exchange current $i_0$ is an important parameter in that it is a rate constant for a particular electrochemical reaction. If we are more than 50 mV from the reversible potential, the rate expression for an electrochemical reaction can be expressed as follows

$$i = i_0 e^{-\beta VF/RT} \qquad (7)$$

or

$$V = \frac{RT}{\beta F} \ln i_0 - \frac{RT}{\beta F} \ln i \qquad (8)$$

$$= a - b \log i \qquad (9)$$

The latter equation is the familiar Tafel[3] equation of electrode kinetics. The value of $i_0$ varies from metal to metal. Typical values are given in Table 1.

Thus we can see that at the same overpotential the hydrogen evolution rate is over ten orders of magnitude greater on platinum than it is on mercury. Thus the enormous effect of the substrate metal on the hydrogen evolution reaction can be appreciated.

## B. Hydrogen Evolution Mechanisms

Two basic mechanisms have been accepted for hydrogen evolution. These are the recombination mechanisms

### TABLE 1

| Metal | $i_0$ A/cm$^2$ |
|-------|----------------|
| Hg | $10^{-13}$ |
| Fe | $\approx 10^{-7}$ |
| Ni | $\approx 10^{-7}$ |
| Pd | $10^{-3}$ |
| Pt | $5 \times 10^{-3}$ |

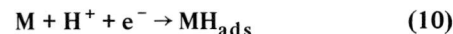

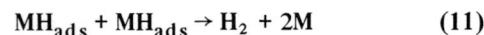

$$M + H^+ + e^- \rightarrow MH_{ads} \qquad (10)$$

$$MH_{ads} + MH_{ads} \rightarrow H_2 + 2M \qquad (11)$$

and the electrochemical desorption mechanism

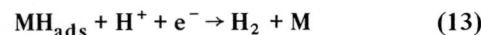

$$M + H^+ + e^- \rightarrow MH_{ads} \qquad (12)$$

$$MH_{ads} + H^+ + e^- \rightarrow H_2 + M \qquad (13)$$

### 1. The Adsorption of Hydrogen

Both mechanisms of hydrogen involve the species $MH_{ads}$. It is this species through which hydrogen enters the metal. The other possible mode of entry

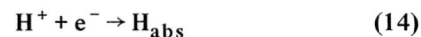

$$H^+ + e^- \rightarrow \underline{H_{abs}} \qquad (14)$$

by which the discharge of a hydrogen ion results in the *absorption* of hydrogen inside the metal, has been shown to be unimportant, at least on iron. Accordingly, it is the coverage and free energy of adsorption of hydrogen which is important for hydrogen entry.

Since this adsorbed hydrogen is involved in hydrogen evolution as well as the entry of hydrogen into the metal, we must consider the dependence of its coverage on potential.

**a. Langmuir Adsorption.** For the condition of low coverage of $MH_{ads}$ one can usually take the equilibrium adsorption isotherm derived for noninteracting species. We obtain the equilibrium isotherm by equating the rates of adsorption and desorption.

$$k_F(1 - \theta_H) \exp\left(-\beta \frac{VF}{RT}\right) = k_b \, \theta \exp(1 - \beta) \frac{VF}{RT} \qquad (15)$$

Here $k_F$ and $k_b$ are constants, $\theta_H$ is the fraction of the surface which is covered by adsorbed hydrogen, $\beta = \frac{1}{2}$ is the symmetry factor for the reaction and depends on the shape of the free energy profile on the reaction coordinate, V is the potential, F the Faraday, R the gas constant, and T the temperature. This results in an isotherm

$$\frac{\theta}{1 - \theta} = k \, \exp\left(-\frac{VF}{RT}\right) \qquad (16)$$

As the potential becomes more cathodic (negative), the coverage with hydrogen will increase.

**b. Temkin Adsorption.** When the coverage of hydrogen is not low, the interaction between the adsorbed atoms becomes appreciable. Also, different sites on the metal surface may have different free energies for hydrogen absorption. For the case in which the free energy of adsorption is of the form

$$\Delta F_{ads} = r\theta_{ads} + const$$

the isotherm becomes

$$r\theta + RT \ln \frac{\theta}{1-\theta} = -VF + const \qquad (17)$$

or

$$\theta \approx const - \frac{VF}{r} \qquad (18)$$

## 2. Kinetics of Hydrogen Evolution[4-7]

**a. Slow Discharge–Fast Recombination, Langmuir.** The rate may be written as

$$i_1 = 2F k_1 C_{H^+}(1-\theta) e^{-\beta VF/RT} \qquad (19)$$

The coverage $\theta$ may be potential dependent. To obtain $\theta$ we use the assumption that the catalytic step is in equilibrium. Then

$$k_2(k'\theta)^2 = k_{-2}(1-\theta)^2 p \qquad (20)$$

and

$$\frac{\theta}{1-\theta} = \frac{k_{-2}^{1/2}}{k_2^{1/2}} \cdot \frac{p^{1/2}}{k'} \qquad (21)$$

where p is the partial pressure of hydrogen. Re-arranging gives

$$\theta = \frac{k_{-2}^{1/2} p^{1/2}}{k_2^{1/2} k' + k_{-2}^{1/2} p^{1/2}} \qquad (22)$$

$$1-\theta = \frac{k_2^{1/2} k'}{k_2^{1/2} k' + k_{-2}^{1/2} p^{1/2}} \qquad (23)$$

Two cases may be distinguished.

Case (1): $\quad k_2^{1/2} k' \gg k_{-2}^{1/2} p_{H_2}^{1/2}$

From Equation (22), $\theta \to 0$ and from Equation (23), $(1-\theta) \simeq 1$. Thus Equation (19) may be written

$$i_1 = 2F k_1 C_{H^+} e^{-\beta VF/RT} \qquad (24)$$

Case (2): $\quad k_2^{1/2} k' \ll k_{-2}^{1/2} p_{H_2}^{1/2}$

From Equation (22), $\theta \simeq 1$, from Equation (23)

$$1-\theta \simeq \frac{k_2^{1/2} k'}{k_{-2}^{1/2} p^{1/2}} \qquad (25)$$

Substituting Equation (25) into Equation (19) gives

$$i_1 = 2F k_1 C_{H^+} k' \frac{k_2^{1/2}}{k_{-2}^{1/2} p^{1/2}} e^{-\beta VF/RT} \qquad (26)$$

For this mechanism $\theta$ did not introduce any additional potential dependence into the rate expression, but this is not always so.

**b. Fast Discharge–Slow Recombination, Langmuir.** The rate may be written as

$$i_2 = k_2(k'\theta)^2 \qquad (27)$$

At first sight the rate would appear to be independent of potential. However, $\theta$ will be determined by the preceding equilibrium which is potential dependent. Thus assuming the discharge step is in equilibrium, then

$$k_1 C_{H^+}(1-\theta) e^{-\beta VF/RT} = k_{-1} k'\theta e^{+(1-\beta)VF/RT} \qquad (28)$$

and

$$\frac{\theta}{1-\theta} = \frac{k_1 C_{H^+} e^{-VF/RT}}{k_{-1} k'} \qquad (29)$$

or

$$\theta = \frac{k_1 C_{H^+} e^{-VF/RT}}{k_1 C_{H^+} e^{-VF/RT} + k_{-1} k'} \qquad (30)$$

Two cases may be distinguished.

Case (1): At low potentials $\quad k_1 C_{H^+} e^{-VF/RT} \ll k_{-1} k'$ .

From Equation (30)

$$\theta \simeq \frac{k_1 C_{H^+} e^{-VF/RT}}{k_{-1} k'} \qquad (31)$$

Substituting Equation (31) into Equation (27) gives

$$i_2 = 2F k_2 \frac{k_1^2}{k_{-1}^2} C_{H^+}^2 e^{-2VF/RT} \qquad (32)$$

Case (2): At high potentials, $k_1 C_{H^+} e^{-VF/RT} \gg k_{-1} k'$ .

From Equation (30), $\theta \simeq 1$, thus

$$i_2 = 2F k_2(k')^2 \qquad (33)$$

For this mechanism at low potentials, or low $\theta$, the coverage introduces a potential dependence into the rate expression.

**c. Slow Discharge–Fast Electrochemical, Langmuir.** The rate is given by

$$i_1 = F C_{H^+}(1-\theta) e^{-\beta VF/RT} \qquad (34)$$

Assuming the electrochemical step to be in equilibrium, then

$$k_3 k'\theta C_{H^+} e^{-\beta VF/RT} = k_{-3} p(1-\theta) e^{(1-\beta)VF/RT} \qquad (35)$$

$$\frac{\theta}{1-\theta} = \frac{k_{-3} p}{k_3 k' C_{H^+} e^{-VF/RT}} \qquad (36)$$

$$\theta = \frac{k_{-3} p}{k_3 k' C_{H^+} e^{-VF/RT} + k_{-3} p} \qquad (37)$$

53

$$1 - \theta = \frac{k_3 k' C_{H^+} e^{-VF/RT}}{k_3 k' C_{H^+} e^{-VF/RT} + k_{-3} p} \quad (38)$$

Two cases may be distinguished.

Case (1): At fairly high potentials, if

$$k_3 k' C_{H^+} e^{-VF/RT} \gg k_{-3} p ,$$

then from Equation (37), $\theta \to 0$ and from Equation (38) $(1 - \theta) \simeq 1$. The rate is then

$$i_1 = F k_1 C_{H^+} e^{-\beta VF/RT} \quad (39)$$

Case (2): At low potentials, if

$$k_3 k' C_{H^+} e^{-VF/RT} \ll k_{-3} p ,$$

then from Equation (37) $\theta \simeq 1$ and from Equation (38)

$$1 - \theta \simeq \frac{k_3 k' C_{H^+}}{k_{-3} p} e^{-VF/RT} \quad (40)$$

Substituting Equation (40) into Equation (34) gives

$$i_1 = F k_1 C_{H^+}^2 \cdot \frac{k_3 k'}{k_{-3} p} e^{-(1 + \beta) VF/RT} \quad (41)$$

The above scheme for obtaining the current-potential relation for a given mechanism is quite general, although a slight change in technique must be used for coupled mechanisms. Coupled mechanisms are those where conditions ($\theta$ or potential) are such that the rate of the reverse reaction may be neglected for both steps of the overall reaction. This means then that we can no longer obtain $\theta$ from the equilibrium condition. Instead we use the steady state condition.

**d. Coupled Discharge–Electrochemical, Langmuir.** In the steady state the rates of the discharge and electrochemical steps are equal, thus

$$k_1 C_{H^+} (1 - \theta) e^{-\beta VF/RT} = k_3 C_{H^+} k' \theta e^{-\beta VF/RT} \quad (42)$$

and

$$\frac{\theta}{1 - \theta} = \frac{k_1}{k_3 k'} \quad (43)$$

$$\theta = \frac{k_1}{k_1 + k_3 k'} \quad (44)$$

$$1 - \theta = \frac{k_3 k'}{k_1 + k_3 k'} \quad (45)$$

Two cases may be distinguished.

Case (1): If $k_1 \ll k_3 k'$, then from Equation (44), $\theta \simeq k_1/k_3 k' \to 0$, and from Equation (45) $(1 - \theta) \simeq 1$. The rate is then

$$i_1 = F k_1 C_{H^+} e^{-\beta VF/RT} \quad (46)$$

Under these conditions, we say that discharge is rate-determining, because the rate expression contains $k_1$, the rate constant for the discharge step.

Case (2): If $k_1 \gg k_3 k'$, Equation (44) gives $\theta \simeq 1$, and Equation (45) gives

$$1 - \theta \simeq \frac{k_3 k'}{k_1} \quad (47)$$

Substituting Equation (47) into Equation (34) gives

$$i_3 = F k_3 k' C_{H^+} e^{-\beta VF/RT} \quad (48)$$

Under these conditions the electrochemical step is rate-determining.

**e. Slow Discharge–Fast Electrochemical, Temkin.** The rate expression is

$$i_1 = F k_1 C_{H^+} e^{-\beta r\theta/RT} e^{-\beta VF/RT} \quad (49)$$

The rate constant $k_1$ will include the pre-exponential $(1 - \theta)$ term, since changes in $(1 - \theta)$ will be small compared to changes in $e^{-\beta r\theta/RT}$. Assuming the electrochemical step is in equilibrium, then

$$C_{H^+} k_3 e^{(1 - \beta) r\theta/RT} e^{-\beta VF/RT} = p k_{-3} e^{-\beta r\theta/RT} e^{(1 - \beta) VF/RT} \quad (50)$$

$$e^{r\theta/RT} = \frac{k_{-3}}{k_3} \frac{p}{C_{H^+}} e^{VF/RT} \quad (51)$$

$$e^{-\beta r\theta/RT} = \left( \frac{k_3}{k_{-3}} \frac{C_{H^+}}{p} \right)^{\beta} e^{-\beta VF/RT} \quad (52)$$

Substituting Equation (52) into Equation (49)

$$i_1 = 2 F k_1 \left( \frac{k_3}{k_{-3} p} \right)^{\beta} C_{H^+}^{(1-\beta)} e^{-2\beta VF/RT} \quad (53)$$

Both the potential dependence and the reaction order with respect to $H^+$ are different from that obtained under Langmuir conditions.

**f. Fast Discharge–Slow Electrochemical, Temkin.** For nonactivated desorption, we may write the rate as

$$i_3 = 2F k_3 C_{H^+} e^{r\theta/RT} e^{\beta VF/RT} \quad (54)$$

Assuming the discharge step to be in equilibrium

$$k_1 C_{H^+} e^{-\beta r\theta/RT} e^{-\beta VF/RT} = k_{-1} e^{(1 - \beta) r\theta/RT} e^{(1 - \beta) VF/RT} \quad (55)$$

$$e^{r\theta/RT} = \frac{k_1}{k_{-1}} C_{H^+} e^{-VF/RT} \quad (56)$$

$$e^{(1 - \beta) r\theta/RT} = \left( \frac{k_1}{k_{-1}} C_{H^+} \right)^{1 - \beta} e^{- (1 - \beta) VF/RT} \quad (57)$$

Then substituting Equation (56) into Equation (54)

$$i_3 = 2F \frac{k_3 k_1}{k_{-1}} C_{H^+}^2 e^{-(1 + \beta) VF/RT} \quad (58)$$

For activated desorption (a desorption step which involves a free energy of activation in addition to the free energy for the desorption process)

$$i_3 = 2F k_3 C_{H^+} e^{(1 - \beta) r\theta/RT} e^{-\beta VF/RT} \quad (59)$$

Substituting Equation (57) into Equation (59)

$$i_3 = 2F k_3 C_{H^+}^{2-\beta} \left(\frac{k_1}{k_{-1}}\right)^{1-\beta} e^{VF/RT} \quad (60)$$

**g. Coupled Discharge—Electrochemical, Temkin.** For nonactivated adsorption, using the steady state assumption

$$k_1 C_{H^+} e^{-\beta r\theta/RT} e^{-\beta VF/RT} = k_3 C_{H^+} e^{r\theta/RT} e^{-\beta VF/RT} \quad (61)$$

$$e^{-(1+\beta)r\theta/RT} = \frac{k_3}{k_1} \quad (62)$$

$$e^{-\beta r\theta/RT} = \left(\frac{k_3}{k_1}\right)^{\beta/(1+\beta)} \quad (63)$$

$$i = F k_1 \left(\frac{k_3}{k_1}\right)^{\beta/(1+\beta)} C_{H^+} e^{-\beta VF/RT} \quad (64)$$

For activated absorption

$$k_1 C_{H^+} e^{-\beta r\theta/RT} e^{-\beta VF/RT} = k_3 C_{H^+} e^{(1-\beta)r\theta/RT} e^{-\beta VF/RT} \quad (65)$$

$$e^{-r\theta/RT} = \frac{k_3}{k_1} \quad (66)$$

$$e^{-\beta r\theta/RT} = \left(\frac{k_3}{k_1}\right)^{\beta} \quad (67)$$

Substituting Equation (67) into Equation (49) gives

$$i = F \left(k_1\right)^{(1-\beta)} k_3^{\beta} C_{H^+} e^{-\beta VF/RT} \quad (68)$$

Under these conditions there is no rate-determining step, the situation being one of mixed control.

**h. Slow Discharge—Fast Recombination, Temkin.** Since the coverage is dependent only on the pressure of hydrogen gas, this case gives the same kinetics as for Langmuir adsorption.

Table 2 contains a summary of the current-potential and coverage-potential relations derived according to the above scheme.

### 3. Mechanisms Followed in Various Metals

Much work has been undertaken to determine what mechanism of hydrogen evolution is followed at each metal. The paths which are probably followed by a number of metals are given in Table 3.[4,7]

From the above discussion it is evident that the coverage of hydrogen on a metal substrate depends both on the mechanism of hydrogen evolution on the metal and on the overpotential. At any potential more negative than the reversible hydrogen potential, the rate of the hydrogen evolution reaction will be constant. When the rate of the reaction is constant the concentration of intermediates (i.e., the hydrogen coverage on the metal electrode) will be constant.

### III. The Entry of Electrolytic Hydrogen Into the Metal

#### A. General Kinetics of Entry

In the past, two views of the probable mechanism for the entry of electrolytic hydrogen evolved. Some Russian workers[8-10] have suggested that hydrogen enters the metal in the same elementary act as that in which it is discharged, and that the intermediate state through which hydrogen enters the metal lattice is not identical with the adsorbed intermediate state which leads to the evolution of hydrogen gas. In other words, the reaction which leads to hydrogen evolution and the reaction which leads to the transfer of hydrogen into the metal are regarded as mutually independent. The other point of view is that the electrolytic

**TABLE 2**

| | $-\dfrac{\partial V}{\partial \log i}$ | | | $-\dfrac{\partial V}{\partial \log J}$ | | | $J = f(L)$ | | |
|---|---|---|---|---|---|---|---|---|---|
| | Langmuir | Temkin | | Langmuir | Temkin | | Langmuir | Temkin | |
| | | Non-Act. | Act. | | Non-Act. | Act. | | Non-Act. | Act. |
| Slow Discharge—Fast Recombination | $\dfrac{2RT}{F}$ | $\dfrac{2RT}{F}$ | $\dfrac{2RT}{F}$ | 0 | 0 | 0 | -- | -- | -- |
| Slow Discharge—Fast Electrochemical | $\dfrac{2RT}{F}$ | $\dfrac{RT}{F}$ | $\dfrac{RT}{F}$ | $\dfrac{RT}{F}$ | $\dfrac{RT}{F}$ | $\dfrac{RT}{F}$ | $i^{-2}$ | $i$ | $i$ |
| Fast Discharge—Slow Recombination | $\dfrac{RT}{2F}$ | $\dfrac{RT}{2F}$ | $\dfrac{RT}{F}$ | $\dfrac{RT}{F}$ | $\dfrac{RT}{F}$ | $\dfrac{RT}{F}$ | $i$ | $i^{1/2}$ | $i$ |
| Fast Discharge—Slow Electrochemical | $\dfrac{2RT}{3F}$ | $\dfrac{2RT}{3F}$ | $\dfrac{RT}{F}$ | $\dfrac{RT}{F}$ | $\dfrac{RT}{F}$ | $\dfrac{RT}{F}$ | $i^{2/3}$ | $i^{2/3}$ | $i$ |
| Coupled Discharge—Recombination | $\dfrac{2RT}{F}$ | $\dfrac{5RT}{2F}$ | $\dfrac{3RT}{F}$ | $\dfrac{4RT}{F}$ | $\dfrac{5RT}{2F}$ | $\dfrac{3RT}{2F}$ | $i^{1/2}$ | $i$ | $i^2$ |
| Coupled Discharge—Electrochemical | $\dfrac{2RT}{F}$ | $\dfrac{2RT}{F}$ | $\dfrac{2RT}{F}$ | 0 | 0 | 0 | -- | -- | -- |

hydrogen on entering the metal must go through an adsorbed state which is identical to the intermediate which leads to hydrogen evolution. The rate of hydrogen entry into the metal will then be determined by the concentration of this absorbed intermediate, the energetics of transfer of hydrogen to the metal bulk and the energetics of the desorption process which leads to hydrogen evolution. The latter point of view stresses the importance of hydrogen coverage of the surface of the metal. In the case of gas phase diffusion, this point was first stressed by Neville and Rideal[11] in 1936. However, the importance of the hydrogen coverage on the permeation of electrolytic hydrogen into metals was overlooked until the work of Bockris and Thacker[12] in 1959.

## B. Quantitative Treatment

The latter point of view will be treated quantitatively. This can be more clearly understood by taking a concrete model. Let us take a metal membrane, one side of which has unit area exposed to electrolyte (see Figure 1). On this side hydrogen is evolved at a potential considerably more negative than the hydrogen reversible potential. On the

other side of the membrane, provisions are made to maintain the coverage of hydrogen on this surface at zero at all times. A hydrogen permeable metal membrane under these conditions will have a steady state flux of hydrogen through the membrane which is as follows.

$$J = \frac{DC_0}{L} \qquad (69)$$

where $J$ is the flux of hydrogen through the membrane, $D$ the diffusion coefficient of hydrogen in the membrane, $L$ is the thickness of the membrane, and $C_0$ is the concentration of hydrogen/cc metal at $x = 0$. Given a coupled discharge recombination mechanism for iron and assuming a Bockris-Thacker[9] reaction sequence for the entry of hydrogen into the metal, we arrive at the following reaction sequence on the cathodic side of the membrane (see Figure 2).

Now $FeH_{ads}$ refers to adsorbed hydrogen on the metal surface and $FeH_{abs}$ refers to absorbed hydrogen directly beneath the metal surface. $k_1$, $k_2$, $k_3$, and $k_{-3}$ are the rate constants for the various steps. Since diffusion through the membrane is the rate-determining step in the permeation

TABLE 3

|     |     |     |     |     |     |     | Al  |     |
|     |     |     |     |     |     |     | D   |     |
| Ti  |     | Mn  | Fe  | Ni  | Cu  |     | Ga  |     |
| D   |     | A   | E, C| A   | A or D |  | A   |     |
| Nb  | Mo  |     | Rh  | Pd  | Ag  | Cd  | Sn  |     |
| D   | D   |     | B   | B   | C or D | A | A   |     |
| Ta  | W   |     | Ir  | Pt  | Au  | Hg  | Tl  | Pb  | Bi |
| D   | A or D |  | B   | B   | D   | A   | A   | A   | D  |

A – Slow Discharge, Fast Recombination
B – Fast Discharge, Slow Recombination
C – Slow Discharge, Fast Electrochemical
D – Fast Discharge, Slow Electrochemical
E – Coupled Discharge Recombination

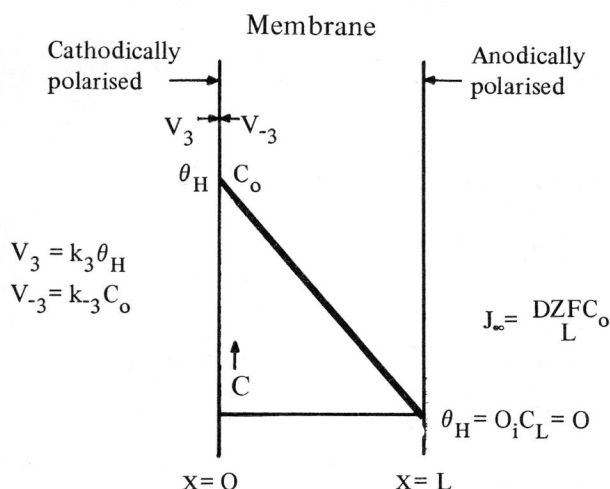

FIGURE 1 – Schematic diagram of the membrane and diffusion boundary conditions.

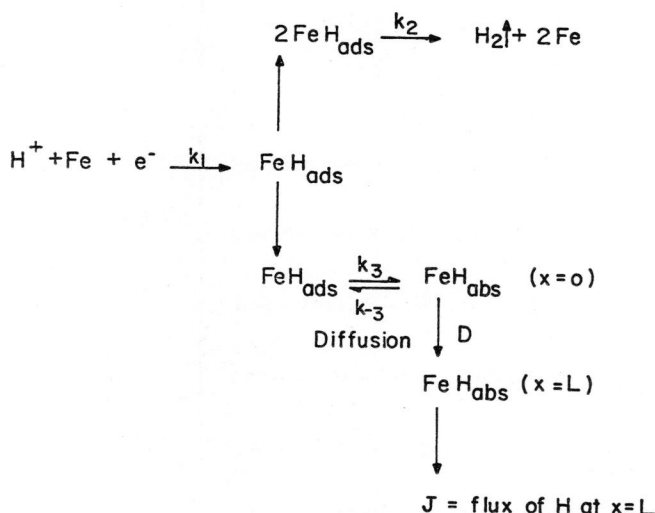

FIGURE 2 – Hydrogen evolution and entry scheme.

56

process, the surface-to-bulk reactions at the cathode surface can be taken to be in equilibrium, i.e.,

$$k_3 \theta \left[1 - \frac{x_0}{x_s}\right] = k_{-3} C_0 (1 - \theta) \qquad (70)$$

where $\theta$ is the hydrogen coverage on the cathode surface of the membrane, $x_0$ is the number of occupied interstitial sites per $cm^3$ directly beneath the cathode surface, $x_s$ is the number of available interstitial sites per $cm^3$ for hydrogen saturation to occur, and $C_0$ is the concentration of hydrogen in the metal at x - 0. For low hydrogen coverages and for low degrees of saturation of the metal, Equation (70) reduces to

$$k_3 \theta = k_{-3} C_0 \qquad (71)$$

In this case, then,

$$C_0 = \frac{k_3 \theta}{k_{-3}} \qquad (72)$$

and the flux of hydrogen through the metal is

$$J = \frac{D}{L} \left(\frac{k_3}{k_{-3}}\right) \theta \qquad (73)$$

From Equation (73) it is clear that the flux of hydrogen through the metal is directly proportional to $\theta$—the coverage of the metal with the adsorbed hydrogen intermediate. The cathodic current is

$$i = k_1 a_{H^+} (1 - \theta) e^{-\beta VF/RT} = k_2 \theta^2 \qquad (74)$$

or

$$\theta = \left(\frac{1}{k_2}\right)^{1/2} i^{1/2} \qquad (75)$$

and

$$C_0 = \frac{k_3}{k_{-3}} \left(\frac{1}{k_2}\right)^{1/2} i^{1/2} \qquad (76)$$

Also,

$$J = \frac{D}{L} \frac{k_3}{k_{-3}} \left(\frac{1}{k_2}\right)^{1/2} i^{1/2} \qquad (77)$$

For small hydrogen coverages we find that

$$J = \frac{D}{L} a_{H^+}^{1/2} \left(\frac{k_3}{k_{-3}}\right) \left(\frac{1}{k_2}\right)^{1/2} e^{-\beta VF/2RT} \qquad (78)$$

Equation (77) gives the relationship between the square root of the current and the permeation that was found by Bodenstein.[2] Equation (78) shows that

$$\frac{\partial V}{\partial \ln J} = -\frac{4RT}{F} = \frac{\partial V}{\partial \ln \theta} \qquad (79)$$

These two relationships show that the permeation of hydrogen through an iron membrane should be proportional to the square root of the applied current density, and that the rate of hydrogen permeation through the membrane should increase by a factor of ten for every increment of 240 mV in the hydrogen overvoltage. Typical plots of these two parameters versus the hydrogen permeation rate are shown in Figures 3 and 4. Incidentally, the independent discharge step mechanism supported by some Russian workers predicts

$$J \alpha i^2 \qquad (80)$$

The discussion of the relationship between the hydrogen evolution reaction and the entry of hydrogen into the metal has thus far been limited to iron. Table 2 gives the

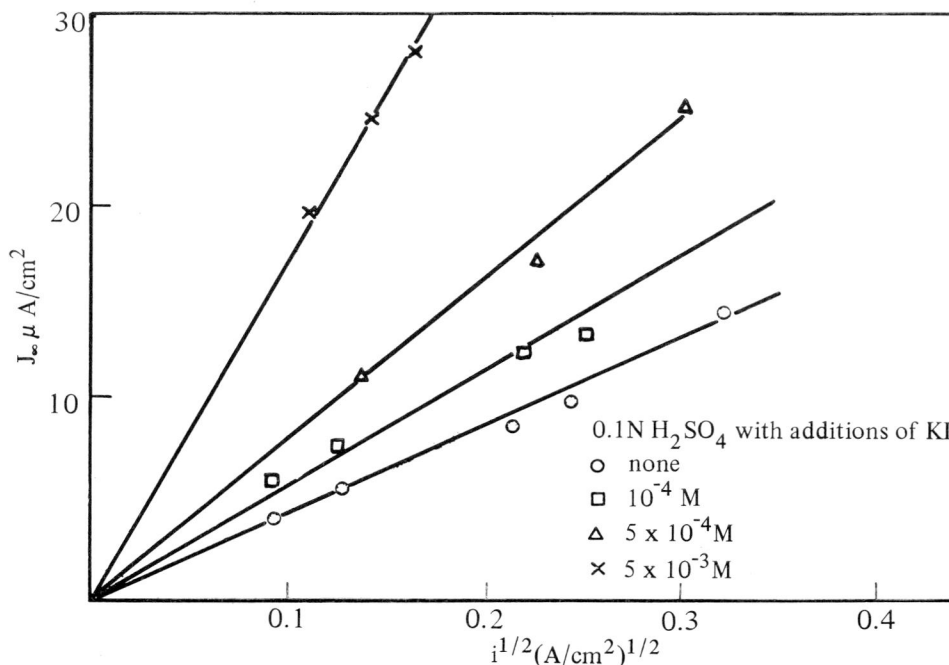

FIGURE 3 — Permeation-current curve for acidic iodide solution, Armco iron, L = 0.77 mm, 25 C.

57

relationships between the hydrogen evolution reaction and the entry of hydrogen into the metal for the other possible mechanisms for hydrogen evolution. The only assumptions are a Bockris-Thacker[12] type mechanism for the entry of hydrogen into the metal. Thus it is evident that the various mechanisms for hydrogen evolution can give different permeation-current and permeation-potential relationships.

## IV. Hydrogen Evolution and Entry Into Metal During Corrosion

During corrosion hydrogen evolution proceeds with simultaneous metal dissolution. For conditions in which other reactions, e.g., oxygen reduction, can be neglected, the partial current density for hydrogen evolution must equal that for the metal dissolution so that the net current is zero. This is illustrated in Figure 5 where the partial currents and corrosion potential are given.

The partial current for hydrogen evolution then gives rise to a source of atomic hydrogen which may enter the metal. The hydrogen evolution current density is now governed not only by the kinetics of the hydrogen evolution reaction but also by the kinetics of metal dissolution.

## V. The Effect of Poisons on the Entry of Hydrogen Into Metals

It has long been known that the addition of chlorides, iodides, etc., increases the entry of electrolytic hydrogen into ferrous metals.

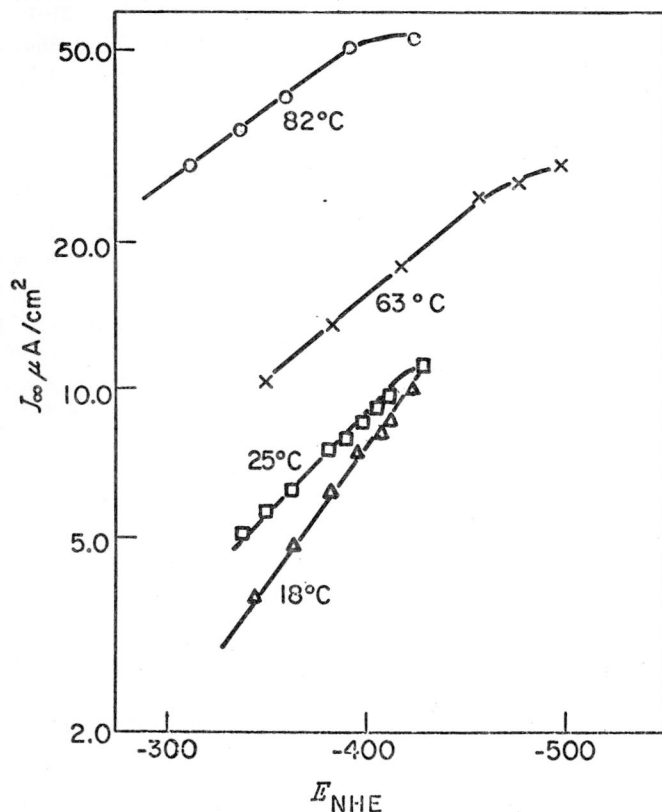

FIGURE 4 — Permeation-potential curves for Armco iron, L = 0.7 mm, 0.1 N $H_2SO_4$.

Kobazev and Montblanova[13] have suggested that the increase in the hydrogen permeation rate on the adsorption of anions is due to a lowering of the M-$H_{ads}$ bond energy. The effect of the lowering of the M-$H_{ads}$ bond energy can be easily understood by considering the energetics of the various reactions in the vicinity of the metal surface. Figure 6 shows the potential energy curves for physical adsorption of $H_2$ (ABC), chemisorption of H (DEF) and absorption of H in an octahedral interstitial cavity directly beneath the cathodic surface (KLM). GHI represents the chemisorption curve for $H_{ads}$ when the M-$H_{ads}$ bond strength W is lowered by an amount $\Delta W$.

The permeation rate at any current density

$$J_i = \frac{D}{L} \frac{k_3}{k_{-3}} \left(\frac{1}{k_2}\right)^{1/2} i^{1/2} \tag{81}$$

Let $J_i'$ be the permeation rate on lowering of the M-$H_{ads}$ bond energy by an amount $\Delta W$. Then

$$\frac{J_i'}{J_i} = \frac{k_3'}{k_3} \frac{k_{-3}}{k_3'} \left(\frac{k_2}{k_2'}\right)^{1/2} \tag{82}$$

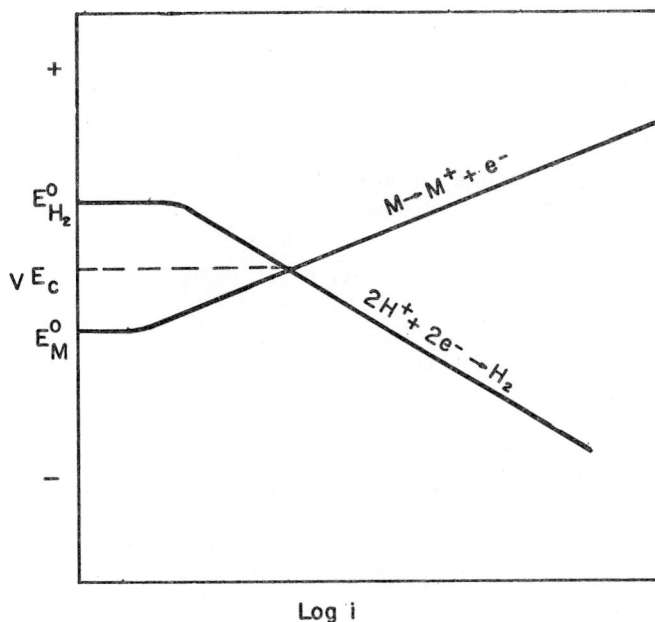

FIGURE 5 — Partial current density on corrosion.

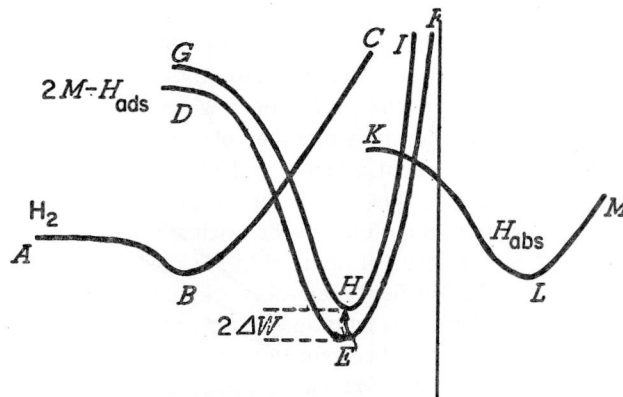

FIGURE 6 — Schematic representation of the potential energy curves for physical absorption of molecular hydrogen, chemisorption of atomic hydrogen, and absorption of atomic hydrogen.

On the basis of the model shown in Figure 6

$$k_3' = k_3 e^{\alpha W/RT} \qquad (83)$$

$$k_2' = k_2 e^{2\beta \Delta W/RT} \qquad (84)$$

$$k_{-3}' = k_{-3} e^{(\alpha-1)\Delta W/RT} \qquad (85)$$

where $\alpha$ and $\beta$ are the slopes of the potential energy curves at the points of intersection. Equations (83), (84), and (85) give the changes which the rate constants for the desorption and absorption steps undergo when the M-$H_{ads}$ bond energy is lowered by an amount $\Delta W$. Substituting Equations (83), (84), and (85) in Equation (82) gives

$$\frac{J_i'}{J_i} = e^{(1-\beta)\Delta W/RT} \qquad (86)$$

Since $\beta < 1$ it can be seen that lowering of W by $\Delta W$ results in an increase in the permeation rate.

The question arises as to how adsorbed ions can decrease W. If one supposes, as have Frumkin and Slygin[14,15] for platinum, that the polarity of the M...$H_{ads}$ is negative towards the solution side, then the lowering of the M...$H_{ads}$ bond energy may be due to electrostatic interaction between $H_{ads}$ and the adsorbed anion, this would explain the effect of ions such as I⁻ and Cl⁻ on the permeation rate through iron. Typical experimental data are given in Figure 3. Bockris and Conway[16] have suggested that the interaction between adsorbed materials and the d-band of the metal could lower W. The

lowering of W in this fashion would explain the effect of sulfur, arsenic, and cyanide on the permeation of hydrogen into iron, as all of these substances are strongly chemisorbed on the metal. Aromatic substances such as naphthalene can be absorbed flat on the metal surface, and the aromatic $\pi$ electrons can interact with the d-band electrons of the metal substrate, thus lowering the M-$H_{ads}$ bond energy. Experimental results for the effect of naphthalene on the permeation of hydrogen into iron are shown in Figure 7. Finally, if adsorption of ions takes place at sites favorable for hydrogen evolution (i.e., with large W), discharge will then occur at other sites where W is weaker. The lowering of W may be due to any of the above three effects or a combination of them, since they can occur simultaneously. Lowering of W increases the activation energy for the discharge process in hydrogen evolution. Thus there is always an increase in the hydrogen overvoltage with absorption of impurities if the discharge step is rate-determining. In the case of a fast discharge—slow electrochemical desorption mechanism, one would expect a lowering of overvoltage with a lowering of W.

Some impurities can lower the hydrogen permeation rate. We have found that additions of valeronitrite, benzonitrile, and naphthonitride to dilute sulfuric acid electrolyte lower the hydrogen permeation rate. Typical results are shown in Figures 8, 9, and 10. The fact that the effects of the aliphatic and aromatic nitrides are mutually similar indicate that all of these substances are adsorbed end-on on the electrode (i.e., vertically adsorbed). Adsorption of these compounds in this fashion would increase the thickness of

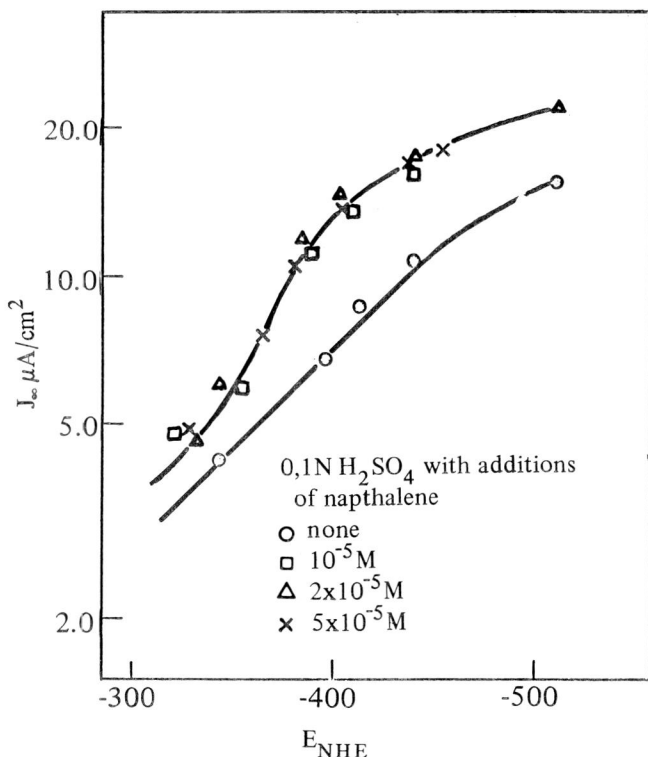

FIGURE 7 — Permeation-potential curves, Armco iron, L = 0.77 mm, T = 25 C.

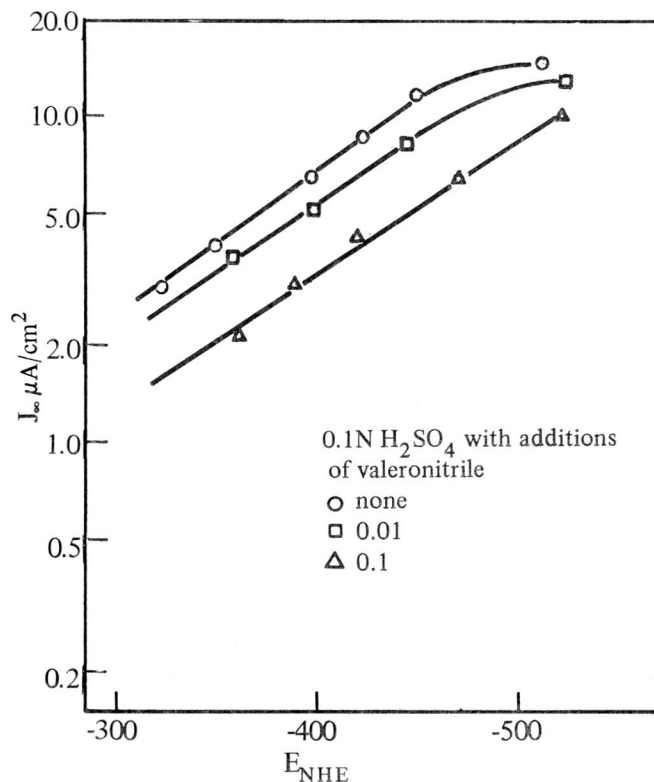

FIGURE 8 — Permeation-potential curves, Armco iron, L = 0.77 mm, 25 C.

the double layer at the metal-electrolyte interface. Furthermore, any interaction between the $\pi$-bonds of the aromatic nitrides and the metal d-band would be eliminated. Since energy would be expended on pushing hydrogen ions through the adsorbed layer, an increase in the overvoltage would be expected. This increase in the activation energy from the discharge step would lower $\theta_H$ without lowering the Fe...$H_{ads}$ bond energy. Thus the permeation rate would be reduced.

Because of the fact that we have not yet found a method for measuring the absolute coverage of hydrogen on a highly corrodible metal such as iron, we cannot determine the absolute values of $k_2$, $k_3$, and $k_{-3}$. Determination of the absolute coverage of hydrogen, together with the known dependence of the hydrogen evolution and permeation rate on temperature, would enable us to construct an actual potential energy profile for the entry of hydrogen into the metal. The lowering of W by adsorption of impurities could then be determined quantitatively. The work thus far has removed the entry of hydrogen into iron from the realm of empiricism and has correlated it with the mechanism of hydrogen evolution.

## VI. Problems Associated with the Investigation of Hydrogen Entry Into Metals

The best way to study the entry of electrolytic hydrogen into metals is to evolve hydrogen on one side of a membrane and measure the permeation rate of the hydrogen through the metal. A device was developed at the Electrochemistry Group of the University of Pennsylvania. This device essentially consisted of a membrane both sides of which were in contact with electrolytic solutions, which were electrochemically isolated. Hydrogen was evolved on one side of the membrane and dissolved anodically at the other side of the membrane.[17,18] The flux of hydrogen through the membrane then is

$$J = \frac{I_A}{F} = D\left(\frac{\partial C}{\partial x}\right)_{x=L} = \frac{DC_0}{L} \qquad (87)$$

where $I_A$ is the measured anodic current. Since currents of the order of $10^{-7}$ A/cm$^2$ can easily be measured, we can determine hydrogen fluxes as small as $10^{-12}$ g of hydrogen atoms/cm$^2$/sec. Since we can easily work with membranes as thin as 0.1 mm, and we know D to be of the order of $10^{-5}$ cm$^2$/sec, we can determine values of $C_0$ as low as $10^{-10}$-$10^{-9}$ g H/cc of Fe. The variation of $C_0$ with potential, current, temperature, and impurity addition directly reflects the changes in the hydrogen evolution kinetics, hydrogen absorption on the metal substrate, and the general energetics of the various processes which occur in going from a hydrogen ion in solution to an absorbed hydrogen atom directly beneath the cathodic surface of the membrane. Thus, the all-important parameter to determine in investigating the entry of hydrogen into a metal is $C_0$; and for a successful determination of $C_0$ we must have a linear gradient of absorbed hydrogen throughout the membrane.

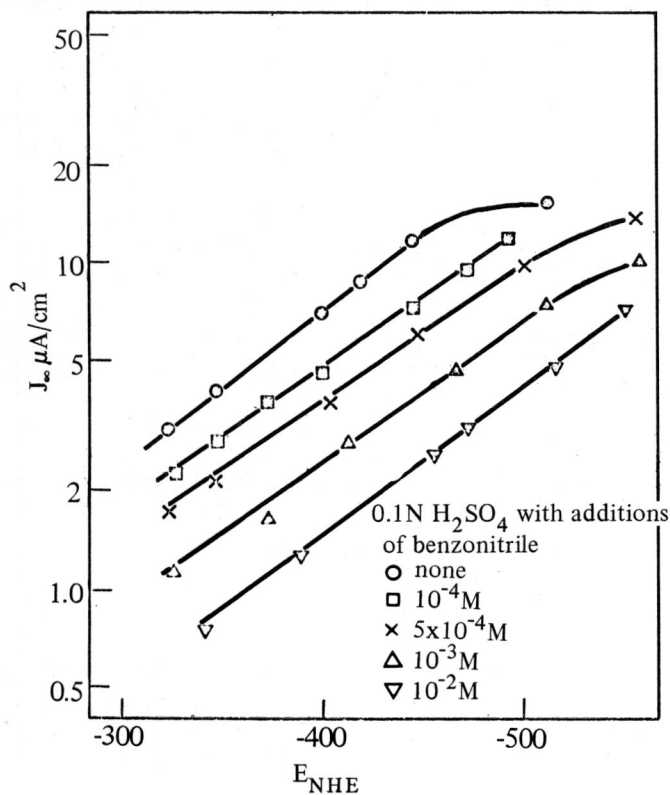

FIGURE 9 — Permeation-potential curves, Armco iron, L = 0.77 mm, T = 25 C.

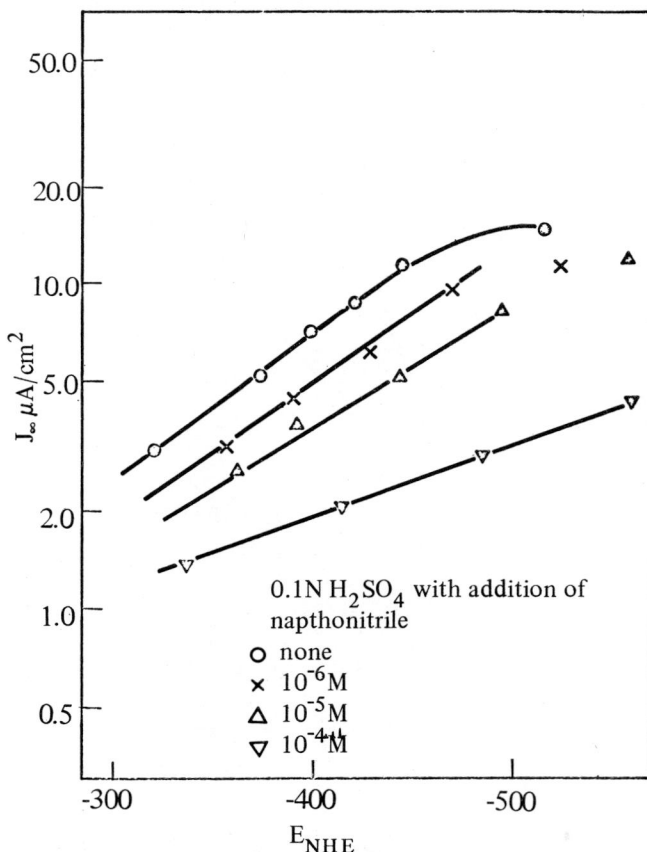

FIGURE 10 — Permeation-potential curves, Armco iron, L = 0.77 mm, T = 25 C.

60

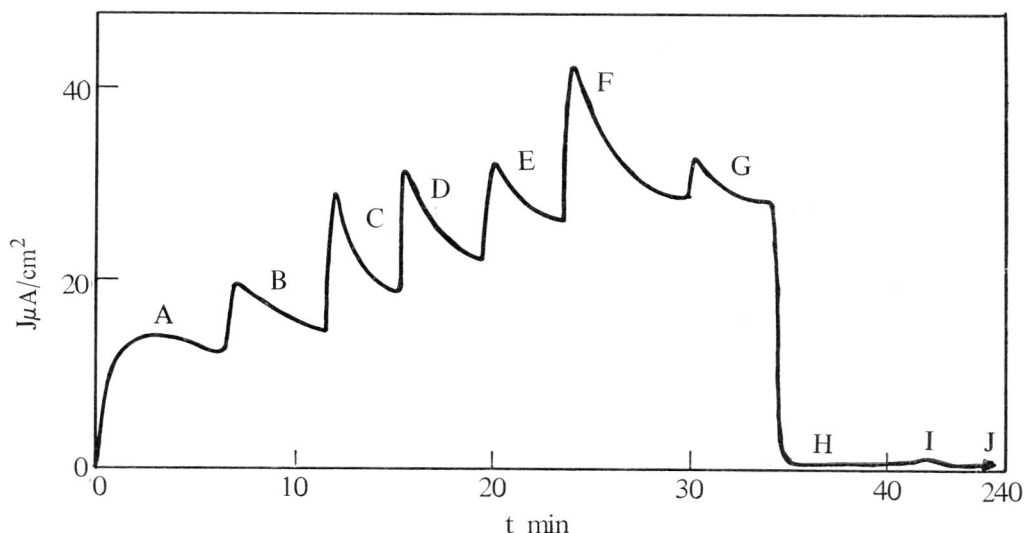

FIGURE 11 — Permeation transient, Armco iron, $L = 0.77$ mm, 0.1 N $H_2SO_4$, cathodic current-A; 0.6 mA/cm$^2$; B 1 mA/cm$^2$; C 4 mA/cm$^2$; D 10 mA/cm$^2$; E 20 mA/cm$^2$; F 40 mA/cm$^2$; G 50 mA/cm$^2$; H 0.6 mA/cm$^2$; I 1 mA/cm$^2$; J 0.6 mA/cm$^2$.

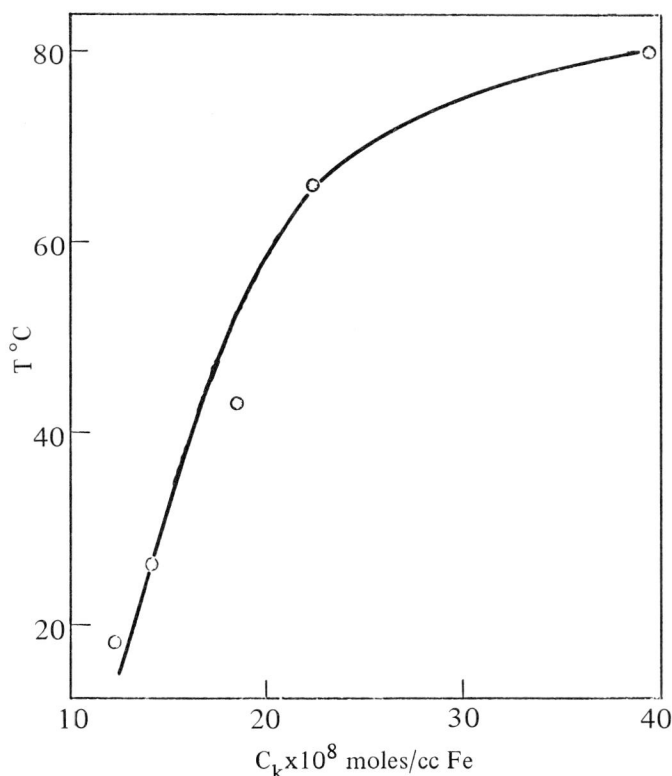

FIGURE 12 — Temperature dependence of critical hydrogen concentration in polycrystalline Armco iron.

In the course of our work we found that above a certain value of $C_0$ $(C_k)$ the premeability of iron membranes is drastically and irreversibly reduced. If during hydrogen evolution we do not exceed $C_k$ we can reproduce transients for hydrogen permeation indefinitely by simply turning on and shutting off current periodically. On exceeding $C_k$, we run into a situation which is shown in Figure 11 and described above. The concentration of hydrogen at which this phenomenon occurs is a function of temperature, as shown in Figure 12.

The following hypothesis is advanced for this phenomenon. When the concentration of hydrogen is low, hydrogen diffuses through the metal without damaging the membrane. However, on reaching a certain critical concentration in the metal, hydrogen molecules will precipitate with sufficient pressure at some hiatus in the metal and cause it to expand to form a crack or blister. The growth rate of such a crack will be determined by the rate of precipitation of hydrogen in the crack, which in turn may be governed by the rate of recombination of hydrogen at the gas-metal interface. The extent of such a void will be determined by the elastic properties of the metal and the equilibrium hydrogen pressure. This pressure will be determined by the concentration of atomic hydrogen in the metal lattice. Cracks in the metal will cut down the hydrogen permeation rate, since they interfere with the path for hydrogen diffusion in the metal. Furthermore, if micro-cracks which are open to the cathode surface are formed, it is possible for hydrogen atoms which have entered the metal surface to recombine at the bottom of such a crack and emerge as molecular hydrogen at the orifice of such a crack. This will occur if the crack width is too small to allow entry of the electrolyte. This again would cut down the permeation rate.

It is obvious that no reasonable values of $C_0$ can be evaluated from permeation transients obtained under the above conditions; hence no meaningful determinations of the kinetics of entry of hydrogen into iron can be elucidated from the data.

If one works with thick membranes and the metal under investigation has a low diffusivity for hydrogen, the occurrence of such phenomena may not be obvious from the permeation transients. Furthermore, under such conditions prolonged times are required to establish a steady state diffusion gradient throughout the membrane. If this time is excessively long, the emerging hydrogen atoms at the other side of the membrane may not reflect conditions at the cathodic surface of the membrane. Table 4 gives maximum recommended thicknesses of membranes to work with when the hydrogen diffusivity in the metal has a particular value. Using these thicknesses of membranes, steady state permeation rates can be determined in about two minutes after initiation of hydrogen evolution. We can easily spot any anomalous effects which may occur in the membrane simply by analyzing the permeation transient.

**TABLE 4**

| $D$ cm$^2$ sec$^{-1}$ | $L$ cm |
|---|---|
| $10^{-4}$ | 0.1 |
| $10^{-5}$ | 0.03 |
| $10^{-6}$ | 0.01 |
| $10^{-7}$ | 0.003 |

In studying the entry of electrolytic hydrogen into metals, the usual precautions of purification, etc., which are enumerated elsewhere[7] should be strictly followed.

## VII. Conclusions

In this paper we give the relationships between the kinetics of the hydrogen evolution reaction, the adsorption of hydrogen on a metal surface, and the entry of hydrogen into a metal. The influence of impurities on these processes is discussed. The most important parameter which awaits determination is the absolute coverage of hydrogen on iron. Some of the pitfalls to avoid when investigating the entry of electrolytic hydrogen into iron are discussed.

## Acknowledgments

We gratefully acknowledge the financial support by the Naval Air Engineering Center, Philadelphia, Pennsylvania, of the work on hydrogen entry into metals.

## References

1. L. Cailletet. *Comp. Rend.,* **58,** 327 (1864).
2. M. Bodenstein. *Z. Electrochem.,* **28,** 517 (1922).
3. J. Tafel. *Z. Phys. Chem.,* **50,** 641 (1905).
4. D. Matthews. Thesis, U. of Pennsylvania, 1965.
5. B. E. Conway and M. Salomon. *Electrochima Acta,* **9,** 1599 (1964).
6. E. Gileadi and B. E. Conway. *Modern Aspects of Electrochemistry,* **Vol. III,** Butterworths, Ed. J. O'M. Bockris and B. E. Conway, p. 347 (1964).
7. J. O'M. Bockris. *Modern Aspects of Electrochemistry,* **Vol. I,** Butterworths, p. 180 (1954).
8. I. A. Bagotskaya. *Zhur. Fiz. Khim.,* **36,** 2667 (1962).
9. L. D. Kovba and I. A. Bagotskaya. *Zhur. Fiz. Khim.,* **37,** 161 (1963).
10. A. N. Frumkin. *Advances in Electrochemistry and Electrochemical Engineering,* **Vol. III,** Ed. P. Delahay, Interscience, 287 (1963).
11. H. W. Neville and E. K. Rideal. *Proc. Roy. Soc.,* **153A,** 89 (1936).
12. J. O'M. Bockris and R. Thacker. Technical Report No. 3, ONR Contract NONR 551 (22) NRO 36-028 (1959).
13. W. Kobazev and V. Montblanova. *Zhur. Fiz. Khim.,* **6,** 38 (1935).
14. A. N. Frumkin and A. Slygin. *Acta Physiochem. URSS,* **5,** 819 (1936).
15. A. N. Frumkin and A. Slygin. *Izvestia Akad. Nauk SSSR, Ser. Khim.,* 773 (1936).
16. J. O'M. Bockris, and B. E. Conway. *J. Chem. Phys.,* **26,** 532 (1954).
17. W. Beck, M. O'M. Bockris, J. McBreen, and L. Nanis. *Proc. Roy. Soc.,* **290A,** 220 (1966).
18. J. O'M. Bockris, J. McBreen, and L. Nanis. *J. Electrochem. Soc.,* **112,** 1025 (1965).

## Discussion

**Dr. Vetter, Freie Universitat Berlin:**

You discussed only that entry of hydrogen into the metal $H_{ads} \rightleftharpoons H_{abs}$ at the cathodic surface is in equilibrium. All your equations for the hydrogen flux through the metal membrane include only the ratio $k_3/k_{-3}$ which is an equilibrium constant and perhaps unknown. Also in the case of simultaneous hindrances of the diffusion and the entry into the metal you will find a proportionality of the flux to the degree of coverage $\theta$ and some of your conclusions may be unchanged. Even an additional slow departure of hydrogen at the exit side can have the same influence. Therefore my question relates to how can you distinguish among all these combinations of fast or slow entry, diffusion and exit. Have you perhaps changed the thickness L of the metal membrane in further investigations or have you analyzed the time function of flux with sudden change in the cathodic current. It must be possible to determine from such measurement the values of hydrogen concentration $C_0$ and of the diffusion constant D. Then a distinction between the mentioned cases seems to me to be possible under certain circumstances.

**J. McBreen:**

**The rate of hydrogen permeation through the metal membranes was found to be inversely proportional to the reciprocal of the thickness of the membrane. Whenever a cathodic current was applied to the membrane, we had a breakthrough time in which no permeation occurred; then we had a slow build-up in the permeation transient which eventually reached a steady state constant value. The time to reach steady state was inversely proportional to the square of the membrane thickness. If after reaching steady state at any particular cathodic current and the cathodic current is increased, we get another transient with identical breakthrough time and transient build-up time. Thus it is clear that diffusion through the membrane is the rate determining step in the permeation process.**

**R. A. Oriani, U. S. Steel Corporation:**

Would you care to comment about how possibly the hydrogen discharge mechanism changes when you go from a pure iron surface to a surface which has two phases as in many steels? Specifically, I am thinking of the Darken-Smith work in 1949.

**J. McBreen:**

At any potential negative to the reversible hydrogen potential the rate of hydrogen evolution (i) depends on the mechanism for hydrogen evolution and the exchange current for the hydrogen reaction ($i_0$), i.e.,

$$i = i_0 \exp (\beta \eta F/RT)$$

In the case of a two phase system we can have two situations:

(A) The mechanism on both phases can be identical (i.e., $\beta$ will be the same on both phases but $i_0$ can differ).

(B) The mechanism on both phases can be different (i.e., both $\beta$ and $i_0$ can differ). In the former case hydrogen evolution will preferably occur on the phase with the highest $i_0$. In the other case the phase preferred for hydrogen evolution will depend on the product of $i_0$ and the exponential term.

**R. A. Oriani:**

May I make a comment on the question of impurities and hydrogen permeation? It seems to me that the adsorption of hydrogen has to follow upon the desorption of water. If you have an energy rich site where things like to adsorb, it is true that the energy of adsorption of hydrogen will be large upon such sites but then the adsorption energy of water would also be large. I suggest that the net energy for the displacement of one substance by another is about the same no matter where you are on the heterogeneous surface.

**J. McBreen:**

Yes, I agree. However my discussion on the effect of impurities on hydrogen permeation does not involve the energy of displacement but rather the absolute value of the metal hydrogen bond energy.

# THE METAL PHYSICS OF STRESS CORROSION

A. J. Forty
School of Physics
University of Warwick

## Abstract

The effects of dislocations on the corrosion of metals are discussed. It is concluded that dislocations might, under certain circumstances, be responsible for the nucleation of corrosion reactions but do not necessarily determine the overall reactivity of the metal. The formation of defects by the corrosion of metals is also considered. The injection of lattice vacancies and the formation of corrosion tunnels are considered to be of considerable importance in the stress corrosion of metals. Finally, some of the mechanical aspects of stress corrosion, particularly the behavior of a porous structure and the metal/corrosion film interface under an applied stress, are discussed.

## Introduction

Discussions of stress corrosion cracking frequently refer to the microstructure of the metal under consideration, both in connection with the activity at the metal/electrolyte interface and with the deformation processes occurring inside the solid. The aim of this paper is to review some of those concepts of metal physics that appear to be relevant to the problem of stress corrosion. Particular attention will be given to the role of crystal defects in corrosion processes but there will also be some discussion of plastic deformation in structures that develop in metals as a result of corrosion. The discussion, by intention, will be peripheral to the main proceedings of the conference but, wherever possible, the ideas developed will be related to the results of specific studies of stress corrosion.

The phenomenon of stress corrosion cracking presents a number of problems which are of direct interest to those concerned with the role of dislocations and other structural defects in the chemical reactivity of solids. In recent years a great deal of emphasis has been placed on the application of the ideas of metal physics to corrosion problems, and it now seems certain that structural defects play an important part in most surface reactions. For example, the work of Gilman and Johnston,[1] Young,[2] Livingston[3] and others on the etching of crystals has shown clearly that the presence of dislocations can have a significant influence on the initiation of dissolution or surface attack; and it is interesting to speculate further on the role of dislocations in corrosion in general.

We are concerned with attempts to extend these ideas to the field of stress corrosion. The atomistic approach that is inevitable when we are considering elementary crystal defects can only apply to idealised and possibly hypothetical systems, and, at best, we can only hope to examine the role of defects in transgranular stress corrosion failure in very simple binary alloys. Our ideas developed in this way might be applied to more complex systems and might even be relevant to intergranular cracking; but in such cases the microstructure is not usually sufficiently well characterized to permit realistic discussion at the atomistic level.

In order to highlight the importance of crystal defects in stress corrosion it is useful to review the various mechanisms that have been proposed to explain this phenomenon. Excellent reviews appear in other contributions to our proceedings and therefore all that is attempted here is a brief summary of the characteristics of these mechanisms. It is in no sense a critique of mechanisms.

The basic features of transgranular cracking which have to be explained by any theory are the following. Firstly it must explain why the simultaneous action of stress and corrosive environment, and not the combined action of these, is essential before failure occurs. According to observations made in recent years[4-6] supporting the two-stage film rupture mechanism this generalization is not quite correct on the microscopic scale, but it may be taken as true for any failure considered macroscopically. Next, a theory must account for the special association between the alloy under test and the particular corrosive environment in which failure occurs. It is essential always to consider the stress corrosion of a *system* of a particular alloy in a particular environment (viz., brass in ammonia, copper-gold in ferric chloride solution). This surely indicates the importance of the chemistry of corrosion. In addition to this there is a significant variation of susceptibility to failure with composition of the alloy. This might also refer to the dependence of the corrosion process on composition but it can alternatively be taken to indicate the importance of the microstructure of the metal, which will also depend on compositon.

Clearly both complex chemical processes and deformation of the metal are involved in stress corrosion, and these are interrelated to a remarkable degree. Nevertheless it is convenient for the present discussion to look at the phenomenon from two extreme points of view.

One group of mechanisms attaches greater importance to the chemical processes involved when the metal is stressed in a corrosive environment, considering that stress corrosion is, in macroscopic terms, localized corrosion enhanced in some way by the applied stress. Accordingly, an understanding of stress corrosion entails an understanding of the electrochemistry of the metal/electrolyte interface, of the structure of the surface of a metal exposed to the active environment and particularly of the way in which surface defects affect the processes of corrosion or dissolution. The effect of the applied stress is considered to be to increase the reactivity of the surface atoms by elastic deformation of the structure or, more likely, plastic deformation of the metal in the vicinity of the surface in connection with etch-pitting and tunnelling at the points of emergence of dislocations. We shall also examine the process of dissolution of a simple binary alloy in some detail; the case where preferential dissolution of one component of the alloy takes place ("dezincification") is particularly interesting because it leads to the possibility of the creation of surface vacancies and vacancy injection into the underlying crystal structure. Vacancy injection might lead to embrittlement of the surface layers and thereby assist crack initiation.

The other extreme point of view suggests that stress corrosion is essentially a process of fracture, following embrittlement of the alloy by corrosion. It has already been suggested that surface embrittlement might occur as a result of vacancy injection. As will be discussed later, vacancies can interact with dislocations or agglomerate to form sessile dislocation loops or voids in the underlying metal. Alternatively, embrittlement might be brought about by dissolution tunnelling which leads to porosity, or by the formation of hard surface films by oxidation of the metal (tarnishing for example). If fracture is an important step in stress corrosion failure it is important to consider the properties of lattice defects inside the metal, particularly to examine the microstructural aspects of fracture and deformation processes in the vicinity of the embrittled surface.

In summary, therefore, this paper will discuss firstly the effects of lattice defects on the chemical reactivity of metals. This will include the discussion of surface struc-

tures, of the role of dislocations in etch-pitting and tunnelling, and the creation of lattice defects by selective dissolution. A discussion will follow of the distribution of lattice strain around the tip of a brittle or semi-brittle crack from the point of view of enhancement of the chemical reactivity of the metal there. Finally, we shall discuss as far as can be done at present the microstructural aspects of the fracture of *two-phase systems*, for the particular cases of the deformation of the porous structure that develops locally in slip bands in some metals by tunnelling corrosion, and plastic deformation and crack initiation at the interface between a metal and a corrosion film.

## Defects and the Chemical Reactivity of Surfaces

The model of the structure of a crystal surface that seems to be currently accepted has been developed over the years by Stranski,[8] Becker and Doring,[9] Burton, Cabrera and Frank[10] and others. Figure 1 shows such a surface containing monatomic steps (S) with kink sites (K), adsorbed atoms (A) and surface vacancies (V). This is the simplest possible situation for a surface of a perfect crystal in contact with its own vapor. Certainly a much more complex structure must exist for a metal in contact with even a weakly corrosive environment. Nevertheless it may be used as the basis for a discussion of dissolution and other corrosion processes, as has been done already by Cabrera and Levine.[11]

Dissolution at low rates is considered to be proceeding by the removal of atoms from kink sites in surface steps, sometimes by direct ionization. The chemical activity of a surface is therefore dependent on the number of kink sites available and thus on the density of surface steps. The density of kink sites in a step and the density of surface steps are not strongly dependent on temperature for metals until the melting point is approached. Accordingly, under most corrosion conditions, simple dissolution should not be

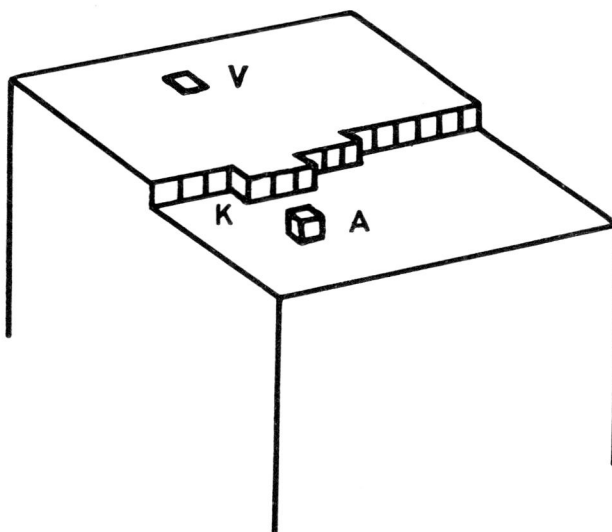

FIGURE 1 — Representation of structure on crystal surface, showing step with kinks (K), adsorbed atoms (A) and surface vacancies (V).

very sensitive to temperature. The density of steps is likely to be dependent on the extent to which the reaction is being driven and the corrosion rate should therefore vary with the nature of the environment as well as the relative potential of the components of the metal.

It is interesting to develop this model of dissolution for the case of simple binary alloys such as copper-gold or even brass. It has already been pointed out that selective dissolution of one component might lead to vacancy injection into the underlying structure and that this might lead to embrittlement.[12] The way in which the creation of surface vacancies and injection of them into the volume of the crystal may occur by selective dissolution has been described in detail by Pickering.[13] Initially, dissolution will occur by the preferential removal of the less noble atoms from kink sites. This eventually leads to electrochemical polarization as fewer of the kinks expose less noble atoms. The increase in driving force necessary to maintain dissolution current might then be sufficient to cause an increasing number of less noble atoms to leave sites in close-packed layers and produce surface vacancies. These newly created surface vacancies can be filled by surface diffusion of adsorbed atoms or of atoms from kink sites, giving rise simply to surface rearrangement. Alternatively, a surface vacancy might be filled by a neighboring atom jumping from the underlying layer, and by a succession of jumps of this kind the vacancy becomes dissolved in the crystal lattice. Pickering[13] has carried out very careful experiments which show conclusively that preferential dissolution of simple binary alloys occurs by a process as outlined above, and X-ray and electron diffraction studies have shown that this is accompanied by a disruption of the crystal structure at considerable depth in the underlying metal, consistent with the build up of a high concentration of vacancies in excess of the equilibrium concentration expected for the normal metal at room temperature.

The continued preferential dissolution of the alloy and injection of vacancies require a rapid volume diffusion of the dissolving atoms from within the specimen to the free surface where ionization can take place. In his paper Pickering points out that the necessary high diffusion rates can occur in the diluted copper-gold remaining after preferential dissolution if an appreciable fraction of the vacancies are associated in pairs as di-vacancies. Under the conditions of high vacancy concentration that might well exist at high dissolution rates, the formation of such vacancy-complexes can be expected. The situation is similar to that of the annealing of vacancies in metals following intensive irradiation.

It is interesting to note that Forty and Humble[4] in their discussion of the tarnishing of brass in ammonia solutions had to invoke enhanced volume diffusion of zinc to account for the high rate at which tarnishing proceeds. They found, for example, that when $a$-brass was immersed in the Mattsson[14] tarnishing solution the oxidation reaction spread to a depth of $10\mu$ in 2 hours. The oxidation reaction depends on dezincification and therefore the rate of tarnishing may be taken to give an order of magnitude of the rate of diffusion of zinc through a copper-rich zone.

The diffusion coefficient calculated in this way is about $10^{-10}$ cm$^2$ sec$^{-1}$. This may be compared with the values of normal diffusion of zinc in $a$-brass at room temperature and at 650 C of $10^{-18}$ cm$^2$ sec$^{-1}$ and $10^{-10}$ cm$^2$ sec$^{-1}$, respectively. It can be seen therefore that the structure of the dezincified zone must be such that the rapid transportation of zinc through it is possible even at room temperature. Again, this can be understood if large numbers of vacancies, probably associated as di-vacancies, in excess of those normally in equilibrium at room temperature are injected from the surface and diffuse into the metal.

Further evidence for the existence of an anomalously high content of vacancies in the tarnished metal was found by Forty and Humble[15] from a study of the annealing behavior of the reacted zone by low energy glancing-incidence X-ray diffraction. It was found that recrystallization of the residual copper occurred at an anomalously low temperature (about 250 C). This can be understood also in terms of a high vacancy concentration in the metal prior to annealing.

Vacancy injection might well be a significant factor in the stress corrosion of simple binary alloys. An excess of vacancies can lead to embrittlement of the metal, either at the surface where cracks can be initiated or at the tip of an already existing crack which can therefore propagate further in a brittle fashion. A supersaturation of vacancies might condense to form sessile dislocation loops or even form macroscopic voids. Excess vacancies might also interact with existing dislocations to cause the latter to climb into a configuration in which they are less mobile in the lattice. In the case of brass in ammoniacal tarnishing solution the dezincification reaction is accompanied by oxidation of the residual copper. The oxidation reaction is allowed to penetrate rapidly even at room temperature because of the very high concentration of vacancies. The microstructural studies of the tarnished layer[4] have shown this to consist of small platelets of copper oxide embedded in the copper. The layer is brittle and cracks form in it in the vicinity of slip bands in the underlying brass.

Referring to Figure 1, it would appear that after an initial period of dissolution all the steps on a crystal surface would be removed. Further dissolution would require the creation of new steps by nucleation within the face or at an edge or corner. This would represent a barrier for further dissolution. In reality, of course, all crystals contain imperfections and the emergence of even a single dislocation at the free surface with a component of its Burgers vector normal to the surface is sufficient to ensure that a permanent step exists. A step attached to an emergent dislocation will retreat by dissolution over the crystal surface to form a dissolution spiral equivalent to the growth spiral commonly observed on the surfaces of crystals growing from vapor or dissolution.[16,17] The tightness of the spiral will depend on the rate at which the dissolution is being driven (i.e., overvoltage). It is interesting to note that the rate of dissolution of a crystal should not be greatly dependent on the number of dislocations that emerge at the surface because a single dislocation is sufficient to ensure that the surface is stepped everywhere. Thus, it does not seem to be possible to account for the enhancement of corrosion rate following the cold working of a metal simply by increase of the density of emergent dislocations. It is far more likely that mechano-chemical effects, such as that described by Hoar and West,[18] occur as a result of the breakdown of a protective film during the cold work. Localized dissolution (or etch pitting) is frequently observed in the vicinity of emergent dislocations or along the traces of slip bands, and the contribution from this to the overall corrosion current clearly will depend on the density of dislocations, and therefore on cold working. This local contribution is small, however, and the effect on the overall current is not likely to give a significant dependence on cold work.

Etch pits are formed when the dissolution reaction is localized at or near structural singularities in the surface. For example, an etch pit can develop around the point of emergence of a dislocation by enhanced activity of the spiral step in that region. The success of dislocation etchants for lithium fluoride[19] depends on an inhibitor, or step poison, which adsorbs into kink sites in steps and thereby slows down the dissolution everywhere except near dislocations. Close to a dislocation fresh kink sites can form rapidly in the attached spiral step and thus rapid attack is possible there. The spiral mechanism probably accounts for etch pitting in very pure metals. The dissolution process in the core of a dislocation is not well understood, although, intuitively, it is expected to be rapid because of the large lattice strain concentrated there. Estimates[20] of the elastic strain energy associated with a dislocation in a crystal give this to be 8 eV per atm.plane. This gives only a very modest increase of the potential of the dislocated crystal relative to that of the perfect structure and it may be concluded from this that dislocations play only a very small part in corrosion. In the case of corrosion of real metals there are other factors which can give rise to localized attack and often obscure the direct effects of lattice strain around dislocations. For example, the segregation of impurities can modify the corrosion rate locally. Because of the lattice strain in the vicinity of dislocations they provide sites for the segregation or precipitation of impurities[21] or for the segregation of an excess of one component of an alloy.[22] The etching of dislocations in metals is often accounted for by chemical inhomogeneity of this kind. The segregation of impurities around grain boundaries is also known to be an important factor in the corrosion of polycrystalline metals.

Many metals are covered with an insoluble oxide film and the etching of these occurs as a result of localized attack through chemical inhomogeneities in the film. The etching of pure aluminum is a particularly interesting example. Small traces of residual impurities segregated at dislocations in the metal are incorporated in the oxide and give rise to penetration of the acid at those points. Thus a pattern of etch pits develops that reveals the presence of dislocations in the substructure of the underlying metal. Structural inhomogeneities in the oxide film on a metal can also lead to localized attack. For example, the electrolytic etching of slip traces in cold worked $a$-brass demonstrated by Jacquet[24] probably occurs as a result of the rupture of

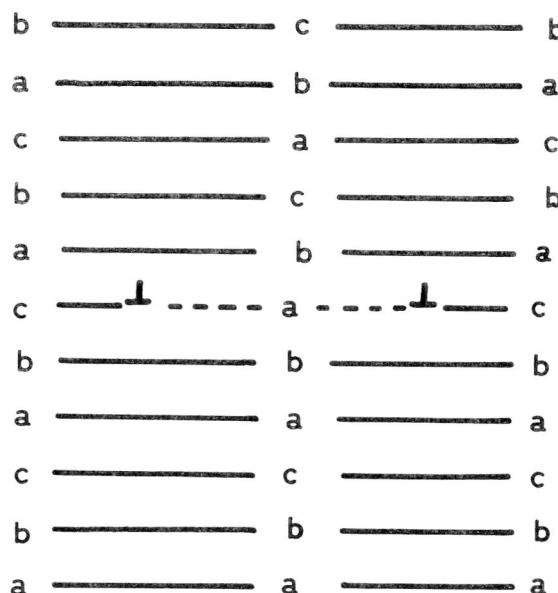

FIGURE 2 — Schematic representation of a stacking fault in an extended dislocation in a f.c.c. metal.

the oxide film by slip in the metal.

The role of stacking faults in stress corrosion has been discussed extensively[25-27] and, although it now seems probable that the correlation with susceptibility to stress corrosion is a consequence mainly of the planar arrangement of dislocations preferred by alloys having low stacking fault energy,[28] it might be worth considering the possibility that localized dissolution at extended dislocations can form a microcrack or pore from which fracture may be initiated. In a metal with low stacking fault energy dislocations are extended into ribbons of stacking fault between a pair of partial dislocations (see Figure 2). The fault can be extended still further by the application of a shear stress normal to the slip plane which forces the partial dislocations apart. The stress required for this is much higher than the critical resolved shear stress but such a condition might prevail locally in a heavily cold worked polycrystalline specimen. Structural disorder around the stacking fault is small and is in any event confined to only one or two atomic layers around the fault. It is not likely therefore that enhanced corrosion occurs for structural reasons. Segregation of impurities or a disturbance of the alloy composition in the faulted structure is expected[29] and this can of course lead to a localized dissolution in a suitable medium.

A special form of localized corrosion that has been found by Nielsen[30] to have special significance in the corrosion of austenitic stainless steel by hot chloride solution is that of etch-tunnelling or tunnel corrosion. Nielson has shown by the electron microscopy of oxide layers extracted from the metal surface after corrosion that the corrosive reaction penetrates slip bands by a tunnelling process. Tunnelling corrosion has also been observed in aluminum by Edeleanu and Law.[31] Both Nielsen and Edeleanu consider that the tunnels follow dislocations. However, experiments on the dissolution of lithium fluoride crystals by Westwood et al[32] show that, although some etch tunnels do indeed follow dislocations, this is not always the case. Emergent dislocations might well provide the sites for the initiation of localized corrosion for the reasons discussed earlier in connection with etch-pitting, but the continued localization of the attack to form a deep tunnel is dependent on other factors not related to the microstructure of the metal. The experiments on lithium fluoride have shown that tunnelling is dependent on having a step poison in the solution that restricts dissolution everywhere on the surface except at the end of the tunnel; because of their slow diffusion down the tunnel there is a reduced number of poison molecules available to inhibit kink and step motion at the end of the tunnel. The balance between rate of dissolution at the end of the tunnel and that over the walls of the tunnel or the free surface is affected also by the increased supersaturation of the solution inside the tunnel where the corrosion is proceeding, and in the case of metals for which the corrosion products are generally insoluble the conditions for pitting or tunnelling must be critical.

## Dislocations and Cracks

Any discussion of enhanced corrosion at the tip of a crack must take into account the microstructure of the metal existing there. A summary of the effects of plastic flow and the distribution of dislocations established around a crack as a result of relaxation of the high stress field concentrated there is given below. There will be no attempt to discuss the mechanics of fracture in metals; this has been done extensively elsewhere[33,34] and also a particularly clear statement of the present understanding of brittle fracture is given in the paper by Tetelman[35] in these proceedings.

The metal around the tip of a crack can undergo plastic deformation as a result of the high strain concentration there, even when the macroscopically applied stress is insufficient to produce extensive deformation elsewhere. The strain pattern will not be uniform. Even in an isotropically elastic solid (such as approximately describes most common metals) it is clear that there is a maximum of normal tensile stress acting across the crack plane ahead of the tip. As shown in Figure 3, this is accompanied by shear stresses with maxima acting in the intersecting 45° planes. These stresses can activate dislocation sources or even force the nucleation of dislocations from the tip of the crack itself, and, depending on the slip geometry preferred by the crystal, can establish a distribution of dislocations around the crack. Figure 4 shows an example where dislocations produced by plastic relaxation around the tip of a cleavage crack in a sodium chloride crystal have been revealed by etching on a transverse section. Similar, but almost certainly more complicated distributions of dislocations exist around cracks in metals (see Figure 3 in the paper by Tetelman, for example). These dislocations can affect corrosion at the crack tip, either by promoting enhanced dissolution by etching or tunnelling or by effecting the rupture of protective films (as will be described later, in the next section).

Vermilyea points out that because of the finite density of dislocations it might be possible for a close-packed surface to develop at the crack tip which is not intersected by a dislocation. Corrosion would then be a very slow process because of the difficulty of nucleating fresh steps. However, it is unlikely that such a situation would exist for long under conditions of stress corrosion because plastic relaxation will occur in the material ahead of the crack and some of the dislocation loops will slip through to promote spiral dissolution. It is well known that diffusion can occur along dislocations at rates several orders of magnitude greater than in the normal crystal lattice.[36] It is probable therefore that dislocations formed by plastic relaxation at the crack tip will also affect the distribution of impurities there and thereby affect crack growth, by enhanced chemical activity or by embrittlement.

## Pores, Tunnels and Stress Corrosion

Corrosion of a metal can develop a porosity by imperfection in film growth, by anodic dissolution of an alloy and redeposition of one of the component metals[37] or by vacancy injection and subsequent agglomeration of vacancies within the metal. Pores or voids, acting as stress raisers, can obviously weaken or "embrittle" the metal by initiating cracks. The fracture of a porous structure is extremely difficult to deal with theoretically and all that can be attempted here is a brief qualitative discussion of the behavior of such a structure when it is stressed to a level at which plastic yielding of the matrix occurs.

The situation for a single pore in a ductile matrix has

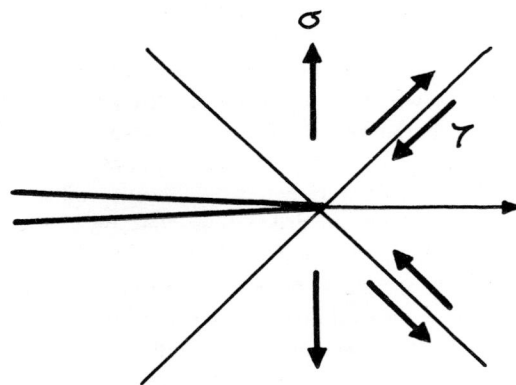

**FIGURE 3 — Distribution of shear stresses around a cleavage crack in the sodium chloride structure.**

**FIGURE 4 — A copy of an optical micrograph showing dislocations around tip of a cleavage crack; dislocations revealed by etching.**

shear stress

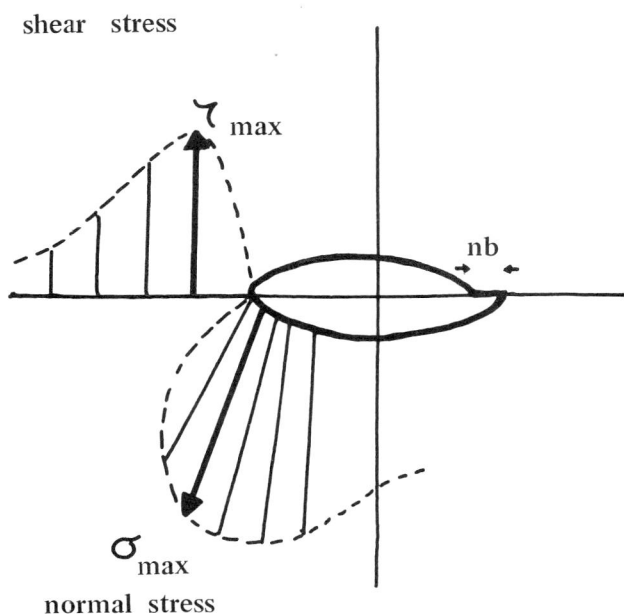

FIGURE 5 — Analysis of normal and shear stresses around a hollow dislocation with large Burgers vector (after Fujita 1958).

been discussed by Fujita[38] and also, in a more sophisticated manner, by Eshelby.[39] According to Fujita a hollow pore or slot lying in an active slip band (a situation that might well exist as a result of preferential dissolution or tunnelling during stress corrosion) may serve as a very effective stress raiser on further deformation. Shear on the slip plane can force dislocations into the pore and effectively convert it into a hollow dislocation having a large Burgers vector. An analysis of the stress field around this, taking for mathematical convenience an elliptical cross-section like that shown in Figure 5, shows an appreciable component of normal stress exerted across the slip plane. It can be shown that this is great enough to initiate fracture if $nb = (Lh/_2)^{1/2}$ where L and h are the cross dimensions of the hole and n is the number of dislocations, each having Burgers vector b, that have been forced into it. If many closely spaced pores are present a complete breakdown of the metal by the linking of the microcracks so formed or by a combination of cleavage and rupture will follow.

The case of corrosion tunnelling into a slip band is interesting from this point of view. If the slip band is activated under an applied stress, dislocations will be forced into the tunnels and locked there. It is possible, therefore, for a stress concentration to develop at the tunnels causing rupture of the surrounding material and consequently a mechanical breakdown of the slip band ensues. It is instructive to consider the situation where a line of tunnels normal to the free surface extend into a slip band. Firstly, suppose shear occurs so that the slip vector (i.e., the Burgers vector of the dislocations forced into the tunnels) is normal to the tunnels. In this case the dislocations will enter the tunnels in the edge orientation and the subsequent stress concentration will be such that the tunnels become linked together by a sidewise rupture or cleavage.

Ultimately a continuous trench will appear in the slip band. Alternatively, if shear occurs so that the slip vector is parallel to the tunnels the trapped dislocations will be in the screw orientation. In this case there will be little or no stress concentration, except possibly at the ends of the tunnels. There should therefore be no tendency for the tunnels to link by rupture; they should merely deepen by further corrosion which should be enhanced by the screw dislocations that are now anchored at the bottom of the tunnels. It should be possible to differentiate between these two situations by making experiments on single crystals with carefully chosen orientations. In more practical circumstances with polycrystalline specimens and with triaxial stressing a combination of mechanical rupture and enhanced corrosion can be expected, so that continuous trenches will form at all slip bands and gradually penetrate deeper into the slip bands by enhanced corrosion.

## The Metal/Corrosion Film Interface

In discussions of stress corrosion it is frequently suggested that the formation of a protective film on the surface of a metal followed by rupture of the film localizes the corrosion process and thereby leads to the initiation of stress corrosion cracks.[40] Not all metals on which films are known to form are susceptible to stress corrosion (pure aluminum, for example). This could be due to the fact that localized rupture of the film by plastic flow in the underlying metal is not always possible, and it is interesting, therefore, to consider more closely the microstructure and mechanical behavior at the metal/film interface; the conditions under which localized rupture of the film can occur should then emerge.

We may consider the general case in which the metal is relatively ductile and the film is harder, and possibly brittle. As Vermilyea has shown, appreciable ductility can occur in some oxide films, but nevertheless it is generally correct to suppose that the film is harder than the metal. It is reasonable therefore to suppose that plastic flow starts in the metal. In all cases of transgranular stress corrosion the alloy deforms by coarse slip, that is by active slip localized in widely spaced bands. Indeed, this is an essential feature of the film rupture mechanism for stress corrosion because this ensures only localized rupture of the film and therefore of further corrosion.

We have to consider the strain caused in the surface film by such a slip band; or, in microstructural terms, to consider the effect of a train of dislocations expanding from a source inside the metal as they meet the metal/film interface. The most important factor is the structure of the interface. In order to simplify the discussion here it will be assumed that the interface is sharp; that is, the transition from metal to film takes place over one or two atomic distances. In a real situation this is not necessarily true as a more gradual transition might occur, especially if the film growth is solid state diffusion-controlled. Nevertheless the principal conclusions to be drawn from a consideration of a sharp interface might still apply with little modification.

If the interface is structurally incoherent the propaga-

69

tion of a dislocation through it cannot readily occur (except, possibly, by renucleation in the second phase, and this might be a difficult process). Thus, dislocations from the active source in the metal will pile up against the interface. This will be the case when the surface film is amorphous or finely polycrystalline. The interface will be incoherent also if the film, though a single crystal, has a structure greatly dissimilar to that of the underlying metal. Again, a pile up of dislocations can be expected. If the film and metal lattices are similar and in parallel orientation the two structures might be constrained to match at the interface. The difference between the lattice spacings of the separate phases will then be accommodated by the introduction of a network of interfacial dislocations.[41] The spacing of these interfacial dislocations will depend on the degree of lattice misfit. For large misfits the interfacial network will be fine-meshed and the penetration of this by slip dislocations can be expected to be difficult. Under these circumstances a pile-up can again be expected at the interface. On the other hand, for a small degree of mismatch the interfacial network will not so readily obstruct the passage of slip and dislocations can pass through the film to the free surface. Effects of this kind have been demonstrated by Evans[42] in a series of experiments in which he deposited various metal films onto a substrate of silver and, after plastic deformation of the composite, extracted the films for examination by transmission electron microscopy. He was able to show that dislocations could slip into the film when the lattice mismatch was small but were blocked when it was high or when the interface was completely incoherent.

Even when the degree of mismatch is small, so that the spacing of the interfacial dislocations is large, it might still be difficult for a large amount of slip to spread into the film. Because of the difference of lattice spacings the Burgers vector of a dislocation must change by a finite amount when it is transferred from the substrate to the film. Transfer must therefore be accommodated by the formation of a residual dislocation which is left behind at the interface. If the Burgers vector in the substrate is $\bar{b}_1$ and in the film $\bar{b}_2$, the Burgers vector of the residual dislocation must be $(\bar{b}_1 - \bar{b}_2)$. The residual dislocation is sessile. As more dislocations slip through the interface its Burgers vector increases, so that for n primary dislocations

the Burgers vector for the residual is $n(\bar{b}_1 - \bar{b}_2)$. The back stress due to this will therefore grow progressively until it is sufficient to block the passage of further dislocations in that slip band. If n is large enough the Burgers vector of the residual becomes big enough to nucleate a new slip dislocation in the film, thus relaxing the stress field at the interface so that the slip band again becomes active. For systems where transfer is possible, however, it is unlikely that enough slip would occur for this before the film cracks.

If dislocations propagate through the film the only result will be the raising of a slip step at the free surface, and, providing the film is not greatly soluble and the slip is less than the thickness of the film, the passivity of the specimen is maintained. If the source of dislocations is so active that the total slip is greater than film thickness further corrosion will occur at the freshly exposed metal in the step.

If the passage of dislocations is blocked at the interface the metal, film and interface become severely strained around the pile-up. This can be relieved by plastic relaxation in the metal by cross-slip, by the nucleation of new slip in the film, by cleavage at the metal/film interface or by cracking through the film. Cross-slip seems to be difficult in alloys susceptible to stress corrosion and, according to ideas about the high strengths of thin films,[43] the nucleation of slip in the second phase is likely to be difficult. Therefore, interfacial cleavage or fracture of the film appear to be the most likely occurrences. Which of these processes occurs will depend on the adhesion of the film to its substrate. For poor adhesion interfacial cleavage will occur; but for good adhesion cracking through the film is possible.

In summary, therefore, the general requirements for film rupture are bad structural misfit at the interface but, nevertheless, good adhesion. There should either be complete incoherence between the two structures (which might be inconsistent with the requirement for good adhesion) or, if the structures are similar, a large degree of lattice misfit. Misfit leads to the piling up of dislocations at the interface because of the blocking action of interfacial dislocations and residual dislocations. The resulting concentration of stress can then lead to rupture of the film if the adhesion is strong enough to resist interfacial cleavage.

## References

1. J. J. Gilman and W. G. Johnston. *Dislocations and Mechanical Properties of Crystals,* Wiley, New York (1957) p. 116.
2. F. W. Young. *J. Appl. Phys.,* **29,** 760 (1958).
3. J. D. Livingston. *J. Appl. Phys.,* **31,** 1071 (1960).
4. A. J. Forty and P. Humble. *Phil. Mag.,* 8, 247 (1963).
5. E. N. Pugh. *Environment Sensitive Mechanical Behavior,* Gordon and Breach, New York (1966) p. 351.
6. A. J. McEvily, Jr. and A. P. Bond. *J. Electrochem. Soc.,* **112,** 131 (1965).
7. D. A. Vermilyea. This conference.
8. I. N. Stranski. *Z. Physik Chem.,* **136,** 259 (1940).
9. R. Becker and W. Doring. *Ann. Physik,* **24,** 719 (1935).
10. W. K. Burton, N. Cabrera and F. C. Frank. *Phil. Trans. Roy. Soc.,* A243, 299 (1951).
11. N. Cabrera and M. M. Levine. *Phil. Mag.,* **1,** 450 (1956).
12. A. J. Forty. *Teknish-Vetenskaplig Forskning,* Swedish Academy of Eng. Sci., **32,** 104 (1963).
13. H. W. Pickering. This conference.
14. E. Mattsson. *Electrochimica Acta,* **3,** 279 (1961).
15. P. Humble. Ph.D. Thesis (Bristol) (1963).
16. F. C. Frank. Advan. Phys. *(Phil. Mag. Suppl.)* **1,** 91 (1952).
17. A. J. Forty. Advan. Phys. *(Phil. Mag. Suppl.)* 3, 1 (1954).
18. T. P. Hoar and J. M. West. *Nature,* **181,** 835 (1958).
19. W. G. Johnston. *Progress in Ceramic Science,* **Vol. 2,** Pergamon Press, New York (1962) p. 3.
20. A. H. Cottrell. Dislocations and Plastic Flow, O.U.P., Oxford (1953).
21. A. H. Cottrell and B. A. Bilby. *Proc. Phys. Soc. A,* **62,** 49

22. A. J. Forty and F. C. Frank. *Journal of the Physical Society of Japan*, **10**, 656 (1955).
24. P. A. Jacquet. *Acta Met.*, **2**, 725, 770 (1954).
25. W. D. Robertson and A. S. Tetelman. A Unified Structural Mechanism for Intergranular and Transgranular Corrosion Cracking, Hammond Metallurgical Laboratory, Yale University, New Haven, Conn. (1960).
26. P. R. Swann and J. Nutting. *J. Inst. Metals*, **88**, 478 (1960).
27. H. W. Pickering and P. R. Swann. *Proc. Second Intern. Conf. on Metallic Corrosion*, National Assn. of Corrosion Engrs., Houston, Texas (1966), p. 128.
28. G. Thomas and W. R. Roser. *Ibid*, p. 66.
29. H. Suzuki. *Science Repts.*, Research Inst. Tohoku University, A4, 455 (1952).
30. N. A. Nielsen. *Proc. Second Intern. Conf. on Metallic Corrosion*, National Assn. of Corrosion Engrs., Houston, Texas (1966), p. 116.
31. C. Edeleanu. *J. Inst. Metals*, **89**, 90 (1960).
32. A. R. C. Westwood and H. Rubin. *J. Appl. Phys.*, **33**, 1002 (1962).
33. F. A. McClintock. *Fracture*, Wiley, New York (1959) p. 523.
34. A. H. Cottrell. *Fracture*, Wiley, New York (1959).
35. A. S. Tetelman. This conference.
36. A. A. Hendrickson and E. S. Machlin. *J. Met.*, **6**, 1035 (1954).
37. L. Graf. *Stress Corrosion Cracking and Embrittlement*, Wiley, New York (1956).
38. F. E. Fujita. *Acta Met.*, **6**, 543 (1958).
39. J. D. Eshelby. *Phys. Status Solidi*, **3**, 2057 (1963).
40. J. J. Harwood. *Stress Corrosion Cracking and Embrittlement*, Wiley, New York, p. 1.
41. J. H. van der Merwe. *Proc. Phys. Soc.*, **A63**, (1950).
42. D. Brame and T. Evans. *Phil. Mag.*, **3**, 971 (1958).
43. D. W. Pashley. *Proc. Roy. Soc. A*, **255**, 218 (1960).

# Discussion

**R. W. Staehle, The Ohio State University:**

For those theories of stress corrosion cracking which depend on slip step emergence there are two important questions:

1. Does slip initiate at the surface (or very near the surface) or within the bulk of the grains?

2. What is the mechanism by which surface films affect the formation of these slip steps?

Would you care to comment on these questions?

**A. J. Forty:**

I cannot give a firm answer to these questions. At first one would suppose that surface sources of dislocations are more important in producing slip steps than those within the grains because they can be activated at lower stresses. However, in most cases of stress corrosion cracking the stress imposed on the specimen is sufficiently great that internal sources can be activated as well as those near the surface. The appearance of slip steps then depends on the ease with which dislocations can emerge at the surface. This would tend to favor surface sources, of course, but, since there are many more internal sources in a grain, the majority of slip lines might still originate from within the bulk of the grains.

The presence of a surface film can have a marked effect on the formation of slip steps. As I indicated at the end of may paper, the passage of dislocations through an interface between the metal and a surface film depends on the degree of misfit. If the misfit is great the passage of dislocations is blocked by a close array of interfacial dislocations (or by a complete lack of cohesion if the misfit is sufficiently great) and a simple slip step is not formed. In this case the film may lift or rupture as a result of stresses concentrated in the pile-up of dislocations. If the degree of misfit is small, dislocations will propagate readily through the interface and slip steps will appear on the surface (through the film) in the normal way. This discussion assumes that the surface film is crystalline and that the interface between film and substrate is sharply defined. There is rather little experimental evidence regarding this assumption for practical stress corrosion systems.

**M. Prazak: State Res. Inst. for Mat. Prot.**

The effect of lattice defects formed under an applied stress seems to be a more important factor in corrosion cracking than the protective film rupture. Bases for this opinion are:

1. The protective (passive) films in general cannot be regarded as a defect-free insulation of metal from the corrosion environment. A typical property of passive systems is the possibility that the film can self-repair some weaker areas or mechanically formed defects, as e.g., cracks. Such defects can be formed also without applied stress.

2. The cracks of the film formed by stressing are not the only defects of the protective film: the film is in many cases perforated also by a corrosion process (e.g., by pitting). The subsequent corrosion of the metal under the film may of course form a notch responsible for initiating a crack in metal, but this mechanism can hardly be responsible for the propagating of the crack.

**A. J. Forty:**

A protective (passive) film is, by definition, one which protects the underlying metal from significant corrosion. Any defects in it are therefore not important from the point of view of normal corrosion. It could be that under applied stress the defects become more effective sites for corrosive attack; but such corrosion will surely be dominated by the rupture of the film by mechanical deformation in the metal and film. Thus, I conclude that, where protective films are formed on the metal, the initiation of stress corrosion is by rupture of the film. The subsequent propagation of a crack, on the other hand, might well be controlled by lattice defects formed in the metal under the applied stress (i.e., slip bands). Indeed, in the case of stainless steel the most likely mechanism for cracking is the initial rupture of a thin surface film followed by tunnelling and ductile fracture in the slip bands exposed to the salt solution. The α-brass/ammonia system is perhaps unusual in that crack propagation as well as initiation seems to occur by the two-stage process of tarnishing followed by rupture.

# ROLE OF OXIDE FILMS IN CREEP RUPTURE

A. J. McEvily, Jr.
University of Connecticut

## Abstract

A study has been made of the possible role of oxide films in the creep rupture behavior of copper, Cu-7%Al and Al-Zn-Mg alloy. Center notched sheet specimens were statically tested in tension at temperatures above half of their absolute melting temperature in air. Extensive blunting of the slit ends occurred prior to the development of visible cracks within the shear zones at the slit ends. After these cracks had grown slowly to some 1/4-inch in length, catastrophic rupture occurred. Electron microscopic examination of replicas of the fracture surfaces in the region of slow crack growth suggests that propagation may have occurred by the repeated formation and rupture of an oxide film. A similar process is considered to be operative in the stress-corrosion cracking of α-brass in ammoniacal solutions.

## Introduction

It has long been recognized that the ambient environment can influence the creep rupture behavior of metals and alloys. However, investigations of creep rupture mechanisms have largely avoided consideration of environmental effects, and have been more concerned with rupture mechanisms leading to the formation and growth of internal voids along grain boundaries. Similarly, experimental studies of rupture mechanisms have generally been aimed at understanding internal void formation. Indeed, tests are often conducted in an inert atmosphere to avoid any complications due to surface oxidation during the creep process. In recent years, however, the importance of environmental effects in many types of fracture processes has been recognized and it seems worthwhile therefore to examine more closely the role of environment in creep rupture. The present investigation is an initial step in this direction, being concerned with a study of the growth of pre-existing flaws in sheet specimens tested in air under creep conditions. Before describing this work, however, it is appropriate to first review briefly some of the known facts about creep rupture processes, and the role of environment therein.

## A Review of the Role of Environment in Creep Rupture

Rupture under creep conditions can occur in either a ductile or a brittle manner. Of these, brittle failures have been studied in greater detail because novel mechanisms are involved, and because of the obvious technological implications.

Brittle fracture in creep invariably involves cracking along grain boundaries. As indicated in the schematic illustration, Figure 1, three general types of cracking are recognized. One of these, surface cracking, is of particular interest in the context of this conference because it is influenced by the environment. The other two modes of cracking, wedge formation and cavitation, can occur in the absence of environmental effects as a result of grain boundary sliding, but in the present investigation they are nonetheless of interest since they influence the topography of the fractographs to be discussed subsequently. OFHC copper is an example of a material in which these internal voids are commonly found. Aluminum on the other hand is an example of a material in which they are not. The degree of susceptibility to void formation appears to depend upon factors such as grain boundary mobility, the nature of particles within the grain boundaries, and the effect of stacking fault energy on dislocation climb.

In the present investigation we will be particularly concerned with possible embrittling effects of oxide films. However, the results of previous investigations indicate that it is impossible to generalize on the role of surface oxide films in creep because, depending upon the applied stress, strain rate, temperature and material, the effect may be deleterious, non-existent or even beneficial. Even in cases where the oxide film may be detrimental, the measure of the effect can vary considerably. For example, Figure 2 indicates two degrees of embrittlement which might occur. In one case, Curve C, the time to rupture is not greatly affected, but the ductility is. In another case, Curve B, both the rupture life and the ductility are decreased. To further complicate matters, aside from possible embrittling effects, in a given instance general oxidation processes may be occurring which lead to accelerated creep rates simply through loss of cross-sectional area. The environment can also affect resistance to creep in other ways. For example, decarburization of a steel in oxygen can lead to loss in strength;[1] dezincification of brass can lead to void formation in the presence of oxide particles;[2] and nickel base alloys strengthened by aluminum compounds can be weakened as the aluminum is taken up by surface oxides.[3] The assessment of the role of the environment may therefore not be a straightforward matter.

An early investigation which indicated that oxidation during creep could be detrimental because of surface cracking was that of Thielemann and Parker.[4] One of their results showed that the rupture lifetime was shortened as the oxygen content of the environment was raised, Figure 3. This figure also brings out the important point that only at long lifetimes where overall plastic deformation processes are suppressed is the effect of the environment manifested. Further, one would expect that any detrimental effects of an environment would be more pronounced the greater the surface to volume ratio. Thielemann and Parker's results shown in Figure 4 confirm this expectation. Note that the size effect is found only in the case of intergranular cracking. No such size effect was found in the case of ductile, transgranular mode failure. In view of the consistency of Thielemann and Parker's results it is somewhat perplexing to find that in tests of steels carried out by Garofalo[5] some years later, no evidence for environmental effects was found. However, Garofalo did indicate that in cases where intergranular rupture occurred at low stress levels, oxidation might decrease the rupture lifetime.

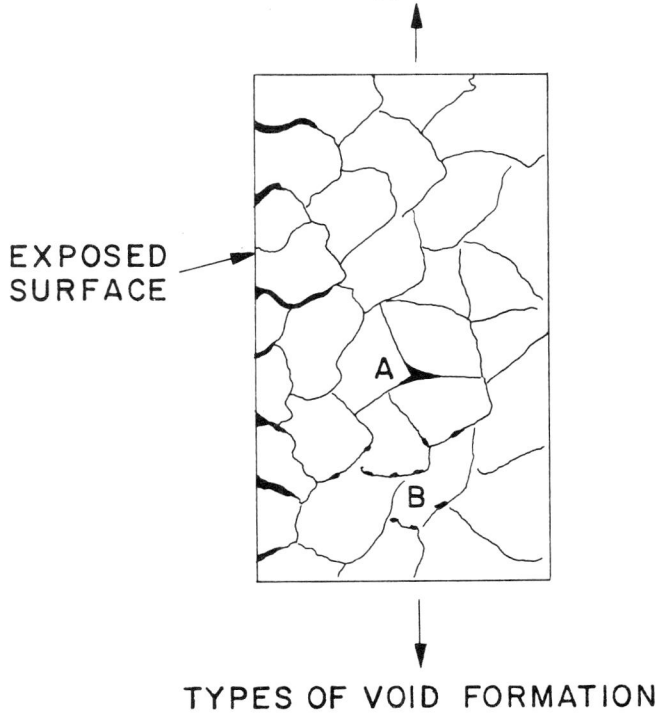

FIGURE 1 — Schematic illustration of the three modes of intergranular creep crack formation. Surface cracking at the exposed surface; wedge formation at the grain boundary triple point at A; and cavitation along the grain boundaries near B.

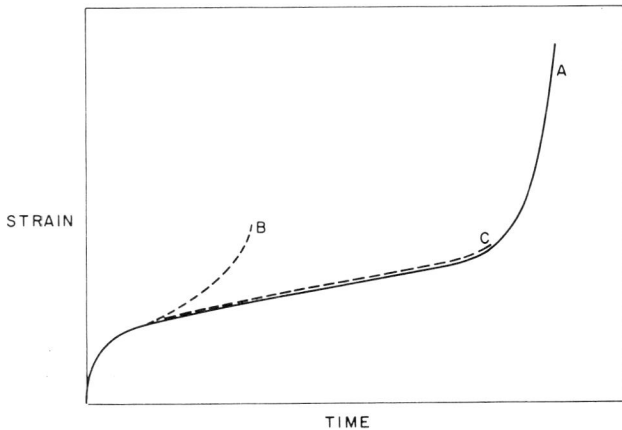

FIGURE 2 — Schematic creep curves. Curve A represents ductile behavior. Curves B and C represent possible modifications of behavior brought about by environmental effects.

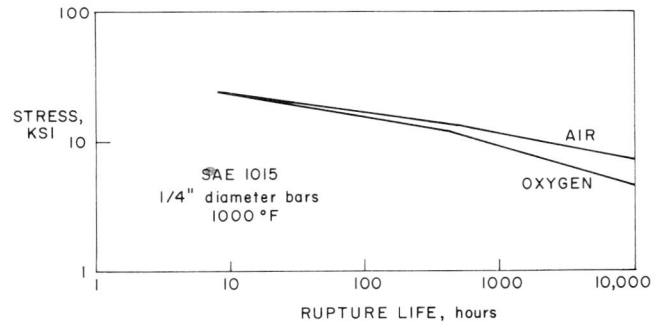

FIGURE 3 — Rupture life of SAE 1015 steel in air and oxygen environments. After Thielemann and Parker.[4]

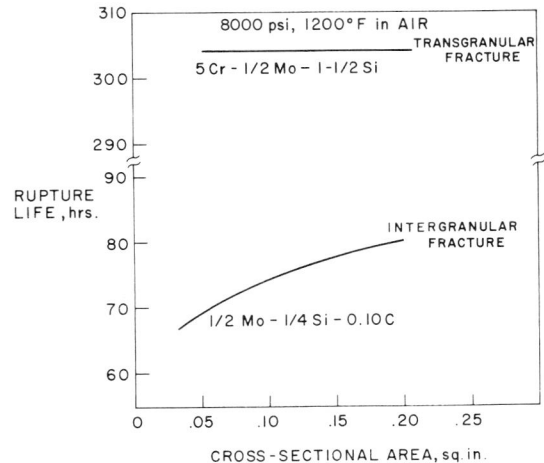

FIGURE 4 — Influence of specimen size on rupture life. After Thielemann and Parker.[4]

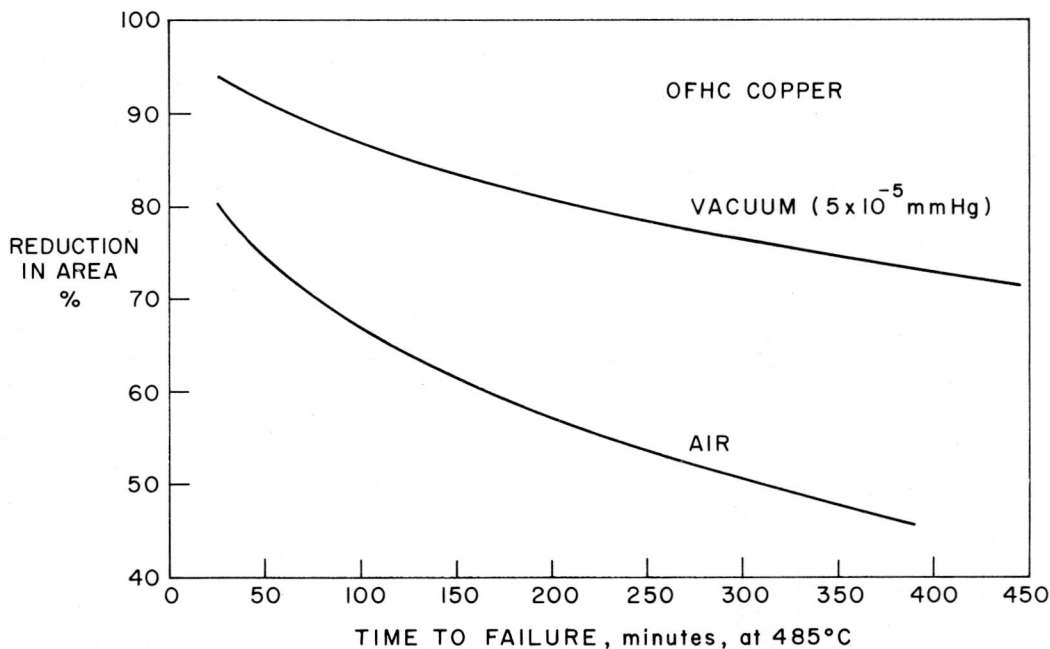

FIGURE 5 — Effect of environment on the reduction in area of OFHC copper tested under creep conditions. After Bleakney.[6]

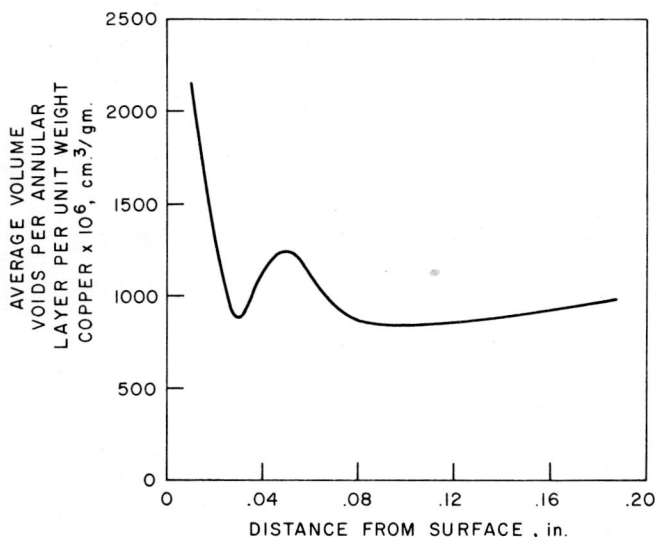

FIGURE 6 — Variation in void density as a function of distance for a surface in OFHC copper. After Boettner and Robertson.[8]

Results of tests on copper performed by Bleakney[6] and shown in Figure 5 indicate that copper tested in air is embrittled to a greater degree than when tested in vacuo. In other tests he showed that the lifetime of copper in air was less than in argon (presumably at the same stress level). On the other hand, test results for silver, a material which does not form an oxide at the temperature of testing,[15] indicated that the environment did not influence the behavior. Bleakney's results also showed that the importance of surface oxidation effects will become increasingly more apparent as other possible rupture mechanisms are suppressed. He observed that copper containing a high density of oxide particles—which promote internal void

formation—was less sensitive to environmental effects than OFHC copper—which has a much lower oxide particle content. Because both stress and the environment were involved in the embrittling process, Bleakney considered the embrittlement to be a form of stress corrosion. Chen and Machlin[16] also observed embrittlement of copper due to an oxygen atmosphere at elevated temperatures.

A most informative paper concerning the nature of the creep rupture process is that of Boettner and Roberston.[8] By determining the density of copper specimens at various stages during the creep process, they demonstrated that voids were nucleated at a very early stage. It was also found that the density of voids was greatest just below the surface, as indicated in Figure 6. This finding was attributed to the ready supply of vacancies available at a free surface. On the other hand, it is possible that the voids may have been created as a result of the rupture of surface oxide films, for the specimens were raised to temperature in air, and a visible oxide film was formed before a protective argon atmosphere was admitted. During subsequent creep deformation, rupture of the initial oxide film may have led to intergranular cracking as in Thielemann and Parker's experiments. Further oxidation would be prevented by the argon atmosphere. Some support for this view is given by the fact that as shown in Figure 6, a secondary maximum in void density occurred just below the region of maximum void density near the surface. This secondary maximum may have arisen because of the high tensile stresses set up in the region ahead of the initial surface cracks. Cracking in the region of high triaxial stress ahead of a notch has been observed by Garofalo[9] in circumferentially notched round bars tested under creep conditions. Where such subsurface cracking occurs in notched specimens the role of the environment may not be particularly important.

74

Boettner and Robertson also noted that the density of a specimen tested in air determined after the removal of the surface oxide film was identical to that of a specimen tested in an inert atmosphere and free of an oxide film. This is an important finding for it implies that the effect of the environment was confined to the near surface region and that no significant long range diffusion leading to internal oxidation or other form of embrittlement causing additional void formation had occurred. In passing it may be of interest to note that they found a greatly reduced tendency for void formation in single crystals of copper free of oxide films, high purity polycrystalline copper, polycrystalline copper formed by the recrystallization of single crystals, and directionally solidified copper. We might therefore expect that the results of tests of specimens in these conditions to exhibit a relatively strong dependence on environmental effects since the usual modes of void formation would be suppressed.

Achter and coworkers have studied the effect of environments on the creep behavior of nickel and nickel base alloys. For example, surface cracking of nickel at 650 C under a 12000 psi tensile stress was found by Sherman and Achter[10] to occur faster in air than in a vacuum of 1 x 10$^{-5}$ mm Hg. On the other hand, Shahinian and Achter found that at 817 C under 2500 psi tensile stress that nickel tested in air had a longer creep life by a factor of 100 than when tested in vacuum. The specimens tested in air, however, were embrittled in the sense that they exhibited virtually zero reduction in area. The increased life in air has been explained by a mechanism of oxide strengthening in which nickel oxide penetrates and fills grain boundary cracks, sustains a tensile stress and arrests thereby the fracture process.[12] Such different results indicate the difficulty of making a priori predictions of the influence of environment on creep behavior.

## Experiments and Results

The experimental portion of this investigation was aimed at obtaining additional information concerning the effects of the ambient environment on the creep rupture process. The first tests consisted of checking the effect of the environment on the rupture lifetime of OFHC copper. The test specimens were thin strips, 1/2-inch wide and 0.0045-inches thick, which contained a central slit. These specimens were tensile loaded to 5000 psi gross stress at 400 C in either air or a purified argon atmosphere. In air the rupture lifetime was 20 hours, whereas in argon the lifetime was in excess of 300 hours; oxidation had clearly resulted in a significant loss in lifetime. (Even in the purified argon atmosphere some oxidation occurred, which underscores the obvious fact that it is not a simple experimental matter to exclude oxygen for the environment in such long time tests.) The thickness of the specimen tested in air had been reduced by the spalling of the oxide layer to about 0.0035 inches, and in order to determine whether the observed reduction in lifetime in air was simply due to this loss in cross-sectional area, a third specimen was exposed for 20 hours in air at 400 C before

being stressed to the 5000 psi level. This specimen did not fail soon after loading as might be expected if the loss in cross-sectional area were entirely responsible for the shortened lifetime in air. In fact failure did not take place until 21 hours had elapsed. Again the final thickness was 0.0035 inches. From these tests it appears that embrittlement is due to combined stress-environmental effects.

In another series of tests the processes of deformation occurring at stress raisers introduced to localize deformation were studied. The specimens measured 2-inches in width and were approximately 1/16-inch thick. Three materials were investigated; OFHC copper and Cu-7Al — both prone to cavitation during creep — and Al-Zn-Mg alloy, 7075-T6, a material much less susceptible to cavitation.

Figure 7 provides an indication of the processes of oxidation and deformation occurring during creep of copper. After 171.5 hours, a blistered scale has formed, and plastic deformation has markedly altered the shape of the stress raising slit. The oxide is most severely cracked in the region of the slit where compressive stresses exist. After 295.8 hours the slit ends have become blunted, and cracks have appeared in the region of high tensile stress at the slit ends. Considerable plastic flow has occurred, but until just prior to rupture, no advance of the crack takes place. The deformation results in a localized thinning of the section immediately ahead of the notch. This deformation is essentially a through-thickness plane stress type of deformation, rather than plane strain. A small amount of slow crack growth, less than 1/4-inch in length, occurred prior to final rupture. Similar observations were made in the case of Cu-7%Al specimens, but the extent of oxidation was much less.

A taper section through the oxide on a copper specimen, Figure 8, indicates its irregular nature. (In many other places the oxide had spalled off exposing the base metal.) Small cracks are evident within the oxide and voids can be seen in the base metal. Many of these voids are connected to the free surface and, as shown in Figure 9, are rimmed by an oxide layer. The intergranular nature of the voids can be seen in Figure 10. A search was made to determine whether grain boundaries in low stress regions away from regions of highest deformation were preferentially oxidized, but only in rare instances was such evidence found. An example is given in Figure 11. In general the metal-oxide interface had an irregular, scalloped appearance.

In the case of the 7075-T6 aluminum alloy, no readily visible surface oxide film forms, but of course one is always present. As shown in Figure 12, the processes of deformation at the tip of a stress raiser—in this instance a fatigue crack—are similar but much more extensive than in the case of copper or Cu-7%Al. (The lesser ductility exhibited by copper and Cu-7%Al is due to their greater tendency for intergranular cracking.) In the aluminum alloy after a remarkable amount of localized deformation has occurred, cracks appear and propagate slowly in the heavily necked down region at the tip of a blunted fatigue crack in the very last stages of the rupture lifetime. The development of constraints against through-thickness plastic deformation set up by nonuniform lateral contraction may be a requirement for crack initiation. By the time such constraints have developed the entire section of these 2-inch wide sheet specimens has been so reduced that the average true local stress is raised considerably above its initial value, and deformation is proceeding rapidly. As in the case of the copper specimens, the extent of slow crack growth is only of the order of 1/4-inch or less in these tests. As shown in Figure 13, along the fracture path considerable plastic flow has occurred, but no internal voids have formed.

Replicas of fracture surfaces in the region of slow crack growth for the alloys tested are shown in Figures 14, 16 and 17. As is usual with electron fractography, the selection of "typical" areas presents something of a problem. In the examples chosen some attempt has been made to demonstrate the range of fracture characteristics encountered, but the main emphasis is placed upon those features which may indicate an influence of environment on the fracture process. A more thorough study is needed to establish the fraction of surface covered by any one fracture type as a function of stress and temperature.

In Figure 14 examples of the fracture surface appearance of OFHC copper are shown. A common finding was the presence of smooth regions indicative of particles surrounded by areas quite mottled in appearance, Figure 14a. Figures 14b and 14c differ considerably from Figure 14a, a finding which suggests that crack growth occurred by a two-stage process involving growth of an oxide film at the crack tip, followed by its rupture and the incremental advance of the crack until it is arrested by becoming blunted in the ductile substrate material. Such a two-stage process has been proposed to account for the growth of stress corrosion cracks in brass exposed to a "tarnishing" ammoniacal solution where similar fractographic features are observed.[13,14] Another point of similarity is that in time extensive creep deformation can occur at the tips of cracks even at room temperature where stress corrosion cracking is usually studied. For example, consider a sheet specimen of annealed brass in which a fatigue crack is grown at 1800 cpm at a peak stress of 17000 psi. If the crack growth process is interrupted periodically and the central crack opening displacement maintained, then clear evidence of the creep deformation processes can be

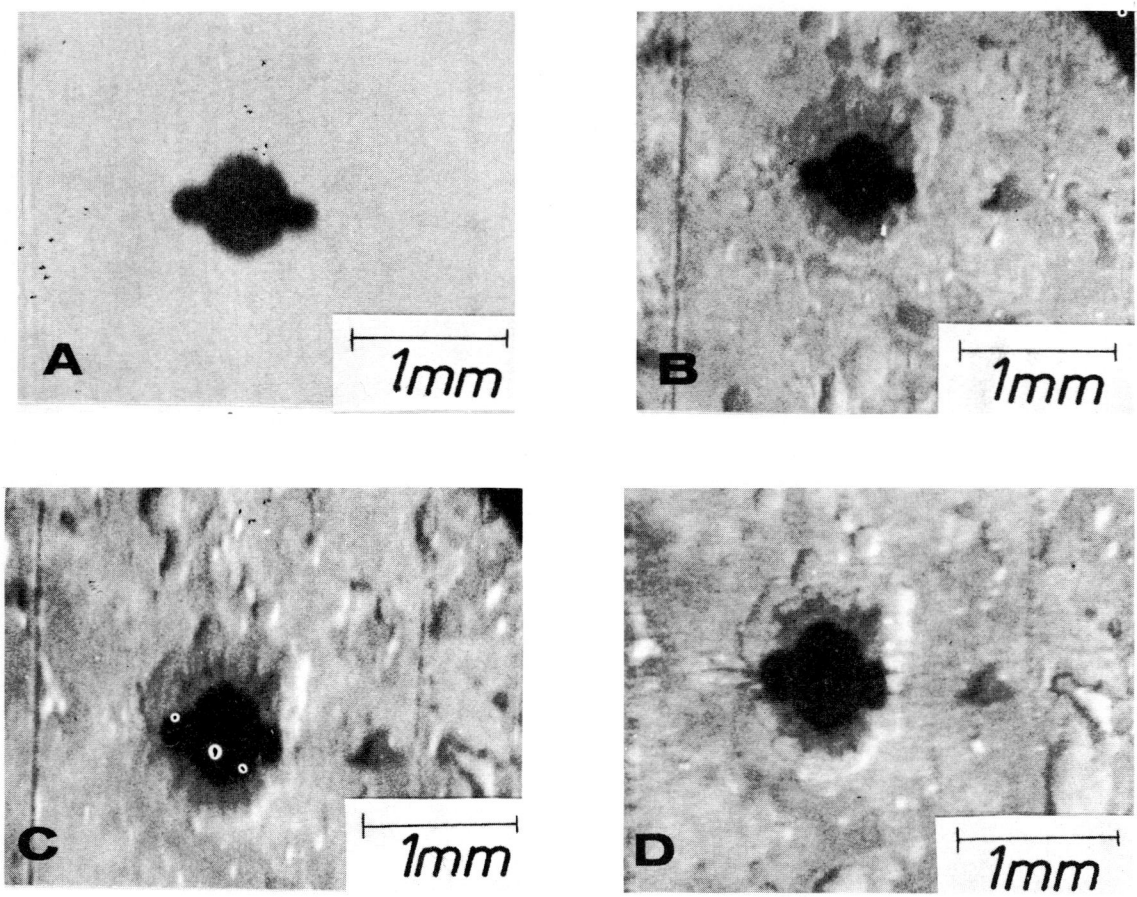

FIGURE 7 — Creep deformation at a slit in sheet specimen of OFHC copper. Tensile axis vertical. Test conditions: 5000 psi gross stress, 400 C. Rupture lifetime: 327 hours. (a) after 18.8 hours, (b) after 176.5 hours (note development of scale), (c) after 234.6 hours, and (d) after 195.8 hours.

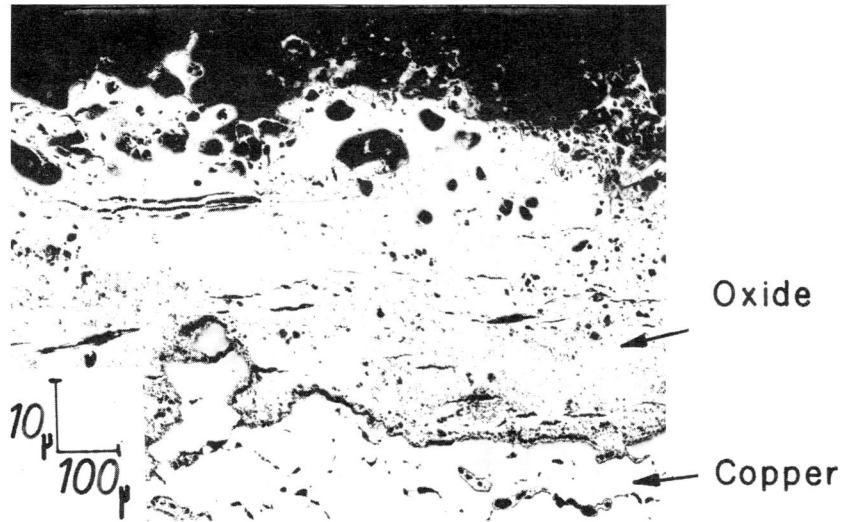

FIGURE 8 – Taper section through oxide film on copper specimen near region of fracture. Taper magnification in vertical direction gives twelve fold increase in magnification. Tensile axis near vertical direction.

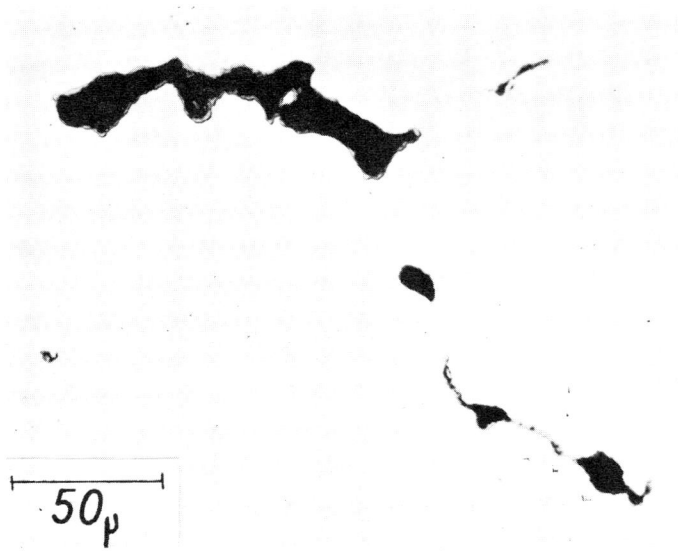

FIGURE 9 – Surface connected voids in OFHC copper rimmed by oxide film.

obtained as shown in Figure 15.

Examples of fracture surface markings on Cu-7%Al are given in Figure 16. Evidence of cavity formation is given in Figure 16a. Indications of slip on at least three slip systems are evident. In Figure 16b, regions heavily pitted, presumably as a result of oxidation, exist along side of smooth regions. A type of veining, characteristic of many smooth regions but of undetermined origin, can also be seen. Much

different in appearance are the regions shown in Figures 16c and 16d, which, as in the case of copper, suggest a two-stage process of crack growth. Only single sets of markings exist over distances some $10\mu$ or more in length in these two figures. The deformation in Figure 16d in particular is much more severe than that in Figure 16a, the latter being suggestive of slip intersecting a free surface.

Examples of the fracture appearance of the aluminum

77

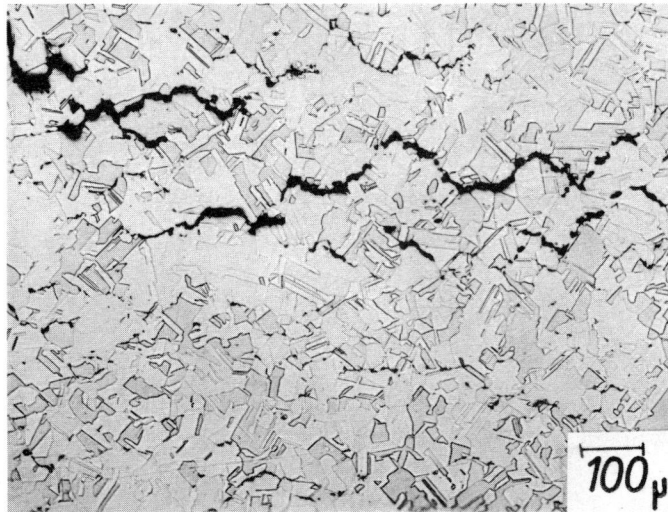

FIGURE 10 — Intergranular cracking in OFHC copper.

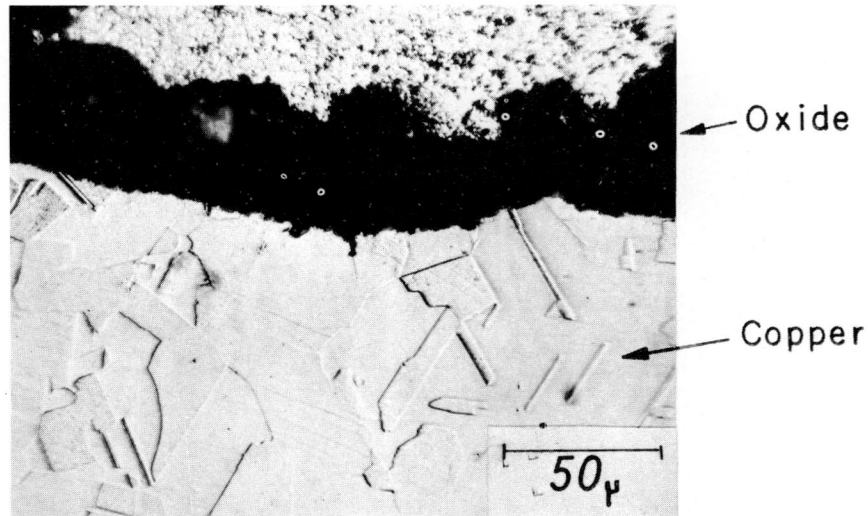

FIGURE 11 — Oxide-metal interfacial region showing rare example of oxide penetrating grain boundary in low stress region.

alloy are shown in Figure 17. Again a wide variety of topographical characteristics was encountered. The figures selected are of regions in which the markings suggest that crack growth occurred by a two-stage mechanism. Certainly the types of markings shown do not fall into the categories of ductile dimpling or cleavage. Incidentally, the usual sort of ductile rupture markings were observed in regions of fast fracture.

In a failure process involving repeated film formation and rupture, the rate controlling process can be either the time required for sufficient plastic deformation to rupture the film to occur at the tip of the crack. Since in a material such as aluminum tested in air the film is extremely thin and forms with great rapidity the rate controlling process

may be that associated with the attainment of a critical strain at the crack tip.

A final experiment was an attempt to replicate matching fracture faces in the region of slow crack growth in the aluminum alloy. If crack growth did occur by a two-stage process leading to the creation of crack arrest marks, then the arrest marks on each surface should correspond. Because of slight differences in replica shrinkage, curvature of the replicas, and variations in shadowing effects, this task proved to be more difficult than anticipated. Nevertheless a degree of correspondence was obtained as shown in Figure 18, providing thereby some further support for the two-stage rupture process.

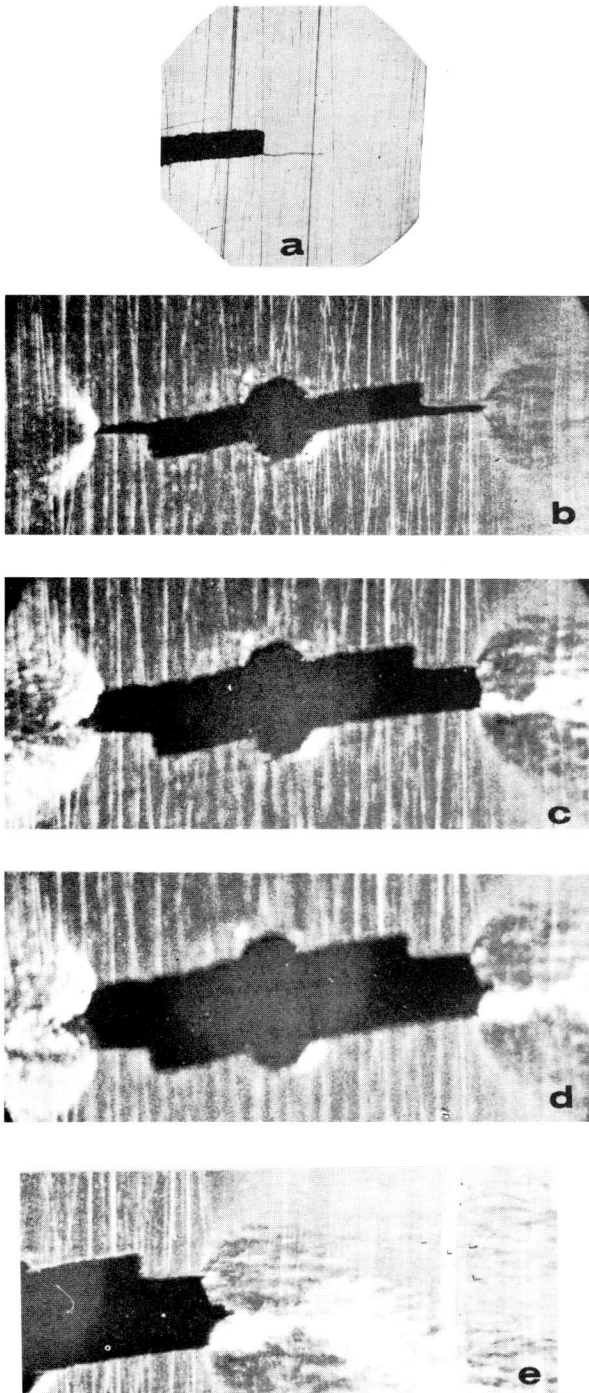

FIGURE 12 — Creep deformation at fatigue crack tip in sheet specimen of Al-Zn-Mg alloy, 7075-T6. Test conditions: 20,000 psi gross stress, 200 C. Rupture lifetime: 86.9 hours (a) starting fatigue crack at right end of slit, (b) after 49.0 hours, (c) after 83.7 hours, (d) after 85.8 hours, and (e) after 86.1 hours.

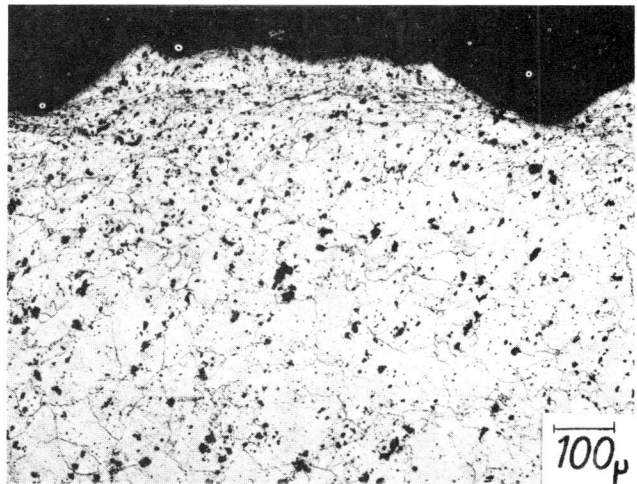

FIGURE 13 — Region near fracture in 7075-T6. Tensile axis vertical. Dark spots are constituent particles. No voids are evident. Note grain flow along fracture edge.

## Concluding Remarks

Results of tests with OFHC copper confirm the view that materials subject to intercrystalline cracking during creep can be further embrittled by the cracking of surface oxide films. Environmental embrittlement is promoted by long exposure times, large surface to volume ratios, and strain gradients such that surface strains are maximized. No evidence of intercrystalline cracking was found in the case of an Al-Sn-Mg alloy, and no evidence was uncovered to indicate that the ambient environment greatly affects the overall creep behavior of any alloys which fail in a transgranular, ductile manner.

Examination of the fracture surfaces in the region of slow crack growth, a stage immediately preceding final rupture, indicates that, as proposed in the case of the growth of certain stress corrosion cracks, a two-stage process of crack growth involving oxide film rupture contributes to crack advance in all materials studied.

## Acknowledgment

The author expresses his appreciation to Mr. J. Ingall and to Mr. R. Benoit for their able assistance in the experimental aspects of this investigation.

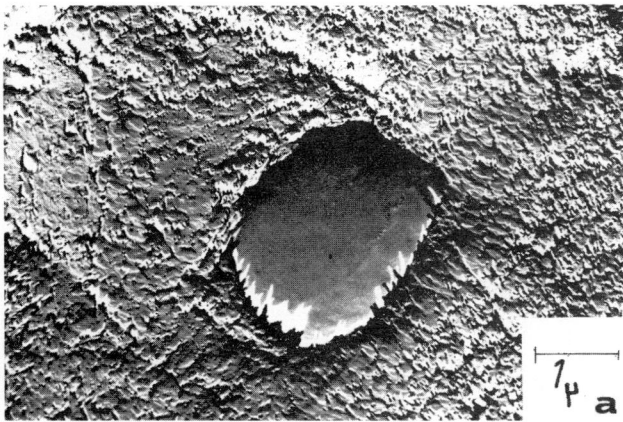
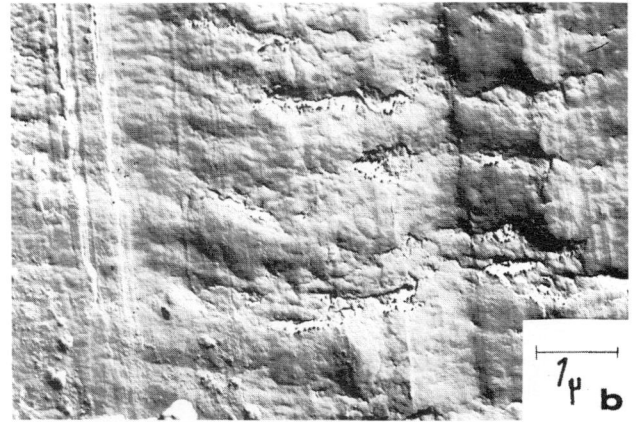

FIGURE 14 — Fracture appearance of OFHC copper in region of slow crack growth. Test conditions: 400 C, 5000 psi. Rupture life: 327 hours.

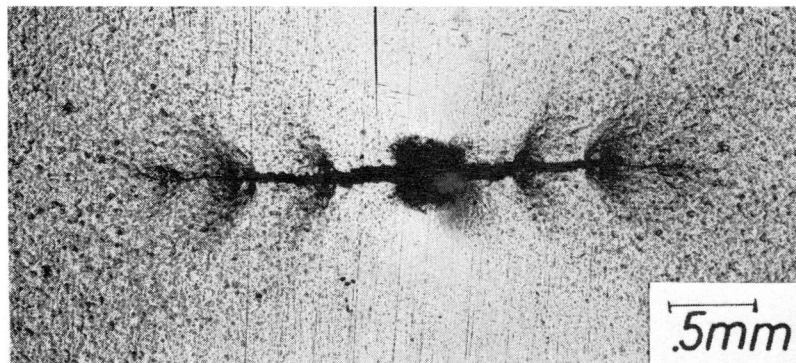

FIGURE 15 — Example of creep deformation at fatigue crack tip in brass at room temperature. Specimen cyclically loaded to 17,000 psi gross stress at 1800 cpm to grow fatigue crack. Marked creep deformation occurred at crack tip whenever test was interrupted and maximum central opening displacement maintained with wedge.

# References

1. W. Betteridge and A. W. Franklin. *J. Inst. Metals*, **85**, 473 (1956-57).
2. R. Resnick and L. Seigle. *Trans AIME*, **209**, 87 (1957).
3. W. Betteridge. *The Nimonic Alloys*, St. Martins Press (1959).
4. R. H. Thielemann and E. R. Parker. *Trans AIME*, **135**, 559 (1939).
5. F. Garofalo. *Proc. ASTM*, **59**, 973 (1959).
6. H. H. Bleakney. *Canadian J. of Technology*, **30**, 340 (1952).
7. H. H. Bleakney. *Canadian Met. Quarterly*, **4**, 13 (1965).
8. R. C. Boettner and W. D. Robertson. *Trans AIME*, **221**, 613 (1961).
9. F. Garofalo. *Proc. ASTM*, **59**, 957 (1959).
10. R. J. Sherman and M. R. Achter. *Trans AIME*, **224**, 144 (1962).
11. P. Shahinian and M. R. Achter. *Trans AIME*, **215**, 37 (1959).
12. T. R. Cass and M. R. Achter. *Trans AIME*, **224**, 1115 (1962).
13. A. J. Forty and P. Humble. *Phil. Mag.*, **8**, 247 (1963).
14. A. J. McEvily and A. P. Bond. *J. Electrochem. Soc.*, **112**, 131 (1965).
15. E. S. Machlin. *Trans AIME*, **206**, 106 (1956).
16. C. W. Chen and E. S. Machlin. *Trans AIME*, **218**, 177 (1960).

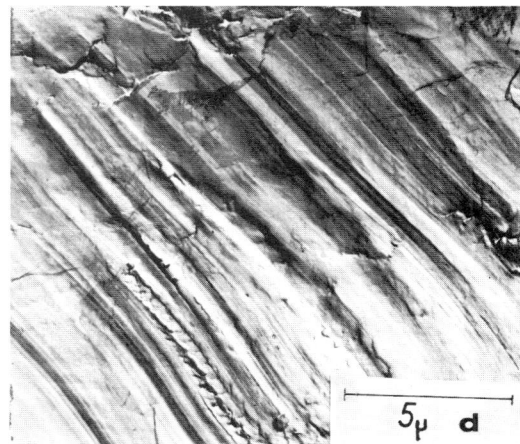

FIGURE 16 — Fracture appearance of Cu-7%Al in region of slow crack growth. Test conditions: 400 C, 9000 psi. Rupture life: 36.1 hours.

FIGURE 17 — Fracture appearance of Al-Zn-Mg alloy, 7075-T6, in region of slow crack growth. Test conditions: 200 C, 20,000 psi. Rupture life: 86.9 hours.

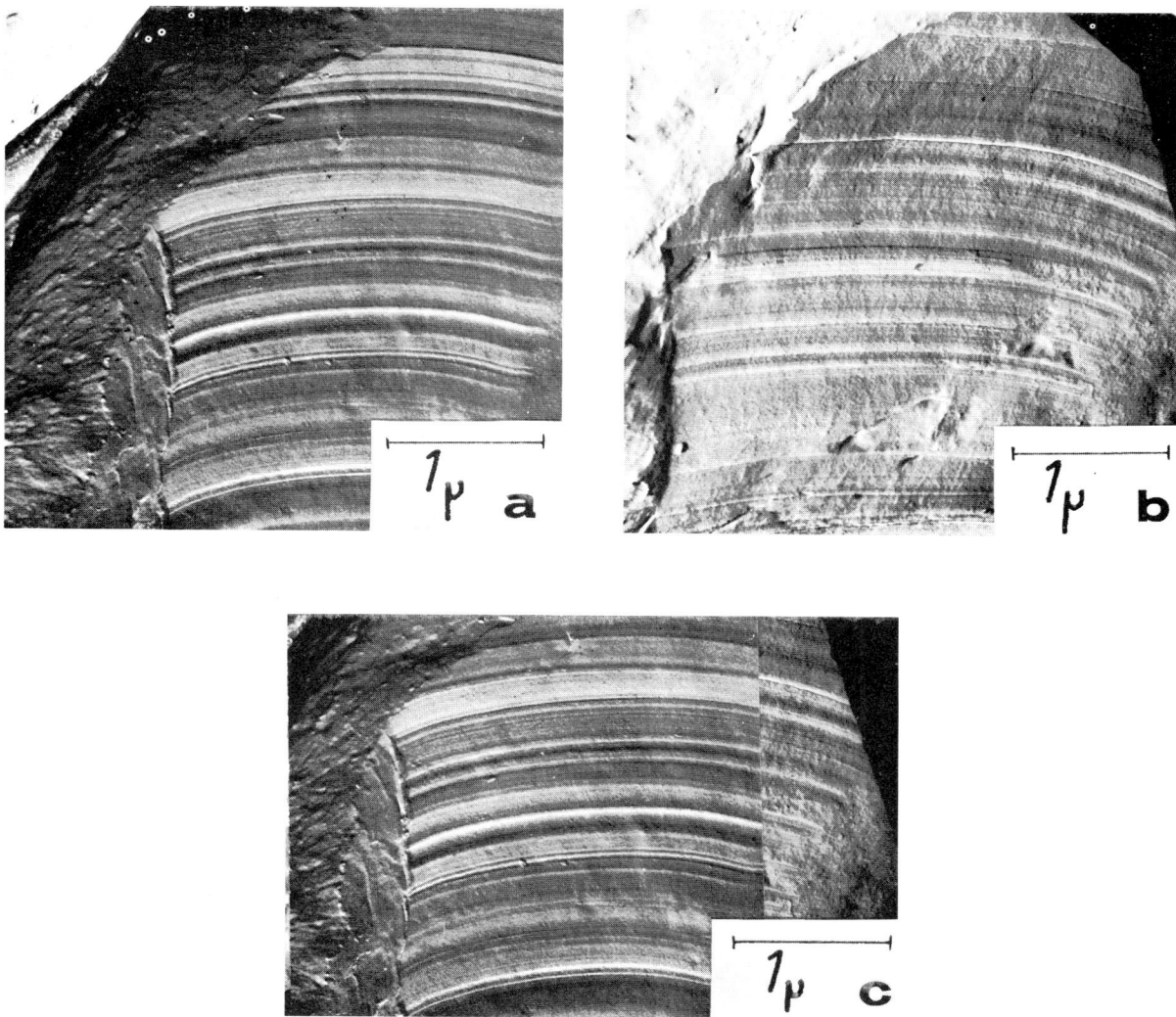

FIGURE 18 — Replicas of mating fracture surfaces of Al-Zn-Mg alloy taken in region of slow crack growth. (a) and (b) are the replicas which are superimposed in (c).

## Discussion

**M. Prazak, State Research Institute for Materials Protection:**

The results of McEvily's experiments performed at higher temperatures in air without the presence of an aqueous environment seem to me to be very valuable for studying the role of oxide films and some other steps of the s.c.c. mechanisms — as e.g., the creep deformation preceding the crack.

In connection with this paper I would like to point out another possible role of some oxide films, especially at higher temperatures. Commonly the corrosionists believe the oxide film to act only as a protective, passive layer, which isolates the metal from the environment. This is nearly true in cases of corrosion under common conditions. On the contrary, the oxide film may possess another property: according the Hoar's suggestion[1] it can act as a solid electrolyte. As an electrolyte the oxide film can accept the role also of a "corrosion medium". The cathodic reaction (ionization of oxygen) may occur overall on the surface of the oxide, while the anodic reaction may concentrate to more active sites in the metal structure. This can be regarded as one of the conditions of s.c.c. The electron and ionic conductance of the oxide (by defects) is

1. T. P. Hoar and L. P. Price. *Trans. Farad. Soc.,* **34,** 867 (1938).

in some cases sufficient for such a mechanism, especially for short distances. The selectivity for corrosion of more active sites (as can be seen in Figure 11 of the paper), is given by the condition of existence of nearly chemical equilibrium at the metal surface. This condition is probably fulfilled, as the oxide film is nearly metal saturated at the metal/oxide interface. (See the general comments on the s.c.c. theory by Prazak.)

The above proposed role of oxide films might be expected analogously also in aqueous environments; their action would be of course at lower temperatures limited to submicroscopic dimensions.

### E. N. Pugh, RIAS:

I would like to show two slides. The first concerns the interpretation of striations on stress-corrosion fracture surfaces. Figure 1, taken from unpublished work by Westwood, Goldheim and myself, illustrates matching intercrystalline fracture surfaces in silver chloride which failed by stress-corrosion in aqueous sodium chloride; one micrograph was reversed during printing to facilitate comparison. The striations were found to be perfectly matching on both surfaces, e.g., consider the region indicated by arrows. This fact rules out the possibility that they correspond to slip steps formed behind the advancing crack front, and indicates that they represent successive positions of the crack tip during discontinuous crack propagation. Failure in this system is thought to occur by the repeated

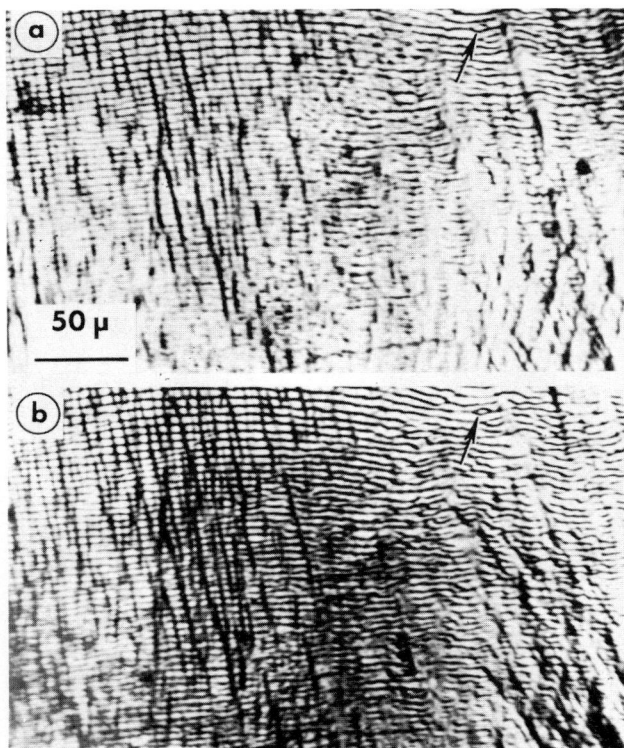

FIGURE 1 – Matching intercrystalline fracture surfaces of silver chloride fractured in 6 N aqueous NaCl presaturated with $AgCl_4^{3-}$ ions, illustrating matching striations.

formation and rupture of a brittle surface film, by a mechanism similar to the oxide-rupture model described by Dr. McEvily. However in this instance the film is not an oxide but is considered to be a defect hardened charge double layer. [A. R. C. Westwood, D. L. Goldheim and E. N. Pugh, *Phil. Mag.*, **15**, 105 (1967)].

I would like to remind Dr. McEvily of the data we obtained at RIAS on the effect of temperature on the failure of pure copper (99.999%) tested at a constant tensile load in air and argon, respectively [E. N. Pugh, W. G. Montague and A. R. C. Westwood, reported by Pugh in "Environment-Sensitive Mechanical Behavior" (A. R. C. Westwood and N. S. Stoloff, ed.) Gordon and Breach, New York (1966), p. 445]. We have since extended the temperature range in these studies and also carried out a test in vacuum ($\sim 10^{-5}$ mm Hg). The results, Figure 2, indicate that there is no significant difference in time to failure at a given temperature in the different environments, despite the fact that specimens tested in air were coated with a thick oxide film while those tested in argon and in vacuum appeared bright and film-free. These observations clearly question the role of oxide rupture in the fracture process and suggest that failure occurs by conventional creep.

### A. J. McEvily:

I would like to thank both Dr. Prazak and Dr. Pugh for their comments on this paper. The point brought out by Dr. Prazak that an oxide film can act as a solid electrolyte certainly seems to be an important consideration in any process involving oxide film rupture. One might expect that both the mechanical as well as electrochemical properties of the film would be affected, and that these effects might be even more important in aqueous stress-corrosion cracking than in creep rupture.

Dr. Pugh has provided evidence of a two-stage process of crack advance in AgCl, and thereby has demonstrated that this type of fracture process is more general than might

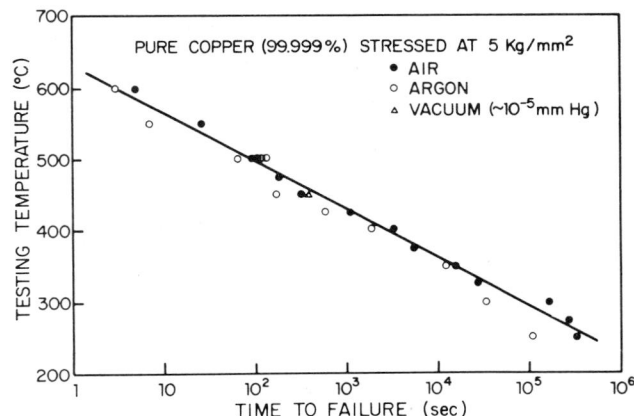

FIGURE 2 – Relationship between testing temperature and time to failure for copper specimens stressed at a constant tensile load in air, argon and vacuum, respectively.

have been initially anticipated. The fact that he found little influence of the environment in the time to rupture for copper of 99.999% purity, may appear to be somewhat surprising in view of the evidence cited in my paper, and it is not at this point a simple matter to reconcile these apparently contradictory results. It is noted however, that in tests of OFHC at 485 C, Bleakney (Figure 6) found that any difference between air and vacuum tests would be infinitely small for failure times of the order of two minutes such as obtained in Dr. Pugh's tests at this temperature. It appears therefore that rupture controlled by bulk creep processes may occur more rapidly than do significant oxidation processes under the conditions of Dr. Pugh's tests. Certainly much longer times were also involved in Thielemann and Parkers' tests (Figure 7) before an effect of the environment became apparent. Nevertheless it seems evident that at this stage more good research is required before a truly satisfactory answer can be given. This will involve consideration of surface to volume effects, a recognition that even at room temperature the ambient environment can affect fatigue behavior, a determination of crack initiation times vs crack propagation times, a determination of the influence of purity, and a detailed study of fracture characteristics and mechanisms.

# AN EVALUATION OF STRESS CORROSION CRACKING MECHANISMS

H. H. Uhlig

Massachusetts Institute of Technology

## Abstract

Various theories for stress corrosion cracking are critically reviewed with the aim of identifying common features leading to a unifying theory. There is strong evidence that a special process of adsorption and bond energy lowering is the unique aspect which permits stress corrosion cracking to occur. The specificity of the various environment-alloy combinations which produce cracking is related to the specificity of adsorption processes leading to reduction in surface energy (stress sorption cracking). The marked effect of extraneous anions to inhibit cracking in otherwise accelerating test media is ascribed to competitive adsorption and to the dependence of adsorption on the prevailing potential. Cathodic polarization prevents cracking by preventing adsorption of damaging anions. Analogously, adsorption processes appear to be the central feature of observed cracking in specific liquid-solid metal combinations and in plastics exposed to specific solvents.

During my many years of association with corrosion problems, I have always sought for and favored unifying principles. The electrochemical theory has admirably served this purpose for aqueous corrosion; Wagner's theory has served similarly for oxidation of metals at elevated temperatures. It is with some hope, therefore, and perhaps also an expression of faith in the self-consistency of nature, that I believe a similar unifying principle underlies environmental causes of fracture for all classes of materials including metals. A description of such a viewpoint is contained in this review, as well as a critical evaluation of other viewpoints which tend to the less satisfying conclusion that the basic fracture mechanism may be specific to each material and different for each environment.

An evaluation of stress corrosion cracking theories applying to metals should probably first clarify the phenomenon to which the theories apply. The term stress corrosion cracking usually relates to failures which require conjointly a tensional stress and a specific environment. Any workable theory must therefore include both factors in the fracture mechanism. Hence, instances of intergranular corrosion, not requiring stress, are not bona fide examples of the kind of fracture presently discussed. For example, artificially aged 4% Cu-Al alloys may fail by intergranular corrosion in many salt solutions or acids, as may 18-8 stainless steels heat treated in the range 400-900 C (carbide precipitation). Simultaneously applied stress in these instances may stimulate crack formation but the corrosion reaction does not depend on stress. It proceeds by the mechanism alone of galvanic action between alloy along grain boundaries and alloy of differing composition constituting the grains. For 70-30 brass and Admiralty metal many different kinds of aqueous solutions, e.g., acid $BiCl_3$, $Na_2MoO_4$, $Fe_2(SO_4)_3$, $Co(SO_4)_2$ cause intergranular corrosion but only aqueous solutions containing ammonia or amines cause stress corrosion cracking.[1] High purity aluminum quenched from 600 C, whether stressed or not, may fail intergranularly in concentrated HCl, but it is resistant to stress corrosion cracking in any environment.

It is also convenient to distinguish stress corrosion cracking from hydrogen cracking, in which the cause of fracture is directly related to hydrogen already present, or which enters the metal lattice through discharge of $H^+$ at the metal surface. Some features of hydrogen cracking are similar to stress corrosion cracking, but the causes differ, at least in detail. Cathodic polarization, for example, accelerates hydrogen cracking but inhibits stress corrosion cracking. This is an important fundamental characteristic and is perhaps even more important as a practical consideration in the design of metal structures.

Corrosion fatigue requiring repeated or alternate tensional stress resulting in typically transgranular failures is also different in mechanism from that of stress corrosion cracking, and requires a theoretical treatment all of its own. The present discussion, therefore, deals with environmental causes of cracking in metals subject to a constant tensional stress which may be residual in the metal or may be applied. The resultant cracks are either transgranular or intergranular depending on the metal and its metallurgical history, and on the composition of the specific environment causing failure.

## Theories of Stress Corrosion Cracking (s.c.c.)

The range of variables and specific conditions entering the phenomena of stress corrosion cracking provides sufficient evidence that the mechanism is not simple nor is it easily derived. Both the chemistry and the metallurgy of stressed metals actively undergoing fracture on exposure to damaging environments are complex and are not well understood. In the meantime, any successful working hypothesis should account for the following facts:

1. Pronounced specificity of environments required for s.c.c. of many metals, and the lack of any general relation to their intensity as corrosive agents.

2. General resistance or immunity of pure metals. Similarly, the marked effect of trace impurities or larger amounts of alloying elements to either inhibit or accelerate s.c.c.

3. Usually beneficial effect of cathodic polarization.

4. Inhibiting effect of extraneous anions. For example, addition of 5% $NaNO_3$ to $MgCl_2$ test solution at 130 C extended the cracking time of cold rolled 18-8 stainless steel from 0.3 to > 200 hours. Similarly addition of 3% NaCl to 60% $CaNO_3$, 3% $NH_4NO_3$ test solution at 108 C extended the cracking time of quenched mild steel from 4.5 to > 200 hours.[2] Ions such as $SO_4^{--}$, $F^-$, $NO_3^-$ were found to be inhibitors for the stress corrosion cracking of a titanium alloy (8% Al, 1% Mo, 1% V) in halide test solutions.[3]

5. Effect of structure (e.g., ferritic vs austenitic stainless steels, $\alpha$ vs $\beta$ brass) and grain size (increasing tendency to failure with increasing grain size).

Several theories have been proposed, but all contain elements of speculation and no one of them has been demonstrated beyond a doubt. Current theories usually resolve themselves into one of two mechanisms: (1) *Electrochemical* including oxide film rupture or tubular corrosion pit modifications. (2) *Stress Sorption Cracking* involving surface energy reduction by adsorbed components of the environment.

In more recent descriptions, there seems to be general concurrence in the view that cracking by either mechanism is related to pile-up of dislocations at barriers of one kind or another. The decrease in required fracture stress with increase of grain size (larger reservoir of dislocations) is strong support of this idea. Furthermore, it is suggested that unless the imperfections accumulate in suitable patterns along complex slip planes or grain boundaries, s.c.c. is not likely. The imperfections, e.g., stacking faults or aggregates of dislocations, may accelerate diffusion and transport of impurity and alloy atoms to the imperfection arrays, causing localized segregation. This can account for resultant preferential dissolution by the electrochemical mechanism, or in turn the composition gradient may favor adsorption of specific components of the environment, followed by reduction of surface energy.

## The Electrochemical Theory

Dix,[4] with Mears and Brown,[5] were apparently the first to propose that galvanic cells are set up between continuous intermetallic precipitates and adjacent metal at grain boundaries or through paths within the grains, the ensuing corrosion acting under stress to open up a crack. The applied stress was considered helpful in rupturing surface films, thereby exposing fresh metal at the tip of the crack, allowing the reaction to continue. Support of this view was derived from potential measurements showing that intergranular crack sensitive paths in various Al alloys, and also in some other metals, were anodic to the grains. Furthermore, cathodic polarization prevented crack initiation, or the growth of cracks already started. The electrochemical mechanism, with certain modifications depending on the metal, was elaborated by U. R. Evans,[6] R. N. Parkins,[7] T. P. Hoar,[8] L. Graf[9] and others.

Following Dix, it was observed that metals such as 18-8 stainless steels, carbon steels, Ag-Au alloys or brass, are subject to failure even though intermetallic compounds do not precipitate and hence cannot be a supposed source of potential difference along crack-sensitive paths. It was proposed that for austenitic stainless steels, ferrite produced by cold work ahead of the yielding crack might constitute the anodic path.[10] But, as was shown later, high nickel steels, e.g., 25% Cr, 20% Ni, which do not undergo a phase transformation when plastically deformed, are susceptible nevertheless. And although cold work itself may sometimes (but not always) markedly accelerate the corrosion rate of metals, e.g., of low carbon steels in HCl or $H_2SO_4$, s.c.c. of such steels is not observed in these media. Instead, cold work produces immunity, not increased susceptibility, of carbon steels in media causing stress corrosion cracking such as hot aqueous solutions containing $NO_3^-$.

Engell and Bäumel[11] expressed doubt that the electrochemical theory could be applied to mild steel because stressed steel wires exposed to nitrate solutions underwent discontinuous extension, the rapid portions of which they interpreted as intermittent cracking. The resultant calculated rate of cracking, i.e., 0.02 cm/second, is equivalent to a current density of 540 amp/cm$^2$ at the tip of the crack, which value is so high as to cast doubt, they stated, on the electrochemical model. In later papers,[12] however, they implied that the discontinuous extension they observed was caused by discontinuous creep which occurred regardless of damaging or non-damaging environments. The average rate of crack propagation, therefore, was much less than the value first estimated and hence their objection to the electrochemical theory based on their original premise was not valid. Swann and Pickering[13] showed that discontinuous extension (creep) of stressed alloys in air (Portevin-Le Chatelier effect) is a common occurrence, usually ascribed to segregation of solute elements to dislocations during active slip. The effect is often observed only at elevated temperatures common to s.c.c. test conditions and suggests, they stated, a relation to factors entering susceptibility. For example, the resulting composition gradients may favor chemical dissolution and crack initiation. It is obvious, in any event, that discontinuous extension of a stressed metal exposed to any environment is not evidence of discontinuous cracking.

The weakness of the electrochemical theory was uncovered through observations that some metals crack only in specific electrolytes, whereas electrochemical action would in fact be expected in a variety of related chemical media of comparable electrical conductivity. Furthermore there appears to be no reasonable electrochemical explanation why additions of extraneous anions to damaging environments should act as inhibitors for s.c.c., e.g., chlorides and acetates for carbon steels in boiling nitrate solutions. Simple galvanic effects between tip and walls of the crack, in other words, are not alone sufficient to explain the cause of fracture.

Keating[14] suggested that stress corrosion cracks are formed by mechanical fracture, the propagation of which is interrupted periodically by barriers which require chemical dissolution before the crack can proceed. Harwood[15] also favored an electrochemical-mechanical process of crack propagation. This mechanism, however, proved unlikely, first on the observation that removal of the damaging environment from a crack followed by further extension of the metal resulted in ductile behavior,[16] and, second, that a crack propagating in stressed 18-8 stainless steel exposed to boiling $MgCl_2$ solution stopped at the interface of 18-8 welded to nickel, the latter metal being immune to chlorides.[17]

A modification of the electrochemical-mechanical model was suggested by Pickering and Swann[18] based on thin-film electron microscopy. They proposed that an observed network of tubular corrosion pits forming along preferred paths such as active slip planes could account for cracking by ductile fracture of the tenuous walls of numerous adjacent pits. This viewpoint, it will be noted, in common with the more general electrochemical theory of Dix and his co-workers does not explain the specificity of environments required for cracking, nor does it explain the peculiar inhibiting effects of various anions in the case of carbon steels, stainless steels and Ti alloys.

The oxide film rupture theory, first mentioned by Dix, was modified and extended by Logan[19] for various metals including aluminum and magnesium alloys, and by Forty and Humble[20] and by McEvily and Bond[21] for α brass. The common point of view is that a film of brittle surface corrosion product ruptures under stress, allowing progressive exposure of metal underneath to further chemical attack. The film-covered sides of the crack may, in some instances, act as cathode. Support of this mechanism was derived from potential measurements or from visible or microscopic examination of metals that had undergone s.c.c. Such a mechanism, however, if applicable at all, is probably not general because (1) s.c.c. in α brass is observed in absence of visible or suspected films, e.g., in alkaline $NH_4OH$, (2) pure metals on which brittle or cathodic corrosion products form quite readily are immune, and (3) tarnished metals in air on which equally brittle films exist do not fail. Farmery and Evans[22] doubted that oxide film rupture could enter the cause of s.c.c. in 7% Mg-Al alloy because cracks, the growth of which was stopped by cathodic polarization, did not necessarily reactivate when the applied current was discontinued. The film rupture hypothesis is also not plausible for cracking of metals like stainless steels exposed to boiling concentrated $MgCl_2$ solution on which an oxide film would have but short life. Potentiostatic anodic polarization curves for 18-8 in boiling 42% $MgCl_2$ solution show no evidence of a passive region.[23] Furthermore, it was demonstrated that an observed decrease of cracking times for 25% Cr, 20% Ni stainless steels following pre-exposure of unstressed specimens to boiling $MgCl_2$ test solution is caused not by dissolution of a supposed oxide film, but instead by metallurgical aging of the alloy at the test temperature (154 C).[24] Similarly, alloys of Cu-Au or Ag-Au, on which oxide or other non-ductile surface films do not form, are nevertheless susceptible to stress corrosion cracking in $FeCl_3$ or aqua regia. Finally, as mentioned earlier, both chloride ions which supposedly break down oxide films, and nitrate ions which supposedly favor oxide films, can act as inhibitors for stress corrosion cracking of mild steel and of austenitic stainless steels respectively. Obviously some factor other than rupture of an oxide or other type brittle film is responsible for s.c.c. in most observed instances of metal fracture.

Hoar and West[25] measured a marked decrease of anodic polarization during active straining of metal wires and supposed that an effect of this kind could act to accelerate electrochemical effects between the tip and walls of the growing crack. Whether the observed decrease of polarization they observed is accounted for by other than simple increased area of exposed metal as the metal yields, is not clear. It seems evident nevertheless that decreased anodic polarization cannot be of prime importance to the s.c.c. mechanism in view of (1) the immunity of pure metals and of various alloys which should be affected electrochemically by active strain no less than are susceptible metals (except for greater overall increased area of fresh metal at surface cracks in susceptible metals) and (2) the required specificity of environments for cracking but lack of correlating specificities for reduced polarization. Furthermore, (3) electrochemical effects, such as discontinuous potential jumps during extension of a stressed metal specimen in an electrolyte are not confined to media which favor oxide films nor to media which cause stress corrosion cracking. Bäumel and Engell[12] found, for example, that discontinuous potential jumps of up to 10 mV in the active direction accompanied discontinuous extension of stressed mild steel exposed to boiling 45% $CaCl_2$ ($O_2$ saturated) solution in which s.c.c. did not occur, as well as in boiling $Ca(NO_3)_2$ solution in which s.c.c. did occur.

In summary, the main support of the electrochemical mechanism is contributed by potential measurements and the inhibiting effect of cathodic polarization. Unexplained is the required specificity of environments for cracking and the inhibiting effect of extraneous ions. Mention might also be made of the unexplained required above-room temperatures for cracking of austenitic stainless steels in chlorides and of carbon steels in alkalis; the transgranular cracking of sensitized 18-8 stainless steels in $MgCl_2$ solution despite well developed corrosion sensitive paths along grain boundaries; the sensitivity of molybdenum-bearing 18-8 stainless steels (Type 316) to s.c.c. in chlorides despite their improved resistance over 18-8 (Type 304) to pitting and to general attack by chlorides; and finally the susceptibility of Ti alloys to s.c.c. in environments such as $CH_3OH$ or $CCl_4$ which are not electrolytes.

## Stress Sorption Cracking

The mechanism of cracking by this name[26] proceeds not by chemical or electrochemical dissolution of metal at the tip of a crack, but instead by weakening of already strained metal atom bonds through adsorption of the environment or its constituents. The surface energy of the metal is said to be reduced, encouraging the metal to part under tensile stress. This mechanism is related to the simplified Griffith criterion of crack formation which equates strain energy in the metal to the surface energy of the incipient crack area. It is essentially the mechanism which Petch and Stables[27] first suggested for hydrogen cracking of steels and which was later emphasized by Uhlig[26] and by Coleman, Weinstein and Rostoker[28] as being applicable to s.c.c. of metals and alloys.

Langmuir[29] showed that only a monolayer of adsorbate (e.g., oxygen atoms) is necessary to decrease affinities of surface atoms for themselves or for their environment, specifically adsorbed species chemically bonded (chemisorbed) to the surface being especially effective in this regard. It is such adsorbed films which prevent cold welding of solids, including metals, placed in contact with each other. Crack initiation is thought to involve a similar decrease in surface affinities with the distinction that only those specific adsorbates are effective which reduce the attractive forces of adjoining metal atoms one for the other located at the extreme root of a notch, subject to high tensile stress, and experiencing some plastic deformation. Certain adsorbed ions, and in some instances adsorbed water, do this more effectively for many metals than does oxygen. The latter adsorbs strongly but presumably retains, unlike adsorbed damaging species, a high affinity for adjacent adsorbed oxygen atoms, thereby preventing release of neighboring bonds necessary to crack initiation.

In addition to explaining the fracture of steels containing hydrogen, crack propagation aided by adsorption has been suggested as explaining the fracture of glass exposed to moisture,[30] the fracture of solid metals by liquid metals[31] and the stress cracking of plastics by specific organic solvents.[26] Obviously electrochemical reaction is not a necessary part of such failures even though many other features resemble s.c.c. in aqueous media.

Support of the view that stress sorption cracking is the prevailing mechanism in s.c.c. of metals comes from the observation of:

(1) Specificity of environments causing cracking. Chemisorption is also specific.

### TABLE 1[31] – Susceptibility of Solid Metals to Embrittlement by Liquid Metals

| Liquid → | Li | Hg | Bi | Ga | Zn |
|---|---|---|---|---|---|
| Steel | C | NC | NC | NC | C |
| Cu alloys | C | C | C | | |
| Al alloys | NC | C | NC | C | C |
| Ti alloys | NC | C | NC | NC | NC |

C = cracking; NC = no cracking

(2) Inhibiting effect of extraneous anions and of cathodic protection. Anions in sufficient concentration tend by mass action to displace adsorbed damaging species. Or they may shift the corrosion potential into regions where the damaging species do not adsorb. For similar reasons, cathodic polarization (cathodic protection) is generally effective because the potential is shifted into regions where damaging species cannot adsorb.

(3) The analogous cracking, as mentioned above, of non-metals by specific environments and of metals by specific liquid metals, including effect of grain size.

The cracking of metals (embrittlement) by liquid metals especially parallels the characteristics of stress corrosion cracking in that only specific solid metal-liquid metal couples are damaging, and also a tensile stress is essential. The cracking tendencies of several metal combinations are shown in Table 1. It is obviously satisfactory to construct a mercury boiler of mild steel, as is done in practice, but not of brass or of titanium, both of which are subject to intergranular attack. Mercury presumably is effective in reducing surface energy along grain boundaries of stressed brass or Ti, but not of iron or steel.

Regarding Item 2 above, increased cathodic polarization (increased applied negative charge to the metal) reduces the probability of anion (negatively charged) adsorption, in addition to increasing the pH of electrolyte at the metal surface which may furthermore decrease adsorption of damaging anions. For many metals, e.g., Al alloys, carbon steels, stainless steels and α brass, cathodic polarization serves to decrease or prevent s.c.c. Anodic polarization, on the other hand, which favors anion adsorption, often increases susceptibility.

The ability of extraneous anions to displace adsorbed species (and hence perform as inhibitors) was demonstrated by Rosenfeld and Maximtschuk.[32] Employing radioactive $Cl^-$ 36, they found that $Cl^-$ readily adsorbed on a Cr surface from aqueous chlorides but that less or no adsorption occurred in presence of added $OH^-$ or $SO_4^{--}$. This condition prevailed even when the potential was shifted in the noble direction (anodic polarization) which otherwise favored increased adsorption of $Cl^-$.

Extraneous anions are not always inhibitors, but may induce susceptibility instead by moving the potential of a metal into regions where damaging species are better able to adsorb. This mechanism probably applies to s.c.c. of 10% Al-Mg alloy induced by addition of $K_2CrO_4$ to dilute NaCl solution. The alloy in absence of chromate corrodes only generally without cracking.

An explanation is still required for the immunity of

pure metals and for the importance of lattice structure. Possible reasons have not advanced beyond the speculative stage[33] but they probably deserve brief mention. There is evidence, for example, that some plastic flow always precedes and accompanies crack formation. The required chemisorption, therefore, may be assumed to take place not generally on the metal surface, but only on mobile dislocations or other type active imperfections as they emerge at the metal surface. Swann and Pickering[13] found that cracks in 5% Au-Cu alloy did not necessarily nucleate at accumulations of static dislocations, the supposition being that segregation of solute atoms is a necessary accompanying process. Alternatively, or in addition, however, it can be concluded that mobile dislocations are necessary either to favor diffusion of solute atoms, as Swann and Pickering suggested, or on emerging at the metal surface, to act as sites where the required adsorption can occur. Since adsorption takes time, the imperfection site must remain on the metal surface a minimum time. Hence only imperfections which are characterized by adequate surface half-life, in combination with suitable adsorbates, are damaging. It is in this respect that impurities may play an important role. It is known, for example, that interstitial C and N atoms are attracted to lattice imperfections, forming Cottrell atmospheres, and that these succeed in pinning or impeding the movement of imperfections. Carbon or N atoms, therefore, may in this way extend the half life of imperfections at the grain boundary surface of iron sufficient for nitrate and hydroxyl ions to chemisorb; similarly nitrogen atoms, which apparently have a greater tendency to segregate at dislocations than do carbon atoms,[34] may make it possible for chloride ions or hydroxyl ions to chemisorb on active slip bands of austenitic stainless steels. Should the imperfections migrate from the surface before adsorption can take place, which is more likely with pure than with impure metals, cracks do not initiate nor do they propagate once formed. In absence of segregation of solute atoms associated with mobile surface imperfections, it is also possible that the necessary chemical affinity for the adsorbing species is lacking.

The higher the stress the greater is the density of mobile surface imperfections favoring adsorption, and hence the more rapid is crack propagation. High concentrations in solution of damaging species insure greater adsorption at available sites and hence also accelerate the crack process. The dependence of s.c.c. on magnitude of stress and on accompanying mobile dislocations suggests that a relation should exist to creep of metals the mechanism of which also depends on mobile dislocations. A relation of this kind was previously proposed by Graf[9] who found analogies between fracture-time stress curves in damaging environments and corresponding creep data. If one assumes the simplified relation that the time, t, to fracture by s.c.c. is inversely proportional to the steady state creep rate R, then

$$R = \frac{k_o}{t} \qquad (1)$$

The steady state creep rate of metals is related to the applied stress $\sigma$ by[35]

$$\sigma = k \log R + const. \qquad (2)$$

Hence the following relation is derived

$$\sigma = -k \log t + k \log k_o + const. \qquad (3)$$

This is identical in form to the empirical linear relation between applied stress and logarithm of fracture time by s.c.c. reported previously to hold for austenitic[36,37] and martensitic[38] stainless steels, for carbon steels,[7] for brass[39] (data replotted) and for Al alloys.[22]

The effect of structure, i.e., body-centered cubic vs face-centered cubic 18-8, is probably best explained by unfavorable geometry of dislocation pile-ups at the many available slip planes of the b.c.c. lattice. Swann[40] suggested that b.c.c. metals in general have superior resistance to transgranular s.c.c. because of the difficulty of slip on any preferred plane as compared to ease of slip on $\{111\}$ planes in face-centered cubic metals. Hence the expected cross slip process in b.c.c. metals is favored, leading to tangled instead of coplanar arrays of dislocations. He also pointed out, however, that the presence of coplanar arrays in any alloy does not always imply susceptibility to s.c.c.

Electrochemistry would seem to be an unnecessary process for crack initiation or propagation except in one detail which may turn out to be relatively important. This concerns the possibility that in some cases metal complexes rather than simple anions adsorb at mobile surface imperfections. The complexes in turn must first form by a reaction, which may be essentially electrochemical in nature, between the metal and the environment. The evidence for this comes from the accelerated cracking of $\alpha$ brass in cupric ammonium complex solutions compared to the long time required in ammonium hydroxide for which appreciable time is presumably required to first form the necessary copper complex. Also $\alpha$ brass is reported to crack in cupric complexes of citric or tartaric acids, but presumably not in the acids themselves.[41] Similarly, polycrystalline AgCl apparently undergoes s.c.c. only in presence of aqueous complex silver ions such as $(AgCl_4)^{---}$.[42]

In summary, the mechanism of stress sorption cracking plausibly accounts for many features of s.c.c. It also satisfactorily relates s.c.c. in aqueous media to the mechanism of similar fracture in metals and non-metals from environmental causes not involving electrochemical reactions. Although details of fracture obviously differ for various materials, a unifying mechanism is made available which ascribes the same basic environmental cause of cracking in stressed metals exposed to damaging electrolytes, non-electrolytes or liquid metals, as well as in stressed plastics or glasses exposed to their specifically damaging environments.

The areas of mechanism particularly requiring additional study relate to (1) the metallurgy of mobile imperfections on which adsorption presumably occurs. For example, can pinning of surface dislocations by adsorbates contribute to true brittle fracture? and (2) the chemistry of surface imperfections which account for $NO_3^-$ but not $SO_4^{--}$ or $Cl^-$ adsorbing with accompanying cracking at grain boundary imperfections of iron, and similarly $Cl^-$ but not $SO_4^{--}$ or $NO_3^-$ adsorbing with resultant s.c.c. at imperfections within the grains of austenitic stainless steels.

## References

1. Wilson Lynes. *Corrosion, 21*, 125 (1965).
2. H. H. Uhlig and V. Agarwala. Unpublished observations.
3. T. Beck and M. Blackburn. Preprint AIAA-ASME Conf., Palm Springs, Calif., March (1967).
4. E. Dix, Jr. *Trans. Am. Inst. Min. Met. Engrs., 137*, 11 (1940).
5. R. Mears, R. Brown and E. Dix, Jr. In *Symposium on Stress Corrosion Cracking of Metals*, p. 323, ASTM-AIME, Philadelphia (1945).
6. U. R. Evans. *The Corrosion and Oxidation of Metals*. pp. 665-93, Ed. Arnold, London (1960).
7. R. N. Parkins. *J. Iron and Steel Inst., 172*, 149 (1952).
8. T. P. Hoar. *Corrosion, 19*, 331t (1963).
9. L. Graf. *2nd Int. Congress on Metallic Corrosion*, NACE, Houston (1963).
10. C. Edeleanu. *J. Iron and Steel Inst., 173*, 140 (1953).
11. H. Engell and A. Baumel. In *Physical Metallurgy of Stress Corrosion Fracture*, T. Rhodin, Editor, p. 341, Interscience, N. Y. (1959).
12. A. Bäumel and H. Engell. *Archiv. f. Eisenhuttenw., 32*, 379 (1961); *33*, 285 (1962).
13. P. Swann and H. Pickering. *Corrosion, 19*, 369t (1963).
14. F. Keating. Symposium on Internal Stresses in Metals and Alloys, p. 311, *Inst. of Metals*, London (1947).
15. J. Harwood. In *Stress Corrosion Cracking and Embrittlement*, W. Robertson, Editor, pp. 1-20, John Wiley and Sons, Inc., New York (1956).
16. R. Bakish and W. Robertson. *Acta Met., 4*, 342 (1956).
17. D. van Rooyen. *J. Electrochem. Soc., 107*, 715 (1960).
18. H. Pickering and P. Swann. *Corrosion, 19*, 373t (1963).
19. H. Logan. *J. Res. Nat. Bur. Stds., 48*, 99 (1952).
20. A. Forty and P. Humble. *Phil. Mag., 8*, (8) 247 (1963).
21. A. McEvily and A. Bond. *J. Electrochem. Soc., 112*, 131 (1965).
22. H. Farmery and U. Evans. *J. Inst. Metals, 84*, 413 (1955-6).
23. S. Barnartt and D. van Rooyen. *J. Electrochem. Soc., 108*, 222 (1961).
24. H. Uhlig and J. Sava. *Corrosion Science, 5*, 291 (1965).
25. T. Hoar and J. West. *Nature, 181*, 835 (1958); *Proc. Roy. Soc., 268A*, 304 (1962).
26. H. Uhlig. In *Physical Metallurgy of Stress Corrosion Fracture*, T. Rhodin, Editor, pp. 1-16, Interscience, N. Y. (1959).
27. N. Petch and P. Stables. *Nature, 169*, 842 (1952).
28. E. Coleman, D. Weinstein and W. Rostoker. *Acta Met., 9*, 491 (1961).
29. I. Langmuir. *J. Am. Chem. Soc., 38*, 2221 (1916); *40*, 1361 (1918).
30. E. Orowan. *Nature, 154*, 341 (1944).
31. W. Rostoker, J. McCaughey and H. Markus. *Embrittlement by Liquid Metals*, Reinhold, N. Y. (1960).
32. I. Rosenfeld and W. Maximtschuk. *Z. physik. Chem., 215*, 25 (1960).
33. H. Uhlig and J. Sava. *Trans. Am. Soc. Metals, 56*, 361 (1963).
34. M. Rudee and R. Huggins. *Acta Met., 12*, 501 (1964).
35. F. Seitz. *Physics of Metals*, p. 144, McGraw-Hill, N. Y. (1943).
36. M. Scheil. In *Corrosion Handbook*, H. Uhlig, Editor, p. 176, John Wiley & Sons, Inc., N. Y. (1948).
37. T. Hoar and J. Hines. *J. Iron and Steel Inst., 182*, 124 (1956).
38. J. Truman, R. Perry and G. Chapman. *J. Iron and Steel Inst., 202*, 745 (1964).
39. A. Morris. *Trans. Am. Inst. Min. Met. Engrs., 89*, 256 (1930).
40. P. Swann. *Corrosion, 19*, 102t (1963).
41. H. Johnson and J. Leja. *Corrosion, 22*, 178 (1966).
42. A. Westwood, D. Goldheim and E. Pugh. *Acta Met., 13*, 695 (1965).

## Discussion

**M. Henthorne, The Carpenter Steel Co.:**

That stress corrosion cracking is related to grain size according to a Petch relationship is not necessarily supporting evidence for the "Stress Sorption Cracking" mechanism. Petch grain size relationships exist for yield stress and flow stress as well as for brittle fracture stress. Since many stress corrosion failures occur under conditions more conducive to plastic deformation than to brittle fracture it would seem likely that in these cases the correlation between grain size and flow stress would be more applicable than that between grain size and brittle fracture stress. This has been found to be true for the case of mild steel in boiling nitrate solutions.[1] Using slow strain rate tensile stress corrosion tests it has been shown that the stress corrosion fracture stress (stress at which a crack is visible by surface examination at 100 X) varies with grain size in the same way as flow stress. Tests over a range of strain rates have indicated that the reason for this correlation is not that a critical stress is required to initiate a visible crack but rather that a critical time is required to form an open crack in a material being plastically deformed.

1. M. Henthorne and R. N. Parkins. Some Aspects of the Influence of Structure Upon Stress-Corrosion Cracking and Grain Boundary Corrosion in Mild Steels, *British Corrosion Journal, 2*, 186 (1967).

**H. H. Uhlig:**

Dr. Henthorne is correct in pointing out that grain size affects yield stress of a metal as well as fracture stress. In each case, smaller grain size increases corresponding stress. It is feasible, therefore, to consider that rate of creep is affected by grain size which in turn affects the nature of imperfection arrays generated at the tip of the yielding crack.

In either event, I would be tempted to conclude that the effect of grain size on s.c.c. supports the mechanism of stress sorption cracking. It certainly does not provide support for the electrochemical mechanism. Mild steel, for example, when cold worked equivalent to at least 50% reduction of thickness, is immune to s.c.c. at any applied stress in a boiling nitrate test solution. Hence one cannot assume that cold work produces anodic sites or paths analogous to those accounting for increased corrosion of cold-worked steel in acids. Furthermore cracking does not occur along slip planes which take part in the plastic deformation process, but along grain boundaries, whether or not they contain cementite inclusions.

**P. R. Swann, Imperial College:**

Stress corrosion typically involves the slow propagation of a crack through ductile material. I think it is doubtful that the atomically sharp cracks you envisage would be stable under such conditions. I would expect that slip would blunt the tip of the crack and render the absorption process ineffective.

**A. R. C. Westwood, RIAS:**

On the basis of the stress-sorption, or any other adsorption-dependent model[1] for embrittlement, one would argue that the reason a propagating crack stays sharp and does not become blunted by plastic flow is that the active species is continuously present at the crack tip, and is continuously reducing the strength of the bonds there so that they fracture at some stress less than that necessary to activate crack-blunting slip in this region.[2]

1.  A. R. C. Westwood and M. H. Kamdar. *Phil. Mag.,* 8, 787 (1963).
2.  A. R. C. Westwood, C. M. Preece and M. H. Kamdar. *Trans. ASM,* 60, 723 (1967).

**D. L. Douglass, Stanford Research:**

If what you say is true, what we really would like to know is how much can various factors lower the surface energy factor which influences K.

How much decrease in stress could you expect due to the fact that $\gamma$ varies to the one-half power?

**H. H. Uhlig:**

Coleman, Weinstein and Rostoker [*Acta Met.,* **9**, 491 (1961)] indicate that the surface energy of 18-8 stainless steel is reduced from a normal value of about 1000 ergs/cm$^2$ to 157 ergs/cm$^2$ in 42% MgCl$_2$ solution at 150 C. Similarly the value for Mg-6% Al alloy is decreased from about 500 ergs/cm$^2$ to 93 ergs/cm$^2$ in NaCl-K$_2$CrO$_4$ solution at room temperature.

**R. A. Oriani, U. S. Steel:**

I would like to characterize the stress sorption cracking theory, as developed by Petch and Stables for example, as a necessary-but-not-sufficient type of argument. Certainly, lowering the surface free energy of a crack surface by adsorption from the environment may make it thermodynamically possible for a crack to propagate, but as every kineticist knows, thermodynamic possibility is not enough to insure that a reaction will in fact proceed, since kinetic barriers have to be overcome.

It is therefore necessary to consider the mechanism of bond-breaking at the terminus of the crack and how it is affected by the environment. If this is what is meant by the stress sorption theory, then there is no argument except one of semantics. However, there is reason to believe that more than semantics is involved since usually the stress

sorption argument involves the quantitative estimate of the surface free energy lowering by adsorption. On the other hand it should be clear that there is no necessary correlation between the lowering of the surface free energy by adsorption and the enhancement of crack propagation by any one substance, since we have well recognized cases of substances which adsorb strongly yet crack propagation is not thereby enhanced. In summary, the problem seems to me to be that of the kinetics of bond breaking and this will be found to bear only a faint relation to the thermodynamics of adsorption.

**H. H. Uhlig:**

Dr. Oriani is right in proposing that the kinetics of bond breaking at the tip of a crack probably plays an important role in stress corrosion cracking. The extent to which this factor alters the purely thermodynamic factor of surface energy reduction probably varies with the system, rate of straining, the impurities present, the surface condition, and degree of cold work. The Rebinder effect, for example, operates not with all substances which adsorb on metals, but specifically with surface active agents and only some of those. It is required, therefore, not only that a substance adsorb on a metal surface preliminary to crack growth, but also that the bond strength between immediately adjacent adsorbate layers favor crack continuation rather than crack healing.

**J. Leja, University of British Columbia:**

In discussing the complexes everybody assumes that the identity of the complex which is actually adsorbing and is reducing the surface energy is known and is determined by the environment. In the case of copper, Drs. Pugh, Benson, and everybody else, consider the copper-ammonia complexes responsible. Nobody mentions the alloying element, zinc, nor the possibility of a bi-metallic complex formed by copper ammine aligning with the zinc of the substrate at the grain boundary or at the slip plane. In analogy with activated adsorption in catalysis, it may be sufficient for a few individual molecules of say, copper ammine to penetrate to the zinc sites and to develop by adsorption an activated copper-zinc-ammine complex of sufficient surface pressure to reduce the surface tension of the solid in a drastic manner.

In most cases, it is the combination of the environment and the alloying element which determines whether the material will stress-corrosion crack, or not. If you remove this alloying element, the character of the solid changes and its susceptibility to stress-corrosion cracking changes. The combination of environment and the constituents of the metal decide the issue of the stress-corrosion cracking.

**H. H. Uhlig:**

Dr. Leja points out correctly that adsorption of the environment is only one aspect of the stress corrosion phenomenon. The effect of alloying and the magnitude of tensile strength are always necessary considerations as well. Specific alloying elements or impurities definitely increase susceptibility of many metals to s.c.c. as numerous data and long experience have shown. The alloying or impurity elements may act in at least three ways. The first is to diffuse to imperfection arrays generated at the tip of a yielding crack and thus alter the geometry, mobility and density of surface sites on which adsorption can occur. Secondly, the alloying constituents associated with imperfections can change the chemistry of the metal surface either favoring or discouraging, depending on the system, subsequent adsorption of the environment. Thirdly, they may increase the half life of surface imperfections beyond the critical minimum time necessary for successful adsorption.

### D. A. Vermilyea, General Electric Research and Development Center:

I would like to raise a point about inhibition which seems to me to argue strongly against the adsorption theory. If you have an inhibitor which adsorbs more strongly than the substance which causes cracking, then the surface energy would be lower in the presence of the inhibitor than in the presence of the agent causing cracking. Hence the crack should proceed faster.

### H. H. Uhlig:

The argument raised by Dr. Vermilyea would be valid if all ions behaved similarly and there were no specifically damaging ions. The extraneous anions which act as inhibitors do so largely by displacing the damaging ion in the electrical double layer adjacent to the metal surface. They decrease the damaging ion activity below the value needed for successful adsorption on the metal surface required for cracking. Should the inhibiting ion adsorb directly on the metal surface, which is certainly a possibility, it must be in the non-damaging category if it is to fit the definition of an inhibitor.

The details of structure and composition which define a damaging anion are of course still not clear. This is one of the forefront problems of s.c.c. regardless of which theory is adopted to explain the phenomenon. One of the requirements is discussed in my reply to Dr. Oriani. The damaging species are presumably those which, if adsorbed, form layers with less attraction to each other on adjacent sides of the crack compared to similar adsorbed layers made up of non-damaging species which exert a greater mutual attraction.

### A. R. C. Westwood, RIAS:

As far as I am aware, the first worker to suggest that adsorbed species could influence the mechanical behavior of a solid by reducing its surface free energy was Rebinder, in 1928.[1] Some disadvantages of this simple, thermodynamic, non-mechanistic approach have been outlined by Westwood and Kamdar,[2] Stoloff and Johnston[3] and Westwood,[4] and it has been recently shown that Rebinder effects in non-metals are not, in fact, related to adsorption-induced changes in $\gamma$, the surface free energy.[5,6] However, if $\gamma$ is defined as the work necessary to create 1 cm$^2$ of surface by a process of division,[7] then undoubtedly certain adsorbed "liquid metal" atoms can embrittle certain solid metals by reducing $\gamma$. The mechanism of this phenomenon remains unclear, and simply stating that it involves a

reduction in surface free energy does not provide any improved understanding. Moreover, current work at RIAS,[8] utilizing liquid metal solutions, also indicates that the occurrence of liquid-metal embrittlement is by no means as specific as earlier thought. Many elements, when available effectively in the liquid state (by being dissolved in some "inert", carrier liquid metal environment) at some temperature appropriate for the particular solid metal, can cause some degree of embrittlement in most common solid metals.

As far as stress-corrosion cracking is concerned, however, there seems to be no unequivocal evidence, as yet, that any manifestation of this phenomenon is due to adsorption-induced reductions in $\gamma$.[9] One problem with the utilization of this concept as a general mechanism for stress-corrosion cracking is the occurrence of discontinuous failure in several embrittlement systems, e.g., $\alpha$-brass in ammonia. In the one system in which failure *is* discontinuous, and for which it is established that the adsorption of some chemical species *is* responsible for embrittlement, namely the complex-ion embrittlement of AgCl, the embrittlement mechanism has been shown to involve the repeated formation and rupture of Frenkel defect-hardened surficial layers.[10]

Professor Uhlig also asks "can pinning of surface dislocations by adsorbates contribute to true brittle fracture"? I think that, for metals, the answer is no. Because of conduction electron screening in a metal, the effects of any chemisorbed species will not be felt at depths greater than a few atom diameters in from the surface. Thus yielding in the vicinity of a crack tip, a bulk phenomenon, could not be significantly affected by the presence of some chemisorbed species. Fracture, on the other hand, which involves the repeated rupture of surface bonds, can be significantly influenced by an adsorbed species. A discussion of these points is given in Reference 11.

1. P. A. Rebinder. *Proc. Sixth Phys. Conf.,* Moscow, 1928. (See also: *Z. Phys.,* **72**, 91 (1931)).
2. A. R. C. Westwood and M. H. Kamdar. *Phil. Mag.,* **8**, 787 (1963).
3. N. S. Stoloff and T. L. Johnston. *Acta Met.,* **11**, 251 (1963).
4. A. R. C. Westwood. *Environment-Sensitive Mechanical Behavior,* Gordon and Breach, New York, 1 (1966).
5. A. R. C. Westwood. *Advances in Material Science, II, Microplasticity,* 365 (1968).
6. A. R. C. Westwood, D. L. Goldheim and R. G. Lye. *Phil. Mag.,* **16**, 505 (1967).
7. R. Shuttleworth. *Proc. Phys. Soc.,* A**63**, 444 (1950).
8. C. M. Preece and A. R. C. Westwood. To be published.
9. E. N. Pugh. *Environment-Sensitive Mechanical Behavior,* Gordon and Breach, New York, 351 (1966).
10. A. R. C. Westwood, D. L. Goldheim and E. N. Pugh. *Phil. Mag.,* **15**, 105 (1967).
11. A. R. C. Westwood, C. M. Preece and M. H. Kamdar. *Trans. ASM,* **60**, 723 (1967).

### H. H. Uhlig:

Many of the points raised by Dr. Westwood seem to me to be ones of semantics. Dr. Oriani has already suggested that kinetic as well as thermodynamic factors perhaps enter the mechanism of s.c.c. This situation does not exclude the probability that reduction of surface energy, whatever one calls it, is an important component of the mechanism for many metal systems, if not the most important component. The Griffith criterion of crack initiation is still a useful construct for understanding the conditions which account for fracture of a brittle solid, even if the assumptions are oversimplified and some of the details have been left out. There is much supporting evidence that this same approach is useful in describing environmentally induced cracking of ductile metals.

To argue that liquid-metal embrittlement occurs generally rather than with specific solid-liquid metal combinations is to tangle with the facts. It is well known that mercury boilers can be and have been constructed successfully of steel, but not of either brass or of titanium. The latter metals are specifically embrittled by liquid mercury whereas iron is outstandingly resistant under a wide variety of temperatures and stresses.

**A. R. C. Westwood, RIAS:**

Actually, iron alloys are very susceptible to embrittlement by mercury, as has been shown by Stoloff et al.[1]

1. N. S. Stoloff, R. G. Davies and T. L. Johnston. *Environment-Sensitive Mechanical Behavior,* Gordon and Breach, New York, 613 (1966).

**H. Spahn, BASF:**

In his paper Prof. Uhlig discusses the effect of stress on SCC mentioning the following relationship between applied stress $\sigma$ and time to failure t:

$$\sigma = -k \log t + \text{const.}$$

which implies that there is no threshold stress.

Figure 1 shows that for 42% $MgCl_2$ solution boiling at 145 C and a Type 347 stainless steel there is a threshold stress which is somewhat less than the 0.2-% offset yield strength of the material at 145 C. In the range of the threshold stress the time to rupture markedly increases from some 10 to more than 1000 hours with the longest experiment being carried on to about 3000 hours without failure of the specimen.

Figure 1 being plotted on a semilogarithmic scale one can see that, at stresses higher than the threshold stress region, the above relationship roughly holds true. The scatter is, however, considerable, and the linear relationship between stress and log time is not too well fulfilled.

Prof. Uhlig points out that a semblance of threshold stress may have its origin in incidental compressive stresses in surface layers of the test specimens. This is certainly not the case for the results of Figure 1 which were obtained on uniaxially loaded tensile specimens with a gage length of 25 mm and a diameter of 7 mm. These specimens were machined, ground and mechanically polished. They were then given a solution annealing treatment at 1050 C (20 minutes) and quenched in water. Finally, they were electropolished in two stages (cf. H. Spahn. *Metalloberflache.* **20**, 91-99 (1966). Using this procedure very low internal stresses could be obtained.

It seems to us that the existence of a threshold stress

has been concealed in many experiments by internal tensile stresses in improperly heat treated specimens. Figure 2 shows in Curve "a" what happens if Type 316 L stainless steel specimens, again in boiling 42% $MgCl_2$ solution, contain internal tensile stresses. A striking observation though not an unexpected one is the finite specimen life at stresses approaching zero. If the specimens were treated in the aforementioned way Curve "b" resulted showing a threshold stress.

Figure 1 in Prof. Uhlig's paper, taken from the work of Hoar and Hines (*J. Iron and Steel Institute.* **182**, 124 (1956)) resembles Curve "a" in Figure 2 and, in fact, shows a finite time to rupture at zero stress.

Taking these observations into account we would suggest not to elaborate too much on the above semilogarithmic relationship connecting it for instance to the steady state creep rate by the equations

$$R = \frac{k_o}{t}$$

and

$$\sigma = k \log R + \text{const.}$$

For the aforementioned stainless steels in boiling 42% $MgCl_2$ solution the more important point seems to be the existence of a threshold stress range which seems to indicate that a certain amount of slip must occur to give rise to stress corrosion cracking.

Figure 1 also indicates the surface state of the specimens after the test. Under the present conditions some pitting had occurred at low stresses after 1000 hours. It is evident that under conditions where heavy pitting occurs a threshold stress cannot be expected.

**H. H. Uhlig:**

**I appreciate knowing about Dr. Spahn's results on s.c.c. of Type 347 and Type 316 L stainless steels which seem to show a threshold stress below which failure does not occur. It is puzzling that the Type 347 steel should show no threshold stress when surface ground and passivated, but a very definite threshold stress when electropolished and passivated. This would seem to indicate, if surface stresses are the cause as Dr. Spahn indicates, that grinding produces marked tensile stresses in surface layers of the steel. However, if a phase transformation of austenite to cold-worked ferrite occurs by grinding, as reported previously by others, the surface stresses therefore ought to be compressional instead because of the volume increase accompanying the phase change.**

**But in addition to uncontrolled surface stresses, other factors may also play a role in the apparent fact that some investigators find a threshold stress while others report its absence. One suspects that, in some tests, galvanic coupling of the stainless steel to a more active metal, or to a stainless steel which has accidentally or otherwise been heat treated to undergo mild carbide precipitation, induces some degree of cathodic protection. Under these conditions stress**

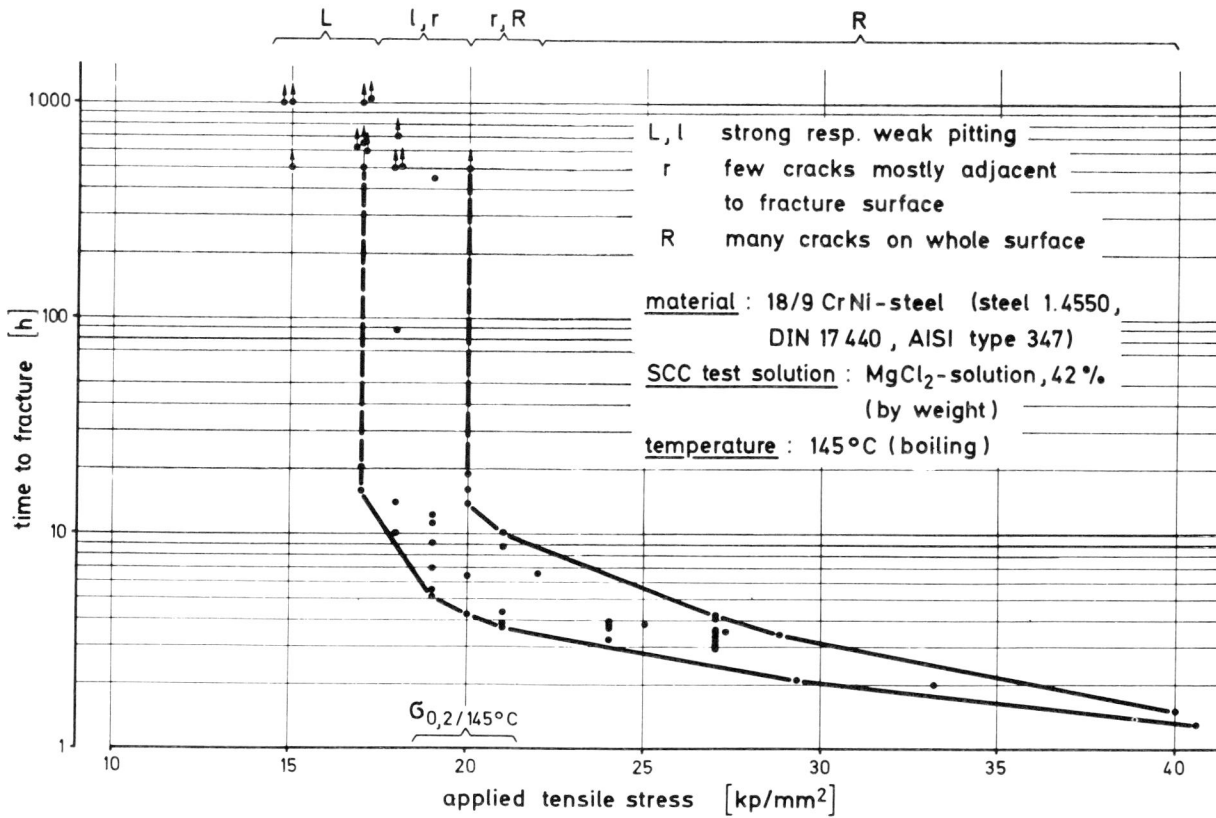

Legend inside Figure 1:

L, l   strong resp. weak pitting
r     few cracks mostly adjacent
      to fracture surface
R    many cracks on whole surface

material : 18/9 CrNi-steel (steel 1.4550,
                DIN 17 440, AISI type 347)
SCC test solution : $MgCl_2$-solution, 42 %
                  (by weight)
temperature : 145°C (boiling)

FIGURE 1 — Effect of applied tensile stress on time to fracture for Type 347 stainless steel exposed to boiling 42% $MgCl_2$.

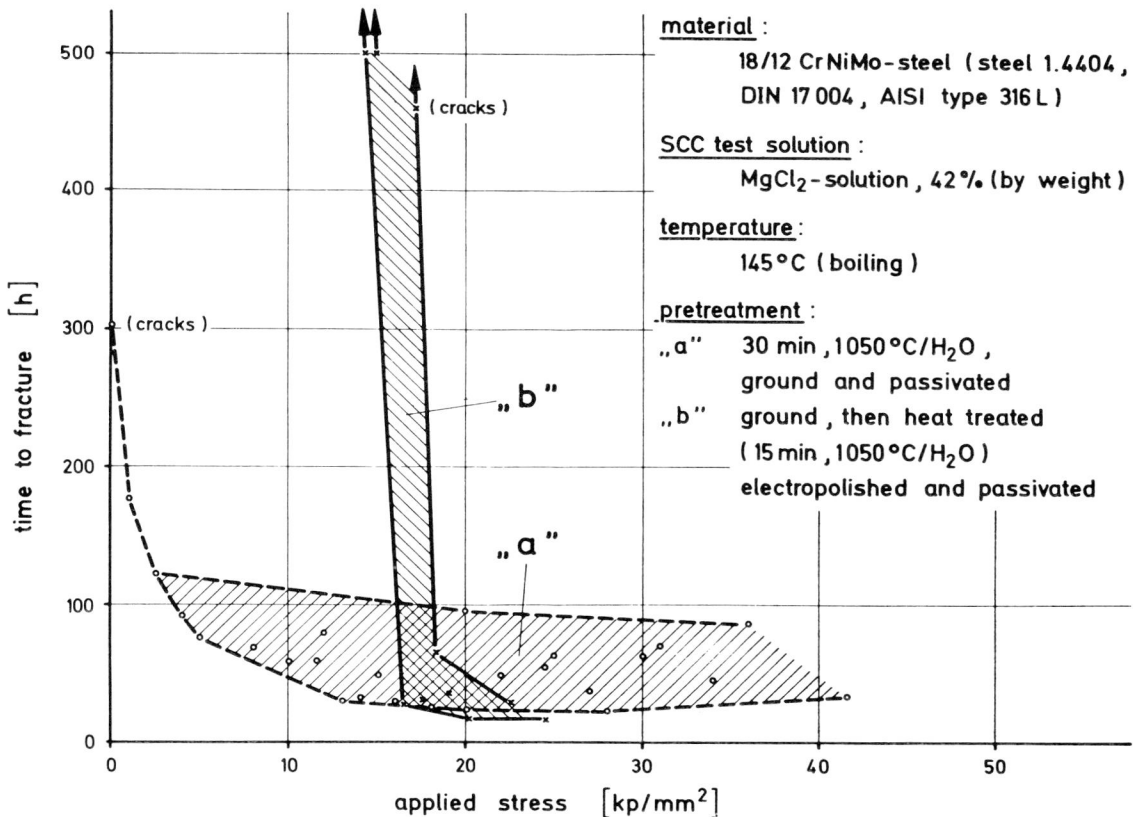

Legend inside Figure 2:

material :
    18/12 CrNiMo-steel (steel 1.4404,
    DIN 17 004, AISI type 316 L)

SCC test solution :
    $MgCl_2$-solution, 42 % (by weight)

temperature :
    145°C (boiling)

pretreatment :
„a"   30 min, 1050°C/$H_2O$,
      ground and passivated
„b"   ground, then heat treated
      (15 min, 1050°C/$H_2O$)
      electropolished and passivated

FIGURE 2 — Effect of applied tensile stress on time to fracture as affected by pretreatment.

corrosion cracking may occur only at highest stresses. This does not imply that Dr. Spahn's experiments were affected in this way, but the point is made that further careful experiments are needed to resolve the discrepant data now appearing in the literature on the matter of whether a threshold stress does indeed exist. The theory of s.c.c. outlined in my paper indicates that a threshold stress in general is not expected.

### J. R. Weeks, Brookhaven National Laboratory:

In general, with the considerable interest expressed at this and previous conferences in the effects of surface adsorption on the stress corrosion process, it is surprising that no experiments have been reported today which demonstrate that this adsorption occurs, and from which the kinetics and free energies of the proposed chemisorptions can be estimated. What evidence do we have that surface adsorptions involving, for example, $Cl^-$, do occur on stainless steel surfaces with sufficient adsorption energies to cause the observed cracking?

### H. H. Uhlig:

The evidence that $Cl^-$ adsorbs on stainless steels comes largely from indirect evidence. For example, Rosenfeld and Maximtschuk[1] found that radioactive $Cl^-$ is adsorbed on metallic Cr and that the amount adsorbed is potential dependent. Additions of extraneous anions, e.g., $SO_4^{--}$ or $OH^-$, were found to desorb $Cl^-$. Hence, if adsorbed $Cl^-$ causes s.c.c., extraneous anions, e.g., $SO_4^{--}$ or $OH^-$, should act as inhibitors of stress corrosion cracking by the stress sorption mechanism. Sulfates are difficult to evaluate because of solubility limitations but $Cl^-$ or acetate ions inhibit s.c.c. of mild steel in boiling $NO_3^-$ test solution, and $OH^-$, $NO_3^-$ or acetate ions inhibit s.c.c. of 18-8 in boiling $MgCl_2$.

The calculated amount by which surface energy is reduced by adsorption is covered in my reply to Dr. Douglas.

1. I. Rosenfeld and W. Maximtschuk. *Z. physik. Chem.,* 215, 25 (1960).

### E. N. Pugh, RIAS:

I would like to make two comments concerning the adsorption model that you have described. First, you suggest that the model is operative in both stress-corrosion cracking and liquid-metal embrittlement. If this is so, I find it difficult to reconcile the fact that pure metals are known to undergo liquid-metal embrittlement with your statement that pure metals are not susceptible to stress-corrosion cracking.

Second, I cannot accept that the adsorption model (or any other model) can account for all cases of stress-corrosion cracking. As a specific example, consider the failure of alpha-brass in non-tarnishing aqueous ammonia. We know that the presence in solution of cupric-ammonium complex ions is a prerequisite for cracking (E. N. Pugh, J. V. Craig, and A. J. Sedriks, This Volume), and, according to the model, we would have to conclude that failure results from the stable adsorption of these ions. However, we

know that increasing the complex-ion concentration of the non-tarnishing solutions leads to increasing rates of weight loss, due to reactions of the type

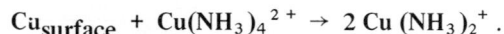

$$Cu_{surface} + Cu(NH_3)_4^{2+} \rightarrow 2\, Cu(NH_3)_2^+ .$$

In view of these reactions and the observed high rates of weight loss, I do not think it is realistic to propose that the cupric complexes are stably adsorbed at the metal surface. It seems more likely that failure in this case occurs by a dissolution-dependent mechanism.

### H. H. Uhlig:

In answer to Dr. Pugh, when liquid metal embrittlement occurs, a solid metal is being contaminated by at least one different liquid metal. Hence the processes of imperfection generation followed by adsorption reflect the behavior of an alloy rather than that of a pure metal. This is not the situation in stress corrosion cracking involving a pure metal and a non-metallic environment.

The adsorbing species in the case of $\alpha$ brass has not yet been identified, so that is hazardous to draw conclusions from circumstantial evidence alone. Furthermore, the corrosion reactions occurring generally over the metallic surface are not a positive indication of the reactions occurring at the tip of an advancing crack. The situation is complicated in addition by the probability that the rate of crack growth is sensitive to concentration of the adsorbing species in the bulk of solution. Rebinder et al, for example, found that the effect of a surface active agent such as oleic acid in paraffin oil on the creep rate or shear stress of several metals was a maximum at 0.2%. This was explained on the basis that, at this concentration, adsorbed oleic acid formed an oriented monolayer on the metal surface which had optimum effect on mechanical properties of the underlying metal. Below this concentration less than a monolayer was adsorbed, and above this concentration a multilayer of disarrayed molecules was adsorbed, either of which had less effect. A similar situation may occur in the stress sorption cracking of solids, whether metallic or non-metallic.

### K. Bohnenkamp, Max-Planck-Institut fur Eisenforschung:

I have two questions:

1. If we assume a continuous penetration of cracks, I am not sure whether the time ($< 10^{-2}$ sec) is sufficient for the specific chemisorption of ions.

2. I do not see the sharp distinction between intergranular corrosion and intergranular stress corrosion. Intergranular corrosion happens in nitrate solutions also without stress but is accelerated on stressed specimens.

### H. H. Uhlig:

The rate of cracking of 18-8 stainless steel in $MgCl_2$ test solution or for mild steel in a nitrate test solution is of the order of 0.5 cm/hr. Most adsorption processes are sufficiently rapid to keep up with new surface formation represented by this order of crack growth.

If one hypothesizes a much more rapid crack rate corresponding to discontinuous cracking, one has first to prove that the discontinuous extension of the specimen is not caused by discontinuous creep rather than by cracking.

There is actually a sharp distinction between intergranular stress corrosion cracking of a metal like mild steel in which an applied stress is necessary, and intergranular corrosion of the same metal in absence of an applied stress. A mild steel stress corrosion cracks at perhaps 0.5 cm/hr, but in absence of stress the rate will be orders of magnitude smaller, if indeed any intergranular corrosion occurs at all. Similarly, a 70-30 brass when stressed in cupric-ammonium solutions may fail intergranularly within minutes, but when exposed to the same solution in absence of applied or residual stress, observable intergranular corrosion, if any, occurs over a period of days. Wilson Lynes[1] studied this matter in detail. Only ammonia or amines caused s.c.c. of brass; many chemical media induced slow intergranular corrosion whether the brass was stressed or not. The large difference in rate of penetration induced by an applied tensile stress is strong support that the mechanism of crack formation differs from the corrosion reaction which operates in the absence of stress.

1. W. Lynes. *Corrosion,* **21,** 125 (1965).

# THE ELECTROCHEMISTRY OF LATTICE DISARRAY

T. P. Hoar
University of Cambridge

## Abstract

The types of disarray that occur in metal lattices are briefly indicated. Simple thermodynamics shows that the influence of disarray—as induced for example by cold work—on *equilibrium* electrochemical properties is small and in any case not measurable in a meaningful way. Kinetic considerations show, however, that the influence of disarray on the *process* of anodic dissolution can be considerable. In *overall* dissolution, the increase of the surface density of sites active for dissolution, produced by disarray, is suggested as the important factor in the rate equation. In *local* dissolution of the microscopic highly disarrayed regions, there may also be a significant reduction of the free energy of activation for dissolution, consequent upon the localized stored energy of disarray.

## Introduction

The concept of lattice disarray has been invoked to explain many corrosion phenomena that occur, or begin to occur, at singularities on the metal surface. Thus, localized attack at grain boundaries, etch pits beginning at emergent dislocations, enhanced corrosion or selective dissolution of one alloy component at highly cold worked surface regions such as scratches or punch marks, corrosion-fatigue fracture[1] and stress-corrosion cracking[2-6] have all been discussed in terms of localized lattice disarray of one kind of another. The idea no doubt arose through the early observations that cold worked metals usually dissolve in acid solutions more rapidly than annealed, and that fine-grained metals often dissolve more rapidly than single crystals. In corrosion in nearly neutral solutions, when oxide films and/or layers of corrosion products are usually present on the metal surface, the influence of disarray in the metal lattice, whether general or localized, is often much less clear-cut, because of the over-riding influence of the non-metallic surface layers: but even in such cases, the corrosion anodes are usually 'bare' metal at gaps or breaks in the oxide film or corrosion-product layer, and the influence of lattice disarray can become apparent.

In view of the widespread use that has been made of the concept of lattice disarray, it is unfortunate that electrochemists have so far made little contribution to a proper understanding of its effects: the mainstream of electrochemical thought was in the past fed very largely by experiments on 'simple' surfaces such as liquid mercury, and in the intensive study of solid surfaces now proceeding the tendency is towards the use of 'well-defined' surfaces produced by anodic polishing on annealed single crystals with the avowed object of minimizing lattice disarray. Equally, although solid-state physicists are making intensive studies on lattice disarray so as to explain the *bulk* structure and properties of solids, they often tend to regard the *surface* as a slightly tiresome complication to be studied later on. The metal/electrolyte-solution interface is indeed a boundary between solid-state physics and classical electrochemistry. While we may appreciate the electrochemist's desire to make its metal side as 'simple' as possible and the solid-state man's wish to ignore its solution side whenever he can, we have to recognize that the interdisciplinary 'interphase', with all its complications caused by lattice disarray in real engineering materials, is of great practical importance *now*, and that in the absence of proper theoretical treatment a number of misconceptions concerning the nature of and effects caused by disarray are retarding progress.

This paper is an attempt to clear up a number of points qualitatively, and to suggest some of the more promising avenues to be explored in new research, in the electrochemistry of lattice disarray.

## Thermodynamics of Disarray

When a metal lattice is put in tension or compression within the elastic region, where Hooke's Law applies, the work done by a stress $\sigma$ producing a strain $\epsilon$, with Young's Modulus $Y = \sigma/\epsilon$, is

$$\sigma \epsilon/2 = \sigma^2/2Y .$$

If the operation is done isothermally, the total energy increase in the metal at absolute temperature T is

$$\sigma^2/2Y + T\alpha\sigma,$$

where $\alpha$ is the coefficient of linear thermal expansion; the second term (often the larger) arises through the thermo-elastic effect. It is readily shown that the extra energy that can be put into a metal by such elastic deformation is, at most, no more than 10 cal/mole.[7]

When the lattice is subjected to cold work, the extra, stored energy can be readily computed from the area under the conventional or true stress/strain curve, and it can be measured calorimetrically by comparison of the heat evolved during the dissolution of cold-worked metal with that similar evolved from annealed material. The extra energy stored in cold worked material is at most some 100 cal/mole.[7]

It is thus evident that the extra energy per mole of metal introduced by elastic or plastic deformation is quite small compared with the chemical energy involved in, for example, dissolution to metal cations. It is true that the calorimetric measurements mentioned above give the total energy increase, i.e., the enthalpy increase $\Delta H_D$ associated with the lattice disarray, whereas the more interesting quantity from the point of view of the electrochemical behavior of the disarrayed metal is the free energy increase $\Delta G_D$; but since

$$\Delta G_D = \Delta H_D - T\Delta S_D,$$

where $\Delta S_D$ is the entropy increase caused by disarray and is obviously positive, $\Delta G_D$ is an even smaller positive quantity than $\Delta H_D$. At temperatures well below the melting point of the metal, $T\Delta S_D$ is in fact fairly small compared with $\Delta H_D$, and we may therefore consider the upper limit of $\Delta H_D$, *ca* 100 cal/mole, as a fair approximation to the upper limit of $\Delta G_D$.

The over-all decrease of free energy of a cold-worked metal in passing from the metallic to the ionized state can thus be expected to be no more than 100 cal/mole greater than that of annealed metal. From the relationship

$$\Delta G = -zFe,$$

where $\Delta G$ is the conventional free energy increase for the passage of 1 mole of metal into the ionized state at electrode potential e, one might therefore expect the electrode potential of a heavily cold-worked metal exposed to a solution of its own z-valent ions to be more negative than that of the annealed metal by $4.2 \times 100/z \times 96,500 = 4.4 \times 10^{-3}/z$ volts, or say 2 mV for a bivalent metal.

So small a potential difference would not be expected to produce appreciable 'galvanic' corrosion when cold-worked and annealed metal were coupled together in a solution containing the metal ions and no other cathodic reactant. Furthermore, if metastable cold-worked material be allowed to come into equilibrium, on open circuit, with its ions in solution, it does so by slight dissolution accompanied by redeposition of its ions in a lattice more nearly conforming to its stable, unworked state: the surface it then presents approximates, in fact, to annealed material. This phenomenon is, of course, no more than an illustration of the general proposition that one cannot have an equilibrium (whether electrochemical or not) when one or more of the phases is in a metastable state. The calculated maximum shift of the equilibrium potential produced by cold work, 2 mV, indeed is not only small but has no real meaning. Attempts to measure such a shift are partly analogous to attempts to measure differences of equilibrium potential between different crystallographic faces of single crystals, which similarly fail because the higher energy planes revert to the most stable plane during the measurements.

## Kinetics of Disarray

A significant difference in electrochemical behavior between cold-worked and annealed metal can be expected only *when the materials are operating as anodes at potentials considerably removed from the equilibrium potential* of the annealed metal, where the reverse reaction of cathodic deposition is negligibly slow. This situation can occur only if a cathodic reaction, other than that of deposition of the metal itself, occurs, either on a separate cathode, or locally on the metal itself as an electron source, at a potential more noble than the 'equilibrium' potential of the metal: that is, if the metal is undergoing either 'anodic' or 'natural' corrosion. Then, if the cold-worked anode *operates more rapidly* than the annealed at the same potential, considerable real differences become measurable and meaningful. A well known *macroscopic* example of the effect is the faster etching under acid attack of cold-worked scratches or punch marks in otherwise unworked metal. The influence of cold work on the rate of anodic dissolution of, for example, mild steel[8] and nickel[9] is also well established.

The over-all rate of anodic dissolution expressed as anodic current density $i_a$ is related to the anode potential e by an equation of general form

$$i_a = A\,n\,\exp\left(\frac{-\Delta G_a^*}{RT}\right)\,\exp\left(\frac{\alpha z F (e - e_o)}{RT}\right)$$

where A is a constant, n the surface density of dissolving sites, $\Delta G_a^*$ the standard free energy of activation of these sites at potential $e_o$,[(1)] $\alpha$ the fraction of $(e - e_o)$ that assists the dissolving ions over the energy barrier, and the other symbols have their usual meanings. Increase of $i_a$ at constant potential thus involves either an increase of n, a decrease of $\Delta G_a^*$, or both. We have suggested, for the large increase (up to $10^4$ times) of $i_a$ during straining of certain iron-nickel[10] and iron-chromium-nickel[11] alloys in hot concentrated chloride solutions (where there is no passivity—on static metal $i_a$ depends exponentially upon e),[11] that the major effect is an increase of n, the energy of activation being little if at all decreased. For the smaller increase in $i_a$ produced *after* cold-work on nickel (a factor

99

of about 10) increase of n is also the likely explanation: we have shown[9],[12] that the experimental enthalpy of activation, $\Delta H_a^* = 10.6$ Kcal/mole, is not altered by cold work, and since the entropy of activation is also unlikely to be influenced, $\Delta G_a^*$ should likewise remain constant.

Increase of n is easily interpreted physically. Sites active for dissolution may be kinks in edges of incomplete planes, other singularities in such edges, or ad-atoms in quasi-equilibrium with the kinks etc.; in each case their surface density will be approximately proportional to the density of emergent dislocations or other regions of disarray in the metal surface, each of which is increased by cold work. It is also reasonable to believe that the very large increase of $i_a$ sometimes found *during* straining is caused by a corresponding very large *evanescent* increase of n — when straining ceases, the newly formed surface quickly 'settles down', or dissolves anodically, to leave a much less active condition. We may note that n is not temperature-dependent at room temperatures: analogously to bulk vacant sites, from which indeed they may arise during anodic dissolution, kink sites are 'frozen in' at room temperatures, in much higher concentration than that corresponding to thermal equilibrium with the close-packed surface.

Decrease of $\Delta G_a^*$ would be less easy to interpret physically: since each and every atom eventually becomes a site active for dissolution, the average decrease could not exceed the average stored energy, at most 100 cal/mole. At room temperature, this corresponds to a factor of *ca* exp(100/2 x 300) = 1.2, far less than the increases in $i_a$ that can be observed.

We have so far considered the *macroscopic* electrochemical effects of disarrayed metal. Disarray is, in fact, distributed in a highly non-uniform way in metals, and we now examine the *microscopic* electrochemical situation.

The maximum amount of stored energy in cold worked metal is, as we have seen, of the order of 100 cal/*mole of total metal*. We can make a crude upper estimate of the extra energy *per mole of disarrayed metal* by considering grain boundaries and dislocations as approximating in energy to that of the liquid state, and vacancies as approximating in energy to that of the vapor state,

although this latter energy is distributed among the several neighbours of the vacancy. The latent heats of fusion of most metals lie in the range 2-5 Kcal/mole,[13] and the latent heats of sublimation in the range 30-120 Kcal/mole.[13] It may be reasonable therefore to suggest an 'average' energy for regions of severe disarray in the range 2-10 Kcal/mole over and above that of the remaining well-arrayed lattice. A conservative estimate of say 3 Kcal/mole for a consequent lowering of $\Delta G_a$ for regions of disarrayed atoms could thus increase $i_a$ by a factor of exp (3000/2 x 300) $\sim$ 150. Such dissolution could only be *selective*, of the disarrayed region and not of the generality of the lattice, in contrast to the *over-all* dissolution depending on the number of available active sites[2] discussed earlier. It could well provide a mechanism whereby microscopically localized slots form from disarrayed material, and provide stress-raising 'starters' for stress-corrosion 'cracks'. More mundanely, it could well explain the initial stage of preferential grain-boundary dissolution.

## Conclusion

A major point made in the present discussion is that, since disarrayed metal, however produced, is in a meta-stable state, with a surface that tends to revert to the stable state when it is in contact with an electrolyte solution, there can never be merit in methods that aim to assess its electrochemical properties by *equilibrium* measurements or calculations. Rather, kinetic measurements of *rate* of anodic dissolution, conveniently under potentiostatic conditions with the potential well removed from the 'equilibrium', are capable of discrimination either (1) between the rate of general dissolution of, say, annealed, cold-worked or straining metal, or (2) between the rate of microscopically localized dissolution of the disarrayed regions of otherwise well-arrayed metal. In the former type of experiment, direct measurements of current are possible: in the latter, microscopic estimates of the relative rates of attack may have to be made.

As well as steady-state current measurements, current transients both slow and fast are of interest, since they give information about the rate of change of a metal surface. The disappearance of disarrayed metal can be assessed from such transients, as can the production of new disarray during straining.

---

[1]Note that for a reversible electrode reaction between stable phases, we commonly make $e_o$ the reversible potential, so that $(e_o - e)$ is the anode overpotential and $\Delta G_a^*$ the 'thermal' free energy of activation at the reversible potential. The present definition avoids the need for defining a reversible potential or an exchange current, which are not meaningful for a non-stable metal phase.

---

[2]Note that when disarrayed regions (other than screw dislocations) dissolve, they are *not* self-perpetuating, whereas active ad-atoms (if in quasi-equilibrium with kink sites) and kink sites (to a very large extent) are.

## References

1. D. Whitwham and U. R. Evans. *J. Iron Steel Inst.,* 165, 72 (1950).
2. T. P. Hoar and J. G. Hines. *J. Iron Steel Inst.,* 182, 124 (1956).
3. T. P. Hoar and J. G. Hines. In *Stress Corrosion Cracking and Embrittlement,* ed. W. D. Robertson, p. 107, Wiley, New York (1956).
4. G. Thomas and J. Nutting. *J. Inst. Metals,* 88, 81 (1959-60).
5. P. R. Swann. *Corrosion,* 19, 102t (1963).
6. T. P. Hoar. *Corrosion,* 19, 331t (1963).
7. A. L. Tichener and M. B. Bever. In *Progress in Metal Physics,* 7, ed. B. Chalmers and R. King, p. 147. Pergamon Press, London (1958).

8. M. T. Simnad and U. R. Evans. *Trans. Faraday Soc.,* **46**, 175 (1950).

9. T. P. Hoar. *J. Inst. Metal Finishing,* **39**, 166 (1962).

10. J. C. Scully and T. P. Hoar. *2nd Int. Congr. Metallic Corrosion,* New York 1963, p. 184. NACE, Houston (1966).

11. T. P. Hoar and J. M. West. *Proc. Roy. Soc.,* **A 268**, 304 (1962).

12. G. K. Notman. Thesis, Cambridge (1960).

13. O. Kubaschewski and E. Ll. Evans. *Metallurgical Thermo-chemistry,* 2nd Edn. Pergamon Press, London (1956).

## Discussion

**J. E. Draley, Argonne National Laboratory:**

I don't understand how you relate the local energy available for the increased reaction rate with the common observation that there isn't very much of this reaction from pure metals, as there is from alloys. I would have thought that the energy difference available from the strain and the local imperfection point of view would be as great for the pure metal as for the alloy. There is quite a difference in behavior, of course.

**T. P. Hoar:**

In alloys, or in impure metals, there are regions of varying sizes where local heterogeneity is very great—a decorated dislocation is a typical region of this kind, not of course present in a pure metal. At such a region, it is reasonable to suppose that the activation energy for the *process* of dissolution may be less than at a less disarrayed region, such as an undecorated dislocation in pure metal.

For increased *rate* of dissolution, it is of course not necessary that the disarrayed metal should be thermodynamically less noble: only that either the activation energy for dissolution should be lower, or the density of active sites greater, or that both these factors should operate.

**R. A. Oriani, U. S. Steel:**

I agree with what Professor Hoar has said, that kinetics in general is far more important than other considerations about strain energy and this sort of thing, however, I would like to expand a little bit on his remarks on the thermodynamic aspects of what stress fields do in thermodynamics.

In the first place, as he has already indicated, what is important is the chemical potential. He called it the energy density per mole of disarrayed atoms, or something of this sort, but really a better term is the chemical potential of the atoms in question. In general, one cannot derive the chemical potential of a matrix atom of a stressed metal from the overall free energy density.

Let me show you a few cases. Suppose one has a body under uniaxial stress, $\sigma$. Let the surface parallel with the applied stress be in contact with some environment, either aqueous or gaseous. We ask what is the chemical potential of an atom, such as iron upon this surface. By virtue of the fact that this surface has a tensile stress in the direction of the surface but a zero stress normal to that surface, the increment of chemical potential of such an atom due to stress is $\overline{V} \sigma^2/2Y$, where $\overline{V}$ is the partial molal volume. However, the chemical potential is not defined anywhere else in this stressed body except at a place where there is an interchange of material with the environment. That is, the chemical potential of the matrix atom of a stressed body is a surface property.

An applied stress can only raise the chemical potential of a matrix atom if that atom is upon a surface having zero normal stress as in the foregoing example. If however there is a surface which has normal to itself a component of the tensile applied stress and which can exchange atoms with the surroundings, the chemical potential of these atoms at such a surface can be lowered by the applied tensile stress. This is not obvious from Professor Hoar's formulations. It happens because the term $\overline{V} \sigma/3$, a term linear in $\sigma$, takes over from the term in $\sigma^2$. This is in fact the basis of Herring's treatment of creep by vacancy diffusion. Similarly, the chemical potential of interstitial solutes is lowered by applied tensile stresses and raised by applied compressive stresses. For the interstitial solute, however, the chemical potential is defined everywhere in and on the stressed body. Those interested in more details are referred to the paper by J. C. M. Li, R. A. Oriani, and L. S. Darken, *Z. physik. Chemie* (N.F.) **49**, 271 (1966).

**T. P. Hoar:**

I am obliged to Dr. Oriani for his interesting comments, which appear to be correct, and for drawing my attention to his recent publication.

**H. H. Uhlig, MIT:**

I have a short comment or question regarding your statement about the cracking of mild steel in nitrate solution. We confirm that a black film is present on the mild steel surface, easily visible. My question relates to the fact that when we add to the nitrate test solution a small amount of an inhibitor like NaCl or Na acetate, the same black film forms, but the specimen does not crack. In light of your described mechanism, why should this be?

**T. P. Hoar:**

We do not know. The formation of the magnetite film appears to be a necessary concomitant of stress corrosion cracking. We do not regard it as a sufficient condition.

**G. Martin, North American Rockwell, Inc.:**

You point out the significant fact that it is not the bulk mass energy of deformation which is important for SCC phenomena, but the local energy associated with a lattice defect or dislocation. This energy has been estimated from the strain energy associated with such defects and found to be of the order of a few electron volts, i.e., of the same order as the energies involved in the chemical reactions. I suggest that at a moving crack tip, because of the local stress concentration, these local energies are even larger than they would be on a flat surface. This may explain the

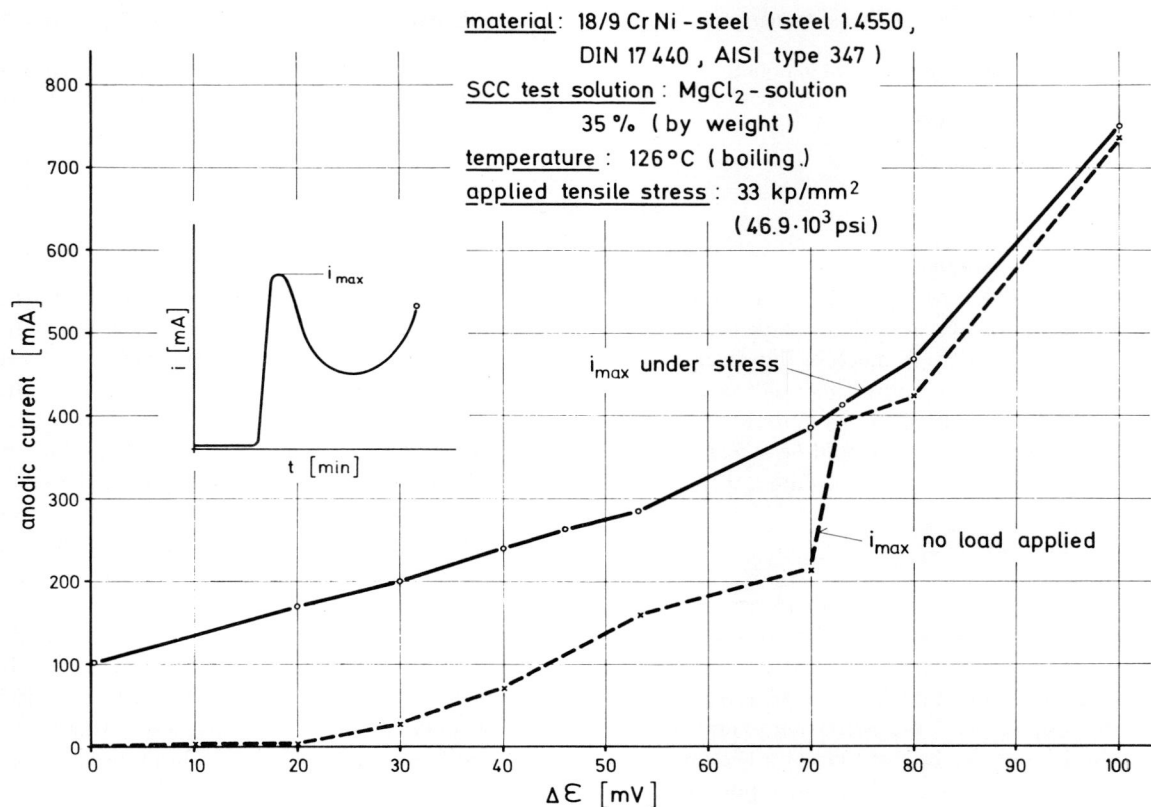

FIGURE 1 — Maximum anodic current vs overpotential for two conditions of load for stainless steel specimens exposed to boiling MgCl₂.

tendency of chemical reactions to occur at the crack tip rather than other portions of the surface.

**T. P. Hoar:**

**Dr. Martin's point is well taken and would bear further investigation.**

**H. Spahn, BASF:**

Dr. Hoar concludes from the exponential dependence of the anodic current upon the potential that iron-chromium-nickel alloys are not passive in concentrated chloride solutions. This conclusion is of utmost importance to the mechanism of SCC of stainless steels, and it seems, therefore, most desirable to have some more experimental evidence on that.

For boiling $MgCl_2$-solution and Type 347 stainless steel we cannot support the above conclusion. Weight loss measurement on unstressed specimens over a period of 300 hrs showed that the corrosion current at open circuit potential is 0.1 $\mu A/cm^2$ for the 35% solution and 1.0 for the 42% solution. In these experiments a reflux-cooler open to the air was used. When bubbling pure hydrogen around the specimen in a boiling 38% $MgCl_2$-solution the steel was passive, too.

Besides the weight loss criterion electrochemical measurements give no indication of an absence of passivity. Figure 1 shows potentiodynamic current-potential curves taken under the conditions indicated. Curve B for an

unloaded specimen clearly shows that, starting from the open circuit potential at about $\epsilon_h$ = -80 mV the current remains extremely low. Then, at about -50 mV — it suddenly increases and the steel is attacked comparatively even with practically no indication of pitting. The more diluted the solution the greater is the difference between the open circuit and the breakthrough potential which manifests itself as the pitting potential by the heavy pitting observed beyond it in the more diluted solutions.

Loaded specimens behave in the same way. They again show extremely low current densities up to the breakthrough (pitting) potential. From there on the current increase is steeper than in the case of an unloaded specimen.

A third argument that at least in the present case the austenitic steel is passive is based on potentiostatic experiments some of which are presented in Figure 2. After having reached a steady open circuit potential, potentials up to 100 mV more noble than the free open circuit potential were applied by means of a potentiostat. It can be seen that on an unloaded specimen (lower curve) at potentials up to 20 mV more noble than the open circuit potential extremely small currents are drawn. Again, beyond that a breakthrough occurs. Specimens loaded with 33 kp/mm² draw an anodic current at the open circuit potential. This is due to the film rupture at gliding parts of the surface which destroys passivity there. This gives rise to an electrochemical differentiation between gliding sites on

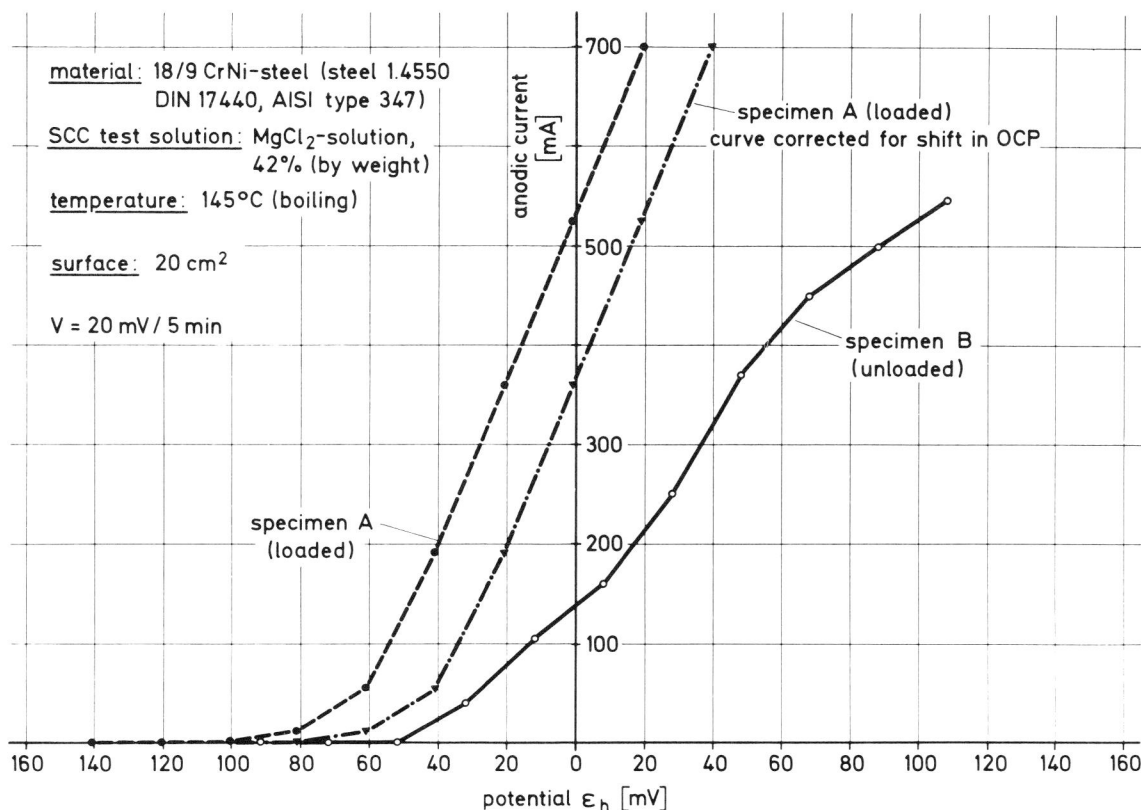

FIGURE 2 — Anodic current vs overpotential for stainless steel at two conditions of load and exposed to boiling MgCl₂.

the surface (active, not yet repassivated) and the (very much greater) non-gliding part of the surface. We agree very much with Dr. Graf in this part of the SCC mechanism and it is felt that the question "active or passive" is a very important one in the mechanistic sense.

The question to Dr. Hoar is: Could the observed i-ϵ dependency also result from the electrochemical conditions prevailing beyond the breakthrough potential?

**T. P. Hoar:**

Dr. Spahn provides, in his Figure 1, some results that are very similar indeed to those we gave some time ago (T. P. Hoar and J. M. West, *Proc. Roy. Soc.*, London, A268, 304, 1962). Our conditions were: 18-8 Cr-Ni (unstabilized) steel, 42 wt% MgCl₂ solution, 154 C. Dr. Spahn says that at about -50 mV (nhe) the current "suddenly" increases and "the steel is attacked comparatively evenly with practically no indication of pitting." This was our experience also, and we take it to mean that the steel is dissolving in the active state. Certainly in more dilute solutions there may well be a passivation and a breakthrough of the passive film at a higher potential, manifested by heavy pitting; but in the hot concentrated solution we believe that the passivation potential is so high and the notional breakthrough potential so low that passivation cannot occur. Nonetheless, it is very possible that the 18-8 surface is covered with a film of nickel metal (nickel is appreciably more noble than iron and chromium under the conditions being discussed), and

that this is responsible for keeping the dissolution current density of *static* 18-8 alloy very small at the operative potential of the stress-corrosion cracking process, say -0.1 to -0.05 V (nhe), as we suggested (T. P. Hoar and J. G. Hines, *Proc. 8th Meeting. CITCE.* Madrid, 1956, p. 273 and esp. p. 286, Butterworth, London, 1958) many years ago. The mechanical rupture of such a film may well be in part responsible for the much greater dissolution rate of *yielding* 18-8 alloy, at the same potential, as suggested by Staehle in his modification of Swann's "coarse slip" hypothesis.

I agree with Dr. Spahn that it will be very interesting to examine the e/i relationship for metals dissolving (usually with anodic brightening) at high positive potentials beyond the "breakthrough" point. Such evidence as there is indicates that limiting current densities are often reached, controlled in the main by the diffusion-convection situation in the liquid near to the metal/solution interface. In boiling concentrated 42 wt% aqueous magnesium chloride, one would expect such a limiting c.d.—scarcely affected by potential—to be of the order of 1 A/cm² for "natural" diffusion-convection (without stirring). This is just about the c.d. required to move a stress corrosion crack forward at the usual rate of 0.5-2 mm/h. It is interesting to note that anodic polarization of cracking 18-8 steel increases the density of cracks but scarcely affects their rate of propagation (J. G. Hines and T. P. Hoar, *J. Applied Chem.*, 8, 764, 1958).

103

# APPLICATION OF FRACTURE MECHANICS TO
# STRESS CORROSION CRACKING STUDIES

R. P. Wei
Lehigh University

## Abstract

The application of linear elastic fracture mechanics to stress corrosion cracking studies is described. Important implications with regard to the analysis of data, specimen size and testing technique are enumerated and limitations are noted. Data are cited to show that critical experiments within the framework of fracture mechanics can provide important clues to the mechanism of crack propagation.

## 1. Introduction

Stress corrosion cracking—which manifests itself in the occurrence of delayed failure of structural components under statically applied loads well below the yield strength of the material—is a problem of long standing. This phenomenon of delayed failure is often referred to as "static fatigue". The traditional measure of stress corrosion susceptibility is given in terms of the time required to produce failure (time-to-failure) at different stress levels obtained from testing "smooth" specimens of the material in the appropriate corrosive environments. The failure time, however, incorporates both the time required for "crack initiation" and a period of slow crack growth so that the separate effect of the environment on each of these stages cannot be ascertained. (A part of this difficulty stems from the lack of a precise definition for crack initiation.) This difficulty is underscored by the experimental results of Brown and Beachem[1] on titanium alloys. Their results showed that certain of the alloys that appeared to be immune to stress corrosion cracking in the traditional tests are, in fact, highly susceptible to environment-enhanced crack growth. The apparent immunity was explained by the fact that these alloys were nearly immune to pitting in the same environment, which was requisite for crack initiation.[1] Since current design practice presumes the presence of crack like defects in structures (see, for example, Reference 2), a considerable amount of effort has been devoted to studying the effect of environments on crack growth in the past few years.

The successful application of linear-elastic fracture mechanics analyses to describe the fracture behavior of high strength materials under monotonically increasing loads[3] has led to a logical extension of these same concepts to the study of slow crack growth under both static and fatigue loads, commonly termed subcritical-crack growth. The use of the crack-tip stress-intensity parameter (K), which governs the intensity or magnitude of the local stresses, to characterize the crack-driving force has met with considerable experimental success. The supporting evidence has been documented by Johnson and Paris[4] recently. The experimental results of Smith et al[5] on a titanium alloy serves as a good example. By using wedge-force-loaded specimens, for which the stress-intensity factor K decreases with crack extension under a constant applied load while the net section stress increases, Smith et al[5] clearly demonstrated the dependence of slow crack growth on K (Figure 1).

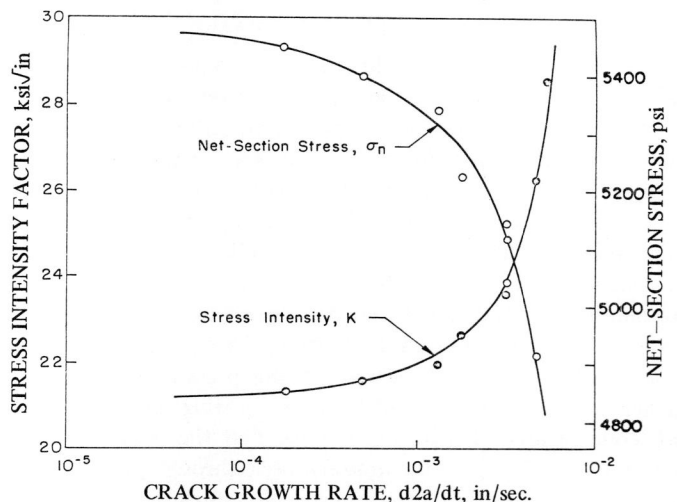

FIGURE 1 — Stress-intensity factor and net-section stress versus crack growth rate for a wedge-force-loaded specimen.[5]

With the increasing interest in applying the fracture mechanics approach to stress corrosion cracking studies in high strength materials, a brief review of the basic justification and limitations in using linear-elastic fracture mechanics analyses to describe crack growth and fracture seems appropriate. Some practical considerations in the design of experiments and test specimens will be given. Recent results on water-enhanced fatigue crack growth in a high strength aluminum alloy will be discussed.

## 2. Analytical Fracture Mechanics Considerations

Since crack extension and stress corrosion attack would occur in the highly stressed region of the crack-tip, the stress distribution in the crack-tip region should be considered. The stress field near crack tips may be divided into three basic types, each associated with a local mode of deformation—the opening mode, I, and two sliding modes, II and III.[6] The opening mode, mode I, is characterized by direct separation of the crack surfaces symmetrically with respect to the plane occupied by the crack. The edge-sliding mode, II, and the tearing mode, III, are akin to models for edge and screw dislocations respectively. For the present discussion, only the opening mode, I, will be considered, although the general discussion will be applicable to the other two modes as well.

The stress and displacement fields associated with the opening mode, mode I, in an isotropic elastic body is given by.[6-8]

$$\sigma_x = \frac{K_I}{\sqrt{2\pi r}} \cos \frac{\theta}{2} [1 - \sin \frac{\theta}{2} \sin \frac{3\theta}{2}]$$

$$\sigma_y = \frac{K_I}{\sqrt{2\pi r}} \cos \frac{\theta}{2} [1 + \sin \frac{\theta}{2} \sin \frac{3\theta}{2}]$$

$$\sigma_{xy} = \frac{K_I}{\sqrt{2\pi r}} \sin \frac{\theta}{2} \cos \frac{\theta}{2} \cos \frac{3\theta}{2}$$

$$u = \frac{K_I}{8\mu} \sqrt{\frac{2r}{\pi}} [(2\kappa - 1) \cos \frac{\theta}{2} - \cos \frac{3\theta}{2}]$$

$$v = \frac{K_I}{8\mu} \sqrt{\frac{2r}{\pi}} [(2\kappa + 1) \sin \frac{\theta}{2} - \sin \frac{3\theta}{2}]$$

For plane strain:

$$\kappa = 3 - 4\nu$$

$$\sigma_z = \nu(\sigma_x + \sigma_y)$$

$$w = 0$$

For generalized plane stress:

$$\kappa = \frac{3 - \nu}{1 + \nu}$$

$$\sigma_z = 0$$

$$w = -\frac{\nu}{E} \int (\sigma_x + \sigma_y) \, dz$$

r and $\theta$ are the radial and angular coordinates measured from the crack tip (Figure 2); $\mu$ is the shear modulus; and $\nu$ is the Poisson's ratio. Higher order terms in r have been neglected in Equation 1. Hence, the stresses and displacements are to be regarded as good approximations in the region where r is small compared to other planar (x-y plane) dimensions, such as the crack length, and exact in the limit as r approaches zero.

The parameter $K_I$ is the stress intensity factor, for mode I, which depends on the loading and the configuration of the body, including the crack size, and governs the intensity or magnitude of the local stresses. The analytical determination of the K factors and the crack-tip stress fields is basically a problem in the mathematical theory of elasticity and, will not be considered here. K factors for many different loadings and body configurations have been catalogued by Paris and Sih.[6] Numerical solutions of $K_I$ for practical test specimens, suitable for routine use, are given in ASTM STP 410 by Brown and Srawley.[9]

It should be noted that the linear elasticity solution for a sharp crack (see Equation 1 for example) gives rise to infinite stresses at the crack tip where the radius of curvature is "zero". In reality, of course, the deformed shape of the crack assumes some finite radius of curvature and the stress level always remains finite. Hence, it is likely that a large deformation theory would predict finite stresses at the crack tip.[10] In addition, the occurrence of local plastic deformation also tends to reduce the stress concentrating effects of the crack. If the zone of plastic deformation is small in comparison with the crack length, and other planar dimensions of the body, then the stress distribution in the large will not be seriously disturbed and the elasticity solutions represent a reasonably accurate

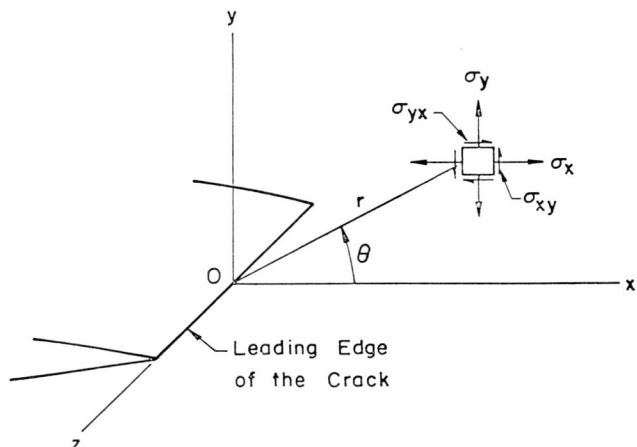

FIGURE 2 – Coordinates and stress components in the crack-tip stress field.

approximation of the stress and displacement fields near the crack tip. Since the small zone of plastically deformed material at the crack tip is contained within the surrounding elastic material, it is reasonable to expect that the behavior in this region would be governed by the surrounding elastic material and thus be characterized by the crack-tip stress-intensity factor $K_I$.

Inspection of Equation 1 suggests that identical stress fields are obtained for identical $K_I$ values. Hence, $K_I$ provides a single parameter characterization of the stress and displacement fields near the crack tip, independent of the size of the crack. This is not strictly true, however, since Equation 1 is only approximate for large values of r. The exact analysis of Inglis[11] shows that for cracks of different sizes, for the same $K_I$, the stresses away from the crack-tip differ considerably; the stresses very close to the crack tip, though, are nearly equal to each other.[12] On the basis of the Inglis solution,[11] Liu[12] showed that if the plastically deformed zone is much smaller than some region, within which the elastic stresses are approximately the same for bodies with different sizes of crack loaded to the same level of $K_I$, the stresses and strains at geometrically similar points, even within the plastic zone, would be the same. Thus, the use of $K_I$ as a single parameter characterization of the crack driving force may be justified.

It should be emphasized that the use of the crack-tip stress-intensity factor $K_I$ to characterize the crack driving force in practical engineering materials is predicated on the assumption of limited plasticity. The applicability of this approach to actual cases must be established by experimentation. The foregoing discussions are also limited to the case of stationary cracks, in contradistinction to moving cracks that are of concern in subcritical-crack growth. The results of Sih[13] suggest that for the usual rates of crack growth and fatigue loading frequencies encountered in subcritical-crack growth studies, modification of the crack-tip stress-intensity factor $K_I$ to include dynamic effects will not be necessary.

## 3. Some Practical Considerations

In the previous section, the basis and limitations for using the crack-tip stress-intensity factor, $K_I$, to characterize the crack-driving force in subcritical-crack growth experiments have been considered. In this section, some practical considerations in the design of experiments and test specimens will be given.

### 3.1 Growth Rate Versus Time-to-Failure

Experimental measurements of stress corrosion susceptibility follow essentially two paths, dictated in part by tradition and in part by practical considerations of experimentation and motivation. The conventional and simpler approach involves the measurement of time-to-failure for precracked specimens under different loads, akin to the traditional stress corrosion tests using smooth specimens. By successive reductions in load, a threshold level of $K_I$ is reached, below which, presumably, no failure can occur

under statically applied loads. This level of $K_I$ has been designated as $K_{Iscc}$.[1] In practice, $K_{Iscc}$ is often defined by the level of $K_I$ at which no failures occur after some finite interval of time. The level of $K_{Iscc}$ in relation to $K_{Ic}$, the plane-strain fracture toughness of the material in air, gives a measure of the stress corrosion susceptibility of the material, and may be used directly in material selection and design.[4] Since only simple test fixtures and instruments (clock) are needed, this procedure is used extensively for routine material evaluations.[1,2] The more complex approach involves the direct study of the crack-growth kinetics, that is, the determination of the rate of crack growth as a function of $K_I$, the crack-driving force, and the test environment. This approach is exemplified by the works of Johnson and his coworkers[14,15] and Van Der Sluys[16] for crack growth under static loads, and the work of Wei et al[17] on fatigue. With this approach, adequate instrumentation will be necessary for monitoring crack growth. A discussion of the relative merits of these two approaches in relation to the study of fundamental mechanisms of stress corrosion cracking will be considered later. Here, the influence of specimen size and geometry on the time to failure will be considered in relation to $K_{Iscc}$ testing and design.

### 3.2 Influence of Specimen Size and Geometry on the Time-To-Failure

The influence of specimen size and geometry on the time-to-failure is evident in the results of Brown and Beachem,[18] Figure 3, and may be demonstrated analytically by considering a crack growth relationship in the form

$$\frac{da}{dt} = F \text{ (K, T, other material, environment and test variables)} \quad (2)$$

The explicit form of the function F need not be specified for this discussion, although the determination of this functional relationship is basic to the study of stress corrosion cracking. For a typical time-to-failure experiment, in which all variables are maintained constant, the crack-tip stress-intensity factor $K_I$ increases monotonically with crack growth from some initial value $K_{Ii}$ to a critical value $K_{Ic}$ (for plane-strain) for fracture. The critical value $K_{Ic}$ (or $K_c$) for fracture has been shown by Steigerwald[19] to be independent of the test environment. Rewriting Equation 2 in terms of the rate of increase in $K_I$

$$\frac{dK_I}{dt} = \frac{dK_I}{da} \cdot \frac{da}{dt} = \frac{dK_I}{da} \cdot F \quad (3)$$

and integrate, the time to failure is given by

$$t_F = \int_0^{t_F} dt = \int_{K_{Ii}}^{K_{Ic}} \frac{dK_I}{\left(\dfrac{dK_I}{da}\right) \cdot F} \quad (4)$$

In this integration, it is implicitly assumed that the righthand side of Equation 3 contains no time-dependent terms. Since $K_I$ can be expressed in the form[9]

$$K_I = \sigma a^{1/2} Y \left(\frac{a}{W}\right)$$

where $\sigma$ = some nominal applied stress

      $a$ = crack length                   **(5)**

$Y\left(\frac{a}{W}\right)$ = calibration parameter reflecting the geometry of the specimen

      $W$ = specimen width

inspection of Equations 4 and 5, shows the obvious dependence of the time-to-failure on the specimen geometry and size. For the purpose of illustration, we may consider the case of a large plate, containing a through-thickness crack of length $2a$, subjected to uniform tensile loading remotely from the crack in a direction normal to the crack plane. The stress intensity factor is then given by

$$K_I = \sigma \sqrt{\pi a}, \quad \sigma = \text{nominal tensile stress} \quad \textbf{(6)}$$

and

$$\frac{dK_I}{da} = \frac{\pi \sigma^2}{2K_I} \quad \textbf{(7)}$$

Thus, the time-to-failure is given by

$$t_F = \frac{2}{\pi \sigma^2} \int_{K_{Ii}}^{K_{Ic}} \frac{K_I \, dK_I}{F} \quad \textbf{(8)}$$

It is obvious that the life of the specimen (or structure) depends on the crack size for given values of the initial $K_I$. It follows, from Equations 4, 5, and 8, that for geometrically similar specimens, loaded to the same level of initial $K_I$, the larger specimen will take a longer time to reach failure.

From the foregoing discussion, it is clear that an indiscriminate choice of "cut-off" time could lead to

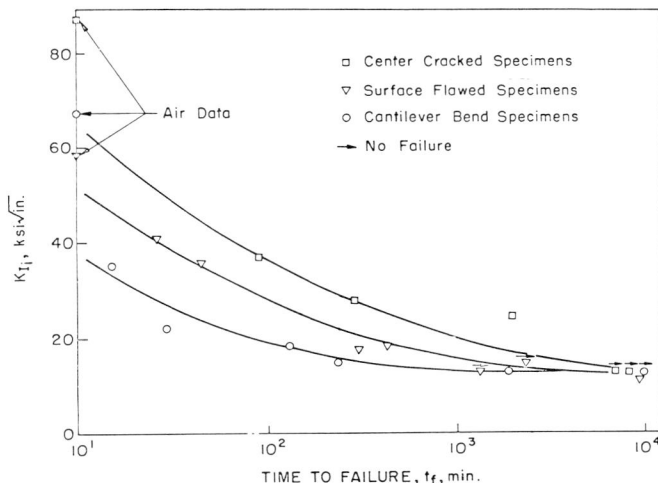

FIGURE 3 – Influence of specimen geometry on the time to failure (AISI 4340 steel).[18]

erroneous estimates of $K_{Iscc}$, (see Figure 3 also), and care must be taken in projecting service life of structures on the basis of laboratory tests. Indeed, the need to establish the functional relationship between the rate of crack growth and the mechanical and chemical processes embodied formally in Equation 2 is indicated. Further considerations will be given in Section 5.

### 3.3 Specimen Types

Various types of test specimens are being used for studying the effects of environments on subcritical-crack growth. The particular choice depends principally on the specific application. The more popular specimens are those containing surface flaws[1,2] and those containing some form of through-thickness cracks.[1] The surface-flawed specimens are primarily used for service simulation tests.[2] Because of the variation of the stress-intensity factor across the entire crack front,[6] the use of this type of specimen for basic studies in stress corrosion cracking will have limited value. In general, those specimens containing a through-thickness crack will be most suitable for use in these studies. The particular choice of a given type of specimen will depend on practical considerations of load and space requirements, availability of material, containment of test environment, etc. K calibration for the various common types of test specimens are given in ASTM STP 410 for crack-length to specimen-width ratios up to 0.6 in most cases.

### 3.4 Specimen Size Requirement

The basis and limitations in the use of the crack-tip stress-intensity factor $K_I$, based on linear elasticity, to characterize the crack-driving force has been discussed in Section 2. The validity of using such a description for a given experiment depends on our ability to fulfill the "limited plasticity" assumption experimentally, which, in practice, involves the design of test specimens such that the dimensions of the crack and the specimen are to be much larger than the size of the plastically deformed zone at the crack tip. The minimum size of the crack and other dimensions of the specimen needed to satisfy the assumption of limited plasticity cannot be predicted at present from theoretical considerations alone; it must be established, in general, by trial. However, the task of designing suitable test specimens for stress corrosion studies are greatly simplified by the results available from the work of ASTM Committee E-24 on Fracture Testing of Metals, which is embodied in ASTM STP 410.[9] Many of the considerations for the design of plane-strain fracture toughness test specimens lend themselves directly to crack growth studies. In connection with the discussion of specimen size, it is useful to keep in mind certain aspects of the crack-tip plastic zone which affect the fracture behavior of plate specimens. (The following discussion of "plane-strain versus plane-stress" follows essentially that given by Brown and Srawley.[9])

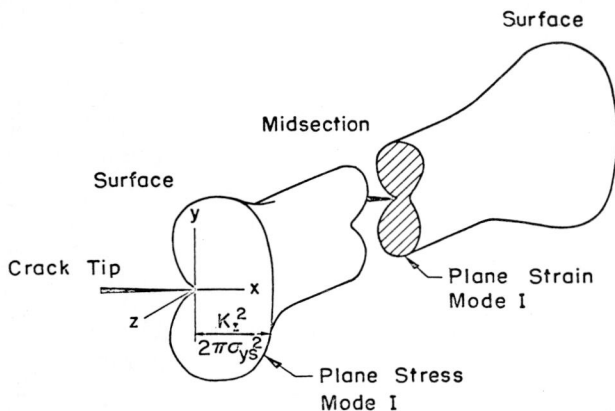

FIGURE 4 — Formal representation of plastic zone at the tip of a through-thickness crack in a plate.[9]

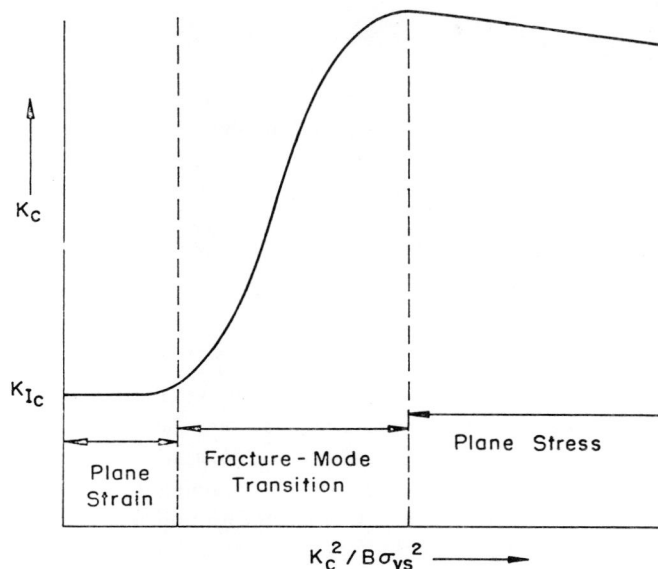

FIGURE 5 — Effect of thickness and fracture mode transition.

Figure 4 shows a formal representation of the shape of a crack-tip plastic zone in a plate-specimen, based on Mises yield limit lines for plane-stress and plane-strain as given by McClintock and Irwin.[20] The shape of the plastic zone that would be obtained by a more complicated elastic-plastic analysis would be somewhat different; the difference, however, is not important for the present discussion. In a sufficiently thick specimen, plane-strain conditions prevail in the mid-thickness region while plane-stress conditions prevail near the faces. The plastic zone extends much farther ahead of the crack near the faces than it does in the mid-thickness region, and the free surface influence extends into the thickness of the specimen for a distance which is proportional to $(K_I/\sigma_{ys})^2$, (a characteristic dimension proportional to the size of the crack-tip plastic zone), where $\sigma_{ys}$ is the uniaxial yield strength of the material. For thickness, $B \gg (K_I/\sigma_{ys})^2$, the crack-tip condition is predominantly plane-strain and the resultant fracture corresponds to that of the opening mode—plane-strain, flat fracture. It is clear that when the thickness is less than some critical value that is proportional to $(K_I/\sigma_{ys})^2$, the constraint-relieving influence of the free faces will extend entirely through the thickness. This relief of constraint tends to suppress opening-mode crack extension because of the increased possibilities of plastic deformation. The resultant fracture would be a slant or shear failure, and tending toward plane-stress. For intermediate thicknesses, the fracture is characterized by a mixture of plane-stress and plane-strain. The variation of fracture toughness, $K_c$, associated with this change is illustrated schematically in Figure 5.

The influence of fracture mode (i.e., plane-strain versus plane-stress) on subcritical crack growth has been reviewed by Johnson and Paris.[4] Available data suggest that the effect of test environment on crack growth under plane-strain and plane-stress conditions may be different. For engineering evaluation of plate materials for specific applications, the thickness of the material is usually specified. A change in the mode of fracture as the crack progresses can occur, and test results must be considered in the light of the fracture mode transition. For simplicity, for studies of the mechanisms of stress corrosion cracking and for material evaluation associated with alloy development, testing under some prescribed mode, such as plane-strain, would be desirable. The tentative recommendations given by Brown and Srawley[9] for plane-strain fracture toughness test specimens offer guidance in determining the appropriate specimen sizes for stress corrosion studies.

For valid plane-strain fracture toughness evaluation by the "pop-in" technique, Srawley and Brown[9] suggested, on the basis of experimental results, that the minimum length of the crack and the minimum thickness of the test specimen should be equal to $2.5(K_{Ic}/\sigma_{ys})^2$, where $(K_{Ic}/\sigma_{ys})^2$ is a characteristic dimension of the material, proportional to the size of the plastic zone at onset of plane-strain fracture instability. Although no specific minimum dimension for the ligament (net section or uncracked region) was indicated by their experimental results, Brown and Srawley suggested that this dimension be set equal to $2.5(K_{Ic}/\sigma_{ys})^2$ also, since the accuracy of K-calibration becomes poor for cracks greater than one-half of the width of the test specimen. Thus, the minimum thickness and crack size become $2.5(K_{Ic}/\sigma_{ys})^2$ and the specimen width, $5(K_{Ic}/\sigma_{ys})^2$.

For crack growth studies, the use of specimens with crack-length to width ratio of 1/2 is obviously inappropriate. It seems that a minimum crack length equal to $2.5(K_I/\sigma_{ys})^2$ would be a reasonable requirement; $K_I$ is the crack-tip stress intensity factor at any stage in time. For experiments where the time-to-failure is to be determined, the size of the specimen should be sufficiently large to provide valid $K_{Ic}$ or $K_c$ measurement at fracture; the crack length at fracture should not exceed 0.5 to 0.6 W (W = specimen width). Precise definition of specimen size requirements for time-to-failure experiments is difficult, since it depends very much on the test procedure employed for attaining different initial $K_I$ levels. Since the time-to-failure will be influenced by specimen size and geometry, failure time, itself, will have no fundamental value. Therefore, it would be more appropriate to consider the minimum specimen size requirement for establishing the $K_{Iscc}$ or $K_{scc}$ levels. In this respect, the dimensions of the specimen should conform to the minimum dimensions for valid fracture toughness testing. For example, in the case of plane-strain, the minimum crack length and specimen thickness requirements are $2.5 (K_{Ic}/\sigma_{ys})^2$ and the minimum specimen width $5 (K_{Ic}/\sigma_{ys})^2$.[9] For $K_{Ic}/\sigma_{ys} = 1/3$, typical of ultra-high-strength steels, these requirements become 0.3 and 0.6 inch respectively. For $K_{Ic}/\sigma_{ys} = 1$, achievable in some steels at a yield strength of 150 to 180 ksi, the requirements become 2.5 and 5 inches respectively. It is obvious that the linear-elastic fracture mechanics approach has been applied principally to studies of high strength materials of limited toughness thus far.

For crack-growth rate or kinetic studies, more definite specification of specimen size is possible For the commonly used specimens (center-cracked specimens and single-edge-cracked specimens tested in tension or bending), a starting crack length equal to 0.2 to 0.3 W would provide a reasonable range for crack growth. For a load that would produce a level of $K_I$ equal to $K_{Ic}$, for plane-strain, when the crack length a increases to 0.5 to 0.6 W, the condition that the crack length be greater than $2.5 (K_I/\sigma_{ys})^2$ is satisfied for 0.2 W $\leq$ a $\leq$ 0.6 W. Thus, for plane-strain, a specimen of W $\geq 5 (K_{Ic}/\sigma_{ys})^2$ with an initial crack length of 0.2 to 0.3 W should be adequate to cover all values of $K_I$ up to $K_{Ic}$. The specimen thickness requirement of $2.5 (K_{Ic}/\sigma_{ys})^2$ was determined on the basis of the "pop-in" criterion.[9] A somewhat thicker specimen or some artificial means, such as the use of shallow face grooves,[9,16] to suppress shear lip development may be necessary to ensure adequate constraint. It is clear that the size of specimen required for this type of investigation can, again, be large.

Considerable reduction in specimen size is possible if stress corrosion cracking experiments are carried out under cyclic (or fatigue) loads. Since the size of the crack-tip plastic-zone is proportional to $(K_I/2\sigma_{ys})^2$,[20] a factor of four reductions is possible; and since fatigue-crack growth can occur at $K_I$ levels below that for crack growth under static loads, further reductions in the specimen size may be

achieved. The use of fatigue-crack-propagation experiments to study the mechanisms for environment-enhanced crack growth may indeed be justified in certain cases. Experimental support for this viewpoint is provided by a comparison of crack growth data on high-strength steels tested under static and fatigue loads.[14,15,17,21-23] The effect of atmospheric moisture, dry and humid hydrogen at one atmosphere, on the rate of crack growth under static and fatigue loads were found to be qualitatively the same.[14,15,17,21-23] The sensitivity to moisture in some medium-carbon high-strength steels and 18Ni maraging steels as a function of microstructure and fracture toughness were also similar.[21-23] These results suggest that the mechanism for environment-enhanced crack growth under static and fatigue loads may indeed be the same; and the use of fatigue-crack propagation experiments merits consideration. It should be noted, however, that in the fatigue test results, the influence of oxygen in retarding crack growth, shown by Hancock and Johnson for static loads,[15] was not observed.

## 4. Experimental Results on 7075-T651 Aluminum Alloy

To gain additional insight into the problem of moisture-enhanced crack growth in high strength aluminum alloys, fatigue-crack propagation experiments were carried out on an 1/4-inch-thick plate of aluminum-zinc-magnesium-copper type alloy (7075-T651) recently[24] to study the effect of water, oxygen and hydrogen on the rate of fatigue-crack propagation over a range of test temperatures (295 to 380 K). Dehumidified high purity argon (99.9995 percent purity) was used as the reference dry environment. This experiment compliments the investigations of Hartman[25] and Bradshaw and Wheeler[26] carried out at room temperature.

Test results showed that water increased the rate of fatigue-crack-growth by about a factor of 10 over this range of test temperatures for crack growth rates ranging from

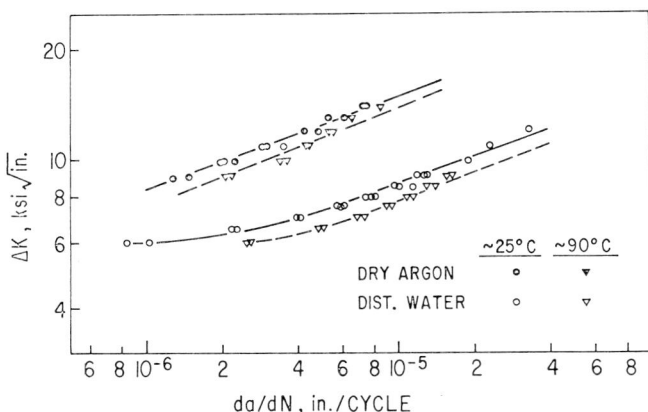

FIGURE 6 — Effect of distilled water on the rate of fatigue-crack propagation in 7075-T651 (bare) aluminum alloy.[24]

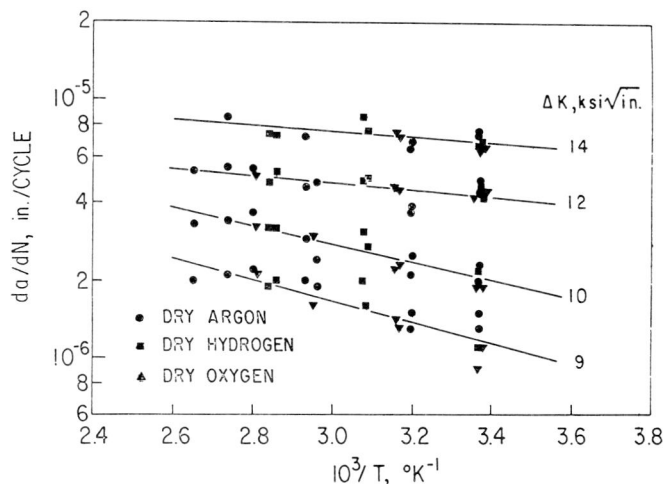

FIGURE 7 — Rate of fatigue-crack propagation in 7075-T651 (bare) aluminum alloy as a function of test temperature in the dry gaseous environments.[24]

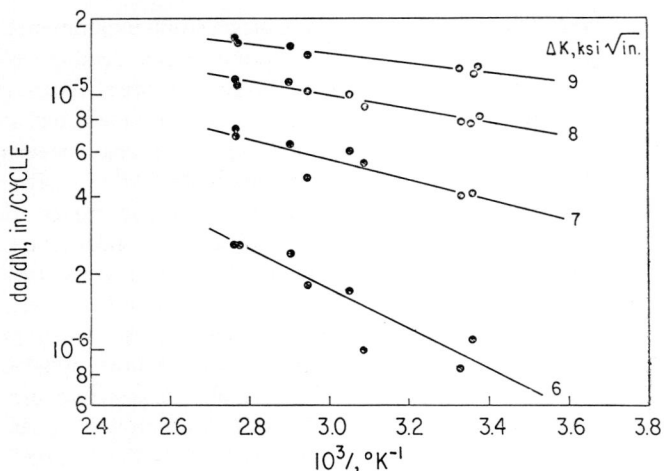

FIGURE 8 — Rate of fatigue-crack propagation in 7075-T651 (bare) aluminum alloy as a function of test temperature in distilled water.[24]

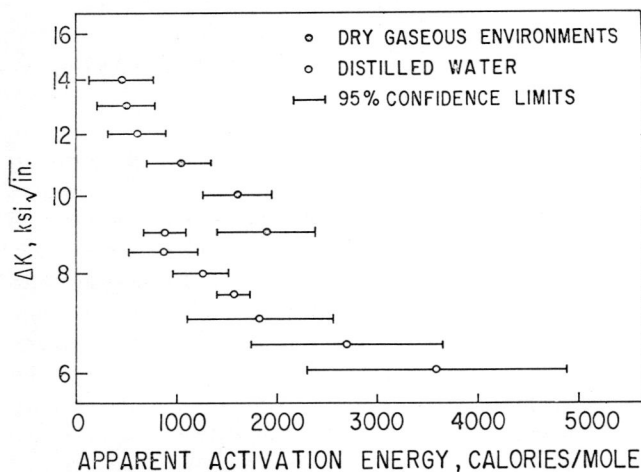

FIGURE 10 — Apparent activation energies for crack growth in distilled water and humid argon.

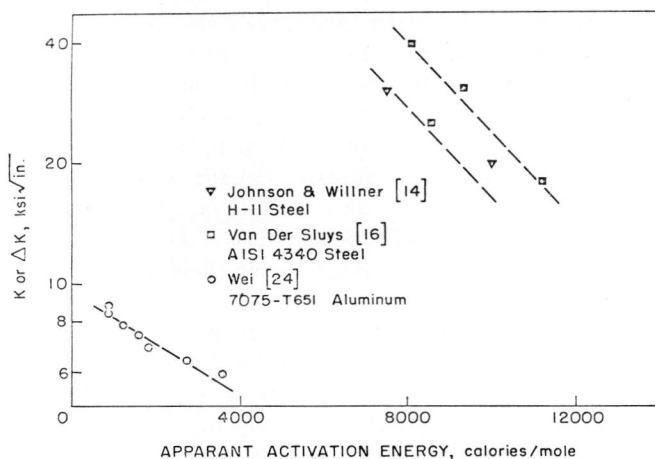

FIGURE 9 — Variation of apparent activation energy with crack-tip stress-intensity factor (7075-T651 aluminum alloy).[24]

be, in reality, associated with a transition in the mode of fracture to plane-stress, rather than being associated with the rate of diffusion of water vapor to the crack tip as suggested by Bradshaw and Wheeler.[26]

The results further indicated that fatigue-crack propagation in this aluminum alloy is controlled by thermally activated processes, both in the inert argon and in the distilled water environments (Figures 7 and 8). The apparent activation energies appear to depend strongly on the crack-tip stress intensity factor (Figure 9). This behavior is in general agreement with that suggested by Li and Johnson.[28] The rate controlling process appears to be that associated with the creation of crack surfaces.[24] However, other chemical processes, such as hydrogen diffusion, cannot be ruled out since no data are available on the activation energy for hydrogen diffusion in a high, triaxial stress field.

## 5. Some Further Discussions

In the light of these experimental results, some further considerations of existing data and the design of experiments may be given. Re-examination of the results of Van Der Sluys[16] and Johnson and Willner[14] suggests a strong dependence of the apparent activation on K (Figure 10) similar to that for the aluminum alloy.[24] In view of these results, a direct comparison of the apparent activation energy for environment-enhanced crack growth with that for some chemical process, determined under conditions of "zero" stress, as a means of identifying the mechanism for stress corrosion cracking is no longer straightforward. Although, "hydrogen embrittlement" may indeed be the mechanism for moisture-enhanced crack growth in high strength steels, additional experimental work will be necessary to confirm this point.[14,16]

The strong dependence of the apparent activation energy on K further suggests that the failure-time approach will not likely lead to an understanding of the mechanisms for stress corrosion cracking. Since the rate of crack growth

$10^{-6}$ to $3 \times 10^{-5}$ inch per cycle (Figure 6), while dry oxygen and dry hydrogen had little effect on crack growth.[24] These results are in essential agreement with the room temperature test results of Hartman[25] and Bradshaw and Wheeler,[26] and supports their contention that the mechanism for water-enhanced crack growth in high strength aluminum alloys is that of "hydrogen embrittlement" suggested by Broom and Nicholson.[27] According to this mechanism, the large acceleration in the rate of crack growth is caused by the superposition, to the crack-tip stress field, of the effect of high-pressure hydrogen gas driven into the crack-tip region by the reaction of water with the freshly created aluminum crack surface. The decreasing effectiveness of water for crack growth rates greater than $10^{-5}$ inch per cycle, shown by Hartman[25] and Bradshaw and Wheeler,[26] was not observed. Since the present results indicate a nearly constant factor of 10 increase in the rate of crack growth from $10^{-6}$ to $3 \times 10^{-5}$ inch per cycle, the decreased effectiveness of water observed by Hartman[25] and Bradshaw and Wheeler[26] may depend strongly on K (see Figure 1), the time to failure will, most likely, be dominated by the initial stage of crack growth. Thus, if an apparent activation energy is determined, it will represent some effective value, biased toward the lower K levels, and would be of little value. Therefore, experiments designed to study the kinetics of crack growth are recommended. For accurate determination of the dependence of crack growth rate on K, some arrangement for maintaining constant K over a reasonable range of crack growth will be highly desirable.[16,24]

Since stress corrosion cracking involves a complex interplay of chemical and mechanical processes, a co-ordinated analytical and experimental program will be necessary for a complete understanding of the basic mechanisms involved.

## 6. Summary

The basis and limitations for the application of linear-elastic fracture mechanics analyses to the study of environment-enhanced crack growth (stress corrosion cracking) is considered. The use of the crack-tip stress-intensity factor to characterize the crack-driving force is justified under the assumption of limited plasticity. Practical considerations of specimen design to fulfill this assumption is considered. In general, the specimen size requirements are the same as that for valid fracture toughness determination on the same material.

The use of fatigue-crack propagation studies for investigating the mechanisms of stress corrosion cracking is justified in certain cases. This approach permits appreciable reduction in the size of test specimen required. Application of this technique to the study of moisture-enhanced crack growth in a high strength aluminum alloy showed that (1) the cause for the large increase in the rate of crack growth by water is the formation of hydrogen gas with high pressure in the region ahead of the crack tip, driven in by the reaction of water with the freshly created crack surface, as suggested by Broom and Nicholson; (2) fatigue-crack propagation in water, as well as in the dry environments, is controlled by thermally activated processes, with apparent activation energies that depend strongly on the crack-tip stress-intensity factor. The rate controlling process appears to be that associated with the creation of new crack surfaces for growth rates in the range of $10^{-6}$ to $10^{-5}$ in/cycle. These results further suggest that experiments in which the rate of crack growth is determined as a function of the crack-tip stress-intensity parameter and the test environment would be more appropriate. Detailed understanding of the mechanisms of stress corrosion cracking will depend on a well coordinated analytical and experimental investigation of the mechanical and chemical processes involved.

## Acknowledgment

The author wishes to acknowledge the support of the Advanced Research Projects Agency, Department of Defense, through the Office of Naval Research under Contract Number Nonr 610(09).

## References

1. B. F. Brown and C. D. Beachem. *Corrosion Science,* 5, 745-750 (1965).
2. C. F. Tiffany and J. N. Masters. *Fracture Toughness Testing and Its Applications,* ASTM STP 381, 249-278 (1965).
3. *Fracture Toughness Testing and Its Applications,* ASTM STP 381 (1965).
4. H. H. Johnson and P. C. Paris. *Journal of Engineering Fracture Mechanics,* 1, 3-45 (1968).
5. H. R. Smith, D. E. Piper and F. K. Downey. *Journal of Engineering Fracture Mechanics,* 1, (1968).
6. P. C. Paris and G. C. Sih. *Fracture Toughness and Its Applications,* ASTM STP 381, 30-83 (1965).
7. G. R. Irwin. *Transactions, Am. Soc. Mechanical Engrs., Journal of Applied Mechanics* (1957).
8. G. R. Irwin. *Structural Mechanics,* Pergamon Press, New York, N. Y., p. 557 (1960).
9. W. F. Brown, Jr. and J. E. Srawley. *Plane Strain Crack Toughness Testing of High Strength Metallic Materials,* ASTM STP 410 (1966).
10. G. C. Sih and H. Liebowitz. *Mathematical Theory of Brittle Fracture,* forthcoming.
11. E. E. Inglis. *Transactions, Institution of Naval Architects,* (London) 60, 219 (1913).
12. H. W. Liu. *Discussion, Fracture Toughness Testing and Its Applications,* ASTM STP 381, 23 (1965).
13. G. C. Sih. *International Journal of Fracture Mechanics,* 4 (1968).
14. H. H. Johnson and A. M. Willner. *Applied Materials Research,* 34 (1965).
15. G. G. Hancock and H. H. Johnson. *Trans. Metallurgical Society AIME* (1966) April.
16. W. A. Van Der Sluys. *Mechanisms of Environment Induced Subcritical Flaw Growth in AISI 4340 Steel.* T. and A.M. Report No. 292, University of Illinois (1966) September.
17. R. P. Wei, P. M. Talda and Che-Yu Li. *Fatigue Crack Propagation,* ASTM STP 415, 460-485 (1967).
18. B. F. Brown and C. D. Beachem. *Specimens for Evaluating the Susceptibility of High Strength Steels to Stress Corrosion Cracking,* Internal Report, U. S. Naval Research Laboratory (1966).
19. E. A. Steigerwald. *Proc. ASTM,* 60, 750 (1960).
20. F. A. McClintock and G. R. Irwin. *Fracture Toughness Testing and Its Applications,* ASTM STP 381, 84 (1965).
21. G. L. Hanna, A. R. Troiano and E. A. Steigerwald. *Trans. ASM,* 57, 658 (1964).
22. G. L. Hanna and E. A. Steigerwald. *Influence of Environment on Crack Propagation and Delayed Failure in High Strength Steels.* Technical Documentary Report No. RTD-TDR-63-4225, Air Force Materials Laboratory (1964) January.
23. W. A. Spitzig, P. M. Talda and R. P. Wei. *Journal of Engineering Fracture Mechanics,* 1, 155 (1968).
24. R. P. Wei. *International Journal of Fracture Mechanics,* 4 (1968).
25. A. Hartman. *International Journal of Fracture Mechanics,* 1, 167 (1965).
26. F. J. Bradshaw and C. Wheeler. *Applied Materials Research,* 5, 112 (1966).
27. T. Broom and A. J. Nicholson. *Journal Institution of Metals,* 89, 183 (1960).
28. Che-Yu Li and H. H. Johnson. *Kinetics of Sub-Critical Crack Growth on High Strength Materials,* Report No. 756, The Materials Research Center, Cornell University, (1967) Aug. 15.

# Discussion

**J. C. Scully, University of Leeds, Leeds, England:**

Dr. Wei has pointed out some limitations of this approach insofar as we cannot use ductile materials. This is a severe limitation since many of the materials that are susceptible to stress corrosion fall into this category.

My criticism of the fracture mechanics approach goes deeper than that, however. It is indeed a very indirect approach. Fracture mechanics is concerned with comparatively large scale parameters whereas the fundamental mechanism of stress corrosion must involve detailed and complex interaction of metal and environments at the tip of a crack. For example, at this conference we have been discussing Professor Uhlig's stress sorption mechanism, Dr. Pickering's preferential dissolution results, and Dr. Pugh's tarnish film rupture. Fracture mechanics cannot contribute to these discussions.

The prefatigued notch bar test is helpful in screening alloys but can offer no explanation. It has been shown[1] that titanium alloys having identical $K_{Ic}$ values exhibit a wide range of $K_{Iscc}$ values. Even different heats of one alloy exhibit different $K_{Iscc}$ values.[1] This is because of the microstructural dependence of stress corrosion processes. Unless these atomistic processes are examined and understood no fundamental mechanism can be elicited.

It is worth observing also that $K_{Iscc}$ values provide poor design criteria since the K values for corrosion fatigue are lower.

I would conclude by emphasizing how limited are the applications of fracture mechanics to a basic understanding: (a) because its use is restricted to high strength alloys, and (b) because its approach is so indirect. Stress corrosion studies are sadly lacking in quantitative data. Because fracture mechanics provide lots of numbers we must be careful in judging how meaningful they are.

1. M. H. Peterson, B. F. Brown, R. L. Newbegin, and R. E. Groover. *Corrosion*, **23**, 142 (1967).

**Martin J. Blackburn, Boeing Scientific Research Laboratory:**

One gets the general impression at this conference that people are proposing models for stress corrosion cracking in which the stress (or strain) conditions are purely incidental. The methods of fracture mechanics may provide some insight into the analysis of the mechanical factors. However, in most cases, cracks are propagating through plastically deforming material and thus the problem is more complex than the elastic solutions used predominately at this time.

**R. P. Wei:**

The author appreciates the discussions by Drs. Scully and Blackburn. In his criticism, Dr. Scully appears to have missed the essential point in the fracture mechanics approach to stress corrosion cracking and other fracture studies. The aim of fracture mechanics analyses is to provide a quantitative description of the stresses and strains in the neighborhood of the crack-tip which is of direct importance to the understanding of the fundamental mechanism of stress corrosion cracking. Of course the use of a linear elastic analysis for the case of real materials which must deform plastically near the crack tip is subjected to certain restrictions. The author has attempted to point out these limitations and provide justification for the use of the stress-intensity factor K, based on linear elasticity, as a "crack driving force" term in his paper.

Criticism of some practitioners of fracture mechanics in the stress corrosion cracking area for not having devoted sufficient attention to the corrosion aspects of the problem may be justified. It would be equally appropriate to apply this criticism in reverse to the stress corrosion people as indicated by Dr. Blackburn's remark that "people are proposing models for stress corrosion cracking in which the stress (or strain) conditions are purely incidental". In many of the experimental investigations on "the fundamental mechanisms of stress corrosion cracking", small test specimens loaded to some average stress level were used. Since the average stress does not really represent the stresses near the crack tip where corrosion and further crack growth takes place, quantitative characterization of the various "mechanisms" would not be possible.

In essence, the author only wishes to emphasize that real progress toward a quantitative understanding of the mechanism of stress corrosion cracking can be achieved only if one meticulously define and control both the chemical and mechanical variables involved. In this regard the author agrees with Dr. Blackburn that, even though the use of fracture mechanics analyses based on linear elasticity as a basis for treating the mechanical aspects of the problem is less than ideal, useful insight into the stress corrosion cracking problem may be obtained if the limitations of these analyses are carefully observed in their application.

Regarding $K_{Iscc}$, the author would tend to agree with Dr. Scully that it is of questionable value in design when fatigue loading is involved. $K_{Iscc}$, in practice, serves only as a convenient (and inexpensive) measure of stress corrosion susceptibility.

# A NOTE ON AN ELECTRON THEORY CONCEPT OF STRESS CORROSION[1]

George Martin
North American Rockwell Corp.

We have recently carried out some experiments on the effects of electron transport through surface layers on surface sensitive properties. This transport was achieved through an ionized atmospheric environment. We tested the stress corrosion resistance of salt coated titanium 8-1-1 alloy at 1000 F[1] and the fatigue life of nickel at 1500 F.[2] In these tests the ionized environment was obtained by surrounding the cylindrical specimen with a platinum Faraday cage kept at a positive or negative potential of about 1000 V/cm relative to the specimen. Additional ionization, in some cases, was obtained by placing the test apparatus in a radiation proof chamber and exposing it to a 25,000 Curie cobalt 60 source. The degree of ionization could be estimated from the current flowing between the Faraday cage and the specimen. All specimens were loaded in torsion under either a steady load for stress corrosion or a cyclic load for fatigue. The experimental device is shown in Figure 1; in this figure the loading device, placed on top, is not shown. Some of the results of the stress corrosion tests, at a stress of 38,400 psi (shear) are shown in Figure 2. The relationship obtained between the space charge current and the fatigue life is shown in Figure 3. The pattern of Figure 2 is typical of an anodic protection system. Important here is that this protection has been achieved with charge densities of about $10^{-9}$ amps/cm$^2$.

Beck[3] calculates that currents of several orders of magnitude larger would be required to affect surface reactions in titanium alloy cracks. Ripling[4] indeed shows that very large currents do inhibit cracking in titanium. However, judging by the effects of the very small current, it appears here that the imposition of a current flow affects some phenomena additional to the surface reactions.

The results of the study of the effect of space charge currents on fatigue cracking also indicate an effect of space charges. Here the primary effect is not one of anodic protection, but presumably an effect on the oxidation rate. Fromhold[5-7] and Fromhold and Cook[8] have shown that space charges affect oxidation rates through modification of the diffusion coefficients. This applies particularly to semi-conductor types of oxides, such as the p-type nickel oxide. The simplest diffusion equation, considering such charges, is

$$J = \mu\, CE - D\, dc/dx$$

where $\mu$ is the mobility, C the charge/carrier, E the charge and the remainder the usual Fick's Law. As a first

---

[1]Ed Note: This paper deviates considerably from the normal interpretations of stress corrosion cracking. During the meeting there was not sufficient time for oral discussion and none is included herein. The essential experimental finding, upon which a proposed theory is based, involves perceptible changes in the stress corrosion behavior as a result of space charge currents. While these effects may be interpreted in terms of electron theory, they may also be interpreted in terms of effects of current transport on the oxide properties. The plasticity of oxides is well known to be affected by dynamic electron transport through the film.

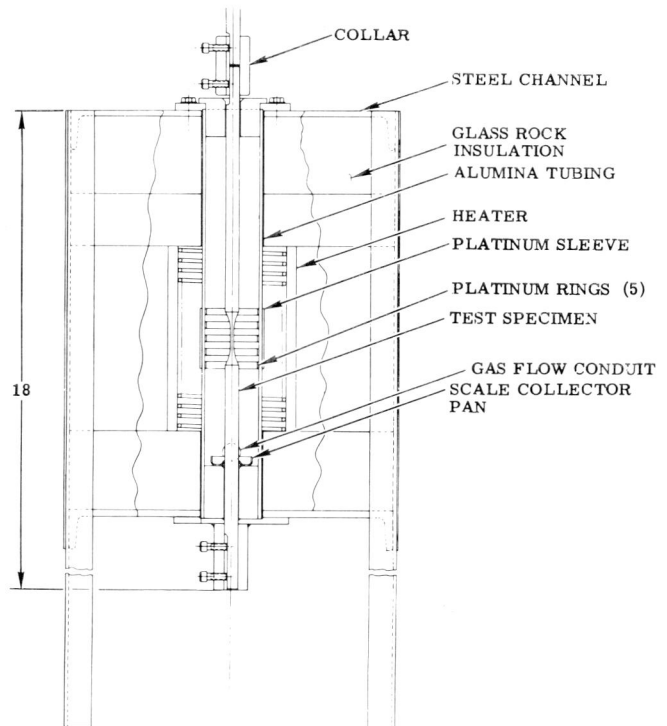

FIGURE 1 — Specimen charging and holding device.

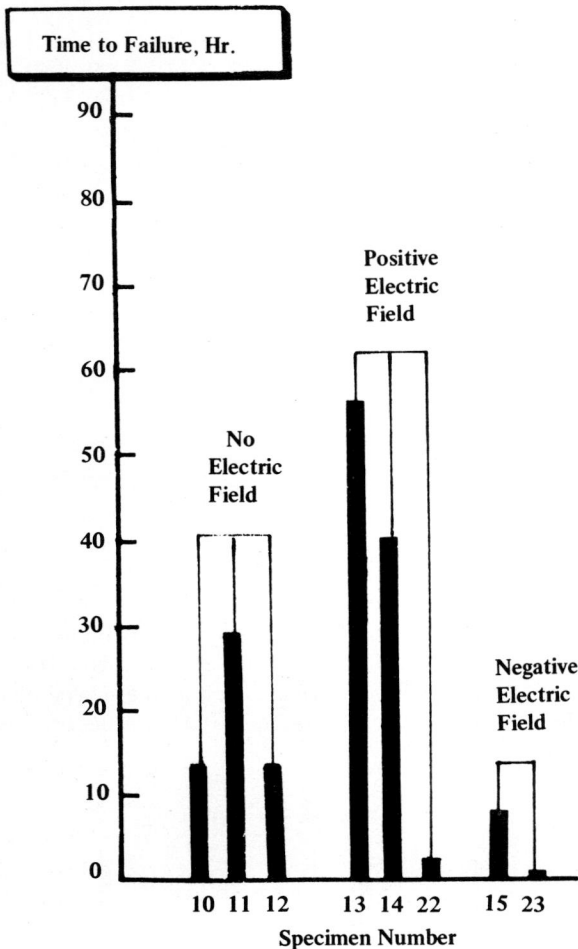

FIGURE 2 — Time to failure of titanium 8-1-1 specimens at 1000 F and 38,400 psi shear load as affected by electric field.

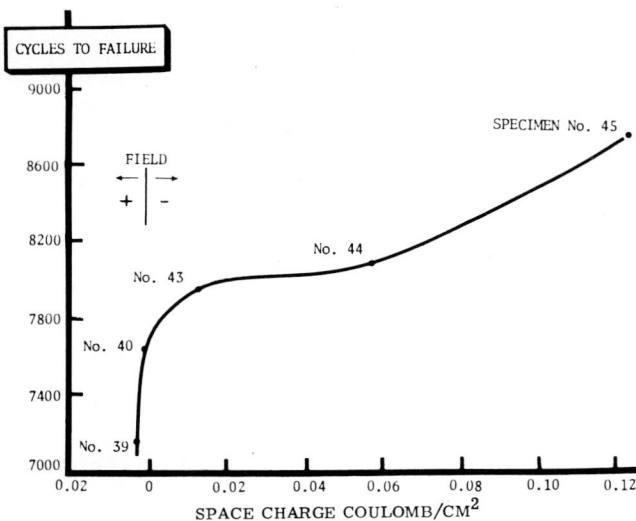

FIGURE 3 — Effect of space charge on fatigue life of nickel at 1500 F.

approximation, charge current and effects on diffusion rates are linear. However, the results show an apparent behavior, especially with small currents, which is not linear. Here again, the possibility of some additional factors cannot be eliminated.

The above experiments were some studies carried out to determine whether a concept involving electron theory of surface crack formation might be tenable.

The current concepts of stress corrosion mechanisms appear to fall into one of two broad categories. Either they are based on electrochemical principles or they are based on solid state phenomena, such as relate to crack formation, within the alloy. It is suggested here that a possible mechanism exists which connects these approaches and allows their co-ordination. Such a concept must be based on a scale including both approaches. Such a scale exists if we consider the potential mechanism in terms of the interface electron transport phenomena.

We have to accept the fact that conduction electrons in a metal do not form a uniform or uniformly distorted field. The actual field is distorted locally due to line and point defects and the resulting perturbations or space charges are likely to affect electron movement throughout a relatively extensive area. The existence of such perturbation is being increasingly acknowledged, as is the present inability of the quantum mechanics approach to analyze them (e.g., Petty[9] or Pippard[10]). However, a number of attempts at solving these problems are now being made. Prange and Sachs simulate an electron-lattice system by a set of interacting quasi-particles, which appears more amenable to analysis, at least under isotropic conditions. Mann[12] estimates the effects of point defects and Podor[13] the effects of edge dislocations. Klotzman et al[14] give an expression for a space charge due to a vacancy and Gilman[15] suggests a moving dislocation viewed as an electron tunneling process. Experimental evidence on the effect of electron perturbations due to lattice dislocations and their movements come from a large number of studies on the effects of point and line defects and of stress on electric conductivity. The latter are particularly significant here, as they suggest a direct relationship between dislocation movement and electron mobility in metals. Additional experimental evidence supporting the equivalence of travelling dislocations and electron movement are data on the phenomenon on exo-electrons. Krogstad and Moss[16] have concluded that these electrons can only be due to the release from the metal surface of electrons carried there by travelling stress induced dislocations.

Once we can express defect movements in terms of electron energy dynamics, the phenomena associated with these movements can be balanced against the energies of the various other, already established, surface reactions. We could, then, write an energy balance for the total local surface energy $F_s$:

$$F_s = F_d + F_c + F_t + F_g + F_a + F_x + F_w$$

which includes the following terms: $F_d$ is the energy associated with a point or line defect; $F_c$ is the energy of the basic chemical reaction, including ionization potentials; $F_t$ is a surface tension energy; $F_g$ secondary surface potential energies caused by local concentration gradients; $F_a$ energies due to adsorption or chemisorption factors; $F_w$ work function; and $F_x$ an energy which may be an externally applied voltage.

In this equation, the terms $F_d$ and $F_t$ are the terms of the energy balance generally considered in solid state mechanics approaches, $F_c$, $F_g$, $F_a$ and $F_x$ are the terms familiar through the electrochemists. A measure of the feasibility of such an equation would be the result of an examination of the order of magnitude of the various terms, particularly of those related to the electron perturbation associated with point or line defects.

No accurate calculation of line or point defect associated electron perturbation energies can as yet be made. However, an order of magnitude estimate could be obtained from the strain energy associated with various defects. For a straight dislocation in an isotropic medium for the most unfavorable case of alignment of the Burgers vector with the dislocation axis, the strain energy is given as[17]

$$F_d = G\,b^2\,L\,\ln\,(1/\sqrt{d}\,b)/4\pi(1 - \nu)$$

where G is the shear modulus, b the Burgers vector, L the total dislocation length, d the dislocation density and $\nu$ the Poisson ratio. For typical metals, $F_d$ is of the order of a few eV/atom plane. Vacancy defect formation or migration energies are also of the order of 0.1-2 eV.[18] These orders of magnitude compare well with those available for the other energy terms. Chemical reaction energies are of the order of

10m - 200 Kcals/mole or about 0.4-8 eV/molecule. If ionization of metal atoms are involved, these energies are somewhat higher, perhaps 5-10 eV for the first stage of ionization.[19] Energies due to local concentrations are probably of the order of concentration change, if only solid solutions are involved. Surface energies are of the order of 1000 dynes/cm or 0.405 eV/atom on the surface. Adsorption and chemisorption energies are also of the same order as those of chemical reactions, i.e., perhaps 0.3 eV/atom site. The work function is of the order of 2 to 4 eV.

From a point of view of feasibility of balance, therefore, the terms in the energy equation are of the same order of magnitude. The most varied terms appear to be those connected with the energies of chemical reactions, which agrees with the general observation that corrosion, i.e., the chemical reactions, play a major role in stress corrosion. It must be emphasized that here we are no longer dealing with an overall or continuum approach, but with surface energy balances over very small areas, such as the area of the energy field surrounding a particular atom. Only if that limitation is realized, does an electron theory concept become feasible.

A full quantitative treatment would require considerable advances in state knowledge of the electron theory in metals generally. So far, relatively few electron physicists have dealt with the problems of surface reactions as involved in SCC. SCC problems are approached by chemists and metallurgists using classical methods and concepts. It is suggested that here is a field of immense and practical importance worthy of a true interdisciplinary approach.

# References

1. G. Martin and S. Tsang. U. S. Air Force Conference on Corrosion, Denver, 1967.
2. G. Martin and S. Tsang. U. S. Air Force Symposium on Nucleonics, Columbus, Ohio, 1967.
3. T. R. Beck. International Symposium on Stress Corrosion 1967.
4. E. J. Ripling et al. Final Report NASA Contract NASr-50, November, 1965.
5. A. T. Fromhold. *Phys. Chem. Solids*, **24**, 1081 (1963).
6. A. T. Fromhold, *J. Chem. Phys.*, **24**, 1309 (1963).
7. A. T. Fromhold. *J. Chem. Phys.*, **41**, 509 (1964).
8. A. T. Fromhold and E. L. Cook. *Phys. Rev.*, **158**, 600 (1967).
9. E. R. Petty. *Metallurgia*, 12 (1964) July.
10. A. B. Pippard. *The Dynamics of Conduction Electrons*, Gordon and Breach, N. Y., 1965.
11. R. E. Prange and A. Sachs. *Phys. Rev.*, **158**, 672 (1967).
12. E. Mann. *Phys. Stat. Sol.*, **13**, 293 (1966) and **11**, 753, 765 (1965).
13. B. Podor. *Phys. Stat. Sol.*, **16**, K 167 (1966).
14. S. M. Klotzman, A. N. Timofeev and I. S. Trakhtenberg. *Phys. Stat. Sol.*, **18**, 847 (1966).
15. J. J. Gilman. Tech. Rep. ONR Contract 3985(06), October, 1966.
16. R. S. Krogstad and R. W. Moss. 6th Symposium of NDT and Physics, Dayton, 1965.
17. D. Kuhlman-Wilsdorf. *Physical Metallurgy*, Interscience, 627 (1965).
18. J. Takamura. *Physical Metallurgy*, Interscience, 700 (1965).
19. E. U. Condon. *Handbook of Physics*, McGraw-Hill, 7-21 (1958).

# PART II

# HOMOGENEOUS NOBLE METAL ALLOYS

# EVALUATION OF SESSION ON Cu, Ag, AND Au ALLOYS

E. N. Pugh and A. J. Forty

The session can be divided into two sections:

## 1. Failure of Cu-Base Alloys in Aq. NH₃

No general agreement was reached concerning the mechanism of failure, nor was it agreed whether a single mechanism is applicable to both tarnishing and non-tarnishing conditions or whether different mechanisms are operative. The oxide-rupture model, again put forward for tarnishing conditions, was not seriously challenged, but on the other hand no new evidence was presented in support of the model.

It was evident that several major questions remain to be answered concerning the oxide-rupture model. For example, the details of the actual film-rupture process remain to be established. In their papers, Forty and Vermilyea assumed that massive glide in the substrate was responsible for rupture of the film. However, Pugh et al questioned whether such glide could occur during crack propagation, and suggested alternatively that the film failed in a brittle fashion when a critical film thickness was attained.

The mechanism of tarnish growth also remains to be established, and, in addition, there is no data available on the kinetics of the oxide-growth process. It is interesting to note that as a result of discussions during the Conference, Pugh et al at RIAS and Booker at Sir John Cass College have agreed to study the growth kinetics using the same alloys but using different methods (ellipsometry and cathodic reduction, respectively).

In non-tarnishing conditions the position is somewhat similar. It appears to be established that cupric-ammonia complex ions are necessary to cause cracking but their role is still in doubt. Pugh et al suggested that cracking proceeds by a dissolution reaction of the type

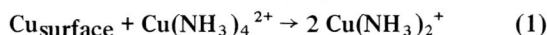

$$Cu_{surface} + Cu(NH_3)_4^{2+} \rightarrow 2\ Cu(NH_3)_2^+ \qquad (1)$$

On the other hand, Uhlig proposed that failure resulted from the adsorption of the cupric complexes at the crack tip, causing a reduction in bond strength.

A major issue to be clarified concerns the behavior of pure copper in non-tarnishing solutions. Pugh et al and Graf both reported that SCC occurred in these solutions (but not in tarnishing solutions), whereas other workers (Booker and Blackwood) observed no cracking in the case of the pure metal. From a mechanistic point of view, it is important to resolve this question, since several models are based on the presence of solute atoms. Note that Reaction (1) does not involve solute atoms. A further point to be clarified is the observed dependence of the path of cracking in non-tarnishing solutions on the dislocation structure of the alloys.

## 2. Failure of Cu-Au and Ag-Au Alloys in Aqueous Ferric Chloride and in Aqua Regia

There appeared to be general agreement that the basic cause of failure in these cases is the preferential dissolution of the less-noble component, resulting in the formation of a gold-rich surface layer. At the same time, the details of the dissolution process remain to be established, as evidenced by the discussion following Pickering's talk.

The precise mechanism of stress-corrosion cracking in these systems received little attention. The model of Swann et al involving the formation of tubular corrosion pits remains a candidate. However, according to Graf, cracking proceeds by continuous anodic dissolution at the crack tip, the faces the crack being protected by the presence of the gold-rich phase. It is evident that critical experiments are necessary to distinguish between these and other models.

# THE STRESS-CORROSION CRACKING OF COPPER, SILVER, AND GOLD ALLOYS

E. N. Pugh, J. V. Craig, and A. J. Sedriks
Research Institute for Advanced Studies
(Martin Marietta Corporation)

## I. Introduction

Despite the equivalence implied in the title, the published literature, and hence this review, is largely concerned with the failure of the copper alloys. Silver alloys, notably the binary Ag-Au system, have received some attention, but there appears to be no evidence that gold-base alloys, i.e., those containing > 50 at.% Au, are susceptible to stress-corrosion cracking.

The literature associated with the stress-corrosion cracking of copper alloys is vast—for example, the bibliography compiled by Rask[1] contains 642 references covering the period 1886-1961—so that any review paper must necessarily be selective. The mechanistic theme of this conference immediately eliminates many of the papers. In addition, the failure of the brasses, which forms a large part of the literature, was extensively reviewed by Bailey[2] in 1961, so that detailed discussion relating to these alloys can be concentrated on the more recent literature. Moreover, the paper by Graf in this volume[3] reviews much of his considerable work in this area and hence it is sufficient to summarize his views here. In addition to these restrictions, it was found that limiting the review to single-phase alloys led to no significant reduction in the volume of interpretable data. Similarly, the environments considered can be limited to several main types.

For the purpose of discussing the major mechanisms which have been proposed, it is convenient to divide the paper into the following sections:

(1) the failure of alpha-phase copper alloys in aqueous ammonia.

(2) the failure of Cu-Au and Ag-Au alloys in aqueous ferric chloride and in aqua regia.

(3) the failure of beta brasses in the presence of water vapor.

Before considering these failures, however, it is useful to discuss the relevant physical metallurgy of the various alloys, with particular regard to their dislocation structures.

## II. Structure and Mechanical Behavior of Alloys

### A. Face Centered Cubic (FCC) Alloys

The FCC alloys considered in Sections III and IV are mainly Cu-Zn, Cu-Al, Cu-Ni, Cu-Au, and Ag-Au. In the absence of embrittling environments, these alloys are ductile at room temperature, glide occurring on the close-packed $\{111\}$ planes in the $\langle110\rangle$ directions.

For the Cu-Zn system, the primary alpha solid solution based on copper is stable at room temperature up to $\sim 37$ wt.% Zn.[4] There is no evidence for long-range order (LRO) in the alpha alloys, but stored-energy measurements by Clarebrough et al[5] indicated that short-range order (SRO) exists in alloys containing > 20 wt.% Zn. The presence of SRO in a lattice is believed to make initial dislocation motion more difficult,[6] and Forty[7] has suggested that this effect may be responsible for a low initial yield rate in the alpha-brasses.

Transmission electron microscopy by Swann and Nutting[8] has shown that the dislocation structure of the deformed alpha-brasses is dependent on the solute content. In the pure metal and in dilute alloys, the dislocations form a "cellular" structure, Figure 1(a), typical of materials which can readily cross-glide, while in alloys containing > $\sim$ 18 wt.% Zn the dislocations tend to be confined to their glide planes, thus forming "planar" arrays, Figure 1(b). From the standpoint of mechanical behavior, the significance of the planar arrays is that localized stress concentrations can be produced when dislocations within such arrays become "piled up" at obstacles, as shown in Figure 1(b).

From the measurements of the radius of curvature of extended dislocation nodes, Howie and Swann[11] have shown that the stacking-fault energy (SFE) of the alpha-brasses decreases with increasing Zn content, Figure 2. The transition from cellular to planar dislocation structures may be due to this reduction in SFE, since it becomes increasingly difficult to constrict the extended dislocations formed in the alloys of low SFE and hence cross-glide becomes increasingly difficult.[12] On the other hand, Kear and Wilsdorf[13] have pointed out that the presence of SRO may also lead to planar glide. They argued that the passage

118

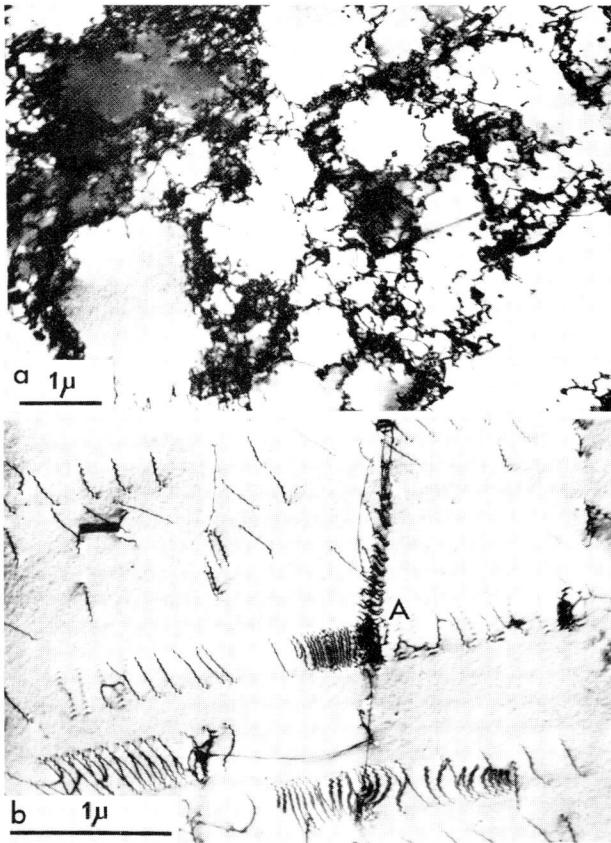

FIGURE 1 — Transmission electron micrographs illustrating: (a) The cellular dislocation structure in pure copper. After Swann.[9] (b) Planar dislocation arrays in an alpha-brass containing ~30 wt.% Zn; note the dislocation pile-ups at A where two slip bands have intersected. After Segall.[10]

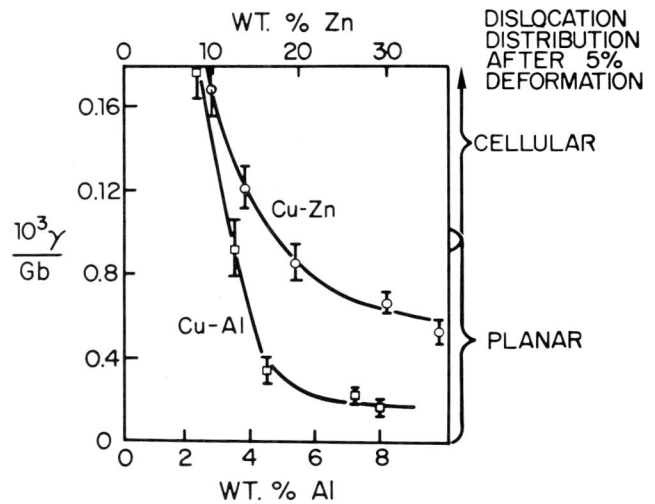

FIGURE 2 — Effects of solute concentration on the stacking-fault energy $\gamma$ (in units of $10^{-3}$ Gb) and dislocation structure of Cu-Zn and Cu-Al alloys. After Howie and Swann.[11]

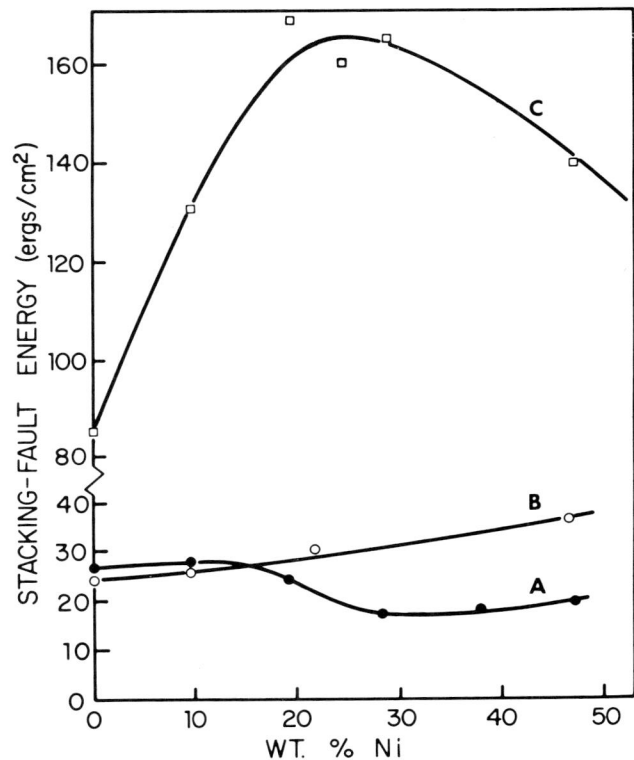

FIGURE 3 — Effect of Ni content on the stacking-fault energy of Cu-Ni alloys. A. After Henderson.[16] B. After Nakajima and Numakura.[17] C. After Harris et al.[18]

of one or two dislocations over the glide plane destroys local order across that plane, so that other dislocations can follow the same path with less difficulty, thus favoring planar configurations.

For the Cu-Al alloys, the primary alpha-phase extends to ~9.5 wt.% Al.[4] As in the case of the Cu-Zn alloys, the dislocation distribution changes from cellular to planar with increasing Al content, the transition occurring at ~3.5 wt.% Al.[8] The addition of Al also causes a reduction in SFE,[11] Figure 2, and it appears that the change in dislocation structure must be attributed to this effect, since there is no evidence for ordering in the alpha-phase.

Both Cu-Ni[4] and Ag-Au[14] exhibit continuous alpha solid solutions. Electron-microscope studies by Ohtani and Dodd[15] have shown that only cellular dislocation structures are formed in the latter, but the structures in the case of Cu-Ni do not appear to have been studied directly. However, several workers have determined the effect of Ni content on SFE, using either X-ray diffraction[16,17] or texture methods.[18] While agreement between the measured values is poor, Figure 3, none of the data reveals a decrease in SFE with increasing solute concentration, and thus, by comparison with the data for Cu-Zn and Cu-Al, Figure 2,

the dislocation distribution would be expected to be cellular for all compositions.

In the case of Cu-Au, the primary alpha solid solution exhibits LRO at compositions above 40 wt.% Au, the $Cu_3Au$ superlattice being obtained at ~51 wt.% Au on cooling below 390 C.[14] Pickering and Swann[19] have shown

119

that fully ordered $Cu_3Au$ may be obtained by annealing for several days at temperatures just below 390 C and slowly cooling to room temperature; the ordered structure was found to contain antiphase domain boundaries. Rapid quenching from temperatures above 390 C was shown to suppress the LRO reaction, retaining the disordered FCC structure.

The dislocation distribution in deformed Cu-Au alloys has been examined by several investigators.[9,13,19,20] Pickering and Swann[19] found that a cellular structure typical of pure copper was retained in alloys containing $< \sim 15$ wt.% Au. Planar arrays were found in quenched (disordered) $Cu_3Au$,[9,13,19] Figure 4(a), and, in view of the apparent high SFE in this material,[9,13] Kear and Wilsdorf[13] concluded that the presence of SRO is responsible for the planar arrays, as discussed above for the case of alpha-brass.

The motion of a dislocation through an ordered $Cu_3Au$ lattice creates an antiphase boundary in its wake, and, to minimize the energy associated with such boundaries, dislocations have been observed[9,20,22,23] to move in pairs of like sign connected by a strip of antiphase boundary, so that the trailing dislocations recreate the original ordered structure. Such pairs of dislocations are termed "super-lattice dislocations".[21] It is unlikely that the associated pair can cross-glide, since this would require the second dislocation to follow exactly in the wake of the first[21] and thus it might be expected that planar glide would occur, giving rise to planar dislocation arrays of the type observed in alpha-brass, Figure 1(b). However, electron-microscope studies indicated that the dislocations are randomly distributed,[9,20] Figure 4(b). At the same time, this structure differs from the cellular structure, cf. Figures 1(a) and 4(b), in that the dislocations frequently exhibit straight segments lying along <110> directions in screw configuration.[9] The origin of this structure is not fully understood, although tentative models have been put forward.[20]

### B. Beta-Brass

The beta-brasses, containing 46.6-50.6 wt.% Zn, normally possess an ordered structure at room temperature, namely the $L2_0$ superlattice.[4] The disordered $\beta$-phase (BCC) is stable at elevated temperatures, but on cooling it undergoes the ordering reaction $\beta \rightarrow \beta'$ at about 460 C. Unlike the case of $Cu_3Au$ discussed above, the ordering reaction cannot be suppressed by quenching. However, the ordered $\beta'$-phase is in fact metastable, and, in particular, can be decomposed by severe strain at room temperature, producing a martensitic phase.[24] Again in contrast to $Cu_3Au$, the $\beta'$-phase does not contain a domain structure as a result of the ordering reaction.[25]

Unlike disordered BCC metals, which generally exhibit wavy glide, i.e., glide on several planes of the <111> zones, room-temperature glide in beta-brass is confined to $\{110\}$ planes, being characterized by straight slip lines in parallel sets or in angular patterns.[26-28] At high strains ($> 5\%$), deformation bands are produced.[26,27,29] Bands of this type are a common feature of easy glide in cubic crystals,

and are considered to result from the interaction of arrays of edge dislocations of opposite sign on parallel glide planes.[30,31]

The occurrence of $\{110\}$ glide and the formation of straight slip steps probably results from the existence of superlattice dislocations, connected by $\{110\}$ antiphase boundaries. This is supported by the analysis by Flinn[25] which indicates that (110) is the plane of lowest anti-phase-boundary energy for screw dislocations, and by the electron-microscope studies of Swann[9] which were claimed to have provided direct evidence for superlattice dislocations in this material. However, more detailed studies by Head et al[32] have cast some doubt on the latter observation. These workers found that about 90% of the dislocations present in their foils were close to screw orientation, gliding on $\{110\}$. However, they were unable to determine unambiguously whether these were single dislocations of <111> Burgers vector, or whether they consisted of a closely-spaced pair of superlattice dislocations, each of $1/2$ <111> Burgers vector.

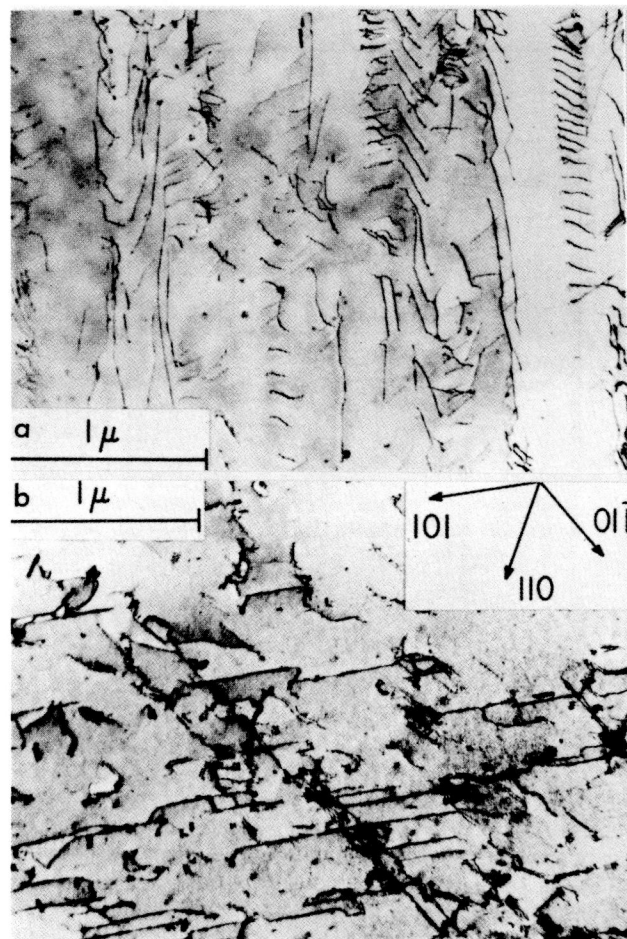

FIGURE 4 — Transmission electron micrographs illustrating the dislocation structures of $Cu_3Au$ after 5% elongation. (a) Disordered. (b) Ordered. After Swann.[9] Note that the dislocations in (b) consist of closely spaced superlattice pairs but these cannot be resolved at this magnification.

The mechanical properties of the single phase binary $\beta'$ alloys have been determined by Bailey.[33] It was shown that in dry air yield occurs at a tensile stress of about 10,000 psi, and fracture at about 75,000 psi, with a maximum elongation of 40%. In constant load tests, also in dry air, these alloys failed by creep rupture at stresses of about 80% of the ultimate tensile stress, but not at stresses substantially below this. Fracture in both tensile and creep tests were found to be transcrystalline. However, failure in the former occurred by cleavage without necking, while in the latter the specimens failed in a ductile fashion. Thus it appears that the fracture mode in dry air is sensitive to strain rate.

Strengthening of the binary alloys may be accomplished by alloying with Al, Mn, Fe, Sn, and Ni, in individual quantities not exceeding 5 wt.%,[34,35] and Zr and Ti in quantities not exceeding 0.4 wt.%.[36] These additions may increase the 0.1% proof and ultimate stresses by factors of 6 and 2 (max), respectively, and may cause a four-fold reduction in tensile elongation.[34-36] The grain size of the complex alloys is generally an order of magnitude lower than that of the binary, and second phases rich in Fe, Ti and Zr, in addition to the Cu-Zn $\gamma$ phase, may be observed, predominantly at the grain boundaries.[34-36]

## III. Failure of Alpha-Phase Copper Alloys in Aqueous Ammonia

### A. Failure of Alpha-Brasses

The failure of alpha-brasses in ammoniacal environments represents the classical example of stress-corrosion cracking. Commonly referred to as season-cracking,[2] this phenomenon has been recognized as a serious practical problem for over 60 years.[37,38] A notable feature of the failure is the specific nature of the environment. Traditionally, it has been considered that the failure requires the presence of ammonia (or certain ammonia derivatives),[2] although more recent work suggests that cracking of alpha-brass can also occur in aqueous solutions containing either nitric acid or cupric nitrate,[39,40] and in certain aqueous citrate or tartrate solutions.[41] In addition to ammonia, the occurrence of cracking requires the presence of moisture,[42] and, although this has not been as conclusively established, it will be seen below, III.A.3, that oxygen is also necessary.

In view of the obvious importance of chemical considerations in this problem, it is worthwhile to begin by discussing this aspect.

### 1. Chemistry of the System

Consider first the behavior of pure copper in aqueous ammonia. The presence of oxygen in solution is necessary for dissolution, and it is generally considered[43-45] that the overall reaction is

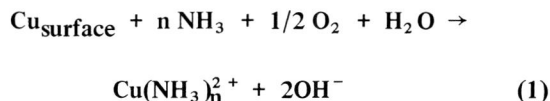

$$Cu_{surface} + n\,NH_3 + 1/2\,O_2 + H_2O \rightarrow$$

$$Cu(NH_3)_n^{2+} + 2OH^- \qquad (1)$$

It has been suggested[45] that the process involves the cathodic reduction of oxygen at the surface of the copper,

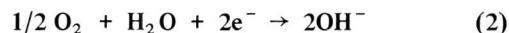

$$1/2\,O_2 + H_2O + 2e^- \rightarrow 2OH^- \qquad (2)$$

and the anodic dissolution of copper in the presence of the complexing agent,

$$Cu_{surface} + n\,NH_3 \rightarrow Cu(NH_3)_n^{2+} + 2e^- \qquad (3)$$

Alternatively, Halpern[43,44] has proposed that the adsorption of dissolved oxygen onto the copper surface represents the first step in the process,

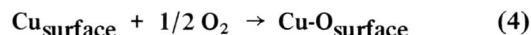

$$Cu_{surface} + 1/2\,O_2 \rightarrow Cu\text{-}O_{surface} \qquad (4)$$

followed by the reaction of ammonia and the ammonium ion with the "copper-oxygen complex" to form the cupric complex, according to,

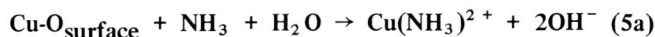

$$Cu\text{-}O_{surface} + NH_3 + H_2O \rightarrow Cu(NH_3)^{2+} + 2OH^- \quad (5a)$$

and

$$Cu\text{-}O_{surface} + NH_4^+ + OH^- \rightarrow Cu(NH_2)^{2+} + 2OH^- \quad (5b)$$

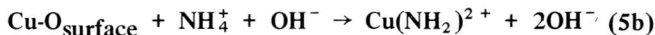

The exact nature of the copper-oxygen complex was not known, but it was considered that it consisted either of a film of adsorbed oxygen or a thin layer of copper oxide.[44] There appear to have been no direct studies of such copper surfaces, but Pickering and Swann[19] have examined thin foils of alpha-brass containing 36 wt.% Zn which had been exposed to either aqueous ammonia or ammonia vapor. Transmission electron microscopy indicated that discrete particles were present on the surfaces and selected area diffraction identified these as cuprous oxide.

In solution, the number of ammonia ligands, n, associated with the cupric complex depends on the ammonia concentration of the solution.[46] The complexes have an octahedral structure, so that in theory the central cupric ion can be associated with six ligands. However, pronounced tetragonal distortion occurs, resulting in two trans ligands being weakly bonded. As a consequence, the addition of the fifth and sixth ligands is difficult, and in fact $Cu(NH_3)_5^{2+}$ is the highest complex which can exist in aqueous solutions. The presence of the cupric complexes gives rise to the characteristic blue color of the solutions, the precise wavelength of the absorption maximum being determined by n. The position of the maximum for each complex (n = 1 to n = 5) has been determined,[47] so that the predominant species in a given solution can be found experimentally by spectrophotometry. In addition, the absorption spectra provide a useful measure of the concentration of the complex ions, e.g., Figure 5, since the maximum optical density in a given ammoniacal solution is directly proportional to the copper content of the solution.

It is well known that the cupric complexes react at copper surfaces to give cuprous complex ions.[46] For the tetramine ion, the reaction is:

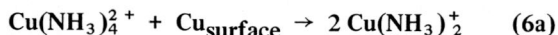

$$Cu(NH_3)_4^{2+} + Cu_{surface} \rightarrow 2\,Cu(NH_3)_2^+ \qquad (6a)$$

The cuprous ion is unstable in oxygenated solutions, reverting to the cupric form,

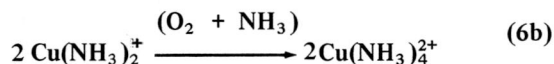

$$2\,Cu(NH_3)_2^+ \xrightarrow{(O_2 + NH_3)} 2\,Cu(NH_3)_4^{2+} \qquad (6b)$$

and it has been suggested that the dissolution process is autocatalytic in the presence of oxygen.[48-50] Note that in addition to the regeneration of the cupric complexes, Reactions (6a) and (6b) indicate that multiplication occurs. The autocatalytic nature of the process has been demonstrated for unstressed sheet specimens of both copper and "70-30 brass" (i.e., brass containing ~ 30 wt.% Zn) immersed in oxygenated ~ 15N aqueous ammonia.[51-52] The predominant complex ion in this case is $Cu(NH_3)_5^{2+}$ for which the autocatalytic process is thought to be:

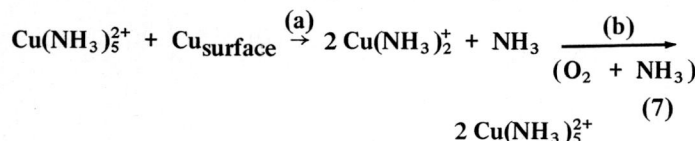

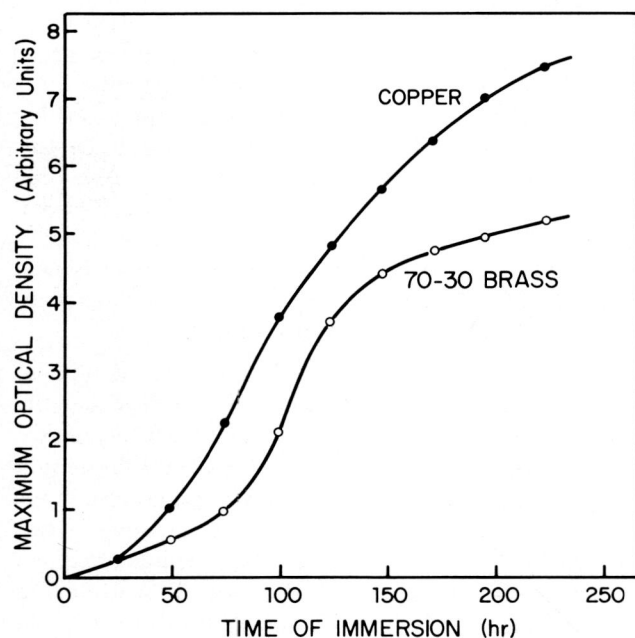

$$Cu(NH_3)_5^{2+} + Cu_{surface} \xrightarrow{(a)} 2\,Cu(NH_3)_2^+ + NH_3 \xrightarrow[(O_2 + NH_3)]{(b)} 2\,Cu(NH_3)_5^{2+} \qquad (7)$$

FIGURE 5 — Relationship between the Cu content of oxygenated ~ 15N aqueous ammonia, as measured by the maximum optical density of the solutions, and the time of immersion of unstressed specimens of copper and 70-30 brass. The copper exists in solutions as the cupric complex $Cu(NH_3)_5^{2+}$. After Pugh et al.[52]

Note that the weakly-bound fifth ligand is thought to play no significant role in the reactions. The copper content of the ~ 15N solution, as measured by the maximum optical density, was shown to increase initially with time of immersion at an increasing rate as predicted by Reactions (7a) and (7b), Figure 5.

It can be seen in Figure 5 that the increase in complex-ion concentration is more rapid in the case of the pure metal. The behavior of the zinc during the operation of the autocatalytic process in brass has not been discussed. While there can be little doubt that zinc enters the solution, where it exists as the stable complex $Zn(NH_3)_4^{2+}$,[46] the mechanism of its dissolution is not understood. Several workers have suggested that "since zinc is much less noble than copper" then zinc will be preferentially removed in ammoniacal solutions[53,54] but there is no evidence for such dezincification at the metal surface. It is interesting to note that if zinc enters solution at a lower rate than copper then transport of copper through the zinc-rich surface layer would be necessary for the operation of the autocatalytic process.

It can be seen in Figure 5 that an inflection occurs in both curves, after ~ 85 and ~ 110 hr, respectively, and that the rate of increase of the maximum optical density subsequently decreases. The inflection in the case of the brass corresponds to the formation of the characteristic black surface film, commonly referred to as the tarnish.[55] The composition and structure of the tarnish will be discussed in the following section but it should be pointed out here that the film consists mainly of cuprous oxide. The inflection is attributed[56] to the fact that Reaction (7a) does not occur at the tarnish surface, so that the autocatalytic process ceases when a continuous surface film is formed. Further dissolution then proceeds by reaction of the tarnish with the environment, presumably by reactions analogous to (5a) and (5b).

The occurrence of the inflection for the copper specimen suggests that a continuous surface film is also formed in that case. While a pronounced tarnish was not observed in the case of the pure metal, the surface condition showed a definite change at the immersion time corresponding to the inflection.[52] Before the inflection, the surfaces appeared bright, and well-defined facets were observed in the optical microscope; after the inflection, the surface appeared relatively dull and no facets were detected. Similar behavior has been observed in weight-loss studies on both copper and 70-30 brass in ~ 15N aqueous ammonia solutions containing various concentrations of $Cu(NH_3)_5^{2+}$ ions (prepared by dissolving copper powder in oxygenated ~ 15N solution, i.e., by Reaction 1), Figure 6(a).[56] The initial increase in the rate with increasing copper content of the solution is due to Reaction (7a), and the maximum in the curves corresponds to the onset of tarnishing of the brass. The close similarity between the data for copper and brass again strongly suggests that a continuous surface film is formed in the case of the pure metal. It is apparent that further study, either ellipsometric or electron-microscopic, is necessary to investigate this question.

The occurrence of tarnishing in brass at a critical complex-ion concentration, Figure 6, has been considered by Pugh and Westwood.[56] Optical-microscope studies of specimens immersed in tarnishing solutions indicated that tarnishing proceeds by the formation and growth of many nuclei, Figure 7. Further, based on the electron-microscope studies of Pickering and Swann,[19] discussed above, it was suggested that small nuclei are also present on surfaces exposed to non-tarnishing solutions but that their growth is limited by continuous dissolution.[(1)] Extending this approach, it was proposed that the formation of a detectable tarnish depends on two competing processes, namely (1) the growth of the tarnish, discussed in the following section, and (2) the dissolution of the tarnish, by reactions analogous to (5a) and (5b). Thus at low complex-ion concentration, rate (1) < rate (2), while at compositions above the critical value rate (1) becomes greater.

To account for this change in relative rates, it was assumed that rate (1) remains essentially unchanged but that rate (2) decreases significantly with increasing complex-ion concentration. This decrease was attributed

---

[(1)]In effect, the particles of cuprous oxide were considered to represent the Cu-O complex in Halpern's model[43] for dissolution, Reactions (4) and (5).

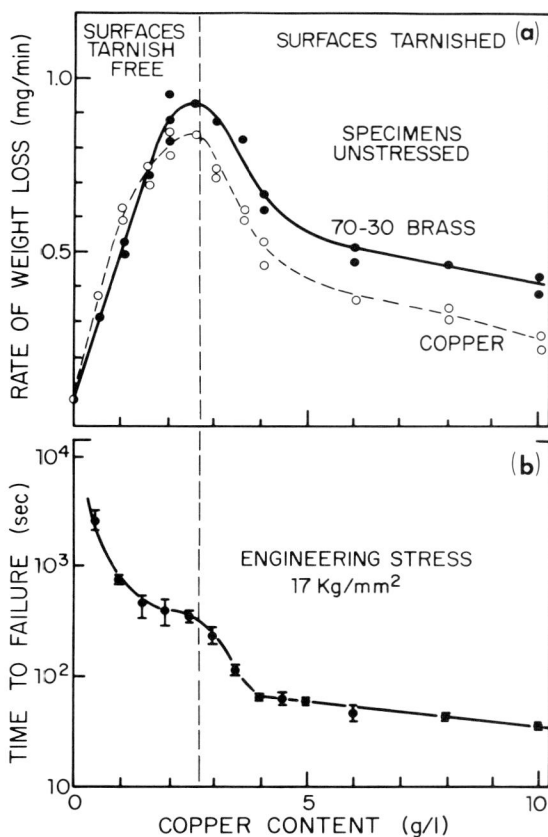

not to the increase in the concentration of the complex ions *per se*, but to the accompanying increase in $OH^-$ concentration, see Reactions (5a) and (5b). The increase in $OH^-$ concentration leads to a reduction in $NH_4^+$ concentration, because of the dissociation reaction

$$NH_3(aq) + H_2O \rightleftharpoons NH_4^+ + OH^- \qquad (8)$$

and Halpern[43] has shown that $NH_4^+$ makes a large contribution to the oxide-dissolution process, the reported reaction rate constants for Reactions (5a) and (5b) being $\sim 84$ and $\sim 1550$ mg/Cu/cm$^2$/hr/mole, respectively.

Based on this model, it was shown that the complex-ion concentration at which tarnishing occurs could be varied over a wide range by controlling the $NH_4^+$ concen-

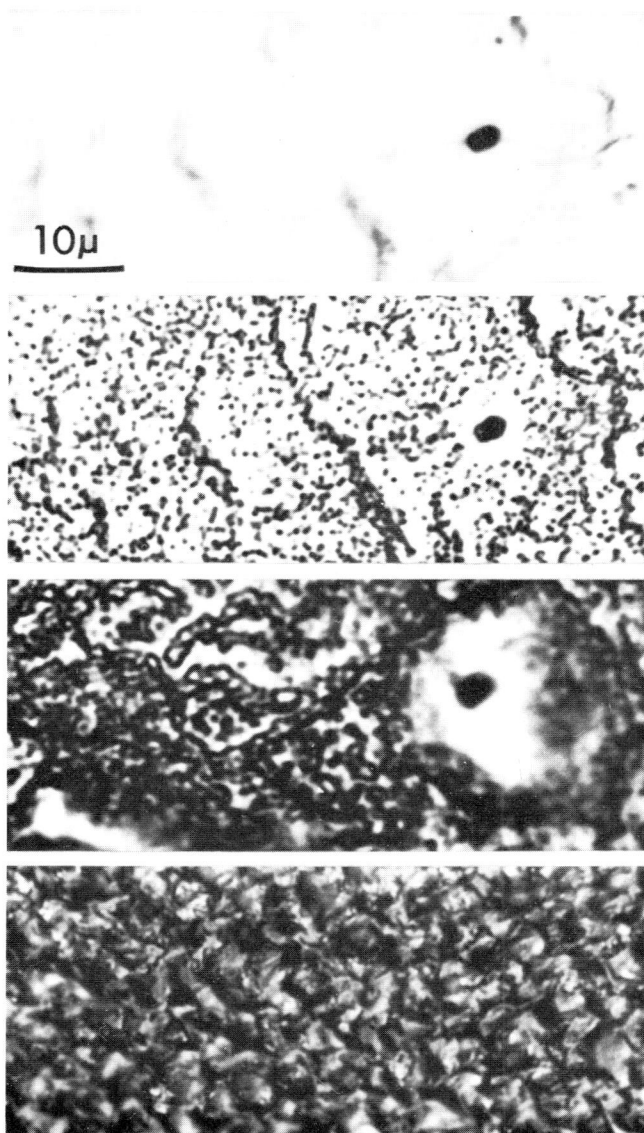

FIGURE 6 — Relationship between the concentration of copper, present as $Cu(NH_3)_5^{2+}$, of $\sim 15N$ aqueous ammonia and (a) the rate of weight loss of unstressed specimens of copper and 70-30 brass and (b) $t_F$ for 70-30 brass. After Pugh and Westwood.[56]

FIGURE 7 — Optical micrographs illustrating the formation of the tarnish on 70-30 brass immersed in $\sim 15N$ aqueous ammonia preconcentrated with 3.5 g/l copper. The micrographs correspond to immersion times of 0, 5, 15, and 180 sec, respectively. After Pugh and Westwood.[56]

tration.[56] For example, by preparing the solutions by dissolving cupric nitrate in $\sim 15N$ aqueous ammonia, i.e., according to

$$Cu(NO_3)_2 + 5NH_3 \rightarrow Cu(NH_3)_5^{2+} + 2NO_3 \quad (9)$$

it was possible to prepare solutions of the same complex-ion concentration as in the standard solutions prepared from copper, but without the accompanying high $OH^-$ concentration. The model predicts that the onset of tarnishing in such solutions should be moved to higher complex-ion concentrations, and this was confirmed by experiments. In fact, tarnishing was not observed in these solutions over the range investigated (0-10 g/l dissolved copper), and the rate of weight loss increased continuously, Figure 8(a). These studies are being extended to more dilute solutions in which it is possible to make use of existing thermodynamic data to provide a quantitative test of the model.[52] Results to date indicate that qualitatively the behavior in 1N solutions is closely similar to that in $\sim 15N$ solutions.

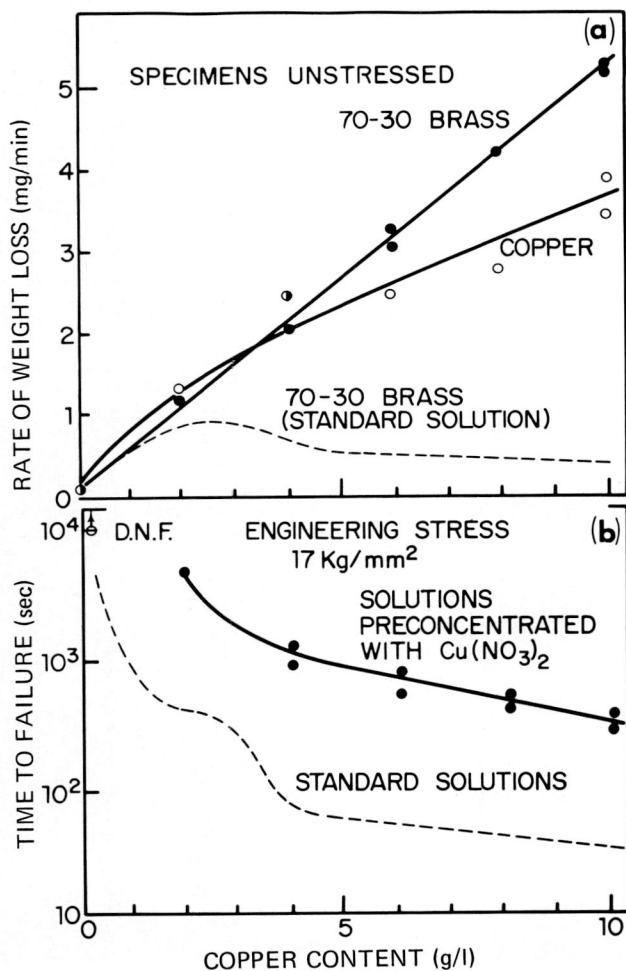

The dependence of the onset of tarnishing on the composition of the environment may also be interpreted by means of potential-pH diagrams of the type developed by Pourbaix.[57] Mattsson[58] has employed this approach in a study of the behavior of an alpha-brass in ammoniacal solutions of varying pH. A diagram, Figure 9(a), was constructed from existing thermodynamic data for pure copper at 25 C in an ammoniacal copper sulfate solution containing 0.05 g-atom/l copper and 1g-mol/l total ammonia. In practice, the solutions were prepared by adding the ammonia partly as $NH_3$ solution and partly as $(NH_4)_2SO_4$, so that by adjusting this ratio the pH was varied in the range 3.9-11.2; the pH value 2.0 was obtained by the addition of sulfuric acid. The copper was added as $CuSO_4 \cdot 5H_2O$ in all cases. The behavior of a brass containing $\sim 37$ wt.% Zn (predominantly alpha-phase but containing a few isolated grains of beta-phase) in these solutions was found to be in reasonable agreement with the diagram, despite the facts that the diagram was constructed for the pure metal and that aging occurred in some pH ranges, reducing the copper contents significantly. Thus, in accord with the diagram, no film formation was observed at pH 2 or in the range 7.8-11.2. Brown-red coatings were

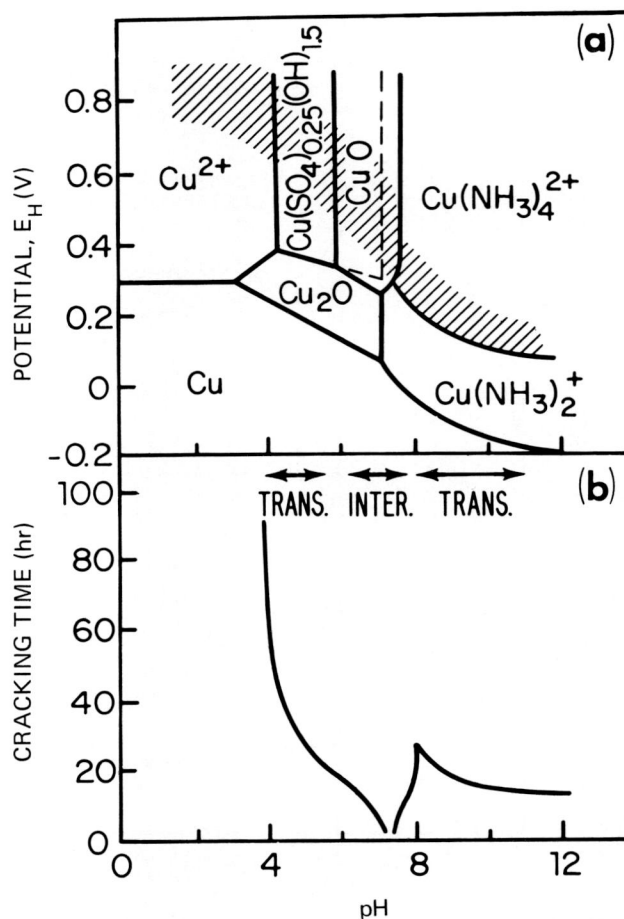

FIGURE 8 — Relationship between the Cu content of $\sim 15N$ aqueous ammonia, preconcentrated by additions of $Cu(NO_3)_2$, and (a) rate of weight loss of unstressed specimens of copper and 70-30 brass and (b) $t_F$ for 70-30 brass. After Pugh and Westwood.[56]

FIGURE 9 — Cracking time for alpha-brass in ammoniacal copper sulfate solutions of varying pH and the corresponding potential/pH diagram. After Mattsson.[58]

124

formed at pH values of 3.9 and 4.7 and these were considered to consist mainly of metallic copper with $Cu_2O$ as a minor constituent. From pH 5.2 to 5.7 thin coatings, about 0.1 $\mu$ thick, were formed. However, from pH 6.3 to 7.3 well-defined tarnish films were in evidence. At pH 7.7 thin grey deposits, judged to be a mixture of copper oxide and $Zn(OH)_2$ and ZnO, were observed.

In Mattsson's experiments, the redox potential was determined at the beginning of the test, see shaded region in diagram, Figure 9(a), but the potentials were not measured during the tests. However, Hoar and Booker[54] have subsequently obtained potential/time curves for a brass containing 30 wt.% Zn immersed unstressed in various Mattsson's solutions in the pH range 4.0-9.0, and have correlated these results with observations on the surface condition. The data, presented in Figure 10, are in good agreement with the predictions of the diagram, a surface film being formed in the pH range 5.8-7.5 at potentials in the range 0.20-0.28 V. X-ray and electron-diffraction studies established that the film consisted of cuprous oxide. Similarly, McEvily and Bond[59] have reported that the potential of stress-corrosion specimens of a brass containing 30 wt.% Zn immersed in a tarnishing Mattsson's solution of pH $\sim$ 7.2 increased from $\sim$ 0.20 to 0.25 V during the test.

Johnson and Leja[60] have criticized Mattsson's diagram, arguing that the $Cu_2O$ region is incorrectly located. As evidence for this, they pointed out that while brass tarnishes in the pH range 6.0-8.0, no detectable tarnish is formed in the case of pure copper. However, it was seen during the discussion of Figures 5 and 6 that a thin oxide may be present on copper. From the diagram, Figure 9(a), it can be seen that $Cu_2O$ can be formed in the pH range 3.0-7.2 either by the anodic oxidation of copper, or by the

cathodic reduction of $Cu^{2+}$, $Cu(SO_4)_{0.25}(OH)_{1.5}$, or CuO. It will be seen in the following section that existing evidence indicates that the oxide is formed anodically. Thus the difference in behavior of the alloy and the pure metal may simply be due to differences in the kinetics of oxide-film growth.

## 2. The Composition and Structure of the Tarnish

Recent papers[51,54-56,59,61,62] on the stress-corrosion cracking of alpha-brass have placed considerable emphasis on the tarnish and hence it is necessary to discuss

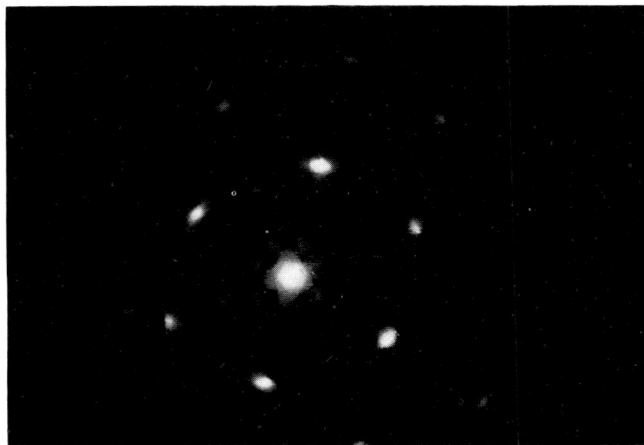

FIGURE 11 — Electron-diffraction pattern from tarnish platelets. After Forty and Humble.[55]

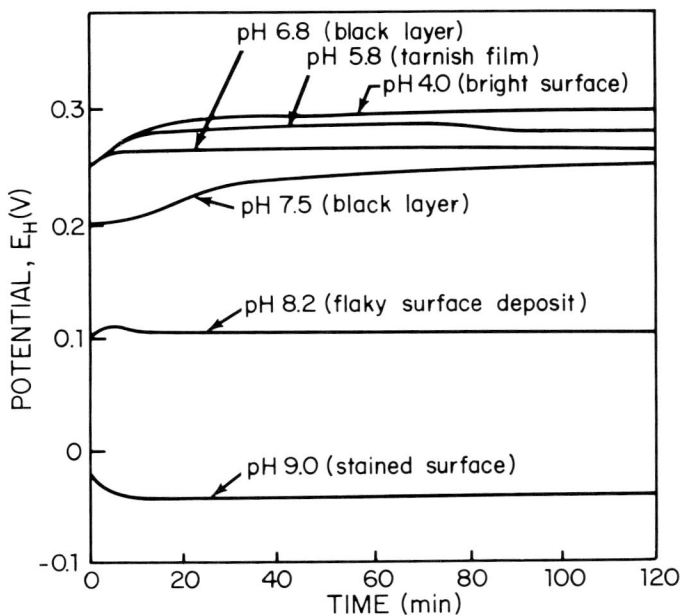

FIGURE 10 — Potential/time curves for unstressed 70-30 brass in ammoniacal copper sulfate solutions of varying pH. After Hoar and Booker.[54]

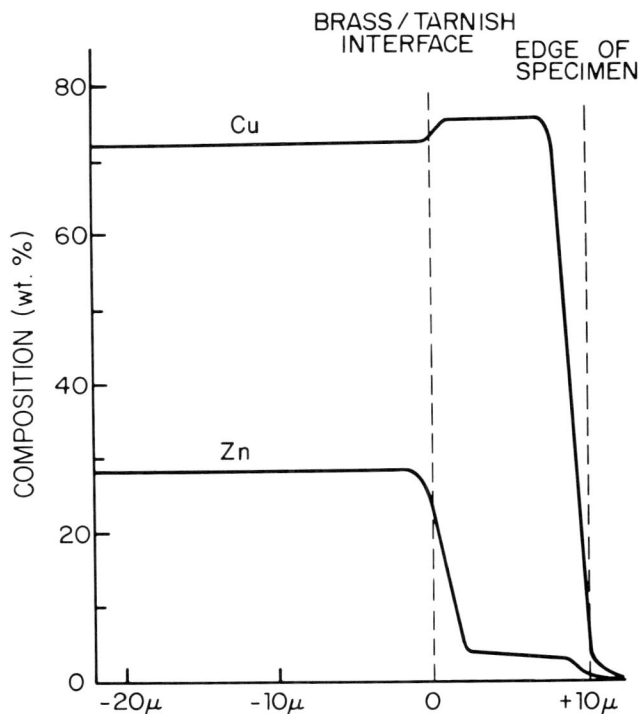

FIGURE 12 — Composition of 70-30 brass after tarnishing, revealed by electron probe X-ray micro-analysis. After Forty and Humble.[61]

the nature of this film in some detail. The tarnish formed on 70-30 brass has been studied by several investigators.[52,54,55,59-61] Visual examination of specimens at successive stages during immersion in tarnishing solutions indicates that the formation of the characteristic black film is preceded by the appearance of a range of interference colors. Electron-microscope studies[55,61] by Forty and Humble of thin flakes of tarnish stripped from the brass surfaces demonstrated that the tarnish consisted of an aggregate of small platelets, about 500 Å in diameter and about 100 Å thick. The electron-diffraction patterns exhibited a regular pattern of spots, typical of a monocrystal, Figure 11, suggesting that the platelets were similarly oriented and therefore grew epitaxially from the brass (monocrystal) substrate. Ring patterns obtained in cases where the platelets were disarranged by electron-beam heating provided evidence for the existence of both cuprous

oxide and residual copper; electron-probe X-ray microanalysis of sections of tarnished specimens has indicated that the tarnish is severely depleted with respect to zinc, Figure 12.[61] X-ray and electron-diffraction studies by other workers[41,54] have confirmed the presence of cuprous oxide in the tarnish. Cuprous oxide can be regarded as FCC with respect to cuprous ions (actually cubic C3), with a lattice parameter of $\sim 4.2$ Å,[63] and since 70-30 brass has a lattice parameter of $\sim 3.7$ Å[64] then the tarnish could be regarded to be formed merely by an expansion of the metal lattice without change in orientation.

Metallographic examination of sections of specimens immersed in tarnishing solutions, Figure 13(a) and (b), has also led to significant conclusions. Examination of sections of specimens partially immersed in tarnishing solutions established that the tarnish penetrates *into* the metal,[52,55,61] Figure 13(a). The position of the tarnish surface relative to the original brass surface depends on the time of immersion and the composition of the solution,

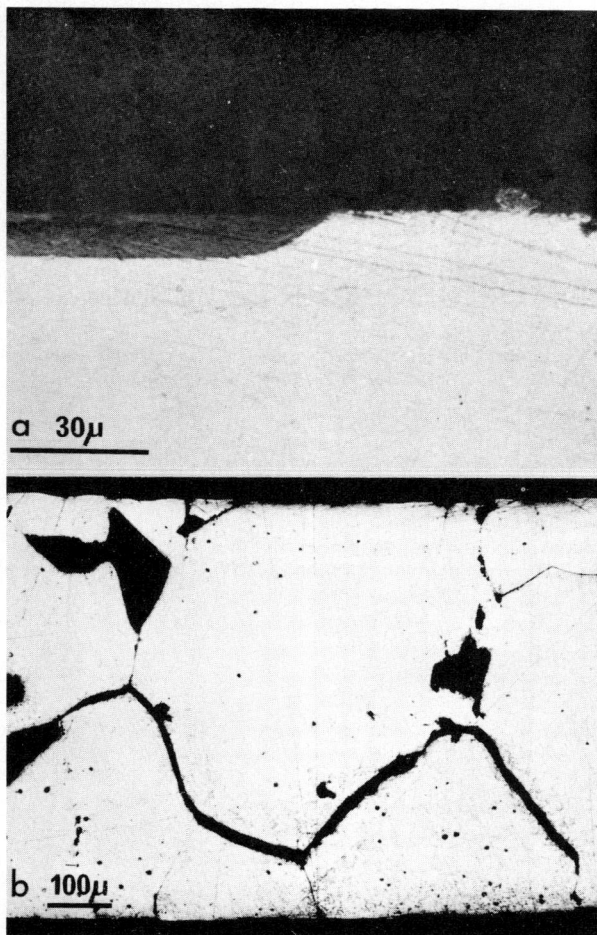

FIGURE 13 — Transverse sections of unstressed 70-30 brass after immersion in tarnishing ammoniacal solutions. (a) Appearance of monocrystal after partial immersion in Mattsson solution for 24 hours. After Forty and Humble.[55] (b) Appearance of polycrystalline material after complete immersion for 72 hours in $\sim$ 15N aqueous ammonia preconcentrated with 8 g/l copper. Note preferential penetration of tarnish along grain boundaries. After Pugh et al.[52]

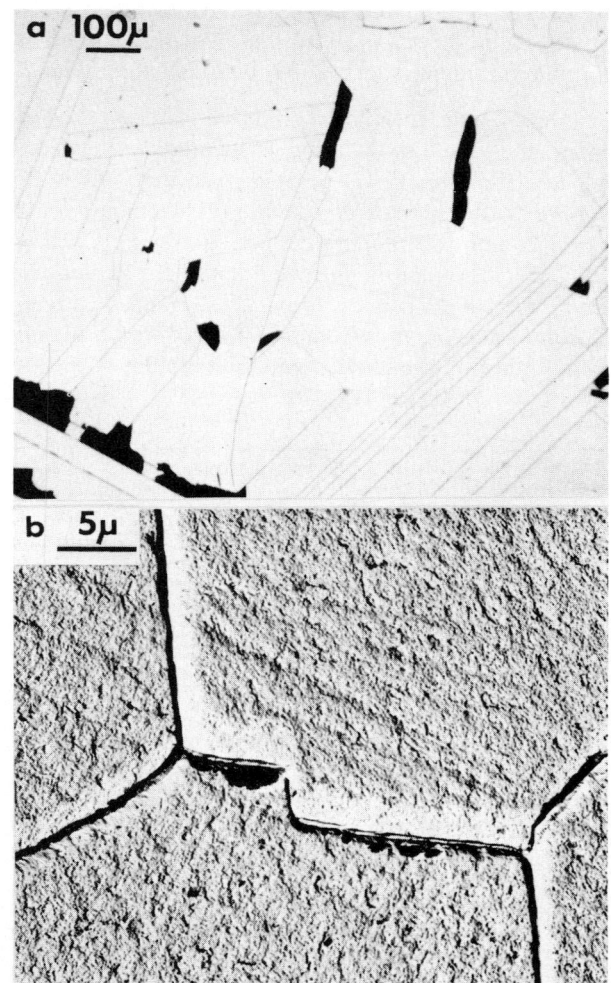

FIGURE 14 — Replicas of surface of tarnish formed on 70-30 brass, examined (a) using the optical microscope and (b) with the electron microscope. These micrographs demonstrate that the structure of the underlying metal has been retained in the tarnish. After Pugh et al.[52]

being determined by both the expansion of the lattice due to the formation of $Cu_2O$ (volume ratio $Cu_2O$: Cu $\sim 1.64$)[63] and by the dissolution of the tarnish by the environment. The surface of the tarnish exhibits a grain structure similar to that of the brass substrate. The structure, delineated by surface grooves, can be seen clearly in replicas, using either the optical, Figure 14(a), or the electron microscope, Figure 14(b); the thickness of the tarnish for the specimens illustrated was $\sim 10~\mu$.[52] The presence of the surface grooves indicates that the grain structure of the brass is retained in the oxide, and that the rate of dissolution of the tarnish is most rapid at grain boundaries and twin interfaces. These metallographic observations, together with the electron-diffraction patterns, leave little doubt that the tarnish is epitaxed to the substrate.

A further significant observation is that when unstressed 70-30 brass specimens are immersed for long periods in tarnishing solutions they become extremely brittle.[65] Handling of such specimens in the absence of the environment causes them to fall into many small fragments. Fracture is intercrystalline in each case and is due to the complete penetration of the grain boundaries by the tarnish, Figure 13(b). These observations demonstrate that tarnish growth occurs preferentially along grain boundaries.

The tarnish appears fully dense when viewed with the optical microscope, but it has been suggested that the layer is in fact porous.[61,66] Forty and Humble[61] based this conclusion on the observation that when glass tubes containing tarnishing solutions were sealed with thin brass foils, leaks eventually developed although the foils remained apparently coherent. Tromans and Nutting[66] have examined replicas of the tarnish formed on 70-30 brass surfaces during exposure to moist ammonia vapor. The published electron micrographs were claimed to provide evidence for cracking and for the existence of pores at grain and twin boundaries, but the interpretation of these micrographs is open to some question. Note that the replica illustrated in Figure 14(b) shows no evidence for porosity at the grain boundaries.

Studies of the rate of growth of the tarnish support the view that the tarnish is fully dense. Using the taper-sectioning method, McEvily and Bond[59] observed that growth obeys a parabolic relationship, Curve A in Figure 15, suggesting that the tarnish is protective and that the tarnishing reaction is controlled by a diffusion process across the film.[63] More recent work[52] has failed to confirm this experimental finding, but has indicated that a limiting thickness is attained, Curve B in Figure 15. Note that this data is also consistent with the process being diffusion controlled. In such cases, the rate of growth is inversely proportional to the thickness of the film, so that the rate decreases with thickness, usually yielding a parabolic relationship.[63] However, in the present case the film is also being continuously dissolved by reaction with the environment, by reactions similar to (5a) and (5b). The rate of dissolution has been found to be constant[56] and assuming that the density of the surface layers of the

tarnish remains essentially unchanged, then the rate of reduction in tarnish thickness by dissolution is also constant. The limiting thickness of tarnish would then correspond to that value at which the rate of growth equals the rate of removal by dissolution. Further exposure to the tarnishing environment caused a continuous reduction in the thickness of the residual metal.[52]

The composition of the solid and the solution have been found to have a significant effect on the tarnishing process. The fact that a thick tarnish does not form in the case of pure copper indicates that zinc plays a role. This is supported by the qualitative observations of Hoar and Booker[54] that the rate of tarnishing increases with increasing Zn content of the brass. The addition of various amounts of zinc to tarnishing solutions had no significant effect on the behavior of immersed copper specimens,[52] demonstrating that the presence of zinc *in the solid* is the important factor. Recent experiments have indicated that other alloying additions, e.g., nickel and aluminum, cause tarnishing,[52] so that the nature of the solute does not appear to be critical.

There appears to be no evidence in the literature that other environments cause tarnishing of brass, so that it seems that the role of ammonia is highly specific. It was seen in the preceding section that the composition of the ammoniacal solution, particularly the pH, critically determines whether tarnishing occurs. In particular, it

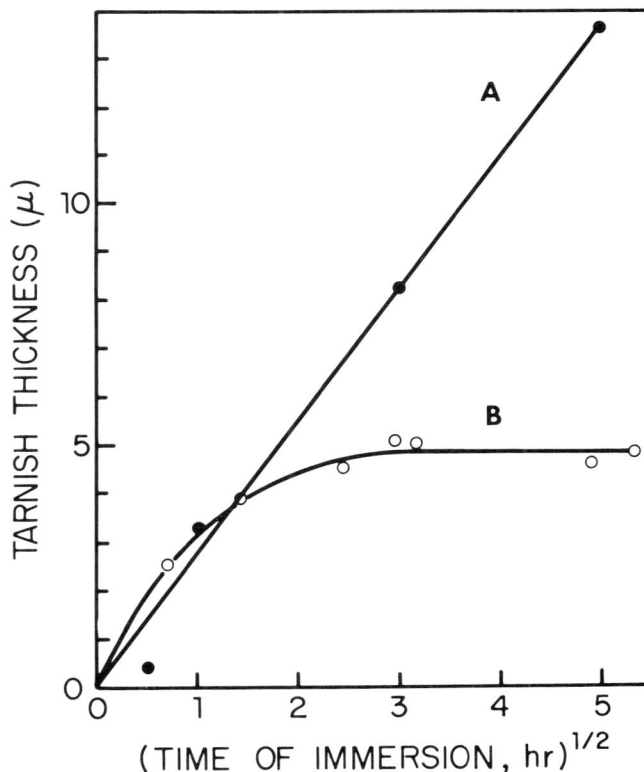

FIGURE 15 — Relationship between thickness of tarnish formed on 70-30 brass and time of immersion in Mattsson's tarnishing solution of pH $\sim$ 7.2. A. After McEvily and Bond.[59] B. After Pugh et al.[52]

should be emphasized at this point that, regardless of other conditions, the presence of a significant concentration of cupric complex ions appears to be a prerequisite for tarnishing to occur.[52,56]

The mechanism of the tarnishing process has received relatively little attention. It is evident from the observation that tarnishing proceeds into the brass that the tarnish is not formed by deposition from solution. Several workers[54,55,61] have suggested that the first stage in the process involves the preferential dissolution of zinc from the metal, but the means by which the resulting porous copper becomes converted to oxide was not made clear. Alternatively, it has been proposed[56,67] that the initial film is formed directly by reaction of surface copper atoms with adsorbed oxygen, i.e., by Reaction (4), and that further growth is then dependent on diffusion across the film. Accepting the general view that cuprous oxide is cation deficient,[63] it was suggested that the process is controlled by the diffusion of cuprous ions across the oxide, which is in turn dependent on the concentration of cation vacancies. Since the tarnish is known to be depleted with respect to zinc, Figure 12, it was argued that the preferential removal of zinc at the tarnish-solution interface is an essential step in the process. Thus, assuming that zinc exists in the oxide as the divalent ion occupying cation sites (associated with a cation vacancy to maintain electrical neutrality), the selective removal of these ions results in the injection of cation vacancies into the oxide lattice.[(2)] It was argued that the presence of these vacancies is primarily responsible for the high rates of cation diffusion necessary for rapid tarnish growth. The specific nature of the ammoniacal environment was rationalized by proposing that the selective removal of zinc results from a surface reaction involving the cupric complex ion, e.g.,

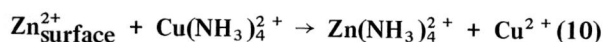

$$Zn^{2+}_{surface} + Cu(NH_3)_4^{2+} \rightarrow Zn(NH_3)_4^{2+} + Cu^{2+} \quad (10)$$

This model is consistent with many of the characteristics of tarnishing. However, it assumes that the tarnish consists essentially of fully dense cuprous oxide, whereas it was seen that other workers[55,61] consider that the tarnish is a porous layer, composed of platelets of the oxide embedded in a matrix of residual copper. Moreover, the selective removal of zinc by Reaction (10) is based on the existence of the stable zinc complex ion. Such a reaction would not be expected to be general, and hence the observation[52] that binary Cu-Al and Cu-Ni alloys also tarnish readily in the presence of a sufficient concentration of cupric-ammonia complexes casts serious doubt on this aspect of the model. It is apparent, then, that the mechanism of tarnishing requires considerable further attention.

Mechanically, the tarnish appears to be completely brittle at room temperature. The brittle nature of the film was demonstrated by Forty and Humble[55] in studies in which tarnished brass specimens were plastically deformed.

[(2)]This approach was based on an earlier suggestion by Forty[7] which invoked dezincification at film free-brass surfaces.

It was shown that glide in the substrate caused cracking of the tarnish and that the shape of the cracks was related to the slip vector in the brass. There is no evidence in the literature for plasticity of the tarnish and this is consistent with studies of cuprous oxide formed by dry oxidation which indicated that the oxide was essentially brittle at temperatures below ~ 700 C.[68]

In summary, then, the tarnish appears to consist largely of crystalline cuprous oxide, which is epitaxed to the brass substrate. The mechanism of tarnish growth is not understood but it appears to be controlled by diffusion of ions across the film. The film is brittle at room temperature.

## 3. Effect of Composition of the Environment on Stress-Corrosion Behavior

In 1944, Althof[69] pointed out that failure of alpha-brass in aqueous ammonia does not occur until the solutions turn blue, and that stress-corrosion life is significantly reduced when large concentrations of copper are introduced into the solutions before the test commences. The importance of the copper content of the solution apparently went unnoticed in the literature for some time, but it has been confirmed by more recent work.[41,51,54,56,70-73] Figure 16 illustrates data for 70-30 brass tested in oxygenated ~ 15N aqueous ammonia, used either "fresh" or "preconcentrated" with 6 g/l of copper powder.[51] It can be seen that at certain stress levels the presence of the copper reduces the time to failure, $t_F$, by two orders of magnitude. Similar reductions have been observed in the case of dilute testing solutions (~ 1N).[41,51,54,70,73]

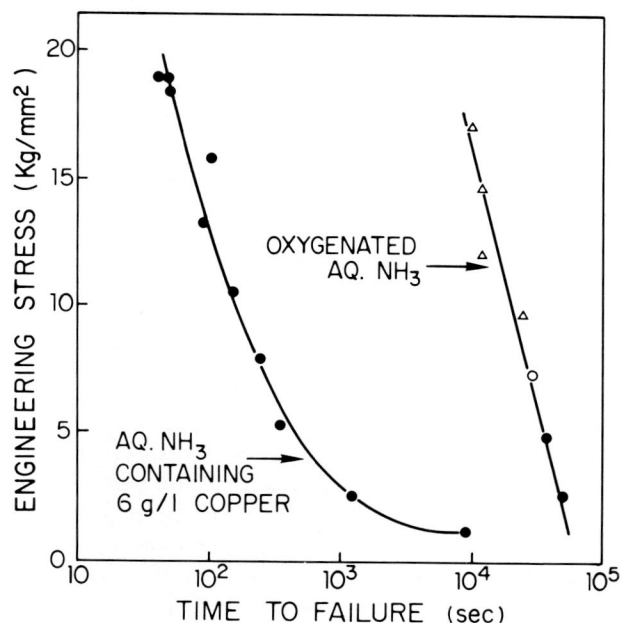

FIGURE 16 — Comparison of $t_F$ for 70-30 brass tested in oxygenated ~ 15N aqueous ammonia and in similar solutions preconcentrated with 6 g/l copper. The copper exists in solution as $Cu(NH_3)_5^{2+}$. After Pugh et al.[51]

The copper exists in the solution as cupric complexes and hence these observations demonstrate the important role of these ions in the stress-corrosion process. The reduction in $t_F$ for any given stress level, Figure 16, can be attributed[51] to the fact that time is required in fresh solutions for the production, via dissolution of the specimen, of a sufficient concentration of these ions to cause failure; in preconcentrated solutions, these ions are present at the beginning of the test. It should be emphasized that failure requires the physical presence of the cupric complex ions in solution, and is not due to the effect of the complex ions on some other property of the solution. It was seen above, for example, that solutions prepared from copper powder contain increased $OH^-$ concentrations, Equation (1), and thus it might be argued that the $OH^-$ ions are responsible for cracking. However, factors such as $OH^-$ concentration can be varied in other ways, but tests in such solutions do not lead to failure in the absence of the complex ions.

Several workers[41,54,56] have demonstrated the importance of the cupric complex ions by showing that $t_F$ decreases as the complex-ion concentration of the test solution is increased, e.g., Figure 6(b). The importance of these ions has also been demonstrated in tests in which the volume of the test solution was varied.[51] For preconcentrated solutions, $t_F$ was independent of volume, while for fresh solutions $t_F$ increased markedly with increasing volume, Figure 17, because in this case increasingly longer times were necessary to produce the required concentration of complex ions.

It has been pointed out[51] that the observations on the effect of volume of the test solution are relevant to certain practical aspects of stress-corrosion failure. Season-cracking is commonly observed in moist industrial atmospheres, and, under these conditions, shallow layers of condensed water formed on the surfaces readily pick up oxygen and ammonia from the atmosphere. The small volume of

solution leads to the rapid formation of large concentrations of complex ions and hence to rapid failure. It is also well known that failure in stressed specimens partially immersed in fresh aqueous ammonia generally occurs at, or just above, the level of the solution. This effect can be attributed to conditions within the meniscus, i.e., small volume and ready access of oxygen.

Tests have also been conducted in solutions preconcentrated with the zinc complex, $Zn(NH_3)_4^{2+}$.[51] The introduction of the zinc caused no detectable change in $t_F$ from that in fresh solutions. Stress-corrosion cracking did occur, but at failure the solutions contained significant concentrations of cupric complexes.

Studies in which the stress-corrosion behavior of 70-30 brass was correlated with spectrophotometric studies of the testing solutions have suggested that the number of ammonia ligands in the complex is not critical. Pugh et al[51] have shown that rapid failure can occur in both $\sim 15N$ and $1N$ solutions in which the predominant complexes are $Cu(NH_3)_5^{2+}$ and $Cu(NH_3)_4^{2+}$, respectively. Johnson and Leja,[60] using solutions similar to those of Mattsson,[58] suggested that most rapid failure occurred in solutions where the complexes are present as $Cu(NH_3)^{2+}$, $Cu(NH_3)_2^{2+}$, $Cu(NH_3)_3^{2+}$, or mixtures of these. It should be noted, however, that comparison of the relative effectiveness of the different complexes in causing cracking requires that tests are carried out in solutions containing identical concentrations of these complexes in which other properties such as pH are also constant. Tests have not yet been conducted under these conditions.

Mattsson's paper of 1961[58] represents a significant advance in this area. Stress-corrosion tests were carried out in the ammoniacal copper sulfate solutions of varying pH, discussed above in connection with the potential-pH diagram, Figure 9(a). The time to produce cracks in loop specimens (i.e., constant strain bend testpieces), as determined by visual inspection through the walls of the glass flasks used for the tests, was found to depend on the pH, as shown in Figure 9(b). More significantly, however, the path of cracking was found to depend on the surface condition of the specimens. It was seen above that solutions in the pH range 6.3-7.3 caused pronounced tarnishing, whereas no film formation was observed in the range 7.8-11.2. Cracking was found to be predominantly intercrystalline in the tarnished specimens, but predominantly transcrystalline in the film-free cases. Cracking was also transcrystalline in the range 3.9-6.3, where again no detectable tarnish was formed.

The occurrence of intercrystalline failure in tarnished specimens and transcrystalline cracking in the absence of this layer has subsequently been confirmed by several workers.[54,56,74] Figure 6(b) illustrates the variation in $t_F$ of 70-30 brass at a constant engineering tensile stress, with the copper content of $\sim 15N$ aqueous ammonia.[56] As noted above, $t_F$ decreases with increasing copper content. However, it can be seen that a well-defined inflection occurred, which coincided with the occurrence of a detectable tarnish (and hence with the maximum in the rate of weight loss curve, Figure 6(a)) and also coincided with a

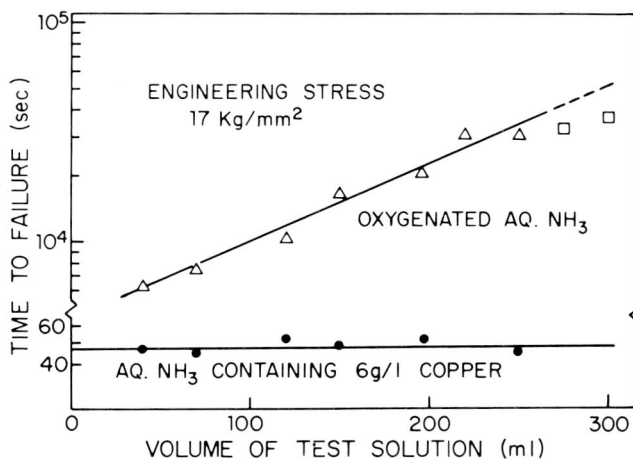

**FIGURE 17 — The effect of varying the volume of the testing solution on $t_F$ for 70-30 brass tested in oxygenated $\sim 15N$ aqueous ammonia and in similar solutions preconcentrated with 6 g/l copper. After Pugh et al.[51]**

transition from predominantly transcrystalline (tarnish-free) to predominantly intercrystalline failure (tarnished). Similarly, when tests were carried out in the tarnishing and non-tarnishing ~15N aqueous ammonia solutions discussed in III.A.1, then two distinct curves were obtained, Figure 8(b).[56] Again, failures were predominantly intercrystalline in the tarnish solutions and transcrystalline in the non-tarnishing cases.

The significance of Mattsson's work is that it demonstrated the controlling role of the environment in determining cracking characteristics and emphasized the importance of defining the environmental conditions. It is clearly impossible to compare observations made by different workers unless it is known whether the test conditions caused tarnishing or not. This information is frequently not available in the earlier literature. An immediate question which arises from Mattsson's work concerns the type of environment which should be used to simulate practical conditions. The fact that season-cracking of 70-30 brass in industrial atmospheres is generally reported to be intercrystalline[75-78] suggests that such conditions cause tarnishing. This is not unexpected since the small volume of solution within the condensed layer of water at the metal surface can be expected to lead to a rapid increase in complex-ion concentration, and hence, by analogy with Figure 6,[(3)] the composition of the solution would rapidly enter the tarnishing range. The wide-spread use of moist ammonia vapor in laboratory tests thus appears to be satisfactory since such conditions lead to tarnishing and to intercrystalline failure in 70-30 brass.[79,80] However, tests in which the specimens are fully immersed in tarnishing ammoniacal solutions appear to be more reliable, since they permit more accurate standardization of the environment.

The data presented by Mattsson, Figure 9, may also prove to be useful in determining the mechanism of cracking, since they permit the stress-corrosion results to be correlated with the potential-pH diagram. Mattsson pointed out that, according to the diagram, in the pH range 7.8-11.2 (transcrystalline stress-corrosion cracking) reduction of $Cu(NH_3)_4^{2+}$ to $Cu(NH_3)_2^+$ (Reaction (6a), above) can take place at a potential high enough to cause anodic dissolution of both copper and zinc. It was considered that this process is likely to be important in the stress-corrosion process in this pH range. The diagram also shows that at pH 2 (no cracking) copper and zinc cannot be anodically dissolved by a corresponding reduction of $Cu^{2+}$ to $Cu^+$. At pH ~7.3 (tarnish, rapid intercrystalline stress-corrosion failure) anodic dissolution is possible by the reduction of either $Cu(NH_3)_4^{2+}$ or CuO. The relevance of these observations to the mechanism of failure is discussed below, III.C.

The effect of oxygen content on the stress-corrosion cracking of 70-30 brass in various Mattsson's solutions has been reported in recent papers. Hoar and Booker[54] found that deaeration of solutions of pH 7.2 caused no detectable

effect on the stress-corrosion behavior or on solution potential/time curves, and in particular, the specimens were tarnished. On the other hand, at pH 5.6 deaeration significantly extended the stress-corrosion life. Johnson and Leja[41] reported somewhat similar results. At pH > 8, absence of oxygen caused the solutions to become colorless in a few hours and stressed brass specimens remained unbroken for 30-40 days; when oxygen was introduced into these solutions, they became colored and cracking occurred within several hours. At pH < 8, $t_F$ was unaffected by the absence of oxygen.

The observations of Johnson and Leja in the solutions of pH > 8 can readily be explained in terms of Reaction (6a) and (6b). Thus, while the reaction of cupric complexes with copper at the metal surface, (6a), is unaffected by the absence of oxygen, the re-oxidation of the resulting cuprous complexes, (6b), does not then occur. Hence the solution becomes colorless and, in the absence of cupric complexes, cracking does not occur. The occurrence of cracking in Hoar and Booker's tests in solutions of pH 5.6 (non-tarnishing) may be due to the fact that the volume of the solution was large and the surface area of the specimen small, so that failure occurred before the solution became sufficiently depleted with respect to the cupric complexes. The fact that the behavior in tarnishing solutions was unaffected by the absence of oxygen is not fully understood, but it suggests that Reactions (6a) and (6b) do not play a role in such solutions.

In considering the effect of oxygen content on the stress-corrosion process, it should be noted that Mattsson's solutions are preconcentrated with copper before the test commences. When specimens are tested in de-oxygenated fresh aqueous ammonia, no significant dissolution occurs, i.e., Reaction (1) does not proceed, and, in the absence of cupric complex ions, the specimens do not undergo stress-corrosion cracking.[52]

The main conclusions of this section are as follows:

(1) The presence of cupric complex ions, $Cu(NH_3)_n^{2+}$, in solution is necessary for the stress-corrosion cracking of alpha-brasses in aqueous ammonia.

(2) The composition of the ammonia solution determines the path of stress-corrosion cracking in 70-30 brass. In solutions of compositions which cause tarnishing, cracking is predominantly intercrystalline, whereas failure in non-tarnishing solutions is mainly transcrystalline.

(3) The presence of oxygen is essential for stress-corrosion cracking to occur in fresh aqueous ammonia, being necessary to produce the cupric complex ions, Reaction (1). In solutions presaturated with the cupric complexes, oxygen appears to be necessary for cracking only in non-tarnishing cases; failure in tarnishing solutions has been reported in de-oxygenated solutions.

---

[(3)]This data is for ~15N aqueous ammonia. However, closely similar results have been obtained in more dilute solutions,[52] which more closely approximate the practical case.

## 4. Effect of Composition of Solid on Stress-Corrosion Behavior

Early reports that copper does not undergo stress-corrosion cracking in ammoniacal environments[80-81] are in accord with the general view[82] that pure metals are immune to this type of failure. However, recent studies by Pugh et al[52,83] have indicated that pure copper does in fact fail by intercrystalline stress-corrosion cracking when it is tested in non-tarnishing solutions preconcentrated with cupric complexes, Figure 18. Failure was not observed in tarnishing solutions, see Figure 19, and this may account for the earlier reports of immunity. Studies of nominally pure metals invariably lead to the question of purity. The copper used by Pugh et al,[83] originally 99.999% copper, was heat treated at 900 C in a vacuum of $10^{-5}$ mm Hg to produce suitable grain sizes, thus it could be argued that the specimens became contaminated, possibly by oxygen. More recent tests[52] have been carried out on annealed material supplied by Dr. L. H. Jenkins, Oak Ridge National Laboratories. These specimens, determined to be 99.999% copper or better by analysis at Oak Ridge, also failed by stress-corrosion cracking in non-tarnishing solutions. The stress-corrosion life of these specimens was significantly shorter than those used in the previous study,[83] but this is thought to be due to their larger grain size.

The influence of Zn content on the susceptibility of alpha-brasses tested in moist ammonia vapor has been studied by Edmunds[81] and by Thompson and Tracy.[80] In both cases, $t_F$ was found to decrease rapidly with increasing Zn content to 20-30 wt.%. More recently, Pugh et al[52] have carried out similar studies in the tarnishing and non-tarnishing $\sim$ 15N aqueous ammonia solutions containing 8 g/l copper. The results are illustrated in Figure 19. The data for the tarnishing solutions are very similar to those of the earlier studies,[80,81] $t_F$ decreasing continuously with increasing zinc content. However, the behavior of specimens tested in non-tarnishing solutions is significantly different. In addition to the fact that pure copper failed in these solutions, $t_F$ showed a general reduction in depend-

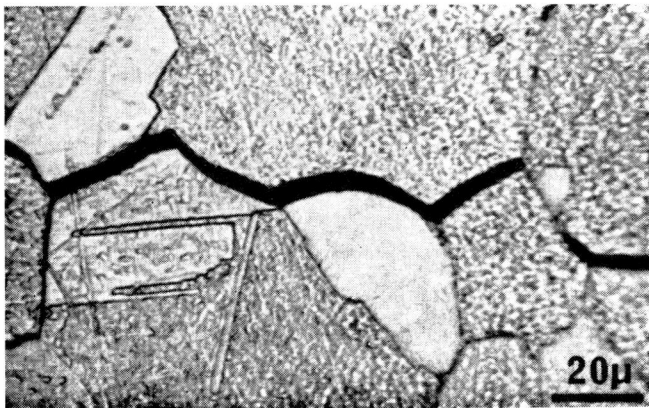

ence on solute concentration. Moreover, while $t_F$ initially decreased with increasing Zn content a discontinuity occurred between 10% and 20%. Examination of the fractured specimens indicated that failure in the non-tarnishing solutions was predominantly intercrystalline for the pure metal and for alloys containing $<$ 20 wt.% Zn, but predominantly transcrystalline in those containing 20% and 30% Zn. Failure in tarnishing solutions was predominantly intercrystalline in all alloys, in agreement with the findings of Thompson and Tracy.[80]

These observations are to some extent in accord with the proposal by Tromans and Nutting[66,84] and Swann[9] that the path of stress-corrosion failure of the alpha-brasses in aqueous ammonia is controlled by the dislocation structure of the deformed alloy. It was proposed that failure is intercrystalline in materials having cellular dislocation structures, and predominantly transcrystalline, depending to some degree on the stress,[66,84] in those where the dislocations form planar arrays (the models on which these proposals are based are described below, III.C). The results for non-tarnishing solutions are in good agreement with this prediction. Thus the transition from cellular to planar dislocation structures occurs at $\sim$ 18% Zn, Figure 2, and the change in crack path takes place between 10% and 20%, Figure 19. However, it should be noted that the path of fracture of specimens tested in tarnishing solutions is independent of the dislocation structure.

The influence of minor alloying elements on the stress-corrosion behavior of the alpha-brasses appears to have received little systematic study in recent years. The most complete study remains that of Wilson, Edmunds, Anderson and Pierce,[85] using a moist ammonia vapor environment (tarnishing). In these studies, reported in 1945, 36 elements were added singly to 70-30 brass. A pronounced beneficial effect was observed in the case of silicon. Increasing the Si content up to 1.6 wt.% caused a

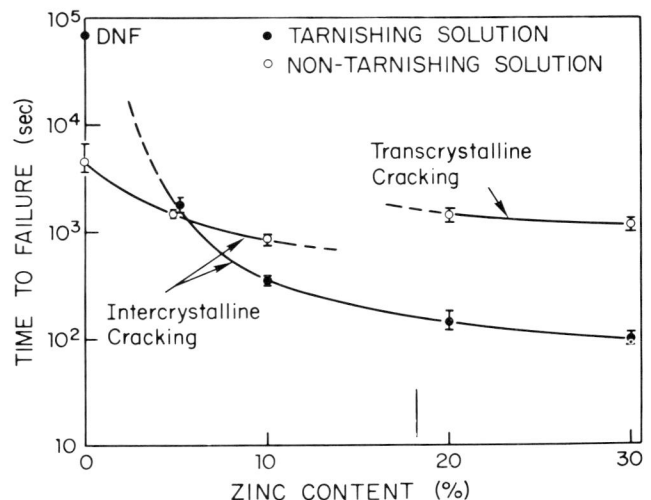

FIGURE 18 — Intercrystalline stress-corrosion cracking in copper tested in a non-tarnishing ammoniacal solution. After Pugh et al.[83]

FIGURE 19 — Effect of Zn content of alloys on $t_F$ for specimens tested at 10% proof stress in tarnishing and non-tarnishing $\sim$ 15N ammoniacal solutions containing 8 g/l copper. After Pugh et al.[52]

131

continuous increase in $t_F$. At 1.5 wt.% Si, for example, $t_F$ for specimens annealed at $\sim 650$ C was $\sim 2000$ min compared with $\sim 180$ min for 70-30 brass. The increasing resistance to stress-corrosion cracking was accompanied by a progressive transition from intercrystalline to trans-crystalline cracking. Increasing the annealing temperature of the 1.2 wt.% Si alloy to $> 700$ C followed by water quenching caused a further significant increase in resistance, $t_F$ now reaching 7000 min in some cases. This added increase was associated with the introduction of a second phase, which, from the published micrographs, appeared to be continuous at the boundaries of the alpha grains. Low-temperature annealing caused the partial decomposition of this phase and led to the loss of much of the added resistance introduced by the high-temperature treatment.

The effects of other elements were less significant. Phosphorus, arsenic, barium, cerium, magnesium, tellurium, tin, beryllium, and manganese caused increased resistance under some instances but not in others. The other elements investigated had no significant effect. None of the elements added accelerated failure and, in particular, the suscepti-bility of commercial 70-30 brass could not be attributed to the presence of impurities.

The following conclusions can be made concerning the effect of composition of the solid on the stress-corrosion process:

(1) While pure copper does not undergo stress-corrosion cracking in tarnishing ammoniacal solutions, recent work suggests that the pure metal is susceptible to failure in non-tarnishing solutions.

(2) The presence of zinc in the solid increases the susceptibility to cracking in both tarnishing and non-tarnishing solutions; the dependence of $t_F$ on the Zn content is particularly large in the former, Figure 19.

(3) The path of fracture of alpha-brasses in non-tarnishing solutions is related to the Zn content, failure being predominantly intercrystalline in dilute alloys (10 wt.% and less) and predominantly transcrystalline in alloys containing $> 20$ wt.%. For

tarnishing solutions, on the other hand, fracture is intercrystalline for all alpha alloys.

(4) With the exception of silicon, the addition of third elements to 70-30 brass causes little significant effect on stress-corrosion susceptibility in moist ammoniacal vapors (tarnishing). Additions of silicon produce a large increase in resistance but its role is not yet understood.

## 5. Effect of Other Factors on Stress-Corrosion Behavior

**a. Grain Size.** Edmunds[81] has shown that $t_F$ for 70-30 brass tested in moist ammonia vapor (tarnishing) decreases with increasing grain size as illustrated in Figure 20. There appears to be no data for specimens tested in non-tarnishing solutions.

**b. Stress.** There have been few attempts to define the stress conditions during stress-corrosion tests. Many workers have determined the relationship between engineer-ing tensile stress (i.e., based on original cross-section area of specimen) and $t_F$ for 70-30 brass tested under constant load. Typical data is presented in Figure 21 for both tarnishing and non-tarnishing solutions.[52] It can be seen that no "threshold" stress exists below which cracking does not occur, but a distinct change of slope occurs, the data forming two distinct branches. Hoar and Booker[54] have suggested that the change of slope occurs at the flow stress, $\sigma_f$, of the material.

While data obtained from such tests is useful for comparative purposes, it is evident that interpretation of the results is extremely complex. The failure process involves three stages, namely (1) initiation of the stress-corrosion crack, (2) propagation of the crack, and (3) final mechanical failure when the effective cross-section of the specimen can no longer sustain the applied load—note that

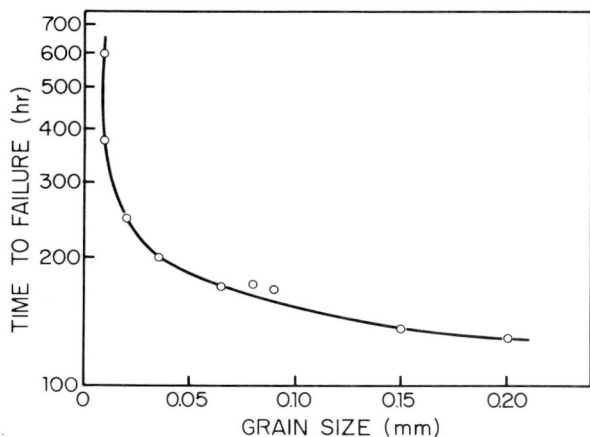

FIGURE 20 — Effect of grain size on $t_F$ of 70-30 brass tested in moist ammonia vapor. After Edmunds.[81]

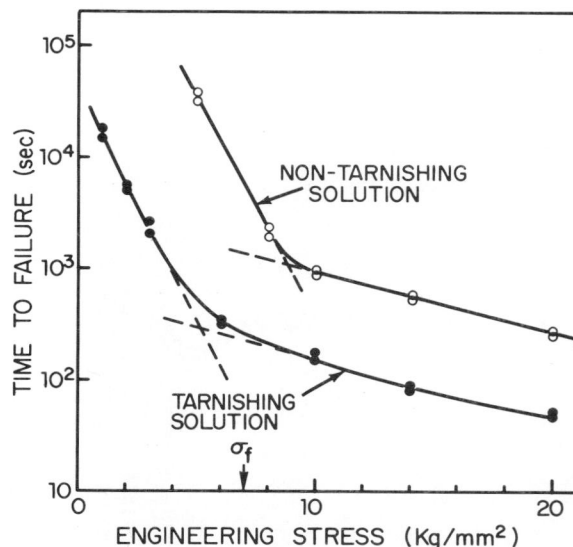

FIGURE 21 — Influence of engineering stress on $t_F$ for 70-30 brass tested in tarnishing and non-tarnishing $\sim 15$N aqueous ammonia containing 8 g/l copper. After Pugh et al.[52]

the distance the stress-corrosion crack propagates before this final stage depends on the stress level. Taking the third stage to be instantaneous, then $t_F$ can be represented by the sum of initiation and propagation times; the relative values of these two stages is generally not known. In addition, the true stress on the specimen increases during the tests as specimen dissolution occurs, and this effect can be expected to be large in the case of non-tarnishing $\sim 15N$ solutions, n.b. dissolution rates in Figure 8(a).

Recently, McEvily and Bond[59] conducted a more detailed study of the stress dependence in the brass-ammonia system. The propagation of stress-corrosion cracks in specimens of 70-30 brass taken from cold-rolled sheet, 0.031 in thick, was studied. Specimens, 2 in wide and containing a central slit, Figure 22, were tested under constant tensile load in Mattsson's tarnishing solution of pH $\sim 7.2$, the rate of cracking being determined by means of an optical microscope. Over a wide range of values, the log of the rate of cracking was found to be a single valued function of $\sigma_g \sqrt{\ell}$, where $\sigma_g$ is the maximum applied gross-section stress, and $\ell$ is the semilength of the crack, Figure 22. The data could be represented by the equation

$$\frac{d\ell}{dt} = A\sigma_g^2 \ell \qquad (11)$$

where A is a constant. The significance of this result will be discussed below, III.C., but it should be noted that the parameter $\sigma_g \sqrt{\ell}$ is related to the stress intensity at the tip of the advancing crack, if the crack length is less than half the sheet width.[86]

Data of this type is not available for non-tarnishing conditions.

c. **Temperatures.** A major difficulty in determining the effect of temperature on the failure of specimens in aqueous ammonia stems from the high vapor pressure of ammonia, which causes excessive losses at temperatures little above room temperature. Thus in tests by Nichols and Rostoker,[87] specimens of 70-30 brass were partially immersed in concentrated aqueous ammonia and ammonia and air were bubbled through the solution. Failure occurred slightly above the solution level, i.e., within the meniscus as discussed above, III.A.3, and $t_F$ showed a slight decrease with increasing temperature in the range 20-75 C. However, it is doubtful whether these results are reliable due to the variation in ammonia content within the meniscus. A similar criticism can be made of the results of Johnson and Leja.[41]

Pugh and Montague[88] have recently studied the temperature dependence of the cracking of 70-30 brass in both the tarnishing and non-tarnishing $\sim 15N$ aqueous ammonia solutions containing 8 g/l copper. The test solutions were contained in a sealed stainless steel container, allowing only a small space above the solution to minimize losses of ammonia from solution, and the specimens were fully immersed. The stress-corrosion data is presented in Figure 23, in which $\log_{10} t_F$ is plotted as a function of the reciprocal of the absolute temperature. It can be seen that linear relationships exist over significant temperature ranges for both types of solution, but that the slopes are significantly different. If it is assumed that no initiation periods exist, then $t_F$ can be regarded to be inversely proportional to the average rate of cracking, and thus the existence of the linear relationships in Figure 23 indicates that the Arrhenius relationship is obeyed. Calculation of activation energies from the slopes of Figure 23 yields values of $\sim 0.43$ and $\sim 0.70$ eV for tarnishing and non-tarnishing solutions respectively.

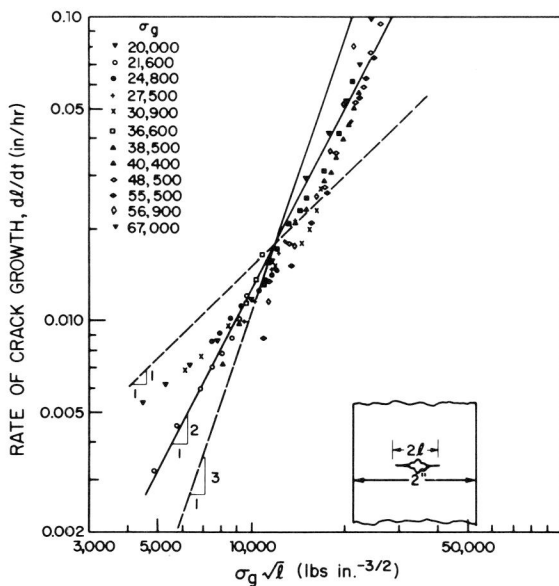

FIGURE 22 — Relationship between the rate of cracking of 70-30 brass tested in a tarnishing ammoniacal solution and the stress-intensity[59] parameter $\sigma_g \sqrt{\ell}$.. After McEvily and Bond.[59]

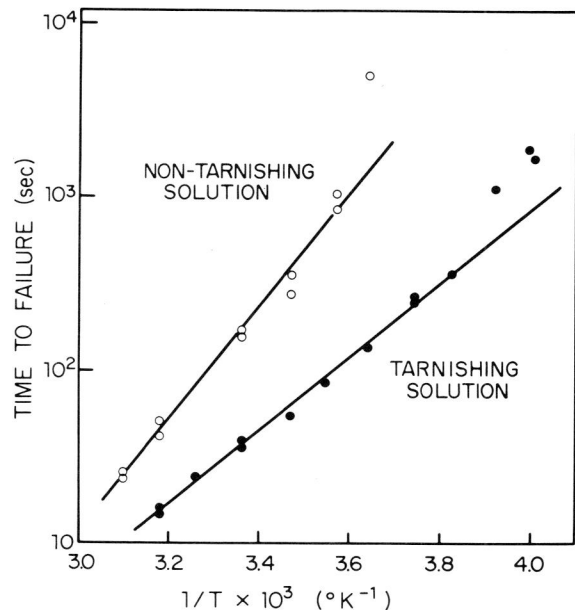

FIGURE 23 — Temperature dependence of $t_F$ for 70-30 brass tested in tarnishing and non-tarnishing $\sim 15N$ aqueous ammonia containing 8 g/l copper. After Pugh and Montague.[88]

It was seen above that the path of cracking of alpha-brass in aqueous ammonia depends on both the composition of the environment, III.A.3, and the Zn content of the alloy, III.A.4. Thus failure is predominantly intercrystalline in all alloys tested in tarnishing solutions, whereas failure in non-tarnishing solutions is predominantly intercrystalline for alloys containing up to ~ 10 wt.% Zn and predominantly transcrystalline for more concentrated alloys. In this section, the path of cracking is discussed in more detail, using examples obtained at RIAS[52] to illustrate the types of behavior. These studies were conducted on annealed sheet specimens, 0.5 mm thick, and having gauge dimensions 10 mm x 3 mm, tested under constant tensile load. In each alloy, the grain size was uniform and was ~ 0.1 mm; for pure copper, the grain size was extremely irregular, although the average was approximately 0.1 mm. In all cases, the micrographs represent sections perpendicular to the surface of the sheet and parallel to the tensile stress; the specimens were plated with nickel before sectioning to ensure edge retention.

a. **70-30 Brass.** Sections were prepared from the fractured specimens tested over a range of engineering stresses in either tarnishing or non-tarnishing solutions of ~ 15N aqueous ammonia, Figure 21. Similar data has been obtained for 1N solutions and examination of sections of failed specimens indicated that the ammonia concentration did not significantly affect the cracking behavior.[52]

Figures 24(a) and 24(b) illustrate the predominantly intercrystalline nature of cracking in tarnishing solutions. In some cases, the main intercrystalline cracks were associated with transcrystalline branches, Figure 24(a), and some degree of transcrystalline cracking was frequently observed at grain-boundary triple points, Figure 24(b). Some transcrystalline cracking can also be seen to be initiated at the specimen surfaces, but in all cases these were shallow relative to the main intercrystalline cracks. These observations are essentially independent of stress over the range studied (2-20 Kg/mm$^2$), although the incidence of the transcrystalline forms of cracking appeared to increase slightly with increasing stress.

In non-tarnishing solutions, the path of cracking showed a greater dependence on stress. At low stress levels, the surfaces displayed facets which appeared to be crystallographic, Figure 25(a), and cracking was mainly intercrystalline. As the stress increased, the surfaces became less faceted and failure became transcrystalline, Figure 25(b). The main transcrystalline cracks displayed considerable branching, Figure 25(c), the degree of branching increasing with increasing stress. Examination of specimens etched to reveal deformation, e.g., Figure 25(c), indicated that while some secondary cracks appeared to be parallel to the traces of slip bands, many others showed no crystallographic dependence.

b. **Effect of Zinc Content.** Sections were prepared from the fractured specimens used in Section III.A.4, Figure 19. In these tests, pure copper and alloys containing 5, 10, 20 and 30 wt.% Zn were tested at their 10% proof stresses in tarnishing and non-tarnishing solutions of ~ 15N aqueous ammonia.

Each of the alloys exhibited intercrystalline cracking in the tarnishing solutions, but the pure metal was immune to failure. With the exception of 70-30 brass, discussed above, cracking in each of the alloys was almost entirely intercrystalline, Figure 26(a). In the non-tarnishing solutions, failure in pure copper and the alloys containing 5 and 10 wt.% Zn was again initially entirely intercrystalline, Figures

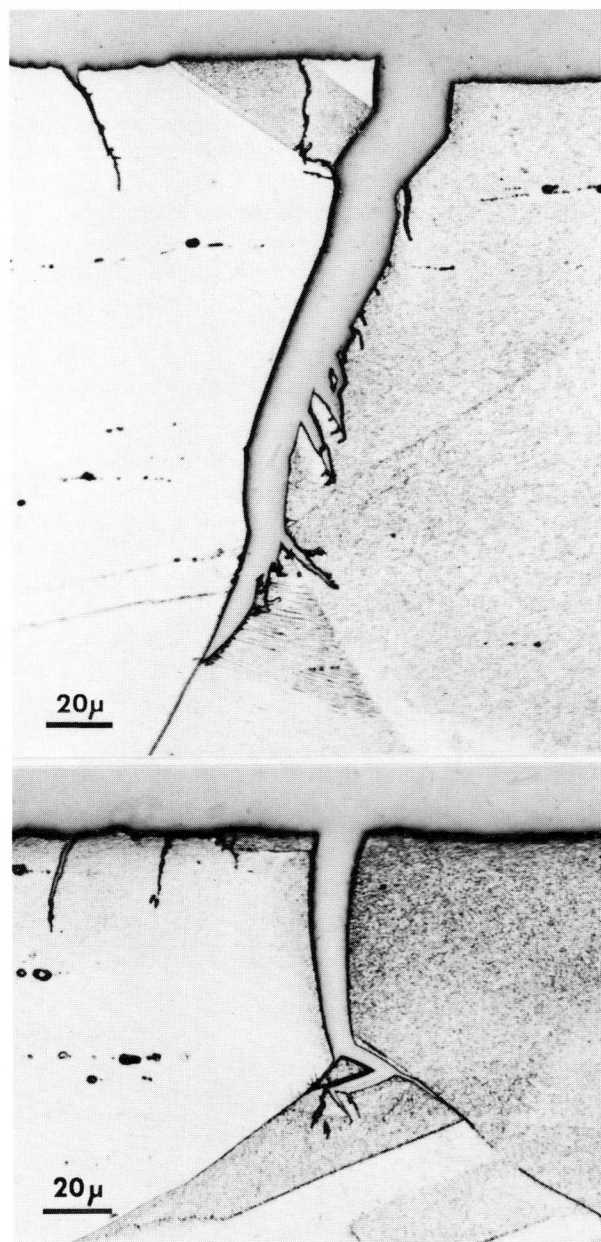

20μ

20μ

FIGURE 24 — Sections illustrating the predominantly intercrystalline nature of stress-corrosion cracking in 70-30 brass tested in tarnishing ~ 15N aqueous ammonia. Various transcrystalline cracks are in evidence but these are small by comparison with the main intercrystalline cracks. After Pugh et al.[52]

134

18 and 26(b), but in the alloys containing 20 and 30 wt.% Zn cracking was predominantly transcrystalline, Figure 25(b). The degree of branching appeared to increase as the Zn content increased from 20 to 30 wt.%.

## 7. Electrochemical Observations

While there have been numerous papers dealing with the electrochemistry of the brass-ammonia system, see Bailey,[2] the results are in general difficult to interpret since the exact composition of the environments is not known. Thus several workers have demonstrated that failure of stressed specimens can be prevented by cathodic protection, either by the application of an external potential[89-91] or by connecting the brass to a more anodic metal,[91] and such observations have been considered to support an "electrochemical mechanism" of failure.[2] However, it is not clear from these papers whether cathodic protection simply prevents the formation of cupric complex ions, shown to be a necessary first step in the stress-corrosion process, III.A.3, or whether it influences the basic role of the complexes in the failure.

Against this background, the electrochemical studies of Hoar and Booker,[54] referred to above in several instances, must be regarded as a significant advance since these workers employed a variety of Mattsson's solutions. In one series of experiments, they studied the effect of an externally applied emf on the stress-corrosion behavior of 70-30 brass tested in the tarnishing solution of pH $\sim$ 7.2. In these tests, the potential of the specimens was controlled potentiostatically from the beginning of the tests, the current flowing to the polarized electrode was measured, and $t_F$ recorded. Some typical results are given in Table 1.

Increase in cathodic polarization can be seen to cause a progressive increase in $t_F$, whereas anodic polarization led to a decrease in $t_F$ and accelerated the formation of the tarnish. At the two lowest potentials, no tarnishing occurred, the specimen surfaces becoming etched; no attempt was made to determine whether this change in

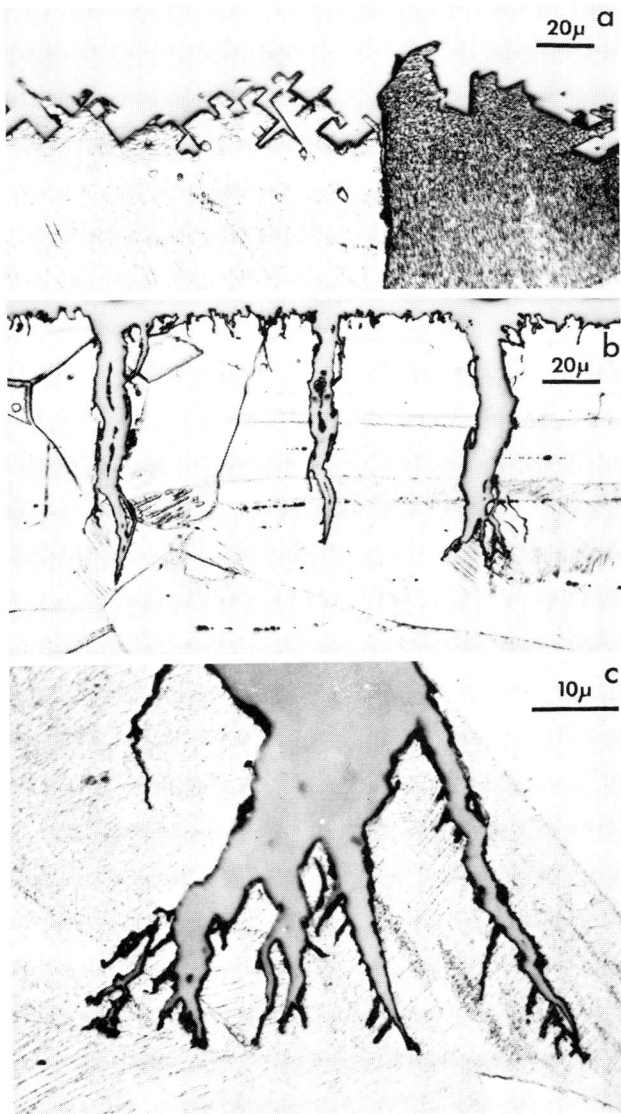

FIGURE 25 — Sections illustrating the behavior of 70-30 brass tested at (a) 5 Kg/mm$^2$, and (b) and (c) 17 Kg/mm$^2$, in non-tarnishing $\sim$ 15N aqueous ammonia. Note well defined facets at the lower stress level, (a), and the branching transcrystalline cracks at the higher stress, (b) and (c). After Pugh et al.[52]

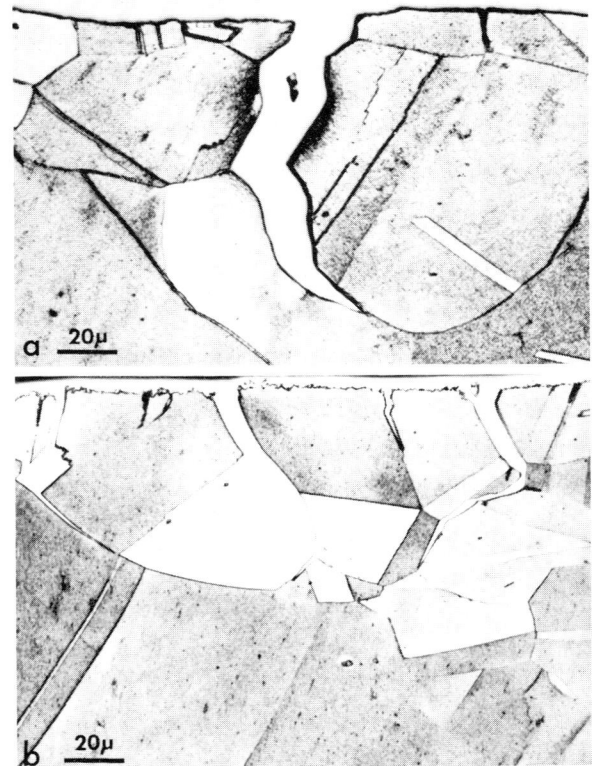

FIGURE 26 — Sections showing the intercrystalline nature of stress-corrosion cracking of an alpha-brass containing 5 wt.% Zn, tested at 10% proof stress in both (a) tarnishing and (b) non-tarnishing $\sim$ 15N aqueous ammonia. After Pugh et al.[52]

surface condition was associated with a change in crack path. Cathodic polarization to any greater degree merely resulted in the deposition of copper from solution. Further experiments were carried out to determine whether propagating cracks could be halted by cathodic polarization. Cracking specimens were polarized to 0.15 V and 0.05

**TABLE 1**

Influence of External E.M.F. on Time to Failure of 70-30 Brass Tested at 11,500 psi in Mattsson's Solution, pH $\sim$ 7.2 After Hoar and Booker[54]

| Polarization | Potential, $e_H$ (V) | External Current Density ($\mu A/cm^2$) | Time to Failure (hr) | Final Surface Condition |
|---|---|---|---|---|
| Anodic | 0.30 | 835 | 2.5 | Black film |
| Zero | 0.25 | 0 | 3.5 | Black film |
|  | 0.24 | 20 | 4.7 | Black film |
| Cathodic | 0.15 | 75 | 21.5 | Etched |
|  | 0.05 | 125 | 219 | Etched |

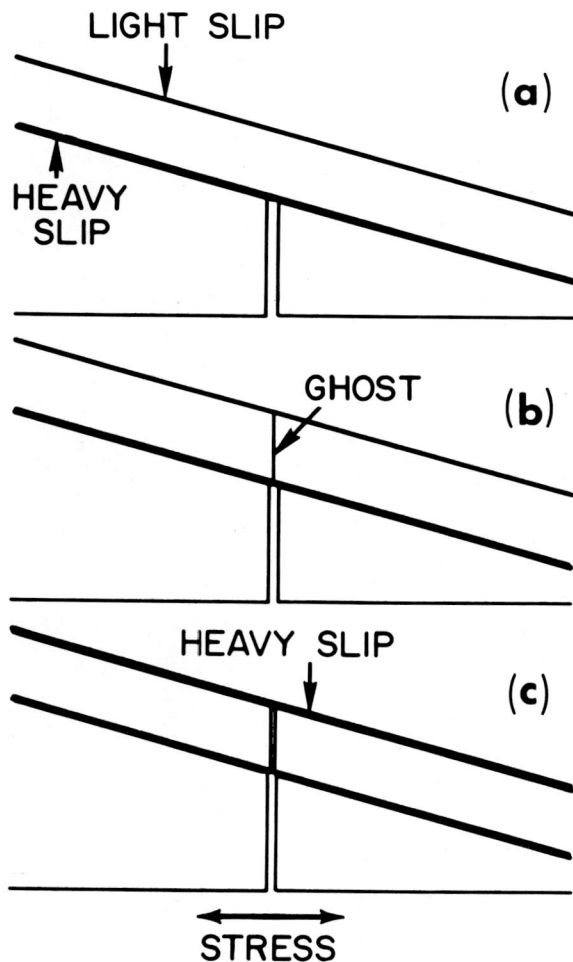

FIGURE 27 — Schematic representation of transcrystalline crack propagation in 70-30 brass tested in aqueous ammonia. After Edeleanu and Forty.[53]

V, respectively, but while $t_F$ was reduced in both cases, the application of the potential did not prevent cracking. Hoar and Booker do not appear to have extended these studies to non-tarnishing solutions.

A major conclusion of these potentiostatic studies is that, in solutions which contain cupric complexes before testing, cathodic polarization decreases the rate of failure but does not appear to completely inhibit failure, except in the case where copper is deposited on the specimen surface. This suggests that the earlier observations of cathodic protection can in fact be attributed to the inhibition of specimen dissolution, preventing the formation of cupric complexes. It is also significant that anodic polarization, which increases the rate of cracking, also appears to increase the rate of formation of tarnish.

*8. Metallographic Observations*

**a. Optical Microscopy.** Edeleanu and Forty[53] have studied the propagation of stress-corrosion cracks in notched monocrystals of 70-30 brass tested by bending in fresh aqueous ammonia of unspecified concentration. The appearance of cracks at the root of the notch followed an incubation period of 1-2 hr, presumably corresponding to the time required to produce a sufficient concentration of cupric complexes to cause failure. From the published micrographs it appears that the specimens remained tarnish-free during the subsequent studies, indicating that the composition of the solution did not enter the tarnishing range, see Figure 6.

The cracks were observed to propagate in bursts, each starting and stopping at a transverse slip band. The process is illustrated schematically in Figure 27. The crack appeared first as a fine "ghost" line, Figure 27(b), which then widened to a readily visible crack as slip occurred in the slip band at which the tip was arrested, Figure 27(c). This stage was followed by a further incubation period.

More recently, Forty and Humble[55] have studied the behavior of similar monocrystals in Mattsson's tarnishing solution of pH $\sim$ 7.1. While the crack-propagation process was not studied directly, it was shown that "crack-like penetrations" can be produced by repeated immersion of unstressed specimens followed by stressing in the *absence* of the environment. Later work on polycrystalline material by Pugh, Montague and Westwood, reported by Pugh,[65] established that intercrystalline failure could be produced in this way and that the resulting specimens were closely similar to those fractured in conventional tests. Note that these observations cast doubt on the classical definition according to which stress-corrosion cracking requires the simultaneous action of stress and corrosive attack.[92] Pugh and Westwood[56] have shown that similar tests using non-tarnishing solutions do not lead to cracking.

**b. Electron Microscopy.** On the basis of fractographic studies, McEvily and Bond[59] have claimed that the fracture of 70-30 brass in tarnishing solutions is discontinuous. The studies, carried out on cold-rolled polycrystals tested under constant load in Mattsson's solution of pH $\sim$ 7.2, indicated that parallel markings existed on the stress-corrosion fractures, Figure 28. It was claimed that these "striations", similar in appearance to those observed on the fracture surfaces of fatigue specimens, define the position of the crack front at successive stages during propagation, and hence provide evidence for a discontinuous fracture process. However, no evidence was presented to distinguish such markings from slip steps, formed on the fracture surfaces in the wake of the advancing crack tip. It was stated that the markings remained parallel over distances much larger than the grain size, but in view of the severe cold work (75% reduction) it could be argued that a preferred orientation exists and that slip steps might thus be expected to be approximately parallel in neighboring grains.

Pugh, Montague and Craig[52] have subsequently attempted to resolve this ambiguity. Preliminary experiments indicated that annealed specimens are unsuitable for such tests, since severe plastic deformation in the relatively soft material during propagation obscures any fine structure on the fracture surfaces. Studies of cold-worked specimens

confirmed the existence of markings, similar to those in Figure 28, but they were observed only on ∼ 10% of the total stress-corrosion fracture surfaces. For example, the field shown in Figure 29(a) contains a central band exhibiting the markings, but this region is bounded on both sides by areas which do not have a striated appearance. Studies of the stress-corrosion fracture surface near the transition to final ductile fracture have shown that the direction of cracking, as determined by the dimpled structure of the ductile region, is perpendicular to the parallel surface markings. This is illustrated in Figures 29(a) and 29(b) in which the two areas are separated by about one field and are shown in the correct relative orientation.

The results of these studies are consistent with the conclusions of McEvily and Bond, but do not rule out the possibility that the surface markings correspond to slip steps. Similar markings have been observed by optical microscopy on the fracture surfaces of the non-metal silver chloride embrittled in certain complex-forming aqueous solutions.[67,93,94] In that instance, it has been found[94] that the markings are matching on both halves of inter-

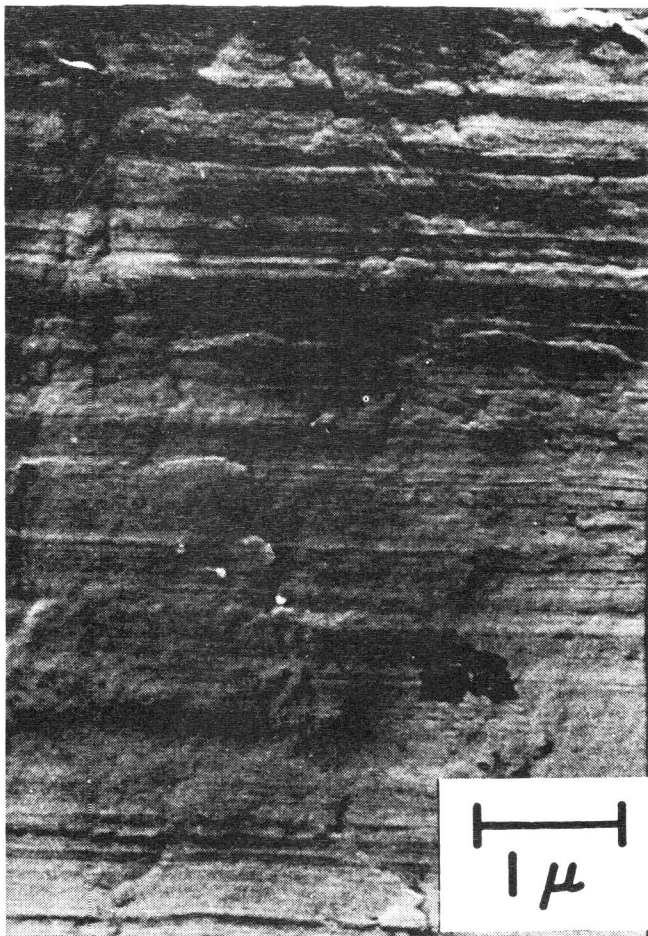

FIGURE 28 — Electron micrograph of replica of the stress-corrosion fracture surface of cold-rolled 70-30 brass tested in tarnishing ammoniacal solution, illustrating "striations". After McEvily and Bond.[59]

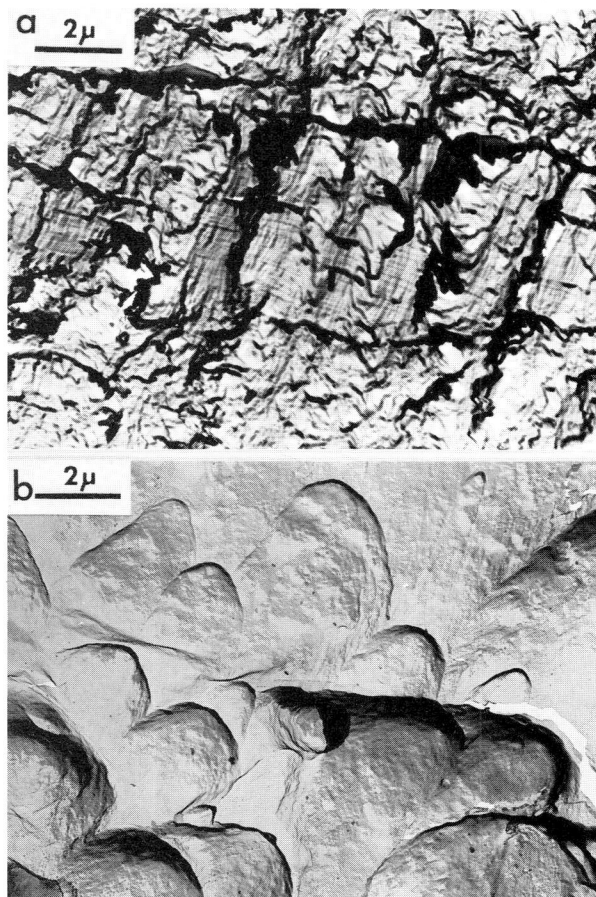

FIGURE 29 — Electron micrographs of replicas of the fracture surface of cold-rolled 70-30 brass tested in tarnishing ∼ 1N ammoniacal solution. (a) Stress-corrosion fracture. Note that the parallel markings, evident in the central band, cannot be detected in the upper and lower regions. (b) Adjacent ductile fracture. After Pugh et al.[52]

crystalline fracture surfaces, thus eliminating the possibility that they correspond to slip steps. Attempts are being made to provide similar evidence for the brass-ammonia case.[52]

At the present time, there is no information on the fracture surfaces of specimens tested in non-tarnishing solutions.

The transmission technique has also been used to provide information on the stress-corrosion process, but some of the results are difficult to reconcile with those for bulk specimens. Tromans and Nutting[66,84] carried out direct stress-corrosion tests on foils of 70-30 brass, stressing being carried out in the microscope specimen holder. Stressed foils immersed for 15 sec in a solution of 2 volume % of 0.88 s.g. ammonium hydroxide in water (*not* preconcentrated with cupric complex ions) were observed to undergo "some form of transgranular stress corrosion"; unstressed foils were reported to be immune to this type of attack. Further study indicated that the "cracks" were initiated on {111} slip planes, and that the initiation of slip-plane attack was directly associated with the emergence of dislocations. While these conclusions appear to be supported by electron micrographs, it is difficult to accept that stress-corrosion cracking could occur in fresh solutions within 15 sec. It was seen above, III.A.3, that cracking in conventional tests in fresh solutions is preceded by long incubation periods, corresponding to the time required to form a sufficient concentration of cupric complexes, e.g., Figure 16.

Tromans and Nutting[66] have also studied thin foils taken from bulk specimens of 70-30 brass stressed for 5 min in Mattsson's tarnishing solution of pH ~ 7.2. The stress-corroded surface was coated with an impermeable lacquer and foils were then prepared by controlled electropolishing from the uncoated side. The electron-microscope studies were again considered to indicate that crack initiation occurred at regions of high dislocation density. In annealed test pieces, pits, considered to be microcracks, were observed at grain boundaries steeply inclined to the surface while there was no evidence of attack within the grains. These findings were consistent with the macroscopic observation that failure of the annealed specimens was intercrystalline. It was not possible to demonstrate a positive relationship between the microcracks and dislocations because of the unfavorable orientation of the susceptible boundaries, but it was argued that such boundaries act as obstacles to mobile dislocations and also that dislocations tend to become trapped there during annealing. Tests on prestrained bulk specimens led to a transition from pure intercrystalline failure to a mixture of inter- and transcrystalline cracking. In this case, examination of the foils indicated that attack occurred at grain boundaries and also at planar arrays of dislocations within the grains. Dissolution of the planar arrays was considered to give rise to a series of microcracks which subsequently linked to form transcrystalline macrocracks. Analysis of attack traces again suggested that attack occurred along {111} glide planes.

## B. Failure of Other Binary Copper Alloys

The most complete study of the stress-corrosion cracking of binary copper alloys remains that of Thompson and Tracy,[80] published in 1949. In addition to copper and Cu-Zn alloys, see above III.A.4, these workers investigated the failure of binary alloys containing up to 0.9 wt.% P, 1.2 wt.% As, 1.0 wt.% Sb, 4 wt.% Si, 30 wt.% Ni, and 5 wt.% Al. The studies were confined to one ammoniacal environment, namely moist ammonia vapor. It was seen above, III.A.4, that this environment causes tarnishing in Cu-Zn alloys, but it is not clear from the paper whether tarnishing occurred in the other systems. Pure copper was immune to failure in the tarnishing environment, but the addition of

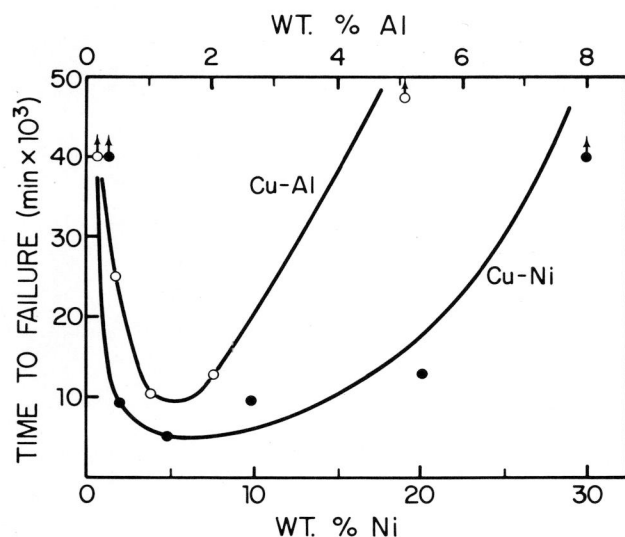

FIGURE 30 — Effect of solute concentration on $t_F$ for Cu-Al and Cu-Ni alloys tested in moist ammonia vapor. After Thompson and Tracy.[80]

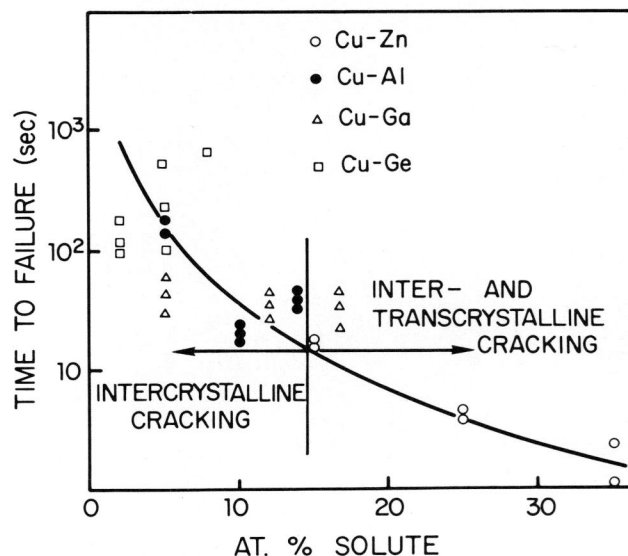

FIGURE 31 — Effect of solute concentration on $t_F$ of various binary copper alloys tested in aqueous ammonia. After Ohtani and Dodd.[15]

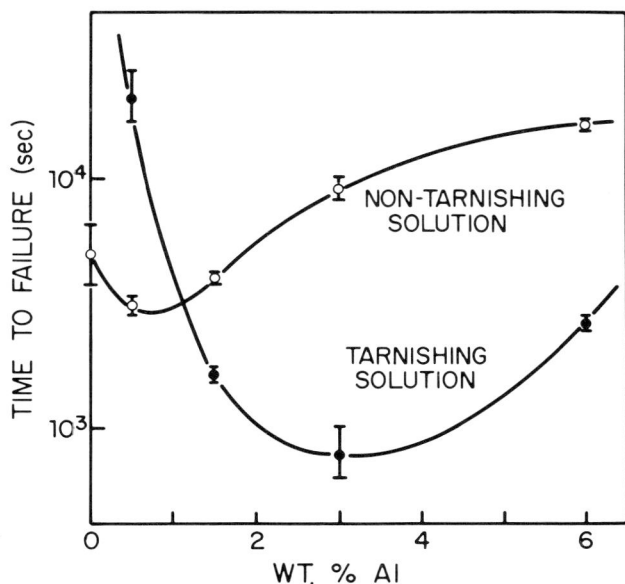

FIGURE 32 — Effect of Al content on $t_F$ of Cu-Al alloys tested in tarnishing and non-tarnishing $\sim$ 15N aqueous ammonia containing 8 g/l copper. After Pugh et al.[52]

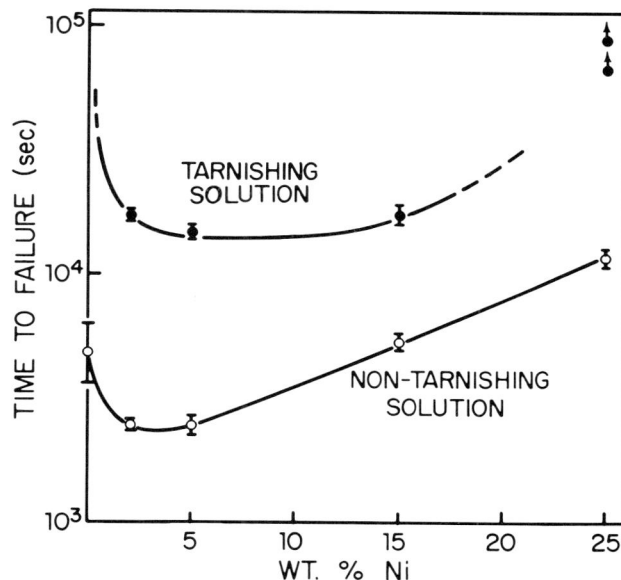

FIGURE 33 — Effect of Ni content on $t_F$ of Cu-Ni alloys tested in tarnishing and non-tarnishing $\sim$ 15N aqueous ammonia containing 8 g/l copper. After Pugh et al.[52]

the binary additions introduced susceptibility to stress-corrosion cracking in each case, $t_F$ decreasing rapidly with increasing solute concentration as for the Cu-Zn system, Figure 19. However, in contrast to the behavior of the brasses, further additions of each solute led to a gradual increase in $t_F$, e.g., Figure 30. Thompson and Tracy did not correlate their stress-corrosion data with observations on the path of fracture.

Ohtani and Dodd[15] have also studied the stress-corrosion failure of various binary copper alloys. The specimens were stressed in tension to produce a constant 5% strain and immersed in 50% aqueous ammonia (not preconcentrated with cupric ions). It was claimed that the data is best presented as a simple function of solute concentration, regardless of the nature of the species. Figure 31 illustrates their data for Cu-Al, Cu-Ga, and Cu-Ge, as well as for Cu-Zn alloys. On the basis of this data, it was suggested that stacking-fault energy, and hence dislocation structure is not a major factor in determining susceptibility to transgranular stress-corrosion cracking, since all Cu-Ge alloys were found to be relatively immune to transgranular attack while the high zinc alloys were quite susceptible, even though, for example, Cu-8 at.% Ge has approximately the same stacking-fault energy as Cu-24 at.% Zn. Unfortunately, no information is available on the surface condition of the specimens. The occurrence of transgranular cracking in the high zinc alloys indicates that the solution does not cause tarnishing in that case, but it is not known whether this is also true for the Cu-Ge alloys.

More recently, Pugh, Craig and Montague[52] have studied the behavior of Cu-Al and Cu-Ni alloys tested in both the tarnishing and non-tarnishing $\sim$ 15N aqueous ammonia solutions containing 8 g/l copper. The results of

stress-corrosion tests are shown in Figures 32 and 33. The curves can be seen to be similar to those obtained by Thompson and Tracy,[80] using the moist ammonia atmosphere, cf. Figure 30. However, it is surprising that the agreement with respect to solute content at the minimum $t_F$ is better for the non-tarnishing solution, the minimum $t_F$ occurring at $\sim$ 1 wt.% Al and $\sim$ 5 wt.% Ni in both cases, see Figures 32 and 33. This suggests that the ammonia-vapor test does not cause tarnishing in these alloys, despite the fact that specimens tested in the tarnishing $\sim$ 15N solution were found to undergo tarnishing as noted in III.A.2.

Comparison of the data of Figures 32 and 33 with that for the Cu-Zn system, Figure 19, shows that the rate of cracking, as indicated by $t_F$, is approximately the same in each system for the non-tarnishing solutions. However, the rate of cracking in tarnishing solutions decreases in the order Cu-Zn > Cu-Al > Cu-Ni. In particular, the failure of Cu-Ni alloys in the tarnishing solutions is slower than in the non-tarnishing solutions.

Metallographic examination of the fractured specimens from Figures 32 and 33 indicated that the relationship between the path of cracking in non-tarnishing solutions and dislocation structure noted for Cu-Zn alloys, III.A.4, was again in evidence. It was seen in II.A that deformed Cu-Al alloys exhibit a transition in dislocation structure from cellular to planar at $\sim$ 3.5 wt.%; failure was found to be predominantly intercrystalline for alloys containing < 3 wt.% Al, Figure 34(a) but at 6 wt.% Al cracking was predominantly transcrystalline, Figure 34(b). For Cu-Ni alloys, the dislocation structure is thought to be cellular for all binary alloys, II.A, and in this system there was no evidence of transcrystalline failure, cracking being inter-crystalline in each case, Figure 34(c). Failure in tarnishing solutions was predominantly intercrystalline for both Cu-Al and Cu-Ni alloys.

It can be concluded that all the binary alpha-phase copper alloys so far investigated have been found to be susceptible to stress-corrosion cracking in ammoniacal environments, the rate and path of failure being dependent on the nature of the solute. Based on the behavior of Cu-Ni and Cu-Al alloys (and Cu-Zn), it appears that the proposed relationship[9,66,84] between the path of cracking and dislocation structure is valid for non-tarnishing solutions. In tarnishing solutions, however, failure is predominantly intercrystalline for all alloys tested, regardless of the dislocation structure of the substrate.

### C. Discussion of Proposed Mechanisms

The major models which have been proposed to account for stress-corrosion cracking have been fully described in recent reviews.[65,95] For the present purpose, it is necessary only to discuss these models in terms of the failure characteristics outlined in the preceding sections.

A major fact, and one which unquestionably underlies the specific action of ammonia, is the essential role of cupric-ammonia complex ions in the failure process, III.A.3. On the basis of the generalized approach suggested by Nichols and Rostoker,[87] it might be considered that failure is mechanical and results from the adsorption of the cupric complexes at the metal surface. However, the adsorption model, discussed more fully below, V.B., is essentially a model for brittle fracture and is unlikely to be operative in the present case, because the cupric complex ions were seen to cause rapid dissolution of the metal, III.A.1, e.g., by reactions:

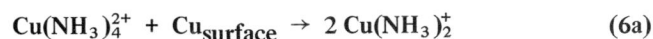

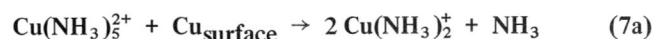

$$Cu(NH_3)_4^{2+} + Cu_{surface} \rightarrow 2\,Cu(NH_3)_2^{+} \tag{6a}$$

$$Cu(NH_3)_5^{2+} + Cu_{surface} \rightarrow 2\,Cu(NH_3)_2^{+} + NH_3 \tag{7a}$$

Such behavior does not favor brittle cracking since excessive dissolution causes blunting of the crack.

It appears more logical to consider that failure occurs by a dissolution-dependent process involving the reduction of the cupric complexes, i.e., by reactions of the type given in (6a) and (7a). This view, first suggested by Mattsson[58] on the basis of the correlation between his stress-corrosion data and the potential-pH diagram, III.A.3, is consistent with existing evidence for non-tarnishing solutions. It was seen that $t_F$ for specimens tested in non-tarnishing solutions decreased as the complex-ion concentration, and hence the rate of dissolution increased, Figures 6 and 8. It was noted, III.A.1, that the reactions involving the cupric complexes become autocatalytic in the presence of oxygen, because the resulting cuprous ions are oxidized to the cupric state, e.g.,

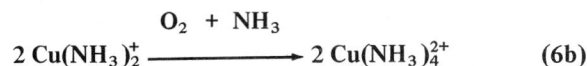

$$2\,Cu(NH_3)_2^{+} \xrightarrow{\;O_2\ +\ NH_3\;} 2\,Cu(NH_3)_4^{2+} \tag{6b}$$

Conversely, if oxygen is removed from the solution then the cupric-ion concentration becomes depleted and hence failure by such a model would be expected to be prevented. Such behavior has been observed, III.A.3. Note also that the reactions do not involve the presence of alloying elements, so that cracking might be expected to occur in pure copper. Earlier reports indicated that the pure metal was immune to such failure, but it was seen above that cracking does in fact occur in non-tarnishing solutions, III.A.4.

There is thus good evidence that failure in non-tarnishing solutions occurs by the surface reactions involving cupric complex ions, e.g., (6a) and (7a). However, several major questions remain to be answered. In particular, the way in which these reactions become localized at the crack tip rather than causing overall dissolution must be accounted for. Other observations to be explained include the apparent dependence of the path of cracking on dislocation structure, and the dependence of $t_F$ on the

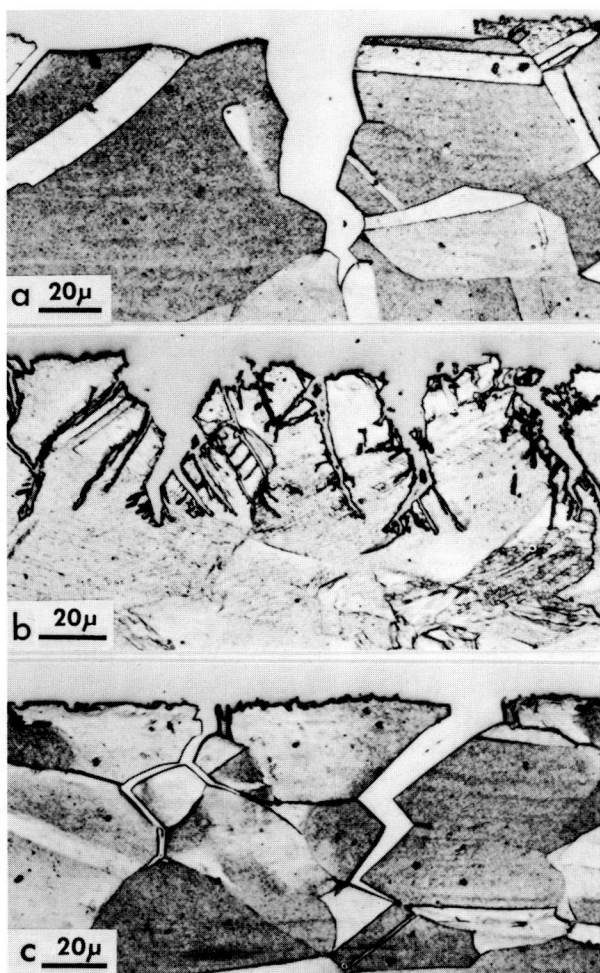

FIGURE 34 — Stress-corrosion cracking in binary copper alloys containing (a) 0.5 wt.% Al, (b) 6 wt.% Al, and (c) 2 wt.% Ni, tested at their 10% proof stress in non-tarnishing ~ 15N aqueous ammonia. Note the change from inter-crystalline to transcrystalline cracking caused by the increase in the Al content, cf. (a) and (b), and the intercrystalline nature of failure in the Cu-Ni alloy. After Pugh et al.[52]

140

solute concentration, III.A.4 and III.B. Each of these points can be rationalized in terms of the model proposed by Tromans and Nutting,[66,84] which suggests that cracking occurs primarily by a single-stage process involving rapid dissolution at dislocations created during stressing. Cracking by such a process can be expected to follow the path of greatest dislocation density and hence to be dependent on the dislocation structure of the solid. Tromans and Nutting considered that preferential dissolution at dislocations resulted from the segregation of solute atoms to these defects during stressing, thus making these sites "more reactive". On this basis, it could be argued that the rate of cracking would increase as the solute concentration increased.

Tromans and Nutting did not consider the chemistry of the process, but it is evident that the model must now be reconciled with the demonstrated importance of the cupric complex ions. In the case of Cu-Zn alloys it could be argued that the cupric complexes react preferentially with the solute, since zinc forms an extremely stable complex ion with ammonia.[46] However, this explanation is unlikely to be valid for Cu-Ni alloys, and certainly does not appear to be applicable to the Cu-Al system, since aluminum does not appear to form complexes with aqueous ammonia.[46] Moreover, the failure of pure copper in non-tarnishing solutions would seem to eliminate the role of solute atoms in the dissolution process. Thus it appears more realistic to accept the proposal that the reaction between the cupric complexes and copper atoms at the metal surface, Reactions (6a) and (7a), represents the basic dissolution reactions, and that the presence of alloying elements simply influences the rate and path of cracking.

Accepting this view, the correlation between path of cracking and dislocation structure can be rationalized if it is assumed that Reactions (6a) and (7a) proceed preferentially at dislocations. While it is generally believed that emergent dislocations in pure metals are more reactive than the matrix, the difference is thought to be small[96] and thus the preferential attack would not be expected to lead to cracking. However, in the absence of experimental evidence, it is not possible to rule out such a mechanism in this specific instance. Etch pit studies on pure copper in preconcentrated ammoniacal solutions are necessary to resolve this question.

An alternative possibility, previously discussed for this system,[72] can be based on the suggestion that stress-corrosion phenomena involve stress-dependent surface reactions.[97] Applied to the present case, this would require that the activation energies for Reactions (6a) and (7a) are significantly reduced at regions of stress in the lattice. The increased rate of cracking associated with the addition of solute atoms could then be attributed to the increased ability of the alloy to sustain stress concentrations. On the basis of this model, the principal regions of stress in materials having cellular dislocations would be expected to occur at grain boundaries, giving rise to intercrystalline attack, while in materials having planar arrays stress concentrations may also exist within the grains, leading to transcrystalline attack. Unfortunately, it is difficult to devise a critical experiment to test the validity of this model.

Other dissolution-dependent models may be advocated. These include the classical film-rupture model proposed by Champion[98] and developed by Logan,[99] according to which the basic cause of cracking is the local rupture of passive surface films by slip-step emergence and the subsequent prevention of repassivation in this area by further plastic deformation, the crack propagating by continued localized dissolution and plastic deformation. In the present case, the passive film could be considered to correspond to the tarnish in tarnishing solutions, but in non-tarnishing solutions the existence of a passive film is in doubt, III.A.1. Moreover, as Parkins[95] has pointed out, the film-rupture model is essentially a model for trans-crystalline cracking; there is no apparent reason for failure by such a mechanism to follow grain boundaries. This criticism also applied to the revised film-rupture model put forward by Swann and his co-workers,[19,100] discussed in IV.B.

A final dissolution-dependent model which must be considered is that proposed by Hoar and his asso-ciates,[54,101-103] based on the concept that a yielding metal is more reactive than the non-yielding metal. Thus it may be argued that the reaction between the complex ions and the surface copper atoms occurs preferentially at the yielding metal at the tip of an advancing crack, the non-deforming metal at the crack faces being less reactive. However, while Hoar and Scully[103] have demonstrated that the anodic current density of an austenitic stainless steel wire maintained at -0.14 V increased with increasing strain rate, the interpretation of this effect remains to be established. For example, it could be argued that the increasing current results not from the disarraying of the metal surface per se, but from the increased frequency of rupture of passive surface films.[65]

The mechanisms discussed above have been considered in terms of the characteristics of failure in non-tarnishing solutions. In tarnishing solutions, significant differences in behavior exist.

(1) The activation energies are different for failures of alpha-brass in tarnishing and non-tarnishing solutions, III.A.5.

(2) The rate of cracking of Cu-Zn and Cu-Al alloys in tarnishing solutions exhibits a greater dependence on solute concentration compared to the rate in non-tarnishing solutions, and, in particular, pure copper does not undergo cracking in the former, III.A.4 and III.B.

(3) The path of cracking in tarnishing solutions is predominantly intercrystalline for all alpha alloys investigated, regardless of the dislocation structure of the metal substrate, III.A.4 and III.B.

(4) In contrast to non-tarnishing solutions, failure of alpha-brass in tarnishing solutions is unaffected by deaeration of the solution, III.A.3.

(5) Cracking in tarnishing solutions can be produced by cycles of separate immersion of unstressed

specimens followed by stressing in the absence of the environment: similar experiments with non-tarnishing solutions do not lead to cracking, III.A.8.

In the light of these differences, it is questionable whether the same mechanism is operative in both types of solution. Mattsson[58] has also attributed the failure of alpha-brass in tarnishing solutions to the dissolution reaction (6a), suggesting that this reaction is prevented within the grains by the presence of the tarnish, but that it can proceed at the grain boundaries because the tarnish was considered to be porous at these regions; presumably the role of stress in such a model is to widen the crack by plastic deformation, thus facilitating access of the solution. On the other hand, Pugh and Westwood[56] have suggested that the mechanisms are basically different and that failure in tarnishing solutions occurs by the tarnish-rupture model.

The original concept on which the tarnish-rupture model is based was provided by Forty and Humble,[55] but the development of the model to its present form is due largely to the subsequent studies of McEvily and Bond.[59] According to the model, failure in tarnishing solutions proceeds by the repeated formation and rupture of the brittle tarnish. This model is illustrated schematically in Figure 35. The first stage involves the formation and rupture of the tarnish layer, Figure 35(a) and (b). The resulting crack does not propagate into the brass substrate but becomes blunted by plastic deformation,[4] Figure 35(c). However, fresh brass is then exposed to the environment, allowing the tarnishing reaction to penetrate further *into* the metal, Figure 35(d). When the tarnish attains a critical thickness cracking again occurs, Figure 35(e), and again the crack becomes blunted when it encounters the substrate, Figure 35(f). Cracking thus proceeds discontinuously, failure being confined to the brittle layer.

The tarnish-rupture model is in qualitative agreement with much of the experimental evidence. The model predicts that the resulting fracture surfaces are striated, Figure 35(g), and thus the fractographic observations reported by McEvily and Bond[59] can be considered to provide strong support for the model. However, it was seen that the interpretation of the markings remains to be established, III.A.8. The occurrence of intercrystalline cracking is fully consistent with the observation that tarnishing proceeds preferentially along grain boundaries, III.A.2. Moreover, the observation that cracking is produced by the separate action of the environment and the stress, III.A.8, is also consistent with the model.

A significant feature of the model is that it indicates that the rate of cracking is determined by the rate of growth of the tarnish. No quantitative correlation has been made of these rates, although Hoar and Booker[54] have claimed that the rate of tarnishing of the alpha-brasses increases with increasing Zn content of the alloy, III.A.2; the rate of cracking in tarnishing solutions was also seen to increase with increasing Zn content, III.A.4. Moreover, the polarization experiments of Hoar and Booker[54] indicated that anodic polarization reduced $t_F$ and also accelerated the formation of the black film, III.A.7. It is evident that quantitative studies of tarnish growth, e.g., by ellipsometry, are necessary to confirm this possible correlation. The effect of such factors as Zn content, application of external potential, and temperature could then be compared for both processes. For example, it would then be possible to compare the temperature dependence of the rate of tarnishing with that reported for the rate of cracking in tarnishing solutions, III.A.5.

Reliable measurements of the rate of tarnish growth would also permit an estimate of the cracking rate and thus allow comparison with experimentally determined values. As McEvily and Bond[59] have pointed out, the model predicts that the rate of cracking $d\ell/dt$, can be approximated by

$$\frac{d\ell}{dt} = \frac{x}{t_x} \qquad (12)$$

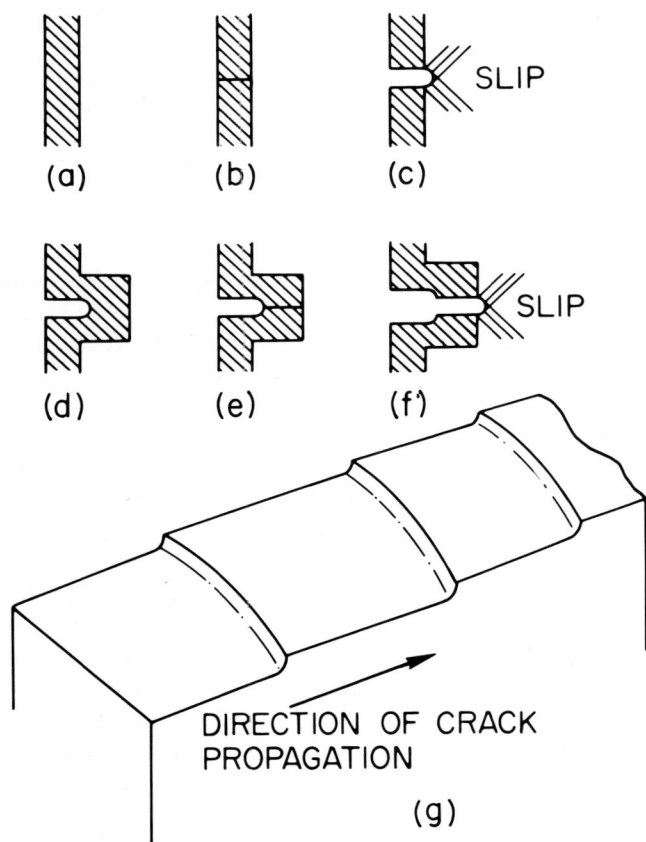

FIGURE 35 — Schematic representation of tarnish-rupture model. After Pugh.[65]

---

[4]This is in contrast to an earlier model proposed by Edeleanu and Forty[53] in which it was suggested that cracks attaining high velocity in brittle surface layers would then propagate for a finite distance into the metal substrate. There is no evidence for this behavior in alpha-brass but it is thought to occur in titanium alloys stressed in liquid nitrogen tetroxide.[104]

where x is the inter-striation spacing and $t_x$ is the time required for the growth of the film to thickness x. On the basis of the data presented in Figure 15, McEvily and Bond considered that growth is parabolic and hence that

$$x = k \sqrt{t_k} \qquad (13)$$

where k is a constant. Substituting for $t_x$ in Relation (12), they obtained

$$\frac{d\ell}{dt} = \frac{k^2}{x} \qquad (14)$$

From the data in Figure 15(A),k was calculated to be $1.2 \times 10^{-8}$ in$^2$/hr and, estimating the interstriation spacing from fractographs such as Figure 28, rates of cracking were calculated to be 0.0006 in/hr at a gross stress of 31,000 psi and 0.0025 in/hr at a gross stress of 67,000 psi. The corresponding experimentally determined rates were 0.004 in/hr and 0.017 in/hr, respectively. The difference between the calculated and observed values can be partly attributed to the uncertainty in measuring the interstriation spacing, see Figures 28 and 29. In addition, it was seen that the reliability of the data of Figure 15, obtained by a taper-sectioning method, is open to some question, III.A.2.

A major question which remains to be answered concerns the mechanism of film rupture and its proposed dependence on film thickness. The work of Forty and Humble[55] suggested that rupture of the surface film resulted from massive slip in the substrate. On the other hand, McEvily and Bond[59] argued that such slip is not necessary, and, as evidence for this, pointed out that crack initiation occurred in severely cold-worked 70-30 brass tested at stresses considerably below the macroscopic flow stress. In their tests, the load was applied to cold-worked specimens *before* exposure to the environment, permitting any initial plastic deformation to occur. In the absence of the solution, no further extension of the statically-stressed specimen was detected, and hence it was concluded that creep can be discounted. Introduction of the environment caused tarnishing and immediate crack initiation. McEvily and Bond pointed out that it is unlikely that the growth of a thin oxide, probably < 1000 Å thick, can lead to a sufficient increase in stress to cause further massive deformation in the substrate. A similar argument can be applied to film rupture during crack propagation. Mechanically, the configuration immediately following blunting of the crack by deformation in the substrate, Figure 35(f), is stable, and further motion of the arrays of dislocations created during blunting would require an increase in the local stress concentration. Again, it can be questioned whether the growth of a thin oxide film at the crack tip can provide a sufficient increase in stress to cause massive glide.

A factor which has not been adequately taken into account in the preceding argument is the role of epitaxial stresses. The increased volume of the oxide over that of the metal (volume ratio $\sim 1.64$) leads to the creation of epitaxial stresses near the oxide-metal interface; the stresses are compressive in the oxide and tensile in the metal. It is possible that the epitaxial stress in the metal, acting in conjunction with the applied tensile stress, causes sufficient dislocation motion to rupture the surface film. Moreover, if it is assumed that the magnitude of the epitaxial stress increases with increasing film thickness then it is apparent that this effect can account for the dependence of film rupture on the thickness of the film.

An alternative approach is to discount the role of dislocations, and to consider that the film-rupture process involves purely brittle fracture. In the absence of evidence of plasticity, the tarnish can be regarded to be completely brittle at room temperature, so that it is possible that rupture occurs when a flaw in the tarnish satisfies the Griffith condition. Developing this approach, and assuming that the size of the flaw is directly proportional to the thickness of the tarnish, Pugh and Sedriks[105] have derived the experimentally observed relationship between the rate of cracking and the stress-intensity parameter $\sigma_g \sqrt{\ell}$, namely

$$\frac{d\ell}{dt} = A\sigma_g^2 \ell \qquad (11)$$

The nature of the flaws was not established. The fact that the tarnish is being continuously dissolved by the environment might be considered to rule out the relevance of surface flaws, since a Joffe effect[106] could be expected. However, the observation that etch grooves are formed at grain boundaries in the tarnish, III.A.2, led Pugh and Sedriks to suggest that these may provide a sufficient notch effect to initiate brittle failure. The alternative that the flaws are internal was also considered.[105]

The possibility that epitaxial stresses may play a role in the brittle fracture of the tarnish must also be considered. The magnitude of these stresses, which are compressive in the oxide, can be expected to be greatest near the tarnish-metal interface, decreasing with distance from the interface. The interaction between these compressive stresses and the applied tensile stresses is not understood in detail, but it might be argued that the film would have to grow to a critical thickness before it becomes subjected to a net tensile stress, and it is possible that this effect may account for the suggested dependence of film rupture on film thickness.

Finally, it should be noted that service failures in brasses are considered to occur under tarnishing conditions so that, in terms of the tarnish-rupture model, it is necessary to reduce the rate of tarnish growth to reduce susceptibility to season-cracking. The most satisfactory solution is clearly to provide a "built-in" inhibitor—that is, the addition of a minor alloying element which would significantly reduce the rate of tarnishing but which would not adversely influence the mechanical properties of the alloy. It was seen, III.A.4, that with the exception of silicon, elements which have been added have had little effect on stress-corrosion resistance.

To summarize this discussion, it is considered that two different mechanisms of stress-corrosion cracking can operate during the exposure of stressed alpha-phase copper alloys to aqueous ammonia. In non-tarnishing solutions, failure is thought to be dissolution-dependent, involving autocatalytic reactions between cupric-ammonia complex ions and copper atoms at the metal surface, Reactions (6) and (7). Failure in tarnishing solutions is believed to occur by the tarnish-rupture model, according to which cracking proceeds by the repeated formation and rupture of the brittle surface film. The latter is considered to be responsible for service failures in commercial alloys.

## IV. Failure of Cu-Au and Ag-Au Alloys in Aqueous Ferric Chloride and in Aqua Regia

Although stress-corrosion failures have been reported in low-carat gold alloys used for jewelry and in silver dental alloys,[107] failure of these alloys cannot be regarded as a serious practical problem. Nevertheless, a significant amount of research has been carried out on Cu-Au and Ag-Au alloys in recent years, presumably because of their attractiveness for mechanistic studies—they exhibit a continuous range of solid solubility, II.A, high-purity alloys can be readily prepared, and there are a number of aqueous environments which cause failure. In addition, Cu-Au alloys exhibit LRO, II.A, and hence studies can be made to determine the effect or ordering on the stress-corrosion process.

### A. Characteristics of Failure

Graf has carried out extensive studies on these and related alloys; these are fully discussed elsewhere in this volume.[3] A major conclusion of his work is that stress-corrosion susceptibility in homogeneous alloys is associated with the presence of alloy components that are more noble than the principal metallic component of the alloy. This is illustrated by data for Cu-Au and Ag-Au alloys tested in aqua regia, Figure 36.[108] The pure metals and the alloys containing $> \sim 40$ at.% Au were not susceptible to stress-corrosion cracking, but failed because general dissolution resulted in a reduction in cross-section and eventual ductile failure. The addition of gold to copper and silver was found to introduce stress-corrosion susceptibility, resulting in the observed decrease in $t_F$. Conversely, gold is not rendered susceptible to stress-corrosion cracking by the addition of the less noble elements copper and silver.

Graf has pointed out that aqua regia dissolves gold as well as copper and silver. However, closely similar behavior was observed with environments such as aqueous ferric chloride which attack only the less noble components.[108] This observation led to the conclusion that a corrosive medium which causes cracking must react with at least the less noble component of the homogeneous alloy. Note that this condition predicts that cracking can occur in a wide variety of environments, in contrast to the conventional view that specific media are required.[82]

The observation that the presence of a noble solute is necessary for the occurrence of stress-corrosion cracking was considered to be general and was claimed to operate in other alloy systems, including those based on aluminum and magnesium.[109] It was acknowledged that exceptions occur, notably the failure of Cu-Zn alloys in aqueous ammonia. However, it was pointed out that the alpha-brasses do not fail in environments such as aqueous ferric chloride, concentrated hydrochloric acid, and nitric acid, and hence the rule breaks down only in the case of ammonia, which was considered "to behave in a special manner towards copper".

On the basis of his work, Graf[3] has concluded that failure in Cu-Au and Ag-Au alloys results from the

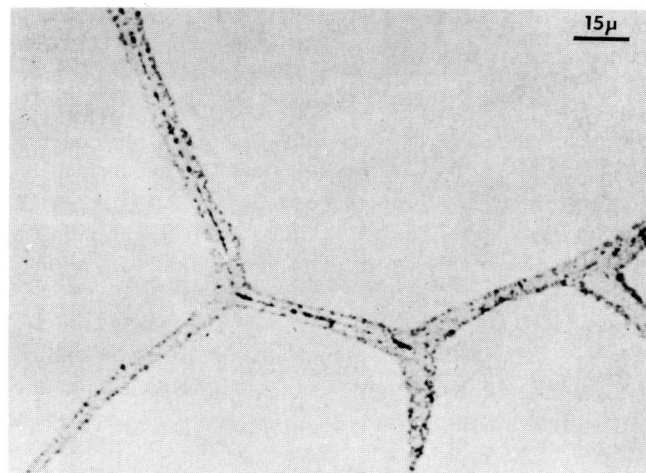

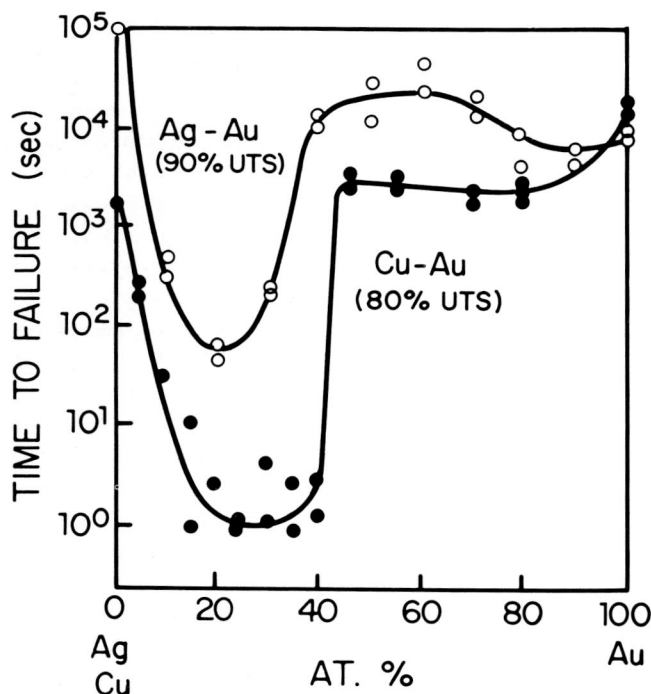

FIGURE 36 — Dependence of $t_F$ of Cu-Au and Ag-Au alloys tested in aqua regia on the Au content. After Graf and Budke.[108]

FIGURE 37 — Section of Cu$_3$Au after exposure (unstressed) to aqueous ferric chloride, illustrating preferential growth of gold-rich phase along grain boundaries. After Bakish and Robertson.[111]

formation of gold-rich surface layers. In environments such as aqueous ferric chloride which do not attack gold, the gold-rich layer was thought to be formed simply by the selective removal of copper or silver. However, in solutions which also dissolve gold, e.g., aqua regia, Graf considered that the gold is re-precipitated. In those solutions where gold is dissolved as a complex ion, e.g., 10% $KCN-H_2O_2$ solution, re-precipitation does not occur and stress-corrosion cracking is not observed.

There is now considerable experimental evidence to support the view that a gold-rich surface layer is formed.

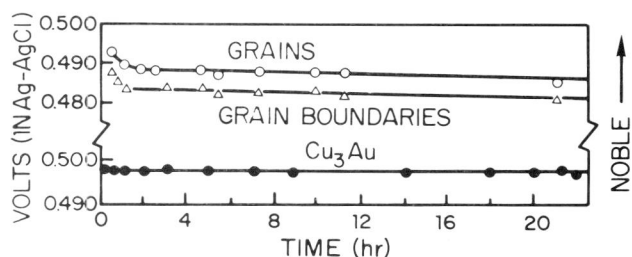

FIGURE 38 – Potential-time relationship for unstressed $Cu_3Au$ immersed in aqueous ferric chloride. After Bakish and Robertson.[110]

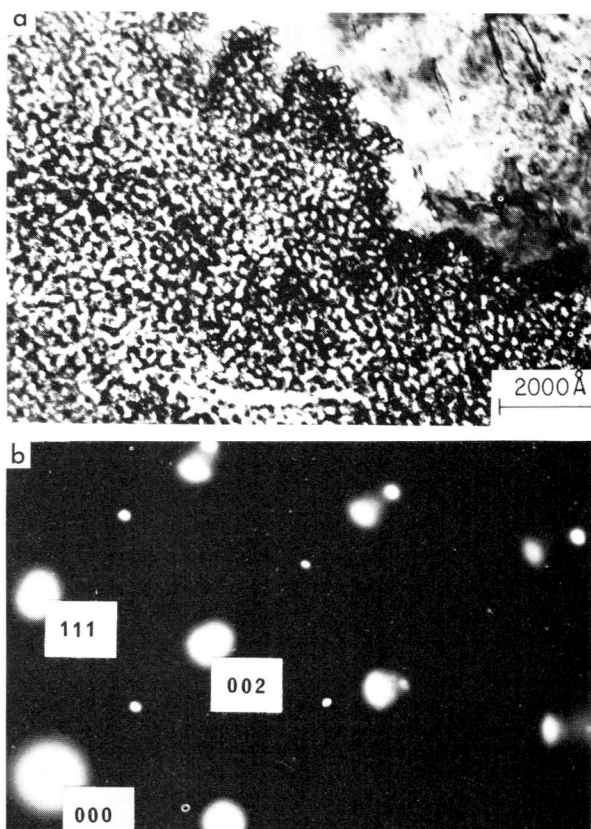

FIGURE 39 – (a) Transmission electron micrograph of foil of a Cu-25 at.% Au alloy (ordered) exposed to aqueous ferric chloride for 1 minute. (b) Selected-area electron diffraction pattern from the corroded area, showing the sharp reflections of the ordered alloy and the diffuse reflections of the gold-rich lattice. After Pickering and Swann.[19]

Bakish and Robertson[110,111] have shown that dissolution of unstressed $Cu_3Au$ in aqueous ferric chloride proceeds by the dissolution of copper only, since not even traces of gold were detected by spectrographic analysis of the solutions. Optical metallographic studies of annealed polycrystals indicated that the reaction proceeds preferentially at grain boundaries, Figure 37, resulting in the formation of what was considered to be a "gold sponge". Continued exposure led to complete intercrystalline penetration of the specimen. Electrochemical experiments revealed that the grain boundaries were anodic with respect to the grains, Figure 38, the potential difference remaining finite and constant for long periods of immersion. Bakish and Robertson reported that the preferential attack in annealed $Cu_3Au$ also occurred at incoherent twin boundaries and subgrain boundaries in addition to grain boundaries; in plastically deformed $Cu_3Au$ additional active sites were found to be located at slip bands, particularly in the vicinity of grain and twin boundaries. In a later paper, Robertson and Tetelman[112] suggested that the activity of the slip bands is largely due to the elastic strain energy of aggregates of dislocations held up by Lomer-Cottrell barriers.

Pickering and Swann[19] studied the dissolution process by means of electron microscopy, using the transmission technique. Foils taken from a series of Cu-Au alloys were immersed in aqueous ferric chloride and aqua regia, and also in solutions which do not cause stress-corrosion cracking. The nature of attack in the solutions which cause cracking was found to be essentially the same for alloys containing 5, 25 and 40 at.% Au; the observations for the 25 and 40 at.% alloys were essentially the same in the ordered or disordered conditions. In each case, selected-area electron diffraction patterns from corroded regions of the foils indicated the presence of a gold-rich lattice in addition to the parent lattice, and established that a strong epitaxial relationship existed between the two lattices. For example, Figure 39 illustrates the results obtained for the alloy containing 25 at.% Au exposed to aqueous ferric chloride.

Consideration of the transmission electron micrographs and the selected-area diffraction patterns led Pickering and Swann to conclude that corrosive attack proceeded by the formation of tubular pits, nucleated at grain boundaries, twin boundaries, and, in the case of ordered material, antiphase boundaries; there was no evidence for preferential attack at emergent dislocations. The clusters of pits were observed to gradually impinge on one another until the whole surface became pitted. While these conclusions concerning the morphology of attack are substantiated by the published micrographs, the conclusion that tubular pits are formed is open to some question.

Comparative studies of foils immersed in non-cracking solutions, e.g., aqueous KCN, revealed that general dissolution occurred; no coherent gold-rich phase or tubular pits were observed in these cases.

More recently, Pickering and Wagner[113] and Pickering[114] have studied the dissolution of Cu-Au alloys by means of several techniques, including X-ray diffraction, electron diffraction, and electron-probe microanalysis. These studies, fully described elsewhere in this volume,[114] provided conclusive evidence for the formation of the gold-rich surface layer in specimens exposed to solutions which cause cracking. These workers also considered the mechanism of dissolution in some detail. No evidence was found for the ionization and reprecipitation of gold, and it was concluded that the gold-rich layer is formed by the preferential anodic dissolution of copper, accompanied by solid-state diffusion of both copper and gold.

The characteristics of the stress-corrosion cracking of $Cu_3Au$ in aqueous ferric chloride have been studied by Bakish and Robertson.[111,115] In polycrystalline specimens, failure was predominantly intercrystalline and the observations were essentially the same for both the ordered and disordered conditions.[111] Cracking also occurred in single crystals and again no differences in behavior was noted for ordered and disordered specimens.[115] Thus it appears that the difference in dislocation structures in the two conditions, II.A., does not lead to a detectable change in stress-corrosion behavior.

Cracking in single crystals was found to be initiated at active sites along slip band clusters.[115] However, further growth of the crack did not follow the trace of the slip band or other crystallographic direction, but invariably proceeded along a path perpendicular to the tensile axis. The papers by Bakish and Robertson imply that preferential dissolution of copper occurs only at the active sites. If this were so, the observation that the cracks do not follow the slip bands would suggest that the cracks, initiated at an active site, can then propagate through the normal lattice. However, on the basis of the electron-microscope observations of Pickering and Swann,[19] it appears more likely that the whole surface becomes attacked, although penetration may be more rapid along certain paths. Thus it is probable that the initial cracks observed by Bakish and Robertson were confined to a shallow surface layer. Tests in which the ferric-chloride solution was removed after crack initiation resulted in the halting of the crack, indicating the essential role of the environment during crack propagation.

Bakish[116] subsequently found that single crystals of $Cu_3Au$ which were immersed, unstressed, in 2% aqueous ferric chloride for one month and then bent, failed by cleavage along $\{110\}$ planes. It was suggested that cleavage occurred through a thin layer of gold-rich "sponge" formed by the preferential leaching of copper along $\{110\}$ planes.

## B. Discussion of Proposed Mechanisms

The preceding section indicates that the stress-corrosion cracking of Cu-Au and Ag-Au alloys involves the formation of a gold-rich surface layer which is epitaxed to the parent lattice. In aqueous ferric chloride, this layer is formed by the selective removal of copper or silver. In the case of aqua regia, which also attacks gold, it has been suggested that this layer is formed by the re-precipitation of gold. Alternatively, it is possible that the formation of the gold-rich layer in aqua regia simply results from a greater rate of removal of copper or silver than gold. It is evident

that, regardless of the precise mechanism of formation, the process requires solid-state diffusion of copper and silver across the layer, and also some rearrangement of gold atoms to maintain a relatively dense film.

Swann and his colleagues[19,100] have suggested that the mechanism of stress-corrosion cracking in these alloys involves the formation of tubular-etch pits. In its most recent form,[100] the model proposes that the failure proceeds by the following stages:

(1) The formation of the gold-rich surface film.
(2) Rupture of the film by slip-step emergence.
(3) Tunnel corrosion at the exposed metal along the slip trace, leading to the formation of tubular pits, Figure 40(a).
(4) Ductile rupture of a slot weakened by many tubular pits, Figure 40(b).

It was noted above that the presence of tubular etch pits was deduced from electron micrographs and from electron-diffraction studies, but that the interpretation of the data is open to some question. The mechanism of formation of such pits has not been fully explained,[65] although Westwood[117] has suggested that it may involve the preferential adsorption of step-poisons.

Alternatively, Graf[3] has proposed that stress-corrosion cracking in these alloys proceeds by anodic dissolution at the crack tip, essentially by a film-rupture mechanism of the type proposed by Champion[98] and Logan,[99] see above, III.C., with the gold-rich layer corresponding to the passive film. This layer is considered to be continuous on the specimen surface and on the faces of the crack, but plastic deformation at the crack tip is thought to continuously rupture the layer, exposing the underlying lattice and thus permitting localized anodic dissolution.

It appears unlikely that this simple concept of anodic dissolution can adequately account for crack propagation, since dissolution was seen to lead to the formation of the coherent surface layer and thus does not in itself cause significant extension of the crack. Clearly, the stage of crack growth corresponds to the rupture of the surface film. In this respect, the failure is analogous to the tarnish-rupture model, III.C., in that cracking results from the formation and rupture of a weak surface film which is

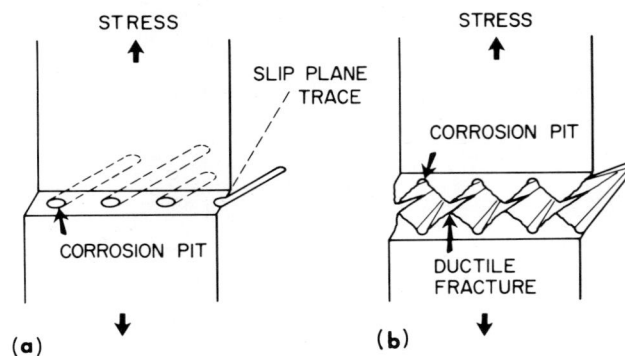

FIGURE 40 — Schematic representation of mechanism of stress-corrosion cracking proposed by Swann et al.[19,100]

epitaxed to the base material and which penetrates into the substrate. In the case of the tarnish, the film is brittle at room temperature, whereas in the present case the observed weakness of the film can be attributed to a high concentration of vacancies and possibly macroscopic voids. There is no direct evidence for the existence of these defects but it is clear that the selective removal of the major alloying component must result in a highly imperfect lattice.

Other similarities exist between the failure of these alloys and that of alpha-brass in tarnishing ammoniacal solutions. For example, the growth of the gold-rich phase in polycrystalline $Cu_3Au$ immersed, unstressed, in aqueous ferric chloride proceeds preferentially along grain boundaries; failure of stressed specimens is intercrystalline. The path of fracture is the same in both ordered and disordered specimens, and therefore is not sensitive to the change in dislocation structure in the two conditions, II.A.

As in the case of the tarnish-rupture model, a major question to be answered concerns the mechanism of film rupture. It is possible that film rupture is essentially continuous in this system, resulting from continuous plastic deformation at the crack tip. On the other hand, the possibility that the film grows to a critical thickness before rupture, as in the tarnish-rupture model, cannot be ruled out. It is evident that further studies, particularly fractography, are necessary to resolve this aspect of the failure process.

## V. Failure of Beta-Brasses in the Presence of Water Vapor

Unlike the case of the alpha-brasses, these materials have received little attention since Bailey's extensive review of 1961,[2] so that this section is largely a critical summary of that paper.

Beta-brasses undergo stress-corrosion cracking in aqueous ammonia, but there is insufficient interpretable data to warrant a discussion of this failure. For example, while it has been shown[34,69,118,119] that cracking in moist ammonia is transcrystalline, there appear to have been no tests in which the composition of the aqueous ammonia was varied, nor has the surface condition of the fractured specimens been discussed in detail. The beta-brasses also fail simply in the presence of water, and it is this type of failure which has received greatest attention.[2] Since binary beta-brass has little commercial application, most of these studies have been carried out on higher-strength alloys containing additional alloying elements, notably aluminum.[34,35,120-122] However, studies of the binary alloys have established that embrittlement does occur,[33] and thus it appears that the role of the additional elements may be simply to modify the basic mechanism of failure. The following discussion is confined largely to the binary alloys.

### A. Characteristics of Failure

Bailey has observed that binary $\beta'$-phase alloys undergo stress-corrosion cracking when they are stressed in moist air

under constant tensile stress of $\sim 80\%$ UTS,[33] while failure does not occur at $\sim 60\%$ UTS.[120] It was seen above, II.B., that creep-rupture also occurs at these high stress levels. However, the failures in moist air differed from the creep failures in that the time to failure was drastically reduced, no necking occurred, and the fracture mode changed from transcrystalline to intercrystalline. A typical intercrystalline stress-corrosion crack is illustrated in Figure 41.

In considering the effects of alloying elements on the susceptibility to intergranular cracking it is necessary to separate the effects of composition of the solid solution from those arising from the introduction of brittle and ductile second phases. In this respect, the reported changes in susceptibility with Zn content must be examined very carefully. In the $\beta' + \gamma$ phase region, the $\gamma$ is precipitated at the grain boundaries[123] as well as within the grains, and the formation of semi-continuous networks of brittle $\gamma$ at the $\beta'$ grain boundaries would tend to localize fracture in these regions even in the absence of moisture. It is significant, therefore, that Bailey[33] describes the fracture of $\beta' + \gamma$ alloys in dry air as tending to an intercrystalline path. Similarly the introduction of substantial amounts of Al, which has a high 'zinc-equivalent', will similarly favor grain-boundary precipitation of $\gamma$.[35] Conversely, the reduction of Zn content to below 46 wt.% results in an $a +$

FIGURE 41 — Intercrystalline crack in binary $\beta'$-brass containing 47.3 wt.% Zn after stressing for 2 hours at 20 tons/in$^2$ in the atomsphere. After Bailey.[2]

$\beta'$ structure, and since $a$ is not embrittled by moisture and is more ductile than $\beta'$ a reduction in the susceptibility would be expected and has been observed.[33]

Nevertheless, it is well established that embrittlement occurs in complex alloys in which it cannot be attributed to the presence of second phases.[34,35,122] In these instances, the alloys fail at stresses well below the 80% tensile stress level required to embrittle binary alloys. This may be interpreted as indicating that strengthening of the $\beta'$ solid solution by alloying increases susceptibility to intergranular cracking. However, even in the case of the higher-strength alloys, failures are obtained only at stresses above those required to initiate plastic flow,[34,35] indicating that dislocation motion is essential for embrittlement to occur.

The exact nature of the aqueous environment is also important in determining susceptibility to intergranular cracking. While data is limited with regard to the effects of changes in environment on the susceptibility of binary $\beta'$ alloys, the complex alloys show a progressive increase in the susceptibility to intergranular cracking as the environment is changed from moist air to distilled water to 3% aqueous sodium chloride.[2,34] Microscopic examination of specimens immersed for long periods in saline solutions revealed no evidence of grain-boundary attack.[120] Further, Perryman[35] has reported that in a 3% NaCl solution the grain boundaries in the highly susceptible 3 and 4% Al alloys were in fact cathodic with respect to the grain interiors, although in a less susceptible binary alloy no significant electrochemical difference was detected.

## B. Discussion of Proposed Mechanisms

From a mechanistic viewpoint, the basic fact which must be explained is the transition in the fracture modes of the binary $\beta'$ alloys tested under constant tensile loads of $\sim 80\%$ UTS in dry air and in the presence of water vapor. In the former, ductile transcrystalline failure occurs whereas failure in the latter is brittle and intercrystalline. The absence of evidence of intercrystalline cracking or grain-boundary sliding[2,33] in the former eliminates the possibility that the grain boundaries are inherently weak in these alloys. Similarly, the possibility that plastic deformation creates a tendency for intercrystalline brittleness, for example, by inducing the strain transformation at grain boundaries, would also appear to be eliminated.

In 1958, Bailey[33] suggested that the adsorption of water might lower the surface-energy requirements, thus facilitating cracking. Similar surface-energy models have been proposed by other workers to account for hydrogen embrittlement,[124,125] stress-corrosion failures in aqueous environments,[82,87,126] and liquid-metal embrittlement.[127,128] Basically, this type of model states that the energy for fracture is reduced if the surface energy of the resulting fracture surface is lowered by the adsorption of specific species from the environment. This concept has been criticized for several reasons.[65] In particular, it has been pointed out that the model provides no insight into the mechanism of embrittlement on an atomic scale, since the proposed reduction in surface energy occurs *after* crack initiation.[129] Consequently, it has been suggested that adsorption-induced embrittlement results from the adsorption and interaction of the embrittling species with strained bonds of the solid, causing a localized reduction in cohesive strength.[129,130]

Recent work[131] on the mechanism of adsorption-induced embrittlement of ductile solids by liquid metals has established the following as prerequisites for failure: (1) some measure of plastic deformation, (2) the existence in the material of stable obstacles to dislocation motion, thus producing stress concentrations at the head of blocked slip bands, and (3) adsorption of the active embrittling species specifically at the sites of the stress concentrations. Extending this model to the water-induced failure of beta-brass, it can be seen that the observed behavior is not inconsistent with any of these requirements. Embrittlement in the binary $\beta'$-phase alloy occurs at stresses where continuous dislocation motion is taking place (leading to transcrystalline creep-rupture in the absence of moisture). Failure is intercrystalline, so that the grain boundaries themselves can be considered to provide barriers to glide. In this context, it is interesting to note that the beta-brasses are embrittled by the liquid-metal mercury, and that failure in that case is also intercrystalline.[34] The final requirement that the embrittling species should adsorb at the site of the stress concentration would appear to require the rupture of surface oxide films to permit access of the environment to the metal surface.

Other characteristics of the intercrystalline failure of beta-brass can be rationalized in terms of the adsorption model. Thus the increase in susceptibility observed on alloying the binary $\beta'$-phase with Al and other elements may be explained in terms of solid-solution strengthening increasing the ability of the lattice to sustain stress concentrations. A similar relationship has been observed between strength and susceptibility to liquid-metal embrittlement.[127] The observation[35] that grain boundaries in susceptible alloys immersed in aqueous chloride solutions showed no indication of corrosive attack also supports the model, since excessive dissolution would not favor a brittle-fracture process. The accelerating effect of chloride ions on the failure can be rationalized if it is proposed that these ions are also strongly adsorbed and have a greater interaction with the strained bonds.[2]

While the existing observations on the intercrystalline failure of beta-brass can in general terms be reconciled with the adsorption model, it must be recognized that the observations are extremely limited and that further work is necessary to provide a critical test of the model. For example, no electron-microscope studies have been carried out on this system, but it is evident that direct experiments on thin foils and fractographic examination would provide valuable information.

Finally, it must be pointed out that a factor which has so far received little attention is the role of hydrogen. There can be little doubt that hydrogen is liberated at cathodic areas during exposure to aqueous environments, and therefore the possibility that the failure represents a form of hydrogen embrittlement must be considered, particularly in view of the bcc structure. The observation[35] that in 3% NaCl solutions the grain boundaries of the highly susceptible aluminum-containing alloys were cathodic with respect to the grains themselves would thus appear significant. It is surprising in view of this result that the electrochemical studies do not appear to have been extended, particularly to an investigation of the effects of anodic and cathodic polarization on the embrittlement behavior.

## VI. Concluding Remarks

On the basis of existing evidence, it appears unlikely that a single mechanism can account for the various failures discussed in the preceding sections, thus strengthening the view[65] that stress-corrosion cracking should be regarded as a generic term and that several different types of failure can occur.

Exposure of alpha-phase copper alloys to tarnishing ammoniacal solutions results in the formation of a brittle oxide film which is expitaxed and which grow into the metal. It is considered that crack propagation in these instances occurs by the repeated formation and mechanical fracture of this surface film. While further studies are necessary to determine the validity of this hypothesis, the possible consequences are far reaching. In particular, the model predicts that susceptibility to stress-corrosion cracking is determined largely by the rate of growth of the oxide film, and hence it advocates a radically different approach to the problem of reducing stress-corrosion susceptibility, namely by control of the oxide-growth process.

The failure of Cu-Au and Ag-Au alloys in the presence of either aqueous ferric chloride or aqua regia is also considered to involve the formation and rupture of a mechanically weak surface film. In these systems, the film consists of a gold-rich phase, epitaxed to the substrate, which is formed by the preferential dissolution of the less noble elements.

The failure of the beta-brasses in the presence of water vapor does not appear to involve film formation and it is possible that embrittlement in this instance results from an effective reduction in bond strength caused by the adsorption of water at regions of stress. On the other hand, the role of hydrogen cannot be discounted in this system, and it may be that this failure represents a form of hydrogen embrittlement.

The cracking of alpha-phase copper alloys in nontarnishing ammoniacal solutions also does not appear to involve film formation, but is believed to occur by a dissolution-dependent process involving the reaction of cupric-ammonia complex ions with copper atoms at the metal surface.

Several other significant conclusions can be drawn. For example, recent work has confirmed the proposal[9,66,84] that the path of cracking of copper alloys in aqueous ammonia can be influenced by the dislocation structure of the alloy. However, this is the case only for non-tarnishing solutions; in tarnishing environments, the practically important case, the path of failure is predominantly intercrystalline regardless of the dislocation structure of the metal. Similarly, the path of failure of Cu-Au and Ag-Au alloys in either aqueous ferric chloride or aqua regia is not influenced by changes in dislocation structure. The report that pure copper undergoes stress-corrosion cracking in non-tarnishing ammoniacal solutions is also significant in that it challenges the traditional view that pure metals are immune to such failures.

## Acknowledgments

The authors are indebted to A. R. C. Westwood for helpful discussions, and to the U. S. Army Research Office (Durham) for financial support.

## References

1. S. Rask. *Recent Advances in Stress Corrosion.* (A. Bresle, ed.) Bulletin No. 25 from the Corrosion Committee of the Royal Swedish Academy of Engineering Sciences, Stockholm (1961) p. 81.
2. A. R. Bailey. *Met. Rev.,* 6, 101 (1961).
3. L. Graf. This Volume.
4. M. Hansen and K. Anderko. *Constitution of Binary Alloys,* McGraw-Hill Book Co., Inc., New York (1958).
5. L. M. Clarebrough, M. E. Hargreaves, and M. H. Loretto. *Proc. Roy. Soc.,* 261A, 500 (1961).
6. J. C. Fisher. *Acta Met.,* 2, 9 (1954).
7. A. J. Forty. *Physical Metallurgy of Stress Corrosion Fracture.* (T. N. Rhodin, ed.) Interscience Publishers, New York (1959) p. 99.
8. P. R. Swann and J. Nutting. *J. Inst. Metals,* 90, 133 (1961-62).
9. P. R. Swann. *Corrosion,* 19, 102t (1963).
10. R. L. Segall. Private Communication.
11. A. Howie and P. R. Swann. *Phil. Mag.,* 6, 1215 (1961).
12. P. B. Hirsch. *Met. Rev.,* 4, 101 (1959).
13. B. H. Kear and H. Wilsdorf. *Trans. AIME,* 224, 382 (1962).
14. G. V. Raynor. *Annotated Equilibrium Diagram Series.* No. 3, Institute of Metals, London (1944).
15. N. Ohtani and R. A. Dodd. *Corrosion,* 21, 161 (1965).
16. B. Henderson. *J. Inst. Metals,* 92, 55 (1961-62).
17. K. Nakajima and K. Numakura. *Phil. Mag.,* 12, 361 (1965).
18. I. R. Harris, I. L. Dillamore, R. E. Smallman, and B. E. P. Beestan. *Phil. Mag.,* 14, 325 (1966).
19. H. W. Pickering and P. R. Swann. *Corrosion,* 19, 373 (1963).
20. B. H. Kear. *Acta Met.,* 12, 555 (1964).
21. N. S. Stoloff and R. G. Davies. *Prog. in Mat. Sci.,* 13, 1 (1966).
22. M. J. Marcinkowski, N. Brown, and R. M. Fisher. *Acta Met.,* 9, 129 (1961).
23. W. Bell, W. R. Roser, and G. Thomas. *Acta Met.,* 12, 1247 (1964).
24. T. B. Massalski and C. S. Barrett. *J. Metals,* 9, 455 (1957).
25. P. A. Flinn. *Trans. ASM,* 218, 145 (1960).
26. A. B. Greninger. *Trans. AIME,* 128, 369 (1938).
27. C. S. Barrett. *J. Metals,* 6, 1003 (1954).
28. I. R. Kramer and R. Maddin. *J. Metals,* 4, 197 (1952).

29. G. Bassi and J. P. Hugo. *J. Inst. Metals,* 87, 155 (1958-59).

30. A. H. Cottrell. *Dislocations and Plastic Flow in Crystals.* Clarendon Press, Oxford (1956).

31. J. Friedel. *Dislocations.* Pergamon Press, New York (1964).

32. A. K. Head, M. H. Loretto, and P. Humble. *Phys. Stat. Sol.,* 20, 505 (1967); 20, 521 (1967).

33. A. R. Bailey. *J. Inst. Metals,* 87, 380 (1958-59).

34. M. E. Whitaker, E. Voce, and A. R. Bailey. *Metallurgia,* 39, 21 (1948).

35. E. C. W. Perryman. *J. Inst. Metals,* 83, 369 (1954-55).

36. E. C. W. Perryman and R. J. Goodwin. *J. Inst. Metals,* 83, 378 (1954-55).

37. C. Diegel. *Verhandl. Ver. Bef. Gewerbefleiss,* 85, 177 (1906).

38. E. S. Berry. *Brass World,* 2, 39 (1906).

39. L. Graf. *Metall,* 18, 1163 (1964).

40. D. H. Thompson. Private Communication.

41. H. E. Johnson and J. Leja. *Corrosion,* 22, 178 (1966).

42. R. G. Johnston. *Sheet Metals Ind.,* 14, 1197 (1940).

43. J. Halpern. *J. Electrochem. Soc.,* 100, 421 (1953).

44. J. Halpern. *J. Metals,* 9, 280 (1957).

45. F. Habashi. *Ber. Bunsenges. Physik. Chem.,* 67, 407 (1963).

46. F. A. Cotton and G. Wilkinson. *Advanced Inorganic Chemistry.* Interscience Publishers, Inc., New York (1962).

47. C. K. Jorgensen. *Absorption Spectra and Chemical Bonding in Complexes.* Pergamon Press, London (1962).

48. E. Yamasaki. *Sci. Rep. Tohoku Imp. Univ. Ser. I,* 9, 169 (1920).

49. E. Zeretskii and G. Akimov. *Zhur. prikl. Khimii,* 11, 1161 (1938).

50. B. C. Y. Lu and W. F. Graydon. *J. Amer. Chem. Soc.,* 77, 6136 (1955).

51. E. N. Pugh, W. G. Montague, and A. R. C. Westwood. *Trans. ASM,* 58, 665 (1965).

52. E. N. Pugh, W. G. Montague, and J. V. Craig. Unpublished work at RIAS under Contract DA-31-124-ARO-D-258.

53. C. Edeleanu and A. J. Forty. *Phil. Mag.,* 5, 1029 (1960).

54. T. P. Hoar and C. J. L. Booker. *Corrosion Science,* 5, 821 (1965).

55. A. J. Forty and P. Humble. *Phil. Mag.,* 8, 247 (1963).

56. E. N. Pugh and A. R. C. Westwood. *Phil. Mag.,* 13, 167 (1966).

57. M. Pourbaix. *Thermodynamics of Dilute Aqueous Solutions.* Arnold, London (1949).

58. E. Mattsson. *Electrochim. Acta,* 3, 279 (1961).

59. A. J. McEvily, Jr. and A. P. Bond. *J. Electrochem. Soc.,* 112, 131 (1965).

60. H. E. Johnson and J. Leja. *J. Electrochem. Soc.,* 112, 638 (1965).

61. A. J. Forty and P. Humble. *Environment-Sensitive Mechanical Behavior.* (A. R. C. Westwood and N. S. Stoloff, ed.) Gordon and Breach, New York (1966) p. 403.

62. A. J. McEvily, Jr. and A. P. Bond. *Environment-Sensitive Mechanical Behavior.* (A. R. C. Westwood and N. S. Stoloff, ed.) Gordon and Breach, New York (1966) p. 421.

63. O. Kubaschewski and B. E. Hopkins. *Oxidation of Metals and Alloys.* Butterworth, London (1953).

64. W. B. Pearce. *Handbook of Lattice Spacings and Structures of Metals and Alloys.* Pergamon, New York (1958).

65. E. N. Pugh. *Environment-Sensitive Mechanical Behavior.* (A. R. C. Westwood and N. S. Stoloff, ed.) Gordon and Breach, New York (1966) p. 351.

66. D. Tromans and J. Nutting. *Corrosion,* 21, 143 (1965).

67. E. N. Pugh and A. R. C. Westwood. *Symposium on Stress-Corrosion Testing.* ASTM, STP 425 (1967). p. 228.

68. J. A. Sartell, R. J. Stokes, S. H. Bendel, T. L. Johnston, and C. H. Li. *Trans. AIME,* 215, 420 (1959).

69. F. C. Althof. *Z. Metallkunde,* 36, 177 (1944).

70. S. Hellsing, O. Lissner, S. Rask, and B. Strom. *Werks. Korros.,* 8, 569 (1957).

71. L. Graf and W. Richter. *Z. Metallkunde,* 52, 833 (1961).

72. E. N. Pugh and A. R. C. Westwood. *High-Strength Materials.* (V. F. Zackay, ed.) John Wiley and Sons, Inc., New York (1965) p. 701.

73. W. Lynes. *Corrosion,* 22, 113 (1966).

74. W. Lynes. *Corrosion,* 21, 125 (1965).

75. W. H. Bassett. *Proc. ASTM,* 18, 153 (1918).

76. W. H. Hatfield and G. L. Thirkell. *J. Inst. Metals,* 22, 67 (1919).

77. H. Moore, S. Beckinsale, and C. E. Mallinson. *J. Inst. Metals,* 25, 35 (1921).

78. D. K. Crampton. *Trans. AIME,* 1930, p. 233.

79. G. Edmunds, E. A. Anderson, and R. K. Waring. *Symposium on Stress-Corrosion Cracking of Metals.* ASTM-AIME (1945) p. 7.

80. D. H. Thompson and A. W. Tracy. *Trans. AIME,* 185, 100 (1949).

81. G. Edmunds. *Symposium on Stress-Corrosion Cracking of Metals.* ASTM-AIME (1945) p. 67.

82. H. H. Uhlig. *Physical Metallurgy of Stress-Corrosion Fracture.* (T. N. Rhodin, ed.) Interscience Publishers, New York (1959) p. 1.

83. E. N. Pugh, W. G. Montague, and A. R. C. Westwood. *Corrosion Science,* 6, 345 (1966).

84. D. Tromans and J. Nutting. *Fracture of Solids.* (D. C. Drucker and J. J. Gilman, ed.) Interscience Publishers, New York (1963) p. 637.

85. T. C. Wilson, G. Edmunds, E. A. Anderson, and W. M. Pierce. *Symposium on Stress-Corrosion Cracking of Metals.* ASTM-AIME (1945) p. 173.

86. H. F. Hardrath and A. J. McEvily, Jr. *Proceedings of Crack Propagation Symposium.* Cranfield, College of Aeronautics, 1, 231 (1963).

87. H. Nichols and W. Rostoker. *Trans. ASM,* 56, 494 (1963).

88. E. N. Pugh and W. G. Montague. To be published.

89. C. L. Bulow. *Symposium on Stress-Corrosion Cracking of Metals.* ASTM-AIME (1945) p. 19.

90. R. H. Brown and R. B. Mears. *Trans. Electrochem. Soc.,* 81, 455 (1942).

91. R. B. Mears, R. H. Brown, and E. H. Dix, Jr. *Symposium on Stress-Corrosion Cracking of Metals.* ASTM-AIME (1945) p. 323.

92. H. Sutton, E. A. G. Liddiard, B. Chalmers, and F. A. Champion. *J. Inst. Metals,* 71, xvii (1945).

93. A. R. C. Westwood, D. L. Goldheim, and E. N. Pugh. *Acta Met.,* 13, 695 (1965).

94. A. R. C. Westwood, D. L. Goldheim, and E. N. Pugh. Unpublished work.

95. R. N. Parkins. *Met. Rev.,* 9, 201 (1964).

96. F. W. Young, Jr. *J. Appl. Phys.,* 32, 192 (1961).

97. W. B. Hillig and R. J. Charles. *High-Strength Materials.* (V. F. Zackay, ed.) John Wiley and Sons, Inc., New York (1965) p. 682.

98. F. A. Champion. *Symposium on Internal Stresses in Metals and Alloys.* Inst. of Metals, London (1948) p. 468.

99. H. L. Logan. *J. Res. Nat. Bur. Stds.,* 48, 99 (1952).

100. P. R. Swann and J. D. Embury. *High-Strength Materials,* (V. F. Zackay, ed.) John Wiley and Sons, Inc., New York (1965) p. 327.

101. T. P. Hoar and J. G. Hines. *Stress-Corrosion Cracking and Embrittlement.* (W. D. Robertson, ed.) John Wiley and Sons, Inc., New York (1956) p. 107.

102. T. P. Hoar and J. M. West. *Proc. Roy. Soc.,* 268A, 304 (1962).

103. T. P. Hoar and J. C. Scully. *J. Electrochem. Soc.,* 11, 348 (1964).

104. A. J. Sedriks, P. W. Slattery, and E. N. Pugh. This Volume.

105. E. N. Pugh and A. J. Sedriks. *Surfaces and Interfaces II: Physical Mechanical Properties.* Syracuse University Press (1968). In press.

106. A. R. C. Westwood. *Fracture of Solids.* (D. C. Drucker and J.

J. Gilman, ed.) Interscience Publishers, New York (1963) p. 553.

107. H. L. Logan. *The Stress Corrosion of Metals.* John Wiley and Sons, Inc., New York (1966).

108. L. Graf and J. Budke. *Z. Metallkunde,* **46,** 378 (1955).

109. L. Graf. *Stress-Corrosion Cracking and Embrittlement.* (W. D. Robertson, ed.) John Wiley and Sons, Inc., New York (1956) p. 48.

110. R. Bakish and W. D. Robertson. *J. Electrochem. Soc.,* **103,** 320 (1956).

111. R. Bakish and W. D. Robertson. *Trans. AIME,* **206,** 1277 (1956).

112. W. D. Robertson and A. S. Tetelman. *Strengthening Mechanisms in Solids.* ASM (1962) p. 217.

113. H. W. Pickering and C. Wagner. *J. Electrochem. Soc.,* **114,** 698 (1967).

114. H. W. Pickering. This Volume.

115. R. Bakish and W. D. Robertson. *Acta Met.,* **4,** 342 (1956).

116. R. Bakish. *J. Metals,* **9,** 494 (1957).

117. A. R. C. Westwood. *Corrosion Science,* **6,** 381 (1966).

118. O. Lissner. *Sheet Metal Ind.,* **30,** 45 (1953).

119. H. L. Logan. *J. Res. Nat. Bur. Stds.,* **56,** 159 (1956).

120. A. R. Bailey. *Metal Ind.,* **80,** 519 (1952).

121. A. R. Bailey, R. McDonald, and L. E. Samuels. *J. Inst. Metals,* **85,** 25 (1956-57).

122. L. E. Samuels and A. R. Bailey. *Metal Ind.,* **85,** 143 (1954).

123. L. E. Samuels. *J. Inst. Metals,* **82,** 227 (1953-54).

124. N. J. Petch and P. Stables. *Nature,* **169,** 842 (1953).

125. N. J. Petch. *Phil. Mag.,* **1,** 331 (1956).

126. E. G. Coleman, D. Weinstein, and W. Rostoker. *Acta Met.,* **9,** 491 (1961).

127. W. Rostoker, J. M. McCaughey, and H. Markus. *Embrittlement by Liquid Metals.* Reinhold Publishing Corp., New York (1960).

128. H. Nichols and W. Rostoker. *Acta Met.,* **9,** 504 (1961).

129. A. R. C. Westwood and M. H. Kamdar. *Phil. Mag.,* **8,** 787 (1963).

130. N. S. Stoloff and T. L. Johnston. *Acta Met.,* **11,** 251 (1963).

131. M. H. Kamdar and A. R. C. Westwood. *Environment-Sensitive Mechanical Behavior.* (A. R. C. Westwood and N. S. Stoloff, ed.) Gordon and Breach, New York (1966) p. 581.

## Discussion

**A. J. Forty, University of Warwick:**

As Dr. Pugh has pointed out, the details of the film-rupture process require attention. However, since this topic is dealt with by several of the following papers, we feel that discussion should be held over until later in the session. Therefore I would now like to invite discussion on other aspects of this paper. One controversial point concerns the behavior of pure copper—does stress-corrosion cracking really occur in the pure metal as the authors suggest? This seems to be a question of fundamental importance because, if it is true, it will invalidate one of the principal characteristics of stress corrosion, that is, that the phenomenon is associated with alloys rather than pure metals.

**A. W. Blackwood, Rensselaer Polytechnic Institute:**[1]

Since receiving a preprint of the note by Pugh et al (*Corrosion Science,* **6,** 345 (1966)) over a year ago, we have attempted to duplicate their observation of stress corrosion in pure copper without success. We have used both deadloading tests and low strain rate tensile tests, and in neither case have we observed anything other than a normal ductile failure in the presence or absence of the environment, with the exception that at every high magnification we observed some form of microscopic cracking. However, this cracking occurs in the presence or absence of an ammoniacal stress corrosion environment preconcentrated with copper.

**E. N. Pugh:**

I can only repeat that cracking occurred in *non-tarnishing* solutions in the two batches of material that we used, both of which were nominally 99.999% copper. Under the constant load conditions used in our test, the final fracture was partially ductile, occurring when the

primary stress-corrosion crack had sufficiently reduced the cross section. There were numerous secondary intercrystalline cracks in other regions of the gauge length. I should also add that Professor Graf has observed stress-corrosion cracking in pure copper; I understand that he will mention this in his talk later in the session.

**E. N. Pugh, Written Discussion:**

Following this conference, stress-corrosion tests were carried out at RIAS on spectrographically pure copper from ASARCO, provided by Dr. Blackwood. Specimens were cut with approximate gauge dimensions 30 x 3 x 2 mm. The major faces were abraded with SiC papers and etched with 50% nitric acid and finally with 4% aqueous ferric chloride. The specimens were then tested at an engineering stress of 10 Kg/mm$^2$ in 15N aqueous ammonia preconcentrated with 8 g/l copper, added as cupric nitrate. Failure did not occur in 10 hours. However, examination of the specimens indicated that numerous intercrystalline cracks were present but these had not propagated to failure because of the elongated grain structure. The surfaces of the testpieces appeared bright and faceted; there was no evidence of tarnishing.

A second series of tests was carried out on specimens which had been heat treated to produce equiaxed grains (annealed for 1 hour at 750 C in a vacuum of 10$^{-5}$ mm Hg). Failure of these specimens occurred in 5-6 hours. The main fracture was partially ductile but many secondary intercrystalline cracks were evident.

After testing, several specimens (of both types) were sent to Dr. Blackwood and he confirmed the occurrence of intercrystalline stress-corrosion cracking. Note that the intercrystalline cracking in the specimens which were *not* annealed would appear to rule out the relevance of contamination in those which were heat treated.

[1]Present Address: American Smelting and Refining Company.

**G. Martin, North American Rockwell, Inc.:**

We talk rather glibly about pure metals, but even in a five nine purity metal there are about $10^{18}$ foreign atoms per cc, most of which are likely to be concentrated at defects and grain boundaries. In these areas, which are the most likely potential centers of cracks origin, impurity concentrations may be very much higher than indicated by an overall analysis. Have you ever carried out any tests to determine such segregation effects?

**E. N. Pugh:**

No. We have not studied segregation effects. However, I would like to point out that while there may be impurity atoms at grain boundaries in the copper specimens which we tested, it is highly unlikely that significant concentrations of zinc exist. Therefore the failure of "unalloyed" copper is difficult to rationalize in terms of models which are based on preferential dezincification. Similarly, failure occurs in numerous binary copper alloys, so that we suggest that failure in non-tarnishing solutions results from the reaction of cupric complexes with the *copper lattice* rather than with the various solute or impurity atoms.

**J. Kruger, National Bureau of Standards:**

What is the role of the copper ammonia complex? Is its only function the provision of the right environment to form a tarnish film at a sufficiently high rate?

**E. N. Pugh:**

We have not observed tarnishing in ammoniacal solutions in the absence of significant concentrations of the cupric complexes and hence we conclude that the presence of the complexes is necessary for rapid tarnish growth, although the details of its role are not understood.

**J. Kruger:**

In that case it should be possible to cause cracking in other, non-ammoniacal, aqueous solutions which cause rapid tarnishing, for example, in the solution used in the work of Miller and Lawless (*J. Electrochem. Soc.*, **106**, 854 (1959)).

**E. N. Pugh:**

I was not aware that rapid tarnishing of copper alloys occurred in other aqueous solutions. It is certainly worth trying the solution that you mention. Of course, another way of testing the model is to grow films by dry oxidation and Dr. McEvily will tell us something about this in his talk later this week.

**J. Kruger:**

Oxide films formed by dry oxidation would not be as suitable as those formed in solution because in order to get sufficiently rapid film growth the temperature would probably have to be quite high. At such high temperatures, creep would occur and we would never be sure we were looking at the same process as that in solution.

**D. A. Vermilyea, General Electric Research and Development Center:**

I would like to comment on the mechanism of tarnishing. In the paper, it is suggested that tarnish grows by some kind of diffusion in the solid state and I would like to argue that such growth is unlikely.

I extrapolated the high temperature diffusion data for copper in copper oxide to room temperature and came up with a diffusion coefficient of $10^{-28}$. If you assume there is one hundred percent copper ion vacancies, and calculate the diffusion rate with that diffusion coefficient over a film one micron thick, you will come up with one-tenth of an ion per centimeter per second, which is very small.

It seems that a more likely mechanism would involve the dissolution of the whole alloy and the reprecipitation of the copper oxide. During the initial exposure when the film has not formed the entire alloy dissolves away, both copper and zinc remaining in solution. Later on copper oxide becomes stable and I would suggest that the role of the increasing amount of cupric complex is simply to raise the potential to the point where the copper oxide becomes thermodynamically stable. Once that happens you precipitate copper oxide. If the oxide remains porous a dissolution-reprecipitation mechanism can continue the growth of the film. The kinetics of dissolution and reprecipitation are plenty fast because of the much larger diffusion coefficient of copper in the aqueous solutions. In fact, the question now is how does it get so slow because a calculation shows the rate might be a hundred times faster than the observed rate.

In many instances of this sort where a film does form by dissolution and reprecipitation, the film does remain porous. This was pointed out some time ago by Mueller who studied the growth of these films. A test of this mechanism would be the temperature coefficient of the tarnish growth, which should be rather low.

**P. R. Swann, Imperial College, London:**

Is there any evidence that a protective oxide film is present at the grain boundary region?

**E. N. Pugh:**

Metallographic sections of polycrystalline brass specimens coated with thick (10-20 $\mu$) tarnish films indicate that the oxide covers the whole surface. The tarnish appears fully dense viewed with the optical microscope, but it is possible that it is in fact porous, as Dr. Vermilyea suggests. It is interesting to recall that Mattsson (*Electrochim. Acta*, **3**, 279 (1961)) suggested that pores in the tarnish are more likely to occur at grain boundaries and that this may account for the intercrystalline failure mode in tarnishing solutions.

**D. Tromans, University of British Columbia:**

The authors state that they are unaware of any direct transmission electron microscope studies on Cu-Ni alloys and conclude solely from published X-ray and texture experiments that the dislocation distributions in these alloys are probably cellular. This conclusion is supported by some unpublished work which I conducted in 1961 on Cu-20 wt.% Ni. Direct transmission electron microscopy of this alloy revealed a cellular dislocation distribution.

### W. D. Sylwestrowicz, Bell Telephone Laboratories:

I would like to comment on the interpretation of Mattsson's (*Electrochim. Acta*, **3**, 279 (1961)) results relating the time of fracture in *a*-brass to pH of the solution.

The data presented by Mattsson show a very complicated dependence of the time of fracture on the pH of the solution, with accompanying changes in the mode of fracture, and, in a limited range of solutions, the formation of a black tarnish on the surface of specimens.

Investigations of Pugh and his collaborators, reported in the paper under discussion, indicate that, depending on whether or not the solution forms a black tarnish, two different relations exist between the time of fracture, the mode of fracture and the content of zinc. All these observations form a very complex picture and have led the authors of the paper under discussion to the conclusion that different mechanisms of stress corrosion occur at different pH of the solution, and that stress corrosion fracture should be considered as a generic term only.

An attempt is made here to present a more coherent picture of the processes occurring in *a*-brass and is based on the data of Mattsson and Pugh et al. It is suggested that two independent phenomena take place in the specimen. One which is a stress corrosion process leading to intercrystalline or transcrystalline fracture, depending on the zinc content of the alloy. The second is a corrosive attack on the specimen resulting in formation of a black tarnish on the surface of the specimen and finally in an intercrystalline

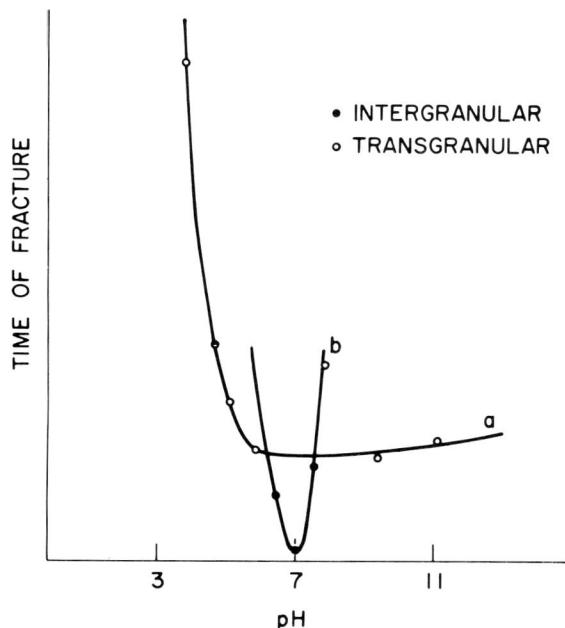

FIGURE 1 — Schematic curves showing time to fracture vs pH for (a) stress corrosion cracking depending on pH and (b) intergranular stress accelerated corrosion.

failure. It should be emphasized that this is not a stress corrosion process. Curve a in Figure 1 shows a possible type of dependence of the time of fracture by a stress corrosion mechanism on pH of the solution. Curve b indicates the time necessary to crack the specimen by a corrosive attack (not stress corrosion) at grain boundaries, occurring in a limited range of pH. These curves were plotted with the use of Mattsson's data.

It appears that in the range of solutions from approximately 5.5 to 7.8 pH dissolution takes place faster than stress corrosion and specimens crack in an intercrystalline mode. Above and below this range of solutions, specimens fail by transcrystalline fracture by a stress corrosion process. Mattsson observed that "Most specimens had both intergranular and transgranular cracks, but generally one type was dominating." This observation supports the view that two processes are occurring simultaneously. Results of Pugh et al (Figure 21 in the paper being discussed) show that in the range of solutions where black tarnish develops, specimens can fail without a threshold stress. They concluded that "It can be seen that no 'threshold' stress exists below which cracking does not occur," (page 132 of the paper being discussed). This clearly demonstrates that in this range of pH cracking does not occur by a stress corrosion mechanism. Further supporting this view are the experiments with unstressed 70-30 brass specimens immersed in tarnishing solutions, (page 126 of the paper being discussed). After prolonged exposure, specimens become extremely brittle. "Handling of such specimens in the absence of the environment causes them to fall into many small fragments." Failure occurred simply by a corrosive attack on grain boundaries. Observations of Pugh, Montague and Westwood, that in tarnishing solutions, polycrystalline specimens crack after repeated immersion of unstressed specimens followed by stressing in the absence of the environment, (page 136 of the paper being discussed) give additional support to the view that in this solution failure occurs by corrosive dissolution of material at the grain boundaries and not by a stress corrosion process. Similar tests using non-tarnishing solutions do not lead to cracking (E. N. Pugh and A. R. C. Westwood, *Phil. Mag.*, **13**, 167 (1966)).

To summarize: In the range of solutions investigated by Mattsson, the observations for *a*-brass can be explained by assuming that two processes take place. A stress corrosion process occurs in all solutions above approximately 3.9 pH and leads to a transcrystalline fracture of specimens. In a narrow range of solutions, of pH values between approximately 6.3 and 7.7, a strong corrosive attack occurs simultaneously on grain boundaries causing intergranular cracking before the specimen can fracture by a stress corrosion mechanism.

### E. N. Pugh:

We appear to have a problem of semantics here. We both consider that two mechanisms of failure can occur in the brass-ammonia system, but, adopting the view that stress-corrosion cracking is a generic term, we refer to *both* types of failure as stress-corrosion cracking. You state that the intergranular cracking occurring in 70-30 brass in tarnishing solutions is *not* a stress-corrosion failure. However, I should point out that this is the case that corresponds to season-cracking, which is generally regarded as the classical example of stress-corrosion cracking.

You also imply that stress is not necessary for failure to occur in tarnishing solutions and you mention our experiments on unstressed specimens as support for this. These experiments simply indicate that in unstressed specimens the tarnish grows preferentially into the metal along grain boundaries and that, given sufficient time, the brittle film will completely penetrate the grain boundaries so that on subsequent stressing, say by handling, failure will occur through the brittle intercrystalline film. We believe that in stressed specimens the film breaks when it attains a certain thickness and cracking then occurs by the repeated formation and rupture of this film.

## Prepared Discussion on
## Stress Corrosion Cracking of Alpha-Brass

**D. Tromans, N. A. Dowds and J. Leja,**
**The University of British Columbia:**

A research program is in progress at the University of British Columbia, Canada, to study the characteristics of stress corrosion cracking of alpha-brass and other alloy systems. The current note presents preliminary observations on intergranular stress corrosion of Cu:30 Zn alloy in three basically different environments: (1) ammoniacal solutions, (2) mercurous nitrate solutions, and (3) citrate and tartrate solutions. The experimental techniques have involved (a) bend tests on strip specimens, (b) time-load Instron experiments on notched rods, and (3) fractographic studies.

## A. Cracking in Ammonia and Mercurous Solutions

### A.1. Strip Specimens

The ammonia solutions and the technique of testing strip specimens were those used earlier and described in the paper by H. E. Johnson and J. Leja (*Corrosion*, **22**, 178 (1966)). The composition and initial conditions of alpha-brass used were also similar to those reported in the earlier work. The results with strip specimens were found to duplicate the previously established U-shaped relationship between the total time to cracking and pH of ammonia solutions, as seen in Figure 2.

### A.2. Instron Tests

Brass rods of 3/8 in diameter, 7 in length, threaded at both ends, were machined halfway along their length to give a 60 degree notch of 0.2 in diameter; then the rods were cleaned in chloroethane and heat treated (protecting the notch from dezincification with a cover tube of brass) at 500 C for 30 minutes in an atmosphere of dissociated ammonia (3 parts $H_2$ and 1 part $N_2$). Subsequent surface cleaning was identical to that of strip specimens, (i.e.,

immersion in 45% $HNO_3$). Interfacial attack at the meniscus was eliminated by protecting the rods with teflon tape to within 0.2 in of the notch. The rods were then introduced into a teflon-pyrex cell surrounding only the vicinity of the notch and containing the stress-corrosive solutions (at various pH, etc.). The whole set-up, rod and cell, was then inserted in an Instron Tensile Testing Machine and taken up to a stress above the yield point across the area of the notch (i.e., a load of 2000 lbs.). The cross-head was then stopped (i.e., load no longer increased), the cell was filled with the solution and the progress of cracking was followed autographically on a load/time plot, shown schematically in Figure 3. [The onset of cracking reduced the cross sectional area in the base of the notch thereby momentarily increasing the stress level; the increase in stress produced a local extension and a corresponding contraction of the electrical strain gauge used to measure the load; hence, since the cross-head was stationary, the cracking process resulted in a decrease of load conditions with time.]

The conditions of testing on Instron were analogous to the bend tests employed with strips, where a progressive decrease in stress took place at the tip of the bend as cracking proceeded; Instron tests produced also a U-shaped relationship between time of cracking and pH of ammonia solutions, as discussed later. All time/load curves, as in Figure 3, showed a period $P_1$-$P_2$ (denoted as initiation time) having a very slow decrease in load with time, followed by a more rapid decrease ($P_2P_3$) with an indication of steps, and a third period of pronounced step-like relationship. The reproducibility of these time/load curves for each environment was unusually high, e.g., (1) time to a 30 lb decrease in load differed only by ±

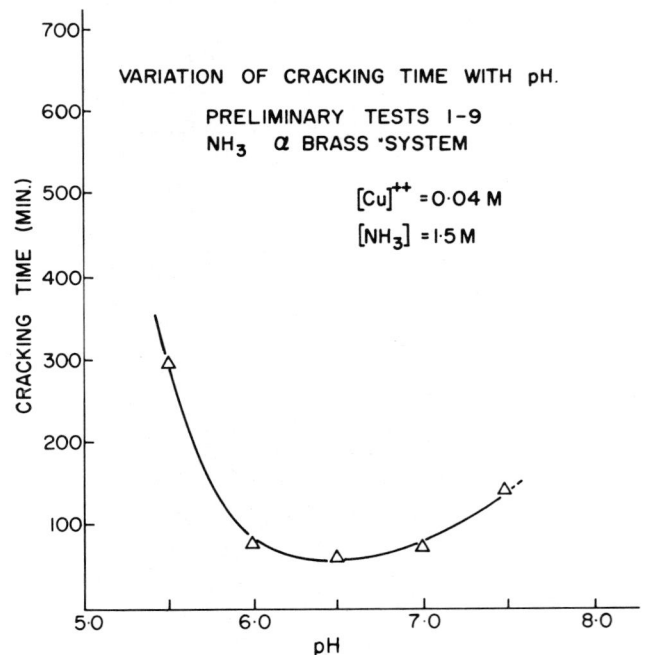

FIGURE 2 — The relationship between the total cracking time in stress corrosion cracking and pH of ammonia solutions, in tests with strip brass specimens.

154

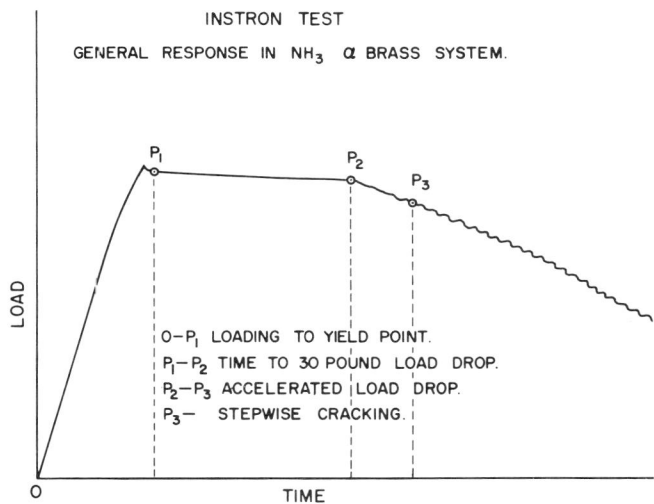

FIGURE 3 — Schematic reproduction of a load/time recording, in tests with notched brass rods under stress in Instron machine.

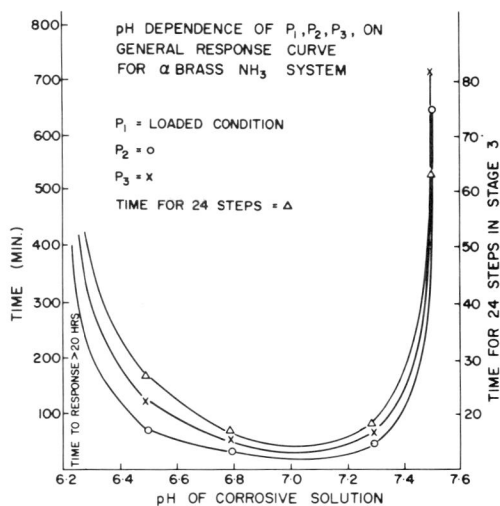

FIGURE 4 — Dependence of the initiation time and the total cracking time on pH of ammonia solutions, in tests with notched brass rods in Instron machine.

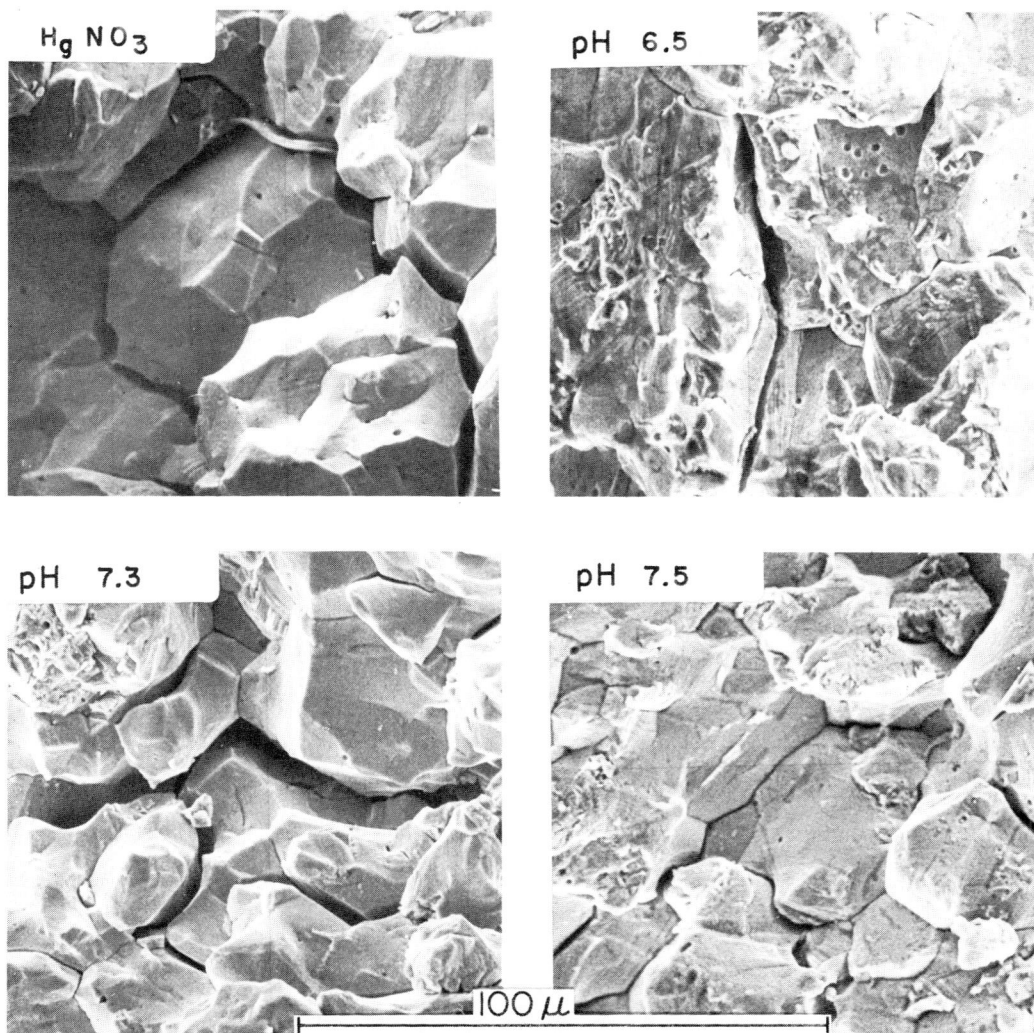

FIGURE 6 — Scanning electron micrographs (25 kv, secondary electron image) of alpha-brass notched rod specimens stress-corrosion fractured in HgNO₃ and ammonia solutions at pH 6.5, 7.3, and 7.5.

1%, (2) the number of steps in the last period was constant for all rods heat-treated in the same manner, and (3) the frequency (the time length) of the steps in the third period was reproducible to ± 1%.

The cracking was found to be predominantly intergranular in all solutions studied.

**A.2a. Effect of pH on Load/Time Curves.** A comparison of load/time curves for ammonia solutions at different pH values shows that:

(1) The initiation period (time length to 30 lb load decrease, which has been arbitrarily chosen as a reference point) varies (a) in the same U-shaped manner as the total cracking time of the strip specimens, Figure 4, (b) appears to depend on the stress applied.

(2) The number of steps in the last period of fast-cracking[1] was found to be (a) independent of pH or environment (the same for ammonia at all pHs, for mercurous nitrate solution, and for potassium citrate solution) and (b) dependent on grain size, as shown by an increase in grain size by annealing at 900 C which reduced the number of steps, and by the fact that when specimens were removed from the Instron before completing the fracture (sectioned longitudinally and the number of grains around which the crack had propagated was counted), there was an agreement within 10-20% with the total number of distinguishable steps—e.g., at pH 6.8, there were found in one test 47 grains and 50 steps, and in another test, 3 grains across the cross-section of the notch and 3 clear steps in the load/time curve.

(3) The frequency (the time length) of steps in the third period was found to follow the same trend as the initiation period (1).

It appeared to us that the initiation period was due to the dissolution of the surface layer of brass which—owing to a lower activity of Zn—should be denuded of Zn atoms and be represented by a predominantly Cu layer. A preliminary test was carried out whereby an additional coating of copper was deposited electrochemically on the notched rod before it was used in Instron test; the initiation time was found to be increased several-fold for a copper layer of 0.004 in thickness, both in ammonia and mercury systems. Similarly, a test in which the rod was first soaked for a time equal to initiation time in the corrosive solution without the application of load and then the load applied, showed that there was an expected decrease in the initiation time.

The chemical activity and the macroscopic appearance of the stress-corrosion fractured areas differed from those of both the mechanically fractured areas and the outside surface of the specimen. For the brass specimens in ammonia system (at all pHs) the stress-corrosion fractured area always appeared yellow irrespective of whether or not the environment produced a tarnish on the outside, or on the mechanically fractured surface. Figure 5 shows two halves of the same specimen, one with a yellow annulus surrounding a tarnished core on the fractured surface of a notch when (at pH 6.8) the stress-corrosion crack was allowed to propagate only part of the way through the specimen (forming an annulus) after which the load was quickly increased to produce a mechanical ductile fracture in the center, thus creating a core which tarnished in the few seconds that elapsed before the specimen was withdrawn from Instron. Figure 5 also shows the other half of the same specimen after its immersion in the cleaning solution (45% $HNO_3$) followed by re-immersion in exactly the same solution in which stress-cracking took place. It is evident that tarnish reforms after the "yellow" surface is cleaned. Clearly, (a) the stress-corrosion *crack propagation does not involve tarnish formation,* and (b) some sort of adsorbed film *prevents tarnish formation* in ammonia systems.

Visual differences, although less marked, were also observed in the appearance of stress-corrosion cracked areas and other surfaces (outside or mechanically fractured) for systems of brass in mercurous nitrate solution and potassium citrate solution.

*A.3. Fractography of Alpha-Brass Specimens*

Irrespective of the corrosive environment tested [ammonia solutions at pH 6.3-7.5, mercurous nitrate solutions (saturated $HgNO_3$ in 1% $HNO_3$, diluted 10 to 1 or 25 to 1)], the fractured surfaces showed identical features. This may be seen in the scanning electron micrographs (kindly carried out by the Japan Electron Optics Demonstration Center, Burlingham, California) shown in Figures 6, 7, and 8. Figure 6 shows stress-corrosion fractured surfaces of specimens in $HgNO_3$, ammonia solutions at pH 6.5, 7.3, and 7.5.

Figure 7 shows a comparison of a stress-corrosion fracture at pH 6.8 and a mechanical ductile fracture of the same specimen. Higher magnification reveals numerous fine striations on the surfaces of grains, as in Figure 8 for pH 7.3 and $HgNO_3$ systems; these fine striations are not always composed of one parallel set but also occur as intersecting sets of parallel lines (see arrowed regions). Figure 9 is a carbon replica electron micrograph of $HgNO_3$ system in which these intersections of parallel striations are clearly visible. Also, in Figure 9, the apparent crystallographic nature of these striations is revealed by the change in direction across both grain boundaries and twin-boundaries.

From this, we conclude that the striations are *slip-steps* arising from *dislocation motion* (on intersecting slip systems) and *not* crack arrests associated with film rupture, as originally proposed by A. J. McEvily and A. P. Bond (*J. Electrochem. Soc.,* **112**, 131 (1965)). Also, it is apparent that the mechanisms of cracking in these two systems, mercurous nitrate and ammonia environments, are basically the same. [When liquid mercury was formed in the notch on using concentrated solutions, no cracking resulted.] It should be noted from the above micrographs that there is no evidence of any appreciable ductile fracture or tearing.

---

[1]Similar step-like periods were observed in other polycrystalline alloys, e.g., in testing notched Al-10Mg alloy (in NaCl + $K_2CrO_4$ solution), and in mild steel wire in boiling 55% $Ca(NO_3)_2$ (117 C).

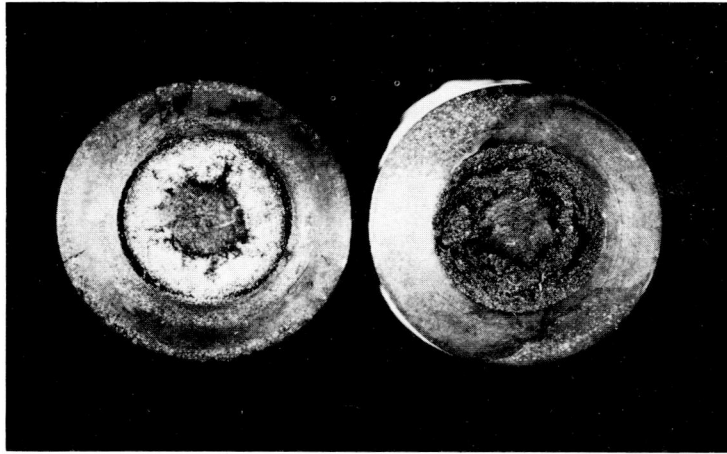

FIGURE 5 — Macroscopic appearance of a stress-corrosion fractured surface in the form of a "yellow" annulus, and a mechanically fractured core covered with a tarnish. The other half of the specimen shows that the yellow annulus acquired a tarnish after acid cleaning and re-immersion in ammonia solution. (Ed. Note: The original picture was submitted in color. The specimen at right has a gold colored annulus and dark gray interior; the one at left has dark gray annulus and interior.)

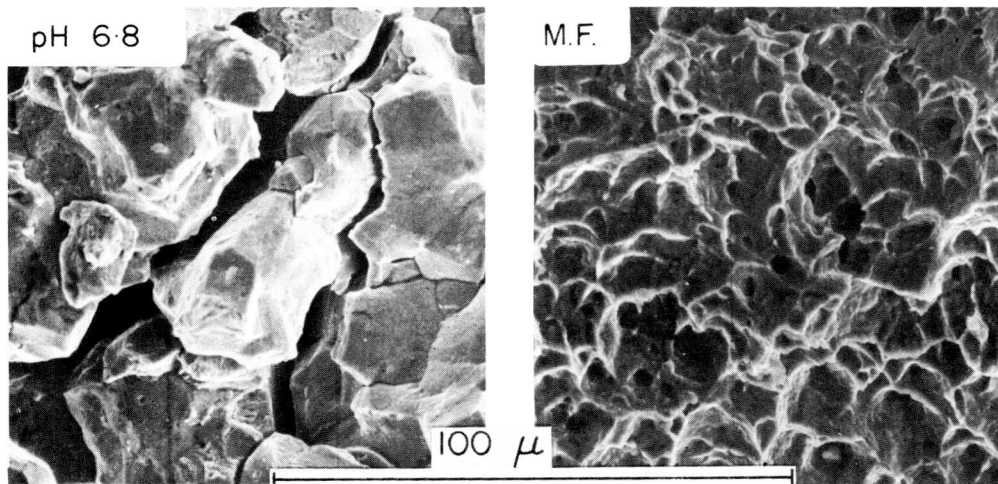

FIGURE 7 — Scanning electron micrograph of adjoining areas of the same specimen fractured by a stress-corrosion cracking in ammonia solution at pH 6.8 (left) and by ductile fracture (right).

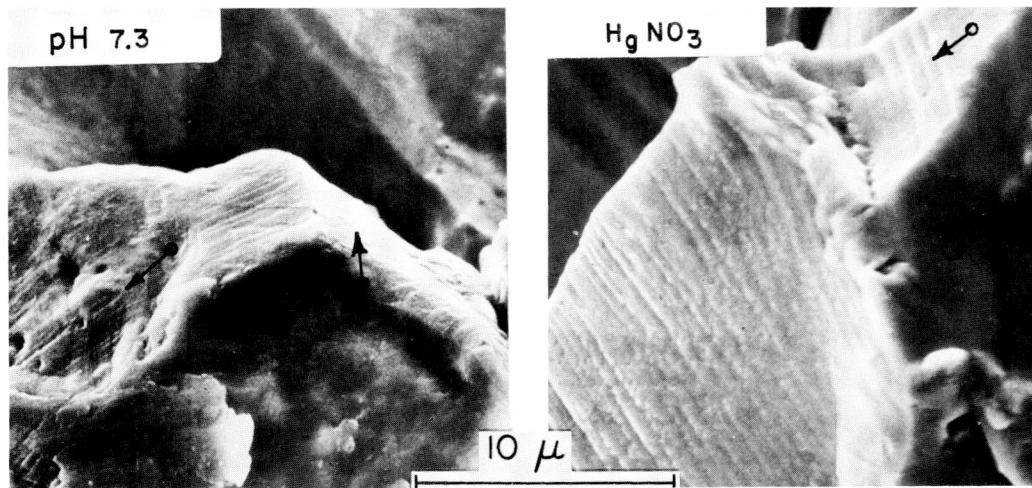

FIGURE 8 — Scanning electron micrographs showing sets of intersecting striations, for ammonia and HgNO₃ s.c.c. specimens.

157

## B.1. Citrate and Tartrate Systems

Strip specimens, stressed by bending over 1/2 in mandrel, were immersed in a range of potassium citrate, sodium citrate and potassium tartrate solutions, of varying Cu concentrations and pH. Generally, very long cracking times were recorded, as seen in Table 1; whereas nearly all specimens in *potassium citrate* systems have cracked, the *sodium* citrate solutions have produced *no cracking* after 98 days; potassium tartrate series produced cracking at one set of conditions.

Instron test on notched brass rod (in saturated potassium citrate solution diluted 1:1 with 1 M Cu sulfate solution) resulted in stress-corrosion fracture within 16-20 hours; the number of steps was the same as for the brass-ammonia system specimens of the same grain size and heat treatment.

Carbon replica electron micrograph showed similar features to those discussed above for ammonia and mercury systems, e.g., an intersecting set of parallel striations, Figure 10.

### Acknowledgments

The contribution of Mr. G. Bacon in the initial stages of this work and the financial support of the National Research Council of Canada are gratefully acknowledged.

**Table 1**

| 1.1 Potassium Citrate | — | 0.6 M Solution |
|---|---|---|
| **Cu Conc** | **pH** | **Time-to-Cracking** |
| 0.05 | 8 | 98 days |
| 0.05 | 9 | 63 days |
| 0.05 | 10 | (no failure) |
| 0.10 | 8 | 55 days |
| 0.10 | 9 | 984 hours (41 days) |
| 0.10 | 10 | 410 hours (17 days) |
| 0.20 | 8 | 1150 hours (48 days) |
| 0.20 | 9 | 240 hours (10 days) |
| 0.20 | 10 | (no failure) |

| 1.2 Sodium Citrate | — | 0.6 M Solution |
|---|---|---|

Cu 0.07 M; pH 6, 7, 8, 9, 10,   no cracking in 98 days

| 1.3 Potassium tartrate | — | 0.6 M Solution |
|---|---|---|

Cu 0.04-1.0 M; pH 11-13 — The only specimen that cracked in 14 days (within 98-day testing period) was the one in pH 13 and 1.0 M Cu concentration.

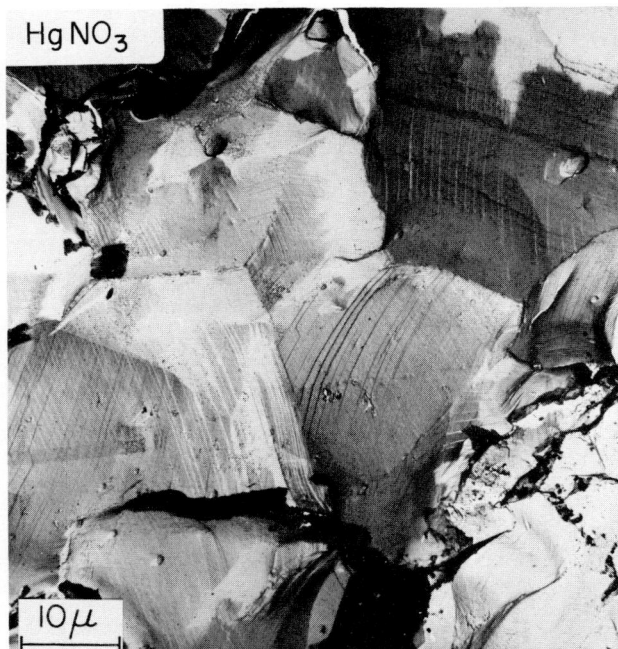

FIGURE 9 – Carbon replica electron micrograph showing sets of intersecting striations on $HgNO_3$ s.c.c. specimen.

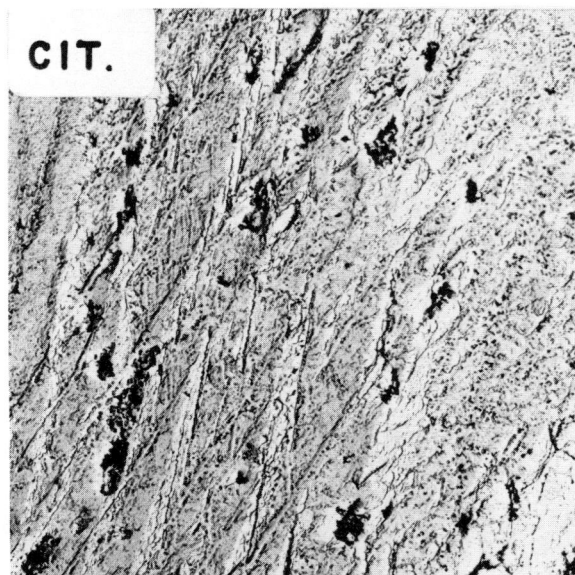

FIGURE 10 – Carbon replica electron micrograph of fracture in a strip alpha-brass specimen stress corroded in potassium citrate solution.

# PREFERENTIAL ANODIC DISSOLUTION IN BINARY ALLOYS

H. W. Pickering
U. S. Steel Corporation

## Abstract

Results of investigations by X-ray diffraction, by electron diffraction, with a rotating disk-ring electrode and with an electron microprobe, and measurements of the polarization capacity enable one to conclude that preferential anodic dissolution of Cu from Cu-Au alloys occurs via solid state diffusion of Cu and Au, and that ionization of Au does not occur. Investigations with the rotating disk-ring electrode on Cu30 atomic percent Zn indicate that the ionization-redeposition mechanism does not operate during dissolution of Cu-Zn alloys. These results provide a better understanding of the mechanism of stress corrosion in these alloys. The consequences of excess vacancies and of concentration gradients near the base of cracks or near other local penetrations are discussed.

## I. Introduction

Since stress corrosion occurs usually in alloys rather than in pure metals, it is important to understand the mechanism by which alloys dissolve in aqueous environments, noting especially those aspects which are not a part of the anodic dissolution of pure metals. It is the purpose of this paper to outline some recently obtained results[1-3] which give improved understanding of the mechanism by which binary Cu-Au and Cu-Zn alloys dissolve in aqueous electrolytes. These results are of special interest to this meeting since the alloys themselves are susceptible to stress corrosion.

When a single-phase binary alloy is anodically dissolved in an aqueous solution, the mode of dissolution may be (a) simultaneous dissolution of the two constituents of the alloy, or (b) preferential dissolution of the less noble metal of the alloy with the more noble metal accumulating on the alloy surface. For the latter mode it is necessary that the difference between the single-electrode potentials of the two constituent metals in the electrolyte, possibly involving complexing agents, be sufficiently large, i.e., several times greater than RT/F, and that the potential of the dissolving alloy be higher than that of the less noble metal and significantly lower than that of the more noble metal.[1] A spongy layer of the remaining more noble metal has been reported after extended dissolution especially for Cu-Zn and Au-Cu alloys.[1-13] Consequently, there must be a mechanism by which the atoms of the less noble metal reach the surface. Three plausible mechanisms exist: (1) Both metals ionize; this ionization is followed by re-deposition of the more noble metal, (2) only the less noble metal ionizes and enters the solution while atoms of the more noble metal aggregate by surface diffusion and (3) only the less noble metal ionizes and enters the solution and atoms of both metals move in the solid phase by volume diffusion.

From the results of the experiments to be described it was possible to arrive at rather definite conclusions regarding the mechanism of preferential anodic dissolution of binary alloys.[1-3] Perhaps the most definitive and important of them is that during anodic dissolution of Cu-Au alloys, solid-state diffusion occurs to a significant extent and ionization of Au does not take place. Also important is the observation that anodic dissolution of Cu-Au alloys is accompanied by an enormous increase in surface area. Finally, results thus far obtained for Cu 30 atomic percent Zn (Cu30Zn) alloy lead to conclusions similar to those arrived at for Cu-Au alloys, i.e., that ionization and redeposition of Cu does not occur during dissolution of Cu-Zn alloys.

## II. Experimental

### A. Cu-Au Alloys

#### 1. Test for Occurrence of Volume Diffusion

The possible occurrence of volume diffusion during anodic dissolution of Cu-Au alloy at 23 C was examined by

X-ray and electron diffraction of the surface layers of dissolved specimens. Let us consider the diffraction patterns which may be expected from alloy left after dissolution via the various mechanisms. For the mechanism of solid-state diffusion the pattern will contain broad diffraction rings resulting from X-ray and electron scattering from alloy regions of variable composition; i.e., the occurrence of volume diffusion leads to a gradual variation in composition, and thus, in lattice parameter, with distance from the electrolyte-alloy interface. If on the other hand one of the alternative mechanisms operates, the diffraction pattern may be expected to exhibit rings only at the Bragg angles corresponding to pure Au and to the original alloy composition, and appreciable diffracted intensity will not be observed at intermediate Bragg angles. That is, both the surface diffusion and the ionization-redeposition mechanisms lead to the formation of crystals on the surface which are relatively pure in Au. The reason for this is that during dissolution of Cu-Au alloy the potential is more noble than the reversible potential for dissolution of Cu (in Cu-Au alloy) in the electrolyte, and therefore no tendency exists for redeposition or aggregation of Cu on the surface. On the contrary especially since dissolution of Cu-Au alloys is generally accompanied by appreciable polarization,[1,8] it may be expected that copper atoms are incorporated into the electrolyte as ions virtually immediately upon becoming atoms in the surface layer.

Investigations of this kind have been conducted by Graf[14] in 1932 on Cu-Au alloys after immersion in various electrolytes. His findings are in accord with the concept of enhanced volume diffusion although definite conclusions cannot be made because of insufficient data on the oxidizing conditions and because of the rather limited resolution in his patterns.

**a. X-ray Diffraction Experiments.** After anodic dissolution of Cu1Au, Cu3Au, Cu5Au, Cu10Au and Cu22Au in 1 M $H_2SO_4$ and in buffered 1 N NaCl (pH 5), X-ray diffraction examination of the specimens shows increased diffracted intensity extending approximately between the Bragg angles, $\theta$, characteristic of pure gold and of the original alloy.[1,3] For example, pattern b of Figure 1, obtained from a Cu5Au specimen after a relatively short period of dissolution in 1 M $H_2SO_4$ at 5 mA/cm$^2$, contains a broad region of diffracted intensity between the $2\theta$ positions corresponding to Cu5Au and pure Au for diffraction of CuK$\alpha$ radiation by {111} planes. The same may be seen for Cu10Au dissolved in the $H_2SO_4$ at 5 mA/cm$^2$ and in the buffered NaCl solutions at 20 mA/cm$^2$ in Figures 2 and 3 respectively, and for Cu1Au dissolved in the $H_2SO_4$ electrolyte at 1 mA/cm$^2$ in Figure 4. In the latter, the specimen for X-ray examination consisted of alloy particles which became detached from the Cu1Au sheet electrode during anodic dissolution and fell to the bottom of the cell (whereas the patterns in Figures 1-3 were obtained directly from the surface layers of the dissolved alloys). Similar results were observed in all the alloys for the first four diffraction lines investigated and for the various current densities employed.[1,3]

At a later stage of anodic dissolution a maximum develops at a $2\theta$ position corresponding to an intermediate Cu-Au composition. With further dissolution the maximum shifts very slowly toward higher gold compositions. The nearly constant position of the maximum with continued

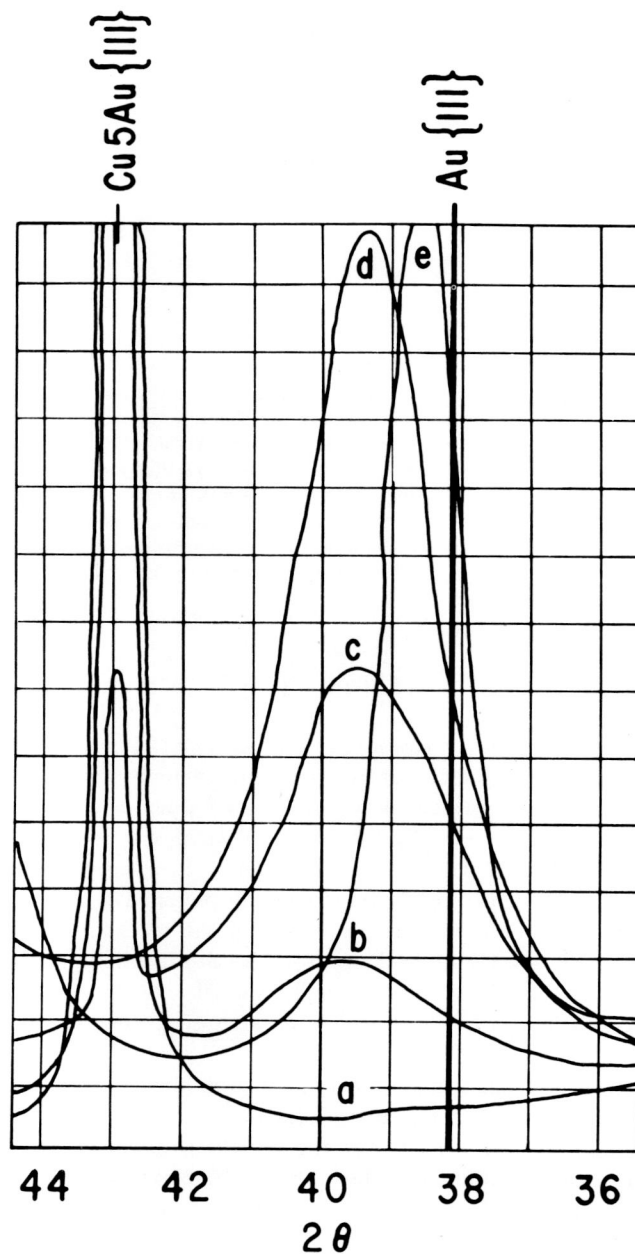

FIGURE 1 — Traces of recorded X-ray intensity for Cu5Au after various amounts of dissolution at 5 mA/cm$^2$ in 1 M $H_2SO_4$, illustrating a broad region of increased diffracted intensity from {111} planes, i.e., for 42.7 > $2\theta$ > 38.2$^0$, corresponding to the presence of a gradient in composition towards the gold-rich side of the original alloy composition. The $2\theta$ position of pure Au is indicated by the vertical line at $2\theta$ = 38.2$^0$. Pattern a, prior to anodic dissolution; pattern b, 3.0 C/cm$^2$ passed; pattern c, 12.0 C/cm$^2$ passed; pattern d, 48.0 C/cm$^2$ passed; and pattern e, 96.0 C/cm$^2$ passed.

160

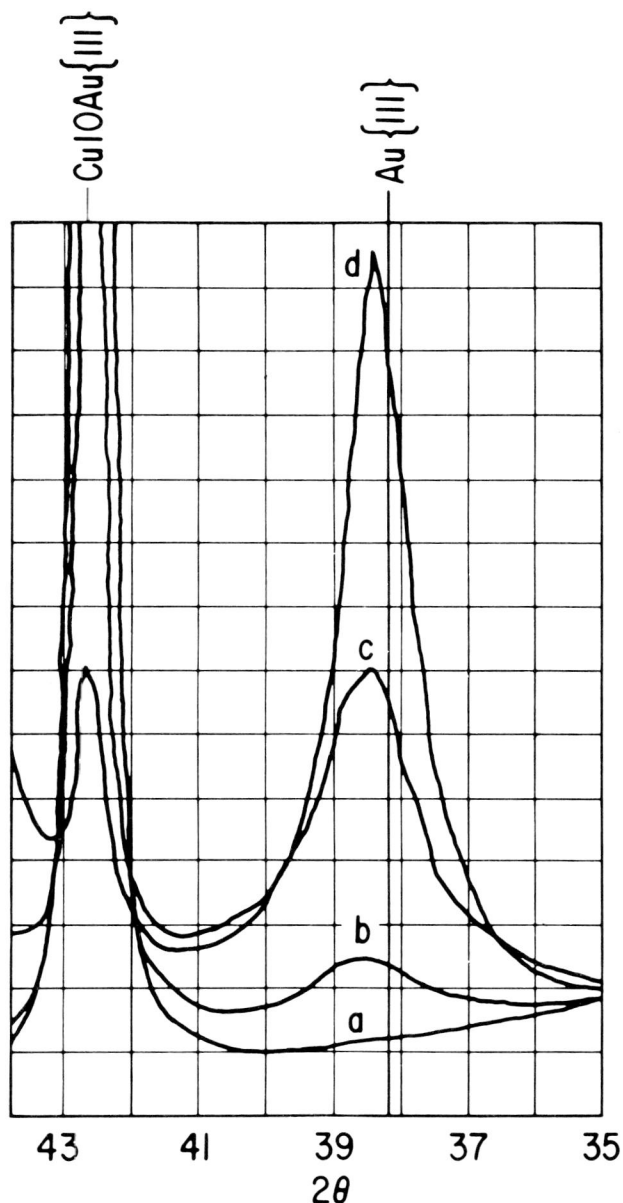

FIGURE 2 – Same as Figure 1 but for Cu10Au. Pattern a, prior to anodic dissolution; pattern b, 0.75 C/cm² passed; pattern c, 3.0 C/cm² passed; and pattern d, 24.0 C/cm² passed.

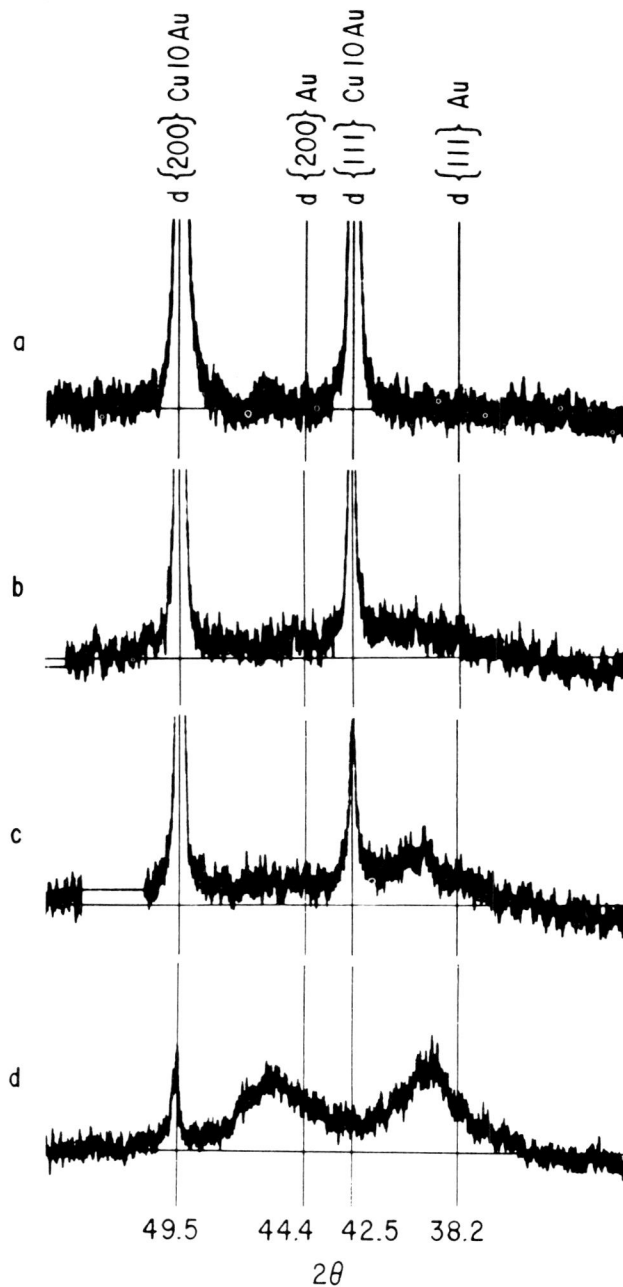

FIGURE 3 – X-ray diffraction patterns for a Cu10Au foil specimen after increasing amounts of dissolution at 20 mA/cm² in buffered 1 N NaCl, illustrating increased diffracted intensity over broad ranges of angle $2\theta$, e.g., $42.5 > 2\theta > 38.2°$ and $49.5 > 2\theta > 44.4$ for diffraction by $\{111\}$ and $\{200\}$ planes of gold-rich Cu-Au alloy, respectively. (a) prior to anodic dissolution; (b) 1.2 C/cm² passed; (c) 2.4 C/cm² passed; (d) 19.2 C/cm² passed.

dissolution, illustrated in patterns c and d of Figures 1-3, indicates the current is maintained primarily by dissolution of Cu from remaining original alloy rather than from the newly formed gold-rich material. Finally when the specimen is very nearly consumed, resulting in partial disintegration, an appreciable shift of the maximum toward the pure Au composition is noted (see pattern e of Figure 1). Prior to this final shift in composition the original alloy peaks are already decreased to background intensity. Optical metallography indicated that the final shift occurred in the absence of original, unreacted alloy, see Figure 5. For the other Cu-Au specimens, unreacted alloy still remains as shown for Cu3Au and Cu22Au in Figures 6 and 7.

For a given current density and time of electrolysis, the position of the maximum, taken as the center of its half-width, is at a lower $2\theta$ value (corresponding to a composition richer in gold), the higher the gold content of the original alloy. This may be seen in the X-ray patterns of Figures 1 and 2 and in Table 1 where the positions of the maxima are given along with the estimated Cu-Au composition corresponding to each maximum; the latter admittedly has wide error limits. It should be noted that the assignment of a definite composition to the maximum implies only a preponderance of material of this composition with other compositions still present. For this reason the term maximum is used, peak being reserved for intensity profiles corresponding to a single composition.

The position of the maximum depends also on the composition of the electrolyte. It occurs at a composition less rich in gold for the $Cl^-$ than for the $SO_4^=$ electrolyte. This may be seen for Cu10Au dissolved in the $H_2SO_4$ and in the buffered NaCl solutions in Figures 2 and 3 and in Table 1. Metallographic examination of these specimens also showed a greater tendency for local penetrations to develop in the alloy during dissolution in the NaCl than in the $H_2SO_4$ electrolyte. Local penetrations after dissolution in buffered NaCl solution may be seen in Figure 8. Large openings in the reacted layer are also apparent.

The intensity of the gold-rich maxima for a given current density and time of electrolysis increases, and the appearance of broad regions of increased diffracted intensity is detected at an earlier stage of dissolution as one increases the gold content of the original alloy from 3 to 22 atomic percent (Figures 1 and 2).

In the case of alloys low in Au the reacted layer adheres rather poorly. For Cu1Au alloy, particles are dislodged and may be collected from the bottom of the cell for subsequent diffraction analysis (Figure 4). The observed dislodging of particles is in accord with industrial experience especially during electrolytic refining of copper containing a small amount of Au. Partial disintegration of the reacted layer also occurs for Cu3Au (see Figure 6).

During the experiment the earliest detection of increased diffraction intensity occurs at what is actually a relatively advanced stage of dissolution corresponding to the passage of $> 0.5$ C/cm$^2$ and to the development of a reacted layer a fraction of a micron in thickness. This is a consequence of the fact that initially when the surface is virtually plane the intensity of diffracted X-rays from regions of variable composition is practically nil since the depth of X-ray penetration is very much greater than the depth of the zones of variable composition; the diffusion

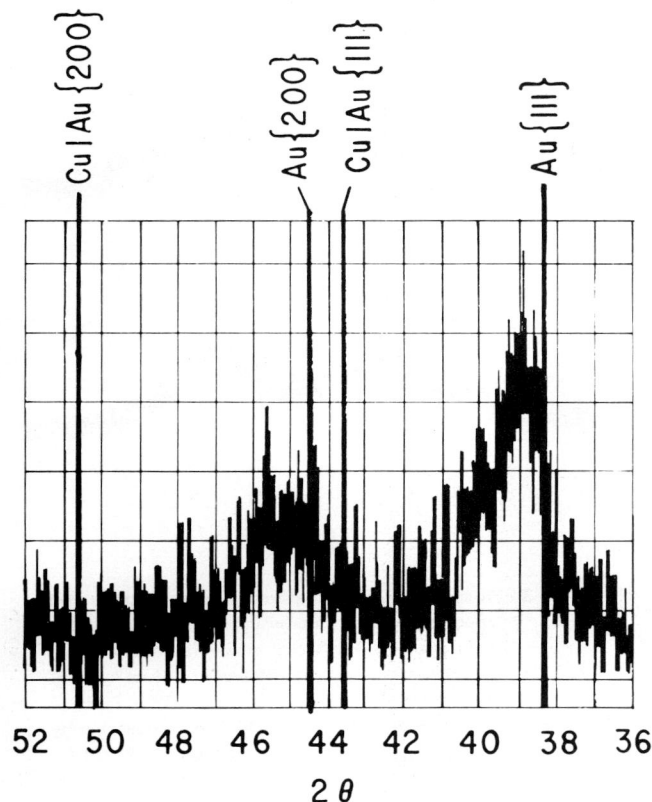

FIGURE 4 — X-ray diffraction pattern of particles which became dislodged from a Cu1Au foil specimen during dissolution at 1 mA/cm$^2$ in 1 N CuSO$_4$ + 0.1 N H$_2$SO$_4$ and fell to the bottom of the cell, illustrating broad regions of increased diffracted intensity at $43 > 2\theta$ 38.2 and $50.6 > 2\theta > 44.4$ for diffraction of CuK$\alpha$ radiation by $\{111\}$ and $\{200\}$ planes of gold-rich Cu-Au alloy, respectively.

**TABLE 1**[1]

| Starting Alloy | Position ($2\theta$) of the Half-Maximum Width, in Degrees | Estimated Compositions[2] |
|---|---|---|
| Cu3Au | 39.8 | Cu60Au |
| Cu5Au | 39.4 | Cu69Au |
| Cu10Au | 38.5 | Cu96Au |
| Cu22Au | 38.2 | Au |
| Cu5Au[3] | 39.5 | Cu68Au |
| Cu10Au[4] | 39.5 | Cu68Au |

[1] Compositions corresponding to the newly formed maxima in the X-ray patterns. These results are for various Cu-Au alloys dissolved mainly in 1 M H$_2$SO$_4$ at 5 ma/cm$^2$ for 80 min.

[2] Approximate average composition estimated from these data and lattice parameter as a function of composition.[11]

[3] Anodically dissolved at 1 ma/cm$^2$ for 400 min.

[4] Anodically dissolved in buffered 1 N NaCl of pH 5 at 20 ma/cm$^2$ for 16 min.[1]

distance and the depth of penetration of X-rays have been calculated to be of the order of a few hundred and a few thousand angstroms, respectively.[1] At a later stage of anodic dissolution, however, the thickness of the layer in which compositional differences exist is very much greater than the actual diffusion distance. This is a result of the occurrence of extensive surface roughening during dissolution[2] (see subsequent section), i.e., since a region of variable composition exists next to every element of surface, the volume of material of variable composition increases roughly in proportion to the surface area.

**b. Electron Diffraction Investigations.** Electron diffraction examination of Cu-Au foils were made in order to confirm the result of the X-ray investigation—that volume diffusion occurs during dissolution of Cu-Au alloy. Information can in this way be obtained at very early stages

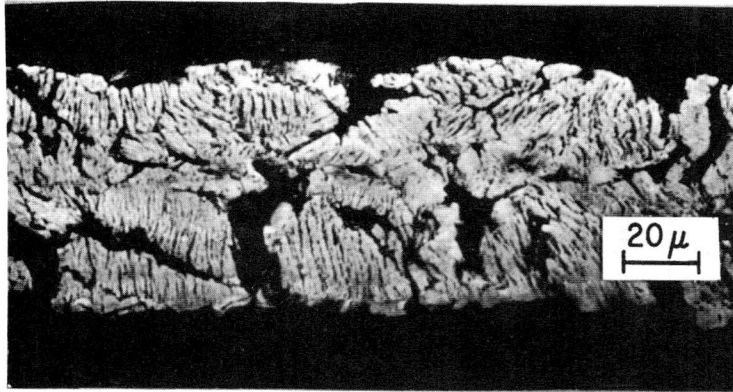

FIGURE 5 — Cross-section of Cu5Au foil specimen after anodic dissolution at 5 mA/cm$^2$ in 1 M H$_2$SO$_4$ for 320 min. (96 C/cm$^2$ passed), illustrating complete penetration of the alloy with a meeting of the reacted layers at about the midplane of the foil specimen.

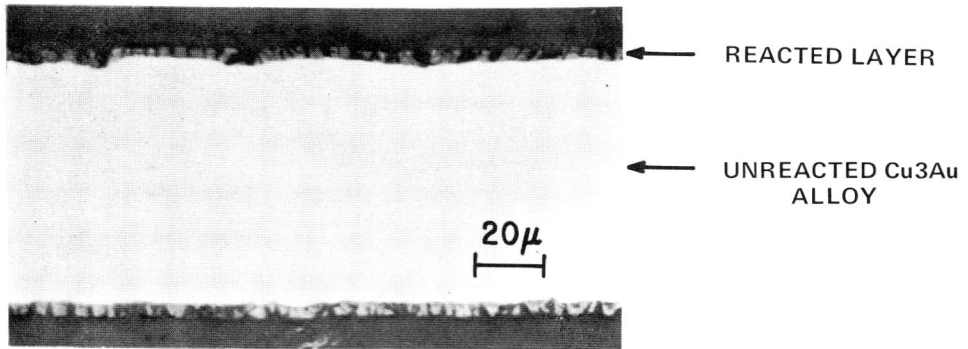

REACTED LAYER

UNREACTED Cu3Au ALLOY

FIGURE 6 — Cross-section of a Cu3Au foil specimen after anodic dissolution at 5 mA/cm$^2$ in 1 M H$_2$SO$_4$ for 80 min. (24 C/cm$^2$ passed).

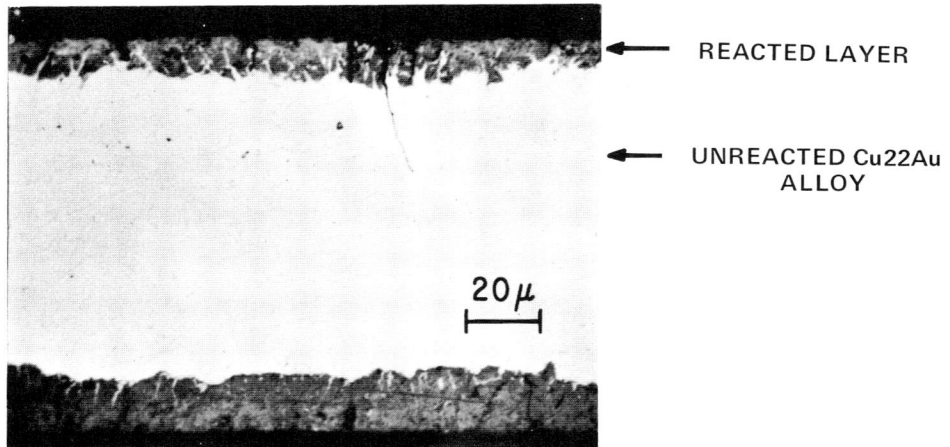

REACTED LAYER

UNREACTED Cu22Au ALLOY

FIGURE 7 — Cross-section of a Cu22Au foil specimen after anodic dissolution at 5 mA/cm$^2$ in 1 M H$_2$SO$_4$ for 80 min. (24 C/cm$^2$ passed).

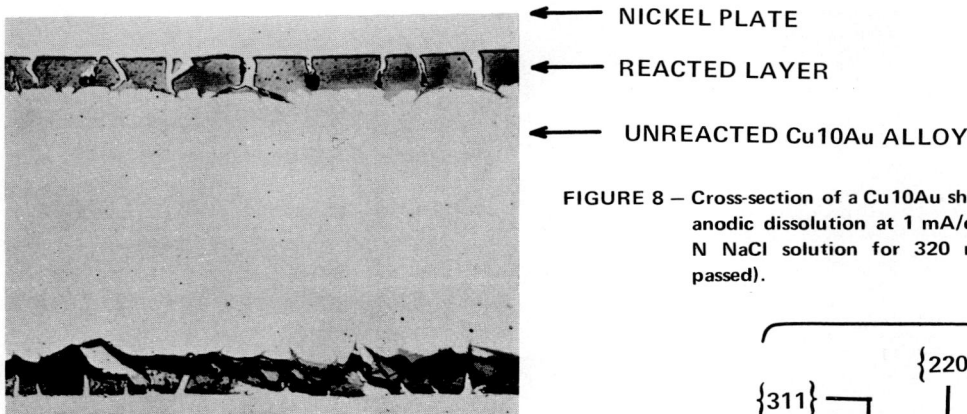

NICKEL PLATE

REACTED LAYER

UNREACTED Cu10Au ALLOY

FIGURE 8 — Cross-section of a Cu10Au sheet specimen after anodic dissolution at 1 mA/cm$^2$ in buffered 1 N NaCl solution for 320 min (19.2 C/cm$^2$ passed).

of anodic dissolution when the surface is still virtually plane, since the depth of penetration of the electrons is of the same order of magnitude as the diffusion distance. After passage of as little as 0.1 C/cm$^2$ broad rings corresponding to intermediate Cu-Au compositions appear in the electron diffraction patterns. This is seen in Figure 9 for Cu10Au anodically dissolved in 1 M H$_2$SO$_4$. Similar results were obtained for the other Cu-Au alloys. Passage of 0.1 C/cm$^2$ corresponds to about 100 atomic layers of dissolved Cu calculated on the basis of a uniform current density. Actually the current density may have been rather non-uniform as a result of geometrical and defect inhomogeneities introduced by scoring during the surface preparation. Consequently the electron diffraction data at 0.1 C/cm$^2$ may correspond to somewhat more than 100 atomic layers of Cu dissolved. The data of Figure 9 and the estimated compositions corresponding to them are tabulated for the first four diffraction planes in Table 2. Differences in the $2\theta$ positions of the maxima for different diffraction planes may be due to different depths of penetration, as well as to limited sensitivity in the patterns.

c. **Electron Microprobe Investigations.** Electron microprobe analysis through the cross-section of an anodically dissolved Cu10Au foil specimen was made in order to

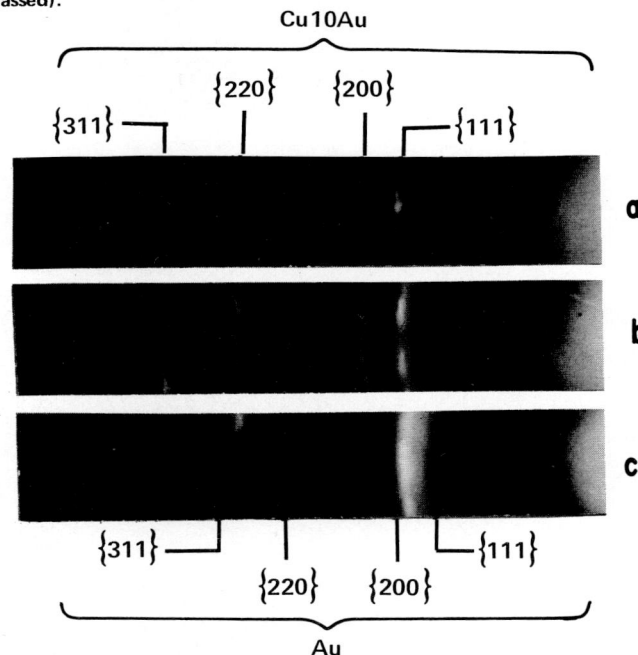

Cu10Au

{311}    {220}    {200}    {111}

a

b

c

{311}    {220}    {200}    {111}

Au

FIGURE 9 — Reflection electron diffraction patterns of Cu10Au after anodic dissolution in 1 M H$_2$SO$_4$, illustrating broad rings at gold-rich compositions in addition to Cu10Au alloy rings, in accord with enrichment by Au in the alloy layer immediately next to the alloy-electrolyte interface. (a) prior to anodic dissolution; (b) after 0.10 C/cm$^2$ passed (1 mA/cm$^2$ for 100 sec); (c) after 0.14 C/cm$^2$ passed (20 mA/cm$^2$ for 7 sec).

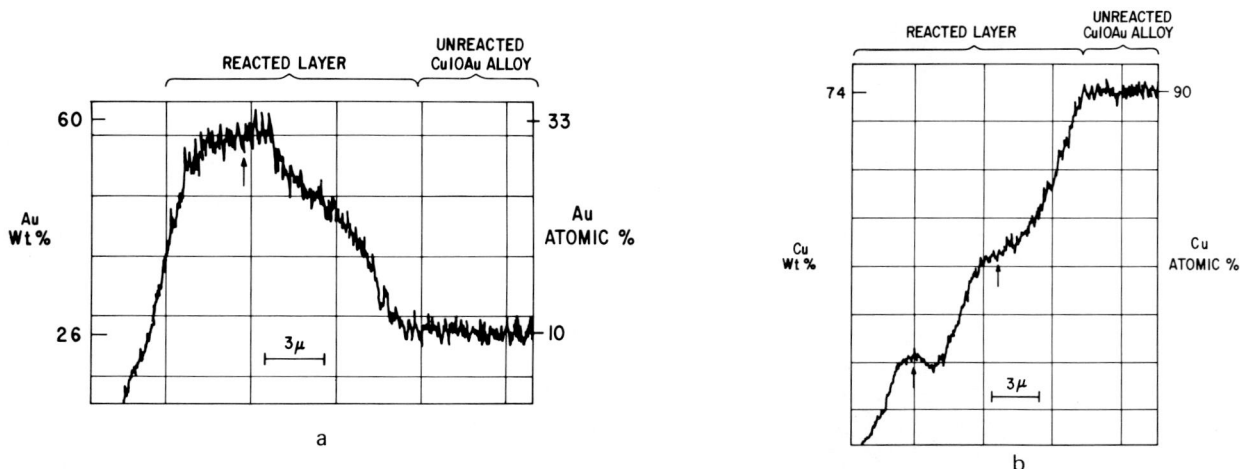

FIGURE 10 — Electron microprobe patterns taken through the cross-section of a Cu10Au foil specimen after anodic dissolution, illustrating increasing Au (pattern a) and decreasing Cu (pattern b) contents in the reacted layer as one proceeds outward from the alloy-reacted layer interface. As the beam approaches the outer surface of the reacted layer only part of the beam intersects it; consequently the intensity falls off even though the element content may actually increase, as in the case of Au in pattern a.

164

determine the gradients of Au and Cu throughout the reacted layer. An overall increase in Au content and decrease in Cu content proceeding outward from the interface between the alloy and the reacted layer were indicated, as shown in Figure 10. This result is consistent with a mechanism of anodic dissolution which involves interdiffusion of the component metals. The curves of the intensity are not smooth but contain plateaus and maxima. These are thought to be due to the presence in the reacted layer of particles of virtually unreacted Cu10Au alloy seen by optical metallography although the effects of porosity in the reacted layer are not known. Porosity may also produce errors in the microprobe determinations of concentration.

### 2. Measurement of Surface Roughening

The occurrence of volume diffusion during anodic dissolution of Cu-Au alloys should lead to severe roughening of the surface, according to theoretical considerations by Harrison and Wagner.[11] They show that a plane surface is unstable when one metal is preferentially removed from a binary alloy with diffusion in the alloy as the rate-controlling step. The salient point may be seen without calculations.[11] The length of the diffusion path from an arbitrary plane in the bulk (parallel with the surface) to the surface varies wherever a perturbation exists in the surface, being shorter at the valley than at the crest of the perturbation. Consequently more atoms are removed from the alloy at the valley than at the crest, and accordingly the interface at the valley recedes faster than at the crest. The amplitude of the perturbation thereby increases with time. Anodic dissolution of Cu from Cu-Au alloy may be expected to proceed similarly, followed by the growth of pores and channels, with the eventual formation of a reacted layer of very high surface area. Formation of a porous layer during dissolution especially for Cu-Zn and Cu-Au alloys has been reported by various authors[1-13] on the basis of metallographic examination, and in one investigation on Cu-Au, individual pores were observed and measured at a few hundred Å diameter by transmission electron microscopy.[12]

Polarization capacity measurements were conducted in order to determine the increase in surface area when Cu is anodically dissolved from Cu10Au in 1 M $H_2SO_4$ at 24 C. Measurements of this kind have been previously made by Bowden and co-workers[16] for a determination of the roughness of various metallic surfaces and by Wagner,[17] by Gerischer and Tischer[18] and by Jaenicke and Schilling[19] in order to determine the decrease in surface area of silver obtained by cathodic reduction of silver chloride. The present measurements were made in a bridge circuit with a low-amplitude, high-frequency (30 kHz) alternating current superimposed on a direct current by which the rate of dissolution was determined. For the experimental conditions employed, the measured capacity is approximately proportional to the surface area of the Cu10Au test electrode.[2] The circuit is shown in Figure 11 and is a modification of one used by Gerischer and Tischer.[18]

The results of these measurements show that the surface area increases sharply during the first 10 to 20 minutes of dissolution, rising by a factor of 20 to > 100 depending on the current density. The rate of increase of area decreases after about the first minute until the total area no longer changes appreciably with time even though dissolution of Cu continues. When the direct current is cut off and anodic dissolution ceases, the capacity data indicate a sharp decrease in surface area (although a direct proportionality between capacity and area may no longer be a good approximation for reasons reported elsewhere,[2]) in accord with the data of Wagner[17] and others[18,19] for analogous conditions. Figure 12 illustrates this behavior for Cu10Au electrodes anodically dissolving at different current densities of 1 and 3 mA/cm². The data are shown in terms of the measured capacity divided by the geometrical area and in terms of the ratio of the measured capacity to the initial capacity $C_O$, where $C_O$ is the value obtained by extrapolation to zero time of the capacity measured during

TABLE 2[(1)]

| Diffraction Plane | Original Cu10Au Alloy Ring | Radius (cm) of | | Pure Au |
| | | Gold-Rich Ring, 1 mA/cm² for 100 sec. (0.10 C/cm²) | Gold-Rich Ring, 20 mA/cm² for 7 sec. (0.14 C/cm²) | |
| --- | --- | --- | --- | --- |
| 111 | 3.47 | 3.30 | 3.15 | 3.09 |
| 200 | 3.96 | 3.80 | 3.61 | 3.56 |
| 220 | 5.56 | 5.43 | 5.16 | 5.04 |
| 311 | 6.48 | – | 5.97 | 5.92 |
| | | Cu40Au[(2)] | Cu85Au[(2)] | |

[(1)]Radii of the electron diffraction rings shown in Figure 9. The values for pure Au are also shown.
[(2)]Approximate average composition estimated from above data and lattice parameter as a function of composition.[15]

165

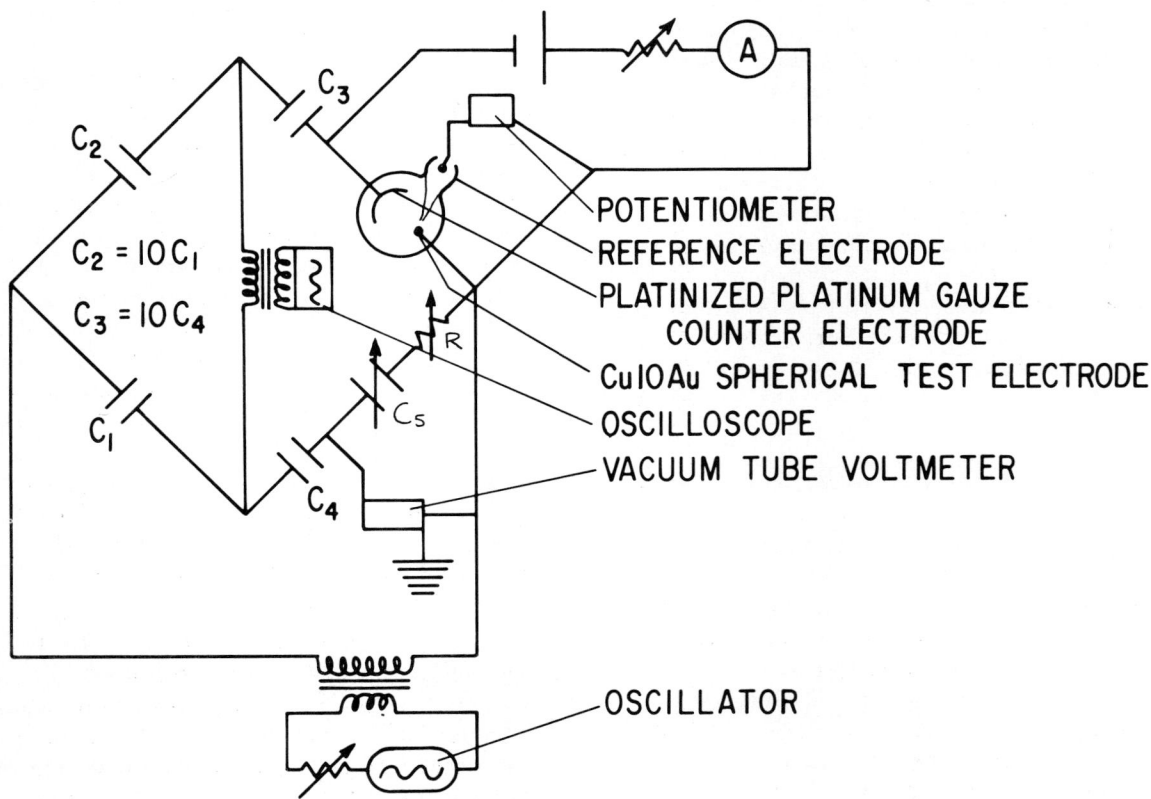

FIGURE 11 — Circuit for measuring the impedance.

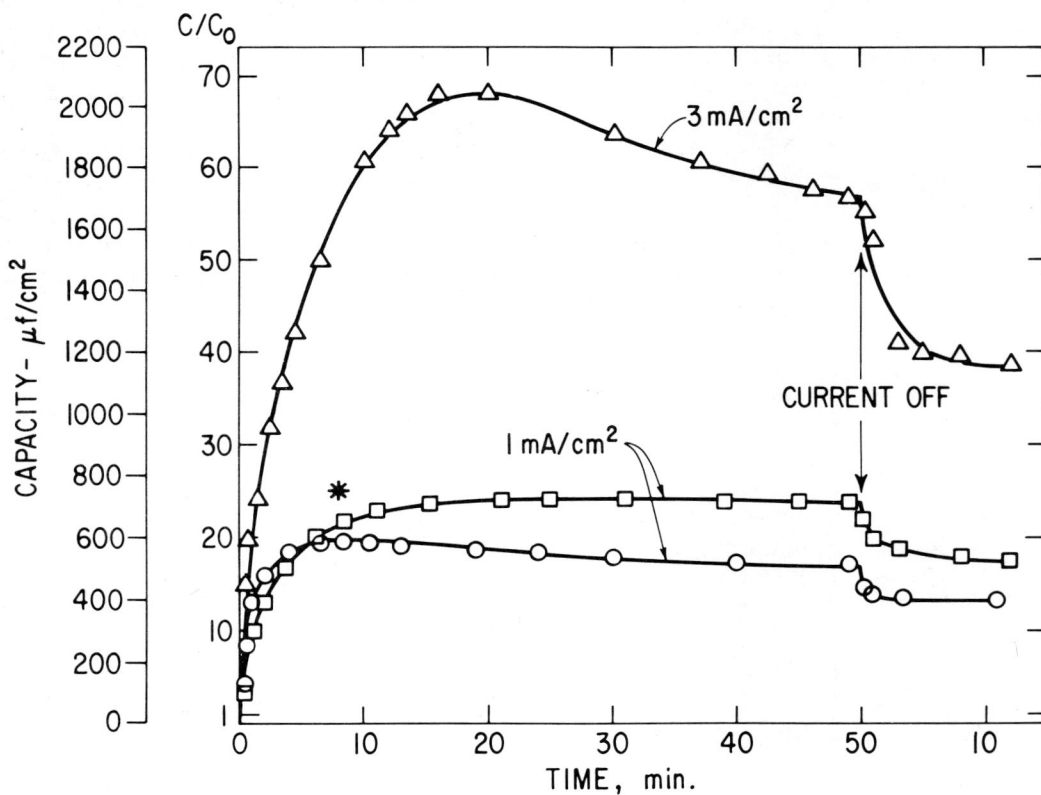

FIGURE 12 — Capacity measured during anodic dissolution and the ratio of the measured capacity to the initial capacity $C_o$ for Cu10Au electrodes dissolved in 1 M $H_2SO_4$ at 1 mA/cm$^2$ (o and □) and 3 mA/cm$^2$ (△). See text for determination of $C_o$. * indicates the C/Co calculated from the BET measurement of area for a Cu10Au electrode which had been dissolved at 1 mA/cm$^2$ for 8 min.

166

anodic dissolution. A reasonably good extrapolation was possible at 1 mA/cm² since at very early stages of anodic dissolution a plot of capacity vs time is nearly linear. The average initial capacity obtained in this manner from data of several Cu10Au electrodes[2] was $C_O = 30 \mu F/cm^2$ with a rather poor reproducibility of about ± 50%.

The subsequent aging of the electrode surface after the current is interrupted occurs mainly within a few minutes; after one hour virtually no further change occurs. The surface area corresponding to the one-hour aged condition, although decreased by about a factor of two from that existing just prior to cut-off of the current, is still greater by more than an order of magnitude than at the start of anodic dissolution, when the surface was essentially plane.

From additional capacity data for other current densities it was established that (a) for a given time of electrolysis the increase in surface area is greater the higher the current density and (b) as one proceeds from a current density of 1 to 5 mA/cm² the surface area increases to larger and larger values prior to leveling off, with the result that more than a one hundred-fold increase in area obtains for Cu10Au electrodes dissolving at 4 or 5 mA/cm².

The eventual leveling off of the surface area while dissolution of Cu continues may be understood in terms of two processes occurring simultaneously with counter-acting effects: Anodic dissolution which tends to increase the area and aging which tends to reduce it.[20] Initially the surface area of the Cu-Au electrode increases rapidly, the rate being determined mainly by the rate of Cu dissolution. As dissolution continues and the surface area becomes large, aging becomes more important in determining the net change in surface area; i.e., when roughening has occurred to a considerable extent such that primary, secondary and tertiary pores and channels penetrate the alloy in various directions, there will be significant amounts of Au-rich alloy, especially near the original surface, where aging may occur in virtually complete absence of Cu dissolution. The decrease in area in these regions may eventually become comparable to the amount of new surface formed near the base of the channels where dissolution of Cu mainly occurs. Thus, the surface area which initially increases sharply continues to increase but at an ever decreasing rate as dissolution continues, and eventually becomes a weak function of the amount of dissolution.

It was confirmed by the BET method that the change in surface area may be determined from measurements of the polarization capacity.[1] After dissolution at 1 mA/cm² for 8 minutes, the BET area of a Cu10Au electrode was found to have increased by about a factor of 25, or something less than twice the increase determined by measurements of the polarization capacity (see Figure 12).[2]

---

[1] The author is indebted to H. H. Podgurski for the BET area determination.

[2] For comparison of the BET area with the area determined from the capacity, one should note that a decrease in area occurs after the current is shut off (i.e., prior to the BET measurement), and that reaction products may remain even after extensive rinsing of the sample. The latter may be expected to give a BET area on the high side.

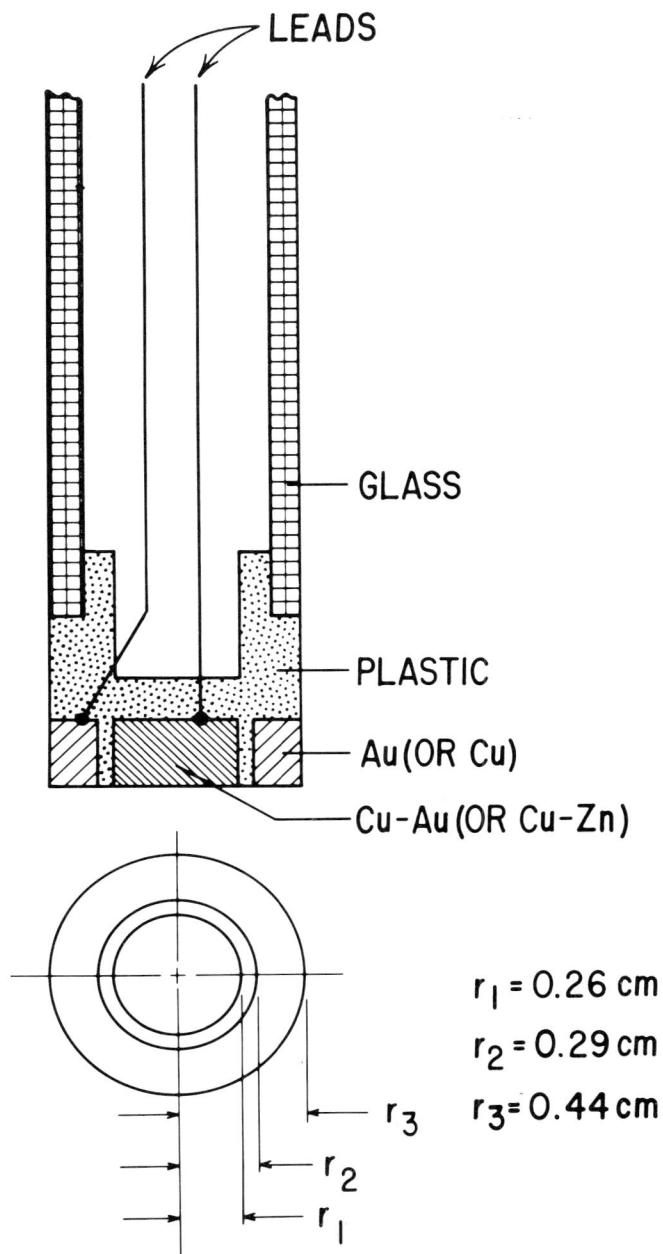

FIGURE 13 — Disk-ring electrode assembly.

$r_1 = 0.26$ cm

$r_2 = 0.29$ cm

$r_3 = 0.44$ cm

### 3. Test for the Occurrence of the Ionization of Au

As a first step in determining if ionization and redeposition of Au may be occurring during anodic dissolution of Cu10Au alloy, the electrochemical measurements were conducted at 23 C in order to determine if Au is ionized.[1] A rotating disk-ring electrode, Figure 13, which was introduced by Frumkin and Nekrasov[21] for the detection of intermediates in electrode reactions, was used. The theory for the interplay of diffusion and convection has been worked out by Ivanov and Levich.[22] The disk electrode of Cu10Au alloy was subjected to anodic dissolution at a current $I_d$ and the resulting potential $E_d$ was measured. The ring electrode (Au) was kept at a potential $E_r$ appropriate for discharge of Au³⁺ with a Wenking

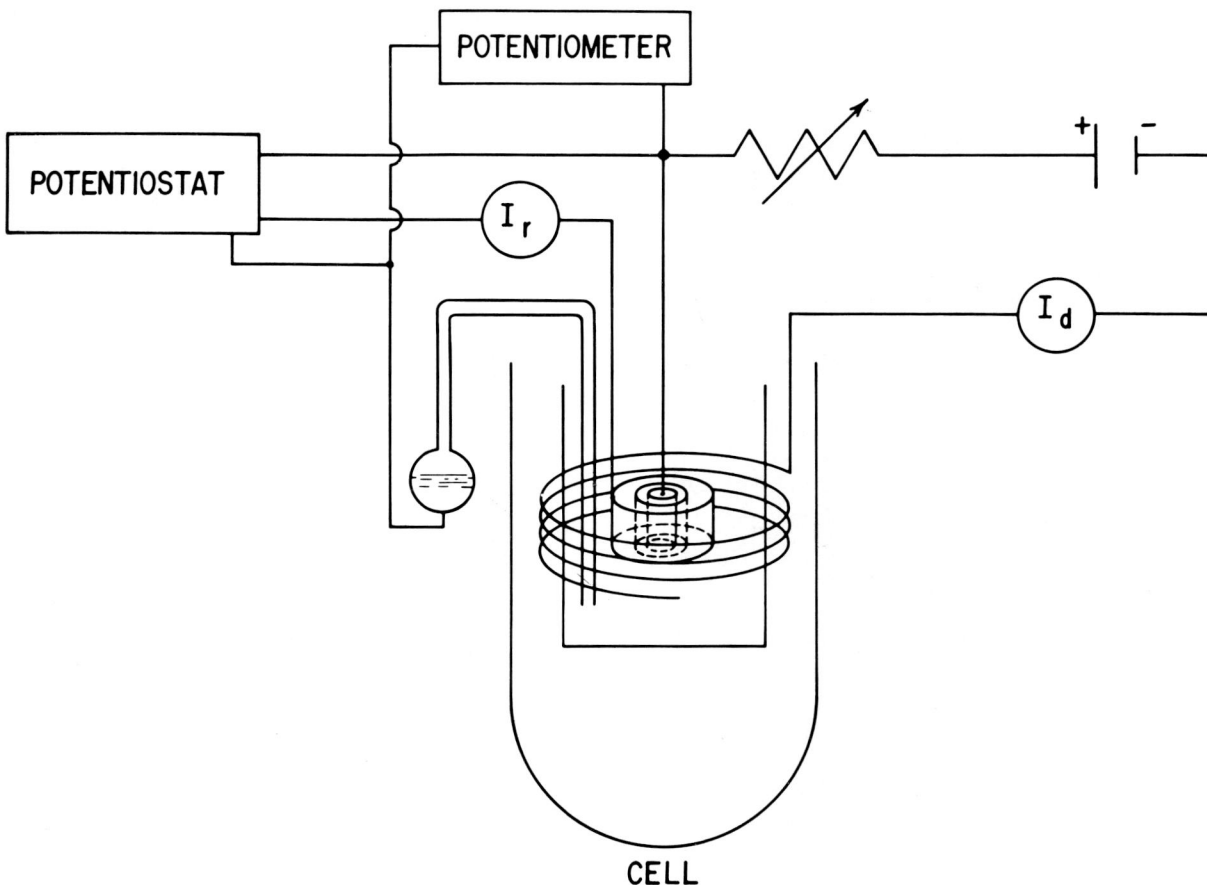

**FIGURE 14 – Circuit used for the ionization and redeposition experiments.**

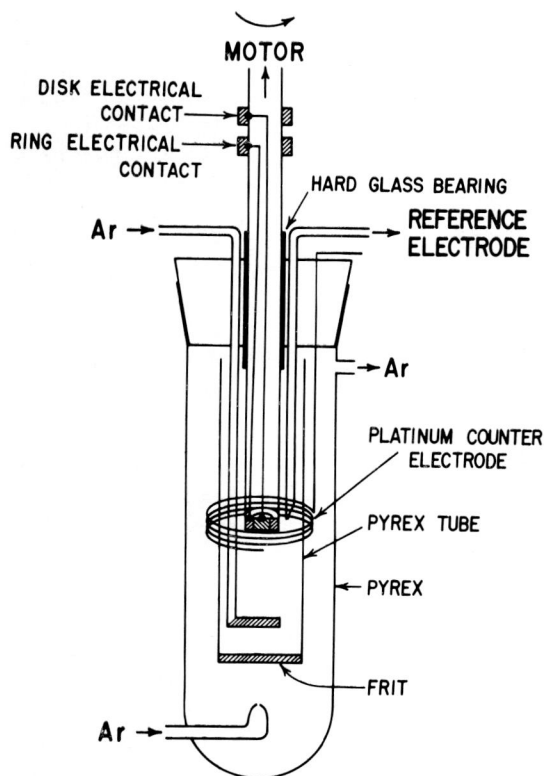

**FIGURE 15 – Cell used for the rotating electrode experiments.**

potentiostat and the resulting current, $I_r$, was measured. The electrolyte was 1 N $CuSO_4$ + 0.1 N $H_2SO_4$ and the rotation speed was 2900 rpm. Oxygen and hydrogen were excluded from the system. Thus at pH $\sim$ 1 only the reaction

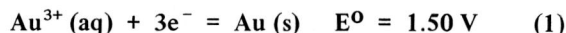

$$Au^{3+} (aq) + 3e^- = Au (s) \quad E^0 = 1.50 \text{ V} \quad (1)$$

may occur at the ring electrode if its potential is between 0.5 and 1.2 V. Accordingly a potential $E_r$ = 1.1 V was selected. The circuit and cell are shown in Figures 14 and 15. Additional experimental details are reported elsewhere.[1]

Let us consider conditions where Au is ionized to a certain extent. By virtue of rotation of the disk-ring electrode assembly, the solution in the hydrodynamic boundary layer containing newly formed $Au^{3+}$ ions is swept outward, thereby transporting $Au^{3+}$ ions to the vicinity of the ring electrode where they are discharged, producing a current $I_r$ in the ring circuit.

The relation between the observed potential $E_d$ of the disk electrode and the applied current $I_d$ is shown in Figure 16 for two different runs. The potential varied only slightly during the period of dissolution. At all applied currents $I_d$, the current at the ring electrode was practically nil, i.e., less than 2 $\mu$A. This indicates that gold is not ionized from the Cu10Au alloy in accord with the fact that the potential of the alloy according to Figure 16 was much lower than the

168

standard electrode potential of Au for Reaction (1). On the basis of this result and of the aforementioned diffraction data, it would seem that dissolution of Cu from Cu-Au alloy must occur virtually exclusively via the interdiffusion of Cu and Au in the alloy, unless the surface diffusion mechanism operates. Appreciable preferential dissolution via surface diffusion, however, is not considered likely, as will be discussed later.

### B. Cu30Zn Alloy

#### 1. Tests for the Occurrence of the Redeposition of Cu on Cu30Zn

When Cu30Zn alloy is subjected to anodic dissolution both components are dissolved, according to previous investigations and results reported below. Hence one wishes to know if copper is redeposited on the alloy surface for conditions under which Cu and Zn are dissolved from the alloy.

Theoretical considerations[1] show that ionization-redeposition of the more noble metal is possible, but only if coupling of the anodic reactions in accord with the concepts of irreversible thermodynamics occurs. This becomes apparent when one considers the dissolution of Cu-Zn alloy. Assume first that the anodic reactions

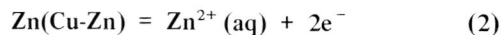

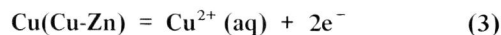

$$Zn(Cu\text{-}Zn) = Zn^{2+} (aq) + 2e^- \qquad (2)$$

$$Cu(Cu\text{-}Zn) = Cu^{2+} (aq) + 2e^- \qquad (3)$$

are independent of each other and also independent of the cathodic redeposition reaction

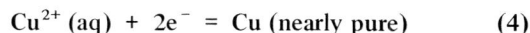

$$Cu^{2+} (aq) + 2e^- = Cu \text{ (nearly pure)} \qquad (4)$$

Since the activity of Cu in Cu-Zn is less than that of pure copper, the single-electrode potential for equilibrium of Reaction (3) in a solution of given $Cu^{2+}$ ion concentration is more noble than that of Reaction (4) involving pure copper. Thus, dissolution of copper from Cu-Zn according to Reaction (3) can take place only if the electrode potential is more noble than the equilibrium electrode potential for Reaction (3) and thereby even somewhat more noble than the equilibrium electrode potential for Reaction (4). Consequently, if a short-circuited couple of Cu-Zn and pure copper is made the anode with a pre-determined current, one has to expect that copper ions enter the solution from the Cu-Zn surface and from the pure copper surface as well, provided that there is no coupling between Reactions (2) and (3). However, if in accordance with the principles of irreversible thermodynamics, coupling between Reactions (2) and (3) occurs,

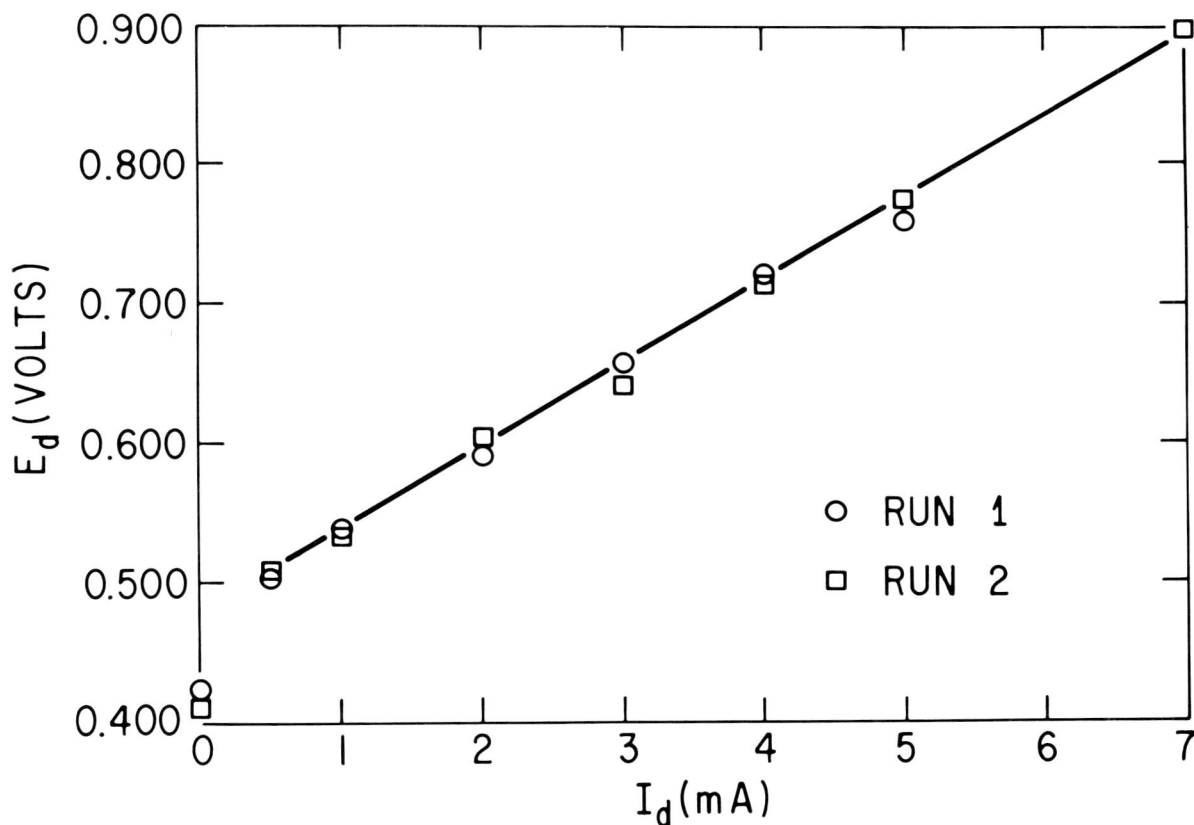

FIGURE 16 — Measured potential $E_d$ (SHE) of Cu10Au disk electrodes in 1 N $CuSO_4$ + 0.1 N $H_2SO_4$ vs the applied current $I_d$.

169

i.e., the cross coefficients in the general rate equations are finite, the anodic dissolution of copper from Cu-Zn alloy according to Reaction (3) may take place at a potential less noble than the equilibrium potential for Reaction (4). The copper ions that enter the solution from the Cu-Zn surface may then be redeposited at the copper surface according to Reaction (4). A realistic atomistic model of this process may be found elsewhere.[1] On the basis of this analysis the following experiments using the rotating disk-ring electrode were made.

**a. Rotating Disk-Ring Experiment 1.** In this experiment the amount of Cu recovered at the ring electrode during anodic dissolution of the Cu30Zn disk electrode was measured and compared to the theoretical value. If $I_o$ is the rate of dissolution of Cu, in amperes, at the disk electrode it can be shown[22,1] that the recovery ratio, $I_{r(Cu)}/I_o$, where $I_{r(Cu)}$ is the current at the ring electrode due to discharge of $Cu^{2+}$ ion, has a value of 0.53 when no redeposition of $Cu^{2+}$ occurs at the disk electrode, and a value $< 0.53$ when redeposition does occur. It should be noted that $I_{r(Cu)}$ is always smaller than $I_o$ since a certain fraction of the $Cu^{2+}$ ions produced at the disk electrode remains in the boundary layer at the rim of the ring ($r = r_3$) and is swept into the bulk electrolyte (1 N $ZnSO_4$ of pH 5). Comparison of the recovery ratios obtained at two speeds

of rotation provides a further check on the tendency of redeposition of Cu at the Cu-Zn disk electrode since $I_{r(Cu)}/I_o$ is independent of rotational speed in the absence of redeposition but not if redeposition occurs.[22,23]

Data obtained at 2900 rpm for different impressed currents to the Cu30Zn disk electrode yield $I_{r(Cu)}/I_o$ values which are the same within the experimental error as the theoretical value of 0.53 calculated for zero redeposition of copper. Table 3 lists these data and $I_{r(Cu)}/I_o$ values for a typical run. $I_{r(Cu)}$ was calculated as the

TABLE 3[1]

| | | | | | |
|---|---|---|---|---|---|
| $I_d$ ($\mu$A) | 50 | 100 | 500 | 1000 | 3000 |
| $E_d$ (V) | 0.252 | 0.264 | 0.301 | 0.320 | 0.387 |
| $I_r$ ($\mu$A) | 62 | 78 | 233 | 435 | 1239 |
| $I_r^o$ ($\mu$A) | 43 | 44 | 55 | 80 | 190 |
| $I_{r(Cu)}/I_o$ | 0.54 | 0.49 | 0.51 | 0.51 | 0.50 |

[1]Typical potentials of the disk ($E_d$), measured current ($I_r$) and interpolated residual currents ($I_r^o$) at the ring, and recovery ratios $I_{r(Cu)}/I_o$ as a function of the dissolution current ($I_d$) applied to a Cu30Zn disk electrode. The electrolyte was 1 N $ZnSO_4$ + 0.05 N $HC_2H_3O_2$ + 0.05 N $NaC_2H_3O_2$ and the potential of the ring electrode was -0.30 V (SHE).

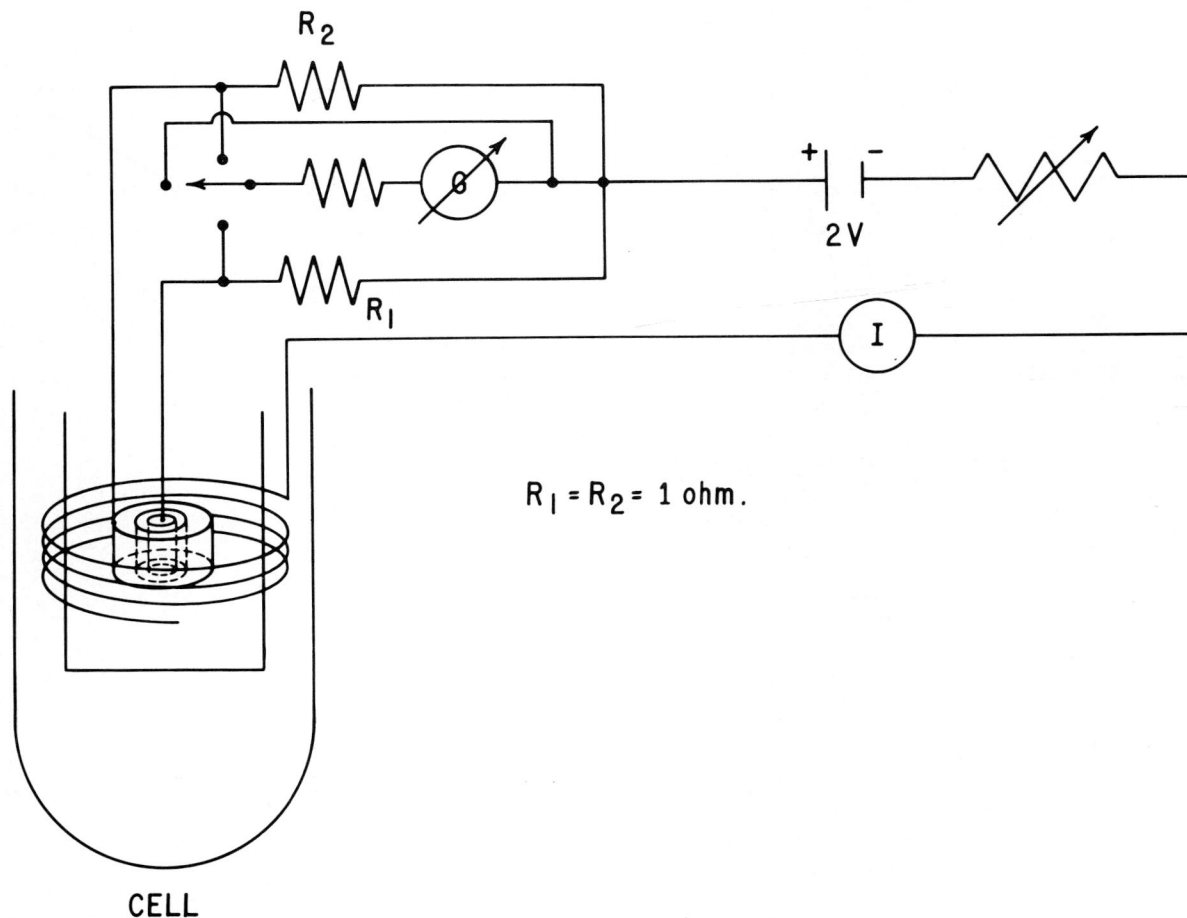

$$R_1 = R_2 = 1 \text{ ohm.}$$

FIGURE 17 — Circuit used to further check for the presence of Cu redeposition during anodic dissolution of Cu30Zn alloy.

measured current at the ring electrode, $I_r$, less the residual $I_r^o$. The latter was necessarily an interpolated value from data obtained intermittently when $I_d = 0$. The current, $I_o$, for dissolution of copper from the Cu30Zn disk electrode was calculated as the impressed current, $I_d$, times the mole fraction of Cu in the alloy. Essentially the same results were obtained for the rotational speeds of 290 and 2900 rpm. These results indicate that redeposition of Cu does not occur during dissolution of Cu30Zn alloy.

**b. Rotating Disk-Ring Experiment 2.** In view of the limited accuracy of the measurements reported in (a) and Table 3, redeposition of a minor fraction of copper of the order of 10 percent or less cannot be ruled out. More definite information was yielded by a second series of experiments where the disk and the ring electrode were practically short-circuited (see Figure 17). The currents $I_d$ and $I_r$ were obtained by measuring the IR drop across resistors $R_1$ and $R_2$ with the help of a galvanometer calibrated before the run. The highest IR drop across the 1 $\Omega$ resistors was 0.47 mV. Thus the potential difference between the disk and the ring electrode was always negligible. The electrolyte was the same as for the first series of experiments and the rotational speed was 2900 rpm. In order to eliminate accumulation of copper ions in the bulk solution, fresh electrolyte was used for each run and measurements were begun with the lowest value of the impressed current $I_d$. Thus the concentration of copper ions at the ring electrode was determined essentially by that prevailing at the disk electrode due to dissolution of the alloy. Results are shown in Table 4. The current at the ring electrode was always anodic. Thus no redeposition of copper was found. On the contrary, copper was dissolved from the Cu ring at the potential prevailing during dissolution of the Cu30Zn alloy.

## III. Discussion

### A. Volume Diffusion at Room Temperature

The occurrence of appreciable volume diffusion at room temperature would normally not be expected on the basis of diffusivities extrapolated from high-temperature measurements. Such an extrapolation implies that (a) equilibrium concentrations of vacancies (and interstitials) are established at room temperature as at elevated temperatures, and (b) the contribution of diffusion along small-angle grain boundaries and along dislocations is negligible at room temperature. Many authors have already pointed out that the second condition may not be satisfied and, therefore, the effective (average) diffusion coefficient at room temperature may be considerably greater than the extrapolated value. The high diffusivities which obtain during anodic dissolution of Cu-Au alloys (as indicated by the appearance in the diffraction patterns of diffracted intensity at $2\theta$ positions corresponding to intermediate Cu-Au compositions), however, are believed to result mainly from the failure to satisfy the first condition. This is discussed in the next section.

*1. The Model of Vacancy Formation at the Surface*

Vacancy formation at the surface may occur when an alloy is subjected to anodic dissolution and only atoms of the less noble component enter the solution.[1,24,25] This represents a situation quite different from the one describing dissolution or vaporization of a pure metal, where transport of material across the interface is believed to occur mainly via kink sites. To see this let us consider the dissolution of a Cu-Au alloy in $H_2SO_4$ (aq), where virtually only copper enters the solution as $Cu^{2+}$ ions according to previous investigations[8,10] and the foregoing results. A partial step on the surface with a sequence of Cu and Au atoms is shown in Figure 18. When a current is

TABLE 4[1]

| $I_d$ ($\mu A$) | $I_r$ ($\mu A$) |
|---|---|
| 48.3 | 1.7 |
| 96.2 | 1.7 |
| 293 | 6.9 |
| 473 | 31.6 |

[1]Dissolution currents at the disk ($I_d$) and at the ring ($I_r$) electrodes for currents ($I_d + I_r$) applied in the anodic direction on the Cu30Zn disk — Cu ring couple in 1 N $ZnSO_4$ + 0.05 N $HC_2H_3O_2$ + 0.05 N $NaC_2H_3O_2$.

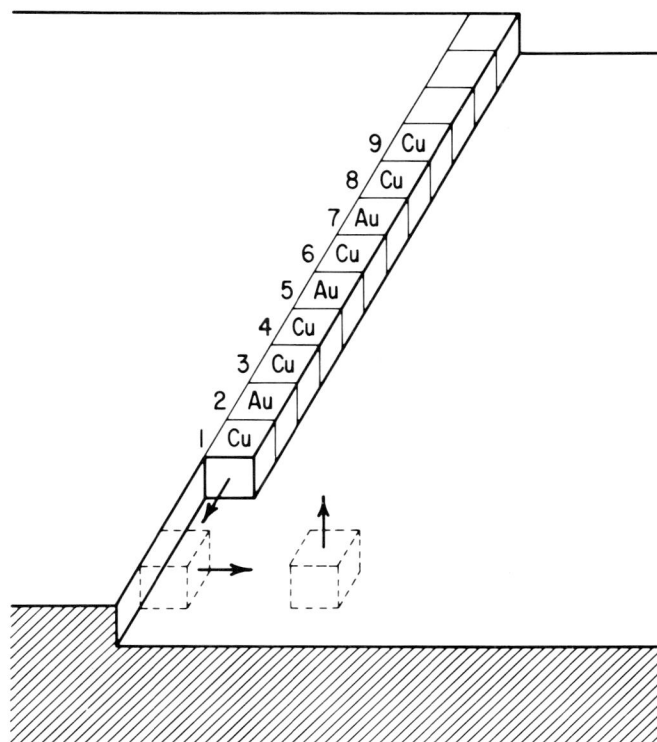

FIGURE 18 — Dissolution of Cu from a Cu-Au alloy via adsorbed Cu atoms as intermediates.

171

passed in the anodic direction, first a copper atom from position 1 may move from its kink position in order to become an adsorbed atom and subsequently to enter the solution as an ion. Then, the gold atom initially at position 2 may also move to become an adsorbed atom. Thus, the Cu atom initially at position 3 now occupies the kink position and may be ionized by the same mechanism which has been assumed for the copper atom initially at position 1, as is also true for the copper atom initially at position 4. The gold atom originally at position 5 becomes the atom at the kink position and thus may also move to become an adsorbed gold atom. In view of the continuous increase of the concentration of adsorbed gold atoms, there is, however, an increasing tendency of gold atoms to move back to the kink positions in the steps. Thus, after removal of a sizeable fraction of copper atoms from the steps, it happens only very rarely that a copper atom occupies a kink position and is free to move from its kink position and to be desorbed as an ion. This leads to electrochemical polarization, i.e., the electrode assumes a potential considerably above the equilibrium potential. The increase in the driving force necessary to maintain a constant current may now make it possible that an atom not at a kink position, e.g., the copper atom at position 8, may enter the solution as a divalent ion. As the driving force is further increased, Cu atoms from complete lattice layers may directly enter the solution as $Cu^{2+}$ ions. In this way, surface vacancies are formed continuously. Surface vacancies in a partially complete step may be filled by lone adsorbed atoms, or by a sequence of movements of atoms in a step. Surface vacancies in a complete lattice layer may also be filled by adsorbed lone atoms. In addition, atoms from the lattice layer underneath the surface may fill surface vacancies, whereby excess monovacancies and also divacancies in the interior of the alloy may be created. By random walk, excess vacancies will appear not only directly next to the surface but also in a certain volume of the crystal underneath the surface. Diffusion of vacancies into the interior of the alloy is limited because of the presence of dislocations which are sinks for vacancies. In view of the continuous production of vacancies at the surface, however, the number of available sinks for vacancies in the vicinity of the surface is reduced and subsequently excess vacancies may diffuse to greater distances from the surface while anodic dissolution is continued. The build-up of an excess vacancy concentration in the vicinity of the surface, which has already been considered by Schottky[24] in conjunction with the oxidation of metals at elevated temperatures and by Forty[25] in conjunction with dezincification at room temperature, would also enhance chemical diffusion, i.e., movement of copper atoms from the bulk alloy to the surface and backward diffusion of gold atoms according to the gradient of the Cu/Au ratio. In this way, more and more copper atoms may enter the solution as $Cu^{2+}$ ions. In the next section it is shown, using the known diffusivities of mono- and divacancies in Cu, that diffusion of Cu in Cu-Au alloy at room temperature may be expected to occur via divacancies rather than monovacancies.

*2. Mobility of Mono- and Divacancies*

Monovacancies seemingly do not account for diffusion of copper in Cu-Au alloy at room temperature. According to Ramstetter, Lampert, Seeger and Schule[26] $D_\square$ in pure Cu at 25 C equals $3 \cdot 10^{-19}$ cm$^2$/sec. Thus the mean square displacement of a monovacancy $\overline{\Delta X^2}$ for t = 1000 sec is only $\overline{\Delta X^2} = 2D_\square t = 6 \cdot 10^{-16}$ cm$^2$, which is of the order of the square of the distance between neighboring Cu atoms. Diffusion of copper atoms via divacancies may be operative, however, since their diffusivity[26] $D_{\square\square} = 1.3 \cdot 10^{-12}$ cm$^2$/sec in copper at 25 C is much higher. Using this value of $D_{\square\square}$ it has been shown for conditions of diffusion to a plane surface,[1] that appreciable true current densities may obtain in the presence of excess divacancies (viz., $10^{-4}$ A/cm$^2$ for an admittedly high divacancy mole fraction of $10^{-2}$). Since vacancies diffuse faster in Au than in Cu,[26a] interdiffusion may be even faster than that calculated. Further, since appreciable surface roughening occurs[2] the apparent current density may be much greater for the same assumed mole fraction of divacancies; conversely, an apparent current density of $10^{-4}$ A/cm$^2$ may be obtained with a divacancy mole fraction which is considerably lower than $10^{-2}$.

### B. On the Modes of Dissolution of Cu-Au and Cu30Zn Alloys

It is noteworthy that virtually no gold is dissolved from Cu-Au alloys, whereas Cu and Zn are dissolved simultaneously from a Cu30Zn alloy. This divergency is understandable since for the Cu-Au alloys the less noble metal is the major component whereas in the Cu30Zn alloy the more noble metal is. Preferential dissolution of zinc from the Cu30Zn alloy, however, may occur at much lower current densities than used in this investigation, in accord with reports that dezincification of brass during immersion in aqueous electrolytes is observed especially when the supply of oxygen is low.[4-6] According to Feller,[13] preferential dissolution of zinc under conditions of anodic polarization does occur when the alloy contains more than 75 atomic percent zinc.

### C. Argument Against the Surface Diffusion Mechanism

Aggregation of absorbed atoms of the more noble metal by virtue of surface diffusion may be expected to lead primarily to the formation of patches of monolayers. In addition, atoms of the more noble metal may pile up on the initial patches of monolayers and thus small three-dimensional crystals of the more noble metal may be formed. Since these crystals may be expected to grow in all three dimensions, there is the tendency to form finally a dense layer of the more noble metal. Hence further anodic dissolution of the less noble metal is prevented. This is to be expected especially if the mole fraction of the more noble metal is high as, e.g., in alpha brass. The surface diffusion mechanism, therefore, seems inadequate to explain preferential anodic dissolution under conditions where stifling of the reaction does not occur.

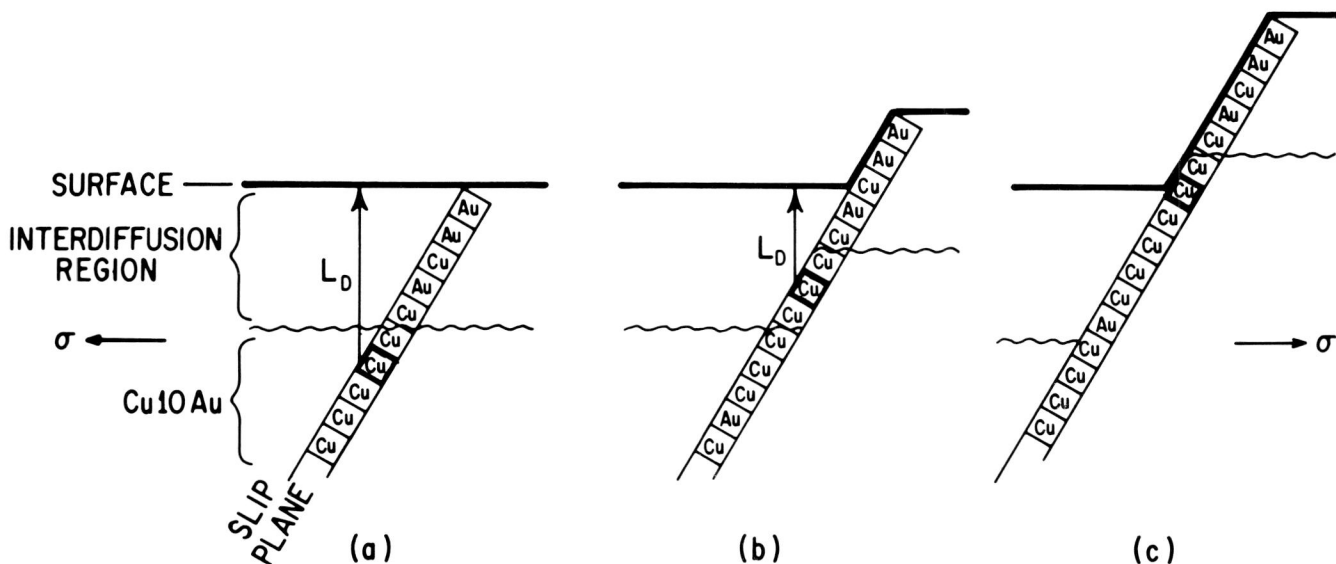

**FIGURE 19** — Schematic drawing illustrating the effect of plastic strain on enhancing dissolution in the vicinity of slip steps by considering in particular the diffusion length, $L_D$, of the Cu atom shown in heavy lines. (a) prior to slip; (b) after 3 dislocations have emerged from the surface along the slip plane $L_D$ is locally shortened; (c) after many dislocations have emerged, unreacted alloy is exposed to the environment.

### D. Relevance of These Results to Stress Corrosion

Several authors, including the present one, have in the past suggested or assumed that the dissolution step associated with stress corrosion of Cu-Au alloy involves ionization and redeposition of Au. On the basis of the results of the aforementioned experiments with a rotating disk-ring electrode, such a mechanism may be ruled out. Rather, stress corrosion in Cu-Au alloys involves interdiffusion of the components in the alloy in accord with the aforementioned X-ray and electron diffraction data.[3]

Similarly, if preferential dissolution of Zn occurs during stress corrosion of brass, interdiffusion of the component metals rather than ionization and redeposition of Cu may be expected. Several authors have suggested that dezincification occurs during the stress corrosion of brass.[25,30]

The occurrence of preferential dissolution via solid-state diffusion leads to the development at the crack tip as elsewhere of (a) a gradient of composition with the surface layers poor in the less noble metal and (b) an excess concentration of divacancies, some of which may dissociate to monovacancies or coalesce to form multivacancies, voids and dislocation loops while others migrate to sinks such as dislocations. Both consequences could be factors contributing toward stress corrosion susceptibility. In the presence of (a) localized plastic strain at the crack tip (or at the base of any perturbation in the surface) may provide for rapid transport of Cu toward the surface of a Cu-Au alloy which otherwise must occur by the relatively slow process of volume diffusion via excess divacancies. Depending on the size of the surface slip step produced, the diffusion path may be merely shortened or in the case of sufficiently large steps "short-circuited" entirely, as schematically shown in Figure 19. It follows that for a given amount of strain the effect is greater the more dislocation motion tends to be confined to a few, rather than many, slip planes, analogous to the case of dislocation-enhanced transport of solute discussed previously.[31] Since large amounts of slip may be expected at the crack tip even for small total strains, this effect could be substantial in providing for much higher currents at the crack tip than elsewhere. Accordingly crack growth occurs, accompanied by tearing of the porous, reacted region[12] which forms as a result of surface roughening and void formation. Segregation of solute (Cu) to the dislocations as indicated by other data[31] may act beneficially especially in the case of the higher Au containing alloys.

Plastic deformation is one means by which the rate of Cu transport to the surface may be increased over that which is possible via interdiffusion of the atoms through the bulk. Another is by diffusion along rapid-diffusion paths such as grain boundaries. Consequently more rapid attack may occur along grain boundaries even in the absence of deformation than elsewhere. This concept is in accord with reports of a tendency for intergranular attack and for stress corrosion cracks to follow grain boundaries in Cu-Au alloys.

---

[3] Extension of these results to anodic dissolution during application of a load to the specimen seems fully justified. Theoretical considerations indicate a very small effect of elastic strain on the single-electrode potential of a metal, about $10^{-4}$ - $10^{-5}$ mV/1000 psi.[27,28] Large scatter exists in the experimentally determined values,[29] but even the largest reported effect is too small by a couple of orders of magnitude to account for ionization of Au at the potentials reported in this work (Figure 16). Further, Gerischer and Rickert[8] report that anodic dissolution of Cu-Au alloy occurs at an even lower potential when the alloy is undergoing plastic deformation, (i.e., appreciable depolarization of the anodic reaction occurs) the potential needed to sustain a given current density being as much as several hundreds mV less than that needed in the absence of deformation.

Consequence (b) may be especially instrumental in the operation of an alternative mechanism for stress corrosion. The presence in the metal of excess divacancies, multivacancies, etc. may greatly restrict dislocation motion.[32,33] In such an event relief of local stress concentrations may occur by crack propagation; that is, the layer ahead of the crack as elsewhere becomes embrittled by the formation of divacancies at the surface, their migration into the alloy and ultimately their coalescense into voids and loops. Mechanisms involving a cleavage step have often been suggested, and Forty[25] has considered embrittlement due to vacancies during stress corrosion of brass.

The X-ray and electron diffraction results for the dissolution of Cu-Au alloy were the same for the NaCl and $H_2SO_4$ electrolytes in that in both electrolytes preferential dissolution of Cu was indicated to occur via interdiffusion in the alloy. Cu-Au alloys have been reported to exhibit stress-corrosion in environments similar to those used in this investigation, viz., in 1 N $NaSO_4$ + 0.1 N $CuSO_4$ + 0.01 N $H_2SO_4$ and in 1 N KCl under conditions of anodic polarization.[8] It also is to be noted that these same environments do not cause stress corrosion (of Cu-Au) in the absence of an impressed current, i.e., during immersion without anodic polarization, as is true generally for immersion of Cu-Au alloys in nonoxidizing environments. In counter-distinction Cu-Au alloys have been reported by Graf[30] and others[10,12] to crack during immersion in many different environments which have in common only that they are strong oxidizing environments. These include aqueous $FeCl_3$, aqua regia, concentrated $HNO_3$, 2% $H_2CrO_4$ (aq) and $NH_3$-$H_2O$-air. Such observations are in accord with the idea that stress corrosion requires a potential providing the possibility of preferential dissolution of one component.[20,1] This idea is different from the main thesis of Graf[30] in that (1) it applies to alloys in which the more noble metal is the principal component as well as to alloys in which it is the lesser component, e.g., $\alpha$-brass, and (2) it explicitly suggests that selective dissolution of the less noble metal is required. Preferential

dissolution of Cu from Cu-Au occurs when the electrode potential exceeds a critical value, which increases with the gold content of the alloy until the potential for oxygen evolution is reached at about 40-45 atomic percent Au.[8] Thus preferential dissolution of Cu and stress corrosion cracking may be expected during immersion of copper-rich Cu-Au alloys in various electrolytes which contain sufficiently strong oxidizing agents or under conditions of anodic polarization in electrolytes which may not contain an oxidant.

A final remark concerns alloys composed entirely of base metals. For alloys of Fe-Ni and Cr-Ni and the commercially important austenitic stainless steels among others, there is a difference in the standard potentials of the component metals of several RT/F. Thus for certain conditions of potential,[1] viz., that the potential of the dissolving alloy be higher than that of the more base metal and lower than that of the less base metal in the environment which may contain complexing agents, preferential dissolution of the more base metal(s) may be encountered. Some data by Hoar and Hines[34] and Barnartt and van Rooyen[35] have appeared which suggest that the surface of austenitic stainless steel becomes enriched in Ni during immersion in 42% $MgCl_2$ solution at 150 C. Hence analogous to the situation with Cu-Au and Cu-Zn, it may be that stress corrosion of the austenitic stainless steels requires a potential which provides for the preferential dissolution of Fe and/or Cr.

## Acknowledgments

The author is especially grateful for the aid of Prof. Dr. Carl Wagner of the Max Planck Institut fur Physikalische Chemie who has made major contributions to the investigations described herein. Gratitude is also expressed to Drs. R. A. Oriani, J. C. M. Li and S. Barnartt for helpful discussion and to Messrs. P. J. Byrne and H. A. Hughes for their skillful assistance in carrying out the experiments, all on the staff of this laboratory.

## References

1. H. W. Pickering and C. Wagner. *J. Electrochem. Soc.,* **114**, 698 (1967).
2. H. W. Pickering. *J. Electrochem. Soc.,* **115**, 690 (1968).
3. H. W. Pickering. *J. Electrochem. Soc.,* **115**, 143 (1968).
4. R. B. Abrams. *Trans. Am. Electrochem. Soc.,* **42**, 39 (1922).
5. G. D. Bengough, R. M. Jones and R. Pirret. *J. Inst. Metals* (London) **23**, 65 (1920).
6. G. D. Bengough and R. May. *J. Inst. Metals* (London) **32**, 81 (1924).
7. L. Graf. *Metallforschung,* **2**, 193, 207 (1947); *Z. Metallkunde,* **40**, 275 (1949).
8. H. Gerischer and H. Rickert. *Z. Metallkunde,* **46**, 681 (1955).
9. F. W. Nothing. *Metall.,* **10**, 520, 1033 (1956).
10. R. Bakish and W. D. Robertson. *Trans. AIME,* **206**, 1278 (1956).
11. J. D. Harrison and C. Wagner. *Acta Met.,* **7**, 722 (1959).
12. H. W. Pickering and P. R. Swann. *Corrosion,* **19**, 369t (1963).
13. H. G. Feller. *Habilitationsschrift, Technische Universitat Berlin* (1965); *Corr. Sci.,* **8**, 259 (1968).
14. L. Graf. *Metallwirtschaft,* **11**, 77 (1932).
15. W. B. Pearson. *Handbook of Lattice Spacings and Structures of Metals and Alloys.* p. 441, Pergamon Press, New York (1958).
16. F. P. Bowden and E. K. Rideal. *Proc. Roy. Soc.,* (London) **A120**, 59, 80 (1928); and K. E. W. Grew. *Discussions Faraday Soc.,* **1**, 91 (1947); and E. A. Conner. *Proc. Roy. Soc.* (London) **A127**, 317 (1930).
17. C. Wagner. *J. Electrochem. Soc.,* **97**, 71 (1950).
18. H. Gerischer and R. P. Tischer. *Z. Elektrochem.,* **58**, 819 (1954).
19. W. Jaenicke and B. Schilling. *Z. Elektrochem.,* **66**, 563 (1962).
20. C. Wagner. Private communication.
21. A. N. Frumkin and L. I. Nekrasov. *Dokl. Nauk S.S.S.R.,* **126**, 115 (1959); *Proc. Acad. Sci. U.S.S.R. Phys. Chem. Sec.,* **126**, 385 (1959).
22. Yu. B. Ivanov and V. G. Levich. *Dokl. Nauk S.S.S.R.,* **126**, 1029 (1959); *Proc. Acad. Sci. U.S.S.R. Phys. Chem. Sect.,* **126**, 505 (1959); V. C. Levich. *Physiochemical Hydrodynamics,* p. 329 ff, Prentice-Hall, Inc., Englewood Cliffs, New Jersey (1962).
23. V. G. Levich. *Acta Physicochim. U.S.S.R.,* **17**, 257 (1942).

24. W. Schottky. *Z. Elektrochem.*, **63**, 784 (1959).
25. A. J. Forty. *Physical Metallurgy of Stress Corrosion Fracture*, (T. N. Rhodin, ed.) pp. 99-115, Interscience Publishers, New York (1959); A. J. Forty and P. H. Humble. *Proceedings 2nd International Congress on Metallic Corrosion*, pp. 80-88 (1963).
26. R. Ramstetter, G. Lampert, A. Seeger and W. Schüle. *Phys. Stat. Sol.*, 8, 863 (1965).
26a. W. Schüle, A. Seeger, D. Schumacher and K. King. *ibid.*, 2, 1199 (1962).
27. W. H. Walker and C. Dill. *Trans. Am. Electrochem. Soc.*, 11, 153 (1907).
28. R. E. Fryxell and N. H. Nachtrieb. *J. Electrochem. Soc.*, 99, 495 (1952).
29. Ling Yang, G. T. Horne and G. M. Pound. *Physical Metallurgy of Stress Corrosion Fracture*. (T. N. Rhodin, ed.) pp. 29-39, Interscience Publishers, New York (1959).
30. L. Graf. *Stress Corrosion Cracking and Embrittlement*. (W. D Robertson, ed.) pp. 48-60, John Wiley and Sons, New York (1956); this volume.
31. P. R. Swann and H. W. Pickering. *Corrosion*, 19, 369t-372t (1963).
32. R. Maddin and A. H. Cottrell. *Phil. Mag.*, **46**, 735 (1955).
33. D. Kuhlmann-Wilsdorf, R. Maddin and H. G. F. Wilsdorf. *Strengthening Mechanisms in Solids*. ASM 137-178 (1962).
34. T. P. Hoar and J. C. Hines. *International Committee for Electrochemical Thermodynamics and Kinetics* (C.I.T.C.E.) Vol. 8, pp. 273, Butterworths, London (1958).
35. S. Barnartt and D. van Rooyen. *J. Electrochem. Soc.*, 108, 222 (1961).

## Discussion

**R. A. Oriani, U. S. Steel Corp.:**

I wish to repeat a suggestion that I have made previously to Dr. Pickering, and to ask if in his work he has observed anything like the suggested effects. The suggestion is to utilize an ordering reaction to prove the existence of enhanced volume diffusion during preferential electrodissolution. Suppose, for example, one begins with an alloy of a composition such that the equilibrium state is a superlattice at room temperature, but the electrodissolution is carried out on the quenched-in disordered state. Then the enhanced volume diffusion under question should, if it actually operates, produce an ordered structure that will be manifested by a characteristic X-ray diffraction superlattice line. Alternatively, beginning with any one composition in an ordering system diffusion would produce a range of compositions so that there should develop a superlattice at some position in the reaction zone.

**H. W. Pickering:**

Some change in the "background" intensity does occur in the vicinity of the superlattice reflections, $\{100\}$ and 110, although definite maxima do not appear. In view of the inherent low intensity of superlattice reflections and to some extent the small volume of ordered alloy, the absence of maxima is not surprising.

I should like to take this opportunity to report some very interesting, although preliminary, results for the Cu-Zn system. Here, conditions for observing phase transformations are more favorable, in view of the presence of intermediate phases. After anodic dissolution of single-phase $\epsilon$-brass, peaks due to $\gamma$-brass appear in the diffraction pattern. Similarly after dissolution of single phase $\gamma$-brass, the diffraction patterns contain a broad region of increased diffracted intensity due to $\alpha$-brass. These and additional results will be reported in detail elsewhere.

**P. R. Swann, Imperial College, London:**

Copper gold alloys dissolve in many environments to form a high density of corrosion tunnels about 200 Å diameter. For the first 500 atom distances at least the tunnels propagate very rapidly (200-300 atom distances per second) and I doubt whether such rates could involve volume diffusion over the 100 atom distances you propose even if the divacancy model is adopted.

I would also like to comment concerning the value of the rotating electrode experiments. The corrosion mechanism leading to the sponge-like morphology you observe is such that a plane dissolution front never develops. Dissolution begins by the formation of pits and tunnels and *if* gold did ionize at the bases of the pits and were deposited on the walls, then the ions would not be caught in the surface stream of electrolyte and would not be detected. I am not proposing that this is the dissolution mechanism but it is a possibility that should be considered since the experiment is designed to determine whether or not the gold does ionize.

**H. W. Pickering:**

(I) **Very high rates of dissolution may result if the reversible potential of the oxidant is somewhat more positive than that of Au so that Au dissolves to an appreciable extent. In this case, dissolution of Cu may occur mainly by successive removal of the uppermost atom layers. Nevertheless the surface becomes enriched in Au, in view of the difference in standard potentials of Cu and Au.** Perhaps, eventually, preferential dissolution via volume diffusion occurs, although this has yet to be shown. The salient point is that appreciable Cu dissolves prior to the establishment of the volume diffusion process. The same initial situation exists also for electrolytes in which Au is virtually inert. However, the number of atom layers of Cu which must be dissolved to establish a given degree of surface enrichment is fewer; even so the number may be considerable if piles or ridges of Au develop prior to the attainment of a high gold concentration over the entire surface. Hence, the initial stage of dissolution may occur via appropriate surface migration and/or dissolution of Au, processes which are inherently more rapid than solid state diffusion.

(II) It is true that deposition of gold at the ring electrode would not be detectable if virtually all gold ions within the pores are reduced immediately. This, however, would require a very pronounced "coupling" of the anodic reactions so that gold ions enter the solution at a potential considerably less noble than the Au(Cu-Au)/Au$^{3+}$ (aq) equilibrium potential, see the detailed discussion (for Cu-Zn alloy) on page 13 of the text. The required intensive "coupling" seems very unlikely. On the basis of the measured potential (Figure 16), we see that a reduction in potential of about 1 volt from the Au(Cu-Au)/Au³⁺ (aq) equilibrium potential is required if Au is to dissolve.

## D. A. Vermilyea, General Electric Research and Development Center:

A major problem in accepting the proposed mechanism is that it involves taking atoms out of the center of the last layer to form a lattice vacancy. The energy required is roughly half the binding energy of atoms in the lattice, which would be about 1.5 eV, and I just don't believe it can happen.

I would like to propose a different mechanism. If we have a step, we remove copper atoms from the kink sites and eventually uncover a gold atom. These gold atoms are left behind as copper is removed from both sides. The gold can probably move along the steps and agglomerate to form nuclei of gold. As the step recedes more gold will accumulate on each nucleus. Some alloy will become surrounded by the gold atoms in the nucleus and cannot be removed because to do so would require removing copper atoms from the close packed plane, and the energy to do that is very high.

Eventually a bit of original alloy will be completely surrounded by a ring of gold, forming a surface region of different composition. It still has some copper which is kinetically hindred from being dissolved. Ultimately there will be several of these gold-copper regions, and as steps try to move past these obstacles the step length increases, the edge energy is raised, and there would be an increased over-voltage for dissolution, as you have shown. This increase could easily amount to several tenths of a volt.

Looking at the cross section of the dissolving alloy, I picture the dissolution as giving rise to rods or fibers as the interface moves down. Rods of copper-gold material are left behind on the surface because, as the surface is dissolved away, new gold will deposit on the nucleii already formed. This gives a fine particle size deposit which could account for the diffraction line broadening.

Just how these hypothetical rods or small particles of original alloy coated with gold might diffract X-rays or electrons is not obvious. However, since the particle size is only 10 or 20 angstroms it seems conceivable that the diffraction might indicate a lattice parameter intermediate between that of the alloy and of gold.

## H. W. Pickering:

(I) I should like to restate that the volume diffusion mechanism is in accord with all the experimental observations, in particular, the diffraction data. This is true for all particle sizes. The same statement may not be made for the surface diffusion or ionization-redeposition mechanisms. This may be shown also for the exceptional (in the sense of particle size) surface diffusion mechanism you present. The relevant experimental observations are as follows.

(1) An increase in X-ray diffracted intensity is observed over a broad range of $2\theta$ extending from the $2\theta$ position of the original alloy to that of pure gold. At a somewhat later time a maximum in intensity appears at an intermediate composition which gradually shifts to a lower

(more gold rich) $2\theta$ position with increasing amounts of dissolution. When the sample is completely penetrated and only gold rich alloy remains, a further shift in composition approaching pure gold occurs.

(2) The particle size is on the order of $\sim 200$ Å rather than less than 20 Å, according to transmission electron microscopy data recently obtained for anodic dissolution of Cu 25 atomic percent Au at 1 mA/cm² in 1 M $H_2SO_4$, in agreement with numerous earlier results for specimens immersed in certain oxidizing electrolytes (H. W. Pickering and P. R. Swann, *Corrosion*, 19, 373t (1963)). The alloy after dissolution appears as a porous network (rather than as rods) with a wall thickness on the order of a couple hundred Å. This is shown in Figure 1.

Your mechanism with a particle size of only a few atomic dimensions does not appear to be in accord with observation (2), and it has yet to be shown whether it can account for any part of observation (1). On the other hand if you allow the "rods" to grow in a lateral direction as seemingly is to be expected in the normal course of events, observation (1) is clearly unsatisfied since the "rods" consist of a core of original Cu-Au alloy and an outer layer of Au.

(II) Whether or not atoms may be readily detached from terrace sites, giving rise to surface vacancies, is a question of the driving force applied. In the case of dissolution of pure Cu, atoms leave the lattice primarily via kink sites. The required overpotential is very low, amounting to less than 5 mV for Cu dissolution at 1 mA/cm² in acidified $CuSO_4$ solution, according to Mattsson and Bockris (*Trans. Faraday Soc.*, 55, 1586 (1959)). One asks then what overpotential is required to dissolve Cu atoms at terrace sites, where the number of bonds with neighbor atoms is roughly 30% more than in the case of kinks for low index planes. I guess that the overpotentials we measure for dissolution of Cu from Cu-Au alloy are high enough, since they are on the order of $> 10^2$ mV, rather than a few mV. It is difficult, however,

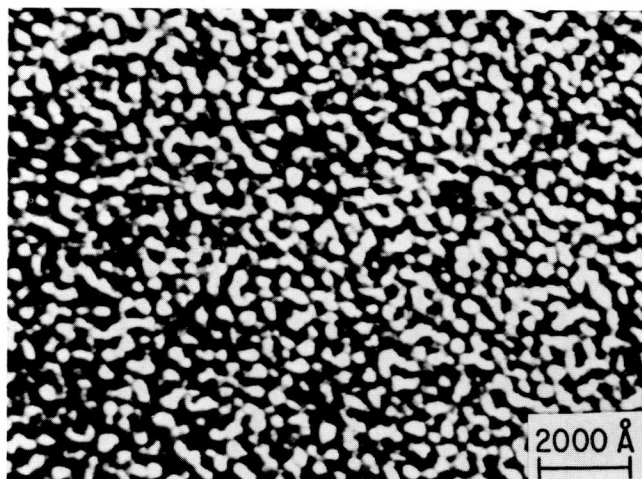

FIGURE 1 — Transmission electron micrograph of an anodically dissolved (50 sec at 1 mA/cm² in 1 M $H_2SO_4$) Cu25Au alloy. Black network is gold-rich alloy. White spots are pores.

176

to formulate a meaningful quantitative argument in view of the complex interaction of forces which exist at a metal-electrolyte interface.

**L. Graf, Max-Planck-Institut fur Metallforschung:**

Dr. Pickering, you suppose the occurrence of volume diffusion during anodic dissolution of Cu-Au alloy at 23 C based on X-ray and electron diffraction of surface layers of dissolved specimens. Your opinion is that only the occurrence of volume diffusion leads to a gradual variation in composition, and thus, in lattice parameter, with distance from the electrolyte-alloy interface. Appreciable preferential dissolution via surface diffusion, however, is not considered likely, because there is supposed to be the tendency to form finally a dense layer of the more noble metal preventing further (anodic) dissolution of the less noble metal. The surface diffusion mechanism, therefore, seems to you to be inadequate to explain preferential (anodic) dissolution under conditions where stifling of the reaction does not occur.

I would like to object, that, with the attack of $HNO_3$ (diluted 1:1) on a Cu10Au alloy whereby gold is not dissolved either, a layer of pure gold forms on the surface, and the attack continues until complete dissolution of the alloy, leaving behind a pure gold precipitation. This is a well-known practice for separating gold from other metals. Also, with the precipitation of a more noble metal from its solutions by a less noble metal, for example of copper with iron, the reaction is not prevented by the copper precipitated on the iron, because the precipitation is porous.

Furthermore, how am I to understand based on your thesis that in aqua regia (diluted 1:1), which dissolves gold, too, nearly the same surface layer arises on a Cu10Au alloy as you found with anodic dissolution and we did in a concentrated $NH_4OH + H_2O_2$ solution, where in both latter cases gold is not dissolved or ionized. I think, all these results are easier to understand with the surface diffusion mechanism considering the variable mobility of the gold atoms in the electrolyte-alloy interface, which depends on the behavior of the attacking solutions.

**H. W. Pickering:**

(I) I believe the salient point to be made about the surface diffusion mechanism is that it is not in accord with much of the diffraction data, as discussed in my reply to Dr. Vermilyea. What we say, in addition, is that the surface diffusion mechanism might not in principle be a satisfactory mechanism, in view of the probability of surface coverage by the more noble metal. I doubt however that the validity of the latter statement can be determined from either of the first two experimental observations you mention. In the first, you have assumed surface diffusion operates, whereas the same result follows if either of the other two mechanisms operate. For example, in the case of volume diffusion a pure Au reacted layer is indicated in the diffraction pattern when the porous alloy near the original alloy-electrolyte interface becomes nearly completely depleted of Cu. In the second, discharge of ions is involved. Since these ions diffuse from the bulk electrolyte to the metal surface, they are generally discharged upon coming in contact with the tips of the protruding deposits. Hence the deposits may grow predominantly in a direction normal to the original metal-electrolyte interface, and in so doing form eventually a porous rather than a protective layer.

(II) From a qualitative point of view, dissolution of Cu-Au in aqua regia may be similar to that which is observed for conditions under which only Cu dissolves, although this has yet to be determined with the help of diffraction data. It is true that the reacted layer which forms after immersion in aqua regia is quite similar in appearance to the reacted layer which forms when dissolution occurs via volume diffusion, but I doubt this really gives a clue as to mechanism.

**A. J. Forty, University of Warwick:**

Perhaps the most important thing that emerges from Dr. Pickering's paper is the conclusion that volume diffusion is the controlling process in preferential dissolution. In order to account for the high rate of the reaction he has to invoke diffusion by a divacancy mechanism. I wonder if this is sufficient?

**H. W. Pickering:**

Calculations presented elsewhere for unidirectional diffusion to a plane surface using the known diffusivity[26] of divacancies in Cu and an assumed divacancy mole fraction of $10^{-2}$ yield a rather high, true current density of $i \sim 2 \times 10^{-4}$ A/cm$^2$ and an "effective thickness" of the interdiffusion zone of $\delta \sim 10^{-6}$ cm after 1000 sec. Although this is a questionably high divacancy concentration, the actual required concentration to produce the same apparent (rather than true) current density may be much lower in view of the demonstrated occurrence of severe surface roughening (Figure 12).[3] Also the diffusivity of divacancies at room temperature is reported to be faster in Au than in Cu.[26a] On the basis of these considerations, divacancies would appear to be sufficient in the case of room temperature diffusion in the Cu-Au alloys.

# SOME ELECTROCHEMICAL FACTORS IN THE
# STRESS CORROSION OF α-BRASS

C. J. L. Booker
Sir John Cass College

## Abstract

The essential thermodynamic background for cracking of copper-zinc alloys in ammonia environments is duscussed. It is currently possible to define the macro-environmental conditions for cracking. These include the formation of corrosion product films, preferential anodic dissolution of zinc at the grain boundaries, and the formation of stable complex ions.

## I. Introduction

The first discussion on the season cracking of brass was reported over 60 years ago,[1] almost half of the 1944 symposium[2] was devoted to the subject and subsequent reviews,[3-5] conferences[6-8] and numerous publications have further elaborated the topic. As a result the complexities of the problem have been partially elucidated, although many details of the mechanism are still unclear.

The purpose of this contribution is to attempt to outline some of the critical electrochemical factors which have emerged in recent studies in ammoniacal and, to a limited extent, in other environments.

## II. Stress Corrosion in Ammoniacal Environments

### A. Background to the Problem

*1. Early Work*

In 1921 it was established[9] that cracking in cold worked cartridge brass could be brought about by ammonia, either in solution or in moist atmospheres, and ammonium compounds; the presence of oxygen and water is necessary[10,11] and carbon dioxide appears to have a synergistic effect.[12] Vapor phase and waterline conditions are often the most severe,[13,14] while in many service failures cracks would seem to be initiated by electrochemical reactions occurring within a condensed aqueous surface film.[11] Clearly, the study of electrochemical processes in such a situation is experimentally very difficult.

*2. Grain Boundary Activity*

Selective electrochemical attack at the grain boundaries

of unstressed α-brass in ammoniacal solutions has been previously investigated[11,15-17] and compared with the cognate copper-gold system.[18-20] These studies have served to account for the intergranular penetration of unstressed brass so widely observed.[21-28] Other experiments involving couples with dissimilar metals[17,29-31] have shown that cathodic polarization of a stressed specimen inhibited while anodic polarization stimulated intergranular cracking. Such effects have been more recently confirmed by potentiostatic studies.[32] These observations have underlined the electrochemical as distinct from the metal-structural aspects of the problem. Furthermore, the important function of complex ion formation has been stressed by Graf[33] as an explanation of the deviation of the brass/ammonia system from his rule for homogeneous solid solution alloys which ascribes stress corrosion susceptibility to the addition of a more noble component to the basis metal. His more recent conclusions are elaborated elsewhere in this volume.

*3. Partial Immersion Conditions and the*
*Importance of Tarnish Films*

The following experiment carried out by the author[14] demonstrates the critical nature of the environment conditions leading to rapid cracking. An annealed 70/30 brass wire, 'stopped-off' at both ends, was carried through a cell and stressed uniaxially with a lever system under an extensometer to follow elongation at the onset of cracking. Aqueous ammonia was added to obtain partial immersion conditions in contact with air. The immersed section of the wire remained bright, the formation of a bluish-green band of corrosion product was observed in the meniscus region, where cracks initiated, while the upper unimmersed part developed a brown tarnish film. If the ammonia level was then raised at the onset of cracking, propagation was arrested as the surface films dissolved off, until fresh cracks were initiated within the new meniscus region. This chain of events could be repeated several times until total immersion was achieved, final fracture actually occurring outside of the exposed gauge length and some considerable time later. Subsequent metallographic examination of the specimen clearly showed a sequence of rings of intergranular cracks corresponding to the successive meniscus exposures. The special properties of this meniscus region have been considered by Russian workers[34] and need not further concern us here.

From this and other work[9,10,28,30,35] it is evident that environmental conditions which discourage the formation of surface films tend to suppress cracking, even when this has been actively initiated, in preference to more generalized attack. The electrochemical factors governing the formation of such surface films will be considered below.

### 4. The Significance of Dissolved Copper

That the presence of dissolved copper, either initially present or intrinsically produced, markedly influences the initiation and propagation of cracking in brass has been widely demonstrated.[13,14,20,28,32,36,37] Indeed, such solutions appeared to provide a favorable basis for developing a test regime for assessing season cracking susceptibility.[38] The copper is generally present as an ammino-complex[11,36,39] of $Cu(II)_{aq}$, together with $Cu(I)_{aq}$ which acquires increased stability in the presence of ammonia.

It has been shown in several investigations that increasing concentration of both complexed copper in solution[32,37,39-41] and zinc in the brass[32,39] facilitates the formation of a characteristic black tarnish. Thus the presence of oxygen in the environment normally serves to stimulate the formation of such complex species—especially when dissolved copper is not initially present—as a precursor to tarnishing reactions and the initiation of intergranular cracking. It has also been found that transgranular cracking may alternatively appear in conditions where no macroscopically visible tarnish film is produced.[28,42]

### B. The Application of the Potential-pH Diagram

#### 1. Background

In considering systematically the complex thermodynamic equilibria between a metal, its solid reaction products and its dissolved states in an aqueous environment the potential-pH diagram as developed by Pourbaix and his collaborators[43] has proved a valuable tool. However, the calculations possible are only as reliable as the accuracy of the primary thermodynamic data. Furthermore, in the departures from equilibrium which occur in corrosion processes where kinetic factors frequently predominate, potential-pH diagrams have recognized limitations.

While Mukaibo and Fueki[44] first attempted to devise a potential-pH diagram to summarize the corrosion behavior of 70/30 brass, taking into account the reduced thermodynamic activity of the zinc, it was clear that its applicability was limited by a lack of understanding of the corrosion behavior of alloys.

#### 2. Mattsson's Diagrams

Mattsson's approach[42] has proved more successful in setting out the electrochemical details of season cracking. These are conveniently summarized in Figure 1. The most significant feature here is the region around pH 7.2 where maximum susceptibility to intergranular cracking occurs with the formation of the now well-characterized[32,45] black tarnish film. Studies of potential-time and polarization relationships by Hoar and Booker[32] under these conditions support the hypothesis of selective dissolution of zinc with the concomitant growth of a pseudo-passivating film of $Cu_2O$ (Figure 2). While the polarization resistance of the anodic process increases with film growth, so the potential rises to remain poised at around the redox-potential of the predominating cathodic depolarizing system, as outlined by the shaded zone in Figure 1:

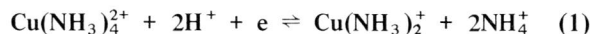

$$Cu(NH_3)_4^{2+} + 2H^+ + e \rightleftharpoons Cu(NH_3)_2^+ + 2NH_4^+ \quad (1)$$

Due to inherent kinetic limitations of solubility and diffusion control the participation of oxygen reduction is of much less significance under these conditions:

$$O_2 + 4H_2O + 4e = 4OH^- \quad (2)$$

However, it has been demonstrated[37,40] that, where the specimen surface/solution volume ratio is large, oxygen is necessary to maintain the concentration of $Cu(II)_{aq}$ by reversing Reaction (1).

The anodic reactions involved in the tarnishing process appear to be

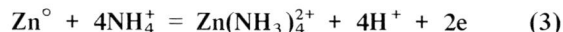

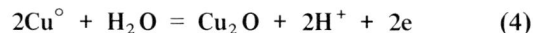

$$Zn^\circ + 4NH_4^+ = Zn(NH_3)_4^{2+} + 4H^+ + 2e \quad (3)$$

$$2Cu^\circ + H_2O = Cu_2O + 2H^+ + 2e \quad (4)$$

while a limited contribution may arise by deposition from solution

$$2Cu(NH_3)_2^+ + 2H^+ + H_2O = Cu_2O + 4NH_4^+ \quad (5)$$

The only change in potential occurring at fracture is an evanescent rise, which has also been confirmed inside a prenotched specimen by McEvily and Bond.[46] Thus the increased electrochemical activity associated with crack propagation is readily sustained by the facile cathodic process (1) without the fall in corrosion potential frequently observed in other systems,[4] although both film rupture[46] and enhanced anodic activity[50] have been demonstrated.

The overall tarnishing process may well be represented

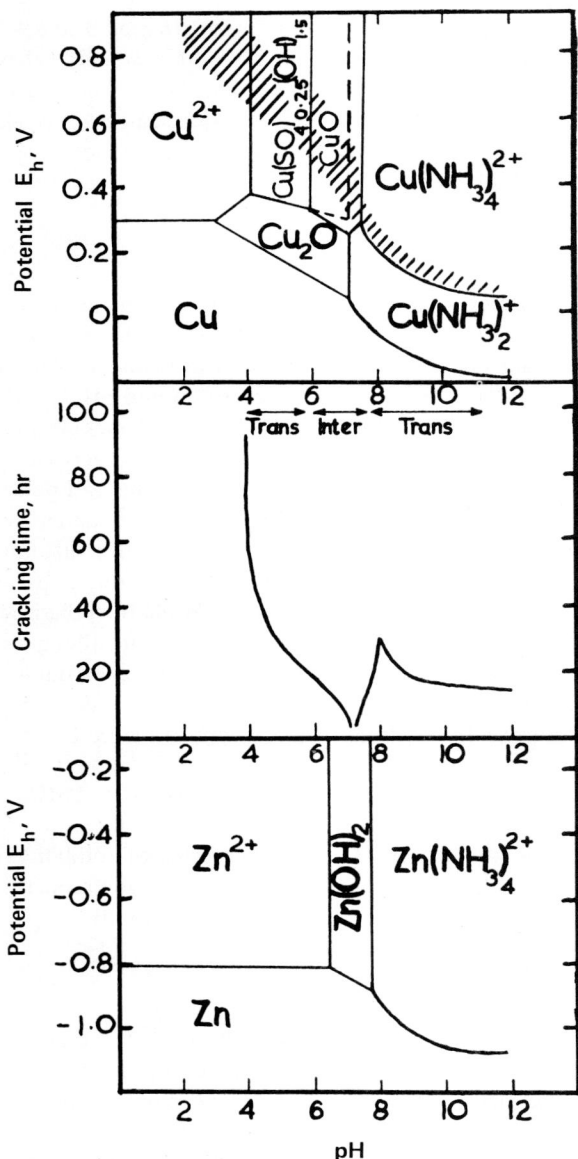

**FIGURE 1 —** Summary of Mattsson's description[42] of the stress corrosion cracking of brass in ammoniacal solutions. (a) Potential-pH diagram for the system Cu-$NH_3$-$H_2O$ at 50 mM dissolved $CuSO_4$ and 1 M total ($NH_4^+$ + $NH_3$); (b) Dependence of stress corrosion cracking susceptibility upon pH; and (c) Potential-pH diagram for the system Zn-$NH_3$-$H_2O$ at 10 mM dissolved Zn and 1 M total ($NH_4^+$ + $NH_3$).

as a combination of Reactions (1), (3), and (4):

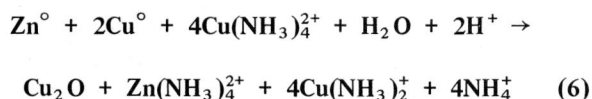

$$Zn^\circ + 2Cu^\circ + 4Cu(NH_3)_4^{2+} + H_2O + 2H^+ \rightarrow$$

$$Cu_2O + Zn(NH_3)_4^{2+} + 4Cu(NH_3)_2^+ + 4NH_4^+ \quad (6)$$

This satisfies the dezincification mechanism proposed by Forty[45] which leads to progression of the overall tarnishing reaction into the metal, forming epitaxial $Cu_2O$ on the brass substrate, while selective penetration at grain boundaries arises from enhanced chemical activity of zinc thereat.

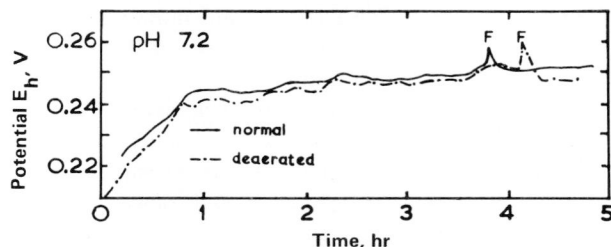

**FIGURE 2 —** Potential-time curves for stressed 70/30 brass wires during the tarnishing reaction in Mattsson's solution showing the negligible influence of oxygen (Hoar and Booker[32]).

However, that this description may be an over-simplification of the situation has been demonstrated by Johnson and Leja,[40,47] who point out that Cu(II) ammine formation involves stepwise formation of a series of complexes $Cu(NH_3)_n^{2+}$ where n = 1 to 5. While the $Cu(NH_3)_4^{2+}$ complex has the widest range of stability, these authors showed by a detailed study under Mattsson conditions that maximum cracking susceptibility actually corresponded to pH 6.5 where the $Cu(NH_3)_2^{2+}$ complex was predominant. It was therefore attractive to suggest that the diammino redox couple $Cu(NH_3)_2^{2+}/Cu(NH_3)_2^+$ provided optimum electrochemical stimulation for good steric and kinetic reasons. However, direct experimental verification of such singular details of mechanism is not easy.

### 3. Recent Modifications

The refinements to Mattsson's diagrams made by Johnson and Leja[47] have been taken up by Letowski and Niemiec[48] and several other controversial features are still open to debate.[49,50] However, these extensions of the original concept are particularly significant because they go some way towards incorporating within the same descriptive framework the more recent extensive studies of Westwood and coworkers[37,39] in concentrated ammoniacal solutions, as well as much earlier data (Section A).

The diagrams shown in Figure 3 represent the extension of Mattsson's calculations to the region of higher pH where the oxide phases again exist as stable domains[47] while, for convenience, the complex ions are limited to the predominating species. The revised data[51] for the solubility of the basic cupric sulfate phase has also been incorporated. This provides a thermodynamic basis for the appearance of tarnishing reactions and associated stress corrosion phenomena in regions of both high and low pH. The complementary method used by Letowski and Niemiec for setting out particular equilibria as a function of total ammoniacal concentration and pH is also shown in Figure 3. The points marked on the lines correspond to the conjugate equilibria between the relevant domains indicated on the potential/pH diagram at a total ($NH_4^+$ + $NH_3$) concentration of 1.0 M, those on the solid line at Cu = 50 mM giving the Mattsson conditions. The lower portion line represents a hundredfold dilution in copper while the upper section is for a tenfold increased concentration

180

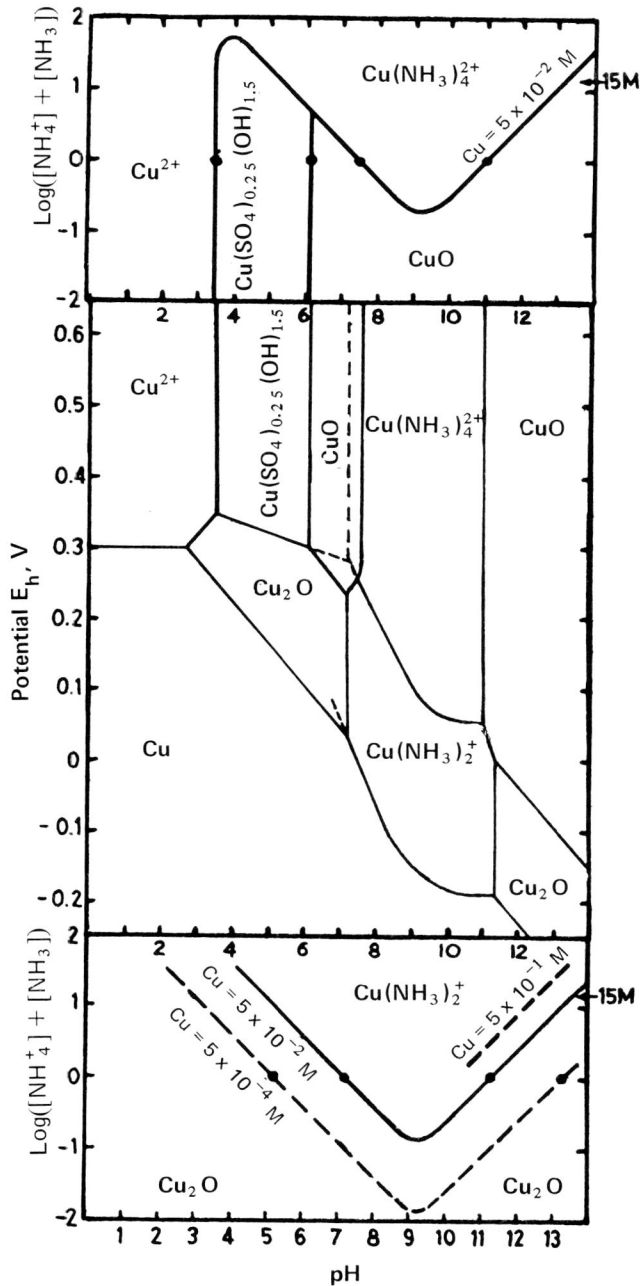

FIGURE 3 — Composite description of the Cu-NH$_3$-H$_2$O system indicating the dependence of the conjugate oxide phase domains on the concentration of dissolved copper and ammoniacal concentration (Letowski and Niemiek[48]). (a) Influence of pH and total (NH$_4^+$ + NH$_3$) activities on the solubility range of CuO; (b) Revised potential-pH diagram for the system Cu-NH$_3$-H$_2$O at 50 mM dissolved CuSO$_4$ and 1 M total (NH$_4^+$ + NH$_3$) showing two conjugate domains for the oxide phases; and (c) Influence of pH and total (NH$_4^+$ + NH$_3$) activities on the solubility range of Cu$_2$O at concentrations of 0.5, 50, and 500 mM dissolved Cu.

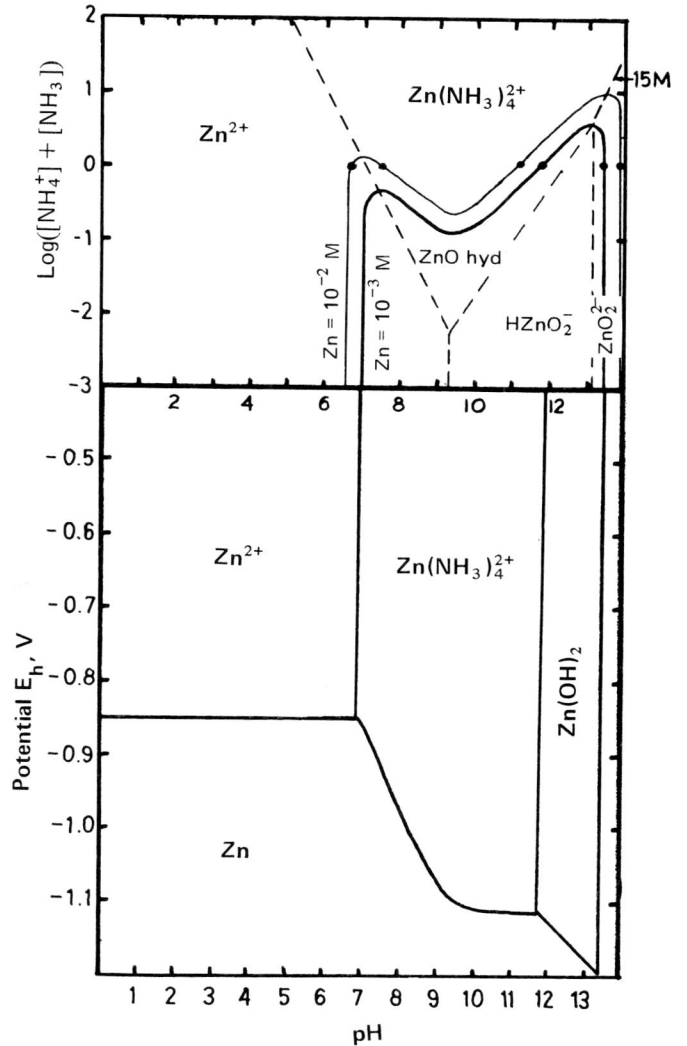

FIGURE 4 — Composite description of the Zn-NH$_3$-H$_2$O system indicating the dependence of the conjugate oxide phase domains on the concentration of dissolved zinc and ammoniacal concentration (Letowski and Niemiek[48]). (a) Influence of pH and total (NH$_4^+$ + NH$_3$) activities on the solubility range of the ZnO species at 1 and 10 mM dissolved Zn and (b) Revised potential-pH diagram for the system Zn-NH$_3$-H$_2$O at 1 mM dissolved Zn and 1 M total (NH$_4^+$ + NH$_3$) showing the single stable domain of Zn (OH)$_2$ at high pH.

which, taken with the 15 M (NH$_4^+$ + NH$_3$) solution condition, represents the region of the Westwood studies[37,39] in which tarnishing was observed. Thus, the extent of the pH range defining the stability domain of the complex ions increases with (a) decreasing copper concentration and (b) increasing ammoniacal content, resulting in a corresponding shrinkage in the area of the oxide domains.

The complementary diagrams for zinc are shown in Figure 4. At Zn = 10 mM there exist two stable domains for Zn(OH)$_2$, only one of which appeared in the original Mattsson diagram (Figure 1). However, at Zn = 1 mM[47] the domain at low pH has disappeared, while at high pH the

181

width is reduced. In the 15 M ammonia condition,[37,39] $Zn(OH)_2$ is not a stable phase.

This form of data presentation provides an explanation of the behavior patterns outlined above (Section A).

**(a) The Delay in Reaching Cracking Conditions in Aqueous Ammonia.** The preferred reaction path under oxygen control is direct dissolution to give predominantly:

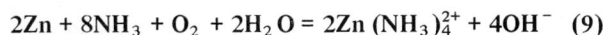

$$4Cu + 8NH_3 + O_2 + 2H_2O = 4Cu(NH_3)_2^+ + 4OH^- \quad (7)$$

$$2Cu + 8NH_3 + O_2 + 2H_2O = 2Cu(NH_3)_4^{2+} + 4OH^- \quad (8)$$

$$2Zn + 8NH_3 + O_2 + 2H_2O = 2Zn(NH_3)_4^{2+} + 4OH^- \quad (9)$$

This may lead to ductile failure under stress if the solution volume is large, but in small volumes relative to specimen area the pH changes, the free ammonia concentration decreases and the dissolved copper concentration rises. These factors increase the thermodynamic probability of surface film formation and hence more selective attack, besides facilitating cathodic depolarization through the progressive formation of the redox couple (1), thus reducing dependence upon oxygen (2).

**(b) The Severity of Meniscus Conditions.** Here we have ready access of both oxygen and ammonia, a confined solution volume and so the time scale of events is compressed.

**(c) Vapor Phase Exposure Conditions.** The solution phase here is minimal, but with a large oxygen catchment area, so that corrosion products may quickly form, while the corrosion processes are probably largely under anodic or resistance control.

**(d) The Influence of Adding Ammonium Salts.** In those cases where the susceptibility to tarnishing and cracking is inhibited by such conditions[30,28,39] the total ammoniacal content is increased and moves the environment condition away from the domain of oxide stability.

**(e) The Influence of Adding Sodium Hydroxide.** This has been shown to increase the degree of tarnishing at lower dissolved copper contents in the 15 M ammonia conditions,[39] which again confirms the prediction from Figure 3.

This approach to the problem is thus complementary to the kinetic and mechanistic studies recently carried out by Westwood et al[37,39] and described by Pugh in this volume.

## C. Polarization Studies

The earlier studies of Hoar and Booker[32] confirmed the electrochemical nature of the mechanism and further details have been elaborated in more recent Cambridge work.[50] These have largely substantiated the interpretation based on the potential/pH diagram. It has proved possible to measure limiting current densities for the diffusion controlled cathodic reactions taking place. Anodic polarization studies under potentiostatic control in static and yielding conditions indicate a maximum in the yielding current at the critical pH 7.3 with the black tarnish film.

Here anodic dissolution at discontinuities in the filmed surface to form the ammino complexes apparently showed a progressive increase with strain rate. The overpotential required to form the stable oxide phases evidently provides a kinetic barrier to hinder rapid repassivation. This is supported by the electron microscope evidence available on the nucleation and growth of the tarnish film.[45] At present a rigorous analysis of the electrode kinetics involved is made very difficult by the complexities of the participating reactions. The general problem is discussed in this volume by Hoar.

## D. Summary

There appear to be three main environmental factors contributing to the specificity of ammonia in the stress corrosion failure of brass.

(a) The formation of corrosion product films play an important role in reducing the overall anodic activity of the surface in respect to general dissolution while still maintaining good electron transport properties to facilitate cathodic processes.

(b) Enhanced preferential anodic dissolution of zinc at grain boundaries associated with concomitant tarnishing and assistance from cooperative crystallographic features lead to "chemical differentiation" of the surface.

(c) The stabilization of the $Cu(I)_{aq}$ valency state by complex formation introduces a very effective cathodic reaction system, which in certain circumstances may participate essentially as an oxygen carrier.

Maximum susceptibility to cracking ensues when all of these factors are operating together. It is now possible to set down in some detail the thermodynamic characteristics of the overall system as a logical step in our understanding of the electrochemical conditions which may lead to various corrosion patterns, and to assess how these may vary with time. However, much less is known about the kinetic factors involved.

Nevertheless, the implication is that wherever these conditions are present in other environments, then a susceptibility to stress corrosion failure may exist. Further testing of this hypothesis is clearly desirable in order to reach a better understanding of the mechanisms operating.

## III. Stress Corrosion in Other Environments

### A. Variety of Reagents

As Johnson and Leja[40] have recently pointed out, cracking has usually been ascribed to ammonia, nitrogen compounds[52] such as a number of amines, or sulfur dioxide.[53] These authors[40] have demonstrated intergranular cracking in copper-containing citrate and tartrate solutions in the pH region where complex ions exist, which extends further the examples reported by Bobylev[53] in solutions of nitrites, carbonates, pyrophosphates and alkalies complexing with copper. Whether or not surface films accompanied cracking was not stated. Graf has also reported further data in this volume.

## B. Pyridine and Ethylene Diamine

These two complexing agents were selected for an exploratory study by Booker and Hoar[54] because the thermodynamic data available seemed to make feasible the calculation of the potential-pH relationships analogous to the ammonia system,[42] employing solutions containing dissolved copper.

However, with both pyridine and ethylene diamine the Cu(I) complex does not appear to gain the stability which it achieves with ammonia, and only in the case of ethylene diamine do the calculations indicate a small stable $Cu_2O$ domain. In general, corrosion experiments indicated a preference for intergranular attack accompanied by severe metal loss rather than true cracking, although some tarnishing was observed with ethylene diamine. This work is being extended to check: (a) the basic thermodynamic data by polarographic studies,[55] (b) the corrosion behavior over a wide range of environment conditions,[56] and (c) the influence of zinc content.[57]

Pentamethylene diamine may also be worthy of further study because it has already been noted that the Cu(I) state achieves stability with this ligand.[58]

## C. Sulfur Dioxide

This system is of particular fundamental and technological interest because in recent Russian electrochemical studies[59,60] on the corrosion of Cu, Fe, and Zn carrying thin condensed moisture films in the presence of oxygen and sulfur dioxide it has been shown that meaningful polarization studies can be made with micro-electrodes. It was demonstrated that: (a) Cu passivates readily, while Zn remains active, (b) the efficiency of cathodic depolarization increases with decreasing film thickness, and (c) sulfur dioxide is over ten times more efficient than oxygen as a cathodic depolarizer.

In relation to these studies it is significant that for stress corrosion cracking of brass in moist sulfur dioxide atmospheres there appears a critical concentration range from 0.5 to 0.05 vol. % $SO_2$ within which cracking appears.[61] At lower concentrations no attack occurs while above this range general surface attack predominates.

There may thus be scope for further electrochemical studies in this system using the micro-electrode technique under stress corrosion conditions.

## IV. Conclusion

While the conditions leading to stress corrosion of α-brass in ammoniacal environments can now be fairly precisely defined in macroscopic electrochemical terms and thus a degree of predictability is available, the intimate details of mechanism on the atomic scale are still far from completely understood. Investigations in other environments are still in a primitive phase, and a more detailed knowledge of the electrochemistry of the complex ions participating is urgently required. The nucleation and growth of surface films which influence the passivation of electrochemically active regions and concomitantly facilitate cathodic depolarization appear particularly important since this may be expected to vary with alloy composition. Polarization studies within condensed moisture films may now be possible, which provides the prospect of securing information more closely related to service environments.

## Acknowledgments

The author is grateful to Drs. Hoar and Rothwell for a view of their data prior to publication, and to Mr. J. B. Cotton of Imperial Metals Industries for his interest in the work.

## References

1. E. S. Sperry. *Brass World*, **2**, 39 (1906).
2. *Symposium on Stress Corrosion Cracking of Metals*, ASTM-AIME, Philadelphia (1944).
3. A. R. Bailey. *Metallurgical Reviews*, **6**, 21, 101 (1961).
4. R. N. Parkins. *Metallurgical Reviews*, **9**, 35, 201 (1964).
5. H. L. Logan. *Stress Corrosion Cracking of Metals*, Wiley, New York (1967).
6. *Stress Corrosion Cracking and Embrittlement.* (W. D. Robertson, ed.) Wiley, New York (1956).
7. *Physical Metallurgy of Stress Corrosion Fracture.* (T. N. Rhodin, ed.) Interscience, New York (1959).
8. *Environment-Sensitive Mechanical Behavior.* Gordon and Breach, New York (1966).
9. H. Moore, S. Beckinsale, and C. E. Mallinson. *J. Inst. Metals*, **25**, 35 (1921).
10. R. G. Johnston. *Sh. Metal Ind.*, **14**, 1197 (1940).
11. T. A. Read, J. B. Read, and H. Rosenthal. *Symposium on the Stress Corrosion Cracking of Metals*, ASTM-AIME, Philadelphia, p. 90 (1944).
12. G. Edmunds, E. A. Anderson, and R. K. Waring. *Symposium on the Stress Corrosion Cracking of Metals*, ASTM-AIME, Philadelphia, p. 7 (1944).
13. A. Morris. *Trans. Amer. Inst. Mech. Engrs.*, **89**, 256 (1930).
14. C. J. L. Booker and T. P. Hoar. Unpublished work.
15. R. Speiser and J. W. Spretnak. *Stress Corrosion Cracking and Embrittlement.* (W. D. Robertson, ed.) Wiley, New York, p. 92 (1956).
16. E. H. Dix. *Proc. Amer. Soc. Testing Mat.*, **41**, 928 (1941).
17. R. B. Mears, R. H. Brown, and E. H. Dix. *Symposium on the Stress Corrosion Cracking of Metals*, ASTM-AIME, Philadelphia, p. 323 (1944).
18. R. Bakish and W. D. Robertson. *J. Electrochem. Soc.*, **103**, 320 (1956).
19. W. D. Robertson and R. Bakish. *Stress Corrosion Cracking and Embrittlement.* (W. D. Robertson, ed.) Wiley, New York, p. 32 (1956).
20. L. Graf. *Proceedings of 2nd International Congress on Metallic Corrosion*, NACE, Houston, p. 89 (1966).
21. H. Moore and S. Beckinsale. *J. Inst. Metals*, **27**, 141 (1922).
22. A. V. de Forest. *Proc. Amer. Soc. Testing Mat.*, **18**, 205 (1918).
23. W. B. Price. *Proc. Amer. Soc. Testing Mat.*, **18**, 209 (1918).
24. J. Czochralski and H. Schrieber. *Korrosion u Metallschutz*, **13**, 181 (1937).
25. D. H. Thompson and A. W. Tracy. *Trans. Amer. Inst. Min. Met. Eng.*, **185**, 100 (1949).
26. M. E. Whittaker, E. Voce, and A. R. Bailey. *Metallurgia*, **39**, 21, 66 (1948).
27. G. Edmunds. *Symposium on the Stress Corrosion Cracking of*

*Metals*, ASTM-AIME, Philadelphia, p. 67 (1944).

28. W. Lynes. *Corrosion*, **21**, 125 (1965).

29. R. H. Brown and R. B. Mears. *Trans. Electrochem. Soc.*, **81**, 455 (1942).

30. C. L. Bulow. *Symposium on the Stress Corrosion Cracking of Metals*, ASTM-AIME, Philadelphia, p. 19 (1944).

31. A. V. Bobylev. Korrozionne Rostreskivanii Latuni — Corrosion Cracking of Brass. *Metallurgizdat*, Moscow (1955).

32. T. P. Hoar and C. J. L. Booker. *Corrosion Science*, **5**, 821 (1965).

33. L. Graf and J. Budke. *Z. Metallkunde*, **46**, 378 (1955).

34. V. V. Skorchelletti and V. A. Tivova. *J. Appl. Chem.*, USSR, **26**, 37 (1953).

35. R. G. Johnston. *Sheet Metal Ind.*, **16**, 664 (1942).

36. F. C. Althof. *Z. Metallk.*, **36**, 177 (1944).

37. E. N. Pugh, W. G. Montague, and A. R. C. Westwood. *Trans. Amer. Soc. Metals*, **58**, 665 (1965).

38. S. Hellsing, O. Lissner, S. Rask, and B. Strom. *Werkst. u. Korros.*, **8**, 569 (1957).

39. E. N. Pugh and A. R. C. Westwood. *Phil. Mag.*, **13**, 167 (1966).

40. H. E. Johnson and J. Leja. *Corrosion*, **22**, 178 (1966).

41. L. Graf and H. R. Lacour. *Z. Metallk.*, **51**, 162 (1960).

42. E. Mattsson. *Electrochim. Acta*, **3**, 279 (1961).

43. M. J. N. Pourbaix. *Atlas d'equilibres electrochimiques*, Gauthier-Villars, Paris (1963).

44. T. Mukaibo and K. Fueki. *J. Electrochem. Soc.*, Japan, **22**, 11, 59 (1954).

45. A. J. Forty and P. Humble. *Phil. Mag.*, **8**, 243 (1963).

46. A. J. McEvily and A. P. Bond. *J. Electrochem. Soc.*, **112**, 131 (1965).

47. H. E. Johnson and J. Leja. *J. Electrochem. Soc.*, **112**, 639 (1965).

48. F. Letowski and J. Niemiec. *J. Electrochem. Soc.*, **113**, 629 (1966).

49. T. P. Hoar and G. P. Rothwell. *Corrosion Science*, in press.

50. T. P. Hoar, P. P. Podesta, and G. P. Rothwell. *Corrosion Science*, in press.

51. A. Burstorff and J. Van Muylder. *Electrochim. Acta*, **9**, 607 (1964).

52. H. Rosenthal and A. L. Jamieson. *Proc. Amer. Soc. Testing Mat.*, **41**, 897 (1941); *Trans. Amer. Inst. Min. Met. Eng.*, **156**, 212 (1944).

53. A. V. Bobylev. *Intercrystalline Corrosion and Corrosion of Metals Under Stress*. (I. A. Levin, ed.) Consultants Bureau, New York, p. 298 (1962).

54. C. J. L. Booker and T. P. Hoar. Unpublished work.

55. C. J. L. Booker and W. A. Ledger. To be published.

56. C. J. L. Booker and R. W. Jones. To be published.

57. C. J. L. Booker and V. Bonfil. Work in progress.

58. E. N. Pugh and A. R. C. Westwood. *High Strength Materials, Proc. 2nd Berkeley International Materials Conference*, 1964. (V. F. Zackay, ed.) Wiley, New York, p. 701 (1965).

59. I. L. Rosenfeld. *Proceedings of the 1st International Congress on Metallic Corrosion*, Butterworths, London, p. 243 (1962).

60. G. B. Klark, M. I. Mikhailovskaya and N. D. Tomashov in Korroziya Metallov i Splavov, Sbornik 1 (N. D. Tomashov, ed.) *Metallurgizdat*, Moscow, 1963. English translation, Corrosion of Metals and Alloys, Collection No. 1 (A. D. Mercer, trans., C. J. L. Booker, ed.) National Lending Library for Science and Technology, England (1964).

61. J. B. Cotton. Private communication (1967).

## Discussion

**A. W. Blackwood, American Smelting and Refining Co.:**

In consideration of the potential-pH factor, especially with respect to the consideration of data of Pugh, did you take into account in your calculation in any way the fact that perhaps thirty percent of the copper present in the solution may be present in the form of the pentammine complex, based on a calculation using the free ammonia concentration and published stability constants of the various complex species. Such a calculation yields a mean coordination number of approximately 4.3 which would indicate that a very significant fraction of the copper present is present in the form of pentammine complex species which might have a very serious effect at high pH on the nature of the potential-pH diagram.

**C. J. L. Booker:**

It is true that I did not take into account the phase-field of the pentammine complex which Pugh and coworkers claim is the predominant species in many of their experiments. This is a refinement which may be thermodynamically significant, although in the interests of simplicity I have chosen to overlook it. However, of more serious importance is the error introduced by neglecting changes in the activity of the dissolved species associated with the increasing concentration of the ammoniacal solution in the high pH region. In these circumstances it is my opinion that we are pushing this approach to the limit of its validity and thus also its practical usefulness.

**H. H. Uhlig, MIT:**

In a paper published about a year and a half ago, Wilson Lynes[1] showed that there are many different chemical media which will cause intergranular corrosion of brass or Admiralty metal but that only ammonia or its derivatives will cause stress corrosion cracking. I should like to submit that sulfur dioxide is in the first category producing intergranular corrosion, not stress corrosion cracking.

1. Wilson Lynes. *Corrosion*, **21**, 125 (1965).

**C. J. L. Booker:**

I am familiar with the interesting range of observations reported in the paper of Lynes. In this respect it is worth remembering too that the "tarnishing" solutions, so specific for stress corrosion *cracking* may equally well bring about *intergranular deterioration* in unstressed material. As for sulfur dioxide, I believe the situation is in need of clarification and with this in mind I am re-investigating the problem.

**E. N. Pugh, RIAS:**

Do your observations provide any additional insight into the mechanism of stress corrosion cracking in the brass-ammonia system?

**C. J. L. Booker:**

I hope my observations provide some contribution to clarifying the environmental factors involved. However, I now feel that further insight is more likely to emerge from a closer study of the kinetics rather than the thermodynamics of the processes involved.

**J. Leja, University of British Columbia:**

In connection with the refinements that are being introduced in the thermodynamics of the system, namely, the activity coefficients, I would like to point out that the potential/pH diagrams for pure copper and for pure zinc are being applied to an entirely different solid, namely, 70/30 brass. In my experience, whenever brass develops a tarnish, copper does not tarnish under identical conditions.

**C. J. L. Booker:**

I have so far been referring to the activity coefficients of the species present in the aqueous environment. It is also thermodynamically desirable to bear in mind the much reduced chemical activity of the zinc present in brass at concentrations up to 30 atomic percent. However, one is nevertheless led to the conclusion that preferential dissolution of zinc and concomitant oxidation of the residual copper are the preferred anodic reactions. The oxidizing environment is provided by the $Cu^I/Cu^{II}$ ammino complex couple. Thus the potential pH diagrams can only be used as indicators of probable reaction paths; the experimental observations provide the verification. It is significant here that the tarnishing reaction is dependent upon the co-dissolution of zinc and, because the tarnish is porous, continued reaction ensues.[1] On the other hand, with pure copper in the tarnishing solutions either film formation may occur, which in this case results in a thin coherent, protective oxide layer appearing on the comparatively compact substrate metal, or else general surface attack may take place. This could well be related to the critical kinetic balance between the rate of film formation and its rate of dissolution in given conditions.

1. A. J. Forty and P. Humble. *Environment Sensitive Mechanical Behavior.* (A. R. C. Westwood and N. S. Stoloff, ed.) Gordon and Breach, New York, p. 403 (1966).

**J. Leja, University of British Columbia:**

This would support the suggestion made by Dr. Vermilyea that although the tarnish penetrates progressively into the metal substrate, it may be formed by reprecipitation.

With regards to the effect of oxygen, I would like to comment that on using very low concentrations of oxygen, e.g., $10^{-8}$ to $10^{-9}$ mole/liter, and limiting the total amount of tarnishing liquid available for the particular brass sample (to say $\sim 5$ ml), the effect of oxygen becomes very pronounced. Less than this amount is insufficient to cause cracking, whereas more than this amount gives corrosion cracking. A rough calculation shows that this limiting amount of oxygen is equivalent to about a monolayer coverage on the sample.

**C. J. L. Booker:**

I have yet to be convinced on your first point. On your second point I would refer you to my Equation (1), where with a small concentration of copper complex in relation to the specimen area the reaction indicated will go far to the right hand side giving predominantly the Cu(I) species present with no further opportunity for cathodic reduction. I think that you also observed that such a solution may become colorless due to depletion in respect to the blue Cu(II) species. Access of oxygen allows my Equation (1) to be reversed and the blue coloration returns, as you found in your experiments. The monolayer calculation is interesting and may lend support to the first step in the mechanism put forward by Pugh and Westwood[1] for their experiments

In conclusion, I would like to draw attention to the

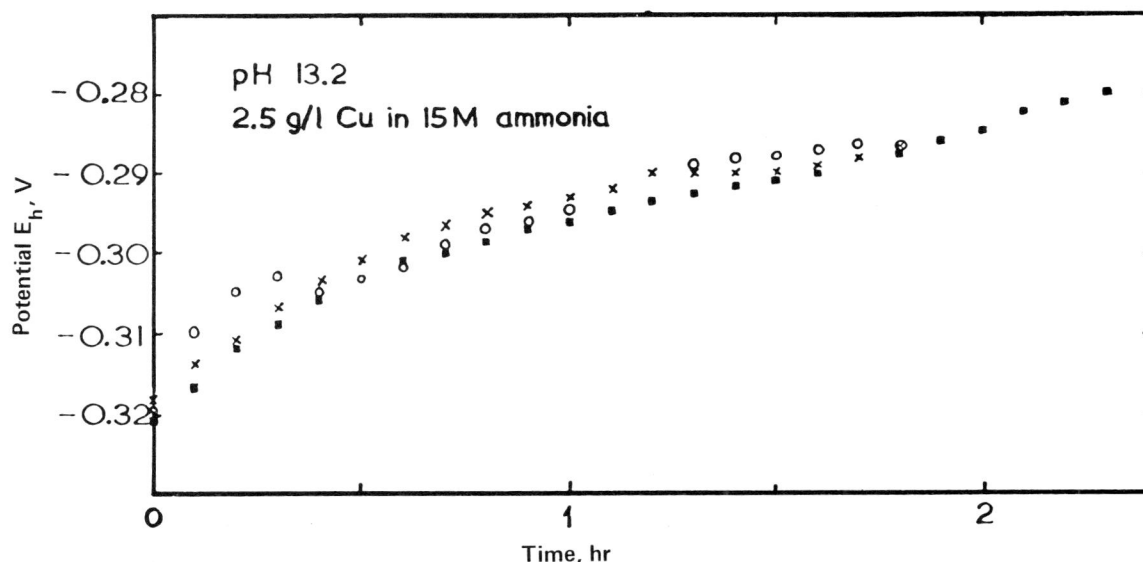

FIGURE 1 — Potential/time curve for 70/30 brass in a 15 N ammonia solution containing 2.5 g/l Cu at pH 13.2 (Booker and Bonfil, work in progress).

data presented in Figure 1; (Booker and Bonfil, work in progress). This shows the corrosion potential v. time characteristic of 70/30 brass in the Pugh and Westwood condition (15 M). A progressive rise is apparent with the onset of tarnishing, but within a much more negative range of potential than occurs under the Mattsson regime (1 M). However, both sets of data are consistent with the concept of the extended potential-pH diagram outlined in this paper. There is thus the prospect of completing a whole set of complementary experiments to study the electro-chemical behavior in this high pH region of the system.

1. E. N. Pugh and A. R. C. Westwood. *Phil. Mag.,* **13**, 167 (1966).

# STRESS CORROSION CRACKING IN HOMOGENEOUS, NON-SUPERSATURATED ALLOYS CONTAINING NOBLE OR NO NOBLE METALS

L. Graf

Max Planck Institute for Metals Research

## Abstract

The stress corrosion cracking of homogeneous non-supersaturated alloys is reviewed. Alloy systems considered include Ag-Au, Cu-Au, Ag-Pd, Ag-Zn, Ag-Cd, Cu-Zn, Brass-Au, Cu-Ni, Cu-Al and Cu-Mn. Experimental results show that, beside two solid solution effects, a pronounced electrochemical process inside the cracks is necessary. For this the difference in potential between the plastically deforming crack roots and the non-deforming crack walls is not sufficient. The crack walls must be covered with a very noble material. It is shown in which way the cathodic areas on the crack walls are formed with alloys containing a noble metal component as well as with alloys containing no noble metal component. On the basis of these results it is shown why no specificity of environment is needed in the first case while it is necessary in the second case.

## I. The Fundamental Causes of Stress Corrosion Cracking in Homogeneous Non-Supersaturated Alloys

### A. The Solid Solution Effects

The stress corrosion susceptibility of homogeneous, non-supersaturated alloys containing noble metals, for instance of AgAu, CuAu, CuPd, FePt, etc., is undoubtedly of less practical importance than the stress corrosion susceptibility of technical homogeneous alloys such as brass, monel or the austenitic stainless steels. Nonetheless, the noble metal binary alloys have proved exceptionally valuable for research into the causes of stress corrosion susceptibility for the technical alloys. For instance, the complete miscibility of the AgAu system and the absence of lattice transformations has made possible the study of stress corrosion susceptibility in a complete solid solution system[1-4] from which the following information of basic significance was obtained (Figure 1).

(1) The stress corrosion susceptibility of homogeneous, non-supersaturated alloys depends, so far as the alloy itself is concerned, only on the solid solution concentration.

(2) Stress corrosion susceptibility appears only on the less noble side of the system.

Thorough research into this strong influence of solid solution formation has shown that this is caused by the following two effects:[5-8]

(i) Solid solution effect I increases the reactivity of the grain boundaries and of other disturbed areas on the grain surfaces;

(ii) Solid solution effect II increases the reactivity of those parts of a solid solution which are being plastically deformed (*in statu deformandi*). Both effects increase strongly with the solute content up to a maximum at 50 At%.

### 1. Evidence of the Number I Solid Solution Effect

*a. Corrosion Tests Without Stress*. The influence of solid solution effect I can be demonstrated by the following experiments[7-9] (Figure 2):

Several sets of unstressed specimens of soft copper and copper with 10 At% gold were corroded in a 2% ferric chloride solution. The specimens were removed, one set at a time, from the solution, thoroughly rinsed, dried and

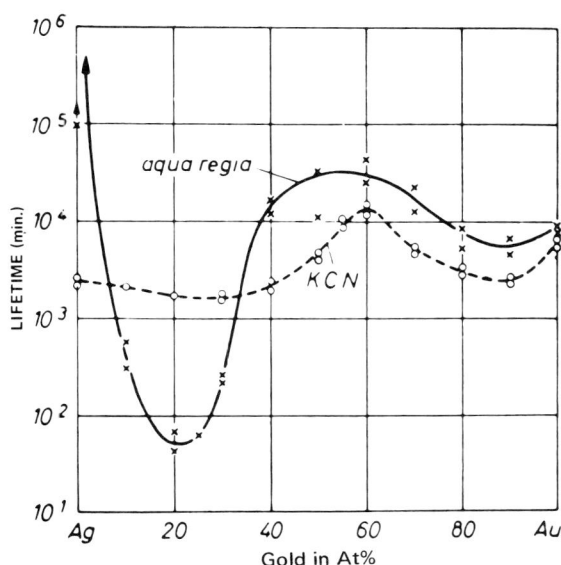

FIGURE 1 – Lifetime vs gold content of Ag-Au alloys in aqua regia and in a 10 percent KCN + $H_2O_2$ solution.

187

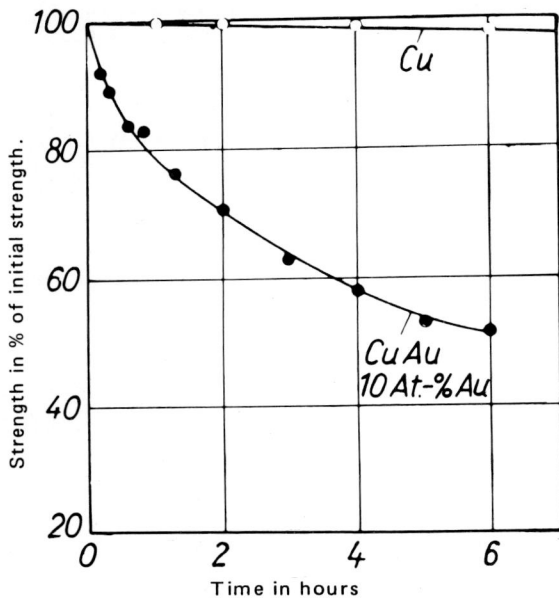

**FIGURE 2 —** Strength of Cu and of a Cu-10 a/o Au alloy vs time of corrosion in FeCl$_3$ solution without stress. Strength measured outside of the solution.

tensile tested. The copper specimens showed only small decreases in tensile strength, due to small reductions of the transverse section by general corrosion, and fractured in a ductile manner. The copper-gold specimens, however, exhibited considerable decreases in tensile strength, becoming more pronounced with prolonged exposure in the solution. In addition the fracture, in areas adjacent to the specimen surface, became increasingly intercrystalline as the time of exposure increased.

*b. Diffusion Tests With Mercury at 120 C.* Diffusion tests on AuCu and CuZn alloys with mercury at 120 C showed that the speed of diffusion along the grain boundaries also depends to a large extent on the solid solution concentration. As Figure 3 shows, the mercury penetrates in a given time more deeply as the concentration of the solid solution increases.

These experiments with unstressed specimens substantiate solid solution effect I and show the increased reactivity of the grain boundaries.

### 2. Evidence of the Number II Solid Solution Effect

*a. Tensile Tests Within the Corroding Agent.* Solid solution effect II can be demonstrated if the forementioned experiments are slightly modified as follows:[6],[8]

Several sets of specimens of copper with 10 At% gold were corroded without application of tensile stresses. At appropriate times half of a set of specimens was removed from the solution, rinsed, dried and tensile tested, while the other half was tested in the corrodent itself. As Figure 4 shows, the first set of specimens showed decreased tensile strengths due to solid solution effect I (Curve a) as already described above. This means that only intercrystalline corrosion occurred. The other half, on the contrary, had much lower tensile strengths due to the stronger attack of the corrodent on areas in a state of plastic flow, (in this case at the grain boundaries) according to solid solution effect II.

*b. Tensile Tests Within Mercury at Ambient Temperature.* The higher reactivity of flowing areas of solid solutions is, moreover, demonstrated with tensile tests in air and in mercury respectively. As shown in Figure 5, the specimens of a copper-gold alloy with 30 At% gold and of brass 67 always fractured at incipient plastic deformation in mercury. In the elastic range, however, the stress-strain relationships are the same in air and mercury. Cold working of the specimens has no effect, but as soon as the higher elastic limit is exceeded, failure will occur. Pure copper, however, does not undergo premature failure when tested in mercury, as Figure 6 shows, or, rather, the effect is too small to be observed with this experiment.

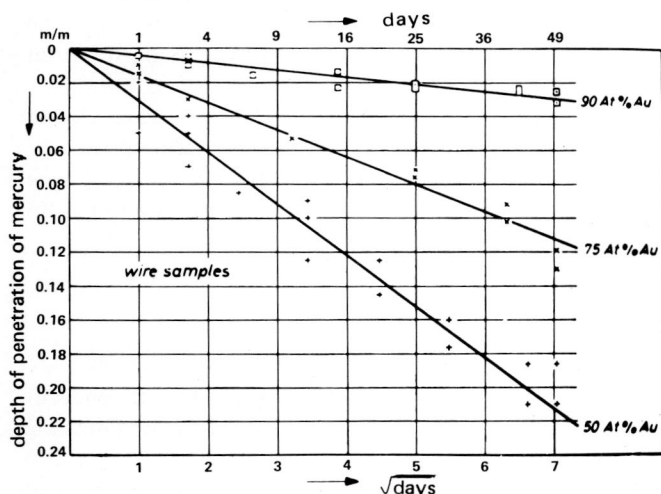

**FIGURE 3 —** Average depth of penetration of Hg in Au-Cu alloys with 10, 25 and 50 a/o Cu vs time of exposure to Hg at 120 C.

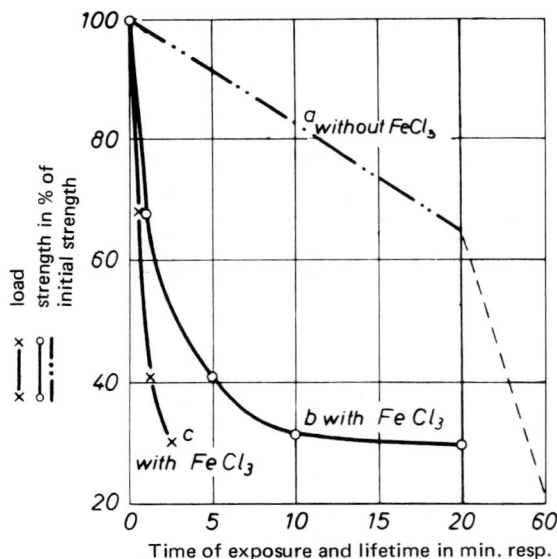

**FIGURE 4 —** Strength and life of a Cu-10 a/o Au alloy vs time of exposure to a 2 percent FeCl$_3$ solution. Curve a: tested outside the solution; Curve b: tested while exposed to the solution; Curve c: lifetime under load in the solution.

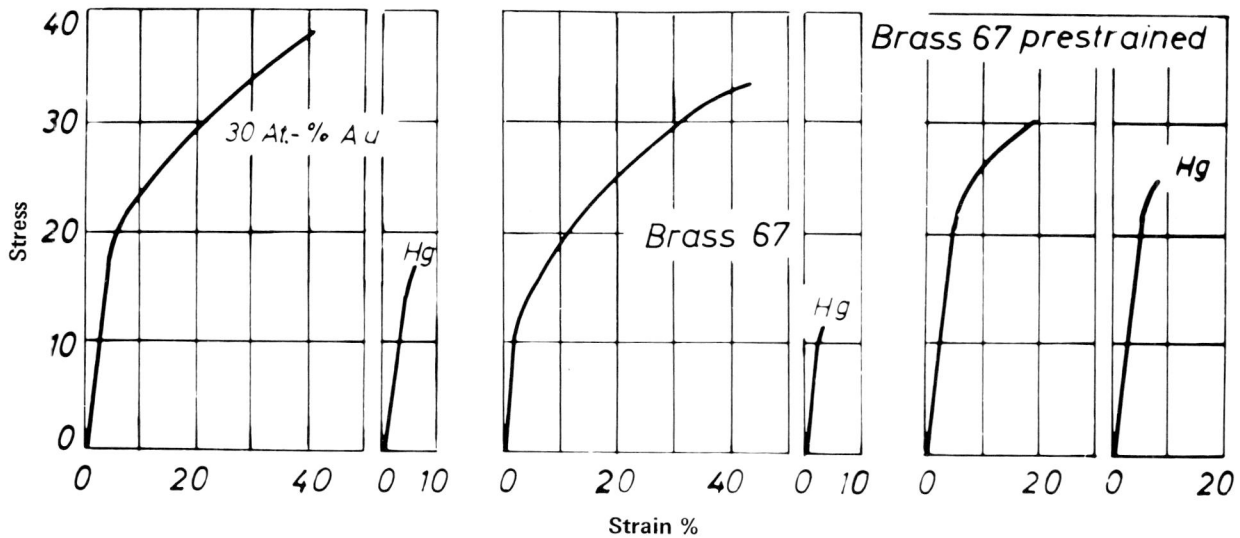

FIGURE 5 — Stress-strain curves of a Cu-Au alloy and of brass 67. Left hand curves: material tested in air. Right hand curves: material tested in mercury as indicated.

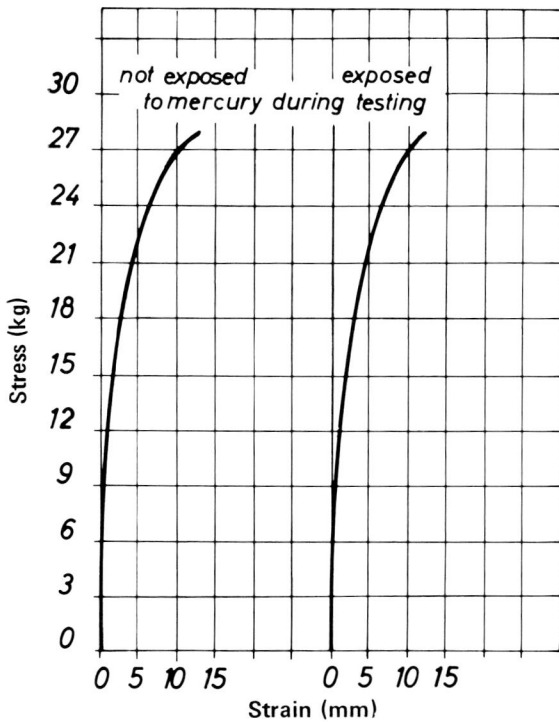

FIGURE 6 — Tensile tests on copper in air and in mercury, showing that there is no difference in strength, if tested in air (left hand curve) or tested in mercury (right hand curve).

The causes of these two solid solution effects are not quite certain. It appears to be possible that an alloying effect prevails in that the lattice distortions and changes in binding forces by the solute atoms give rise to an enhanced dissolution at stationary and moving lattice defects. More detailed studies of these atomistic aspects are therefore desirable.

## B. Requirement of an Electrochemical Process Within the Crevices and Cracks

These two solid solution effects underlie, without any doubt, the embrittlement of solid solutions in liquid metals as well as stress corrosion cracking in aqueous solutions, but in the latter case they alone do not suffice to cause susceptibility.[3,5,8] Were it so, all solid solutions would be susceptible, which fortunately is not the case. Stress corrosion cracking can occur only if a pronounced electrochemical process acts within the cracks. Accordingly, the following general statements can be made: in any homogeneous solid solution the two solid solution effects exist inherently, but whether or not they will become operative and produce stress corrosion cracking depends upon the presence or absence of a pronounced electrochemical process within the crevices or cracks. Therefore only the electrochemical aspects have to be examined to predict stress corrosion susceptibility in a homogeneous, non-supersaturated alloy. The following will discuss a general outline of the stress corrosion cracking process and the effect of tensile stress according to our findings.[8] Next the origin of a pronounced electrochemical process in the cracks will be discussed.

## C. Outline of the Stress Corrosion Process

Due to the combination of solid solution effect I and a pronounced electrochemical process, the grain boundaries and defects in the grain surfaces are preferentially attacked, leading to the formation of crevices. Without tensile stress, the attack along the grain boundaries or of the defects in the grain surfaces ceases in most cases, due to increasing obstruction of diffusion within the crevices. Under tensile stress, as soon as the crevices are deep enough, they begin to open with plastic flow at their roots and better

189

penetration of the corrodent. Now solid solution effect II becomes operative: plastic flow enhances the dissolving process at the roots of the crevices.

In the early stages of stress corrosion the rate of flow and increase in reactivity at the roots are small, but as the process continues the transverse section of the sample decreases and the stress at the roots increases. As a result the flow rate at the roots and the chemical reactivity increase at an accelerated rate. Once flow has started it cannot cease as long as tensile stresses and corrodents are present. The material at the roots cannot work-harden, because it is continuously removed by the corrodent. The combination of tensile stress, the two solid solution effects and the electrochemical process within the crevices or cracks maintains a mechanism of crack propagation characterized by autocatalytic acceleration, in agreement with the observations.

## II. Electrochemical Process Within the Crevices and Cracks

After this brief summary of the influence of solid solutions effects and the outline of the stress corrosion process, we will now examine the means by which a pronounced electrochemical process can occur in the cracks and crevices. This is a matter of basic significance for the appearance of stress corrosion cracking. In order that the agent attacks only at the roots of the cracks or crevices, their walls must be cathodically polarized and the roots themselves anodically polarized. However, the difference in potential existing between the deforming crack root and the non-deforming walls is insufficient to introduce a pronounced electrochemical process. For this to occur, the walls must be covered with a very noble material.

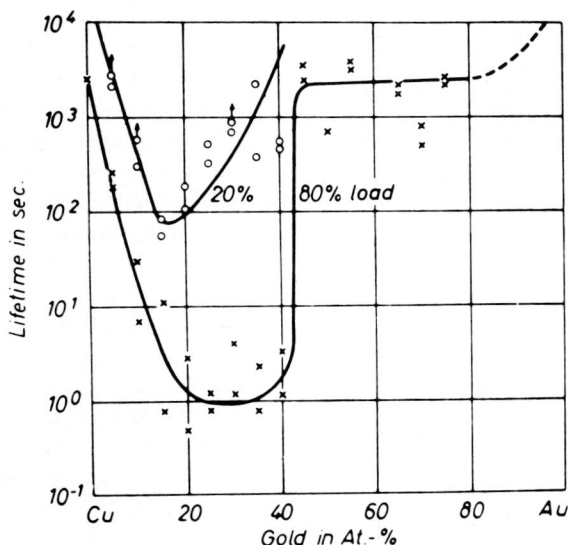

FIGURE 7 – Lifetime of Cu-Au alloys vs gold content in aqua regia under different load. On the gold-rich side there is only surface attack.

### A. Alloys Containing Noble Metals

#### 1. Silver and Copper Base Alloys with Gold

In the case of alloys containing noble metals, such as AgAu, CuAu, etc., such a covering of the crack walls with a very noble material occurs in a very simple manner. When attacked by agents which cannot dissolve the noble component, this remains not only on the surface, but also on the walls of crevices or cracks. Thus, these become strongly cathodically polarized relative to the plastically flowing crack roots not covered by noble atoms. On the other hand, if the noble metal component is also dissolved, as for example when aqua regia acts on AgAu or CuAu alloys, etc., then, at sufficiently high ion concentration, it is partially precipitated by the base component of the alloy. As a result noble cathodic areas are formed in this case too on the crack walls, resulting in a pronounced electrochemical process and the occurrence of stress corrosion, as Figures 1 and 7 show. If, however, the noble metal component dissolves as a complex compound, e.g., when 10% KCN solution with $H_2O_2$ added acts on AgAu or CuAu alloys, the ion concentration at the phase boundary is too low to permit adequate reprecipitation by the base component of the alloy. As a result no pronounced electrochemical process and thus no stress corrosion can occur. This has too been shown experimentally (Figure 1).

Since the cathodic areas of these alloys consist of noble metal, any attacking agent which does not form complex compounds with the noble metal component will introduce stress corrosion. Accordingly, the environment must not be as specific as has been generally assumed to date.

We should note here too that, if the noble metal component is not dissolved, no stress corrosion will occur when a given concentration of the noble component is exceeded. Figures 8 a-c show examples of this. When the parting limit is reached, the lifetime becomes infinite, since the surface is no longer attacked. In addition, the results shown in the graphs lead to the conclusion that any attacking agent not forming complex compounds will initiate stress corrosion.

If the noble metal component is also dissolved by the attacking agent, so that no parting limit is reached, as for instance when aqua regia acts on AgAu or CuAu alloys, etc. (see Figures 1 and 7), here also rather surprisingly the stress corrosion susceptibility decreases above approximately 30 At% Au, and vanishes completely above approximately 45 At%, whereas the surface attack continues. Accordingly, the lifetime is here always finite, but one determined only by surface attack. Thus on the noble metal side of a homogeneous solid solution system with a noble metal as an alloy component, no stress corrosion will occur. This is explained by the fact that when alloys with more than 45-50 At% gold are subjected to corrosion in aqua regia the gold is no longer, or at most insufficiently precipitated by the copper in the alloy. As a result no adequate cathodic covering of gold can form on the crack or crevice walls and there is the consequent absence of the required electrochemical process.

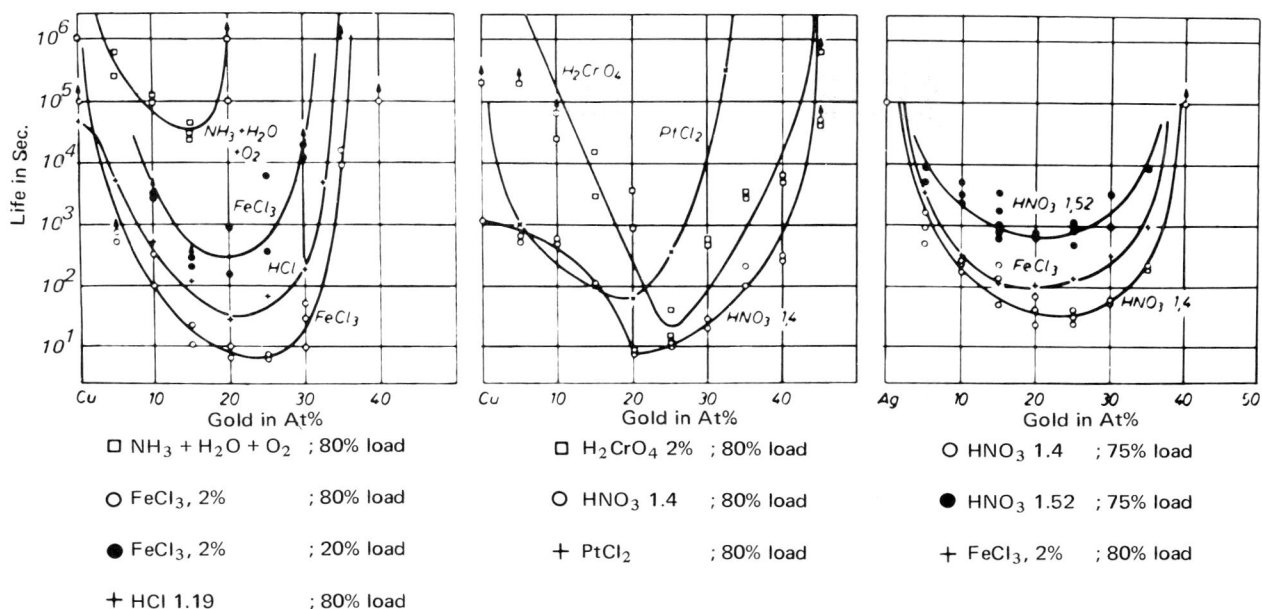

FIGURE 8 — Lifetime vs gold content of Cu-Au and Ag-Au alloys in various reagents (in which gold is not attacked).

## 2. Silver-Base Alloys with Palladium

By way of a further interesting example, let us examine stress corrosion susceptibility in the AgPd system.[1] Here both components have practically the same equilibrium solution potential. Therefore, when attacked by nitric acid, no stress corrosion would be expected since, on dissolution of the solid solution, no cathodic areas and no pronounced electrochemical process can develop within the crevices. As predicted, experiments with stressed alloys in nitric acid showed no stress corrosion and only general dissolution for the entire alloy system.

In contrast to nitric acid, stress corrosion cracking was observed, e.g., in an alloy with 15 At% palladium within a few minutes when the corrodent was aqua regia, 2% aqueous ferric chloride solution or oxygen-bearing hydrochloric acid. This can be explained as follows: due to the low solubility of silver chloride, the potential of silver is shifted to considerably less noble values. Since, on the other hand, palladium chloride is highly soluble, palladium is much more noble than silver in these solutions. Thus, cathodic areas of palladium form as a prerequisite to the electrochemical process and lead to stress corrosion. No stress corrosion cracking occurs on the palladium-rich side of the system.

## 3. Silver Base Alloys with Zinc or Cadmium

A particularly interesting case is the occurrence of stress corrosion in silver-rich AgZn and AgCd alloys with, for example, 30 At% Zn or Cd, in 10% FeCl₃ solution.[10] Here the solvent metal is more noble than the alloying component, and in accordance with the interpretation previously developed no stress corrosion would be expected. If stress corrosion nevertheless occurs, it must be because corrosion in the ferric chloride solution allows the

required electrochemical process to develop. In this case a question must be asked concerning the cathodic covering on the crack walls. Our research has produced the following answer: these alloys are corroded in the FeCl₃ solution and AgCl is formed. This is insoluble and thus covers both sample surface and crack or crevice walls. The AgCl, however, is then reduced by Zn or Cd to Ag and this forms on the crack or crevice walls. Ag is considerably more noble than the alloys concerned, and thus forms the cathodic areas required for a pronounced electrochemical process. Therefore stress corrosion cracking occurs.

## B. Alloys Containing No Noble Metals

Let us now turn to homogeneous technical alloys containing no noble metals, such as α-brass, monel or the austenitic stainless steels containing Cr and Ni. Here the cathodic areas on the crack or crevice walls can form only from suitable solid corrosion products, and this cannot take place under the influence of every agent. This explains why in this case only certain agents initiate stress corrosion and, with this, the "specificity of enviroment".

## 1. α-Brass

a. Concentrated Copper Tetramine Solution. We will examine first of all α-brass[11] where, as is well known, ammonia is capable of causing stress corrosion. From our findings to date, attack by this agent must cover the crack or crevice walls with solid corrosion products which are more noble than the solid solution and thus act as cathodes. Our task is therefore to determine the nature of these corrosion products and to explain their origin.

When ammonia or agents containing ammonia act on brass in the presence of oxygen, copper tetramine and zinc tetramine are formed. These are both highly soluble, so that it seemed that no solid corrosion products would be

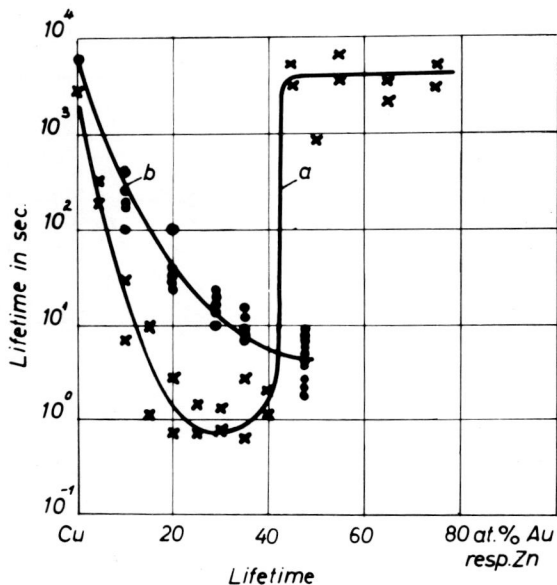

FIGURE 9 — Lifetime of (a) Cu-Au alloys in aqua regia and of (b) Cu-Zn alloys in a concentrated copper tetramine solution vs Au resp. Zn content. The minimum of lifetime is reached in the first case at ca. 30 a/o Au, in the second case at ca. 50% Zn.

FIGURE 10 — Lifetime of brass 63 and of a Cu-10 a/o Au alloy vs different additions to a concentrated copper tetramine solution.

formed. However, in certain conditions copper tetramine will form cupric oxide (CuO) by the reaction

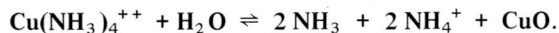

$$Cu(NH_3)_4^{++} + H_2O \rightleftharpoons 2\,NH_3 + 2\,NH_4^+ + CuO.$$

The formation of cupric oxide is favored as the concentration of ammonium ions and ammonia decreases in a concentrated solution of copper tetramine. This results from sustained reaction with copper and zinc and from evaporation losses. Cupric oxide forms preferentially within the cracks owing to the depletion of the agent due to reduced diffusion. Cupric oxide now functions as the cathodic areas on the walls of the crevices or cracks and thus makes possible the establishment of the pronounced electrochemical process required to propagate stress corrosion cracks. Therefore, the dependence of cracking time on solute content is not quite the same as with copper-gold or silver-gold alloys; the minimum lifetime is here at 50% of the solute content (Figure 9).

The importance of cupric oxide to the cracking process can easily be demonstrated by adding ammonium chloride or sulfate to a saturated copper tetramine solution.[12] These additions increase the ammonium ion concentration and prevent, if high enough, the occurrence of stress corrosion cracking by displacing the equilibrium away from the formation of the required cupric oxide. In Figure 10, the life of 70/30 brass stressed to 80% of its ultimate tensile strength is plotted against the amount of ammonium chloride or sulfate, added to a saturated copper tetramine solution. An addition of 0.03 gram-equivalent ammonium chloride per litre completely eliminates stress corrosion susceptibility. Due to its lesser dissociation, somewhat more ammonium sulfate is needed to prevent

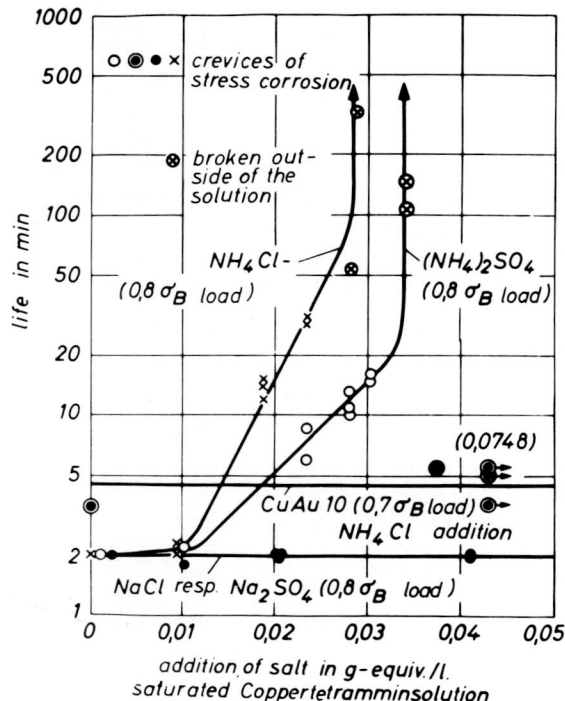

stress corrosion cracking. As expected, additions of sodium chloride or sulfate do not affect stress corrosion susceptibility. If in the solid solution gold is substituted for zinc, additions of ammonium chloride or sulfate to the copper tetramine solution do not eliminate stress corrosion cracking, because here gold forms the cathodic areas.

We can now understand why stressed brass does not exhibit stress corrosion cracking if submerged in a large volume of aqueous ammonia solution. Here no cupric oxide can form, because the equilibrium in this solution is completely displaced to the left. In contrast, specimens exposed to wet ammonia vapor crack after a short time, because the copper tetramine, which forms in the thin liquid layer on the surface, soon reaches concentrations that permit the formation of cupric oxide. Therefore, it is expedient to stress corrode brass in a saturated copper tetramine solution in order to shorten time to failure.

b. Copper Nitrate Solutions. As our experiments with brass have also shown, even ammonia-free solutions containing $Cu^{++}$ ions can cause stress corrosion, though to a lesser degree.[13] Figure 11 shows the life of brass in a 0.5 molar copper nitrate solution relative to zinc content. Life here is about two orders of magnitude longer than in concentrated saturated copper tetramine solution. Figure 12 shows the relationship of the life of brass 80, 70 and 63 to the concentration of the copper nitrate solution and its pH value. Stress corrosion occurs primarily in the concentration range 0.1-1.0 mol/litre copper nitrate solution. In the dilute solutions (pH = 3.4-3.5) a thick, reddish-brown crystalline coating forms on the sample surface. This increases life by stifling the electrochemicaL process in the

192

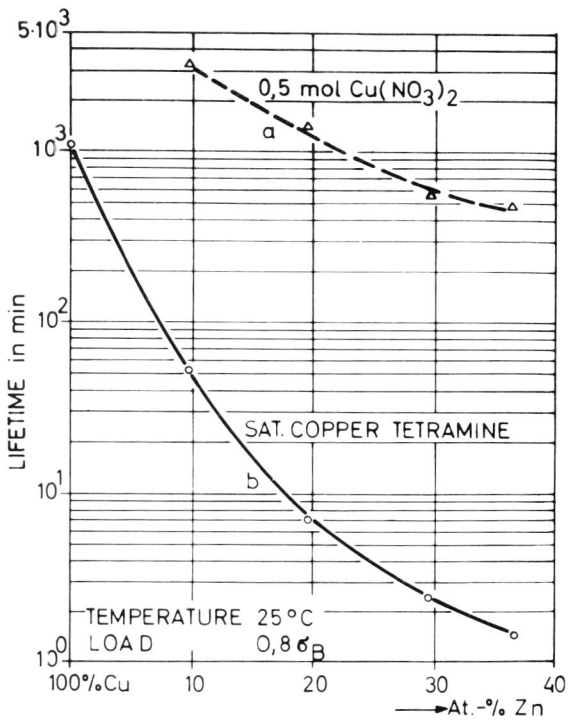

FIGURE 11 — Lifetime of Cu-Zn alloys vs Zn-content (a) in a 0.5 mol $Cu(NO_3)_2$ solution; (b) in a concentrated copper tetramine solution.

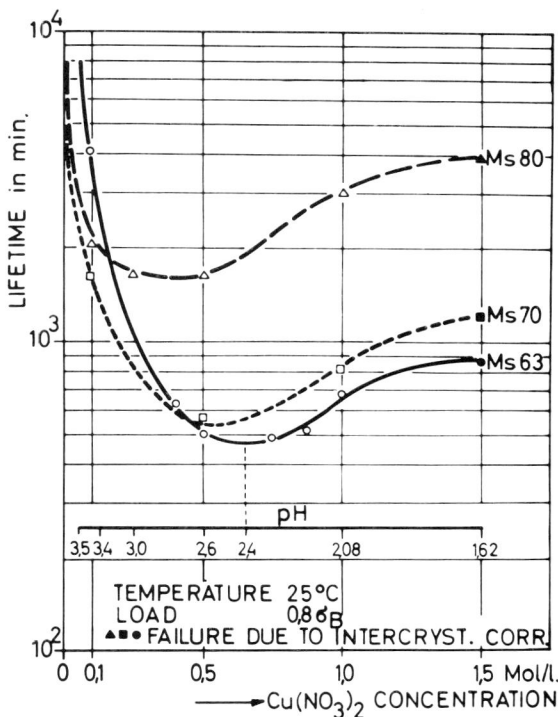

FIGURE 12 — Lifetime of brass 80, 70 and 63 vs concentration of $Cu(NO_3)_2$ solution (resp. the pH-value of them).

cracks. As the copper nitrate concentration increases (and the pH value decreases) the formation of the coating lessens and cracking lifetime becomes shorter, until at approximately 0.5 mol solution strength only a microscopically visible layer remains (pH value approximately 2.6). At this point the minimum life, that is to say the maximum stress corrosion susceptibility, has been reached. As the concentration increases still further the sample surface remains free from corrosion products, but the life curves now begin to rise again until at solution strength approximately 1.5 mol they level out to a more or less horizontal pattern. This is certainly caused by the fact that in these relatively acid solutions (pH in the region of 1.6) the life of the samples is limited only by considerable attack on the grain boundaries, with no further evidence of stress corrosion. Consequently, there is a clear connection between the formation of the coating on the surface and the stress corrosion susceptibility. If too thick a coating forms, crack development is restricted; if too thin a coating, the stress corrosion susceptibility is correspondingly lessened.

This can be seen most clearly in Figure 13. Here a stressed sample was corroded at approximately 70 C in 1-mol copper nitrate solution. As the result of a severe temperature drop in the solution, formation of the coating also decreases, becoming less as the solution grows colder. It can be seen that in the hotter solution, where a thick coating has been formed, no cracks have developed. As the temperature drops and less coating is formed, the cracks become more frequent. This shows clearly that the cracks are not caused by rupture of a dense coating on the surface.

X-ray examination of the coating shows that it consists of crystallites of $Cu_2O$. These form as follows: in an aqueous solution of $Cu(NO_3)_2$ and in the presence of Cu, a certain amount of $CuNO_3$ is always formed, the quantity being dependent on the reaction $Cu^{++} + Cu = 2 Cu^+$. This is hydrolyzed in the aqueous solution in accordance with the reaction

$$CuNO_3 + H_2O \rightleftharpoons CuOH + HNO_3,$$

and since CuOH is not stable, $Cu_2O$ is immediately formed by the reaction $2 CuOH \rightarrow Cu_2O + H_2O$. Since $Cu^+$ ion concentration on the sample surface is low, only a low

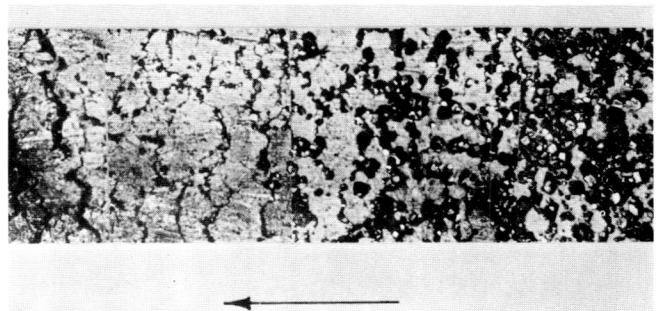

FIGURE 13 — Brass 70, covered with $Cu_2O$ the density of which depends on the drop of temperature in a $Cu(NO_3)_2$ solution. Temperature decreases in the direction of the arrow.

193

concentration of the products of the hydrolysis reaction will in turn be present. Accordingly only a relatively small number of crystallization nuclei form from the $Cu_2O$, but as a consequence of the unvarying $Cu^+$ ion concentration during the whole process these are able to form proper crystallites. The process represents a crystallization out of a homogeneous system, and this is characteristic of hydrolysis reactions. Thus the covering on the sample and the crack walls comprise discrete crystallites and not a smooth microcrystalline coating as with CuO. This is shown diagrammatically in Figure 14. This coating of the crack walls with discrete crystallites is clearly the reason for the absence of smooth narrow cracks, such as those formed in the presence of copper tetramine, and their replacement by more extensive cracks with characteristic thickening and protrusions at the sides, as seen in Figures 15 and 16.

Since CuO is no longer stable below pH ≈ 7, nor $Cu_2O$ below pH ≈ 2.0, the relationship between the stress corrosion susceptibility and the pH value observed by E. Mattsson[14] can easily be understood. Figure 17 illustrates

Mattsson's findings relating life and pH value in ammonium solutions containing $Cu^{++}$ and $SO_4^{--}$ ions. The figure also shows our own values for life in relationship to pH value in copper nitrate and copper sulfate solutions. These show that stress corrosion is still present at pH values in the region of 1.5. We should note here that the pH value on the surface is always somewhat smaller than in the cracks, so that $Cu_2O$ can still form in the cracks when this is no longer possible on the surface. This is direct evidence that noble covering layers on the surface or their rupture can have no basic effect on the occurrence of stress corrosion. Thick covering layers can of course restrict or delay the occurrence of stress corrosion in stress corrosion susceptible alloys, and their rupture naturally leads to the development of stress corrosion. In such cases the stress corrosion susceptibility of a material is merely allowed to take effect, but it is not caused by the pattern just described.

*c. Ferric Chloride Solutions.* Brass alloys 63 and 70 are in certain conditions also susceptible to stress corrosion in $FeCl_3$ solutions.[15] Tests were carried out in 2% $FeCl_3$

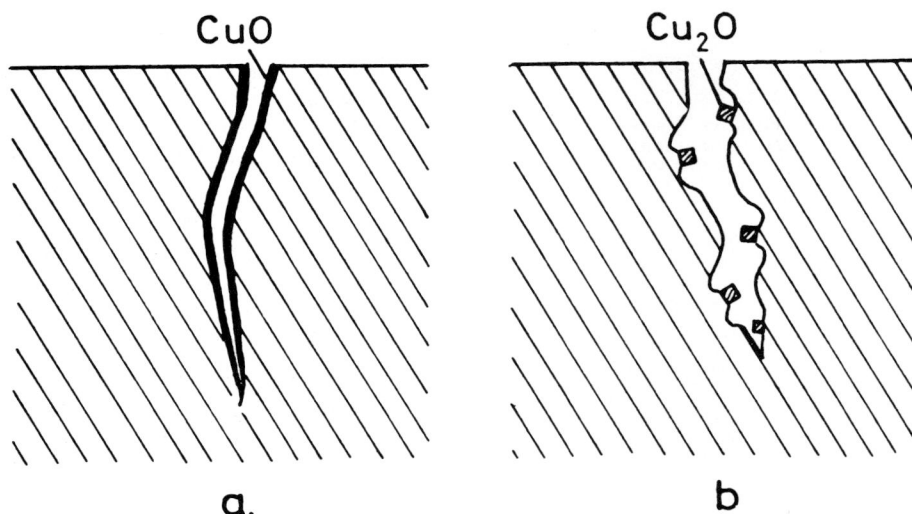

FIGURE 14 — Shape of cracks (diagrammatically) caused (a) by a concentrated copper tetramine solution forming CuO; (b) by a $Cu(NO_3)_2$ solution, forming $Cu_2O$.

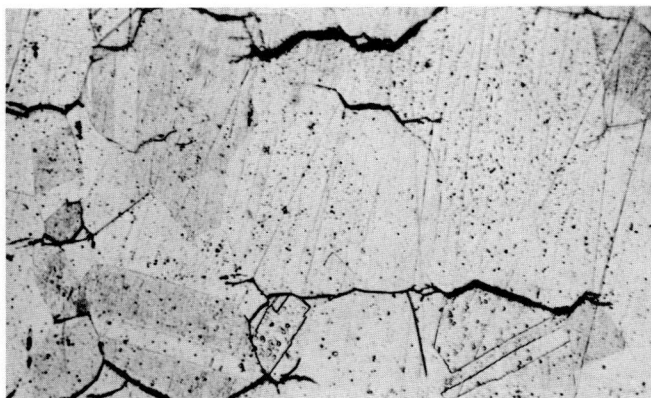

FIGURE 15 — Brass 70 with stress corrosion cracks caused by a concentrated copper tetramine solution.

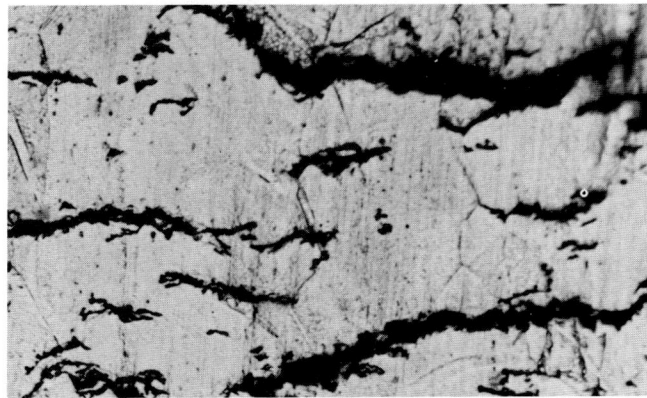

FIGURE 16 — Brass 70 with stress corrosion cracks caused by a 0.5 mol $Cu(NO_3)_2$ solution.

solution, which attacks these alloys as a result of the oxidizing effect of $Fe^{+++}$ ions:

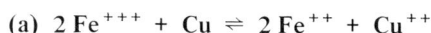

$$(a) \quad 2\,Fe^{+++} + Cu \rightleftharpoons 2\,Fe^{++} + Cu^{++}$$

$$(b) \quad 2\,Fe^{+++} + Zn \rightarrow 2\,Fe^{++} + Zn^{++}$$

This process causes the solution to lose $Fe^{+++}$ and gain $Cu^{++}$ and $Fe^{++}$ ions, and these in turn have a reducing effect on the $Cu^{++}$ ions and cause the precipitation of Cu. Further investigations proved that the reduction of the $Cu^{+}-$or $Cu^{++}$ ions occurs with greater probability by the zinc of the brass than by $Fe^{++}$ ions. During this experiment, relatively small quantities of 2% $FeCl_3$ solution must be used in order that after a relatively short reaction time the change in the concentrations of $Fe^{+++}$ and $Fe^{++}$ ions can lead to the return reaction corresponding to (a) above. In this way, copper cathodic areas required for the pronounced electrochemical process are thus formed, but only in the case of brass 63 or 70 is a sufficiently high potential difference available, whereas this is not the case with brass 80. Accordingly, the latter material is not sensitive to stress corrosion in 2% $FeCl_3$ solution. These experiments show most clearly how many possibilities exist of forming cathodic areas on the crack or crevice walls of brass. Depending on the nature of the attacking agent and the conditions obtaining, they can be formed of Cu, CuO or $Cu_2O$. This explains why, in principle, in the case of technical alloys no firm predictions as to absolute non-susceptibility to stress corrosion could be made, since it is impossible in practice to take into account all conceivable conditions affecting corrosion and to know all chemical reactions during the corrosion process.

## 2. α-Brass With Small Amounts of Gold

*a. Brass 70 resp. Copper with Variable Gold Content up to 5 $^a$/o Gold.* It is possible to carry out several additional interesting and informative experiments using brass.[16] If, for example, brass 70 is alloyed with small quantities of gold, all attacking agents which do not undergo complex reactions with gold will cause stress corrosion to occur, since the cathodic areas are able to develop from the gold irrespective of the nature of the agent. Figure 18a shows the relationship between lifetime and gold content in brass 70 in the range 0.25-5 At% gold, when immersed in solutions of aqua regia, 2% $FeCl_3$, saturated copper tetramine, and copper nitrate. In the case of brass containing no gold, life in aqua regia and $FeCl_3$ solution is governed only by resistance of the sample surface to attack, whereas the other two agents cause stress corrosion here too. However, with only a gold content of 0.25 At%, life of the sample decreases noticeably when attacked by aqua regia and $FeCl_3$ solution, and stress corrosion occurs. This is increasingly evident, as the gold content is increased, so that sample life falls away steeply.

The addition of such small amounts of gold have no practical influence on the strength of the solid solution effects, merely on the electrochemical process. The stress corrosion susceptibility under the influence of aqua regia or

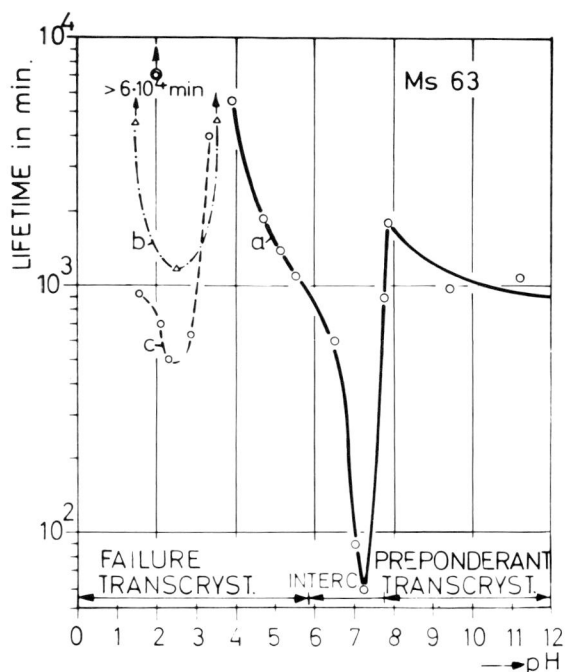

FIGURE 17 — Lifetime of brass 63 vs pH-value. Curve a: exposed to ammoniacal copper sulfate solutions of different pH values, after E. Mattsson. Curve b: exposed to a 0.5 mol $CuSO_4$ solution with different amounts of $H_2SO_4$, to alter the pH value. Curve c: exposed to $Cu(NO_3)_2$ solutions of different concentrations, to alter the pH value.

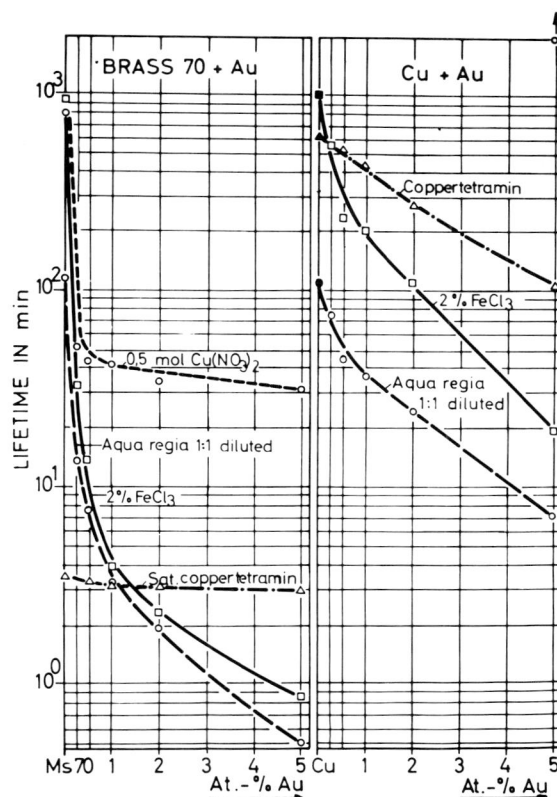

FIGURE 18 — Lifetime vs gold content of brass 70 and Cu-Au alloys in different reagents.

FeCl₃ depends solely on the latter. As a result we are able to investigate the effect of the electrochemical process on the stress corrosion susceptibility without any simultaneous change in the solid solution effects.

It is significant that the addition of gold to samples subjected to copper tetramine and copper nitrate solutions has practically no effect on life. This is certainly explainable by the fact that the gold becomes free as ultra-fine particles during corrosion and is completely surrounded by the $CuO$ or $Cu_2O$ also formed, so that it cannot constitute coherent cathodically effective areas. The rapid decrease in lifetime in the copper nitrate solution when the first addition of 0.25 At% gold is made is remarkable, subsequent additions have only a very weak effect on the life of the samples (Figure 18a).

This unusual result can certainly be explained by the fact that, as described above, the nucleation rate of $Cu_2O$ is low as a consequence of its precipitation from a homogeneous system (hydrolysis). Thus only a few discrete $Cu_2O$ crystallites form. However, if finely-divided gold is also freed in the corrosion process, this assists the nucleation of the $Cu_2O$, the result being an even coating comprising a great many small $Cu_2O$ crystallites on the crack and crevice walls. This leads to a more pronounced electrochemical process. Accordingly, the cracks formed here are narrower and smoother than those produced when copper nitrate acts on brass containing no gold (compare Figure 19 with Figure 16).

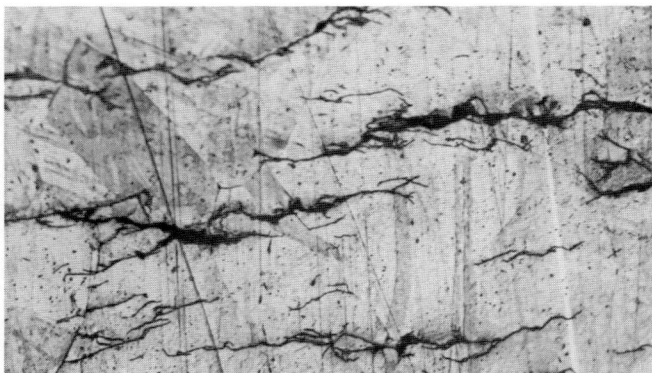

FIGURE 19 — Brass 70 with 2 a/o Au. Stress corrosion cracks, caused by a $Cu(NO_3)_2$ solution.

Figures 18a and b compare the effect of given gold additions to brass 70 with the effect of identical quantities of gold added to copper. The stress corrosion susceptibility of the copper alloys at the same gold content is considerably lower (and the life thus longer) than in the case of brass 70. Since the electrochemical processes in brass 70 + Au and CuAu samples having the same gold content, are of the same strength when corroded in aqua regia and FeCl₃ solution (cathodic areas formed from gold), the lower stress corrosion susceptibility of CuAu must be caused by reduced solid solution effects due to the smaller solute concentration. This applies similarly to the action of copper tetramine, but in this case cathodic areas of CuO are formed and the gold added to the sample does not affect the electrochemical process. This was shown by the tests made with brass 70 + Au (Figure 18a). Therefore, the decrease in lifetime as the gold content is increased can be attributed with some certainty to the increasing influence of solid solution effects on stress corrosion susceptibility. The latter is thus determined at a constant electrochemical process strength.

In the case of non-alloyed copper (Figure 18b) the influence of aqua regia or FeCl₃ solution causes no stress corrosion, since neither solid solution effects nor a pronounced electrochemical process take place. Life is determined solely by surface attack. When gold is added in quantities ranging up to approximately 0.5 At% there is a steep drop in life, caused by the appearance of stress corrosion. After this comes a more gradual fall corresponding more or less to that experienced in copper tetramine. It is thus possible to conclude that from this gold content upwards, even when subjected to aqua regia and FeCl₃ solution, the drop in life as gold content increases is solely conditioned by the resulting increase in solid solution effects. Only in the region of the steep drop in life, around 0.5 At% gold, is the life entirely dependent on the electrochemical process. This is borne out by the absence of this initial steep drop in life when the alloy is subjected to the action of copper tetramine. Since in this case the cathodic areas consist of CuO, a pronounced electrochemical process is present even when the copper is non-alloyed. This process is sufficient in itself to cause slight stress corrosion susceptibility, even in the absence of the solid solution effects. This has been confirmed by microscopic investigations. As gold is added, the solid solution effects become active and govern the subsequent decrease in life, the strength of the electrochemical process remaining unaltered as described above.

*b. Copper With 2 ª/o Gold and Variable Zinc Content up to 30 ª/o Zinc.* It is possible to study the solid solution effects on CuZn alloys with far more clarity if the relationship of life to zinc content in the range 0-30 At% zinc is investigated both *with* and without a constant gold content of, for example, 2 At%. The results are shown in Figures 20a and b. Let us first examine the behavior of the gold-free alloys (Figure 20a): here only copper tetramine causes stress corrosion, and we obtain a sharp drop in life with increasing zinc content. Since the cathodic areas are CuO, their formation and thus the strength of the electrochemical process which then occurs are constant and independent of the zinc content. Accordingly, the drop in life is attributable solely to the increase in solid solution effects which takes place as the solid solution concentration rises. The action of aqua regia or FeCl₃ solution takes the form only of a surface attack, despite the presence of solid solution effects, since no electrochemical process can take place.

If the alloys, like the copper samples, contain 2 At% gold (Figure 20b), then the influence of aqua regia or FeCl₃ solution causes a similar sharp drop in life as in the case of copper tetramine when no gold has been added. Here too the drop is governed solely by solid solution effects, since

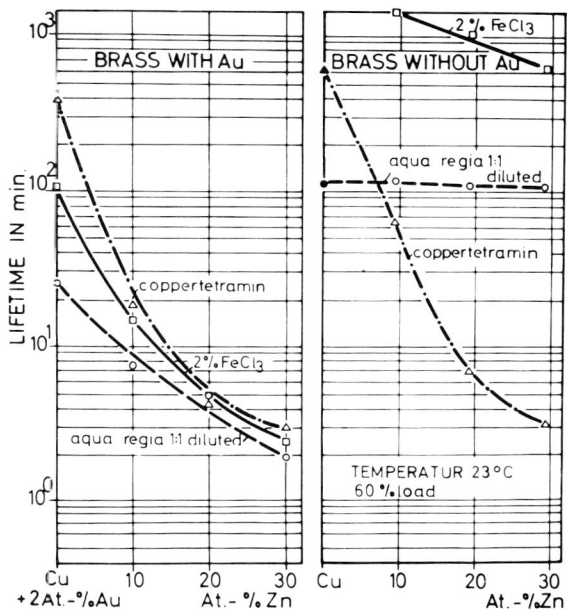

FIGURE 20 — Lifetime vs zinc content of Cu-Zn alloys in different reagents. On the left: Cu-Zn alloys containing 2 a/o Au; on the right: Cu-Zn alloys containing no Au.

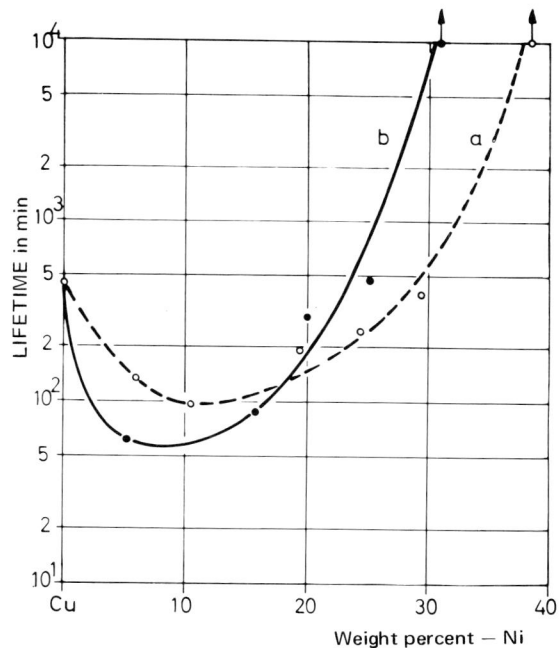

FIGURE 21 — Lifetime vs nickel content of Cu-Ni alloys in a concentrated copper tetramine solution. Curve a: alloys containing no Fe; Curve b: alloys containing ca. 0.3% Fe.

the gold content and hence the strength of the electro-chemical process are constant. Stress corrosion appears in copper containing 2 At% gold also, and the life is thus somewhat reduced already without zinc. When subjected to the action of copper tetramine any comparison of the lifetime graphs with and without gold alloying should take into account the fact that in Figure 20b the solid solution concentrations no longer amount to 10, 20 and 30 At%, but have been increased by the alloying of 2 At% gold to actual values of 12, 22 and 32 At%. As a result the graph of lifetime for the alloys containing gold in Figure 20b runs somewhat lower than that for the gold-free alloys in Figure 20a.

### 3. Copper-Base Alloys With Nickel, Aluminum and Manganese

After this detailed discussion of the causes of stress corrosion in brass, I would like to refer briefly to a number of other homogeneous, non-supersaturated alloys with a copper base, such as CuNi, CuAl and CuMn. The same basic conclusions apply here as for brass, since the behavior of the copper relative to the presence of ammonia is the deciding factor. The less noble components cause only the solid solution effects. The stress corrosion susceptibility need not necessarily have the same relationship to the alloy components in this case as when zinc forms one such component. It can, for example, be influenced to a greater or lesser degree by the varying nature of the resulting corrosion products.

Copper-nickel alloys, on the high copper side, provide an instructive example of this.[17,18] Figure 21 shows the relationship between life and nickel content in a saturated copper tetramine solution (Curve a). After an initial fall,

the life increases again after an alloy of 10% by weight of nickel has been reached, although in the case of pure copper-nickel alloys it does not vanish entirely until a level of approximately 40% by weight of nickel is passed, whereupon the alloy is no longer attacked by the copper tetramine as a result of the high nickel content. This secondary upward movement of the lifetime graph is probably attributable to the much reduced solubility of the nickel complex in an ammonia solution compared with that of a zinc complex. Accordingly, as the nickel content increases, an increasing quantity of nickel hydroxide is precipitated in the cracks and crevices. The gel-like nature of this precipitate restricts the diffusion process in the cracks and crevices, thus prolonging life.

If a low iron content of 0.1-0.3% is present, as is normally the case in technical CuNi alloys, the stress corrosion susceptibility disappears as early as approximately 30 wt.% of nickel (Curve b). The viscous, amorphous ferrous hydroxide precipitated in this case during corrosion is strongly surface-active, and appears to form with the nickel hydroxide a substance which coheres so thoroughly within the cracks that even at 30% nickel content the corrosive agent is completely prevented from entering the cracks and crevices.

Copper-manganese alloys[18] also exhibit the same pattern as shown by the graph in Figure 22. This is also attributable to the corrosion products having blocked access by the agent to the cracks and crevices.

In the case of copper-aluminum alloys,[18] on the other hand, the lifetime decreases steadily in relation to increasing aluminum content until 20 At%, the solubility limit, is reached. This can be seen in Figure 23, Curve b.

This concludes the remarks on homogeneous, non-supersaturated alloys with a copper base. Further homoge-

197

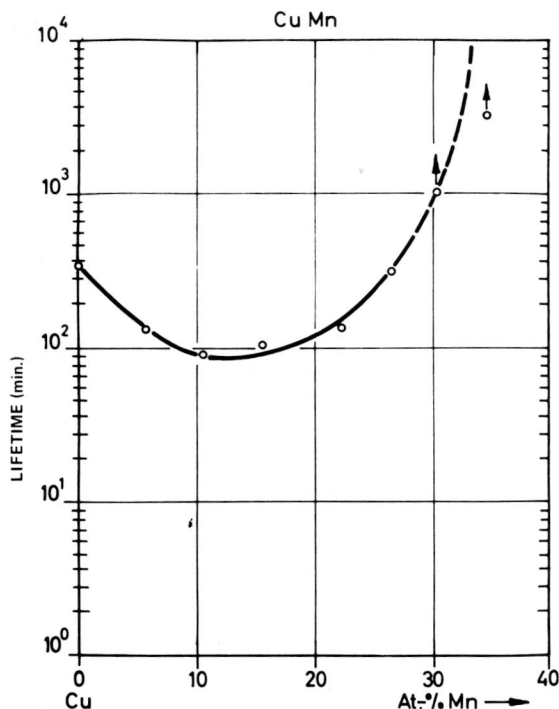

**FIGURE 22 — Lifetime vs manganese content of Cu-Mn alloys in a concentrated copper tetramine solution.**

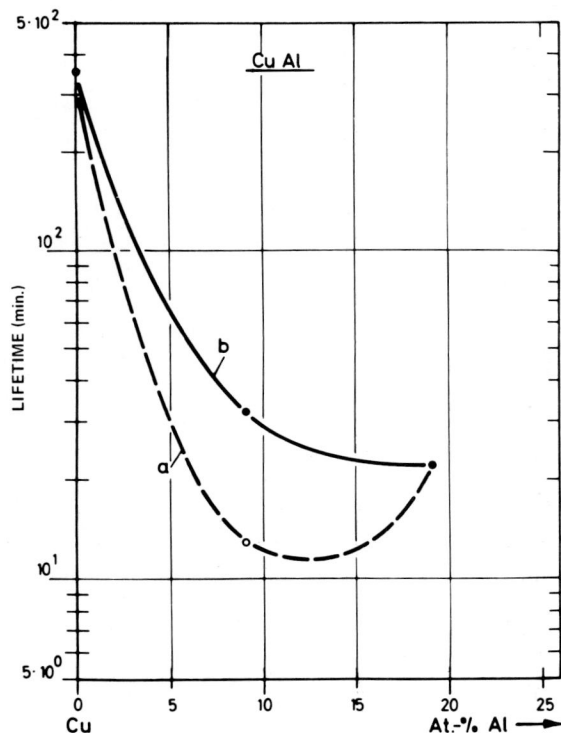

**FIGURE 23 — Lifetime vs aluminum content of Cu-Al alloys in a concentrated copper tetramine solution. Curve a: Samples not protected at the solution/air boundary. Intercrystalline cracks and fracture there. Curve b: Samples protected at the solution/air boundary. Transcrystalline cracks and fracture within the reagent.**

neous alloys of technical importance are those with a nickel or an iron base, for example the alloy monel, which contains approximately 70% nickel and 30% copper, or the austenitic steels containing Cr and Ni. Since I shall be dealing with the latter in the "Austenitic Alloys" session, I will restrict myself here to the NiCu alloy known as monel metal.

The context of these remarks does not allow me to do more than mention the most important findings of our investigations.[19]

### 4. Monel

Since in the case of monel metal the base is considerably less noble than the alloying component, it would be reasonable to anticipate strong stress corrosion susceptibility in the presence of nearly all corrodents, since one would assume the formation of cathodic areas consisting of copper. However, this is not the case, since all the agents attacking the nickel also dissolve the copper, and the strong tendency of copper to form complex compounds does not permit reprecipitation to take place. As a result no copper cathodic areas are formed, and no pronounced electrochemical process can occur in the cracks and crevices. This explains the well known lack of stress corrosion susceptibility of monel metal.

Quite recently stress corrosion has in fact been observed in damp hydrofluoric acid vapor containing air. In addition we have been able to establish that it also occurs in hydrofluoric acid containing $Cu^{++}$ ions. As our tests demonstrated, certain conditions permit $Cu_2O$ to form. Here too this material supplies the cathodic areas which make possible the electrochemical process required for the occurrence of stress corrosion. Figure 24 is a spatial diagram showing the relationship of life to the HF and $CuF_2$ concentrations for an alloy with approximately 70% nickel, 30% copper. As will be seen, the stress corrosion susceptibility is strongly dependent on the $CuF_2$ content of the hydrofluoric acid solution. As the $CuF_2$ content increases, life is reduced, with the minimum displaced towards the higher hydrofluoric acid concentrations. Further details regarding the conditions of the formation of $Cu_2O$, etc., may be taken from the quotation concerned.

### Conclusions

1. The causes of stress corrosion susceptibility of homogeneous non-supersaturated alloys are considered to arise from two solid solution effects operating together with a pronounced electrochemical process. The two solid solution effects involve an increased dissolution at the grain boundaries and of other disturbed areas on the grain surfaces, and further an increased dissolution of parts which are being plastically deformed.

2. The pronounced electrochemical process in the cracks arises from the roots being anodically polarized and the walls being cathodically polarized. However, the difference in potential between the deforming crack roots and the non-deforming crack walls is insufficient. Therefore, the

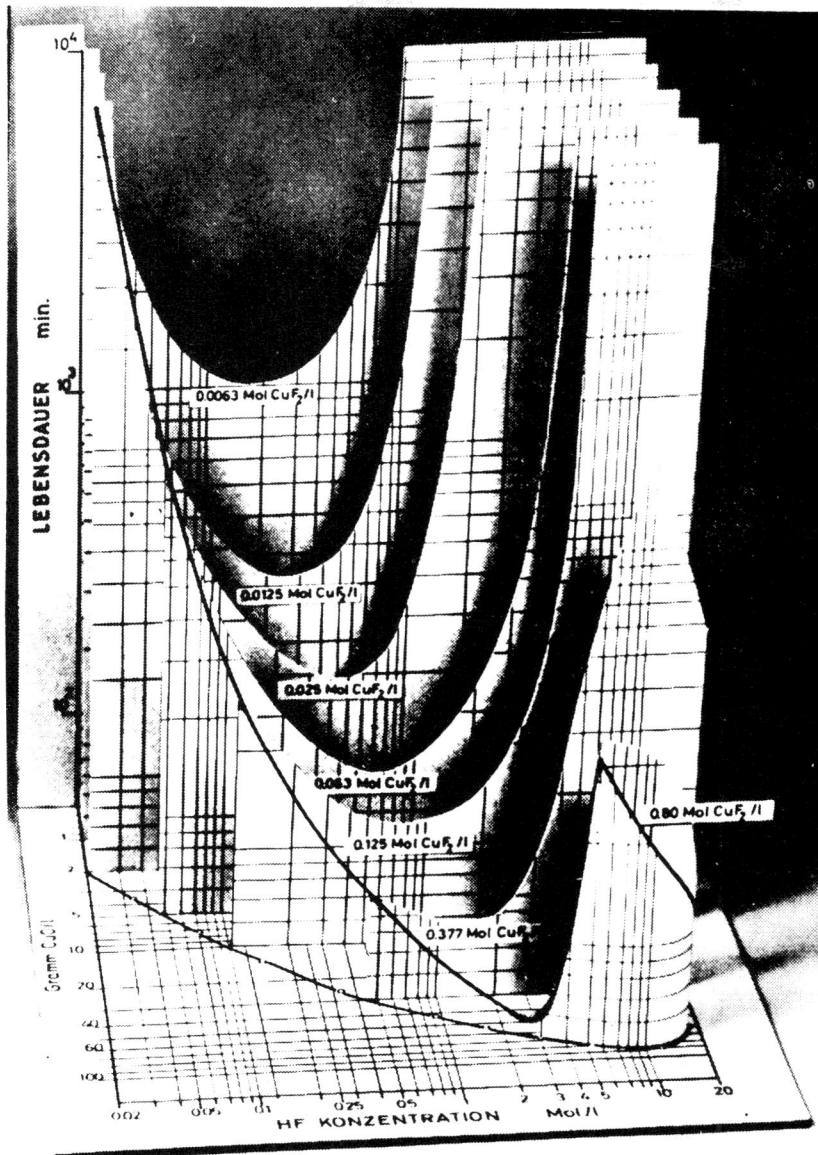

FIGURE 24 — Three-dimensional diagram of the lifetime of a Ni-30 a/o Cu alloy vs concentration of the HF solution and concentration of the CuF$_2$ content in it.

crack walls must be covered with a very noble material.

3. In the case of alloys containing noble metal components the cathodic areas on the crack walls are formed from the noble metal either remaining or else reprecipitated during corrosion.

4. In the case of alloys containing no noble metal components, the cathodic areas on the crack walls can form only from suitable solid corrosion products. This, however, cannot take place under the influence of every agent. This explains why only certain agents initiate stress corrosion. Now, the "specificity of environment" is understandable. It is shown with brass, for example, that the cathodic areas are formed from CuO in ammonia containing solutions, from $Cu_2O$ in copper nitrate solutions and from Cu in 2% $FeCl_3$ solution.

## References

1. L. Graf. *Proceedings Second International Congress on Metallic Corrosion,* New York, N. Y. (1963). Publ. by NACE, Houston, Texas, 1966.
2. L. Graf. *Zeitschrift für Metallkunde,* 38, 193 (1947).
3. L. Graf and J. Budke. *Zeitschrift Metallkunde,* 46, 378 (1955).
4. L. Graf. *Stress Corrosion Cracking and Embrittlement.* W. D. Robertson, Editor. Publ. by John Wiley and Sons, Inc., New York (1956).
5. L. Graf and H. Klatte. *Zeitschrift Metallkunde,* 46, 673 (1955).
6. L. Graf and H. Klatte. *Zeitschrift Physikalische Chemie, Neue Folge,* 10, 306 (1957).
7. L. Graf and H. Klatte. *Zeitschrift Physikalische Chemie, Neue Folge,* 11, 342 (1957).
8. L. Graf. *Werkstoffe und Korrosion,* 8, 329 (1957).
9. L. Graf. *Acta Metallurgica,* 6, 116 (1958).
10. L. Graf and N. Wieling. In course of publication.

11. L. Graf and H. R. Lacour. *Zeitschrift Metallkunde*, **51**, 152 (1960).
12. L. Graf and W. Richter. *Zeitschrift Metallkunde*, **52**, 834 (1961).
13. L. Graf and W. Wittich. *Werkstoffe und Korrosion*, **17**, 471 (1966).
14. E. Mattsson. *Recent Advances in Stress Corrosion*. Ed. by Ake Bresle. Publ. by Almqvist Wiksell, Stockholm, 1961. E. Mattsson. *Electrochimica Acta*, **3**, 279 (1961).
15. L. Graf and N. Wieling. In course of publication.
16. L. Graf and W. Wittich. *Werkstoffe und Korrosion*, **17**, 595 (1966).
17. L. Graf, H. R. Lacour, W. Richter and W. Wittich. *Zeitschrift Metallkunde*, **54**, 406 (1963).
18. L. Graf. *Metall*, **18**, 1287 (1964).
19. L. Graf and W. Wittich. *Werkstoffe und Korrosion*, **17**, 385 (1966).

## Discussion

**H. H. Uhlig, MIT:**

Dr. Graf, we have benefitted a great deal by your contributions to the factors influencing stress corrosion cracking of homogeneous noble metal alloys. I have a question regarding your mechanism of cracking in the brasses described in your paper. I wonder if you have tried adding chlorides in general to your ammonium ion solutions rather than ammonium chloride or sulfate alone. For example, sodium or magnesium .chloride might act as inhibitors. Many salts are expected to act as inhibitors. They do not necessarily need to displace the reaction you have on the board.

My question, therefore, is whether you think there is a displacement effect on your postulated reaction or whether added salts can act as inhibitors independent of any displacement.?

**L. Graf:**

Besides $NH_4Cl$ and $(NH_4)_2SO_4$ we added NaCl and $Na_2SO_4$ to a concentrated $Cu(NH_3)_4(OH)_2$ solution. By the first two additions stress corrosion cracking was prevented, but not by the latter two. Consequently, there is no effect of inhibition of NaCl or $Na_2SO_4$ additions on stress corrosion cracking. Moreover, it is understandable, that they cannot have any influence on the equilibrium

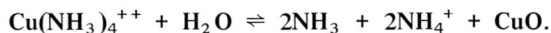

$$Cu(NH_3)_4^{++} + H_2O \rightleftharpoons 2NH_3 + 2NH_4^+ + CuO.$$

I am sure, that, with additions of $NH_4Cl$ or $(NH_4)_2SO_4$, there is a real displacement of the reaction to the left. We know that CuO is necessary as cathodic areas on the crack walls for producing a marked electrochemical process and for causing stress corrosion cracking. The influence of other salts was not investigated, so I cannot say whether they act as inhibitors or not. There may be some effects in this direction.

**H. H. Uhlig, MIT:**

Do you think that nitrates cause cracking because they are cathodically reduced to ammonium salts?

**L. Graf:**

As soon as nitrates are reduced to ammonium salts, it is possible that stress corrosion cracking is caused but that also depends on the conditions of the respective solutions.

Moreover, we were able to show that 0.5 M copper nitrate solution causes stress corrosion cracking to proceed rapidly. In the presence of copper a certain quantity of dissociated $CuNO_3$ arises, depending quantitatively on the reaction $Cu^{++} + Cu \rightarrow 2 Cu^+$. $CuNO_3$ hydrolyses in aqueous solutions, corresponding to

$$CuNO_3 + H_2O \rightarrow CuOH + HNO_3$$

CuOH is not stable and immediately forms $Cu_2O$, corresponding to $2 CuOH \rightarrow Cu_2O + H_2O$. $Cu_2O$ was identified microscopically as well as with X-rays. It produces the cathodic areas on the crack walls, necessary for a marked electrochemical process which causes stress corrosion cracking.

**C. J. L. Booker, Sir John Cass College:**

Could I ask your opinions of the explanations proposed in my paper?

**L. Graf:**

I agree with you that it is very important to know the reactions which lead to the production of CuO or $Cu_2O$, since the presence of one of these oxides is necessary for the appearance of stress corrosion cracking. But our opinions differ respecting their role. With other scientists you suppose that the formation of a surface film from these oxides should be decisive for the appearance of stress corrosion. We, however, came to the result that CuO or $Cu_2O$ only provide the cathodic layers on the crack walls, necessary for a marked electrochemical process. For, according to our understanding, stress corrosion cracking in homogeneous alloys is caused by the co-operation of the solid solution effects and a marked electrochemical process in the cracks.

Further, I think, there is no selective dissolution of zinc from brass, and, therefore, the crack growth cannot depend on it. It is well known that the dissolution of brass in copper-containing ammonia solutions mostly occurs by the strong oxidizing $Cu^{++}$-ions which are present in such a solution. The cathodic process consists in the reduction of $Cu^{++}$ ions, the anodic process in the oxidation of Cu (and Zn) to $Cu^+$ (or $Zn^{++}$) ions. The $Cu^+$ ions are oxidized by the atmospheric oxygen in the solution, by which their concentration increases very quickly and, therefore, the dissolution of brass is accelerated.

**K. Vetter, Free University of Berlin:**

You speak about a cathodic reaction on the wall of the cracks and an anodic reaction at the root of cracks. My question is: What is the cathodic reaction at the walls? In your model, there does not appear to be reducible species to gain electrons on the surface of the copper oxide.

**L. Graf:**

The cathodic reaction at the walls of the cracks consists mainly in the reduction of $Cu^{++}$ ions to $Cu^{+}$ ions. The anodic reaction at the roots of the cracks is the oxidation of Cu (and Zn) atoms of the alloy to $Cu^{+}$ or $Zn^{++}$ ions. There are sufficient $Cu^{++}$ ions in a concentrated $Cu(NH_3)_4(OH)_2$-solution due to the dissociation of the copper-ammonia complex as well as due to the oxidation of the $Cu^{+}$ ions by means of the dissolved atmospheric oxygen in the solution. The direct dissolution of copper or brass in a solution containing oxygen and Cu ions to form copper and zinc complexes does not play an essential part. This follows from the fact that the dissolution of copper or brass is accelerated autocatalytically in an ammonia solution containing oxygen due to the increase of the $Cu^{++}$ ion concentration (S. W. Katz, *Metalloberflaeche,* 3 (A), 101 (1949); "Kupfer" in "Korrosion and Korrosions-schutz," herausgeg, v.F. Toedt, Verlag W.de Gruyter u. Co., Berlin, 1955, S.257).

**M. Prazak, State Research Institute for Materials Protection:**

The author mentioned that it is expedient to stress corrode brass in a saturated copper tetramine solution in order to shorten time to failure. This fact shows one more possible process taking part in the mechanisms of stress corrosion cracking in the case of more noble metals. With these metals (e.g., Cu, Ag) the existence of *exchange currents* of detectable values can be expected. In the presence of more active sites caused by mechanical processes in the metal lattice it is possible that the anodic part (a) of the exchange current occurs on the more active sites, while the

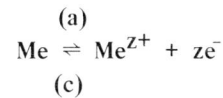

$$\text{(a)}$$
$$\text{Me} \rightleftharpoons \text{Me}^{z+} + z\bar{e}$$
$$\text{(c)}$$

cathodic part (c) of the exchange current occurs previously on the less active sites (low index planes). Such a "recrystallization" of metal surface in presence of electrolyte can be well shown in a macroscopic form in superheated solutions. Thus the "corrosion" of active sites may occur without any other depolarization.

The rate of the exchange process depends of course on the concentration of metal ions present in the solution; therefore the presence of copper tetramine, as well as free or other complex Cu ions in the copper nitrate or organic acids (as mentioned in the Uhlig paper 1) can accelerate the process by raising the exchange current.

The effect of the exchange current is to be expected especially under electrochemical conditions near the equilibrium, where also solid corrosion products as CuO can form according the equation given by Prof. Graf.

**L. Graf:**

It is not easy to decide whether high exchange currents may influence and accelerate s.c.c. We found s.c.c. of brass 70 and 63 in aqueous copper nitrate solutions depending on the concentration or rather on the pH, but the time to cracking was 100 times longer than in a concentrated copper tetramine solution.

In a solution of one mol/l copper nitrate s.c.c. occurs, because, at its pH-value of 2.08, $Cu_2O$ is still stable and forms cathodic areas on the crack walls producing a pronounced electrochemical process in the cracks necessary for the occurrence of s.c.c. But in a solution of 1.5 mol/l copper nitrate with a pH-value of 1.62 $Cu_2O$ is no more stable and cannot form, therefore no s.c.c. occurs.

However, at this lower pH-value considerable intercrystalline corrosion occurs, and we had, up to now, no explanation for this. Maybe this is caused by high exchange currents. In copper sulfate solutions, the same principle operates. See L. Graf and W. Wittich, *Werkstoffe und Korrosion,* 17, p. 471 (1966).

# ROLE OF SURFACE FILM IN
# STRESS CORROSION CRACKING

Saburo Shimodaira and Michinori Takano
Tohoku University

## Abstract

The mechanism of the transition from transgranular to intergranular cracking in the brass-ammonia system was investigated from the standpoint of crystal structure, and the role of the surface film produced in the corrosive environment was determined from the measurement of stress-strain curves. The mechanism of stress corrosion cracking was explained in terms of the surface film theory. The stress corrosion micro-trenches nucleated on freshly produced slip steps and were independent of the stress corrosion cracking susceptibility and the mode of cracking. Intergranular cracking was caused by the retardation of slip step emergence due to the formation of a thick cuprous oxide film. The transition from transgranular to intergranular cracking depends on the mechanical properties of the surface film produced in the corrosive environment. The stress-strain curves in the brass-ammonia system can be explained in terms of the surface film theory.

## I. Introduction

Recently, studies on stress corrosion cracking have been undertaken from the viewpoint of dislocation theory. Electron microscopic examinations of processes involved in stress corrosion cracking has provided a valid ground in applying the dislocation theory to the study of stress corrosion cracking. The present authors have investigated the mechanism of stress corrosion cracking of austenitic stainless steels and brasses using an electron microscope and the following trends were observed: (1) In both alloy-corrosive systems stress corrosion micro-trenches nucleate at freshly produced slip steps in crystal grains regardless of the susceptibility to stress corrosion cracking. Susceptible and non-susceptible alloys are distinguished by the fact that dissolution after slip step emergences continues an appreciable extent in the former alloys but not in the latter; (2) Although stress corrosion micro-trenches predominantly nucleate at slip steps in the interior of crystal grains, the path of cracking changes either intergranular or transgranular depending on the nature of the surface oxide film.

The transition from transgranular to intergranular cracking under stress corrosion is well known in the brass-ammonia system to depend on the corrosive environment,[4-7] the composition of alloys[8-10] and the degree of pre-strain.[11-12] It is the concensus of numerous investigators[4-7,13] that the transition of cracking path is closely related to the surface film produced in the corrosive environment. In previous electrochemical studies,[4,6,7,14,15] however, the detailed nature of the corrosion process of alloys deformed plastically under stress cannot be determined, and consequently, it has been difficult to clearly explain the mechanism of cracking. The film rupture theory which assumes the mechanism to be due to the formation of the surface film in the corrosive environment and the subsequent breakdown under stress has been developed by Logan,[16] Forty and Humble[17] and McEvily and Bond.[18] None of these investigators have developed fully satisfactory descriptions of the process from initiation to the propagation of cracks.

The present authors investigated the mechanism of the transition from transgranular to intergranular cracking from the standpoint of the crystal structure and of surface film produced in the corrosive environment. Stress-strain curves were obtained in the brass-ammonia system in order to explain the mechanism of stress corrosion cracking in terms of the surface-film theory.

## II. Experimental

The chemical composition of brass specimens are listed in Table 1. Sheet specimens were used for the transmission-electron microscopic observations; they were also used for examining the effect of corrosives. Sheet specimens and sheet tensile specimens were 100 x 5 x 0.1 mm and 20 x 10 x 0.1 mm, respectively. The bulk tensile specimens for the stress corrosion test were 15 x 3 x 3 mm. Specimens were wrapped in thin brass foils of the same composition and

**TABLE 1 – Chemical Composition of Specimens**

|  | Cu (%) | Zn (%) | Pb (%) | Fe (%) |
|---|---|---|---|---|
| Bulk Specimen | R | 30.82 | 0.011 | 0.015 |
| Sheet Specimen | 70.02 | R | 0.006 | 0.003 |

annealed at 600 C margin: 1 hour for bulk specimens and 30 minutes for the sheet specimens. The observation of stress corrosion micro-trenches of the sheet specimens in the corrosive environment was carried out in the same way as described previously.[1] The stress-strain measurement of each tensile specimen in the corrosive environment was performed using an Instron tensile test machine (Type TT-CM-L), with a strain rate of $5.5 \times 10^{-5}$ $sec^{-1}$ for the bulk specimens and $4.1 \times 10^{-5}$ $sec^{-1}$ for the sheet specimens. The bulk specimens were also deformed at a strain rate of $1.1 \times 10^{-3}$ $sec^{-1}$ to examine the effect of strain rate. An experiment was conducted to examine the effect of applied stress under the constant load of 33% $\sigma_T$ or 66% $\sigma_T$ ($\sigma_T$: tensile strength, 30 Kg/mm$^2$). The specimens used were all annealed and electropolished prior to the measurement. The stress-strain measurements in solution were carried out with specimens fully immersed. The experiment in the ammonia vapor environment was carried out in a sealed stress corrosion test cell which contained a 28% ammonia solution. Care was taken to avoid direct contact of the specimen with the liquid phase. Measurements were started immediately after ammoniacal water was poured. The corrosive environments used are listed in Table 2. Since in Mattsson's solution (pH 7.4) the slip lines which formed during stress corrosion cracking remained in the tarnish film, they could be observed by means of optical microscopy (Section III.C., Figure 7), and micro stress corrosion behavior and fracture surface in this environment were examined using carbon replicas (Section III.C., Figures 8, 9, and 10).

## III. Results

### A. Microscopic Stress Corrosion Behavior

Stress corrosion behavior of the sheet specimens in Mattsson's solution with pH 2.0, 7.4 or 10.0 and in 3% NaCl aqueous solution is shown in Figure 1 (a), (b), (c) and (d), respectively. Figure 1 shows that stress corrosion micro-trenches in each corrosive nucleate predominantly along the slip steps produced under stress. In addition,

preferential corrosion was also observed at grain boundaries, dislocation ends, and twin boundaries. General corrosion was observed frequently at pH 10.0. Despite the fact that intergranular cracking is observed only at pH 7.4, the morphology of micro attack was the same at pH's 2.0, 7.4 or 10.0 in Mattsson's solution and in 3% NaCl aqueous solution. At pH 7.4, however, the micro-trenches tend to extend quickly over the brass surface. A typical example of the corrosion trenches spread over the surface is shown in Figure 2. From the selected area diffraction pattern obtained from the preferentially corroded region, it is clear that the corrosion products consisted of $Cu_2O$ and Cu. The $Cu_2O$ grew epitaxially on the copper metal produced by dezincification. Two straight lines in Figure 2 can be considered as the initial slip traces produced in the brass specimen, but not in the films of $Cu_2O$ and Cu on the surface.

### B. Stress-Strain Measurement

The relation between the appearance of the surface film and the path of stress corrosion cracking of the bulk specimens at a strain rate of $5.5 \times 10^{-5}$ $sec^{-1}$ is summarized in Table 3. The table shows that in Mattsson's solution (pH 7.4) in which a black and thick oxide film develops, intergranular cracking occurs, whereas, when the surface film produced in the corrosive is thin and the surface exhibits general corrosion, transgranular cracking occurs. In an aqueous solution of 3 percent sodium chloride the surface of the specimens maintained the as-polished state without visible films, and stress corrosion cracking did not occur. The results shown in Table 3 agree with those of other investigators.[4-7,13]

The effect of the strain rate on the stress corrosion cracking behavior of the bulk specimens in each corrosive environment is shown in Figures 3 and 4. At a high strain rate of $1.1 \times 10^{-3}$ $sec^{-1}$, the strain required to cause failure was larger than that at $5.5 \times 10^{-5}$ $sec^{-1}$, and the specimens were markedly affected by plastic deformation as shown in Figure 3. In this case, in Mattsson's solution (pH 7.4) in which intergranular cracking occurred, a few cracks were present, but in a 1 M $NH_4OH$ + 1/4 M $CuCl_2$ aqueous solution in which transgranular cracking occurred many cracks were initiated all over the surface of the specimen. In the ammonia vapor in which transgranular cracking occurred, many cracks were present in the lower portion of the specimen near the liquid phase. Fracture of each specimen showed an appearance similar to ductile failure. At a strain rate of $5.5 \times 10^{-5}$ $sec^{-1}$ however, the strain

**TABLE 2 – Corrosive Environments Used for the Stress Corrosion Test**

| Micro-Stress Corrosion Behavior of Thin Brass Foils | Stress-Strain Measurement |
|---|---|
| Mattsson's Solution (0.05 M $CuSO_4$ + 0.5 M $(NH_4)_2SO_4$ Aq. Sol.) (pH 2.0, 7.4 and 10.0) | Mattsson's Solution (pH 7.4) 1 M $NH_4OH$ + 1/4 M $CuCl_2$ Aq. Sol. Ammonia Vapor |
| 3% NaCl Aq. Sol. | 3% NaCl Aq. Sol. |

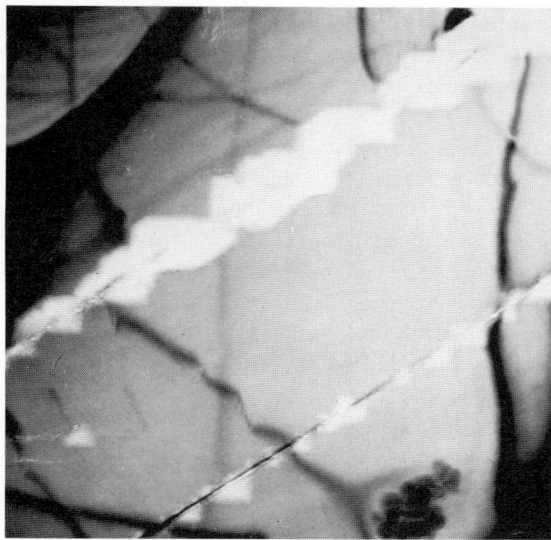

a

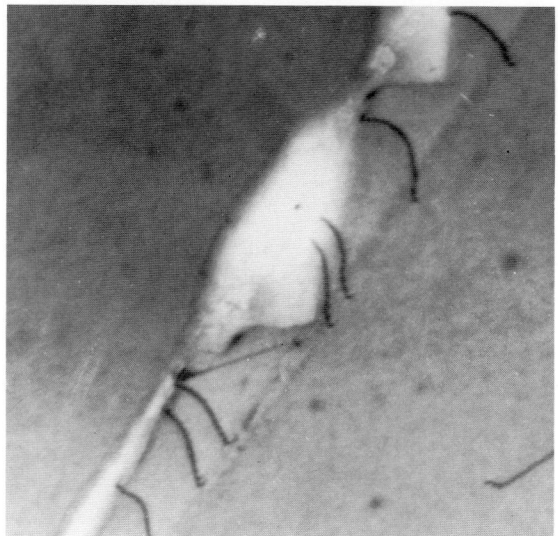

b

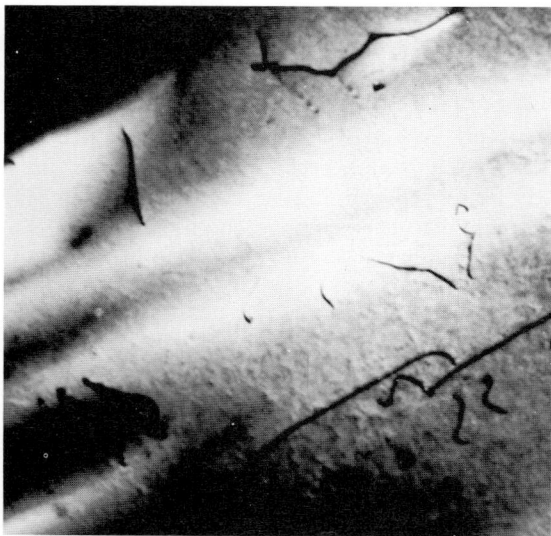

c

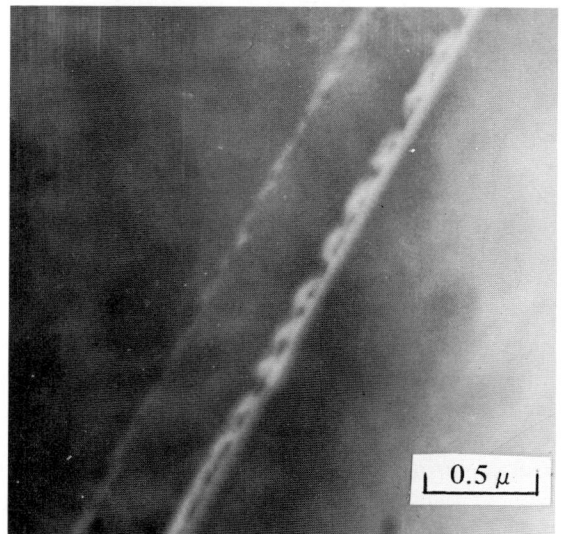

$\llcorner$ $0.5\ \mu$ $\lrcorner$

d

FIGURE 1 — Stress corrosion micro-trenches at freshly produced slip steps in deformed thin foil specimens in Mattsson's solution for 3 min at (a) pH 2.0, (b) pH 7.4, (c) pH 10.0, and (d) in 3% NaCl aqueous solution for 3 min.

TABLE 3 — Results of the Stress Corrosion Test for
70Cu-30Zn Bulk Specimens in Various
Environments ($\dot{\epsilon}$, 5.5 x $10^{-5}$ sec$^{-1}$ )

| Corrosives | Path of Cracking | Surface Color |
|---|---|---|
| Mattsson's Solution (pH 7.4) (0.05 M $CuSO_4$ + 0.5 M $(NH_4)_2SO_4$ Aq. Sol.) | Intergranular Cracking | Black |
| 1 M $NH_4OH$ + 1/4 M $CuCl_2$ Aq. Sol. | Transgranular Cracking | Light Brown |
| Ammonia Vapor | " | Dark Brown |
| 3% NaCl Aq. Sol. | No Cracking | Bright |

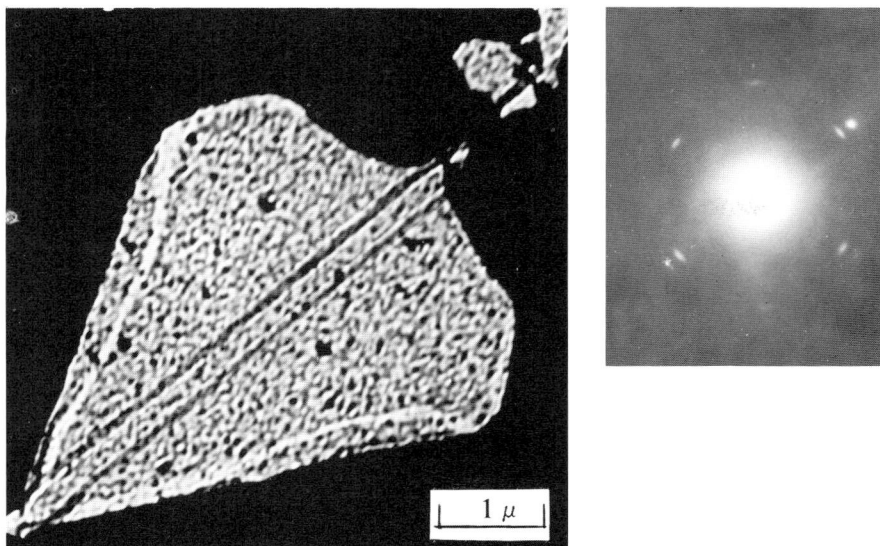

FIGURE 2 — Typical example of the thick oxide film of $Cu_2O$ produced in a deformed thin foil specimen in Mattsson's solution with pH 7.4 for 3 min.

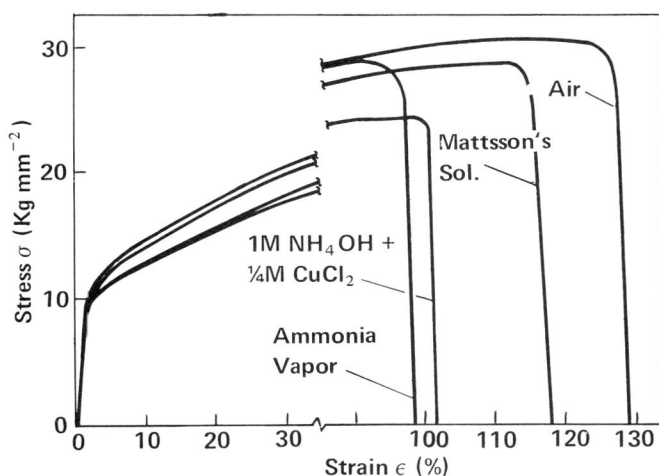

FIGURE 3 — Stress-strain curves for bulk tensile specimens in various corrosive environments, $\dot{\epsilon}$, 1.1 x $10^{-3}$ sec$^{-1}$.

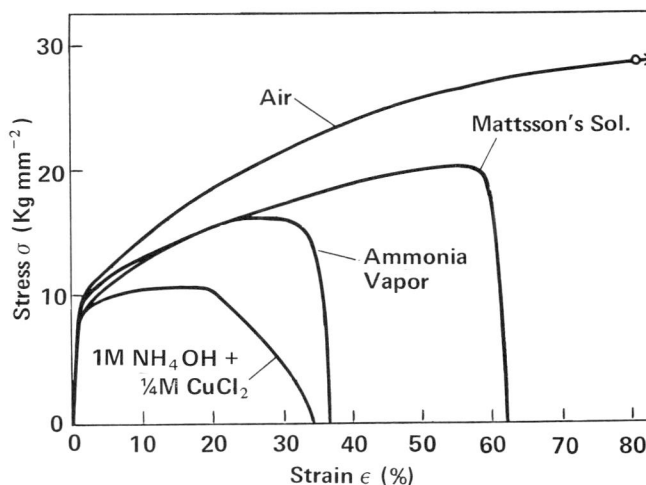

FIGURE 4 — Stress-strain curves for bulk tensile specimens in various corrosive environments, $\dot{\epsilon}$, 5.5 x $10^{-5}$ sec$^{-1}$.

required to cause failure in each corrosive was about one-half of that at 1.1 x $10^{-3}$ sec$^{-1}$ as shown in Figure 4, and all the specimens failed with many cracks. Under the same strain rate, the stress, strain and time to failure during stress corrosion in the transgranular cracking environment were small compared with those in the intergranular cracking environment in the liquid corrosive. In the ammonia vapor, however, the stress required to cause failure was as high as that in the air in the case of the strain rate of 1.1 x $10^{-3}$ sec$^{-1}$, and was nearly equal to that in Mattsson's solution (pH 7.4) even in the case of the strain rate of 5.5 x $10^{-5}$ sec$^{-1}$.

In order to clearly demonstrate the effect of the corrosive on stress corrosion cracking, the stress-strain curves of the sheet specimens were measured. The result obtained at a strain rate of 4.1 x $10^{-5}$ sec$^{-1}$ is shown in Figure 5. The sheet specimens did not fail within the strain of 50% both in the air and in the aqueous solution of 3% sodium chloride. The mode of cracking was intergranular in Mattsson's solution (pH 7.4), and transgranular in the ammonia vapor and in the 1 M NH$_4$OH + 1/4 M CuCl$_2$ aqueous solution. The stress and the strain required to cause failure in Mattsson's solution (pH 7.4), in which intergranular cracking occurred, were much larger than those in the corrosives in which transgranular cracking occurred. The stress-strain behavior of the sheet specimens in each corrosive shown in Figure 5 agrees well with that of the bulk specimens shown in Figure 4. However, in the case

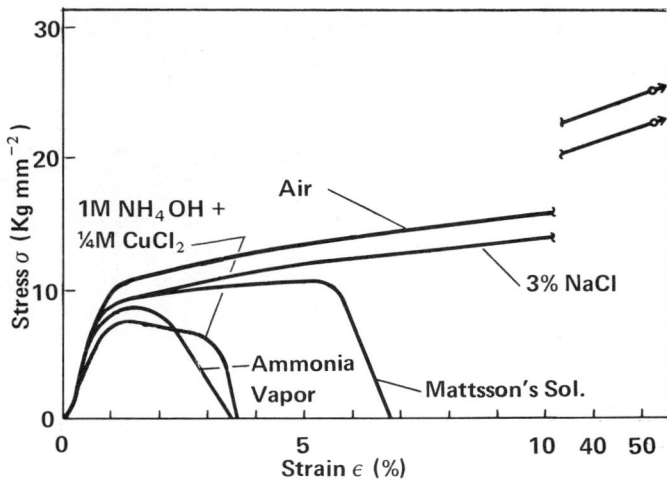

FIGURE 5 — Stress-strain curves for sheet tensile specimens in various corrosive environments, $\dot{\epsilon}$, 4.1 x $10^{-5}$ sec$^{-1}$.

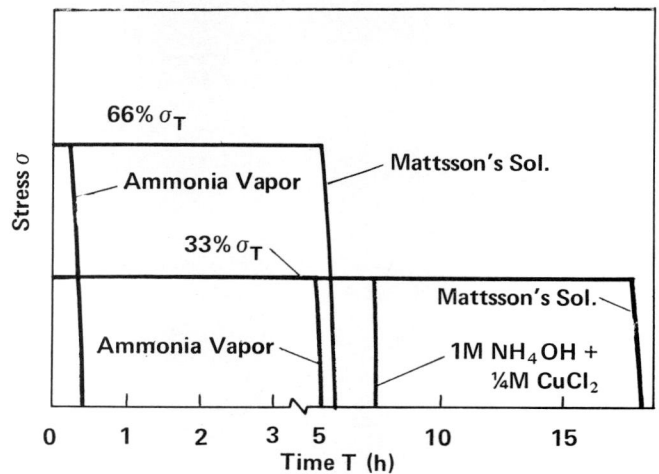

FIGURE 6 — Load-time curves for bulk specimens in various corrosive environments.

of the sheet specimens, the proportion of the surface area to the thickness was large, so a pronounced effect of the corrosives was found; the decline of the stress started at the strain of about 5.5% in Mattsson's solution (pH 7.4) and at the strain of 2 to 3% in the transgranular cracking environment.

The load vs time curve obtained from the bulk specimens in each corrosive under the constant load is shown in Figure 6. The load of 66% $\sigma_T$ in the 1 M NH$_4$OH + 1/4 M CuCl$_2$ aqueous solution could not be applied to the specimens. This result can be predicted from the fact that the stress required to cause failure in this corrosive was very small as shown in Figures 4 and 5. In the ammonia vapor the specimens failed in a short time (18 minutes) under the load of 66% $\sigma_T$. The time to failure in each corrosive under the same load was longer in the intergranular cracking environment than in the transgranular cracking one.

### C. Microscopic Observation

Figure 7 represents the slip lines in the surface tarnish film on the bulk specimens which failed in Mattsson's solution (pH 7.4). Under the high strain rate of 1.1 x $10^{-3}$ sec$^{-1}$ or the large constant load of 66% $\sigma_T$ the slip lines were greatly disturbed and the slip process at the grain boundary was also remarkable as shown in Figure 7 (a) and (b). The specimens were considerably affected by plastic deformation during the cracking. On the other hand, at a low strain rate of 5.5 x $10^{-5}$ sec$^{-1}$ or at a small constant load of 33% $\sigma_T$, the slip lines produced in the surface tarnish film were uniformly distributed in regular array and stress corrosion cracking proceeded without apparent plastic deformation as shown in Figure 7 (c) and (d). Figure 8 represents the result obtained from an electron microscopic observation of the stress corrosion behavior of these surface films. Figure 8 (a), (b) and (c), (d) correspond

to the micrographs obtained under the same condition, as shown in Figure 7 (a), (b) and (c), (d), respectively. Figure 8 (a) and (b) show that the whole surface film was affected by plastic deformation and disturbed by the mechanical tensile stress. At a strain rate of 1.1 x $10^{-3}$ sec$^{-1}$, as shown in Figure 8 (a), the disturbance of the surface film was especially remarkable. Although the microcracks produced at the initial slip steps remained in the tarnish film at a constant load of 66% $\sigma_T$, as shown in Figure 8 (b), a mechanical disturbance appeared in the surface film. In Figure 8 (c) and (d), microcracks remained in the tarnish film, but the surface film was not plastically deformed, showing a smooth surface film. The microcracks nucleated in the surface film can be divided in two types: (1)Those which were short and discontinuous in rows as indicated in Figure 9 (a), and (2) those which were long and straight as shown in Figure 9 (b). It is considered that these different types of microcracks, which were also observed in the earlier work of Forty and Humble[17] on the surface tarnish film of brass in Mattsson's solution, can be related to the crystal orientation of brass and to the direction of stress.

The stress corrosion behavior varies depending on the strain rate or the load in the constant load test. This variation can be recognized in the observation of the fracture surface. The present result is shown in Figure 10. Figure 10 (a) represents the fracture surface which mechanically failed in air at a strain rate of 1.1 x $10^{-3}$ sec$^{-1}$. Figure 10 (b) and (c) show the fracture surfaces of the specimens which failed in Mattsson's solution (pH 7.4) at the strain rate of 1.1 x $10^{-3}$ sec$^{-1}$ and at the constant load of 66% $\sigma_T$, respectively. The fractographs in Figure 10 (b) and (c) are similar to the one in Figure 10 (a), showing the appearance of some mechanical cracking. Figure 10 (b) shows a predominant contribution of the mechanical failure. In Figure 10 (d) obtained in Mattsson's solution (pH 7.4) at the strain rate of 5.5 x $10^{-5}$ sec$^{-1}$, the microfissures which might occur secondarily remained in

a

b

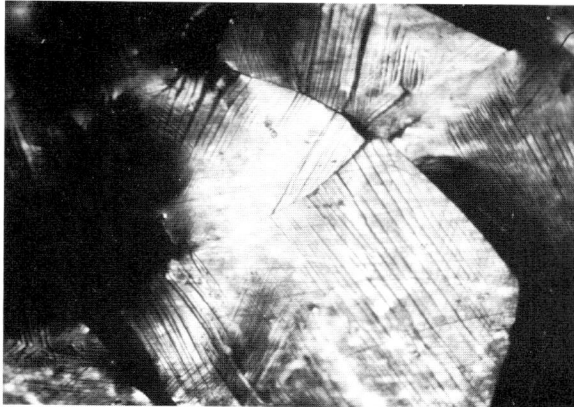

c

d

FIGURE 7 — Slip patterns produced in the tarnish on the failed specimens in Mattsson's solution (pH 7.4) X100: (a) $\dot{\epsilon}$, 1.1 x $10^{-3}$ $sec^{-1}$, (b) 66% $\sigma_T$, (c) $\dot{\epsilon}$, 5.5 x $10^{-5}$ $sec^{-1}$, (d) 33% $\sigma_T$.

the fracture surface. This fractograph is similar to the micrograph of the fracture surface obtained at the same strain rate in Mattsson's solution (pH 7.4) as shown in Figure 8, suggesting the progression of crack propagation by corrosion.

## IV. Discussion

Tromans and Nutting[19] have reported that the preferential attack of the thin brass foil in Mattsson's solution (pH 7.4) occurs at grain boundaries and at individual dislocations adjacent to grain boundaries, and these micro-attacks are associated directly with intergranular microcracking. Ronnquist[20] has also demonstrated that the micro-attacks occur at grain boundaries, under a small stress and at slip steps in the grain under a large stress. In the present experiment, however, stress corrosion micro-trenches with various pH values nucleated preferentially at the slip steps in the grains in Mattsson's solution. In the stress corrosion test of the bulk specimens in Mattsson's solution intergranular cracking occurred at pH 7.4, but not

at pH 2.0 nor 10.0[3] (Mattsson[4] observed transgranular cracking at a high or low pH value). A similar micro-corrosion behavior within grains was also observed in the alloy-corrosive system resistant to stress corrosion cracking.[2] The fact that transgranular micro-trenches occur at the three pH's but intergranular cracking occurred at the middle pH suggests that the initiation of the nucleus and the propagation of cracks in stress corrosion cracking cannot be elucidated according to the same mechanism. The authors previously reported that the chemical composition of the surface film produced in the corrosive was independent of the stress corrosion susceptibility and the path of cracking.[21,22]

Among the numerous micro-trenches nucleated on the slip steps in the early stage, a few of them grow up into cracks. This fact can be explained as follows: Stress corrosion cracking occurs in the corrosive environment where the action of passivators is stronger than that of activators, and therefore repassivation in the slip steps usually prevails in a short time. Furthermore, the stress field in the alloys is microscopically non-uniform. Under

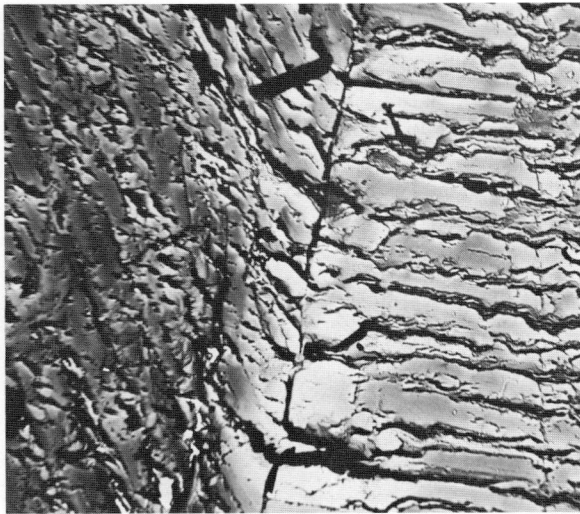

a

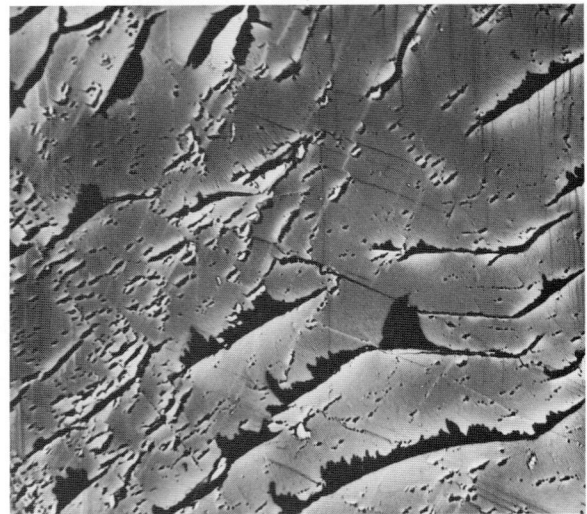

b

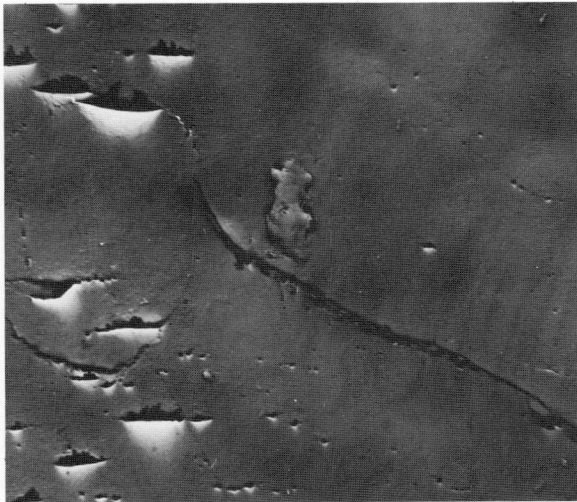

c

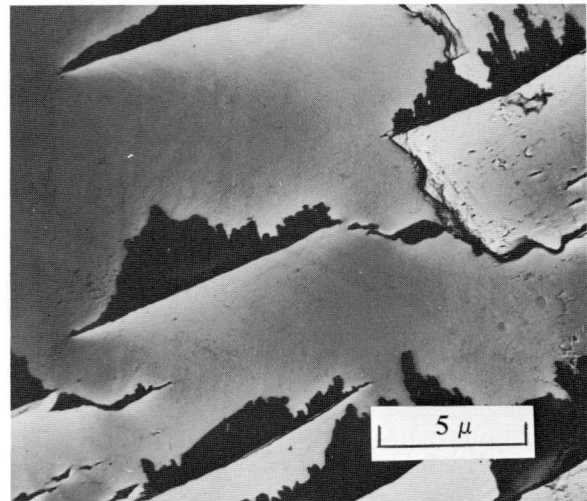

d

FIGURE 8 — Electron micrographs of the surface tarnish for the same specimens as in Figure 7: (a) $\dot{\epsilon}$, 1.1 x 10$^{-3}$ sec$^{-1}$, (b) 66% $\sigma_T$, (c) $\dot{\epsilon}$, 5.5 x 10$^{-5}$ sec$^{-1}$, (d) 33% $\sigma_T$.

these conditions, the corrosion rate of the micro-trenches into the interior of the alloy would differ with the lapse of time. At the tip of the deeply corroded regions on the slip plane, a microscopic stress concentration occurs, and the movement of dislocations on such a slip plane should be further promoted, exposing the fresh slip plane easily to the corrosive. Passivators such as dissolved oxygen would also hardly diffuse to the tip of the deep micro-crevices. The corrosion of these freshly produced slip planes, therefore, would be accelerated, leading to crack propagation. Then the preferential corrosion would penetrate not only along the same slip planes but also along appropriately oriented conjugate slip planes.

The above explanation is concerned with transgranular cracking when the applied stress is large enough to rupture the surface film. Even if the applied stress is not sufficient to rupture the surface film, when corrosion pits are formed, transgranular cracking should initiate at the pits because of the absence of the surface film at the basal part of the pits.

Forty and Humble,[17] Pickering and Swann,[23] and Hoar and Booker[24] reported that the corrosion products on the brass surface in various ammonia environments consisted of small platelets of cuprous oxide. In the present work, under the condition which induced intergranular cracking, the cuprous oxide developed epitaxially on the copper metal which was produced by dezincification of brass. The grain size of cuprous oxide was about one micron as seen in Figure 2. From the relationship between the surface film and the path of cracking (Table 3), it is found that the transgranular cracking occurs when the surface film is not thick.

From the results mentioned above, it is considered that

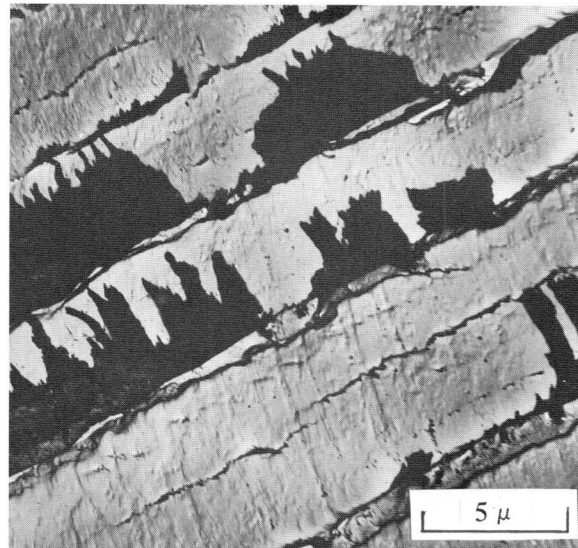

a

b

FIGURE 9 — Microcrack patterns produced in the tarnish on the failed bulk specimens in Mattsson's solution (pH 7.4): (a) short and discontinuous rows, (b) long and straight rows.

the mechanical properties of the surface film (crystal grain size, thickness, porosity, hardness and strength, etc.) play an important role in the propagation of stress corrosion cracks. In the intergranular cracking environment, a cuprous oxide film is first formed at the slip steps produced under stress. This cuprous oxide film consists of a thick tarnish layer which retards the development of the subsequent slip steps thereby hindering the development of micro-trenches. On the other hand, at a high-angle grain boundary where the formation of the oxide film is imperfect, slip steps can form more easily. The possibility of solute segregation also may enhance intergranular corrosion. On the other hand, a relatively weak oxide over the bulk grain promotes transgranular cracking.

On the basis of the role of the surface film mentioned above, the stress-strain curves in the corrosive environment can be explained as follows: In the intergranular cracking environment such as Mattsson's solution (pH 7.4) a thick tarnish layer of $Cu_2O$ that nucleated at the slip steps is formed and the progression of the subsequent slip steps is retarded. A larger stress in this environment is required than in the 1 M $NH_4OH$ + 1/4 M $CuCl_2$ aqueous solution in which the oxide film is scarcely formed and the specimens are generally corroded. On the other hand, in the transgranular cracking environment such as the 1 M $NH_4OH$ + 1/4 M $CuCl_2$ aqueous solution, the micro-corrosion products at the slip steps do not grow into the tarnish layer, and the corrosion proceeds along the slip planes with the progression of slip steps. The stress-strain curves, therefore, in this environment should show a small value from the early stage compared with that in Mattsson's solution (pH 7.4). In this case the micro-corrosion at the initial slip step itself would develop into cracks, resulting in transgranular cracking, and the time to failure becomes shorter than that in the intergranular cracking environment.

In the ammonia vapor in which transgranular cracking occurred a large stress was required at the early stage of the stress-strain curves. In the present experiment the stress-strain measurement was immediately started after the specimens were exposed to the ammonia vapor, so the condensation of the ammonia vapor on the specimen surface as a thin film of ammoniacal aqueous solution was insufficient at first. At a high strain rate of 1.1 x $10^{-3}$ $sec^{-1}$ in the ammonia vapor, therefore, the corrosive action becomes weak at the early stage of the stress-strain curves and only the mechanical action is predominant. The above mentioned phenomenon is seen clearly in Figure 3, in which the stress at the initial stage in the ammonia vapor is nearly equal to that in the air. However, when the ammonia vapor is condensed on the specimen surface the electrochemical corrosion starts in the surface. In this case according to Pugh and Westwood[6] the following autocatalytic reaction at the specimen surface takes place and the corrosion will be accelerated:

$$Cu(NH_3)_5^{2+} + Cu_{surface} \rightarrow 2Cu(NH_3)_2^+ +$$

$$NH_3 \xrightarrow[(O_2 + NH_3)]{} 2Cu(NH_3)_5^{2+}$$

Although in the ammonia vapor an induction period is required before the corrosion starts, once corrosion started, the concentration of $Cu(NH_3)_5^{2+}$ ions on the specimen surface increase and the corrosion at the active sites such as slip steps becomes very rapid. From the above-mentioned point of view, the behavior of the stress-strain curves and the load-time curves in the ammonia vapor differs from that in aqueous solutions.

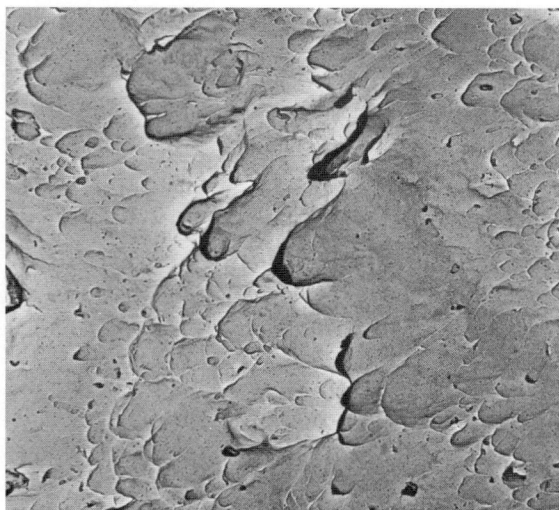

a

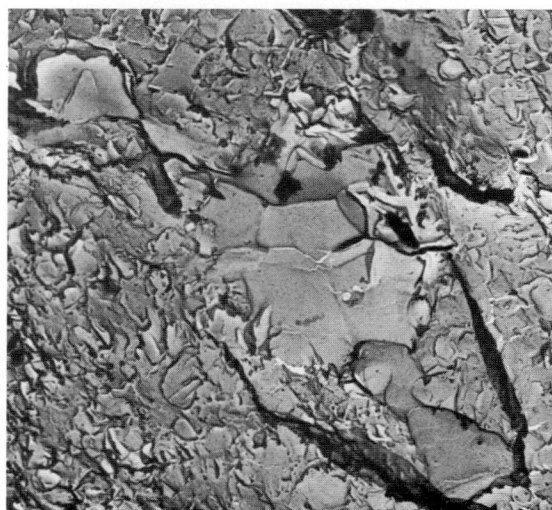

b

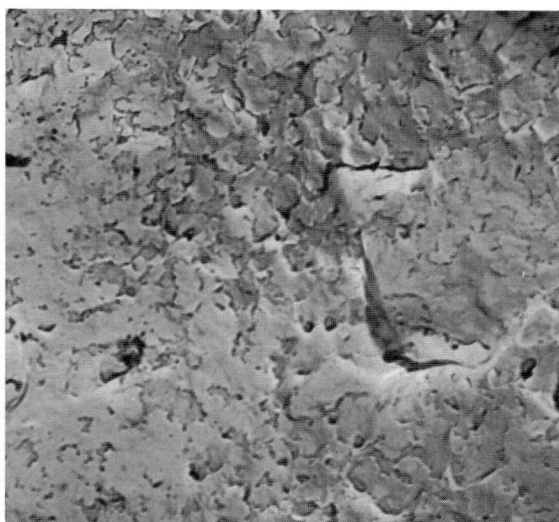

c

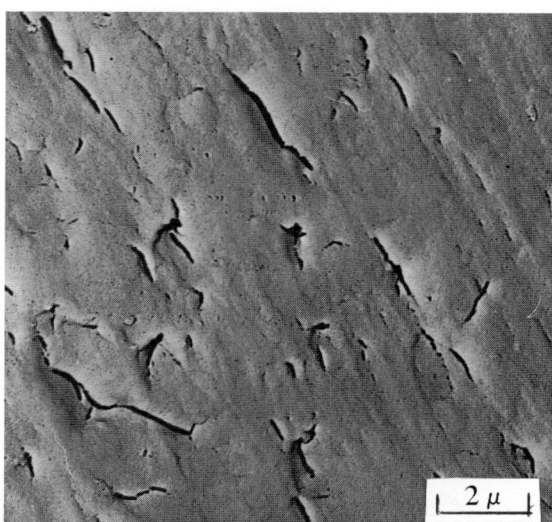

d

FIGURE 10 — Micro-fractographs of the failed bulk specimens: (a) $\dot{\epsilon}$, 1.1 x $10^{-3}$ $sec^{-1}$ in air, (b) $\dot{\epsilon}$, 1.1 x $10^{-3}$ $sec^{-1}$ in Mattsson's solution (pH 7.4), (c) 66% $\sigma_T$ in Mattsson's solution (pH 7.4), (d) $\dot{\epsilon}$, 5.5 x $10^{-5}$ $sec^{-1}$ in Mattsson's solution (pH 7.4).

At a high strain rate the strain required to cause failure increased twice as much as that at a low strain rate, as shown in Figures 3 and 4. Under the constant load test of 66% $\sigma_T$ the specimen was also subjected to large deformation. Thus, at a high strain rate or a high constant load the fractographs show an appearance similar to the mechanical failure. The slip lines on the specimens surface failed in Mattsson's solution (pH 7.4) are shown clearly in Figures 7 and 8.

From the present results it is suggested that the mechanism of stress corrosion cracking depends on the strain rate or the load. It has been observed under a high strain rate and constant load that the propagation of cracking occurs due to an alternate progression of corrosion and mechanical fractures or a mechanical fracture which is accelerated by the lowering of surface energy of alloys as a result of the adsorption of the corrosive substances. On the other hand, under a small strain rate or a low constant load the stress corrosion cracking is caused by a mechano-chemical reaction, in which the slip steps produced under stress act as the chemically active sites and local penetration of corrosion is accelerated. In this case the stress corrosion cracking can be regarded morphologically as a sort o pitting.

## V. Conclusions

1. Stress corrosion. micro-trenches in the brass-corrosive system are independent of the stress corrosion cracking susceptibility, and initiate predominantly at the

210

slip steps in all cases.

2. Under the condition susceptible to intergranular cracking, a thick cuprous oxide film is developed on the surface of brass. The surface film interferes with the subsequent development of slip steps in the grains. In the grain boundaries the slips can occur easily under stress, and therefore the grain boundaries become chemically active and the corrosion penetrates along these boundaries, resulting in intergranular cracking.

3. The transition from transgranular to intergranular cracking depends on the mechanical properties of the surface film produced in the corrosive environment.

4. Stress-strain curves in the brass-ammonia system can be explained in terms of the surface-film theory.

5. Stress corrosion cracking should be explained by a different mechanism based on the magnitude of stress or strain rate.

## References

1. M. Takano and S. Shimodaira. *J. Japan Inst. Metals*, **29**, 553 (1965).
2. M. Takano and S. Shimodaira. *Trans. Japan Inst. Metals*, **7**, 186 (1966).
3. M. Takano and S. Shimodaira. *Trans. Japan Inst. Metals*, **7**, 193 (1966).
4. E. Mattsson. *Electrochimica Acta*, **3**, 279 (1961).
5. W. Lynes. *Corrosion*, **21**, 125 (1965).
6. E. N. Pugh and A. R. C. Westwood. *Phil. Mag.*, **13**, 167 (1966).
7. H. E. Johnson and J. Leja. *Corrosion*, **22**, 178 (1966).
8. M. E. Whitaker. *Metallurgia*, p. 21, p. 66 (1948) November, December.
9. A. K. Lahiri and T. Banerjee. *Corrosion Science*, **5**, 731 (1965).
10. P. R. Swann. *Corrosion*, **19**, 102 (1965).
11. W. D. Robertson and A. S. Tetelman. *Strengthening Mechanism in Solid*, ASM, Ohio, p. 217 (1960).
12. Y. Murakami, H. Yoshida and Y. Ikai. *J. Japan Inst. Metals*, **29**, 1215 (1965).
13. W. Lynes. *Corrosion*, **22**, 113 (1966).
14. F. C. Althof. *Z. Metallk.*, **36**, 177 (1944).
15. T. A. Read, J. B. Reed and H. Rosenthal. *Symposium on the Stress Corrosion Cracking of Metals*, ASTM (1944).
16. H. L. Logan. *J. Res. Nat. Bur. Stand.*, **48**, 99 (1952).
17. A. J. Forty and P. Humble. *Phil. Mag.*, **8**, 247 (1963).
18. A. J. McEvily and A. P. Bond. *J. Electrochem. Soc.*, **112**, 131 (1965).
19. D. Tromans and J. Nutting. *Corrosion*, **21**, 143 (1965).
20. A. Ronnquist. *Third International Congress on Metallic Corrosion*, Moscow, p. 151 (1966).
21. M. Takano, K. Hashimoto, W. Suetaka and S. Shimodaira. *J. Japan Inst. Metals*, **28**, 237 (1964).
22. M. Takano and S. Shimodaira. *Corrosion Science*, **8**, 55 (1968).
23. H. W. Pickering and P. R. Swann. *Corrosion*, **19**, 373 (1963).
24. T. P. Hoar and C. J. L. Booker. *Corrosion Science*, **5**, 821 (1965).

## Discussion

**R. W. Staehle, Ohio State University:**

It is my understanding that intergranular stress corrosion cracking of the brasses exposed to ammonia solutions occurs only under film-forming conditions. According to your model what are the essential criteria for shifts between the intergranular and transgranular cracking modes?

**S. Shimodaira:**

The intergranular cracking will occur when the surface film is physically and electrochemically stable at a certain slip rate, but the cracking will be transgranular when the surface film is not stable.

**R. W. Staehle:**

You suggest that some type of surface film exists in all cases?

**S. Shimodaira:**

Yes. The surface films are always formed in the stress corrosion cracking.

**R. W. Staehle:**

Then you conclude that a weak film permits transgranular cracking and a strong film promotes intergranular cracking?

**S. Shimodaira:**

The stability of the surface films are determined by alloy elements, strain rates and corrosive environments. The surface films will become relatively unstable with the increase of strain rates, and the transgranular cracking will occur even if the intergranular cracking occurs at low strain rates.

**E. N. Pugh, Research Institute for Advanced Studies:**

I think that you may be overlooking the role of dislocation structure—which is dependent largely on alloy composition—in determining the path of cracking.

**S. Shimodaira:**

The distribution of dislocations in the alloys are closely related to the modes of slip processes. Freshly produced slip steps are very important because they are the origin of active sites. But the stress corrosion cracking is essentially a sort of corrosion and the nature of the surface films, especially the repassivation of the activated sites of slip steps in the surface films, will determine the processes of the stress corrosion cracking. If you change the alloy elements or the corrosive environments, you will find the change in the nature of the surface films. The surface films are the most important factor in the stress corrosion cracking.

# PART III

# HOMOGENEOUS IRON-CHROMIUM-NICKEL ALLOYS

# EVALUATION OF SESSION ON AUSTENITIC Fe, Cr, AND Ni ALLOYS

D. L. Douglass and D. van Rooyen

The mechanism of SCC in austenitic alloys appears as garbled now as it did before the meeting. The bulk of the work presented concerned the physical metallurgical aspect of SCC with much emphasis on the role of dislocation substructure. It is not clear from the presentations as to where we stand on this subject. There was some evidence that dislocations play a predominant role, but there was some conflicting evidence that there is little or no effect.

There was an attempt to answer the question of specificity in terms of complexes formed during the general corrosion process followed by selective adsorption. The evidence for this analysis is still lacking, however, and such an analysis must still be considered as speculative.

The electrochemical aspects of SCC were conspicuous by their absence. The thermodynamic treatment of the electrochemistry of lattice disarray appears to offer an interesting approach but needs experimental verification.

There is a need for more cross fertilization of ideas and work between the metal physicists and the electrochemists. An obvious deficiency is that one group tends to ignore the other in that either one or the other aspect of SCC is studied but not both on the same material. Critical experiments must be designed to prove or disprove the film-rupture theory, the adsorption theory, or the surface enrichment theory.

The one unambiguous conclusion was that there does not appear to be one unifying theory of SCC in austenitic alloys (or any other alloys) and that there will never be a concensus. Further attempts to formulate such a unified theory will be futile and should be abandoned.

# STRESS CORROSION CRACKING OF IRON–NICKEL–CHROMIUM ALLOYS

R. M. Latanision and R. W. Staehle
The Ohio State University

## I. Introduction

This review considers stress corrosion cracking in iron-nickel-chromium alloys in aqueous environments. The important commercial alloys in this alloy system are the stainless steels, Incoloys, and Inconels; nominal compositions of specific alloys are summarized in Table 1. Some of these alloys are shown with reference to the ternary Fe-Ni-Cr phase diagram in Figure 1. Most of the research as well as manufacture of economical commercial alloys has been concerned with alloys containing less than 40% chromium; therefore, the discussion will be limited to that region of compositions.

The Fe-Ni-Cr alloys have performed satisfactorily in many applications and the emphasis in this article on susceptibility to stress corrosion cracking should be considered only in the context of the limited and specific environments which cause cracking.

Commercial manifestations of stress corrosion cracking in Fe-Ni-Cr alloys are shown in Figures 2-4. Figure 5 compares fracture strengths of Type 304 stainless steel tested under various conditions of tensile loading, stress rupture, fatigue, neutron irradiation, cold work and stress corrosion cracking. Clearly, the stress corrosion cracking situation is the most debilitating of the various engineering load situations.

There are four important classes of stainless steels:

(1) **Martensitic:** Iron-chromium alloys which are hardenable by heat treatment and contain chromium in the approximate range of 11 to 18%.

(2) **Ferritic:** Iron-chromium alloys which are not hardenable by heat treatment and contain chromium in the approximate range of 15 to 30%.

(3) **Austenitic:** Iron-nickel-chromium alloys which are hardened by cold working and are predominantly face centered cubic. These alloys contain generally 6-22% nickel and 16-26% chromium.

(4) **Precipitation Hardening:** Iron-nickel-chromium alloys which are hardened additionally by precipitation hardening.

In addition to the above there are the Incoloys and Inconels which are austenitic or face centered cubic alloys. These two categories are distinguished by the former containing nickel in the range of 30 to 50% and the latter being the higher nickel alloys. The various classes of alloys above exhibit different susceptibilities to cracking in various environments.

Considered herein will be brief descriptions of the physical metallurgy and electrochemistry relevant to the subject of stress corrosion cracking. The general phenomenon of intergranular corrosion without stress will not be considered since it has been reviewed elsewhere[3] and since the mode of penetration is different from that of stress corrosion cracking. Stress corrosion cracking of iron-nickel-chromium alloys in chloride, caustic, oxygenated, and miscellaneous environments will be discussed in this review. Case histories are not discussed in this review because they add nothing in particular to the understanding of the mechanistic aspects of cracking; also Reference 4 already provides an excellent summary of case histories.

## II. Physical Metallurgy

Detailed discussions of the properties of iron-nickel-chromium alloys are given in a number of texts[5-9] and only those properties of particular interest to stress corrosion cracking will be discussed in this section.

### A. Phase Fields and Alloy Composition

**1. Austenite and Austenitic Stability.** The three binary phase diagrams[10] and ternary isotherms at 800 and 1100 C for the Fe-Ni-Cr ternary system are given in Figures 6 and 7. The ternary diagram at 400 C was given in Figure 1.

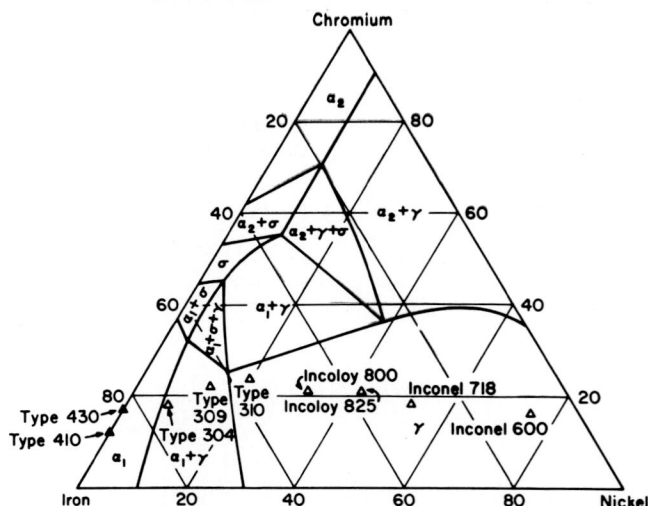

FIGURE 1 – Isotherm of iron-nickel-chromium alloy system at 400 C (Pugh and Nisbet[1]).

TABLE 1—Chemical Composition Limits and Ranges for Stainless Steels (Weight Percentages)

| Designation or Type Number | C | Mn Max. | Si Max. | P Max. | S Max. | Cr | Ni | Other Elements |
|---|---|---|---|---|---|---|---|---|
| **I. Martensitic Chromium Steels** | | | | | | | | |
| 403 | 0.15 Max. | 1.00 | 0.50 | 0.040 | 0.030 | 11.50-13.00 | | |
| 410 | 0.15 Max. | 1.00 | 1.00 | 0.040 | 0.030 | 11.50-13.50 | | |
| 414 | 0.15 Max. | 1.00 | 1.00 | 0.040 | 0.030 | 11.50-13.50 | 1.25-2.50 | |
| 416 | 0.15 Max. | 1.25 | 1.00 | 0.06 | 0.15 Min. | 12.00-14.00 | | Mo:0.60 Max. |
| 416 Se | 0.15 Max. | 1.25 | 1.00 | 0.06 | 0.06 | 12.00-14.00 | | Se:0.15 Min. |
| 420 | Over 0.15 | 1.00 | 1.00 | 0.040 | 0.030 | 12.00-14.00 | | |
| 431 | 0.20 Max. | 1.00 | 1.00 | 0.040 | 0.030 | 15.00-17.00 | 1.25-2.50 | |
| 440A | 0.60-0.75 | 1.00 | 1.00 | 0.040 | 0.030 | 16.00-18.00 | | Mo:0.75 Max. |
| 440B | 0.75-0.95 | 1.00 | 1.00 | 0.040 | 0.030 | 16.00-18.00 | | Mo:0.75 Max. |
| 440C | 0.95-1.20 | 1.00 | 1.00 | 0.040 | 0.030 | 16.00-18.00 | | Mo:0.75 Max. |
| 501 | Over 0.10 | 1.00 | 1.00 | 0.040 | 0.030 | 4.00-6.00 | | Mo:0.40-0.65 |
| 502 | 0.10 Max. | 1.00 | 1.00 | 0.040 | 0.030 | 4.00-6.00 | | Mo:0.40-0.65 |
| **II. Ferritic Chromium Steels** | | | | | | | | |
| 405 | 0.08 Max. | 1.00 | 1.00 | 0.040 | 0.030 | 11.50-14.50 | | Al:0.10-0.30 |
| 430 | 0.12 Max. | 1.00 | 1.00 | 0.040 | 0.030 | 14.00-18.00 | | |
| 430F | 0.12 Max. | 1.25 | 1.00 | 0.06 | 0.15 Min. | 14.00-18.00 | | Mo:0.60 Max. |
| 430F Se | 0.12 Max. | 1.25 | 1.00 | 0.06 | 0.06 | 14.00-18.00 | | Se:0.15 Min. |
| 446 | 0.20 Max. | 1.50 | 1.00 | 0.040 | 0.030 | 23.00-27.00 | | N:0.25 Max. |
| **III. Austenitic Chromium-Nickel Steels** | | | | | | | | |
| 201 | 0.15 Max. | 5.50-7.50 | 1.00 | 0.060 | 0.030 | 16.00-18.00 | 3.50-5.50 | N:0.25 Max. |
| 202 | 0.15 Max. | 7.50-10.00 | 1.00 | 0.060 | 0.030 | 17.00-19.00 | 4.00-6.00 | N:0.25 Max. |
| 301 | 0.15 Max. | 2.00 | 1.00 | 0.045 | 0.030 | 16.00-18.00 | 6.00-8.00 | |
| 302 | 0.15 Max. | 2.00 | 1.00 | 0.045 | 0.030 | 17.00-19.00 | 8.00-10.00 | |
| 302B | 0.15 Max. | 2.00 | 2.00-3.00 | 0.045 | 0.030 | 17.00-19.00 | 8.00-10.00 | |
| 303 | 0.15 Max. | 2.00 | 1.00 | 0.20 | 0.15 Min. | 17.00-19.00 | 8.00-10.00 | Mo:0.60 Max. |
| 303 Se | 0.15 Max. | 2.00 | 1.00 | 0.20 | 0.06 | 17.00-19.00 | 8.00-10.00 | Se:0.15 Min. |
| 304 | 0.08 Max. | 2.00 | 1.00 | 0.045 | 0.030 | 18.00-20.00 | 8.00-12.00 | |
| 304L | 0.03 Max. | 2.00 | 1.00 | 0.045 | 0.030 | 18.00-20.00 | 8.00-12.00 | |
| 305 | 0.12 Max. | 2.00 | 1.00 | 0.045 | 0.030 | 17.00-19.00 | 10.00-13.00 | |
| 308 | 0.08 Max. | 2.00 | 1.00 | 0.045 | 0.030 | 19.00-21.00 | 10.00-12.00 | |
| 309 | .20 Max. | 2.00 | 1.00 | .045 | .030 | 22.00-24.00 | 12.00-15.00 | |
| 309S | .08 Max. | 2.00 | 1.00 | .045 | .030 | 22.00-24.00 | 12.00-15.00 | |
| 310 | .25 Max. | 2.00 | 1.50 | .045 | .030 | 24.00-26.00 | 19.00-22.00 | |
| 310S | .08 Max. | 2.00 | 1.50 | .045 | .030 | 24.00-26.00 | 19.00-22.00 | |
| 314 | .25 Max. | 2.00 | 1.50-3.00 | .045 | .030 | 23.00-26.00 | 19.00-22.00 | Mo:2.00-3.00 |
| 316 | .08 Max. | 2.00 | 1.00 | .045 | .030 | 16.00-18.00 | 10.00-14.00 | Mo:2.00-3.00 |
| 316L | .03 Max. | 2.00 | 1.00 | .045 | .030 | 16.00-18.00 | 10.00-14.00 | Mo:3.00-4.00 |
| 317 | .08 Max. | 2.00 | 1.00 | .045 | .030 | 18.00-20.00 | 11.00-15.00 | Ti:5 x C, Min. |
| 321 | .08 Max. | 2.00 | 1.00 | .045 | .030 | 17.00-19.00 | 9.00-12.00 | Cb-Ta:10 x C, Min. |
| 347 | .08 Max. | 2.00 | 1.00 | .045 | .030 | 17.00-19.00 | 9.00-13.00 | Cb-Ta:10 x C, Min., |
| 348 | .08 Max. | 2.00 | 1.00 | .045 | .030 | 17.00-19.00 | 9.00-13.00 | Ta:0.10 Max., Co:0.20 Max. |

TABLE 1 (cont'd.)

| Designation or Type Number | C | Mn Max. | Si Max. | P Max. | S Max. | Cr | Ni | Other Elements |
|---|---|---|---|---|---|---|---|---|
| **IV. Precipitation Hardening Stainless Steels** | | | | | | | | |
| PH 15-7 Mo | .07 Max. | .70 | .40 | | | 15.00 | 7.00 | 1.15Al, 2.25Mo |
| 17-4 PH | .04 Max. | .40 | .50 | | | 16.50 | 4.25 | .25Cb, 3.6Cu |
| 17-7 PH | .07 Max. | .70 | .40 | | | 17.00 | 7.00 | 1.15Al |
| AM-350 | .10 Max. | .75 | .35 | | | 16.50 | 4.25 | 2.75Mo, 0.10N |
| AM-355 | .13 Max. | .85 | .35 | | | 15.50 | 4.25 | 2.75Mo, 0.12N |
| **V. Others** | | | | | | | | |
| Inconel | | | | | | | | |
| 600 | .04 Max. | .20 | .20 | | .007 | 15.8 | 76.0 | 7.20Fe |
| 625 | .05 Max. | .15 | .30 | | .007 | 22.0 | 61.0 | 3Fe, 4Cb, 9Mo |
| 718 | .04 Max. | .20 | .20 | | .007 | 19.0 | 52.5 | 18.0Fe, .60Al, .80Ti, 5.2Cb, 3Mo |
| X750 | .04 Max. | .70 | .30 | | .007 | 15.0 | 73.0 | 6.75Fe, .80Al, 2.50Ti, 0.85Cb |
| Incoloy | | | | | | | | |
| 800 | .04 Max. | .75 | .35 | | .007 | 20.5 | 32.0 | 46.0Fe, .30Cu |
| 804 | .06 Max. | .9 | | | .007 | 29 | 43.7 | 24.50Fe, .40Cu |
| 825 | .03 Max. | .65 | .35 | | .007 | 21.5 | 41.8 | 30Fe, 1.80Cu, 0.15Al, 0.90Ti, 3.0Mo |
| Nimonic | | | | | | | | |
| 75 | .10 Max. | .45 | .45 | | .007 | 20.5 | 77.6 | 0.50Fe, .20Al, .35Ti |
| Tenelon | .08 Max. | 14.70 | .52 | .025 | .006 | 18.0 | | .13Mo, .11Cu, 40N |
| Croloy | | | | | | | | |
| 16-1 | .03 Max. | | | | | 16.75 | 1.09 | 1.51Mo, .90Cu |
| Carpenter | | | | | | | | |
| 20 | .07 | .7 | | | | 20.0 | 29 | 2.00Mo, 3.00Cu |
| 7 Mo[1] | .20 | 1.0 | | | | 23-28 | 2.5-5 | 1-2Mo |
| CD4MCu | .04 | 1.0 | | | | 25-27 | 4.7-6.0 | 1.75-2.25Mo, 2.75-3.25 Cu |

[1]Carpenter 7 Mo is Type 329.

Of special interest are the single phase $a$-Fe (ferritic) and $\gamma$-Ni (austenitic) regions and the two phase $a$-$\gamma$ region. The $\gamma \rightarrow a$ transformation is very sluggish with the result that the nominally two phase ($a + \gamma$) alloys are generally single phase unless the alloy is deformed or unless certain gamma stabilizing impurity elements (such as N, C) are absent. Carbon, nitrogen, manganese, cobalt, nickel, and copper contribute to the stability of austenite; chromium, tungsten, tantalum, molybdenum, columbium, silicon, titanium, vanadium, and aluminum stabilize the ferrite. The amount of nickel necessary to maintain a stable austenitic structure with respect to the presence of other ferrite or austenite stabilizers has been quantified in an euqation by Post and Eberly[11] as follows:

$$Ni = \frac{(Cr + 1.5 Mo - 20)^2}{12} - \frac{Mn}{2} - 35 C + 15$$

This equation is valid for the following range of compositions:

| Element | Range of Composition (%) |
|---|---|
| C | 0.03 - 0.20 |
| Mn | 0.4 - 4.0 |
| Si | 0.30 - 0.50 |
| Cr | 14.0 - 25 |
| Ni | 7.5 - 21 |
| Mo | 0.1 - 3 |

Nitrogen is a very potent stabilizing element. It lowers the Fe-N eutectoid to 590 C at 2.35 weight percent compared with 723 C and 0.80 weight percent for carbon.[12] The effect of nickel on stabilizing austenite is shown in Figures 6 and 7. This element lowers the

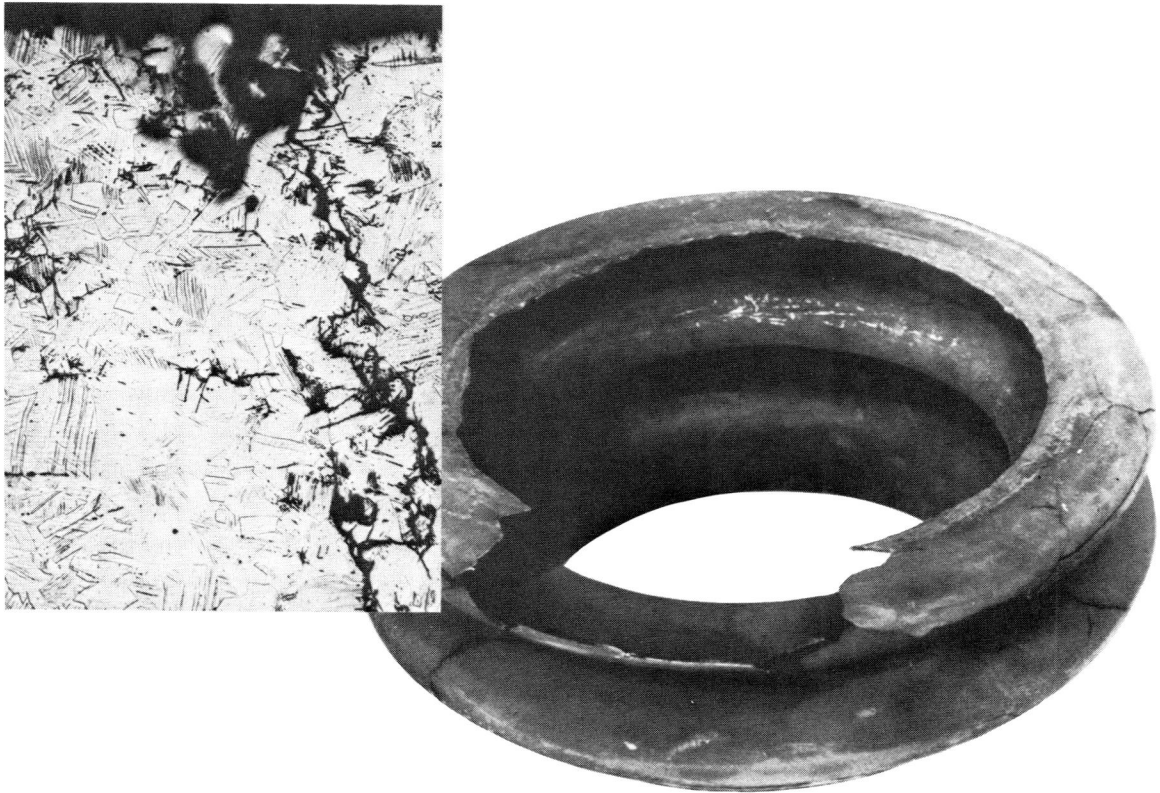

FIGURE 2 — Cold formed stainless steel bellows exposed to gaseous environment containing trace chlorides
No stresses present except those due to forming.

FIGURE 3 — Intergranular stress corrosion crack from nonsensitized stainless steel cladding of uranium-containing fuel
pin. External environment contained less than 1 ppm chloride and less than 5 ppm oxygen.[2]

FIGURE 4 — Stainless steel autoclave cracked on the bottom
due to chlorides from tap water used as
coolant.

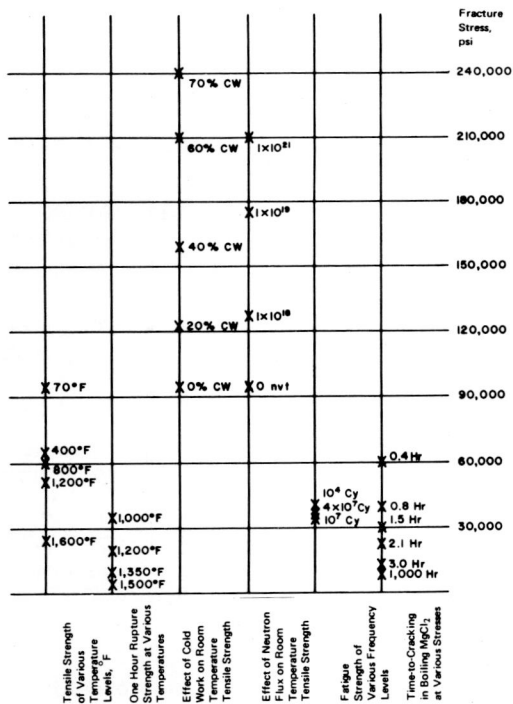

| | | | | | | Fracture Stress, psi |
|---|---|---|---|---|---|---|
| | 70% CW | | | | | 240,000 |
| | 60% CW | 1×10²¹ | | | | 210,000 |
| | | 1×10¹⁹ | | | | 180,000 |
| | 40% CW | | | | | 150,000 |
| | 20% CW | 1×10¹⁸ | | | | 120,000 |
| 70°F | 0% CW | 0 nvt | | | | 90,000 |
| 400°F | | | | | 0.4 Hr | 60,000 |
| 800°F | | | | 10⁴ Cy | | |
| 1,200°F | | | | 4×10⁷Cy | 0.8 Hr | 30,000 |
| 1,000°F | | | | 10⁷ Cy | 1.5 Hr | |
| 1,600°F | | | | | 2.1 Hr | |
| | 1,200°F | | | | 3.0 Hr | |
| | 1,350°F | | | | 1,000 Hr | |
| | 1,500°F | | | | | |

Tensile Strength of Various Temperature Levels, °F — One Hour Rupture Strength at Various Temperatures — Effect of Cold Work on Room Temperature Tensile Strength — Effect of Neutron Flux on Room Temperature Tensile Strength — Fatigue Strength of Various Frequency Levels — Time-to-Cracking in Boiling MgCl₂ at Various Stresses

FIGURE 5 — Comparison of fracture strengths for Type 304
stainless steel tested under various conditions
of loading, metallurgical structure, and environment.

$\gamma \rightarrow \gamma + a$ boundary significantly. The Fe-Mn diagram shows that Mn is slightly more potent than nickel in lowering the same transformation line.[12] The combined effect of manganese and nitrogen on the stability of austenite is shown in Figure 8 from work by Carney.[13] Carney also showed that the addition of 3% nickel to the alloys of Figure 8 raised the 0.25% nitrogen line from about 16 to about 18% Cr.

The final structures of alloys in this system are greatly affected by cooling rate and impurities. Figure 9 shows a pseudo binary diagram for an Fe-18Cr-8Ni base to which carbon is added.[14] The diagram indicates that both ferrite and carbide are stable at room temperature for a stainless steel having the normal carbon content (0.05-0.08%). However, rapid cooling from 1050-1100 C prevents the formation of both carbide and ferrite. Figure 10 shows approximate ranges of metastability and stability for the important phases.[15] It is clear from comparing this figure with Figure 1 that several of the normally "stable" stainless steels are not stable at room temperature.

Owing to the condition of metastability in which most common austenitic stainless steels exist, they tend to transform to martensite during plastic deformation or cooling below room temperature. Since the degree of decomposition of the austenite is related to its stability, the extent of transformation will be retarded by increased concentration of austenite stabilizing elements and by

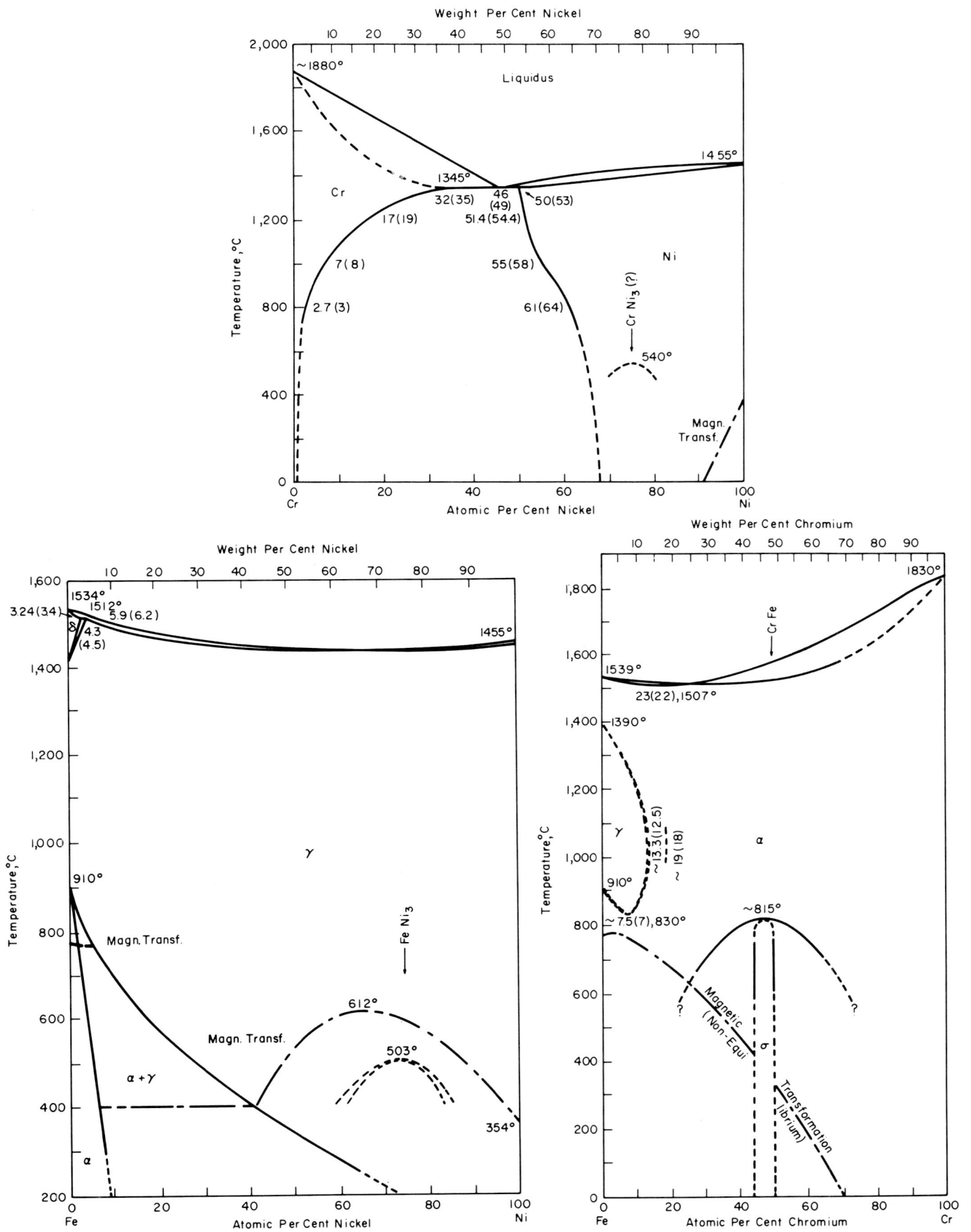

FIGURE 6 — Binary phase diagrams for the Fe-Ni, Fe-Cr, Cr-Ni systems (Hansen[10]).

219

FIGURE 7 — Ternary phase diagrams at 800 and 1100 C (Pugh and Nisbet[1]).

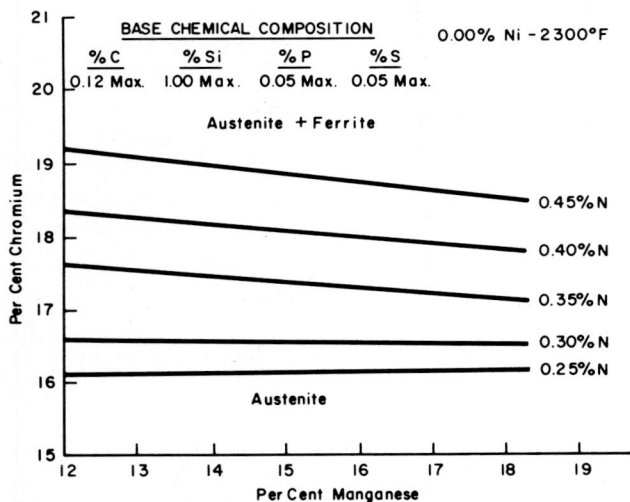

FIGURE 8 — Effect of manganese and nitrogen on the stability of Fe-Cr base alloys. Based on heating at 1260 C for one hour and quenching (Carney[13]).

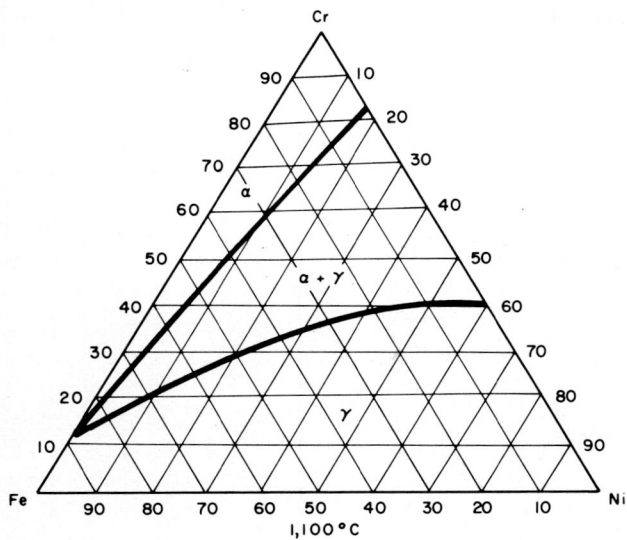

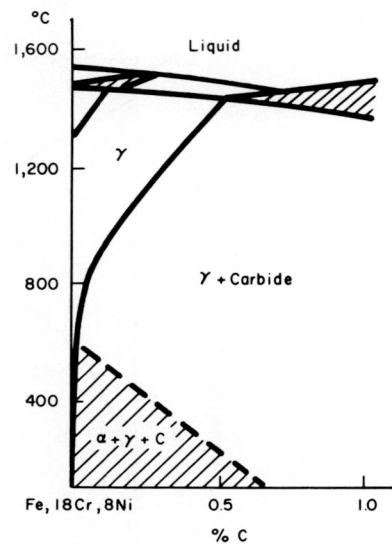

FIGURE 9 — Pseudo binary phase diagram for a Fe + 18Cr + 8Ni base with varying carbon concentration (Brick and Phillips[14]).

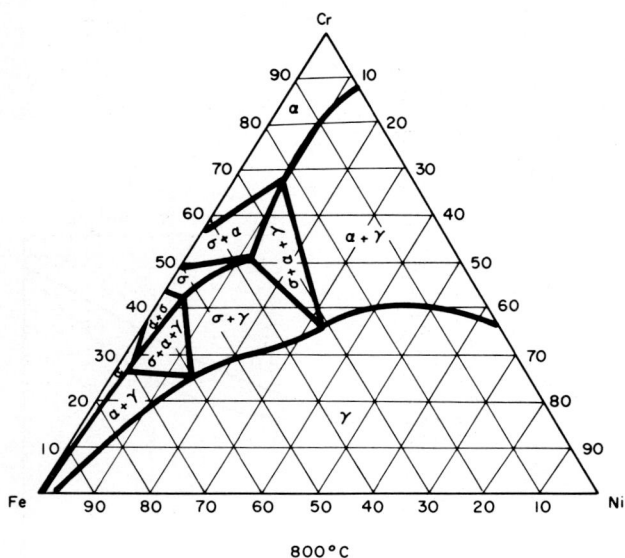

$A_M$ = Metastable Austenite

$A_S$ = Stable Austenite

F = Ferrite (from Austenite)

$F_D$ = Delta (High-Temperature) Ferrite

M = Acicular (Martensitic) Structure

C = Carbide

P = Pearlite

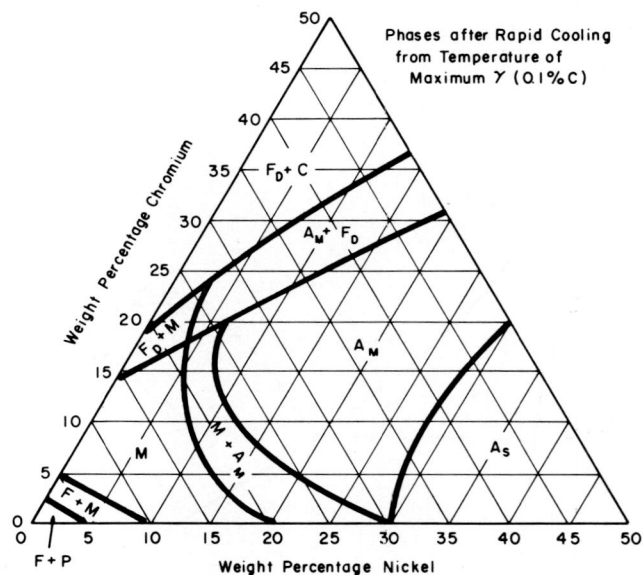

FIGURE 10 — Phases after rapid cooling from temperature of maximum gamma (0.1 percent carbon) (Metals Handbook[15]).

220

performing plastic deformation at relatively higher temperatures. Stainless steels containing nickel in the 7-10% range harden rapidly upon plastic deformation not only as a result of strain hardening but also as a result of the strain induced transformation of metastable austenite. These simultaneous hardening processes tend to make cold fabrication and machining more difficult and also will have significance with respect to slip step emergence at the surface—a factor of direct significance in cracking mechanisms to be discussed later.

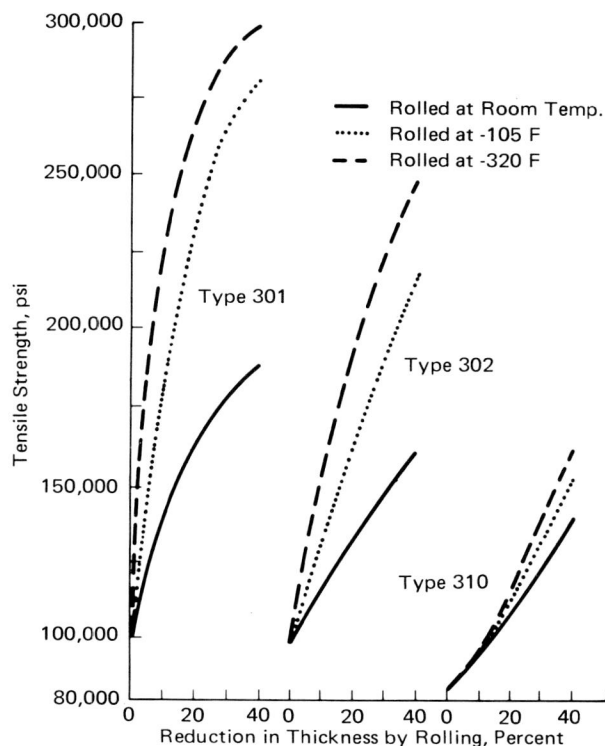

FIGURE 11 — Effect of rolling temperature on tensile strength of Types 301, 302, and 310 stainless steel (Krivobak and Talbot[16]).

Figure 11 summarizes the effect of cold rolling temperature, amount of plastic deformation, and alloy type on the hardening increment due to martensite formation.[16] Clearly the 310 stainless steel (containing 19-22% Ni) is on the verge of being completely stable. An Fe-16Cr-20Ni alloy is completely stable to very low temperatures with $M_s$ = 4°K and $M_d$ = 77°K.[17] Douglass et al have obtained evidence of martensitic transformation in Type 310 stainless steel after 50% cold rolling followed by annealing.[18]

The transformation from austenite to ferrite has been studied in a number of investigations which have considered temperature, alloy composition, degree of mechanical deformation, strain rate and neutron radiation. According to these studies the austenite-martensite transformation proceeds according to the following sequence:[19] The deformation and/or cooling of the fcc austenite results in the formation of stacking faults; the stacking faults then transform to a hexagonal epsilon phase. At the intersection of the ribbons of epsilon, nuclei of martensite are formed which then grow as the deformation and/or cooling continues.

A further indication of the metastability of the single phase produced, as discussed earlier by quenching from 1050 C, is that carbides will precipitate from the supersaturated austenite if given the opportunity by heating in the range 500-800 C. The most damaging effects of carbide precipitation are apparent in a susceptibility to intergranular corrosion, and also in a decreased ductility, particularly notch ductility.

**2. Sigma Phase.** In addition to phases already discussed Cr-Ni stainless steels contain varying quantities of sigma phase. Sigma has a distorted complex tetragonal space lattice (a = 8.799 Å, C = 4.544 Å)[20] which is extremely brittle. In the austenitic stainless steels, sigma may form on exposing the alloys between 565 and 925 C. In Fe-Ni-Cr alloys changes toward equilibrium in this temperature range occur at a very slow rate. Indeed, Rees and coworkers[21] were not convinced that equilibrium conditions were reached in alloys heated in this range for periods of 100 to 200 days.[21] This increased sluggishness undoubtedly explains why sigma is rarely found in austenitic stainless steels which are used at temperatures below 565 C. The equilibrium relations of the sigma phase in these alloys are shown in Figures 1, 6, and 7. The locations of a number of common Cr-Ni stainless steels shows that sigma is often a stable microconstituent. However, it should be remembered that the phase limits are shifted by most of the alloying elements present in the steels. Thus, many of the borderline compositions never exhibit sigma formation even on long time exposures within the range 565-925 C. On the other hand some alloying elements enhance sigma formation with the ferrite stabilizing elements, particularly Mo and Si, being especially effective. These elements lower the chromium range in which sigma precipitation occurs. Thus 18-8 compositions alloyed with Mo or Si are susceptible to sigma formation. It is unlikely that the 15Cr-35Ni alloy lying deep in the austenitic region will ever be embrittled by sigma precipitation. These elements also increase considerably the rate of transformation. A 20Cr-10Ni-3Mo stainless steel may exhibit some sigma even on air cooling through the temperature range in which sigma forms.

**3. Delta Ferrite.** Finally, as shown in the preceding ternary diagrams, equilibrium cooling of alloys containing Cr-Ni compositions found in commercial austenitic stainless steels produces duplex ferrite-austenite microstructures. Quenching many Fe-Cr-Ni alloys from the austenite region will retain the high temperature delta-ferrite as indicated in Figure 10. In more highly alloyed steels, such as 18-8-3 Mo, the delta transformation to austenite is only partly arrested by quenching and austenite may form at the grain boundaries of the parent delta phase.

*B. Mechanical Properties*

The mechanical properties of commercial Fe-Ni-Cr alloys are generally well known and are readily available.[23-26] Typical values for the tensile properties of

221

some of these alloys are presented in Table 2.[27] High ductility and rapid work hardening are characteristic of austenitic alloys.

The effect of alloy composition on the room temperature tensile properties of austenitic Fe-Ni-Cr alloys is summarized in Figure 12[28] where it is shown that the chromium addition is the most potent strengthening agent of the three major constituents. The effect of temperature on the tensile strength of selected high purity alloys from the same study as Figure 12 is shown in Figure 13.

## III. Chemical Properties

A characteristic feature of stress corrosion cracking is the specificity of environment-metal combinations which are susceptible to cracking. This section will describe important aspects of thermodynamics and kinetics which are relevant to interpreting the effect of environment and metal chemistry.

### A. Thermodynamic Data

With respect to interpreting stress corrosion cracking it is instructive to categorize the data of aqueous thermodynamics into metallic dissolution and environmental reduction processes. The processes of metallic dissolution and the relationship to potential and pH have been conveniently and clearly summarized by Pourbaix[29] in his potential-pH diagrams which for iron, nickel, and chromium are shown in Figure 14. These diagrams apply strictly only to equilibrium properties of the pure elements. However, they can be reasonably applied to the dissolution processes of alloys in that the dissolution of nickel from a Fe-Ni-Cr alloy would not be expected at a potential appreciably below that of the standard reduction potential for the $Ni^{++} + 2e \rightleftharpoons Ni$ equilibrium. These diagrams also apply strictly at room temperature having been evaluated only at 25 C; however, the relative values of the equilibria may be taken as applying over a wide range of temperature. A final limitation, but most significant, is that imposed by the effect of anions such as chloride which tend to render otherwise protective corrosion products nonprotective.

Despite the above limitations there are a number of important conclusions which can be obtained from a study and comparison of the diagrams of Figure 14:

1. At potentials more active than that for chromium oxidation no metal dissolution will occur; at potentials above that for nickel oxidation all three alloy elements will dissolve; and at potentials between the standard reduction potentials of nickel and iron both iron and chromium will be oxidized but nickel will not. These trends may be especially significant in the chloride stress corrosion cracking.

2. In the general region of neutral and alkaline pH, film formation processes may be significant if the chloride concentration is low.

3. At high pH the dihypoferrite and dinickelite ions are formed. These are probably significant with respect to caustic cracking. It should be noted particularly that at room temperature and in deaerated solutions of high pH iron is oxidized significantly but nickel is not.

Equally important as the metal dissolution equilibria are those involving reduction of environmental species such as hydrogen ions, dissolved oxygen, ferric ions and others. Again, these equilibria are summarized by Pourbaix.[29] Table 3 summarizes reduction equilibria for species of significance to stress corrosion cracking of Fe-Ni-Cr alloys.

### B. Electrode Kinetic Process

Since the progress of cracking involves such complicating factors as crevice geometries, transient processes

**TABLE 2—Some Properties of Typical Stainless Steels (After Guy[27])**

| Type | Grade | Condition | C | Cr | Ni | Other Elements | Yield Strength $10^3$ psi | Tensile Strength $10^3$ psi | % Elongation in 2 Inches |
|------|-------|-----------|---|----|----|----------------|----------------|-----------------|---------------|
| Martensitic | 420 | Annealed | 0.15+ | 13 | | | 65 | 100 | 30 |
| | 420 | Heat-treated | | | | | 120-200 | 150-300 | 12-2 |
| Ferritic | 405 | Annealed | 0.08- | 13 | | 0.2Al | 35 | 60 | 20 |
| | 446 | Annealed | 0.35- | 25 | | | 60 | 85 | 25 |
| Austenitic | 301 | Annealed | 0.15 | 17 | 7 | | 40 | 120 | 80 |
| | 301 | Work-hardened | | | | | 50-175 | 130-200 | 60-10 |
| | 304 | Annealed | 0.08- | 18+ | 8+ | | 40 | 95 | 70 |
| | 304 | Work-hardened | | | | | 50-150 | 100-180 | 50-10 |
| | 310 | Annealed | 0.25- | 25 | 20 | | 50 | 100 | 50 |
| | 321 | Annealed | 0.08- | 17+ | 8+ | 0.5Ti | 40 | 85 | 60 |
| | 17-7PH | Cold-rolled | 0.07 | 17 | 7 | 1.2Al | | 200-235 | 0-2 |
| | 17-7PH | Age-hardened | | | | | | 275-315 | 0-2 |
| | 201 | Annealed | 0.15 | 17 | 4.5 | 6.5Mn | 55 | 115 | 55 |
| | 202 | Annealed | 0.15 | 18 | 5 | 8.5Mn | 55 | 105 | 55 |

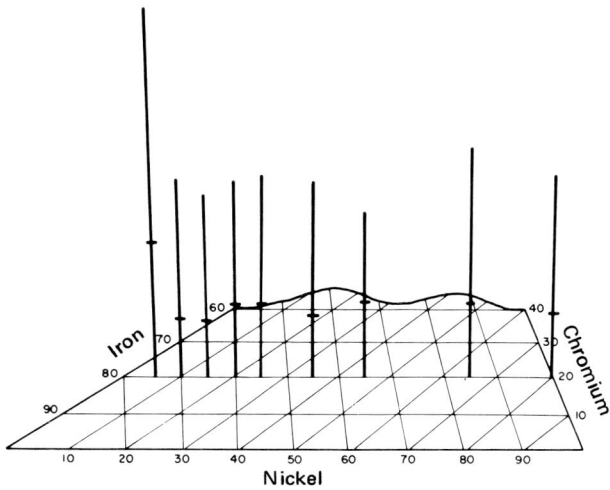

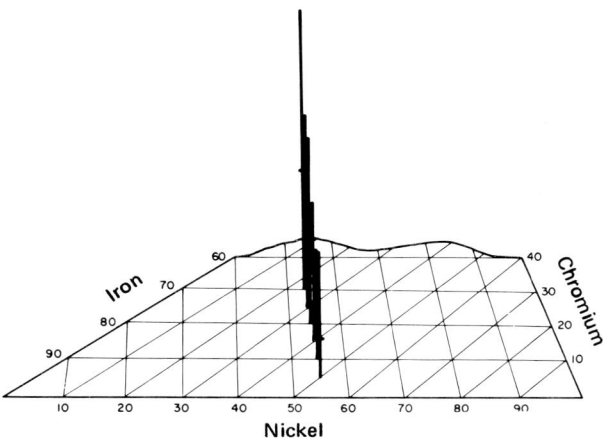

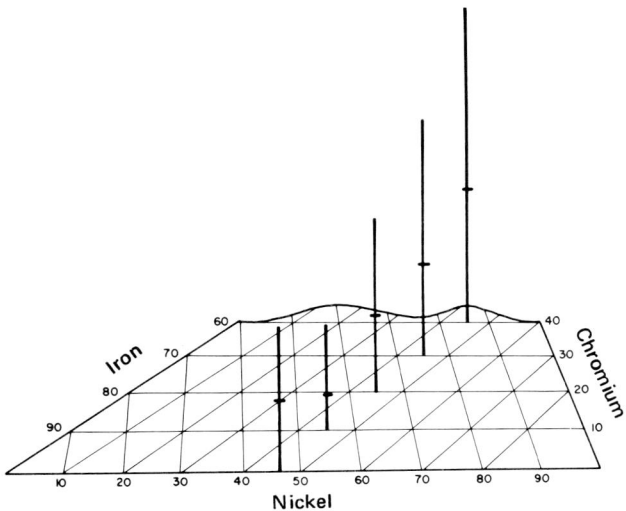

FIGURE 12 — Effect of Fe/Cr, Ni/Cr, and Fe/Ni on the yield and tensile strengths of Fe-Ni-Cr alloys tested at room temperature. Height of line is tensile strength and lower mark is 0.2% offset yield strength. Data obtained from 0.38 mm wire specimens. Total impurities less than 500 ppm (Staehle[28]).

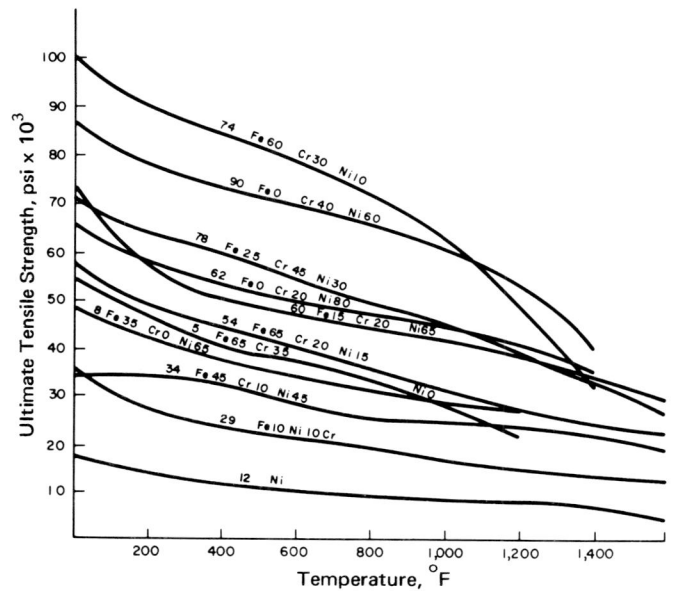

FIGURE 13 — Ultimate tensile strength of Fe-Ni-Cr alloys as a function of temperature for 0.38 mm diameter wire specimens. Total impurities less than 500 ppm (Staehle[28]).

TABLE 3—Electrode Potentials[1]

| Environmental Half Cells | Equilibrium Equation $E_o$ (volts) |
|---|---|
| $ClO_4^- + 8H^+ + 8e^- = Cl^- + 4H_2O$ | $= 1.389 - 0.0591\ pH + 0.0074 \log \dfrac{ClO_4}{(Cl^-)}$ |
| $O_2 + 4H^+ + 4e = 2H_2O$ | $= 1.228 - 0.0591\ pH + 0.0147 \log P_{O_2}$ |
| $NO_3^- + 3H^+ + 2e^- = HNO_2 + H_2O$ | $= 0.934 - 0.0886\ pH + 0.0295 \log \dfrac{(NO_3^-)}{(HNO_2)}$ |
| $Fe^{+++} + e = Fe^{++}$ | $= 0.771 + 0.0591 \log \dfrac{Fe^{+++}}{Fe^{++}}$ |
| $2H^+ + 2e = H_2$ | $= 0.000 - 0.591\ pH - 0.0295 \log P_{H_2}$ |

[1]From Pourbaix[29] and all values at 25 C. Equations are equal to $E_o$.

associated with film breaking, alloys whose surface composition may be changing with time, and complex environments, there are no directly applicable data from the area of electrode kinetics which provide definitive information with respect to identifying environment-metal combinations which crack. However, there are relevant background data which are considered useful and are discussed below.

Condit, Beauchamp, and Staehle have studied the polarization behavior of ternary Fe-Ni-Cr alloys in sulfuric acid potentiokinetically.[30] Curves from the 20Cr base composition and varying iron/nickel ratios are given in Figure 15. The general trend with increasing nickel is for the critical current density to decrease, the minimum passive current density to decrease, and the corrosion potential and the primary passive potential to become more noble. These trends suggest generally that increasing nickel permits film formation processes to passivate the surface more readily. There does not appear to be any precipitous change in any of the critical features of the polarization curves as the nickel is increased except for the change from 0 to 10% nickel.

223

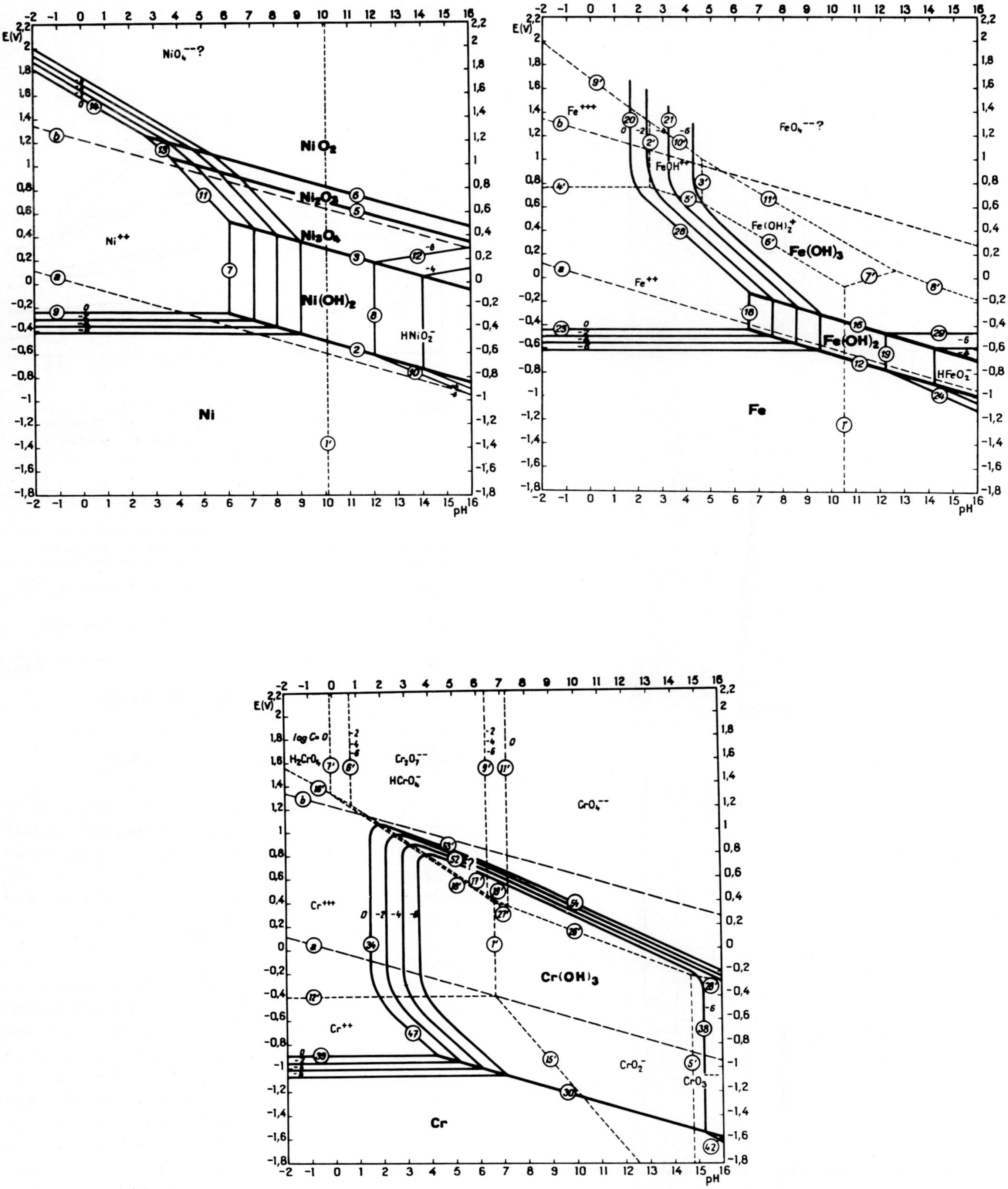

FIGURE 14 — Potential-pH diagrams for iron, nickel, and chromium in aqueous environments at 25 C. Numbers on the diagrams refer to the equilibrium equations which define the various lines (Pourbaix[29]).

224

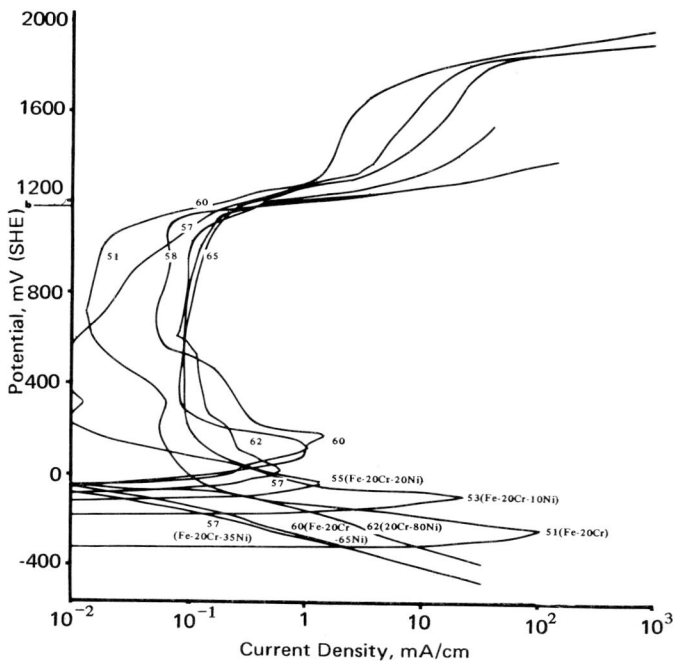

FIGURE 15 — Potentiokinetic polarization curves for Fe-Ni-Cr alloys having a 20Cr base determined in 1 N $H_2SO_4$ at 25 C and a scan rate of approximately 80 mv/min (Condit, Beauchamp, Staehle[30]).

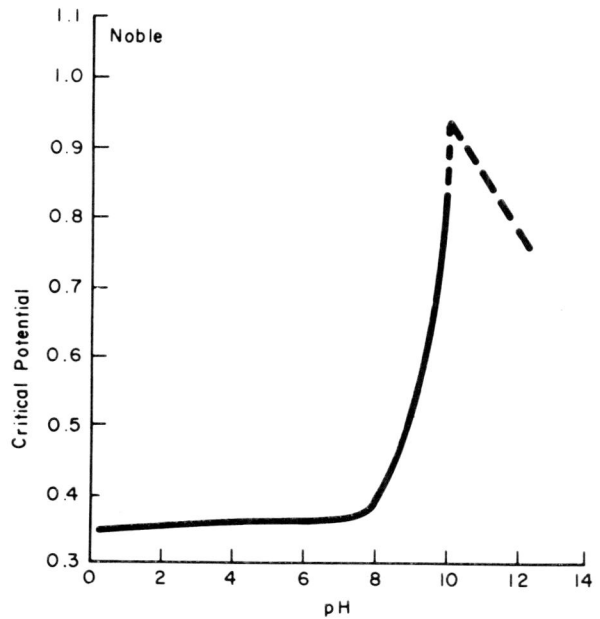

FIGURE 17 — Effect of pH on the critical potential for pitting of Type 304 stainless steel in 0.1 N NaCl at 25 C (Leckie and Uhlig[32]).

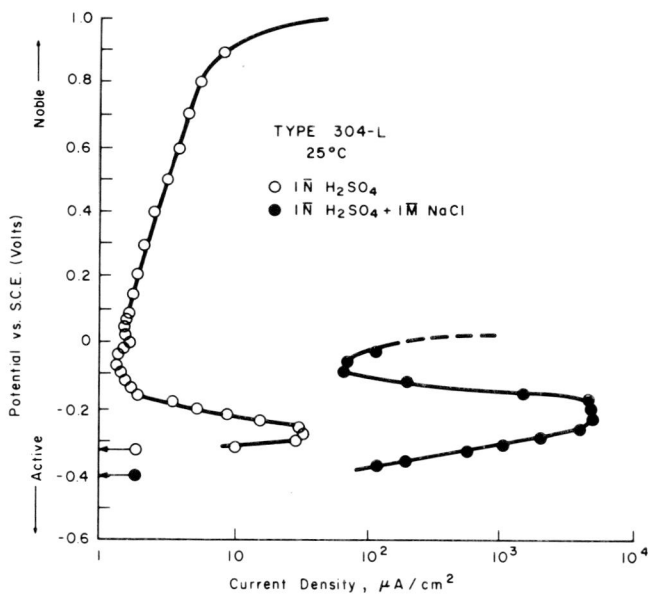

FIGURE 16 — Potentiostatic anodic polarization curves of Type 304L stainless steel in 1 N $H_2SO_4$ and in 1 N $H_2SO_4$ plus 1 M NaCl (Greene and Judd[31]).

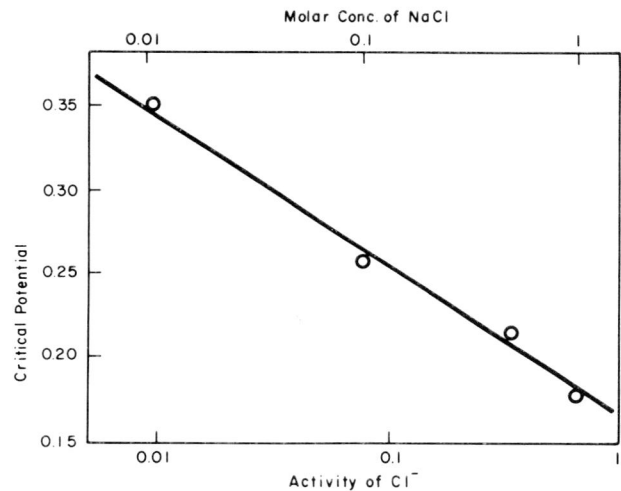

FIGURE 18 — Effect of chloride ion activity on steady state critical potential for pitting of Type 304 stainless steel at 25 C (Leckie and Uhlig[32]).

Greene and Judd have compared the dissolution behavior of Type 304-L stainless steel in sulfuric acid with and without chloride.[31] Figure 16 shows an increase in anodic dissolution kinetics of two orders of magnitude due to the addition of 1 M NaCl to a 1 M $H_2SO_4$ solution. Further, the addition of chloride increases considerably the current density in the formerly passive range of potentials.

Leckie and Uhlig have extensively investigated important factors affecting the pitting of 18-8 type stainless steel using the pitting potential as a criterion for judging the effects of environmental variables.[32] The effect of pH and chloride ion activity are summarized in Figures 17 and 18. They suggest that the steep rise in pitting potential at neutral pH is due to the preferential adsorption of $OH^-$ which decreases the anodic dissolution rate. This trend is reasonable also in view of the effect of increasing pH on the solubility of the iron hydroxide at neutral pH as shown in Figure 14. The decrease in pitting potential resulting from an increase in chloride activity emphasizes the difficulty of passivating these materials in the presence of $Cl^-$.

225

## IV. Cracking in Chloride Environments

This section describes the effects of important environmental and metallurgical variables on the stress corrosion cracking of Fe-Ni-Cr alloys in environments containing chlorides. Mechanistic considerations are described in Section VII.

### A. Environmental Factors

**1. Metallic Cations.** The effect of the chloride ion on the stress corrosion cracking of Fe-Ni-Cr alloys has been the most extensively investigated of environments causing cracking because of the ubiquity of the chloride ion and the virulence of the cracking that often results.

Increasing the chloride ion concentration increases the rate of cracking as shown by Figure 19 from Edeleanu for the cracking of 18-8 and 18-8 Ti steels in boiling $MgCl_2$ solutions.[33] However, since the boiling point varies with concentration, Figure 19 does not demonstrate the effect of chloride ion concentration unambiguously. In the same paper he shows similar results for variations in concentration of NaCl. Warren, using a "wicking" experiment in which the chloride solution is transported to the specimen surface from the solution through a porous material, obtained the data shown in Figure 20 for the cracking of Type 304 at 100 C.[34] Staehle, conducting experiments in single phase aqueous solutions at 260 C on Type 304 obtained the data shown in Figure 21 for two oxygen concentrations.[35] These experiments utilized wires stressed under constant load.

The morphology of cracks in the above experiments is transgranular. Figure 22 shows a typical case of a branched crack from Warren's work.[34]

There is great difficulty in defining a minimum chloride concentration below which cracking will not occur because

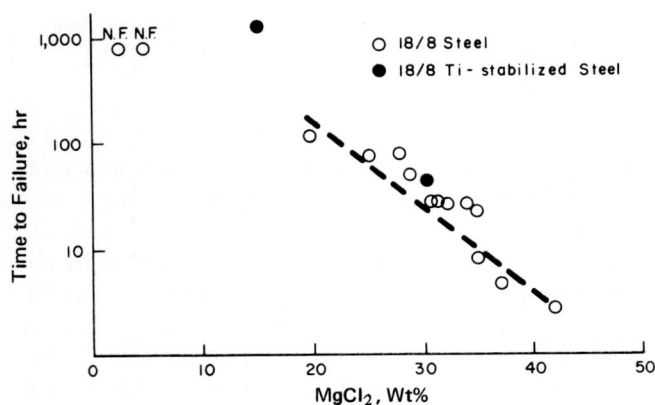

FIGURE 20 — Effect of chloride added as NaCl on cracking of Type 304 stainless steel at 100 C. Solution transported by porous material to specimen (Warren[34]).

of effects of the metal cations, pH, other reducible species, adsorbed species, and concentrating processes such as wetting and drying or boiling.

One of the most widely used environments for studying the chloride stress corrosion cracking of alloys is boiling $MgCl_2$. This was first used extensively by Scheil to study cracking of various stainless steels.[36] While this environment can be considered generally to give reliable results for the relative susceptibilities of various alloys to cracking, certain precautions should be exercised in its use. All the $MgCl_2$ should be taken from the same lot; the boiling temperatures should be maintained constant; and the solution should be boiled for a period of time prior to use.[38,39,78,79] Special care should be used in specifying both the temperature and chloride concentration. Pershke and Kalinin in 1932 checked the effect of $MgCl_2$ concentration on the boiling point and obtained the data plotted in Figure 23.[40] Owing to the relatively steep slope in the region of 20-50% extreme care should be used by investigators in controlling temperatures and concentration of tests.

The effects of various metallic cations have been extensively investigated. Figures 24 and 25 from work by Thomas et al[41] and Warren[34] epitomize the trends due to the most used cations — $Mg^{++}$, $Fe^{+++}$, $Ca^{++}$, $Na^+$, $Li^+$. Berg and Hendrikson[42] have investigated the effects of various cations on stainless steels of various composition at various temperatures and at various chloride concentrations but their results are not definitive with respect to cation effects.

Table 4[52] summarizes a wide variety of experiments performed to ascertain effects of metallic cations. Cracking was transgranular except where noted to be intergranular. A

FIGURE 19 — Effect of concentration of boiling $MgCl_2$ solutions on time to failure of 18-8 stainless steels. Specimens completely immersed (Edeleanu[33]).

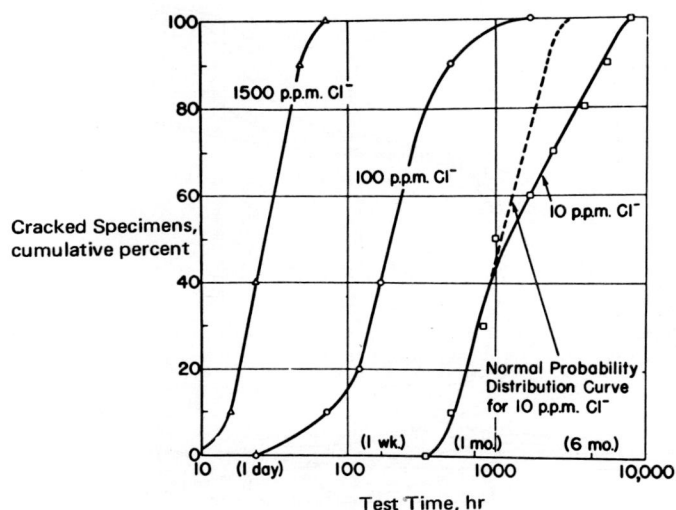

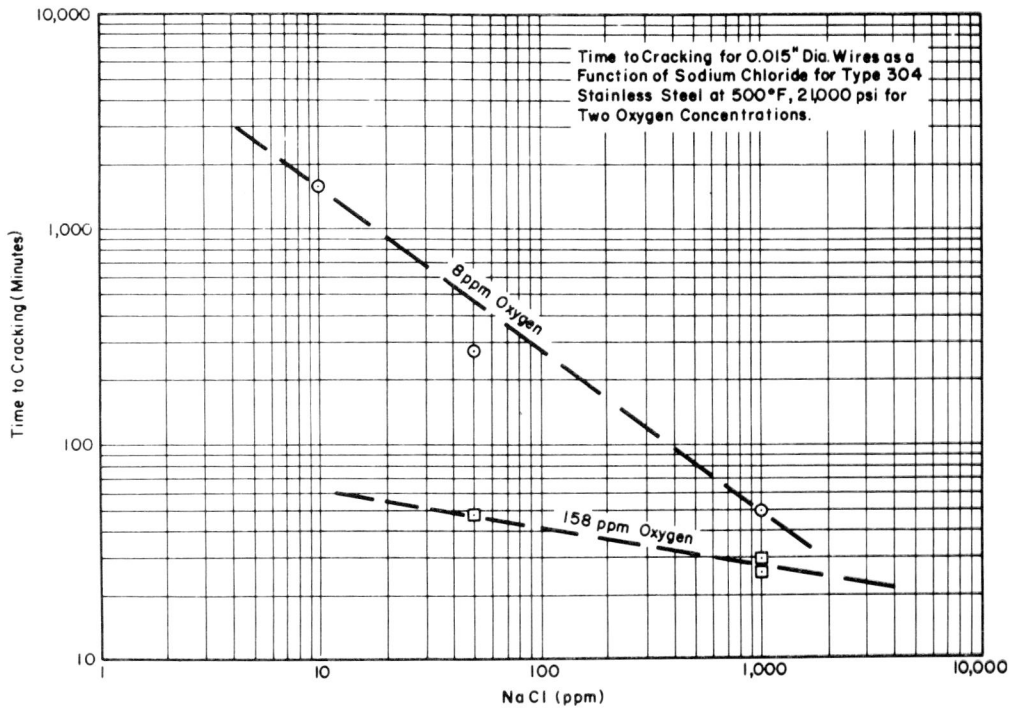

FIGURE 21 — Effect of chloride and oxygen on time to cracking of Type 304 wire held at constant load in single phase aqueous environment (Staehle[35]).

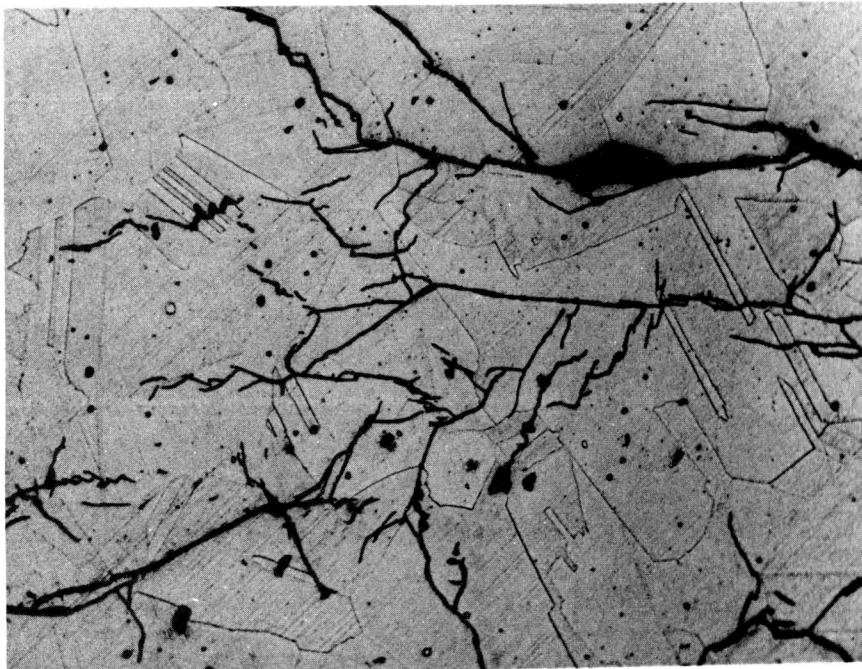

FIGURE 22 — Typical transgranular, branching nature of stress corrosion cracks in austenitic stainless steel, 100X (Warren[34]).

227

clear explanation for the effects of the various cations is not presently available although some reasonable suggestions can be made. The more rapid cracking in MgCl$_2$ vs CaCl$_2$ and CaCl$_2$ vs NaCl may be the result of differences in pH. Increasing the pH will reduce the cathodic reaction rate. Such a trend is indeed suggested by Figure 24. The acceleration due to ferric ions may be the result of the relatively high potential of the Fe$^{+++}$/Fe$^{++}$ redox reaction shown in Table 3. The retardation of cracking due to the addition of SnCl$_2$ observed by Leu and Helle[54] may be the result of the great effect tin has in reducing the exchange current for hydrogen ion reduction. The aqueous equilibrium data for the water-tin system suggests that tin would be stable on the metal surface.[29] If so, the tin would be available on the metal surface to adversely effect the hydrogen reduction kinetics. Other effects of anions may be due to inhibition of anodic or cathodic processes, degree of dissociation of the chloride, and mass transport processes.

   **2. Hydrogen Ion Concentration (pH).** The hydrogen ion is a cation but unlike the metallic cations, such as Mg$^{++}$, Ca$^{++}$, Li$^+$, etc., H$^+$ is a reducible species with its half cell potential lying above that of iron and chromium dissolution half cells over a wide range of pH and slightly

above nickel for a less wide range. Increasing the concentration of hydrogen ions increases the reaction rate of their reduction (consequently increasing the corrosion current of the mixed electrode) and increases the solubility of hydroxides (renders them less protective). If the progress of a stress corrosion crack is taken to operate as a local electrochemical cell, the cracking rate should decrease with increased pH.

   The addition of HCl to the boiling MgCl$_2$ solutions has been found to accelerate cracking by reducing the time for crack initiation. Hoar and Hines found for wire specimens

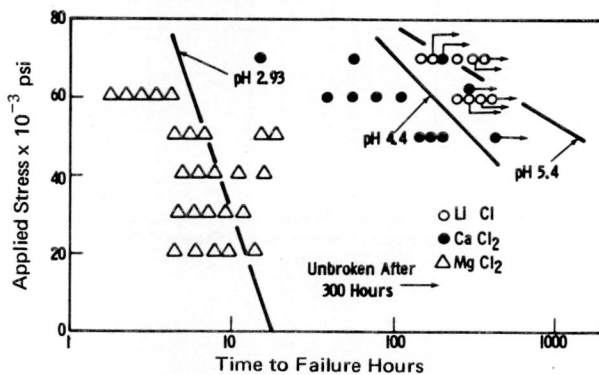

FIGURE 24 — Effect of various cations on time to failure of Type 304 stainless steel in boiling solutions at 125 C. Chloride concentrations approximately 27% and pH taken at 80 C (Thomas et al[41]).

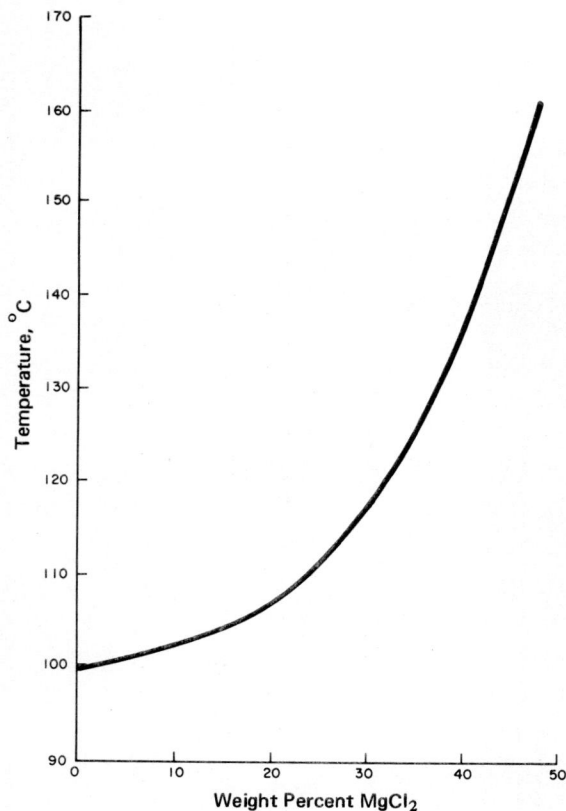

FIGURE 23 — Dependence of boiling point of aqueous MgCl$_2$ solutions on concentration (Pershke and Kalinin[40]).

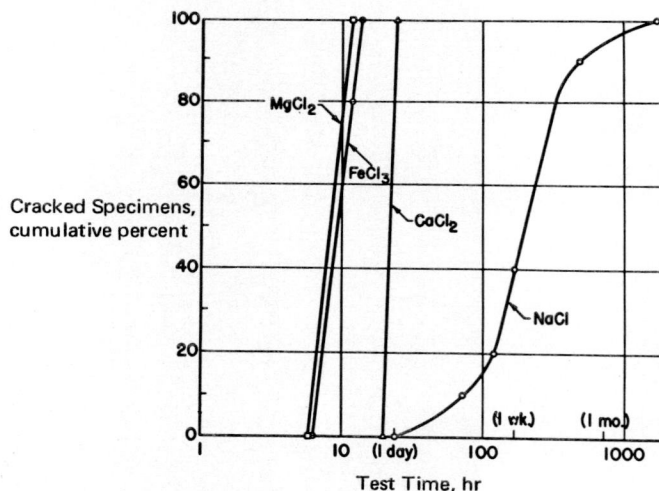

FIGURE 25 — Effect of various cations on the cracking of Type 304 in the wicking test at 100 C (Warren[34]).

228

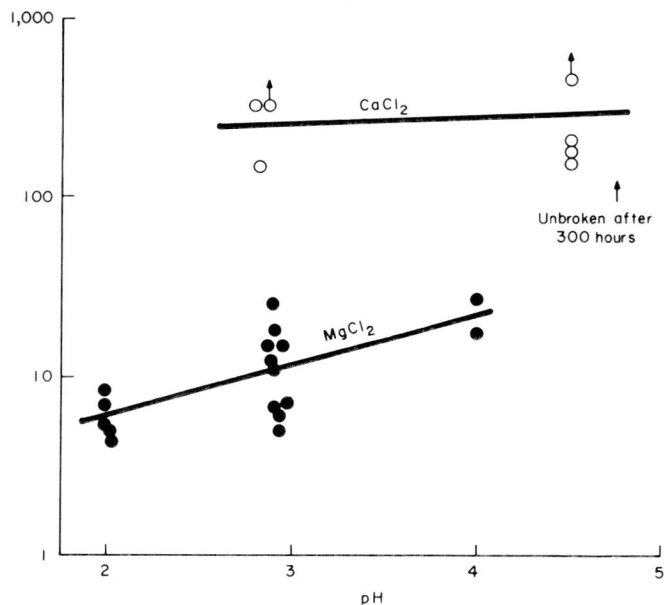

FIGURE 26 — Effect of pH on the time to failure of Type 304 exposed in boiling MgCl$_2$ and CaCl$_2$ solutions at 125 C (Thomas et al[41]).

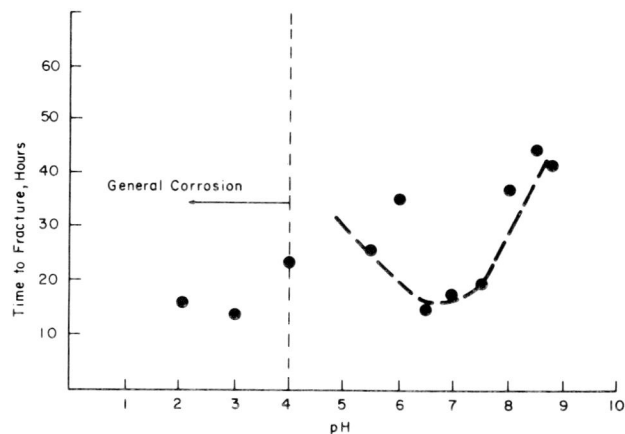

FIGURE 27 — Effect of pH on time to failure of 18.8 stainless steel in 40% CaCl$_2$ solution at 100 C (Anderson[58]).

TABLE 4—Stress Corrosion Cracking of Austenitic Fe-Mo-Cr Alloys in Chlorides[1]

Test Environment (Liquid Phase)

| Reagent[1] | Concentration | Temp. | Material[2] | Applied Stress (psi) | Hours of Exposure | Cracks[3] | Ref. |
|---|---|---|---|---|---|---|---|
| BaCl$_2$ | 10%, 30%, Sat'd | Boiling | 18-6 C.R. | >Y.P. | − | No | 43 |
| C$_2$H$_5$Cl | H$_2$O-free | − | 18-8S − | − | − | No | 44 |
| C$_2$H$_5$Cl | 0.5% H$_2$O | − | 18-8S − | − | − | Yes | 44 |
| CaCl$_2$ | 10 & 20% | Boiling | 18-6 C.R. | >Y.P. | − | No | 43 |
| CaCl$_2$ | 25% | Boiling | 18-10 − | >Y.P. | 50 | Yes | 33 |
| CaCl$_2$ | 50% | Boiling | 18-6 C.R. | >Y.P. | − | Yes | 43 |
| CaCl$_2$ | Sat'd | 100 C | 18-8 A | >Y.P. | − | Yes | 45 |
| CdCl$_2$ | 1705 ppm | 205 | 18-8 − | 10,000 | 8 | No | 52 |
| CdCl$_2$ | 1705 ppm | 205 C | 18-8 − | 26,500 | 17 | Yes | 52 |
| CrCl$_3$ | 10%, 30% & 50% | Boiling | 18-6 C.R. | >Y.P. | − | No | 43 |
| CrCl$_3$ | 25% | Boiling | 18-10 − | >Y.P. | 115 | No | 33 |
| CuCl$_2$ | Sat'd | Boiling | 18-6 C.R. | >Y.P. | − | No | 43 |
| CuCl$_2$ | 1 g/l | 345 C | 18-8 C.R. | >Y.P. | 1165 | Yes (IG) | 47 |
| FeCl$_3$ | .05%, .10% & 20% | Boiling | 18-6 C.R. | >Y.P. | − | No | 43 |
| FeCl$_3$ | 0.1% & 5% | Boiling | 18-8S A | >Y.P. | 240 | No | 46 |
| FeCl$_3$ | 0.5 ppm | 345 C | 18-8 S | − | 44 | Yes (IG) | 48 |
| FeCl$_3$ | 0.1 g/l | 345 C | 18-8 C.R. | >Y.P. | 53 | Yes (IG) | 48 |
| FeCl$_3$ | 6.6% | R.T. | 18-8 S | 35,000 | 96 | Yes (IG) | 44 |
| HCl | 40 ppm Cl$^-$ | 343 C | 304SS C.R. | >Y.P. | 24 | Yes (IG) | 53 |
| HF + 0.2% Fluosilicic Acid | 12% | 83 C | 18-8 A | >Y.P. | − | Yes | 49 |
| HgCl$_2$ | 10% & Sat'd | Boiling | 18-6 C.R. | >Y.P. | 1 | No | 43 |
| HgCl$_2$ | 25% | Boiling | 18-10 − | >Y.P. | 31 | No | 33 |
| HgCl$_2$ | Sat'd | R.T. | 18-8 S | 35,000 | 48 | Yes (IG) | 44 |
| H$_2$O | Distilled | 205 C | 18-8SCb A | 40,000 | 120 | No | 50 |
| H$_2$O | 1% HCl | R.T. | 18-8 S | 35,000 | 840 | No | 44 |
| KBr | 10, 30 & 50% | Boiling | 18-6 C.R. | >Y.P. | − | No | 43 |
| KCl | 10, 30 & 50% | Boiling | 18-6 C.R. | >Y.P. | − | No | 43 |
| KCl | 50% | Boiling | 18-8 A | >Y.P. | 240 | No | 46 |
| KCl | Sat'd | Boiling | 18-10 A | >Y.P. | 4 | Yes | 33 |
| KF | 10, 30 & 50% | Boiling | 18-6 C.R. | >Y.P. | 69 | No | 43 |

[1]The fact that cracking was not observed in certain environments should not be taken as proof that it will never occur. Positive and negative results may be better an indication of relative trends.
[2]A = Annealed; C.R. = Cold Rolled; and S = Sensitized.
[3]Transgranular cracking unless otherwise noted.

229

TABLE 4 (Continued)

| Reagent[1] | Concentration | Temp. | Material[2] | Applied Stress (psi) | Hours of Exposure | Cracks[3] | Ref. |
|---|---|---|---|---|---|---|---|
| LiCl | 10% | Boiling | 18-6 C.R. | >Y.P. | — | No | 43 |
| LiCl | 30% | Boiling | 18-6 C.R. | >Y.P. | 183 | Yes | 43 |
| LiCl | 50% | Boiling | 18-6 C.R. | >Y.P. | 63 | Yes | 43 |
| $MgCl_2$ | 5-60% | Boiling | 18-8 A | >Y.P. | — | Yes | 36 |
| $MgCl_2$ | 5% | R.T. | 18-8 S | 35,000 | 840 | No | 44 |
| $MnCl_2$ | 33% | Boiling | 18-10 A | >Y.P. | 1216 | Yes | 33 |
| NaBr | 10, 30 & 50% | Boiling | 18-6 C.R. | >Y.P. | — | No | 43 |
| NaCl | 1% | 250 C | 18-9 – | <Y.P. | 1.5 | Yes | 51 |
| NaCl | 50-1500 ppm | Boiling | 18-8 A | >Y.P. | 240 | No | 46 |
| NaCl | 3% | 250 C | 18-9Cb – | >Y.P. | 1.6 | Yes | 51 |
| NaCl | 20% | Boiling | 18-10 A | >Y.P. | 96 | Yes | 33 |
| NaCl | 20% | 220 C | 18-9Cb – | >Y.P. | 1.1 | Yes | 51 |
| NaCl | 50% | 267 C | 18-9Cb A | 40,000 | 116 | Yes | 51 |
| NaCl | 50 ppm Cl | 345 C | 304 C.R. | >Y.P. | 24 | Yes(IG) | 53 |
| NaCl | Sat'd | Boiling | 18-10 A | >Y.P. | 18 | Yes | 33 |
| NaCl | 5% | R.T. | 18-8 S | 35,000 | 840 | No | 44 |
| NaF | Sat'd | Boiling | 18-6 C.R. | >Y.P. | — | No | 43 |
| $NH_4Cl$ | 9-25% | R.T. | 18-8 S | 60,000 | — | Yes(IG) | 44 |
| $NH_4Cl$ | 33% | Boiling | 18-10 A | >Y.P. | 28 | Yes | 33 |
| $NH_4Cl$ | Sat'd | Boiling | 18-6 C.R. | >Y.P. | — | No | 43 |
| $NiCl_2$ | 25% | Boiling | 18-10 A | >Y.P. | 779 | Yes | 33 |
| $SnCl_2$ | 50% | Boiling | 18-10 A | >Y.P. | 430 | No | 33 |
| $SrCl_2$ | 10, 30 & 50% | Boiling | 18-6 C.R. | >Y.P. | — | No | 43 |
| $ZnCl_2$ | 5% | Boiling | 18-8S A | >Y.P. | 240 | No | 46 |
| $ZnCl_2$ | 33% | Boiling | 18-10 A | >Y.P. | 200 | Yes | 33 |
| $ZnCl_2$ | 50% | Boiling | 18-6 C.R. | >Y.P. | 69 | Yes | 43 |
| $ZnCl_2$ | Sat'd | Boiling | 18-8 A | >Y.P. | — | Yes | 45 |

[1] The fact that cracking was not observed in certain environments should not be taken as proof that it will never occur. Positive and negative results may be better an indication of relative trends.

[2] A = Annealed; C.R. = Cold Rolled; and S = Sensitized.

[3] Transgranular cracking unless otherwise noted.

of 18-8 steel stressed to 48,000 psi that the addition of 0.02 percent lowered the cracking time from 300 to 25 minutes;[55] Barnart and van Rooyen found a decrease of a factor of 3-9 when 0.10% HCl was added to the $MgCl_2$ solution and the specimens were stressed at 40,500 psi.[56] Uhlig and Lincoln[57] added HCl and NaOH to a boiling $MgCl_2$ and showed that lowering pH decreases time to cracking and raising pH increases time to cracking. The data of Thomas et al in Figure 26 support the observation of Uhlig and Lincoln with respect to the change of pH in a $MgCl_2$ solution; however, Figure 6 shows that over the pH range 3 to 4.5 there is little effect in a boiling $CaCl_2$ solution.[41] Anderson[58] in studying the pH range from 2 to 8.5 observed a general increase in susceptibility with lowered pH but found that general corrosion resulted below pH 4 as shown in Figure 27. The effect of various cations on cracking shown in Figure 23 may be due more to pH than to cation effects. (The pH corresponding to the cation is noted therein.)

The general pattern of pH effects in concentrated and boiling solutions in the 100 to 160 degree range appears to follow the predicted trend qualitatively but certainly not quantitatively. A variation of the hydrogen ion concentration of several orders of magnitudes produces a change in cracking times of significantly less than a factor of ten; and in some cases, virtually no effect of pH is even observed.

Such behavior suggests either that the slow step in the reduction process is not related significantly to concentration of hydrogen ions or, more simply, that the slow step in the cracking process is not related strongly to the reduction process.

Neumann and Griess investigated that effect of pH and oxygen concentration on the cracking of Type 347 at 300 C in a solution containing 100 ppm NaCl.[59] Their data in Table 5 show no significant effect in the range of pH 2.8 to 10.5 at room temperature. Scharfstein and Brindley show that a change from pH 6-8 and 7.0-8.8 at 10 ppm NaCl and 85 C significantly reduces cracking.[60]

TABLE 5–Effect of pH on Stress Corrosion Cracking of Type 347 Stainless Steel (Neumann and Griess[59])

| pH | Chloride Concentration (ppm) | Number of Specimens | Time, Hours First Crack | 100% Cracking |
|---|---|---|---|---|
| 2.8 | 100 | 18 | 100 | 400 |
| 6.5 | 100 | 6 | 200 | 300 |
| 10.5 | 100 | 6 | 200 | 300 |
| 2.8 | 50 | 4 | 200 | 400 |
| 6.5 | 50 | 4 | 400 | 600 |
| 10.5 | 50 | 4 | 200 | 300 |

Rideout has investigated the effect of pH as changed by nitric acid on the stress corrosion cracking of sensitized Type 304 stainless steel in a 10 ppm chloride solution at 90 C and his results are summarized in Figure 28.[61] The results are qualitatively similar to those of Figure 27 indicating an absence of cracking at lower pH. However, the reason for the absence of cracking of Figure 28 may be due to a passivation process and that of Figure 27 to accelerated dissolution. Figure 28 also shows that both transgranular and intergranular cracking can progress simultaneously. A reason for the absence of transgranular cracking at pH 3 is not presently obvious.

3. **Additional Reducible Species.** Barnartt and van Rooyen have demonstrated that for the boiling $MgCl_2$ experiment at 146 C the replacement of bubbling nitrogen with bubbling oxygen produced no effect on potential-time curves or time to cracking.[56] Uhlig and Lincoln reached the same conclusions.[57] Barnartt and van Rooyen also demonstrated that the propagation of stress corrosion cracks is associated with copious evolution of hydrogen. Hoar[84] has argued that the open circuit potentials observed during cracking of stainless steels in $MgCl_2$ (-100 mv SHE) are too high to permit hydrogen reduction to take place especially since some overpotential is required and thus the cathodic reductant is more probably oxygen. According to the hydrogen ion equilibrium in Table 3, it would be impossible for hydrogen ions to be reduced above pH 2. The apparent contradiction can probably be rationalized in terms of local processes inside the crack which (a) keep the hydrogen ion concentration low, (b) keep the potential relatively active, and (c) possibly change the activity coefficient of hydrogen ions. These suppositions have yet to be proven, but the evidence of Barnartt and van Rooyen with respect to the primacy of the hydrogen reduction seems overwhelming.

As the pH increases and hydrogen ion concentration is still further reduced, it is clear that the disparity in potential as well as the decrease in hydrogen ion concentration will eventually become a limiting factor and some alternate reducible specie is required. Neumann and Griess,[59] Staehle et al,[50] and Williams[62] have shown that in neutral solutions some oxygen is required and that in the absence of oxygen no cracking occurs. The well known chloride-oxygen relationship of Williams is given in Figure 29 where it is shown that at high chloride little oxygen is required and vice versa. Unfortunately, this was determined in a wetting and drying situation and therefore must be taken as a qualitative indication of trends. However, the same trend at 260 C is evident from Figure 21 already discussed which was based on experiments in single phase water. Table 6 from Neumann and Griess shows that the oxygen is required at pH 10.5 at 300 C. Unfortunately, they did not conduct a zero oxygen experiment at the lower pH. Since the oxygen solubility is important in the consideration of reaction rates, Figure 30 from Pray et al is included to show the combined effect of pressure and temperature on oxygen solubility in water.[63]

In considering the combined effects of pH discussed in the previous section and oxygen the general trend seems to be that for pH lower than 4-5 the cracking rate will be increased with decreasing pH owing to the effect of hydrogen ion concentration. Above this point the primary reducible specie is oxygen.

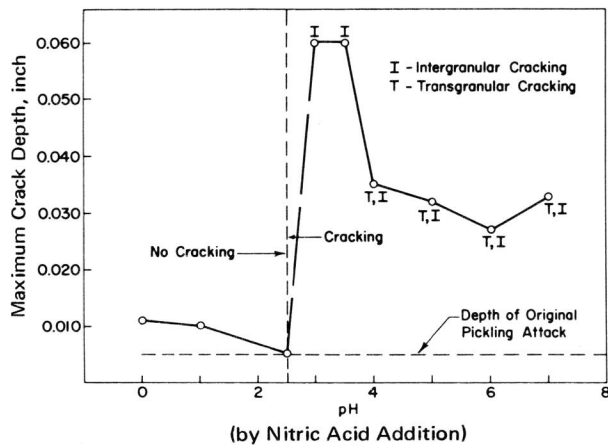

FIGURE 28 — Effect of pH on the maximum crack depth of Type 304 exposed in the stressed condition for 96 hours in a 10 ppm Cl⁻ (NaCl) solution. Specimens sensitized and pickled, pH changed by nitric acid additions (Rideout[61]).

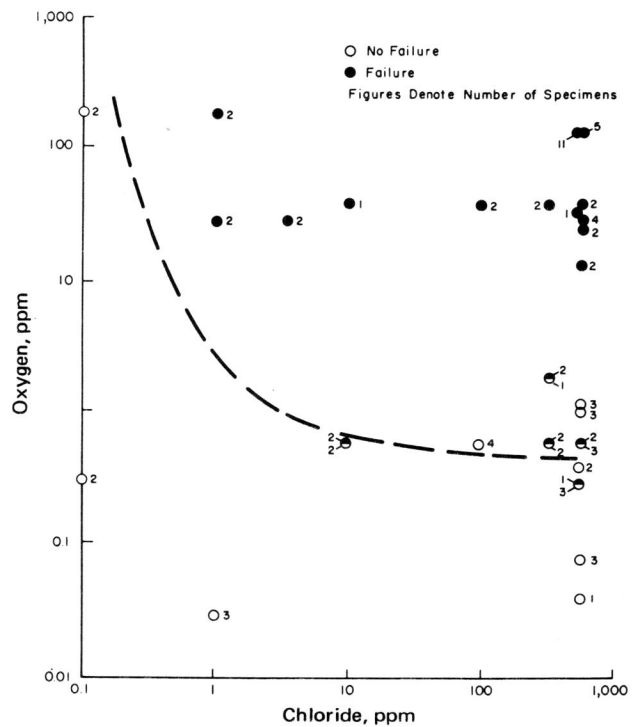

FIGURE 29 — Proposed relationship between chloride and oxygen content of alkaline phosphate treated boiler water and susceptibility to stress corrosion cracking of austenitic stainless steel exposed to the steam phase with intermittent wetting (Williams[62]).

**TABLE 6–Effect of Oxygen Concentration on Stress Corrosion Cracking of Type 347 Stainless Steel at 300 C and 100 ppm Chloride Concentration (Neumann and Griess[59])**

| Oxygen Concentration (ppm) | pH | Number of Specimens | Time, Hours First Crack | Time, Hours 100% Cracking |
|---|---|---|---|---|
| 1200 | 2.8 | 18 | 100 | 400 |
| 50 | 2.8 | 18 | 100 | 300 |
| <1 | 2.8 | 2 | 200 | 400 |
| 1200 | 10.5 | 6 | 200 | 300 |
| 50 | 10.5 | 6 | 200 | 300 |
| <1 | 10.5 | 2 | 100 | 200 |
| 0[(1)] | 10.5 | 4 | >2000[(2)] | – |

[(1)] Contained a 10 to 20 ppm excess of sulfite ions.
[(2)] No cracks during 2000-hour test.

Other species which might perform the necessary reduction process include $Fe^{+++}$, $NO_3^-$, $NO_2^-$, $Cr_2O_7^=$, $H_2O_2$, $Cl_2$, $Br_2$. It would be expected that these species would accelerate cracking unless they happen to adsorb and become anodic inhibitors. Edeleanu has shown that the first four of these additional reducible species can accelerate cracking.[33]

**4. Other Environmental Species, Inhibitors.** Table 7 summarizes work on effects of miscellaneous additions on cracking in chloride environments. A wide variety of additions for chloride solutions have been studied for the purposes of (a) developing inhibitors, (b) accelerating cracking tests, and (c) assessing the virulence of industrial environments. The effect of the various additions will be discussed in that order.

Cracking of Fe-Ni-Cr alloys can be inhibited by eliminating the reducible species, raising the pH, adding an inorganic inhibitor which stifles the anodic reaction, and adding an organic inhibitor which stifles anodic and/or cathodic processes. While the elimination of hydrogen ions is relatively difficult, the elimination of dissolved oxygen is relatively easy through the use of sulfite ($SO_3^=$) or hydrazine ($N_2H_4$) which react with oxygen according to the reactions:

$$N_2H_4 + O_2 \rightarrow 2H_2O + N_2$$

$$SO_3^= + 1/2\,O_2 \rightarrow SO_4^=$$

Thus, in the neutral to higher pH ranges where the hydrogen ions do not contribute to the reduction process the addition of sulfide and hydrazine should be effective inhibitors. Phillips and Singley have shown both inhibitors to be effective in the liquid and vapor phases at 260 C with the effectiveness being greater in the liquid phase.[64]

The chromate ion has been found to reduce or prevent cracking by Scharfstein and Brindley,[60] Logan and Sherman,[46] and Neumann and Griess.[59] Acceleration was noted by Edeleanu and Snowden,[65] and no effect was

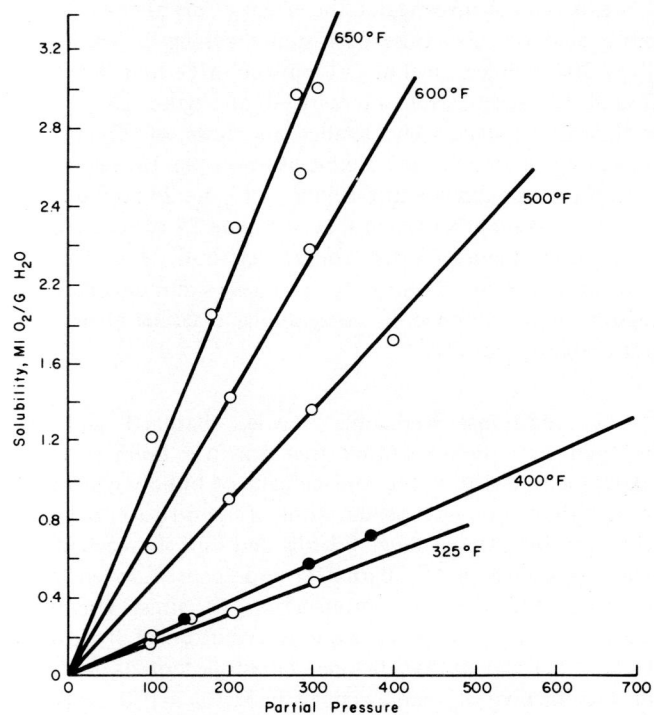

**FIGURE 30 – Solubility of oxygen in water with varying partial pressure (Pray et al[63]).**

noted by Phillips and Singley.[64] $CrO_4^=$ is the stable species above pH 7.29 and $Cr_2O_7^=$ below.[29] Despite the high potential for the $Cr^{+6}$ oxidation state, suggesting that this species might accelerate cracking, the product of the oxidation is a solid product–$Cr_2O_3$ or $Cr(OH)_3$–which would be expected to stifle anodic reactions. The solid product is stable above the general pH region 3-4 which is the region of industrial significance. At lower pH the reduction is directly to $Cr^{+3}$ and in this region the $Cr^{+6}$ would be expected to accelerate cracking. The general effect of chromate can be taken to be as follows. Above a minimum concentration of chromate in the range of 100-300 ppm and above pH 4-5 chromate can be expected to inhibit or greatly retard cracking in the liquid phase.

Phosphates have been shown to have a beneficial effect by Phillips and Singley,[64] Neumann and Griess,[59] Scharfstein and Brindley,[60] and Hoar and Hines.[66] The action of the phosphate differs greatly from the chromate in that there is no oxidation process involved; the phosphates act to control the pH with the $PO_4^{-3}/HPO_4^{-2}$ equilibrium being at pH 12.03 and $HPO_4^{-2}/H_2PO_4^{-1}$ being pH 7.29. The action of the phosphate can then be expected to keep the hydrogen ion concentration low especially by acting in the region of the crack. The phosphate ion may also adsorb preferentially to inhibit the anodic reaction. Of special interest, Neumann and Griess found that the phosphate addition had no effect at a pH of 2.8 but was effective at pH 10.5. (Jackson and Overman[67] studied the effect of inhibitors using radioactive tracers and suggested that the primary effect of phosphate is due to its role in competitive adsorption.)

**TABLE 7—Effects of Various Environmental Additions in Cracking of Austenitic Stainless Steels in Chlorides**

| Addition | Concentration | Chloride Base | Alloy | Phase | Temp. °C | Effect and Comments | Ref. |
|---|---|---|---|---|---|---|---|
| **Nitrates** | | | | | | | |
| $Al(NO_3)_3$ | 300 ppm | 50 ppm NaCl | T-347 | L,V | 260 | 40% cracking in vapor 1% cracking in liquid | 64 |
| $NaNO_3$ | 100-1000 ppm | 50; 500 ppm NaCl | T-347 | L | 260 | Cracking eliminated when $NO_3/Cl$ mole ratio $> 1$ | 64 |
| $NaNO_3$ | 125 ppm | 50 ppm NaCl | T-347 | L,V | 260 | 35% cracking in vapor, 1% cracking in liquid | 64 |
| $NaNO_3$ $+Na_3PO_4$ | 55-1080 ppm | 50; 500 ppm NaCl | T-347 | L | 260 | 100% cracking of pH $< 8$ 0-10% cracking at pH $> 8$ | 64 |
| $NaNO_3$ $+Na_2SO_3$ | 150 ppm 65 ppm | 500 ppm NaCl | T-347 | L | 260 | No cracking | 64 |
| $NaNO_3$ | 1% | 3.5% NaCl | T-304 | boiling L | $\sim 100$ | No cracking | 46 |
| $NaNO_3$ | 0-6% | $MgCl_2$ | 18-8 | boiling L | 130 | No cracking above 4% | 68 |
| $NaNO_3$ | [no air] | NaCl | 18-8 Nb | dewpoint | 285 | Fracture | 65 |
| **Chromates** | | | | | | | |
| $K_2CrO_4$ | 1000,1500 ppm | 10,100,550 NaCl | T-304,-347 | L | 85 | No cracking | 60 |
| $K_2CrO_4$ | | 3.5% NaCl | T-304 | boiling L | 100 | No cracking | 46 |
| $K_2CrO_4$ $+NaOH$ | 2% | 3.5% NaCl | T-304 | boiling L | 100 | No cracking | 59 |
| $Na_2CrO_4$ | [no air] | NaCl | 18-8 Nb | dewpoint | 292 | Fracture | 65 |
| $?CrO_4$ | 100-500 ppm | 20; 100 ppm NaCl | T-347 | L | 300 | Cracking at 100 ppm $CrO_4^=$, None at 250 and 500 ppm | 59 |
| $?CrO_4$ | 260 ppm | 50 ppm NaCl | T-347 | L,V | 260 | No effect | 64 |
| **Phosphates** | | | | | | | |
| $K_3PO_4$ | 1-100 ppm | 50 ppm NaCl | T-347 | L,V | 260 | 40-70% cracking in vapor 1-10% cracking in liquid | |
| $Na_2HPO_4$ | [plus air] | none intentional | 18-8 Nb | dry 72 hr | 330 | 0.0005 in deep cracks | 65 |
| $Na_2HPO_4$ | [plus air] | NaCl | 18-8 Nb | dewpoint | 300 | No cracking + 0.004 in cracks | 65 |
| $Na_2HPO_4$ | [plus air] | NaCl | 18-8 Nb | dry 72 hr | 330 | No cracking | 65 |
| $Na_2HPO_4$ $+NaOH$ | 100-1475 ppm adjust pH to 11 | 50-550 ppm NaCl | T-304,-347 | L | 84 | No cracking | 60 |
| $Na_3PO_4$ | 200,1475 ppm | 50; 550 ppm NaCl | T-304,-347 | L | 84 | No cracking | 60 |
| $Na_3PO_4$ | 1000 ppm | 50 ppm NaCl | T-347 | L | 84 | No cracking | 64 |
| $?PO_4$ | 50-300 ppm | 20-100 ppm NaCl | T-347 | L | 200 300 | Cracking:low pH all $PO_4^=$ conc. Cracking:high pH, low $PO_4^=$ | 59 |
| **Nitrites** | | | | | | | |
| $NaNO_2$ | 250 ppm | 50 ppm NaCl | T-347 | L,V | 260 | 50% cracking in vapor 40% cracking in liquid | 64 |
| $NaNO_2$ | 0.1 N | 0.5 N NaCl | T-304 | boiling | $\sim 100$ | Crack in presence of $NO_2$ but not with $Cl^-$ above? | 46 |
| $NaNO_2$ | 0.5% | 50 ppm NaCl | T-304 | boiling L | $\sim 100$ | No cracking | 46 |
| $NaNO_2$ | 2% | 3.5% NaCl | T-304 | boiling L | $\sim 100$ | No cracking | 46 |
| $NaNO_2$ | [no air] | NaCl | 18-8 Nb | dewpoint | 300 | 0.005 in deep cracks | 65 |
| $NaNO_2$ | [no air] | NaCl | 18-8 Nb | dry 72 hr | 330 | No cracking | 65 |
| $NaNO_2$ $+NaOH$ | 1% | 3.5% NaCl | T-304 | boiling L | $\sim 100$ | No cracking | 65 |
| $NaNO_2$ $+FeCl_3$ | 2% | 3.5% NaCl | T-304 | boiling L | $\sim 100$ | No cracking | 46 |
| $NaNO_2$ $+NH_4NO_2$ | 1% 1% | NaCl | T-304 | V, boiling L | $\sim 100$ | No cracking (pH 4.6-7) | 65 |

TABLE 7 (Continued)

| Addition | Concentration | Chloride Base | Alloy | Phase | Temp. °C | Effect and Comments | Ref. |
|---|---|---|---|---|---|---|---|
| Permanganate | | | | | | | |
| $KMnO_4$ | 0.2% | 3.5% NaCl | T-304 | boiling L | $\sim 100$ | No cracking | 65 |
| Iodide | | | | | | | |
| KI | 100 ppm | 50 ppm NaCl | T-304 | boiling L | $\sim 100$ | No cracking | 65 |
| Na I | 0-10% | $MgCl_2$ | 18-8 | boiling | 130 | No cracking above 6% | 68 |
| Fluoride | | | | | | | |
| NaF | 420 ppm | 50; 500 ppm NaCl | T-347 | L,V | 260 | No effect at 500 ppm $Cl^-$ $\sim 10$% cracking at 50 ppm $Cl^-$ | 64 |
| Sulfite | | | | | | | |
| $Na_2SO_3$ | 100 ppm | 50; 500 ppm NaCl | T-347 | L,V | 260 | 75% cracking in 500 ppm $Cl^-$ V 10% cracking in liquid | 64 |
| $SO_3^{\equiv}$ | 110 ppm | | | | | | |
| $+NO_3^{\equiv}$ | 125 ppm | 500 ppm NaCl | T-347 | L,V | 260 | 5% cracking in vapor | |
| + lignin | 200 ppm | | | | | 1% cracking in liquid | 64 |
| Hydrazine | 8.7 ppm | 50 ppm NaCl | T-347 | L,V | 260 | 35% cracking in $Cl^-$ vapor 5% cracking in $Cl^-$ liquid | 64 |
| Flurosilicate | 100,450 ppm | 50; 500 ppm NaCl | T-347 | L,V | 260 | No effect | 64 |
| Borate | | | | | | | |
| $Na_2B_4O_7$ | [plus air] | none intentional | 18-9 Nb | dry 72 hr | 330 | Cracks 0.002 in deep | 65 |
| Carbonate | | | | | | | |
| $Na_2CO_3$ | [plus air] | none intentional | 18-8 Nb | dry 72 hr | 330 | Cracks 0.005 in deep | 65 |
| $Na_2CO_3$ | [plus air] | none intentional | 18-8 Nb | dewpoint | 275 | No cracking | 65 |
| $Na_2CO_3$ | [plus air] | none intentional | 18-8 Nb | dry 200 hr | 330 | Cracks 0.006 in deep | 65 |
| $Na_2CO_3$ | [plus air] | NaCl | 18-8 Nb | dewpoint | 284 | Complete fracture | 65 |
| $Na_2CO_3$ | [plus air] | NaCl | 18-8 Nb | dewpoint | 312 | Complete fracture | 65 |
| Hydroxide | | | | | | | |
| $NH_4OH$ | 2 N [plus air] | NaCl | 18-8 Nb | dewpoint | 290, 300 | Varying cracking | 65 |
| Sulfate | | | | | | | |
| $UO_2SO_4$ | 0.4 m | | | | | General cracking | |
| $+H_2SO_4$ | 0.02 m | 25-100 ppm NaCl | T-347 | boiling | 300 | with 10 and 1200 ppm | |
| $+CuSO_4$ | 0.005 m | | | | | $O_2$ and pH 2.8,6.5,10.5 | 75 |
| Acetate | | | | | | | |
| $CH_3COONa$ $.3H_2O$ | 0-5% | $MgCl_2$ | 18-8 | boiling | 130 | No cracking above 1.7% | 68 |
| Organics | | | | | | | |
| Lignin | 200 ppm | 50 ppm NaCl | T-347 | L,V | 260 | No effect | 64 |
| Morphalene | 230 ppm | 500 ppm NaCl | T-347 | L,V | 260 | No effect | 64 |
| Octadecyl- amine acetate | 50 ppm | 50 ppm NaCl | T-347 | L,V | 260 | No effect | 64 |
| Tannin | 200 ppm | 500 ppm NaCl | T-347 | L,V | 260 | No effect | 64 |
| Triamylamine + Propargyl alcohol | 20 ppm 125 ppm | 50 ppm NaCl | T-347 | L,V | 260 | 55% cracking in vapor No effect in liquid | |
| Sodium Gluconate | 307 ppm | 50 ppm NaCl | T-347 | L,V | 260 | No effect | |
| Versene | 451 ppm | 50 ppm NaCl | T-347 | L,V | 260 | 60-70% cracking in liquid | 64 |
| Versenol | 485 ppm | 50 ppm NaCl | T-347 | L,V | 260 | and vapor | |

TABLE 7 (Continued)

| Addition | Concentration | Chloride Base | Alloy | Phase | Temp. °C | Effect and Comments | Ref. |
|---|---|---|---|---|---|---|---|
| Others<br>Brine<br>glutamic acid<br>levulinic acid<br>cereal<br>bean sauce<br>tar acids<br>filter aid<br>filter oil<br>pulping process<br>chloronated<br>  solvents | | Wide range | Various<br>18-8 | Various | Various | Cracking | 75 |

The nitrate ion has been shown generally to prevent cracking by Phillips and Singley,[64] Logan and Sherman,[46] and Agarwala.[68] The mechanism for this effect appears to involve competitive adsorption between $NO_3^-$ and $Cl^-$ since the products from the nitrate reduction are soluble (e.g., $HNO_2$) and cannot produce an insoluble precipitated species. Such a competitive adsorption process is suggested by the data of Phillips and Singley who found that at 260 C a molar ratio of $NO_3^-/Cl^- > 1$ prevented cracking providing the pH remained above 8. Uhlig and Gilman have investigated the effects of nitrate additions on the pitting of 18-8 stainless steels by $FeCl_3$ and found that the critical $NO_3^-$ activity to prevent pitting is given by the equation

$$\log (Cl^-) = 1.92 \log (NO_3^-) + 1.34$$

The suggestion of competitive adsorption as a controlling process when species such as $PO_4^{-3}, NO_3^-, I^-, F^-,$ $MnO_4^-$, $NO_2^-$, and acetate are added appears to be well founded. The pitting studies by Uhlig and Gilman,[69] Matthews and Uhlig,[70] Leckie and Uhlig[36] and the cracking studies by Agarwala,[68] and Phillips and Singley[64] argue strongly for the effectiveness of the competitive adsorption process.

Organic inhibitors have been investigated by Phillips and Singley,[64] Podovaev and Balezin,[71,73] Balezin et al,[72] and Podovaev et al.[74] The results of Phillips and Singley are summarized in Table 7 and the materials used were shown to have little significance. The work of Podovaev and Balezin[71] included studies of electrode kinetics, open circuit potential, and cathodic protection combined with the inhibitors. They showed clearly that the action of the inhibitors could be associated with effects on anodic and cathodic processes depending on the inhibitor.

The effects of various chemistries likely to be of industrial importance have been discussed by Copson and Cheng,[75] Edeleanu and Snowden,[65] and many others. English and Griess[76] have investigated uranyl sulfate environments containing chloride. Since most of these random environments have little mechanistic significance, they will not be discussed further.

**5. Effect of Temperature.** Temperature can influence the cracking rate by affecting reaction kinetics of electrochemical processes, dislocation motion, mass transport, solubility of precipitates, and epitaxial film growth. To date no unambiguous study relating mechanisms to the temperative dependence has been conducted. This discussion will consider first the effect of temperature on processes occurring in boiling $MgCl_2$ solution; secondly, the effect of temperature in relatively dilute solutions will be considered.

The most thorough investigation of the temperative dependence of cracking in $MgCl_2$ solutions has been

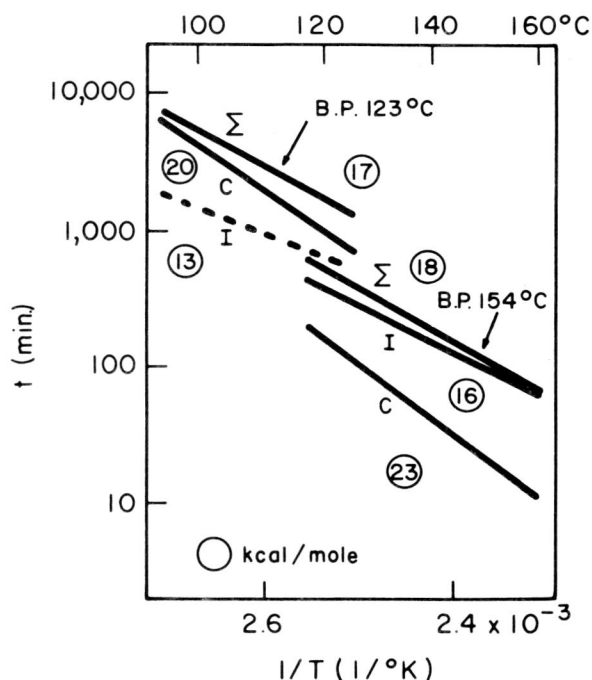

FIGURE 31 — Temperature dependence of stress corrosion cracking parameters in $MgCl_2$ solutions with boiling points of 154 C and 123 C. Tensile specimen, 5 mm diameter, t-time; T-absolute temperature; A-activation energy; $\Sigma$-time to fracture; I-induction period; C-crack propagation period (Kohl[78]).

conducted by Kohl who considered initiation and propagation process, two chloride solutions, and the effect of applied potential.[78] Figure 31 from Kohl summarizes the effect of temperature on the total cracking time ($\Sigma$), initiation period (I) and propagation period (C) for the case of open circuit potential. (I + C = $\Sigma$). For the solution boiling at 154 C (44-45 wt/o $MgCl_2$) the activation energy was 16 kcal/mole for the induction period and 23 kcal/mole for the crack propagation period. For the solution boiling at 123 C (33-34 wt percent $MgCl_2$) the activation energies were 13 kcal/mole for the induction period but 20 kcal/mole for the propagation period. The diameter of specimens was 5 mm. Kohl also determined activation energies for induction and cracking periods under potentiostatic control at -360 and -300 mv (SCE) which correspond to -118 and -58 mv (SHE). He found that the data scatter was considerably reduced and time of initiation and cracking to be lower with the activation energies in the same general range. His data are summarized in Figure 32. Hoar and Hines have also investigated the temperatuve dependence of initiation and cracking periods in $MgCl_2$ environments for 18-8, 18-8-LC, 18-8 Ti, 18-8-3 Mo steels at several stresses.[79] They suggest values of activation energies of 40 and 10 kcal/mole for the induction and crack propagation periods respectively, the former being much higher than that of Kohl. Since Kohl took his values from extensometer readings and Hoar and Hines from potential-time measurements, the basis for comparison may be somewhat different and the apparent disparity in data may not be real. Hoar and Hines also report cathodic potential-current polarization curves obtained as a function of temperature in boiling $MgCl_2$.[136] Approximate values for the activation energy in the range of potential actually operating during the stress corrosion process have been estimated as 15-16 kcal/mole. This can be compared with an approximate activation energy for the corrosion of an Fe-15Ni-20Cr alloy in 1 N $H_2SO_4$ in the range 5-16 kcal/mole obtained by Condit et al.[30]

Thomas et al have investigated the effect of temperature on the time to cracking for Type 304 at three different magnesium chloride concentrations — 31%, 27%, 17.5%.[41] Calculations from their data show approximate activation energies of 46, 23, and 10 kcal/mole, respectively, at those chloride concentrations. Thomas and others suggest that the variation in chloride concentration produces a very small, if any, effect on the cracking time and state that the temperature is a much more significant variable than the chloride concentration.

Andersson has investigated the effect of temperature on the time to cracking for 18-8 stainless steel in 40% $CaCl_2$.[58] If his data are plotted to find an activation energy, a value of about 7 kcal/mole is obtained. He also finds that cracking occurs as low as 70 C.

At this point, it is not appropriate to analyze further the comparison of activation energies because of the lack of data and the undoubtedly complex multiple processes which act simultaneously. However, it is interesting to compare Kohl's data for initiation processes with the temperature dependence of the corrosion current calculated

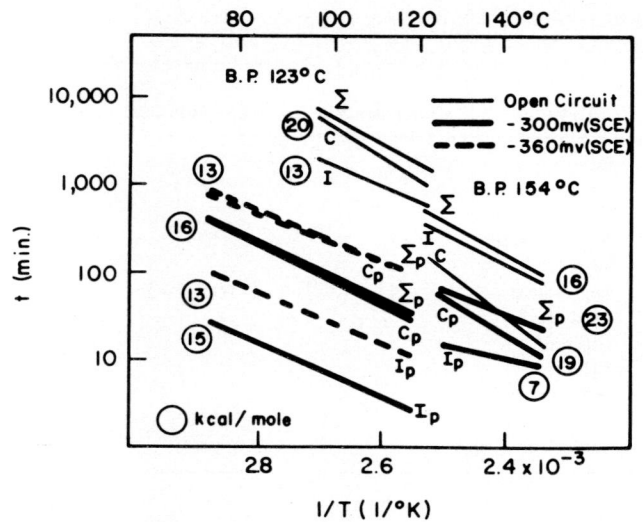

FIGURE 32 — Temperature dependence of stress corrosion cracking parameters in $MgCl_2$ solutions with boiling points of 154 C and 123 C under applied potentials. Tensile specimen, 5 mm diameter, $\Sigma$p-time to fracture with fixed potential; Ip-induction period with fixed potential; Cp-crack propagation period with fixed potential (Kohl[78]).

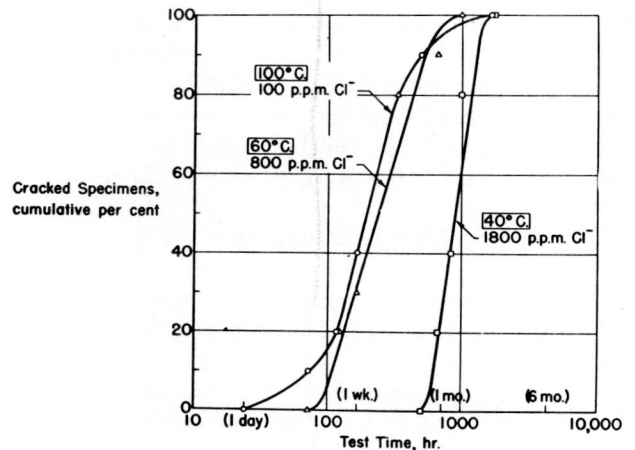

FIGURE 33 — Effect of temperature on the time to cracking of Type 304 stainless steel exposed to water with chloride adjusted to provide the same rate of chloride concentration at three temperatures. U-bends from 16-gauge stock (Warren[34]).

from Hoar and Hines' cathodic polarization experiments. The values are certainly in the same range and suggest that the initiation process is controlled by a dissolution mechanism. The activation energies for propagation from Kohl, while slightly higher than his incubation values, are also in the range of dissolution processes.

Warren has investigated the effect of temperature on the cracking of Type 304 in his "wicking test" in which the solution is transported to a U-bend specimen through a porous material.[34] For a 100 ppm solution of NaCl he finds mean cracking times of about 160, 600, and 3800 hours for 100, 80, and 60 C. Figure 33 from Warren's work shows the effect of temperature for what he suggests are

236

equivalent rates of chloride transport. The significant factor here is the low temperature of 40 C at which cracking is observed.

Various investigations have been conducted in autoclaves at higher temperatures, but owing to the inability of measuring exact cracking times detailed conclusions regarding the effect of temperature are not forthcoming. Significant results and parameters of these investigations are summarized in Table 8.

The data of Table 8 suggests that temperatures as low as 75 C and very dilute chloride concentrations are adequate for cracking. While the various investigations appear to disagree, the conditions under which each experiment was run vary widely. For example, wetting and drying is much more severe than complete immersion.

Work by Frey and Staehle covering the 150-289 C temperature range for Type 304, 309, 310, and Incoloy 800 is summarized in Figures 34 and 35.[82] Figure 34 shows the effect of alloy and stress at 10 ppm NaCl, 12-17 ppm oxygen. All alloys are tested as 0.38 mm diameter wires in unaxial tension at the same fraction of their yield stress, and time to cracking was recorded to the nearest minute. Clearly the higher nickel alloys are more resistant, but are nonetheless susceptible even at the relatively low stresses. Figure 35 plots time to cracking for the first T304 specimen to crack at 100% of the yield stress as a function of temperature at 10 ppm chloride and 10 ppm oxygen. The unusual effect in Figure 35 is the great retardation of cracking at the higher temperatures where normally more rapid cracking would be expected. This effect is probably the result of a competitive film formation which prevents the initiation of cracking in these dilute solutions.

Pickett and Nelson have studied the effect of temperature on crack morphology over the range 289-342 C and find that cracking in a 0.1 g/liter (100 ppm) $FeCl_2$ solution changes from transgranular at the lower temperature to

TABLE 8–Summary of Autoclave Data Showing Effect of Temperature
on Cracking in Chloride Environments

| Temperature Range °C | Environment | Alloys | Significant Results | Ref. |
|---|---|---|---|---|
| 100-210 | 875 ppm NaCl vapor condensation | T-316, T-347 | No cracking below 120 C in 120 hours. Cracking in 1 hour at 210 C (2%) | 79 |
| 205 | 875 ppm NaCl vapor condensation | T-347 | Relatively high chloride concentration required for cracking in liquid phase whereas cracking in vapor condensation occurred at 50 ppm | 50 |
| 150-250 | 10-5000 ppm $Cl^-$ with $Na^+$, $K^+$, $Ca^{++}$, $Mg^{++}$ cations total immersion | Experimental 18 and 26% Cr, 5-15% Ni, 0-4.5% Mo | Cracking absent 150 C and 10 ppm. Increase cracking with increasing chloride above 50 ppm at 150 C | 42 |
| 75-300 | 100 ppm NaCl, oxygen 7-50 ppm total immersion | T-347 | No cracking at 100 C and below at about 10 ppm. $Cl^-$ cracking at 150 C and above at about same rate | 59 |
| 73-100 | 5-550 ppm NaCl total immersion | T-304, T-347, T-304 sensitized | Cracking as low as 73 C and 10 ppm $Cl^-$. Type 347 cracks much more rapidly than 304 | 60 |
| 274-330 | Dried deposit and contaminated water film in dewpoint test. Various additives | 18-8 type experimental steels | Temperature not so significant as additives | 65 |
| 235-320 | Environment inside hollow of stressed tensile specimen | T-304 | Cracking produced at $Cl^-$ as low as 5 ppm. Some oxygen required. No definite temperature dependence observed | 81 |

intergranular at the higher temperature.[83] Typical photomicrographs are shown in Figure 36. This pattern of a transgranular-intergranular shift in mode of cracking occurred over a range of cold work. Also it was found that oxygen is not required for cracking in this temperature range and chloride content.

Definitive work on the temperature dependence of cracking in dilute chloride solutions is sparse and few clear conclusions are possible. The data of Frey and Staehle[82] and Pickett and Nelson[83] in Figures 35 and 36 respectively

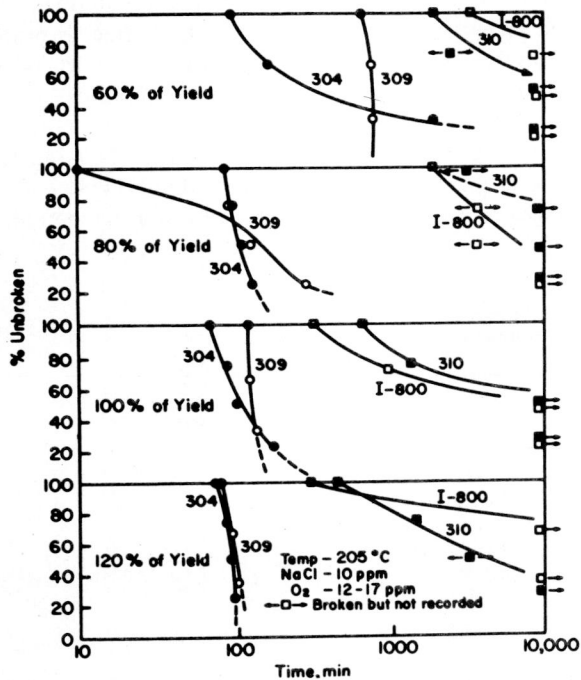

FIGURE 34 — Stress corrosion cracking at 205 C for several Fe-Ni-Cr alloys at various stresses. Tensile specimen, 0.38 mm diameter (Frey and Staehle[82]).

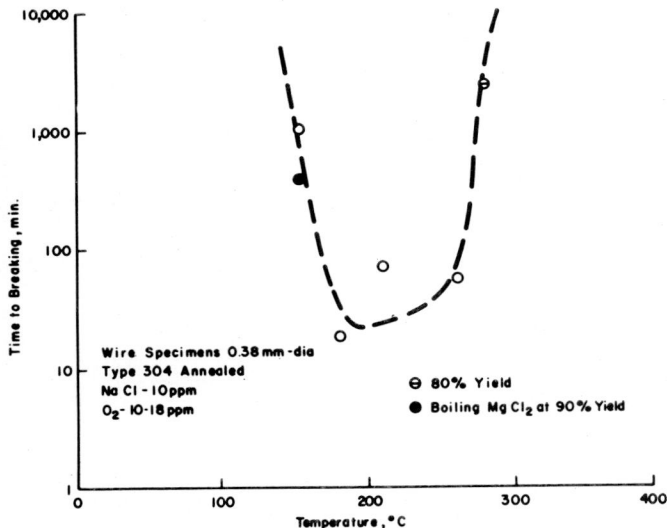

FIGURE 35 — Time to cracking for Type 304 stainless steel loaded to 100% of its yield stress as a function of temperature in autoclave tests. Tensile specimen, 0.38 mm diameter (Frey and Staehle[82]).

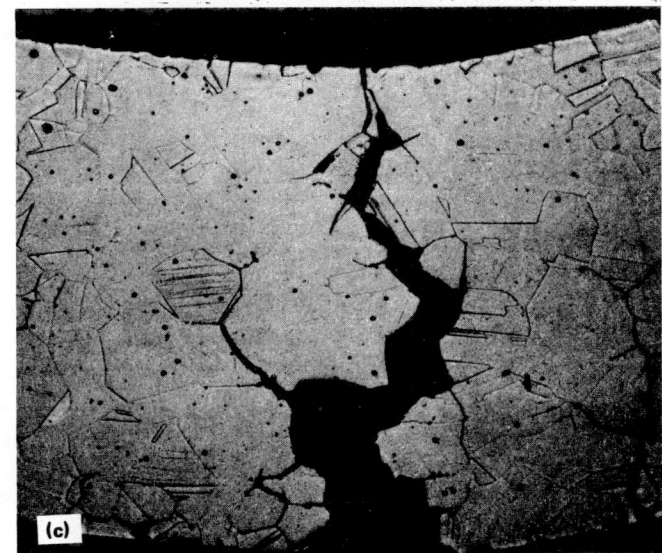

FIGURE 36 — Cracking of nonsensitized Type 304 stainless steel exposed to 0.1 g/l $FeCl_2$ solution (Pickett and Nelson[83]). (a) 10% cold work, exposed at 550 F for 2 days; (b) 20% cold work, exposed at 600 F for 2 days; and (c) 10% cold work, exposed at 650 F for 1 day.

show that competitive processes are operating but their nature is not defined. The temperature dependence of cracking in boiling MgCl$_2$ solutions has been well defined by Kohl[78] and Hoar and Hines[79] but a mechanistic basis is yet to be ascertained.

**6. Effects of Stress and Prestrain.** The general effect of stress on the cracking of Fe-Ni-Cr alloys is summarized in Figure 37 from work by Denhard[85] which was conducted in boiling MgCl$_2$. All specimens were quench annealed. Typical of almost all stress corrosion of these alloys are the two distinctly different slopes on stress vs log failure time coordinates. The equation for these lines is

$$\log t_f = C_1 + C_2 \, \sigma$$

where $C_1$ and $C_2$ are constants for the two lines and $\sigma$ is the applied stress. The clearly evident inflection in the curves normally occurs in the region of the yield stress for annealed specimens. Thus the 310 stainless steel with its higher strength would be expected to crack at higher stresses and because of its higher nickel content the curve would be shifted to longer cracking times. A final important feature of Figure 37 is the minimum stress below which cracking will not occur. Such a stress is called a threshold stress. There has been considerable controversy concerning whether a true threshold stress really exists in view of the finite nature of the semilogarithmic dependence of $t_f$ and $\sigma$ noted above. However, it probably is reasonable when studying fully annealed materials to assume that a threshold stress exists as defined by no cracking in some specified length of time. Such a threshold stress would depend on the environment and the temperature.

Shimose et al have studied the combined effects of temperature, oxygen, and chloride on the threshold stress of 18-8 and 18-8 + 2.4 Mo steels in liquid and vapor environments.[86] All specimens were fully annealed with no machining stresses present. These results are summarized for the 18-8 steel in Figure 38. Important observations

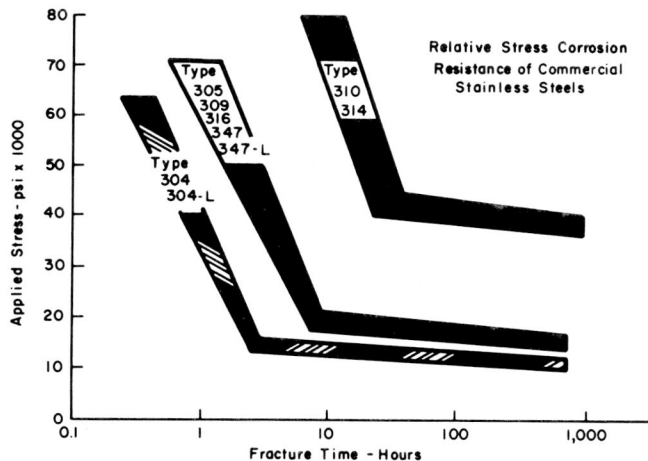

TEMPERATURE
① 180°C, O$_2$
② 180°C, Air
③ 250°C, O$_2$
④ 250°C, Air
—— Vapor Phase
- - - - Liquid Phase

FIGURE 38 — Relation between Cl$^-$ ion concentration and apparent threshold stress in air atmosphere. U-bends and beam specimen; 1.5 mm thick (Shimose et al[86]).

from this work are: (a) increasing the chloride greatly decreases the threshold stress; (b) specimens immersed in liquid require considerably longer to crack than those in the vapor; (c) the use of air above the solution accelerates cracking in liquid and vapor phases; (d) the steel containing molybdenum has a lower threshold curve in every case. Accelerated cracking in the vapor phase compared with the liquid is in accord with the data of Staehle et al.[50] Inhibition of cracking in the liquid at the higher temperature with low oxygen content agrees with the data of Frey and Staehle[82] shown in Figure 35. The important feature of the paper by Shimose et al is the combined effect of chloride and stress. Thus, as the reactant concentration is increased, the cracking rate is increased.

Birchon and Booth investigated the effect of pH on the threshold strain for cracking at 270 C with 5 ppm Cl$^-$ for specimens exposed to a liquid-vapor interface.[37] They found that the threshold strain for cracking increased about a factor of two for 18-8 and 18-8 Mo when the pH was increased from 7 to 10. The lower threshold strain for the base alloy was about $1 \times 10^{-3}$ and for the molybdenum-containing alloy about $1.5 \times 10^{-3}$.

The effect of applied potential on the stress required for cracking has been studied by H. Ternes[87] and his data are summarized in Figure 39. As the potential becomes increasingly noble, cracking is accelerated but with a concomitant decrease in slope of fracture time vs stress. The reason for such behavior is not presently obvious although it may relate to problems involved with transporting the mass of corrosion products out of the crack and the influence of crack yawning.

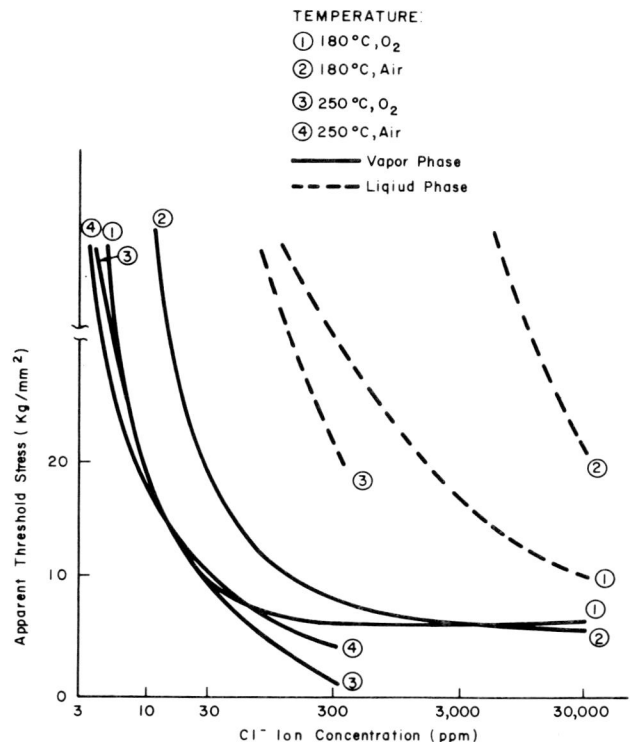

FIGURE 37 — Composite curves illustrating the relative stress corrosion resistance of commercial stainless steels in boiling 42% MgCl$_2$. Tensile specimen, 1/8 inch diameter (Denhard[85]).

239

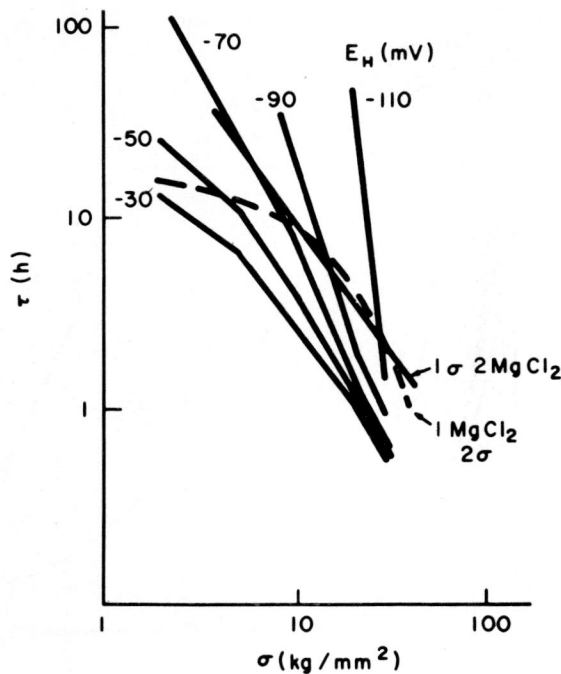

FIGURE 39 — Variation of time to fracture ($\tau$) with applied stress ($\sigma$) for an Fe-18Cr-9Ni alloy in boiling MgCl$_2$. Tensile specimen, 3.5 mm diameter (work of H. Ternes[87] taken from Kohl[78]).

rise but did affect both the potential at which the potential-time curve assumed a negative slope and the subsequent time until cracking occurred. The significance of these trends will be discussed in the section on mechanisms.

Sources and the significance of residual stresses will not be considered here since such a discussion would contribute nothing fundamental. Residual and applied stress can be assumed to be additive; but it is unfortunate that residual

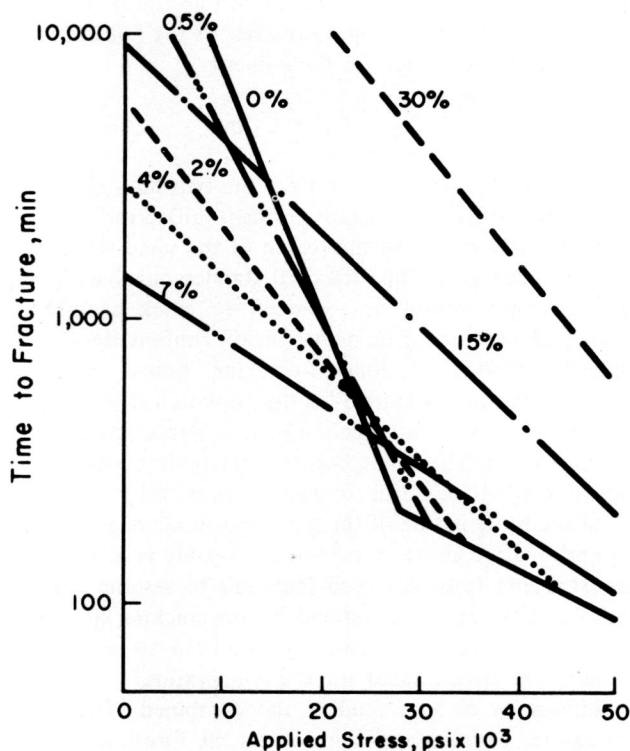

FIGURE 40 — Time to cracking versus stress for various amounts of prestrain for 18-8 Ti specimens exposed to boiling MgCl$_2$. Tensile specimen, 0.02 inch diameter (Hines[88]).

Hines has investigated the effect of prestrain on the time to fracture vs stress behavior of 18-8 Ti wires exposed to boiling MgCl$_2$.[88] His results are summarized in Figure 40. The interesting feature of this work is the effect of prestrain on time to fracture at stresses below about 25,000 psi; cracking time goes through a minimum and then rises above 7% prestrain. Thus, prestrain exerts an accelerating effect on cracking at low prestrain but retards cracking at higher prestrain. The effect of cold work in Type 302 has been studied by Greeley et al,[89] on Type 316 by Hawkes et al,[90] on Type 309 by Burkhart et al,[91] and on Type 310 by Cochran and Staehle.[92] In all cases prestrains or cold work up to 20% accelerated cracking and the trend, except in the work of Burkhart et al, is for still higher prestrains to reduce the cracking rate.

There is occasionally some disparity in the effect of cold reduction on cracking depending on the method of deformation. Prestrain would give relatively uniform deformation whereas swaging or cold rolling would give nonhomogeneous deformation especially at the surface which is also exposed to the environment. For example, Logan and McBee[116] find in their studies of Types 301, 304, and 302 that cracking time generally is increased up to 20-30 percent cold reduction (contrary to the data above); but their cold reduction was performed by rolling where the surface layers are more heavily deformed than in the interior.

Hoar and Hines investigated the effect of applied stress on the potential-time behavior of an 18-8 Ti steel in boiling MgCl$_2$ and their results are summarized in Figure 41.[79] Stress was found not to affect the early stage of potential

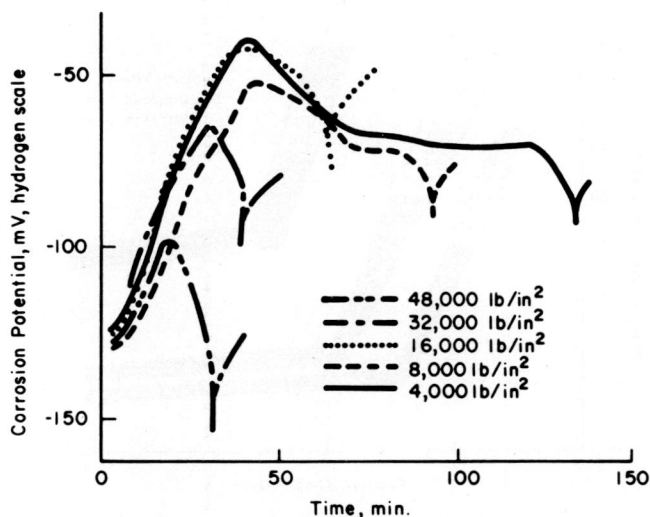

FIGURE 41 — Typical potential-time curves for various applied stresses. 18-8-Ti stainless steel in MgCl$_2$ at 151-154 C. Tensile specimen, 0.02 inch diameter (Hoar and Hines[79]).

stresses are difficult to assess quantitatively. Discussions of failures due to residual stresses have been given by Scheil,[36] Heger[77] and Suss.[93]

**7. Surface Preparation.** The effect of surface preparation on the stress corrosion cracking of Fe-Ni-Cr alloys has been investigated extensively by Cochran and Staehle and their data are shown in Figure 42.[92] The material used was large grained and fully annealed Type 310 stainless. There is approximately a factor of four difference between the mean cracking times of the rough mechanical polish and the vacuum annealed specimens. The mechanically polished specimens (SMP, MMP, RMP) exhibited significantly greater scatter (higher slope on probability paper) than those which were vacuum annealed (VA) electropolished (EP) and chemically polished (CP). From Figure 42 it is clear that surface preparation may be a critical factor in mechanistic studies. The trends noted in Figure 42 appear to result primarily from effects in initiation processes as determined from potential-time studies of specimens under stress. Kohl has shown a trend similar to that of Cochran and Staehle in comparing machined specimens with those from which the machined surface was electrolytically removed.[78] He found a mean cracking time of 25.7 minutes for the former and 104 minutes for the latter with the difference being primarily in the initiation times—4.5 vs 87 minutes. In tests at 205 C in dilute chloride environments, Staehle et al have shown that both electropolished and pickled specimens were less susceptible than abraded specimens.[50] Scheil also studied several surface preparations but his results are not conclusive.[36] Barnartt and van Rooyen[56] found that "reactivating" the previously vacuum annealed surface of specimens by electropolishing and cathodic HCl treatments reduced the cracking time in boiling $MgCl_2$ by a factor of three—a result similar to that of Cochran and Staehle. Again the primary effect of the surface treatment was to reduce the induction period.

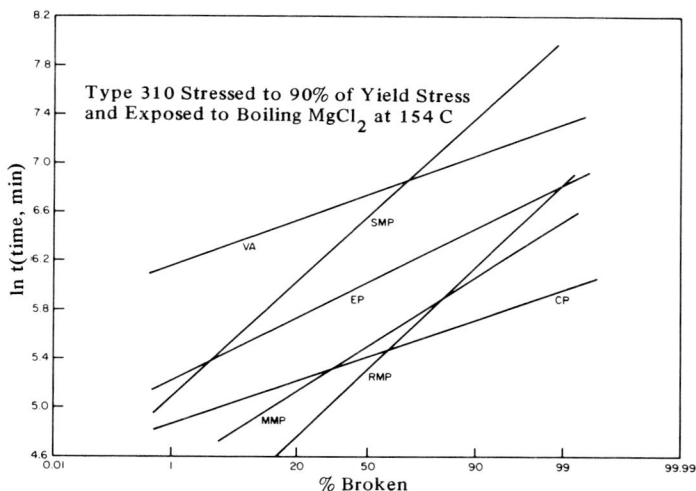

FIGURE 42 — Natural logarithm of the time to failure as a function of percent of specimen cracked for various surface treatments. SMP-smooth mechanical polish; MMP-medium mechanical polish; RMP-rough mechanical polish; VA-vacuum annealed; EP-electropolished; CP-chemically polished (Cochran and Staehle[92]).

Hoar and Hines studied the effect of surfaces prepared by pickling and pickling followed by either 10 hours of heating in air at 200 C or 2 hours at 400 C and found the results given in Figure 43.[79] The effect of the surface preparation was primarily in changing the induction period as noted by the period of potential rise. Koziol and Christopher also studied the effect of preoxidation of Types 304 and 347 stainless steel tubing.[239] Preoxidation was performed by exposing specimens to steam at 316 C for 48 hours. The internally pressurized tubular specimens were tested at 316 C in a solution containing 1000 ppm chloride and 40 ppm oxygen. The preoxidized specimens were found to be very susceptible relative to other conditions tested. Preoxidation was found to have little effect on Type 347 and the 347 behaved in all tests better than 304. Swaging 15% was found to give some improvement probably because the surface layers were relatively highly cold worked and correspond actually to the more resistant prestrains shown by Hines in Figure 40.

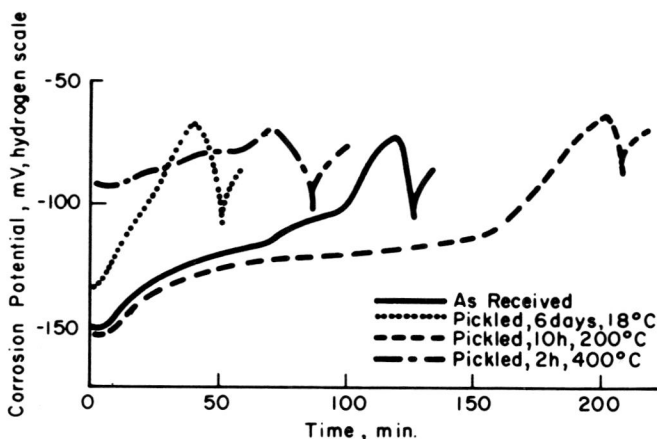

FIGURE 43 — Typical potential-time curves for specimens treated to give various surface conditions. 18-8 stainless steel in $MgCl_2$ at 153 C and at 48,000 psi. Tensile specimen, 0.02 inch diameter (Hoar and Hines[79]).

Koziol and Christopher also investigated the effect of a diffused nickel surface on their 18-8 alloys and found that this treatment conferred the greatest resistance to cracking and also reduced pitting considerably.[239] The nickel layer was prepared by electroplating a 0.1 to 0.15 mm thick deposit and diffusing at 1010 C for 100 hours.

Leu and Helle studied the effects of prepassivation and found that specimens exposed for increasingly longer periods to air at room temperature became increasingly susceptible to cracking.[54] The number of cracks was greatest in these specimens exposed for the longest time. Also if specimens were passivated, stressed, and repassivated, they were more resistant than those which were passivated only once. This trend is in accord with work on the passivity of stainless steel by Mahla and Nielsen[94] and Radavich[95] who found that films of increasing thickness were less ductile and more susceptible to cracking. Of possible interest regarding oxide films is the data of Berg who found that various techniques of surface preparation produce a significant change in the weight losses for Type 304 exposed to water environments in the 300-400 C range.[96] Finally, Rhodin has studied the effect of various oxidizing treatments on the oxide film composition of Type 304 relative to the base alloy composition and his results are summarized in Figure 44.[97] Significantly, there is a difference in the relative enrichments between passivation in aqueous media and higher temperature oxidation and, in particular, silicon is enriched in the aqueous environments.

Uhlig and Sava conducted an interesting experiment to assess the importance of the oxide film. They removed the oxide film from a Type 310 stainless steel by pickling at intermediate times before failure and found that the time of failure was unaffected.[98] This is contrary to the implicit suggestion of Hoar and Hines in Figure 43 which would imply that the total time to cracking would be increased after an intermediate pickle. The alternative model for the factor controlling time to cracking proposed by Uhlig and Sava involves a metallurgical aging process which would be independent of surface preparation. It is doubtful however, that the results of Cochran and Staehle[92] shown in Figure 42 could be explained by such a process. Further, there is certainly some ambiguity in the work of Uhlig and Sava since the critical processes of local crack initiation may have begun before pickling, and the pickling may not have been deep enough. Also, a hydrochloric or sulfuric acid pickle or a cathodic activation might have yielded different results.

While ambiguity exists concerning the role of surface treatments, they nonetheless appear to exert an important influence on the induction period of the cracking process. Thin, adherent, and apparently deformable films tend to provide more resistance than thicker and apparently more brittle ones. Surface films do not appear to exert a decisive effects, actually preventing cracking, but rather an effect in degree.

8. **Neutron Irradiation.** The effect of neutron irradiation on the stress corrosion cracking has been investigated by Cupp,[99] Davies et al,[100] and Knights.[101] All experiments involved irradiation and subsequent exposure to boiling $MgCl_2$. After integrated fast exposure of $5.5 \times 10^{19}$ neutrons/$cm^2$ Cupp found no effect. The work of Davies et al and Knights involved specimens irradiated in the range 1 - $3.25 \times 10^{20}$ fast neutrons/$cm^2$, and they found that irradiation lowered the threshold stress for cracking from a pre-irradiation value of 7000 psi to 3000 psi after irradiation. Also the cracking times at higher stress were shifted 10-20% to shorter cracking times. Knights suggests that the evidence is in favor of a real effect of irradiation rather than spurious effects which might have occurred as a result of handling the irradiated specimens. However, it must be noted that apparently slight changes in surface condition can alter greatly the cracking behavior, and the relatively small differences attributed to irradiation could be due, as well, to these surface effects. The data of Leu and Helle, for example, shows a decrease in cracking time as a result of prolonged exposure to laboratory air.[54]

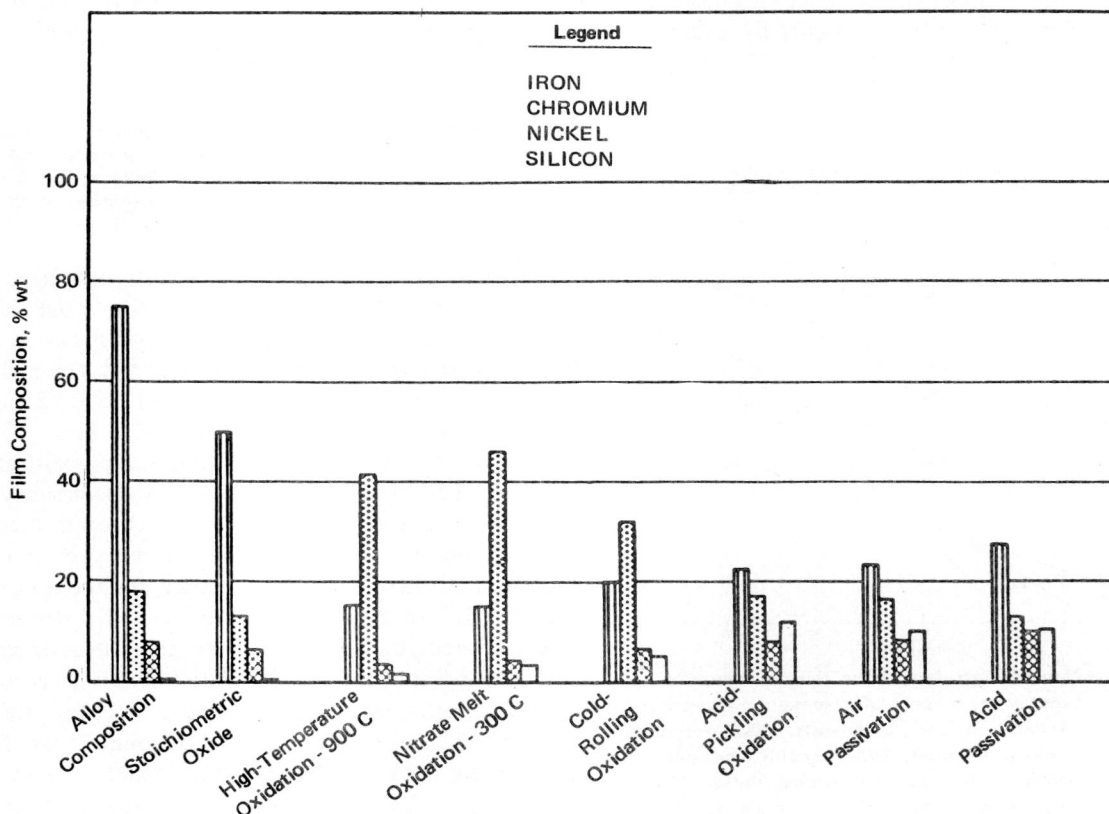

FIGURE 44 — Effect of surface treatment on oxide film composition for Type 304 stainless steel (Rhodin[97]).

**9. Phase.** The most aggressive environment is one in which wetting and drying can occur. This permits chlorides to concentrate far above the normal and at the same time exposes the material to a readily accessible oxidizing agent—oxygen. The wicking experiments by Warren[34] shown in Figure 33 are a good example of the accelerative effect of wetting and drying with cracking occurring as low as 40 C. The experiments of Shimose[86] summarized in Figure 38 compare directly the very rapid cracking in the vapor with the much slower cracking for specimens immersed in the liquid below. The experiments of Staehle et al[50] also show that the vapor region is much more aggressive than the single phase liquid. In boiling $MgCl_2$ experiments it is the general observation that cracking occurs in the vapor region above the boiling solution rather than in the liquid. To prevent this preferential attack the common practice is to immerse the specimens completely.

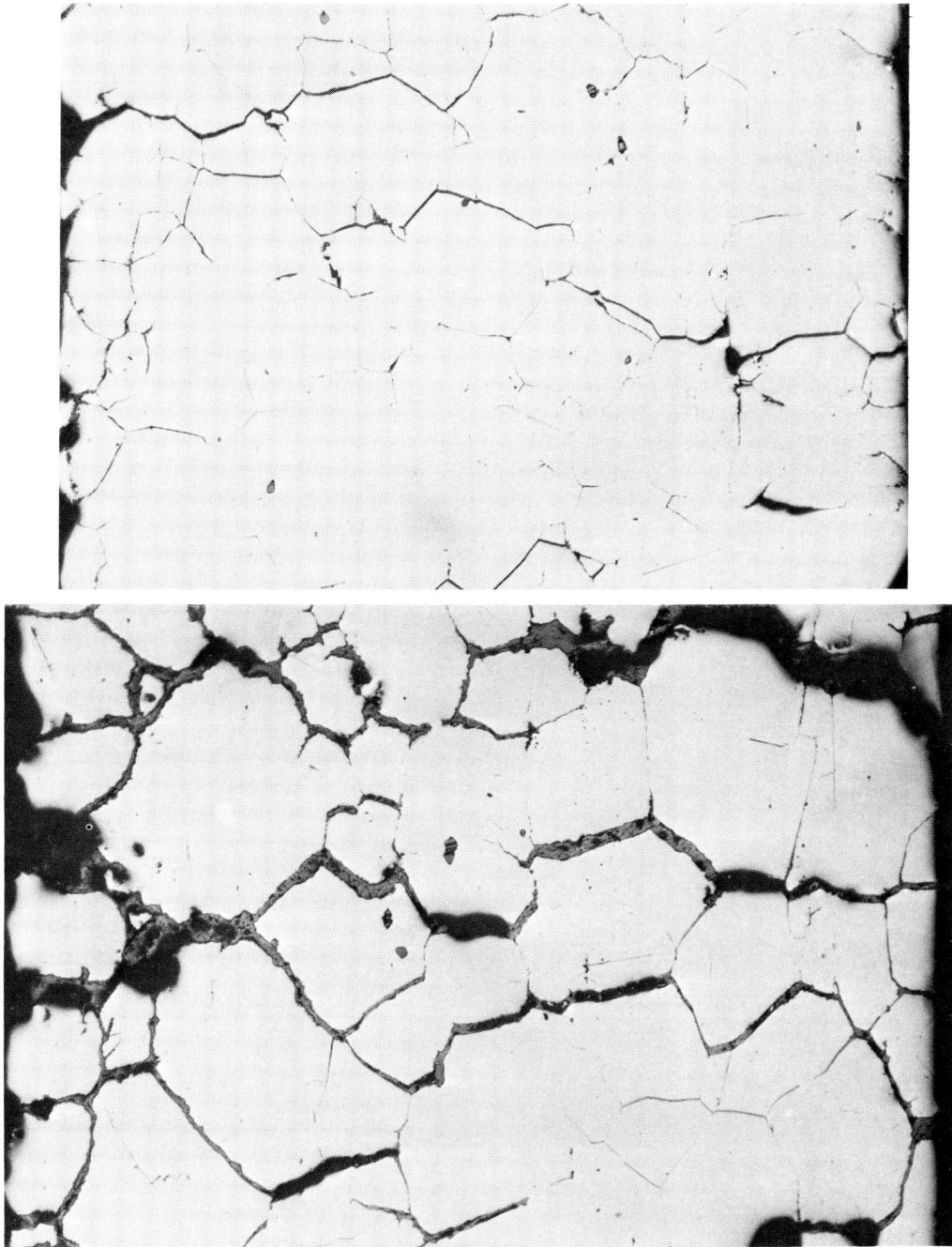

FIGURE 45 — Full cross section along the axis of stress showing intergranular attack present in specimens tested at zero stress (upper) and 15,000 psi (lower). These specimens were Type 304L stainless steel coated with NaCl and tested at 1100 F. As polished. Upper—80X; lower—90X (Pickering et al[104]).

243

Pearl et al[48] have studied various commercial Fe-Ni-Cr alloys in nuclear superheat environments and find that Type 304 is susceptible to both transgranular and intergranular cracking. The intergranular cracking is probably due to the simultaneous sensitization which occurs at superheater temperatures (500-650 C). Chloride appears to build up as a result of its entrainment in the steam from the boiler. It is often difficult to prevent moisture carry over. Also in nuclear reactors some oxygen is present owing to the radiolytic decomposition of water. A comprehensive review of all work conducted in a superheat materials development program at General Electric has also been published. Type 310 stainless steel, Inconel 600, Incoloy 800, Hastelloy-X and Type 406 stainless steel were found acceptable in the superheat experiments.

Pickering et al studied the effect of nominally dry salt coatings in the cracking of Type 430, 304, 304L and 347 stainless steels in the temperature range 590-760 C.[104] The aggressiveness of salts was found to be (in decreasing order) NaF, NaCl, NaBr. Type 304 was more susceptible to cracking than 304L or 347 and Type 430 was not susceptible. The attack was intergranular and did not require the presence of stress. Figure 45 compares stressed and nonstressed specimens. Stress somewhat accelerated the attack. The mechanism of cracking was postulated to involve preferential oxidation of chromium to a nonprotective chromate. The tendency toward this hot salt cracking appears to be partly associated with the fact that the alloy was in the sensitizing region.

### B. Alloy Additions

The relative effect of the various alloying additions appears to be about the same regardless of the chloride environment used. Raising the nickel above 10-15% generally retards cracking; lowering the nitrogen also retards cracking. The behavior of important commercial alloys will be discussed first. Then the results of special studies using experimental alloys to assess the effects of individual additions will be reviewed. Nickel and chromium are dealt with first. Then the various alloy additions are considered in reverse order of their occurrence as groups in the periodic table. Thus, the nitrogen-phosphorous group is considered first, followed by carbon-silicon, etc. This approach is considered efficacious in view of the many apparent similarities which elements from the same group produce on the cracking behavior.

**1. Commercial Alloys.** The predominating trend in the general behavior of commercial alloys in chloride environments follows the pattern summarized in Copson's well known curve of Figure 46.[105,106] The ferritic stainless steels with no nickel do not crack nor does Inconel 600.[36,59,110] Royuela and Staehle have compared various commercial Fe-Ni-Cr alloys having intermediate nickel compositions exposed in boiling MgCl₂ at 90% of their annealed 0.2% offset yield and obtained the data in Table 9.[107] Inconel-600 is a generally corrosion resistant material and immune to cracking; however, some instances of

cracking have been observed and these are discussed by Copson.[106] Such cases have been associated with sensitization at grain boundaries, hydrogen charging and contamination with molten lead. Other instances of Inconel cracking are discussed in Section V, which considers cracking in nonchloride environments.

The effect of stress on time to failure for important 300 series stainless steels has already been given in Figure 37. Hoar and Hines have investigated the stress-time behavior of 18-8 steels with Mo, Ti, and Nb additions.[79]

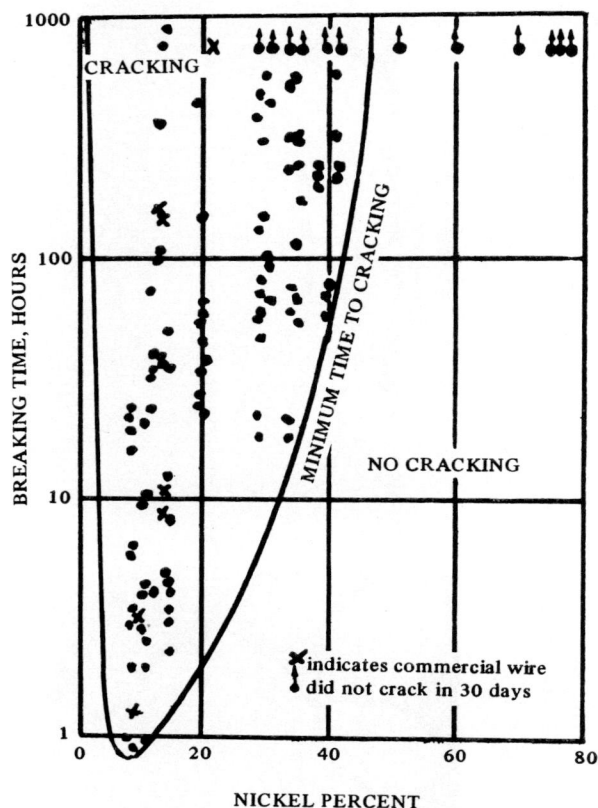

**FIGURE 46 —** Effect of increasing the nickel content on the susceptibility of Fe-18Cr base wires in boiling 42% MgCl₂ (Copson[105]).

**TABLE 9—Average Cracking Time for Commercial Fe-Ni-Cr Alloys Exposed in Boiling MgCl₂ at 154 C[107(1)]**

| Alloy Designation | Nickel Concentration (wt. %) | Average Time to Cracking (minutes)[(2)] |
|---|---|---|
| Type 304 | 9 | 587 |
| Type 310 | 20 | 601 |
| Incoloy 800 | 32 | 1,795 |
| Incoloy 825 | 42 | 6,662 |
| Inconel 718 | 53 | 10,153 |

[(1)]Specimens 0.38 mm diameter wires, vacuum annealed and rapidly cooled, stressed at 90% of 0.2% offset yield strength.
[(2)]Each value the average of ten specimens.

244

Sheil investigated a variety of austenitic and ferritic stainless steels as well as possible alternative alloys.[36] He found that increasing nickel followed the well established trend noted above. Alloys which did not crack after exposures of 400-768 hours included Inconel-600, and Hastelloy-A, B, C. Type 430 (ferritic) did not crack but pitted extensively; Type 405 (ferritic) also did not crack but pitted extensively; Type 421 (martensitic with 1.9 Ni) cracked intergranularly; Type 329 (ferritic with 2-5 Ni) cracked. Other early investigations were conducted by Scheil and Huseby,[108] Franks et al,[43] Scheil et al,[45] and by Hodge and Miller.[109]

Neumann and Griess studied the cracking behavior of a number of commercial alloys and their results are given in Table 10.[59] Of special interest is the cracking of Croloy 16-1 (1% Ni) and Carpenter 7 Mo (2.5-5% Ni), both of which are predominantly ferritic, in view of the absence of cracking in Type 430 where no nickel is present.

This review does not consider cracking mechanisms in the stainless steels which are hardened by martensitic transformations since this is the subject of a review in another part of this volume.[111] The manganese containing stainless steels are discussed in the subsequent section describing the effects of manganese on cracking.

The precipitation hardening austenitic and semi-austenitic alloys will not be discussed extensively except for a few notes. These alloys appear generally to be subject to cracking in chloride environments. The cracking of 17-10 P and 17-14 Cr-Mo has been studied by Denhard[85] and his results are summarized in Figure 47. Cracking in these alloys was transgranular. Staehle has studied the cracking of A-286 at several heat treatments exposed in boiling $MgCl_2$ and results are summarized in Figure 48.[28] The stresses in Figure 48 were all at 90% of the yield but there is a factor of ten difference in mean cracking times. It must be concluded that heat treatment influences the local chemistry in such a way that cracking processes are changed. Figure 49 is a typical micrograph of a cracked specimen of A-286. The cracking tends to be intergranular.

TABLE 10—Stress-Corrosion Cracking Behavior of Several Alloys in Water Containing 100 ppm Chloride and 50 ppm Oxygen at 300 C and in Boiling 42 Percent $MgCl_2$ (Neumann and Griess[59])

| Alloy | pH | Observations[1] |
|---|---|---|
| Croloy 16-1 | 2.8 | No cracks 600 hr[2] |
|  | 6.5 | Cracks < 200 hr |
|  | 10.5 | No cracks 2000 hr[3] |
|  | $MgCl_2$ | Cracks < 100 hr |
| Carpenter 20 Nb | 2.8 | Cracks < 100 hr |
|  | 10.5 | Small crack found after 2000 hr[3] |
| Carpenter 7 Mo (annealed) | 2.8 | Small cracks after 2500 hr[3] |
|  | 10.5 | Small cracks after 2500 hr[3] |
| Carpenter 7 Mo (hardened) | 2.8 | Cracks < 100 hr |
|  | 10.5 | Small cracks after 2500 hr[3] |
| CD4MCu | 2.8 | Cracks < 500 hr |
|  | 10.5 | Small cracks after 2500 hr[3] |
| Incoloy | 2.8 | Cracks < 500 hr |
|  | 6.5 | Small cracks after 2000 hr[3] |
|  | 10.5 | No cracks 2000 hr[2] |
| Incoloy 804 | 2.8 | Small cracks after 2000 hr[3] |
|  | $MgCl_2$ | Cracks < 100 hr |
| Inconel | 2.8 | No cracks 2000 hr[2] |
|  | 6.5 | No cracks 1000 hr[2] |
|  | 10.5 | No cracks 1300 hr[2] |
|  | $MgCl_2$ | No cracks 125 hr[2] |
| Ni-o-nel | 2.8 | Cracks < 300 hr |
|  | 6.5 | Cracks < 100 hr |
|  | 10.5 | One complete failure and one small crack 1500-2000 hr |

[1]Four specimens per test.
[2]Duration of test.
[3]Cracks were not visible at end of test but were found on sectioning the specimens.

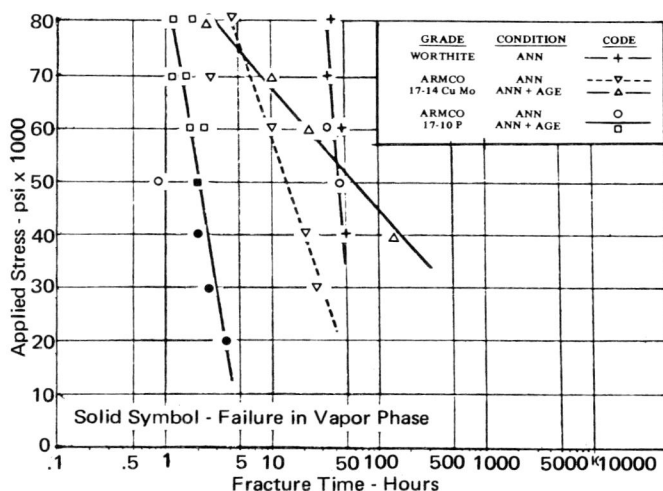

FIGURE 47 — Results of tensile type stress corrosion tests on Worthite, Armco 17-10 P, and Armco 17-14 Cu-Mo in boiling 42% $MgCl_2$ (Denhard[85]).

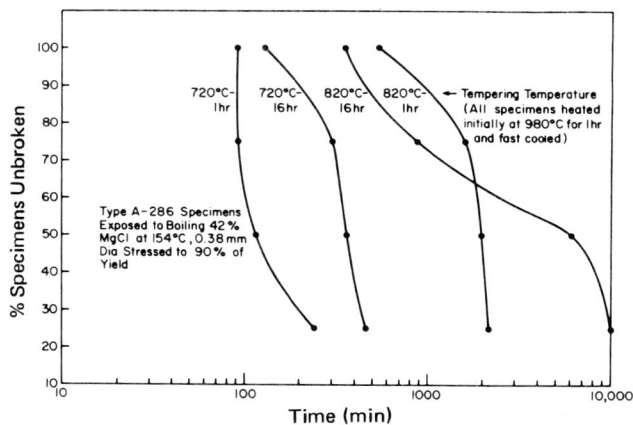

FIGURE 48 — Cracking of A-286 in boiling $MgCl_2$ after four different heat treatments (Staehle[28]).

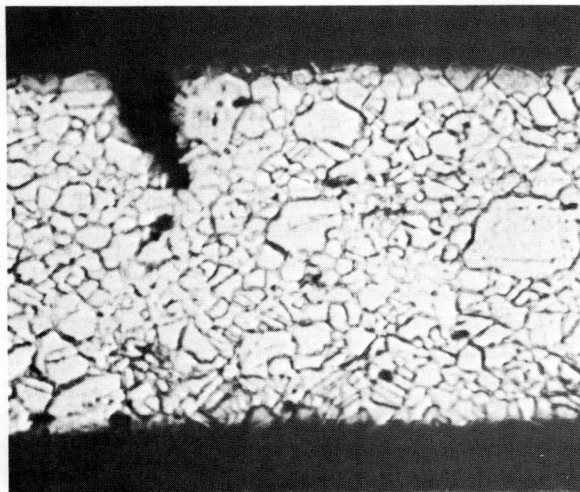

FIGURE 49 — Optical micrograph of A-286 tempered at 720 C for one hour, then exposed to boiling MgCl$_2$. Specimen cracked in 90 minutes; 125X (Staehle[28]).

Bloom[112] has studied a variety of hardenable steels and stainless steels in various environments and finds 17-7 PH susceptible to cracking in salt fog environments whereas 17-4 PH is not.

**2. Nickel and Chromium.** The qualitative effect of nickel on cracking is summarized in Copson's curve, Figure 46, for an alloy base containing 18-20% Cr.[105] Interpretation of the effect of nickel is complicated by the chromium concentration, the $\gamma$ - $\alpha$ phase transformation, the effect of impurities (notably nitrogen), and the crystal structure of the $\alpha$ and $\gamma$ phases. These complications will be considered in detail in Section IV.B.3. on nitrogen, and in Section VII on mechanisms. Despite these complications the overall effect of nickel remains remarkably consistent with Copson's trends.

The beneficial effect of nickel was first noted by Rocha[113,114] who studied the combined effect of nickel and cold work on the cracking in 60% CaCl$_2$ at 100 C containing 0.1 HgCl$_2$. His results in Figure 50 show effects of cold work consistent with the data of Hines[88] and effects of nickel consistent with Copson.[105] Edeleanu investigated the effect of nickel between 6 and 20% with an 18 Cr base in MgCl$_2$ and obtained results which agree with Copson's.[33] Denhard has investigated the stress-time dependence of Fe-18Cr base alloys (containing 8-50% Ni) tested in tension in boiling MgCl$_2$; the alloys were quench annealed.[85] His data appear to be the best available with respect to stress dependence and are summarized in Figure 51. The curves are shifted upward and to the right reflecting the chemical effect of nickel and also the effect of nickel on hardening behavior. Ryabchenkov and Gerasimov have also investigated the effect of nickel additions to an Fe-18-20Cr base and the combined effect of manganese and nickel additions to an Fe-18Cr base alloy.[115] Their results, Figure 52, from tests in boiling MgCl$_2$ show that manganese additions are deleterious but the inhibiting effect of nickel at 40% predominates and ultimately stifles cracking.

Riedrich and Kohl have investigated the effect of nickel additions to Fe-Cr-Mn base alloys and obtained the results shown in Figure 53.[117] These alloys become susceptible in the range of 1-3% nickel depending on the amount of manganese in the alloy.

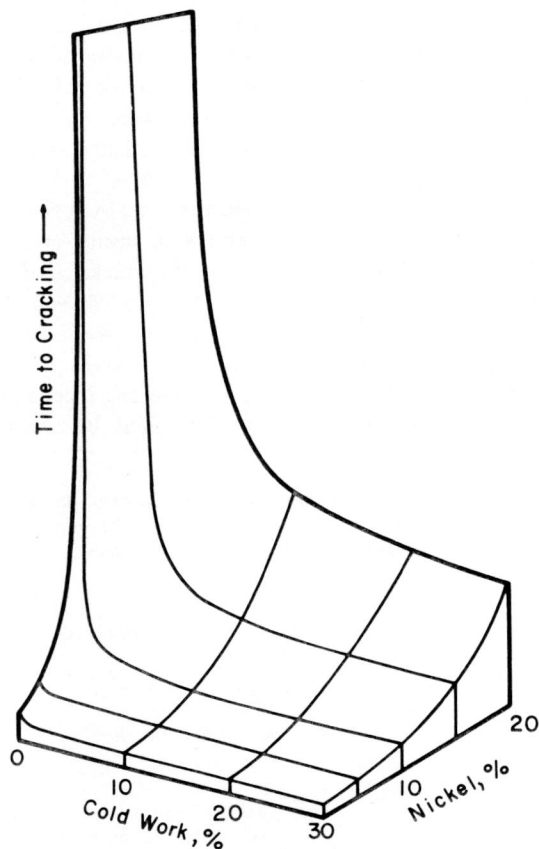

FIGURE 50 — Effect of nickel content and cold work on stress corrosion cracking susceptibility of 18Cr, 8-12Ni stainless steels when loaded to 28,000 psi and exposed to a solution of 60% CaCl$_2$ and 0.1 HgCl$_2$ at 100 C (Rocha[114]).

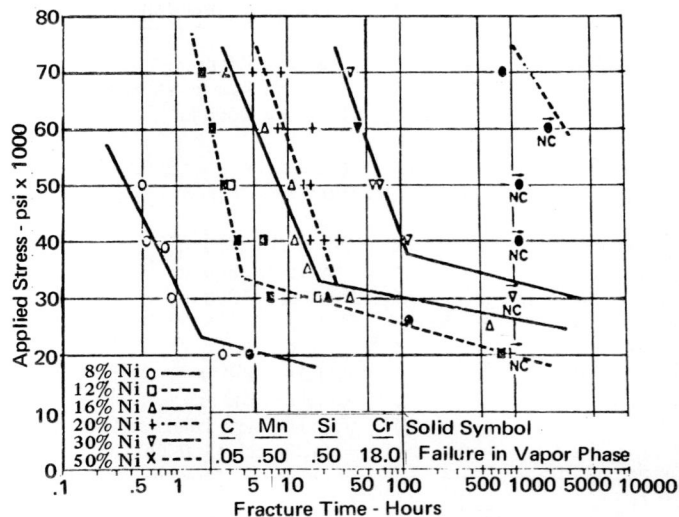

| | C | Mn | Si | Cr | Solid Symbol |
|---|---|---|---|---|---|
| 8% Ni o —— | | | | | |
| 12% Ni □ ---- | | | | | |
| 16% Ni △ —— | | | | | |
| 20% Ni + ---- | | | | | |
| 30% Ni ▽ —— | | | | | |
| 50% Ni X ---- | .05 | .50 | .50 | 18.0 | Failure in Vapor Phase |

FIGURE 51 — Effect of nickel in inhibiting stress corrosion cracking of Fe-Ni-Cr alloys in boiling MgCl$_2$ (Denhard[85]).

Bond has shown that additions of nickel in the range of 1% to Fe-20Cr steels cause transgranular cracking in $MgCl_2$ environments despite their body centered cubic structure.[118]

Copson[105] and Royuela and Staehle[107] have studied the behavior of Fe-Ni alloys in boiling $MgCl_2$ and their results are summarized in Table 11. The results were similar to those for the Fe-18Cr-Ni alloys. Copson showed the cracks to be transgranular and Royuela and Staehle detected both intergranular and transgranular cracking.

There is a clear trend for susceptibility to cracking to follow the nickel content regardless of the crystal structure (ferritic vs austenitic) and alloy base (Fe, Fe-Cr, Fe-Cr-Mn).

The effect of chromium variation on the Fe-Ni base has not been so extensively studied. The first extensive study by Denhard[85] showed that increasing chromium in a Fe-12Ni base increased its susceptibility to cracking in boiling $MgCl_2$. His data are summarized in Figure 54. A range of Ni-Cr variations has been studied by both Truman and Perry[119] (10-25 Cr, 15-45 Ni) and Evans and Burr[120] (16-35 Cr, 8-41 Ni). These results tend to show a minimum in cracking generally at 20% Cr with less susceptibility at higher and lower chromium. The work of Truman and Perry was more specific with respect to cracking times. They also investigated $MgCl_2$, $CaCl_2$, 3 and 10% NaCl at 250 C, NaCl at 330 C, condensing steam and caustic with most tests being in tension. Typical results from their work are summarized in Figure 55. Royuela and Staehle[107] have investigated the effect of a broad range of chromium and

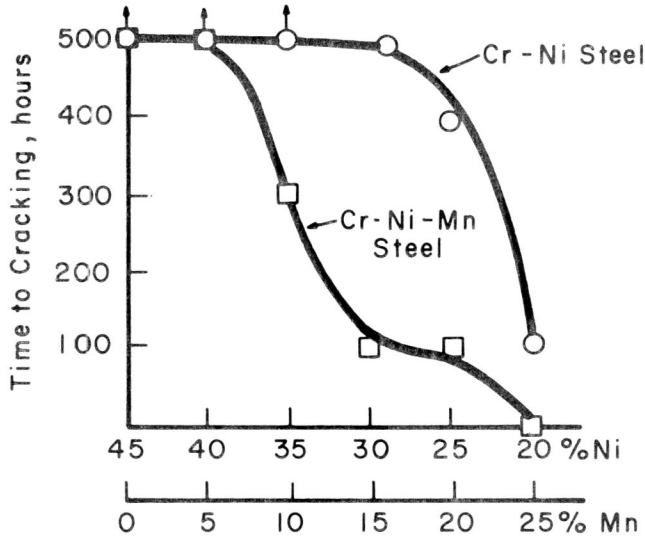

FIGURE 52 — Resistance of Cr-Ni and Cr-Ni-Mn steels to corrosion cracking in boiling 42% $MgCl_2$ (Ryabchenkov and Gerasimov[115]).

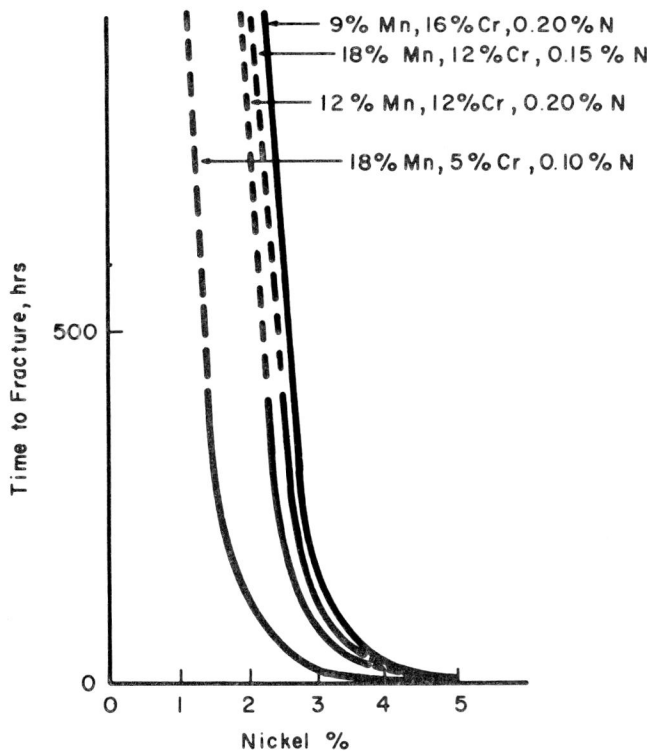

FIGURE 53 — Effect of nickel additions to Fe-Cr-Mn base alloys tested in boiling $MgCl_2$ (Riedrich and Kohl[117]).

TABLE 11 — Cracking Behavior of Fe-Ni Alloys Exposed to Boiling $MgCl_2$

| | Copson[1] | Royuela and Staehle[2] | |
|---|---|---|---|
| Ni Wt. Percent | Time to Cracking (days) | Ni At. Percent | Time to Cracking (minutes) |
| 0 | N.C. (11 days) | | |
| 2.02 | 7 | | |
| 4.96 | <3 | 5 | 350 |
| 8.67 | <3 | 10 | 500 |
| 27.88 | N.C. (7 days) | 25 | 1000 |
| 41.79 | N.C. (7 days) | 30 | N.C. (15,000) |
| 99.41 | N.C. (7 days) | 45 | N.C. (15,000) |

[1]U-Bends, duplicate specimens.
[2]0.38 mm diameter wires tested at 90% of 0.2% offset yield.

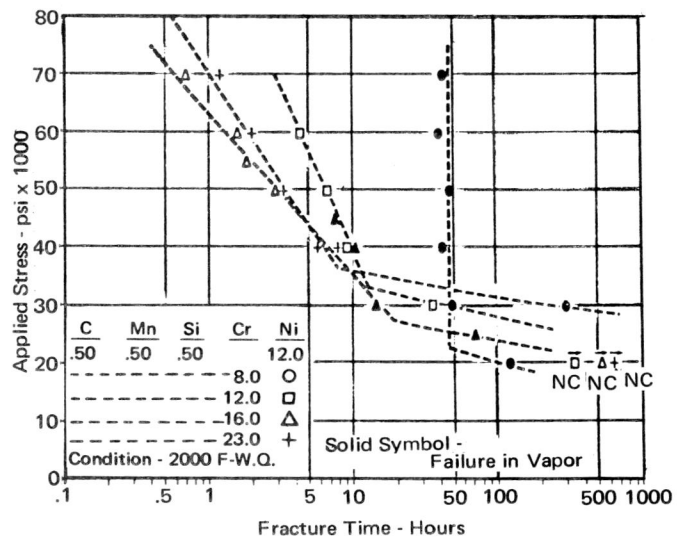

FIGURE 54 — Effect of variations in chromium content on stress corrosion cracking of Fe-Ni-Cr alloys in boiling $MgCl_2$ (Denhard[85]).

nickel variations and their results are shown in Figure 56. The chromium effect has been plotted for Fe-10% nickel base and in the 5-12% chromium range no cracking is observed. Above 15%, cracking is progressively accelerated to 25% Cr. Note that the Fe-5Cr alloy did not crack but pitted. Cracking on all alloys was verified by optical metallography.

For Fe-Ni alloys with about 10-20% nickel the general trend of chromium effects appears to be one of inhibition in the 5-12% range, acceleration between 12 and 25% and inhibition above this value.

3. **Group VB (N, P, As, Sb, Bi).** Lang has investigated the effect of the group VB elements on the behavior of a Fe-16 Ni-20 Cr base alloy in boiling $MgCl_2$ environments and found that they reduce considerably the time to cracking.[102] Her results are summarized in Table 12. These elements are grouped together because of their chemical similarity and their tendency to promote hydrogen pickup

**TABLE 12—General Effect of Group VB Elements on the Cracking of a Fe-20Cr-18Ni Alloy (Lang[102])**

| Addition (wt. %) | Average Life (days) |
|---|---|
| Base Alloy | 17,20 |
| Nitrogen | |
| 0.003 | 10,23 |
| 0.017 | 6 |
| 0.028 | 1 |
| Phosphorous | |
| 0.065 | 1 |
| 0.35 | 1 |
| Arsenic | |
| 0.043 | 1 |
| Antimony | |
| 0.020 | 10 |
| 0.10 | 2 |
| Bismuth | |
| 0.013 | 4 |
| 0.032 | 5 |

U-Bend specimens exposed to boiling $MgCl_2$ at 154 C.

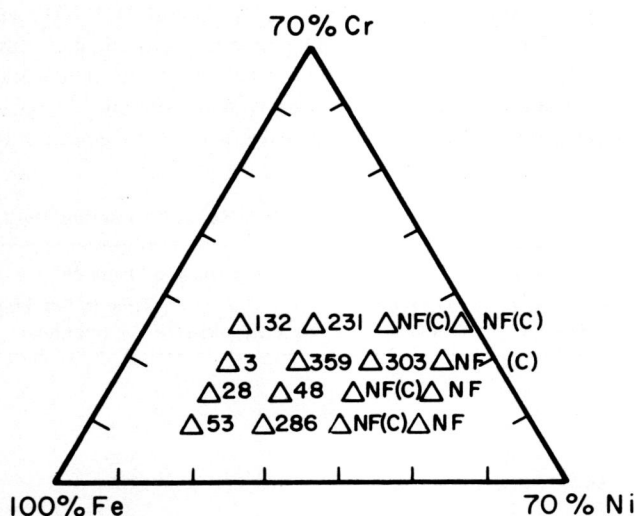

(a)

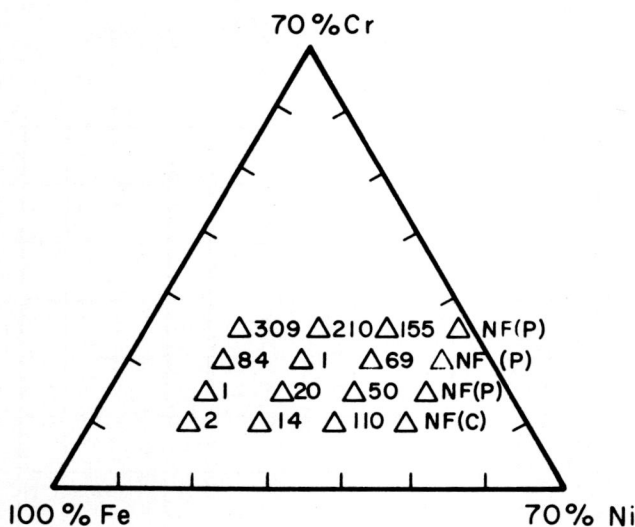

(b)

FIGURE 55 — Time to fracture in hours for alloys as shown above in: (a) boiling 42% $MgCl_2$ at 40,000 psi; (b) 3% NaCl at 250 C/2000 psi $O_2$ and 20,000 psi. NF-not failed in 500 hr; NF(C)-not failed but cracked; NF(P)-not failed but pitted (Truman and Perry[119]).

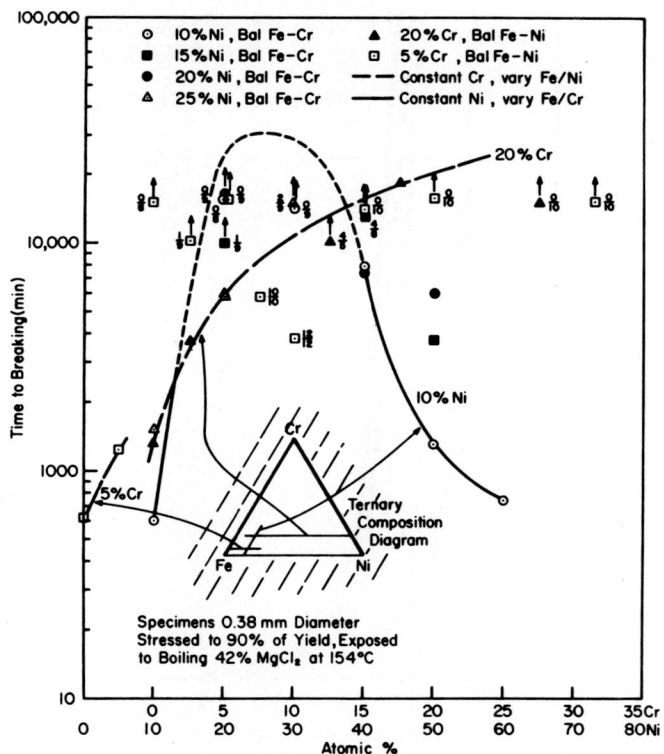

FIGURE 56 — Summary of the effects of nickel and chromium variations on cracking (Royuela and Staehle[107]).

during cathodic charging as well as their similarity in increasing susceptibility to cracking.

*(a) Nitrogen.* Uhlig et al were the first to identify the significance of nitrogen in accelerating the cracking of an austenitic stainless steel.[121] Removing nitrogen and carbon from 18-8 type steels produced ferritic materials which did not crack. When nitrogen and carbon were added, the alloys became austenitic and more susceptible to cracking. They found that an Fe-19 Cr-20 Ni would not crack without nitrogen or carbon and would not crack even with a 0.17% addition of carbon. Adding nitrogen rendered the alloy slightly susceptible especially when cold rolled. Uhlig and White continued the study of nitrogen effects together with several other alloy elements.[122] Their essential conclusion centered about the stabilization of austenite vs ferrite: Factors which stabilized the austenite would promote cracking (a necessary but sometimes not sufficient condition); factors which stabilized ferrite retarded cracking. Uhlig and Sava continued the inquiry into the effect of nitrogen by comparing the aging effects of a relatively pure Fe-19 Cr-20 Ni alloy with Type 310 and found an aging phenomenon in the latter but not in the former.[98] They concluded that the aging effect is due primarily to nitrogen diffusion to dislocations and that this result in some way is significant in the mechanism of cracking—possibly by providing sites for preferential reaction due to solute enhanced chemical reactivity of dislocations.

The several investigations of Uhlig,[121,122] as well as Lang,[102] van Rooyen,[123] Vaughan et al,[124] and Uhlig and Sava[125] show that additions of nitrogen increase the susceptibility of stable alloys containing about 20% Ni and 16-20% Cr. Figure 57 shows the general effect of nitrogen in these stable alloys. The extensive data on nitrogen effects are summarized in Table 13 and support the trends of Figure 57. Uhlig and White's data in Table 13 show clearly that a stable alloy (17-21% Ni) will not crack if the nitrogen is below about 0.05% but will crack at higher concentrations. For about the same nitrogen (0.1%) it is interesting to note that raising the nickel from 8-10% to 17-21% increases time to cracking from 1.2 to 149 hours. Barnartt and van Rooyen[56] show that an Fe-20 Ni-16 Cr alloy containing 0.010 nitrogen resists cracking.

Barnartt and van Rooyen[56] and Barnartt, Stickler, and van Rooyen[129] studied in additional detail the electrochemical differences between the nonsusceptible pure Fe-20 Ni-16 Cr alloy and Type 304. Of special interest is Figure 58 which shows that crack propagation in a laminated plate of 18-8 alloy bonded to the pure Fe-20 Ni-16 Cr alloy stops when cracks reach the high purity material. Application of anodic current did not cause cracks to continue but produced only slightly exaggerated dissolution at the base of the cracks. Thus, despite the prior existence of a crack with its presumed pH gradient, higher crack tip stresses, etc., the crack would not progress when it encountered the nonsusceptible material. When the 18-8 was bonded to a susceptible Fe-20 Ni-16 Cr-1.5 Mo alloy, the cracks continued. Barnartt and van Rooyen showed, at a potential anodic to the initial corrosion potential (-300 mv vs about -380 SCE), that the 18-8 exhibited vigorous hydrogen evolution whereas the Fe-20 Ni-16 Cr did not. While the presence of hydrogen was verified mass spectrographically, this result is unusual because the -300 mv SCE potential corresponds to -58 mv SHE and this corresponds to the $H_2/H^+$ equilibrium at about pH 1. Such an experimental result may be an important clue which suggests that nitrogen functions catalytically to affect the hydrogen ion reduction in a yet undetermined way. In the work by Barnartt, Stickler, and vay Rooyen the Fe-20 Ni-16 Cr alloy was convincingly shown not to be suscep-

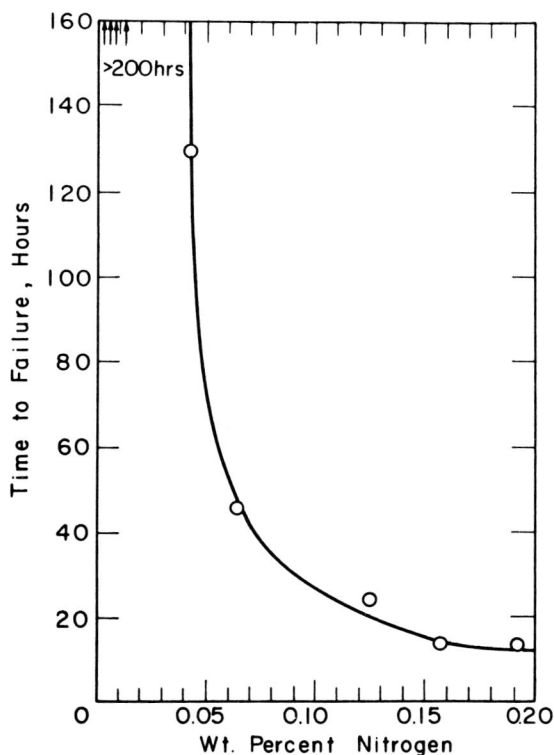

FIGURE 57 — Effect of nitrogen on cracking time of low carbon 19Cr-20Ni stainless steel exposed to boiling MgCl$_2$ (Uhlig and Sava[125]).

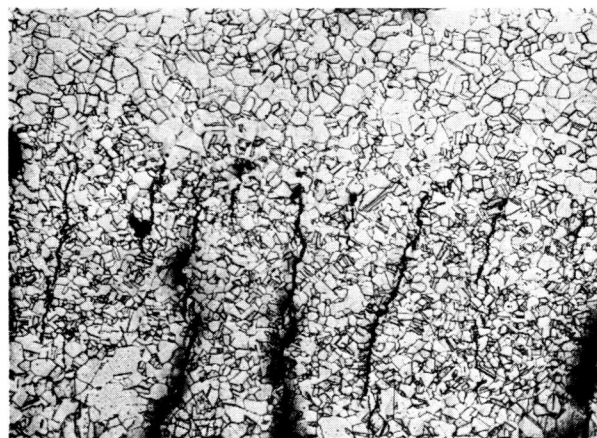

FIGURE 58 — Cracks stopping upon reaching "pure" 16Cr-20Ni alloy after penetrating 18-8 exposed to boiling MgCl$_2$ (van Rooyen[123]).

## TABLE 13—Effect of Nitrogen on Cracking of Fe-Ni-Cr Alloys in Boiling MgCl$_2$

| Investigator | Base Alloy | Test Conditions | Nitrogen Content (wt. %) | Time to Failure (hours) | |
|---|---|---|---|---|---|
| Vaughan et al Ref. 124 | 8-10% Ni 17-20% Cr | U-Bend 42% MgCl$_2$ | 0.0004[1] | N.C. > 500[2] | |
| | | | 0.0003[1] | N.C. > 500[2] | |
| | | | 0.006 | N.C. > 500[2] | |
| | | | 0.023 | Crack < 24 | |
| | | | 0.043 | Crack < 24 | |
| | | | 0.3 | Crack < 24 | |
| | | | 0.3 | Crack < 24 | |
| van Rooyen Ref. 123 | 14 Ni 16.3 Cr Levitation Melted | wire, 0.025 in 42% MgCl$_2$ 48,000 psi | – | 28 | |
| | | | 0.046 | 13 | |
| | | | 0.12 | 14 | |
| | | 40,000 | – | 34 | |
| | | | 0.007 | 40 | |
| | | 35,000 | – | 60 | |
| | | | 0.007 | 54 | |
| | | | 0.012 | 57 | |
| | | | 0.03 | 50 | |
| | 20 Ni 16 Cr | wire, 0.025 in 42% MgCl$_2$ 40,000 psi | | | |
| | | 1.35 Mn + 0.1 C | 0.12 | 120 | |
| | | 1.45 Mn + 0.1 C | 0.03 | > 200 | |
| | | 1.45 Mn + 0.01 C | 0.12 | 30 | |
| | | 1.45 Mn + 0.01 C | 0.03 | 70 | |
| | | 1.45 Mn + 0.25 C | 0.016 | > 150 | |
| | | 1.45 Mn + 0.34 C | 0.016 | > 150 | |
| | | –  0.1 C | 0.0025 | > 150 | |
| | | –  0.2 C | 0.0025 | > 150 | |
| Lang Ref. 102 | 20 Ni 18 Cr | U-Bends Boiling MgCl$_2$ at 154 C | | 480,408 | |
| | | | 0.003 | 552 | |
| | | | 0.003 | 240 | |
| | | | 0.017 | 144 | |
| | | | 0.028 | 24 | |
| Uhlig Ref. 121 | 8-9 Ni 17-20 Cr | U-Bends Boiling 42% MgCl$_2$ | – | > 63 | |
| | | | 0.001 | > 260 | |
| | | | 0.009 | > 60 | |
| | | | 0.15 | 0.12 | |
| | | | 0.24 | 0.12 | |
| Uhlig & White Ref. 122 | 8-10 Ni 17-20 Cr | U-Bends Boiling 42% MgCl$_2$ % C | | | Mag. Prop. as Quenched |
| | | 0.012 | < 0.001 | > 260 | Mag. |
| | | 0.015 | 0.009 | > 200 | Sl. Mag. |
| | | 0.007 | 0.001 | > 260 | Mag. |
| | | 0.004 | 0.005 | > 260 | Mag. |
| | | 0.013 | 0.15 | 1.2 | Non-Mag. |
| | | 0.007 | 0.24 | 1.2 | Non-Mag. |
| | | 0.34 | N.A.[2] | 3.4 | Non-Mag. |
| | | 0.15 | N.A.[2] | 2.5 | Non-Mag. |
| | 17-21 Ni 18-22 Cr | 0.008 | 0.005 | 300,183 | Non-Mag. |
| | | 0.01 | 0.002 | > 200 | Non-Mag. |
| | | 0.01 | 0.051 | > 290 | Non-Mag. |
| | | 0.01 | 0.115 | 149 | Non-Mag. |
| | | 0.23 | 0.016 | > 250 | Non-Mag. |
| | | 0.17 | 0.005 | > 300 | Non-Mag. |

[1]Less than 10 ppm total impurities.
[2]N.C. not cracked, N.A. not analyzed.

tible to cracking by conducting experiments at relatively noble potentials.

The alloys used by Riedrich and Kohl,[117] discussed previously, which were shown in Figure 53 to be resistant without nickel present also contained 0.10 to 0.20% nitrogen. Thus, here were austenitic alloys which contained high nitrogen but were not susceptible to cracking without the presence of nickel.

Van Rooyen has investigated the effects of quinary additions such as Ti, Mn, Al, and Si to Fe-Cr-Ni-N alloys.[123] Such additions might have the effect of reacting by compound formation with the nitrogen to render it less deleterious. Table 14 regroups the data of van Rooyen's to suggest that within a certain range titanium additions suppress the adverse effect of nitrogen. There is likewise a significant effect of Mn, Al and Si. Unfortunately, van Rooyen's data are not sufficiently or statistically extensive to provide the basis for a strong conclusion.

These data from the various studies above suggest that there is a minimum nitrogen content required for susceptibility to cracking in austenitic Fe-Ni-Cr alloys; and this delimitation is in the range of 0.03-0.05% nitrogen. The proposition by Uhlig[121,122] that the primary effect of nitrogen is to affect austenitic stability is ambiguous. If the nitrogen content is lowered, clearly, the 18-8 alloy becomes ferritic; but it is also low in nitrogen and the low nitrogen alloy (at least the austenitic ones) will not crack. It is certainly possible that low nitrogen alloys will not crack regardless of whether they are ferritic or austenitic. Such a trend is analogous with the nickel effect which does not depend on either the ferritic or austenitic structure as shown in the previous section. Further experiments where nitrogen is added to ferritic Fe-Cr-Ni steels are required to

resolve this point. It also appears that the nickel must be present for the nitrogen to exert its effect in view of the Fe-Cr-Mn results of Riedrich and Kohl.

Further consideration of the implications of van Rooyen's data of Table 13 suggest that the effect of numerous alloy elements which reduce susceptibility to stress corrosion in chlorides may exert their influence through reaction with nitrogen. By mass action, the reaction of certain alloy additions, X, with nitrogen may remove nitrogen from solution by X + N = XN. Increasing the concentration of X lowers the nitrogen in solution according to

$$\frac{[X][N]}{[XN]} = K$$

Thus, the beneficial effect of chromium in the 5-12% range may be an example of this effect. Likewise the effect of silicon, aluminum, and the titanium noted above. Whether the nitrogen content is lowered below some critical value by using high purity materials, or by the mass action effect, the result may be the same. Of course, the various alloy additions may have other effects which render them beneficial or detrimental and these may suppress the effect of nitrogen.

The section which discusses mechanism will consider in greater detail the possible effects which nitrogen exerts on alloy susceptibility.

*(b) Phosphorous.* Phosphorous additions were shown, Table 12, to be detrimental by Lang.[102] Work has not been extensive. Ronnquist reports that a 0.2% P addition to an Fe-18 Cr-11 Ni alloy loaded to 20% of the yield and tested in boiling $MgCl_2$ reduces the mean cracking time from 48 to 19 hours.[127] Tufanov,[126] testing in the same medium, finds that a 0.044% addition of phosphorous reduces the rupture time of an Fe-12 Ni-18 Cr alloy from 20-22 hours to 4-9 hours. Royuela and Staehle found that the addition of 0.08% P to an Fe-15 Ni-20 Cr alloy reduced its average cracking time from 110 hours to 27 hours when tested at 90% of the yield stress in boiling $MgCl_2$ at 154 C.

Davis et al[128] have examined the dissolution behavior of the phosphorous-containing alloy of Royuela and Staehle above by using the electron microscope to compare alloy foils exposed to boiling $MgCl_2$. Figure 59 compares foils before and after exposure and with and without phosphorous. The alloy containing phosphorous dissolves very differently, exhibiting highly oriented dissolution sites. These dissolution patterns are not associated with precipitates nor with dislocations. The peculiar geometric nature of the patterns appears to be unique to the dissolution behavior of the homogeneous alloy. Figure 60 compares photomicrographs of alloys with and without phosphorous exposed at 315 C to high chloride and oxygen. The alloy containing phosphorous has a much higher density of cracks. Figure 61 shows photomicrographs of two alloys containing phosphorous which were exposed to boiling $MgCl_2$.

TABLE 14–Effect of Quinary Additions on Time to Breaking of Fe-Ni-Cr-N Alloys[1] (Ref. 123)
(Base Alloy Fe-14Ni-16Cr)

| Additions (wt. pct.) | | Average Time to Breaking at Indicated Stress (Hours) | | |
|---|---|---|---|---|
| Ti | N | Ti + N | | Ti Only |
| | | (40,000) | (48,000) | (48,000) |
| Base Alloy (14Ni-16Cr) | | 34 | 28 | – |
| – | 0.046 | – | 13 | – |
| 0.05 | 0.040 | 29 | 12 | 50 |
| 0.18 | 0.049 | 25 | 24 | 17 |
| 0.31 | 0.047 | 41 | 17 | – |
| 0.44 | – | – | – | 27 |
| 0.65 | 0.036 | – | 21 | 23 |
| Other Alloy | | | | |
| 1.84 Mn | 0.041 | – | 48 | – |
| 0.09 Al | 0.041 | – | 22 | – |
| 0.45 Si | 0.044 | – | 31 | – |

[1]Levitation melted alloys; wire specimens 0.025 inch diameter. 1-5 specimens tested per point, usually 2. Tested in boiling $MgCl_2$.

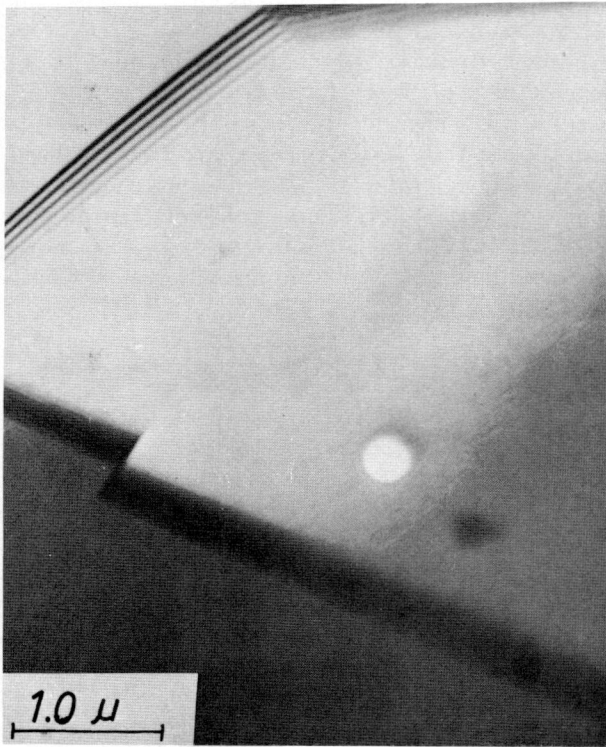

**(a)**

**(b)**

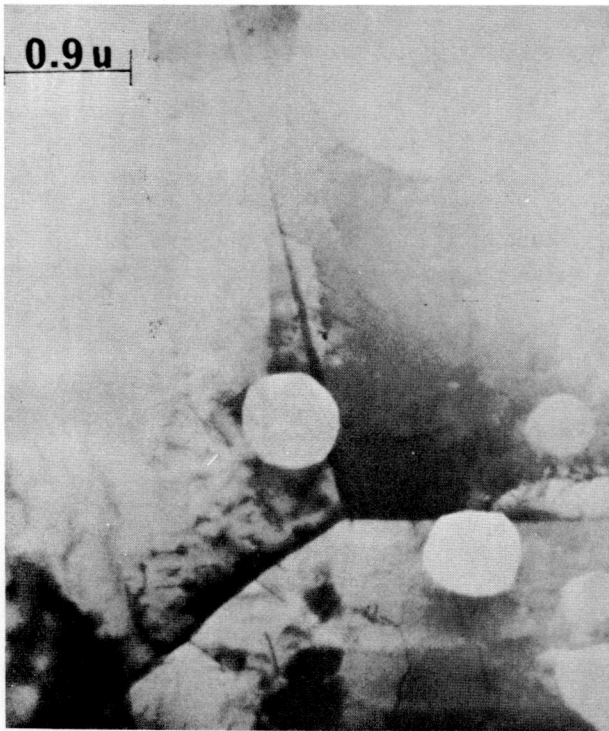

**(c)**

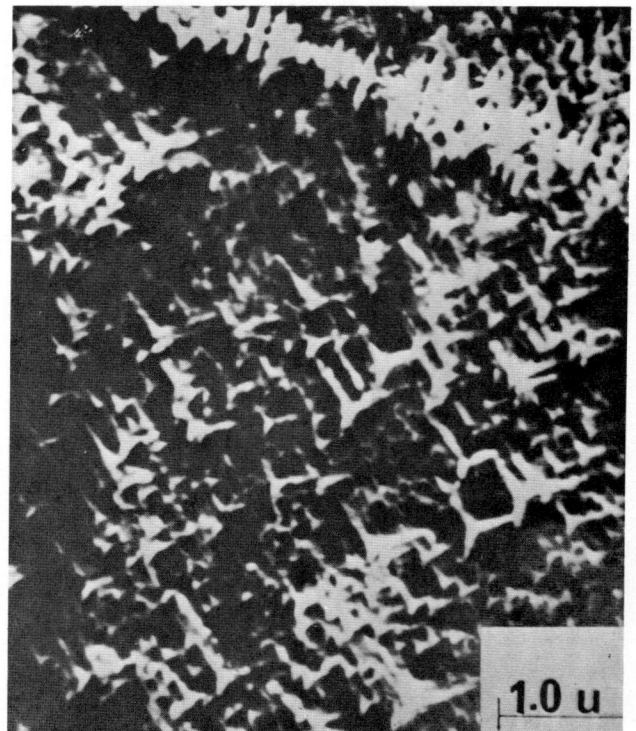

**(d)**

FIGURE 59 — Electronmicrographs showing the effect of P addition on the dissolution behavior of an Fe-20Cr-15Ni alloy exposed to boiling MgCl$_2$. (a) Base alloy, annealed, no P added; (b) Base alloy, annealed, .16 at% P added; (c) Same as (a), but after exposure to MgCl$_2$; and (d) Same as (b), but after exposure to MgCl$_2$ (Davis et al[128]).

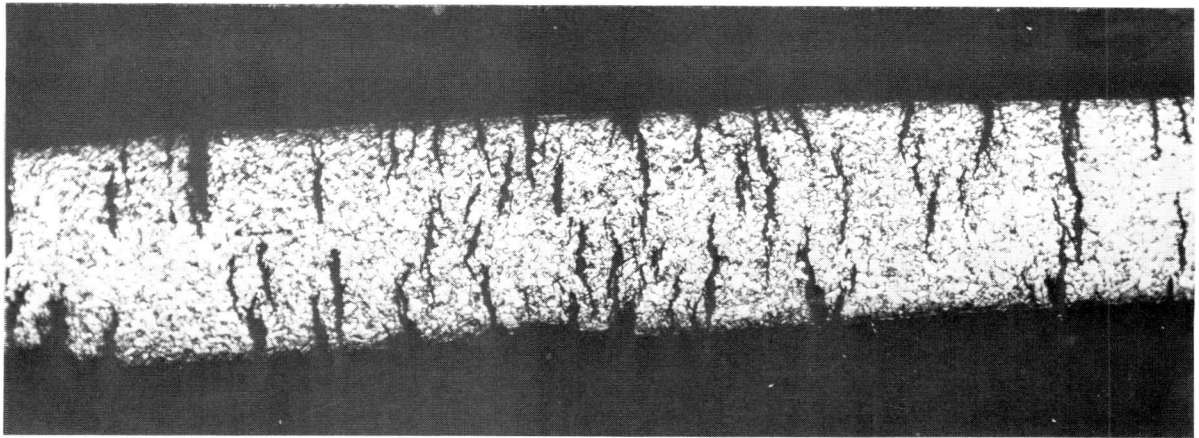

FIGURE 60 — Typical cracks in a Fe-20Cr-15Ni alloy containing 0.16 P. Test performed in a 100 ppm Cl⁻ - 500 ppm $O_2$ solution at 315 C and under a stress of 40,000 psi (Royuela and Staehle[107]).

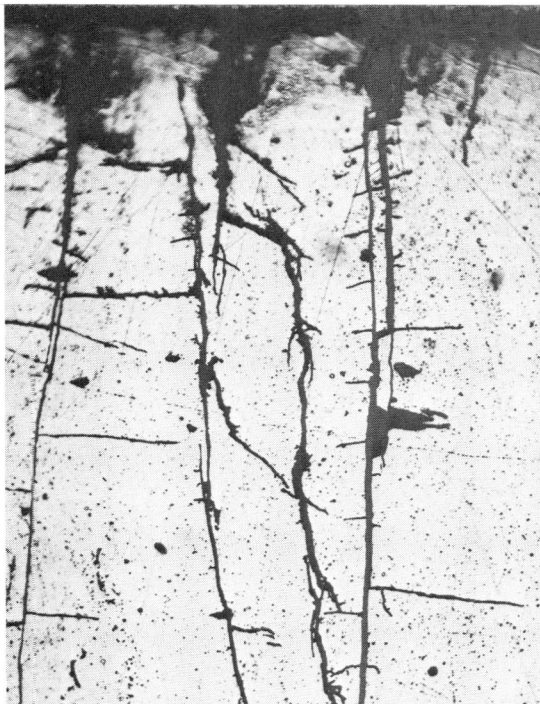

(a)

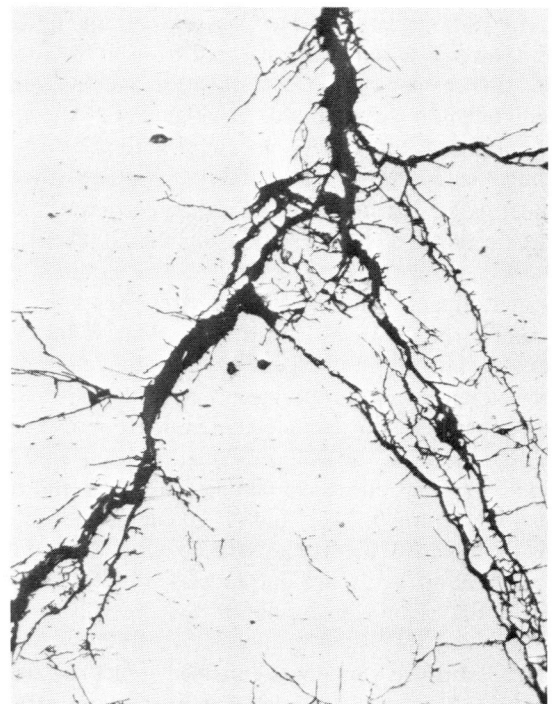

(b)

FIGURE 61 — Stress corrosion cracks in two alloys containing phosphorus exposed to boiling $MgCl_2$. (a) 20Ni-18Cr-.07P (250X) and (b) 21Ni-19Cr-0.35P (250X).

**4. Group IVB (C, Si, Ge, Sn, Pb).** Of the group IVB elements, carbon and silicon have been most widely investigated. Unlike group VB, these elements are generally beneficial; however, carbon and silicon differ in their effects on the stability of austenite with carbon being a potent austenite stabilizer and silicon being a ferrite stabilizer. Thermodynamically, carbon forms a variety of soluble species and gases in water and has a narrow range of stability which is in the region of the equilibrium hydrogen electrode. Silicon is oxidized to $SiO_2$ but can form an

intermediate gas $SiH_4$ that is apparently analogous to $CH_4$.

*(a) Carbon.* The most thorough analysis of the data for effects of carbon appears to have been performed by Hines and Jones who considered the combined effects of carbon and molybdenum.[130] Their results, a statistical mapping of the combined effects of these two elements on the cracking of alloys with nickel in the 5.7 to 19.8% range and Cr 16.4 to 26.6% are shown in Figure 62. Considering only the effect of carbon, (Mo and Ti are considered subsequently) there appears to be a minimum in cracking time between

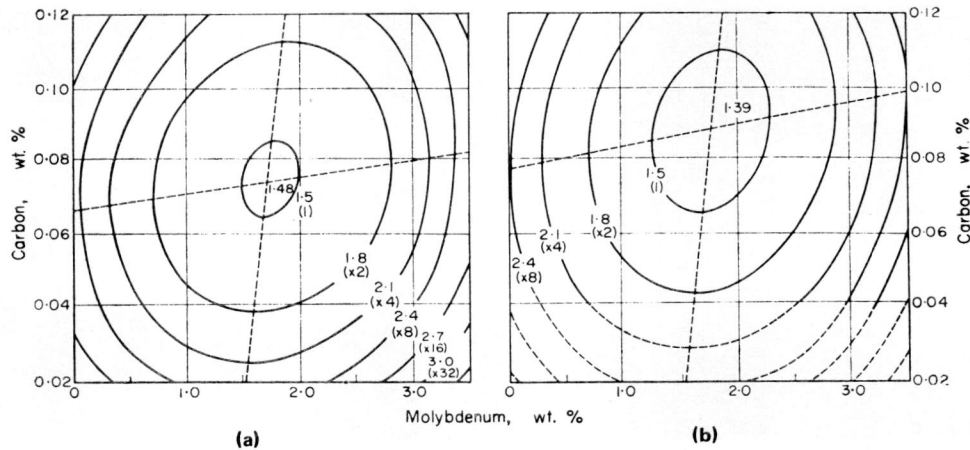

**FIGURE 62** – Contour map showing the effects of carbon and molybdenum on log $t_f$ for steels containing 10% Ni at their 0.1% proof stresses. (a) Unstabilized steels (Ti = 0.00%) and (b) Stabilized steels (Ti = 6 x C). The contour interval of 0.3 represents a factor of two on life. The loci of carbon and molybdenum minima (i.e., the carbon or molybdenum content corresponding to the worst steel at a given molybdenum or carbon content) are indicated as interrupted lines (Hines and Jones[130]).

0.06 and 0.10% carbon. The location of the minimum within this range is somewhat affected by both the titanium stabilization with respect to sensitization and the addition of molybdenum. The trend of Figure 62 showing a minimum in cracking time is in accord with the suggestion of Uhlig et al[121,122] who have proposed that the resistance is at first diminished by the addition of carbon; but they claim this is the result of stabilizing the austenite phase.

Van Rooyen[123] has investigated the effects of carbon alone and carbon with variations in Mo, Mn, N, and Ni. His results are summarized in Figure 63. Van Rooyen finds that wire specimens of alloys having an Fe-14 Ni-16 Cr base and carbon above 0.1% are completely resistant for at least 160 hours at stress up to 60,000 psi. Lang,[102] using a 20 Ni-18 Cr base finds that alloys containing 0.01, 0.03 and 0.10% carbon crack in 9, 16, and > 30 days, respectively, compared with 17-20 days for the base alloy. This confirms the trend found by Hines and Jones without the complication of the phase transformation that prevails in Uhlig's work.

Uhlig's analysis which was discussed earlier (his data are in Table 13) suggested the carbon exerted its effect by influencing the $a \rightarrow \gamma$ transformation. However, Lang's data suggest that the carbon effect is generally independent of the transformation since the alloy used in her investigations was quite stable. The general trend for carbon effects appears to involve an initial increase in susceptibility with small carbon additions in the range of 0.01 to 0.06 and a subsequent decrease in susceptibility until, above 0.1%, the alloy is generally immune. The position of the minimum appears to be affected by alloy additions such as Ti and Mo which form carbides. This suggests that the influence of carbon involves solid solution effects. It is also tempting to suggest as did Uhlig and White,[122] that carbon may affect the nitrogen behavior rather than having an intrinsic effect.

*(b) Silicon.* The earliest work on the beneficial effects of silicon appears to have been done by Uhlig and White[122]

and Bourrat and Hochman.[131] Results from these early studies are summarized in Table 15. Significant improvements can be made at 1% silicon and still further improvement in the range of 3-4% regardless of whether the additions are made to stable or unstable austenitic stainless steels.

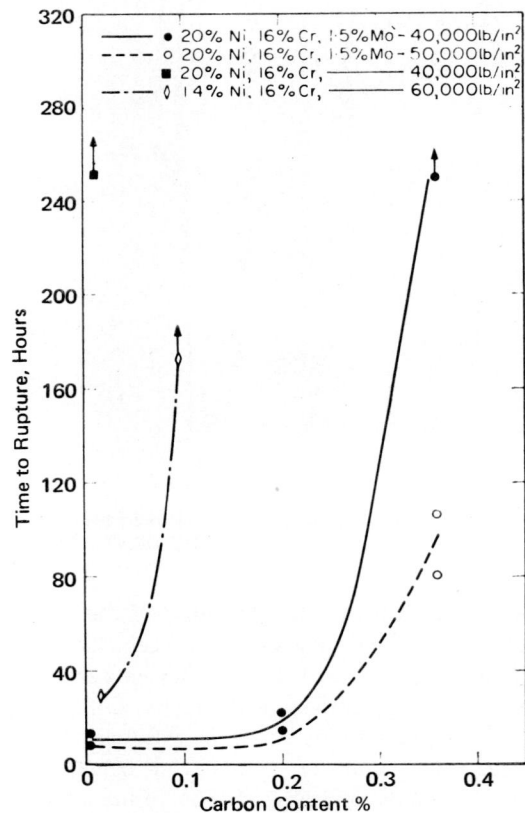

**FIGURE 63** – Effect of carbon on times to failure of stainless steel in boiling $MgCl_2$ (van Rooyen[123]).

254

TABLE 15–Effects of Silicon on the Cracking of Fe-Ni-Cr Base Alloys[1]

| Investigator | Base Alloy | Other Additions | Percent Si | Time to Failure (hrs.) |
|---|---|---|---|---|
| Phelps Ref. 132 | 16.8 Cr + 13.3 Ni | | 3.87 | 142 |
| | 18.9 Cr + 9.4 Ni | | 0.43 | 10 |
| Lang Ref. 121 | 18 Cr + 20 Ni | | 0 2.09 | 480,408 >720 |
| Uhlig & White Ref. 122 | T 304 | | 1.1 3.7 | 31 >250 |
| | 17 Cr + 9 Ni | (0.01N,0.03C) (0.09N,0.008C) (0.05N,0.03C) | 1.35 1.3 2.7 | >250 41 >250 |
| | T 310A | | 0 2.0 | 20 >200 |
| | T 310B | (0.44Cu,0.14Mo) | 0 2.0 | 5.5 13.0 |
| Bourrat & Hochman Ref. 131 | 15-18 Cr 14 Ni | | 0.06 1.0 2.2 3.3 4.0 4.1 | 158 700 193-672 >1000 >1000 >1000 |

[1]All tests in boiling 42% $MgCl_2$. Annealed specimens.

An extensive program has been and is being conducted by the French in connection with the development of alloys containing silicon. Much of this has been done by Compagnie des Ateliers et Forges de la Loire de France.[133] Their alloy designations for silicon-containing alloys are given in Table 16.

Important observations from their work are: Increases in silicon to austenitic or ferritic-austenitic alloys make a significant improvement but incipient cracks are still observed in the 4% silicon alloys in the single phase and two phase specimens exposed to boiling $MgCl_2$. Such cracks are usually only a few grains deep and appear to be arrested in ferrite grains. The addition of molybdenum greatly accelerates cracking and negates the beneficial effects of silicon. The addition of silicon tends to impair mechanical properties if concentration and heat treatment are improper.

The beneficial effect of silicon appears to operate by stifling the anodic process. In view of the effect of silicon on both austenitic and ferritic alloys it must be assumed that the role of silicon is more related to electrochemical effects than structural (i.e., transformation) effects.

*(c) Germanium, Lead, Tin.* Extensive work on these elements has not been done. Lang[102] found that lead additions of 0.001 and 0.003% had no effect in boiling $MgCl_2$ when added to an Fe-20 Ni-18 Cr base alloy. Van Rooyen found that tin additions tended to have a beneficial effect as shown in Table 17. The data are too sparse to serve as the basis for a convincing analysis. It might be noted that both lead and tin have relatively low exchange currents for hydrogen reduction and therefore might be expected to improve resistance to cracking in low pH solutions; however, because of their relatively low melting points the use of these elements may not be feasible.

**5. Group IIIB (B, Al, Ga, In, Tl).** This group has not been extensively investigated and only boron and aluminum have been considered. The effect of boron additions has been investigated by Lang,[102] Tufanov,[126] and Uhlig and White.[122] Uhlig and White concluded that boron in the range of 0.08 to 0.20% added to a low carbon and nitrogen alloy did cause susceptibility in an otherwise nonsusceptible alloy. Lang found that a 0.01% addition of boron accelerated cracking by a factor of about two; but Tufanov found that a 0.1% addition was beneficial by a factor of two.

Lang[102] and van Rooyen[123] investigated the effect of aluminum. Lang found 0.04% addition to be significantly deleterious; and van Rooyen investigating the same concentration observed the same trend. Royuela and Staehle[107] investigating an alloy containing about 0.1 weight percent aluminum found a factor of five improvement. While the data are meager the general trend of boron and aluminum appears to be similar to that of carbon: at low concentrations increased susceptibility tends to be observed; but at higher concentrations, some improvement is noted.

| | Designation | C | Cr | Ni | Mo | Si | Mn | Cu | $N_2$ | S | P |
|---|---|---|---|---|---|---|---|---|---|---|---|
| Austeno-ferritic | Uranus 50 | 0.027 | 19.9 | 8.1 | 2.6 | 0.6 | 0.9 | 1.7 | 0.092 | 0.006 | 0.008 |
| | Uranus 50-Si | 0.026 | 10.0 | 9.4 | 2.7 | 3.0 | 0.9 | 1.6 | 0.068 | 0.008 | 0.009 |
| | Uranus ST | 0.027 | 20.0 | 7.4 | – | 0.6 | 0.8 | – | 0.067 | 0.011 | 0.009 |
| | Uranus ST-Si | 0.027 | 19.5 | 8.6 | – | 2.8 | 1.0 | – | 0.069 | 0.012 | 0.010 |
| Austenitic | Uranus S | 0.016 | 18.3 | 14.0 | – | 4.0 | 1.1 | – | 0.060 | 0.007 | 0.009 |
| | Uranus SD | 0.016 | 17.3 | 15.4 | 2.6 | 4.0 | 1.0 | – | 0.055 | 0.011 | 0.012 |
| | ICN 472 BC | 0.013 | 17.5 | 12.1 | – | 0.5 | 0.8 | – | 0.052 | 0.012 | 0.011 |
| | ICN 164 BC | 0.014 | 17.7 | 14.3 | 2.6 | 0.5 | 0.7 | – | 0.092 | 0.013 | 0.013 |

**6. Group IIB (Zn, Cd, Hg).** This group has not been extensively investigated, except for studies by Beauchamp[52] and Royuela and Staehle,[107] probably because of their relatively low melting point. Beauchamp found that an addition of 0.2% Cd prevented cracking in the vapor of a 205 C test with a 875 ppm chloride solution at 10,000, 20,000, and 30,000 psi. The base alloy, essentially a Type 304, cracked readily under these conditions. Royuela and Staehle[107] showed about a factor of five improvement by adding 1% zinc to an Fe-15 Ni-20 Cr alloy.

**7. Group IB (Cu, Ag, Au).** The standard reduction potentials of copper, silver, and gold are progressively more noble and all are noble to the hydrogen electrode. Silver and gold have not been investigated extensively and copper relatively infrequently—usually together with another quaternary addition.

The effect of copper has been investigated by Hines and Jones,[130] Tufanov,[126] Truman and Perry,[119] and Riedrich and Kohl.[117] Hines and Jones investigated effects in the range of 1% and found slight but not significant improvement after copper was added together with molybdenum. Truman and Perry also investigated the interaction

**TABLE 17–Effect of Tin Additions on the Stress Corrosion of a 14Ni-16Cr Alloy[1] (Ref 123)**

| Tin Concentration (wt. percent) | Average Time to Failure (hr) |
|---|---|
| 0.0015 | 72 |
| 0.017 | 102 |
| 0.33 | 26 |
| 0.44 | 28 |
| Base Alloy (14Ni-16Cr) | 28 |

[1]Base alloy stressed at 48,000 psi; alloy with Sn additions stressed at 50,000 psi. Boiling $MgCl_2$.

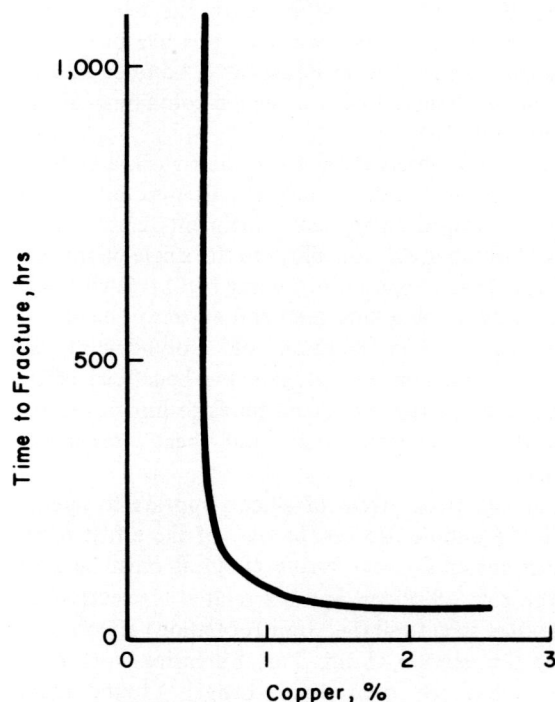

FIGURE 64 — Effect of Cu additions to a 12Mn-18Cr-1.4Ni-.25N alloy on cracking susceptibility in boiling $MgCl_2$ (Reidrich and Kohl[117]).

of copper at 2 and 4% concentrations with molybdenum and found, likewise, no significant effect. Tufanov found that adding 0.68% Cu reduced the lifetime by about 50%.

Riedrich and Kohl investigated the effect of copper additions to the austenitic Fe-Cr-Mn-N base alloy discussed previously in Figure 53. They found that copper exerted the same effect as nickel. Copper, like nickel, considerably decreased the lifetime as shown in Figure 64. The rationalization for this effect will be discussed in the section on cracking mechanisms.

Effects of silver appear not to have been discussed in the open literature. Royuela and Staehle[107] found that a 5% addition of gold to an Fe-15 Ni-20 Cr base accelerated cracking by a factor of about 20 in a boiling MgCl2 experiment. This acceleration is believed to be due to both the enrichment of gold on the surface and its high hydrogen exchange current.

**8. Group VIIIA (The Platinum Elements and Fe, Co, Ni).** Since iron and nickel are a part of the base alloy for this system they will not be discussed as additions.

Cobalt has not been extensively investigated. Uhlig and White[122] added cobalt to a Type 304 base and found that increasing the cobalt content renders the alloy less susceptible according to the following:

| Alloy | Cracking Time in 42% Boiling MgCl$_2$ (hrs) |
|---|---|
| Type 304 | 0.2 |
| + 1.8 Co | 1.5 |
| + 6.0 Co | 3.1 |
| +13.7 Co | 5.5 |

Such an effect should be expected since cobalt and nickel are electrochemically similar. Adding cobalt should be equivalent to adding more nickel.

The effect of platinum elements (Os, In, Pt, Ru, Rh, Pd) has been investigated by Lang,[102] van Rooyen,[123] and Royuela and Staehle.[107] These alloys all have relatively high hydrogen exchange currents and are substantially noble to the hydrogen electrode. The general finding is that the platinum elements greatly accelerate the cracking process. Lang found that 0.21% Ru accelerated cracking by a factor of 20; van Rooyen found at least a factor of 5 increase in cracking rate. Royuela and Staehle found that the platinum elements accelerate cracking by a factor of 10-100 depending on the element (Pb, Pd, Rh, Ru) with Pt having the greatest effect. Royuela and Staehle also found that cracking of alloys containing the platinum elements is always intergranular in boiling MgCl2 and at 315 C in 0.1% NaCl and 500 ppm oxygen. Figure 65 shows the typically intergranular cracking resulting from the addition of platinum elements.

**9. Group VIIA (Mn, Re).** The effect of manganese on the cracking of Fe-Ni-Cr alloys has been studied by a number of investigators. Very little work has been done on effect of rhenium, no doubt because of its cost and scarcity.

Barnartt et al[129] added 1.45 weight percent Mn as well as Ti and Mo (separately) to the Fe-20 Ni-16 Cr base which had been shown to be immune to cracking. While titanium and molybdenum additions induced susceptibility, manganese did not. This experiment probably provides the least ambiguous information on effects of Mn. Van Rooyen[123] investigated the effect of manganese additions and his significant results are summarized in Table 18. In general manganese in the 1-4 weight percent range appears to exert little significant influence in either direction. At less than 1 weight percent there appears to be a slight tendency for manganese additions to accelerate cracking.

The investigations by Riedrich and Kohl[117] in Figures 53 and 64 show that Mn alloyed with Fe-Cr-N bases does not initiate cracking. Cracking only begins when the nickel or copper is added. According to Figure 53 there is a slight tendency for increasing Mn (in the 9-18% range) to accelerate cracking at a given nickel concentration. The work of Ryabchenkov and Gerasimov[115] already summarized in Figure 52 showed the same trend; Mn additions (10-25% Mn) accelerate cracking. Royuela and Staehle have exposed Type 202 (18 Cr-8 Mn-5 Ni) and Tenelon (18 Cr-15 Mn-0.4 N) stressed to 90% of the 0.2% offset yield to boiling 42% MgCl2 and find that average cracking times are 6.5 and 105 minutes compared with the much longer times for the non-Mn austenitic alloys. Photomicrographs of typical cracks in these alloys are shown in Figure 66. The higher Mn content promotes both intergranular cracking as well as intergranular oxidation in the Tenelon.

TABLE 18—Effect of Manganese Additions to Various Fe-Ni-Cr Base Alloys on Stress Corrosion Cracking in Boiling MgCl$_2$[1] (Ref. 123)

| | Cracking Time (hr.) Under Stress (psi) | | |
|---|---|---|---|
| | 35,00 | 40,000 | 48,000 |
| Base Alloy Fe-14Ni-16Cr Levitation Melted | 60 | 34 | 28 |
| + 0.45 Mn | – | 15 | 14 |
| + 1.96 Mn | 43 | – | 23 |
| + 1.84 Mn + .041 N | – | – | 48 |
| Base Alloy Fe-20Ni-16Cr Vacuum Melted | – | >250 | – |
| + 1.47 Mn + 0.0007 N | – | >200 | – |
| + 1.45 Mn + 0.016 N | – | >130 | – |
| + 1.7 Mn + 0.05 N | – | 125 >130 | – |
| Base Alloy Fe-20Ni-16.5Cr Air Melted | – | – | – |
| + 1.44 Mn + 1.03 Mo | – | 8 | – |
| + 1.56 Mn + 0.002 Mo | 170 | | |
| Base Alloy Fe-20Ni-16Cr Levitation Melted | – | – | – |
| + 1.45 Mn + 0.1 C | – | >150 | – |
| + 1.45 Mo + 0.1 C | 11 | | |

[1]0.025 inch diameter wire specimens.

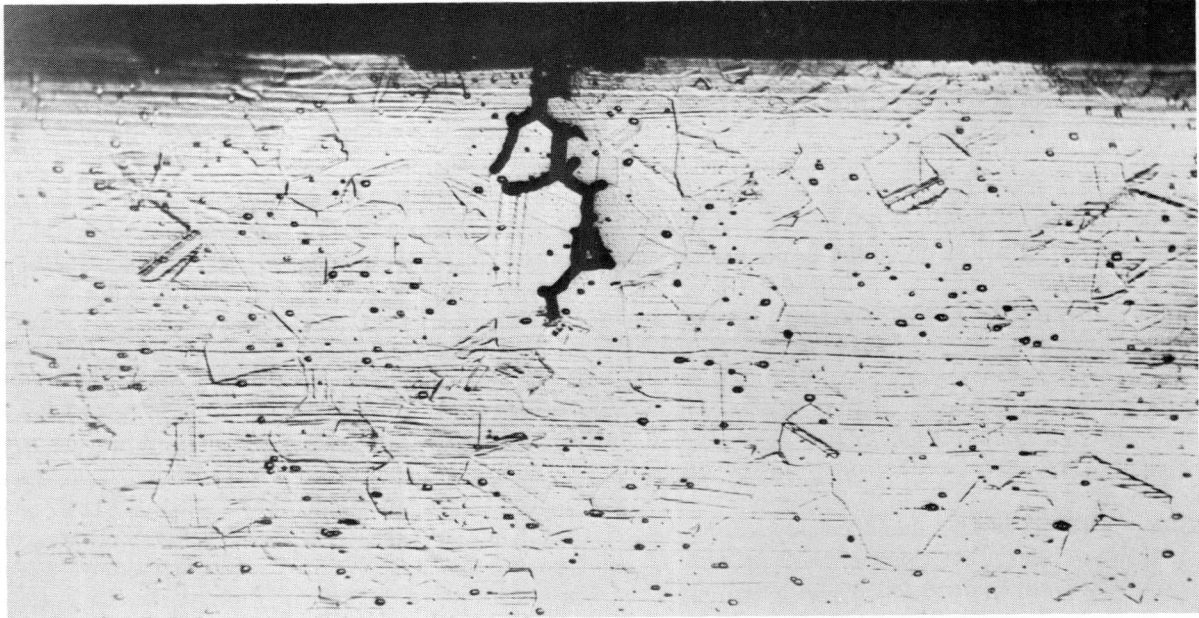

FIGURE 65 — Typical intergranular cracking in a Fe-20Cr-15Ni alloy containing 1.5% Ir. Tests performed in a 100 ppm Cl⁻ - 500 ppm $O_2$ solution at 315 C under a stress of 40,000 psi (Royuela and Staehle[107]).

Manganese in relatively low concentration (0.1-4.0%) appears to have little significant effect. At higher concentrations (> 5%) manganese tends to have a somewhat deleterious effect.

Rhenium additions have not been studied except for the work of Royuela and Staehle[107] who found that additions of about 4% to an Fe-15 Ni-20 Cr alloy accelerated cracking by a factor of approximately ten in boiling $MgCl_2$ solutions. As the platinum elements, rhenium promotes intergranular cracking.

**10. Group VIA (Cr, Mo, W).** The effect of chromium has been already discussed. The influence of molybdenum has been extensively investigated; and tungsten has received very little attention. These elements tend to be similar with respect to metallurgical compound formation and all have relatively high melting points. Chromium and molybdenum also act to reduce pitting. The addition of chromium to iron reduces pitting until it stops in the region of 24-30% Cr.[134] The addition of about 2.5% molybdenum to Type 304 gives Type 316 which is then much more resistant to pitting.[135] Chromium differs considerably from molybdenum and tungsten with respect to stable species in aqueous solutions.[29] Chromium is oxidized to $Cr^{++}$ at a potential in the region of -1.0 volt; the oxidized species is stable over a range of pH up to 4-5. On the other hand both Mo and W are oxidized at more noble potentials in a range of -0.2 volts; the range of pH over which the soluble oxidized species are stable is greatly restricted relative to that for chromium.

The extensive investigations into the effect of molybdenum appear to have been prompted by the significant improvement in pitting resistance resulting from the Mo additions to 18-8 type base. Figure 62 which was discussed

earlier to show the combined effects of carbon and molybdenum illustrates the general influence of molybdenum, namely, to increase cracking susceptibility. Barnartt et al provided unequivocal proof that the Mo addition alone is decisive by adding 1.5% to an immune Fe-20 Ni-16 Cr alloy whereupon it immediately became susceptible.[129] Figure 63 shows that the presence of 1.5% molybdenum displaces the point of optimum benefit of carbon additions from about 0.05 to 0.30%. Van Rooyen also investigated the interaction between Mn and Mo (presumably the addition of Mn would counteract the ferrite forming tendency of Mo) and up to 6.29% Mn was not able to negate the deleterious effect of 4% Mo. Van Rooyen also found that Mo begins to exert its significant detrimental effect at about 0.1-0.2% in a 20% Ni alloy.

Truman and Perry investigated the effect of Mo additions to Fe-Ni-15 Cr alloys with nickel at 15, 25, 35, and 45% concentrations and found no significant effects of 2.5 and 5.0 Mo additions.[119] Quinary copper additions to the Fe-Ni-Cr-Mo alloys also produced little effect. There was some tendency as predicted by Hines and Jones,[130] for the 5% Mo addition to be beneficial.

Hoar and Hines[79] have compared in considerable detail the behavior of an 18-8 and 18-8 Mo steel exposed to boiling $MgCl_2$ with respect to times to failure as affected by stress, potential-time behavior, and temperature dependence of induction and fracture times. The primary effect of the molybdenum appears to be in reducing the induction time as shown in Figure 67. A comparison of failure time vs stress plots for 18-8, 18-8 Ti, 18-8 LC and 18-8-3 Mo is shown in Figure 68. Molybdenum is detrimental by a wide range.

Molybdenum additions appear clearly detrimental in

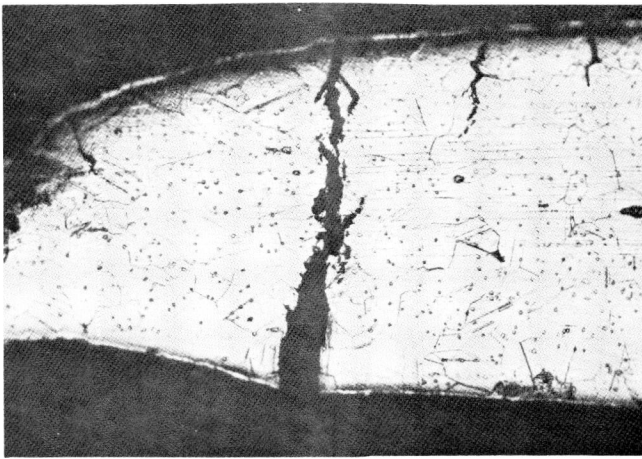

**(a)**

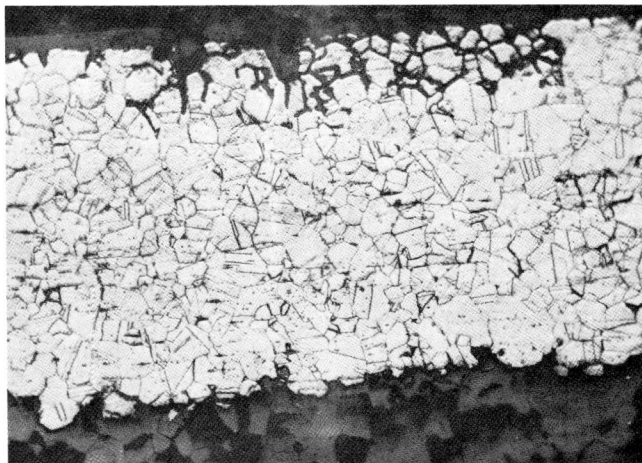

**(b)**

FIGURE 66 — Typical cracking in (a) Tenelon and (b) Type 202 stainless steel exposed to a 100 ppm $Cl^-$ - 500 ppm $O_2$ solution at 315 C at a stress of 40,000 psi (Royuela and Staehle[107]).

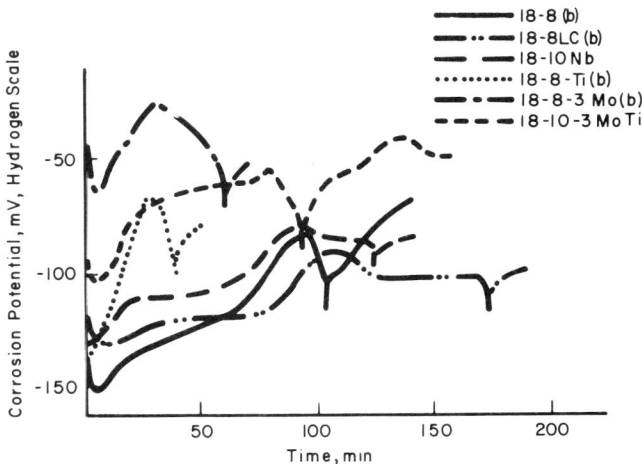

FIGURE 67 — Typical potential-time curves for stressed specimen in $MgCl_2$ at 151-153 C. Steels 18-8 (b), 18-8-LC (b), 18-10 No, and 18-8-3Mo (b) at 48,000 psi; 18-8-Ti (b) at 32,000 psi, and 18-10-3Mo-Ti at 24,000 psi (Hoar and Hines[79]).

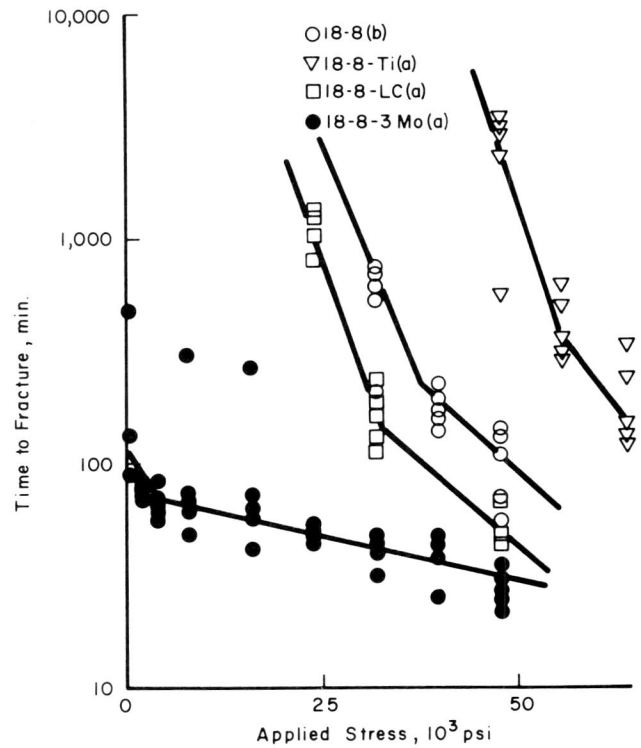

FIGURE 68 — Variation of time to fracture with applied stress for steels 18-8 (a) at 154 C; 18-8-LC (a) at 152 C; 18-8 Ti (a) at 153 C; and 18-8-3Mo at 151 C. All in $MgCl_2$ (Hoar and Hines[79]).

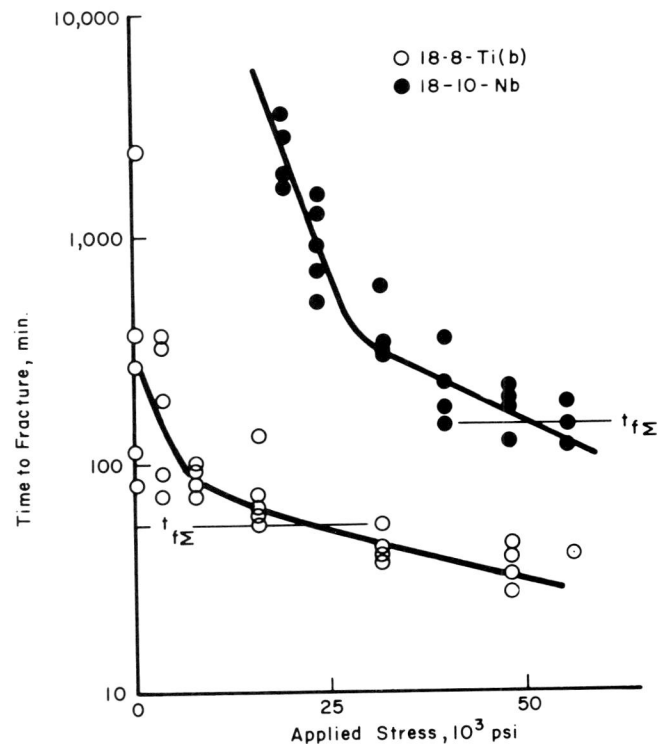

FIGURE 69 — Variation of time to fracture with applied stress for 18-8 Ti (b) at 152 C and 18-10-Nb at 154 C in $MgCl_2$ (Hoar and Hines[79]).

259

TABLE 19—Effect of Columbium Additions on the
Susceptibility of Fe-Ni-Cr Alloys[1]

| Investigator | Cb (wt. pct.) | Cracking Time (hr.) |
|---|---|---|
| Uhlig and White[122] | | |
| 19.1 Cr 9.1 Ni <.002 C <.005 N | 0.46 | 60 |
| 19.0 Cr 9.0 Ni .004 C <.002 N | 1.00 | 29 |
| 19.1 Cr 9.1 Ni <.002 C <.008 N | 1.30 | 22 |
| Tufanov[126] | | |
| 18 Cr 12 Ni | 0.00 | 20-22 |
| 18 Cr 12 Ni | 0.62 | 7-12 |
| 18 Cr 12 Ni | 0.72 | 11-18 |
| 18 Cr 12 Ni | 1.30 | 8-12 |
| 18 Cr 12 Ni | 1.60 | >12 |

[1]Specimens tested in boiling $MgCl_2$.

the 0.1 to 4.0% range when added to 8% Ni and 20% Ni base alloys. Because of its chemical similarity to chromium, it is reasonable to suggest that adding Mo to a 16-20% Cr steel is simply the same as the deleterious effect which results from increasing chromium within certain compositional ranges as shown in Figure 56. By analogy, if the addition of Cr to Fe-Ni alloys is beneficial within other compositional limits, so might the addition of Mo. This possibility has yet to be tested.

The only data showing the effect of tungsten have been obtained by Tufanov[126] who found that a 2.7% addition to an Fe-18 Cr-12 Ni alloy reduced the life by a factor of four. In view of the effects of Mo, such a trend is certainly to be expected.

**11. Group VA (V, Cb, Ta).** Of these elements only columbium has been extensively investigated, probably because of its use as a stabilizing element to prevent sensitization. The effects of Cb and Ti additions to 18-8 type base alloys are compared in Figure 69 from work by Hoar and Hines.[79] The Cb-containing alloy is almost a factor of ten better than the one containing Ti. As already shown in Figure 67 this effect appears to be primarily in the lengthening of the initiation stage. Uhlig and White[122] and Tufanov[126] investigated the effect of Cb additions and found that they decrease resistance to cracking in boiling $MgCl_2$ solutions. Results are summarized in Table 19.

The general effect of Cb additions is to lower cracking times. Uhlig and White suggest that this effect is the result of the influence Cb has on stabilizing the austenitic crystal structure on fast cooling.

**12. Group IVA (Ti, Zr, Hf, Lanthanides).** Of this group, titanium has been the most extensively investigated, probably because of its use as an element which stabilizes stainless steels with respect to sensitization.

Figures 67 and 69 have already demonstrated that titanium additions are deleterious. The most unequivocal experiment was that of Barnartt et al[129] who showed that the addition of 0.54% titanium produced susceptibility in an otherwise resistant Fe-20 Ni-16 Cr alloy. Lang[102] and Tufanov[126] show an increased susceptibility for additions

of Ti in the 0.04-0.5% range. Uhlig found that an 0.62% addition did not cause cracking in a ferritic alloy. Van Rooyen's work on titanium has been previously summarized in Table 14 and shows that the titanium alone does not affect susceptibility significantly.

An addition of less than 0.01 Zr produced an increase in susceptibility of the same extent as 0.045 Ti according to Lang.[102] She also added 0.009 Ce but no unusual effect was observed.

**13. Other Elements.** Of the remaining elements which have not been discussed, only sulfur and oxygen are found in steels. Neither of these have been investigated extensively with respect to effects on cracking in chloride environments. Only Lang[102] has investigated the effect of sulfur and found that additions of 0.057 and 0.33% reduced the life of an 18 Cr-20 Ni alloy. Overman has found that MnS inclusions in stainless steels are preferentially dissolved and cracks can initiate at such sites.[67]

## C. Metallurgical Structure

Features of the metallurgical structure of Fe-Ni-Cr alloys which affect considerations of stress corrosion cracking in chloride environments are the austenite-martensite transformation, duplex austenite-ferrite structures, sensitization, prestrain, weld structure, and grain size. The effect of prestrain has already been discussed; and the other factors will be discussed below. The effect of weld structure will not be discussed here since it appears to add nothing of fundamental significance; however, practically, the constraints involved in welds are often the source of stress sufficient to cause stress corrosion cracking.

**1. Austenite-Martensite Transformation.** Tafaute and Rocha first suggested a positive correlation between the austenite-martensite transformation and susceptibility to stress corrosion cracking of stainless steels.[137] Edeleanu performed an extensive metallographic study of the relationship between cracks and what appears to be martensite platelets.[33] His examination showed that initial stages of attack are associated with structural features which he called quasi-martensite. Figure 70 shows typical examples of this preferential attack. As a result of these observations, Edeleanu[33][138] suggested that cracking is, as proposed by Tafaute and Rocha,[137] associated with the formation of martensite. An important justification for postulating the susceptible martensite was the necessity to explain a path of easy transgranular corrosion. It is of interest to point out that Vaughan et al[124] noted that a transformed structure could be identified on the vases of stress corrosion cracks in stainless steels. Edeleanu's pro-posal was vigorously opposed by Heger and Dulis on the grounds that higher nickel alloys, in which martensite does not form, are susceptible to cracking.[139] Nathorst opposed the idea on the basis that martensite could not form at the low stresses where cracking can be initiated.[140] A further objection to this martensite transformation concept is based on the occurrence of transgranular cracking in 18-8 type materials in superheat environments which exceed the M\ temperature. (This was discussed in a previous section.) Finally, as will be shown later, the transgranular path is

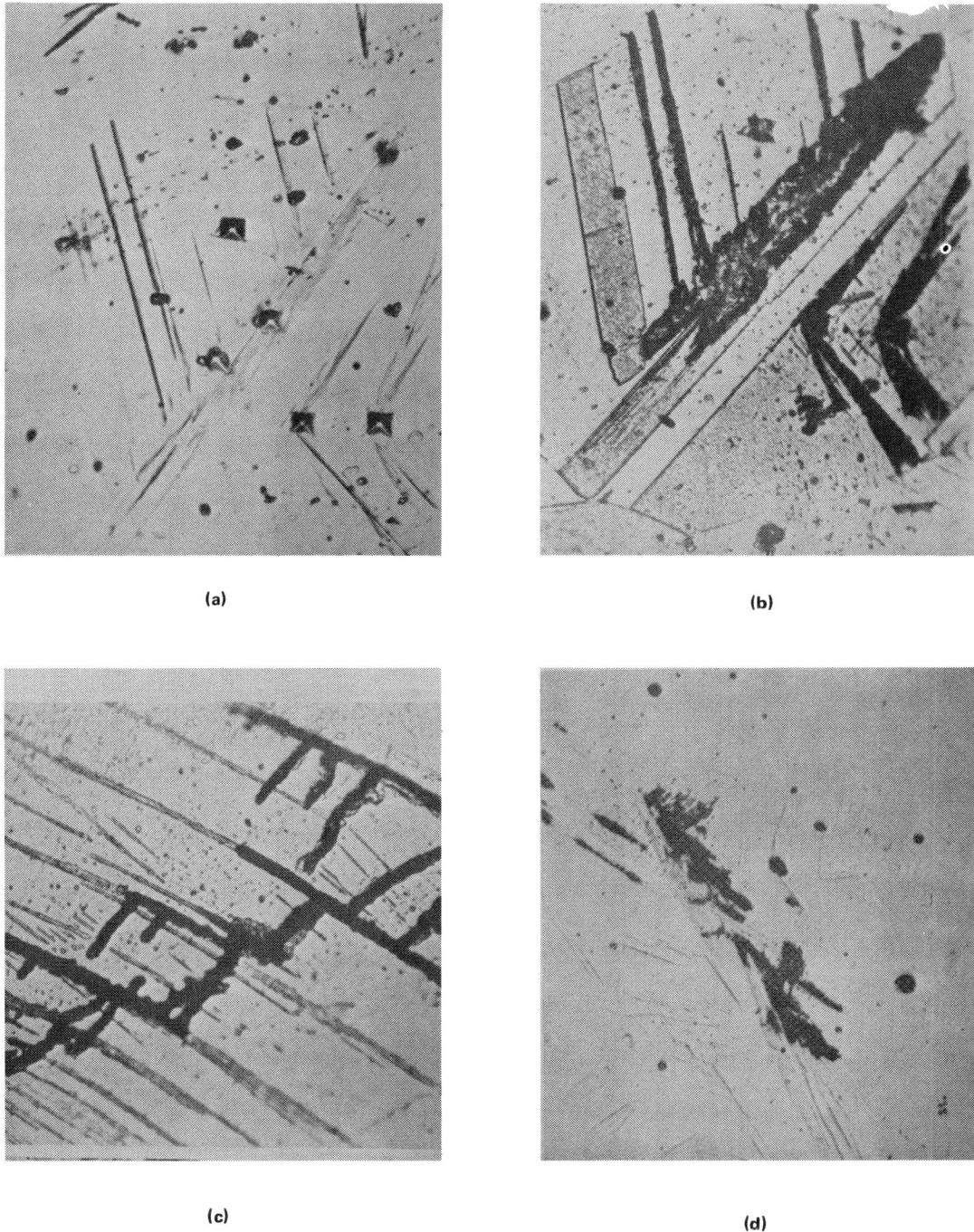

(a)

(b)

(c)

(d)

FIGURE 70 — Photomicrographs showing occurrence and corrosion of quasi-martensite. (a) Quasi-martensite in strained 18-8 stainless steel (500X); (b) Same as (a), but after 8 hr exposure to $MgCl_2$ (500X); (c) Cracks and plates of quasi-martensite in 18Mn-4Cr-8Ni steel; and (d) Selective corrosion of martensite plates in a 15Cr-8Ni-.07C steel exposed to $MgCl_2$ (500X) (Edeleanu[33][138]).

261

probably associated with slip processes.

Hines and Hoar investigated the effect of prestrain (8%) and refrigeration (-196 C) on cracking susceptibility.[141] Both treatments, when applied to a fully softened and large grained material, cause a significant increase in the number of small cracks observed; however, neither the potential-time behavior nor the time-to-fracture vs stress behavior were affected. They concluded that the initiation but not the propagation process was affected. Photomicrographs show the formation of martensite associated with crack tips.

Uhlig and White found that deformation at temperatures, as low as that of liquid nitrogen, produced an increased resistance to cracking in boiling $MgCl_2$ according to the curves of Figure 71.[122] However, specimens deformed at room temperature and then refrigerated exhibited no such increased resistance. These observations are consistent with the results of Hines and Hoar discussed earlier, who also found that refrigeration alone did not increase susceptibility. Hines and Hoar did note that the mode of attack changed after refrigeration to produce more small cracks—presumably as the result of more sites for initiation. Thus, some structural change results from refrigeration without strain. It may be that simultaneous refrigeration and strain causes martensite to form directly on the active slip planes thus preventing further slip from initiating subsequent cracks; whereas, when refrigeration and strain are performed separately, the martensite is not thusly constrained.

Using the arguments implied in Figure 71 and from the fact that Fe-Cr ferritic steels do not crack, Uhlig and White suggested that any chemical or mechanical factor which tended to cause ferrite formation would reduce the susceptibility to stress corrosion cracking. A principal basis of the argument, experimentally, was the observation that a ferritic 18-8 (low C, N) alloy is resistant to cracking in $MgCl_2$ solutions.

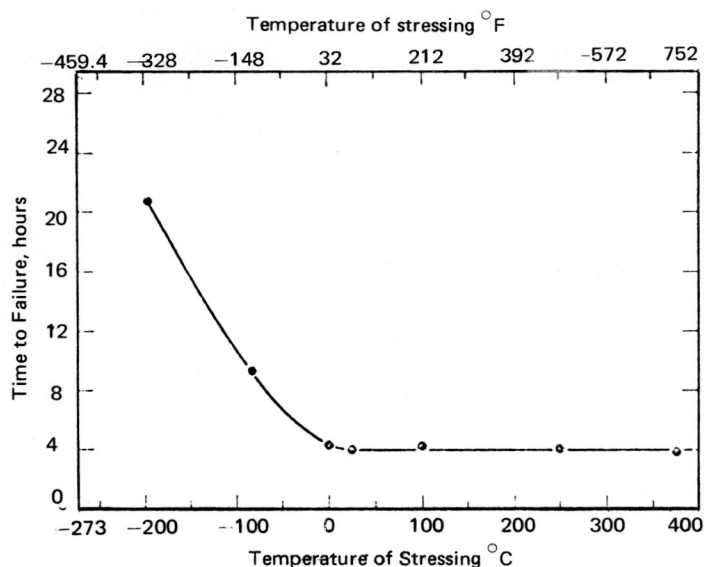

There are several objections to Uhlig and White's contention. First, ferritic steels containing nickel do crack as shown by Bond.[118] Second, the improved resistance to cracking may be explained by the stifling of slip processes as noted above. Finally, the effect due to lowering the nitrogen content may retard cracking independent of crystal structure effects since it has been already shown that low nitrogen in stable austenitic steels also prevents cracking.

The critical experiments to distinguish transformation and crystal structure effects from simple effects of alloy chemistry have yet to be performed. Such experiments should take care to obviate anomalies due to surface preparation, specimen geometry, etc., and should certainly include electron metallographic support.

2. **Duplex Austeno-Ferritic Structures.** The basis for the existence of two phase austenite-ferrite structures has already been discussed in section II.A. Increasing the fraction of ferrite generally increases the resistance of alloys to stress corrosion cracking in chlorides as shown in Figure 72 from work by Edeleanu.[33] Flowers et al have studied certain stainless steels and found also that increased ferrite retards cracking.[142] Figure 73 shows photomicrographs containing known quantities of ferrite. As noted in Figure 72 the general effect of increasing the ferrite concentration is to reduce the alloy's susceptibility to cracking; and the basis for this contention is presumably epitomized by Figure 74 which shows the crack progress to be temporarily stifled by a ferrite grain.

An argument often used to explain the trends of Figures 72 and 74 assumes that the ferrite is resistant to cracking according to the well known resistance of ferritic Fe-Cr stainless steels. When an advancing crack meets a ferrite grain, the grain must mechanically fracture before the crack can progress. An alternate argument can be made on chemical grounds: the two phase alloy must have a distribution of alloy elements between · ferritic and austenitic phases. The ferrite will contain a relatively low

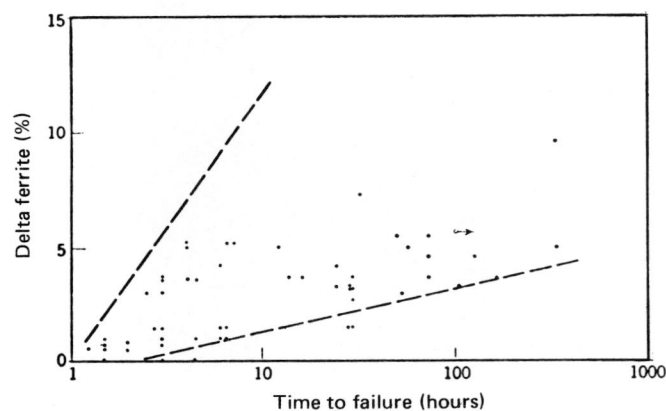

FIGURE 71 — Effect of temperature of stressing on time to failure of sheared 18-8 specimens in 42% $MgCl_2$ at 154 C (Uhlig and White[122]).

FIGURE 72 — Effect of delta ferrite content on the time to fracture of U-bend specimens in boiling 42% $MgCl_2$. Below 3% delta, the times plotted are those at which specimens were found cracked; above 3% delta the time of last examination before cracking is plotted (Edeleanu[138]).

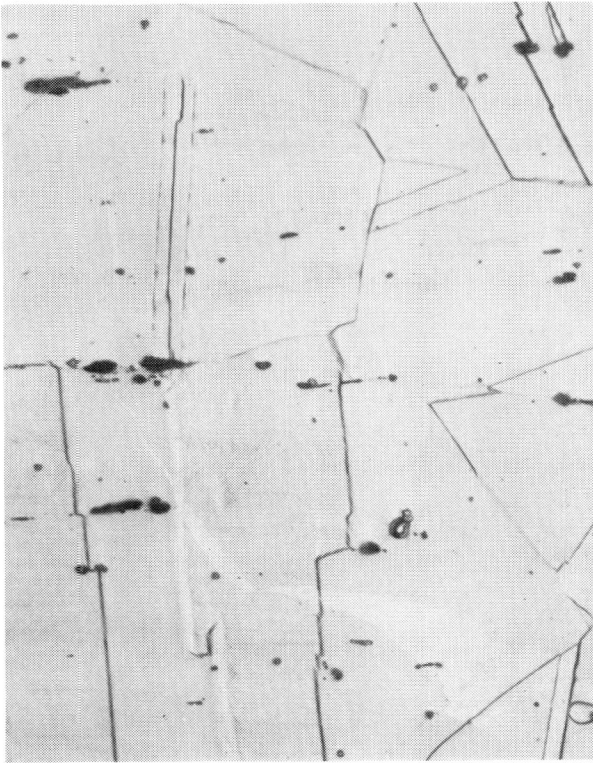

(a)

(b)

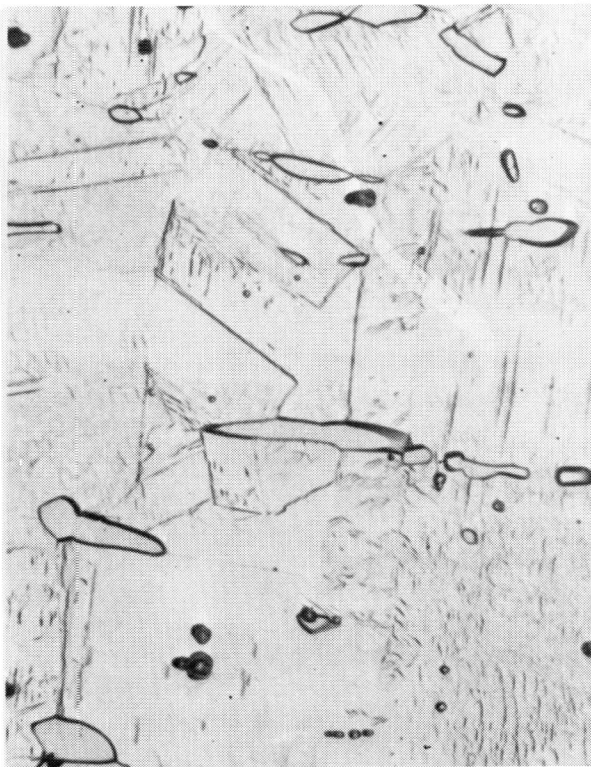

(c)

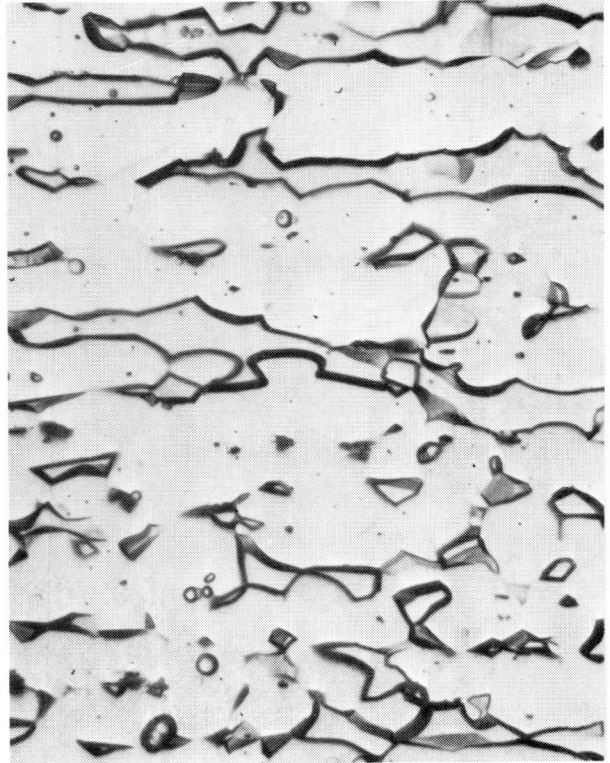

(d)

FIGURE 73 — Optical micrographs showing the incidence of ferrite in various Fe-Ni-Cr alloys. (a) 18Cr-8Ni steel (high carbon), 0% ferrite; (b) 17Cr-8Ni + .006 Zn, 0.6 vol.% ferrite; (c) 18Cr-8Ni (extra carbon), 4.6 vol.% ferrite; and (d) 18Cr-8Ni (high Si, Mn, C), 21.9 vol.% ferrite (Beauchamp[52]).

263

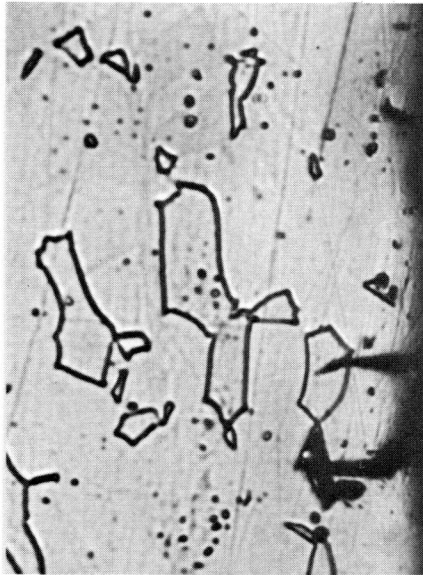

(a)

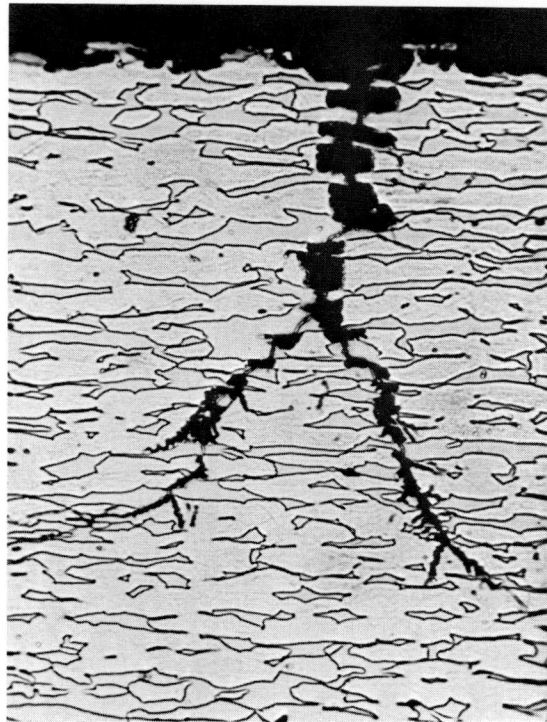

(b)

FIGURE 74 — Cracking in duplex Fe-Cr-Ni alloys in 150 C water at 40 kg/mm. (a) Uranus ST-Si (600X), (b) Uranus 50-Si (600X).

nickel concentration with the austenite a higher one. Since the unstable alloys contain an average nickel content of 7-10%, then the austenite will still be in the range of significant susceptibility but somewhat higher nickel; and the ferrite will be relatively depleted. Thus, the nickel concentration may be sufficient to permit some, but considerably slowed, cracking of the ferrite and the austenite will crack at about its usual rate. While a more rigorous discussion of cracking rate as a function of nickel concentration will be presented later, the data of Riedrich and Kohl, already discussed, showed clearly that cracking rate decreased with decreasing nickel.[117] Also, Copson's data for Fe-Cr-Ni and Fe-Ni alloys show a reduced cracking rate with reduced nickel.[105] Another alternative argument based on mechanical grounds has been advanced by Hines and Hugill to account for their observation that the advancing crack avoids the ferrite.[143] They contend that the ferrite is in compression as a result of its higher coefficient of thermal expansion; therefore, when a crack approaches the ferrite, it cannot pass through because only tensile stresses can propagate cracks. However, as the ferrite is actually formed at a temperature higher than that for testing, it would seem that the ferrite may actually be in residual tension. In fact, the tensile-compressive stress argument is probably a poor one.

As cracks progress through the duplex austenite-ferrite structure the relative amount of local attack associated with successive austenite and ferrite grains can vary. Hines and Hugill[143] show extended dissolution in the ferrite whereas Edeleanu and Snowden[65] and Flowers et al[142] show the

cracks in ferrite to be very narrow with extended dissolution of the austenite. Edeleanu in discussing the paper of Hines and Hugill suggests that these observations of differential dissolution are the result of alloy segregation effects with the result that segregation in the different alloy chemistries may produce contrary effects.

A final argument proposed by Denhard[85] for the ameleorating effect of ferrite suggests that the multiplicity of slip in the ferrite compared to austenite would tend to slow the cracking.

A clear explanation of the transgranular cracking in duplex alloys is yet to be expounded. The trend of data suggest that the chemical segregation argument is most efficacious.

3. Sensitization. Sensitization of Type 304 stainless steels appears to have an uncertain effect on the incidence of stress corrosion cracking. Simultaneous transgranular cracks and intergranular cracks have been observed in a nitric acid solution containing chloride, Figure 28, and in nuclear superheat environments.[103] Scharfstein and Brindley compared the susceptibility of sensitized and unsensitized Type 304 in dilute chloride environments in the 80-100 C range.[60] They found that cracking in the sensitized material proceeded more rapidly and was predominantly intergranular.

Rideout investigated the effect of sensitization on Type 304 stainless steel and found that the sensitization caused cracking, in very dilute chloride environments, to be accelerated. Further, cracking tended to be intergranular

264

although intergranular-transgranular transitions were observed.[240]

Backensto and Yurick studied the behavior of 300 series stainless steels exposed to a variety of test solutions including $H_2S$, $NH_4Cl$, and varied pH and the degree of aeration.[145] They found that most of the cracking was intergranular; the addition of air, as opposed to 100% inert gas, accelerated cracking; increasing the pH reduced cracking; adding $H_2S$ increased cracking rate; and the addition of an amine type inhibitor accelerated cracking.

When alloys are sensitized, it appears generally that cracking will progress more rapidly and will be predominantly intergranular. Whether the resultant cracking is in fact stress-aided intergranular corrosion or indeed stress corrosion cracking is at this point questionable.

**4. Grain Size.** The effect of grain size on the cracking of stainless steels has been studied by Coleman et al[146] and by Barnwell et al.[147] Both studies found that cracking is accelerated by increasing the grain size; however, the change is not spectacular except at lower stresses as shown in Figure 75. Coleman et al argue that the grain size effect supports a surface energy argument for crack propagation according to a model first developed by Petch and Stroh.[148-150] Barnwell[147] suggests that the grain size effect is more related to initiation processes at the metal surface involving early microslip. As will be shown in the section on mechanistic aspects, this latter view is probably more in keeping with the observed phenomenology.

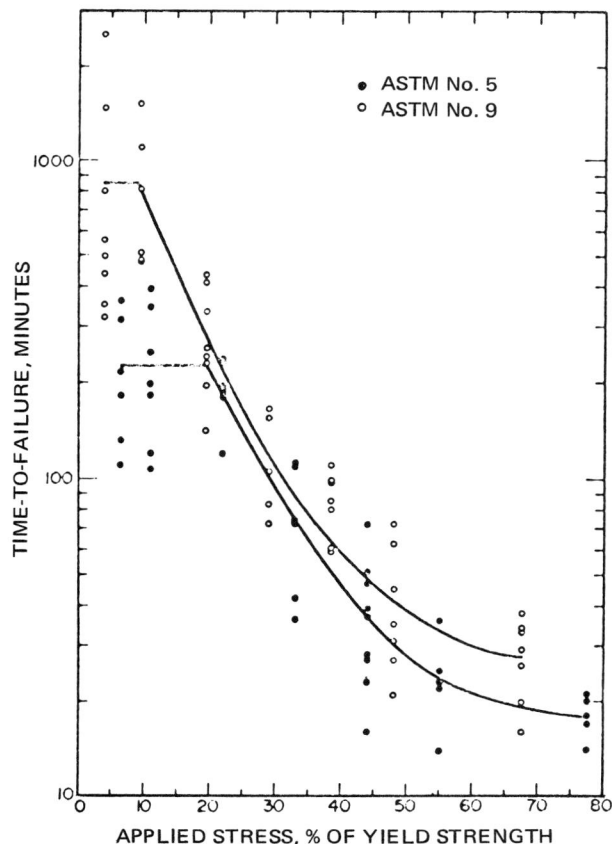

## V. Non-Chloride Environments

The previous discussion considered the many factors involved in the cracking of Fe-Ni-Cr alloys in chloride containing environments. This section considers environments which cause cracking in the absence of chlorides. This discussion will be less extensive owing to the paucity of data.

### A. Other Halide Environments

Despite the chemical similarity of the halogens only the chloride ion has been reported to cause cracking of Fe-Ni-Cr alloys.[151] While there is the mention that the fluoride ion can cause cracking, the evidence was not definitive with respect to absence of chloride ion.

### B. Caustic Solutions

Stress corrosion cracking of Fe-Ni-Cr alloys occurs at high pH in the absence of chloride. Cracking can be intergranular and/or transgranular; oxygen is not required; relatively high concentrations are necessary for cracking; and increasing nickel tends to inhibit cracking. The work in this area is not extensive despite the commercial importance of the problem and no fundamental studies have been reported.

The basis for the susceptibility to caustic cracking appears to involve the stability of soluble species of iron and nickel at high pH. The dihypoferrite ($HFeO_2^-$) and dinickelite ($HNiO_2^-$) ions are stable at high pH according to the half cell equilibria:[29]

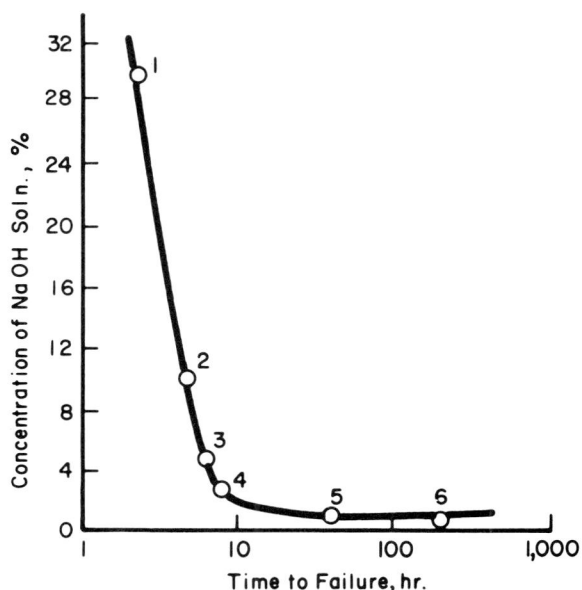

$$Fe + 2H_2O = HFeO_2^- + 3H^+ + 2e^-$$

$$Ni + 2H_2O = HNiO_2^- + 3H^+ + 2e^-$$

FIGURE 75 — Effect of grain size and applied stress on the time to failure of annealed Type 302 stainless steel wire exposed to boiling $MgCl_2$ (Barnwell et al[147]).

FIGURE 76 — Dependence of time to failure of essentially Type 321 stainless steel on concentration of NaOH solution. Tests at 42,000 psi, 330 C (Siderov and Ryabchenkov[152]).

265

**TABLE 20—Effects of Concentration, Stress, and Temperature with KOH and NaOH Solutions (Snowden[51])**

| | Effect of Concentration at 300 C and 10 tons/in$^2$ | | Effect of Stress at 300 C | | | Effect of Temp. with 10 tons/in$^2$ Stress | | |
| Wt.% | Life with KOH, h | Life with KOH, h | Applied Stress tons/in$^2$ | Life with 20% KOH, h | Life with 20% NaOH, h | Temp. C | Life with 20% KOH, h | Life with 20% NaOH, h |
|---|---|---|---|---|---|---|---|---|
| 50 | 7.8 | 2.1 | 20 | 2.0 | --- | 300 | 3.8, 19.8 | 1.1, 1.8 |
| 20 | 3.8, 19.8 | 1.1, 1.8 | 10 | 3.8, 19.8 | 1.1, 1.8 | 250 | 12.2, 55.7 | 3.6, 1.6 |
| 5 | 51.2, 17.6 | 6.4, 15.1 | 75 | --- | 137 | 200 | 40.8, 82.6 | 177.8 |
| 1 | 17.9, 150, UB[1] | | 5 | 16.9, 30.3 | 112, 118 | 175 | 43.7, 195.3 | |
| 0-1 | 551 UB[1] | | 2 | 28.5, 88.5 | 400 UB[1] | 150 | 500 UB[1] | |

[1]UB = Unbroken.

However, these equilibria are not equally reducible by the hydrogen ion equilibrium as shown in Figure 14; and only the iron appears to be significantly oxidized with nickel being sparingly so. This trend suggests that increasing nickel would inhibit caustic cracking, which it does. Chromium forms a soluble species ($CrO_3^=$) but more sparingly than either nickel or iron at the same pH.

1. **Environmental Factors.** Siderov and Ryabchenkov investigated the effect of NaOH concentration on the cracking of Type 310 at 330 C and obtained the results of Figure 76 showing that the concentration of NaOH below which cracking would not occur is about 0.1 to 1%.[152] Cracks were intergranular and transgranular with the latter predominating. Picket et al investigated the cracking of Type 304 and found similar trends.[47] Snowden[156] used Type 347 to investigate the effects of concentration, stress, temperature and the composition of NaOH with KOH. His results are summarized in Table 20. In general, NaOH appears to be about twice as aggressive as KOH. This same trend was noted by Coriou and Grall.[157] The concentration dependence of Snowden's work appears to agree with that of Sidorov and Ryabchenkov. The cracking of all specimens showed no prior susceptibility to sensitization. Snowden also investigated the effect of dewpoint and superheat environments on the cracking of contaminated Type 347 in a temperature range of 275-350 C. The contamination was applied by immersing specimens in a 30% solution. The most significant finding of these experiments was the shifting in mode of cracking. Contrary to the results of solution tests described in Table 20, the cracking for the NaOH contaminated solutions was predominantly transgranular. Specimens contaminated with KOH cracked intergranularly below 380 C (the melting point of KOH) and transgranularly above. Figure 77 shows typical intergranular and transgranular cracks from the work of Snowden.

Wheeler and Howells[155] investigated the effect of NaOH concentration on the cracking of Type 347 in liquid sodium and water environments at 360-450 C. Oxygen was purposely excluded. Their results are shown in Table 21. Cracking in very high caustic concentrations at 399 C and 362 C appears to be stifled; whereas cracking was observed

**TABLE 21—Incidence of Cracking in Type 347 Stainless Steel U-Bends Exposed to Hydroxide Solutions (Wheeler and Howells[155])**

| Temp. C | Mixture | Days | Cracking |
|---|---|---|---|
| 454 | 16% NaOH in Na | 30 | yes |
| 454 | 30% NaOH in Na | 20 | yes |
| 454 | 60% NaOH in Na | 30 | yes |
| 454 | 100% NaOH | 14 | yes |
| 454 | 96% NaOH in $H_2O$ | 30 | no |
| 399 | 100% NaOH | 30 | no |
| 399 | 95% NaOH in $H_2O$ | 30 | no |
| 362 | 100% NaOH | 30 | no |
| 362 | 80% NaOH in $H_2O$ | 1 | yes |

when the concentration reaches 100%. All cracking in this study was transgranular.

The effect of LiOH on the cracking of Type 347 was studied by Pement using cold formed bellows specimens.[153] Concentrations were varied from $10^{-4}$ to 5 molar and specimens were tested at 160, 289, and 315 C. Oxygen was purposely excluded from the experiments. Cracking occurred at all three temperatures; an 0.1 molar concentration appeared to be the approximate division for susceptibility with only one crack observed at this concentration. Intergranular cracking was observed in all cases. Pement states that the cracking in LiOH solutions was less aggressive than in NaOH solutions; and he suggests that this may result from the lower ionization and lower solubility of the LiOH.

The effect of additions to caustic solutions has been investigated. Siderov and Ryabchenkov studied the effect of NaCl additions to a 3% NaOH solution at 330 C and found that the cracking was progressively inhibited as the concentration increased according to the trend in Figure 78.[152] Gulyaev et al[154] investigated the effect of air, nitrogen, and argon additions on cracking in NaOH solutions and found that these additions inhibited cracking. However, the mechanism for their effect is not clear.

Wheeler and Howells investigated the effect of phosphate addition to NaOH + KOH solutions and found that an $Na_3PO_4$/(NaOH + KOH) ratio of 1:4 was sufficient to prevent cracking.[155] Their well known data are shown in Figure 79.

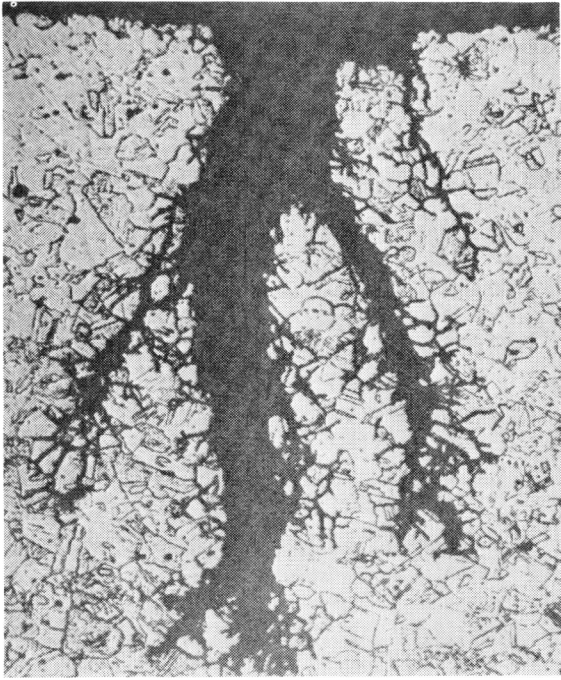

(a)

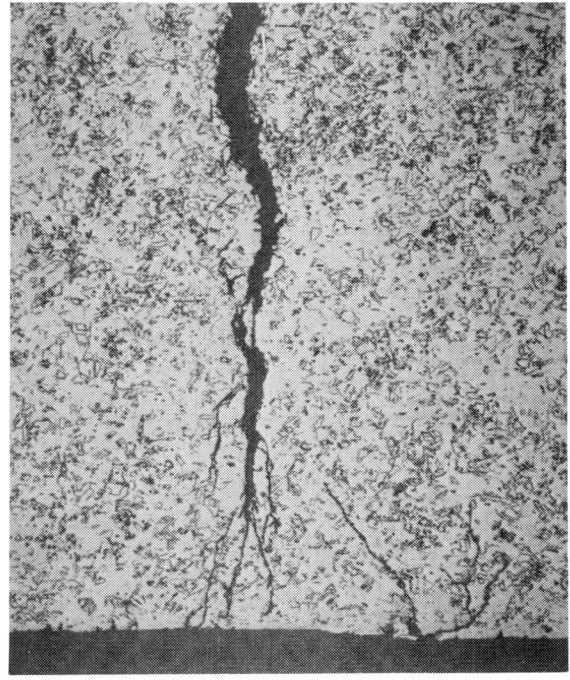

(b)

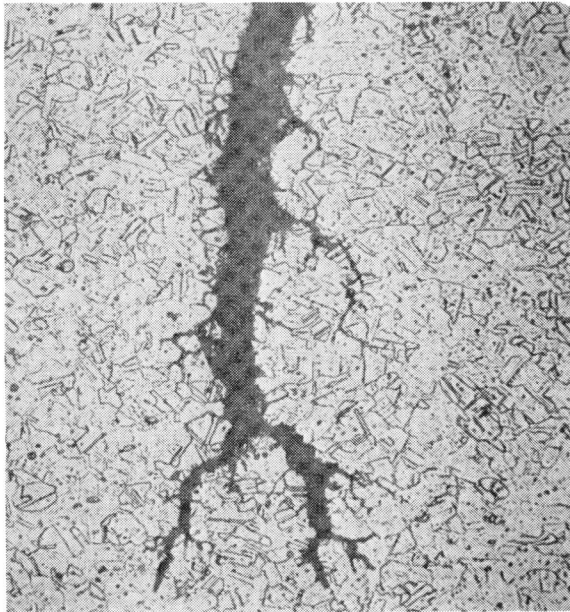

(c)

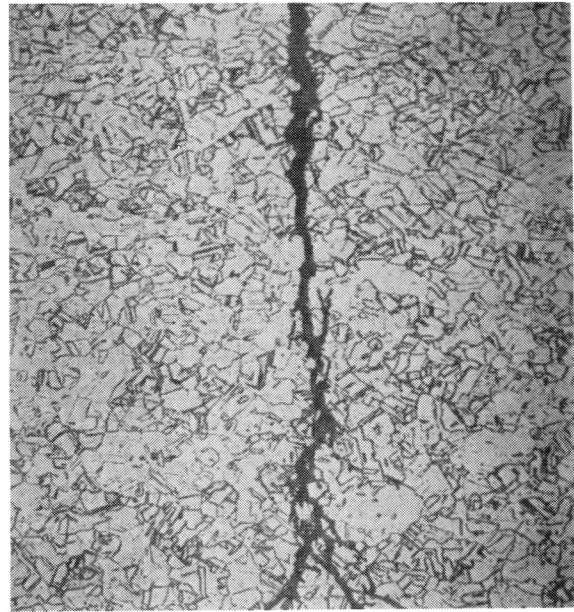

(d)

FIGURE 77 — Typical stress corrosion cracks in 18-9 Nb stainless steel exposed to hydroxide solutions under various conditions. (a) Intergranular cracking with 50% NaOH solution at 300 C (200X); (b) Transgranular cracking with NaOH on steam (100X); (c) Intergranular cracking with KOH below its MP in steam (200X); and (d) Transgranular cracking with KOH heated above its MP in steam (200X) (Snowden[156]).

267

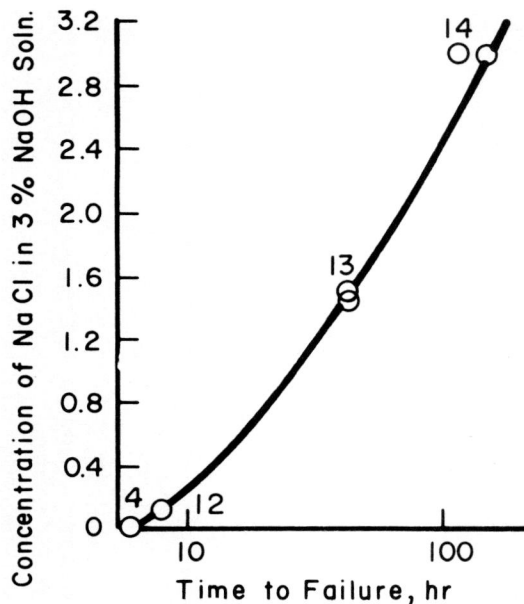

**FIGURE 78** — Dependence of time to failure of essentially Type 321 stainless steel on concentration of NaCl in 3% NaOH (Siderov and Ryabchenkov[152]).

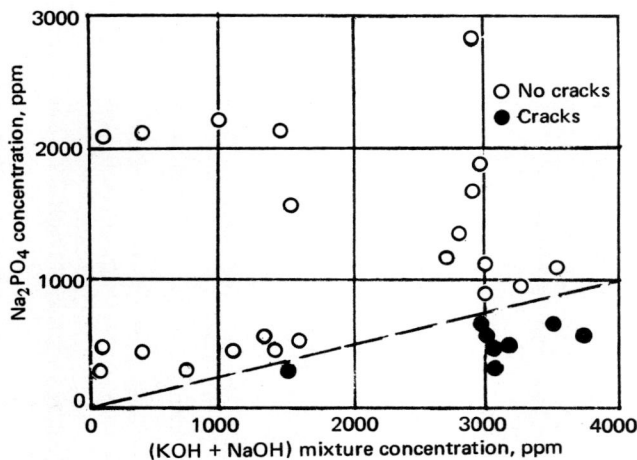

**FIGURE 79** — Influence of $PO_4^{-3}/OH^-$ ratio on cracking of U-bend specimen of Type 347 stainless steel. Concentration ratios of over 1:4 seems to inhibit caustic stress corrosion cracking (Wheeler and Howells[155]).

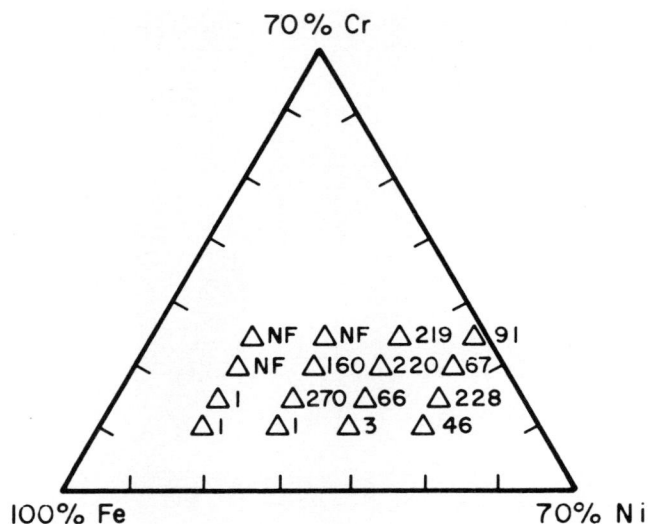

**FIGURE 80** — Time to failure in hours for alloys as shown above in 50% NaOH at 300 C/2000 psi $O_2$, and 20,000 psi. F-failed, perforated by cracking; C-cracked but not perforated; U-not cracked; and U(P)-not cracked but some elongated pits (Truman and Perry[119]).

**2. Metallurgical Factors.** Copson[49,105] first investigated the effect of alloy composition on the cracking of Fe-Ni binary alloys exposed to boiling 33% NaOH at 118 C. His results, summarized in Table 22, show cracking from iron to an Fe-38 Ni alloy. Cracking was intergranular. While his solution contained NaCl and PbO contamination, these appear to have had no effect. Truman and Perry investigated the effect of 50% NaOH at 300 C (with some dissolved oxygen) on the cracking of various specially prepared Fe-Ni-Cr alloys; and their results are summarized in Figure 80.[119] Cracking here is retarded by increasing chromium as well as increasing nickel. Snowden has investigated the effect of caustics on the cracking of various commercial alloys and his results are summarized in Table

23.[51] This table omits data obtained at 5% concentrations and also omits data obtained in KOH since they both tended to give the same results as the 20% NaOH solutions.

Snowden studied the effect of carbon content and heat treatment. He found that low carbon stainless steels (less than about 0.05% C) crack transgranularly while those of higher carbon contents crack intergranularly. Intergranular cracking of the higher carbon alloys persists despite ice brine quenching of specimens annealed at 1050 C. This tendency to shift cracking mode according to the difference in carbon content persists in NaOH and KOH solutions as well as in the steam phase. The wholly transcrystalline cracking of the alloys studied by Truman and Perry and summarized in Figure 80 is probably rationalized by the fact that the carbon content of their materials was in the 0.02-0.05 range.

The general effect of the major alloying elements appears to be epitomized by Table 22 from Copson, Table 23 from Snowden, and Figure 80 from Truman and Perry:

(a) Cracking occurs in Fe-Cr alloys without nickel.

(b) Increasing nickel generally retards cracking; Inconel-600 does not crack.

(c) Increasing chromium generally retards cracking.

(d) A reversion in the nickel effect is observed at 15, 20, and 25% chromium at intermediate nickel concentrations with cracking being accelerated after being decelerated at lower nickel concentrations.

The general trends in intergranular and transgranular cracking modes are summarized in Table 24. While the intergranular and transgranular cracking propensities appear almost capricious, important underlying trends show that transgranular cracking is favored both by low carbon content in the alloy and high caustic concentrations.

**TABLE 22–Stress Corrosion Cracking of Iron-Nickel U-Bends in Caustic (Copson[105])**

| Solution | | Conditions | |
|---|---|---|---|
| Distilled water | 5000 ml | Temperature: | Boiling (255 F) |
| Sodium hydroxide, NaOH | 2500 g | Time: | 14 days |
| Sodium chloride, NaCl | 10 g | Specimens: | U-bends, 6 x 0.5 x |
| Lead oxide, PbO | 10 g | | 0.25 in |

| Composition of Material, % | | | | | Appearance at 14 Days |
|---|---|---|---|---|---|
| Ni | C | Mn | Si | Fe | |
| 0.06 | 0.17 | 0.41 | 0.01 | Bal. | Microexamination disclosed cracks |
| 2.02 | 0.19 | 0.46 | 0.18 | Bal. | Microexamination disclosed cracks |
| 4.96 | 0.15 | 0.51 | | Bal. | Visible cracks |
| 8.53 | 0.12 | 0.53 | 0.19 | Bal. | Cracked in two |
| 37.75 | 0.01 | 0.50 | 0.15 | Bal. | OK at 14 days |
| 99.41 | 0.10 | 0.24 | 0.02 | 0.13 | OK at 14 days |

**TABLE 23–Behavior of Various Fe-Cr-Ni Alloys in Caustic Alkali Environments (Snowden[156])**

| Cr | Ni | Other Additions | Life[1] | Life[2] |
|---|---|---|---|---|
| 18.24 | 10.78 | .... | 3.7 h | 117 h (Na$_2$SiO$_3$ added 42 h to NaOH |
| 17.80 | 8.70 | .... | 8.1 h | 632 h |
| 18.56 | 9.00 | 0.61Ti | 17.8, 284.7, 302 h, 515 h NF | .... |
| 18.48 | 9.20 | 0.52Ti | 4.05 h | 341 h NF |
| 17.72 | 9.55 | 0.35Mo, 0.78Ti, 0.224S | 42.7 h | |
| 17.76 | 8.35 | 2.83Mo | 8.9 h | 189 h NF, 307 h |
| 17.84 | 9.50 | 1.22Nb | .... | 18 h, 90 h NF, 110 h |
| 17.72 | 8.75 | 0.80Nb | 1.6, 1.8, 15.3 h | 15 h, 276 h NF |
| 17.16 | 8.40 | 0.66Nb | 3.7, 37 h | .... |
| 15.90 | 11.84 | 1.23Mo, 1.10Nb | .... | 15 h |
| 12.32 | 12.60 | 0.29Mo, 0.18Cu | 1.2, 20.2 h | 343 h |
| 23.93 | 21.70 | .... | 14.6, 150.8 h | 679 h NF |
| 20.76 | 0.15 | .... | 2.5, 6.5 h | .... |
| 20.50 | 0.16 | 2.08Mo, 1.17Nb | 1.0, 58.6 h | 485 h NF, 1012 h Nf |
| 21.64 | 0.15 | 2.05Mo, 1.19Nb | 55.0 h | .... |
| 13.88 | 5.51 | 1.75Mo, 0.38Nb, 1.63Cu | 6.2, 10.7, 37.9 h[3] | 909 h NF[4] |

[1]Obtained on specimens at 10 tons/in$^2$ and 300 C in solution of 20% NaOH.

[2]Obtained on NaOH contaminated specimens tested at 13 tons/in$^2$ in steam at 330 C and 1500 lb/in$^2$ (superheated).

[3]Aged 2 h 560 C.

[4]Aged 1 h 550 C.

**TABLE 24–General Cracking Modes of Fe-Ni-Cr Alloys Exposed to NaOH and KOH Solutions (Based on Snowden's work[156])**

| | NaOH (MP 318 C) | | KOH (MP 380 C) | |
|---|---|---|---|---|
| | Intergranular | Transgranular | Intergranular | Intergranular |
| Superheat | Change to IG when sodium silicate added | TG cracking in superheat above and below MP | IG below MP of salt | TG above MP of salt |
| High Temperature Solutions | IG for solutions up to 50% NaOH at 300 C | Inter-Trans mode at 75% NaOH 300 C | IG for solutions up to 50% KOH at 300 C | Entirely intercrystalline at 75% KOH |
| | High carbon (>0.05 C) IG | Low carbon (<0.05 C) | High carbon | Low carbon |

269

## C. Water-Oxygen

Since 1959 several instances of stress corrosion cracking in nonsensitized Fe-Ni-Cr alloys in nominally high purity water and in water containing oxygen have been reported. Such instances have occurred in austenitic stainless steels, intermediate nickel alloys, and the Inconels. It has been clearly established that the intergranular cracking observed is not the result of sensitization. However, numerous objections have been raised suggesting that the cracking results from various contaminants. The data, objections, and rationalizations are discussed below.

Coriou et al have shown that Inconel-600 as well as Hastelloy B and C are subject to intergranular cracking at 300 and 350 C in single phase water.[158] The oxygen was approximately 0.1 ppm, lead less than 0.01 ppm, and chloride less than 0.1 ppm. For specimens stressed in constant strain loading slightly above the yield point, cracking occurred in 3-5 months with the cracking somewhat more extensive at higher temperature. Type 304 stainless steels did not crack in the same conditions at 350 C. Cracking was not extensive and metallographic examination was often required to identify the cracks. Inconel 600 and stainless steel were also compared in steam at 650 C; extensive intergranular cracking occurred in the Inconel after a four month test and no cracking occurred in the stainless steel after 15 months. A second series of experiments was reported after numerous objections were raised concerning the above results, in which the specimens were stressed at constant load and the oxygen was less than 0.003 ppm before and after the test. The cracking was much more extensive and occurred in a shorter time. The cracking from the constant strain and constant load experiments is compared in Figure 81.

The objection raised to Coriou's paper (see the discussion appended to Reference 158) were based on possible lead and/or oxygen contamination and on the fact that such cracking had never been observed before in a number of extensive investigations. However, Coriou's work appears to be above reproach and his data must be taken as legitimate observations of intergranular cracking in high purity water. It is likely that the previous experiments did not really duplicate Coriou's work with respect to time, stress, or detail of metallographic examination. With respect to lead contamination Copson and Dean[159] showed cracking due to this species to be transgranular rather than intergranular. If chlorides had caused cracking, certainly the stainless steel specimens would have cracked first. Finally, oxygen is probably not legitimately a "contaminant" but rather a part of the water system; it is doubtful that oxygen plays a significant role in this cracking because of its very low (0.003 ppm) concentration.

Copson and Dean conducted a series of experiments to study the cracking of Inconel-600 in crevice and noncrevice geometries.[159] These experiments, in which air was used as a "contaminant", were conducted at 316 C, pH adjusted to 10, and extended for slightly less than four months. In this work cracking was observed only inside the crevice of double U-bend specimens; and the cracking in this case, as in Coriou's, was intergranular. This cracking occurred as early as two months after exposure.

The intergranular stress corrosion cracking of nonsensitized stainless steels in high purity boiling water reactor environments was first observed by General Electric in 1962 and results of examinations have been published in a number of reports.[160-163] Figure 3 shows a cross sectional view of a fuel rod which is clad with Type 304 and which contains $UO_2$ nuclear fuel and a montage of the cracking distribution. Figure 82 presents a series of optical micrographs showing detailed cross sectional views of the cracking. The cracking is clearly intergranular. An important feature of these cracks is the occasional observation of oxide product which appears epitaxial and occurs usually without preference over the length of the crack.

(a)

(b)

FIGURE 81 — Intergranular failure of Inconel in high purity water at 350 C. (a) Constant stress experiment (48 kg/mm²) 150X and (b) Constant strain experiment (0.5%) 150X (Coriou, et al[158]).

(a)

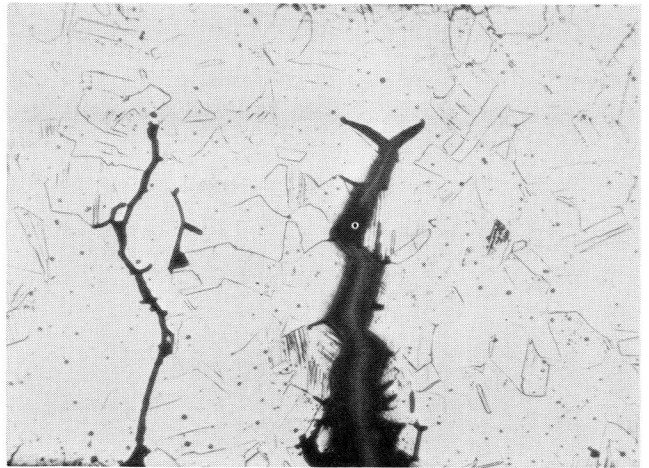

(b)

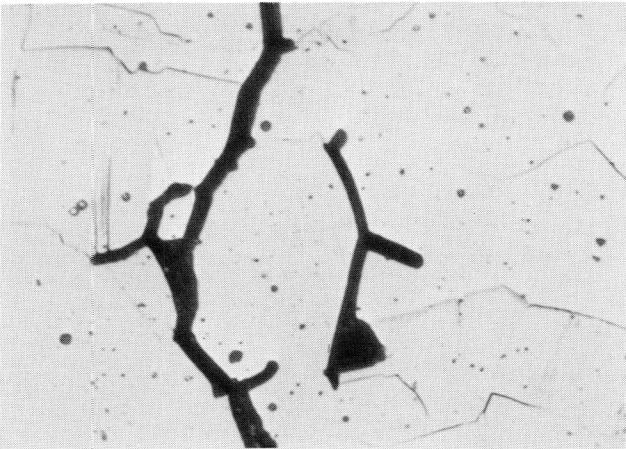

(c)

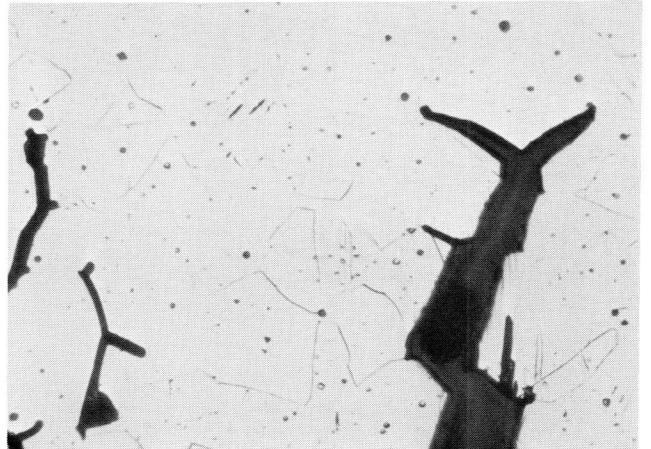

(d)

FIGURE 82 — Intergranular cracking of Type 304 stainless steel cladding material exposed to boiling water reactor environments at 300 C (Staehle[163]).

FIGURE 82e — Incoloy-800 fuel rod cladding failure showing intergranular crack. Fuel clad tubing was 0.425 inch O.D. with 0.011 inch wall, collapsed, cold worked, weld-drawn Incoloy-800. Fuel assembly exposure, 6650 MWd/TU average (Howard and Duncan[242]).

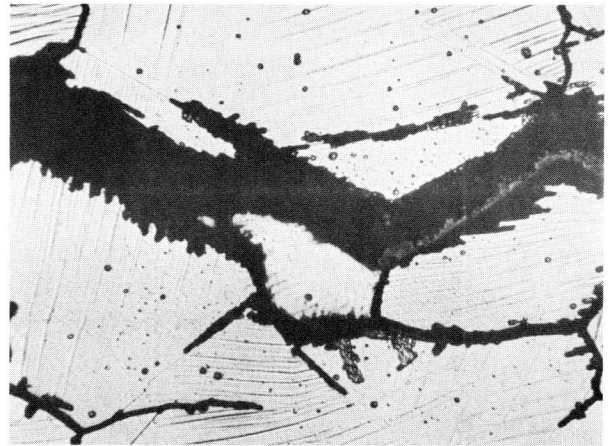

FIGURE 82f — Type 304 stainless steel fuel rod cladding failure from VBWR tests. Corrosion along grain boundaries, strain markings and quasi-martensite platelets. (1000X) (Lees[162]).

271

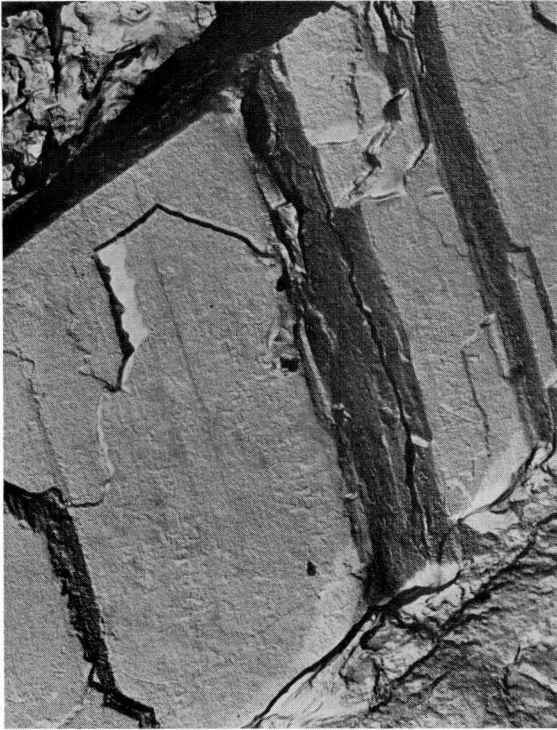

(a)

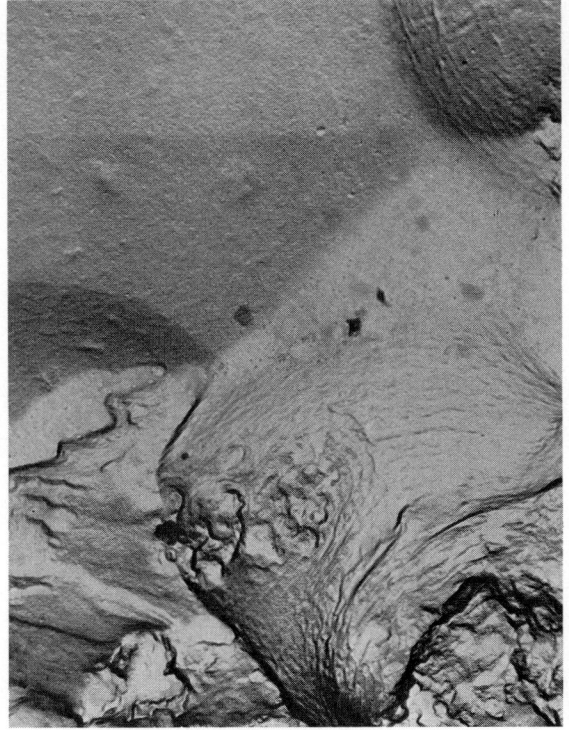

(b)

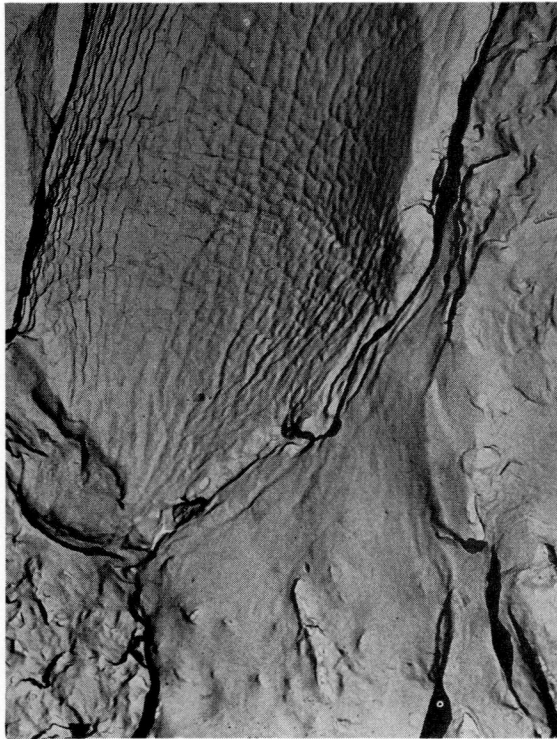

(c)

(d)

FIGURE 83 — Electron fractographs from failures described in Figure 82 (Staehle[163]).

272

Figure 82e shows an intergranular failure of Incoloy 800 exposed to essentially the same conditions as Figures 82a-d. Figure 82f shows details of crack morphology of a cold worked Type 304 fuel rod exposed to the same conditions as Figure 82a-d. Of particular significance here is the preferential penetration into the grain. This suggests that the slip process may be significant with respect to this kind of cracking. Figure 83 shows typical electron fractographs taken from the surfaces of the cracks in Figure 82a-d. This type of cracking occurred only in regions where the $UO_2$ fuel had received the highest depletion of $U^{235}$ and was further accentuated by high heat fluxes and small clad-fuel clearances. The concensus regarding the environmental conditions required for this cracking is that it is due to the presence of oxygen resulting from radiolytic decomposition of the water by the reactor flux field. Thus, the intergranular cracking shown in Figures 3, 82, and 83 was produced by a water-oxygen environment in which oxygen is in the range of 1-5 ppm and the temperature is in the range of 315 C. A final most important characteristic of this cracking is the necessity of dynamic stressing resulting from the inexorable expansion of the nuclear fuel.

Incoloy-800 has been observed to crack intergranularly also in the boiling water reactor environments.[160]

The principal characteristics of the cracking discussed above are as follows:

(a) All cracking is intergranular.

(b) Inconel-600 will crack in high purity water with oxygen in the range of 0.003 ppm and stainless steel will not.

(c) Increasing the oxygen together with a crevice accelerates cracking of Inconel-600; and the presence of radiolytic oxygen will cause cracking of Type 304 and Incoloy-800.

(d) Relatively high stresses are required and dynamic stressing (i.e., low creep rates) accelerate cracking.

There are certain objections to categorizing the above observations together as well as numerous uncertainties. These are discussed below:

(a) Cracking of the stainless steel and Incoloy may be chloride cracking that results from the progressive pickup of chloride on the surfaces. The accumulation of chloride would be accelerated by boiling; and the intergranular crack morphology of Figure 82 may be the result of a process similar to that observed by Pickett et al[47] shown in Figure 36.

(b) The cracking tendency could be related to grain boundary precipitates or equilibrium solute segregation processes which are not the same for the stainless steels and Inconels.

(c) Other processes such as differential dissolution cells, differential passivity, or preferential oxidation may be operating; but the same process may not operate on all alloys.

(d) Another possible process for cracking involves intergranular hydrogen embrittlement according to a process observed in nickel by Wilcox and Smith.[164] They observed intergranular fracture in hydrogen charged nickel.

Grain boundary cracks initiated at 7-9% elongation.

(e) The cracking may be related to the intergranular corrosion observed when testing in the nitric-$Cr^{+6}$ experiments described in the next section.

## D. Nitric-$Cr^{+6}$

A solution of boiling nitric acid containing chromium in its hexavalent oxidation state causes accelerated intergranular corrosion of nonsensitized stainless steels. Stress is not required in this case so it must be classed as an intergranular corrosion phenomenon. Such a result and the testing techniques were first described by DeLong[165] in 1949 and Shirley and Truman[166] in 1952. Owing to the intergranular nature of attack and the fact that it occurs in nonsensitized stainless steel, its use was applied by Armijo primarily to evaluate alloys for their susceptibility to intergranular stress corrosion cracking observed in boiling water nuclear reactors as discussed in the previous section.[167,168]

Rationalizations and techniques applying to these experiments have been considered by numerous authors.[169-175] Nonsensitized stainless steels which corrode intergranularly in this test are Types 304, 347, 321, 316, 316L, and Incoloy 800. A typical photomicrograph of intergranular corrosion in the nitric-$Cr^{+6}$ test is shown in Figure 84. Armijo in his extensive study of this test found the following: stress accelerates penetration but, in the absence of stress, corrosion is still relatively rapid; cathodic protection completely stops penetration as shown in Figure 85; and there appears to be distinct incubation and propagation stages.[167] In a second paper, Armijo showed conclusively that the preferential dissolution was associated with solute redistribution and was not the result of grain boundary strain energy alone.[168] This is shown in Figure 86 by preferential dissolution at grain boundaries and dislocations. However, strain energy no doubt activates the solute redistribution. In support of this Chaudron has shown that a high purity Fe-18 Cr-10 Ni steel is immune to preferential grain boundary attack in the nitric-$Cr^{+6}$ test.[176] Coriou et al have found that increasing grain size and increasing cold work accelerates intergranular penetration.[177]

The nitric-$Cr^{+6}$ test has been used by Coriou et al to rationalize the preference for intergranular cracking in Inconel-600.[158] He prepared a series of Fe-17 Cr alloys (containing about 0.02% C and 0.49 Si) to which nickel was added and exposed the alloys to the solution. The results, summarized in Figure 87, show relatively high intergranular attack of the nickel-rich alloy. This seems to confirm the trend of susceptibility of the high nickel alloys to cracking in high purity water. Armijo and Pickett have used the test to assess the effect of silicon, carbon, manganese, sulfur, phosphorous, nitrogen, and oxygen additions to an Fe-14 Cr-14 Ni alloy. They found serious intergranular attack only in alloys containing phosphorous and silicon. The results from the nitric-dichromate tests were compared with those from the $FeCl_2$ test at 341 C which was previously described (see Figure 36 c). The two tests both show that

273

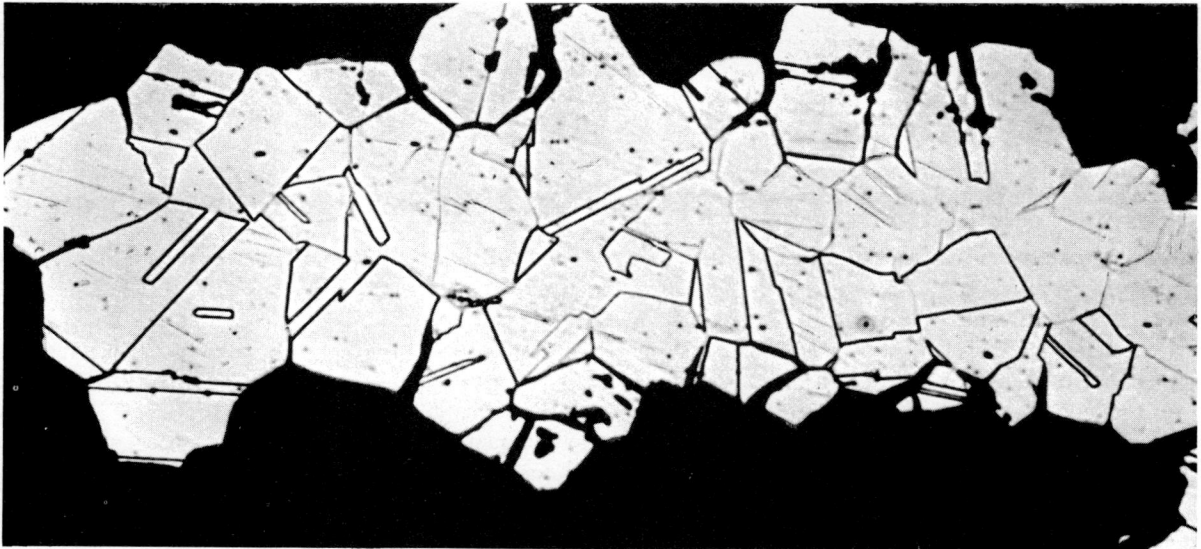

FIGURE 84 — Typical intergranular attack of annealed Type 304 stainless steel in boiling nitric-Cr$^{+6}$ solution (Armijo[167]).

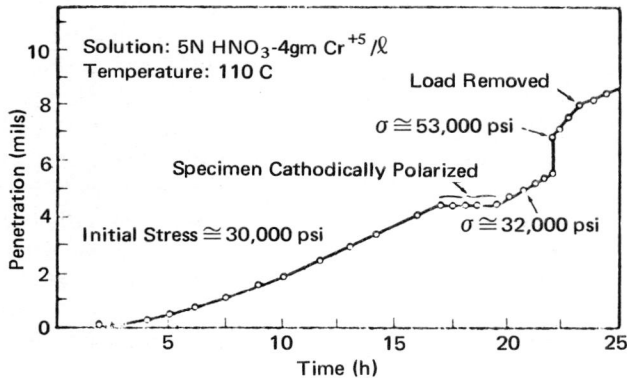

FIGURE 85 — Intergranular penetration versus time for Type 304 in HNO$_3$-Cr$^{+6}$. Note that cathodic polarization completely stops cracking (Armijo[167]).

phosphorous promotes intergranular cracking; but with respect to carbon, intergranular cracking occurs in the FeCl$_2$ test while not in HNO$_3$-Cr$^{+6}$ and the reverse is true for silicon.

While the HNO$_3$-Cr$^{+6}$ test appears to be a useful method for evaluating susceptibility to intergranular dissolution, its application has three distinct drawbacks:

(a) Most intergranular stress corrosion processes occur at neutral pH where the product of Cr$^{+6}$ reduction is a solid product; and only at relatively low pH is the product soluble (Cr$^{+3}$) as in the HNO$_3$-Cr$^{+6}$ test. This is easily seen in Figure 14.

(b) The HNO$_3$-Cr$^{+6}$ test operates at a much higher potential than would be expected in aqueous dissolution processes which are governed either by the hydrogen ion half cell or the reduction of oxygen in very dilute oxygenated solutions.

(c) The nitrate ion adsorbs in such a way to stifle pitting and stress corrosion processes as discussed in a

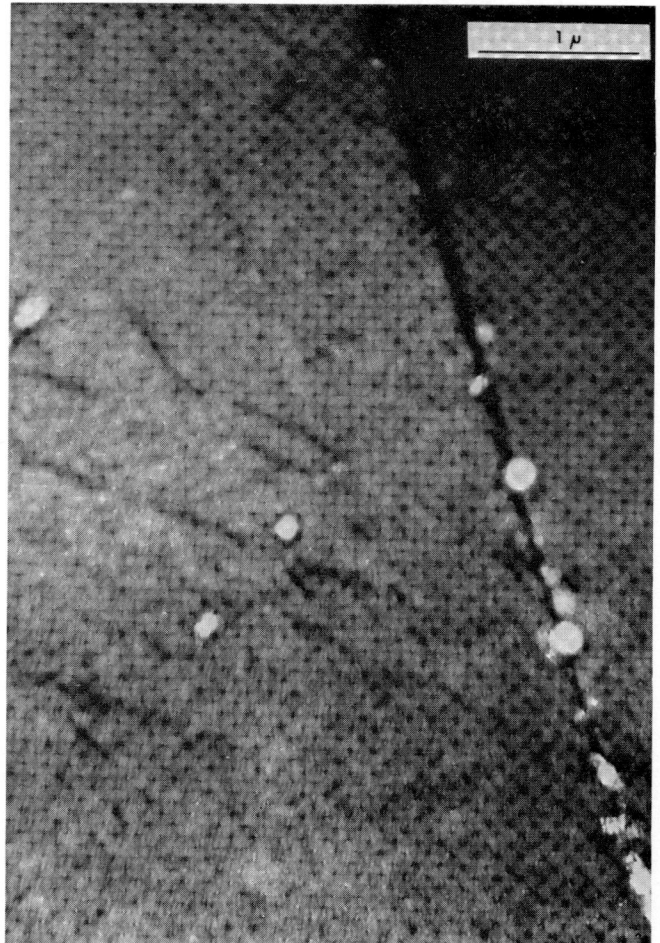

FIGURE 86 — Electron micrograph showing the typical corrosion of austenitic stainless steels heat treated for 1 hr at 1000 or 900 C after exposure to nitric acid-Cr$^{+6}$ at 80 C (Armijo[168]).

274

previous section. Such an adsorbate is not usually present in normal cracking systems.

## E. Lead Contamination

The intergranular cracking of Inconel-600 in molten lead has been discussed by Copson.[106] However, Copson and Dean have recently shown that Inconel-600 will crack transgranularly in aerated water at 316 C containing lead in various forms.[159] A typical photomicrograph is shown in Figure 88 and their data are summarized in Table 25. The cracks shown in Figure 88 are clearly transgranular and their patterns suggest a strong crystallographic influence.

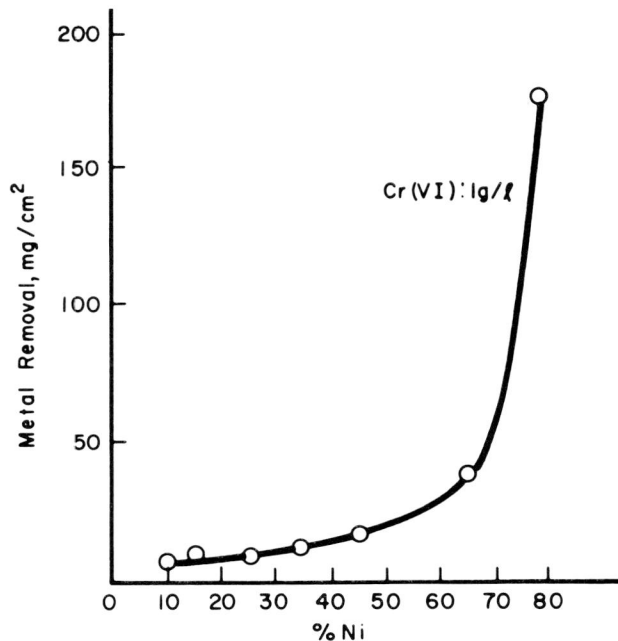

FIGURE 87 — Influence of nickel content on the corrosion of Fe-17Cr-Ni austenitic stainless steel after 70 hours in nitric-Cr$^{+6}$ solution (1g/liter) at 108 C (Coriou et al[158]).

TABLE 25 — Results of Tests Involving Lead as a Contaminant (Dean and Copson[159])

| Alloy No. | Type of U-Bend | Time to Cracking, Weeks | | | |
|---|---|---|---|---|---|
| | | Test 5 | Test 6 | Test 7 | Test 8 |
| 9A | Single | 8 | 8 | 4 | OK |
| 11A | Single | 8 | 8 | 6 | 6 |
| 9A | Double, Outer | 8 | 8 | 6 | OK |
| 9A | Double, Crevice | 8 | 8 | 6 | 8 |

OK = No cracking at end of test, which lasted 1350 hours in Tests 5, 6 and 8 and 1000 hours in Test 7.

Contaminants
    Test 5: Mixture of lead powder and hydrocarbon.
    Test 6: Lead powder.
    Test 7: Lead oxide, PbO.
    Test 8: Hydrocarbon containing fractional percentage of lead.

## VI. Initiation and Propagation — Experimental Observations

Extensive studies have been conducted to illucidate the nature of initiation and propagation of stress corrosion cracks in chloride solution, and virtually nothing has been done in this respect in the other environments. The discussion herein will be based on data from chloride studies but may be applicable generally to cracking in other environments.

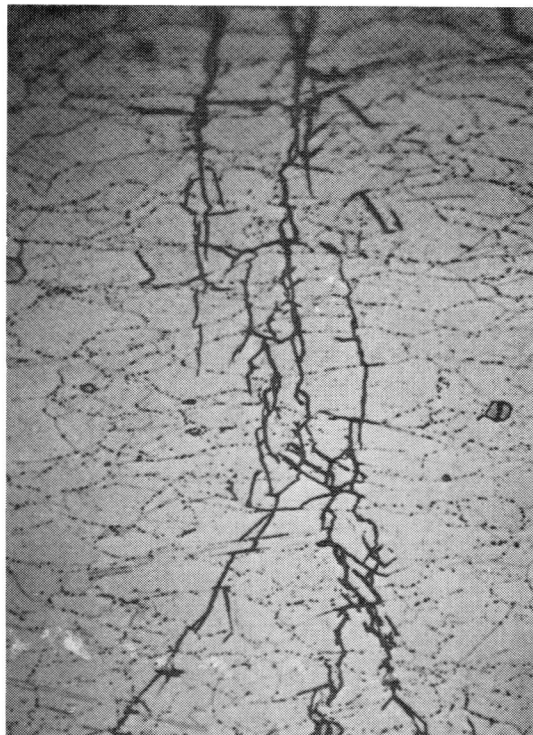

FIGURE 88 — Stress corrosion cracking of Inconel-600 in air-saturated distilled water, pH 10, at 316 C and in the presence of PbO contamination (Copson and Dean[159]).

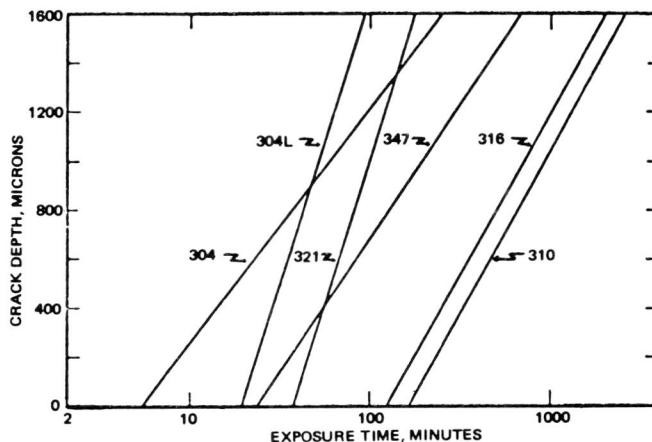

FIGURE 89 — Crack depth as a function of the logarithm of exposure time in 42% MgCl$_2$ for various Fe-Ni-Cr alloys (Eckel[179]).

Initiation and propagation stages have been delineated by several investigators. Eckel has plotted crack length (observed metallographically) versus exposure time for various stainless steels in boiling $MgCl_2$ and determined the time for zero crack length as shown in Figure 89.[179] He finds that the crack length vs time obeys a semilogarithmic relationship:

$$\log t = D/M + \log t_o$$

where $t$ = total time (minutes); $D$ = maximum crack depth (microns); and $M$, $t_o$ = slope and intercept, respectively, both functions of the material.

While this relationship was developed using U-bend specimens, the trends are certainly reasonable and the data fit closely the semilog relationship.

Hoar and Hines in 1954 were the first to perform serious studies of the initiation and propagation of stress corrosion cracks in stainless steels exposed to chloride solutions; they used dilatometry combined with potentiometry. Their subsequent studies utilized these measurements to interpret effects of stress, alloy composition, temperature, and environmental variations. Figure 90 summarizes the correlation between potential and extensometric measurements.[55] Potential-time measurements on nonstressed and stressed specimens are the same except for the final drop in potential observed at breaking of the stressed specimens. Hines has compared metallographic observation with these potential-time curves and suggests that a scheme according to Figure 91 exists.[88] Comparison of this figure with Figure 90 suggests that the fine cracking may not be observed extensometrically and some question regarding such measurements must be raised. Hines provides convincing support for the division of the potential-time curve into the stages shown in Figure 91. The use of the potential-time curve to study effects of stress and alloy composition has already been described in Figures 41 and 67. Kohl, as previously described in the discussion of temperature effects, has used extensometry to

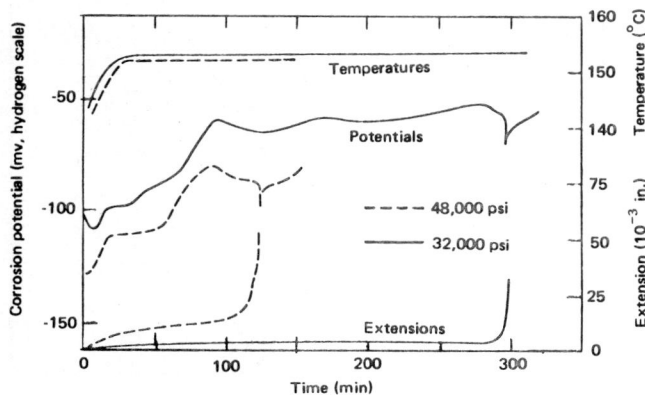

define initiation and propagation stages.[78] Others have studied the delimitation between initiation and propagation stages but in less detail.[90,181]

On a macroscopic scale, it appears that initiation and propagation stages can be identified. However, the measurements of potential, dilation and optical metallography are necessarily gross measurements and incapable of fine resolution. It would appear that the initiation or incubation stage is neither a nucleation type process nor the growth of a critical flaw; the arguments will be presented in Section VII on mechanisms.

The crystallographic nature of the crack propagation process has been studied using single crystals by Reed and Paxton[182] and Paxton et al.[183] Cracking in an Fe-20Cr-20Ni alloy was found to occur on the (100) plane with the highest normal stress. The general crack plane in an Fe-20Cr-14Ni alloy and in Type 304 was approximately normal to the tensile axis. Cracking times for the three alloys were 70-170 hours for Fe-20Cr-20Ni, 16-62 hours for Fe-20Cr-12Ni, and 4-17 hours for the Type 304. Striations were observed on the fracture surfaces. While the authors propose that a fracture process is involved, subsequent work to be discussed suggests that propagation is a dissolution process. Despite the (100) nature of the fracture face in the 20 Ni alloy, cracking was observed to be parallel to slip traces on the surface. Smith and Staehle[184] have presented metallographic evidence that cracking follows a clear crystallographic pattern by virtue of regular interactions with twins; and Logan[185] has shown clear evidence for crystallographically dependent side branching. Smith and Staehle also showed a cross-hatch pattern which developed during the cracking of Type 310 stainless steel. These are shown in Figure 92. Reed and Paxton also showed evidence for a crystallographically dependent interaction of advancing cracks with a spurious twin interface in a single crystal.[182]

Ronnquist shows clear evidence for crystallographic propagation in the early stage of cracking of an Fe-18Cr-11Ni steel and for the occurrence of such processes

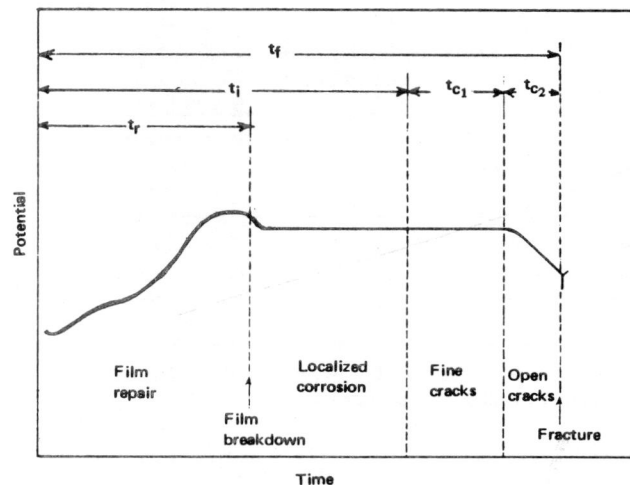

FIGURE 90 — Extension-time, potential-time, and temperature-time curves for 18-8 Nb stressed at 48,000 and 32,000 psi (Hoar and Hines[55]).

FIGURE 91 — Relation of $t_f$, $t_r$, $t_i$, $t_{c1}$, and $t_{c2}$ to the progress of stress corrosion on an idealized potential-time curve (Hines[88]).

on $\{111\}$ planes.[217] Lehtinen has studied the crystallography of advancing crack tips using transmission electron metallography and found the crack tip direction at 30 degrees from the [111].[218] Note that the [110] direction is 35 degrees from the [111] suggesting that crack observed by Lehtinen is advancing along the bisector of the glide planes.

Hines and Hugill[143] suggest, but do not prove, that cracking propagates locally along $\{111\}$ type planes; and

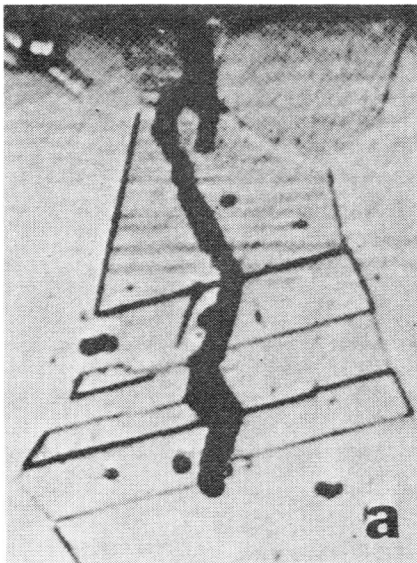

(a)

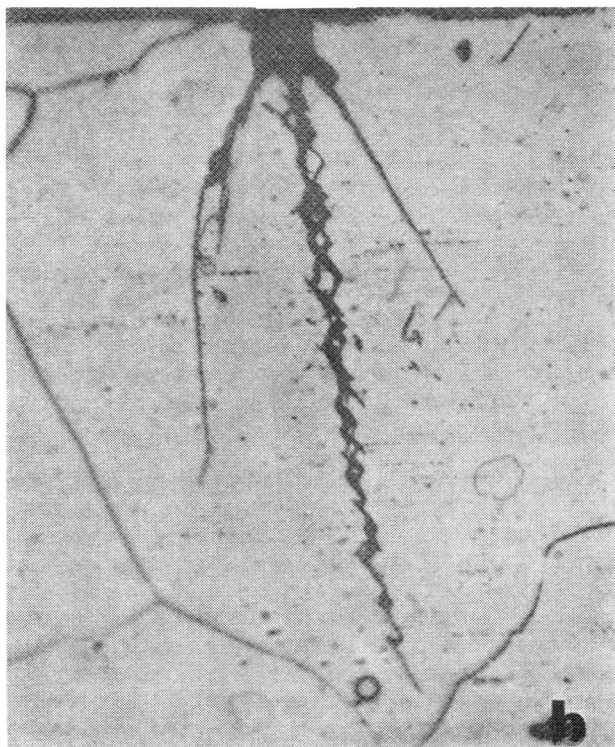

(b)

Denhard, in his discussion of the Hines-Hugill paper, describes his experiments on stainless steel which show that cracks follow $\{111\}$ planes on a local scale. It is the general observation that prior cold work and high residual stresses yield more highly branched cracks than in annealed materials and this was shown in a controlled way by Hines and Hugill.

Scully and Hoar have studied the gross distribution of cracks at the base of a notch and found that the cracking pattern follows the maximum shear lines.[216] The presence of the notch was equivalent to the short single initial crack of Hines and Hugill which, after progressing a suitable distance, bifurcated to follow the planes of maximum shear.

Available evidence suggests that crack propagation, at least locally, follows the slip planes in the gamma alloys; however, the studies of Paxton, which show cracking on the (100) planes, raise questions which have yet to be answered. The definitive study on propagation mechanisms has yet to be done.

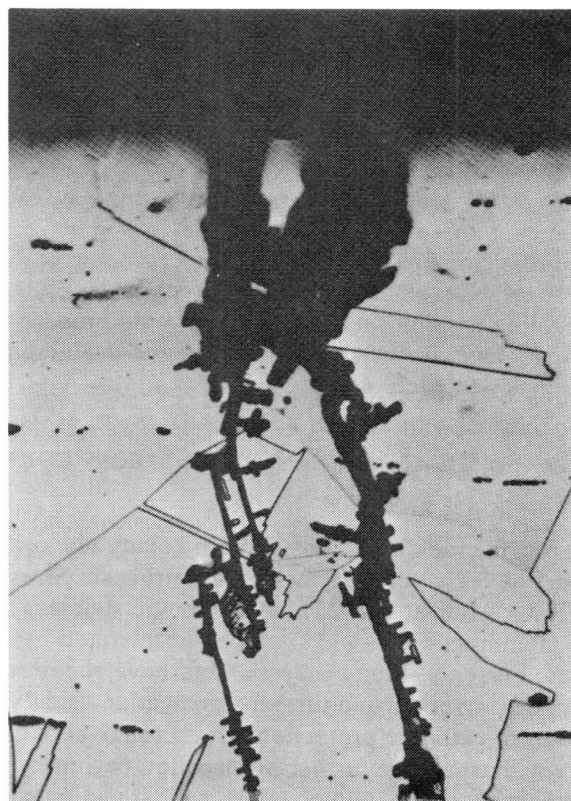

(c)

FIGURE 92 — Optical photomicrographs showing cracks having apparent crystallographic preference. (a) Fe-15Ni-20Cr in 1 w/o NaCl at 260 C (Staehle and Smith[184]). (b) Type 310 stainless steel in boiling MgCl$_2$ (Staehle and Smith[184]). (c) Type 304 stainless steel in dilute Cl$^-$ at 575 C (Logan[241]).

The effect of specimen size on cracking in stainless steels has been studied by Kohl[78] and Hines.[88] Kohl found that changing the specimen diameter from 2 to 8 mm increased the cracking time from approximately 20 to 210 minutes for a load of 60,000 psi on an 18-8 type alloy in boiling $MgCl_2$. Hines studied size effects in the same range using potential-time measurements but at lower applied stress and obtained data in Figure 93. The increased diameter increased all the significant parameters of the potential-time curve. This suggests that the early stage of cracking may not be a surface-dependent process.

## VII. Mechanisms

Previous sections have considered for the most part experimental observations which are presumably the "facts" and extensive speculation has been avoided. However, it is necessary that some underlying rationalization be provided so that reliable predictions can be given regarding expected performance of commercial materials in their respective environments. Such an underlying set of principles is also required if the efforts of alloy design for new environments are to be optomized. The previous discussions of the experimental facts will be used as boundary conditions in assessing the validity of proposed mechanisms.

A useful theory of stress corrosion cracking of the Fe-Ni-Cr alloy must explain at least the role of the following:

(a) Major alloying elements such as nickel.

(b) Minor alloying elements and contaminants.

(c) Major environmental species including chloride, oxygen, and hydroxides.

(d) Stress.

(e) Temperature.

(f) The restriction of lateral dissolution at the crack tip. (The lateral dissolution criterion.)

(g) Initiation and propagation stages.

In the following description the various proposals for cracking mechanisms will be considered with respect to their efficacy in explaining the above objectives. Criticisms will be offered in view of presently known phenomenology.

### A. Increased Anodicity of Strained Material

This idea suggests that the tip of a pit or discontinuity will corrode more rapidly owing to the higher stress resulting from stress concentration. An implicit concept here is that the stress raises the internal energy of the material thereby making it dissolve more rapidly. Such an idea would, for example, meet the restricted lateral dissolution criterion since the deformed volume is relatively small.

This concept is not useful for the following reasons:

1. It is nonspecific with respect to susceptible alloys. The variations in time to cracking cannot be correlated in any way with the capacity to sustain a high internal energy due to elastic strain.

2. In the case of Fe-Ni-Cr alloys exposed to boiling $MgCl_2$ environments, dislocations do not dissolve nor do cell walls having high dislocation densities. If the dislocation core which possesses the highest known elastic strain energy does not dissolve, then it is unreasonable that the tip of a crack should dissolve due to elastic strain energy alone.[184]

3. Slip processes will occur at stresses much lower than that required for significant accumulation of strain energy. Plastic flow with the resultant rupture of films or disarray of the lattice is a very potent accelerant to dissolution.

4. Transgranular to intergranular transitions cannot be rationalized.

There is no evidence that this is a useful concept and further consideration should be dropped.

### B. Strain Accelerated Precipitation of Anodic Phases

The theory advanced in detail by Edeleanu[110,138] suggests that the strain at the base of a crack accelerates the decomposition of unstable austenite to martensite. The resulting martensite presumably is more anodic and hence dissolves rapidly. The narrow region of transformed structure could meet the restricted lateral dissolution required.

This concept was strongly criticized[139,140] as described earlier primarily on the grounds that stable austenitic alloys (up to 50% nickel) will crack. Also unexplained are:

1. The transgranular-intergranular transitions.

2. Cracking above the $M_s$ temperature.

3. Cracking in fully austenitic Fe-Cr-Mn-N-Ni alloys.

There are numerous other objections and this theory must be considered as having little value in the Fe-Ni-Cr systems.

### C. Film Rupture

The film rupture theory as originally suggested by Logan suggests that stress corrosion cracks proceed by successively breaking a passive film.[186,46] At the point of

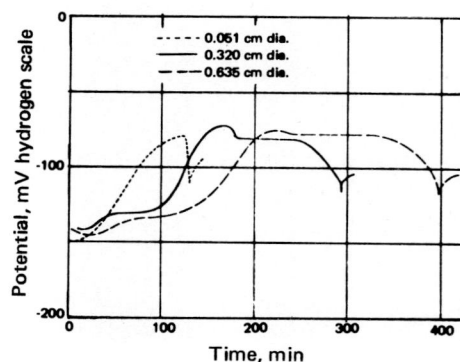

FIGURE 93 — Typical potential-time curves for 18-8-Ti steels at stresses near the 0.1% proof stress (Hines[88]).

rupture, dissolution proceeds until repassivation occurs. Early discussions of the significance of this theory were generally nonspecific. Four important modifications of this theory have been proposed.

**1. Successive Rupture of Brittle Oxide.** The most useful rationalization of cracking in copper alloys appears to involve the formation of a relatively thick tarnish film.[187] This film grows to a thickness on the order of a micron, is broken by the action of stress, reforms, and is rebroken. The total length of crack is thus the number of ruptures times the average thickness of the tarnish layer.

The possibility that such a mechanism operates is suggested by the brittle appearance of cracks. Corroboration for this suggestion has come from the short bursts of crack progress observed in movies[188] and from the fractographic examinations which show evidence of striations. These striations appear to be on the order of the same thickness as the successively formed brittle oxide film.

No critical experiments have been reported to test the validity of this mechanism for the Fe-Ni-Cr alloys. However, it is unlikely that such a process involving an oxide formation is possible in stainless steels because the passive film is normally on the order of 100 Å or less.

**2. Successive Rupture of an Embrittled Layer in the Metal.** Forty[189] has suggested that a subsurface layer of the metal is embrittled by a process related to dezincification. Presumably, this embrittled layer would be successively broken and reformed according to the above mechanism.

Again no critical experiments have been conducted to assess the possible validity of this mechanism in Fe-Ni-Cr alloys. However, it should be noted that in studies of the properties of thin foils after exposure to boiling $MgCl_2$ no significant tendency toward brittleness has been noted.

**3. Successive Rupture of an Ennobled Layer.** In alloys where one of the components has its half cell potential in the same range or above that for the predominant reducible environmental species this component will remain on the surface. When a slip step breaks this surface, dissolution occurs until the surface re-ennobles. There is strong evidence that such a process may be important in the cracking of Fe-Ni-Cr alloys. This will be discussed in detail in a subsequent section, and it will be shown how numerous observations of alloy effects on cracking can be explained on this basis.

**4. Successive Rupture of a Thin Passive Film.** This idea suggests that slip processes break the relatively thin passive film and dissolution proceeds until repassivation occurs. Scully[190] and Hines[191] described in detail how such a process might operate during crack propagation. This process will be discussed and compared with the ennoblement model in a later section.

### D. Dislocation Coplanarity

During the slip process, dislocations may either remain in a single slip plane (remain coplanar) or they may cross slip on intersecting slip planes. Figure 94 compares structures observed in the electron microscope of annealed, strained (planar, cellular arrays) and aged materials. Numerous arguments have been advanced which relate susceptibility to stress corrosion cracking to the relative coplanarity of dislocations. The alloy chemistry is suggested to control physical features of the material such as the stacking fault energy or the degree of ordering which exert constraints on the degree of coplanarity of dislocation arrays. Two essential themes have been proposed for explaining how dislocation coplanarity can be used to rationalize the effect of alloy composition on susceptibility to stress corrosion cracking.

Robertson and Tetelman proposed that a high stacking fault energy enhances susceptibility to intergranular cracking because it would be possible in such instances to preferentially develop a high normal stress at the grain boundaries.[192] A sufficiently high normal stress together with the predisposition of the alloy to dissolve intergranularly would be the criterion for intergranular cracking. They proposed that transgranular cracking occurred at structurally reactive static sites which were associated with dislocation pileups at Cottrell-Lomer barriers. This suggestion was based on observations by Robertson and Bakish of preferential dissolutions apparently associated with such sites in copper-gold single crystals.[193] Since Cottrell-Lomer barriers are stabilized by low stacking fault energies, this condition would also favor transgranular cracking.

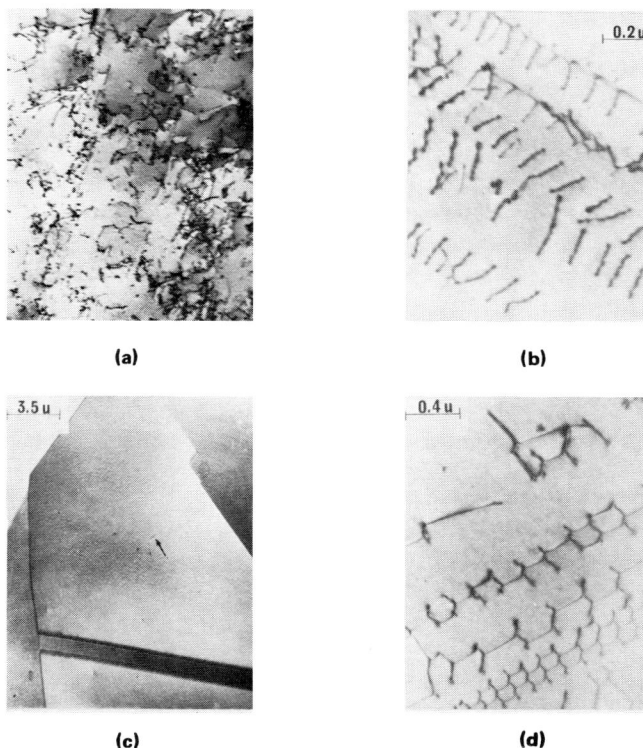

(a)  (b)

(c)  (d)

FIGURE 94 — Electron micrographs showing typical dislocation arrangements in austenitic stainless steels. (a) Annealed structure in 45Ni-20Cr steel; (b) Planar arrays in 45Ni-20Cr steel after 5% strain; (c) Cellular array in 15Ni-20Cr-.1P steel after 5% strain; and (d) Defect structure in 45Ni-20Cr steel after 5% strain and aging for 1 hr at 870 C (Smith and Staehle[184]).

Transition to intergranular cracking from the transgranular mode would occur as the stacking fault energy is raised because easy cross slip would prevent the formation of stable intra-grain pileups although sufficient forces could still be exerted by pileups at grain boundaries to cause intergranular cracking. The essence of these arguments is that low stacking fault energy (high degree of dislocation coplanarity) favors stress corrosion cracking and those alloys whose chemistries yield low stacking fault energies will crack either intergranularly or transgranularly.

Swann and coworkers[194,197] have also presented arguments which favor dislocation coplanarity as an important factor in determining the susceptibility of a given alloy to cracking. Their argument differs from that of Robertson and Tetelman and suggests that transgranular cracking is associated with slip step emergence. A high degree of coplanarity gives a more discrete step having a greater probability of breaking the surface film; whereas the lower degree of coplanarity would produce a much less discrete break in the surface with the result that the surface film may not be broken significantly. These two situations are compared in Figure 95. Swann[196] presents evidence that austenitic stainless steel type alloys which are susceptible to cracking, due either to impurities or to nickel concentrations, exhibit strong tendencies toward coplanar dislocation arrays. His correlation between stacking fault energy and cracking time as a function of nickel is shown in Figure 96.

Swann and Embury[194] demonstrated clearly that preferential dissolution was associated with coplanar dislocation motion. However, a most important restriction was made, namely, that the dislocation be mobile at the time of exposure to the environment. With respect to the importance of coplanar glide they also demonstrated that coplanar dissolution would not occur in a martensitic structure produced by refrigerating austenite. This was presumably due to stifled slip in martensite.

Swann had originally suggested that dislocation coplanarity, and therefore susceptibility to cracking, was associated only with the stacking fault energy. However, Douglass et al and Thomas et al pointed out that, despite the relatively higher stacking fault energy of the higher nickel alloys, coplanar dislocation arrays were still observed.[198,199] They advanced the concept that short range order would also constrain dislocations to coplanar slip (i.e., once SRO is destroyed, it is energetically easier to continue slip on a single slip plane than to reinitiate on other planes). Thus, it would be possible to rationalize coplanar glide in relatively high stacking fault energy materials if SRO exists. Unfortunately, no direct experimental evidence was obtained for short range order but it was argued that there is great difficulty in obtaining the necessary resolution because of the similarity of scattering factors of iron, chromium, and nickel. Also analogous systems were shown to exhibit the required ordering. While these authors presented a rationalization for explaining coplanar glide in high stacking fault energy materials, they did not show why cracking did not occur in alloys where

coplanar glide was observed. A possible suggestion was advanced by Thomas et al[199] that, despite the coplanar glide and local disordering which might provide a site for dissolution, the atoms in non-cracking alloys rearranged too quickly to serve as site for dissolution.

Burr suggests that the SRO argument may not be necessary.[201] He points out that the apparently similar coplanarity of Type 304 and Incoloy-800 observed by Thomas et al, and rationalized by SRO rather than stacking fault energy predominating, may simply be the result of not comparing the alloys over a sufficiently wide range of strains. All early deformation is noted to be coplanar and the transition to cellular arrays occurs at various strains and with varying rapidity in different alloys. Burr also points

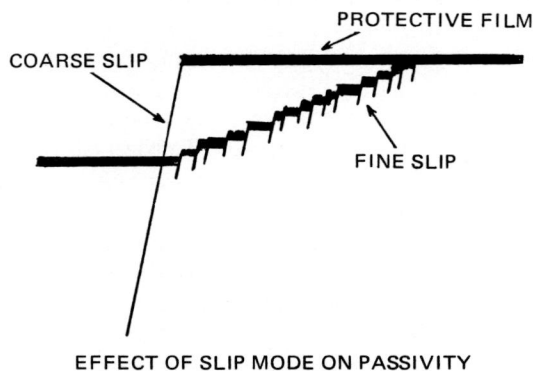

EFFECT OF SLIP MODE ON PASSIVITY

FIGURE 95.— Effect of slip mode on the breakdown of surface films (Pickering and Swann[194]).

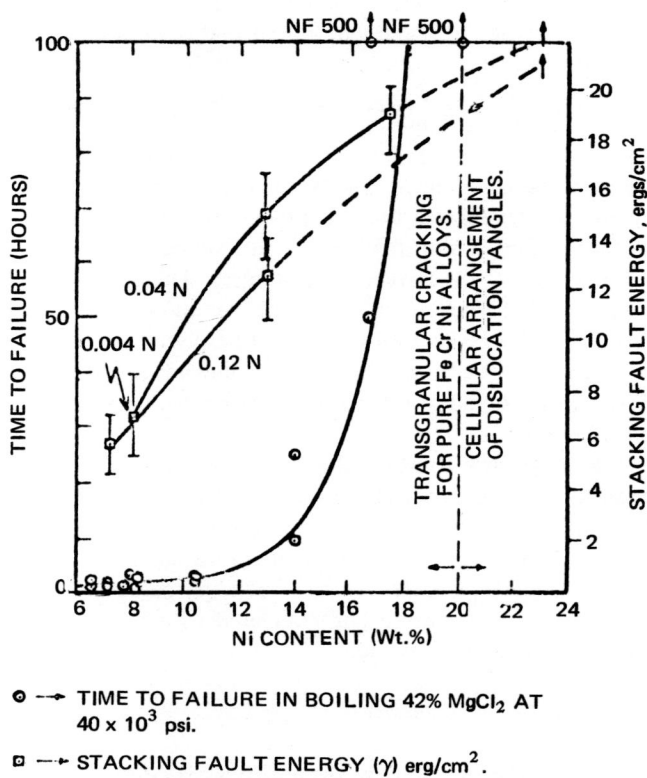

⊙ —► TIME TO FAILURE IN BOILING 42% $MgCl_2$ AT $40 \times 10^3$ psi.

▫ —► STACKING FAULT ENERGY ($\gamma$) erg/cm$^2$.

FIGURE 96 — The effect of nickel on the stacking fault energies and times for stress corrosion failure of approximately 18% Cr stainless steels (Swann[196]).

out that the stacking fault energy at which a significant early transition in coplanarity occurs may be higher than that measured by node techniques.

Pickering and Swann[197] and Swann and Embury[194] propose that the slip step emergence permits dissolution tunnels to be initiated. These dissolution tunnels are then the paths for crack progress into the metal. (Details of tunnel growth are considered in a subsequent section.)

Numerous authors have used the coplanarity and stacking fault energy concepts to explain effects of alloy composition. While nitrogen and phosphorous have little effect on the stacking fault energy, Ronnquist[127] and Thomas et al[199] suggest that the accelerating effect of these additions can be accounted for by the SRO hypothesis. The difference between nonsusceptible Fe-16Cr-20Ni base and manganese containing alloys and the susceptible alloy of the same base with Mo and Ti was suggested by Barnartt et al,[129] and Stickler and Barnartt[200] to correlate well with the coplanarity argument. Evans and Burr conducted a simultaneous study of cracking, stacking fault energy measurements, and dislocation configurations for a wide range of Fe-Ni-Cr alloys plus some alloys with quaternary additions of molybdenum and silicon.[120] They found that increasing nickel increased stacking fault energy while decreasing cracking; and molybdenum effects agreed with Barnartt et al.[129] However, there was no correlation between dislocation distribution and the beneficial effects of both high Cr and quaternary silicon additions. They attributed the latter to the influence of these elements in improving passivity.

The essential situation concerning coplanarity appears presently to suggest the following. Dislocation coplanarity exists over a wider range of alloys than would be predicted by the trends in stacking fault energy. Dislocation coplanarity on the higher stacking fault energy materials can be rationalized by postulating short range order; however, the existence of short range order has yet to be proven. Dissolution appears best explained by slip step emergence rather than slip induced chemical inhomogeneities.

Despite some apparently good qualitative agreement between trends in coplanarity and susceptibility to stress corrosion cracking there are a number of objections to this argument as a useful tool:

1. Tests in boiling $MgCl_2$ show that transgranular cracking occurs in ferritic stainless steels, containing about 1% nickel as well as in the austenitic stainless steels.[118] The difference in crystal structure and stacking fault energy seem too great to rationalize such an occurrence on the basis of coplanarity arguments.

2. Cracking of Fe-Ni-Cr alloys in caustic solutions exhibits variations in cracking mode from intergranular to transgranular due to changes in carbon content and environmental chemistry while over the same range of variables cracking is completely transgranular in chloride environments. (See Table 24.)

3. Inconel cracks transgranularly in lead-containing aqueous environments, intergranularly in water-oxygen environments, and not at all in chloride containing environments.[159]

These examples, and numerous others, question why the cracking mode changes based only on environmental alterations and why the mode does not change in the body centered cubic structure. Presumably, the cracking mode should be insensitive to the environment if the primary effect of alloy chemistry is to control the nature of the slip processes.

*E. Lattice Disarray and Slip Step Emergence*

Hoar and Hines first discussed the current density requirements for an advancing stress corrosion crack assuming that the entire distance traversed was consumed by dissolution.[136] They found that current densities on the order of 1-2 $A/cm^2$ are required. Note that this current density applies after conditions of initiation, as discussed in Figure 91, are established. This also assumes that there is no brittle fracture step involved in propagation. Stainless steels are so ductile that any brittle or cleavage aspect of propagation seems impossible and will not be considered. Swann and Embury provide convincing evidence from acoustical measurements that brittle fracture processes are not involved in the propagation of stress corrosion cracks.[194] West and Fairman using sensitive extensometry also concluded that no discontinuous mechanical steps exist in crack propagation and suggest a continuous dissolution process.[214]

The 1-2 $A/cm^2$ current density is very large with respect to normal corrosion currents for stainless steels in boiling $MgCl_2$ which are in the range of 0.01-1.0 $mA/cm^2$.[136] Peak anodic current densities in boiling $MgCl_2$ (limited by concentration polarization) have been observed to be as high as 100 $mA/cm^2$ which is almost the same order as that required for crack propagation.[107]

In order to rationalize high current densities at a crack tip, Hoar and Hines suggested generally that yielding metal or successive breaking of an oxide film would lead to very rapid dissolution and furnish the current densities required for crack propagation.[79,136]

Hoar and West in 1956 first described experiments of anodic depolarization due to dynamically straining stainless steel wires in boiling $MgCl_2$.[202] Using a current density of 0.5 amps/$cm^2$ a potential of +0.52 V (SHE) was obtained for a static wire specimen in stagnant solution. When the specimen was strained in stagnant solution at 5%/sec at the same current density the potential fell to 0.35 V. Finally when the solution was circulated to reduce concentration polarization and the specimen was similarly strained at the previous current density, the potential lowered to -0.150 V which corresponds very closely to that at the maximum potential plateau shown in Figure 91.

Additional investigations were performed by Hoar and West,[204] and Hoar and Scully,[203,205] West,[206] and van Rooyen.[123] Figure 97 shows the effect of strain rate on the anodic current density at an applied potential of -0.14 V (SHE). Increasing the strain rate clearly increases the current density substantially. Hoar and West[202] and Scully and Hoar[205] note that the depolarization is greater for alloys which are susceptible to cracking. According to Hoar and West, nickel exhibits no strain induced depolarization; and according to Scully and Hoar a series of Fe-Ni alloys exhibit the greatest depolarization at compositions where cracking susceptibility is the greatest. Van Rooyen[123] found that there was little difference among the depolarization observed on susceptible and nonsusceptible stainless steels and on nickel of various purities.

Experimental work to date on strain induced depolarization has established neither a firm difference among alloys, the uniqueness of chloride solutions as a cracking environment, nor a reliable mechanism for explaining the effect; and, while the concept is attractive, additional interpretive work is required.

Hoar and West[204] analyzed the increased reaction rate as being due to an increased number of reactive sites and/or an increased thermal activation of metal atoms at the emerging ledge. West discussed the specificity of environments which cause cracking in terms of the deformability of the ions involved and noted that the chloride ion was relatively deformable and would allow the metal cation to squeeze into its solvation sheath relatively rapidly. West[207] advances an argument to show that the specificity of alloys which crack depends on the nature of the propagation process; this in turn requires that slip planes be a minimum distance apart for significant dissolution to operate. A separation of about one micron is suggested and he suggests that such widely separated slip is characteristic of low stacking fault energy alloys and pure metals which do not crack. It is important to note that West's model is one of progressive ledge dissolution wherein each emergent ledge is dissolved in turn as it emerges. Various models for this process are shown in Figure 98. A significant objection to West's model is that it does not account for shift in the transgranular or intergranular mode of cracking. Partial support for the lattice disarray model comes from work on the electron metallographic examination of thin foils stressed and exposed to various environments. In summary, this work shows that significant dissolution is produced only by moving dislocations. The first unequivocal demonstration of the process was published by Swann and Embury[194] who showed preferential dissolution associated moving dislocations. A review of the work to date on dissolution processes as affected by moving dislocations together with their experimental work has been published by Smith and Staehle.[184] Figure 99 epitomizes the geometrical aspects of slip step dissolution. Typical patterns for this "slip step dissolution" observed in Fe-Ni-Cr alloys are shown in Figure 100. The dissolution is noted by the light areas. Dissolution in nonstressed alloys is random pitting. These slip step dissolution patterns were observed on pure iron, pure nickel and several alloys exposed to boiling $MgCl_2$. It is therefore clear that slip step dissolution, to some extent, can occur on susceptible as well as nonsusceptible (to cracking) materials. If such dissolution is an integral part of stress corrosion cracking, then it is a necessary but not sufficient condition. It is to be further noted that such dissolution can proceed entirely through a foil (500-1200 Å) after only a few dislocations have moved. This suggests that the mechanical emergence of ledges is not required but that the advancing dissolution can nucleate its own ledge sites.

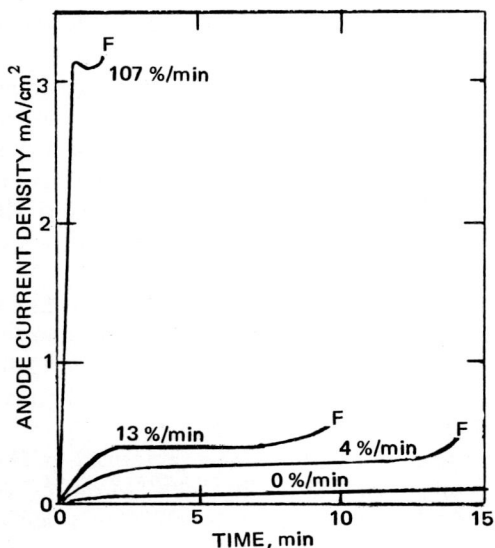

FIGURE 97 — Current density-time curves for 18Cr-8Ni wires strained at 4, 13, and 107% min. while maintained at -0.14 V (SHE). F-fracture (Hoar and Scully[203]).

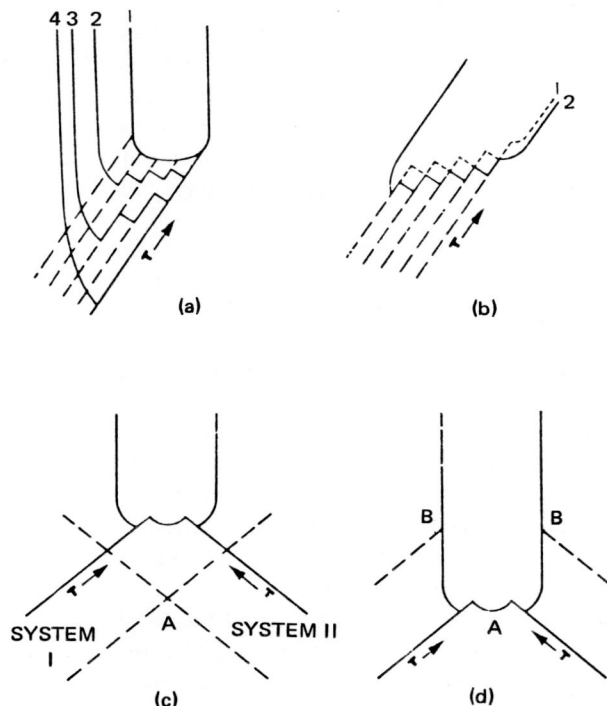

FIGURE 98 — The profile of an advancing crack. (a) Progressive stages for crack inclined to a single system of active slip planes; (b) The constant profile for a crack propagating down the slip plane; (c) and (d) Successive stages for a crack moving through two active slip systems (West[207]).

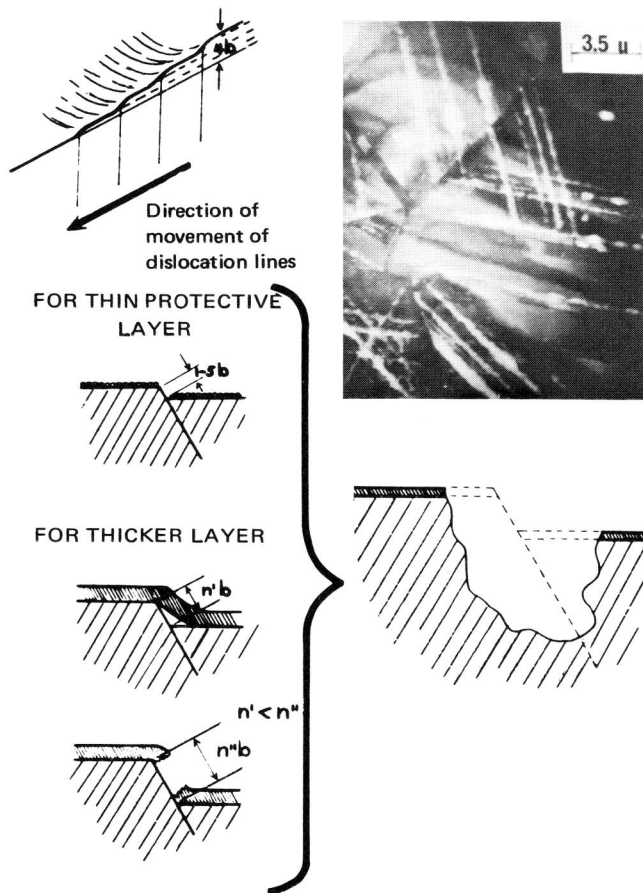

FIGURE 99 — Schematic drawing illustrating the geometrical aspects of slip step dissolution (Smith and Staehle[184]).

Direction of movement of dislocation lines

FOR THIN PROTECTIVE LAYER

FOR THICKER LAYER

$n' < n''$

An interesting observation is to be made with respect to the dependence of crack velocity on concentration polarization. It would appear that incipient cracks are not easily propagated until they reach a sufficient depth. At this critical depth local yawning takes place (as well as significant specimen dilation) and the concentration polarization is reduced permitting the cracks to progress rapidly. If the cracks are unable to yawn, the crack growth rate is undoubtedly limited by concentration polarization.

The significant objection to the slip step dissolution concept is the lack of an obvious mechanism for restricting lateral dissolution; i.e., once a ledge is formed it should continue to dissolve. The fact that such a ledge is stifled at some stage in its development is considered to be the cornerstone in a useful theory described later, which defines alloy-environmental situations which are susceptible to cracking.

A final objection to the slip step dissolution model as obtained from examining thin foils is its apparent lack of specificity with respect to intergranular and transgranular transitions when the environment changes. This specificity must therefore be provided by interactions of environment-metal chemistry.

## F. Processes for Restricting Lateral Dissolution— Film Formation and Noble Element Enrichment

When a slip step emerges, it is reasonable that the ledge so produced should continue to dissolve until it meets a boundary or other discontinuity. The fact that the lateral dissolution is stifled rapidly, despite reinitiation at the crack tip, gives the appearance of a crack: a stress corrosion crack. There are two processes by which lateral dissolution can be stifled. One is a film formation or passivation process. Second is the enrichment of the surface layer in one of the alloy components the half cell potential of which is noble to the corrosion potential. These two processes will be discussed with respect to explaining observed SCC phenomena.

Hines[191] and Scully[190] have considered a mechanism for the advancing crack in Fe-Ni-Cr alloys in chloride environments which bases the restricted lateral dissolution on the following factors: film formation, crack progress by strain induced depolarization, and the susceptibility of alloys based on the coplanarity argument. The build up of a film is evidenced by the increasingly noble potential observed in the potential-time curves typified in Figure 91. The stage of potential rise is due to anodic reactions at weak spots in the initial air-formed film leading to repair by precipitation, oxygen adsorption, or formation of hydroxides. After the potential rise, local corrosion begins, and the film breaks down. In the next stage cracks progress owing to the dissolution of yielding metal. As the crack progresses, the film on the crack walls is repaired and serves as a cathodic site.

There are a number of objections to the above model:

1. It is highly doubtful that slip processes really vary so much over the austenitic range to cause the difference in cracking and noncracking which is observed. Measurements of slip line separations have yet to be made over critical ranges.

2. The fact that ferritic stainless steel containing 1% nickel are subject to transgranular cracking in MgCl$_2$[118] raises a question as to the importance of minimizing cross slip.

3. The fact that the range of susceptible alloys in chloride environments varies little from dilute to concentrated solutions raises a serious question as to whether the nature of the film formation process is such as to distinguish susceptible from nonsusceptible alloys.

4. There is no particular reason why cracking should not begin immediately upon exposing the specimen to solution. The initiation of slip processes, in fact, would be easier in the imperfect film.

An alternative process is possible for rationalizing the dependence of cracking on alloy composition, completely independent of the nature of slip processes. The increase in potential shown in Figure 91 could also be the result of nickel enrichment on the surface as depicted by Figure 101. As the alloy dissolves, the surface is successively enriched in nickel as the more active iron and chromium dissolve. The fact that nickel enrichment might occur in the potential regime of Figure 91 was suggested by Barnartt and van

283

Rooyen[56] and Hoar.[84] Assume that the slip step model is combined with the enrichment process as shown in Figure 102. After the surface has enriched the slip step forms. The composition of the step has a lower nickel concentration than that of the enriched surface; and the step dissolves until the nickel is enriched to the same composition as the pre-existing surface. This process is repeated as the crack progresses. The "slip step enrichment" concept can now be applied to rationalizing Copson's curve as in Figure 103. At high nickel compositions the slip step composition is not appreciably different from that of the enriched surface and cracking is stifled. At very low nickel (< 1%) sufficient nickel is not available and prior enrichment cannot occur. Between these limits the possibility of enrichment is adequate and the difference in noble element concentration is relatively significant. Cracking will occur at various rates depending on the distance from the end points of noble alloy composition. Further support for this model comes

from Barnartt who shows that the potential-time curves for the pure components (Fe, Ni, Cr) in boiling $MgCl_2$ are relatively flat. Slight increases in potential are no doubt due to film formation processes. A detailed discussion of this rationalization has been submitted for publication.[209]

One of the predictions of the slip step enrichment model is that other elements similar electrochemically to nickel should cause transgranular cracking in chloride solutions. Bond has observed transgranular cracking of ferritic alloys containing about 1% of copper as well as the cracking in the alloy to which 1% nickel was added[118] (despite the ferritic structure). Riedrich and Kohl found no cracking in austenitic Fe-Cr-Mn-N alloys even though they were austenitic; however, the addition of either Cu or Ni at 1-4% caused transgranular cracking to occur.[117] In this case Mn is electrochemically similar to Cr despite its austenitizing tendency and Mn therefore cannot enrich. Final evidence for the applicability of the mechanism is

IMPORTANT CHARACTERISTICS
OF DISSOLUTION PATTERNS

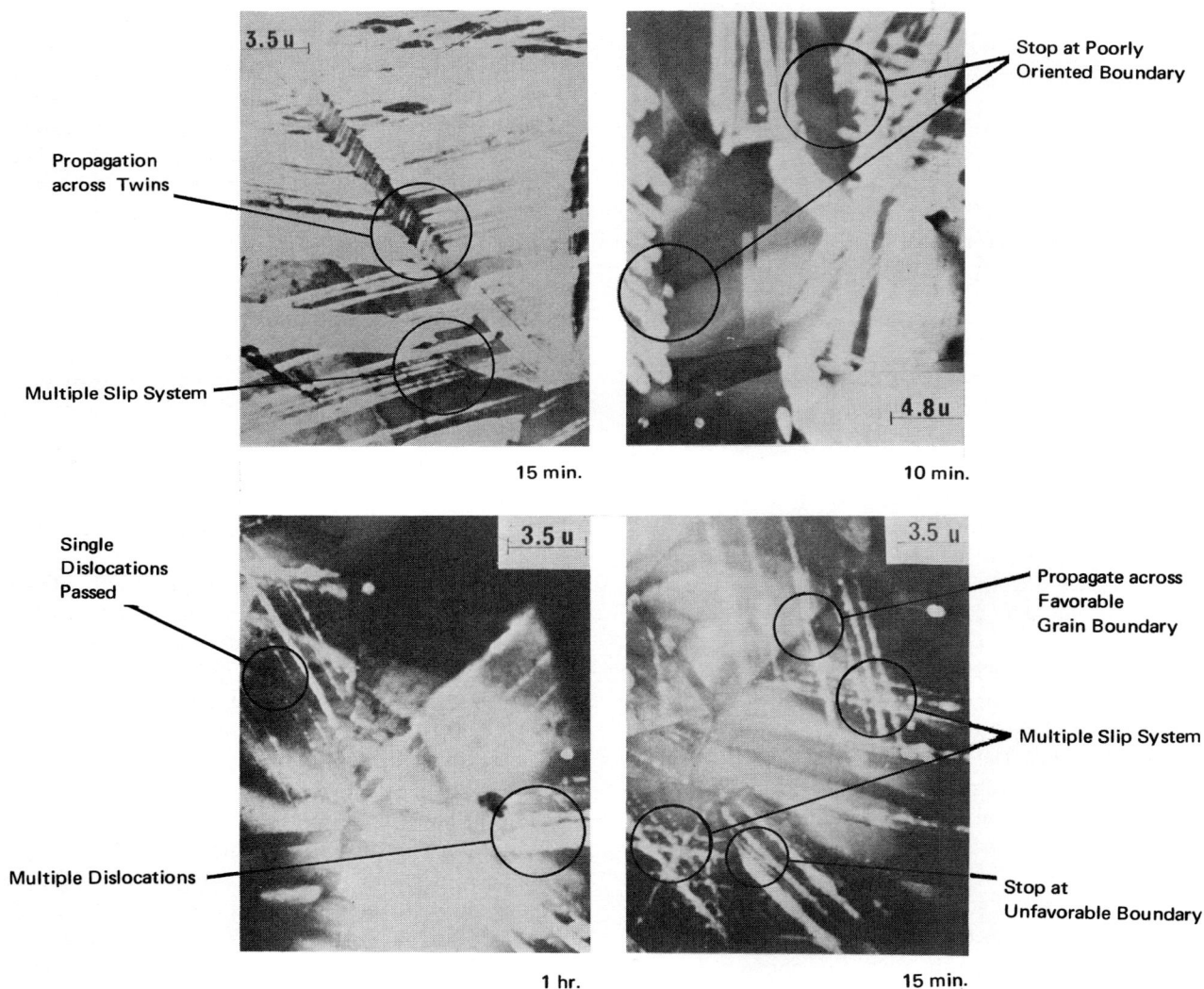

FIGURE 100 — Electron micrographs of various alloys exposed to boiling $MgCl_2$. These figures illustrate important physical features of dissolution arrays. Times shown are of exposure to environment. All specimens in stressed condition (Smith and Staehle[184]).

284

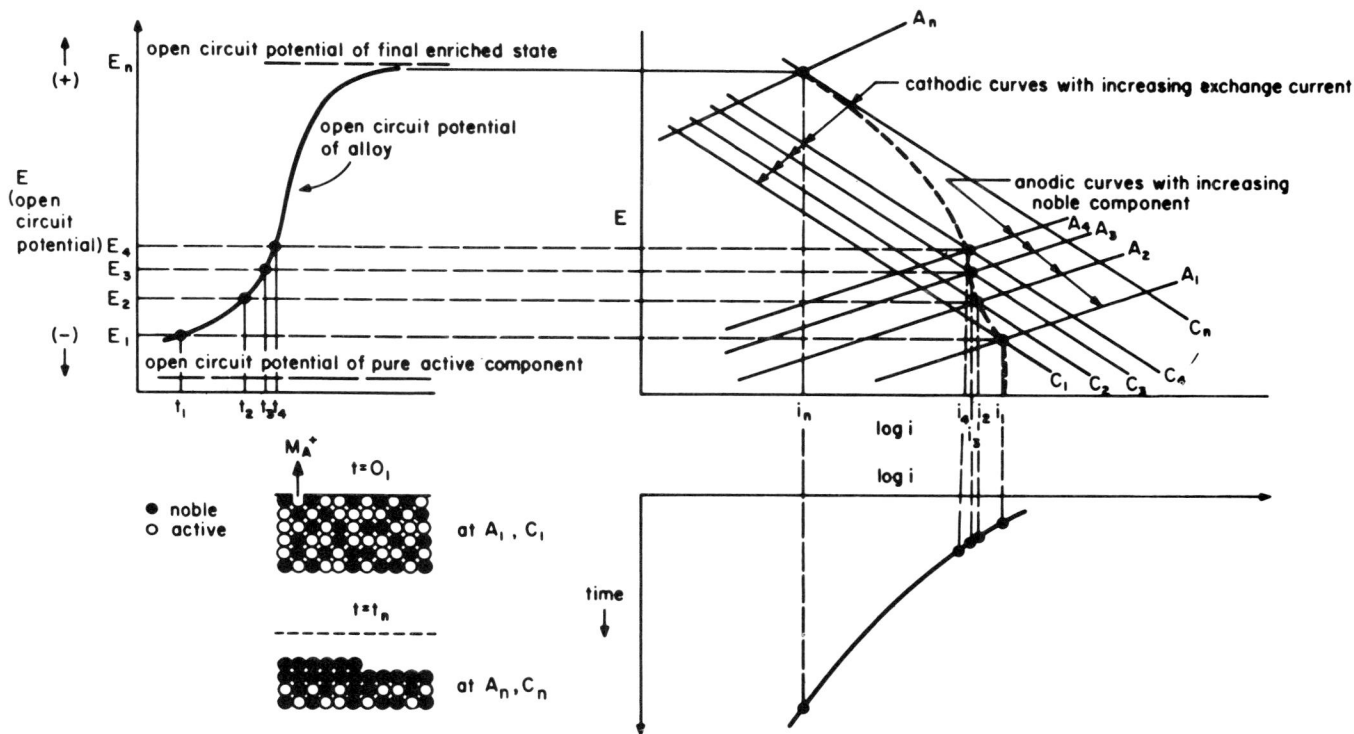

FIGURE 101 — Description of process by which noble element enriches on a metal surface. Upper left shows potential-time plot indicative of enrichment. Upper right shows rationalization of potential-time plot according to operation of kinetic processes; lower right shows effect on corrosion current; lower left shows composition of final surface (Staehle[209]).

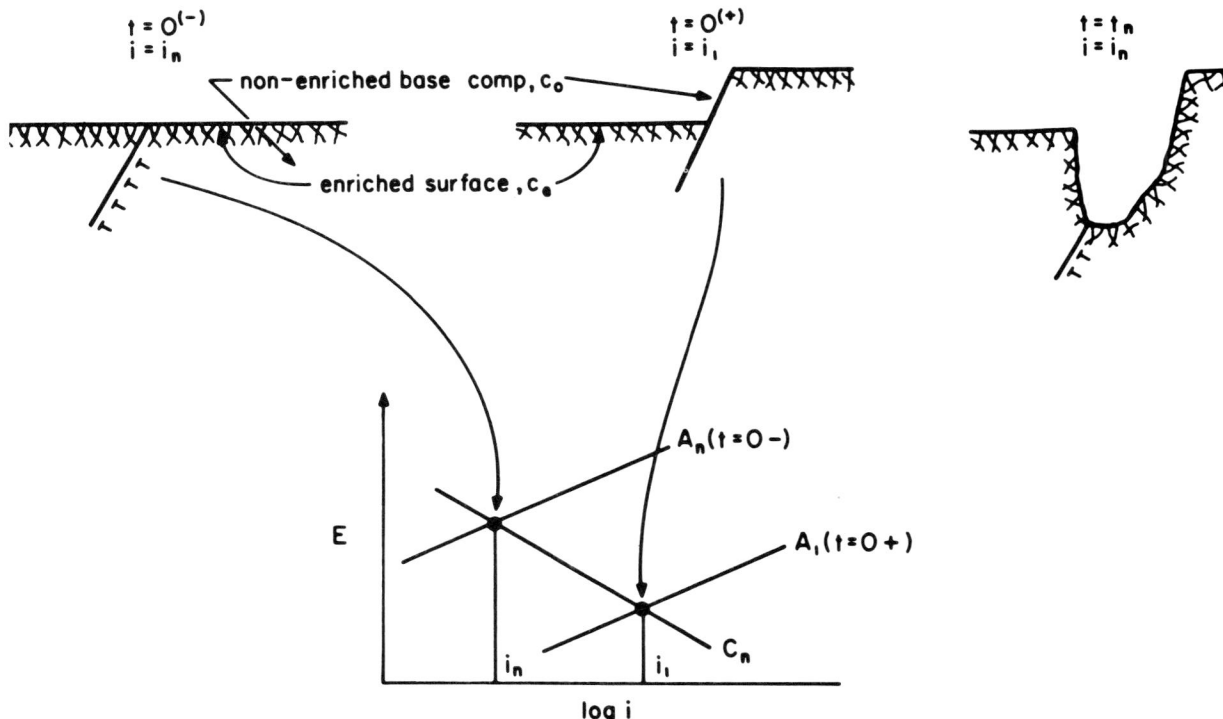

FIGURE 102 — Sequence of events involved with the emergence of a slip step on a previously enriched surface having a concentration, $C_e$ (Staehle[209]).

285

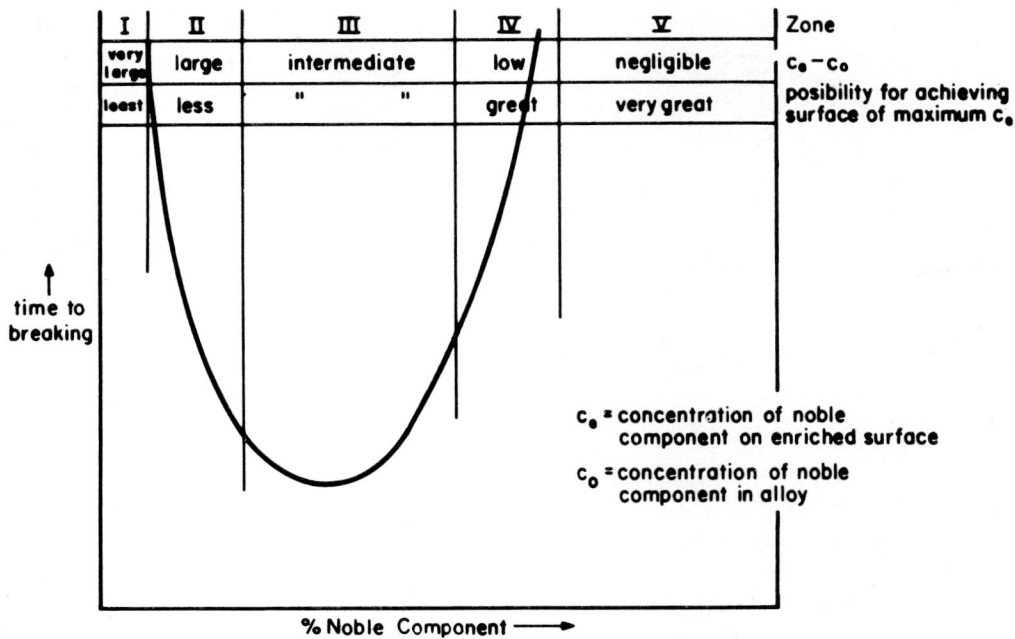

| Zone | I | II | III | IV | V | Zone |
|---|---|---|---|---|---|---|
| | very large | large | intermediate | low | negligible | $c_e - c_0$ |
| | least | less | " " | great | very great | posibility for achieving surface of maximum $c_e$ |

$c_e$ = concentration of noble component on enriched surface

$c_0$ = concentration of noble component in alloy

FIGURE 103 — Schematic relationship between time to fracture curve for active-noble alloys and the difference in noble element concentration, Ce-Co, and the surface enrichment rate (Staehle[209]).

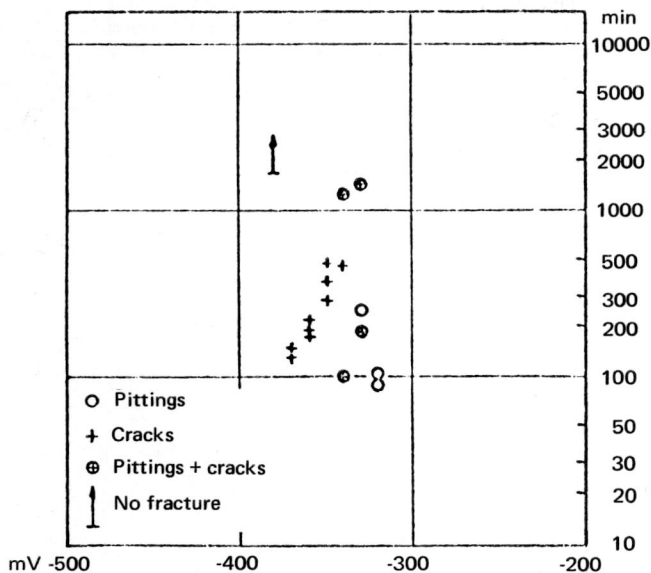

- O   Pittings
- +   Cracks
- ⊕   Pittings + cracks
- |   No fracture

FIGURE 104 — Time to fracture vs potential for cold drawn 18-8 steel in 40% CaCl₂ at 100 C. Load: 20 kg/mm² (Brennert[212]).

suggested by experiments in which the corrosion potential is raised above the half cell potential for nickel with the result that restricted lateral dissolution was no longer possible and extended cracks were observed.[212]

The above suggests a possible alternative for explaining the effect of Mn, Mo, and Ti additions to the Fe-16Cr-20Ni studied by Barnartt et al.[129] Mn is similar to Cr electrochemically, so in 1% concentration does not change the dissolution process. Mo and Ti, on the other hand, form stable reaction products in the potential and pH range

studied and would be expected to assist in restricting lateral dissolution. Numerous other alloying and environmental effects can be more easily rationalized on electrochemical grounds than on the basis of affecting slip processes. The process described above also provides an answer to Uhlig's question on Copson's paper[105] which asked why Fe-Ni alloys could crack whereas Fe-Cr alloys did not. The activity of Fe and Cr is such that enrichment processes are not possible whereas they are for the Ni in the Fe-Ni alloy. Further support for this model comes by analogy with the work of Graf on the cracking of homogeneous noble metal alloys.[210] He found a minimum in cracking time similar to Copson's. It is also noteworthy that relatively high reduction half cells (Fe$^{+++}$, NO$_3^-$) were required for cracking. Thus the active constituent must be oxidized and it could not have been in a hydrogen ion half cell environment. Additional support for the enrichment model comes from work on the crack morphology as a function of applied potential by Brennert.[212] Typical results in Figure 108 show that below certain potentials no cracks are observed while at relatively high potentials only pitting and general corrosion were observed. Only at intermediate potentials in the region of the corrosion potential was cracking actually observed. Thus at relatively noble potentials nickel would go into solution so that only pitting or nonrestricted lateral dissolution was observed.

The slip step enrichment as well as the slip step passivation models offer a means for explaining the initiation as well as propagation stages. Thus initiation is a single slip step dissolution event and propagation is simply a continuation. Such a process may be somewhat discontinuous owing to the repassivation which occurs before the next slip step event. Such a chemically discontinuous pattern would account for the striations observed by West and Fairman[214] and Logan et al.[215]

While the enrichment process seems to be the more reasonable process for explaining restricted lateral dissolution in the chloride cracking, the film formation is probably more reasonable in hydroxide cracking. Here cracking does not go through a minimum with nickel but starts at the nickel free end and becomes stifled as nickel is increased. This dependence has been previously explained as relating to the stability of dissolved species ($HFeO_2^-$ vs $HNiO_2^-$) with respect to the environmental half cell.

Despite the evidence for the nickel enrichment concept no direct proof is available that nickel is in fact enriching. Definitive experiments have yet to be conducted. However, Ronnquist has observed preferential enrichment of Cr in the corrosion products from stainless steel corrosion in boiling $MgCl_2$ with only traces of Fe and Ni.[219] Nielsen,[229] likewise, has observed preferential enrichment of Cr in the oxide with nickel being less than half that expected based on uniform dissolution of the alloy. The observations of Nielsen and Ronnquist are exactly in the order of the electrochemical prediction of the dissolution process. Note that some nickel will be dissolved when the surface is fully enriched since the corrosion potential will inevitably rise with enrichment.

It is appropriate here to comment briefly on the electrochemistry of Fe-Cr-Ni alloy cracking in boiling $MgCl_2$ solutions since it is at least obliquely relevant to the mechanisms of this section. The only extensive studies have been conducted by Hoar and Hines,[136,211] and Barnartt and van Rooyen.[56] In their 1956 paper, Hoar and Hines discussed the evidence showing oxygen to be the reducible species and gave the thermodynamic arguments to show that $H^+$ reduction is unreasonable—in $MgCl_2$ solutions. However, the direct observation of hydrogen evolution by Barnartt and van Rooyen[56] suggests that there may be significant deviation from ideal behavior. Hoar and Hines estimated current densities for crack propagation, estimated activation energies for the exchange current of the reduction reaction, and estimated trends in the corrosion current of a nonstressed specimen. In their 1958 paper Hoar and Hines defined regions of potential and externally applied current density in which cracking would and would not occur. The propagation of cracks was arrested by external currents which reduced the potential below -0.14 V (SHE). It was also found that a strong initial cathodic treatment would provide such a degree of passivity that much smaller current densities would be protective. Barnartt and van Rooyen determined anodic and cathodic polarization curves for 18-8 and the high purity Fe-16Cr-20Ni alloy. They found that hydrogen evolution was possible on anodically polarized 18-8 but not the Fe-16Cr-20Ni alloy.

While Hoar and Hines as well as others have demonstrated that cracking of stainless steels can be prevented by going to more active potentials (cathodic protection), Acello and Greene have demonstrated that anodic protection would be beneficial if the environment although containing chloride exhibited an active-passive

transition.[213] This polarization in the passive region would stifle cracking. They also demonstrated that such a region exists providing that the chloride concentration is sufficiently low. They found that Type 304 would crack in $10 N H_2SO_4$ + 0.5 N NaCl solution in 0.5-48 hours whereas when protected at +0.5 V (SCE) cracking did not occur in 1300-2700 hours. The effect of chloride on the polarization behavior is shown in Figure 105. Acello and Greene also studied the corrosion rate of the $H_2SO_4$-NaCl solution in protected (+0.5 V SCE) and nonprotected conditions. Their results in Table 26 show that the addition of chloride stifles the anodic corrosion in sulfuric acid—a result which must correspond with its tendency to adsorb.

## G. Tunneling

Swann and coworkers[194,195,197] have proposed a process of crack initiation and advance which involves preferential tunneling followed by mechanical tearing. The process is epitomized by Figure 106. The initial site for preferential attack is an emergent slip step where the chemical reactivity is enhanced by the film breaking. The tunnels progress into the metal by a chemical process until their progress is stifled, due probably to mass transfer limitations. The weakened region is torn and the tunnels reinitiate.

The critical question in this mechanism concerns the process by which tunnels grow—their initiation being reasonably accounted for by dynamic slip step emergence. There are several experimentally verified mechanisms for local dissolution processes which would produce tunnel

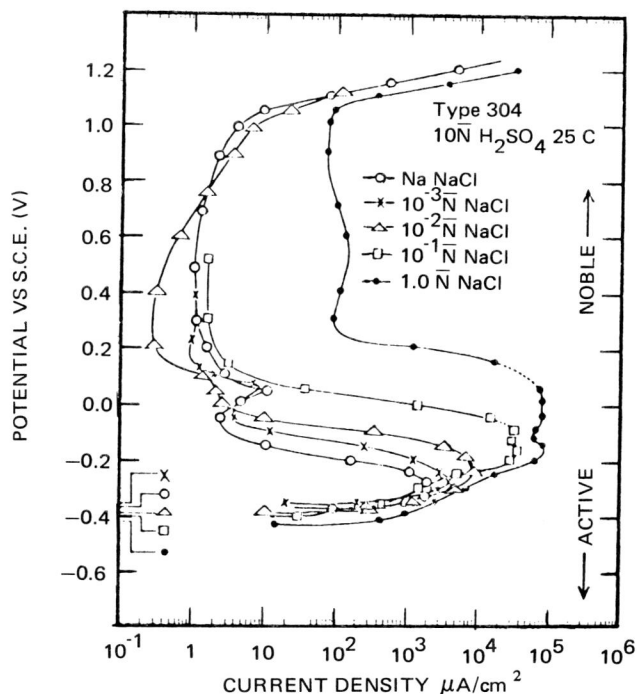

FIGURE 105 — Effect of chloride on the anodic polarization of Type 304 stainless steel in 10 N $H_2SO_4$ (Acello and Greene[213]).

geometries. These have been recently reviewed by Dean et al.[222] While none of these mechanisms presently offer a clear explanation for alloy or environmental dependence, they offer numerous reasonable possibilities. Again, as with the slip step propagation model, the tunneling dependent processes must meet the restricted lateral dissolution criterion.

A simple explanation for tunneling involves preferential dissolution at dislocations. Their arrangement in a coplanar

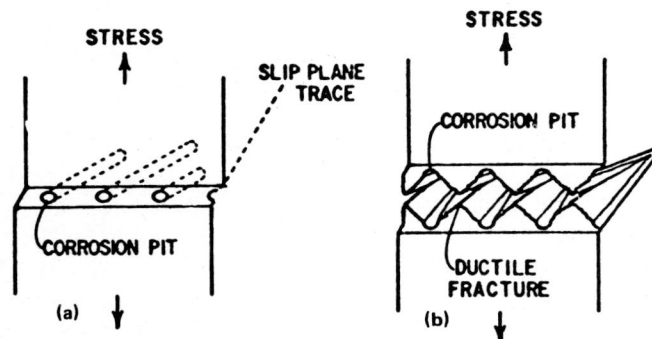

FIGURE 106 — Schematic representation of the stress corrosion cracking mechanism. (a) Tubular pits initiated at areas where surface films have been ruptured by slip. (b) Ductile tearing along a plane containing the tubular pits. The stress is increased across the plane because of the reduced cross section and the stress raising effect of the pit (Swann and Embury[194]).

pile up array would offer an ideal situation, once dissolved, for the crack development shown in Figure 106. However, the strain energy of a dislocation, even its core, offers only a 1-10 mv change in the equilibrium potential; and so any dissolution beyond the normal etch pit geometry would not be expected. Indeed, preferential and extended dissolution of unadorned dislocations has never been observed. If chemical segregation either by strain induced equilibrium redistribution or strain sensitive precipitation occurs at dislocations, it is then possible for a sufficient potential difference to develop for preferential dissolution to take place. The observation of Robertson and Bakish[193] discussed by Robertson and Tetelman[192] of preferential dissolution along [110] directions in strained CuAu crystals is probably an excellent case of dissolution at solute enriched dislocations. It is possible that the dislocations were enriched in copper. Thus, in the ferric chloride solution, the Cu would be oxidized leaving the gold behind on the walls of the tunnels. Preferential dissolution at solute enriched dislocations has been observed in aged Fe-Si alloys by Suits and Low[224] and Pickering.[226] Pickering, in fact, performed an elegant experiment using thin foils in which enriched and nonenriched dislocations were present. The former dissolved and the latter did not. Tromans and Nutting[226] have observed preferential dissolution at dislocations in Cu-Zn alloys exposed to stress corrosion cracking environments. These dissolution pits were observed to link up. Armijo found evidence for preferential

TABLE 26 — Comparison of Corrosion Rates Protected vs Unprotected
(Acello and Greene[213])

| Type | Environment Air Exposed (30 C) | Corrosion Rate (mpy) | |
| | | Unprotected | Protected |
|---|---|---|---|
| 310 | N H$_2$SO$_4$ | 0.35 | — |
| | N H$_2$SO$_4$ + 10$^{-5}$ N NaCl | 0.27 | 0.028 |
| | N H$_2$SO$_4$ + 10$^{-3}$ N NaCl | (1) | 0.040 |
| | N H$_2$SO$_4$ + 10$^{-1}$ N NaCl | 2.10 | 0.082 |
| | N H$_2$SO$_4$ + 0.5 N NaCl | 2.10 | — |
| 310 | 10 N H$_2$SO$_4$ | 295.00 | — |
| | 10 N H$_2$SO$_4$ + 10$^{-5}$ N NaCl | 330.00 | 0.038 |
| | 10 N H$_2$SO$_4$ + 10$^{-3}$ N NaCl | 9.00 | 0.029 |
| | 10 N H$_2$SO$_4$ + 10$^{-1}$ N NaCl | 25.00 | 0.050 |
| | 10 N H$_2$SO$_4$ + 0.4 N NaCl | — | 0.023 |
| | 10 N H$_2$SO$_4$ + 0.5 N NaCl | 26.00 | — |
| 304 | N H$_2$SO$_4$ | 15.70 | — |
| | N H$_2$SO$_4$ + 10$^{-5}$ N NaCl | 14.00 | 0.016 |
| | N H$_2$SO$_4$ + 10$^{-3}$ N NaCl | 2.93 | 0.045 |
| | N H$_2$SO$_4$ + 10$^{-1}$ N NaCl | 3.20 | 0.020 |
| | N H$_2$SO$_4$ + 0.5 N NaCl | 2.46 | — |
| 304 | 10 N H$_2$SO$_4$ | 1,340.00 | — |
| | 10 N H$_2$SO$_4$ + 10$^{-5}$ N NaCl | 1,930.00 | 0.016 |
| | 10 N H$_2$SO$_4$ + 10$^{-3}$ N NaCl | 1,125.00 | 0.040 |
| | 10 N H$_2$SO$_4$ + 10$^{-1}$ N NaCl | 77.00 | 0.210 |
| | 10 N H$_2$SO$_4$ + 0.5 N NaCl | 113.00(2) | 1.600 |

(1)Specimen remained passive during corrosion test.
(2)Specimens exposed to this environment cracked without anodic protection.

dissolution at dislocations in specimens exposed to $HNO_3$ + $Cr^{+6}$ environments.[227] Figure 86 shows one example.

The direct evidence for preferential dissolution at dislocations in Fe-Cr-Ni alloys is open to question. While there is no question that tunnel type dissolution is occurring, there is a serious question as to the mechanism. Smith and Staehle, in examining numerous thin foils in various conditions and of various compositions, found no evidence for preferential attack at static dislocations.[184] Scully's observation of platinum decoration at dislocations is probably the result of initial etch pitting dissolution. The observation by Tromans and Nutting of dissolution at dislocations is probably more likely slip step dissolution resulting from moving dislocations and the pitting dissolution claimed at dislocations is probably the random dissolution observed by Smith and Staehle on dislocation free specimens. The absence of solute enhanced dissolution in $MgCl_2$ environments can probably be explained by the relatively small difference in the Fe, Ni, Cr atom sizes and thus no solute segregation is expected.

Despite the lack of direct observation of preferential dissolution at dislocations, the observations of Nielsen[220] shown in Figure 107 indicate that preferential tunnel type dissolution is taking place, that it is crystallographic, and that it is preceding an advancing crack. Such evidence is strong support for Swann's model.

If dislocation reactivity is not a suitable rationalization for Nielsen's observations,[220] another must be found. It is also noteworthy that his first fractographic studies both of fracture faces and corrosion product fans showed evidence of striations already discussed[229] and no tunnels were evident. In this case, the oxide material was simply that extracted from the cracks. However, for the observations of tunnels as in the first two photos of Figure 107, an extra step was performed in specimen preparation. Before removing the corrosion product oxide from the surface, the specimen was first oxidized to strengthen the film for handling in the electron microscope and to prevent tearing during bromine dissolution. Here the tunnels were observed. Both the aggregate of spires as well as the wispy appearing ones may in fact be the result of the whisker growth described by Gulbransen and Copan[230] and may have nothing to do with preferential penetration into the metal. There is, in fact, a very close resemblance between the various manifestations of Nielsen's tunnels and Gulbransen and Copan's blades and "grass." It is also noteworthy that Nielsen showed no definite relationship between the tunnels and slip step dissolution as reported by Dean et al and described below.[222] Despite these objections the apparent precursor tunneling at the right of Figure 107c at the tip of the advancing crack appears legitimate and remains as support for Swann's argument.

Other alternative proposals have been suggested in lieu of the concept of dislocation reactivity. Pickering and Swann have studied homogeneous tunnel formations in Cu-Au alloys and found that tunnels will progress crystallographically with concomitant enrichment of gold on the tunnel surfaces. These tunnels were not associated with dislocations nor other structural inhomogeneties—thus the

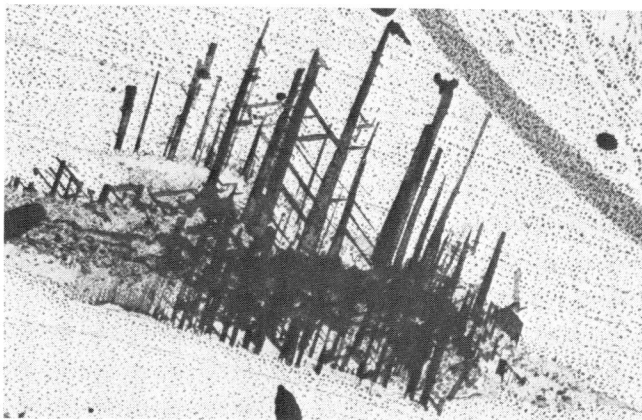

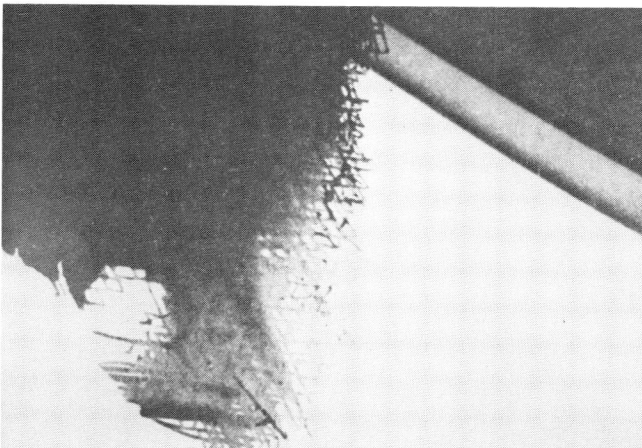

FIGURE 107 — Corrosion tunnels in Type 304 stainless steel exposed to boiling $MgCl_2$ (Neilsen[220]).

basis for calling them homogeneously nucleated. The acuity of these tunnels was observed to decrease with increasing gold as depicted schematically in Figure 108, and a noncracking environment produced nonspecific dissolution. The trend of tunneling shown in Figure 108 is in accord with the relationship observed by Graf for the susceptibility of these alloys to cracking.[210] An objection to applying this process directly to interpreting tunneling of the type in Figure 107c is the general proliferation of tunnels. Something relatively specific seems to be required. However, this process may still be useful for mechanistic interpretations.

Westwood has proposed that tunnel growth may occur by a step poison mechanism.[231] His experiments on LiF have shown clearly that the morphology and growth of tunnels is sensitive to the nature of environmental species. As has been already demonstrated in these discussions, adsorption of critical species is an important factor in dissolution kinetics and crack propagation behavior. While there is no specific evidence for tunnel growth in metals as influenced by step poison, the idea is sufficiently attractive to consider further. At this time, there is no way of determining the applicability of such a mechanism to Swann's model.

Finally, an investigation by Dean et al has been conducted using a technique similar to that of Nielsen's (i.e., oxide was stripped from stressed specimens after exposure to boiling $MgCl_2$).[222] This investigation included commercial alloys varying in nickel from Type 304 to Inconel 600. The incidence of tunnels was found generally to correlate with the susceptibility of the alloys to cracking. Further, a definite correlation between tunnels and slip step emergence was demonstrated as shown in Figure 109. These tunnels exhibited a more irregular appearance than those of Nielsen in Figure 107. This seems more reasonable for an internal corrosion process. Also, neither tunnels nor slip step traces were observed on specimens taken from surfaces in compression. The mechanism of propagation of these tunnels was taken as involving slip step activated dissolution at the base of the tunnels. Thus, if irregularities form in the initial dissolution trench, subsequent dislocations are likely to interact only with these irregularities, form slip steps and become pinned between the discontinuities. Thus the tunnel progresses in the slip plane by successive slip step dissolution. The restricted lateral dissolution criterion is provided by nickel enrichment as described in the previous section. After a sufficient number of dislocations accumulate between the advancing tunnels, their back stress causes a slip step between the tunnels and dissolution occurs; but it does not catch up with the advancing tunnels since the amount of dissolution per slip step event is almost independent of the number of dislocations taking part in the process. Such a process would give the geometry shown in Figure 107.

While the tunnel model is generally attractive, it may depend more on the ennoblement process to explain the effect of alloy chemistry on cracking susceptibility. Further, it would appear that the tunneling process is a specific variation on the general theme of slip step dissolution. Cracks, in general, especially as evidenced by numerous striations from fractography, appear to progress with extended linear fronts perpendicular to the direction of propagation and do not progress as a point front as in tunneling. In other words, the cracks progress by simply deepening trenches with each successive increment in depth being the result of a step emergence. This view is also supported by the dissolution arrays of Figure 100. The intermittent dissolution which could give rise to tunneling is infrequent compared to that which produces extended trenches.

### H. Surface Energy

It has already been demonstrated here, as well as in the literature, that certain environmental species adsorb in

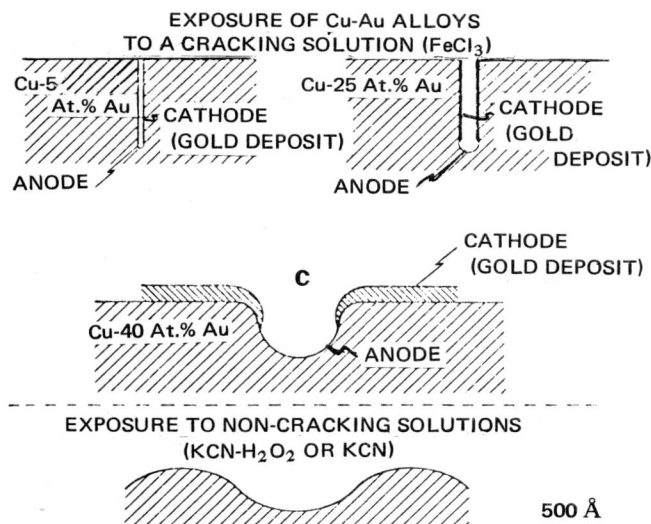

FIGURE 108 — Cross section showing the geometry of attack for Cu-5, 25, and 40 a/o Au alloys exposed to cracking solutions and for Cu-Au alloys exposed to noncracking solutions. The radius to depth ratio of the pits is drawn to scale (Pickering and Swann[197]).

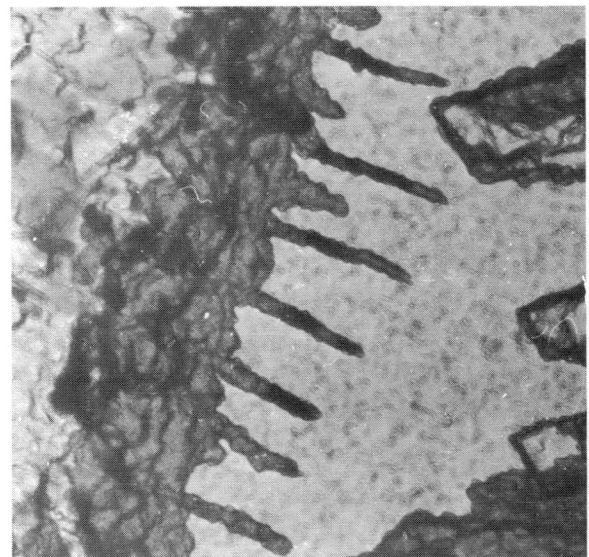

FIGURE 109 — Oxide film from Type 304 stainless steel stressed above yield point and exposed to boiling $MgCl_2$ for 30 minutes (Dean et al[222]).

290

preference to others. Associated with such adsorptions must be varying degrees of surface energy lowering. Uhlig,[223] Nichols and Rostoker,[232] and Coleman et al[233] have proposed that this concept be applied to interpreting stress corrosion cracking in aqueous environments. The essence of these proposals involves an interaction of the critical environmental species with the stressed metal bonds at the crack tip causing bond breaking and consequent advance of the crack.

This concept is considered to have limited application to cracking in this alloy system for the following reasons:

1. Yielding with attended step emergence is clearly operating at the base of cracks in ductile alloys. Any scheme of bond breaking would require an infinitely sharp crack which does not exist.

2. Greater energy lowering will come from dissolution than adsorption. Thus, dissolution processes are favored.

3. Crack advance is fairly clearly an electrochemical dissolution process. The findings advanced in this review are too numerous to disregard. There are also numerous processes available to explain restricted lateral dissolution.

4. The role of species which produce peculiar or unusual effects of inhibiting or accelerating cracking are no doubt explicable in terms of adsorption, but this adsorption probably affects electrode kinetic processes.

5. The grain boundary size dependence of Coleman et al[233] can be more easily explained by effects of grain size on slip step emergence. Thus the probability of a emergence increases with increasing grain size owing to the increased back stress which can be developed on a given slip plane.

### I. Chloride Ion Migration

Bergen[234] and Thomas and Allio[235] have proposed that the specific action of the chloride ion as well as the effects of nickel on the cracking of Fe-Ni-Cr alloys can be rationalized in terms of reversible chloride ion migration through the crack film toward the region of highest stress. The chloride then acts to break down the film thereby allowing metal dissolution. The distribution of chloride ions in a stress gradient was demonstrated by radioactive tracer measurements of the chloride concentration along a beam specimen stressed in three point loading.[67,234] The chloride concentration was found to be maximum at the region of highest stress. When the stress was removed, the chloride distribution was again random. Special precautions in specimen preparation were taken to avoid spurious effects. Redistribution was measured on specimens stressed out of solution; these specimens have been thoroughly washed to remove surface chlorides so that all chloride was incorporated in the surface oxide film. When a specimen of Type 305 was stressed, the ratio of chloride at the point of maximum stress to that at zero stress was about 1.6. No redistribution occurred on Incoloy 800. Bergen suggested that the diffusion of chloride in a higher nickel alloy would be inhibited because the Ni-O bond is stronger than the Ni-Cl bond.

While the redistribution of chloride may be an experimentally verifiable observation, application of this concept to cracking in chloride environments is questionable for the following reasons:

1. As shown earlier, not only does Incoloy 800 crack in chlorides but so does Incoloy 825 (about 42% nickel) as well as other alloys containing up to 50% Ni. Neither the above data nor its predictions are in accord with these data.

2. The chloride concentration in the environment, especially 42% $MgCl_2$, probably overwhelms any that is transported in the oxide film. When a slip step emerges chloride must be immediately available in large quantities. It is inconceivable that the necessary flux of $Cl^-$ could be sustained by solid state diffusion in an oxide film.

### J. Wedging Action of Corrosion Products

Nielsen first demonstrated clearly that corrosion products of significant volume are produced within an advancing stress corrosion crack in stainless steels exposed to chloride environments.[229] He also showed that these corrosion products could exert a measurable stress. Pickering et al[236] studied quantitatively the forces exerted by oxide products. They found that pressures of 4000-7000 psi could be exerted by corrosion products building up in a constricted region. In a particular experiment designed to show that these pressures could propagate a crack, a small stainless steel plate was inserted into a notch with about 0.001 in clearance. Corrosion in this gap due to exposure to a chloride environment at 206 C produced sufficient stress to propagate cracks as shown in Figure 110. X-ray analysis of these stresses at the base of the notch showed that the yield point had been reached (in this case noncracking titanium was used as the notch material while stainless steel was used as the insert).

The work of Pickering et al clearly demonstrates that stresses due to corrosion products can be significant and probably in many cases the critical factor in propagating cracks in engineering structures.

Whether the wedging action effect determines environment—alloy combinations which crack may be questioned.

FIGURE 110 — Photograph of failed Type 347 stainless steel specimen. Specimen is slightly opened to illustrate cracks at base of notch (Pickering et al[236]).

For example, the less passive ferritic stainless steels would be expected to crack more readily. On the other hand the more passive higher nickel alloys would be expected to produce less volume of corrosion products and hence be less susceptible—which they are. The effect of wedging would be aggravated in higher pH solutions where $Fe(OH)_3$ is more insoluble. Wedging is probably important only in propagation and not in initiation. The data of Pickering et al show clearly that the concept of a threshold stress is meaningless in engineering materials. A crack may be easily started due to machining stresses and propagated by corrosion product build up.

### K. Hydrogen as a Critical Species in Cracking

Vaughan et al proposed that absorption of hydrogen is a critical process in the stress corrosion cracking of stainless steels in chloride environments.[124] They suggested that susceptibility is related to the amount of hydrogen absorbed as well as the mobility of hydrogen in the material. Electron metallographic evidence showed that in a susceptible alloy (containing nitrogen) hydride plates reoriented under stress in a direction perpendicular to the applied stress; whereas in a nonsusceptible alloy hydrogen did not reorient. It was further demonstrated that the hydrides dissolve preferentially in boiling $MgCl_2$. Thus, the susceptibility of an alloy to cracking would be related to its capacity to form hydrides as well as whether the hydrides reorient on application of stress. Presumably, hydrogen becomes available from hydrogen reduction inside the crack.

There are a number of observations which support the contention proposed above. The results of Lang[102] summarized in Table 12, show that group VB elements accelerate cracking considerably. Some of these elements (Sb, As) are often used to accelerate hydrogen absorption during cathodic charging. Barnartt and van Rooyen[56] showed that hydrogen was emmanating from a stainless steel specimen undergoing cracking in boiling $MgCl_2$. Shively et al[237] showed that Type 310 could be embrittled by hydrogen absorption but only under severe conditions of charging. Barnartt and van Rooyen also found that hydrogen was readily produced at anodic potentials in a susceptible 18-8 alloy but not in a pure resistant Fe-16Cr-20Ni alloy.

Despite the apparent attractiveness of the suggestion, there are a number of objections which must be considered:

1. Cathodic charging is a severe state of affairs and it is unlikely that such an intense situation exists at the base of a crack, especially in view of the relatively high concentration of positive ions being produced as the crack advances.

2. The thermodynamic argument pointed out by Hoar,[84] while apparently not explaining the hydrogen evolution of Barnartt and van Rooyen, clearly suggests that high pH solutions would not cause cracking owing to the increasing lack of available $H^+$ ions. Furthermore, at neutral pH and above, it has been clearly demonstrated that oxygen

is required for crack propagation. Further, hydrogen ions are consumed in the oxygen reduction according to:

$$O_2 + 4H^+ + 4e \rightarrow H_2O$$

It appears from the present evidence that hydrogen absorption may not be a determining factor in cracking but in low pH ranges may exert a secondary influence.

## Conclusions

### Chloride Cracking

The evidence suggests that major alloying elements (Fe, Ni, Cr) as well as the impurities exert their effects on controlling susceptibility to cracking through electrochemical and physicochemical avenues. Crack initiation as well as propagation appears to be controlled structurally by slip step emergence with subsequent rapid dissolution in the region of the step; however, this slip step process will occur as well in nonsusceptible as susceptible alloys. There is little evidence that dissolution at solute enriched static dislocations is a significant consideration. Chemical processes appear to control the extent and role of reaction after slip step emergence. These chemical effects specifically involve transient anodic dissolution, rate and type of reduction reaction, the formation of protective films, and the adsorption of various species which may accelerate or decelerate these processes.

It appears that the effect of nickel can be best explained according to a model which involves the preferential enrichment of nickel on the surface. The effect of nitrogen appears not to involve either the slip process or dislocation reactivity but rather some aspect of hydrogen ion discharge, hydrogen absorption, or the anodic process. The temperature dependence of cracking appears to be controlled through its effect on electrochemical reaction. Stress exerts its effect through controlling the rate of slip step emergence. The uniqueness of chloride ion with respect to the cracking process appears to involve the manner of ion adsorption in competition with other ions and the subsequent dissolution of the metal possibly as a complex ion. The detailed nature of this process is uncertain.

### Hydroxide Cracking

Cracking at high pH is characterized by intergranular and transgranular cracking depending on the pH and carbon content of the alloys. Factors controlling susceptibility in this system again appears to involve chemical reaction processes. Major alloying additions appear to exert their effect through controlling the nature of the soluble species. The $HNiO_2^-$ ion requires a more noble potential for its formation than does the $HFeO_2^-$. Cracking susceptibility starts with iron and iron-chromium alloys and decreases until relatively high nickel concentrations are reached. At this point the susceptibility ceases.

Of particular note is the intergranular cracking of nonsensitized stainless steels and Inconels in high purity water containing varying amounts of oxygen. Susceptibility seems to be associated with relatively higher stresses than required for either chloride or hydroxide cracking. Both the chemistry and physical metallurgy of this process are presently obsure with respect to mechanistic interpretation.

Lead additions to high purity water cause Inconel 600 to crack transgranularly. While the details of this process are also obscure, owing to lack of phenomenonlogical data, it would appear that a process of environmental ennoblement, operating similar to that of nickel in chloride cracking, may be a key factor.

While considerable phenomenological information is available, detailed understanding is limited and no completely satisfactory mechanisms are yet available. Future work should emphasize and investigate the following:

1. Oxidation and reduction processes as affected by critical species in the alloy and environment. The transient nature of these processes especially should be considered.

2. Slip processes at the metal surface, at internal barriers, and at the crack tip as affected by alloy structure and chemistry.

3. Mass transport and oxidation-reduction processes as affected by restricted geometries such as tunnels or extended cracks.

# References

1. J. W. Pugh and J. D. Nisbet. *Trans. AIME,* **188,** 268 (1950).
2. E. A. Lees. *Analysis of Failure of Type 304 Stainless Steel Clad Swaged Power Fuel Assembly,* GEAP-4400 (1963) October.
3. M. Streicher. *J. Electrochem. Soc.,* **106,** 151 (1959).
4. ASTM-STP-264 (1960).
5. J. G. Parr and A. Hanson. *An Introduction to Stainless Steel,* ASM, Metals Park (1966).
6. C. A. Zapffe. *Stainless Steels,* ASM, Cleveland (1949).
7. *The Making, Shaping and Treating of Steel,* H. E. McGannon, ed., U. S. Steel (1964).
8. J. G. H. Moneypenny. *Stainless Iron and Steel,* **1** and *Stainless Steel in Industry,* **II,** London, Chapman-Hall (1951 and 1954).
9. E. E. Thum. *The Book of Stainless Steels,* ASM (1935).
10. M. Hansen. *Constitution of Binary Alloys,* 2nd Edition, McGraw-Hill Book Co., Inc., New York (1958).
11. C. B. Post and W. S. Eberly. *Trans. ASM,* **39,** 868 (1947).
12. M. Hansen and K. Anderko. *Constitution of Binary Alloys,* McGraw-Hill Book, Co., Inc., New York (1958).
13. D. J. Carney. Data reported in *The Making, Shaping, and Treating of Steels,* 1117 (1964).
14. R. M. Brick and A. Phillips. *Structure and Properties of Alloys,* McGraw-Hill, New York (1949).
15. *Metals Handbook,* 1261 (1948 Edition).
16. V. N. Krivobak and A. M. Talbot. *Proc. ASTM,* 50 (1950).
17. J. F. Breedis and W. D. Robertson. *Acta Met.,* **10,** 1077 (1962).
18. D. L. Douglass, G. Thomas, and W. R. Roser. *Corrosion,* **20,** 15t (1964).
19. T. J. Pashos. *Stainless Steel Fracture Investigation Program,* GEAP, 4915 (1965) July. (Summarized therein is the work of about ten investigations.)
20. D. P. Shoemaker and B. G. Bergman. *Acta Cryst.,* **7,** 857 (1954).
21. W. P. Rees, B. D. Burns and A. J. Cook. *JISI,* **162,** 325 (1949).
22. H. Thielsch. *Welding Journal,* **29,** 5775 (1950).
23. ASTM-STP-369 (1965).
24. The International Nickel Company, Technical Bulletins.
25. *Metals Handbook.* Eighth Edition, **I** and **II,** ASM, Metals Park (1964).
26. W. F. Simmons and J. A. Van Echo. *Report on the Elevated Temperature Properties of Stainless Steel,* ASTM Publication (1965).
27. A. G. Guy. *Elements of Physical Metallurgy,* Addison Wesley, Reading, Mass., 390 (1960).
28. R. W. Staehle. Unpublished results.
29. M. Pourbaix. *Atlas of Electrochemical Equilibria in Aqueous Solutions,* Pergamon Press, New York (1966).
30. D. O. Condit, R. L. Beauchamp, and R. W. Staehle. Unpublished results.
31. N. D. Greene and G. Judd. *Corrosion,* **21,** 15 (1965).
32. H. P. Leckie and H. H. Uhlig. *J. Electrochem. Soc.,* **113,** 1262 (1966).
33. C. Edeleanu. *JISI,* **173,** 140 (1953).
34. D. Warren. *Proceedings of the Fifteenth Annual Industrial Waste Conference,* Purdue University (1960) May.
35. R. W. Staehle. Paper presented at the Sixty-ninth Annual Meeting of the American Society for Testing Materials, Atlantic City (1966).
36. M. A. Scheil. *Symposium on Stress Corrosion Cracking of Metals,* ASTM-AIME, 395 (1944).
37. D. Birchon and G. C. Booth. *Second International Congress on Metallic Corrosion,* NACE, 33 (1963).
38. H. Kohl. *Werkstoffe u. Korrosion,* 729 (1963).
39. M. A. Scheil. Comment on Reference 33.
40. V. K. Pershke and S. K. Kalinin. *J. Chem. Ind.* (Moscow), No. 12, 16 (1932).
41. K. C. Thomas, H. M. Ferrari, and R. J. Allio. *Corrosion,* **20,** 89t (1964).
42. S. Berg and S. Henrikson. *Recent Advances in Stress Corrosion,* Bulletin No. 25, Corrosion Committee, Royal Swedish Academy of Engineering Sciences, Stockholm, 63 (1961).
43. R. Franks, W. D. Binder, and C. M. Brown. *Symposium on Stress Corrosion Cracking of Metals,* ASTM-AIME, 411 (1944).
44. J. C. Hodge and J. L. Miller. *Trans ASM,* **28,** 25 (1940).
45. M. A. Scheil, O. Zmeskal, J. Waber and F. Stockhausen. *Welding Journal,* **22,** 499s (1943).
46. H. J. Logan and R. J. Sherman. *Welding Journal,* **35,** 389s (1956).
47. A. E. Picket, W. L. Pearl and M. C. Rowland. *Nuclear Applications,* **1,** 453 (1965).
48. W. L. Pearl, G. G. Gaul, and G. P. Wozadlo. *Nuclear Science and Engineering,* **19,** 274 (1964).
49. H. R. Copson. *Welding Journal,* **32,** 75s (1953).
50. R. W. Staehle, F. H. Beck, and M. G. Fontana. *Corrosion,* **15,** 373t (1959).
51. P. P. Snowden. *JISI,* **194,** 181 (1960).
52. R. L. Beauchamp. M. S. Thesis, The Ohio State University (1963).
53. R. N. Duncan. *Stainless Steel Failure Investigation Program,* 4th Quarterly Report, GEAP-5150 (1966) April.

54. K. W. Leu and J. Helle. *Corrosion,* **14,** 249t (1958).
55. T. P. Hoar and J. G. Hines. *Stress Corrosion Cracking and Embrittlement,* ed. W. D. Robertson, John Wiley and Sons, New York (1956).
56. S. Barnartt and D. van Rooyen. *J. Electrochem. Soc.,* **108,** 222 (1961).
57. H. H. Uhlig and J. Lincoln, Jr. *J. Electrochem. Soc.,* **105,** 325 (1958).
58. B. Anderson. *Corrosion,* **18,** 425t (1962).
59. P. D. Neumann and J. C. Greiss. *Corrosion,* **19,** 345t (1963).
60. L. R. Scharfstein and W. F. Brindley. *Corrosion,* **14,** 588t (1958).
61. S. P. Rideout. Paper presented at NACE 20th Annual Conference, March 9-13, 1964.
62. W. L. Williams. *Corrosion,* **13,** 539t (1957).
63. H. A. Pray, C. E. Schweickert, and B. H. Minnich. *Ind. Engr. Chem.,* **44,** 1146 (1952).
64. J. H. Phillips and W. J. Singley. *Corrosion,* **15,** 450t (1959).
65. C. Edeleanu and P. P. Snowden. *JISI,* **186,** 19.
66. T. P. Hoar and J. G. Hines. *JISI,* **177,** 240 (1954).
67. R. F. Overman. *Corrosion,* **22,** 48 (1966).
68. V. S. Agarwala. M. S. Thesis, Massachusetts Institute of Technology, 1966, Advisor H. H. Uhlig.
69. H. H. Uhlig and J. R. Gilman. *Corrosion,* **20,** 289t (1964).
70. J. W. Matthews and H. H. Uhlig. *Corrosion,* **7,** 419 (1951).
71. N. I. Podobaev and S. A. Balezin. *Zhur-Priklad Khim.,* **33,** 2290 (1960).
72. S. A. Balezin, V. V. Romanov, and M. I. Podobaev. *Doklady Acad. Nauk,* SSSR, **123,** 902 (1958).
73. S. A. Balezin and N. I. Podobaev. *Zhur. Priklad Khim,* **33,** 1311 (1960).
74. N. I. Podobaev, S. A. Balezin and V. V. Romanov. *Zhur. Priklad. Khim,* **33,** 1311 (1960).
75. H. R. Copson and C. F. Cheng. *Corrosion,* **13,** 397t (1957).
76. J. L. English and J. C. Griess. *Corrosion,* **20,** 138t (1964).
77. J. J. Heger. *Metal Progress,* **109** (1955) March.
78. H. Kohl. *Corrosion,* **23,** 39 (1967).
79. T. P. Hoar and J. G. Hines. *JISI,* **182,** 124 (1956).
80. W. W. Kirk, F. H. Beck, and M. G. Fontana. *Physical Metallurgy of Stress Corrosion Fracture,* ed. T. N. Rhodin, Interscience, New York (1959).
81. H. L. Logan, M. J. McBee, and M. Romanoff. *Materials Research and Standards,* 635, (1963) August.
82. J. W. Frey and R. W. Staehle. To be published in a special volume of *Corrosion* magazine containing proceedings on NACE of conference on High Purity Water held in Los Angeles, Spring, 1967.
83. A. E. Pickett and W. B. Nelson. *Stainless Steel Failure Investigation Program.* Fifth Quarterly Progress Report, compiled by R. N. Duncan, GEAP 5194.
84. T. P. Hoar. *Corrosion,* **19,** 331t (1963).
85. E. E. Denhard. *Corrosion,* **16,** 359t (1960).
86. T. Shimose, A. Takamura, K. Hori, and K. Shimogori. *Transactions of the Japan Institute of Metals,* **6,** 83 (1965).
87. H. Ternes. Thesis, Bergakademie Clausthal, 1963, reviewed by H. Kohl in Reference 78.
88. J. G. Hines. *Corrosion Science,* **1,** 2 (1961).
89. D. J. Greeley, V. J. Russo, R. K. Saxer, and J. R. Myers. *Corrosion,* **21,** 327 (1965).
90. H. P. Hawkes, F. H. Beck, and M. G. Fontana. *Corrosion,* **19,** 247t (1963).
91. E. R. Burkhart, J. R. Myers, and R. K. Saxer. *Corrosion,* **22,** 21 (1966).
92. R. W. Cochran and R. W. Staehle. *Corrosion,* **24** (1968).
93. H. Suss. *Corrosion,* **17,** 61t (1961).
94. E. M. Mahla and N. A. Nielsen. *Trans. Electrochem. Soc.,* **89,** 167 (1946).
95. J. F. Radavich. *Corrosion,* **15,** 613t (1959).
96. P. H. Berge. *J. Electrochem. Soc.,* **112,** 670 (1965).
97. T. N. Rhodin. *Corrosion,* **12,** 123t (1956).
98. H. H. Uhlig and J. P. Sava. *Corrosion Science,* **5,** 291 (1965).
99. C. R. Cupp. *Physical Metallurgy of Stress Corrosion Fracture,* Interscience, New York (1959).
100. M. J. Davis, D. A. Landsman, and W. E. Seedon. AERE-R 5014, UKAEA Research Corporation, Harwell, Berks.
101. C. F. Knights. AERE-M 1899, UKAEA Research Group, Harwell, Berks.
102. F. S. Lang. *Corrosion,* **18,** 378t (1962).
103. H. D. Ongman. *Nuclear Superheat Project Final Report,* GEAP-5087 (1965) December.
104. H. W. Pickering, F. H. Beck and M. G. Fontana. *Trans ASM,* **53,** 793 (1961).
105. H. R. Copson. *Physical Metallurgy of Stress Corrosion Fracture,* Interscience, New York (1959).
106. H. R. Copson. *First International Conference on Metallic Corrosion,* Proceedings, Butterworths, London (1961).
107. J. Royuela and R. W. Staehle. Unpublished results.
108. M. A. Scheil and R. A. Huseby. *Welding Journal Suppl.,* 361S (1944) August.
109. J. C. Hodge and J. L. Miller. *Trans ASM,* **28,** 25 (1940).
110. C. Edeleanu. *JISI,* **173,** 140 (1953).
111. R. N. Parkins and E. H. Phelps. Review of Stress Corrosion Cracking in Iron Base Alloys, Conference on Fundamental Aspects of Stress Corrosion Cracking, September, 1967, The Ohio State University, Columbus, Ohio.
112. F. K. Bloom. *Corrosion,* **11,** 351t (1955).
113. H. J. Rocha. *Stahl u. Eisen,* **62,** 1091 (1942).
114. H. J. Rocha. *Tech. Mitt. Krupp Forschungsber,* **5,** 1 (1942).
115. A. V. Ryabchenkov and V. I. Gerasimov. *Zaschita Metallov,* English translation, **1,** 38 (1965).
116. H. L. Logan and M. J. McBee. Data from Materials Research and Standards published in *The Stress Corrosion of Metals,* by H. L. Logan, Wiley, New York (1966).
117. G. Riedrich and H. Kohl. *Berg und Huttenmannishche Monatshefte,* **108,** 1 (1963).
118. A. P. Bond. Paper presented at the Sixty-Ninth Meeting of the American Society for Testing Materials, Atlantic City (1966).
119. J. E. Truman and R. Perry. *Brit. Corr. Jnl.,* **1,** 60 (1966).
120. T. E. Evans and D. J. Burr. *Brit. Corr. Jnl.,* **1,** 192 (1966).
121. H. H. Uhlig, A. White, and J. Lincoln, Jr. *Acta Metallurgica,* **5,** 473 (1957).
122. H. H. Uhlig and R. A. White. *Trans ASM,* **52,** 830 (1960).
123. D. van Rooyen. *Proceedings of First International Conference on Stress Corrosion Cracking,* Butterworths, London (1961).
124. D. A. Vaughan, D. I. Phalen, C. L. Peterson, and W. K. Boyd. *Corrosion,* **19,** 315t (1963).
125. H. H. Uhlig and J. P. Sava. Massachusetts Institute of Technology, Topical Report (1966).
126. D. G. Tufanov. *Metallovedenie i Termicheskaya Okrabotka Metallov,* 15 (1964) April.
127. A. Ronnquist. *Current Corrosion Research in Scandinavia,* Helsinki (1964).
128. J. A. Davis, T. J. Smith, and R. W. Staehle. Unpublished results.
129. S. Barnartt, R. Stickler, and D. van Rooyen. *Corrosion Science,* **3,** 9 (1963).
130. J. G. Hines and E. R. W. Jones. *Corrosion Science,* **1,** 88 (1961).
131. J. Hochman and J. Bourrat. *Comptes Rendus de l'Academie des Sciences,* **255,** (1962) December 17.
132. E. H. Phelps. Paper presented at Sixty-Ninth Meeting of American Society for Testing Materials, Atlantic City (1966).
133. Quarterly progress report for January 1966, under Euratom Contract 033-64-9 TEE F (RD), Compagnie des Ateliers et Forges de la Loire.
134. R. F. Steigerwald. *Corrosion,* **22,** 107 (1966).
135. M. A. Streicher. *J. Electrochem. Soc.,* **103,** 375 (1956).
136. T. P. Hoar and J. G. Hinès. *Proc. of Eighth Meeting of the International Committee of Electrochemical Thermodynamics and Kinetics,* (CITCE), Madrid, Butterworths Scientific Publications (1956).
137. W. Tafante and H. J. Rocha. *Tech. Met.,* 427 (1950)

December.

138. C. Edeleanu. *Stress Corrosion Cracking and Embrittlement,* Wiley, New York (1956).

139. J. J. Heger and E. J. Dulis. Discussion of Reference 33, *JISI,* **175,** 390, 1953.

140. H. Nathorst. Discussion of Reference 33, *JISI,* **175,** 390, 1953.

141. J. G. Hines and T. P. Hoar. *JISI,* **184,** 166 (1956).

142. J. W. Flowers, F. H. Beck, and M. G. Fontana. *Corrosion,* **19,** 186t (1963).

143. J. G. Hines and R. G. Hugill. *Physical Metallurgy of Stress Corrosion Fracture,* Interscience, New York (1959).

144. E. E. Denhard. Discussion of Reference 143.

145. E. B. Backensto and A. N. Yurick. *Corrosion,* **18,** 169t (1962).

146. E. G. Coleman, D. Weinstein, and W. Rostoker. *Acta Met.,* **9,** 491 (1961).

147. V. L. Barnwell, J. R. Myers, and R. K. Saxer. *Corrosion,* **22,** 261 (1966).

148. N. J. Petch. *JISI,* **174,** 25 (1953).

149. A. M. Stroh. *Adv. Phys.,* **6,** 418 (1957).

150. N. J. Petch. *Phil. Mag.,* **1,** 337 (1956).

151. ASTM-STP 264, *Stress Corrosion Cracking of Austenitic Cr-Ni Stainless Steels,* (1960).

152. V. P. Sidorov and A. V. Ryabchenkov. *Metallovedenie i Okrabotka Metallov,* 25 (1958) June.

153. F. W. Pement. *Bettis Technical Review,* 112 (1960).

154. V. N. Gulyaev, P. A. Akol'zin, E. S. Gromova, and E. N. Ivanov. *Teploeneigetika,* No. 9, 50 (1961).

155. G. C. Wheeler and E. Howells. *Power,* p.86 (1960) September.

156. P. P. Snowden. *JISI,* **197,** 136 (1961).

157. H. Coriou and L. Grall. Rapport CEA-R2600, Centre d'Etudes Nucleaires de Saclay.

158. H. Coriou, L. Grall, C. Mahieu, and M. Pelas. *Corrosion,* **22,** 280 (1966).

159. H. R. Copson and S. W. Dean. *Corrosion,* **21,** 1 (1965).

160. Progress Reports on High Power Density Program sponsored by Atomic Energy Commission at General Electric under Contract Number AT(04-3)-361.

161. W. H. Arlt and S. R. Vandenberg. *Fuel Failure Examinations and Analyses in the High Power Density Program,* The General Electric Company, GEAP-4360.

162. E. A. Lees. *Analysis of Failure of Type 304 Stainless Steel Clad Swaged Powder Fuel Assembly,* General Electric Company, GEAP-4400.

163. R. W. Staehle. Investigation of Cracking in Stainless Steel Fuel Elements, The Ohio State University Research Foundation, C00-1319-30.

164. B. A. Wilcox and G. C. Smith. *Acta Met.,* **13,** 331 (1965).

165. W. B. deLong. *ASTM-STP,* **97,** 211 (1949).

166. H. T. Shirley and J. E. Truman. *JISI,* **171,** 354 (1952).

167. J. S. Armijo. *Corrosion,* **21,** 235 (1965).

168. J. S. Armijo. *Corrosion Science,* **7,** 143 (1967).

169. M. M. Kurkpov, G. V. Akimov and N. N. Bordign. *Doklady Acad. Nauk.,* SSCR, **87,** 625 (1952).

170. M. M. Kurpkov, G. V. Akimov, and N. N. Bordign. *ibid.,* p. 93.

171. A. B. McIntosh. *Chem. and Ind.,* 687 (1957).

172. J. E. Truman. *J. Appl. Chem.,* **4,** 273 (1954).

173. M. A. Streicher. *J. Electrochem. Soc.,* **106,** 161 (1959).

174. H. Coriou, J. Hure, and G. Plante. *Electrochem. Acta,* **5,** 105 (1961).

175. H. Coriou, A. Desestret, L. Grall, and J. Hochman. *Corrosion et Anticorrosion,* **14,** 163 (1966).

176. G. Chaudron. AEC Euratom Program, Quarterly Progress Report No. 6, EURAEC-976 (1963) October-December.

177. H. Coriou, L. Grall, G. Kurku, and G. Plante. *Colloque de Metallurgy,* **IV,** 75 (1960).

178. J. S. Armijo and A. E. Pickett. *Stainless Steel Failure Investigation Program,* Sixth Quarterly Progress Report, General Electric Company, GEAP-5281.

179. J. F. Eckel. *Corrosion,* **18,** 270t (1962).

180. T. P. Hoar and J. G. Hines. *JISI,* **177,** 248 (1954) June.

181. G. H. G. Kraft, J. Z. Amacker, J. R. Myers, and R. K. Saxer. *Corrosion,* **21,** 188 (1965).

182. R. E. Reed and H. W. Paxton. *First International Congress on Metallic Corrosion,* 301 (1961).

183. H. W. Paxton, R. E. Reed, and R. Leggett. *Physical Metallurgy of Stress Corrosion Fracture,* Interscience, New York (1959).

184. T. J. Smith and R. W. Staehle. *Corrosion,* **23,** 117 (1967).

185. H. L. Logan. *Metals Engr. Quarterly,* **5,** 32 (1965).

186. H. L. Logan. *J. Res. Nat. Bur. Standards,* **48,** 99 (1952).

187. E. N. Pugh, J. V. Craig, and A. J. Sedriks. This volume.

188. C. Edeleanu. *Physical Metallurgy of Stress Corrosion Fracture,* Interscience, New York (1959).

189. A. J. Forty. *ibid.,* p. 99.

190. J. C. Scully. *Corrosion Science,* **7,** 197 (1967).

191. J. G. Hines. *Corrosion Science,* **1,** 21 (1961).

192. W. D. Robertson and A. S. Tetelman. *Strengthening Mechanism in Solids,* J. J. Harwood, ed., ASM, Metals Park (1962).

193. R. Bakish and W. D. Robertson. *Acta Met.,* **3,** 513 (1955).

194. P. R. Swann and J. D. Embury. *High Strength Materials,* Zackey, ed., Wiley and Sons, New York (1965).

195. P. R. Swann. *Scientific American,* **214,** 73 (1966).

196. P. R. Swann. *Corrosion,* **19,** 102t (1963).

197. H. W. Pickering and P. R. Swann. *Corrosion,* **19,** 373t (1963).

198. D. L. Douglass, G. Thomas, and W. R. Rosser. *Corrosion,* **20,** 15t (1964).

199. K. C. Thomas, R. Stickler, and R. J. Allio. *Corrosion Science,* **5,** 71 (1965).

200. R. Stickler and S. Barnartt. *J. Electrochem. Soc.,* 343 (1962).

201. D. J. Burr. *Corrosion Science,* **5,** 733 (1965).

202. T. P. Hoar and J. M. West. *Nature,* **181,** 35 (1958) March 22.

203. T. P. Hoar and J. C. Scully. *J. Electrochem. Soc.,* **111,** 348 (1964).

204. T. P. Hoar and J. M. West. *Proc. Roy. Soc.,* **268,** 304 (1962).

205. J. C. Scully and T. P. Hoar. *Second International Congress on Metallic Corrosion.*

206. J. M. West. *Corrosion Science,* **1,** 178 (1961).

207. J. M. West. Chapter 7, *Electrodeposition and Corrosion Processes,* Van Nostrand, New York (1965).

208. R. W. Staehle. Presented at Spring, 1967 AIME Meeting in Los Angeles.

209. R. W. Staehle. Submitted to *Corrosion* magazine.

210. L. Graf. *Stress Corrosion Cracking and Embrittlement,* Wiley, New York (1956).

211. J. G. Hines and T. P. Hoar. *Jnl. Appl. Chem.,* **8,** 764 (1958).

212. S. Brennert. *Recent Advances in Stress Corrosion,* Royal Swedish Academy of Engineering Sciences, Stockholm (1961).

213. S. J. Acello and N. D. Greene. *Corrosion,* **18,** 286t (1962).

214. J. W. West and L. Fairman. *Brit Corr. J.,* **1,** 67 (1966).

215. H. L. Logan, M. J. McBee, and D. J. Kahan. *Corrosion Science,* **5,** 729 (1965).

216. J. C. Scully and T. P. Hoar. *Corrosion,* **20,** 174t (1964).

217. A. Ronnquist. *Corrosion et Anticorrosion,* **14,** 3 (1966).

218. B. Lehtinen. *J. Sci. Inst.,* **44,** 234 (1967).

219. A. Ronnquist. Comment on Reference 220.

220. N. A. Neilsen. *Corrosion,* **20,** 105t (1964).

221. R. M. Latanision. Unpublished results.

222. M. F. Dean, F. H. Beck, and R. W. Staehle. *Corrosion,* **23,** 192 (1967).

223. H. H. Uhlig. *Physical Metallurgy of Stress Corrosion Fracture,* Interscience, New York (1959).

224. J. C. Suits and J. R. Low, Jr. *Acta Met.,* **5,** 285 (1967).

225. H. W. Pickering. *Acta Met.,* **13,** 437 (1965).

226. D. Tromans and J. Nutting. *Corrosion,* **21,** (1965).

227. J. S. Armijo. *Corrosion Science,* **7,** 143 (1967).

228. J. C. Scully. Conference Proceedings, *Physical Basis of Yield and Fracture.*

229. N. A. Nielsen. *Physical Metallurgy of Stress Corrosion Fracture,* p. 121.

230. E. A. Gulbransen and T. P. Copan. *Physical Metallurgy of*

*Stress Corrosion Fracture*, Interscience, New York (1959).

231. A. R. C. Westwood. *Corrosion Science*, **6**, 387 (1966).
232. H. Nichols and W. Rostoker. *Trans. ASM*, **56**, (1963).
233. E. G. Coleman, D. Weinstein, and W. Rostoker. *Acta Met.*, **9**, 491 (1961).
234. C. R. Bergen. *Corrosion*, **20**, 269 (1964).
235. K. C. Thomas and R. J. Allio. *Nature*, **206**, 82 (1965) April 3.
236. H. W. Pickering, F. H. Beck, and M. G. Fontana. *Corrosion*, **18**, 230t (1962).
237. J. H. Shively, R. F. Hehemann, and A. R. Troiano. *Corrosion*, **23**, 215 (1967).

238. I. B. Casale. *Corrosion*, **23**, 314 (1967).
239. J. J. Kozoil and S. S. Christopher. Contract AT(30-1)-3256, U. S. Atomic Energy Commission, Final Research Report, September, 1966.
240. S. P. Rideout. *Second International Conference on Metallic Corrosion*, Butterworths, London.
241. H. L. Logan. *The Stress Corrosion of Metals*, Wiley (1966).
242. C. L. Howard and R. N. Duncan. *High Power Density Development Project*, Twenty-Fifth and Twenty-Sixth Quarterly Progress Reports, June-November 1966, GEAP-5405, December 1966.

# Discussion

### D. A. Vermilyea, General Electric Research and Development Center:

On the nickel enrichment theory, 18-8 stainless steel is presumably protected by essentially a layer of pure nickel. In your experiments with thin foils in which you produced slip in magnesium chloride and observed a corrosion groove along the slip step, wouldn't you expect nickel to be immune to such groove formation?

It seems that if nickel does the protecting of 18-8 stainless steel then a major difference between pure nickel and 18-8 should be observed in the thin foil experiments.

### R. W. Staehle and R. M. Latanision:

**We agree that the results from the thin foil observations are ambiguous with respect to differentiating the cracking susceptibility of nickel from 18-8. The reason for this is not presently clear. However, the electron microscope cannot easily distinguish depth of dissolution trenches among the various specimens. The relative susceptibilities to cracking also may be related to differences in propagation processes rather than initiation processes. For the moment we think that it is important to note that slip step dissolution is a real phenomenon and its extent is large relative to the number of dislocations involved. Exactly how this process actually applies is open to question at this time.**

### S. B. Brummer, Tyco Laboratories, Inc.:

It seems to me that your explanation of the maximum in susceptibility with respect to Ni content can be tested. If I understand you correctly, differential dissolution could still occur at the low Ni end but enrichment with Ni would be too slow to give a suitable groove. I think that the current transients for the corrosion of the unstressed alloys should be relatable to your hypothesis. Specifically, you should find that those alloys which are most susceptible should show a very large decrease in their corrosion rate with time. By appropriate masking of the material, so as to expose only relevant regions, you might get quite spectacular effects as a function of Ni composition.

In connection with your remarks concerning strain depolarization,[1] West[2] has recently pointed out that van Rooyen's[3] experiment is not valid. Specifically, West reports work of Scully[4] and claims that the reason that van Rooyen was unable to find the strain depolarization reported by Hoar and Hines[1] and Hoar and West[5] was that he did not eliminate ohmic polarization. At the high current densities which are involved, the potential of the dissolving metal is significantly altered by the ohmic contribution. It seems then that we cannot rule out strain depolarization as important in some stress corroding systems.

References for Brummer Discussion

1. T. P. Hoar and J. G. Hines. *J. Iron Steel Inst.*, **177**, 248 (1954).
2. J. M. West. *Electrodeposition and Corrosion Processes*, Van Nostrand, London (1965).
3. D. van Rooyen. *Proc. First International Congress on Metallic Corrosion*, London, 1961; Butterworths, London, 84 (1962).
4. T. P. Hoar and J. C. Scully. *Trans. Electrochem. Soc.*, **111**, 348 (1964).
5. T. P. Hoar and J. M. West. *Proc. Roy. Soc.*, **268A**, 304 (1962).

### R. W. Staehle and R. M. Latanision:

**Dr. Brummer's suggestion concerning current transients is a matter which we are presently pursuing. Our present work indicates that the concept of enrichment and the rates thereof are easier to discuss than to prove.**

**Regarding your criticism of van Rooyen's work, I frankly doubt that ohmic polarization is a major consideration. Obtaining the large increases in current for the straining vs the nonstraining case requires that special attention be given to selection of potentials as well as time at potential prior to straining. Some of the reasons for this are discussed in a forthcoming paper based on a thesis by one of my M.S. students, Tomomi Murata. We are currently investigating this whole matter of strain induced depolarization from a more fundamental point of view.**

### N. A. Nielsen, Du Pont Company:

On the question of deposition of nickel from solution onto stressed stainless steel undergoing corrosion-cracking we do not know that corrosion of Type 430 stainless steel will displace nickel from solution in boiling 42% $MgCl_2$. We have obtained visible deposits of nickel on Type 430 steel exposed to boiling 42% $MgCl_2$ containing as little as 0.1% $NiCl_2$. It remains to be shown conclusively that this happens on an austenitic steel during the corrosion-cracking process.

### R. W. Staehle and R. M. Latanision:

**Depositing nickel ions from solution and enriching them on the surface may be two different processes.**

Depositing $Ni^{++}$ on the surface will occur for the same thermodynamic reason that Ni will not dissolve: e.g., the equilibrium potential of the $Ni \rightleftharpoons Ni^{++} + 2e$ reaction relative to the corrosion potential. If nickel ions are in solution, they will contribute an additional reduction reaction, $Ni^{++} + 2e \rightarrow Ni$, thereby changing the oxidation kinetics of the Type 430. In some experiments using stressed Type 430 exposed to boiling $MgCl_2$ we found that the addition of about 1% $NiCl_2$ caused failure about four times faster. The failure was due to pitting rather than cracking. The role of nickel was presumably that of an additional reducible species.

#### J. Kruger, National Bureau of Standards:

Have you considered the possibility that the role of the nickel is to provide ions that go into the lattice of a film and thereby change its properties in such a way that stress cracking is promoted or stopped?

#### R. W. Staehle and R. M. Latanision:

Your suggestion is very attractive. It is fairly clear to us from work underway in our own and other laboratories that a film actually forms on Fe-Cr-Ni alloys in stainless steel when exposed to boiling $MgCl_2$ as well as other chloride containing environments. If this film forms, then what is the role of the nickel if it does enrich? It is possible that it may affect the film properties. However, in our laboratory we have studied polarization behavior in $H_2SO_4$ and over a wide range of Fe-Cr-Ni alloys and find little difference in the parameters of the active-passive behavior of various alloys despite great changes in susceptibility to cracking. Of course the more meaningful data are those obtained in chloride solutions.

#### H. H. Uhlig, MIT:

One observation indicates, I think that this whole matter relates to structure and not to nickel enrichment. If one takes an 18-8 stainless steel containing a certain amount of carbon and nitrogen it is face-centered cubic in the quenched state and it is susceptible to stress corrosion cracking in boiling magnesium chloride. If, on the other hand, one takes a similar composition alloy with the same nickel and chromium contents, but reduces the carbon and nitrogen so that the alloy now quenches to the body-centered cubic structure, it will not crack. The nickel content is precisely the same.

Or if one takes an austenitic 18-8 stainless steel (face-centered cubic) containing carbon or nitrogen and then severely cold works the alloy (preferably at liq. $N_2$ temperature favoring transformation) to completely form the body-centered cubic structure, nickel, carbon and nitrogen contents remaining the same, the alloy is now *not* susceptible to stress corrosion cracking in $MgCl_2$.[1,2] These facts indicate that it is structure that determines susceptibility and not nickel enrichment of the surface.

References for Uhlig Discussion

1. H. Uhlig, R. White and J. Lincoln. *Acta Met.*, **5**, 473 (1957).
2. H. Uhlig and R. White. *Trans. Am. Soc. Metals,* **52**, 830 (1960).

#### R. W. Staehle and R. M. Latanision:

The question whether alloy structure or alloy chemistry is critical is an intriguing and fundamentally significant question. As I see the essence of your argument, ferritic steels are resistant and austenitic ones are not. There is, however, abundant evidence that ferritic structures do crack. Figure 11 from Nielsen's paper shows transgranular cracking in a ferritic steel. Figure 74 of our review shows cracks in ferrite grains. Paul Bond (1968 NACE meeting in Cleveland, April, 1968) has found cracking in several ferritic alloys to which noble additions of Ni and Cu have been made. It must therefore be concluded that ferritic structures do, without question, sustain cracking; however, such cracking does not occur if the alloy is only of the Fe-Cr type.

The question of effects of nitrogen and carbon effects may relate to pitting and its influence on cracking as suggested by Graf's second paper of this conference. He found that an increase in pitting decreases the cracking. This may be significant relevant to work by Streicher (see our Reference 135) who found that additions of nitrogen to stainless steel accelerates pitting while additions of carbon and molybdenum decelerate pitting. These three elements have exactly the opposite effects on the cause of cracking.

Finally, the experiment on the cold work material should be interpreted in terms of Figure 40 of our paper which is based on work of Hines. As the cold work increases above a level of about 10% cracking is progressively stifled. We suggest that your "severe" cold work simply prevented cracking according to this already well established trend of cold work effects.

#### L. R. Scharfstein, Carpenter Steel Co.:

The cause of stress corrosion cracking in the martensitic stainless steels is an often debated subject. Several years ago, when undertaking work in an attempt to elucidate this problem,[1] we were amazed to see an extra-ordinary effect due to the presence of small additions of nickel to the alloy when tests were conducted in boiling 42% by weight $MgCl_2$. These results were never reported. Since A. P. Bond[2] has recently reported a similar effect due to the presence of nickel in ferritic stainless steels, I believe that our results should be added to this growing literature.

The analyses of the two martensitic 12% Cr stainless steels studied were already published.[1] The major differences in composition were: Steel A contained 0.13% C and 0.38% Ni whereas Steel B contained 0.05% C and 1.76% Ni. Nitrogen contents (not previously reported) were 0.034% and 0.024%, respectively. Steel A is commercially known as Type 403 or 410 while B is called Stainless No. 404. Steel A may be hardened to a greater degree ($R_c$ 41) than B ($R_c$ 36) but both alloys are fully martensitic when austenitized and cooled to room temperature.

Table 1 summarizes results obtained in boiling 42% by weight $MgCl_2$. The specimen used resembled a tensile specimen with a test cross-section of 0.125 in. The specimens were loaded in direct tension through a lever system. The softest test samples ($R_b$ 80 and 90) were tested

**TABLE 1—Direct Tension Tests in Boiling 42% by Weight MgCl$_2$** (12% Cr Steels)

| Steel | Hardness | Load, psi | No. of Specimens Cracked/ No. of Specimens Tested | Time to Fracture, hr. |
|-------|----------|-----------|---------------------------------------------------|-----------------------|
| A | R$_b$ 80 | 30,000 | 0/5 | N.C. |
| B | R$_b$ 90 | 30,000 | 0/2 | N.C. |
| A | R$_c$ 19 | 70,000 | 0/5 | N.C. |
| B | R$_c$ 18 | 70,000 | 5/5 | 2-4 |
| A | R$_c$ 34 | 90,000 | 0/4 | N.C. |
| B | R$_c$ 34 | 90,000 | 9/9 | 12-28 |

NOTES:

N.C. means no cracks were observed in 200 hr., the total test duration.
A contained 0.38% Ni, B contained 1.76% Ni.
A contained 0.13% C, B contained .05% C.

**TABLE 2—Room Temperature Tensile Strength**

| Steel | Hardness | Yield Strength, 0.2% Offset, psi | Tensile Strength, psi |
|-------|----------|----------------------------------|-----------------------|
| A | R$_b$ 80 | 40,000 | 75,000 |
| B | R$_b$ 90 | 50,000 | 75,000 |
| A | R$_c$ 19 | 85,000 | 110,000 |
| B | R$_c$ 18 | 70,000 | 85,000 |
| A | R$_c$ 34 | 115,000 | 145,000 |
| B | R$_c$ 34 | 124,000 | 150,000 |

in the solution annealed (705 C) condition. Steel A was hardened to R$_c$ 19 by annealing (705 C), air cooling, austenitizing (982 C), oil quenching and tempering at 649 C, and to R$_c$ 34 by tempering at 538 C. Steel B was hardened to R$_c$ 18 as above but was tempered at 593 C. Steel B was tempered at 510 C in order to obtain a hardness of R$_c$ 34. As can be seen from the above tempering temperatures, the two steels respond to tempering slightly differently. Likewise, the mechanical properties are somewhat different as can be seen from Table 2. The structures were fully martensitic when hardened and tempered.

In order to determine whether steels A and B had different responses to other chemical media and to electrochemical polarization, wires were prepared from each steel and tests were conducted in apparatus resembling van Rooyen's.[3] Media evaluated (besides 42% boiling MgCl$_2$) included: dilute HCl + SeO$_2$, dilute H$_2$SO$_4$ + SeO$_2$, dilute acetic acid + (NH$_4$)$_2$S, boiling 3% NaCl, and boiling 3% NaCl + CS$_2$. Although many tests were performed with anodic, cathodic and no applied currents (at several tensile loads), only little differences were found in the behavior of steels A and B—except in MgCl$_2$ without applied currents. Only Steel B appeared susceptible to stress corrosion cracking in boiling 42% by weight MgCl$_2$ without an applied current. The environments purported to accelerate hydrogen embrittlement (such as dilute acetic acid + (NH$_4$)$_2$S) acted more quickly upon Steel A but both steels did crack, and fracture paths appeared to be very similar. In fact, the crack path in all environments, for both steels, was extremely similar. The cracks follow an intergranular path associated with the prior austenite grains. The one major exception, is the crack path in Steel B when tested in boiling 42% MgCl$_2$, either without an applied current or

with anodic polarization. As can be seen from Figures 1, 2, 3, and 4 the cracks have more of a transgranular appearance, as well as much more branching. Figures 5 and 6 are examples of cracks in other media or under cathodic polarization.

I believe that these data do show that although the 12% chromium martensitic steels are susceptible to hydrogen embrittlement and anodic accelerated cracking, the presence of 1.76% Ni in the alloy leads to a unique cracking behavior in boiling 42% MgCl$_2$ without any applied current.

References for Scharfstein Discussion

1. L. R. Scharfstein and C. M. Eisenbrown. *Nature,* 188, No. 4750, 572-573 (1960) November 12.
2. A. P. Bond. Minutes of Subcommittee *Corrosion Resistance of High Alloy Weldments,* High Alloys Committee, Welding Research Council, 9/26/66 and 3/8/67. In addition, *Reports of Progress,* Welding Research Council, XXII, No. 10, p. 22 (1967) October.
3. D. van Rooyen. *First International Congress on Metallic Corrosion,* Butterworth and Co., London, p. 134 (1962).

**R. W. Staehle and R. M. Latanision:**

We believe that this enhanced susceptibility to cracking which results from the presence of nickel is in accord with the trends predicted by the nickel-enrichment proposal.

**M. R. Louthan, Jr., Savannah River Laboratory:**

Stress corrosion cracking of austenitic stainless steels has been under study at Savannah River Laboratory for several years. Many of our observations are in general agreement with the conclusions of Prof. Staehle; however, our studies of stress corrosion cracking of a Fe, Cr, Mn, N alloy are not in agreement with the reference cited in his review (Reference 117 in review).

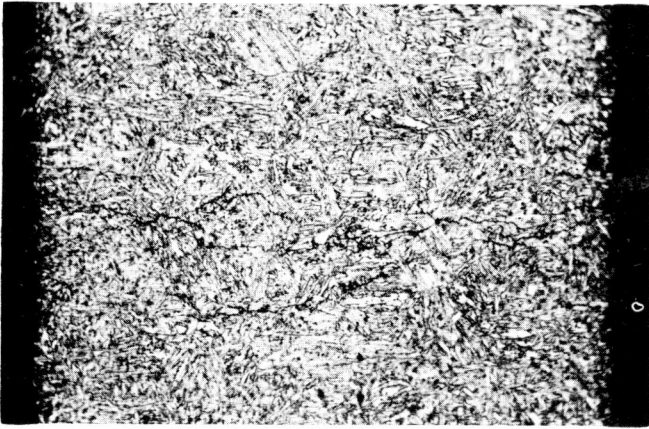

FIGURE 1 – Cracks in Steel B, containing 1.76% Ni, after anodic polarization (0.1 ma/cm$^2$) for 1 hour in boiling 42% MgCl$_2$. Hardened wire (R$_c$ 20) stressed at 45,000 psi.

FIGURE 4 – Cracks in Steel B, R$_c$ 34, after 17 hr exposure to boiling 42% MgCl$_2$ at 90,000 psi. No applied current.

FIGURE 2 – Same as Figure 1, unetched.

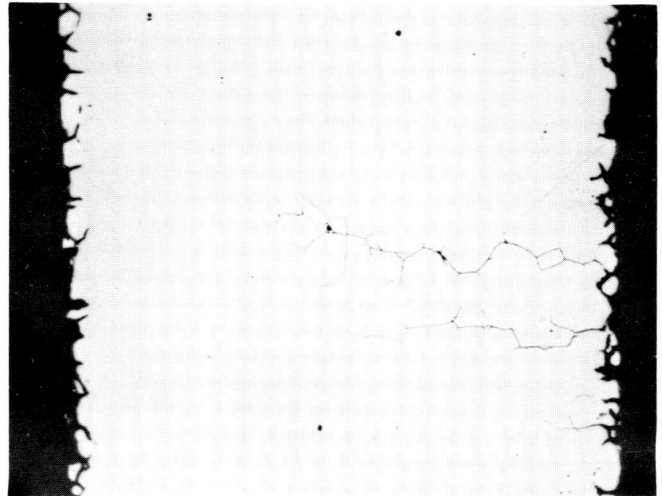

FIGURE 5 – Cracks in Steel B, R$_c$ 34, after 4.7 hr exposure to boiling 3% NaCl, pH = 4, at 90,000 psi.

FIGURE 3 – Cracks in Steel B, R$_c$ 34, after 0.5 hr exposure to boiling 42% MgCl$_2$ at 90,000 psi. No applied current.

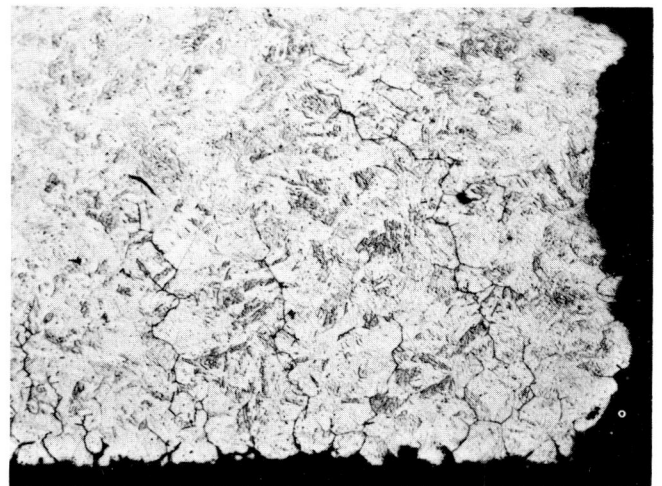

FIGURE 6 – Cracks in Steel A, R$_c$ 34, after cathodic polarization (2 ma/cm$^2$) for 5 hr in boiling 3% NaCl (pH = 2), stressed to 90,000 psi.

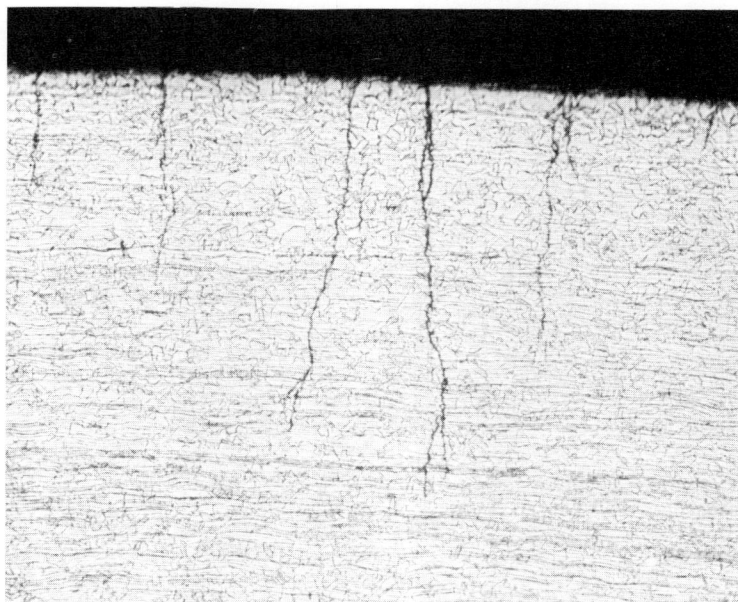

FIGURE 7 — Transgranular stress corrosion cracks in a low Ni steel exposed 19 hours to $MgCl_2$-$H_2O$ solution at 150 C.

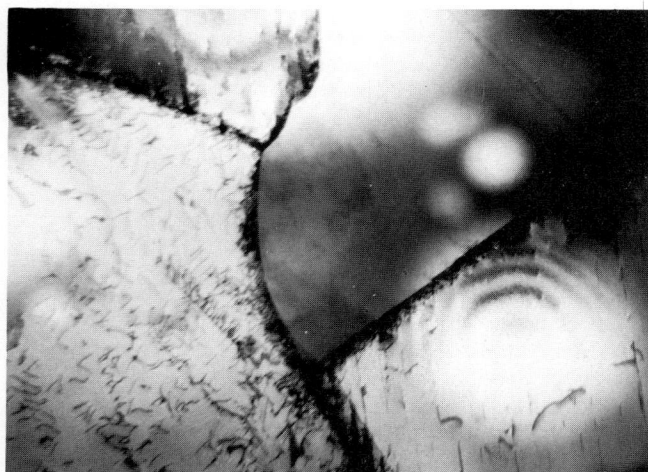

FIGURE 8 — Dislocation substructure in lightly cold worked low Ni steel.

We have studied stress corrosion cracking in a low Ni, Mn- and N-stabilized, austenitic stainless steel (Tenelon. Composition in wt %: C, 0.08-0.12; Mn, 14.5-16.0; P, 0.045 max; S, 0.03 max; Ni, 0.75 max; N, 0.35 min; Cr, 17.00-19.00; Fe, balance) and found that it was susceptible to transgranular cracking in both $MgCl_2$ and $MnCl_2$ solutions. Severe cracking (Figure 7) occurred after only 19 hours of exposure in $MgCl_2$ solutions at 150 C. This observation differs from the work of Riedrich and Kohl (Reference 117 in review), which suggested that cracking in austenitic Fe, Cr, Mn, N alloys occurred only when nickel or copper (in amounts of approximately 2% or greater) was added to the alloy. The observation of a necessity for nickel or copper was used as evidence to support the theory that enrichment of nickel (or copper) at the crack surface and subsequent corrosion at the enriched region played an important role in the cracking process. The statement by Latanision and Staehle that "Mn is similar to Cr electrochemically ... and the related activity of Fe and Cr is such that enrichment processes are not possible" apparently suggests that enrichment should not occur in the steel we studied. Transmission electron microscopy studies, however, show that the stacking fault energy of the steel is quite low and that coplanar dislocation motion is common (Figure 8). We believe that these results support the "dislocation coplanarity" theory of crack propagation along sites made anodic by localized dislocation movement (see Reference 1 for discussion of SRL results). Thus, although the proposed enrichment process may be operative in some austenitic stainless steel, it does not appear to explain cracking in the Fe, Cr, Mn, N system.

Reference for Louthan Discussion

1. M. R. Louthan, Jr. *The Role of Dislocation in Transgranular Stress Corrosion Cracking of Austenitic Stainless Steels,* USAEC Research and Development Report DP-1008, E. I. Du Pont de Nemours & Co., Savannah River Laboratory, Aiken, South Carolina (1966).

**R. W. Staehle and R. M. Latanision:**

This observation by Louthan on the cracking of Tenelon is indeed important because it suggests that either the nickel enrichment idea is not a general criterion or that there may be other means for obtaining restricted lateral dissolution. However, it should be noted that Tenelon does contain about 0.7% Ni and this amount may be sufficient to promote cracking via the nickel enrichment process. To answer this question unequivocally, an alloy with absolutely no nickel but of otherwise identical Tenelon composition should be tested. (Ed. Note: These data of Louthan's should be compared with Kohl's given next in this discussion of the Staehle-Latanision paper.)

# Intergranular and Transgranular Stress Corrosion Cracking of Austenitic Mn-Cr and Mn Steels in Seawater

## By H. Kohl

In order to round off the picture of s.c.c. of f.c.c. steels, a brief report shall be given on the behavior of austenitic Mn-Cr- and Mn-alloyed steels in sea water. There are two kinds of s.c.c.

1. Mn-Cr-steels with a higher carbon content in welded or sensitized condition are susceptible to s.c.c. with intergranular crack propagation.

2. Mn-Cr- and Mn-steels will fail by s.c.c. in sea water even in the solution heat treated and water quenched condition, if tensile stresses at a higher level are applied. In this case crack propagation is primarily transgranular.

Results shall be given for the following steel: C, 0.54; Si, 0.51; Mn, 18.25; Cr, 4.64; Ni, 0.58; and N, 0.106.

### Intergranular s.c.c. in Sea Water

A specimen of this steel with 0.2 in diameter in sensitized condition will fail by intergranular s.c.c. in cold artificial sea water under a load of 31 tons per square inch after about 100 hours.

Figure 9 shows a cracked specimen and a micrograph. Crack propagation is strictly intergranular.

In Figure 10 applied stress is plotted vs time to fracture. Variation of time to fracture with applied stress shows a pronounced influence of tensile strain on intergranular attack in sea water.

Figure 11 gives the area of sensitivity to s.c.c. as affected by annealing time and temperature. U-bend specimens were used for these tests. Cr-rich carbides at grain boundaries appears to be the critical factor. Anodic polarization and increased temperature shorten time to fracture. Cracking is prevented by cathodic protection.

Table 1 gives some steels which are susceptible to intergranular s.c.c. in sea water. To become sensitive, precipitation of Cr-rich carbides is necessary. Intergranular s.c.c. does not occur, either if carbon content is very low or if no Cr is added. That is why usual stainless Cr-Ni-steels

and f.c.c. Mn-steels do not show this s.c.c. Steels of the compositions in Table 2 also are susceptible only after a sensitizing annealing or in welded condition.

Precipitation of Cr-rich carbides will cause Cr-depleted grain boundaries, which leads to differences in potential of grain and grain-boundary. The variation of time to fracture with applied stress in Figure 10 shows that this is primarily a stress corrosion cracking phenomena.

### Transgranular s.c.c. in Sea Water

Specimens were solution heat-treated at 1922 F and water quenched. Spring loaded specimens which were machined from solution heat treated material and tested with machined surface failed by s.c.c. in boiling artificial sea water. Closer examination found that austenitic Mn-Cr- and Mn-steels exhibit transgranular s.c.c. in boiling and cold sea water. Figure 12 shows two cracked specimens and a micrograph. Cracks propagate transgranularly with some crystallographic orientations.

With the steel mentioned at the beginning, variation of time to fracture with applied stress was investigated and results are given in Figure 13 for specimens in boiling, aerated, artificial sea water.

One series of tests was conducted with specimens with machined surface. Another used surfaces where 0.020 inches were removed electrolytically. Figure 13 shows that at high stresses specimens with machined and electrolytically removed surface layers behave similarly. Specimens with machined surfaces cracked at much lower stresses than the electrolytically prepared ones.

Figure 14 shows the variation of time to fracture with testing temperature for transgranular s.c.c. in sea water. At room temperature, specimens will crack after about 250 hours under the given conditions.

Table 2 gives some steels which are susceptible to transgranular s.c.c. in sea water.

**TABLE 1—Composition of Alloys Showing Intergranular Stress Corrosion Cracking in Sea Water**

|   | C | Si | Mn | Cr | Ni | N |
|---|-----|-----|-----|-----|-----|-----|
| 1 | 0.2 | 0.5 | 1 | 18 | 10 | — |
| 2 | 0.2 | 0.5 | 7 | 18 | 10 | 0.2 |
| 3 | 0.2 | 0.5 | 10 | 18 | 3 | 0.2 |
| 4 | 0.2 | 0.5 | 6 | 12 | 10 | — |
| 5 | 0.2 | 0.5 | 8 | 9 | 6 | — |
| 6 | 0.1 | 0.5 | 20 | 9 | 2 | 0.2 |
| 7 | 0.5 | 0.5 | 18 | 5 | — | 0.1 |

**TABLE 2—Composition of Alloys Showing Transgranular Stress Corrosion Cracking in Sea Water**

|   | C | Si | Mn | Cr | Ni | N |
|----|-----|-----|-----|-----|-----|-----|
| 8 | 0.5 | 0.5 | 18 | 5 | — | 0.1 |
| 9 | 0.4 | 0.5 | 18 | — | 3 | 0.1 |
| 10 | 0.4 | 0.5 | 18 | — | — | 0.1 |
| 11 | 0.5 | 1.0 | 20 | — | — | — |

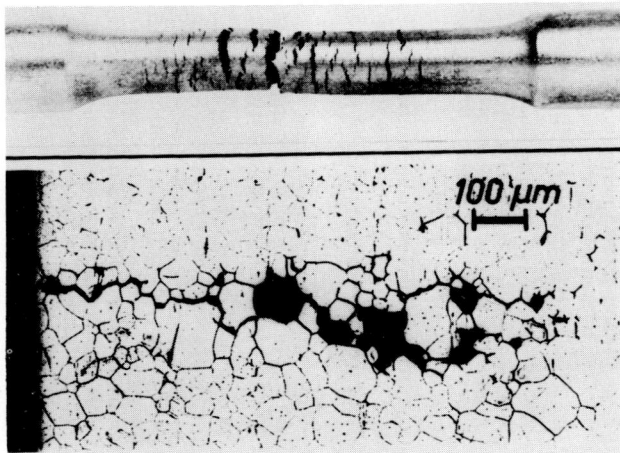

FIGURE 9 — Macro and microviews of sensitized specimens cracked intergranularly after exposure to sea water, room temperature.

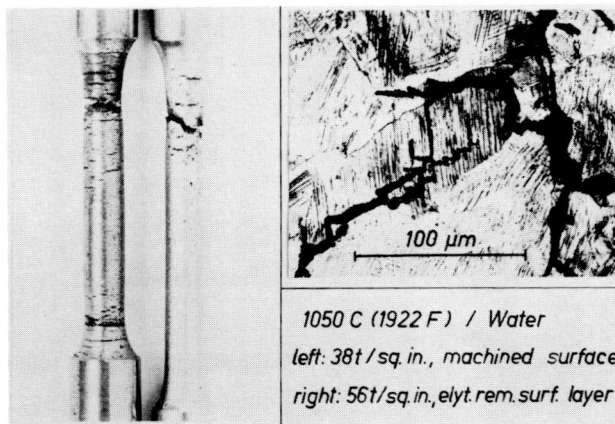

1050 C (1922 F) / Water

left: 38 t / sq. in., machined surface

right: 56 t / sq. in., elyt. rem. surf. layer

FIGURE 12 — Macro and microviews of quench annealed specimens cracked transgranularly after exposure to boiling sea water.

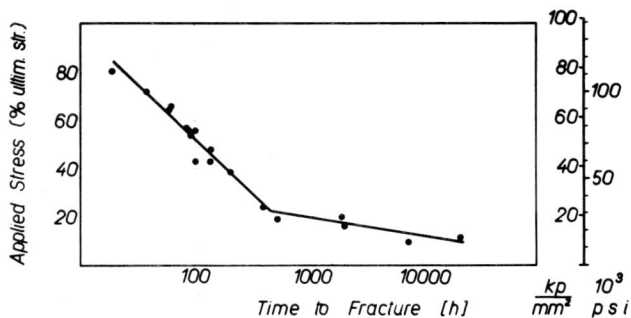

| C | Si | Mn | Cr | N | specimen |
|---|----|----|----|---|----------|
| 0,5 | 0,5 | 18,2 | 4,6 | 0,1 | 5 mm (0,2 in) diam. |

seawater roomtemp.    650°C (1200°F)/1 h

FIGURE 10 — Effect of applied stress on the cracking of sensitized specimens exposed in sea water at room temperature.

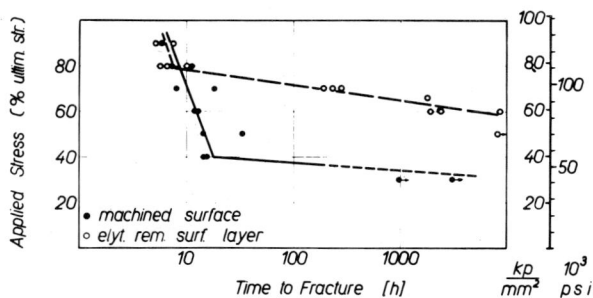

machined surface
elyt. rem. surf. layer

| C | Si | Mn | Cr | N | specimen |
|---|----|----|----|---|----------|
| 0,5 | 0,5 | 18,2 | 4,6 | 0,1 | 5 mm (0,2 in) diam. |

boiling seawater    1050°C (1922°F) / water

FIGURE 13 — Effect of stress on the time to fracture of quench annealed specimens with two different surface preparations.

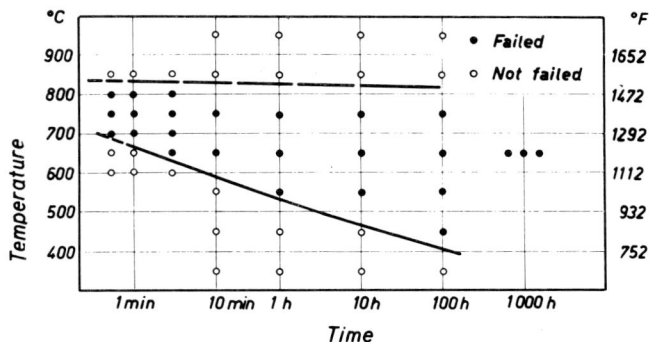

Failed
Not failed

| C | Si | Mn | Cr | N | seawater roomtemp. |
|---|----|----|----|---|----|
| 0,5 | 0,5 | 18,2 | 4,6 | 0,1 | |

U-bend spec. 0,1 in sheet

FIGURE 11 — Effect of heat treating, temperature, and time on the cracking of specimens exposed to room temperature sea water.

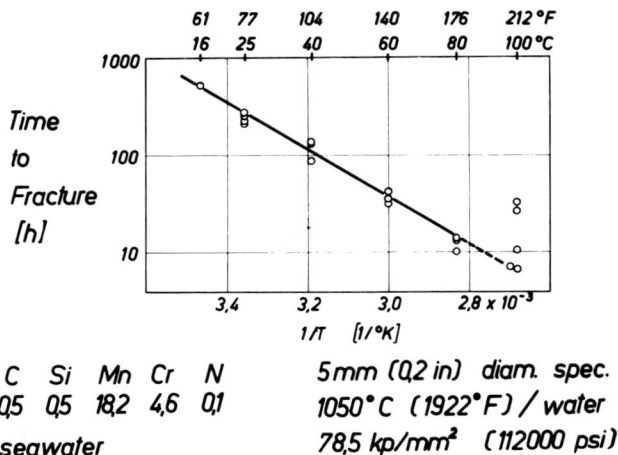

| C | Si | Mn | Cr | N | 5 mm (0,2 in) diam. spec. |
|---|----|----|----|---|----|
| 0,5 | 0,5 | 18,2 | 4,6 | 0,1 | 1050°C (1922°F) / water |

seawater    78,5 kp/mm² (112000 psi)

FIGURE 14 — Effect of temperature on the time to fracture of quench annealed specimens.

**H. Spahn, BASF Ludwigshafen am Rhein, Germany:**

As to the question whether grooves form during SCC of austenitic steels or if such grooves are artifacts (due to electropolishing), I would like to emphasize that grooves can form, at least in 42% boiling MgCl₂ solution and on Type 347 stainless steel. They form at stresses close to the 145 C yield point (about 28,500 psi for Type 347) or below and were observed in many potentiostatic experiments, from which Figure 15 gives an example. As this picture shows, grooves are formed in the early stages of the specimen lifetime at the stress level indicated.

At higher stresses no grooves appear. Instead, the cracks start directly from the surface. From this it can be concluded that the formation of grooves bears no principal mechanistic importance. They are, however, a typical feature under the aforementioned conditions and must be regarded as the result of the primary stage in the localization of the electrochemical attack. They clearly differ from pits in that their longer axis is perpendicular to the direction of the applied stress. By using a scanning electron microscope one can show that this stress oriented growth is very pronounced even in the early part of an SCC experiment.

**R. W. Staehle and R. M. Latanision:**

**The grooves which we discussed in our review are observable only in the electron microscope and are not seen, as are yours, in the optical microscope. Note our Figure 100. The reasonability that such grooves continue to progress as a sort of stepwise trenching due to slip processes is corroborated by Figure 92.**

**M. R. Louthan, Jr. and M. L. Holzworth,**
**Savannah River Laboratory:**

The authors have done an excellent job in presenting a comprehensive review article of a most difficult subject. In connection with the discussion of the possible role of hydrogen absorption in stress corrosion cracking, reference is made to the work of Vaughn et al (Reference 124 in Latanision's and Staehle's review), who reported a hydride phase in cathodically charged Type 304 stainless steel. In

work recently completed and submitted for publication in *Corrosion*, we found no hydride phase, but did observe a cph phase similar to that reported by Vaughn et al. This phase was identified as ε martensite, which formed during cathodic charging because absorbed hydrogen significantly lowered the stacking fault energy of the austenite matrix. Because absorbed and adsorbed hydrogen promote different effects in austenite, we suggest that if hydrogen is involved in stress corrosion cracking of Fe, Cr, Ni alloys, failure is promoted by the surface effects caused by the *ad*sorption, rather than *ab*sorption, of hydrogen.

**R. W. Staehle and R. M. Latanision:**

**Your work is certainly interesting. We are greatly concerned, however, that results from cathodic charging be applied to the interpretation of stress corrosion cracking of stainless steels in chloride environments. The evidence is very strong that most of the reduction process responsible for crack propagation does not operate near the crack tip but at some distance removed. Further the severe acuity of the crack tip would favor formation of hydrogen because of the lowered surface energy requirements and the activity of neutral hydrogen on the surface at the crack tip would be lowered. These, too, are also plausible but questionable arguments. It seems that the critical experiments have yet to be run.**

**M. Prazak, State Research Institute for**
**Materials Protection, Prague:**

An essential question in stress corrosion cracking is how apparently brittle cracks can occur in ductile alloys. When notches or fissures are present initially, the application of stress in the absence of an environment causes plastic flow at their base and these incipient cracks can be healed. The movies presented on Tuesday evening (especially the ones by Nielsen on stainless steel and Priest, Beck and Fontana on magnesium alloys) show two notable results. First, plastic deformation preceds the advancing crack. Second, the crack itself in its first stage is very sharp. See Figure 16a.

Figure 16 illustrates the sequence of events for plastic blunting of an initially sharp crack in the absence of an

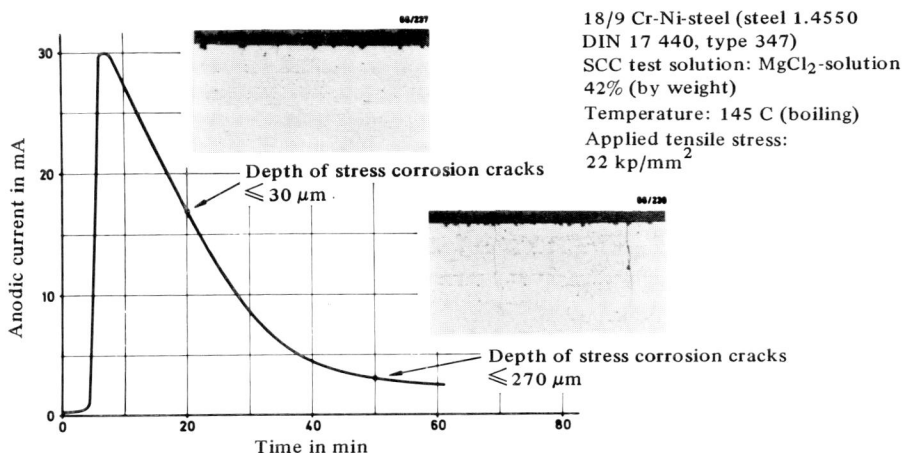

18/9 Cr-Ni-steel (steel 1.4550
DIN 17 440, type 347)
SCC test solution: MgCl₂-solution
42% (by weight)
Temperature: 145 C (boiling)
Applied tensile stress:
22 kp/mm²

Depth of stress corrosion cracks
≤ 30 μm

Depth of stress corrosion cracks
≤ 270 μm

FIGURE 15 — Typical plot of anodic current vs time for specimen at controlled potential.

environment. The notch is widened and the material at the crack tip is hardened. Thus, the notch essentially repairs itself.

When an environment is present and cracking occurs, the above process is disturbed in some way. The hardened metal at the crack tip is cracked in some way by the environment.

I should like to suggest several environmental processes which might be critical in stress corrosion cracking and heretofore have not been extensively discussed:

1. The liquid medium at the crack tip may be nearly at equilibrium owing to the very high concentration of ions of the corrosion product. If the crack sides are at this near equilibrium condition, then preferential attack might occur at the crack tip because of the high strain energy. This process would be analogous to thermal grooving at grain boundaries.

2. Studies of electrocapillary phenomena show that surface tensions of metals decrease at potentials both active

and noble to the potential of zero charge. The environment-surface forces involved herein may be of sufficient magnitude to decrease the applied forces required to produce cleavage as shown in Figure 17.

## Effect of Plastic Strain on the Susceptibility of Metals and Alloys to Stress Corrosion Cracking

### M. Smialowski

It may sometimes be observed during stress corrosion tests that the fracture of tensile specimens exposed to a constant load does not cross the reduced section, but chooses some longer path, e.g., across the taper where the tensile stresses are comparatively low. This chiefly occurs at applied loads somewhat higher than the yield strength. A thorough study of the relationship between the applied load and time to fracture reveals a minimum followed by a

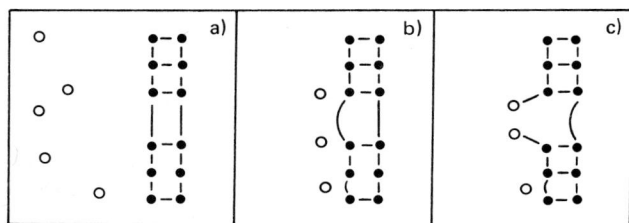

FIGURE 16 — Processes involved in blunting a prior fissure in a ductile material.

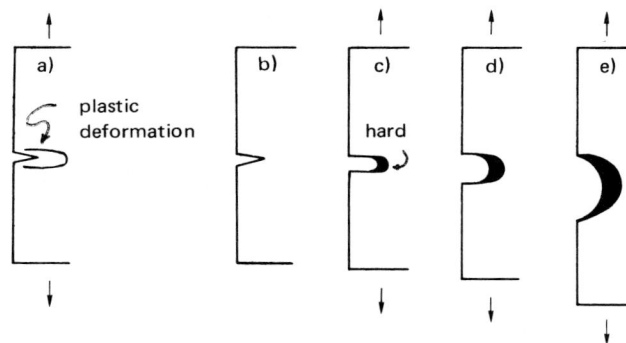

FIGURE 17 — Schematic of processes involved in band breaking due to adsorption of environmental species.

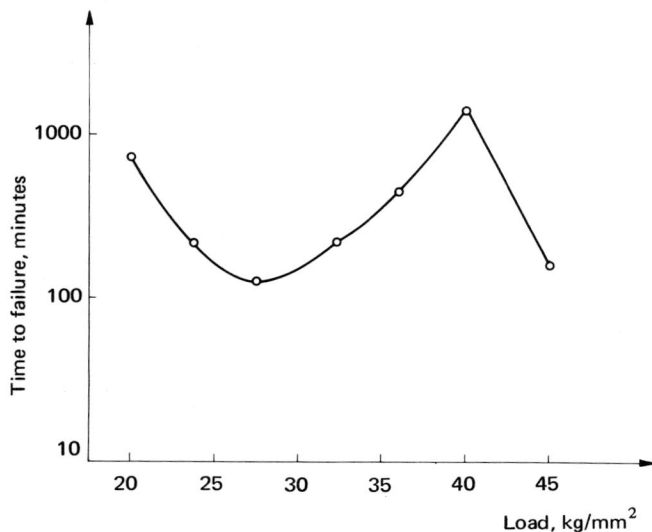

FIGURE 18 — Relationship between the applied tensile load and log time to fracture for Type 302 stainless steel in boiling 35% $MgCl_2$ solution at 125 C.[1]

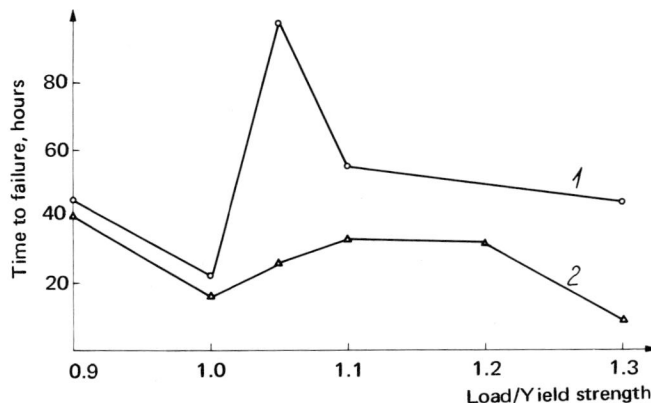

FIGURE 19 — Relationship between the ratio of applied tensile load to yield strength and time to fracture for low-carbon iron (Curve 1) and 0.14% C steel (Curve 2) in 45% $NH_4NO_3$ solution spray at 95 C.[2]

304

maximum of the curve.[1] Such phenomena were observed for both transgranular cracking of austenitic 18Cr-8Ni stainless steel in magnesium chloride[1] as shown in Figure 18 and intergranular cracking of iron and annealed mild steel in ammonium nitrate solutions,[2,3] Figure 19.

Forty[4] postulated that the susceptibility to stress corrosion cracking of alpha-brass and similar alloys with some degree of short range order should increase and then decrease with increasing amounts of cold work. Hines[5] observed a pronounced minimum of the time to fracture for 7% cold-worked 18-Cr-8Ni-Ti steel specimens in boiling 42% $MgCl_2$ solution, and similar results were found by Greeley et al.[6] These authors explained the longer time to fracture stated for the more heavily cold-worked alloy by the transformation of austenite into strain-induced martensite. In a later work, Burkart et al[7] confirmed this viewpoint, since for a 24Cr-12Ni steel, in which cold working does not produce the martensite, no increase of the time to fracture with the amount of cold work was observed.

The explanation based on the martensite transformation does not fit results shown in Figure 18 since the straining occurred at 125 C. As shown by Cina[8] and others, plastic deformation of 18Cr-8Ni steels above 100 C does not involve the transformation of austenite into martensite. There were no traces of martensite in specimens used in Figure 18 after the tests.

Recent electron-microscopic studies done by Rychcik et al[9] have shown that the stress at which the time to fracture attains minimum involves a dislocation arrangement with few dislocation loops distributed relatively uniformly and thereby produces low density barriers to the free movement of dislocations. Such a structure may be assumed to enable dislocations to move along slip planes over a path approximately as long as the diameter of the grain or the distance between the grain boundary and the twin boundary. At stresses higher than that corresponding to the minimum of the curve in Figure 18, dense dislocation loops are formed which may obstruct the movement of dislocations and reduce considerably their free path.

The above results seem to support the views on the essential role of the dislocation substructure in the stress corrosion cracking of f.c.c. alloys.

As shown in Figure 19, a similar relationship between the applied load and time to fracture was observed by Zabik[2,3] for the intergranular corrosion of iron and annealed low-carbon steel in ammonium nitrate. Zabik suggests that the increase of the time to fracture at stresses somewhat higher than the yield strength is due to the formation of slip bands. These reduce the probability of a critical piling up of dislocations at the grain boundaries, this piling up being necessary for the occurrence of the intergranular stress corrosion. At higher stresses than A.L./Y.S. ~ 1.2, the critical piling up of dislocations may

not only occur at the grain boundaries, but on slip bands and pearlite lamellae as well, and this causes a renewed decrease in the time to fracture. In an annealed 0.28% C steel, Zabik[1] did not observe such effects. The time to fracture decreased regularly with increasing load. This was evidently due to the much lower ductility of that steel when compared with low-carbon iron and annealed 0.14% C steel.

References - Smialowski Discussion

1. M. Smialowski and M. Rychcik. *Corrosion*, (1967). In press.
2. W. Zabik. *Zeszyty Naukowe Politechniki Slaskiej*, Nr. 92 (1963).
3. M. Smialowski. *Corrosion et Anticorrosion*, 13, 270 (1965).
4. A. J. Forty. *Physical Metallurgy of Stress Corrosion Fracture*, Interscience, New York (1960).
5. J. G. Hines. *ibid.*
6. P. J. Greeley, V. J. Russo, R. K. Saxer and J. R. Myers. *Corrosion*, 21, 327 (1965).
7. E. R. Burkart, J. R. Myers and R. K. Saxer. *Corrosion*, 22, 21 (1966).
8. B. Cina. *J. Iron Steel Inst.*, 177, 406 (1954).
9. M. Rychcik, S. Gorczyca and A. Korbel. Paper in preparation (1967).

## Concentration vs Boiling Temperature of Magnesium Chloride Solutions

M. A. Streicher and I. B. Casale

### Introduction

The temperature of boiling magnesium chloride solutions, which are used to detect the susceptibility of stainless steel alloys to stress corrosion cracking has a pronounced effect on the measured time to failure. A discrepancy between the boiling-point-concentration relationship was brought to our attention when a series of 42 wt % solutions was prepared in the Engineering Materials Laboratory and a boiling point observed that was apparently low by almost 10 C compared with values often cited in the literature. In an attempt to resolve this discrepancy, atmospheric boiling-point data were assembled from the literature for $MgCl_2$ solutions in the 0-46 wt % concentration range. These data were supplemented by new experimental determinations on 40-46 wt % $MgCl_2$—the concentration range of greatest interest in stress corrosion tests—for which little information was available.

The concentration in general use was apparently proposed by Scheil,[1] who reported preparing a "solution containing approximately 1375 gm of $MgCl_2 \cdot 6H_2O$ and 150 ml $H_2O$ boiling at 309 F (154 C)... This solution contains about 42 wt % $MgCl_2$. Numerous authors[2-5] have cited this paper and have reported preparing 42 wt % $MgCl_2$ solutions with boiling points of 154 C.

In 1961 Barnartt and van Rooyen[6] called attention to the inconsistency in the reported boiling point. They measured a boiling point of 146 C at 730 mm Hg for a 42.5 wt % $MgCl_2$. These data, when corrected to 760 mm Hg, yield a value of 147.0 C, in good agreement with data published by Pershke and Kalinin[7] in 1932, which plot to

[1]For these studies one must use specimens whose tapered parts are properly isolated from the corrosive medium.

305

146.5 C at the same concentration. Their comments appear, however, to have been disregarded by others,[12-17] except for Thomas, Ferrari, and Allio,[8] Scully and Hoar,[9] and Kohl.[10,11]

Evidently investigators have either been preparing 42 wt % solutions and assuming a boiling temperature of 154 C, or they have been adding water to $MgCl_2 \cdot 6H_2O$ to adjust the boiling temperature to 154 C and assuming a 42 wt % solution. Because of the hygroscopic nature of the hydrate, the later procedure is probably the one being used. Inspection of still-sealed bottles of reagent-grade $MgCl_2 \cdot 6H_2O$ (minimum assay 99.0%) revealed that varying amounts of water had been absorbed by the crystals. As a check on the "purity" of the hydrate, 600-gm samples were removed from four freshly opened bottles and the boiling points measured. These varied by as much as 5 C. On the basis of boiling-point data discussed below, the actual $MgCl_2 \cdot 6H_2O$ content was as low as 97 wt %.

## Procedure and Results

All available data at 1 atm from the original literature sources were critically analyzed[24] and the "best" data selected. In addition, the boiling temperatures of four solutions in the 40-46 wt % concentration range were measured. Experimental details are given in Reference 24.

"Best" data from the literature and our experimental measurements are plotted in Figure 20 for 0-46 wt % $MgCl_2$. Data for the range of special interest (40 to 46%) are shown on an expanded scale in Figure 21. There is good agreement among the results of Pershke and Kalinin,[7] Barnartt and van Rooyen,[6] Thomas, Ferrari, and Allio,[8] and this investigation.

Because the boiling-point curve is essentially linear between 40 and 46 wt % $MgCl_2$, all the data shown in Figure 21 (except for Scheil's value[1]) were fitted by the least-squares method to a linear equation. The resulting equation

$$t, °C = (3.51)(wt \% MgCl_2) - 2.91 \qquad (1)$$

should not be used to extrapolate beyond the 40-46 wt % $MgCl_2$ concentration limits. The temperature is the boiling point at 1 atm. The boiling point for 42.0 wt % $MgCl_2$ calculated from the equation is 144.5 ± 0.5 C; conversely, a solution boiling at 154.0 C has a concentration of 44.7 ± 0.2 wt % $MgCl_2$.

## Discussion

As shown above, the preparation of a particular magnesium chloride solution by weighing the hydrate is not a reliable technique. Because boiling points of solutions above 40 wt % vary rapidly with concentration, the boiling temperature affords a sensitive means of determining and controlling the concentration. Note that a 0.3 wt % increase in $MgCl_2$ increases the temperature of 1 C in the high (40-46 wt %) concentration range.

The importance of reproducibility and control of temperature of these solutions for stress corrosion tests is

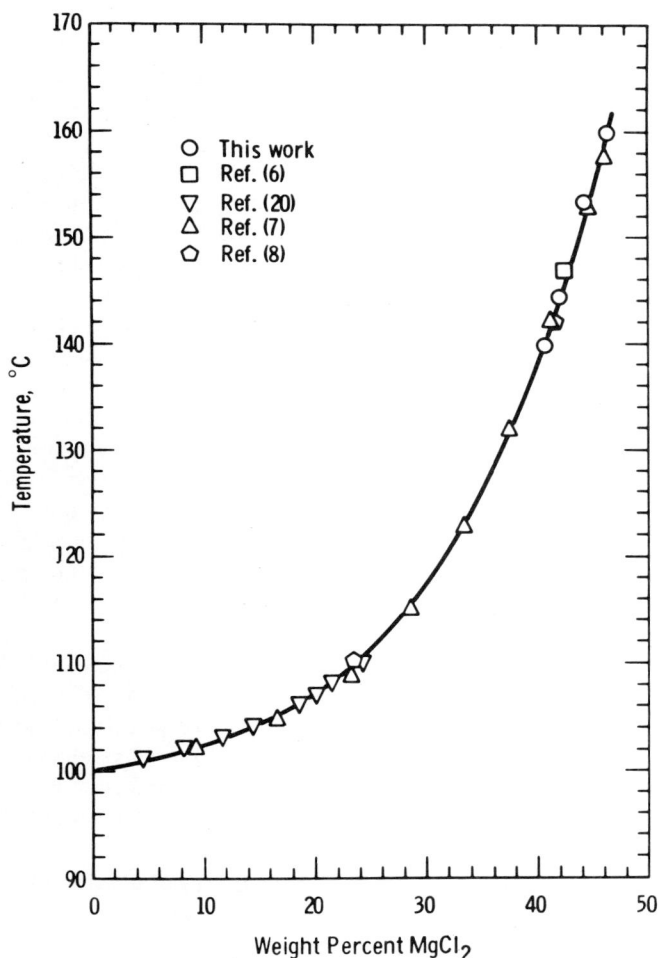

FIGURE 20 – Boiling points of aqueous $MgCl_2$ solutions at one atmosphere as a function of concentration.

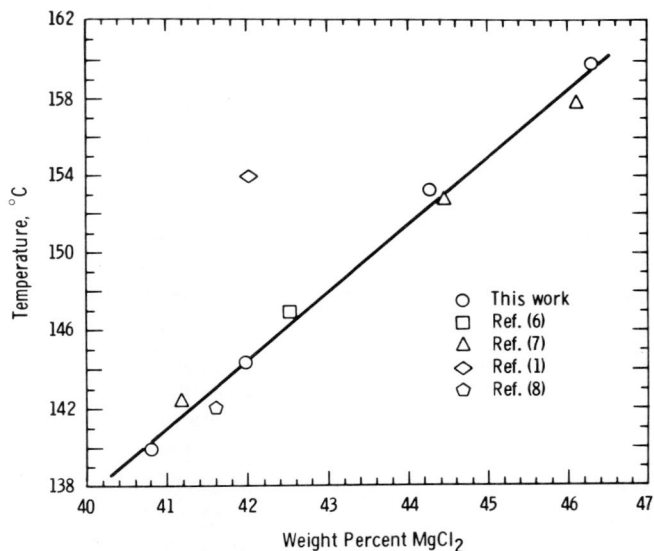

FIGURE 21 – Boiling points of aqueous $MgCl_2$ solutions at one atmosphere as a function of concentration. Equation of line: t, °C = 3.51 (wt % $MgCl_2$) - 2.91.

306

well illustrated by the work of Hoar and Hines[2] and of Thomas, Ferrari, and Allio.[8] These investigators found that the time to failure of austenitic stainless steel in "42%" solutions (actually 44.7% for Hoar and Hines) is increased by a factor of 4 when the temperature is decreased by 10 C in the 120-150 C range. The data of Thomas, et al[8] and Hoar and Hines[2] were confirmed by Kohl.[10] Thus temperature has a major effect on the time to failure.

In contrast, the effect of $MgCl_2$ concentrations above 35 wt % on the time to failure appears to be small.[1] Thomas, Ferrari, and Allio[8] and Kohl[10] found no significant change in time to failure when the $MgCl_2$ concentration was changed from approximately 45% to 35%, provided the temperature was held constant. Kohl found that, below 35% at constant temperature, the time to failure increases with decreasing $MgCl_2$ concentrations.

## Conclusion

The above results show that a magnesium chloride solution of a given concentration is most accurately

---

[1] A report[18] ascribing a major effect on the time to failure to the $MgCl_2$ concentration appears to be based on tests in which the temperature was decreased as well as the salt concentration.

prepared by measuring the temperature of the boiling solution. For example, to prepare a 45.0 ± 0.2 wt % $MgCl_2$ solution, add water to boiling reagent-grade hexahydrate until the temperature is decreased to 155.0 ± 0.5 C at 760 mm Hg. Temperature corrections for pressure variations within ± 30 mm Hg of 1 atm may be made through use of the following relationship.[7]

$$\Delta t/\Delta p = 2.5 \, C/60 \, mm \, Hg = 0.04 \, C/mm \, Hg \quad (2)$$

Because of the major effect of temperature, it is essential, particularly in extended-time tests, to hold the temperature constant throughout the test period. The use of appropriate reflux condensers and ground-glass joints and frequent measurements of the boiling temperature are a necessary part of the test procedure.

The test results of various investigatiors can be compared only if the test conditions are defined and standardized. It is therefore proposed that a 45.0 ± 0.2 wt % $MgCl_2$ solution, which has an atmospheric boiling point of 155.0 ± 0.5 C (311.0 F) be considered for general use in stress corrosion tests where constant test-solution conditions are desirable.

## References

1. M. A. Scheil. *Symposium on Stress Corrosion Cracking of Metals,* ASTM-AIME, Philadelphia, 1945 (Std. Tech. Publ. No. 64, p. 395).
2. T. P. Hoar and J. G. Hines. *J. Iron and Steel Inst.,* London, **182,** 124 (1956).
3. K. W. Leu and J. N. Helle. *Corrosion,* **14,** 249t (1958).
4. H. H. Uhlig and J. Lincoln, Jr. *J. Electrochem. Soc.,* **105,** No. 6, 325 (1958).
5. R. E. Reed and H. W. Paxton. *First International Congress on Metallic Corrosion,* p. 301, London, Butterworths (1962).
6. S. Barnartt and D. van Rooyen. *J. Electrochem. Soc.,* **108,** No. 3, 222 (1961).
7. V. K. Pershke and S. K. Kalinir. *J. Chem. Ind.* (Moscow), No. 12, 16 (1932).
8. K. C. Thomas, H. M. Ferrari and R. J. Allio. *Corrosion,* **20,** 89t (1964).
9. J. C. Scully and T. P. Hoar. *Second International Congress on Metallic Corrosion,* p. 184, Houston, National Association of Corrosion Engineers (1966).
10. H. Kohl. *Werkstoffe u. Korrosion,* **16,** 364 (1965).
11. H. Kohl. *Corrosion,* **23,** 39 (1967).
12. E. R. Burkart, J. R. Myers and R. K. Saxer. *Corrosion,* **22,** 21 (1966).
13. R. W. Staehle. Ohio State University Research Foundation, Columbus, Contract AT(11-1-1319), August 30, 1966.
14. G. H. G. Krafft, J. Z. Amacker, R. K. Saxer and J. R. Myers. *Corrosion,* **21,** 188 (1965).
15. M. R. Louthan. *Corrosion,* **21,** 288 (1965).
16. H. Coriou, L. Grall, C. Mahieu and M. Pelas. *Corrosion,* **22,** 1280 (1966).
17. D. A. Vaughan, D. I. Phalen, C. L. Peterson and W. K. Boyd. *Second International Congress on Metallic Corrosion,* p. 216, Houston, National Association of Corrosion Engineers (1966).
18. C. Edeleanu. *J. Iron and Steel Inst.,* London, **173,** No. 2, 140 (1953).
19. H. Gerlach. *Caliche,* Santiago, Chile, 8, 298 (1926).
20. H. Gerlach. *Tha., Z. anal. Chem.,* **26,** 413 (1886).
21. P. de Heene. *Acad. Roy. Sci. Belg.,* Mem. cour. in 8° 31, No. 4 (1881).
22. L. Kahlenberg. *J. Phys. Chem.,* **5,** 339 (1901).
23. C. H. Sluiter. *Proc. Royal Acad. Sci.,* Amsterdam, **17,** 1036 (1915).
24. I. B. Casale. Boiling Temperatures of Magnesium Chloride Solutions - Their Application in Stress Corrosion Studies. *Corrosion,* **23,** 314-317 (1967) October.

# ELECTRON MICROFRACTOGRAPHY OF
# STRESS-CORROSION CRACKING

N. A. Nielsen
E. I. du Pont de Nemours & Co., Inc.

## Abstract

A survey of appearances of the fracture surfaces of stress corrosion cracks in Fe-Cr-Ni alloys is reported for austenitic, ferritic, and austenitic-ferritic alloys. Low and high magnifications are studied using optical and electron microscopes. Fractographs show strong indications of cleavage fracture. Striated appearances suggest alternating electrochemical and mechanical processes. Considerable additional work is needed to define the significance of fractographic observations on surfaces of stress corrosion cracks.

## Introduction

The first application of microscopy to the study of metal fractures was made in 1722 by Reaumur who classified several irons and steels by their fracture-surface appearance. This event and the important subsequent history of fractography are described by Henry and Plateau[1] in their handbook on "Microfractography." Included are the systematic modern observations of Zappfe from 1941 to 1951 of the fracture surface characteristics of many different metals (including the first observation of striations in fatigue fracture surfaces). His studies with the light microscope defined "fractography" and developed it into an important metallographic tool.

The term microfractography appears to have been first used by Crussard in 1956 and denotes the application of the electron microscope, with its advantages of great depth of field and resolution, to fractographic examination. Microfractography is thus synonymous with electron fractography and electron microfractography, terms commonly used in the United States.

In recent years electron fractography has received new emphasis as a tool for the investigation of the micromechanisms of fracture processes in metals.[2-4] In metallurgical research and in service failure analysis the fine-scale morphology of fracture surfaces provides a description and an identification of the fracture.

A fracture can often be characterized as ductile or brittle solely by its macroscopic characteristics. Confirmation is obtained by electron fractographic examination and at the same time the fracture mode is identified as intergranular or transgranular (or both) while the mechanism of fracture is identified as involving plastic rupture (microvoid coalescence producing rupture dimples), or cleavage ("river pattern structure") or fatigue (here crack growth can involve both plastic fracture and cleavage mechanisms). This basic terminology has been developed primarily in the analysis of service failures, particularly of high strength engineering alloys where electron fractography is now commonly employed to provide the key information for identification of the cause of failure.

It is obvious to those who have utilized the techniques of electron fractography that this tool has a far broader potential applicability in the more complex fracture processes where special environmental conditions have a controlling effect. Most of the reported fractographic work to date has not considered the role of environment on fracture morphology. There is little doubt, however, that the utility of electron fractography will increase greatly once we learn how to interpret unambiguously fracture morphology which develops in the failure of stressed metals and alloys exposed to specific active environments. Such areas of expanded application exist in the phenomena of stress-corrosion cracking (SCC), stress accelerated intergranular corrosion, hydrogen embrittlement, liquid metal embrittlement, corrosion fatigue, etc. In the present paper the writer will discuss only some applications of electron fractography to stress-corrosion cracking of stainless steels. The investigations are still in progress. What is presented here is intended to illustrate how electron fractography can contribute to a better understanding of the complexities which becloud the present picture of the mechanism(s) of

SCC in stainless steel.

The first use of electron fractography by the writer was reported at the Pittsburgh Conference on Physical Metallurgy of Stress-Corrosion Fracture in 1959.[5] It was indicated then that electron fractography can provide information on:

(1) the ductile-brittle characteristics of the fracture surface,

(2) fracture face corrosion and corrosion product formation in the crack system, and

(3) the role of any metallic or nonmetallic phases in embrittling alloys by providing preferential paths for fracture.

In a more recent paper[6] concerned with an electron microscopic study of the nature of initial corrosion sites in stressed stainless steel, it was shown that the transitional changes from an initial corrosion-tunnelling penetration of slip planes through recognizable microcracks to ultimate fracture of Type 304 stainless steel could be followed by oxide replication of appropriate specimens. This is broadly the area in which intensive use of electron microscopy (fractography) can provide answers to many of the present questions on corrosion-cracking mechanisms. But implied in this potential contribution of electron fractography is the reliable interpretation and complete analysis of the information inherent in the fractographs. In present usage electron fractographs contain more information than can be analyzed. The role of corrosion in the fracture process adds an additional dimension of complication to a precise interpretation of fracture surface morphology.

## Fractography of Cr-Ni-Fe Stainless Steel

The differences in the macrocharacteristics of "brittle" fracture by SCC and ductile fracture on normal tensile loading are shown in Figure 1. Here in a Type 304 steel tensile specimen which had been exposed to boiling 42% $MgCl_2$ the flat, brittle-appearing outer zone (SCC fracture surface) contrasts with the sponge-like, porous appearance of the normal shear failure of the steel.

When examined at higher magnification with both the light and electron microscope, the SCC fractures are found to contain several structural features which are more readily interpreted in terms of brittle fracture than in terms solely of an electrochemical theory of SCC. Feathery, fern-like, dendritic surface morphology is commonly observed, as well as faceted and cleavage-like surfaces with river pattern markings and areas showing finely spaced striations. Figure 2 shows a photomicrograph of the dendritic feature in an SCC fracture of Type 316 stainless steel tubing. Figure 3 is a carbon replica of similar fracture surface structure photographed in this case so that comparison can be made with an electron micrograph of the same area.

It is not easy to correlate light fractographs with electron fractographs of identical areas. The difference in depth of field of the two instruments is, in part, the answer. Also, a precise orientation of the specimen is required for photomicrography (illumination must be at normal incidence to the area of interest which must be smooth enough

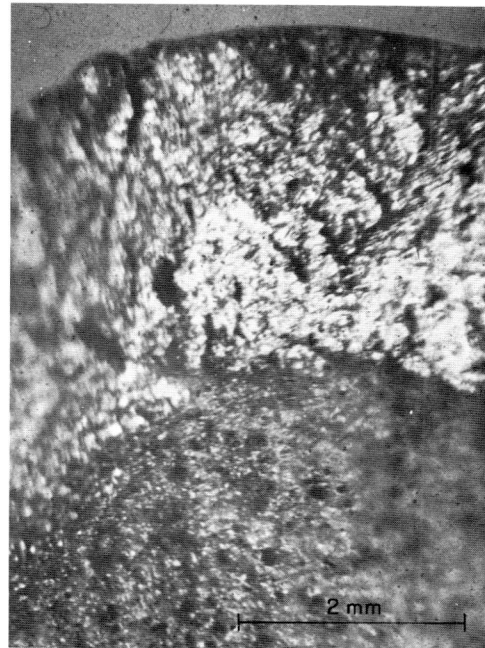

FIGURE 1 — Photomacrograph of fracture in Type 304 stainless steel tensile specimen (stress-corrosion cracked in periphery).

FIGURE 2 — "Feather" morphology in SCC fracture of Type 316 stainless steel tubing.

to reflect light back along the same optical path). The shallow depth of field emphasizes the dendritic or feathery character of the fracture morphology. In the electron microscope, however, the whole replica, three dimensionally, is in focus and its angle of tilt to the electron beam becomes of importance only in the taking of stereomicrographs (an extremely valuable practice and recommended for reliable interpretation of the fracture surface topography).

Figure 4 is the electron fractograph corresponding to the structure encircled in black ink in Figure 3. In this case the areas were chosen to permit the viewer to conclude that the same structure is, in fact, shown in each fractograph.

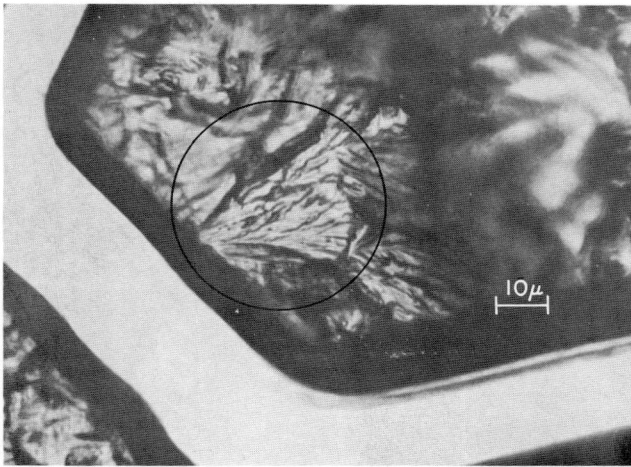

**FIGURE 3 — Photomicrograph of carbon replica of Type 316 SCC fracture.**

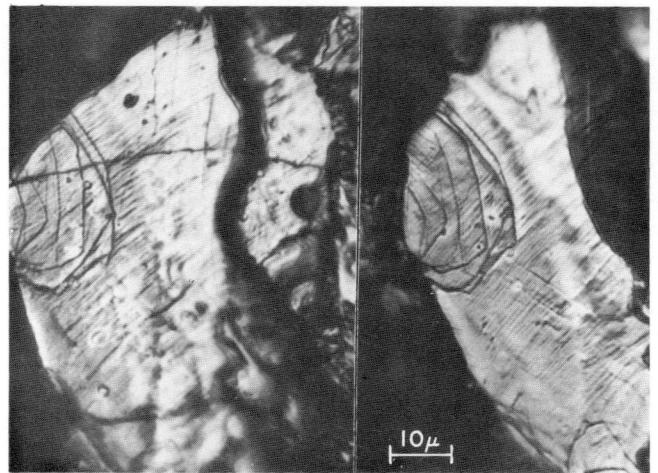

**FIGURE 5 — Matching detail found in fracture surfaces of Type 304 stainless steel failed in boiling 42% MgCl$_2$.**

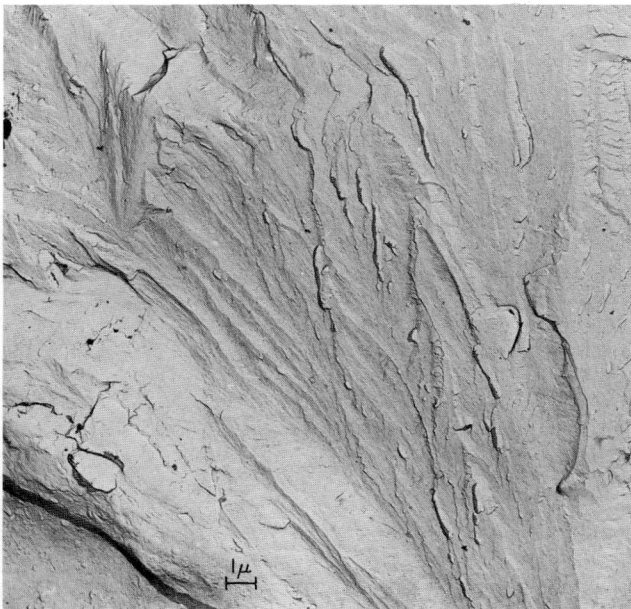

**FIGURE 4 — Electron micrograph of circled area shown on Figure 3.**

**FIGURE 6 — Mixed modes of stress-corrosion crack propagation in Type 304 stainless steel (oxide replica).**

Even so, it is seen that the fan-shaped outlines of the feature are no longer so easily identifiable in the electron fractograph. The structure shown here would be identified as cleavage or perhaps quasi-cleavage based on the nomenclature established in electron fractography.

In study of SCC of austenitic stainless steels, the use of tubing is particularly advantageous since the residual tensile stresses present from manufacture make the tubing susceptible to failure in boiling· 42% MgCl$_2$ (if a final stress-relief heat treatment is not specified by the purchaser). In Type 304 tubing the fracture mode in SCC is not always entirely transgranular. A small percentage of the fracture surface consists of reflective facets which represent grain surfaces exposed by intergranular decohesion. It is possible, how-

ever, that some of the highly reflective surfaces in SCC fractures in high tensile strength tubing may result from true cleavage following a plane of martensite present in the austenite matrix.

Figure 5 is included to show that fracture surfaces can be matched rather precisely. At 750 X the "cleavage-step" markings have the same configuration and there is a strong suggestion that their mode of formation was mechanical rather than electrochemical. (These surfaces also show a high density of slip or deformation markings.) Whatever corrosion did occur in the generation of these surfaces was

310

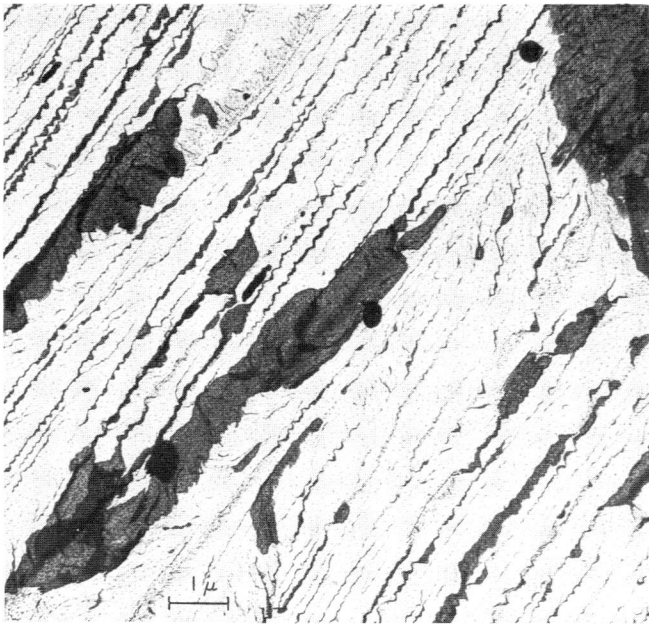

FIGURE 7 — Striated structure of SCC fracture in Type 304 stainless steel (oxide replica).

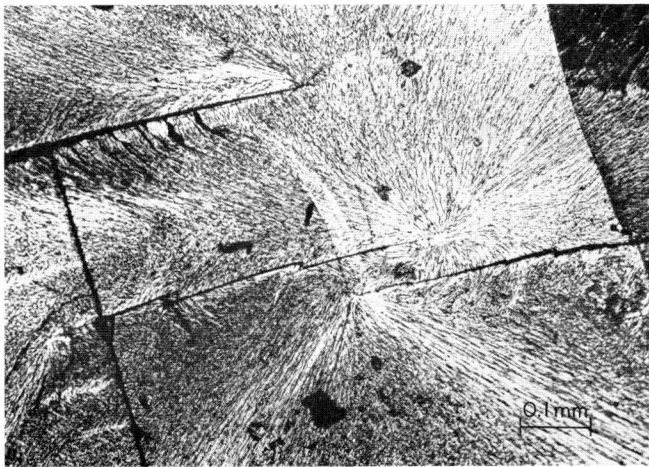

FIGURE 9 — Fracture surface detail at tip of secondary crack showing cleavage-type morphology.

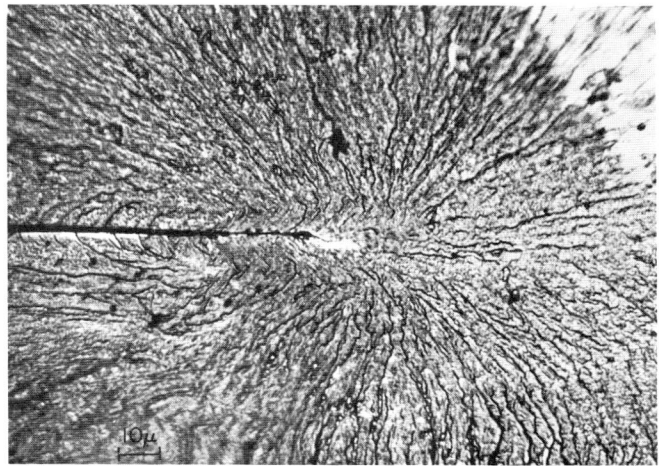

FIGURE 8 — SCC fracture surface with orthogonally directed secondary cracks in cast stainless steel.

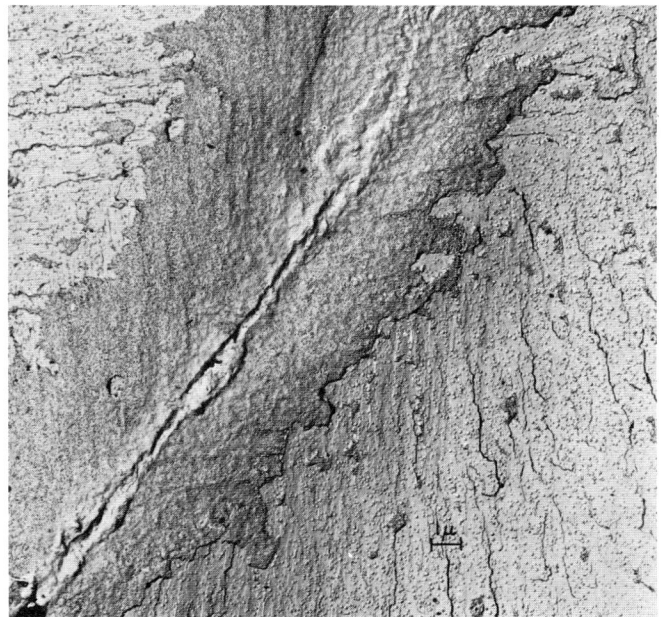

FIGURE 10 — Electron fractograph (carbon replica) of crack tip shown in Figure 9.

not sufficiently intense to obliterate the matching detail disclosed in this pair of photomicrographs. Attempts are now being made to determine how well the detail in corresponding electron fractographs can be matched.

Areas of intergranular separation in SCC of austenitic stainless steels can be identified very readily by electron fractography. Figure 6 shows mixed modes of crack propagation. The smooth central area is a grain surface which is surrounded by areas of transgranular fracture. It is probable that the intergranular decohesion occurs as a result of the fortuitous orientation of a grain boundary coincident with the path of an advancing transgranular stress corrosion crack.

The transgranular fractures frequently exhibit "river markings" similar to cleavage detail found in brittle

fractures where the environment plays no role in the failure process. Closely spaced striations are also a common feature. The latter are presently interpreted as crack-arrest lines and were suggested by Nielsen[5] to result from periodic propagation of the crack. Logan, McBee and Kahan[7] have also commented on the significance of striation formation in Type 321 stainless steel also fractured in boiling 42% $MgCl_2$. Striations of this nature occur in other slow strain SCC systems, e.g., aluminum and copper alloys; and they will likely be found in other stress-corrosion cracked alloys when electron fractography is applied in the failure analyses.

McEvily and Bond[8] have discussed striation formation during SCC in alpha brass and in a 5.5 Al-2.5 Zn magnesium alloy. Their interpretation is in terms of a mechanism of periodic rupture of anodic films or tarnish layers. The common conclusion developing in the investigation of striation markings is that the mechanism of SCC does not involve solely a confined form of electrochemical corrosion but does involve small steps of mechanical fracture alternating with short stages of crack advancement by anodic dissolution. In the case of austenitic stainless steel this periodic process appears to be crystallographically oriented and produces a surface having a sawtooth profile. The electron fractograph shown in Figure 7 is one of a stereopair which shows this type of topography.

The dark patches present in Figures 6 and 7 are corrosion products randomly extracted with the oxide replica from the original fracture surfaces. That such corrosion products also play a role in the SCC mechanism has been theorized by Nielsen[5] and by Pickering, Beck and Fontana.[9]

## Fractography of Ferrite-Containing Stainless Steels

The fractography of ferrite-containing austenitic stainless steel and of ferritic stainless alloys which fail by SCC can also provide information pertinent to an improved understanding of SCC mechanisms. Figure 8 shows an area in a highly magnetic cast experimental stainless alloy containing 18% Cr and 10% Ni which developed orthogonally directed cracks upon exposure (without applied stress) to boiling 42% $MgCl_2$. The area of examination appears to have fractured in what appears to be a brittle fashion with fracture initiating from the tip of the center crack in a sunburst pattern (Figure 9). This same area around the crack tip is shown in the electron fractograph of Figure 10. Stereo-examination of the "white flag" area of Figure 9 shows that it is an etched area of smoother topography than the remainder of the fracture surface. The topography of the fracture is based on parallel terraces separated by small steps, exactly the same as river patterns in cleavage fracture. Again, however, while the crack apex appears to have functioned as a stress-raiser to initiate a radiating cleavage fracture, this topography developed at a slow rate simulating, as in the case of the fully austenitic alloys, the appearance of fast brittle fracture. This is an example of the very real dilemma present in correctly interpreting the brittle-appearing fracture surface morphologies produced by SCC in the boiling 42% $MgCl_2$ test.

In high-chromium, low-nickel stainless alloys which have a duplex ferrite-austenite structure, the pattern of SCC in the stressed alloy, surface and the fracture surface morphology can also be quite different from what is observed in fully austenitic alloys. In Figure 11 an orthogonal system of stress-corrosion cracks is shown in the surface of a stressed U-bend of a wrought experimental alloy containing 20% Cr and 4% Ni and 2% Mo. The fracture structure which these crack surfaces exhibit is typically chevron and fan-shaped, radiating outward in the direction of macrocrack propagation (Figure 12). Electron micrographs of these chevrons would normally be inter-

preted as showing cleavage facets (Figure 13); and again under other circumstances of fracture (absence of corrosive environment) there would be no difficulty involved in accepting this as an example of truly brittle fracture.

Rather different SCC fracture morphology is found in a laboratory heat of a 22% Cr, 5% Ni stainless alloy also having a duplex ferrite-austenite structure. These alloys are of interest because of the structural role of ferrite in lengthening the time to failure in 42% $MgCl_2$ tests. Babakov et al,[10] for example, have shown that a 20% Cr, 5% Ni, 0.2% Ti alloy has higher resistance to SCC than an 18% Cr, 10% Ni, Ti-containing stainless steel. The path of crack propagation through these dual-structured alloys is always transgranular through the austenite and either intergranular along ferrite-austenite boundaries or transgranular through the ferrite, depending upon the percentage of ferrite present and its geometrical form and distribution. The α-γ alloys, therefore, are potentially valuable materials for electron fractographic studies of SCC. The bimodal fracture path is barely resolvable in the photomicrograph at 1000 X in Figure 14. The open ends of the miniature chevrons are

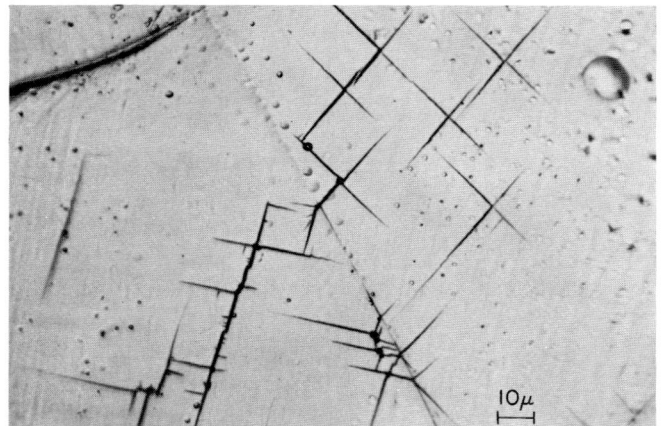

FIGURE 11 — Orthogonal system of SCC in surface of U-bend specimen (20% Cr-4% Ni-2% Mo stainless steel).

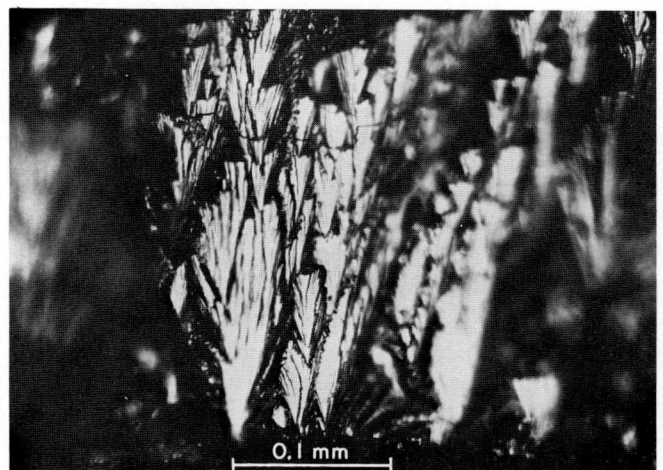

FIGURE 12 — Chevron markings in SCC fracture of 20% Cr-4% Ni-2% Mo alloy.

312

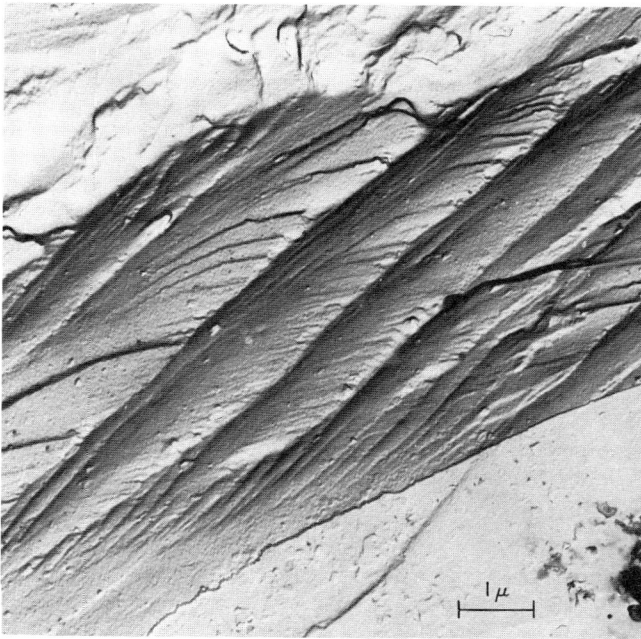

FIGURE 13 — Electron fractograph showing cleavage-type detail in SCC fracture chevrons.

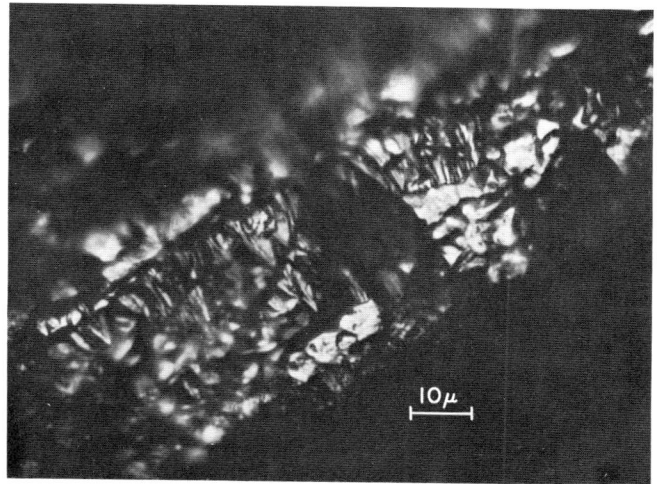

FIGURE 14 — Bimodal SCC fracture path in 22% Cr, 5% Ni stainless steel (mixed $\alpha$-$\gamma$ alloy).

present in the austenite and point in the direction of macrocrack propagation. The electron fractograph in Figure 15 (oxide replica) shows the junction of intergranular fracture in ferrite and transgranular fracture in austenite in this alloy. There is considerable secondary cracking present in the austenite surface and the chevron or river-pattern markings can also be recognized. The two phases can be seen to differ in their oxidation resistance. The ferrite is distinguished by a more coarsely mottled structure than the austenite (larger oxide crystallites form on ferrite in the oxide replication procedure than form on austenite).

## Summary

The broad application of electron microscopy to SCC research has already resulted in many important contributions to our knowledge of the SCC behavior of stainless steel. It has provided new information on (a) surface structural changes occurring in the initiation of corrosion cracking, (b) on the nature of subsurface dislocation structure, and (c) on fracture surface morphology of microcracks and of the macrocracks which result in ultimate failure.

This paper has been limited to a report of some examples of electron microfractography applied to ultimate fractures. In the cases described, fracture surface morphologies normally characteristic of brittle fracture are encountered. There are more features suggestive of cleavage failure than any other form of fracture. The existence of striated topography argues strongly for an electrochemical-mechanical mechanism of crack propagation.

However, because electron microfractography in its

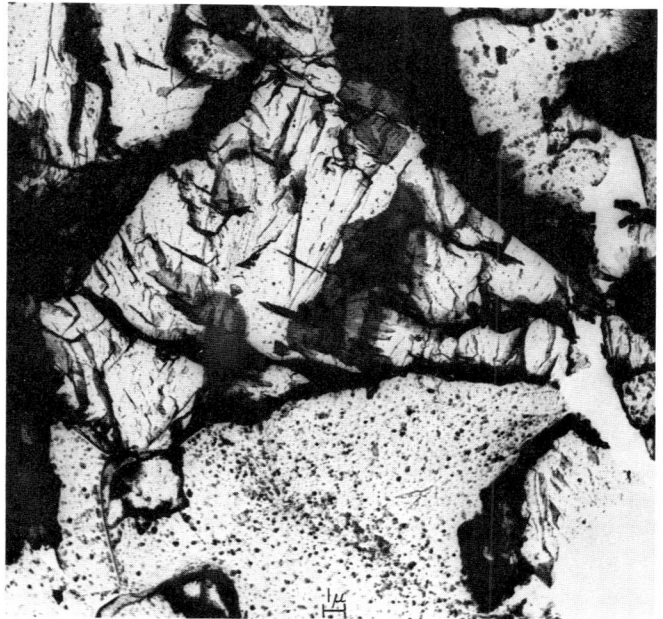

FIGURE 15 — Electron fractograph (oxide replica) of 22% Cr-5% Ni, $\alpha$-$\gamma$ stainless steel.

application to stress-corrosion cracking research is still in the exploratory stage, completely decisive analysis and interpretation of the information in fractographs cannot yet be made. The current quandary which must be resolved in the explanation of the similarity of features found in SCC fractures in stainless steel to features found in fractures known to have taken place without accompanying electrochemical corrosion. Future work with the electron microscope and the correlation of fractographic structure with data on chemical composition and crystallography of the same fracture surfaces are required for an unequivocal answer.

313

# References

1. G. Henry and J. Plateau. *Microfractography,* Editions Metaux, Paris.
2. C. D. Beachem and R. M. N. Pelloux. "Fracture Toughness Testing and Its Applications," *ASTM STP,* No. 381, pp. 210-245, Am. Soc. Testing Materials, Philadelphia (1965).
3. Electron Fractography Handbook, Technical Report ML-TDR-64-416, Air Force Materials Laboratory, Wright-Patterson AFB, Ohio, January 31, 1965.
4. *Symposium on Electron Fractography,* 1967 Annual Meeting of ASTM, Boston, June 29, 1967 (to be published).
5. N. A. Nielsen. "Physical Metallurgy of Stress Corrosion Fracture," (T. N. Rhodin, ed.) *Metallurgical Society Conferences,* Vol. 4, pp. 121-154, Interscience Publishers, New York (1959).
6. N. A. Nielsen. *Corrosion,* **20,** 104t-110t (1964) March.
7. H. L. Logan, M. J. McBee, and D. J. Kahan. *Corrosion Science,* **5,** 729-730 (1965).
8. A. J. McEvily and A. P. Bond. "Environment Sensitive Mechanical Behavior," (A. R. C. Westwood and N. S. Stoloff, ed.) *Metallurgical Society Conferences,* Vol. 35, pp. 421-443, Gordon and Breach (New York), 1966.
9. H. W. Pickering, F. H. Beck, and M. G. Fontana. *Corrosion,* **18,** 230t-239t (1962) June.
10. A. A. Babakov, A. V. Kryukov, and V. N. Ippolitova. *Zashchita Metallov,* **3** (1), 38-42 (1967).

# Discussion

**J. E. Draley, Argonne National Laboratory:**

If I understand correctly, the pointed end of the fan is nearer the surface of the specimen so the propagation direction is in the direction of the widening fan, is that right?

What this brings to mind is penetration of the metal by something from points on the surface, and spreading or diffusion as penetration proceeds. The penetrant that comes to my mind is hydrogen. I don't think there is any evidence at the moment for this substance, but the shape suggests diffusion of something in the metal.

Most of us think there is some metal removed as the crack propagates, at least over the area where the crack is formed. Have you addressed yourself to trying to determine what this is in your microscopic studies? I thought there might be clues in the character of the surface.

**M. R. Louthan, Jr.,Savannah River Laboratory,
E. I. du Pont de Nemours and Co., Inc.:**

Fractography has also been used at the Savannah River Laboratory as a tool to study stress corrosion cracking. Our observations are in general agreement with Nielsen's, in that we have seen evidence of mechanical fracture throughout the rupture faces of transgranular stress corrosion cracks in austenitic stainless steels. We have also seen similar topographic features in stainless steel specimens that developed surface cracks as a result of cathodic charging with hydrogen, indicating that hydrogen may be involved in transgranular stress corrosion cracking processes.

Cathodic charging of hydrogen into austenitic stainless steels will often cause cracking on the $\{111\}$ planes and along grain boundaries.[1] Prolonged charging will cause grain dropping to occur, and the initial cellulose acetate carbon replica from a charged surface will contain entire grains and grain fragments. Subsequent replication and fractographic studies of areas where grains have been removed show topographic features quite similar to those Nielsen has found in transgranular stress corrosion failures. These similarities can be seen by comparing the circled areas in Figure 1 with Figures 4, 5, 13, and 15 in Nielsen's paper.

Although we have not examined a sufficient number of hydrogen-charged specimens to draw any conclusions at this time, we have presented this comparison of cracks caused by stress corrosion and by hydrogen charging in the hope that it will provoke further studies along these lines.

1. D. A. Vaughan, et al. *Corrosion,* **19,** 314t (1963).

**N. A. Nielsen:**

**The fan-shaped fracture morphology is correctly interpreted by Dr. Draley. There is a progressive broadening of this feature in the direction of crack propagation. The suggestion he makes for the role of hydrogen in the development of such fracture surface morphology should be given serious consideration. The above comments by Dr. Louthan relate directly to this point.**

**I have recently been informed by Dr. H. Okada of the Tokyo Research Institute of Yawata Iron and Steel Co., Ltd. that they also have cracked Type 304 stainless steel by cathodic charging with hydrogen. Cracks formed parallel to slip lines and were accompanied by martensite formation on aging of the hydrogen-charged Type 304 steel. The evidence is accumulating that more attention must be given to the role of hydrogen in mechanism research on stress-corrosion cracking of the austenitic alloys.**

**The observation of thin films of corrosion deposits on crack surfaces confirms the occurrence of electrochemical corrosion in the cracking process. We believe that high resolution electron micrographs of mating fracture surfaces will permit identification of the sites or areas of metal loss by corrosion as well as the degree of corrosion. Such studies are in progress.**

**T. P. Hoar, University of Cambridge:**

I am concerned that many of your pictures are very similar to patterns seen after electrochemical deposition of metals from solution or after the opposite process, electrochemical dissolution. The flat planar areas correspond to close packed planes and the lines would correspond to ledges. Can you show evidence therefore, that we are observing cleavage and not dissolution processes?

**H. Spahn, BASF:**

In his electron microfractographic work, did Dr. Nielsen observe etch pits or etch figures? In a French publication Mencarelli [Memoires Scientifiques Rev. Metallurg., LIX,

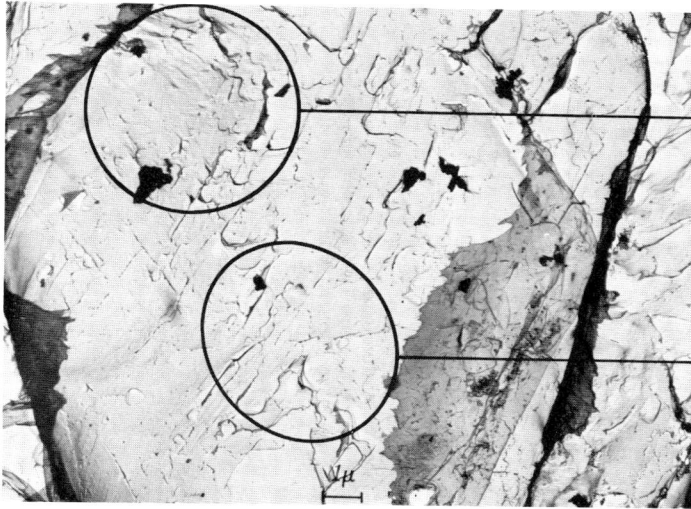

Compare with Figures
in Nielson's Paper

Figure 4

Top of Figure 13

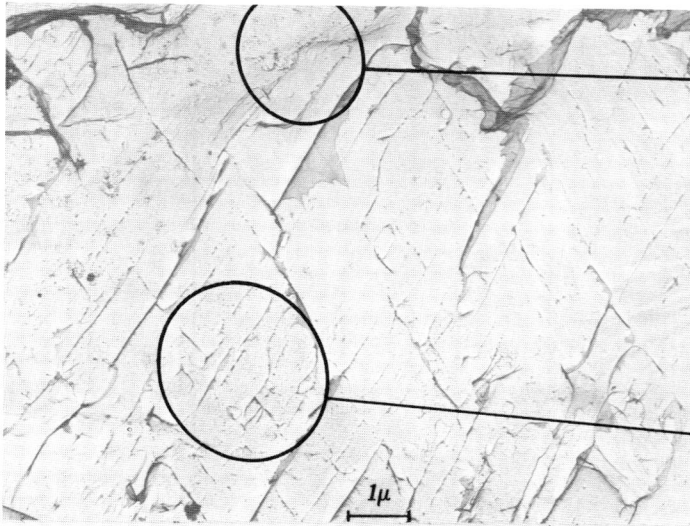

Figure 15

Figure 15

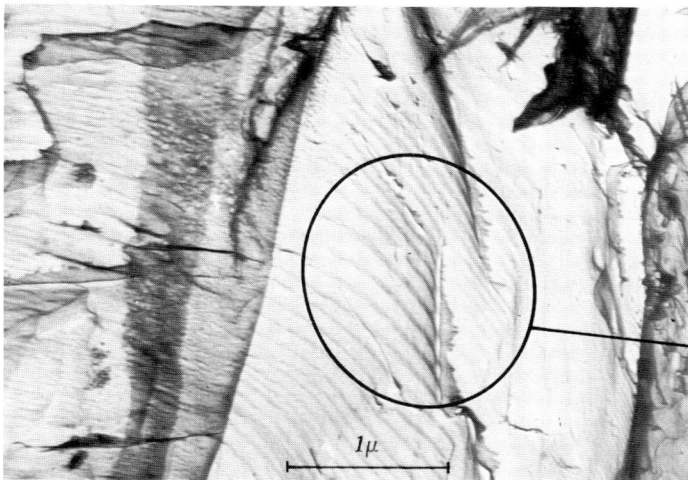

Figure 5
and
Figure 13

FIGURE 1 — Typical fractographic appearance of rupture surfaces produced in austenitic stainless steels during cathodic
charging of hydrogen.

315

Nr. 12, 1962, Seite 809-817] observed this on fracture surfaces of similar austenitic stainless steels. The appearance of etch figures can be understood if one assumes that part of the fracture surface behind the tip of the crack always remains in the active state while the crack is advancing. In support of this is the observation we made on Type 347 stainless steel in 42% $MgCl_2$-solution at 140 C and which showed that gas bubbles evolved from the cracks which can only be assumed to be hydrogen from the cathodic reaction in active dissolution.

### W. P. Hubner, AB Atomenergi:

I have a question concerning the parallel striations on stress corrosion fractures of stainless steel which you show for instance in Figure 7 of your paper. Have you been able to find out whether these striations are parallel to or normal to the direction of crack propagation or maybe both? I am somewhat doubtful as to the interpretation that they are crack-arrest lines, since we in similar studies at Stockholm have always found the striations to be more or less parallel to the direction of crack propagation and never normal, which they should have been in some cases at least, if they really were crack-arrest lines.

### P. R. Swann, Imperial College:

Is there any possibility that any of the striations you observe are sections through sets of corrosion tunnels?

### E. N. Pugh, RIAS:

I would like to discuss the striations that you showed on the fracture surfaces of stress-corroded austenitic stainless steels. By analogy with the work on the brass-ammonia system, it might be suggested that cracking proceeds by a brittle film-rupture mechanism—that is, that failure occurs by the repeated formation and rupture of a brittle surface film. I can see the objection to such a model since it is difficult to imagine a suitable surface film in this system. However, what alternative explanations can be put forward for the presence of the striations, and, in particular, how can they be reconciled with the model advocated earlier today by Staehle and Latanision?

### N. A. Nielsen:

In answer to Dr. Hoar's question, I have anodically etched stainless steel in boiling 42% $MgCl_2$ at various voltages and current densities and have not observed any features on the etched surfaces resembling those found on surfaces developed by stress-corrosion cracking.

The thought occurred to me also that the "dendritic" and fan-shaped features observable by light microscopy on fracture surfaces might be dendritic deposits of nickel. Neither the electron microprobe nor microspot testing techniques have so far confirmed this supposition. The electron fractography carried out to date gives strong indication and suggests that cleavage fracture may be involved in the failure mechanism. Whether this is, in fact, true remains to be determined by further research on scc.

I am grateful to Dr. Spahn for bringing the paper by Mencarelli to my attention. It is an important work on the microfractography of stress-corrosion cracks in stainless steels and I will refer to it again in the following discussion.

The evolution of hydrogen during active scc of stainless steel in boiling 42% $MgCl_2$ is a characteristic feature and is shown very clearly in a time-lapse movie of crack propagation which I made several years ago.

We have not observed any etch pits in our fracture surface studies. Mencarelli did, however, because his cracking medium contained ferric chloride (40% $MgCl_2$ plus 2% $FeCl_3$). My own interpretation of his etch pits is that they indicate that the surface in which they formed was *passive* and not active. Ferric chloride will produce general etching on an active stainless steel surface. The surface must be at least partially passive if well-defined geometric etch pits are to be obtained.

If we had a complete understanding of the mechanism of striation formation in stress-corrosion fracture surfaces, we would have the key information needed to explain fracture surface morphology. Mencarelli considers the striations to have a unique morphology and orientation which differentiate them from fatigue striations and from cleavage steps in true brittle fracture. In his paper cited above by Dr. Spahn, Mencarelli states that these lines are more or less normal to the thickness direction of the specimen but that there are local variations due to the polycrystalline structure of the steel and the presence of twins. We have yet to make a systematic study of this question. We know, however, that in localized regions of an active macrocrack system the direction of localized crack advance need not be the same as the direction of macrocrack propagation. Therefore, the formation of

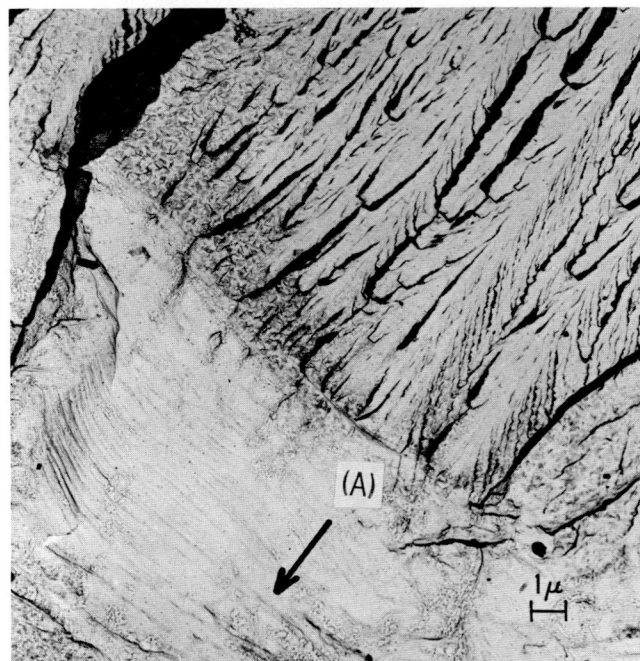

FIGURE 2 — Electron fractograph of termination front of transgranular stress-corrosion crack in Type 316 stainless steel. (Black arrow shows direction of crack propagation. At (A) parallel striations have penetrated alloy matrix in advance of visible crack front.)

fracture surface striations need not necessarily be, and probably most often will not be, normal to the direction of macrocrack propagation. In further reply to Dr. Hubner's discussion, the electron fractograph in Figure 2 below shows the termination front of a transgranular crack. (The specimen was broken open mechanically along the line of the crack front). There are several narrow bands of parallel striations which make a high angle with the termination line (see Point A). Here it appears that several of the lines have actually penetrated into the alloy ahead of the visible crack front.

If corrosion-cracking is crystallographically oriented, the $\{111\}$ planes will determine the micromechanism of corrosion-cracking either by a corrosion-tunneling mechanism or by periodic emergence of slip steps separated by regions of anodic dissolution (Staehle and Latanision).

Thus, it is possible that the striations can be the result of the lateral intersection of corrosion tunnels, in answer to Dr. Swann's question.

To reply to Dr. Pugh's discussion, my understanding of the Staehle-Latanision concept of the scc mechanism (alternating slip step emergence, anodic attack and surface enrichment in nickel producing a brittle layer which ruptures mechanically) is that a striated surface morphology would be expected.

I wish to thank Dr. Williams for his description of the features in the purely mechanical fracture surface of the specimen referred to in the above discussion.

### J. C. Williams, The Boeing Co.:

The band of apparent striations is not related to fatigue striations but has been termed serpentine glide by Beacham. Occurrence of serpentine glide is not uncommon; however, the factors which influence its occurrence are not well known. Dr. R. M. N. Pelloux of Boeing Scientific Research Laboratories has recently pointed out to me that this effect results during the initial stages of opening (blunting) of a very sharp crack. The crack is blunted by a double shear until conditions for hole formation (dimple rupture) are met. The case at hand is similar to that of a fatigue test specimen which is mechanically failed after propagating the crack by fatigue. Presence of the band of serpentine glide is good evidence of a sharp stress-corrosion crack.

# THE EFFECT OF ORDERING AND STACKING FAULT ENERGY
## ON THE SENSITIVITY TO STRESS CORROSION CRACKING

A. Ronnquist
Swedish Institute for Metal Research

## Abstract

The correlation between susceptibility to stress corrosion cracking and properties of the metal such as stacking fault energy and ordering are discussed. Detailed consideration is given to problems associated with the measurement of the stacking fault energy using the node technique. Results show that there is a great uncertainty in node measurements and therefore considerable doubt as to the significance of correlations among alloys. The suggestion is made that correlations of stress corrosion susceptibility only with factors associated with deformation processes may be insufficient to specify the cracking susceptibility. Special attention should be given to the combined effects of complex forming tendencies of the environment together with factors affecting deformation processes.

## Introduction

Since 1959 when Swann and Nutting[1] published the observed attack on stacking faults in a thin foil of brass, a number of papers on the influence of stacking fault energy on stress corrosion cracking have appeared.[2-6] The subject is reviewed by Parkins.[7] Swann and Nutting suggested that the preferential attack on stacking faults was due to the stress concentration associated with the preferential dissolution. However, in a later paper it is suggested that the stacking faults determine the dislocation configuration.[3] Thus, with a lower stacking fault energy, planar dislocation arrangements are favored. These, in turn, tend to promote stress corrosion cracking.

Tromans and Nutting[8] concluded from later studies that the mechanism for initiating stress corrosion is basically the same for both intergranular and transgranular modes of failure. Failure occurs at regions with high local dislocation densities. These regions are at the grain boundaries in the case of intergranular cracking and at dislocation pile ups in the case of transgranular cracking. A prerequisite to stress corrosion cracking is the segregation of solute atoms to the dislocations which thus changes the chemical reactivities of these regions. Transgranular cracking will occur only in alloys of low stacking fault energy, for example, less than 20 ergs/cm$^2$ where extensive dislocation pile ups are likely to form. Increasing the amount of plastic strain in such alloys produces more pile ups and increases the tendency for transgranular cracking to occur. Finally, Tromans and Nutting suggest that stress

corrosion cracks propagate primarily by a single stage mechanism involving a rapid rate of chemical attack at dislocation sites and linking of these corrosion sites to form a crack.

Ordering has also been suggested as an important factor causing coplanar dislocation arrangements.[2]

The present paper will discuss the influences of both ordering and low stacking fault energy. Also considered will be the relation between crystal structure and the stages of initiation and propagation. The distribution of active sites will be related to the applied stress. Finally, a suggested model for stress corrosion cracking is presented which includes consideration of both the electrochemical factors as well as factors affecting dislocation geometry.

## Effect of Stacking Fault Energy on Stress Corrosion

The three methods commonly used for determining stacking fault energy are based on measuring (1) twin boundary frequency, (2) extended dislocation nodes, and (3) separation of partial dislocations. Most of the measurements of stacking fault energy in connection with stress corrosion work have used the extended dislocation nodes.

Most of the values appearing in the literature are based on a limited number of measurements, and the reliability of fault energy values has been unknown. The effect of orientation of the dislocation node in the (111) plane has usually been neglected. In an earlier paper[6] a systematic correlation has been shown between the radius of a curved node boundary and its orientation in the slip plane. Two

**TABLE 1—Composition of the Two Steels Studied**

| Steel No | Weight in ppm | | | | | | | | | | | | | |
|---|---|---|---|---|---|---|---|---|---|---|---|---|---|---|
| | Ni | Cr | C | O | S | N | P | Cu | Co | Sn | B | Si | Al | Mo |
| 18:11 | 10.82[1] | 18.0[1] | 24 | 22 | 53 | 33 | 10 | 50 | 20 | 10 | 1.9 | 70 | 120 | 50 |
| 18:11-2P | 11.00[1] | 18.1[1] | 20 | 24 | 20 | 54 | 0.19[1] | 40 | 20 | 10 | 1.0 | 250 | 80 | 50 |

[1]Weight in percent.

18:11 austenitic stainless steels of high purity have been investigated (Table 1). Strips were cold-rolled to 300 micrometer thickness and annealed in evacuated silica tubes for 2 hours at 1030 C. After a water quench, tensile specimens were deformed to 1% plastic elongation at room temperature. Thin foils were prepared and examined in a Siemens, Elmiskop I, microscope. Extended nodes both singly and in networks were photographed at 40,000 to 60,000 magnifications. Nodes which were in good contrast, completely formed, and not apparently distorted by nearby dislocations were photographed at a magnification of 100,000. The radius of the central portion of each bounding dislocation was measured by comparisons with sets of arcs printed into a lantern slide and equivalent to radii between 200 and 3000 Å. The measured values were corrected as suggested by Howie and Swann.[9] Each radius was measured by three independent observers. Considerable care was taken to prevent comparison and discussion of results during measurements.

The distributions of corrected radii in the two steels are shown in Figure 1. The values from each of the three observers have been plotted. For one, steel values between 300 Å and 2800 Å were obtained. The arithmetic mean radius for the phosphorus-free steel was 1600 ± 350 Å. This value may be compared with the radii of the most symmetric nodes. Individual radii agreed within 10%, which was 1530 ± 250 Å. Thus, for this material results obtained from symmetrical and unsymmetrical nodes are not significantly different.

Similar results have been obtained in the case of the phosphorus containing steel. The addition of 0.2% of phosphorus to the steel reduced the mean value of the radius from 1600 to 1460 Å. The change in radius R is just outside significance at the 95% level.

A criticism of the node method is that it neglects variations in dislocation line tension with orientation in the slip plane. Figure 2 shows the relation between corrected R-values and the orientation of the partial in the slip plane expressed by $\alpha$ (Figure 3) which locates the dislocation lines with respect to a [110] direction. Theoretical calculations of the influence of self-stress of dislocations on the shape of the extended nodes has been done by Brown,[10] who suggests that the values of stacking fault energy deduced earlier must be multiplied by a factor of 2.3. The importance of having the node geometry in mind is pointed out by Jossang et al.[11] Hirsch and coworkers[12] suggest that the best method of obtaining approximate stacking fault energies from nodes, where $\gamma$ and the

character of the node is unknown, is to use a formula relating $\gamma$ to the width of the node.

$$\gamma = \frac{0.3 \, Gb^2}{W}$$

Uncertainties in possible relationships between stacking fault energies and susceptibility to stress corrosion cracking[13] arise from the poor reliability of available determinations of stacking fault energies.

It has been reported that alloys with low stacking fault energy do not show a coplanar dislocation arrangement as

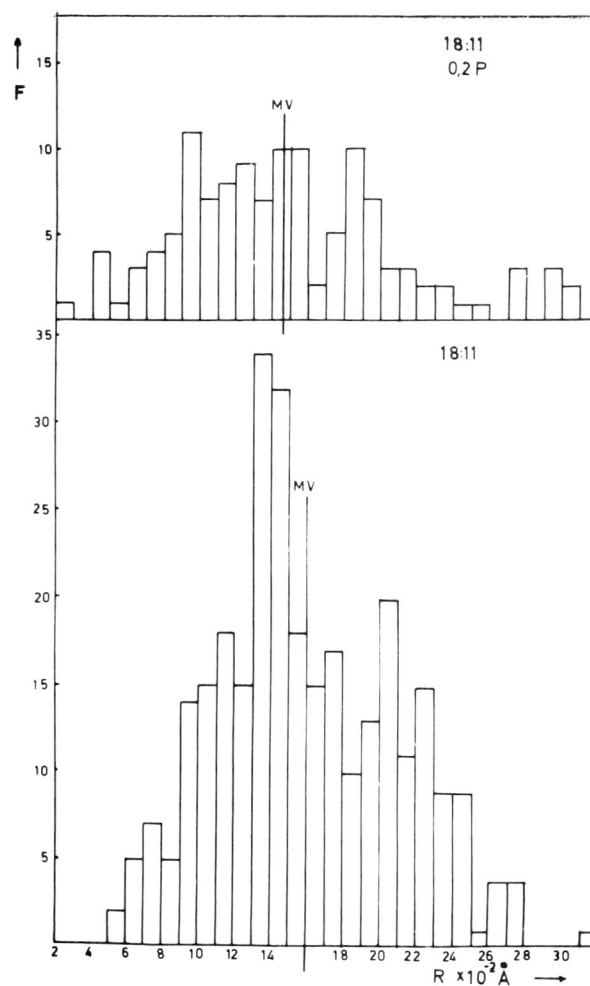

FIGURE 1 — Histogram of values of R as measured by three different observers.

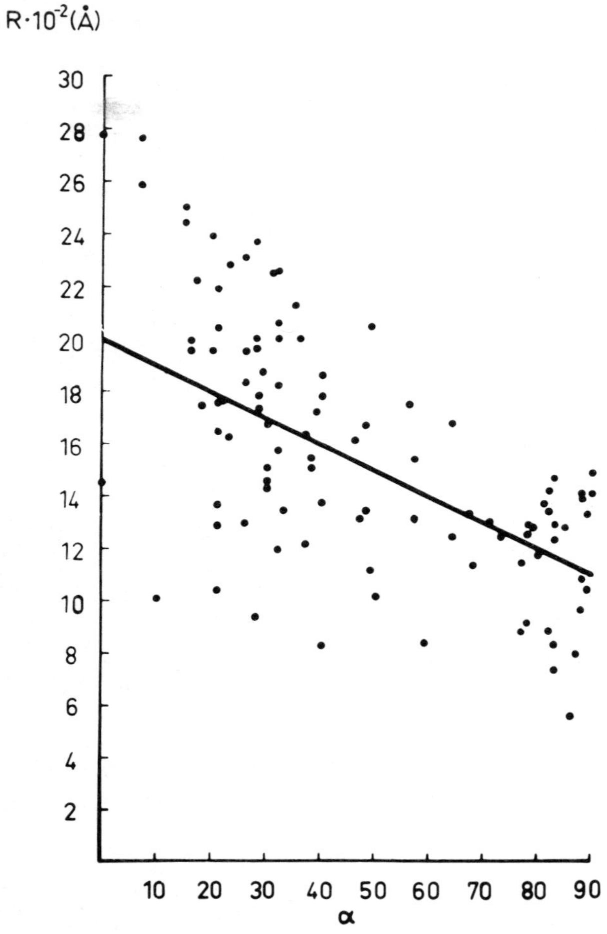


**FIGURE 2 – Corrected R-values as a function of α.**

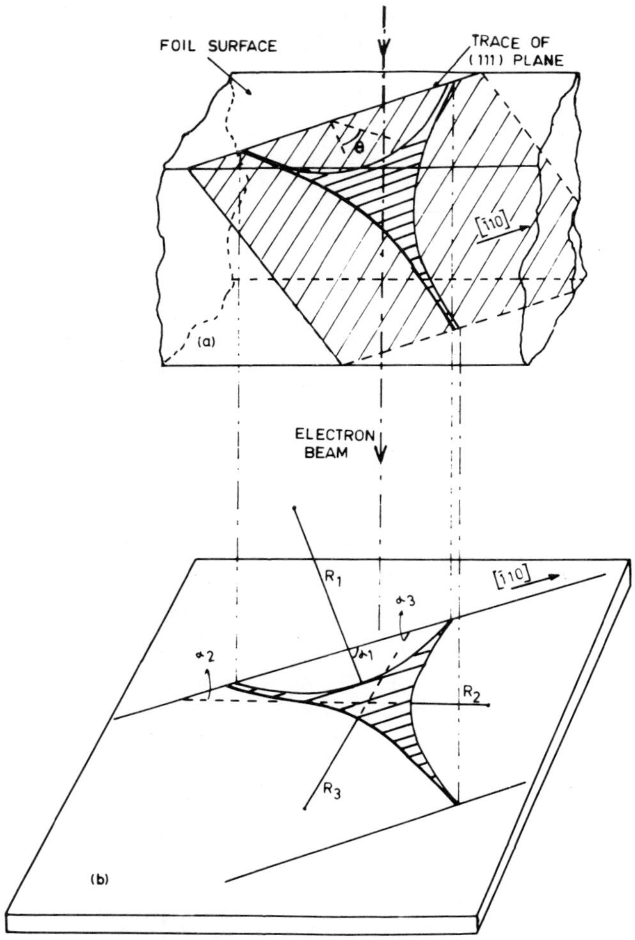


**FIGURE 3 – Geometric relation between a node in the thin foil (a) and the electron image (b).**

one would expect. Swann has suggested that much of the apparent contradiction may be avoided by considering that the stacking fault energy is not the only factor which determines the distribution of dislocations. However, it has been found that alloys containing tangled dislocation arrays are susceptible to stress corrosion cracking, and this is not in accord with the presumed importance of coplanar arrays. This apparently contradictory state of affairs may result from the fact that dislocation arrays examined in the electron microscope are often from materials which have been deformed more than the strain associated with local stress corrosion sites.

## Ordering–Influence on Stress Corrosion

As mentioned above, ordering might also be a factor determining the distribution of dislocations during a deformation process. The influence of ordering has earlier been studied by Pickering and Swann[14] and Douglass, Thomas and Roser.[2] A number of papers dealing with the mechanical properties and ordering has appeared during the last years, and are critically reviewed by Stolof and Davies.[15] Very little information is available on iron, chromium, and nickel systems. Bell et al[16] conducted a diffraction analysis of dislocation pairs to detect order in solid solutions. They conclude from the observations of super dislocations that ordering is present in the stainless steel and particularly near the $(Fe,Cr)_3N$ composition. The results confirm earlier suggestions that short range order exists in these alloys and that ordering is responsible for the observed increases in stacking fault energy.[2] In the present work ordering was studied by means of electron microscopy and resistometric determinations. The variations of the resistivity with the annealing time and temperature cannot wholly be explained by the metallographically observed phase changes (Figures 4 and 5). The steel used was even investigated by means of neutron diffraction. However, the scattering factors for the different kinds of alloying elements do not differ enough to give a suitable diffraction pattern to state a change in ordering. The ordered domains might even be too small to yield significant data. Using thin foils produced by electrolytic thinning from one side from stress corroded material, it has been seen frequently that the crack path is located adjacent to dislocation pile ups (Figure 6), which in a few cases have been interpreted as superlattice pile ups (Figure 7).

## Microscopic Investigations
## Initiation of Stress Corrosion

Active sites on the metal surface and their distribution have been studied as a function of different amounts of applied stress. Stressed specimens have been oxidized either in an atmosphere of chlorine or of oxygen. The oxidation furnace has been described elsewhere.[17] The nucleation of the chlorides and oxides was studied in the electron microscope using carbon replicas.

As solid corrosion products are formed on the metal surface during the exposure in magnesium chloride solution, the initial stages of the stress corrosion process could be studied simply by extracting the products on two plastic replicas. By means of a second replica of the same area, more detailed information was obtained about local attack and its relation to the metal structure.

Independent of the corroding environment, $MgCl_2$, $O_2$ or $Cl_2$, the chemical attack occurs along slip lines (Figures 8 and 9). From the stress corrosion experiments in dry gases the variation of the distribution of active sites with the applied load could be followed. The observed results are summarized as follows. A specimen which was fully annealed without applied stress oxidized as expected: the different grain surfaces show a different number of oxide nuclei which is typical in the case of an anisotropic crystal (Figure 8). When loaded a fraction of the yield stress, the grain boundaries are heavily attacked, and some of the slip directions are decorated by oxide nuclei.[1]

When loading the specimen above the yield stress, the trends are distinctly changed: the grain surfaces are covered by nuclei, and now the nuclei are distributed mainly along slip directions.

---

[1] There is a difference between $\alpha$-brass and stainless steel. In the case of $\alpha$-brass only grain boundaries are attacked and the grain surfaces are covered with a random distribution of oxide nuclei; but in the case of stainless steel, even at a load far beyond the yield stress, the slip directions are decorated.

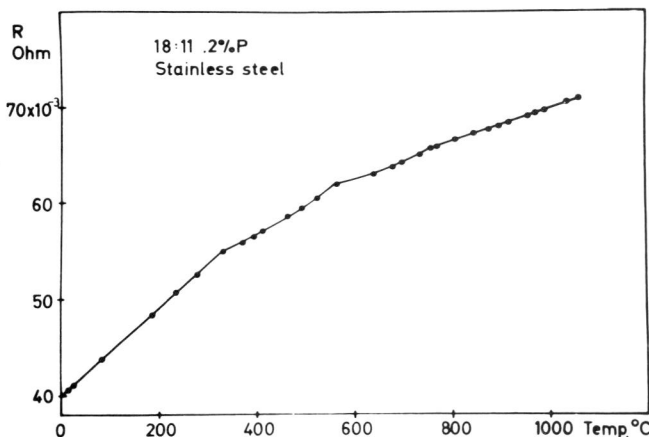

FIGURE 5 — Metallographic structure after heat treatment at 1050 C and then annealed one week at (a) 450 C, (b) 550 C, (c) 750 C, and (d) 1050 C.

FIGURE 4 — Resistance as a function of temperature at equilibrium in 18:11 0.2 P steel.

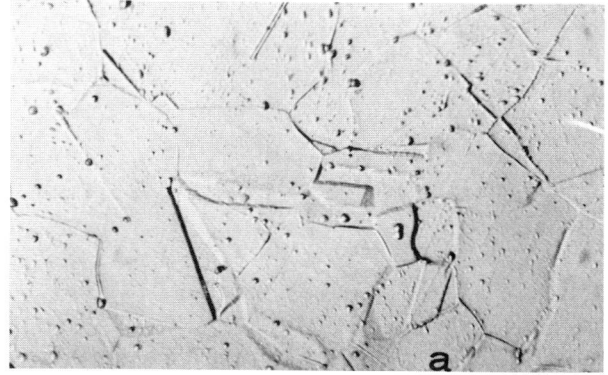

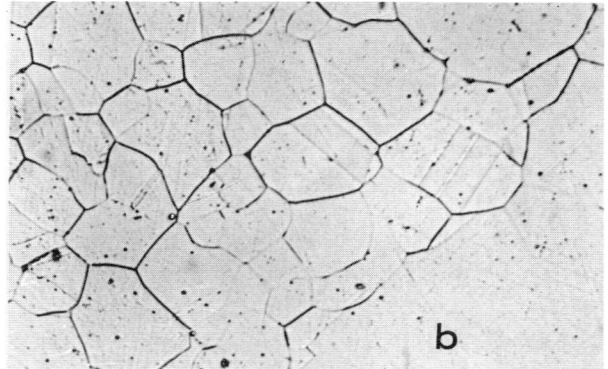

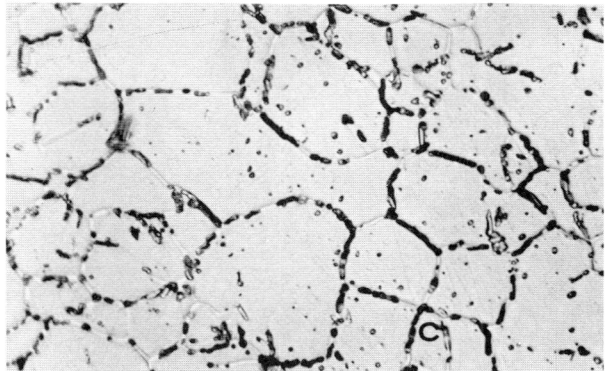

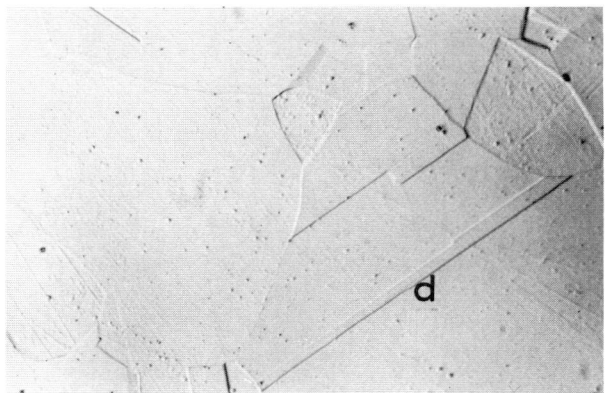

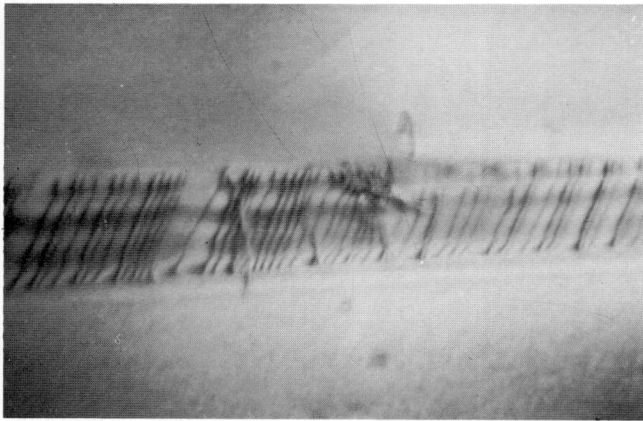

FIGURE 6 — Dislocation pile up at the tip of a crack.

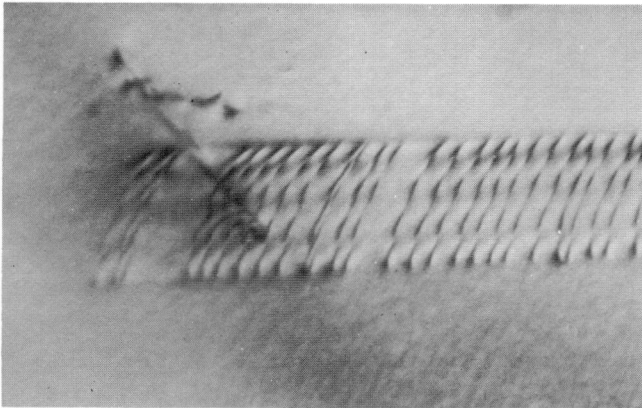

FIGURE 7 — Superlattice dislocation pile up.

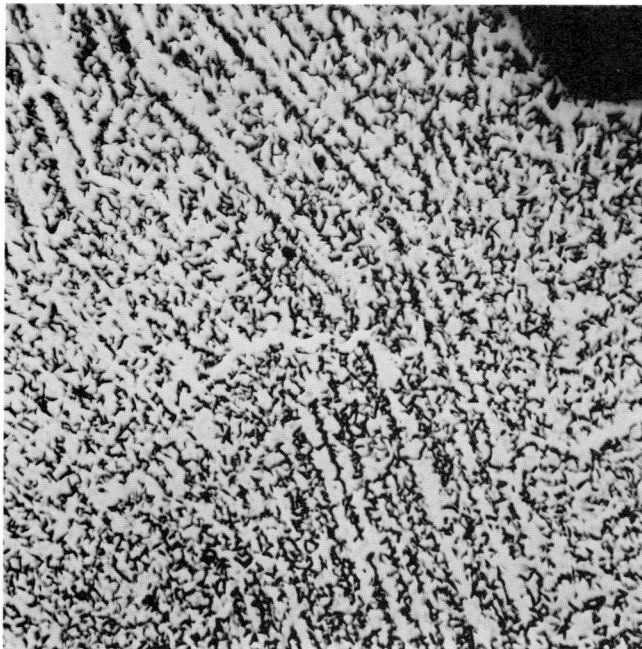

FIGURE 8 — Extracted corrosion products onto a plastic replica from stress corroded steel in $MgCl_2$ solution.

The fact that preferential reaction can occur at slip lines in gaseous environments suggests that the electrochemical processes in the liquid environment may not be too significant. It is more likely that the factors affecting initiation are those relating to slip processes.

## Propagation of Stress Corrosion

The propagation of stress corrosion cracks has been studied by electron metallographic examinations of thin foils of stress corroded material. Foils were prepared by electrolytical thinning from one side. The propagation has also been studied using the optical microscope. Due to the favorable shape of the specimens in the form of strip it was possible to investigate them in the light microscope without any further preparation. Using the interference contrast technique the slip lines were clearly visible. The results can be summarized here as follows: The propagation of cracks seem to follow a dislocation pile up. The dislocation pile up may be either of superlattice character or of an ordinary type. In the bottom of macro-cracks, micro-cracks were formed. The micro-cracks were usually formed along slip directions where slip had not occurred (Figure 10). The results from the thin foil studied were also in agreement with the observation that slip had not occurred. The dislocation pile up usually stopped inside the grain and did not go through the grain. These observations suggest that there is reason to believe that the dislocations are formed close to the tip of the corrosion crack.

## Effect of Applied Stress

The time to fracture as function of applied load has been determined and a typical result is given in Figure 11. It is obvious that there is a relation between time to

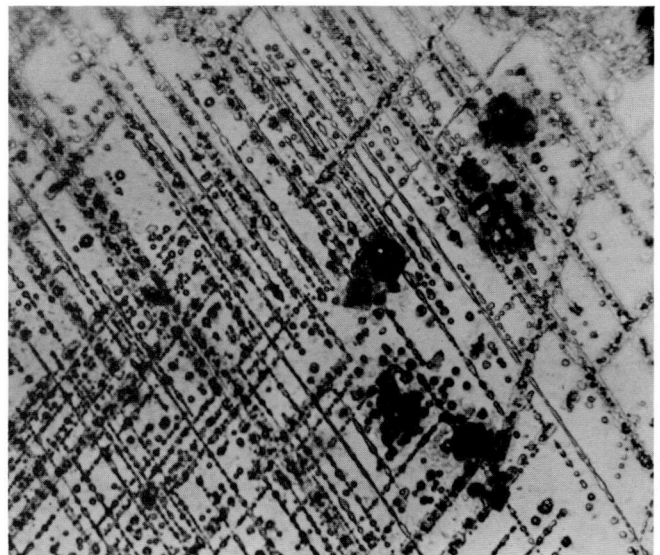

FIGURE 9 — Light optical photograph of stress corroded steel in $Cl_2$ gas loaded 40% of yield point.

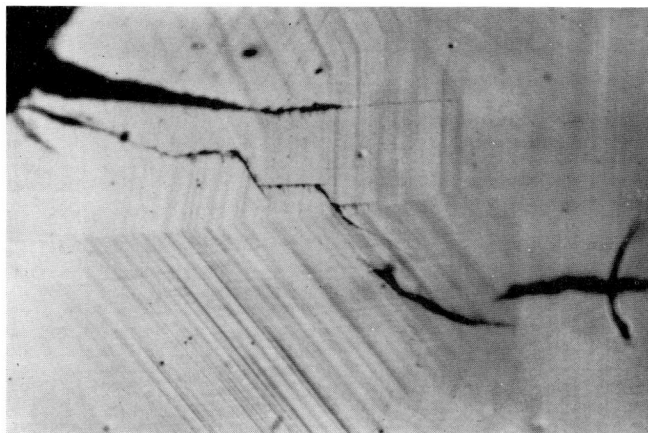

FIGURE 10 – Light optical photograph of micro-cracks at a tip of a macro-crack.

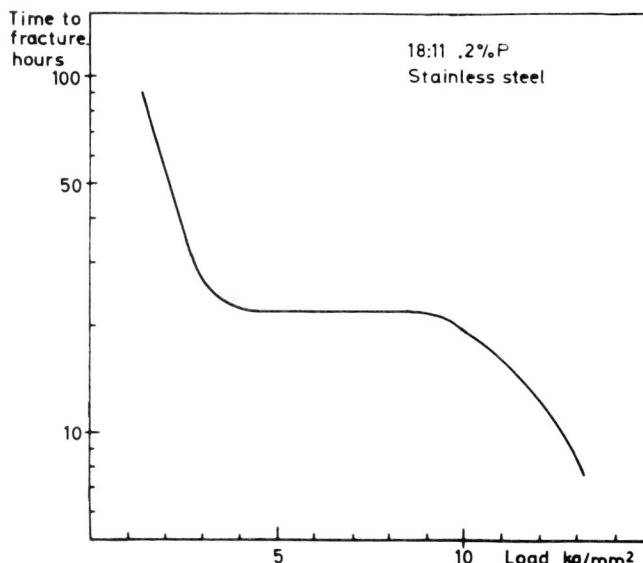

FIGURE 11 – Relation between time to fracture and applied stress.

fracture and number of activated dislocation sources. As the stress field around the tip of a pit or a crack is higher than in the outer matrix, it is reasonable to assume that sources close to such a tip are more easily activated.

## Discussion

There are a number of typical characteristics of transcrystalline stress corrosion cracking which must fit into a final theory. The failure by cracking is caused by the common action of stress and corrosion causing a brittle-appearing fracture in a ductile material. Stress corrosion cracks are formed in a limited number of specific environments: for stainless steel, those containing chloride, and for brass, those containing ammonium ions. None of the suggested theories fully explain all these facts. The available theories are referred to one of the groups: (a) those in which crack propagation is attributed essentially to electrochemical processes[18,19] and (b) those in which it is explained in terms of mechanical processes triggered by corrosion.[20,21]

The theories by Forty[20] and Robertson and Tetelman[21] have their support from many metal physical observations. They both explain why a stress corrosion crack follows specific crystallographic directions. They even explain why materials with different stacking fault energies will behave in different ways. However, none of the theories explains the specific effect of the chemical environment.

According to Pickering and Swann[14] stress corrosion cracks are formed by tubular attack in the alloy exposed to solutions which cause stress corrosion cracking. Solutions which do not cause stress corrosion cracking produce a uniform surface roughening. It is further proposed by Pickering and Swann that when susceptible alloys are exposed to corrosive environments a mechanically weak pitted structure is produced along active planes and that ductile fracture occurs through this corroded region. They suggest that the observed rate of pitting can achieve the rate of propagation of stress corrosion cracks. In a later paper,

Swann and Embury[22] modify the theory to include the effects of surface film rupture on crack nucleation. An important point in the Swann theory is that it suggests relationships between the physical properties of the alloy (as stacking fault energy and short range order) and the character of stress corrosion cracking. Although Swann and Embury have made an attempt to understand the influence of the environment, their theory still does not explain why only specific environments cause stress corrosion cracking.

A recently delivered theory by Staehle[23] is based on a preferential dissolution causing a noble surface film on the alloy which during the mechanical deformation will crack. In this way anodic surfaces are formed in a bottom of a crack and the propagation of the crack is determined by the electrochemical dissolution of the alloy. However, it also does not explain why the specific electrolytic environments are necessary to cause stress corrosion cracking.

The available theories which are based essentially on the processes of plastic flow obviously do not account for processes occurring in the electrolyte. A useful theory must combine these considerations. Based on available data the most likely possibility is that the formation of complex ions is involved.

Mattsson showed that transcrystalline cracking in α-brass occurs in ammoniacal solutions containing amine complex ions of copper and zinc. At pH on the acidic side where the complexes are unstable transcrystalline cracking will not occur; but on the basic side where the complexes are stable transcrystalline cracking will occur. It is also typical that when copper sulfide is added to the solution, the time to fracture will drastically decrease. Similar observations have been obtained in the present work. When ferric chloride is added to the magnesium chloride solution the time to fracture will decrease from 60 hours to about 4 hours. The interpretation of these observations must involve an interference between the formed complexes and

323

the metal surface; and a suggested hypothesis is based on a coordination of the metal physical behavior of the metal and the interaction of formed complexes in the solution on the metal surface. The assumption of an effect of the environment on the mechanical behavior has its support from a number of published data. One of the first works indicating an effect of surface active agent was published by Rehbinder in 1928; and Rehbinder and Wennstrom observed that the flow of lead, tin and copper sheets under constant load was much faster if small amounts of surface actants were present in the hydrocarbon bath in which the metal was emerged. They even reported an effect on both the indentation hardness and tensile properties of metals in various electrolytes. A "Rehbinder effect" was also reported by Benedicks[24] and Ruben, who studied steel in different electrolytes. An extensive review of the effect of environment of mechanical properties of metals is delivered by Kramer and Dehmer.[25]

Liquid metal embrittlement of solid metals is suggested by Westwood and Kamdar[26] to be determined by the reduction of the surface energy. Analogies between stress corrosion cracking and embrittlement by liquid metals have been proposed by Nichols and Rostoker.[27] Coleman, Weinstein and Rostoker[28] investigated the effect of stress corrosion media on the fracture stresses. From the Stroh-equation for brittle fracture they calculated the surface energy from fracture stresses as a function of the grain size. The surface energy on stainless steel is assumed to be at least $10^3$ ergs/cm$^2$ and was reduced to 157 ergs/cm$^2$ in a magnesium chloride solution. This drastic change in surface energy effected by the magnesium chloride solution might be taken as evidence for explaining stress cracking as a pure embrittlement process. However, the fact that cathodic protection will stop the progress of cracks suggests strongly that electrochemical processes play a significant role.

If it is assumed that the active component in the electrolyte is a complex, e.g., $FeCl_4^-$, one will be able to explain the variation in sensitivity with pH of the solution. One will even be able to explain the variations with different halogenide solutions as the polarization of the bond metal-halogenide varies. A good evidence for an effect of an iron complex is the observation that the time to fracture will drastically decrease when $FeCl_3$ is added to the $MgCl_2$ solution as mentioned above.

A suggested model for stress corrosion cracking[29] is summarized as follows:

1. Etch pits are formed along active slip planes due to dislocation movement out to the metal surface.

2. A stress field is built up close to the tip of the pit and this supports an activation of dislocation sources in the same area.

3. Dislocations are chemically dissolved.

4. The driving force for dissolution due to strain energy and chemical dissolution in most environments is not sufficient to cause cracking. But by an interaction between the suggested complexes and the metal surface the metal-metal-bond can, according to Reference 28, easily be broken.

5. The incubation period involves formation of pits, and a general corrosion during which the concentration of $FeCl_4^-$ is raised.

# References

1. P. R. Swann and J. Nutting. *J. Inst. Met.*, 88, 478 (1959/60).

2. D. L. Douglass, G. Thomas, and W. R. Roser. *Proceedings 2nd Int. Congr. Met. Corr.*, New York, 1963. Published by NACE, 1966, p. 66.

3. P. R. Swann. *Ibid*, p. 188.

4. S. Barnartt, R. Stickler, and D. van Rooyen. *Corr. Science*, 3, 9 (1963).

5. A. Ronnquist. Current Corrosion Research in Scandinavia, Helsinki, 1964, Almqvist & Wiksell, Stockholm, 1965, p. 121.

6. A. Ronnquist and D. Dulieu. *Brit. J. Appl. Phys.*, 15, 1569 (1964).

7. R. N. Parkins. *Met. Rev.*, 9, 201 (1964).

8. D. Tromans and J. Nutting. *Fracture of Solids*, Edited by D. C. Drucker and J. J. Gilman, John Wiley and Sons, New York, p. 637 (1963).

9. A. Howie and P. R. Swann. *Phil. Mag.*, 6, 1215 (1960).

10. L. M. Brown. *Phil. Mag.*, 10, 441 (1964).

11. T. Jossang, M. J. Stowell, J. P. Hirth and J. Lothe. *Acta Met.*, 13, 279 (1965).

12. P. B. Hirsch, A. Howie, R. B. Nicholson and D. W. Pashley. *Electron Microscopy of Thin Crystals*. Butterworths, p. 427 (1965).

13. N. Ontani and R. A. Dodd. *Corrosion*, 21, 161 (1965).

14. H. W. Pickering and P. R. Swann. *Proceedings 2nd Int. Congr. Met. Corr.*, New York, 1963. Published by NACE, p. 128 (1966).

15. N. S. Stoloff and R. G. Davies. *Progr. Material Science*, 13, 1 (1966).

16. W. Bell, W. R. Roser, and G. Thomas. *Acta Met.*, 12, 1247 (1964).

17. A. Ronnquist. *Corrosion et Anticorrosion*, 14, 3 (1966).

18. T. P. Hoar and J. G. Hines. *J. Iron Steel Inst.*, 182, 124 (1956).

19. J. G. Hines. *Corrosion Science*, 1, 21 (1961).

20. A. J. Forty. *Recent Advances in Stress Corrosion*. Ed. A. Bresle, p. 22, Roy. Swedish Acad. Eng. Sci., Stockholm, (1961).

21. W. D. Robertson and A. S. Tetelman. *Strengthening Mechanisms in Solids*, p. 217, ASM (1962).

22. P. R. Swann and J. D. Embury. *Proc. 2nd Int. Materials Symp. Conf.*, Berkeley, Calif. (1964).

23. R. Staehle. Communicated at a seminar at the Swedish Inst. Met. Res. Stockholm, 1967.

24. C. Benedicks and G. Ruben. *Jernkont. Ann.*, 129, 37 (1945).

25. I. R. Kramer and L. J. Demer. *Progr. Materials Sci.*, 9, 133 (1961).

26. A. R. C. Westwood and M. H. Kamdar. *Phil. Mag.*, 787 (1963).

27. H. Nichols and W. Rostoker. *Trans, ASM*, 56, 494 (1963).

28. E. G. Coleman, D. Weinstein, and W. Rostoker. *Acta Met.*, 9, 491 (1961).

29. A. Ronnquist. *Jernkont. Ann.*, 151, 765 (1967).

# Discussion

**J. R. Weeks, Brookhaven National Laboratory:**

In your complex model, is the role of oxygen in solution that of oxidizing the Fe to $Fe^{+++}$, or do you presume it becomes involved in the adsorbate itself? $Cl^-$ ions have been observed to adsorb on the surface of Fe or ferritic steels; is the role of the Cr and Ni, then, one of providing the internal metastable structure and dislocation networks? There appears to be (from the previous discussion) some objection to the presence of complexes involving $Fe^{+++}$; do Cr and Ni also form complexes, such as $CrCl_4^-$, in solution that can adsorb strongly enough to reduce the cohesive energy at the crack tips?

**A. Ronnquist:**

It is likely to assume that the role of oxygen is to oxidize $Fe \rightarrow Fe^{+++}$. Considering the pH in the solution and the complex constants, I cannot see why e.g. $Fe(Cl)_4^-$ should not be present.

**L. R. Scharfstein, The Carpenter Steel Co.:**

I find it extremely difficult to imagine that an iron tetrachloride complex immediately adjacent to the surface of yielding, or rapidly dissolving, steel should contain trivalent iron. Even if dissolved oxygen is available to oxidize divalent to trivalent iron, surely the availability of oxygen in the vicinity of the crack should be minimal. In my opinion therefore, the equilibrium between trivalent and divalent iron at the surface in the region of straining steel should favor the reduced state.

**A. Ronnquist:**

This is a point, but it does not explain the role of $Cl^-$, which is known to accelerate a stress corrosion process.

**D. L. Douglass, Stanford Research:**

Earlier I mentioned that we are concerned about the role of the structural aspects versus the electrochemical aspects with respect to the specificity of the chloride ions. I think insofar as dislocation structures per se are concerned, there is still not a clear-cut case, but I think the evidence for ordering is very limited. About the only evidence we have really seen are the superdislocations that Axel showed in one of the earlier slides. Suffice it to say, there is considerable room for additional work in this area.

**R. A. Dodd, The University of Wisconsin:**

While it is true that various researchers have claimed to observe superdislocations in austenitic stainless steels, such observations are rather uncommon and generally unsubstantiated by careful tilt/contrast experiments. Similar criticism must apply to Dr. Ronnquist's data, particularly since simple visual inspection of the micrographs suggests that the paired dislocations are actually dipoles.

**A. Ronnquist:**

The examination done of the contrast changes, when tilting the specimen in the microscope is a better proof.

# SOME EFFECTS OF NITROGEN ON THE RESISTANCE TO STRESS CORROSION CRACKING OF TYPE 304 STAINLESS STEEL WIRES

W. A. Mannheimer
Universidade do Brasil
and
H. W. Paxton
Carnegie-Mellon University

## Abstract

The stress corrosion cracking of nitrided stainless steel was evaluated in boiling $MgCl_2$ environments. It is shown that a significant increase in specimen lifetime is produced by nitriding in the 500-950 C range. Electrochemical measurements suggest that the mechanism for improvement due to nitriding probably results from a cathodic protection effect.

## I. Introduction

Many investigators have studied the effect of composition on the cracking behavior of austenitic stainless steels. Nickel has been shown by Copson[1] to be particularly effective in suppressing stress corrosion, if the amount runs to several tens of percent. Lang[2] has made a systematic study of the addition of alloying elements to a steel containing 20% Ni and 18% Cr. The elements of group V, nitrogen, phosphorus, arsenic, antimony and bismuth, as well as ruthenium, molybdenum and aluminum are reported as being harmful, and carbon (0.1%) and silicon are beneficial.

Both carbon and nitrogen have potent effects on $M_S$ and on the propensity for forming $\delta$-ferrite during annealing treatments in the vicinity of 1050-1100 C. Since neither martensite nor $\delta$-ferrite in this class of materials are susceptible to cracking in chloride solutions, it is common for experiments to use materials of high nickel content, which lead to stable austenite at all temperatures from liquid down to below room temperature. This helps to avoid misleading results caused by the influence of other alloying elements on microstructure. Whether conclusions drawn from work on these high Ni steels can be transferred directly to 18-8 remains to be clearly demonstrated.

The influence of nitrogen in solution is confirmed by the work of Uhlig and White.[3] They compared the behavior of commercial Type 304 steel, which had a nitrogen content of 0.02-05% with a similar laboratory alloy, in which the nitrogen content was held to 0.001-0.009%. While the former cracked in a few hours, the laboratory alloys did not crack even in tests carried to more than 260 hours.

The original purpose of the work described here was to investigate the effects of increasing the nitrogen content in the surface on the stress corrosion cracking of austenitic stainless steel. It was hoped that by introduction from a nitriding atmosphere, a supersaturation of dissolved nitrogen would occur without nitride precipitation. This would permit studies over a wider range of dissolved nitrogen than in homogeneous specimens and perhaps permit cracking behavior to be more clearly identified with the effects of this dissolved nitrogen on structure, stacking fault energy and perhaps on the cracking plane.

However, preliminary work showed that a surface nitride film formed quite rapidly. The increase in resistance to cracking showed a spectacular improvement, and hence this unsuspected benefit was investigated rather thoroughly, and is the basis of this paper. The original purpose, while not yet examined critically, may still be well worth while if suitable techniques can be developed.

## II. Experimental Procedure

The majority of experiments were performed on 0.047 in diameter commercial wire of Type 304 austenitic stainless steel of composition (as furnished by the supplier) given in Table 1. Louthan[4] has reported small differences in stress corrosion behavior among batches of the same nominal composition. For the general and intergranular corrosion test, samples were prepared from 1/16 in sheet of Type 304 stainless steel of similar composition. The analysis for this steel is also given in Table 1. This material was also used for the preparation of larger amounts of nitride.

For stress corrosion experiments, 21 in long wires were straightened by pulling to 85 lbs (49,000 psi) on an Instron machine, subsequently annealed in argon at 1050 C for one

TABLE 1

| Material | Cr | Ni | Si | Mn | C | P | S | Cu | Mo |
|---|---|---|---|---|---|---|---|---|---|
| 304 wire | 18.90 | 10.97 | 0.39 | 1.64 | 0.050 | 0.029 | 0.010 | (1) | (1) |
| 304 sheet | 18.83 | 9.33 | 0.55 | 1.82 | 0.059 | 0.027 | 0.005 | 0.20 | 0.34 |

(1)Not available.

hour, and quenched from the annealing temperature. The specimens had a grain size of 4-5 (ASTM) after this treatment.

Nitriding was done in an atmosphere of cracked ammonia, in a vertical furnace having a hot zone 14 in long, with a temperature variation of $\pm 5$ C in the most unfavorable case. $NH_3/H_2$ mixtures were obtained with a gas mixing train, most experiments being made with a 75% $NH_3$-25% $H_2$ mixture. Control specimens (blanks) were obtained by treating in hydrogen.

Immediately before heat treatment in the nitriding furnace, the specimens were pickled for two minutes, at room temperature, in a 10% $HNO_3$-10% HF solution. They were then washed in running water, rinsed with ethanol, and wiped with acetone-soaked cotton.

Resistance to stress corrosion cracking was evaluated using boiling 42% $MgCl_2$ solution. The wire specimens were held vertically in an apparatus very similar to the one described by Hoar and Hines.[5] In brief, it consists of a reaction vessel having a reflux condenser, and heated by a small electric furnace. The specimens were held in Type 304 steel grips well outside the apparatus, and loaded by a lever arrangement to a load of 60,000 psi.

To avoid preferential failure at the liquid-vapor interface,[5-7] the specimens were coated with epoxi-cement except for a short length which was immersed completely.

Because it was impractical to test all samples at a certain time after heat treatment (as for instance Hoar and Hines did), randomness with respect to this variable was deliberately accepted. Specimens have been tested anywhere from 48 hours to 8 weeks after heat treating. The reproducibility of the experiments, as shown by the failure times of the hydrogen annealed blanks, is normal for this type of experiment.

Upon failure, the fracture area of the specimens was mounted for metallographic examination. The etchant used was a mixture of equal parts of concentrated hydrochloric acid, distilled water and concentrated hydrogen peroxide.

Electrochemical experiments were performed by following the potential of the stress corroding wires with time and by investigating polarization curves with a potentiostat. In both cases, the basic corrosion cell was modified with the inclusion of two side arms, to provide connection to a standard calomel electrode (SCE) and for a platinum counter-electrode (Figure 4). The platinum wire dipped into cold saturated $MgCl_2$ solution; this prevents attack on the platinum, as reported by Hoar.[8]

The values of E.M.F. reported are subject to small errors due to liquid junction potentials, thermal gradients, bridge resistance, and resistance in the test wire and cell. No

corrections for these were made in this work. The absolute values of E.M.F. determined in this work compare very well with those reported by Hoar and Hines, and Barnartt and van Rooyen,[9] and because the same experimental arrangements were used in all runs, small differences are expected to cancel out in relative comparisons.

In the potentiostatic studies, unless otherwise noted, discrete changes of E.M.F. of 10 mV were made every two minutes, with the current reading being made 90 seconds after the change.

## III. Experimental Results

The experimental results from this investigation can be divided into four main categories: nature and morphology of surface layer formed in nitrided Type 304 steel; study of stress corrosion cracking resistance of nitrided Type 304 steel; electrochemical and metallographic observations on stress corrosion cracking of nitrided Type 304 steel; diverse supporting experiments.

### A. Nature and Morphology of Surface Layer Formed in Nitrided Type 304 Steel

Nitriding of Type 304 stainless steel results in the formation of a surface layer containing metallic nitrides. A survey of the phases formed in the range 400-950 C is presented here. The large number of variables, together with the complexity of the system, which is at least a quaternary (Fe-Cr-Ni-N) prevented a complete study, and a completely adequate understanding of the reactions involved was not obtained.

The four basic morphologies observed are shown in Figures 1 to 4. They were formed at 400, 550, 700 and 950 C, respectively, by nitriding in 75% $NH_3/H_2$.

The layer formed at 400 C is very hard, brittle, of high resistance to chemical attack, and presumably consists of a metallic nitride. Attempts to identify it by X-ray diffraction were not conclusive. From the best results obtained, it is suggested that among the possible nitrides in the Fe-Cr-Ni system, the fit for $(Fe_3Ni)N$ is the closest. This is an ordered face centered cubic phase, based on the $Fe_4N$ phase in the Fe-N system.[10] Because of its metallographic aspect, this layer will be referred to as "white layer" in the following discussion.

At higher temperatures, a second layer is observed growing into the "white layer". Eventually, at 700 C, the whole nitride layer is of this type. It is also hard and brittle, but not chemically resistant. By dissolution of nitrided samples in concentrated hydrochloric acid, it was possible

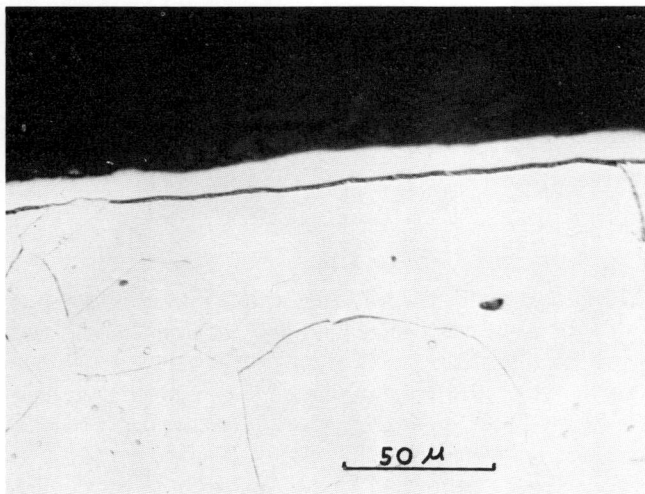

FIGURE 1 — Type 304 stainless steel, nitrided in 75% NH$_3$/H$_2$ at 400 C for 60 hours; HCl-H$_2$O$_2$ etch.

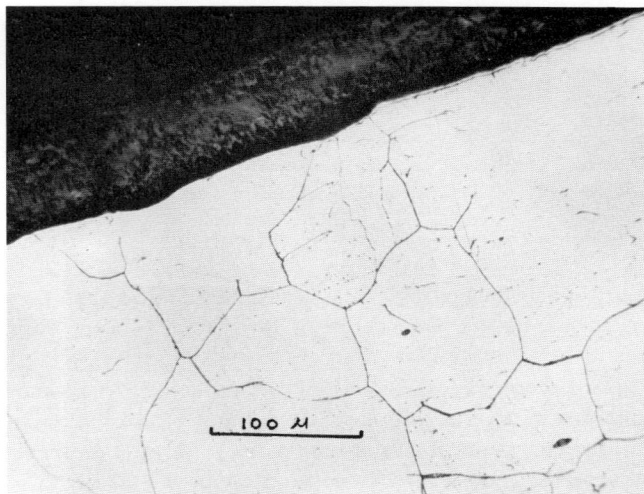

FIGURE 3 — Type 304 stainless steel nitrided in 75% NH$_3$/H$_2$ at 700 C for 1 hour; HCl-H$_2$O$_2$ etch.

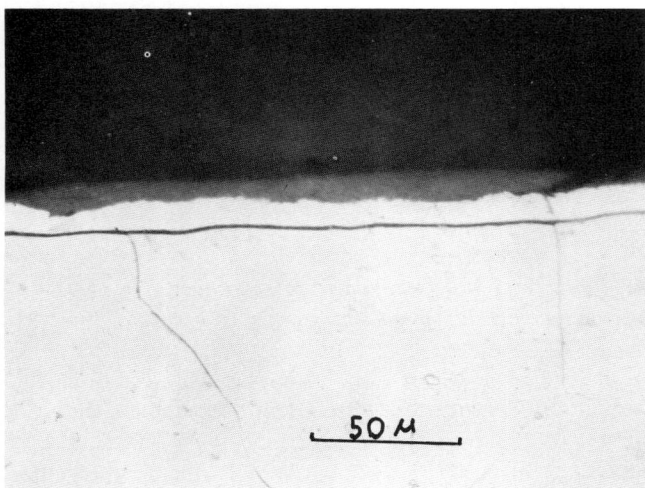

FIGURE 2 — Type 304 stainless steel nitrided in 75% NH$_3$/H$_2$ at 550 C for 6 hours; HCl-H$_2$O$_2$ etch.

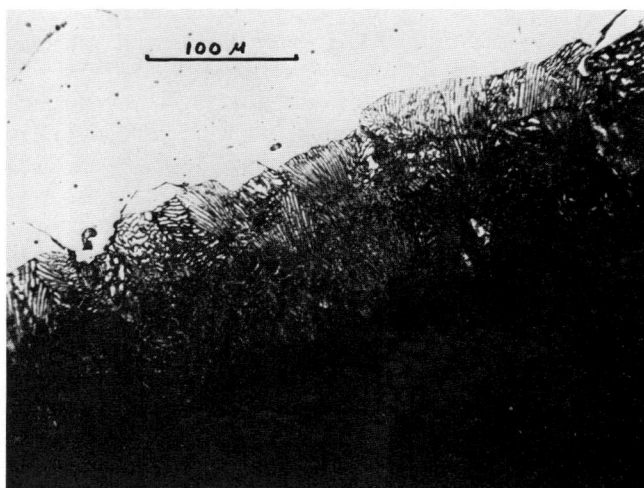

FIGURE 4 — Type 304 stainless steel nitrided in 75% NH$_3$/H$_2$ at 950 C for 1 hour; HCl-H$_2$O$_2$ etch.

to isolate a constituent which was identified as CrN by X-ray diffraction.

At 950 C, the layer assumes a morphology shown in Figure 4. Dissolution of the nitrided specimen in concentrated hydrochloric acid permitted the extraction of a nitride, which also proved to be CrN. Precipitates of similar pearlitic nature, have been observed on the grain boundaries in Fe-Cr-Mn-N alloys by Hsiao and Dulis,[11] and reported, perhaps incorrectly, as Cr$_2$N. No evidence of the presence of Cr$_2$N was found in this investigation. Samples were quenched from the nitriding temperatures, and it was established that the pearlitic structure was formed isothermally at the nitriding temperature.

## B. Stress Corrosion Cracking Resistance of Nitrided Type 304 Steel

The resistance of nitrided wires to stress corrosion cracking was surveyed in boiling MgCl$_2$ after nitriding for various times at the following temperatures: 400, 500, 550, 600, 700, and 950 C. The results are summarized in Table 2, and in Figures 5, 6, and 7. Detailed investigation was made at two temperatures: at 550 C, the slow onset of the protective effect is such as to make study possible; and at 700 C, the rapid achievement of protection makes for the convenient preparation of the large number of specimens required for electrochemical studies.

At 400 C, as already discussed, only the "white layer" was formed. No improvement in stress corrosion behavior was observed, specimens which were nitrided for 24 and 60 hours failing in 1.6 ± 0.7 hours.

At 500 C, a modest improvement is apparent, but no specimen survived 100 hours testing time. The achievement of even this modest improvement required extremely long nitriding times. Warpage of the wire was a serious problem, which rendered many samples useless for a uniaxial test.

**TABLE 2—Stress Corrosion Resistance of Type 304 Wires Nitrided in 75% $NH_3/H_2$ Mixture**

| Nitriding Temperature | Observations | Surface Layer |
|---|---|---|
| 400 C | no protection, even after long nitriding times (60 hrs.) | $Fe_3Ni\,N$ (?) |
| 500 C | modest protection after long nitriding times (72 hrs.) | $Fe_3Ni\,N$ (?) + + CrN |
| 550 C | increased protection after intermediate nitriding times (6-48 hrs.) | $Fe_3Ni\,N$ (?) + + CrN |
| 600 C | good protection after short nitriding times (30 mins.) | $Fe_3Ni\,N$ (?) + + CrN |
| 700 C | good protection after very short nitriding times (5 mins.) | CrN |
| 950 C | good protection, but specimen brittle | CrN |

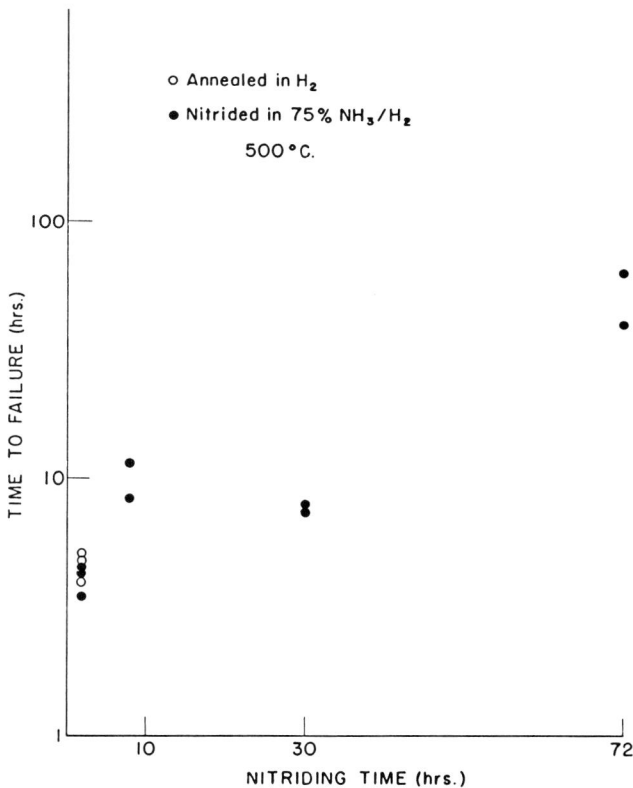

FIGURE 5 — Time to failure of Type 304 stainless steel wires in boiling $MgCl_2$ as function of nitriding time at 500 C.

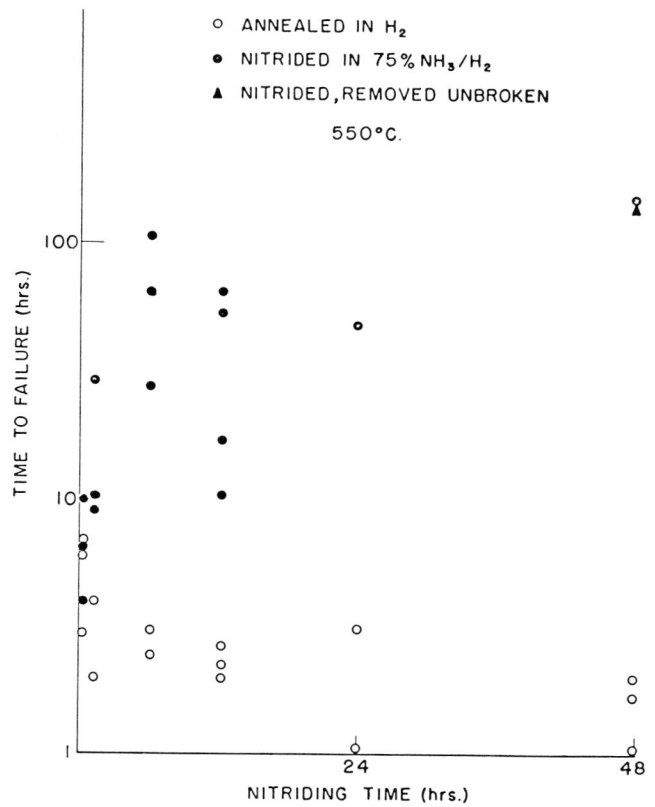

FIGURE 6 — Time to failure of Type 304 stainless steel wires in boiling $MgCl_2$ as function of nitriding time at 550 C.

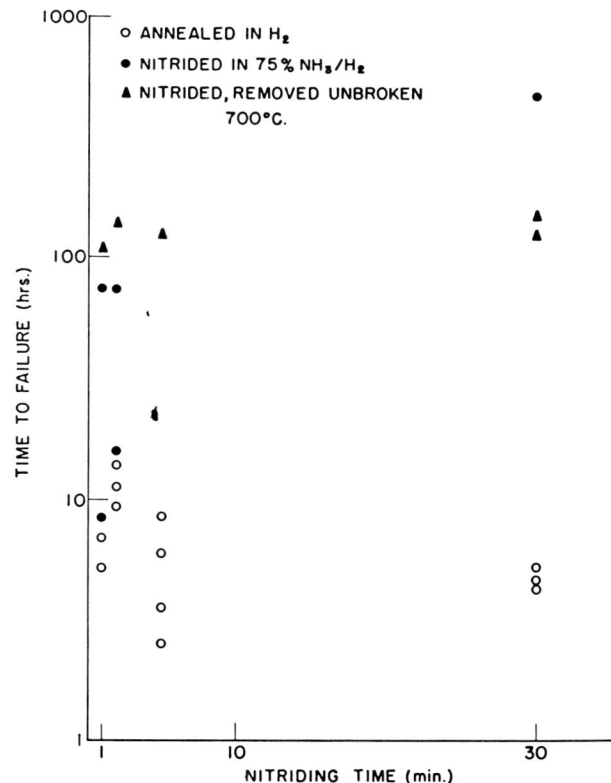

FIGURE 7 — Time to failure of Type 304 stainless steel wires in boiling $MgCl_2$ as function of nitriding time at 700 C.

Very non-uniform penetration of the nitride layer was observed, and the warping of the wire is attributed to this.

At 550 C, much better resistance was obtained, nitriding for less than 24 hours, already improving the life of the specimen by one order of magnitude. At very long nitriding times, warpage of the specimens was again recorded.

At 600 C, the behavior was quite similar to that observed at 700 C. The surface layer has CrN precipitated in most of its thickness with only a narrow band of "white layer" present. The onset of protection is very rapid, specimens nitrided for 30 minutes resisting stress corrosion cracking for more than 100 hours.

At 700 C, the layer is, as previously described, entirely of the CrN type. An improvement, although erratic, is already apparent after one minute nitriding time, and specimens nitrided five minutes survive for 100 hours or more. Tests were arbitrarily discontinued after 100-200 hours when the specimens were unbroken, except for occasional ones which were tested to failure. In these cases, heavy decomposition and cracking of the protective epoxi coat was present, and the specimens, more often than not, failed above the liquid level, in the chloride-vapor region, by a combination of stress corrosion and general corrosive decay.

Specimens nitrided at 950 C showed, in general, good protection after nitriding for one hour. However, the specimens became quite brittle, and occasional failures were recorded which could be correlated to the shock produced by the failure of another specimen on the test rig. Because of this, and as there seems to be no practical advantage in operating at this rather high temperature, no further investigations were made under these conditions.

We conclude from the stress corrosion tests, that, subject to the considerations on general corrosion to be discussed later, the optimum temperature range of nitriding is between 550 and 700 C, for times in the range 1-24 hours, according to the operating temperature.

## C. Metallography

The nitride layer cracked profusely on loading to the stress level of 60,000 psi and permitted ready access of the corrosive environment to the underlying stainless steel, as shown in Figure 8. The layer containing CrN was subject to attack during the exposure to $MgCl_2$. In specimens which had been heavily nitrided, and which were strongly pro-

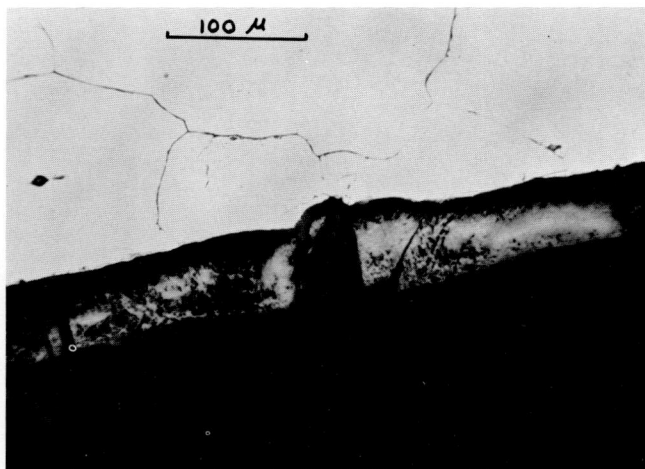

FIGURE 8 — Type 304 stainless steel nitrided in 75% $NH_3/H_2$ at 700 C for 1 hour, loaded to 60,000 psi in tension; $HCl-H_2O_2$ etch.

tected, there were in general no large areas where the nitride layer had been completely removed. When a specimen remained unbroken for a very long time, a gradual deterioration of the layer became evident. In an attempt to correct for sensitization of Type 304 steel, heat treated in the range where protection was achieved, specimens after being nitrided for one hour at 700 C, were annealed in argon for one hour, at various temperatures around 1000 C, and quenched from this temperature. (These specimens are referred to as "double annealed".) The nitride layer grows inward during the anneal, with the morphology characteristic of the annealing temperature. It was found that stress corrosion protection was lost by this treatment; failure times ranged from 1 to 3 hours. It was further found that the anneal in argon had to be at a temperature above approximately 980 C in order to result in the effective loss of stress corrosion protection.

The general conclusion from metallographic examination would, therefore, be that a layer consisting of precipitated CrN (and chromium depleted Fe-Ni) formed between 500 and 950 C is required for the establishment of stress corrosion resistance, and that this resistance is maintained until there is substantial deterioration of the layer over parts of the surface of the wire.

## D. Electrochemical Measurements

The results from the electrochemical observations will be discussed on the basis of the schematic curves. In general, while these curves were very characteristic in shape for each specimen, reproducibility in absolute values was somewhat variable. This was specially true in the maximum potential reached before fracture, as well as in the duration of the phenomenon which is responsible for the peak. Such a variation is indeed expected from the nature of the measured potential, which represents the average potential of specimens undergoing highly localized corrosion, and where neither the anodic nor the cathodic sites are probably stable or reversible. This is presumably a manifestation of the same factors which determine the variation in time to failure, and in the number of cracks observed in specimens of identical heat treatments.

Figure 9 shows the typical variation of potential (measured against a standard calomel electrode) with time, for a nitrided and a blank specimen.

The curve for the blank is very similar to that described by Hoar and Hines,[5] both in form and magnitude of potential. When the $MgCl_2$ solution was initially poured into the reaction cell, a potential in the vicinity of -420 mV was observed; this potential slowly increased as the solution came to its boiling point, and was about -390 mV when the wire was ready to be loaded, and the test initiated. Sharp transient peaks were recorded during the loading of the specimen. The precise interpretation of these peaks is not clear; they may be related to transient electric phenomena in the apparatus due to the loading movements, or to an expression of the behavior described by Hoar and West[12] due to the rapid yielding of the wires upon loading. After some time, a potential was established which slowly

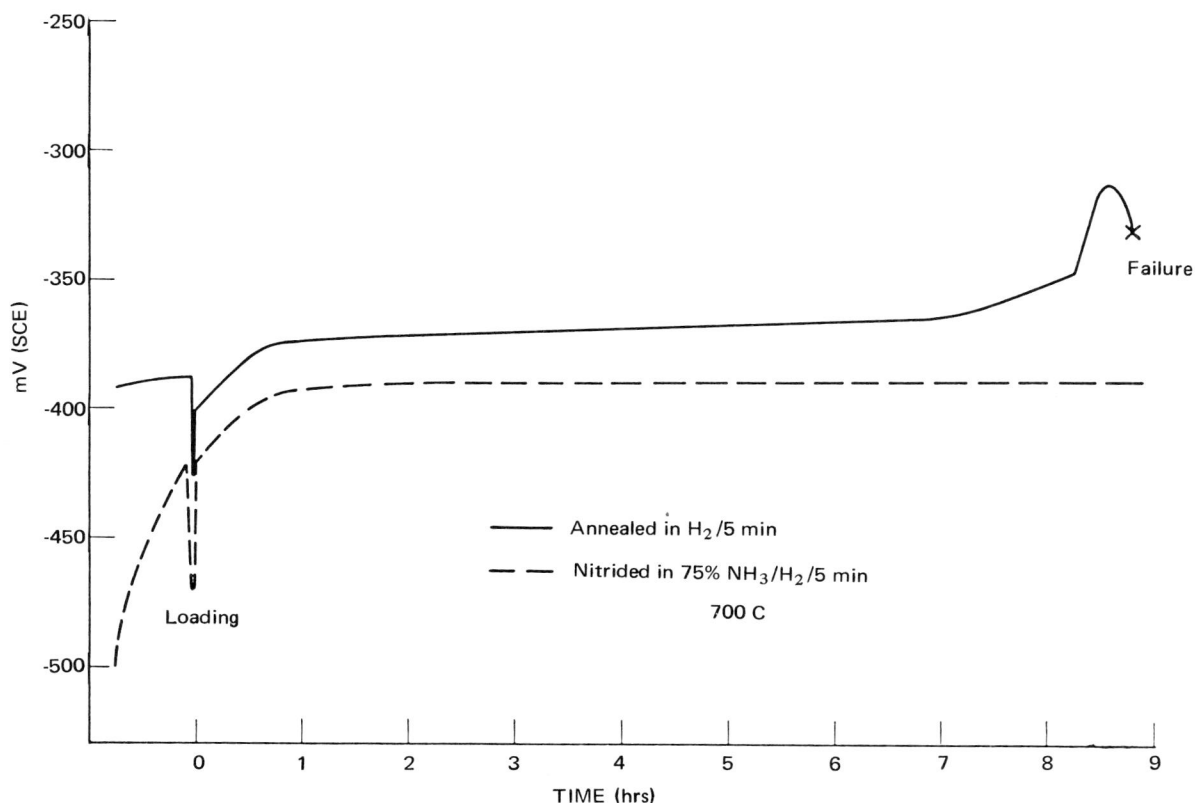

**FIGURE 9** — Potential/time curves for hydrogen annealed and nitrided Type 304 stainless steel wires, loaded to 60,000 psi in boiling $MgCl_2$ solution. (Schematic.)

increased over a variable period of time; this has been associated by Hoar and Hines with an induction period. Eventually, the potential started to increase faster, and then abruptly went through a maximum. Rupture of the specimen occurred at some time after it had reached the maximum.

Nitrided specimens started at a much lower potential (close to -500 mV), and this increased to about -420 mV when the test was initiated. After loading, and after a transient period, a potential in the vicinity of -390 mV was established and maintained until the specimen was removed unbroken.

For some specimens which were nitrided under conditions which led to eventual failure in times of the order of 10-100 hours (nitrided for various times at 550 C), it was possible to obtain potential-time measurements for the whole experiment, up to failure. These curves typically showed no sharp maximum before the moment of breakage. A slow, continuous, but sometimes irregular drift, towards higher potentials was recorded up to the moment of failure. This occurred at potentials between -340 and -370 mV.

A similar behavior was recorded for "double annealed" specimens. Again, there was no maximum to indicate impending failure, and the final potentials observed were in the range -370 to -380 mV.

On the other hand, specimens nitrided at 400 C, which

were not protected against stress corrosion, were observed to have curves entirely similar to those of the blank specimens.

Figure 10 shows the potential-current curves obtained for blanks and for specimens nitrided at 700 C for one hour. The wires were loaded to 60,000 psi and the load removed, in order to have specimens, which through unloaded, had the nitride layer ruptured as in a stress corrosion test. Two examples of each are shown, to illustrate the degree of reproducibility achieved in the experiment. It should be mentioned that current, rather than current density is plotted. The area of wire exposed to the boiling solution was approximately 1 cm², but it is not known which area should properly be assigned to the anode or cathode. The anodic area in the case of cracking specimens is certainly quite small. Qualitatively, the following features of the curves may be pointed out:

The nitrided wire has a cathodic current approximately 5 times that of the blanks. The anodic current increases as the potential rises, up to -300 mV, and then goes through a minimum at -270 mV. The reason for this minimum, which is very distinct, is unknown. It lies, as will be seen, outside the potential range in which specimens remain unbroken when undergoing stress corrosion. It is probably related to the nitride-rich layer, because it is absent in blank specimens.

The potential at which the specimens become anodic

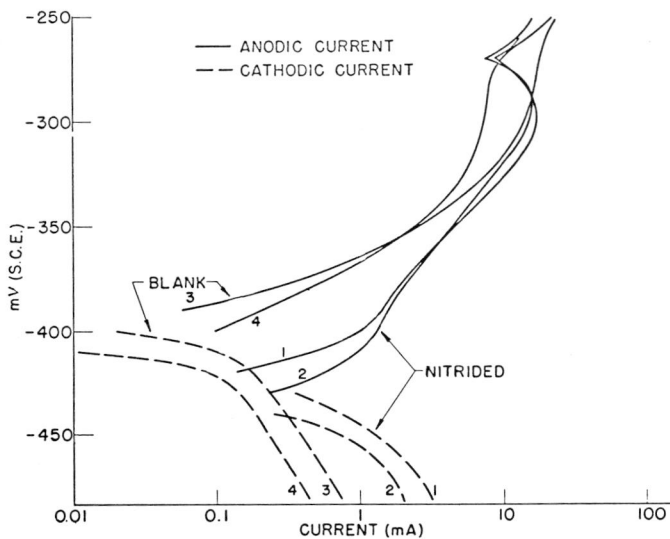

FIGURE 10 — Potential/current curves for Type 304 stainless steel wires, hydrogen annealed and nitrided at 700 C, unloaded, in boiling MgCl$_2$ solution.

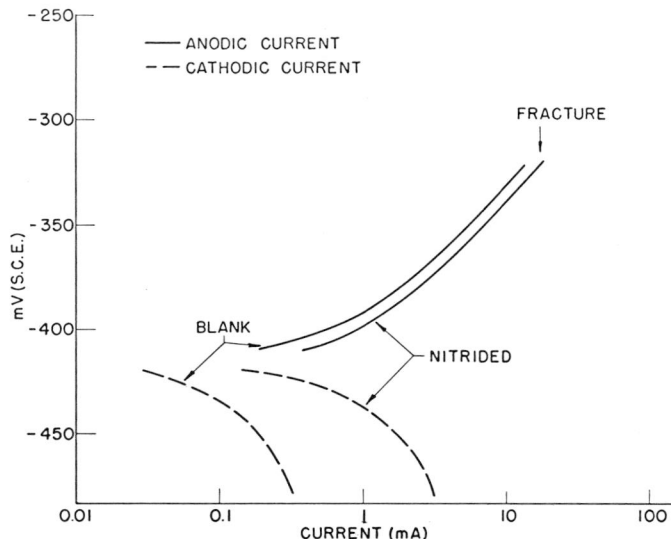

FIGURE 11 — Potential/current curves for Type 304 stainless steel wires, hydrogen annealed and nitrided at 700 C, loaded to 60,000 psi, in boiling MgCl$_2$ solution.

shows a difference of the order of 20 mV between the nitrided and the blank specimen. This is the same difference observed in the values of the open potential measurements.

When the same experiment is performed with the specimens under load, the results are as shown in Figure 11. The same factor of 5 is observed in the cathodic current, but the remainder of the two curves is very similar. The same potential at which they become anodic is indicated, and the anodic parts of the curves follow closely to the point of failure at about -320 mV for both specimens.

The potential at which the specimens broke was subject to a variation of about 10 mV, but tended to vary with the rate at which the potential was changed on the potentiostat. Fracture occurred at a lower potential the slower the potential was changed. This is to be expected, if one considers that similar numbers of electrons are necessary in each case to affect the corrosion corresponding to the observed cracking, and that for slow traversing times, proportionately more coulombs pass through the specimen at each potential.

### E. Mechanical Behavior of Nitrided Wires

The presence of the hard, brittle, nitride layer on the surface of the test wires modified their behavior in tension, as would be expected from the composite structure produced. In order to evaluate any influence of this on the stress corrosion susceptibility, stress-strain curves were determined for different nitriding times and temperatures, as well as for blanks and double-annealed specimens, and this variation compared with cracking behavior. It was found that the differences in mechanical behavior were related only to the presence of hard nitride layers, both by the "white layer" and the "CrN layer", and not related in any way to stress corrosion resistance.

### F. Intergranular and Generalized Corrosion

Because the heat treating temperatures used in this

work are in the range in which austenitic stainless steels may become subject to the phenomenon of sensitization and intergranular cracking, the susceptibility to this phenomenon after nitriding was investigated. The acidified copper sulfate test (Strauss test) was used.[13] Heavy generalized attack on the CrN layer, whenever this was present, was observed. This led to the dissolution of the layer, by action on the matrix around the CrN particles; these were not attacked, and could be recovered from the solution and identified. Intergranular corrosion was in all cases comparable to that observed on blank specimens, and could perhaps be controlled by the use of low carbon grades. During the execution of the Strauss test it was observed that the nitrided specimens displaced copper upon being immersed in the cold reagent. Table 3 shows the results of a survey of this effect, and attention is drawn to its correlation with stress corrosion cracking susceptibility.

The results of the Strauss test indicate that general corrosion resistance of the stainless steel may be affected to an important degree by the nitriding process. The eventual application of nitriding as a means of preventing stress corrosion should therefore be preceded by a careful evaluation of the behavior of the nitrided material in the environment of contemplated usage.

## IV. Discussion

The factors which determine the onset of CrN precipitation in the layer above approximately 500 C are subject to speculation. No thermodynamic data on the activity of nitrogen or metallic components are available for the calculation of the free energy of formation of CrN in this system. Nucleation kinetics may also be an important factor. An approximate calculation, under the assumption that all available chromium in the layer is precipitated as CrN, leads to a maximum volume fraction of 25% of CrN. Therefore, it is reasonable to assume that the layer consists of particles of CrN in a matrix of chromium-depleted (in

**TABLE 3—Effect of Acidified Copper Sulfate Solution on Austenitic Stainless Steel After Several Heat Treatments**

| Heat Treatment | Copper Displacement | Stress Corrosion Behavior |
|---|---|---|
| Annealed in $H_2$ at 700 C | No[1] | Cracks |
| Annealed in argon at 1050 C | No | Cracks |
| Nitrided in 75% $NH_3/H_2$ at 700 C | Yes | Protected |
| Nitrided in 75% $NH_3/H_2$ at 550 C | Yes | Protected |
| Nitrided in 75% $NH_3/H_2$ at 400 C | No | Cracks |
| Double annealed – | | |
| 700 C/$NH_3$ - 1050 C in argon | No | Cracks |
| Iron-15% nickel | Yes | ------ |

[1]This specimen was initially covered with a faint layer of copper, which disappears after some minutes.

the limit, pure Fe 15% Ni) alloy.

The morphology of the CrN layers formed at higher temperatures is strongly reminiscent of those observed under appropriate conditions in the internal oxidation of dilute alloys. The theory of this process has recently been reviewed by Rapp.[14]

The kinetics of internal oxidation have been successfully predicted in many cases for dilute solutions, as a diffusion controlled process. The indications are that the kinetics, in the precipitation of CrN at 700 C, are controlled in a similar manner since the depth of penetration appears to be a parabolic function of time.

All the evidence from the present investigation indicates that the observed immunity against stress corrosion cracking shown by nitrided wires is due to an electrochemical effect. It has been shown that once the wires are maintained at a potential which leads to an anodic current, they crack in much the same fashion whether they are nitrided or not.

It is suggested that the precipitation of chromium nitride at the surface of the metal results in a chromium-depleted, iron-nickel rich phase, which is more active than, and cathodically protects, the underlying austenitic stainless steel.

It is well known that stress corrosion cracking in austenitic stainless steels can be stopped by cathodic protection; this protection can be achieved by imposing a protective potential with an outside E.M.F. source, or by the presence of more active, consumable, surface layers. This form of cathodic protection is well exemplified by the galvanizing of steel. Such a protective coating has, for instance, recently been reported by Kitamura and Morita,[15] who obtained improved stress corrosion resistance on 18-8 steel with the use of sprayed aluminum layers.

One would expect chromium content to have a large effect on the electrochemical behavior of Fe-Ni alloys, especially as it varies across the 10-13% limit usually associated with the appearance of continuous passive films in stainless steels. Several investigators have studied the anodic behavior of binary alloys, and Beauchamp[16] has investigated the behavior of the iron rich corner of the Fe-Cr-Ni ternary, in 1 N sulfuric acid. A large decrease in

the anodic current is observed with the addition of 10 and 20% Cr to Fe-10% Ni. The potential at which the alloy becomes anodic is very similar in sulfuric acid to that observed in $MgCl_2$, namely -420 mV (SCE). Some caution is however required in applying these results directly to the $MgCl_2$ system, because one would, among other things, expect the oxidation conditions to be quite different. A comparable investigation in boiling $MgCl_2$ would therefore supply most welcome information.

The observation that Fe-15% Ni displaces copper from acidified copper sulfate solution, in the same fashion as protected specimens, is in agreement with the proposed behavior.

The effect of the "double anneal" on the stress corrosion behavior of nitrided samples can also be readily understood. The anneal temperature of 1050 C is high enough to permit appreciable chromium diffusion from the unaffected matrix, so that the chromium content of the depleted outside layer is again raised, in a manner identical to that which occurs when sensitized steels are heated to this temperature.

## V. Conclusions

1. Type 304 austenitic stainless steel wires, nitrided in $NH_3/H_2$ mixtures in the range 500-950 C, and tested at a stress of 60,000 psi in boiling $MgCl_2$, showed significant increase in stress corrosion life, as compared to specimens treated in hydrogen.

2. An examination was made of the surface layers formed during nitriding in the range 400-950 C. Specimens nitrided in the range 500-950 C had CrN precipitated, and its presence was associated with stress corrosion protection.

3. Protected wires can be broken by the application of anodic currents with a potentiostat.

4. Nitriding has little influence on sensitization, but renders the steel susceptible to generalized chemical attack under certain conditions.

5. It is concluded that the prevention of stress corrosion cracking is due to cathodic protection, in which the consumable anode is found by a region of chromium-depleted alloy, in the vicinity of CrN precipitates.

## Acknowledgments

The continuing support of the Office of Naval Research is greatly appreciated. Valuable discussions have been held with many friends on our own faculty and with Professor R. W. Staehle and R. A. Rapp (Ohio State University). The unusual competence of W. Poling in the experimental part of this program has been a considerable factor.

## References

1. H. Copson. *Physical Metallurgy of Stress Corrosion Fracture.* Interscience, New York, p. 240 (1959).
2. F. S. Lang. *Corrosion,* 18, 378t (1962).
3. H. H. Uhlig and R. A. White. *Trans. ASM,* 52, 830 (1960).
4. M. R. Louthan, Jr. AEC Research Report, Contract AT(07-2)-1, September (1964).
5. T. P. Hoar and J. G. Hines. *JISI,* 182, 124 (1956).
6. G. H. G. Kraft, J. Z. Amacker, R. K. Saxer, and J. R. Myers. *Corrosion,* 21, 188 (1965).
7. C. R. Cupp. *Physical Metallurgy of Stress Corrosion Fracture.* Interscience, New York, p. 270 (1959).
8. T. P. Hoar. *Recent Advances in Stress Corrosion.* Bull. No. 25, Corrosion Committee of the Royal Swedish Acad. of Eng. Sci., Stockholm (1961).
9. S. Barnartt and D. van Rooyen. *J. Electrochem. Soc.,* 108, 222 (1961).
10. ASTM Special Technical Publication 48-L, ASTM, Philadelphia (1962), Card 9-318; after J. W. Wiener and J. A. Berger. *J. Metals,* 7, 360 (1955).
11. C. M. Hsiao and E. J. Dulis. *Trans. ASM,* 52, 855 (1960).
12. T. P. Hoar and J. M. West. *Proc. Roy. Soc.,* A 268, 304 (1962).
13. *ASTM Standards,* Part 3, p. 427, A 393-63 (1964).
14. R. A. Rapp. *Corrosion,* 21, 382 (1965).
15. Y. Kitamura and S. Morita. *Corr. Eng.,* 12, 16 (1963).
16. R. L. Beauchamp. Ph.D. Thesis, Ohio State University, Columbus, Ohio, (1966); cited in D. O. Condit and R. W. Staehle Report COO-1319-46, The Ohio State University Research Foundation (1966).

## Discussion

**T. P. Hoar, University of Cambridge, Cambridge, England:**

What do you believe is the essential reason for the nitriding exerting its effect? Is it the greater electrochemical activity of surface or the brittleness of the surface?

**H. W. Paxton:**

I believe that the effect is due primarily to greater electrochemical activity of the surface, and not to any mechanical constraint or assistance from the film itself. In his thesis, Mannheimer describes a variety of experiments which rule out this second possibility.

**R. W. Staehle, The Ohio State University:**

I think it is very significant that the cathodic curve for the nitrided specimen shows a displacement to the right. This was also observed by Barnartt and van Rooyen in comparing low and high nitrogen alloys. The presence of nitrogen apparently accelerates the reduction process.

**H. W. Paxton:**

This may very well be true, but the subject needs systematic study which was not possible in the present work.

# RELATIONSHIP OF DYNAMIC STRAINING AND PITTING EXPERIMENTS TO INTERPRETING THE MECHANISM OF CRACKING IN AUSTENITIC STAINLESS STEELS

L. Graf and G. Springe
Max Planck Institut fur Metallforschung

## Abstract

The causes of stress corrosion cracking of an austenitic stainless steel in boiling $MgCl_2$ are shown to be the same as those in homogeneous, nonsupersaturated, nonferrous alloys, i.e., two solid solution effects combined with a pronounced electrochemical process inside the cracks. The former are intrinsic properties of solid solutions, therefore only the origin of the cathodic areas on the crack walls were to be determined, because the potential difference between the flowing crack roots and the nonflowing crack walls is not sufficient. Nonstraining material is shown to form a stable protective film in boiling $MgCl_2$ which, moreover, acts cathodically on the crack walls whereas the plastic flowing crack roots are not passivated and act as anodes. With the help of schematic current density-potential diagrams the potential range is shown in which stress corrosion cracking can occur. Experiments in which pitting was allowed to commence prior to stressing showed that the onset of cracking, once stress had been applied, was significantly delayed. These pitting experiments show the importance of competing electrochemical processes and also verify the electrochemical nature of the cracking.

## I. Causes of Stress Corrosion Cracking in Homogeneous Non-Supersaturated Alloys

This paper describes an investigation into the mechanism of stress corrosion cracking of a carbon stabilized austenitic stainless steel, Fe-18Cr-11Ni-0.025C (Steel No. 4306). Using previously established interpretations obtained in the study of nonferrous solid solution alloys,[1,2] this alloy would be expected to exhibit the same solid solution effects already observed;[2,3] namely:

1. An increased reactivity at the grain boundaries and at disturbed areas in the grain surfaces.

2. An increased reactivity at regions in a state of flow.

Both effects are affected by the concentration of components in the solid solution having a maximum at 50 $^a$/o. Stress corrosion only occurs, however, if, in addition to these effects, a pronounced electrochemical process takes place within the cracks, for which the crack walls must be polarized cathodically and the roots anodically in order to direct the attack exclusively at the roots of the cracks and to protect the crack walls. Previous findings have shown that a potential difference alone between the crack walls and the crack root, even in a state of plastic flow, is not a sufficient condition for propagating stress corrosion cracks.[4] It is important that the crack walls be significantly more noble than the solid solution. Therefore, determining the nature of material on the walls of the crack would establish the sufficient condition for cracking because the solid solution effects are always present.

## II. Electrochemical Processes Within Advancing Stress Corrosion Cracks

### A. The Cathodic Reaction and Substrate Material on Crack Walls

In accordance with Ternes,[5] and contrary to Saxena,[6] we found that Steel No. 4306 is passivated in a stable manner in a boiling $MgCl_2$ solution, even in the absence of oxygen. The polarization curve does not show the shape typical for a passivating material; namely, the pronounced active peak and the very low current densities in the passive region which is independent of the potential. There is only a steep ascent (Figure 1). However, as may be seen in the schematic diagram of Figure 2, this is due to the fact that the rest potential in this case lies very close to the pitting potential. Because the cathodic current density strongly increases with the decreasing of the potential, the typical features of a passive material are concealed. According to both our findings and those of Ternes,[5] and contrary to the assumption of Hoar,[7] the cathodic part of the reaction consists of the production of $H_2$. Hydrogen evolution is observed at active cracks.

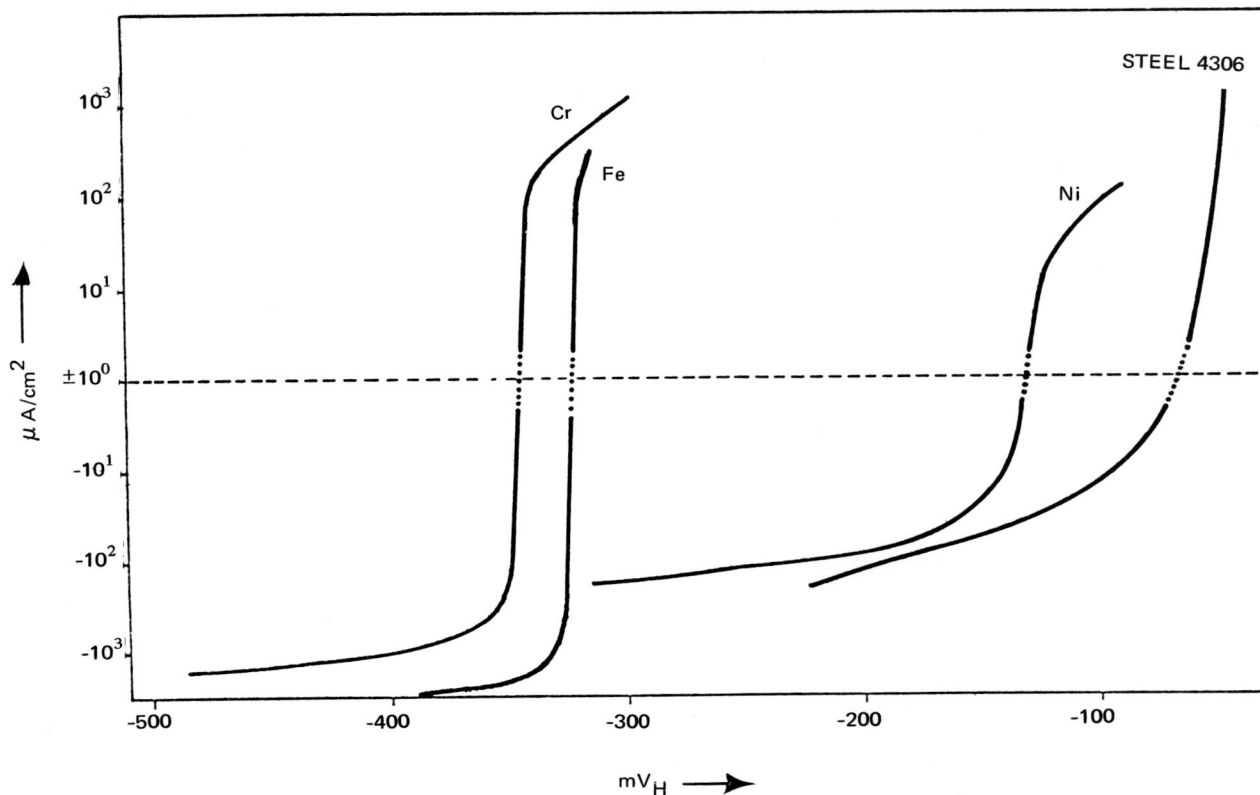

FIGURE 1 — Kinetic current-potential curves for ground samples of Cr, Fe, Ni, and steel No. 4306 (18% Cr, 11% Ni, 0.025% C) in boiling MgCl$_2$ solution (142 C), 160 mV/h.

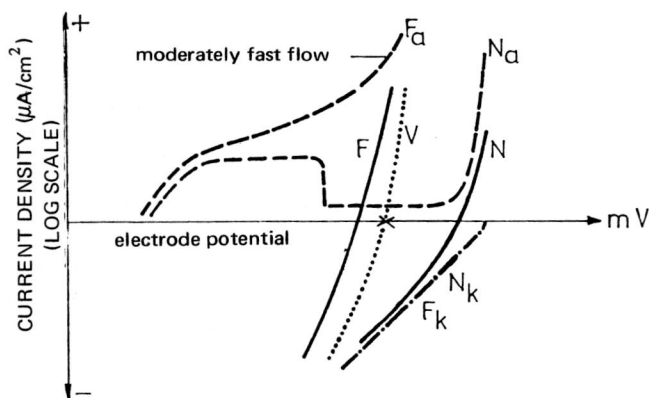

FIGURE 2 — Schematic current-potential curves of austenitic stainless steel in boiling MgCl$_2$ solution (142 C); N, N$_a$, N$_k$ : for nonflowing regions, F, F$_a$, F$_k$ : for moderately fast flowing regions, V = F + N : sum curve for the deforming sample, x : corrosion potential.

## B. Behavior of the Crack Roots (Experiments Under Plastic Strain)

**1. Boiling MgCl$_2$ Solution.** Available information suggests that the cathodic layer on the crack walls is formed of a passive film. The crack roots, however, are probably not passivated due to dynamic plastic flow. In order to prove this, corrosion potentials were measured of the steel being studied during steady plastic strain in a boiling MgCl$_2$ solution. Strain rates used were 0.82 x 10$^{-4}$ and 9.6 x 10$^{-4}$ per minute respectively. The experiments were carried out in such a way that a period of strain, lasting 20 or 10 minutes, respectively, was followed by an equally long period without strain.

The corrosion potential with respect to time is shown in Figure 3. The continuous parts of the curve give the change of potential during the periods of strain, the dashed parts show the change during periods without strain. During the periods of strain the potential of the samples always becomes less noble, particularly so in the case of the higher strain rate; and, moreover, a stress corrosion process took place with the formation of cracks and the ultimate fracture of the sample. With the lower strain rate, therefore, the potential became more strongly negative towards the end of the test. During periods without strain, the potential became more noble again, which suggests that repassivation occurs as soon as the flow processes stop. It is peculiar that the potential of the sample with the higher strain rate increases again after passing through a minimum although the sample is still in the state of strain. This will be explained later.

336

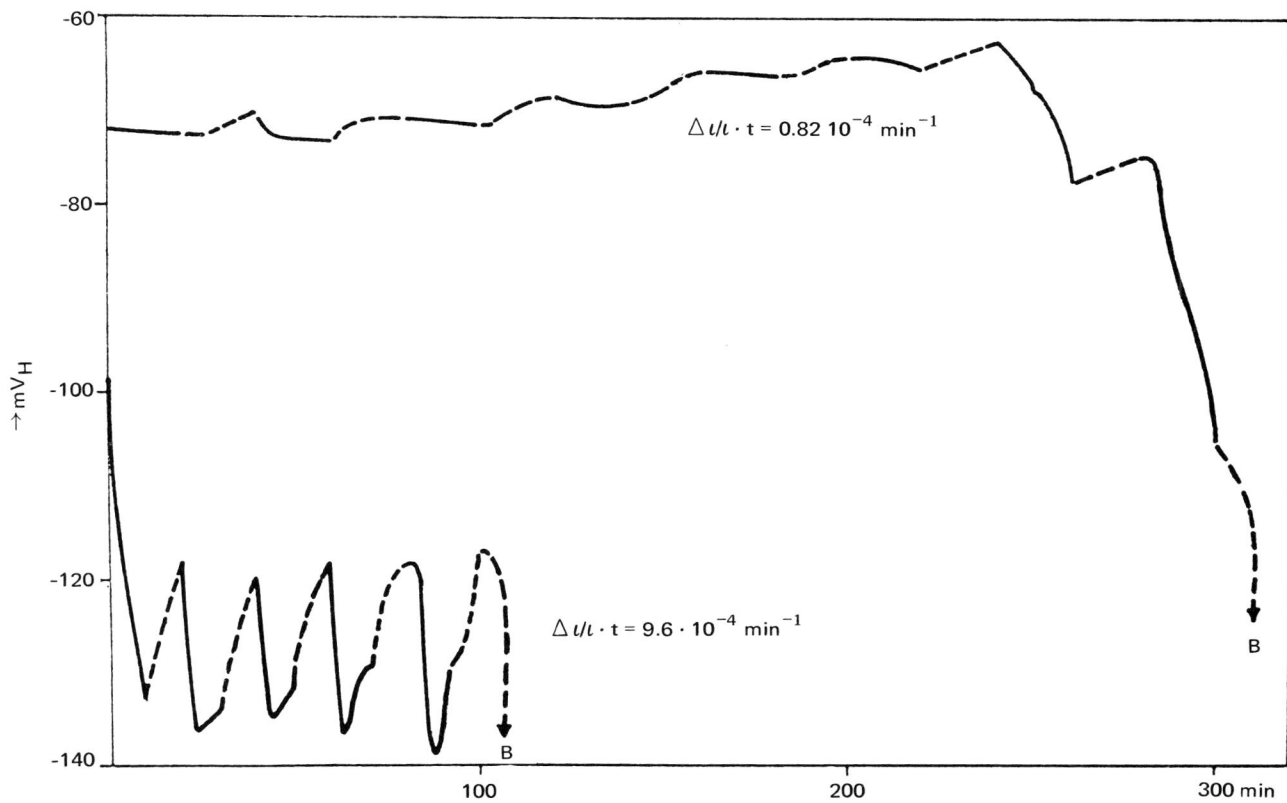

FIGURE 3 — Corrosion potential vs time of solution annealed steel No. 4306 (18% Cr, 11% Ni, 0.025% C) in boiling MgCl₂ solution (142 C). Full parts of the curves: periods of constant strain. Dashed parts: periods without strain.

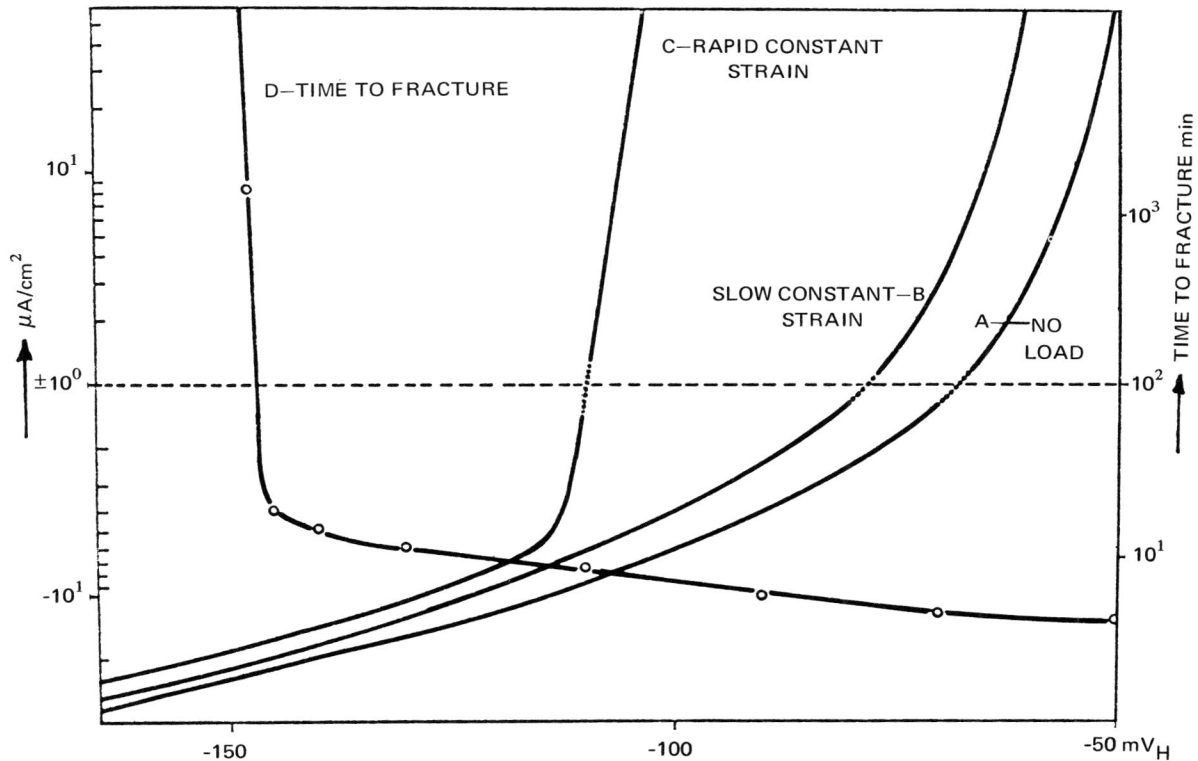

FIGURE 4 — Kinetic current-potential curves of Steel No. 4306 (18% Cr, 11% Ni, 0.025% C) in boiling MgCl₂ solution (142 C), 160 mV/h. Curve A: sample unstressed. Curve B: sample under slow constant strain (1.6 x $10^{-4}$/min). Curve C: sample under fast constant strain (4.8 x $10^{-4}$/min). Curve D: life vs potential, load 80% UTS.

**2. 17% HCl- and 13% HNO$_3$-Solutions.** To further clarify the behavior of dynamic straining, an annealed sample was exposed to a 17% HCl solution, in which the sample dissolves actively and shows no stress corrosion. Under strain produced by a load of 80% of the ultimate tensile stress, the sample showed only a slight decrease of potential from -175.3 mV$_H$ to -177 mV$_H$. In contrast, a similar sample was equally loaded and strained in a passivating 13% HNO$_3$ solution and here a sharp decrease of potential from +400 to +140 mV$_H$ occurred. In both cases, the decrease of potential which was produced by the short-time and intensive flow process occurring under load, reversed and vanished in a few minutes. The significantly greater decrease of potential of the passivated sample is caused by the cracking of the passive film as well as by the plastic deformation (solid solution effect II). It is noteworthy that no stress corrosion occurs in this case. This is well understandable by the fact that in a strongly passivating agent the regions of plastic flow can also be repassivated in a short time. Therefore, no sufficient time continuous electrochemical differentiation occurs here. Straining in the elastic region caused only a negligible shift in potential of 2 mV.

### C. Influence of Plastic Flow on Current-Potential Curve

The influence of plastic flow on the shape of the current-potential curve of Steel No. 4306 was studied potentiokinetically at 160 mV$_H$ per minute in boiling MgCl$_2$ solution (142 C). Specimens were solution annealed samples that were strained at strain rates of $1.6 \times 10^{-4}$ and $4.8 \times 10^{-4}$ per minute (Figure 4).

The polarization curves for the strained specimens are displaced towards less noble potentials and more anodic currents respectively indicating a considerable electrochemical differentiation between flowing and nonflowing regions. This difference can be reasonably applied to the flowing active roots of the cracks and the nonflowing passivated crack walls. In the potential region where significant difference of current exists, the material should be susceptible to stress corrosion cracking.

### D. Relationship Between Stress Corrosion Susceptibility and Current-Potential Curves

Cracking times in boiling MgCl$_2$ solutions were investigated as a function of potential to determine whether the supposed correlation exists between cracking susceptibility and the potential-current curves of Figure 4. A time-to-fracture vs potential curve from these cracking studies is superimposed on Figure 4 and shows that there is susceptibility to stress corrosion in those potential regions at which a significant disparity exists in current density between static and rapidly straining material. In reality, the electrochemical differentiation between the flowing active roots of the cracks and the nonflowing passive crack walls is considerably greater than is indicated by the displacement of the polarization curves. For in the strained samples a mixed potential from flowing and nonflowing regions is measured and not the potential from only flowing regions. Therefore, stress corrosion susceptibility begins at a more negative potential than one expects from the corresponding displacement of the current-potential curves.

From the steep rise in lifetime below -147 mV$_H$ we may conclude that at this potential the marked electrochemical differentiation between flowing and nonflowing regions disappears. This value must therefore be at the active-passive transition of the unloaded, nonflowing steel. Hoar and West,[8] as well as Hines and Hoar[9] found a value of -150 mV$_H$ for the potential of the active-passive transition. Ternes[5] found a value of -145 mV$_H$. This close correspondence of the active-passive transition with the results of our measurements confirms the correctness of our considerations.

For further information we consider the schematic diagram in Figure 5. As to observe the marked electrochemical differentiation between flowing and nonflowing regions disappears, if the corrosion potential falls below the active-passive transition and the nonflowing regions thereby become active. This is achieved through polarization of the samples at a potential value more negative than -147 mV$_H$. Then the dotted curve in Figure 5 corresponds to the total polarization curve of the deforming sample. According to the analysis of Figure 5, susceptibility to stress corrosion is not suppressed in this case by cathodic protection in the normal sense, but rather by activation of the nonflowing regions.

### E. The Effect of Strain Rates

Considering the significance of Figure 5, it must be possible also by using high strain rates to displace the

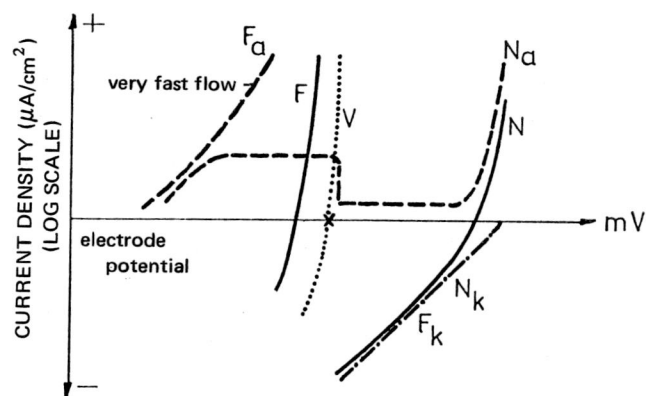

**FIGURE 5** — Schematic current-potential curves of austenitic stainless steel in boiling MgCl$_2$ solution (142 C). N, N$_a$, N$_k$: for nonflowing regions; F, F$_a$, F$_k$: for very fast flowing regions; V = F + N: sum curve for the deforming sample; x: corrosion potential.

corrosion potential so far towards negative values that the sample becomes active and susceptibility to stress corrosion disappears.

In Figure 3, in the curve corresponding to the slower strain rate, it is conspicuous that a marked decrease of potential occurs only near the end of the test, when a greater number of stress corrosion cracks appears and grows and the flow processes at the crack roots become more and more stronger. In the rapidly strained sample the cracks appear very earlier and the local flow rates at the roots of the cracks are very high, so that the potential falls very quickly to more negative values.

However, when the corrosion potential of the sample drops below the active-passive transition due to the high anodic current loading of the flowing regions (crack roots) the passivity even of the nonflowing regions (crack walls) ceases and the marked electrochemical differentiation between these and the flowing regions vanishes. Therefore, the crack growth of the still straining sample stops and with that the flow processes are no longer concentrated on the crack roots, whereby the local flow rate decreases. In this condition the sample ennobles itself again, i.e., its potential increases even though it is being strained.

In accordance with these considerations, the most negative potential reached by the more rapid straining in Figure 3 must correspond to the potential for active-passive transition. One obtains a value of -135 to -139 $mV_H$, varying a little from the more exact value of -147 $mV_H$ obtained from the disappearance of stress corrosion through cathodic polarization. This shows how difficult it is to measure the activation potential. It also may be noted here that Ternes[5] gives as his measured "cathodic protection potential" (i.e., no break in a round sample with a diameter of 3.5 mm under 30 kp/mm$^2$ in 150 hours) a value of -130 $mV_H$ for the more exact position of which he assumes a value of -145 $mV_H$ which is supported by extrapolation of the crack propagation rate to zero.

These tests confirm that it is also possible to suppress the stress corrosion process by sufficiently high strain rates.

*F. Relationship Between Stress Corrosion and Pitting*

The occurrence of pitting tends to suppress cracking. In stress corrosion tests in which the sample potential with respect to time was continuously recorded, it was found that samples whose potential only slowly and immaterially ennobles after the loading exhibited a life over the average. To determine the significance of this effect, specimens were exposed unstressed to boiling MgCl$_2$ for different lengths of time prior to stressing. The samples were then stressed to 80% of the ultimate tensile strength. After waiting 64 minutes before loading, the rupture occurred after 194 minutes, while immediately loaded samples broke after 29 minutes. Under microscopic examination, the long-lived samples exhibited, in addition to stress corrosion cracks, moderate pitting which did not occur in the short-lived samples. This suggested that the retardation of cracking was associated with simultaneously active pitting. During this

active pitting the concentration of H$^+$ and Cl$^-$ increases inside the pits[13] and the local attack increases.

This additional anodic process lowers the corrosion potential according to the principle of summing partial currents. This lowered corrosion potential tends to stifle cracks as the potential for the active-passive transition is approached. The pitting provides, in effect, sacrificial anodes.

If, on the other hand, the samples are already under tensile stress before pitting begins, the flowing regions cause a polarization to more negative potentials. In this way the potential is removed from the pitting potential and stress corrosion occurs. In this case the flowing regions function as sacrificial anodes. These considerations were confirmed by the following experiments.

A cold-rolled sample in boiling MgCl$_2$ (142 C) showed a lifetime of approximately 4 minutes when the sample was loaded to 80% of its ultimate tensile strength immediately after addition of the solution and anodic polarization to -50 $mV_H$. Under the same conditions, but without polarization, the average life amounted to about 8 minutes. If, on the other hand, after addition of the agent, the sample was prepolarized for only 2 minutes to -50 $mV_H$ and then loaded without polarization, it did not break within 1000 minutes. As the microscopic results showed, pitting was produced in this 2 minutes of prepolarization. Neither did stress corrosion occur when the load was applied 30 seconds before the end of the 2 minute long polarization to -50 $mV_H$.

A supplementary series of tests was conducted at 100 C in a room-temperature-saturated MgCl$_2$ solution. The corrosion potential was -110 $mV_H$ and specimens were stressed to 80% of their ultimate tensile strength. Following are the significant results.

1. When the samples were exposed to the solution immediately after loading the average time to failure was 64 minutes.

2. When the samples were polarized to -80 $mV_H$, with a current density of 10 ma/cm$^2$, immediately after addition of the solution, the samples broke after 16 minutes.

3. When the polarization of -80 $mV_H$ was imposed only during the first 5 minutes after addition of the solution, then no fracture occurred in the samples within 1200 minutes. The samples showed distinct pitting after termination of the test.

This series of tests confirms the close relationship between pitting and stress corrosion and shows, as already before pointed out, that one of the two corrosion mechanisms can be almost completely suppressed by promoting the other.

Based on the above trends, the observations of Barnartt, et al[10] that a pure Fe-16Cr-20Ni alloy is resistant to cracking whereas alloys with 1.5 Mo or 0.5 Ti are susceptible, can also be explained in electrochemical terms. Parenthetically, it should be noted that experiments by Ohtani and Dodd[12] suggest that the stacking fault rationalization used by Barnartt et al based on Forty's proposal[11] may not be a useful idea. The potential-time curves of these steels show a sharp potential increase after the beginning of the test only with 1.5% Mo or 0.5% Ti alloy additions, while without these additions, or with 1.5% Mn respectively only a very slow potential ennobling was exhibited. The latter suggests the occurrence of pitting, which was also actually observed while molybdenum additions lower the susceptibility to pitting, as is well known.

Thus, predictions from experiments conducted herein appear to explain the trends in cracking observed by Barnartt et al due to various alloy elements, i.e., alloy chemistries which promote pitting tend to suppress cracking and vice versa.

## III. Conclusions

1. Previously established interpretations of the causes of stress corrosion susceptibility in homogeneous nonferrous solid solution alloys are also applicable to a carbon stabilized austenitic stainless steel, Fe-18Cr-11Ni-0.025C (Steel No. 4306). These causes are two solid solution effects in cooperation with a marked electrochemical process in the cracks. Because the former are intrinsic properties of solid solutions, only the origin of the cathodic material on the crack walls was to be determined necessary for a marked electrochemical process.

2. In the present case the strong cathodic polarization of the crack walls is due to their passivation as against the crack roots in the state of plastic flow which are not passivated in a boiling $MgCl_2$ solution (142 C). Therefore, susceptibility to stress corrosion occurs only when the corrosion potential of the sample lies in the passive range of the alloy. This range of potential is noble to the potential of an active-passive transition in the metal-environment system studied.

3. Susceptibility to cracking may be eliminated by dynamic straining if the associated open circuit is negative to the active-passive transition potential.

4. Susceptibility to cracking can be substantially reduced by arranging conditions which permit active pitting to operate. This can be done by adding certain alloying elements or by allowing pitting to start prior to stressing.

## References

1. G. Springe. Dissertation Technische Hochschule Stuttgart (1966).

2. L. Graf. *Proc. Second International Congress on Metallic Corrosion,* New York, N. Y., p. 89-101, 1963. (Publ. by the National Association of Corrosion Engineers, Houston, Texas, 1966).
L. Graf. *Acta Met.,* **6**, 116 (1958).
L. Graf. *Werkstoffe und Korrosion,* **8**, 329 (1957).

3. L. Graf and H. Klatte. Zeitschrift fur Physikalische Chemie, *Neue Folge,* **10**, 306 (1957); **11**, 342 (1957).
L. Graf. *Werkstoffe und Korrosion,* **8**, 329 (1957).

4. L. Graf and W. Wittich. *Zeitschrift fur Metallkunde,* **56**, 380 (1965).
L. Graf and W. Wittich. *Werkstoffe und Korrosion,* **17**, 385, 471, 595 (1966).
L. Graf. *Werkstoffe und Korrosion,* **18**, 1 (1967).

5. H. Ternes. Dissertation Bergakademie Clausthal, 1963.

6. M. N. Saxena. Mechanism of Stress Corrosion Cracking in Austenitic Stainless Steels. Thesis at the University of Wisconsin, Ph.D., 1965. Engineering, Metallurgy, University Microfilms, Inc., Ann Arbor, Michigan.

7. T. P. Hoar. *Proc. Second International Congress on Metallic Corrosion,* New York, N. Y., p. 14-22, 1963. (Publ. by National Association of Corrosion Engineers, Houston, Texas, 1966).

8. T. P. Hoar and F. M. West. *Proc. Roy. Soc.,* **268**, A 304 (1962).

9. J. G. Hines and T. P. Hoar. *J. Appl. Chem.,* **8**, 764 (1958).

10. S. Barnartt, R. Stickler and D. van Rooyen. Sci paper 62-139-55-Pl.24 (1962). Westinghouse Res. Lab., Pittsburgh; S. Barnartt and D. van Rooyen. *J. Electrochem. Soc.,* **108**, 222 (1961).
R. Stickler and S. Barnartt. *J. Electrochem. Soc.,* **109**, 343 (1962).

11. A. J. Forty. *Physical Metallurgy of Stress Corrosion Fracture.* (T. N. Rhodin, ed.) pp. 99-115, Interscience Publ., New York (1959).

12. N. Ohtani and R. A. Dodd. *Corrosion,* **21**, 161 (1965).

13. E. Brauns and W. Schwenk. *Archiv. Eisenhuettenwesen,* **32**, 387 (1961).

## Discussion

**K. Bohnenkamp, Max-Planck-Institut fur Eisenforschung**

In Figures 3 and 5 of the text it is shown that the electrochemical differentiation between flowing and non-flowing regions disappears or is small below the activation potential. That means the solid solution effects are small. The question is, are these effects necessary for stress corrosion. At least for the growth of the cracks, I think, it would be sufficient, if the repassivation is slower than the formation of new active surfaces coming from the plastic flow at the tips of cracks.

**L. Graf:**

Our investigations of homogeneous nonferrous alloys showed that the susceptibility to stress corrosion depends very strongly on the solute concentration as well as on a marked electrochemical process in the cracks. Since the austenitic stainless steels, for example Fe-13Cr-11Ni-0.025C (Steel No. 4306), have a high solute concentration, there is no reason that here, the solid solution effect should not be active. As shown by Copson, susceptibility of stress corrosion depends on the nickel content very strongly.

I understand that you question the cooperation of the solid solution effects, since they, evidently, play no part at the stress corrosion cracking of mild steels. But, here, the great influence of the C and N content shows that there are some other causes of the susceptibility to stress corrosion. The causes of it are surely not the same at all metallic materials.

Concerning your second question, the crack growth, we suppose, according to our results, that, during the stress corrosion process, the roots of the cracks are constantly active and no repassivation occurs there. This may be, as you say, because the repassivation is slower than the formation of new active surfaces caused by the plastic flow of the crack roots.

# CARBON AND NITROGEN EFFECTS IN THE STRESS CORROSION CRACKING OF AUSTENITIC STAINLESS STEELS

J. Bade and R. A. Dodd
University of Wisconsin

## Abstract

The effects of nitrogen and carbon on the stress cracking of austenitic stainless steels in chloride environments vary with the base composition of the steel.

Steels which intrinsically are either highly crack-susceptible or highly crack-resistant are little affected by higher interstitial contents. Steels of intrinsically moderate crack resistance are made more crack-prone by nitrogen additions and rather less crack-prone by carbon additions.

Transmission electron metallography indicates that these interstitials may exert significant influences on the defect structure, depending on the initial stacking fault energy, but the overall correlation between defect structure and stress cracking propensity is poor.

Since carbon and nitrogen seem to exert their greatest effect in the region of the Fe-Cr-Ni phase diagram where austenite is unstable, it is suggested that these elements play some important role in the structural stability of alloy atoms at the crack tip. Changes from austenitic to ferritic structures are accompanied by a chemical change. This local chemical change may provide a local dissolution at the crack tip.

## Introduction

Evidence concerning the effect of interstitial solutes, carbon and nitrogen, on the propensity to stress corrosion cracking of austenitic stainless steels is not clearcut. Tromans and Nutting[1] have suggested that segregated interstitial impurities are essential to the transgranular stress corrosion cracking of alloyed austenites, but this is not in accordance with the fact that austenitic stainless steels prepared from zone refined iron and "Specpure" chromium and nickel display about the same sensitivity to cracking as more impure alloys.[2] Also, Uhlig and White[3] reported that carbon and nitrogen, present in greater than trace amounts, seem to produce opposite effects, carbon reducing the susceptibility to stress corrosion cracking and nitrogen increasing it. Yokota et al[4] agree with this observation.

Swann attempted to account for the apparently opposite effects of carbon and nitrogen in terms of different substructures present in the plastically deformed alloys.[5] Austenitic stainless steels containing nitrogen in excess of nominal amounts were found to deform essentially by coplanar glide of dislocations, while carbon produced dislocation tangling or (at higher strains) a cellular substructure. Various opinions have been expressed concerning the reason why a coplanar mode of dislocation glide should correlate with an increased propensity to transgranular cracking. They include the suggestion of a preferred electrochemical attack along a continuous plane of disordered material in a short-range-ordered matrix,[5] the segregation of solute atoms to the coplanar groups of dislocations,[1,6,7] and the easier rupture of protective surface films by the higher slip steps associated with coplanar glide.[8,9] The precise mechanism remains obscure, and this fact, together with the uncertainties in the behavior of carbon and nitrogen in stainless steels, led to the present work.

## Experimental

Small ingots of the desired compositions were prepared by induction melting the high-purity components[(1)] in magnesia crucibles in a helium atmosphere. After homogenizing, the ingots were rolled into strips from which specimens were cut for evaluation of stress corrosion susceptibility and structural examination. All specimens were sealed in evacuated Vycor capsules and quenched from 1000 C. Corrosion testing was done in boiling 42%

---

[(1)]Glidden Super Pure "Plast-Iron" typically containing 0.002% C and 0.004% N. Johnson Matthey Specpure Nickel and Chromium.

$MgCl_2$ using a previously described spring-loading arrangement for straining the specimens.[10]

The compositions of the alloys investigated and the average fracture times are given in Table 1. The chromium and nickel contents refer to the accurately weighed amounts, but all alloys were analyzed for carbon and nitrogen whether these were deliberate alloying additions (added as spectrographic graphite and chromium nitride) or merely present as nominal interstitial impurities.

Although actual fracture times are quoted, little significance attaches to the absolute values since these vary with surface preparation, specimen geometry, etc. Therefore, close agreement with other investigators is not to be expected, but the constancy of the present technique ensures that the differences in cracking times presently observed are attributable only to compositional effects.

## Stress Corrosion Cracking Data

In addition to being listed in Table 1, the average fracture times are shown in Figure 1 in a way that relates them to the alloy constitution. The full line represents the approximate boundary of the austenite phase field at 1000 C. The boundary may be reasonably correctly located in (b) and (c), i.e., in the presence of moderate interstitial contents, but in (a) evidently it should be located at somewhat lower Ni and Cr contents because some of the carbon and nitrogen-free alloys were two-phase. Specifically, in (a) the 20Cr 10Ni, 25Cr 20Ni, and 30Cr 20Ni alloys contained large amounts of martensite after quenching from 1000 C. According to the slip step height model, martensitic steels should be resistant to transgranular cracking on account of the fine slip in deformed martensite,[11] although composition variations in the regions adjacent to carbides may cause martensitic steels to crack.[12] In the present instance the initial corrosive attack appeared to occur at the austenite/martensite interface; this point will be examined later.

In a macroscopic sense all the other alloys were austenitic and will be discussed on this basis. Although certain differences are apparent between Figures 1 (a), (b), and (c), the predominant observation in all three cases is that nickel and chromium contents primarily determine fracture times. The effect of higher nickel contents in promoting resistance to stress corrosion cracking is well known,[5,13,14] and it is now seen that decreasing the chromium content has a similar effect. For instance, 20Cr 30Ni and 10Cr 20Ni alloys have fracture times in excess of 500 hours irrespective of the interstitial contents. Practical chromium levels are considerably in excess of 10 $^W$/o, and it is possible that the lower amount of chromium diminishes the protective value of the surface film and promotes a general corrosive attack rather than the localized corrosion necessary for stress cracking. However, an alternative explanation may be that 20Cr 30Ni and 10Cr

TABLE 1 – Chemical Compositions (wt. %) and Fracture Times of Steels

|  | Cr | Ni | C | N | Average Fracture Time (Hr) |
|---|---|---|---|---|---|
| Low-nitrogen Low-carbon steels | 20 | 10 | 0.006 | 0.005 | 1.2 |
|  | 20 | 15 | 0.018 | 0.003 | 60 |
|  | 20 | 20 | 0.015 | 0.006 | 140 |
|  | 20 | 30 | 0.011 | 0.006 | >500 |
|  | 10 | 20 | 0.012 | 0.004 | >500 |
|  | 25 | 20 | 0.022 | 0.005 | 50 |
|  | 30 | 20 | 0.036 | 0.005 | 150 |
| Low-nitrogen High-carbon steels | 20 | 10 | 0.150 | 0.009 | 46 |
|  | 20 | 20 | 0.027 | 0.003 | 218 |
|  | 20 | 30 | 0.050 | 0.010 | >500 |
|  | 10 | 20 | 0.028 | 0.005 | >500 |
| High-nitrogen Low-carbon steels | 20 | 10 | 0.012 | 0.044 | 3.6 |
|  | 20 | 20 | 0.018 | 0.051 | 54 |
|  | 20 | 30 | 0.010 | 0.029 | >500 |
|  | 10 | 20 | 0.012 | 0.013 | 500 |
|  | 25 | 20 | 0.017 | 0.037 | 58 |

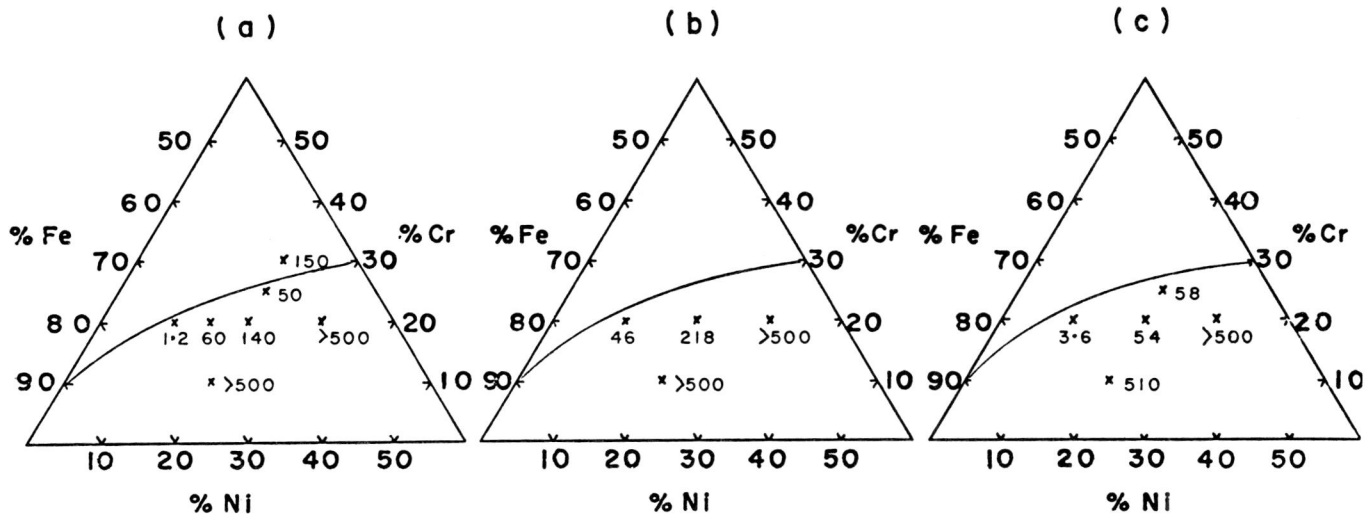

FIGURE 1 – Stress corrosion fracture times (hours) for various austenitic stainless steels: (a) carbon and nitrogen as nominal impurities, (b) .15 > C > .027, and (c) .051 > N > .013.

20Ni alloys are remote from the phase boundary and do not easily transform as a result of plastic deformation.

In comparison with the above observations the effects of both carbon and nitrogen are relatively minor, although it can be seen that these elements do indeed tend to exert opposing effects on fracture times, the situation varying with the base composition. The 20Cr 10Ni 0.044 N steel is considerably more crack-prone than the 20Cr 10Ni 0.150 C composition—fracture times of 3.6 and 46 hours, respectively—but a direct comparison with a low-interstitial austenitic composition near 20Cr 10Ni unfortunately is not possible. However, earlier observations by one of the investigators suggests that such a steel would not behave substantially differently from the 20Cr 10Ni 0.044 N composition. In other words, the base austenitic 20Cr 10Ni steel is so extremely crack-sensitive that nitrogen additions do not affect the situation. The longer fracture time associated with carbon additions will be discussed later in terms of structure. The base 20Cr 20Ni fracture time of 140 hours is increased to 218 hours by the addition of only 0.027% C, while 0.051% N reduces the time to 54 hours

Thus, a steel of moderate stress corrosion susceptibility is quite sensitive to interstitial effects, suggesting that practical control of interstitial elements is particularly worthwhile in this case. The 20Cr 30Ni and 10Cr 20Ni fracture times are apparently unaffected by carbon and nitrogen additions. This fact is particularly interesting in the case of nitrogen additions because in one of the steels, at least, nitrogen does promote coplanar glide of dislocations.

## Dislocation Substructures

It has been observed that nitrogen in austenitic stainless steels promotes coplanar glide of dislocations, and also that the effect may relate to the existence of short-range order rather than to a lowering of stacking fault energy by nitrogen.[5] The last suggestion is relevant to some stress corrosion models, but the necessity of coplanar dislocation motion occupies a central position in most current theories of transgranular cracking, generally through the effect on slip step height.[11]

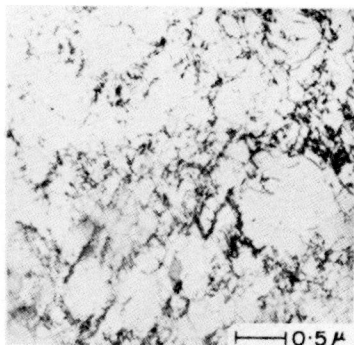

20% Cr, 10% Ni, 0.005% N

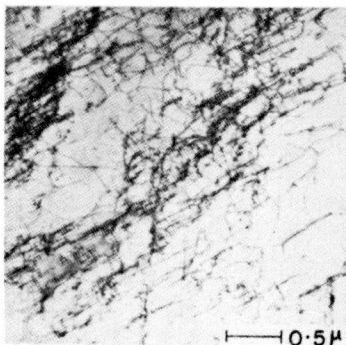

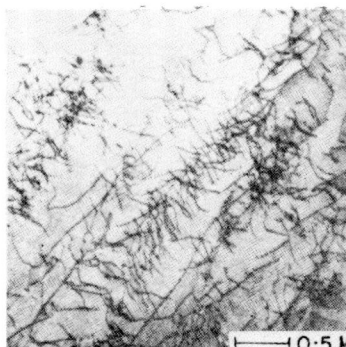

20% Cr, 20% Ni 0.005% N

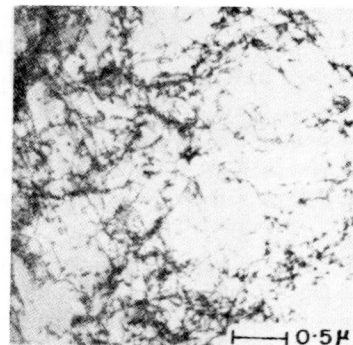

20% Cr, 30% Ni 0.005% N

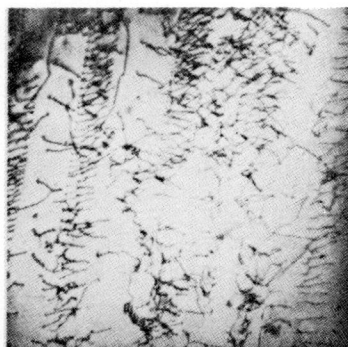

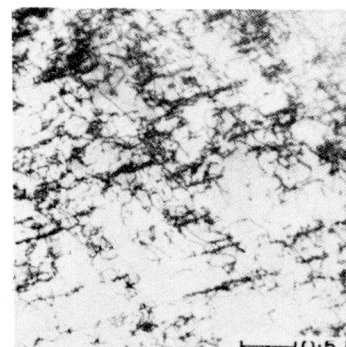

20% Cr, 10% Ni 0.05% N

20% Cr, 30% Ni 0.05% N

20% Cr, 20% Ni 0.05% N

FIGURE 2 — Effect of nitrogen on the structure of austenitic stainless steels of constant chromium and varying nickel concentrations (7% strain).

In Figure 2 is shown the effect of nitrogen on the structure of strained (7%) alloys of constant 20% Cr and varying Ni contents. In all cases the effect of nitrogen in promoting coplanar dislocation glide is quite pronounced. However, as noted there is not always a concomitant effect on stress cracking susceptibility. To reiterate, a base 20Cr 10Ni steel is already so susceptible to stress cracking that nitrogen additions have no added effect. Conversely, a base 20Cr 30Ni steel is highly immune to cracking and cannot be made susceptible through nitrogen in interstitial solution. Only the steels of moderate stress cracking susceptibility are adversely affected by nitrogen.

The effect of nitrogen on the structure of steels of constant 20% Ni and various Cr contents is shown in Figure 3. A consistent effect is not observed, perhaps largely because only 0.013% N was obtained in the 10Cr 20Ni steel. Taking this last fact into account it seems probable

that in these steels also nitrogen promotes coplanar motion of dislocations.

The effect of carbon on dislocation substructure has been examined only with respect to 20Cr 10Ni and 20Cr 20Ni steels. In both cases pronounced tangled substructures are formed in plastically strained alloys, as shown in Figure 4, and the effect is probably quite general. These facts are in complete agreement with earlier observations.[5]

## Nucleation Sites for Corrosion and Fracture Modes

The platinum decoration technique developed by Nielsen[15] offers an effective way of examining the sites of initial corrosive attack and relating them to any subsequent mode of fracture, i.e., transgranular or intergranular. For this purpose, specimens were electropolished, slightly strained, and immersed for 15 seconds in boiling 42% $MgCl_2$ containing chloroplatinic acid. Direct carbon replicas

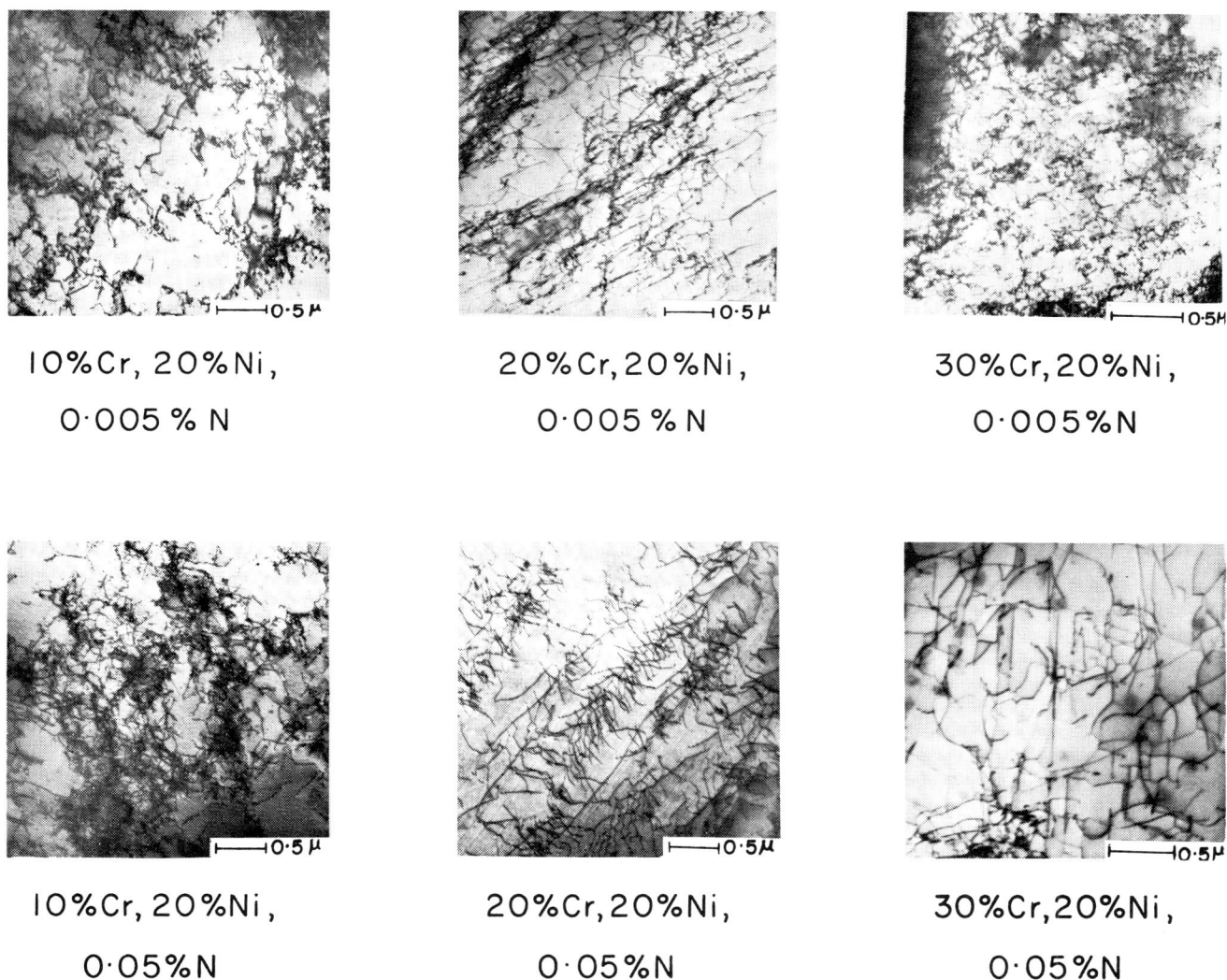

10%Cr, 20%Ni,
0·005 % N

20%Cr, 20%Ni,
0·005 % N

30%Cr, 20%Ni,
0·005%N

10%Cr, 20%Ni,
0·05%N

20%Cr, 20%Ni,
0·05%N

30%Cr, 20%Ni,
0·05%N

FIGURE 3 — Effect of nitrogen on the structure of austenitic stainless steels of constant nickel and varying chromium concentrations (7% strain).

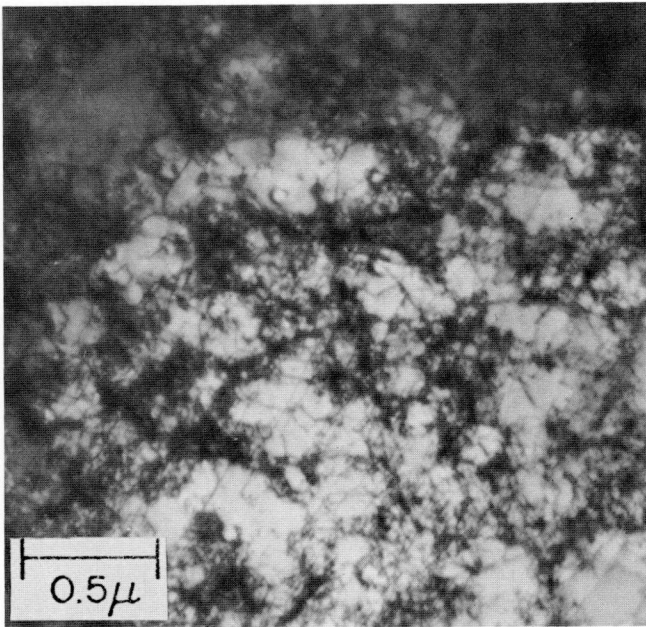

a

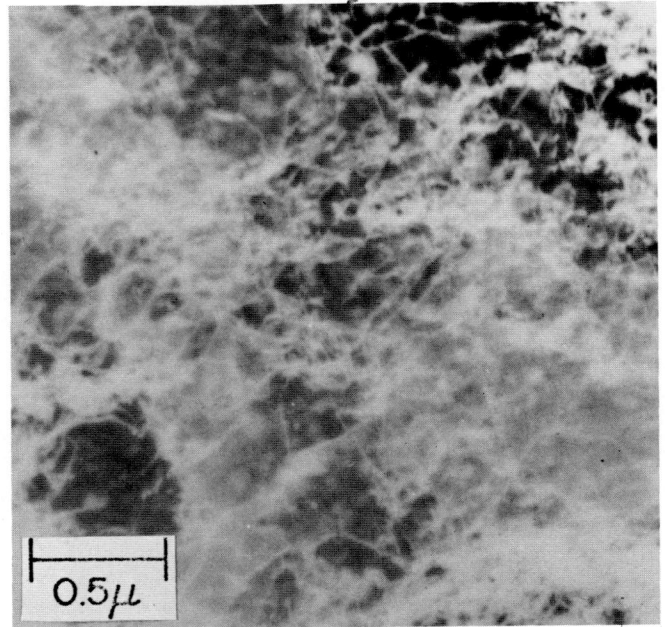

b

**FIGURE 4 — Effect of carbon on the structure of strained austenitic stainless steels.**

of the corroded surfaces were taken, the deposited platinum being extracted with the replica.

Figure 5 shows platinum decoration at austenite/martensite interfaces in the 20Cr 10Ni steel. This steel has an abnormally short fracture time, a fact which probably depends in part on the relative proportions and distributions of the two phases.

Figures 6-8 illustrate the way the severity of slip line corrosion varies with composition, and some micrographs of fracture modes are shown in Figure 9.

Considerable slip line attack occurs in the 20Cr 10Ni 0.150 C steel, notwithstanding the probable small slip step height associated with the tangled substructure of Figure 4. In fact, this alloy cracked transgranularly (Figure 9) showing that lack of coplanar dislocation glide does not preclude the possibility of transgranular cracking. On the other hand, the 20Cr 20Ni 0.027 C alloy which possesses a very similar dislocation substructure (Figure 4) shows no evidence of slip line attack even at high magnifications (Figure 8). The small slip line spacing, and hence small slip step height, is well evidenced. This alloy cracks predominantly intergranularly (Figure 9).

In the basic 20Cr 20Ni alloy there is considerable random pitting attack together with a relatively minor deposition of platinum along slip lines. The fracture mode of this alloy could not be uniquely characterized, and appeared to be mixed inter- and transgranular. This correlates with the weak slip line attack and the moderate resistance to stress corrosion cracking of this alloy.

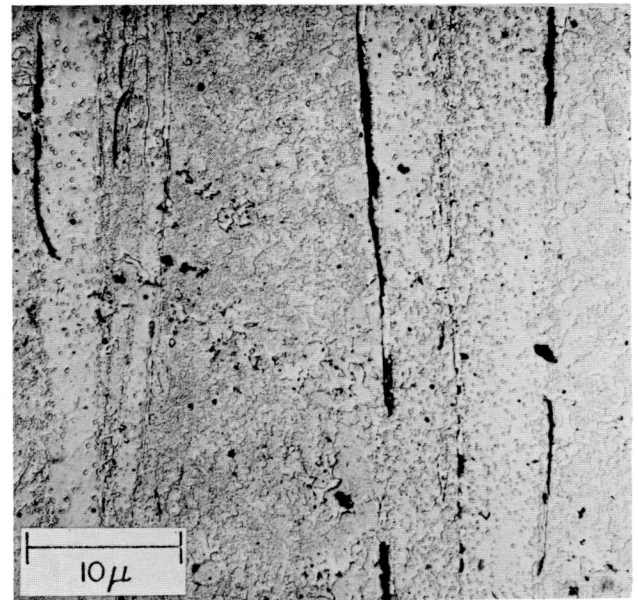

**FIGURE 5 — Martensitic/austenitic interface in Fe-20Cr-10Ni-0.005N-0.006C steel. Corroded regions denoted by platinum decoration.**

The remaining fractures depicted in Figure 9 are transgranular, as anticipated in view of the coarse slip (or coplanar glide) evidenced in these instances.

## Conclusions

It has been demonstrated earlier that coplanar glide of dislocations is not a sufficient criterion for transgranular

346

stress corrosion cracking.[14,16] This fact is re-emphasized by the present behavior of certain compositions, notably 20Cr 30Ni, which are quite resistant to stress cracking whether or not they contain nitrogen, and despite the fact that the presence of nitrogen promotes a coplanar dislocation structure.

It may be generally true that a tangled dislocation substructure correlates with intergranular cracking or perhaps complete immunity to stress cracking,[5] but the behavior of the 20Cr 10Ni 0.15 C composition shows that an alloy possessing such a substructure may indeed crack transgranularly. In other words, a coplanar dislocation substructure is not even a necessary condition attaching to transgranular stress cracking, so that homogeneous slip and

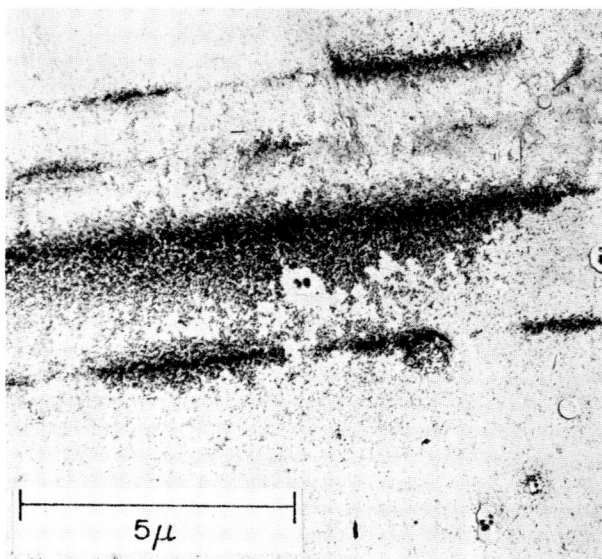

FIGURE 6 — Corrosion at slip lines in Fe-20Cr-10Ni-0.009N-0.15C steel.

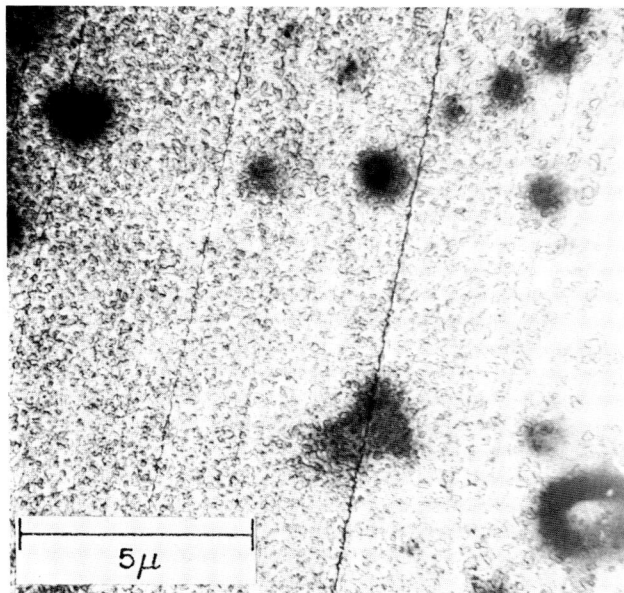

FIGURE 7 — Random pitting and some slip line corrosion in Fe-20Cr-20Ni-0.006N-0.015C steel.

concomitantly small slip steps do not necessarily imply the absence of transgranular stress cracking. The tangled dislocation substructures of Figures 4 (a) and (b) suggest that the 20Cr 10Ni 0.15 C and 20Cr 20Ni 0.027 C alloys deform identically, yet the alloys crack trans- and intergranularly respectively.

Various possibilities can be adduced to account for the above dilemma. For instance, the possibility of electrochemical attack at slip steps, leading to transgranular cracking, may be related to the kinetics of repassivation at the step, as emphasized by Scully.[17] Since the necessary electrochemical information is unavailable, this possibility cannot be examined further, although certainly there is no justification for assuming similar kinetics for different alloys. As an alternative, the possibility of phase transformations being responsible for transgranular stress cracking may require re-examination. Edeleanu first discussed the possible importance of a strain-induced austenite → martensite transformation,[18] but later theories of cracking have tended to reject this possibility on the grounds that stress cracking can occur at temperatures at which martensitic transformations are unlikely to occur. Still, the overwhelming impression gained from the present cracking data is that the principal consideration governing transgranular cracking susceptibility is the proximity of the alloy composition to the boundary of the austenite phase field, and this leads to the following suggestion.

The known phase boundaries of the Cr-Fe-Ni system at 400 C[14] can be assumed to correspond to equilibrium at 150 C (stress cracking test temperature), and Figure 10 clearly indicates that the crack-prone austenites are within or close to $(\gamma + \alpha)$ or $(\gamma + \sigma)$ equilibrium regions. Thus, if the average alloy composition places an alloy in the metastable austenite phase region, local diffusion may permit small volume elements to attain the composition of the equilibrium second phase. In the case of, say, a 20Cr 10Ni steel the second phase will be ferrite of lower nickel content than the co-existing equilibrium austenite, and it is

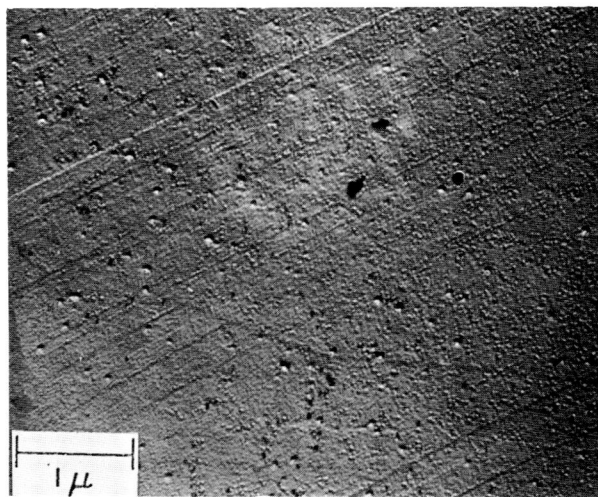

FIGURE 8 — Electron micrograph showing absence of slip line corrosion in Fe-20Cr-20Ni-0.003N-0.027C steel.

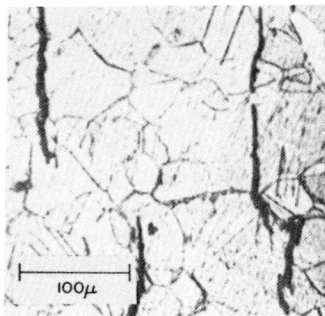

20% Cr, 10% Ni
0.005% N, 0.006% C

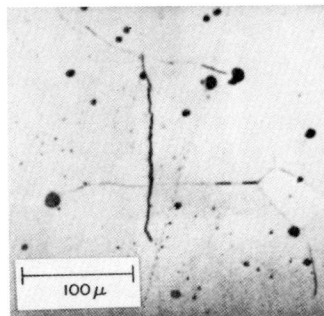

20% Cr, 10% Ni
0.044% N, 0.012% C

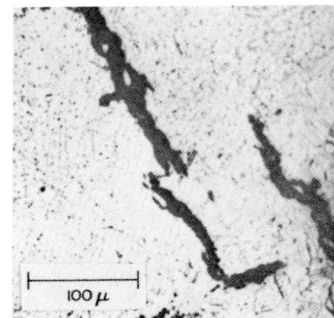

20% Cr, 10% Ni
0.009% N, 0.150% C

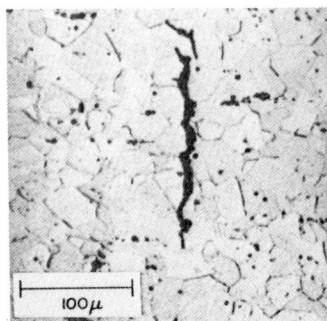

20% Cr, 20% Ni
0.051% N, 0.018% C

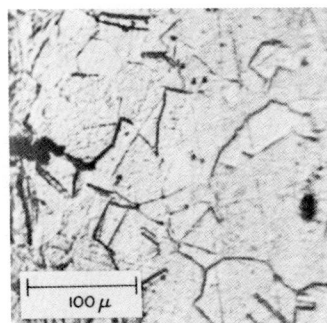

20% Cr, 20% Ni
0.003% N, 0.027% C

FIGURE 9 — Fracture mode versus composition of austenitic stainless steels.

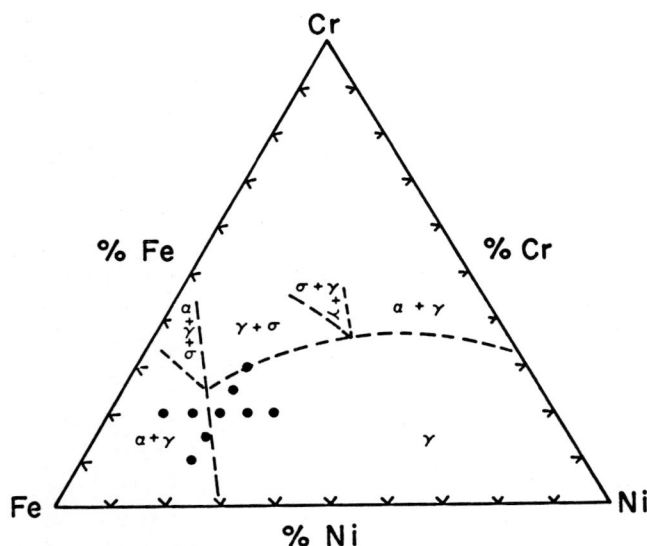

FIGURE 10 — Austenite phase boundaries at 400 C (after J. W. Pugh and J. D. Nisbet. *Trans. AIME*, 188, 268 (1950)). Full circles denote compositions of present investigation.

possible that preferential surface dissolution of nickel will aid the formation of small volume elements which are ferritic from a composition standpoint. Furthermore, even if the average alloy composition corresponds to stable austenite, local composition fluctuations corresponding to a two-phase alloy can still occur, such fluctuations being particularly likely if the average composition is near the phase boundary. The "transformed" regions will be rapidly removed by anodic dissolution if they form at a surface or crack tip. Further fluctuations will eventually result in the newly exposed region at the crack tip attaining a two-phase composition, the probability of this occurring within unit time being dependent on (a) local diffusion rates near the crack tip; these will be increased by dislocation motion in this region of high stress concentration and also by higher temperatures, (b) the remoteness of the average composition from the phase boundary. Thus, on the basis of this model a steel such as 20Cr 30Ni is highly resistant to transgranular stress cracking because, even if a pre-existing crack is assumed, the probability of composition fluctuations leading to a two-phase composition in the small volume element at the crack tip is very small. As outlined above, the model does not predict immunity to transgranular stress cracking for any austenitic stainless steel composition, but merely points to the probability of a long or a short fracture time.

The model is illustrated schematically in Figure 11 for a 20Cr 10Ni steel. The initially random solid solution of 11 (a) shows compositional changes (depletion in nickel) in the slipped region in 11 (b). The assumed ferritic volume

Random   70 Fe, 20 Cr, 10 Ni   solid solution

○ — Fe
● — Ni
◐ — Cr

(b)

At the corrosion test temperature (150–154° C) defect–aided diffusion occurs in the slipped region, and a small volume element may achieve the chemical composition of the thermodynamically stable second phase (ferrite). This involves a loss of nickel from this region.

The outlined element corresponds in composition to stable ferrite.

(c)

The ferritic element is anodically dissolved, further slip occurs at the notch and the entire process repeats. Ductile tearing may assist fracture.

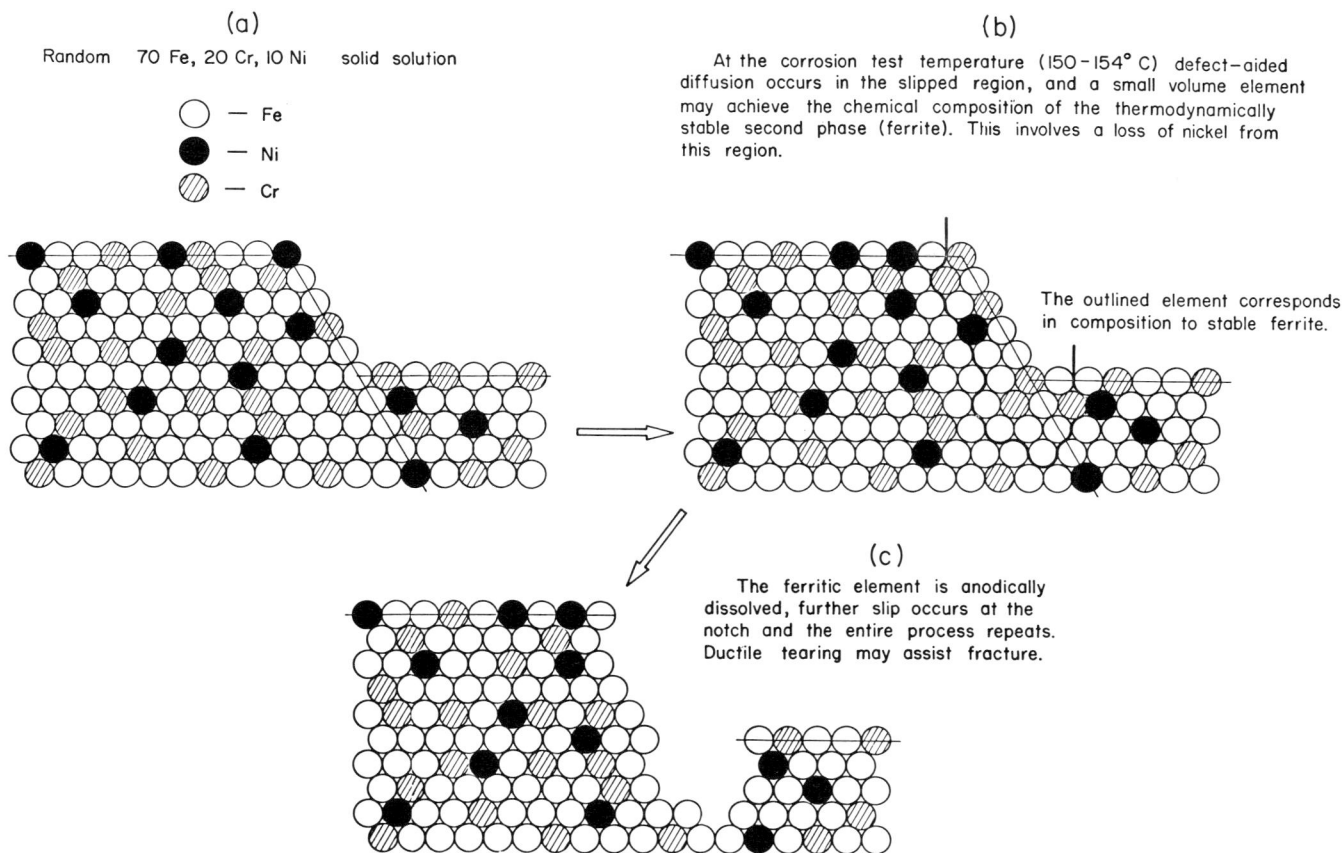

**FIGURE 11** — Schematic illustration of diffusion at a slip step in Fe-20Cr-10Ni austenitic stainless steel to form the stable phase (ferrite), which is then anodically dissolved.

element is highly anodic with respect to the surrounding austenite matrix, and is rapidly dissolved to give the configuration of 11 (c). Further slip now occurs, and the sequence is repeated.

The role of interstitial atoms is of secondary, although not necessarily negligible, importance. However, in the 20Cr 30Ni steel nitrogen additions can indeed be said to produce a negligible effect since the fracture time with or without nitrogen additions is always in excess of 500 hours. According to the ideas outlined above, this is simply because the probability of the required composition fluctuation is small in this alloy. The difference in transgranular stress cracking behavior of the 20Cr 10Ni 0.15 C and 20Cr 10Ni 0.044 N alloys (average fracture times of 46 and 3.6 hours, respectively) may be due to the coplanar dislocation glide in the latter alloy forming lamellar regions of abnormally high diffusion rates and hence abnormally high probabilities of the required composition fluctuations. A crystallographically simple fracture path ensues. The probability of the required composition fluctuations is equally high for the 20Cr 10Ni 0.15C steel, but the tangled substructure suggests that the "transformed" volumes form at random locations leading to a locally "zig-zagged" fracture path (although still transgranular as observed) and a longer fracture time.

An extension of this same argument can account for the differences in cracking behavior between 20Cr 10Ni

0.15C and 20Cr 20Ni 0.027C. Thus, the former alloy lies nearer the phase boundary and so may transform as discussed above. The lack of slip line corrosion in the latter alloy (Figure 8) is consistent with the observed freedom of this alloy from transgranular cracking, which in turn may be related partly to a low probability of composition fluctuations, but perhaps equally to the absence of a comparatively well-defined crystallographic corrosion path due to the tangled substructure. The observed intergranular stress cracking of this alloy is presumably due to segregation of interstitials at grain boundaries. If this intergranular cracking could be prevented, while at the same time retaining a tangled substructure, it might reasonably be predicted that this alloy would *eventually* crack transgranularly as a result of composition fluctuations.

Convincing proof of the above suggestions is lacking at the present time. Hot stage transmission electron microscopy has shown no evidence of phase transformations at 150 C in any of the steels, but in any event the model specifies only local nuclei formation, and growth of the nuclei into visible (electron-optical) particles is hardly to be expected at the test temperatures employed.

In summary, coplanar dislocation glide is neither necessary nor sufficient for transgranular stress cracking in austenitic stainless steels. According to the model, all these alloys have a finite probability of cracking transgranularly. However, control of dislocation substructure does effect some control over the cracking phenomenon by giving rise to a continuous fracture path (coplanar substructure) or a discontinuous fracture path (tangled substructure). Such control seems to be practically worthwhile for certain alloys at least, and can be effected by control of the amount and nature of interstitial elements.

## Acknowledgments

The authors gratefully acknowledge the sponsorship of the Air Force Office of Scientific Research through Grant AF-AFOSR-221-63.

## References

1. D. Tromans and J. Nutting. *Corrosion*, **21**, 5, 143 (1965).
2. N. Ohtani and R. A. Dodd. *Corrosion*, **21**, 5, 161 (1965).
3. H. H. Uhlig and R. A. White. *Trans. Amer. Soc. Metals*, **52**, 830 (1960).
4. K. Yokota, S. Morika and J. Ito. *Japan Inst. Metals*, 52nd General Meeting (1963).
5. P. R. Swann. *Corrosion*, **19**, 3, 102 (1963).
6. H. W. Pickering and P. R. Swann. *Corrosion*, **19**, 373 (1963).
7. P. R. Swann and H. W. Pickering. *Corrosion*, **19**, 369 (1963).
8. H. L. Logan. *Second International Conference on Metallic Corrosion* (1963).
9. P. R. Swann and J. D. Embury. *Proc. 2nd International Materials Conference*, Berkeley, Calif., 1964, in press.
10. D. Klarstrom, K. Kon, N. Ohtani, and R. A. Dodd. *Proc. 3rd International Corrosion Congress*, Moscow, U.S.S.R., 1966, in press.
11. P. R. Swann. *United States Steel Corporation Report*, P 717 Pr 291 (1965) April 6.
12. N. A. Tiner and C. B. Gilpin. *Corrosion*, **22**, 10, 271 (1966).
13. H. R. Copson. *Physical Metallurgy of Stress Corrosion Fracture*, p. 247, Interscience, New York (1959).
14. T. E. Evans and D. J. Burr. *British Corrosion Jnl.*, **1**, 5, 192 (1966).
15. N. A. Nielsen. *Corrosion*, **20**, 3, 104 (1964).
16. D. L. Douglass, G. Thomas, and W. R. Roser. *Corrosion*, **20**, 15 (1964).
17. J. C. Scully. Paper presented to the 1966 Annual Conference of the Stress Analysis Group of the British Institute of Physics during a Symposium, *The Physical Basis of Yield and Fracture*.
18. C. Edeleanu. *Stress Corrosion Cracking and Embrittlement*, p. 126, Jonh Wiley, New York (1956).

## Discussion

**D. L. Douglass, Stanford Research:**

The dislocation structures observed are determined to a large extent by the amount of strain and may change from coplanar arrays at about 5% strain to tangles or cellular arrays at 15% strain. Any conclusions must therefore be tempered somewhat unless the structure is known for various strains.

**R. A. Dodd:**

Dr. Douglass' observation is well taken, but not unreservedly applicable to the situation. Certainly, at 15% strain the dislocation structure will consist of tangles or cellular arrays, irrespective of the stacking fault energy. However, in practice, typical stress cracking may occur even at stresses below the macroscopic elastic limit so that only a rather small amount of localized plastic strain is necessary for stress cracking to occur. Under these conditions (or at somewhat higher stresses) the type of dislocation configuration which exists is very dependent on stacking fault energy and/or short-range order, and we believe that observations of the dislocation structures corresponding to 5-7% strain offers a reasonable correlation with practical situations.

**H. W. Paxton, Carnegie-Mellon University:**

I have a question and a comment. I hope the question doesn't sound impertinent, but I notice in your paper that you think you are forming martensite in a 30% chromium, 20% nickel alloy after quenching from 1000 C. In going back to your method of analysis I notice you just use the initial amounts of chromium and nickel. I wonder how much chromium you boiled out of this in your induction process, and if you have any direct analysis. You really shouldn't form martensite in this composition!

The comment on the idea of fluctuations which form martensite has been bandied around for many years in the phase transformation game. In particular, Kaufman who tried to make this one work, has been pushed to try to invoke the fluctuations at very high temperatures and even then can't prove it.

**R. A. Dodd:**

The alloys were melted quite carefully, and chromium losses are believed minimal. However, Professor Paxton's doubts concerning the existence of martensite in a quenched 30% Cr 20% Ni steel are justified. We made a casual assumption that the constituent was martensite but, in fact, it was probably delta ferrite. Of course, this change does not in the least detract from the comments in our paper on the importance of the amounts and distribution of other phases in relation to transgranular stress cracking susceptibility.

Regarding the second point raised by Professor Paxton, our suggestions relate to the possibility of composition fluctuations producing small volume elements of the stable phase, ferrite or sigma, not martensite. We do not know if Kaufman's analysis is applicable to our ideas, but we would again emphasize the fact that stress cracking propensity correlates closely with the degree of austenite metastability.

**J. C. Scully, University of Leeds:**

Over the past year or so I have been considering stress corrosion generally with reference to a very simple question: Why do cracks not stop? Since many susceptible alloys are passive we have to explain the highly localized activity at the tip of the crack in electrochemical effects arising from the physical metallurgical behavior of the alloy. In low strength ductile alloys the width of the slip step is probably important in denuding the local environment of passivating species. In high strength alloys localized "pop-in" crack propagation under plane strain conditions may promote a similar effect. In both cases the same general effect is observed: too much fresh metal surface is created too rapidly for the environment to repassivate adequately. As a result either anodic dissolution and/or hydrogen entry occur and promote cracking.[1-3]

1. J. C. Scully. *Corrosion Sci.*, 7, 197 (1967).
2. J. C. Scully. The Electrochemical Parameters of Stress Corrosion, *Corrosion Sci.* (in press).
3. J. C. Scully. The Mechanical Parameters of Stress Corrosion, *Corrosion Sci.* (to be published).

### R. A. Dodd:

**Dr. Scully's ideas may be applicable to many cases of stress cracking, but do these include the stress cracking of austenitic stainless steels in boiling magnesium chloride solutions? Surely no passive film is present, making a depassivating/repassivating model inappropriate.**

### H. R. Copson, International Nickel Co., Inc.:

The speaker raised a question about the path of the cracking in our tests in boiling 42 percent magnesium chloride solution (*Physical Metallurgy of Stress Corrosion Fracture,* p. 247, Interscience, New York, 1959). Micro-examinations were made of all specimens. This showed typical branching transgranular cracks. The path of the cracks was always transgranular regardless of the nickel content of the alloy.

### E. E. Denhard, Armco Steel Corp.:

This paper was of special interest to me because it parallels some work that our laboratories have been conducting.

I agree with the authors' conclusion that coplanar dislocation glide is probably neither necessary nor sufficient to account for transgranular stress corrosion cracking in austenitic stainless steels. However, I would have liked to have seen both the carbon and nitrogen ranges expanded for the alloys they investigated. For example, we find that iron-chromium-nickel alloys that contain as much as 35 to 50 percent nickel can be readily stress corrosion cracked if sufficient nitrogen is present. Since alloys of this type can tolerate nitrogen up to approximately one percent of the chromium content without danger of gassiness, an upper limit of .18 to .20 percent nitrogen might have been considered.

Similarly, carbon content beyond the .150 percent upper limit would have been an interesting area to test. Alloys of this type become extremely resistant to stress corrosion cracking.

Although we are primarily concerned with the mechanistic phenomena at this conference, we of course have as an ultimate objective a commercial realization of alloys that are resistant to stress corrosion cracking. In essence, I agree with the remark made by Dr. Uhlig that these alloys are strongly structurally dependent insofar as stress corrosion cracking is concerned. By expanding the carbon and nitrogen ranges, we are adding greater assurance that the austenite stability is maintained, providing of course that we do not add secondary constituents which will effect the stress corrosion process. Although most of the alloys that Mr. Bade and Professor Dodd investigated were reported to be fully austenitic, our tools for measuring this aspect are still grossly limited. It seems highly possible that localized regions of martensite could be present on an atomic basis even though the macro indications of the material are face-centered cubic. If the latter conjecture is correct, then the recent work of Matsushima, Uhlig and others who point a finger at hydrogen embrittlement of austenitic stainless steels cannot be ignored.

# INFLUENCE OF CARBON AND NICKEL CONTENT ON STRESS CORROSION CRACKING OF AUSTENITIC STAINLESS ALLOYS IN PURE OR CHLORINATED WATER AT 350 C

H. Coriou, L. Grall, P. Olivier, and H. Willermoz
Centre d'Etudes Nucleaires de Saclay

## Abstract

Fe-Cr-Ni alloys have been exposed to high purity water at 350 C and the influence of nickel and carbon concentrations studied. Variation in carbon concentrations are shown to exert no effect on the tendency for intergranular cracking in an Inconel-600 type alloy. Intergranular cracking was observed in Inconel 600 regardless of the presence or absence of chloride.

It was shown in previous studies[1-3] that austenitic nickel-chromium-iron alloys of high nickel content were sensitive to a characteristic phenomenon of stress corrosion cracking. This process always took the form of intergranular cracking and occurred in demineralized water or in steam in the absence of oxygen, at temperatures ranging from 300 to 650 C. This phenomenon has the following general characteristics: the time necessary for cracks to appear was always long, of the order of several months; a reduction in the level of stress increased very considerably the breaking time; finally, the addition of a slight creep accentuated the sensitivity to this type of cracking. One rupture of Inconel 600 tube in service conditions was observed in a nuclear reactor and appears to be related to this process.[4]

The present work considers the influence, on an essentially intergranular process, of new factors likely to be involved: (1) Lowering of the carbon content and consequently of the intergranular carbide precipitate density, and (2) varying the nickel content of the alloy in water containing chloride rather than the pure water used previously.

## I. Influence of Lowered Carbon Concentration

*Experimental*

Taking commercial Inconel 600[1] as the basis of comparison, an alloy of similar composition was specially melted under vacuum. The composition of the resulting alloy is compared with the commercial alloy in Table 1. The special alloy has the desired low carbon content (20 ppm).

The alloy was rolled to 1 mm thick sheet and quench annealed from 1050-1100 C. Samples were cut and pickled and prepared by a process described earlier.[3] The specimens are stressed by bending in stainless steel jigs (Figure 1). They are electrically insulated from the support. The stress applied is always a little higher than the yield strength and the metal sustains a slight permanent deformation of about 0.5 percent maximum.

TABLE 1 – Composition (Weight Percent)

| Material | C | N | Ni | Cr | Mn | Si | P | S |
|---|---|---|---|---|---|---|---|---|
| Inconel 600 | 0.040 | 0.032 | 78.4 | 14.9 | 0.1 | 0.2 | – | 0.007 |
| Inconel 600 - type alloy | 0.002 | 0.004 | 77.3 | 18.0 | 1.1 | 0.5 | 0.007 | 0.007 |

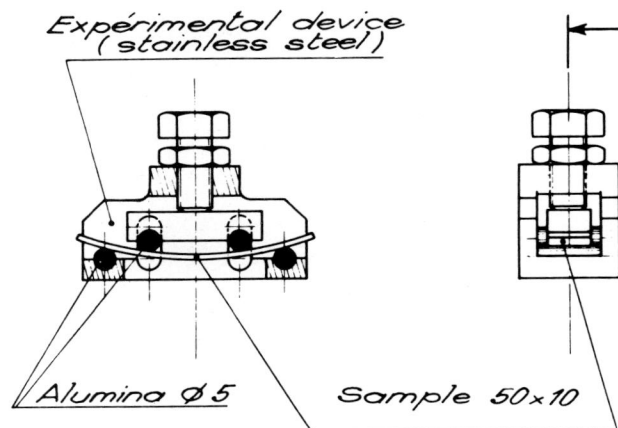

FIGURE 1 — Stainless steel jig for bended specimen.

---

[1]Trade name, The International Nickel Co., Inc.

The samples are placed in an 18/10 stainless steel testing loop at 350 ± 1 C (180 bars). The water is continuously purified by a mixed bed ion exchange resin and the resistivity is maintained at about 1 MΩx cm when cold. Two series of experiments were carried out using this system: (a) the water is degassed to give an oxygen concentration lower or equal to 0.003 mg/l; (b) an overpressure of 5 kg/cm$^2$ of oxygen is introduced and the water is saturated with this gas throughout the test. The experiments are conducted under these conditions for a period of eight months, the specimens being inspected monthly.

## Results and Discussion

Optical metallography of longitudinal sections of the low carbon alloy showed intergranular cracking in speci-

mens exposed to both low (Figures 2 (a) and (b)) and high (Figure 3) oxygen environments similar to that observed previously in the commercial Inconel 600.[3] For comparison, Figure 4 shows a specimen of the special alloy exposed without stress.

The special and commercial alloys were characterized by examination of carbon replicas in the electron microscope. Figure 5 from the special low carbon alloy exhibits sparse and random precipitation. On the contrary, the commercial alloy in Figure 6 shows relatively large amounts of precipitates predominantly at the grain boundary. Moreover two distinct kinds of component are observed as shown in Figures 7 (a) and (b). These two precipitates differ in size and morphology.

The observations above suggest that (a) lowering of the carbon content and the resulting elimination of intergranular carbide precipitation plays no apparent part in the

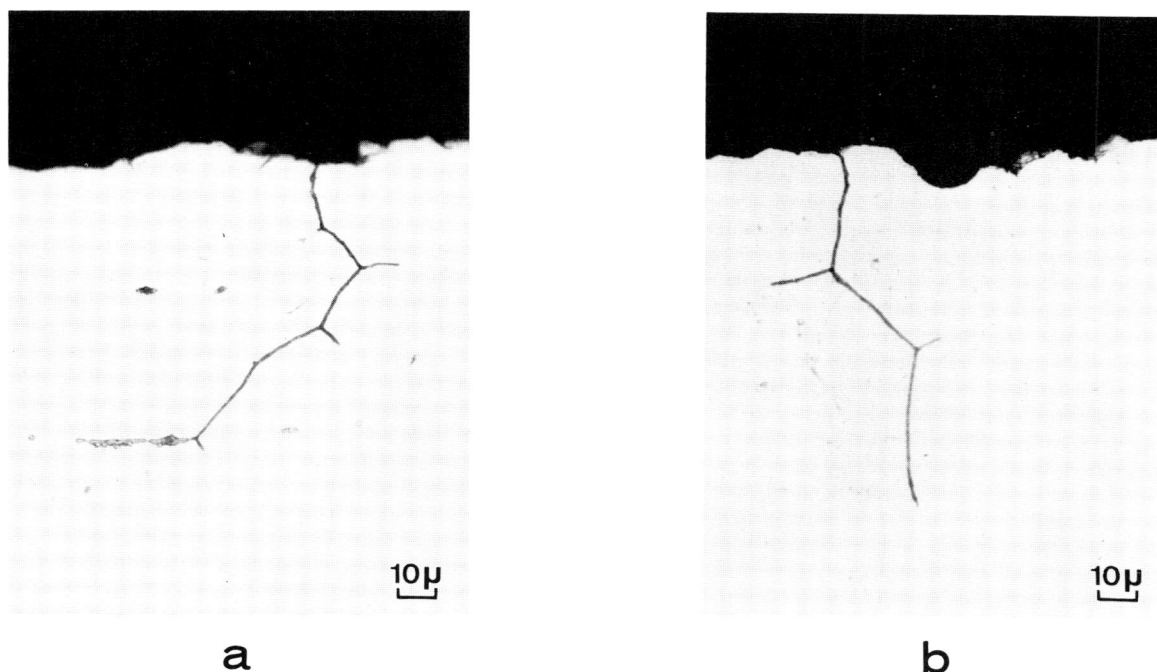

a

b

FIGURE 2 — (a) and (b) Intergranular cracks on extra low carbon Inconel 600-type alloy after an eight months test under stress in circulating demineralized water at 350 C with low oxygen content ( ≤ 0.003 mg/l).

FIGURE 3 — Intergranular crack on extra low carbon Inconel 600-type alloy. Same conditions as Figure 2 but in oxygen saturated water.

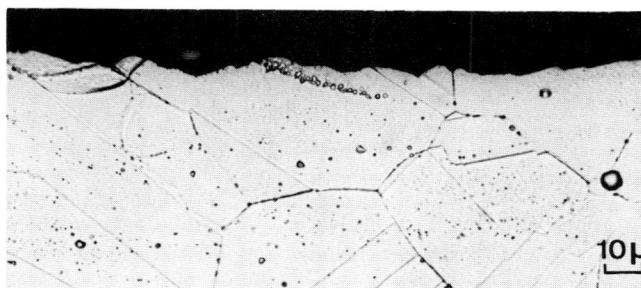

FIGURE 4 — Nonstressed specimen of extra low carbon Inconel 600-type alloy after eight months in demineralized and low oxygen-containing water at 350 C.

353

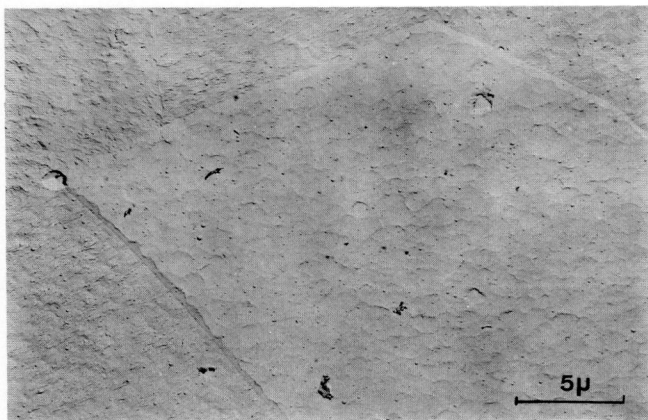

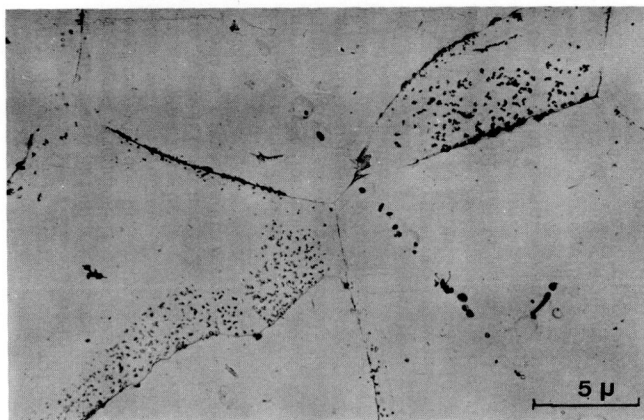

FIGURE 5 — Grain boundary structure of extra low carbon Inconel 600-type alloy. Note absence of intergranular carbide precipitation (carbon content: 20 ppm).

FIGURE 6 — Commercial Inconel 600-inter and intragranular carbide precipitations (carbon content: 400 ppm).

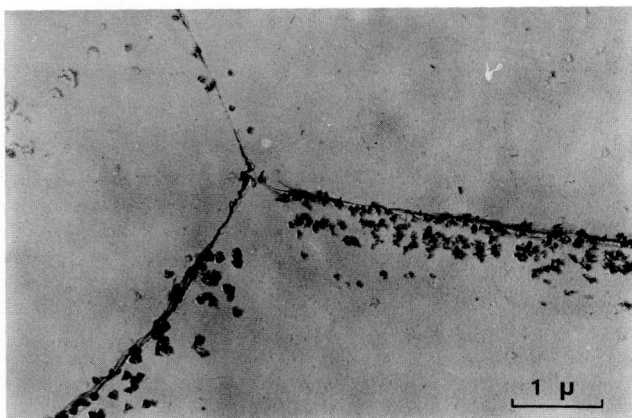

**a**

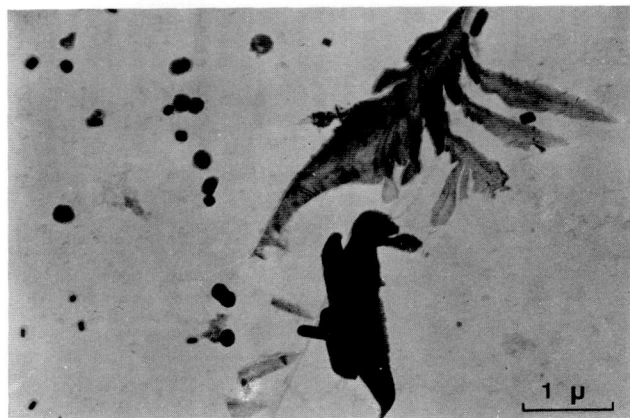

**b**

FIGURE 7 — Two types of precipitates at grain boundaries of commercial Inconel 600: (a) Fine carbide precipitation, (b) Coarse carbide precipitation.

phenomenon of intergranular cracking investigated and (b) the oxygen content does not significantly influence the process.

## II. Influence of Nickel Content in Water Containing Chloride

*Experimental*

The compositions of alloys having various nickel contents are given in Table 2. Chromium is constant (17-18%) and nickel varies from 10 to 77%. It will be noted that in every case the carbon content is low. The 77% nickel type is that studied in the first part of this work and is thus comparable to Inconel 600, while the 10% nickel alloy is similar to 304 ELC stainless steel. These alloys were prepared and stressed the same as in the previous section.

**TABLE 2—Composition Weight Percent**

| Material | C | N | Ni | Cr | Mn | Si | Fe |
|---|---|---|---|---|---|---|---|
| IN-15 | 0.020 | 0.017 | 10.1 | 17.5 | 1.0 | 0.3 | bal. |
| IN-16 | 0.025 | 0.010 | 14.9 | 17.2 | 1.0 | 0.5 | " |
| IN-17 | 0.020 | 0.008 | 24.5 | 17.1 | 1.0 | 0.5 | " |
| IN-18 | 0.025 | 0.004 | 34.7 | 17.3 | 1.1 | 0.5 | " |
| IN-19 | 0.010 | 0.004 | 44.3 | 17.3 | 1.1 | 0.5 | " |
| IN-20 | 0.010 | 0.004 | 64.5 | 17.5 | 1.1 | 0.5 | " |
| IN-32 (Inconel 600 - type alloy) | 0.002 | 0.004 | 77.3 | 18.0 | 1.1 | 0.5 | " |

For each alloy two nonstressed samples were tested for purpose of comparison. The test was carried out in a stainless steel autoclave completely lined with Zircaloy 2.

The experimental medium is demineralized water (resistivity $\rho \geqslant 1$ M$\Omega$x cm) to which sodium chloride is added to give, at the experimental temperature (350 ± 2 C),

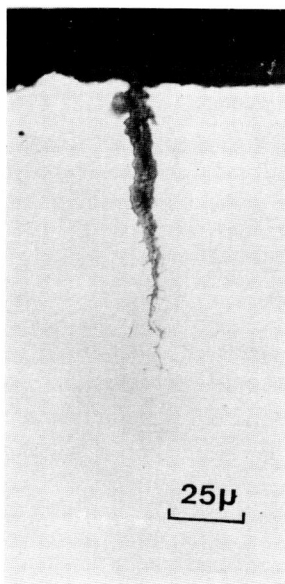
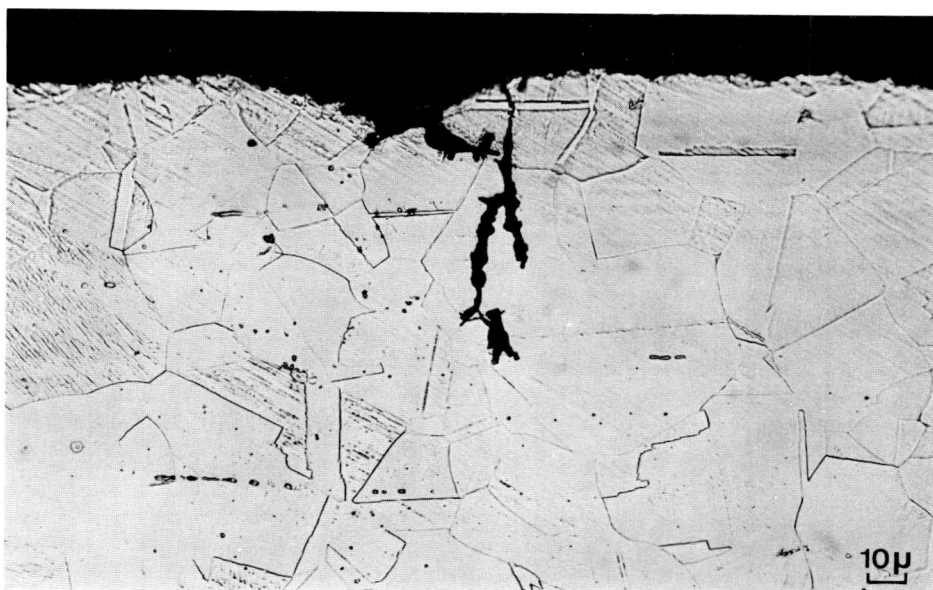

a

b

FIGURE 8 — (a) and (b) Transgranular cracking of 18% Cr-10% Ni alloy after a six months test under stress in static 350 C water containing 1 g/l Cl⁻.

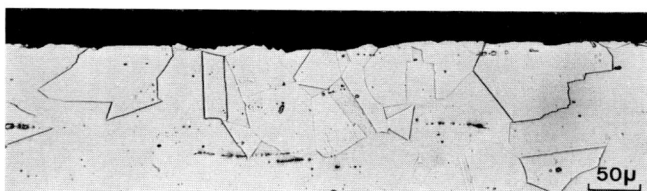

FIGURE 9 — Absence of any type of cracking on an 18% Cr-35% Ni alloy after the same test as Figure 8 (a) and (b).

FIGURE 11 — Unstressed specimen of extra low carbon Inconel 600-type alloy after six months in 1 g/l Cl⁻ bearing water at 350 C.

a

b

FIGURE 10 — (a) and (b) Intergranular cracking of extra low carbon Inconel 600-type alloy after the same test as Figure 8 (a) and (b), and 9.

a chloride ions concentration of 1 g/l. The solution is degassed (oxygen content lower or equal to 0.003 mg/l). The test is conducted under these conditions for six months, at the end of which the samples are removed and subjected to a systematic metallographic analysis according to the procedure used in the preceding study. The chloride content of the water is verified monthly and the solution renewed when the autoclave is open to inspect the specimens.

*Results and Discussion*

1. The 10% nickel alloy, representing a 304 ELC stainless steel, undergoes characteristic transgranular cracking (Figures 8 (a) and (b)). This observation can be compared to the well known phenomenon of stress corrosion cracking of this same type of steel in chlorinated solutions at low temperature.

2. The 15% nickel alloy shows slight signs of a cracking process similar to the 10% nickel alloy.

355

3. On alloys containing from 25 to 65% nickel, no trace of any cracking phenomenon was observed. Figure 9 shows a cross sectional micrograph of a 35% nickel sample.

4. The 77% nickel alloy exhibits clear evidence of the intergranular cracking phenomenon shown previously (Figures 10 (a) and (b)). For comparison, Figure 11 shows structure of an unstressed reference sample.

From these observations it can be concluded that the occurrence of stress corrosion cracking in chloride-containing water at 350 C seems to depend on the composition of the alloy and particularly on its nickel content. In effect, all other conditions being equal, the variation of this single parameter leads to the absence of cracks or to the appearance of one or other of the possible cracking processes.

## III. Conclusions

Considering the above results together with those from previous studies the following significant trends emerge with respect to the cracking of Fe-Ni-Cr alloys in 350 C water.

1. The cracking process is always very slow and shows up only after several months of testing.

2. The type of mechanical stress applied and its magnitude considerably modify the sensitivity to cracking and its severity.[3] A tensile stress produces more numerous and deeper cracks, appearing more rapidly than does a bending stress. A reduction in stress increases the lifetime of the sample. The addition of a slight creep makes the phenomenon more sensitive. The influence of these factors and the direction in which they act prove that we are dealing with a stress-dependent corrosion process.

3. Among the various parameters only the variation in nickel content of the alloy shows a determining influence. No change can be found in the typically intergranular cracking observed on alloys of the Inconel 600 type, in connection with the following: (a) oxygen saturation or degassing of the water, (b) a 1 g/l concentration or the absence of chloride ions in solutions, and (c) presence of carbon or its reduction to trace amounts in the metal.

4. The nickel concentration is the predominating factor. The liability to crack, as a result of corrosion under a stress slightly above the yield strength, in water at 350 C, is illustrated by Figure 12. It is found in effect that whether or not annealed Type 304 ELC stainless steel cracks, depends on whether or not the water is chlorinated, and when the phenomenon does occur it is transgranular. On the other hand, Inconel 600-type alloys show cracking in every case and the cracks are always intergranular.

5. The intermediate alloys with nickel concentrations between the values A and B in Figure 12 do not crack under the conditions of these experiments. The two extremes thus defined cannot be determined with precision until more information is available. Trends are probably liable to variation, for example, with temperature. However they show that alloys of medium nickel concentration are of definite technological interest. This diagram shows in addition that the well known beneficial effect of an increased nickel content on the stress corrosion cracking of stainless steels in chloride solutions becomes, on the contrary, unfavorable when the values are too high under the conditions considered here. However, we observe at the same time that this is due to the appearance of another and quite different category of phenomenon, on which the action of a conventional factor such as the presence of chloride ions becomes effectively negligible even for a concentration as high as 1 g/l. This result differs sharply from that of the usual pattern in chlorinated solutions, the prototype of which is represented by magnesium chloride solution boiling at 154 C.

6. As we stated previously[3] the main question raised by the phenomenon of intergranular cracking thus concerns the specific influence of nickel above a certain minimum concentration on the properties of the grain boundaries of austenitic alloys.

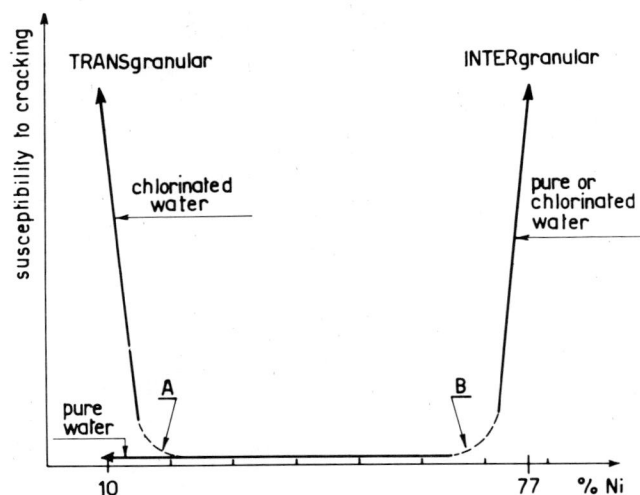

FIGURE 12 — Schematic diagram showing the influence of nickel content on the cracking processes occurring in 18% chromium austenitic alloys, when stressed slightly above the yield point in 350 C water (demineralized or containing 1 g/l chloride ions).

## References

1. H. Coriou, L. Grall, Y. LeGall and S. Vettier. *Stress Corrosion Cracking of Inconel in High Temperature Water.* Third Metallurgy Conference on Corrosion, Saclay, 1959. North Holland Publishing Co., Amsterdam, 161-169.

2. H. Coriou, L. Grall, M. Pelras and S. Vettier. *Stress Corrosion Cracking in Chloride Media and in High Temperature Water of Nickel Containing Alloys.* Paper presented at Colloquium of the European Society of Atomic Energy, Studsvick, Sweden, 1962.

3. H. Coriou, L. Grall, C. Mahieu and M. Pelras. Sensitivity to Stress Corrosion and Intergranular Attack of High-Nickel Austenitic Alloys. *Corrosion,* **22**, 10, 280-290 (1966) October.

4. B. Gronwal, L. Ljungberg, W. Hubner and W. Stuart. Intercrystalline Stress Corrosion Cracking of Inconel 600 Inspection Tubes in the Agesta Reactor. *Aktiebolaget Atomernergie,* A.E. 245, Stockholm, Sweden (1966).

## Discussion

**J. E. LeSurf, Chalk River Nuclear Laboratories:**

We have seen propagation of intergranular crevices on Inconel-600 in high purity water in the absence of external stress. Figures 1 and 2 show unstressed samples exposed out-of-flux in in-reactor loops in NRX, i.e., in irradiated water; Figure 3 is from an out-reactor loop.

1. This specimen was in the two-phase (steam/water) coolant of a boiling in-reactor water loop. The water had neutral pH, with av. 4.6 ppm $O_2$ in the steam phase and av. 0.1 ppm $O_2$ in the water phase. (Exposure time—89 days at 288 C.)

2. This sample was exposed in the separated steam from a fog-cooled (water mist in steam) radiation, dosed with ammonia to inhibit oxygen formation ($< 0.005$ ppm $O_2$ in the steam phase). (Exposure time—161 days at 300 C.)

3. This sample was exposed in an out-reactor pressurized water loop for 257 days at 288 C. The water was dosed with 10 ppm $NH_3$ and 0.01-0.05 ppm $O_2$ was maintained by hydrogen peroxide injection.

The material was annealed sheet, deep drawing quality, with presumably very little internal stress.

In all cases, significant intergranular penetration has occurred, up to $7 \times 10^{-3}$ inches. The as-received material had slight intergranular crevices to a maximum depth of 0.5 $\times 10^{-3}$ in, presumably from the manufacturer's pickle. The manufacturer now recommends vapor-blasting the surface with zirconia instead of pickling. We have subsequently exposed crack-free material in two locations. These samples have not yet been examined.

**W. P. Hubner, Corrosion Laboratory, AB Atomenergi:**

As to the difference between the French results and those of Copson and coworkers, I would like to ask Dr. Grall two questions.

Have you interrupted your tests for examination and inspection of the specimens? As I understand, in Copson's test, the testing period is not a continuous one, but is frequently interrupted for various times. This could have quite an influence on the build up of corrosion products and on the water chemistry in general.

The other question is: Have you in your experiments found any difference between specimens with crevices or those free of crevices? Have you found any effect of any kind of crevice in your specimens?

**H. R. Copson:**

Dr. Hubner asked a question about the effect of interrupting the tests. This generated an important thought in my mind. On the one hand we are concerned with the details of laboratory autoclave test procedures, and on the other hand we are trying to translate the laboratory results to service performance. This is not always easy or reliable. For evaluating the service performance of materials there is nothing better than actual service experience. Alloy 600 has been used in steam generators of pressurized water reactors for some time and the performance has been excellent.

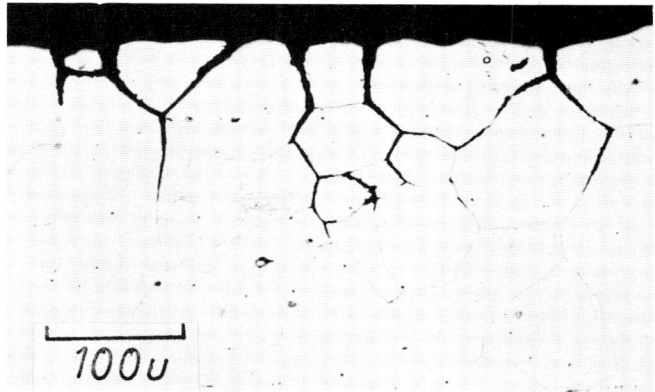

FIGURE 1 — Inconel-600 in steam/water, 89 days and 288 C.

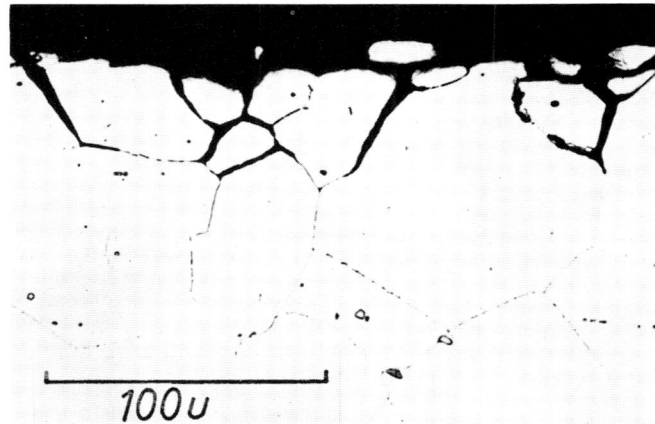

FIGURE 2 — Inconel-600 in dry steam, 161 days at 300 C.

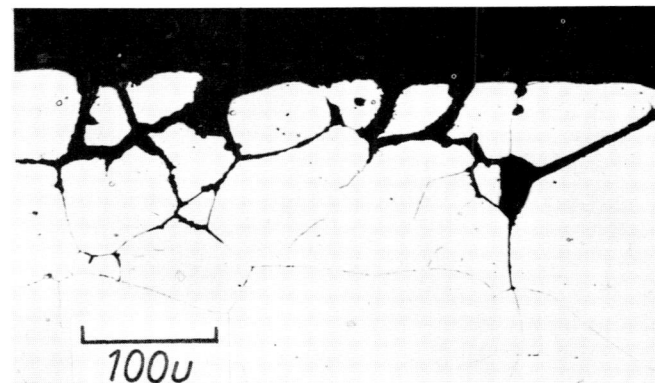

FIGURE 3 — Inconel-600 in pressurized water, 257 days at 288 C.

**F. W. Pement, Westinghouse Electric Corp.:**

I would like to ask about some experimental details. First, was there any appreciable thermal cycling or temperature variation during the time in the six months' test period, and, second, for those tests in which specimens were four-point loaded on alumina rods, what was the condition of the alumina at the end of the tests?

**E. E. Denhard, Armco Steel Corp.:**

It seems to me that the high nickel alloys characterized by the Inconel 600 type must fail by a mechanism other than the familiar transgranular stress corrosion cracking. Perhaps this is an environmentally affected stress rupture test since, as far as I know, it has only been observed to occur at high temperatures in the presence of steam.

In alloys of this type, the increased nickel greatly restricts carbide solubility and this in turn is reflected by decreased intergranular corrosion resistance, particularly in the presence of strong oxidizing chemicals. This is evidenced by the extremely high corrosion rate of Inconel 600 in boiling 65% nitric acid.

Perhaps the intergranular fracture path of this material is a grain boundary oxidation phenomena hastened by the particular form of oxygen present and the temperature and stress present.

**H. R. Copson:**

Our general chairman has asked us to bring out areas of disagreement. We have one here which pertains to the behavior of Alloy 600 in high purity water. Results obtained in the United States seem to be different from those reported in this paper.

The story starts some 10 or 15 years ago when interest began to develop in the use of Alloy 600 for heat exchanger tubing in pressurized water nuclear reactors. This interest was based on the realization that in water and steam environments it is difficult to exclude chlorides completely. Thus there is always a possibility that evaporation can form high local concentrations of chlorides. Experience gained from many years of laboratory tests, plant tests, and service performance established that high nickel alloys are resistant to stress corrosion cracking in hot concentrated chloride solutions under conditions where austenitic stainless steels fail rapidly. So far this is in agreement with the present paper.

In addition to resistance to chlorides, however, it was necessary to establish that Alloy 600 was suitable for the environmental conditions encountered in pressurized water reactors. Accordingly extensive further test programs were carried out in the United States. These showed that Alloy 600 had low corrosion rates, low crud release rates, acceptable activity build-up, excellent weldability, and resistance to pitting, intergranular corrosion, and stress corrosion cracking under simulated service conditions. These qualifying tests led to the continuing successful use of Alloy 600 in pressurized water reactors.

This, however, is not the complete story. In recent years there have been reports, such as described here today, showing intergranular corrosion and cracking of Alloy 600

in certain high pressure high temperature water environments. Naturally we were surprised by this, and have made repeated attempts to reproduce such attack in pure water. One series of tests was run at Battelle Memorial Institute on specimens and water received from France. Careful microexamination showed the absence of intergranular attack of any of these Alloy 600 specimens. All this was published in *Corrosion,* **21,** page 1-8, 1965.

Continued laboratory testing soon revealed that certain contaminants in the water could promote attack. One of these was lead. In combination with tensile stresses a lead contaminant produced cracking which usually was predominantly transgranular, although in some instances the cracking was partly or largely intergranular. Another harmful contaminant was oxygen, but oxygen was detrimental only in the presence of both crevices and high tensile stresses. With this combination intergranular stress corrosion cracking occurred in the crevice area. The first results with these contaminants were included in the 1965 paper.

We have continued the laboratory testing, and another paper dealing with oxygen contamination has been accepted by *Corrosion* for publication in 1968. This describes stress corrosion tests in pressurized water at 600 F using double U-bends and double bent beam specimens. The tests were conducted in autoclaves for up to 3000 hours. The composition of the gas phase and the pH were controlled. The materials tested included Alloys 600, 625, 800, stainless steels Type 304, 304L, 347, and some experimental laboratory compositions. In these tests no attack was observed in specimens stressed at 90 percent of the room temperature yield strength. No attack was observed when hydrogen constituted the gas phase. No attack was observed when crevices were absent. The combined action of a high stress, a high oxygen concentration, and a crevice did promote intergranular attack and cracking in the crevice area in all the alloys tested. The severity of the attack increased with the oxygen concentration. Many specimens heated for 2 hours at 1250 F showed deeper attack than annealed specimens. However, solution heat treatment, low carbon content, or the presence of carbide stabilizers did not eliminate the attack. Variations in composition within the normal range of Alloy 600 were unimportant. Differences in behavior among the several alloys tested were minor compared with the environmental effects.

This covers rather briefly the main points I wished to discuss. There is an unresolved discrepancy between the results described and the data in the paper which was just presented.

**L. Grall:**

As for an eventual influence of contaminants, such as lead or oxygen, the problem has already been discussed and a precise answer has been given in *Corrosion* (October 1966, p. 288-290). The conclusion is that none of these factors is to be considered. On the other hand, we never introduced a "crevice effect" in any test we made. So the phenomenon which has been evidenced is proper to the material itself.

About experimental details, we may be precise about the various points as follows:

1. The specimens do not undergo any thermal cycling, even during recurring shutdowns for examination, because the inertia of the apparatus under pressure is high and the cooling rate is low.

2. The alumina rods show no trace of any damage during test and they keep intact. Identical tests have been made with sintered zirconia or Zircaloy 2 previously oxidized in steam at 400 C: the results obtained were similar.

# PART IV

# CARBON STEELS*

*Evaluation of this session included with evaluation of session on High Strength Steels.

# STRESS CORROSION CRACKING OF LOW CARBON STEELS

R. N. Parkins
The University of Newcastle Upon Tyne

One of the disquieting features associated with the phenomenon of stress corrosion cracking in mild steels is that, since some of its characteristics were first recorded[1] over 50 years ago, there appears to have been a continuing increase in the number of environments in which it has been observed to occur and in the frequency of its occurrence. These trends are not surprising perhaps from certain viewpoints, but they are disquieting because, although knowledge of the problem has increased in this time, it remains the case that understanding of the environmental aspects of the phenomenon in particular is still so poor that it is frequently impossible to decide with confidence and without recourse to experiment whether or not untried environments will promote such failure. It is true that preventative measures are available and some of these are dependent upon manipulation of the electro-chemistry of cracking, e.g., cathodic protection or the use of inhibitive additions, but these methods have *ad hoc* experiment as their basis rather than enlightened thought related to the nature of the reactions whereby cracks are propagated. Fortunately, the metallurgical and stress parameters that measure the contribution of these factors to the promotion of intergranular penetration by certain environments are better understood and it is with these aspects of the phenomenon that this review is opened.

## Effects of Steel Structure and Composition

*Influence of Composition*

Attempts to crack relatively pure iron in bulk form in boiling nitrates have not met with any success[2,3] nor have failures been produced in iron or mild steel previously heated in moist hydrogen to remove carbon or nitrogen.[2-4] Radeker and Grafen[5] claim that "...A pure iron melted in a vacuum was shown to be highly susceptible to cracking...", but since their, so-called, pure iron contained 0.27% of quoted impurities, the chief of which was copper (0.10%), the result hardly seems to justify the ignoring of the weight of evidence from other workers. There is, however, one piece of work that appears genuinely to be at variance with the results that show pure iron and moist hydrogen treated steel to be resistant to cracking, and this concerns the observation of Flis et al[6] that polycrystalline whiskers of iron are prone to cracking in ammonium nitrate solution at 75 C. Although the purity of the whiskers that they used does not appear to have been measured, they state that the method of production was one that normally gives a purity of about 99.99%, which is similar to that of the bulk iron specimens that could not be cracked.[2,3] Flis et al, by implication, consider that the fact that their results were obtained on whiskers in no way invalidates their application to bulk material, but clearly there is a discrepancy and for the protagonists of either viewpoint to ignore this is inadequate. The most obvious reason for the discrepancy would be one involving size effect, but the most pressing need is for the results on whiskers to be confirmed and preferably extended to include tests in nitrates other than that of ammonium, especially since the potentials at which the tests were performed in ammonium nitrate appear to coincide with a range in which, according to Szklarska-Smialowska,[7] failure of wire specimens is by general, not intergranular, corrosion.

The introduction of carbon into bulk pure iron results in susceptibility to cracking,[2,3] so that it is not surprising that, where an extensive range of commercial mild steels has been studied,[2] there is a strong correlation between the carbon content of the steel and its cracking propensity. The nature of the relationship is not simple however, since although a small amount of carbon (< 0.10%) produces susceptibility, the resistance to cracking increases as the carbon content increases.[2,8,9] Since decarburized steel and bulk pure iron are resistant to cracking it is clear that the relationship between carbon content and cracking propensity must pass through a maximum at some concentration of carbon between 0% and about 0.2%. The exact value is of little consequence since commercial mild steels are rarely made with less than about 0.05% C and at this concentration the material is very susceptible to cracking, although it is conceivable that the concentration to which the carbon has to be reduced in order to delay or prevent cracking could be of practical interest. Parkins[2] found that moist hydrogen treatments that reduced the carbon below 0.02% were effective in preventing cracking under the conditions of testing that he employed although Logan[10] and Munster and Grafen[9] have produced cracks in steels containing

0.01% and 0.004% C respectively. These discrepancies are probably not of any great significance when it is remembered that structure, as well as composition, exerts an influence upon cracking propensity and also that the removal of carbon by treatment in moist hydrogen almost certainly leaves the surface of specimens with much less carbon than the interior. (The carbon contents quoted by Parkins were average values taken through the thickness of the specimens; Logan and Munster and Grafen used steels prepared with low carbon from the melt.) The important facts appear to be that bulk carbon-free material is not susceptible, the introduction of relatively small amounts of carbon promotes cracking and the latter becomes less severe as the carbon content is increased further.

It appears likely that nitrogen can act in a similar manner to carbon, although the importance of this to the cracking of normal commercial steels is controversial. Stromeyer[11] was the first of a number of workers to suggest that iron nitride could be the cause of inter-crystalline cracking in boiler plates, arising from a belief that ageing and stress corrosion cracking are related to one another. German workers[12,13] also have long argued that a steel resistant to intergranular cracking can be produced by fully killing the steel with aluminum, so that nitrogen is fixed as aluminum nitride and thereby rendered incapable of entering into any precipitation phenomenon. A sophisticated mechanism of cracking involving $Fe_4N$ was suggested by Waber and McDonald.[4] Thermodynamic considerations show that $Fe_4N$ should be anodic with respect to ferrite and, if a continuous film of this phase is formed, a susceptible crack path will be provided. Since it is readily shown that such a film is not existent in normal steels, it is suggested that it is laid down in advance of the crack tip by the activation of the precipitation through the plastic strain that will occur in this region. Although Waber and McDonald claim support for their suggested mechanism from the correlation of cracking propensity with the amount of 'free nitrogen' in the steel, the analysis of other results[2] on the same basis gives an insignificant correlation and indeed at relatively high nitrogen contents ($\sim 0.05\%$) cracking resistance is conferred. However, by far the most convincing evidence that nitrogen may behave in essentially the same manner as carbon in promoting cracking has been provided by Uhlig and Sava[3] who prepared a nitrogen steel from decarburized electrolytic iron, which was resistant to cracking, and found that the introduction of 0.043% N produced marked susceptibility. Here again the result is not necessarily in conflict with others,[2,14] since the intro-duction of intermediate amounts of nitrogen appear to promote susceptibility while larger quantities confer resistance and the effect of nitrogen has been shown[3] to be dependent upon heat treatment. The effects of nitrogen therefore appear to be essentially the same as those of carbon, but so far as normal commercial steels are concerned it would seem that carbon is the more important element in view of the fact that the nitrogen content of such steels is usually relatively small, whereas the carbon content is greater and frequently within the range wherein high susceptibility is experienced. This generalized state-ment is not in agreement with that of Munster and Grafen[9] who claim that, although nitrogen is extremely important, especially in the sense that it shortens the lifetime at very small stresses, the magnitude of the nitrogen content in the range 0.005 to 0.10% is unimportant. However, these statements are not particularly convincing in the light of their results and appear to arise because of their method of assessing results. This is by comparing lifetimes at equivalent fractions of the tensile strength of the different steels, but since the tensile strengths vary considerably with composition the basis of comparison appears false. The results are replotted in Figure 1 on the basis of applied stresses, from which it appears difficult to make any deduction other than that increasing carbon contents cause an increasing resistance to cracking and that varying the nitrogen from $< 0.0005$ to 0.0344% produces no obvious trend.

Of the remaining elements that may occur in mild steels, either by accident or design, the only ones that appear to have been claimed to exercise a significant effect are Al, Ti, Cr and Cu. Most of the work involving Al additions has been reported by German workers, who have been concerned with relatively small quantities ($< 0.1\%$) of the order used in deoxidizing steels or the production of, so called, non-ageing steels. Fry[15] appears to have been one of the first to state that deoxidizing steel produced increased resistance to intercrystalline corrosion and has subsequently been supported by other workers of whom Houdrement et al[13] are typical. They state that in a series of tests in hot sodium nitrate involving 90 heats of unkilled steel and 180 heats of killed steel, only 11% of the heats of the unkilled steel were resistant to cracking whereas 76% of the "...thoroughly deoxidized" heats developed no cracks. The compositions of these steels, which presumably ranged widely, are not given, so that it is impossible to determine if any other factors could explain the results, although the size of the sample suggests that there should be some significance in the general conclusion. Against these suggestions that aluminum killing improves the resistance to cracking may be placed the results of other workers. Thus, Pearson and Parkins[16] tested a number of steels containing

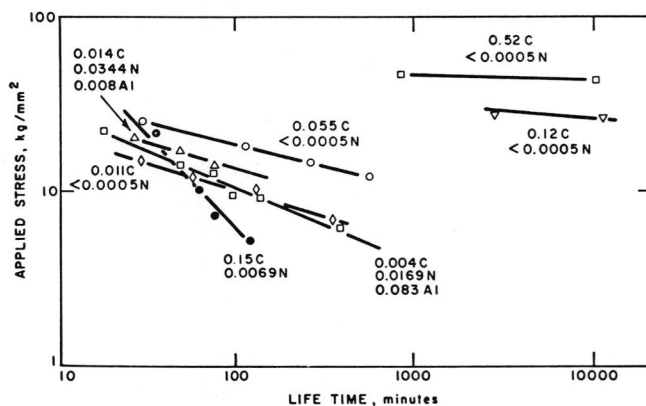

FIGURE 1 — Lifetimes of various steels in boiling 60% $Ca(NO_3)_2$ as a function of applied stress. Results taken from R. Munster and H. Grafen[9] and replotted.

about 0.07% Al, including a steel in which half of the heat was cast without any aluminum addition while the remainder was killed with 0.089% Al, but in no case was there any obvious improvement in stress corrosion resistance clearly resulting from the aluminum addition. Similarly the results of Munster and Grafen,[9] replotted in Figure 1, show no obvious benefits from the presence of aluminum in amounts of the order used for deoxidation, although these authors claim, without convincing proof, that aluminum can have a beneficial effect "...with higher carbon contents". Radeker and Grafen[5] state that the "...most favorable aluminum content..." for resistance to cracking in alkali is between 0.02 and 0.03%, since any further increase is without effect. However, this conclusion appears to be based upon the fact that one steel containing 0.002% Al cracked more readily than eight steels containing 0.02% or more of aluminum, and since the other elements present in these steels are not quoted it is impossible to decide if the result could be explained in some other manner. In summary, it appears that there is no clear indication of the effect upon stress corrosion of mild steels of deoxidation with aluminum, although many of the results quoted as indicating a beneficial effect are possibly capable of alternative interpretations. In practical terms, there seems to be no justification for the use of fully killed steels as a means of avoiding stress corrosion, since apart from any doubts as to the exact effect of aluminum additions there is ample evidence, even from German workers, that they are not effective in completely preventing cracking. A similar conclusion may be arrived at in respect of titanium additions in that there is some evidence of a beneficial effect[9] to be put against evidence of no effect,[16] although even in the former case the steel was susceptible to cracking. The conflicting results in these cases may be related to the fact that the beneficial effect was observed in a steel containing 0.46%, whereas in the results that indicated the titanium addition was without effect the amount present was only 0.15%.

The magnitude of these titanium additions is significantly higher than those considered in relation to aluminum and usually involved in deoxidation practice. With aluminum contents of the same order there is evidence of a marked improvement in resistance to cracking. Herzog[17] has reported that aluminum itself had a beneficial effect when present in amounts between 0.5 and 2.0%, although complete immunity from cracking did not exist in the normalized condition. With chromium contents between 2 and 4% and with 0.8% Al resistance to stress corrosion was observed even with less than 0.1% C. Confirmation of the beneficial effects of aluminum and chromium, when present separately in amounts ranging from 0.3 to 1.0% has been presented[18] and an explanation offered in terms of the effects of these elements upon oxide film formation based upon potential/time curves for the steels while immersed in a boiling mixed nitrate solution. In the same paper,[18] the deleterious effect of copper additions in the range 0.30 to 1.0% is indicated. The stress corrosion of certain low alloy, as opposed to mild, steels is known to occur, Houdrement et al[13] referring to the cracking of a

Ni/Cr steel in mixed nitrates and Loginow and Phelps[19] to C/Mn, Ni/Cr/Mo and Cr/Mo steels in anhydrous ammonia. Some idea of the range of steels susceptible to cracking in alkaline solutions is available from an industrial survey.[20] However, carbon and nitrogen apart, there has been little systematic investigation of the effects of alloying upon stress corrosion of steels in boiling nitrates or alkalies and, in any case, alloy steels are not the concern of this part of the present review.

## Influence of Structure

Although mild steels are not normally subjected to the range of heat treatments applied to, say, low alloy steels, there are nevertheless wide structural variations possible in mild steels as the result of differences in composition or differences in heat treatment. Thus, in addition to the annealed and normalized conditions that are so frequently met, welding and stress relieving treatments may produce martensite or tempered structures, the susceptibility of which to intergranular cracking is therefore of practical importance. The effects of heat treatments, and their associated structures, upon the cracking susceptibility of mild steel is therefore worthy of study and has received a certain amount of attention.

There appears to be general agreement[5,13] that the higher the austenitizing temperature, for whatever reason, the more susceptible is a steel likely to be to cracking. The most likely explanation of this effect appears to be associated with grain size, it having frequently been remarked upon that coarse grained materials crack more readily than those of smaller average grain diameter. Houdrement et al[13] suggest that this is because, for the same total quantity of a precipitating phase that is responsible for cracking, it "...will become more enriched in the grain boundaries as the grain becomes coarser." Coleman et al[21] have suggested an alternative explanation based upon the observation that the stress to initiate a stress corrosion crack, arbitrarily defined as one visible at the surface at a magnification of 20x, is dependent upon the grain size according to a relationship of the type observed originally by Petch[22] for the brittle fracture of mild steel. The existence of such a relationship for the stress corrosion of a mild steel in a boiling nitrate solution[23] is apparent from Figure 2, but the interpretation of such results as indicative of a surface energy mechanism for cracking, following Coleman et al,[21] or by "stress-sorption cracking", as referred to by Uhlig and Sava[3] appears open to doubt. An explanation[23] more in keeping with the facts is that the grain size dependence of the, so-called, stress to initiate a stress corrosion crack is a manifestation of the grain size dependence of the plastic properties of the steel, which are involved in the type of test to which Figure 2 refers.

It is the case, of course, that the austenitizing temperature is not the only factor involved in establishing the ferritic grain size of a mild steel, which is the particular grain size with which intergranular stress corrosion in mild steels is concerned. Thus, cooling rate from the austenitic condition is at least as important, although the effect of this in terms of ferritic grain size has received no attention. Nevertheless, the effects of different cooling rates have been studied to some extent and there appears to be unanimity among the various workers[3,13,14,24,25] that, in cooling from about 920 C, water quenching renders steels more susceptible than oil quenching and that the resistance to cracking increases as the cooling rate is decreased further through air cooling to furnace cooling. However, it needs to be stressed that these trends are relative and that even with very slow cooling, especially from high austenitizing temperatures, many mild steels are still readily susceptible to stress corrosion. The general effect of variation in cooling rate is clearly the opposite of that which would be expected if its influence was related to ferritic grain size and it would appear that it is possibly through the form and distribution of the carbon that cooling rate controls cracking propensity.

The effects upon cracking tendencies of tempering following quenching and of annealing in similar temperature ranges has received a considerable amount of attention but the results from various workers show inconsistencies. The majority have found that the susceptible water quenched condition can be mitigated by tempering at relatively high temperatures. Thus, Nehl and Werner[8] found that steels with less than 0.15% C could be made resistant if they were tempered in the range 600-780 C following quenching, while Athavale and Eilender[14] found an improvement in cracking resistance following tempering at 650 C and Smialowski et al[24] observed maximum resistance after tempering at 500-600 C. The results of Houdrement et al[13] are reproduced in Figure 3 and indicate agreement with the aforementioned results. On the other hand the results of Uhlig and Sava,[3] shown in Figure 4, indicate that tempering for 1/2 hour in the range 100-250 C increased the resistance to cracking and that above 250 C failure had not occurred in 200 hours, unless tempering was carried out at about 450-500 C when

marked susceptibility returned. This result was reproduced, in general form, on three different steels and is clearly contrary to that of other workers in that the latter observed increased resistance from high temperature tempering whereas Uhlig and Sava observe the opposite effect. The fact that Houdrement et al[13] show that tempering for 4-12 hours above 600 C following oil quenching results in a distinct deterioration in cracking resistance may be taken as a measure of support for part of the effects observed by Uhlig and Sava, but this result refers to oil quenching and when the same workers studied the effects of tempering following water quenching their results showed a trend opposite to those of Uhlig and Sava.

An explanation of these inconsistencies could conceivably lie in the cooling treatment, i.e., whether rapid

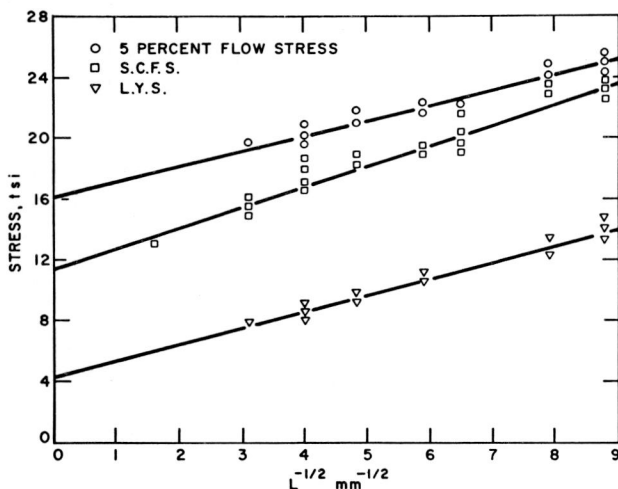

FIGURE 3 — Effect of 1/2 hr tempering, following quenching from 900 C, on the resistance to failure of a 0.26% C steel stressed at 40 kgm/mm$^2$ and immersed in a boiling calcium-ammonium nitrate solution. (E. Houdrement, H. Bennek and H. Wentrup,[13] *Stahl und Eisen.*)

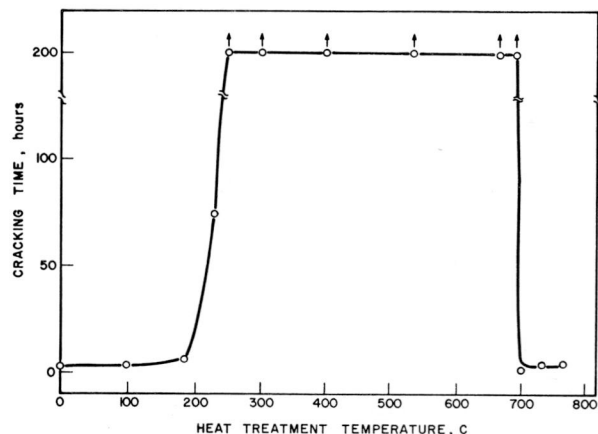

FIGURE 2 — Effect of grain size on yield stress, 5% flow stress and stress corrosion fracture stress (S.C.F.S.) for 0.08% C steel in 8 N Ca(NO$_3$)$_2$. (M. Henthorne and R. N. Parkins,[23] *British Corrosion Journal.*)

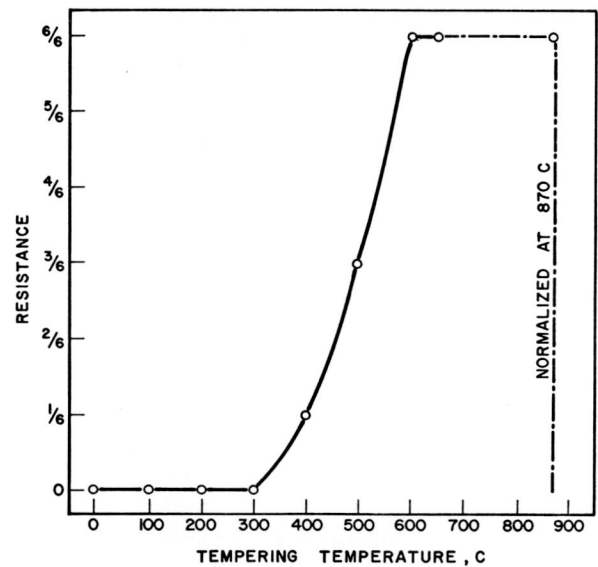

FIGURE 4 — Effect of temperature of 1/2 hr heat treatment of 0.06% C steel quenched from 925 C on cracking in boiling calcium-ammonium nitrate solution. (H. H. Uhlig and J. Sava,[3] *Trans. Amer. Soc. Metals.*)

or slow, following tempering, but here again what little work exists shows discrepancies. Thus, Houdrement et al[13] report that heat treatments at 650 or 730 C and furnace cooling improve cracking resistance, but the results of Munster and Grafen[9] on a 0.02% C steel indicate otherwise. They found that water quenching from 730 C followed by a 4 hour treatment at 500 C and water quenching increased the cracking susceptibility over that observed after air cooling, but direct quenching from 710 C into liquid nitrogen gave increased resistance, in contrast to the results of Houdrement et al. Munster and Grafen carried out similar treatments on a steel containing 0.0069% N and 0.015% C and obtained results essentially the same as those for the 0.02% C steel. The explanation that is put forward by Munster and Grafen for these results is concerned with the formation of a "...thickly covered sediment...of tertiary cementite...at the grain boundaries..." the amount of which increases with heat treatments that produce increased susceptibility. Some of the micrographs shown in their paper support such a suggestion, although since the specimens with which other micrographs are concerned varied in composition as well as heat treatment comparison is not as simple as the authors imply and their conclusions are open to objection.

The association of intergranular cracking with the presence of cementite at the grain boundaries has been suggested[2] as an explanation of the importance of the carbon content of commercial mild steels in controlling cracking propensity. It is well known that decrease of the carbon content of mild steels results in a change in the distribution of the carbide from an essentially pearlitic form at, say, 0.2% C to discrete particles in the grain boundaries without any pearlite at about 0.07% C and less. Since it is the latter steels that are the most susceptible to intercrystalline corrosion the inference is obvious and a method of testing the data is clearly to subject a pearlitic mild steel of relatively high crack resistance to sub-critical annealing to divorce the pearlite and cause the carbide to be dispersed, at least in part, as discrete particles at the grain boundaries. That such heat treatments result in markedly increased susceptibility to cracking is apparent from Figure 5. Since it is readily shown that $Fe_3C$ is cathodic to ferrite in nitrate solutions, the location of stress corrosion at the grain boundaries and in the vicinity of the carbides there, must be associated with attack upon the ferrite. It has been suggested[2] that this could be due to the ferrite in the vicinity of the carbides being disarrayed by dislocations piled-up against the carbide particles but no supporting evidence is forthcoming from thin film electron microscopy and the interpretation now preferred[23] is one involving carbon, either in solution or as carbide, segregated at the grain boundaries acting as a very efficient cathode and thereby stimulating the anodic reaction. The micrographs of Figures 6 and 7 may be offered in support of such a suggestion, both showing the appearance of foils dipped in a boiling nitrate solution for a few seconds and then examined in an electron microscope. Figure 6 shows a tongue of metal containing a grain boundary protruding from the edge of the foil and Figure 7 the intense attack on

the material immediately adjacent to a grain boundary carbide particle. That the tongue of metal apparent in Figure 6 is a boundary to which carbon and possibly nitrogen has segregated is suggested by the work of Phillips[26] who has shown, by transmission electron microscopy, that electropolished foils show ridges at grain boundaries, without visible evidence of precipitates, providing the carbon and nitrogen contents are below 0.0001% and that the sample has not been quenched from about 690 C. This is in line with the observation of Munster and Grafen[9] that quenching from 710 C into liquid nitrogen caused a steel to have increased crack resistance. It also anticipates the results of Uhlig and Sava[3] showing the marked deterioration in crack resistance as the result of tempering quenched steels at 450-550 C followed by air cooling, although Uhlig and Sava have stated that the activation energies they determined (35-48 kcal per mole) are appreciably higher than the activation energies for diffusion of carbon ($\sim$ 22 kcal per mole) or of nitrogen (18 kcal per mole) in $a$-iron and therefore "...the important process entering stress corrosion cracking is not limited by diffusion of interstitial atoms...". However, it does not explain the inconsistencies of the results of these workers with those of others and there is clearly a need for a systematic investigation of such treatments, especially in view of the wide range of mild steels used by the various workers studying the effects of sub-critical heat treatments.

*Grain Orientation and Dislocations*

The orientation difference of adjacent grains across their common boundary, and which may be expressed as a grain boundary energy, is an obvious parameter to include in a mechanism of intergranular stress corrosion. Moreover, since grain boundary energy increases with orientation difference it may be thought that high angle grain boundaries, separating crystals of relatively large mis-orientation, would be the most susceptible to intergranular corrosion. Logan[27] reported results for coarse grained, wet hydrogen treated, mild steel showing that the differences in orientation of crystallographic planes bounding stress corro-

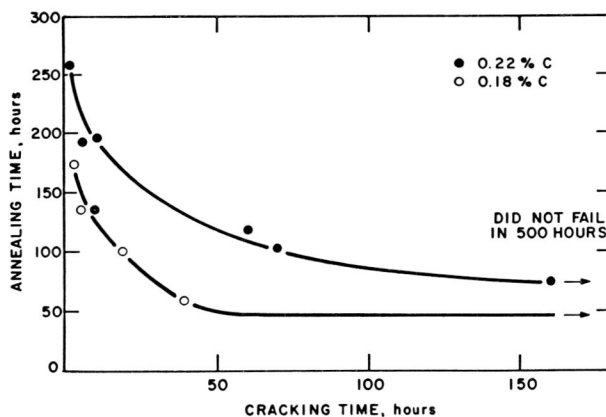

FIGURE 5 — Effect of annealing at 700 C on the cracking susceptibility of two mild steels immersed in boiling calcium-ammonium nitrate solution. (R. N. Parkins,[2] *Journal Iron and Steel Institute.*)

365

FIGURE 6 — Preferential attack adjacent to a grain boundary in a thin film of annealed 0.08% C steel. (M. Henthorne and R. N. Parkins,[23] *British Corrosion Journal.*)

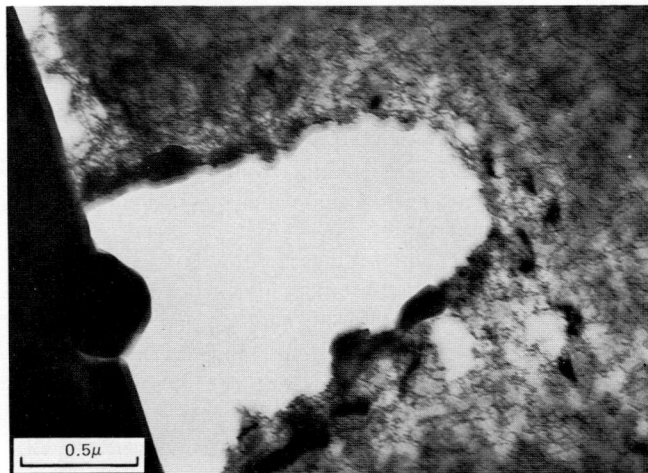

FIGURE 7 — Preferential attack near a grain boundary carbide particle resulting from immersion of thin film in hot nitrate solution for 5 seconds. (M. Henthorne and R. N. Parkins,[23] *British Corrosion Journal.*)

sion cracks were greater than 10 degrees for 69% of the cracks that he considered, from which he concludes that cracks generally originated at high energy grain boundaries. However, since Logan does not appear to have measured the misorientation across boundaries that did not crack or measured the distribution of misorientations in the specimen as a whole, the experiment would hardly appear to be unequivocal. Smialowski[28] also is a protagonist of the hypothesis that the intergranular stress corrosion of iron is primarily due to differences in the free energy of iron atoms situated in differently oriented crystal faces and grain boundaries. Supporting results are claimed by Flis et al[6] who made electrochemical measurements on single crystals of iron having varying crystal planes exposed to the action of the electrolyte. That the anodic dissolution rate and open circuit potential were observed to vary according to the plane exposed is not unexpected, although the variations are small in comparison with the electrochemical differences between other structural features, e.g., different phases, present when mild steel undergoes stress corrosion. In any case, it appears doubtful if the different electrochemical properties of different crystal faces can afford an adequate explanation of stress corrosion cracking, as is apparent from the elegant work of Robertson and Bakish[29] on copper alloys. The atomic configuration along a grain boundary where it meets an outer surface is not an equilibrium one, since it involves arbitrary edges of adjacent crystals which are unstable with respect to close-packed planes. If some mechanism exists, such as dissolution, whereby atoms can be removed from the boundary region, the original boundary line expands to a groove having more stable planes as sides. But once the equilibrium groove angle is achieved, it is preserved while metal atoms are removed more or less at random from both the free surface and the surface groove. This affords an explanation of grain boundary etching but not of stress corrosion cracking. It may be argued[28] that the case is different for iron

immersed in nitrates, because the latter passivate different crystal planes in differing degrees, but the essential idea of the explanation offered by Robertson and Bakish is still valid.

The strain energy associated with the core of a dislocation has obvious similarities to the energy of a grain boundary and the concept discussed above for intergranular stress corrosion could be extended to include a significant contribution by line defects. The involvement of dislocations in stress corrosion mechanism for mild steels has sometimes been made[2,3,6] but there is, as yet, little direct evidence in support. It seems most likely that dislocations will act indirectly, either in transporting solute atoms,[3,23] or in causing crack tips to be film-free.[30]

## Effects of Stress and Strain

Many authors have shown that the time to cracking increases markedly as the tensile stresses on specimens are decreased and the results shown in Figure 1 may be regarded as typical. Although having no mechanistic background, the time to fracture as a function of stress may be estimated, by a method given by Engell et al,[31] from a knowledge of the rate of crack growth and the specimen size. A threshold stress is usually observed, below which the probability of cracking is remote, but the value of this can vary widely from a very few tons/sq in to levels approaching the tensile strength, depending upon the composition and structure of the steel and upon the details of the test method employed in its determination. It appears undesirable therefore to quote threshold stresses in any sense in which they can be used for design purposes, unless precautions are taken to ensure that the details of the method of determination are taken into account, and especially since the majority of industrial stress corrosion failures in low carbon steels probably arise from fabrication and not design stresses. For constant test conditions, the threshold stress appears to increase with carbon content[2,9] and there is some additional support for such a relationship arising from industrial experience[16,32] of welded structures, where the residual welding stresses would be expected to be close to the yield strengths of the materials concerned.

There is ample evidence in the literature[16,19,20,32,33,34] of the beneficial effects to be derived from the stress relieving of welded structures in relation to stress corrosion cracking. A full stress relieving anneal at about 650 C is by far the most efficient treatment although this may not always be feasible, in which case partial stress relief at lower temperatures or controlled low temperature stress relief by localized heating may be useful. Since these latter treatments do not reduce the residual stresses to very low values it is important that they are not applied to the very low carbon steels that may crack with tensile stresses of only 3 or 4 tons/sq in, although even in these cases a useful increase in life may be obtained by partial stress relief. It has sometimes been suggested that the beneficial effects of low temperature treatments derive from structural changes that they engender in the steel, rather than from relieving residual stresses. That this is not so is readily shown[33] by the fact that the reimposition of applied stresses to welded specimens previously subjected to a short sub-critical anneal causes them to crack very readily.

The function of stress in the stress corrosion cracking of low carbon steels, like its function in the failure of other materials, has been variously suggested as being to hold cracks open to allow the interchange of soluble reactants and products, to fracture passivating oxide films[35] or to assist crack propagation by producing short bursts of purely mechanical rupture.[36] The evidence that is usually adduced in support of a film rupture mechanism or of crack propagation involving bursts of mechanical rupture, is sharp fluctuations in potential of stress corroding specimens or of some dimension of the latter that indicates a rapid change in the state of strain of the specimen. There is however, an alternative explanation[30] of such fluctuations related to the fact that at the temperatures involved in stress corrosion testing mild steels in boiling nitrates, such steels exhibit a serrated stress-strain curve indicative of discontinuous plastic flow even in the absence of stress corrosion crack propagation. Moreover, the rate of crack propagation typically observed in the stress corrosion of mild steels is such as can be accounted for entirely in electrochemical terms[30] and without recourse to arguments involving bursts of mechanical rupture.

This is not meant to imply that stress plays an insignificant role in stress corrosion, although intergranular penetration in the absence of stress is possible with mild steels immersed in boiling nitrates. However, to be sustained to an appreciable depth such penetration needs anodic stimulation or the application of a tensile stress.[23] This suggests that the function of stress is simply to keep open the initial fissure or crack to prevent the latter being blocked by corrosion products and this may well be true for the relatively low carbon steel to which this result refers, since an applied stress of only 2.8 tons/sq in was capable of producing complete failure in this steel in less than 2 days. However, for other steels cracking is only produced with much higher stresses, usually in excess of the yield stress, suggesting that stress has a greater part to play in the mechanism of cracking than that of simply holding open the crack. Perhaps the important factor in these steels is not stress as such, but the plastic strain that it produces in appropriate circumstances. In some cases it has been reported[37] that cracking could only be produced in notched specimens and, although there appears to have been no systematic investigation of the influence of pre-cracking mild steel specimens before corroding in boiling nitrates or alkalies as has been made for other systems,[38] the inference here also would appear to be that the function of stress is more than that of simply pulling apart the sides of a crack.

There are apparently conflicting results of the effect of cold plastic deformation in its influence upon stress corrosion of mild steels, some workers[2,14] having shown that moderate amounts of plastic deformation increase the susceptibility to cracking while others[3,30] have shown that mild steel cold rolled to about 70-85 percent reduction in thickness or prestrained in tension by various amounts is more resistant to stress corrosion. Such differences may be due, at least in part, to variations in experimental methods, but there is also the possibility that they are related to differences in the compositions of the steels used by different workers. Thus, where cold work has been shown to reduce susceptibility the experiments have been conducted on steels of high inherent susceptibility having appropriate compositions, whereas those steels that required plastic deformation to induce cracking were of higher carbon content and therefore inherently more resistant. There is a clear need for a thorough investigation of this aspect of the subject, but it appears that the effect of deformation as expressed in these results may be associated with the distribution of soluble carbon in relation to the grain boundaries.

There is some support for this suggestion from Uhlig and Sava.[3] They show that cold rolled steel becomes susceptible to cracking again after annealing for 1/2 hour at 500 C. The offered explanation of these results is that cold rolling removes "...excess interstitial atoms in the ferrite matrix and along the grain boundaries" and that "...the grain boundaries are distorted to such an extent that continuous paths in the metal favorable to fracture do not exist." Subsequent appropriate heat treatment causes a specific concentration of interstitials to return to the recrystallized grain boundaries and susceptibility to cracking returns. Thin film electron microscopy should enable the validity of these suggestions to be examined. Uhlig and Sava go on to state that "...stress relief of cold worked steel at 400 to 650 C, which is apparently sometimes specified, may actually reduce resistance to stress corrosion cracking rather than increase resistance." It would be unfortunate if this statement was interpreted to mean that stress relieving treatments at 400 to 650 C were always likely to be detrimental, especially in view of the large amount of industrial experience that shows the beneficial effect to be derived from such treatments in relation to welded fabrications.

## Effects of Environmental Composition

Although many authors have recognized that the environments that promote stress corrosion cracking must have properties somewhere between those that produce rapid general corrosion and those that produce complete passivation, a precise definition of the properties of a crack producing electrolyte is still not forthcoming. From a more practical viewpoint, Galvele[39] has recently suggested a form of test, based upon the measurement of the currents flowing from potentiostatically polarized specimens plastically deformed at a constant strain rate, which may be able to be used in distinguishing susceptible from non-susceptible solutions, but the method first requires testing against the range of environments known to produce cracking before its usefulness can be established with certainty. Of the environments that have been associated with stress corrosion in mild steels, those based upon nitrates and hydroxides have received most study, although media based upon $H_2S$ have had a good deal of attention in the U.K., because of the cracking problem that existed in gas making plant, while cracking in anhydrous liquid $NH_3$ has attracted attention in the U.S.A. Logan[40] gives a list of most of the references in the literature to cracking media.

### Nitrate Solutions

From various studies[13,25,41-43] of the stress corrosion of mild steels in boiling nitrates with different cations, it appears that those with acidic cations are the most potent, as is apparent from the threshold stresses for the failure of a 0.05% C steel in various nitrates over a range of concentrations shown in Table 1. This suggests that a nitrate solution that does not produce rapid or extensive cracking by itself can be made much more aggressive by small additions of acid and this is found to be so.[43] On the other hand, movement of the pH to higher values by the addition of alkali causes a marked increase in resistance to cracking at values of pH above about 7, a result confirmed by Szklarska-Smialowska.[7] The effects of other additions to nitrates appears to be such that they may be placed into one or other of two categories according to whether cracking is accelerated or retarded.[36,41,43,44] Thus oxidizing additions, such as $KMnO_4$, $MnSO_4$, $NaNO_2$ and $K_2Cr_2O_7$, accelerate cracking while hydroxides and other salts, especially those forming insoluble iron products, such as $Na_2CO_3$, $H_3PO_2$, $Na_2HPO_4$ and $CO(NH_2)_2$ retard or prevent failure. The presence of oxygen in solutions of nitrates is claimed by Smialowska and Ostrowska[45] to be of the greatest importance in assisting the cracking mechanism, yet Herzog and Portevin[25] claim that oxygen is without effect. Although it may be an oversimplification to

state that the potency of a nitrate based solution depends upon its pH and the presence or otherwise of oxidizing additions or substances capable of forming insoluble iron salts, since particular cations may exert an effect, these generalized statements appear broadly true, subject to a systematic and detailed study of the whole question of solution composition.

TABLE 1 – Threshold Stress Values (tons/sq in) of 0.05 C Steel in Nitrate Solutions of Various Concentrations[1]

| | Solution Concentration | | | |
|---|---|---|---|---|
| Nitrate | 8N | 4N | 2.5N | 1N |
| $NH_4NO_3$ | 1.0 | 1.5 | 3.5 | 6.0 |
| $Ca(NO_3)_2$ | 2.5 | 3.5 | 6.0 | 11.5 |
| $LiNO_3$ | 2.5 | 4.0 | 9.5 (2N) | 11.5 |
| $KNO_3$ | 3.0 | 4.5 | 7.0 | 12.0 |
| $NaNO_3$ | 4.0 | 9.5 | 11.0 | 13.0 |

[1]R. N. Parkins and R. Usher,[43] Butterworths.

### Hydroxide Solutions

The uncertainties that exist in relation to the effects of solution composition with nitrate based media are multiplied and the whole picture is even more confused in relation to the literature on hydroxide solutions. Although there is general agreement[13,46,47] that the lowest concentration at which boiling caustic solutions appear to produce stress corrosion is about 5% NaOH, many workers have not found it possible to produce cracking in relatively pure solutions. Thus, the literature contains statements[48,49] to the effect that only solutions containing $Na_2SiO_3$ promote cracking while others claim that $SiO_2$ is not necessary to produce cracking[50] or, indeed, that it may possibly have some inhibitive effect.[51] Similarly, Schroeder et al[44] claim that small amounts of the oxidizing salts $KMnO_4$, $NaNO_3$ or $Na_2CrO_4$ caused cracking in conditions where pure NaOH did not produce failure, yet $NaNO_3$ is added to boiler water to prevent cracking and bubbling oxygen through a boiling solution stops cracking,[5] in contrast to its reported effect in nitrate solutions.[45] The situation in respect of preventative treatments, involving control of the composition of feed water to boilers wherein caustic cracking probably still constitutes an industrial hazard of appreciable proportions, also leaves much to be desired. The maintenance of a $Na_2SO_4$/NaOH ratio in excess of 2.5 is still widely practiced as a means of preventing caustic cracking, presumably because there is much experience of boilers not failing in these circumstances. However, the statistical evidence of Weir[52] is that no benefit is derived from the maintenance of a high sulfate/hydroxide ratio and there is ample practical experience of cracking in boilers where the water conditions have met the specified minimum ratio. The evidence[53] in support of the $NaNO_3$ and coordinated phosphate treatments for the prevention of caustic cracking in boilers is more convincing, although it is by no means universally accepted that nitrate treatment is completely effective or that the use of tannins for the same purpose may be regarded as having been established beyond all doubt.

Much of the confusion surrounding caustic cracking may arise from the fact that a reliable laboratory test has not been available and much of the published data has come from measurements on operating boilers without the degree of control necessary in properly conducted experiments. Various devices have had to be adopted in order to produce cracking in laboratory tests, notably that of making a variety of additions to the caustic solution, one obvious interpretation of which is that cracking may only occur within a restricted range of electrode potentials and that these additions operate by causing the free corrosion potential to fall within this range.

Wenczel and Wranglen[54] observed a drop in the load carrying capacity of wires tested in the narrow range of potentials from -1150 to -800 mV (SCE) in 40% NaOH and this type of result has subsequently been confirmed.[47] Using a slow strain rate tensile test with potentiostatic control and taking the reduction in area of the test piece as a convenient quantitative measure of the stress corrosion cracking propensity, Humphries and Parkins[55] have studied the effects of various additions to 35% NaOH upon the cracking of a mild steel. The type of result obtained is apparent from Figure 8, which indicates the ease of distinction between additions without effect and those having a restraining influence. Additions of $Al_2O_3$, $Cu_2O_3$, $KMnO_4$, $NaNO_3$, $Na_2SO_4$, PbO, $Pb_3O_4$ or ZnO were found to have no effect within the restricted range of potentials in which cracking occurs in pure 35% NaOH.

In conditions where no external polarization was applied, some of these substances caused the free corrosion potential to fall within the critical range and the range and intensity of cracking may then be intensified, while other additions may cause the free corrosion potential to take values where cracking does not occur and so may produce

an inhibitive effect. Such substances, which include $NaNO_3$ and $Na_2SO_4$, both of which are extensively employed in boiler water treatment to prevent caustic cracking, may be termed "unsafe" inhibitors. The only substances, of those tested, that were found to have a truly inhibitive effect were valonea and quebracho tannins and $NaH_2PO_4$, although $Na_2SiO_3$ and oxygen appear to confer partial inhibition, as is apparent from Figure 8.

*Environments Other Than Nitrates and Hydroxides*

From time to time various environments have been associated with the detection of stress corrosion cracks in mild steel; but these substances have received little or no systematic study and in some instances it may be doubtful if in fact they are capable of promoting stress corrosion. The stress corrosion of welded mild steel plant in gas and coke works where it is exposed to crude coal gas liquors has been associated[56] with the presence of $NH_3$, $H_2S$, $CO_2$ and HCN in the condensate over a range of compositions. The statistical evidence collected from 87 different plants that pointed to these constituents as being important was supported by some laboratory work involving synthetic liquors, but the work was not primarily concerned with the mechanism whereby these substances acted to produce cracking, although the suggestion was made that the cyanide was principally responsible for grain boundary attack, by forming soluble iron complexes in alkaline solution. Elsewhere,[57] it has been reported, but not confirmed,[56] that HCN solutions containing 2.6 to 3.5 g/l cause transgranular cracking in mild steel.

Moist $H_2$ is reported[58] as causing the failure of cold-drawn high-carbon steel wire when loaded to only 40% of its breaking load, although this failure may have resulted from hydrogen embrittlement, in the light of the work that has been carried out in relation to failures in "sour" oil well equipment. What appears to be a classical case of stress corrosion cracking in a mild steel boiler tube has been ascribed[59] to the presence of fuming sulfuric acid with a free $SO_3$ concentration of about 3.6%. The cracking originated from the fire side of the tube, where the operating temperature would be about 400 F although there is some suggestion that the cracking continued after the boiler was taken out of service, which is of interest in the sense that attempts have sometimes been made to explain the property of nitrates or hydroxides that causes them to produce cracking by comparison with the properties of sulfates, which are assumed not to promote stress corrosion.

While relatively little is known about environments such as those just mentioned, failures in anhydrous ammonia have received more systematic study.[19] It is considered that the presence of contaminants in ammonia is necessary for the occurrence of stress corrosion and that air, of normal carbon dioxide content, is the most important contaminant in producing failure of ammonia vessels in service. It is suggested that the effect of $CO_2$

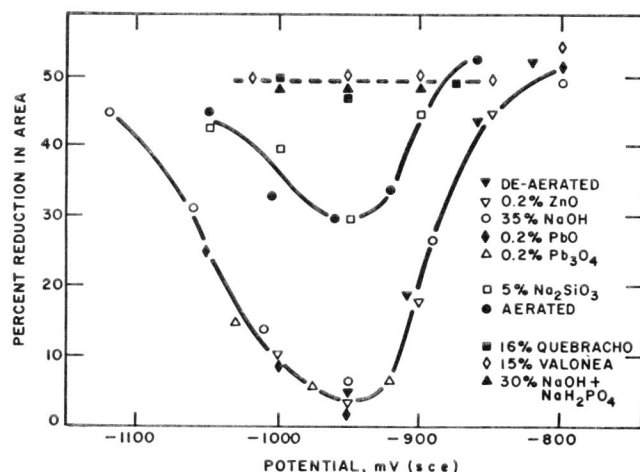

FIGURE 8 — Effects of various additions to 35% NaOH upon reduction in area of mild steel at various potentials strained at 4.2 x 10$^{-6}$ sec$^{-1}$. (M. J. Humphries and R. N. Parkins,[55] *Corrosion Science.*)

369

results from the formation of ammonium carbonate which, in turn, increases the ammonium ion concentration. Oxygen reacts with the ammonium ions according to

$$O_2 + 2NH_4^+ + 4e \rightarrow 2OH^- + 2NH_3$$

and the overall reaction is

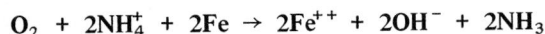

$$O_2 + 2NH_4^+ + 2Fe \rightarrow 2Fe^{++} + 2OH^- + 2NH_3$$

Water in amounts greater than 0.1% was found to inhibit stress corrosion cracking of the steels used in the fabrication of ammonia vessels, believed to be the result of film formation. An interesting observation arising from this work, and one having considerable practical implications, was that cracking continued to occur after periods of exposure up to five years, even though the highest failure rate occurred in the first year. A similar statement could be made in relation to cracking in coal gas liquors.[56]

### Electrochemical Control

Although the foregoing sections on the effects of environment composition on stress corrosion in carbon steels may give some indication of the immensity of the problem, there is a clear need for some rationalization of the situation if *ad hoc* testing or expensive industrial failures are going to be replaced by other means whereby the potency of environments may be assessed. It may turn out that there will be so many exceptions to any general rules that may be stated as to make the latter worthless, although some comfort may be found in the suggestion that the metallurgical aspects of the problem, in terms of composition and structure, begin to appear as consistent through a number of different environments. Moreover, if rationalization of the environmental aspects of the problem is achieved, it appears likely that this will derive from electrochemical studies, rather than from the type of approach that has been used hitherto.

It is well established that the stress corrosion of mild steels in many of the environments mentioned is amenable to electrochemical control, cracking being prevented by cathodic protection or stimulated by movement of the potential in the anodic direction.[16] Systematic studies have been made[7] of cracking over a wide range of potentials in 5 N $NH_4NO_3$, although much of that particular paper is concerned with the peculiarities of the cathodic polarization of iron in this solution, and similar work[54] has been carried out in 40% NaOH. An attempt is made in another paper[60] presented at this conference to rationalize these and additional results.

The fact that movement of the potential in the cathodic direction results in a considerable increase in lifetime over that observed at the free corrosion potential may be taken as an indication that the mechanism of stress corrosion in low carbon steels in nitrates and hydroxides does not involve hydrogen embrittlement. This contention is supported by the fact that addition to nitrate solutions of

sulfur or selenium, both of which are known to assist atomic hydrogen penetration, produce either no effect or increase the time of failure of mild steel specimens.[43]

Various attempts have been made to relate the polarization curve for iron or steel immersed in different solutions to the potency of the latter from the stress corrosion viewpoint. Engell and Baumel[36] produce results showing the anodic parts of the current/potential curves for iron crystals immersed in boiling 55% $Ca(NO_3)_2$ or 66% $(NH_4)_2SO_4$, being examples of solutions that, respectively, do and do not promote stress corrosion. The potent solution is characterized by its ability to passivate iron at or near the free corrosion potential, which is not the case in the sulfate solution. Hot perchlorate and chloride solutions, which do not produce stress corrosion in mild steels, yield current/potential curves appreciably different from that for $Ca(NO_3)_2$. In 30% NaOH, iron is not passive at the free corrosion potential, but it is claimed that, since a small amount of dissolved oxygen is necessary for this solution to produce cracking, the oxygen shifts the potential to higher values and passivation thereby results. The essential point of the Engell and Baumel thesis, which appears to be that stress corrosion susceptibility arises in those transient regions between activity and passivity, is possibly too naive in view of the facts that cracking can occur over a range of potentials[7,54,60] and there are many solutions that show an active/passive transition but which do not promote stress corrosion in low carbon steels. Nevertheless the more sophisticated electrochemical studies, of which that by Engell and Baumel is one, of recent years appear much more likely to provide an understanding of the environmental aspects of stress corrosion in mild steels than have earlier approaches.

### Importance of Oxide Films

Much of the electrochemical work relating to stress corrosion of mild steels has been discussed in the light of the part played by oxide films in the cracking mechanism. Straub and Parr[61] were probably first to suggest that, in hydroxide solutions, a coherent coating of $Fe_3O_4$ formed on the steel and this rendered the metal resistant to further attack by the hydroxide unless the film was broken and fresh steel exposed. Other workers have subsequently expressed similar views, Logan,[35] typically, claiming that the potential difference between filmed and film-free areas leads to electrolytic action whereby stress corrosion occurs. That oxide films form, at least in certain situations where stress corrosion occurs, is well established, but what is not well understood is their significance to the crack propagation mechanism. It seems reasonable to assume that if a continuous film forms over the tip of a crack the latter will stop propagating, unless the film is subsequently ruptured by the action of stress or by chemical action. Whether films located in such regions do in fact form is open to doubt since there is the possibility that the local conditions at a crack tip are not conducive to film formation[43] and the potential fluctuations that accompany plastic straining of mild steel, and which have been taken as supporting a film rupture mechanism of cracking, can be interpreted differently.[30] In any case, there appears to be two aspects of stress corrosion in mild steel that are difficult to account for in terms of a simple film rupture theory; one is that there must be many solutions that result in film formation but not in stress corrosion, since the environments that produce it are highly specific, and the other that the cracking is intergranular and not transgranular.

Various aspects of film formation in relation to stress corrosion in mild steels are discussed in detail elsewhere[60] and it is probably sufficient for present purposes to suggest that the evidence currently available is most consistent with oxides playing a secondary role in the sense that, while they may stop cracks from propagating, they do not cause stress corrosion.

*Reactions Involved*

The evolution of gas bubbles from stress corroding mild steels has been observed by a number of workers. Engell and Baumel[36] state that the gas "...seems to be nitrogen" and suggest the reaction

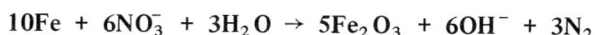

$$10Fe + 6NO_3^- + 3H_2O \rightarrow 5Fe_2O_3 + 6OH^- + 3N_2$$

assuming the passive layer to be $Fe_2O_3$. The same authors state that decomposition of the nitrate results in the formation of nitrite, the $NO_2^-$ is assumed to be an oxidizing agent and its removal, by urea additions, would be expected to shift the potential of iron to less noble values and cause an increase in the lifetime of specimens undergoing stress corrosion. Results of experiments involving urea additions are given in support. However, this result appears to contradict some due to Smialowski,[62] who states that, in the absence of air, $NO_2^-$ is formed and this prevents cracking by acting as an inhibitor. Other work[43] involving the addition of 1% $NaNO_2$ to 4 N $NaNO_3$ indicates that such an addition assists cracking to some extent.

Smialowski et al[63] quote the analysis of the gas collected during prolonged corrosion of mild steel in $NH_4NO_3$ at 100 C as containing 98% $N_2$ but "...the yield of this product is negligible" and they suggest a summarized reaction

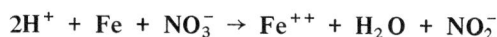

$$2H^+ + Fe + NO_3^- \rightarrow Fe^{++} + H_2O + NO_2^-$$

the production of the inhibiting $NO_2^-$ being increased by the oxidation of $Fe^{++}$ according to

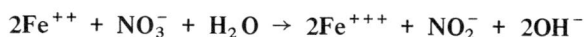

$$2Fe^{++} + NO_3^- + H_2O \rightarrow 2Fe^{+++} + NO_2^- + 2OH^-$$

If such reactions are imagined to occur at the tip of a crack and the products are confined within the latter it is difficult to understand why the cracking is not inhibited by the $NO_2^-$, assuming this to be inhibitive as suggested by Smialowski,[62] and neglecting any consideration of the effect of the $OH^-$. If the crack yawned due to deformation new solution would be drawn in and the problem would be

alleviated or, on the other hand, it is conceivable that the $NO_2^-$ is formed by cathodic reduction according to[7]

$$NO_3^- + H_2O + 2e \rightarrow NO_2^- + 2OH^-$$

which avoids the problem. It is possibly largely a matter of speculation as to which, if any, of these various equations are of primary or even secondary relevance to the propagation of stress corrosion cracks in mild steel. Such a viewpoint is particularly likely to be taken by those who consider that some rationalizing link exists between the various media that produce stress corrosion. On such a basis it is possible to offer an explanation[60] of the potential dependence of cracking in hydroxides and nitrates in terms of reactions involving the formation of the soluble species $HFeO_2^-$, $Fe^{++}$ and $Fe^{+++}$ with the potential/pH diagram as the unifying link.

## Conclusions: Cracking Mechanism

The various cracking mechanisms that have been suggested from time to time to account for the stress corrosion of low carbon steels have the same essential characteristics as those that have been advanced in explanation of cracking in other materials.[64] Some of these have been considered on previous pages and there would appear to be little to be gained from a restatement of these and other ideas at this point. Rather will the opportunity be taken for summarizing the present position from a mechanistic viewpoint, however subjectively, and for indicating where additional work would assist in elucidating the mechanism.

The fact that intergranular disintegration of mild steels in nitrate solutions by anodic stimulation in the absence of stress has been demonstrated suggests that any mechanism must contain a structural parameter that recognizes an inherent susceptibility of the grain boundary regions to corrosive attack. For commercial mild steels, the feature that seems to be associated with inherent susceptibility to intergranular corrosion is the carbon content and distribution, although nitrogen, not normally present in sufficient amount to play a critical role in commercial materials, may play a similar part if it is present in appropriate proportions. The effects of heat treatments may be related to the distribution of carbon with respect to the grain boundary regions, but there is a need for a systematic study of this point. It may turn out that such studies would also offer an explanation of the suggestion, not yet unequivocal, that cracks only propagate in the vicinity of high angle boundaries, since the latter may be associated with a susceptible carbon distribution.

Although there is a fair amount of evidence pointing to carbon as an important factor in the stress corrosion of mild steels its exact function remains obscure. Its distribution may be expected to influence the deformation characteristics of the steel but the fact that intergranular corrosion may proceed in the absence of stress suggests that its primary role is electrochemical. It may be the case, as has been proposed, that carbides or carbon segregates act as very efficient cathodes thereby facilitating the anodic reaction, but there is a clear need for electrochemical studies to ascertain the real significance of such a statement. Nor would the confirmation of such a mechanism preclude any effect that carbon distribution may have upon deformation characteristics, which are probably of importance in crack propagation in the presence of stress. The role here is secondary however, and unlike that proposed by Uhlig and Sava,[3] who suggest that the function of C and N atoms at boundaries is to lock defects that coalesce into cracks by chemisorption of critical ionic species. Their 'stress-sorption cracking' mechanism relies heavily on the results of Engell and Baumel[36] interpreted as indicative of cracking proceeding discontinuously and in spurts at exceptionally high rates, but the validity of such an interpretation is rather doubtful.[30,64]

The function of stress in crack propagation appears to be primarily concerned with preventing blockage of the crack by corrosion products, although it may also influence, through attendant plastic strain, the distribution of soluble C and N, a possibility requiring further study. It is conceivable that the stress assists crack propagation by mechanical rupture, but there is no necessity to invoke such an argument in the sense that the rates of crack propagation observed are not in excess of those that may result from purely electrochemical propagation.[30]

The uncertainties in any cracking mechanism for mild steels occur most frequently in relation to the reactions into which the environment enters and it is in this field that the need for further work is most urgent. There are, of course, some obvious comments to be made, such as that oxide films probably play a significant role in assisting the localization of the corrosion, that initial air-formed films, if continuous, need to be penetrated in an incubation period that will precede grain boundary corrosion or cracking and that insoluble products if formed over crack tips or within the confines of a crack may stop further crack propagation. The exact nature or composition of the oxide is possibly of lesser significance since, while cracks propagate in hydroxides in the presence of $Fe_3O_4$ but not $Fe_2O_3$ films, in nitrates cracking occurs in the presence of either, and in other environments that produce cracking, such as gas liquors, the surface films are likely to be different again. It is equally clear that for crack propagation to continue the tip must be in a state where metal may pass into solution and this will be achieved only if the environment permits the potential of the metal to lie within certain restricted ranges. All of this tends to suggest that when the point is reached whereby the properties of a potent solution may be precisely defined it will be seen to involve a rather fine balance between a number of characteristics. Such an outcome seems likely in view of the highly specific nature and relatively small numbers of environments known to promote stress corrosion in mild steels.

# References

1. J. H. Andrew. *Trans. Faraday Soc.*, 9, 318 (1914).
2. R. N. Parkins. *J. Iron Steel Inst.*, 172, 149 (1952).
3. H. H. Uhlig and J. Sava. *Trans. Amer. Soc. Metals*, 56, 361 (1963).
4. J. T. Waber and H. J. McDonald. *Stress Corrosion Cracking of Mild Steels.* Corrosion Publishing Co., Pittsburgh, 1947.
5. W. Radeker and H. Grafen. *Stahl und Eisen*, 76, 1616 (1956).
6. J. Flis, J. Miebuch and M. Smialowski. *Corrosion*, 20, 184t (1964).
7. Z. Szklarska-Smialowska. *Corrosion*, 20, 198t (1964).
8. F. Nehl and W. Werner. *Stahl und Eisen*, 59, 1155 (1939).
9. R. Munster and H. Grafen. *Archiv fur das Eisenhutt.*, 36, 277 (1965).
10. H. L. Logan. *Physical Metallurgy of Stress Corrosion Fracture.* Edited by T. N. Rhodin, Interscience Publ., 295, 1959.
11. C. E. Stromeyer. *J. Iron Steel Inst.*, 79, 404 (1909).
12. W. Ruttman. *Tech. Mitt. Krupp*, 4, 23 (1936).
13. E. Houdrement, H. Bennek and H. Wentrup. *Stahl und Eisen*, 60, 575, 791 (1940).
14. G. Athavale and W. Eilender. *Korr. und Metallschutz*, 16, 127 (1940).
15. A. Fry. *Krupp Monatshefte*, 7, 185, (1926).
16. C. E. Pearson and R. N. Parkins. *Welding Research*, 3, 95r (1949).
17. E. Herzog. *Corros. et Anticorros.*, 2:3, 59, 91 (1954).
18. R. N. Parkins and A. Brown. *J. Iron Steel Inst.*, 193, 45 (1959).
19. A. W. Loginow and E. H. Phelps. *Corrosion*, 18, 299t (1962).
20. N.A.C.E. Technical Practices Committee 5C. *Corrosion*, 7, 295 (1951).
21. E. G. Coleman, D. Weinstein and W. Rostoker. *Acta Metallurgica*, 9, 491 (1961).
22. N. J. Petch. *J. Iron Steel Inst.*, 174, 25 (1953).
23. M. Henthorne and R. N. Parkins. *British Corrosion Journal*, 5, 2, 186 (1967).
24. M. Smialowski, E. Gasior and C. Bieniosek. *Bull. Acad. Polanaise de Science et Lettres*, A1, No. 2, Suppl. (1950).
25. E. Herzog and M. Portevin. *Metaux et Corrosion*, 24, 40 (1949).
26. V. A. Phillips. *Acta Metallurgica*, 11, 1139 (1963).
27. H. L. Logan. *Physical Metallurgy of Stress Corrosion Fracture.* Edited by T. N. Rhodin, Interscience Publishers, p. 295, 1959.
28. M. Smialowski. *First International Congress on Metallic Corrosion*, Butterworths, p. 357, 1961.
29. W. D. Robertson and R. Bakish. *Stress Corrosion Cracking and Embrittlement.* Edited by W. D. Robertson, Wiley, p. 32, 1956.
30. M. Henthorne and R. N. Parkins. *Corrosion Science*, 6, 357 (1966).
31. H. J. Engell, K. Bohnenkamp and A. Baumel. *Archiv. fur das Eisenhutt.*, 33, 285 (1962).
32. F. A. Champion. *Chemistry and Industry*, 967 (1957).
33. R. N. Parkins. *British Welding Journal*, 2, 495 (1955).
34. R. N. Parkins. *British Welding Journal*, 8, 24 (1961).
35. H. L. Logan. *J. Res. Nat. Bur. Standards*, 48, 99 (1952).
36. H. J. Engell and A. Baumel. *Physical Metallurgy of Stress Corrosion Fracture*, Edited by T. N. Rhodin, Interscience Publishers, p. 341 1959.
37. C. D. Weir. *Proc. Inst. Mech. Eng.*, 163, 18 (1950).
38. B. F. Brown and C. D. Beacham. *Corrosion Science*, 5, 745 (1965).
39. J. Galvele. Ph.D. Thesis, University of Cambridge, 1966.
40. H. L. Logan. *The Stress Corrosion of Metals.* Wiley, 1966.
41. M. Smialowski. *Korr. Met.*, 14, 111 (1938).
42. D. Cubicciotti and W. Boyer. *Weld. J. Res. Suppl.*, 15, 1403 (1950).
43. R. N. Parkins and R. Usher. *First International Congress on*

*Metallic Corrosion,* Butterworths, p. 289, 1961.

44. W. E. Schroeder, A. A. Berk and R. A. O'Brien. *Met. and Alloys,* 8, 320 (1937).

45. M. Smialowski and T. Ostrowska. *Corr. et Anticorr.,* (1957) March.

46. A. A. Berk and W. F. Waldeck. *Chemical Engineering,* 57, 235 (1950).

47. H. Grafen and D. Kuron. *Archiv. fur das Eisenhutt.,* 36, 4 (1965).

48. F. G. Straub and T. A. Bradbury. *Power Plant Eng.,* 40, 104 (1936).

49. W. C. Schroeder and A. A. Berk. *Amer. Inst. Min. Met. Eng.,* 120, 387 (1936).

50. C. D. Weir. *Proc. Inst. Mech. Eng.,* 163, 18 (1950).

51. E. P. Partridge, C. E. Kaufman and R. E. Hall. *Trans. Amer. Soc. Mech. Eng.,* 64, 417 (1942).

52. C. D. Weir. *Trans. Amer. Soc. Mech. Eng.,* 70, 253 (1948).

53. C. D. Weir and P. Hamer. *Chem. and Ind.,* 71, 1040 (1952).

54. J. Wenczel and G. Wranglen. *Corrosion Science,* 4, 137 (1964).

55. M. J. Humphries and R. N. Parkins. *Corrosion Science,* 5, 7, 747 (1967).

56. R. N. Parkins and R. Usher. *J. Applied Chemistry,* 9, 445 (1959).

57. H. Huckholtz and R. Pusch. *Stahl und Eisen,* 62, 21 (1942).

58. W.P. Rees. *Symposium on Internal Stresses in Metals and Alloys,* Inst. of Metals, London, p.333, 1948.

59. British Engine Boiler and Electrical Insurance Co. Ltd, Technical Report, New Series Volume II, p.56, 1954.

60. M. J. Humphries and R. N. Parkins. This Conference.

61. S. W. Parr and F. G. Straub, University of Illinois Bulletin, p177, 1928.

62. M. Smialowski. *First International Congress on Metallic Corrosion,* Butterworths, 1961. Discussion p. 295.

63. M. Smialowski and Z. Szklarska-Smialowska. *Corrosion,* 18, 1t (1962).

64. R. N. Parkins. *Metallurgical Reviews,* 9, 201 (1964).

# CAUSTIC CRACKING OF MILD STEEL

K. Bohnenkamp
Max-Planck-Institut fur Eisenforschung

## Abstract

Experiments were carried out primarily in boiling solutions. Specimens of different steels were held at constant electrode potentials under tensile stress with a constant load. The experimental results indicate, that the intergranular stress corrosion in sodium hydroxide is limited to a narrow range of anodic potentials. Apart from a sufficient stress, an appreciable amount of plastic deformation is also necessary. Plastic deformation was also necessary in boiling solutions of calcium nitrate. Only specimens with a higher content of nitrogen fractured here at a stress below the lower yield point. Stability against intergranular stress corrosion was observed only on specimens of a steel with a higher carbon content. Some specimens of steels alloyed with aluminum or titanium resisted stress corrosion only after special heat treatments.

## I. Introduction

Stress corrosion of steels has been investigated by many workers.[1] However, it has not been possible to give a generally accepted explanation of mechanistic processes. Experiments on intergranular stress corrosion have been conducted primarily in concentrated nitrate solutions, or in concentrated alkalis. The work of Gräfen and Kuron[2] is the most recent publication on stress corrosion in concentrated alkalis. Experiments show that the carbon and nitrogen content of the steels play a deciding role. It has been shown[4-9] that the intergranular attack does not disappear in steels with carbon contents below 0.02%.[3] Long and Uhlig[9] observed that the intergranular stress corrosion of specimens quenched from 925 C and tempered then three hours at 550 C disappears only for zone refined iron with a carbon content lower than 5 ppm and a nitrogen content lower than 0.3 ppm.

## II. Experimental Procedure

The present investigations on mild steels were performed mostly in boiling 33% sodium hydroxide (bp 120 C). The analyses of the steels are given in Table 1. The diameter of the cylindrical specimens was 8 mm. The surface of the test section, which was turned down to 5 mm, was ground. In most cases the specimens were annealed for half an hour at 950 C under vacuum and then removed from the furnace, cooling somewhat slower than in air.

The arrangement of the experimental cell is shown in Figure 1. After the temperature of the experiment had been reached, the specimens were stressed in uniaxial tension with constant load. The electric potential, which plays an important role besides the mechanical stress,[2,5,6,8] was supplied by an electronic potentiostat. A mercury/mercuric oxide electrode with the same sodium hydroxide concentration as the test solution served as a reference electrode. The potential of this electrode is $E_h$ = 80 to 90 mV. All potentials are given with reference to the standard hydrogen electrode. The electrolyte container, made of commercial steel, served as the opposite electrode. The top and bottom of the cell were closed with rubber stoppers. A few comparative tests with a Teflon electrolyte container and a platinum electrode gave results which did not differ from those obtained with the steel container. The latter was admittedly attacked in places. Glass containers were strongly attacked in boiling sodium hydroxide, and did not last long enough. Moreover, the dissolved silicates influenced the course of the stress corrosion.

For comparison, some experiments were conducted in boiling solution of calcium nitrate. Here we used glass vessels, platinum electrodes as opposite electrodes and mercury/mercuric chloride as reference electrodes.

## III. Dependence on Potential

Figure 2 shows the variation of time to fracture with potential for Armco iron (C). In this series of experiments the load was 30 kg/mm², just above the upper yield point.

TABLE 1—Analyses of Steels Tested (wt. %)

|   | C | N | Al | Ti | Si | Mn | P | S | Cu | O |
|---|---|---|---|---|---|---|---|---|---|---|
| A | 0.003 | 0.003 | 0.003 | | <0.001 | <0.001 | 0.004 | 0.007 | | 0.003 |
| B | 0.004 | 0.014 | 0.001 | | <0.001 | <0.001 | 0.003 | 0.002 | | 0.002 |
| C | 0.02 | 0.006 | 0.003 | | 0.003 | 0.018 | 0.011 | 0.009 | <0.003 | |
| D | 0.11 | 0.009 | 0.004 | | 0.01 | 0.31 | 0.022 | 0.039 | 0.03 | |
| E | 0.33 | 0.004 | 0.007 | | 0.29 | 0.73 | 0.011 | 0.03 | 0.1 | |
| F | 0.103 | 0.014 | 0.085 | | 0.015 | 0.002 | 0.002 | 0.004 | | |
| G | 0.009 | 0.006 | 0.031 | | 0.004 | 0.003 | 0.002 | 0.002 | | 0.002 |
| H | 0.005 | 0.016 | 0.12 | | 0.012 | 0.002 | 0.002 | 0.001 | | 0.002 |
| I | 0.105 | 0.005 | 0.019 | 0.73 | 0.014 | 0.003 | 0.004 | 0.004 | | |

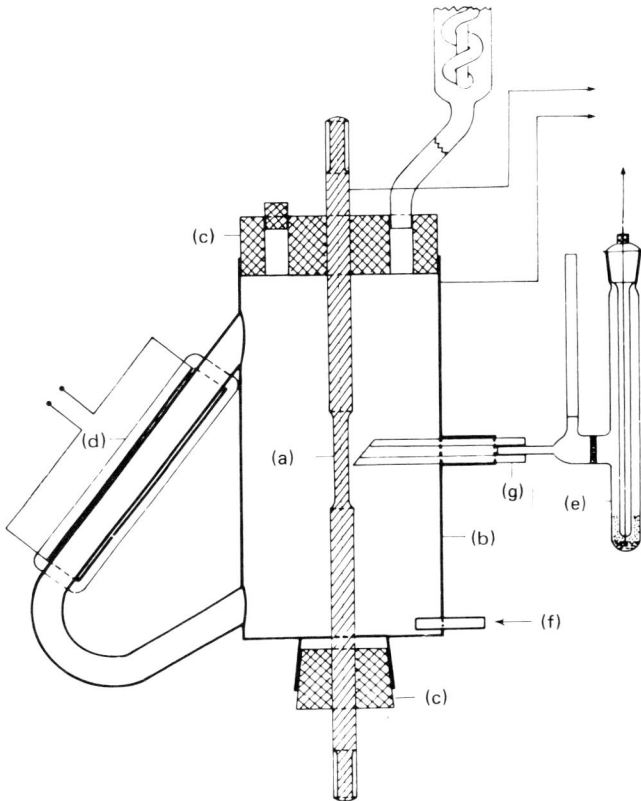

FIGURE 1 — Cross-section of a cell. (a) Specimen; (b) vessel; (c) rubber; (d) heating element; (e) reference electrode; (f) gas inlet; (g) Teflon.

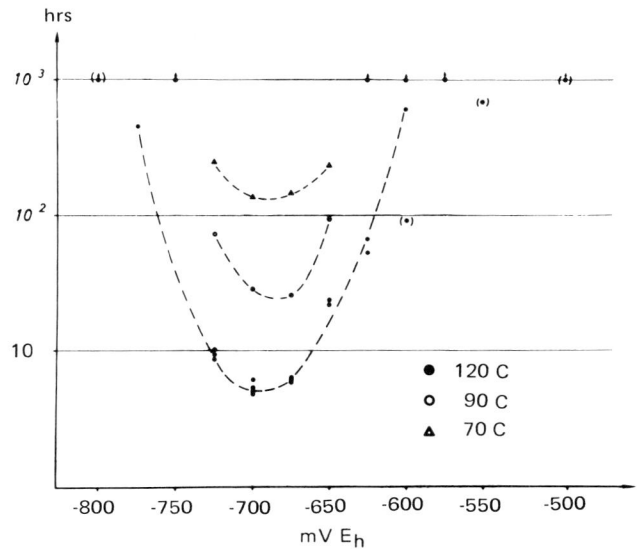

FIGURE 2 — Time to fracture of specimens of steel C as a function of potential $(E_h)$. Stressed with 30 kg/mm$^2$ in NaOH (33%). (●) after first holding for 3 hours at $E_h$ = -700 mV.

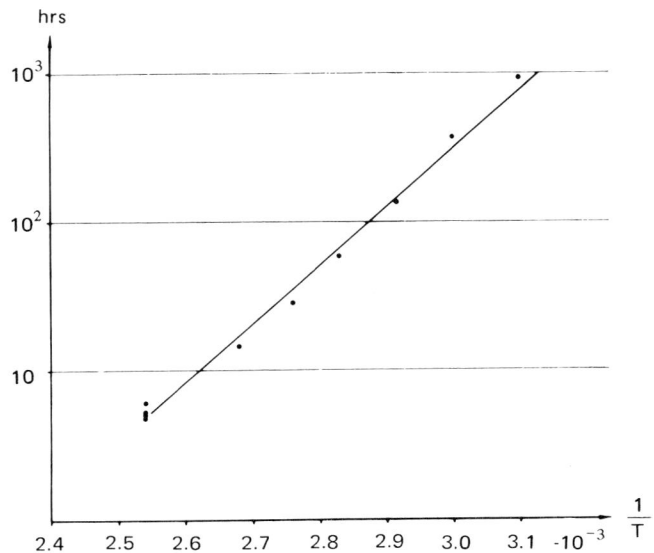

FIGURE 3 — Steel C. Time to fracture as a function of the reciprocal temperature. Stressed with 30 kg/mm$^2$ in NaOH (33%). $E_h$ = -700 mV.

The incidence of intergranular stress corrosion in sodium hydroxide is, according to the experimental results, limited to a narrow potential region. The minimum time to fracture occurs at a potential $E_h$ = -700 mV. This is true also for lower temperatures. When the times to fracture measured at various temperatures are plotted against the reciprocal of the absolute temperature, an approximately straight line is obtained. This is shown in Figure 3. The slope corresponds to an activation energy of about 18 Kcal/Mol.

The measurements plotted in Figure 2 in brackets are for specimens which were first held for 3 hours at $E_h$ = -700 mV and then polarized to the potentials shown in the diagram. During the holding period at $E_h$ = -700 mV, cracks appeared which were up to 300 $\mu$ deep (see Figure 7). Nevertheless, these specimens fractured, after switching to the other potentials shown in Figure 2 only after longer times, or not at all within 1000 hours. The shorter times to

375

fracture, compared with the normal specimens, measured at $E_h$ = -600 mV and $E_h$ = -550 mV can be explained by the increased mechanical stress and by a drop in electric potential within the cracks. The experiments described here show, in any case, that not only the formation of cracks, but also their growth is limited to a narrow potential range.

A series of experiments in which hydrogen, instead of nitrogen, was passed through the electrolyte, gave the same times to fracture at potentials which were only 25 mV more noble. The dependence of the incidence of stress corrosion on the oxygen content of the sodium hydroxide which is observed in practice must therefore arise from the fact that the corrosion potential depends upon the oxygen content.[4]

In experiments in 25% sodium hydroxide (boiling point 113 C), the shortest time to fracture was 14 hours at $E_h$ = -675 mV. Two tests in 20% sodium hydroxide (boiling point 109 C), which were carried out at $E_h$ = -650 mV and $E_h$ = -625 mV, were stopped after 850 and 1000 hours, respectively. Cracks were observed on the sample tested at -650 mV.

The experiments on specimens of the other steels which were stressed in boiling sodium hydroxide (bp 120 C) showed nearly the same potential dependence of the intergranular stress corrosion as in Figure 2. The potentials with the lowest times to fracture lay at $E_h$ = -660 mV for the specimens A (pure iron), at $E_h$ = -700 mV for the specimens B (pure iron with nitrogen), D (technical steel), I (steel alloyed with titanium) and at $E_h$ = -750 to -725 mV for the specimens F, G, H (steels with aluminum). Specimens of the steel E (technical steel) did not show cracks, when normalized.[10]

Gräfen and Kuron,[2] in their experiments in sodium hydroxide, also observed that the incidence of intergranular stress corrosion is limited to a narrow range of potentials. One reason for the fact that this range lay at less noble potentials, could be the use of glass vessels. In a few trials, in which the sodium hydroxide was boiled in a glass vessel before the experiment began, the times to fracture at $E_h$ = -700 mV were found to be longer by a factor of 8.

The fractured specimens had numerous cracks over the whole test length. Figure 4 shows the intergranular progress of a crack in a specimen which had fractured at another place. On specimens which were tested outside the critical potential range, and removed after 1000 hours, no intergranular cracks were observed even after bending the specimen. Crack-like corrosion running across the grains was observed only after tests in which specimens C and D were tested 1000 hours at $E_h$ = -850 mV and at the corrosion potential around $E_h$ = -900 mV. In Figure 5 a micrograph is shown. A further test on a specimen C, which was cathodically polarized ($E_h$ = -1050 to -1000 mV) did not show cracks.

## IV. Comparison with Current-Potential Curves

Recently several papers have been published on the electrode reactions of iron in sodium hydroxide.[11-13] Most important for the present investigation is the discovery that

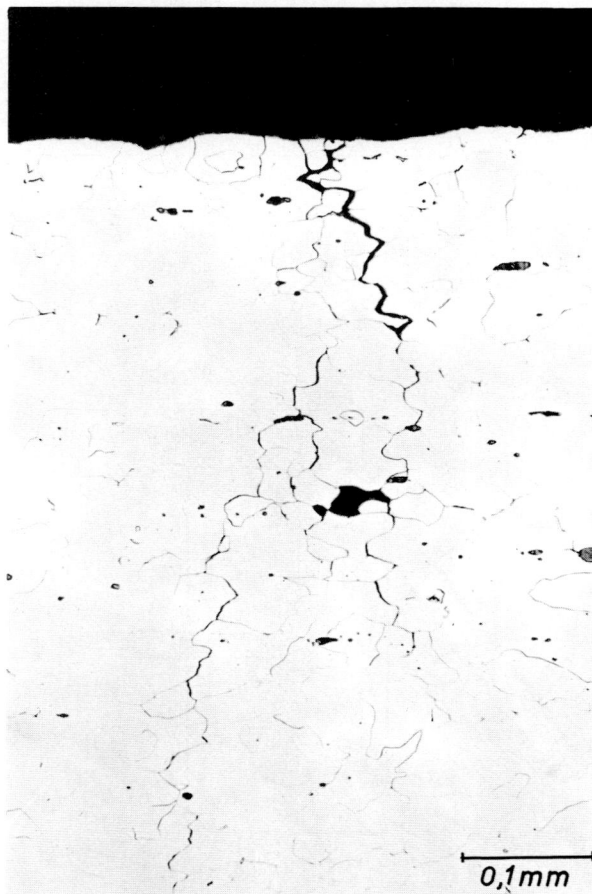

FIGURE 4 — Steel C. Optical micrograph of a cross section through the axis of a specimen stressed with 30 kg/mm$^2$ in boiling NaOH (33%). $E_h$ = -700 mV. Specimen fractured after 4.8 hours.

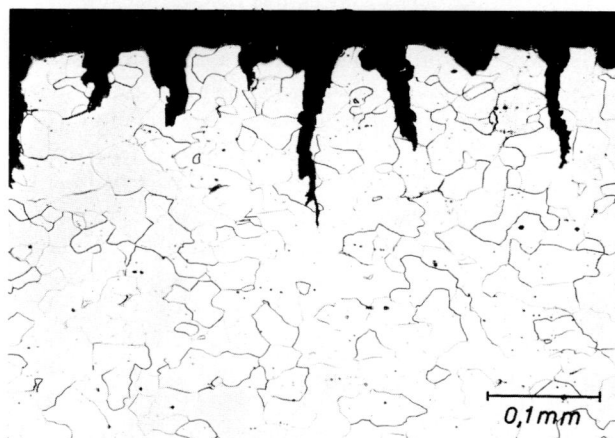

FIGURE 5 — Steel C. Optical micrograph of a cross section through the axis of a specimen tested 1000 hours with the load of 30 kg/mm$^2$ in boiling NaOH (33%). $E_h$ = $E_{corr}$ ≈ -900 mV.

in the neighborhood of $E_h$ = -700 mV a protective film of $Fe_3O_4$ is formed, and around $E_h$ = -300 mV a protective film of $\gamma$-$Fe_2O_3$ is formed. The current-potential curves measured herein at 120 C gave no stationary values. The measurements plotted in Figure 6 were carried out in a Teflon vessel with a platinum cathode and a magnetic stirrer. The potential was raised to $E_h$ = +300 mV ($\bullet$) and then lowered (o) in the same steps of 50 or 100 mV. It was held a minute at each value. The passivation occurs according to Figure 6 around $E_h$ = -800 mV. Analyses and micrographs after experiments at constant potentials showed that the anodic currents decreasing with time could be nearly accounted for at $E_h$ $\geq$ -600 mV by the dissolution of iron and formation of the oxide layer according to $Fe \rightarrow Fe^{3+} + 3e^-$ ($Fe + 4OH^- \rightarrow FeO_2^- + 3e^- + H_2O$ and $3Fe + 8OH^- \rightarrow Fe_3O_4 + 4H_2O + 8e^-$ or $2Fe + 6OH^- \rightarrow Fe_2O_3 + 3H_2O + 6e^-$). At $E_h$ = -800 mV the amount of oxidized iron corresponded nearly to $Fe \rightarrow Fe^{2+} + 2e^-$ ($Fe + 4OH^- \rightarrow FeO_2^{2-} + 2H_2O + 2e^-$ and $Fe + 2OH^- \rightarrow Fe(OH)_2 + 2e^-$ or $3Fe + OH^- \rightarrow Fe_3O_4 + 4H_2O + 8e^-$). At $E_h$ = -850 mV the specimen remained active up to 24 hours. The amount of iron dissolved in 6 hours was 10% higher than corresponding to the current-time curve. The reason for this is probably the appreciable cathodic partial current. Analyses showed also a dissolution of iron at $E_h$ = -900 mV and -1000 mV. At $E_h$ = -800 mV very small anodic or even cathodic currents were reached after 30-60 minutes. With increasing potential the anodic currents fell off more slowly.

At the start of the experiments on stress corrosion somewhat smaller current densities were observed than in Figure 6 as a result of the heating lag. After plastic strain the current usually increases initially by several milliamperes. In spite of the remarkable differences between single experiments, the currents fell off more slowly than in the experiments carried out with the Teflon vessel and a

platinum electrode. At $E_h$ $\geq$ -650 mV the average current densities remained after 1000 hours between 0.1 and 0.5 $mA/cm^2$. At potentials -800 mV $\leq$ $E_h$ $\leq$ -700 mV were appreciably lower values or even cathodic currents sometimes observed. In a trial with a platinum anode in an iron vessel a current was observed independent of potential between -600 mV and +500 mV but dependent on stirring rate. The current density referred to the platinum anode (9 $cm^2$) lay around 0.4 $mA/cm^2$ similar to the values during the stress corrosion experiments. A comparative test with two platinum electrodes in a Teflon vessel showed in the potential range -750 mV $\leq$ $E_h$ $\leq$ +500 mV current densities |i| less than 0.01 $mA/cm^2$. Unlike the experiments with the Teflon vessel on specimens which had been tested for longer times in the critical potential range in the steel containers, the formation of an $\alpha$-$Fe_2O_3$ layer was observed some tenths of a millimeter thick. Since the diameter outside the strained test section did not change appreciably, it must be assumed that the iron came from the cathodic steel container. Here iron must go into solution as a divalent ion and must be oxidized at the anode according to $FeO^{2-} \rightarrow FeO_2^- + e^-$. Under the easily removed layer of $\alpha$-$Fe_2O_3$ was a thin strongly adhering layer which also appeared on specimens tested in the Teflon vessel. An X-ray diffraction photograph of this layer after a test at $E_h$ = -700 mV showed $Fe_3O_4$-reflections.

According to Figure 2 a strong correlation exists between the time to fracture and the potential. However, the total currents show appreciable scatter at the same potential. A comparison of Figures 2 and 6 shows that the potential region where stress corrosion occurred corresponds to the region of passivation. A complete passivation of specimens strained and stressed can be assumed only at $E_h$ $\geq$ -600 mV. The decrease of current with time at $E_h$ = -800 mV may also be due to a protective layer. Nevertheless, the specimens did not crack here.

For comparison, the current density measurements made on an iron-chromium-carbide specimen with 1.95% chromium[14] are also given in Figure 6 ($\triangle$). The holding times at each potential were again 1 minute. This current-potential curve indicates a preferential dissolution of iron carbide. According to Langenscheid and Naumann[15] this is valid for cementite but not for the pure iron nitrides. Corresponding current-potential curves in boiling calcium nitrate solution (bp 115 C) showed lower current densities for the iron-chromium-carbide specimen than for the steel C. For the stress corrosion in calcium nitrate a preferential dissolution of the visible cementite precipitates seems therefore to be improbable.[3,5]

## V. Influence of Stress and Strain

In order to follow the growth of the cracks, specimens C loaded with 30 kg/mm$^2$ at $E_h$ = -700 mV were removed after 1 to 5.7 hours before appearance of fracture. The maximum penetration depth of the cracks, observed in micrographs, are given in Figure 7. The measurements show that the cracks form quickly and suggest that they grow continuously. The acceleration of crack growth with

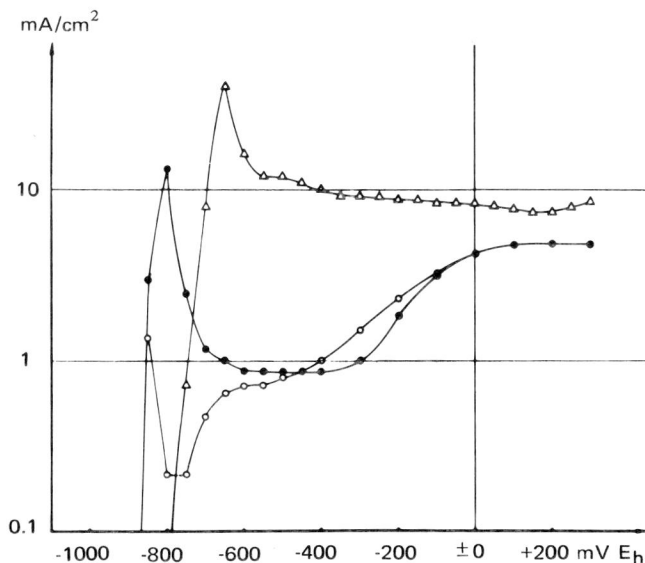

FIGURE 6 – Current densities as a function of potential in boiling NaOH (33%). $\bullet$ ○ Steel C, $\triangle$ Fe$_3$C with 1.9% Cr; $\bullet$ $\triangle$ Increasing potential, ○ Decreasing potential; Holding time one minute.

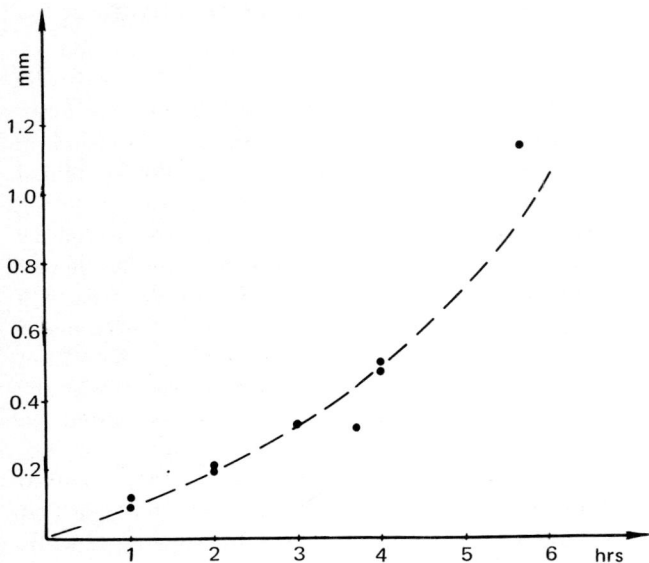

FIGURE 7 – Steel C. Penetration of deepest cracks as a function of time. Stressed with 30 kg/mm$^2$ in boiling NaOH (33%). $E_h$ = -700 mV.

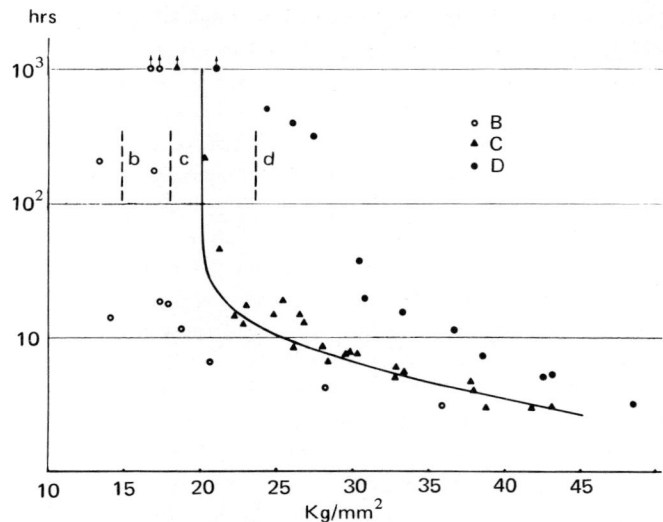

FIGURE 9 – Time to fracture as a function of the stress (calculated from the cross section after plastic elongation) in boiling NaOH (33%). $E_h$ = -700 mV. Specimens B (○), C (▲), D (●). b, c, d values of the lower yield points.

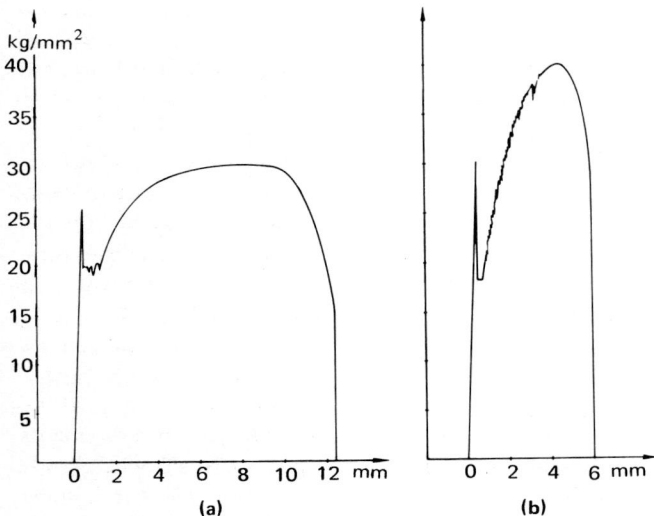

FIGURE 8 – Steel C. Stress-strain-curves. (a) Room temperature. (b) 120 C (in oil). Strain velocity 2 mm/min. 1 mm ≈ 3% of test length.

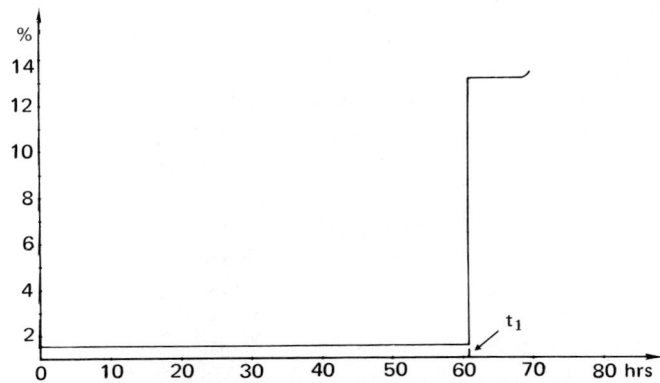

FIGURE 10 – Steel C. Strain of the test length as a function of time. Stressed with 26 kg/mm$^2$ in boiling NaOH (33%). $E_h$ = -700 mV. $q(t < t_1) \approx q_o$, $q(t \geqslant t_1) \approx q_1 < q_o$.

decreasing cross-sectional area, i.e., with increasing stress, is in agreement with the relationship derived in an earlier paper[6] on stress corrosion in calcium nitrate. This relationship is

$$\frac{dr}{dt} = -k\,(\sigma(t) - \sigma_O) = -k\,\left(\frac{L}{\pi r^2\,(t)} - \sigma_O\right) \qquad (1)$$

where r is the radius of the rest of the cross section, k the rate constant, $\sigma_O$ the lower limiting stress and L the load.

In a further series of experiments, the mechanical stress was varied. Figure 8 shows examples of stress-strain curves which were obtained at the given strain rate from two test samples of steel C, in one case at room temperature in air, and in the second case at 120 C in an oil bath. The elastic extension of the samples outside the test section is also included in the plotted measurements. It is striking that the tensile strength is greater at 120 C than at room temperature. That was observed only on specimens of the steels C and D and could possibly be due to the increased diffusion rate of carbon and nitrogen. At lower strain rates, even greater stresses were reached. Also, the stress fluctuations of the specimens tested at 120 C remained until fracture. If the strain was stopped after exceeding the upper yield point a new yield point was observed after only 20 minutes at room temperature.

In the experiments in boiling sodium hydroxide, the load was constant. The strain rate on crossing the yield point was approximately 50% per second. After that, a further extension was observed only some time before fracture. Tests made at random with specimens which were strained previously in air or with specimens slowly strained in boiling sodium hydroxide did not show appreciably different times to fracture.

Most of the experiments were carried out in such a way that the specimen was first strained just above the upper

378

yield point, and then tested at the load shown in the diagram. In Figure 9, the times to fracture of specimens B, C, and D are plotted against the stress. In this case the stress was calculated with respect to the diameter of the specimens after the experiments. This corresponds well with the value after plastic strain. The observed times to fracture show that when the stress is below a certain critical value, approximately equal to the lower yield point, no stress corrosion appears. This agrees with the results of our experiments with calcium nitrate.[5,6] For austenitic steels with no extended yield point, on the other hand, no such minimum stress is required.[1] The dependence of the times to fracture of mild steels on the stress could be described by the integration of Equation (1). The curve for the specimens C was calculated with $\sigma_O$ = 20 kg/mm$^2$, $\sigma_B$ = 50 kg/mm$^2$, observed at the lowest strain rate (0.05 mm/min) at 120 C, and with $\alpha$ = 1.7. From the accommodation of the curve it follows that k $\approx$ 10$^{-4}$ mm$^3$/min-kg. For the specimens B and D the lowest stress $\sigma_O$ corresponds closely to the lower yield point. The few experiments on specimens of pure iron (A) showed similar values as the specimens B. The lower stress limit seems to be here appreciably higher than the yield point of 5 kg/mm$^2$.

In experiments with steel E, none of the normally normalized specimens, which were strained in the critical potential range $E_h$ = -800 to -600 mV with 50 kg/mm$^2$ over the upper yield point, fractured within the test period of 1000 hours. Also no cracks were observed in micrographs. The observation that the susceptibility to intergranular stress corrosion disappears at higher carbon concentration agrees with the results of other workers.[3,8,10]

Experiments with specimens C, which were strained previously in air up to 30% showed on the other hand mostly longer times to fracture.[4,7] Especially remarkable was the inhibiting influence on a specimen with a neck. The fracture took place outside the neck.

When the specimens (C, D) were loaded under the upper yield point the times to fracture varied considerably for a given load. Only after a long time, a sudden plastic elongation was observed. In a few such experiments the strain was recorded during the experiment. A curve so obtained is given in Figure 10. Specimens which were loaded in oil at 120 C, instead of boiling sodium hydroxide, showed the same behavior. Accordingly, the sudden extension cannot be due to corrosion attack. In all experiments in which plastic flow was recorded, the measured times between plastic flow and fracture agree with those obtained from specimens which were plastically deformed at the start of the experiment. Accordingly, plastic deformation seems to be a necessary condition for crack formation. This was confirmed by an experiment in which the specimen flowed after 72 hours and was discharged and removed immediately after that. In a micrograph no intergranular attack was observed.

That the plastic deformation is a necessary condition for the formation of cracks was also shown in experiments in which the specimens A, B, and C were stressed only up to the lower yield point. None of the specimens tested in such a way showed any cracks.

## VI. Comparative Tests in Calcium Nitrate

Some experiments on specimens B, C, D, and E were conducted in a boiling concentrated solution of calcium nitrate. The potential ($E_h$ = 0) was close to the corrosion potential. A specimen E stressed with 50 kg/mm$^2$ showed no stress corrosion in this solution either. The times to fracture of specimens C and D were shorter, up to a factor of 5, than in sodium hydroxide at the same stresses. But the lower stress limit was in this case also around the lower yield point. Specimens of the steel C, which were stressed only up to the lower yield point and not strained, did not show stress corrosion, just as in sodium hydroxide. This was tested also in some experiments in which the load was applied very slowly and continuously at a rate of 0.15 kg/mm$^2$ hour. Fracture occurred, in this case also, only when the lower yield point was exceeded and the specimen was plastically strained. At stresses between the upper and lower yield points the specimens cracked only when they were plastically strained. The times between plastic flow and fracture agreed again with those obtained from specimens which were plastically deformed at the start of the experiment. A specimen loaded between the upper and lower yield point, which strained only after 94 hours and was then immediately cathodically polarized did not show any cracks, just as in the corresponding experiment in sodium hydroxide.

A significantly different behavior to that found in sodium hydroxide was exhibited only by specimens B. Specimens tested in sodium hydroxide at $E_h$ = -700 mV and stressed with 13 and 16 kg/mm$^2$ did not show cracks after holding times of 1000 hours. Specimens tested in calcium nitrate at $E_h$ = 0 mV stressed with 10, 13, and 15 kg/mm$^2$ cracked after 1.4 to 3.8 hours. A specimen stressed with 7 kg/mm$^2$ showed small cracks after 1000 hours. Corresponding to the stress strain curves measured at 120 C in oil, which showed lower and upper yield points around 15 and 19 kg/mm$^2$, none of the above specimens showed noticeable plastic deformation. Stress corrosion in calcium nitrate at stresses below the lower yield points has been observed by other authors too.[4,5,8,16]

## VII. Variation of Load and Potentials

As already mentioned, a new yield point arises after deformation with constant load. In the experiments in sodium hydroxide further noticeable extensions were observed only some time before fracture. Nevertheless, the question remained, whether creep processes at the peaks of the cracks are the deciding factor. The experiments were not able to settle this question.

Specimens C, which were discharged after straining to just below the lower yield stress and further stressed a week later, showed appreciably longer times to fracture than normally, if not stressed too much the second time. A similar effect was observed also by Engell and Bäumel[5] in experiments in calcium nitrate.

In further experiments, specimens of the steel C were first stressed with 30 kg/mm$^2$ at potentials $E_h$ = -950 mV or $E_h$ = -500 mV and after 5 to 7 days polarized to $E_h$ = -700 mV. Although in two cases the stress was lowered then to 25 kg/mm$^2$, the times to fracture were not noticeably longer than in the normal case. The longer times to fracture first mentioned could therefore be interpreted as being due to a stopping of the formation of cracks with a protective passive layer at $E_h$ = -700 mV, rather than a reduced creep rate.

In a third series of experiments, stresses in specimens C tested at $E_h$ = -700 mV were lowered to smaller values after 2 or 4.5 hours. Cracks of 200 or 600 $\mu$ depth would be expected. The specimens fractured only if the mean stress for the estimated remaining cross section was higher than the original lower yield point.

## VIII. Other Heat Treatments

Specimens C quenched in water fractured only with higher stresses. Experiments with specimens which were held after cooling from 950 C for one hour at 700 C and then quenched in water, confirmed once more that the formation of the cracks starts only after a plastic deformation. The stress-strain curves of such a specimen after quenching, and a specimen removed after being tested in

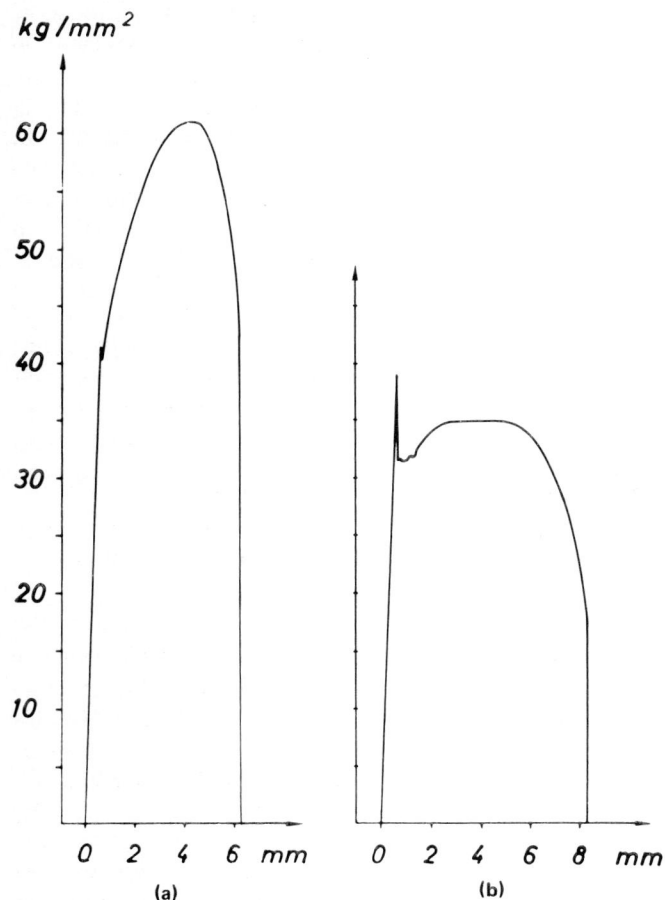

FIGURE 11 — Steel C. Stress-strain-curves of specimens tempered 1 hour at 700 C, then quenched in water. Strain velocity 2 mm/min. 1 mm ≈ 3% of test length. Measured at room temperature. (a) after quenching. (b) after 250 hours in boiling NaOH (33%).

sodium hydroxide with a load of 29 kg/mm$^2$ for 250 hours are given in Figure 11. The latter specimen had not flowed and showed no formation of cracks. The stress-strain curve of a specimen which had been tempered for 250 hours at 120 C in air was practically identical. On the other hand, an appreciable plastic deformation was observed on specimens with the same heat treatment loaded in sodium hydroxide, which had fractured.

Specimens C, which were tempered one hour at temperatures of 400 to 700 C and then cooled in the furnace or in air did not show appreciable changes of time to fracture. Times to fracture of specimens first quenched and then tempered at 300 C (one-half hour) or 400 C (one hour) were longer by a factor of 2 to 4.

A series of specimens E was tested in which the carbon distribution was changed from fine pearlite to spherical dementite precipitates by means of a heat treatment at 700 C for 72 hours. The specimens pretreated in this way showed a slightly reduced strength and were tested with a stress of only 40 kg/mm$^2$ over the upper yield point. In contrast to the normalized specimens, intergranular fracture occurred. This agrees with the observations of Parkins[3] and indicates that it is not really the carbon content which is critical but rather the distribution of carbon.

## IX. Specimens Decarburized or Nitrided

A few experiments were carried out on specimens E, which had been surface-decarburized half an hour at 850 C in moist hydrogen and finally normalized in a vacuum like the other specimens. The depth of the clearly decarburized zone was only about 150 $\mu$. Nevertheless, the pretreated specimens fractured after times of 9 to 45 hours. This indicates that the high carbon content inhibits the formation, but not the growth, of cracks. Parkins[3] found the same in experiments in calcium nitrate.

Further experiments were performed on specimens C and E, which had been nitrided by heating at 600 C in a dry hydrogen-ammonia mixture, and finally normalized. The first group of specimens had an average content of 0.01% nitrogen. On the surface of the specimens the content must be assumed to be higher. In micrographs, nitride precipitates could be seen only in specimens of steel C. No decarburization of the nitrided specimens was found. The nitrided specimens E fractured in times similar to those of the surface decarburized specimens. For the nitrided specimens of steel C a distinct reduction of the time to fracture was observed only at low stresses. That the formation of cracks happens only after a plastic deformation was confirmed also here.

For more strongly nitrided specimens C with 0.07% and 0.12% nitrogen stressed with 31 kg/mm$^2$ we observed times to fracture longer by a factor of 3 than the normal specimens C. But stress-strain curves showed also higher yield points and higher rupture stresses.

## X. Alloyed Specimens

The results discussed so far for unalloyed steels show

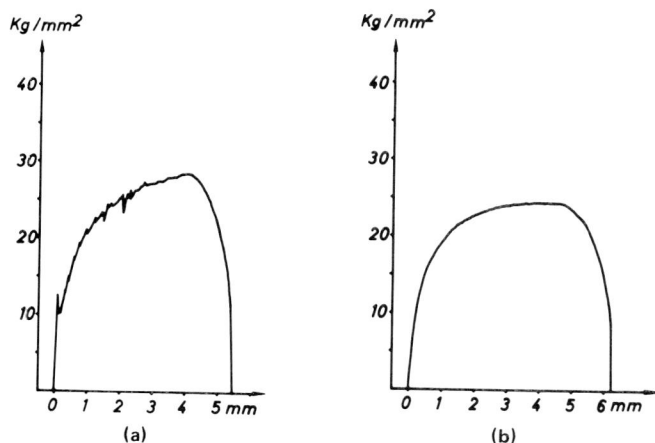

FIGURE 12 – Stress-strain-curves. Strain velocity 2 mm/min. 1 mm ≈ 3% of test length. (a) Specimen of steel H tempered 6 hours 750 C, 15 hours 670 C, 8 hours 600 C, then furnace cooled. Measured at 120 C. (b) Specimen of steel I tempered half an hour at 750 C, 2 hours at 650 C, then furnace cooled. Measured at room temperature.

the favorable influence of a high carbon content (steel E) and the unfavorable influence of nitrogen. To decide whether nitrogen alone is the real cause of the intergranular attack, we tested specimens of steels alloyed with aluminum[8,17] and titanium[8,19] (see Table 1). The aluminum additions in the steels F, G, and H were higher at least by a factor of 2.5 than corresponding to AlN, the titanium additions in the steel E by a factor of 2 higher than corresponding to TiN and TiC.

The stress-strain curves showed sharp yield points only for the specimens alloyed with aluminum. Here the carbon is not, or at least not completely, precipitated as $Al_4C_3$. The specimens of steel alloyed with titanium (I) showed nearly continually differentiable curves. Figure 12 shows examples of stress-strain curves.

After the normal heat treatment only the specimens F and I were tested. The loads lay at 80 to 90% of the rupture loads observed at 120 C. In the critical potential range, the specimens of both steels showed intergranular stress corrosion. The shortest times to fracture of specimens F were 20 to 30 hours, of specimens I, 3 to 6 hours. Only a specimen of the steel I tested with a lower stress held 1000 hours and did not show cracks. A corresponding increase of the lower stress limit was observed also by Münster and Gräfen[8] for a similarly alloyed steel tested in calcium nitrate. This is probably connected with our own result that the lowest stress for cracking of the specimens A is appreciably higher than the yield point.

Further experiments were performed on specimens which were tempered 2 hours at 750 C after normalizing. After this heat treatment, which did not change the stress-strain curves remarkably, all specimens F did not show cracks after 1000 hours. The same was found for a specimen F tested in calcium nitrate.

Specimens of the steels G and H, which were tested only after heat treatments, cracked nevertheless comparatively quickly. The times to fracture were between 5 hours with a stress of 25 kg/mm² and 26 hours with a stress of 15

kg/mm². No noticeable influence of the different heat treatments was found. These results with the specimens G and H support the hypothesis that enrichment of carbon at the grain boundaries leads to the intergranular stress corrosion, too.

The specimens I alloyed with titanium showed, after heat treatments at 750 and 650 C and cooling in the furnace, appreciably longer times to fracture, from 150 to 1000 hours. Two specimens tested 1000 hours did not show any cracks. The observation that steels with sufficiently low contents of free carbon or nitrogen are resistant to the intergranular stress corrosion agrees with the results of Long and Uhlig.[9]

## XI. Conclusions

The experimental results show that the intergranular stress corrosion of mild steel in sodium hydroxide is limited to the region of the passivation potential. This is true for crack formation and crack growth, and can be accounted for by the fact that the protective layer remains incomplete in the case of specimens stressed above the lower yield point, and the grain boundaries remain active. Apart from the critical potential range, an appreciable plastic deformation is necessary, at least for the formation of cracks. How far the creep processes (rather than the stress and lattice defects) facilitate crack growth, cannot be deduced with certainty from the experimental results.

Specimens with around 0.02% nitrogen tested in calcium nitrate fractured even if they were stressed below the lower yield point. Experiments on nitrided specimens of a technical steel with 0.33% carbon, which was normally resistant to stress corrosion, showed that the nitrogen also plays a deciding part for the stress corrosion in sodium hydroxide. But the experimental results on specimens alloyed with aluminum or titanium contradict the assumption that the intergranular attack may be caused only by the nitrogen.

The experimental results and micrographs of specimens with low carbon contents indicate that the carbide precipitates visible in the microscope are not the cause of selective corrosion. In contrast to the observed higher rate of dissolution of iron carbide in sodium hydroxide compared to iron, a smaller rate of dissolution of the carbide, compared to the iron, was observed in calcium nitrate. On account of the similarity of the intergranular stress corrosion in sodium hydroxide and calcium nitrate it therefore appears improbable that the preferred dissolution of carbide precipitates in sodium hydroxide plays a deciding part. Nevertheless, enrichment of dissolved carbon and nitrogen or submicroscopic precipitates at the grain boundaries must be deciding factors.

381

# References

1. H. Ternes. *Werkstoff u. Korrosion*, **14**, 729 (1963).
2. H. Gräfen and D. Kuron. *Arch. Eisenhuttenwes.*, **36**, 285 (1965).
3. R. N. Parkins. *J. Iron Steel Inst.*, **172**, 149 (1952).
4. W. Rädeker and H. Gräfen. *Stahl u. Eisen*, **76**, 1616 (1956).
5. H. J. Engell and A. Bäumel. *Arch. Eisenhuttenwes.*, **32**, 379 (1961).
6. H. J. Engell, K. Bohnenkamp and A. Baumel. *Arch. Eisenhuttenwes.*, **33**, 285 (1962).
7. H. H. Uhlig and J. Sava. *Transactions ASM*, **56**, 361 (1963).
8. R. Münster and H. Gräfen. *Arch. Eisenhuttenwes.*, **36**, 277 (1965).
9. L. M. Long and H. H. Uhlig. *J. Electrochem. Soc.*, **112**, 964 (1965).
10. W. Rädeker and B. N. Mishra. *Werkstoff u. Korrosion*, **17**, 193 (1966).
11. W. W. Lossen and B. Kabanow. *Shurmal Fisitcheskoji Chemii*, **28**, 914 (1954).
12. K. E. Heussler, K. G. Weil, and K. F. Bonhoeffer. *Z. Phys. Chem.*, **15**, 149 (1958).
13. W. Schwarz and W. Simon. *Ber. Bunsenges. Phys. Chem.*, **67**, 108 (1963).
14. W. Jellinghaus. *Arch. Eisenhuttenwes.*, **37**, 181 (1966).
15. G. Langenscheid and F. K. Naumann. *Arch. Eisenhuttenwes.*, **36**, 505 (1965).
16. M. Henthorne and R. N. Parkins. III Intern. Congr. on Met. Corrosion, Moskau, 1966.
17. E. Houdremont, H. Bennek, and H. Wentrup. *Techn. Mitt. Krupp Forsch. Ber.*, **3**, 111 (1940).
18. E. Baerlecken and W. Hirsch. *Stahl u. Eisen*, **73**, 885 (1953).

# Discussion

**H. H. Uhlig, MIT:**

I would like to ask if you can estimate from your data the lowest temperature at which steel will crack in a caustic soda solution. There have been such estimates made in the literature. I wonder if you have explored this point?

**K. Bohnenkamp:**

**Our experiments shown in Figure 3 showed no limit. Up to 50 C we found log $\tau$ proportional to $1/T$.**

**H. H. Uhlig, MIT:**

But in practice there is a temperature limit below which it is accepted that conditions are safe and above which they are unsafe. You apparently have not confirmed such a limit in your own experiments.

My second question is, have you studied the effect of heat treatment on carbon steels?

**K. Bohnenkamp:**

**We found also longer times to fracture for quenched specimens if we took the same stresses.**

**H. H. Uhlig, MIT:**

You mentioned that you had to plastically strain your specimen a slight amount in order to observe susceptibility. We found that if we severely cold worked mild steel it became immune in the boiling nitrate test solution. Is this also true of caustic soda?

**K. Bohnenkamp:**

**We observed also longer times to fracture at the same loads on specimens which had previously been subjected to higher stresses (see Section V).**

**T. P. Hoar, University of Cambridge:**

We are presently conducting experiments on the mechano-chemical effect on this system and the results relate to the potential at which cracking is a maximum.

We find that the magnetite film does not reform after it has been broken by traction until the traction is stopped.

Perhaps $Fe_2O_3$ may be broken by traction but reforms quickly and prevents dissolution even on metal still undergoing traction.

I should also like to suggest that the role of various ions that cause inhibition may be significant in causing the potential to shift from regions of potential where cracking occurs to those where cracking does not occur.

**H. H. Uhlig, MIT:**

If I understand correctly, specimens *at the corrosion potential* would have cracked in a longer time.

**K. Bohnenkamp:**

**That is to be expected, but we observed transgranular cracks (Figure 5) at $E_h$ = -850 and -900 mV. Concerning the potential dependence I would like to point out that we observed the (active) corrosion potential around $E_h$ = -900 mV. But after anodic polarization—which may happen also by oxygen in solution—we found corrosion potentials in the critical range around $E_h$ = .700 mV.**

**H. H. Uhlig, MIT:**

Anodic polarization can apparently lead to intergranular penetration in absence of applied stress which I would call intergranular corrosion and not stress corrosion cracking. If steel specimens are allowed to remain in the calcium nitrate test solution without applied stress and without applied potential, there is no intergranular penetration or cracking. I believe others have made similar observations.

**J. E. LeSurf, Atomic Energy of Canada:**

In discussion, Herb Uhlig stated that no intergranular corrosion of carbon steel occurs in the absence of stress or anodic polarization. In contradiction, I should like to submit micrographs 1, 2, and 3, showing intergranular penetration of SAE 1010 carbon steel on unstressed coupons in high purity water. It is possible that some residual internal stress may remain in this hot rolled material, but no external stress is applied. The micrographs chosen for submission were exposed in pressurized water

382

(1), steam/water mixture (2), and dry steam (3), all in irradiated coolant. No such attack was found on the as-received material or control samples processed without exposure. Neither has any intergranular attack been found on the low alloy steels (2 1/4Cr-1Mo and 1 1/4Cr-1/2Mo) in any of the tests conducted.

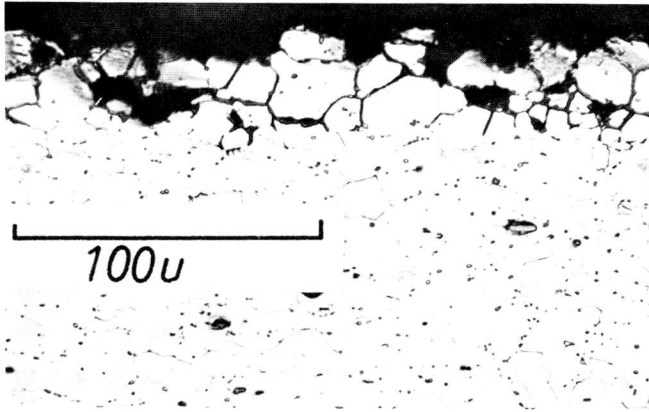

FIGURE 1 — SAE 1010 steel exposed 161 days in ammoniated pressurized water at 288 C (O₂ < 0.005 ppm).

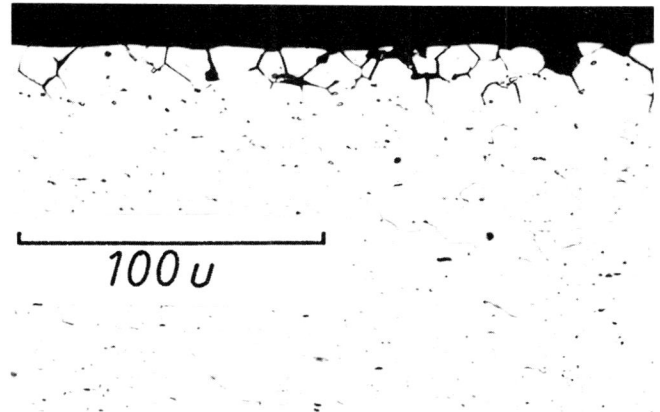

FIGURE 2 — SAE 1010 steel exposed 130 days in ammoniated steam-water mixture at 288 C (O₂ < 0.005 ppm).

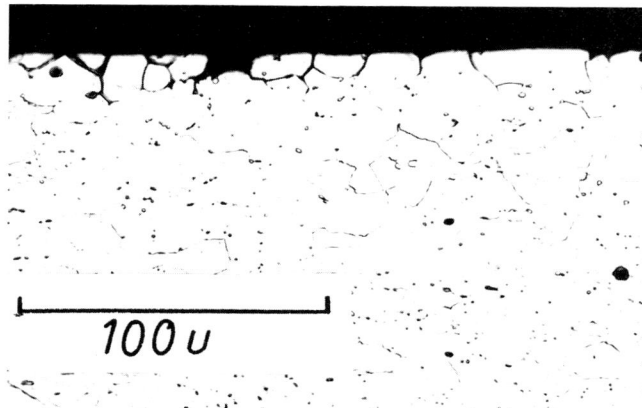

FIGURE 3 — SAE 1010 steel exposed 161 days in dry steam (NH₃-10 ppm, O₂ < 0.005 ppm).

# THE INFLUENCE OF OXIDE FILMS ON STRESS CORROSION CRACKING OF CARBON STEELS

M. J. Humphries and R. N. Parkins
The University, Newcastle upon Tyne

## Abstract

In sodium hydroxide solutions stress corrosion cracking of low carbon steels occurs in the presence of $Fe_3O_4$ films but not $Fe_2O_3$, while in nitrates cracks are readily produced in the presence of either oxide. It is suggested that the important feature associated with such results is not the nature of the oxide as such, but the range of potentials within which cracking occurs and which also determines the type of oxide formed. In hydroxide the range of potentials for cracking agrees reasonably with that in which $HFeO_2^-$ are stable, while in nitrates, accepting the generation of highly acid conditions within cracks, the equivalent range agrees reasonably with that in which $Fe^{++}$ or $Fe^{+++}$ form. Within the ranges of critical potentials in both types of solution, plastic straining of filmed specimens results in a large increase in anodic current, the magnitude of which is considerably greater than would appear likely from consideration of the area of unfilmed metal exposed by the film rupturing. This extra anodic activity may reflect enhanced dissolution arising from plastic straining of the metal independent of any effect associated with the presence of an oxide film.

## I. Introduction

The many hypotheses that have been propounded in attempts to account for the stress corrosion cracking of alloys have included a high proportion in which oxide films play a critical part. In the stress corrosion of low carbon steels in caustic solutions an early suggestion, by Straub and Parr,[1] was that a coherent coating of $Fe_3O_4$ formed on the steel and that this rendered the metal resistant to further attack by the hydroxide unless the film was broken and fresh steel exposed. Stresses below the yield point do not produce breaks in the film, so that the chemical action does not become selective, whereas under high stresses the oxide film cracks in the strained areas and chemical attack progresses. Subsequently, the same idea has been expressed by others, Logan,[2] in particular, claiming that the potential difference between filmed (cathodic) and film-free (anodic) areas leads to electrolytic action whereby stress corrosion occurs. Venczel and Wranglen,[3] using a potentiostatic method to investigate the cracking of steel wires, observed peaks in the polarization current coincident with sudden extensions of the wires accompanying periodic load increases and these current fluctuations were attributed to rupture of the surface oxide film and its repair.

It appears to be reasonably well established that both potential and current fluctuations occur when mild steel is plastically deformed in the boiling nitrate or hydroxide solutions in which it is susceptible to stress corrosion cracking. The significance of such transients to the stress corrosion mechanism is not established and there is an alternative explanation[4] to that in which it is supposed that a potential or current fluctuation is evidence of discontinuous crack propagation. In any case, there are visual differences between the oxide films that form on mild steels in different aggressive nitrate solutions[5] and the location of the oxide film with respect to the underlying metal structure suggests that simple film rupture hypotheses are inconsistent with certain aspects of stress corrosion in low carbon steels. Thus, in nitrate solutions it is observed[6] that visible oxide films first form on grain surfaces but not in those regions where a grain boundary cuts the surface and develops a shallow trench that later is recognizable as a crack. Such observations are not necessarily consistent with the suggestion[7,8] that the cause of stress corrosion is that oxide covered grains act as cathodes while unfilmed boundary regions act as anodes in a local electrochemical cell, a line of argument that could be confusing the cause and the effect. If oxide films form over grain surfaces but not over grain boundaries this would appear to indicate that the filming is directed by some initial difference between the boundary and the grain surface. This difference should not be ignored, as is usually the case in hypotheses involving the driving force in stress corrosion as the potential difference between filmed and unfilmed areas, especially since complete intergranular disintegration of mild steel in boiling nitrate is possible with anodic stimulation and in the absence of stress.[9] Since such stimulated penetration follows the grain boundaries, as do stress corrosion cracks proper in mild steels, it is difficult to escape the conclusion that the regions of preferential corrosion or cracking are present in the virgin material. Moreover, if selective corrosion was simply dependent upon the existence of discontinuities in an oxide film resulting from rupture thereof, then it may reasonably be expected that stress corrosion cracks in mild steel would show at least a significant proportion of transgranular path, which they manifestly do not.

When the present work was initiated it appeared that oxide films were formed during the stress corrosion cracking of low carbon steels in both hydroxide and nitrate environments, but the extent to which these films were involved in the cracking mechanism was obscure, as was the exact nature of the films. The films formed and the parts they play have frequently been assumed to be identical in both hydroxide and nitrate solutions, yet there has been no single investigation in which both types of environment has been investigated from this viewpoint. It was in the hope of establishing some of the facts relating to these points that the present work was undertaken and is still progressing.

## II. Experimental Techniques

The analysis of the steel used in this work is given in Table 1. Machined test pieces were vacuum annealed at 1080 C, followed by a slow cool to 650 C and a subcritical anneal at this temperature for 170 hours. This treatment produced ferritic grain sizes in the range $\ell^{-\frac{1}{2}}$ = 2.5 - 4 mm$^{-\frac{1}{2}}$ and a structure that was known to be highly susceptible to stress corrosion.

**TABLE 1—Composition of Steel Specimens**

|  | C | N | Mn | S | Si | P |
|---|---|---|---|---|---|---|
| wt.% | 0.08 | 0.002 | 0.35 | 0.03 | 0.01 | 0.02 |

The tensile test pieces used were machined in the conventional manner to a 0.5 inch gauge length over which the diameter was 0.1 inch. The specimens were subjected to one or other of two types of test in small hard-beam testing machines incorporating a load cell, the output from which was recorded throughout a test. In one type of test, the specimen was subjected to a continuous, slow, strain rate, which was 4.2 x 10$^{-6}$ sec$^{-1}$, unless otherwise stated. At this and lower strain rates the maximum load and reduction in area both gave a reliable indication of the presence or otherwise of intergranular stress corrosion cracks, as confirmed by metallographic examination. In the other type of test, the specimen was subjected to a constant strain by locking the cross heads of the testing machine when the required load was achieved. In this case the load began to relax when cracking had reached the point where macroscopic yielding was initiated and a convenient measure of the stress corrosion propensity is the time to total fracture.

For tests in caustic solutions, the latter was contained in a mild steel tube that surrounded the specimen and was closed at the ends with rubber stoppers. The cell was heated by an electrical resistance wire on the outside. The upper stopper carried a counter electrode in the form of a cylinder of platinum foil, 1 inch diameter and 1 inch long, supported upon two polytetrafluoroethylene rods that passed through the upper stopper. A platinum wire passed through one of these rods to provide an external electrical connection to the counter electrode. Potentials were measured with respect to a saturated calomel electrode that was connected to the corrosion cell by a string bridge contained within a polytetrafluoroethylene tube. The string bridge was arranged so that its tip was close ($\sim$ 1-2 mm) to the center of the gauge length of the test specimen. A reflux condenser, constructed in polytetrafluoroethylene, entered the cell through the upper stopper. The tests involving nitrate solutions were carried out with an identical arrangement, except that it was constructed in glass.

All solutions were prepared using analytical grade reagents and demineralized water. The test procedure involved boiling the solution in contact with the specimen before applying potentiostatic control and starting the testing machine motor to apply load.

Potentiostatic polarization curves were determined for the steel in each test solution at the boiling point. A potential stepping technique was employed, the potential being changed in 50 mV increments, starting in the cathodic region, and the polarization current was measured after 30 seconds had elapsed at each set potential. These measurements were made using the stress corrosion test cells.

The oxide films formed at various potentials and in different solutions were stripped and examined by X-ray and electron diffraction and by electron or optical microscopy. The stripping technique involved coating the film with a formvar solution, scratching to expose bare metal in a grid-like pattern, and immersion of the specimen in an alcoholic solution of iodine or bromine which rapidly penetrated along the oxide/metal interface freeing the oxide from the metal. The stripped films were washed with dry methanol. X-ray diffraction was preferred to electron diffraction for identification of the oxides since the extra accuracy of the X-ray method was necessary to distinguish between certain of the oxides involved which had very similar lattice constants. Powder photographs were taken using a 9 cm camera with iron radiation taken from a lithium fluoride monochromator. Electron diffraction was mostly used in examining the orientation of crystallites in stripped films.

## III. Results

### A. Stress Corrosion in 35% NaOH

Constant strain rate tests in boiling 35% NaOH at potentials from -960 to +540 mV (hydrogen scale) indicated that cracking only occurred within a restricted range of potentials, wherein both the maximum load reached during the test and the reduction in area at fracture showed reduced values (Figure 1). The critical range of potentials is from about -900 to -600 mV, in good agreement with previous results,[3,8] although the limits are somewhat dependent upon solution composition and other test conditions.[10]

In one series of tests, carried out at -710 mV and at a strain rate of 8.3 x 10$^{-7}$ sec$^{-1}$, straining was discontinued after various times and the specimens examined metallographically to ascertain the point of crack initiation. The results are shown in Table 2 from which it is clear that stress corrosion cracks, detectable by metallographic examination at 700x, in specimens held at the most critical potential, are not found until the stress is appreciably in excess of the initial yield stress (12 tons/sq inch) or until the specimen has been in contact with the solution for a considerable period of time. Since preoxidation of a specimen for 24 hours at zero load and -710 mV did not shorten the time to fracture it would appear that crack initiation is dependent upon the achievement of a particular value of stress or strain.

Constant strain tests at a potential of -710 mV and with the specimens strained to generate stresses of 15-20

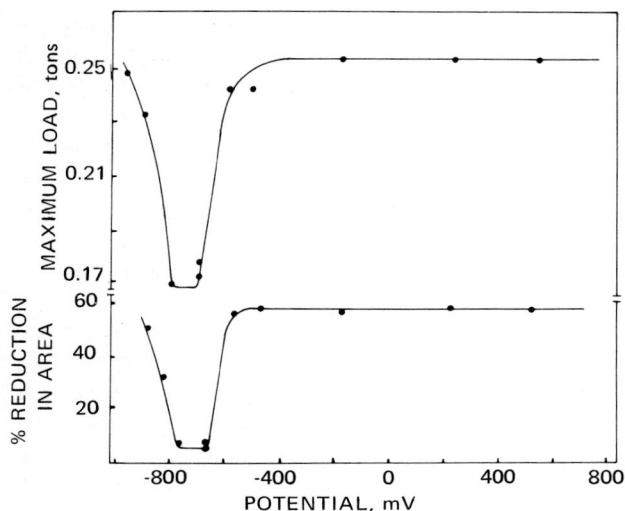

FIGURE 1 — Mechanical properties of mild steel, strained at $4.2 \times 10^{-6}$ sec$^{-1}$ in boiling 35% NaOH, as a function of potential.

TABLE 2—Crack Depths in Specimens Tested for Various Times in 35% NaOH at a Potential of -710 mV and Strain Rate of $8.3 \times 10^{-7}$ sec$^{-1}$

| Duration of Test (hours) | Nominal Stress (tons/sq in) | Crack Length (mm) |
|---|---|---|
| 19 | 13 | 0 |
| 22 | 13.9 | 0 |
| 26 | 15.0 | 0 |
| 46 | 20.0 | 0.03 |
| 48 | 20.8 | 0.05 |
| 54 | 21.0 | 0.25 |
| 60 | – | total fracture |

tons/sq inch failed to produce any cracking in times up to 7 days. If after such a test the specimen was subjected to a constant strain rate test intergranular cracks were produced as readily as in tests on virgin specimens. If, however, a specimen was initially strained at a sufficiently low rate to allow cracks to be formed and the crosshead then stopped, whether or not the cracks continued to propagate depended upon whether the continuous slow straining was stopped before or after the maximum load was reached. In the former case the cracks ceased to propagate, but if continuous straining was continued until the maximum load was passed then the cracks continued to propagate under the constant strain conditions that obtained once the crosshead was stopped. In the latter case crack propagation was accompanied by load relaxation until fracture was completed at almost zero load. The load relaxation was discontinuous, the chart record showing obvious steps, but since at the test temperature this steel exhibits marked strain-aging behavior, giving a serrated stress-strain curve, the explanation of these discontinuities may involve arguments[4] other than those based upon bursts of mechanical rupture.

There is clearly a strong suggestion in most of these results that stress corrosion of mild steel in NaOH requires, among other things, continuing plastic deformation if cracks are to be initiated and propagated.

## B. The Properties of Oxides Formed in 35% NaOH

Samples of oxides were prepared by oxidation in boiling 35% NaOH for 24 hours at various controlled potentials. The powder photograph of the oxide removed from a specimen prepared at -710 mV gave a diffraction pattern corresponding exactly to that given by David and Welch[11] for $Fe_3O_4$. The lattice parameter was 8.394 Å, in close agreement with reported values.[11] An oxide prepared at -50 mV gave reflections corresponding to those of $\gamma$-$Fe_2O_3$ with a lattice parameter of 8.355 Å, again in close agreement with values available in the literature. At intermediate potentials (-480 mV), the structure of the oxide corresponded to neither that of $Fe_3O_4$ or $\gamma$-$Fe_2O_3$, the measurements obtained from the X-ray photograph of this oxide being listed in Table 3. The diffraction pattern contained more lines than that of $Fe_3O_4$, and in this respect more closely resembled that for $\gamma$-$Fe_2O_3$, although the latter does not give a reflection corresponding to (222), while the oxide prepared at -480 mV gave such a reflection. Moreover, the lattice parameter of this oxide corresponded very closely to that of $Fe_3O_4$. It is possible to index all of the lines for this intermediate oxide by choosing a unit cell twice the size of that for $Fe_3O_4$, as is apparent from Table 3. This would correspond to an ordered structure and would appear to be more acceptable than one based upon a unit cell dimension of $\sqrt{2}$. $a_{Fe_3O_4}$, which also permitted indexing of the lines, but the formation of which from the structure of either $Fe_3O_4$ or $\gamma$-$Fe_2O_3$ would require considerable atomic re-arrangement. It is probable that between the compositions $Fe_2O_3$ and $Fe_3O_4$ a range of iron oxides of steadily increasing ferric ion content can form.[12] With increasing content of ferric ions in the oxide increasing numbers of vacancies should be formed in order to maintain electrical neutrality. It follows that the oxide formed at -480 mV, a potential between that at which $Fe_3O_4$ exists (-710 mV) and that at which $\gamma$-$Fe_2O_3$ exists (-50 mV) is likely to contain both vacancies and ferric ions, the ordering of which could lead to the formation of a structure in which the unit cell corresponded to two $Fe_3O_4$ unit cells. The chemical composition of an oxide formed at -480 mV may be expected to lie somewhere between $Fe_3O_4$ and $Fe_2O_3$, although the fact that the unit cell dimension was very close to that of $Fe_3O_4$ suggests that the transition from $Fe_3O_4$ to $\gamma$-$Fe_2O_3$ was just beginning.

The implication of these results to stress corrosion of mild steel in NaOH solutions is that the critical range of potentials within which cracking occurs is associated with the formation of $Fe_3O_4$ films and that at higher potentials, where cracks are not propagated, the ferric iron content of the film increases to that of $\gamma$-$Fe_2O_3$. At lower potentials cathodic protection occurs. In the hope of throwing some light on the question of whether these oxides played a significant role in the cracking mechanism, or whether their presence in different potential ranges was simply incidental, various additional examinations of oxide films were made.

Films used for electron microscopy had to be stripped from specimens after only 2-4 hours in boiling 35% NaOH, otherwise they were opaque to the electron beam. Films formed in the critical range of potentials for cracking consisted of square platelets, of size $4\mu$, and generally similar to those formed[13] upon iron and mild steel in high purity water at 250 C. Select area diffraction showed that a high degree of preferred orientation existed among the platelets, there being a similarity with the epitaxy of platelets formed in high purity water. The $Fe_3O_4$ film that was comprised of these platelets contained large numbers of holes or pores between some of the platelets, the pores frequently joining to form a continuous fault within the film. Films formed at -360 mV consisted of very small crystallites ($\sim 0.2$-$0.4$ $\mu$) having angular characteristics but without an obvious specific shape. The crystallites were appreciably more randomly oriented than were the platelets in the $Fe_3O_4$ film, but there were fewer pores apparent in the $Fe_2O_3$ film. Optical examination in transmitted light revealed no differences between the films that did not reflect the differences observed by electron microscopy. Both films exhibited features in the optical microscope that perpetuated the structure of the metal from which they had formed. Thus grain boundaries and sub-grain boundaries corresponding to those in the metal substrate were detectable. In some cases stripped films of $Fe_3O_4$ showed a network of holes corresponding to grain boundaries in the underlying metal, but whether these holes were produced in

stripping the film, or were indicative of the grain boundary regions being partially unfilmed, it is impossible to state. On the other hand, attempts to measure the capacitance of films of $Fe_3O_4$ and $Fe_2O_3$ in situ on the specimens on which they were formed were unsuccessful because of porosity in the films.

The behavior of $Fe_3O_4$ and $Fe_2O_3$ films upon straining while attached to the specimens on which they were formed was the same in both cases. A network of cracks formed in positions corresponding to the grain boundaries of the metal substrate while additional cracks, roughly parallel to one another and normal to the principal tensile stress, developed over the grain surfaces, as is apparent from Figure 2. The results were the same in specimens strained in silicone oil at 120 C, the temperature of boiling 35% NaOH, and in air at 20 C. Possibly of greater significance are the results obtained upon straining specimens while immersed in boiling NaOH. Oxidation of specimens for 24 hours at -710 mV in boiling 35% NaOH produced a large increase in anodic polarization current when the specimen was rapidly plastically deformed while its potential was maintained at -710 mV. No such effect was observed with specimens held at -360 mV, except for a relatively small increase in anodic current immediately following ductile fracture of the

TABLE 3—Comparison of Oxide Formed in 35% NaOH at -480 mV With Characteristics of Known Oxides

| γ-Fe₂O₃ | | Fe₃O₄ | | α-Fe₃O₄ | | | Unknown Oxide | |
|---|---|---|---|---|---|---|---|---|
| Index | Intensity | Index | Intensity | Index | $(\epsilon h^2 + k^2 + \ell^2)$ | Calc. $\sin^2 \theta$ | Obs. $\sin^2 \theta$ | Intensity |
| 100 | 0.5 | | | | | | | |
| 111 | 0.5 | 111 | 1.0 | 222 | 12 | 0.0399 | 0.0392 | M. |
| 210 | 0.6 | | | | | | | |
| 211 | 0.5 | | | 422 | 24 | 0.0798 | 0.0797 | M.W. |
| | | | | 520; 432 | 29 | 0.0964 | 0.0967 | W. |
| 220 | 4.2 | 220 | 3.4 | 440 | 32 | 0.1064 | 0.1068 | M.S. |
| | | | | 442 | 36 | 0.1197 | 0.1194 | W. |
| 300 | 0.2 | | | | | | | |
| | | | | 611 | 38 | 0.1264 | 0.1275 | V.W. |
| 310 | v.f. | | | | | | | |
| | | | | 621 | 41 | 0.1363 | 0.1361 | W. |
| 311 | 10.0 | 311 | 10.0 | 622 | 44 | 0.1463 | 0.1461 | V.S. |
| 320 | v.f. | | | | | | | |
| | | 222 | 0.6 | 444 | 48 | 0.1596 | 0.1591 | V.W. |
| 321 | v.f. | | | | | | | |
| | | | | 721 | 54 | 0.1796 | 0.1800 | V.W. |
| 400 | 3.3 | 400 | 3.4 | 800 | 64 | 0.2128 | 0.2118 | M.S. |
| | | | | 662 | 76 | 0.2527 | 0.2535 | W. |
| 421 | 0.2 | | | | | | | |
| | | | | 664 | 88 | 0.2926 | 0.2925 | W. |
| 422 | 1.6 | 422 | 1.1 | 844 | 96 | 0.3192 | 0.3195 | M. |
| 511 | 4.5 | 333; 511 | 4.1 | 666; 10,22 | 108 | 0.3591 | 0.3590 | M.S. |
| 520 | v.f. | | | | | | | |
| 521 | 0.3 | | | | | | | |
| 440 | 6.5 | 440 | 6.2 | 880 | 128 | 0.4256 | 0.4260 | M.S. |
| 611 | v.f. | | | | | | | |
| 620 | 0.6 | 620 | 0.3 | 12,40 | 160 | 0.5320 | 0.5330 | V.W. |
| 533 | 1.1 | 533 | 0.8 | 10,66 | 172 | 0.5719 | 0.5718 | W. |
| 622 | v.f. | 622 | 0.2 | 12,44 | 176 | 0.5852 | 0.5846 | V.W. |
| 444 | 0.5 | 444 | 0.4 | 888 | 192 | 0.6385 | 0.6384 | V.W. |
| | | | | 12,83 | 217 | 0.7215 | 0.7202 | V.W. |
| 642 | 0.6 | 642 | 0.5 | 12,84 | 224 | 0.7448 | 0.7447 | V.W. |
| 731 | 2.0 | 731 | 1.9 | 14,62 | 236 | 0.7847 | 0.7846 | M. |
| 800 | 1.0 | 800 | 0.9 | 16,00 | 256 | 0.8512 | 0.8520 | M. |
| 822 | 0.3 | 822 | 0.4 | 16,44 | 288 | 0.9576 | 0.9578 | W. |

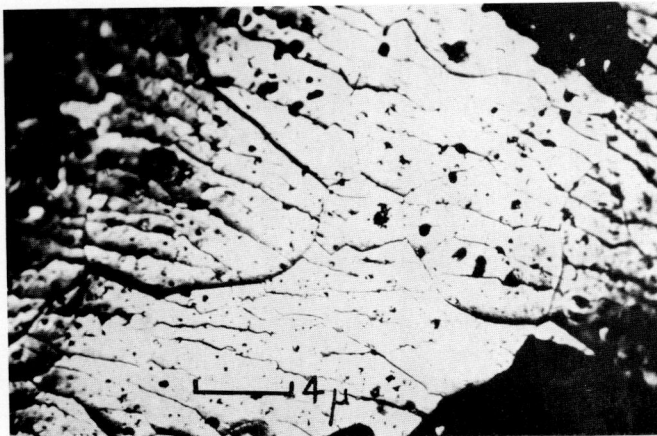

FIGURE 2 — Appearance of oxide film on mild steel after loading to 0.7 x U.T.S.

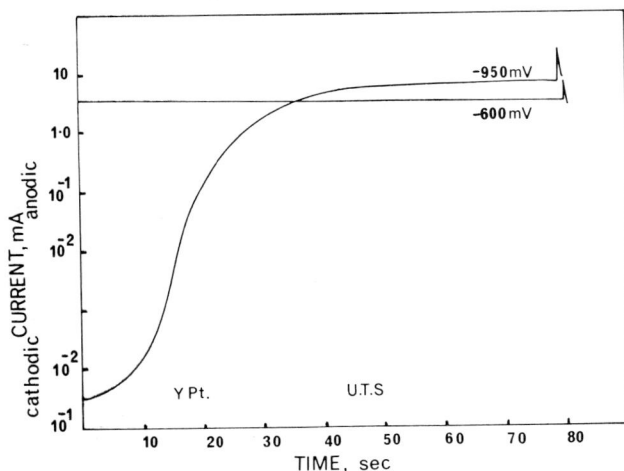

FIGURE 3 — Variation of polarization current during straining of mild steel in boiling 35% NaOH after preoxidation at different potentials.

specimen. The effects are apparent from Figure 3. The results at -710 mV were dependent upon the time of preoxidation and the strain rate. If preoxidation was for less than about 5 hours increase in the anodic polarization current on plastic deformation was not observed in all cases. Examination of the specimens after testing indicated that, after relatively short times of preoxidation, the thickness of the oxide film varied considerably between specimens and between different areas of the same specimen. The effect of strain rate was such that if it was less than about $10^{-3}$ sec$^{-1}$ the polarization current remained almost constant until the specimen fractured, when a jump in the anodic direction was observed. The fact that increased anodic currents were observed only in the range of potentials within which stress corrosion occurs is apparent from Figure 4. This shows the potentiostatic polarization curves 30 seconds after the potential was established and after the polarization current had reached a static or equilibrium value on unstressed specimens. Within the critical range of potentials, plastic deformation after the current had reached a static value caused the polarization current to rise almost to those values noted after only 30 seconds polarization of the unstressed specimens. (Total current, as opposed to current density, is used in plotting Figure 4 since the effective exposed area of specimen is not known with certainty. In every case the same total length of specimen was in contact with the electrolyte, so results are comparable, but since the counter electrode was arranged to extend over only the reduced part of the test specimen and the remainder was not stopped-off, the effective area may be less than the exposed area of 10 cms$^2$.)

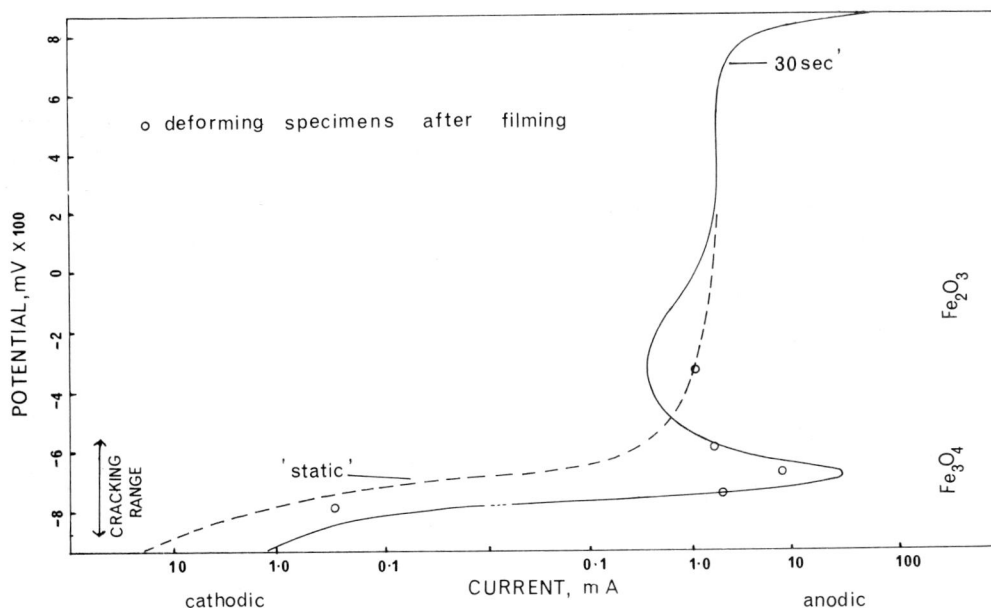

FIGURE 4 — Polarization curves for mild steel, in boiling 35% NaOH, determined under various conditions.

388

Constant strain tests in boiling 4 N NaNO$_3$ and NH$_4$NO$_3$ solutions indicated that intercrystalline stress corrosion cracking occurred over a considerably greater range of potentials than was the case with the hydroxide solution. Figure 5 shows the time to fracture for specimens in NaNO$_3$ initially strained to produce a stress of 16 tons/sq inch, stress corrosion occurring over the range -60 to +1340 mV with a minimum lifetime at +940 mV. In NH$_4$NO$_3$, intergranular cracking, as confirmed by metallography, was experienced over a similar range of potentials and again with a minimum lifetime at +940 mV, as is apparent from Figure 6. With NaNO$_3$ cathodic protection resulted from the application of potentials of -160 mV or less, but in NH$_4$NO$_3$ solutions, the stress corrosion that was observed down to -260 mV was replaced by general corrosion at lower potential and failure resulted from thinning of the specimen. The latter occurred by the formation of overlapping, oxide filled, pits rather than by uniform thinning, as is apparent from Figure 7. Szklarska-Smialowska[14] working with 5 N NH$_4$NO$_3$ at 75 C also found a sharp increase in the time to failure at potentials in the region of -360 to -460 mV followed by an equally sharp drop at even lower potentials ($\sim$ -500 mV). The sharp rise was still associated with intercrystalline failure but at more active potentials, where the failure time was again reduced, failure was due to general corrosion associated with a "...layer (of Fe$_2$O$_3$ · H$_2$O or Fe$_2$O$_3$ + Fe$_3$O$_4$) that adhered less closely, and corrosion grew much faster, but remained uniform." Clearly there are some differences between these results and those obtained in the present investigation, the most obvious causes of which would be the different concentrations of NH$_4$NO$_3$ and the different temperatures at which the experiments were conducted. Szklarska-Smialowska also states that failure by general corrosion occurred in the range of potentials -110 to +190 mV, whereas in the present work failure in this region was by intergranular cracking, as with the potentials above and below this range. This difference is more difficult to understand, especially since Szklarska-Smialowska shows failure from general corrosion occurring in about the same time interval as that for intergranular cracking at slightly higher or lower potentials. This odd result may be associated with the fact that Szklarska-Smialowska used fine wires, 0.045 cm diameter, in her work.

Maximum crack propagation rates in NaNO$_3$ and NH$_4$NO$_3$ did not vary very much with potential, except at the lowest values at which intergranular cracking was observed. At all other potentials the maximum crack propagation rates were of the order of $10^{-3}$ mm/sec, with NH$_4$NO$_3$ producing a rate that exceeded that in NaNO$_3$ by a factor of about two. These rates are considerably faster than the maximum propagation rates observed in 35% NaOH, which were of the order of $10^{-5}$ mm/sec.

One further difference between the behavior of stressed mild steel in hydroxide and nitrate solutions concerns the effect of continuing plastic deformation upon crack propagation. The results quoted earlier indicate that for con-

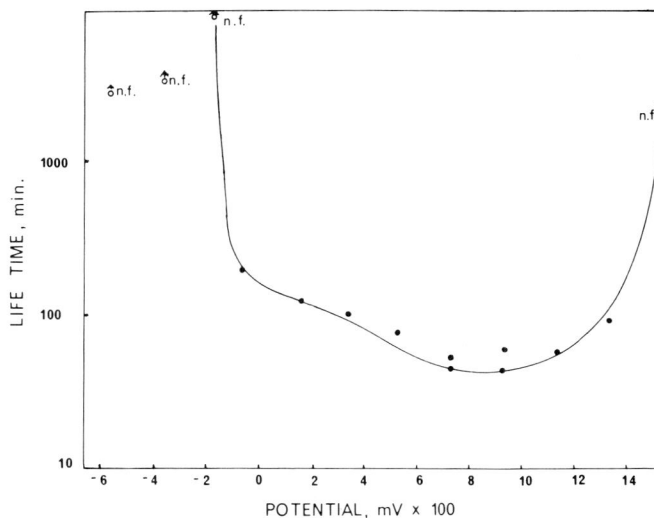

FIGURE 5 — Fracture time of mild steel specimens at various potentials in boiling 4 N NaNO$_3$.

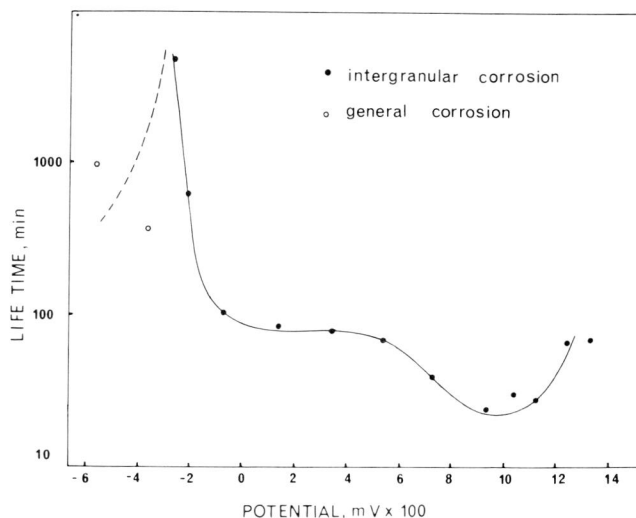

FIGURE 6 — Fracture time of mild steel specimens at various potentials in boiling 4 N NH$_4$NO$_3$.

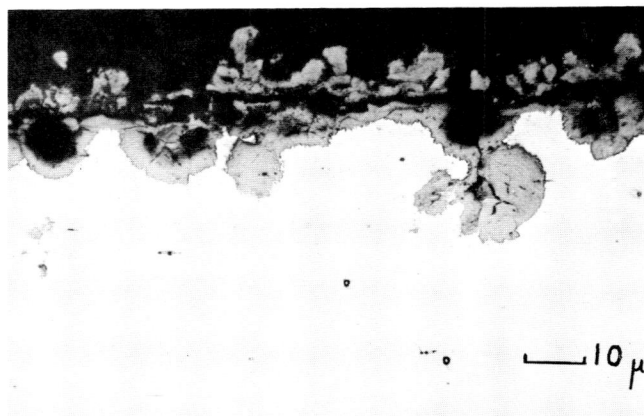

FIGURE 7 — Overlapping, oxide filled pits in mild steel tested in boiling 4 N NH$_4$NO$_3$ at a potential of -400 mV.

tinuing intergranular penetration in hydroxide the stress needs to be such as to result in continuing deformation. Although this also assists intergranular corrosion in nitrates, it is by no means vital and indeed it is possible to obtain complete intergranular disintegration of mild steel in boiling nitrate by anodic stimulation in the absence of stress,[9] an effect not produced by hydroxide solutions.

## D. The Properties of Oxide Films Formed in Nitrates

Although there are many references in the literature to the formation of visible oxide films on mild steel immersed in nitrate solutions there has been little systematic investigation of these and it is usually assumed that they are of $Fe_3O_4$. Szklarska-Smialowska[14] gives the results of some X-ray studies in connection with her work on the effect of potential upon the cracking of mild steel in $NH_4NO_3$, which are summarized in Table 4.

There are some odd features about these results not the least of which is the fact that $Fe_2O_3$ forms at a more active potential than $Fe_3O_4$, a result not expected from thermodynamic considerations. Additionally, there is the peculiar result shown in the potential range -280 to -100 mV, where anodic dissolution without film formation is claimed to occur, yet at potentials both more active and more noble $Fe_3O_4$ is stated to form. In the present work visible films formed over the whole range of potentials from -560 to +1340 mV in $NH_4NO_3$ and from -160 to +1340 mV in $NaNO_3$ and indeed the only major difference between the results of tests in these nitrates was that complete cathodic protection was possible with the sodium salt but not with that of ammonia. Moreover, although X-ray examination has indicated that $Fe_3O_4$ is formed towards the active end of the range of potentials within which stress corrosion was observed, $\alpha$-$Fe_2O_3$ has so far been observed only towards the more noble end, e.g., at +940 mV. The latter corresponds to the potential at which both $NH_4NO_3$ and $NaNO_3$ produce the shortest failure times and the results in nitrates are clearly different from those in hydroxide in that, in the latter, failure did not occur at potentials where $Fe_2O_3$ films formed.

The microstructural characteristics of oxide film formation during stress corrosion in nitrates at the free corrosion potential are known[5,6] and there is no reason for assuming that the general characteristics are essentially different from those observed in hydroxides, especially in regard to lack of continuity of the films. The behavior of filmed specimens upon straining in boiling nitrate has been studied in some detail by Galvele and Hoar[15] and their results, in general terms, indicate marked increases in anodic polarization current accompanying film fracture. In the present work a few tests in boiling 4 N $NH_4NO_3$ have been performed for the purpose of comparing these with those in 35% NaOH shown in Figure 4. These results are shown in Figure 8, the specimens having been preoxidized for 45 minutes before straining at a rate of $3 \times 10^{-3}$ sec$^{-1}$. Clearly, as with hydroxide solutions, there are considerable increases in the anodic polarization current accompanying plastic deformation of the metal and the fracture of its oxide. It is interesting to note that the plastic deformation results in the Flade potential moving about 400 mV in the noble direction. It is of further interest to note that the maximum anodic currents sustained in $NH_4NO_3$ are about two orders of magnitude higher than those sustained in NaOH while bearing in mind that the crack propagation rates in these solutions also differ by two orders of magnitude.

## IV. Discussion

The salient points that have emerged from this investigation are:

1. The ranges of potentials with which cracking is observed are -900 to -600 mV in hydroxide, -260 to +1340 in $NH_4NO_3$ and -60 to +1340 mV in $NaNO_3$.

2. In both types of solution, $Fe_3O_4$ films are formed towards the active end of the relevant range of potentials and $Fe_2O_3$ films at more noble potentials. In hydroxide cracking appears to be associated only with $Fe_3O_4$ formation, but in nitrates cracking occurs in the presence of both $Fe_3O_4$ and $Fe_2O_3$ films.

3. In both types of solution, plastic deformation of preoxidized specimens produces a large increase in anodic current within the range of potentials wherein cracking occurs.

4. In hydroxide, crack propagation required continuing slow plastic deformation to prevent stifling. From previous work[9] it is known that, in nitrates, while such deformation increases the rate of crack propagation somewhat, it is not a necessary requirement for intergranular corrosion, which may lead to disintegration in the absence of any applied stress if the reactions are anodically stimulated.

TABLE 4—Results of X-Ray Studies

| Potential Range | Type of Corrosion | Film Characteristics |
|---|---|---|
| More active than -500 mV | General corrosion | $Fe_2O_3 \cdot H_2O$ or $Fe_2O_3$ + $Fe_3O_4$ |
| -480 to -220 | 'Slight' stress corrosion | $Fe_3O_4$ |
| -280 to -100 | 'Strong' stress corrosion | No visible deposit (anodic dissolution) |
| -100 to +200 | General corrosion | $Fe_3O_4$ |
| +200 to +800 | 'Strong' stress corrosion | 'incomplete passivation film' ($Fe_3O_4$) |
| +800 to +1500 | 'Slight' stress corrosion | 'passivating oxide' |

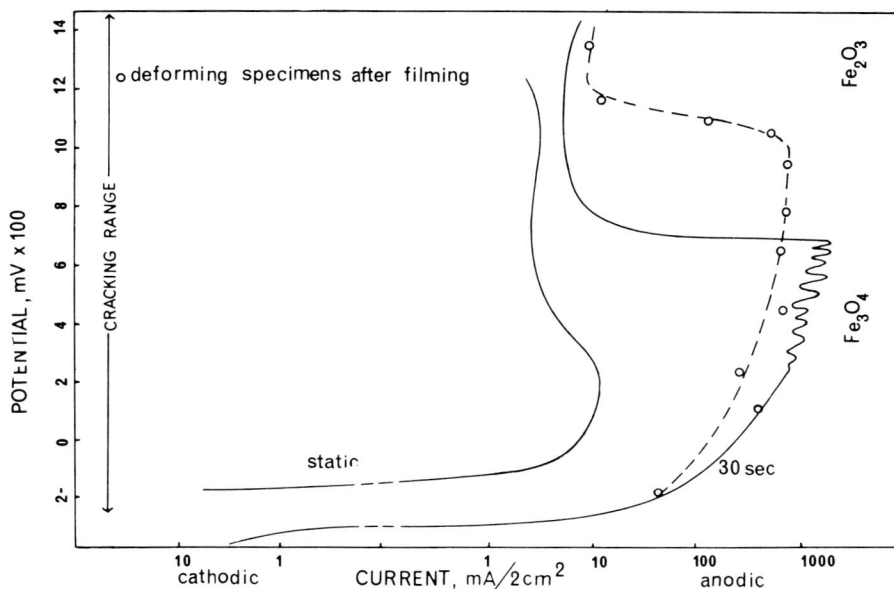

FIGURE 8 — Polarization curves for mild steel, in boiling 4 N NH₄NO₃, determined under various conditions.

The fact that cracking in hydroxide solutions occurs at potentials where $Fe_3O_4$ forms but not where $Fe_2O_3$ exists could be interpreted as strong evidence for these oxide films playing a critical part in the mechanism, possibly because the resistivity of $Fe_3O_4$ is one to two orders of magnitude less than that of $Fe_2O_3$. In nitrates, however, cracking occurs just as readily in the presence of $Fe_2O_3$ as when $Fe_3O_4$ films exist and since, in this particular context, there is no obvious reason for distinguishing between the properties of the oxides in the two different environments it is difficult to escape the conclusion that the coincidence of the cracking limit with the change in oxide type in hydroxide is not a critical factor in cracking behavior. There is in any case an alternative explanation for the fact that cracking was observed in the range -600 to -900 mV in 35% NaOH and this is that this corresponds reasonably to the range of potentials within which soluble $HFeO_2^-$ is likely to form. The potential-pH diagram at the temperatures involved and in the solutions used in the present work is difficult to establish with high precision, since all of the physico-chemical data required does not exist, but recalculation of the positions of the domain boundaries in the $Fe-H_2O$ system, assuming Fe, $Fe_3O_4$ and $Fe_2O_3$ as solid substances, for 120 C indicates that $HFeO_2^-$ should be stable over the range -700 to -1100 mV in 35% NaOH. Bearing in mind the paucity of reliable data, this range agrees reasonably with that in which intergranular cracking was observed. The calculation also indicates that $Fe_2O_3$ should form at potentials only slightly more active than -700 mV, i.e., the formation of $Fe_2O_3$ and the limit of stability of $HFeO_2^-$ are virtually coincident.

If the range of potentials within which cracking occurs in hydroxide is determined by the limits within which soluble iron products form, it is reasonable to ask if the same considerations hold for nitrate solutions. The pH values of the solutions used in the present work were in the region of four, which suggests that the upper limit of

potential at which cracking should cease cannot be much above +200 mV, the point beyond which $Fe^{++}$ are no longer stable. The lower limit of potential should correspond to that at which Fe is the thermodynamically stable phase and for $NaNO_3$, which is without the complication that arises with $NH_4NO_3$ at low potentials, the lower limit of cracking occurs when cathodic protection becomes possible. However, the agreement between the observed and expected upper limit of potential for cracking, +1340 mV as compared with +200 mV, is poor. The observed value of +1340 mV could be accounted for if the relevant pH was less (0-1) since $Fe^{+++}$ could then form at the higher potentials and the limit would correspond to that for oxygen evolution, i.e., about +1300 mV. It has previously been suggested[5] that stress corrosion in nitrates involves the build-up of acidity within the confines of the crack and the observation that extensive intergranular penetration is possible in the absence of stress if anodic stimulation is applied supports this suggestion.

It appears therefore that the potential ranges for stress corrosion in hydroxide and nitrate solutions can be accounted for in terms of the potentials at which soluble iron, as $HFeO_2^-$, $Fe^{++}$ or $Fe^{+++}$, can form and without recourse to arguments involving oxide films fulfilling the primary role. This is not meant to imply that oxide formation is without effect. Thus in hydroxide solutions, and in nitrates at certain potentials, grain boundary corrosion is not sustained, due to blockage by oxide, beyond relatively small amounts of penetration, unless stress is applied and the crack yawns to produce film rupture. In hydroxide in particular, such an effect appears critical and accounts for the fact that cracks could only be propagated under conditions where continuous slow plastic deformation occurred. The results shown in Figures 4 and 8 clearly show that film rupture leads to a large increase in anodic current over the ranges of potential within which cracking occurs, indicating that if a crack becomes blocked

391

with oxide its further propagation is likely if the obstruction is broken. However, the general relevance of the results of Figures 4 and 8 to stress corrosion cracking remains to be considered.

One possible interpretation would be that film rupture simply results in the anodic current returning to that associated with the unfilmed metal, as would be expected to happen with any method of film removal. However, there are problems associated with such a simple interpretation, since the increase in surface area upon straining is not likely to be more than about 5% and, assuming the increase in surface area to be equated to the area of unfilmed metal exposed, the increase in anodic current should be appreciably less than that observed. In fact the area of film-free metal exposed will be greater than 5%, since some of the oxide exfoliates on straining, as is apparent from Figure 2, but, although precise measurements of exposed areas are not available, it is equally clear from Figure 2 that the area of unfilmed metal will be significantly less than that of the original specimen. It would appear, therefore, that the increase in anodic current upon plastically straining filmed specimens may arise in part at least, from effects other than the exposure of bare metal and one possible effect would be that dissolution of the metal is increased by the straining, perhaps because of its influence on the distribution of carbon atoms. There is some evidence[9] that the latter play an important part in stress corrosion cracking of mild steels, possibly because of their efficiency as cathodic sites. If these suggestions for the significance of the results shown in Figures 4 and 8 are correct, they do not alter the earlier remarks about the controlling factor in the potential dependence of cracking being the formation of soluble iron. Thus, film cracking occurs just as readily with $Fe_2O_3$ as with $Fe_3O_4$ in

hydroxide, and there is no reason for assuming that the transportation of carbon atoms in the metal, if this is important, is likely to be different in the presence of different films, yet cracking is not observed over the whole range of potentials at which these effects can occur.

## V. Conclusions

1. The part played by oxide films in stress corrosion cracking of mild steels is probably restricted to that of blocking cracks. While cracking in hydroxide solutions occurs in the presence of $Fe_3O_4$ but not in the presence of $Fe_2O_3$, in nitrates the shortest times to failure are observed in the range of potentials where $Fe_2O_3$ forms. It is considered, therefore, that the nature of the oxide is of little significance.

2. The straining of specimens coated with oxides at various potentials results in an increase in anodic current within the range of potentials wherein cracking occurs for both hydroxide and nitrate solutions. The magnitude of the current increase appears to be considerably greater than could be accounted for on the basis of the area of unfilmed metal produced by film rupture. The difference could possibly be due to the fact that metal dissolution is enhanced by plastic strain.

3. The fact that cracking occurs only within restricted ranges of potential is most readily accounted for by the suggestion that cracking is associated with the formation of readily soluble iron. In hydroxide, the range of potentials for cracking agrees reasonably with that for the formation of $HFeO_2^-$, and in nitrates, accepting the build-up of acidity within the cracks, with that for the formation of $Fe^{++}$ and $Fe^{+++}$.

## References

1. S. W. Parr and F. G. Straub. *Univ. Illinois Bull.*, 177 (1928).
2. H. L. Logan. *Jnl. Res. Nat. Bureau Standards*, 48, 99 (1952).
3. J. Venczel and G. Wranglen. *Corrosion Science*, 4, 137 (1964).
4. M. Henthorne and R. N. Parkins. *Corrosion Science*, 6, 357 (1966).
5. R. N. Parkins and R. Usher. *First International Congress on Metallic Corrosion*, 289 (1961).
6. R. N. Parkins. *Jnl. Iron Steel Institute*, 172, 149 (1954).
7. W. C. Schroeder, A. A. Berk and R. A. O'Brien. *Metals and Alloys*, 8, 320 (1937).
8. H. Grafen and D. Kuron. *Archiv. Eisenhutt.*, 36, 4 (1965).
9. M. Henthorne and R. N. Parkins. *Br. Corros. J.*, 2, 186 (1967).
10. M. J. Humphries and R. N. Parkins. *Corrosion Science*, 7, 747 (1967).
11. I. David and A. J. E. Welch. *Trans. Faraday Soc.*, 52, 1642 (1956).
12. M. C. Bloom and L. Goldenberg. *Corrosion Science*, 5, 623 (1965).
13. E. M. Field and D. R. Holmes. *Corrosion Science*, 5, 361 (1965).
14. Z. Szklarska-Smialowska. *Corrosion*, 20, 1981 (1964).
15. J. Galvele and T. P. Hoar. Unpublished work.

## Discussion

**A. J. Sedriks, RIAS:**

I notice that your environment-induced failures are intergranular and that you use this observation to strengthen the argument against the possibility that failure involves the rupture of oxide films. Whether such an argument is valid or not depends on which stress corrosion cracking model is being considered. For instance, failures of alpha brass in certain types of ammonia environments[1] and alpha titanium in nitrogen tetroxide[2] can be explained in

terms of an oxide rupture model which involves the repeated formation and rupture of oxide at the crack tip. In such a model preferential penetration of oxide along grain boundaries would be expected to produce *intergranular* cracks that propagate discontinuously.

I would like to ask a question. Your load relaxation measurements show discontinuities and you consider this is not necessarily evidence for discontinuous crack propagation. Have you looked for evidence of discontinuous crack propagation by fractography or possibly metallographic sections? I am thinking in terms of trying to stop the crack before it propagates completely through the specimen, completing the fracture in air and examining the surface at the tip of the original crack where there would be less chance of secondary corrosion taking place. I am suggesting that if the cracking process involves only anodic dissolution there should be no evidence of discontinuous growth.

1. E. N. Pugh, J. V. Craig and A. J. Sedriks. *The Stress Corrosion Cracking of Copper, Silver, and Gold Alloys,* this volume.
2. A. J. Sedriks, P. W. Slattery and E. N. Pugh. *Stress Corrosion Cracking of Alpha Titanium in Non-Aqueous Environments,* this volume.

## M. J. Humphries:

I have not been able to make use of fractography or metallography to examine the fracture surfaces, because relatively heavy corrosion products on the fracture surfaces prevent any meaningful conclusions from being drawn. The work on discontinuous load relaxation to which I refer was carried out by Dr. Henthorne (*Corrosion Science*, 6, 357 (1966)).

## M. Smialowski, Institute of Physical Chemistry:

As shown by Dr. Szklarska-Smialowska,[1] cathodic polarization of iron in ammonium nitrate solutions to more negative potential values than -280 mV (corrosion potential) causes reduction of $NO_3^-$ to $NO_2^-$ ions, and further to $NO^-$, $N_2$ and $NH_3$. Under these circumstances, iron rapidly dissolves due to a chemical reaction, probably by forming complex ions containing $NH_3$, Fe and $NO_2^-$ or $NO_3^-$. Because of the $OH^-$ formation, $Fe_3O_4$ can be produced at the cathode. At more negative potential values, the pH at the iron surface and the concentration of $NO_2^-$ can be high enough to produce $Fe_3O_4$ and $Fe_2O_3$ in agreement with thermodynamic considerations. These show that all iron oxides and hydroxides have almost equal equilibrium potentials.[2] Experimental determinations have also shown that the critical passivation potential of iron in alkaline solutions is only slightly more positive than the thermodynamic potentials for the formation of the iron oxides and hydroxides.[3]

Anodic polarization of iron within the potential range from -280 mV to -100 mV causes dissolution of iron. At about -100 mV, the passive oxide layer begins to be formed.

Between -100 mV and 200 mV, the general corrosion predominates, since within this potential range the anodic current is at its maximum and, therefore, the rate of the general corrosion is higher than that of intercrystalline corrosion.

Since processes accompanying the polarization of iron in ammonium nitrate solutions are extremely complicated, the studying of these phenomena presents many special difficulties and problems. During measurements, the use of a tight diaphragm between the anodic and cathodic compartments of the electrolytic cell is obligatory in order to avoid mixing of both the reaction products. On the other hand, the immersion of an iron sample to a limited volume of $NH_4NO_3$ involves a rapid increase of the pH value from about 5 to 7 or even more, and this causes decrease of the corrosion rate.[4]

Another point I would like to comment concerns the controversial effect of carbon. As shown by Dr. Flis,[5] who used for his investigations many differently prepared whiskers and samples of zone refined iron, the presence of carbon seems not to be necessary for the occurrence of the intercrystalline corrosion of iron in ammonium nitrate solutions.

1. Z. Szklarska-Smialowska. *Corrosion,* 20, 198t (1964).
2. B. Kortum. *Treatise on Electrochemistry,* Ed. by Elsevier Publishing Co., p. 521 (1965).
3. J. G. N. Thomas and T. J. Nurse. *Brit. Corros. J.,* 2, 13 (1967).
4. M. Smialowski and Z. Szklarska-Smialowska. *Corrosion,* 18, 1t (1962).
5. J. Flis, J. Mieluch and M. Smialowski. *Corrosion,* 20, 184t (1964); J. Flis. *Corrosion Science,* in press.

## R. N. Parkins:

The work on iron whiskers that has been referred to was carried out by Flis and is mentioned in my review paper. I quote from the original paper...."Two series of experiments were made: one at -0.140 V and 20 C, the other at -0.050 V and 75 C. In these conditions polycrystalline whiskers were intergranularly attacked". At the same conference another paper was presented, by Szklarska-Smialowska from the same laboratory as Flis, and again I quote from the original...."At potentials ranging from -0.1 to 0.2 V, there was general corrosion—with no apparent tendency to intergranular attack". Both pieces of work refer to 5 N ammonium nitrate at 75 C and there is clearly some discrepancy. I would merely suggest that the evidence from these whisker experiments, while interesting and worthy of further consideration, is not so strong that we must consider as worthless the weightier evidence of workers from various laboratories that pure bulk iron cannot be made to fail by stress corrosion cracking.

Again I must state that the weight of the evidence currently available is very much in favor of the suggestion that increasing the carbon content of low carbon steels increases their resistance to cracking.

## E. H. Phelps, United States Steel Corp.:

In postulating that carbide particles at the grain boundaries are highly significant is it not implied that there is a small cathode with a large anode in a conducting solution leading to localized anodic attack. This seems to be the wrong way round and would lead to general anodic attack on the grain.

## R. N. Parkins:

Although the suggestion that carbide particles or dissolved carbon segregated at the grain boundaries are important in crack propagation, in so far as they provide local cathodic sites, we envisage the anodic sites as being relatively local also. The greater proportion of exposed grain surfaces are passivated by oxide films, for which there is a fair body of evidence.

In any case there is evidence from the electron microscopy carried out by Phillips that local electro-chemical effects can arise from carbon segregated at grain boundaries, even though these effects resulted from contact with electropolishing solutions.

## H. H. Uhlig:

May I point out that decorated etch pits show the same effect. Dislocations do not always etch out in the usual etching solutions, but if the dislocations are decorated by interstitial impurities they can be recognized. This probably means that some electrochemical effect accompanies decoration of the dislocation, but a massive compound, such as a carbide, does not always appear to be necessary.

## K. Bohnenkamp, Max-Planck-Institut fur Eisenforschung:

I think we must look at the distribution and the form of the carbides. In low carbon steels the carbon is usually present in the form of grain boundary carbides or enriched at the grain boundaries. But at higher carbon contents we get pearlite rather than grain boundary carbides. This causes a significant difference in susceptibility. Further, I would like to remark that we have similar stress corrosion in sodium hydroxide and in nitrate solutions. But we observed in sodium hydroxide higher anodic current densities on a compact carbide specimen than on the iron specimen (see Figure 6 of my paper). I think that this observation raises questions for your interpretation. Moreover, if we polarize the specimens anodically with external currents, I do not see that we need local cathodes, at least not for the start of the penetration of cracks.

## R. N. Parkins:

Presumably the answer to this is that, near the free corrosion potential, the current changes very sharply for very small potential changes, for both ferrite and carbide. It is very difficult therefore to make measurements which are strictly valid, since even 1 or 2 mV potential change can produce a marked change in current. There is nothing surprising in the result mentioned by Dr. Bohnenkamp and it is not necessarily conflicting with the visual observations of various workers that the greater attack is observed on the ferrite.

## J. A. S. Green, RIAS:

My discussion concerns the role of carbides in the stress corrosion cracking of mild steel in $Ca(NO_3)_2$ solutions.

Up to the present attempts to stress crack spec-trographically pure iron in nitrate solutions have been unsuccessful. However the addition of small amounts of carbon, < 0.1% C, produces susceptibility to stress corrosion. Further addition of carbon tends to increase the resistance to stress corrosion.[1]

In small quantities (< 0.1%) carbon is generally present in the region of the ferrite grain boundaries either as particles of $Fe_3C$ or in interstitial solution. There have been suggestions in the literature[1] that carbon in the grain boundary plays an important role in the stress corrosion cracking of mild steels.

Examination, by transmission electron microscopy, of metal foils which had been immersed in boiling $Ca(NO_3)_2$ for a few seconds showed that intense corrosion occurred at regions of ferrite immediately adjacent to grain boundary carbide particles.[2] Such an observation suggests that cementite is cathodic to ferrite and that it may be providing an efficient cathodic site for the corrosion reaction.

The possible cathodic action of cementite was first suggested by Hoar and Havenhand[3] for the general corrosion of mild steel in dilute acids and was subsequently confirmed by Staicopolus[4] by cathodic polarization measurements in chloride- and sulfate-containing solutions.

However solutions containing chloride and sulfate ions do not cause stress corrosion of mild steels. The polarization studies described here were carried out both on spectrographically pure iron and cementite in 1 N $Ca(NO_3)_2$ solutions which do cause stress corrosion of mild steels.

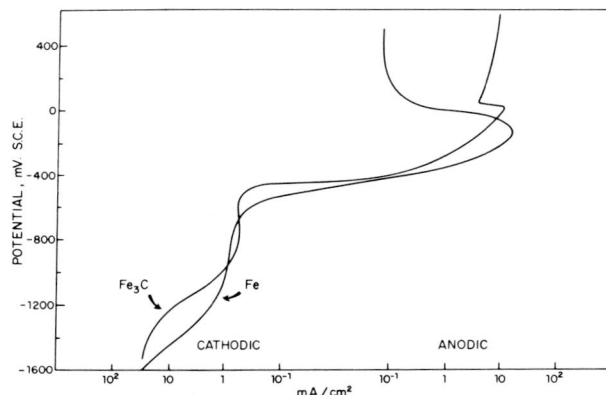

FIGURE 1 — Polarization curves of spectrographically-pure iron and cementite in 1 N $Ca(NO_3)_2$ at 20 C.

Figure 1 illustrates the anodic and cathodic polarization curves of pure iron in 1 N $Ca(NO_3)_2$ at 20 C. In the region of the free corrosion potential these curves illustrate particularly well a marked difference in polarization between pure iron and cementite. For instance in the case of pure iron there is a potential change of about 180 mV over a current density range of three orders of magnitude for small cathodic currents in the neighborhood of its corrosion potential whereas for cementite the equivalent potential change is only about 60 mV. In boiling 1 N $Ca(NO_3)_2$ the difference in the potential change between the curves corresponding to iron and cementite is around 20 mV for the same current density range.[5]

The steeper slope in the case of pure iron as compared to cementite would suggest a greater efficiency of cementite in being able to pass current without marked polarization. These results then tend to support the suggestion that carbide particles may be involved in stress corrosion crack propagation by acting as efficient points for cathodic discharge.

1. *Stress Corrosion Cracking of Low Carbon Steels,* by R. N. Parkins in "Fundamental Aspects of Stress Corrosion Cracking", Columbus, Ohio (1967).

2. M. Henthorne and R. N. Parkins. *British Corrosion Journal,* in the press. See also Figures 6 and 7 of Reference 1.

3. T. P. Hoar and D. Havenhand. *Journal Iron and Steel Institute,* **133**, 239 (1936).

4. D. N. Staicopolus. *J. Electrochem. Soc.,* **110**, 1121 (1963).

5. J. A. S. Green and R. N. Parkins. Electrochemical Properties of Ferrite and Cementite in Relation to Stress Corrosion of Mild Steels in Nitrate Solutions. *Corrosion,* **24**, 66 (1968).

# PART V


# HIGH STRENGTH STEELS

# EVALUATION OF SESSION ON FERRITIC AND MARTENSITIC IRON BASE ALLOYS[1]

## E. H. Phelps and R. N. Parkins

The session on ferritic and martensitic iron base alloys was highlighted by the excellent review on hydrogen in metals by R. A. Oriani. He showed that many of the apparently anomalous phenomena in permeation and diffusion of hydrogen can be rationalized in terms of trapping theory. Of definite practical value is his suggestion that steady-state permeation experiments be used to determine input fugacity.

The experimental results obtained by H. H. Johnson show that cracking of very high strength steels can be induced by hydrogen gas at one atmosphere pressure. The available evidence does not establish whether this cracking is caused by a surface adsorption effect or by absorption of hydrogen into the metal. Even if a volume effect is involved, however, it does not appear possible to account for the cracking in terms of the "planar pressure" theory.

The paper by H. P. Leckie shows that cracking may be induced in high strength maraging steels in sodium chloride solution by the application of active potentials. The data indicate that this cracking is hydrogen embrittlement caused by a stress-sorption mechanism. This paper emphasizes the difference between the corrosion conditions within a sharp crack and in the bulk solution. Within a crack, hydrolysis of corrosion products and restricted diffusion cause increased acidity which may stimulate both anodic dissolution and hydrogen ion discharge. As a result, data on the effect of environmental conditions can only be analyzed on a qualitative basis. Gerberich and Hartbower used an acoustic method to monitor slow crack growth in a high yield strength steel after cathodic charging in acid containing a poison and during exposure in distilled water. The results showed that crack propagation under either condition was discontinuous. It was furthermore concluded that hydrogen diffusion was the controlling mechanism for both types of cracking.

The methods of fracture mechanics were shown to have a definite area of usefulness in the review paper by R. P. Wei. This area will become increasingly important in future research on stress corrosion of the higher strength steels. At the present time, the quantitative influence of the mechanical conditions at the tip of a crack on stress corrosion and hydrogen embrittlement crack propagation still remains to be established.

The importance of potential control for stress corrosion studies on carbon steels in nitrate and caustic solutions was emphasized in the papers by Humphries and Parkins and by Bohnenkamp. Although there appears to be general agreement as to the general effects of carbon, its specific function in grain boundary corrosion still is not clear. Electrochemical reactivity and film rupture as a result of stresses at grain boundary particles appear to be important under specific conditions which depend on steel composition and microstructure and also upon the environment.

The most important areas for future research on steels are (1) to establish the microstructural features which control crack propagation by active path corrosion and hydrogen embrittlement mechanisms, (2) to determine the critical chemical and electrochemical properties of the specific environments which interact with these microstructural features. Other fruitful areas for research are (1) establishment of a quantitative relationship between fracture toughness and stress corrosion behavior, (2) development of methods to control hydrogen entry, and (3) establish quantitative relationships between the stress conditions at the tip of an advancing crack and the rate of crack propagation.

---

[1]Also includes evaluation of carbon steels.

# A REVIEW OF THE STRESS CORROSION BEHAVIOR OF STEELS WITH HIGH YIELD STRENGTH

E. H. Phelps
U. S. Steel Corporation

## Introduction

Stress corrosion cracking is recognized as an important consideration in the use of the higher strength steels and as a result, there is a substantial amount of stress corrosion research done on these materials. A large portion of the work, however, consists of screening tests conducted on candidate alloys in specific alloy development programs, and another large portion consists of empirical studies on preventive methods. These screening programs and empirical tests usually serve their intended purposes, but in many cases they do not result in a clear picture of the metallurgical and environmental factors that control the cracking mechanism. As a result, our understanding of the mechanisms involved in the stress corrosion cracking of the higher strength steels has been for the most part far outpaced by the accumulation of data on performance under specific environmental conditions.

The intent of this discussion is to review the stress corrosion behavior of steels with high yield strength, with emphasis on those aspects of the mechanism(s) that have been reasonably well established. The steels to be covered in the discussion include low alloy and alloy steels, hot work die steels, maraging steels, and martensitic and precipitation-hardenable stainless steels. The environments to be covered include neutral corrosives typically represented by saline solutions and seacoast atmospheres where dissolved oxygen is the principal corrodent, and acidic corrosives where the hydrogen reaction is predominant. Recent studies on the effect of gaseous environments on the performance of the higher strength steels will also be discussed. The behavior of these steels in liquid metal environments is not included in this discussion.

## Effect of Steel Composition and Structure on Stress Corrosion Behavior

### Environments Not Containing Hydrogen Sulfide

Several comprehensive investigations[1-5] have been conducted to establish the influence of alloy composition, heat treatment, metallurgical structure, test procedure, stress level, and environmental conditions on the stress corrosion behavior of the higher strength steels. In addition, several summary papers have been published.[6-8]

Phelps and Loginow[1] report the results of extensive tests with bent beam specimens exposed to the marine atmosphere (80-foot lot) at Kure Beach, North Carolina, and to the semi industrial atmosphere at Monroeville, Pennsylvania. They found that martensitic alloy and stainless steels, when heat treated to high yield strength levels of over 200,000 psi, were susceptible to stress corrosion cracking in both of these atmospheres. The semi austenitic precipitation-hardenable stainless steels were similarly susceptible in the marine atmosphere but not in the semi industrial atmosphere. Tempering of these types of steels at temperatures over 1100 F conferred resistance to cracking although it also caused a reduction in yield strength. Protective coatings that were anodic to steel were found to be very effective in preventing cracking. Cold worked and stress relieved austenitic stainless steels, with very high yield strengths of 215,000 to 264,000 psi, were found to have excellent resistance to stress corrosion cracking.

In alternate immersion tests with AISI 4330M and 4340 alloy steel billet material in 3.5 weight percent sodium chloride solution, Davis[2] found that the transverse grain direction was more susceptible to cracking than the longitudinal direction and that the method of surface finishing used could have a pronounced effect on stress corrosion behavior. In an extension of this work, Davis et al[3] found that the above two steels and H-11 hot work die steel were resistant to cracking at yield strengths below 200,000 psi and that at yield strengths above this level, the times to failure for these steels correlated reasonably well with their notch sensitivity as measured with circumferentially notched tensile specimens. Steels with low ratios of notched-to-unnotched tensile strength generally showed the shortest times to failure, whereas steels with high ratios showed longer times to failure or were resistant.

Setterlund,[4] and Dean and Copson,[5] and Phelps[8] present data on the stress corrosion performance of maraging steels. The results show that the maraging steels, when heat treated to very high strengths, are susceptible to stress corrosion cracking in marine and industrial atmospheres and in laboratory test environments. The times-to-failure for these steels as a class, however, are generally longer than observed for martensitic alloy and stainless steels at the same strength level. Furthermore, the results show that the stress corrosion resistance of these steels can be strongly affected by their structure and thermal histories. Dean and Copson point out, for example, that heat treatments which cause precipitation reactions or establish composition gradients at grain boundaries are harmful, as is coarse grain size.

Brown[7] presents a summary plot of the time-to-failure versus yield strength of a large number of high strength steels in several corrosives including sea water, tap water, distilled water, and humid air or argon. Although not stated by Brown, the data shown were presumably obtained by a number of different investigators using a variety of test procedures. As a result of the large amount of scatter obtained, Brown concludes that "Either the susceptibility to stress corrosion cracking is not overwhelmingly controlled by yield strength or the test procedure is faulty, or both." He indicates that no pattern emerged with respect to steel class (data were included for martensitic, maraging, and precipitation-hardening steels) with the possible exception that the stainless steels were somewhat more prone to show cracking (possibly because of their greater tendency to form pits). He furthermore concludes that many steels begin to show some tendency to stress corrosion cracking as their yield strength is increased and above 175,000 psi their susceptibility may be acute.

In his summary, Phelps[8] presented the plot shown in Figure 1, which shows the stress corrosion failure time as a function of yield strength for five different types of steel—constructional alloy steels with yield strengths up to 150,000 psi, ultra-high strength steels with yield strengths over 150,000 psi, hot work die steels, and martensitic and precipitation-hardenable stainless steels. Each point represents the average failure time for at least five specimens of the bent beam type representing a particular steel with a specific heat treatment. The specimens were stressed to 75

percent of the yield strength and exposed to the marine atmosphere at the 80-foot lot at Kure Beach, North Carolina. Figure 1 shows that the constructional alloy, ultra-high strength, and hot work die steels are resistant to marine atmosphere stress corrosion cracking at yield strengths up to about 180,000 psi. From this yield strength to about 210,000 psi, some of the steels were resistant whereas some were susceptible. All steels at yield strength levels about 210,000 psi were susceptible to failure. The pattern of results was practically the same for the 12 percent chromium and precipitation-hardening stainless steels except that certain of them (as found by Brown) were susceptible in the yield strength range 150,000 to 180,000 psi. Phelps also points out that although 18Ni-8Co-5Mo maraging steel is susceptible to stress corrosion cracking in a marine atmosphere when it is heat treated to very high yield strengths (250,000 psi and above), the times to failure observed are about an order of magnitude longer than those for other ultra-high strength steels at the same yield strength. It is of interest to note that Phelps found a much more positive correlation between stress corrosion behavior and yield strength than was indicated by Brown. This apparent difference is believed to have resulted from the fact that Brown included in his plot the results from several different test environments, some of which were very mild, whereas Figure 1 was based only on results obtained in a severely corrosive marine atmosphere.

In making the present review it has been apparent that most of the investigators studying the stress corrosion behavior of the higher strength steels have used different test procedures and environments. Furthermore, where internal checks have been made, it has been found that the test procedure (type of specimen, surface finish, test duration) can have a pronounced influence on the results obtained, and it goes without saying that the environment (as will be discussed later in this review) can have a controlling influence. Because of these differences, any summary statements may be subject to qualification when compared with the results of any specific investigation. Recognizing this limitation, however, the author believes that the stress corrosion behavior of the higher strength steels in environments not containing hydrogen sulfide may be summarized as follows:

1. The results of a large number of stress corrosion investigations on higher strength steels strengthened by heat treatment have shown that steels with yield strengths over about 200,000 psi are susceptible to stress corrosion cracking in natural atmospheres. The behavior of the various steels is generally the same regardless of the type of alloy, composition, structure, or heat treatment and is more dependent on the yield strength of the steel than any other apparent factor.

2. The maraging steels exhibit longer times to failure and in this sense may be considered superior to the ultra-high strength alloy and stainless steels. The maraging steels have also been found to be relatively more sensitive to structure and prior thermal history than other steels.

3. One investigator found a general correlation between notch sensitivity (in air) and stress corrosion

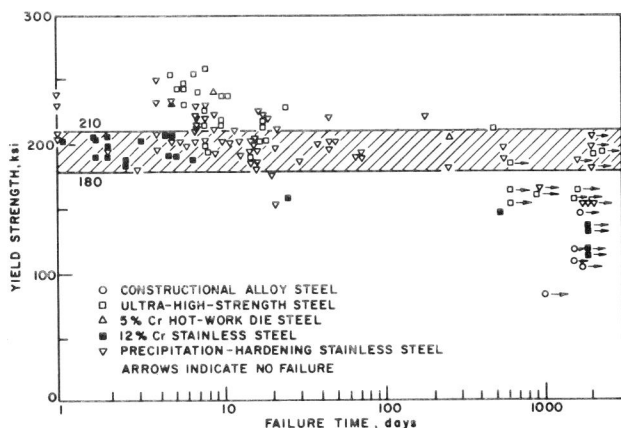

FIGURE 1 – Stress corrosion behavior of steels exposed to marine atmosphere at 75 percent of the yield strength. Phelps.[8]

behavior but such a correlation was not apparent in the studies of other investigators. More work is definitely needed to establish whether any correlation exists between toughness parameters and stress corrosion behavior.

4. As a class, austenitic stainless steels strengthened by cold working have remarkably good resistance to stress corrosion cracking in marine atmospheres.

### Environments Containing Hydrogen Sulfide

It is generally recognized that steels with high yield strengths are much more susceptible to stress corrosion cracking when exposed to environments containing hydrogen sulfide than when this substance is not present. This area is of intense interest in the oil industry because a substantial portion of the crude oil and gas found in various parts of the world contains hydrogen sulfide, and hence the steels used in drilling and recovery of these "sour" products must either have inherent resistance to sulfide cracking or be protected in some manner. As a result of this interest, a large body of information has been developed on the performance of steels in environments containing sulfide.

Committee T-1B of the National Association of Corrosion Engineers has studied the service performance of oilfield hardware in sour crude oils[9] and their report states that susceptibility to cracking increases with increasing yield strength and that steels of the type used for API Grade N-80 pipe exhibit borderline susceptibility. The report recommends that steels for use in sulfide environments be tempered at 1150 F minimum to maintain a hardness value less than Rockwell C 22 (about 115,000 psi tensile strength) and a yield strength less than 90,000 psi.

In a recent paper, Hudgins, et al[10] presented the following generalizations concerning the performance of steels in hydrogen sulfide environments.

1. "None of the materials tested... completely resists sulfide cracking at yield strengths significantly above 100,000 psi when loaded at or above the yield strength with the sole exception of K Monel."

2. "There appears to be a minimum hardness below which cracking does not occur for a given condition of stress. This hardness increases with decreasing $H_2S$ concentration."

Thus, from past experience in the oil industry, it is evident that the property most often used to distinguish susceptible and nonsusceptible steels is hardness, with steels having hardnesses greater than Rockwell C 22 being considered susceptible. As pointed out by Hudgins, et al, however, under severe conditions of stress and cold work and with high hydrogen sulfide concentrations, steels with much lower strength may be subject to cracking.

Attention was focused on the problem of sulfide corrosion cracking as a result of field failures in the early 1950's,[11] and since that time the results of a number of investigations have been reported. Schuetz and Robertson[12] concluded that the basic cause of failure was embrittlement caused by hydrogen absorbed into the steel as a result of the cathodic corrosion reaction and that the principal factors determining failure in service were stress

level (residual and applied) and the hydrogen content. They further showed that if the strength and applied stress level were sufficiently high, both ferritic and martensitic structures were susceptible to cracking but that austenitic steels were resistant under the same conditions. Fraser and coworkers[13,14] showed that for a given type of steel, such as normalized API Grade N-80, poor resistance to cracking was associated with high strength, low ductility and high alloy content (especially manganese, molybdenum, and nickel). High carbon content was found to be beneficial. Baldy and Bowden[15] found that martensite in the steel was detrimental and that this effect overshadowed compositional effects. Hudgins, et al[10] however, conclude that the presence of martensite is not a necessary condition for cracking.

In a recent study, Treseder and Swanson[16] presented additional results which showed that at hardness levels below about Rockwell C 22, nickel contents of about one percent and above are detrimental. Above Rockwell C 22, nickel did not have much effect. Snape,[17] however, found that with the exception of carbon, changes in alloy content did not influence cracking behavior. Susceptibility to cracking increased with increases in carbon content. In these studies, nickel-free and nickel-containing steels (up to 3%) were studied at yield strength levels of from 87,000 psi to 207,000. Snape also found that quenched and tempered steels were more resistant than normalized or normalized and tempered steels and that small differences in microstructure could have a profound effect on cracking resistance.

Kihara[18] describes service failures encountered in several propane storage tanks in Japan fabricated from alloy constructional steel with a yield strength of about 100,000 psi. The leakage type failures were attributed to sulfide corrosion cracking of welded joints caused by hydrogen sulfide and water in the propane. The results of an extensive research program showed that the sensitivity of welded joints to cracking increased markedly with increasing tensile strength and that the cracking could be avoided if the hydrogen sulfide content of the propane was maintained at a sufficiently low level. Epoxy-isocyanate coatings were found to be effective in preventing cracking. Surprisingly, however, post-weld heat treatment at 550 C (1022 F) was found to decrease cracking resistance.

Phelps[8] also presents results on the sulfide corrosion cracking resistance of alloy constructional steels in the welded condition. His data show that welding has a detrimental effect because it introduces a zone of high hardness (and high strength) in the heat affected zone. The use of a post-weld heat treatment was effective in reducing the hardness and increasing the cracking resistance of the heat affected zone.

In summary, it is evident that the presence of hydrogen sulfide in the environment is extremely detrimental from the standpoint of stress corrosion cracking of the higher strength steels. There seems to be reasonably good agreement between various investigators that this type of cracking is caused by absorption of hydrogen into the steel which causes hydrogen embrittlement. Corrosion is important because the cathodic reaction in the corrosion process supplies the hydrogen which enters the steel. It is not clear, however, whether or not the corrosion process in sulfide is also important from the standpoint of causing fissures or "corrosion notches" which would accentuate the hydrogen effect. With respect to metallurgical factors, it is generally accepted that steels with hardness values over about Rockwell C 22 can be expected to be susceptible to stress corrosion cracking in sulfide environments whereas steels with hardness values below this limit are generally resistant. As a general rule, changes in composition and heat treatment which increase strength will tend to reduce sulfide corrosion cracking resistance. However, the role of specific elements in the steel in the cracking process has not been established. It is generally agreed that tempering (at 1150 F minimum) is beneficial for both normalized and as-quenched steels. Both ferritic and martensitic structures are susceptible whereas austenitic structures are resistant.

## Influence of Electrochemical Polarization

### Active Path Corrosion vs Hydrogen Embrittlement

Although it is clear from the previous discussion that for sulfide environments there is general agreement that the mechanism of cracking is predominantly one of hydrogen embrittlement, similar agreement does not exist among workers concerning the mechanism of environmentally induced failures in environments not containing sulfides (or other promoters of hydrogen entry). The determination of the mechanism in these solutions is complicated by the fact that not only are corrosion and tensile stresses involved, as in typical stress corrosion cracking, but that hydrogen generated on the specimen surfaces (even in the absence of promoters) may also play a decisive role in the cracking process. Thus, in order to establish the mechanism of cracking in high strength steels, it is necessary to establish the relative importance of the anodic corrosion process and

of hydrogen generated by the cathodic process. Brown[7] presents an excellent discussion of factors relating to these two cracking mechanisms, and Figures 2A and 2B are from his paper.

Figure 2A depicts cracking by an "active path" corrosion process in which the crack progresses by an anodic corrosion mechanism at the tip of the crack. The path taken by the corrosion process may pre-exist in the metal, as a result of a grain boundary precipitation process, for example, or it may be formed as a result of plastic deformation and/or precipitation processes immediately in front of the crack tip. The important feature is that the crack tip moves by the occurrence of an anodic corrosion process; the cathodic process does not have any influence except to react with the electrons created in the anodic process.

Figure 2B depicts cracking by a "hydrogen embrittlement" mechanism in which the controlling factor in the propagation of the crack is the absorption of atomic hydrogen into metal at cathodic areas. In this case the function of the anodic process is simply to furnish electrons for the cathodic reaction.

Although the above discussion is simplified it does serve to emphasize the difference in the two mechanisms from the standpoint of the electrochemical reactions involved. This difference has served as the basis for the development of an electrochemical polarization method for distinguishing between the two cracking mechanisms. Phelps and Mears[19] have described the electrochemical basis for this method as follows:

"If it is assumed that the corrosion occurring is electrochemical and that complete anodic control is not obtained, the application of cathodic current will serve to reduce the amount of corrosion. When the applied cathodic current is sufficiently high, corrosion is stopped completely. Therefore, if stress corrosion is caused by localized corrosion along an active path through the steel, the application of cathodic current would be expected to suppress the corrosion reaction and to result in a longer time to failure. Conversely, the application of anodic current would be expected to increase the amount of corrosion. Since anodic current may also produce more general attack by increasing the anodic area, it is not possible to definitely predict the effect of anodic current on the time to stress corrosion failure.

On the other hand, if hydrogen generated by general corrosion is the cause of stress corrosion cracking, the application of cathodic current would be expected to generate more hydrogen and shorten the time to failure. The application of anodic current would be expected to generate less hydrogen and lengthen the time to failure."

### Utilization of Polarization Method in Mechanism Studies

The first known use of electrochemical polarization as a method to elucidate the mechanism of failure was by Uhlig in 1950.[20] Using a 13 percent chromium martensitic stainless steel which had been heat treated to a hardness of

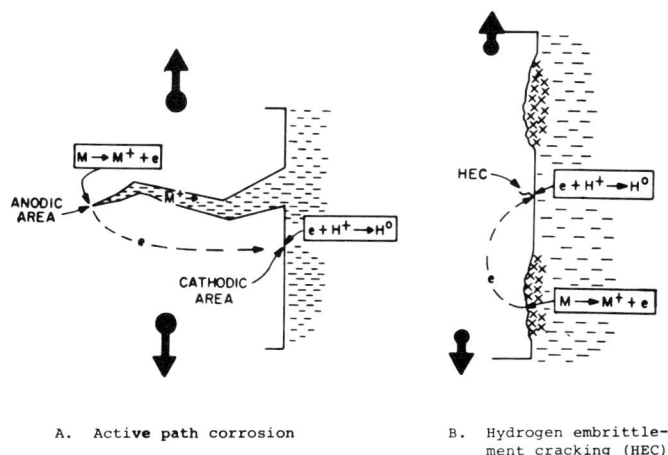

A. Active path corrosion

B. Hydrogen embrittlement cracking (HEC)

FIGURE 2 – Schematic representation of cracking by active path corrosion and hydrogen embrittlement mechanisms. Brown[22]

Rockwell C 47, Uhlig conducted experiments with applied current and found that the time-to-failure was shorter at a high cathodic current density than at a lower current density. Other experiments were conducted in dilute sulfuric acid containing phosphorus in carbon disulfide to promote entry of hydrogen into the steel. Failure occurred with or without applied cathodic polarization. Uhlig summarized his results by suggesting that stress corrosion cracking in the high strength martensitic stainless steel tested occurred by a hydrogen embrittlement mechanism.

In recent years the method has been used very effectively by Brown[7,21,22] Phelps and his coworkers,[1,19,23,24] Truman, et al,[25] and Hughes, et al.[26] Brown[7] found that the time-to-failure for a heat treated AISI Type 410 stainless steel was shortened with the application of anodic current and greatly lengthened with the application of a small cathodic current. This behavior is characteristic of corrosion along an active path through the steel. At high cathodic current densities, relatively short cracking times were observed, indicative of hydrogen embrittlement. In water containing 0.5 percent acetic acid and 0.1 percent ammonium sulfide, small cathodic currents decreased the fracture time, whereas anodic currents greatly extended the fracture time. Brown concluded that this behavior indicated that hydrogen embrittlement was the cracking mechanism in this environment. The absence of cracking with high anodic currents indicated that active path corrosion does not occur. In water saturated with hydrogen sulfide and also containing 6 percent sodium chloride and 0.5 percent acetic acid, impressed currents did not change the cracking time. This behavior was interpreted as indicating either a dual process or that the cracking mechanism (in this environment) was not electrochemical.

Bhatt and Phelps[23,24] found that in neutral salt solutions the time-to-failure for a very high strength 12 percent chromium martensitic stainless steel containing molybdenum and vanadium (12CrMoV stainless) was shortened by anodic currents and lengthened by small cathodic currents, indicative of an active path corrosion process. High cathodic currents decreased the failure time, indicating hydrogen embrittlement. At pH 1 both anodic and cathodic polarization shortened the failure time, indicating active path corrosion in the former case and hydrogen embrittlement in the latter. The mechanism without current was not clear from the experiments but other evidence indicated it to be hydrogen embrittlement. The same pattern of results was obtained at pH 12.5 except that cracking did not occur without applied current or with low values of cathodic current. This resistance was attributed to the onset of passivity.

These authors found that their polarization results and potential measurements could be effectively interpreted in terms of the equilibrium potential—pH diagram for iron, as shown in Figure 3. The points shown on this figure represent the solution potential (with and without polarization) and pH conditions utilized in the experiments with the 12MoV steel. The designations H or APC with each point refer to whether the mechanism of cracking was diagnosed as active path corrosion or hydrogen embrittle-

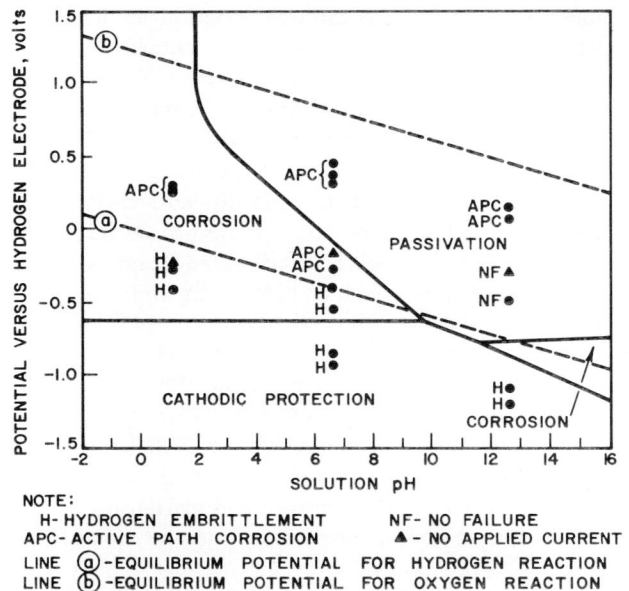

NOTE:
H- HYDROGEN EMBRITTLEMENT        NF- NO FAILURE
APC- ACTIVE PATH CORROSION        ▲ - NO APPLIED CURRENT
LINE ⓐ -EQUILIBRIUM POTENTIAL FOR HYDROGEN REACTION
LINE ⓑ -EQUILIBRIUM POTENTIAL FOR OXYGEN REACTION

FIGURE 3 — Equilibrium potential-pH diagram with stress corrosion results obtained with 12MoV stainless in 3 percent sodium chloride solution. Bhatt and Phelps.[24]

ment as a result of the response of the time-to-failure to anodic or cathodic polarization. It is noteworthy that the mechanism of cracking was diagnosed as hydrogen embrittlement for experiments in which the potential was equal to or more anodic than the reversible hydrogen potential. The diagnosis was active path corrosion for all experiments in which the potential was more cathodic than the reversible hydrogen potential. The above results were supported by hydrogen permeation experiments in which it was found that hydrogen permeated the steel under all of the conditions diagnosed as hydrogen embrittlement, whereas it did not permeate the steel under the conditions diagnosed as active path corrosion.

Truman, et al[25] used electrochemical polarization extensively in studies on stress corrosion cracking of martensitic 13 percent chromium stainless steels. They concluded that when these steels are tempered at temperatures above 450 C (842 F), an active path mechanism is predominant. For steels tempered at this temperature or below, they considered that the evidence is convincing for a hydrogen embrittlement mechanism. They argue that this mechanism prevails even for cracking that occurs with anodic polarization in neutral 3 percent sodium chloride solution by pointing out that the acid solution, which forms in pits, leads to hydrogen evolution near the region of triaxial stress at the tip of the advancing crack (and hence produces a very localized embrittlement).

In polarization studies with alloy steel BS970:EN25 (0.37% C, 2.4% Ni, 0.7% Cr, 0.5% Mo) heat treated to a yield strength of about 200,000 psi, Hughes, et al[26] found that this steel was susceptible to either stress corrosion or hydrogen embrittlement in either an acid (0.1 N HCl) or a neutral (3% NaCl) solution, depending upon the potential. Without polarization, the mechanism was found to be corrosion along an active path in the salt solution and hydrogen embrittlement in the acid solution.

In Reference 23 Bhatt and Phelps describe the various types of curves which may be expected from the use of the polarization method. These various curves of time-to-failure against applied current are shown in Figure 4. Bhatt and Phelps point out that all of the curves shown have been obtained experimentally with the exception of Curve G.

Curve A represents the case where only hydrogen embrittlement is obtained, whereas Curve B shows only active path corrosion. Both processes are shown in Curves C and D with the significant difference that Curve D has an open zone where failure is not observed. Where both anodic and cathodic polarization shorten the cracking time, as in Curve E, it is not possible to determine which mechanism prevails without applied current. Curves F and G might be expected in acid solutions when the corrosion potential is anodic to the reversible hydrogen potential. With Curve H neither anodic nor cathodic polarization have any effect on cracking time. A possible explanation would be that a hydrogen embrittlement mechanism is involved, but that the mechanism by which hydrogen enters the steel is not electrochemical.

## Influence of Environment

*Environments Not Containing Hydrogen Sulfide*

A characteristic feature of stress corrosion cracking of the higher strength steels is that a relatively large number of environmental conditions have been found to cause the phenomenon. In tests designed to determine whether anions other than chloride would cause cracking of 12MoV

stainless steel at a high strength level, Phelps and Mears[19] obtained the results summarized in Table 1. They found that a substantial number of anions other than chloride caused stress corrosion cracking of the steel. Furthermore, it is evident in Table 1 that the anion present has a

TABLE 1 – Stress-Corrosion Behavior of USSS 12MoV Stainless[1] in Various Salt Solutions Phelps and Mears[19]

| Chemical | Concentration | Initial pH | Average Time to Failures |
|---|---|---|---|
| NaF | 1.0 M | 7.7 | 22 min |
| NaCl | 1.0 M | 6.2 | 28 min |
| NaBr | 1.0 M | 6.7 | 11 min |
| NaI | 1.0 M | 8.9 | 6 min |
| $NaH_2PO_4$ | 1.0 M | 3.6 | 6 min |
| $Na_2HPO_4$ | 1.0 M | 8.9 | NF 620 hr |
| $Na_3PO_4$ | Sat | 12.3 | 60 min |
| $Na_2SO_4$ | 1.0 M | 7.0 | 5 min |
| $NaNO_3$ | 1.0 M | 5.7 | 18 hr |
| $Na_2SO_3$ | 1.0 M | 9.4 | 49 hr |
| $NaClO_3$ | 1.0 M | 7.8 | 205 hr |
| $NaC_2H_3O_2$ | 1.0 M | 8.2 | 520 hr |
| $NaNO_2$ | 1.0 M | 8.1 | NF 840 hr |
| $NaHCO_3$ | Sat | 8.9 | NF 840 hr |
| $Na_2CO_3$ | 1.0 M | 11.5 | NF 840 hr |
| NaCN | 1.0 M | 11.8 | NF 840 hr |
| NaOH | 1.0 M | 12.0 | NF 840 hr |

[1]Steel tempered at 800 F to obtain yield strength of 207,000 psi.

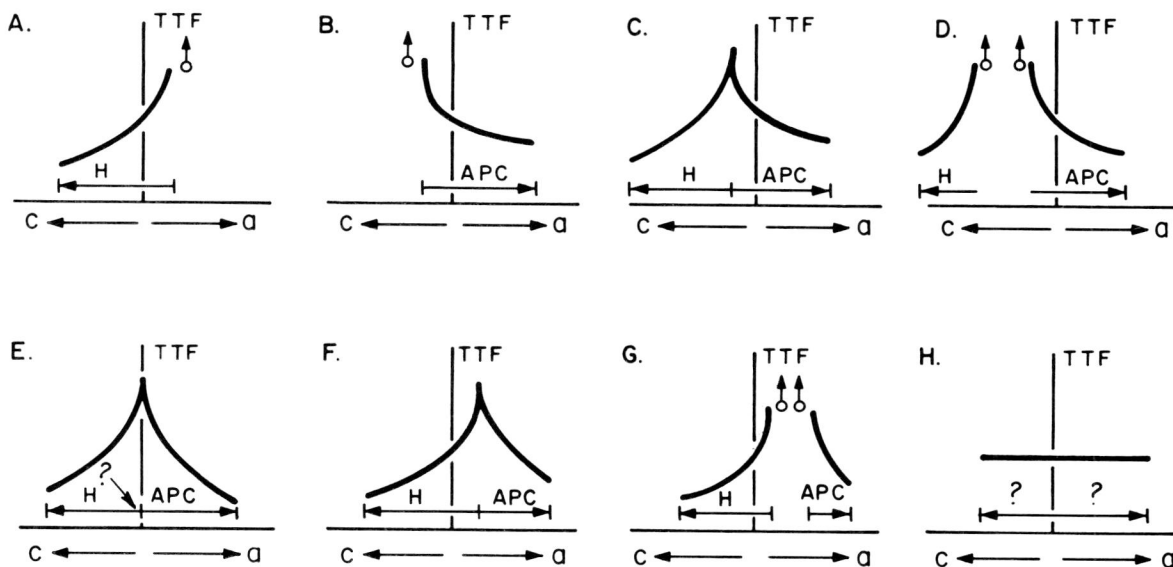

NOTE:
APC – ACTIVE PATH CORROSION   a – ANODIC POLARIZATION   H – HYDROGEN EMBRITTLEMENT
TTF – TIME TO FAILURE   C – CATHODIC POLARIZATION   ♀ – NO FAILURE

FIGURE 4 – Effect of anodic and cathodic polarization on time to failure. Bhatt and Phelps.[24]

pronounced effect on cracking time and that several anions cause cracking in shorter times than chlorides. Bhatt and Phelps[23] used the same steel in experiments in which the pH was varied from 1 to 13 in aerated 3 percent sodium chloride solution. The time-to-failure gradually increased and the corrosion rate decreased as the pH was increased from 3 to about 11. At pH values greater than 11, stress corrosion cracking did not occur and the rate of corrosion was negligible. At pH 1, the time-to-failure was very short and a high corrosion rate was observed. In studies with maraging steels, both Leckie[27] and Green and Haney[28] have found a pronounced minimum in time-to-failure at pH values of between 10 and 12. These investigators attribute this phenomenon to partial inhibition of the anodic process by sodium hydroxide, leading to an increase in the anodic reaction rate at localized sites. Green and Haney[29] also found a minimum in the time-to-failure for 4340 steel and H-11 steel at pH 11 to 12, although it was not as pronounced as that observed with the maraging steel.

Several investigators have commented on the relative severity of various test environments. In studies on hardenable stainless steels, Bloom[30] found that the response to different environments varied with the hardness of the steel. In a severe marine atmosphere, cracking occurred at Rockwell C 40 and above, whereas in a severe industrial atmosphere cracking occurred at Rockwell C 45 and above. Salt fog and aqueous salt solutions also caused cracking at Rockwell C 45 and above. Phelps and Loginow[1] found substantially shorter times-to-failure in a marine atmosphere than in a semi industrial atmosphere. Furthermore, the latter atmosphere did not cause cracking of semi austenitic precipitation-hardenable steels which were susceptible in marine atmospheres. In tests with maraging steels, Setterlund[16] found that the marine atmosphere at the 80-foot lot at Kure Beach, North Carolina, was more severe than the marine atmosphere (200 yards from beach) at Newport Beach, California, or the industrial atmosphere at Bayonne, New Jersey.

From the above results it is evident that the chemistry of the environment can have a controlling influence on the stress corrosion behavior of the higher strength steels, from the standpoint of both inherent tendency for cracking and the time required for cracking. Furthermore, a general parallelism seems to exist between cracking time and the inherent corrosivity of the environment. One of the puzzling features of the present state of research on the higher strength steels, however, is the fact that many environmental conditions, which are only slightly corrosive, if at all, have been found to cause cracking (or slow crack propagation) in steels heat treated to very high strength levels. Steigerwald[31] utilized precracked tensile specimens to study the behavior of 300M steel heat treated to a yield strength of 245,000 psi in various liquid environments. The stress level used was 75,000 psi or 84 percent of the strength obtained without a liquid environment. The results obtained are presented in Table 2. Most of the nonaqueous solvents tested caused delayed failure, although the times-to-failure were always longer than in aqueous environments. Steigerwald points out that the solvents with the lowest

TABLE 2–Influence of Various Environments on Failure Time of 300M Steel[1] Steigerwald[11]

| Environment | Failure Time, min |
|---|---|
| Recording ink | 0.5 |
| Distilled water | 6.5 |
| Amyl alcohol | 35.8 |
| Butyl alcohol | 28.0 |
| Butyl acetate | 18.0 |
| Acetone | 120 |
| Lubricating oil | 150 |
| Benzene | 2247 |
| Carbon tetrachloride | NF-1280 |
| Air | NF-6000 |

[1] Tempered at 600 F to obtain yield strength of 245,000 psi.

dielectric constants, benzene and carbon tetrachloride, resulted in the best performance. In his studies with high strength maraging steels, Setterlund[16] observed cracking in bent beam specimens (not precracked) exposed to tri-chloroethylene. In this case the cracking was attributed to corrosion by traces of free hydrochloric acid in the trichloroethylene.

Steels heat treated to very high strength levels have also been found to be susceptible to slow crack growth in gaseous environments containing various amounts of water vapor. Hanna, et al[32] found that air with a dew point of 35 F and moist argon with a dew point of 45 F were as effective in promoting delayed failure of precracked tensile specimens of 4340 steel (yield strength of 214,000 psi) as was immersion in distilled water. In tests with this steel, in which the moisture content of the argon was systematically varied, it was found that rapid crack growth was apparent in argon with a -7 F dew point but that argon with a dew point of -3 F gave no indication of delayed failure. On the basis of these results the critical dew point to initiate failure was estimated to be -5 F, which corresponds with a water content of only one grain per cubic foot of gas. These authors attributed the observed cracking to embrittlement by hydrogen absorbed into the lattice as a result of a surface corrosion process.

Johnson and Willner,[33] in tests conducted with H-11 steel at a yield strength level of 230,000 psi, found that the stress intensity parameter $K_{IC}$ required to induce slow crack growth varied with relative humidity of argon, as shown in Figure 5. For relative humidities in excess of about 60 percent, it was found that crack initiation and growth characteristics were identical in humid argon and in distilled water, suggesting that at high relative humidities water vapor condenses at the crack tip. For lower relative humidities, cracking was attributed to a lowering of surface energy by an adsorption process.

Although previous studies have shown that high pressure hydrogen can have an embrittling effect on steels with high strength,[34,35] it has only recently been shown by Hancock and Johnson[36] that hydrogen gas at atmospheric pressure is capable of causing substantial embrittlement of martensitic high strength steel (H-11 steel heat treated to a yield strength of 230,000 psi). Subcritical crack growth occurred with precracked tensile specimens at a much more rapid rate in hydrogen at one atmosphere than in humidified argon (100% RH). The addition of as little as 0.7 volume percent of oxygen terminated crack growth in either environment. These investigators consider that adsorbed hydrogen is the source of the embrittlement and that the adsorption is localized in the region of the crack tip. Stress is necessary because simple exposure to hydrogen without stress had no embrittling effect. The inhibiting effect of oxygen is attributed to its ability to adsorb in preference to hydrogen at the crack tip. The authors conclude that their results support the contention that hydrogen embrittlement is a probable cause of delayed failure of martensitic high strength steels. They furthermore point out that their results are difficult to reconcile with the "planar pressure" theory of hydrogen embrittlement because the internal pressure generated in voids should not exceed the one atmosphere external pressure.

*Environments Containing Hydrogen Sulfide*

In experiments aimed at the effect of environment on sulfide cracking, Fraser and Treseder[37] found that hydrogen sulfide was the constituent responsible for cracking of higher strength tubular steels and that the presence of a liquid water phase was also essential; cracking of a susceptible steel did not occur in water saturated hydrogen sulfide gas or in a kerosene solution of hydrogen sulfide. The addition of acetic acid to water saturated with hydrogen sulfide appreciably increased its severity and resulted in cracking of several steels which were not susceptible without the addition of acetic acid. The general effect of temperature is that severity of cracking increases with decreasing temperature. These authors did not find any correlation between rate of general corrosion and cracking tendency. Fraser, et al[13] found that distilled water saturated with hydrogen sulfide and carbon dioxide was more severe than distilled water saturated only with hydrogen sulfide.

Hudgins, et al[10] studied the effect of pH on the behavior of notched C-ring specimens made from tubular steels with hardness values of Rockwell C 33 ± 1. The specimens were stressed to 115 percent of the deformation, which produced yielding. Their results, presented in Figure 6, show that the pH of solutions containing hydrogen sulfide does not have a very marked effect on cracking time until the pH is raised well into the alkaline range. This contrasts with a pronounced effect of pH in chloride solutions not containing sulfide. It is noteworthy that the latter solutions caused cracking at pH values up to about 4, the pH range in which hydrogen evolution is the expected cathodic reaction, but did not cause cracking at higher pH values. In studies of the effect of hydrogen sulfide concentration, these authors found that solutions containing one ppm hydrogen sulfide would cause cracking in notched and highly stressed steels of approximately the same hardness levels as would be cracked by concentrated or sour solutions (3000 ppm $H_2S$). However, the times-to-failure were much longer in the dilute sulfide solutions than in the concentrated ones (several months compared with a few hours). It is concluded that below one ppm a significant increase in useable hardness can be realized (to Rockwell C 29).

Treseder and Swanson[16] conclude from their studies that a "sour" environment, defined as one which required special materials, is one in which the partial pressure of hydrogen sulfide is greater than 0.001 atmosphere.

*Summary of Environmental Effects*

It is evident from these various studies that environmental factors do, in fact, have a controlling influence on the stress corrosion behavior of the higher strength steels. For very high strength steels, seemingly innocuous environments such as distilled water, humidified gases, hydrogen, and various organic solvents prove to be aggressive from the

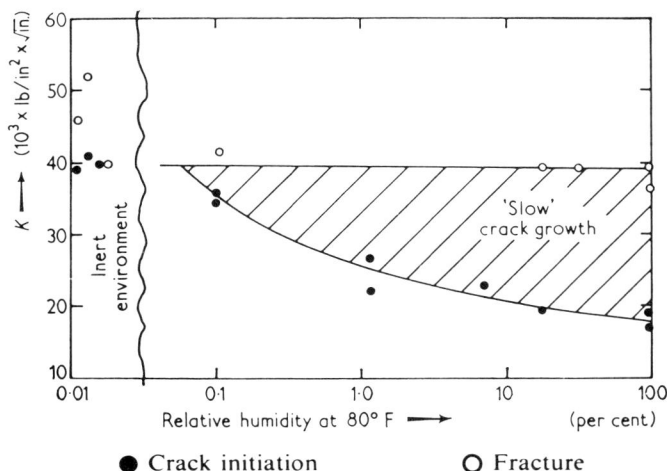

FIGURE 5 — Influence of relative humidity on crack initiation and fracture in H-11 steel at 230,000 psi yield strength. Johnson and Willner.[33]

● Crack initiation    O Fracture

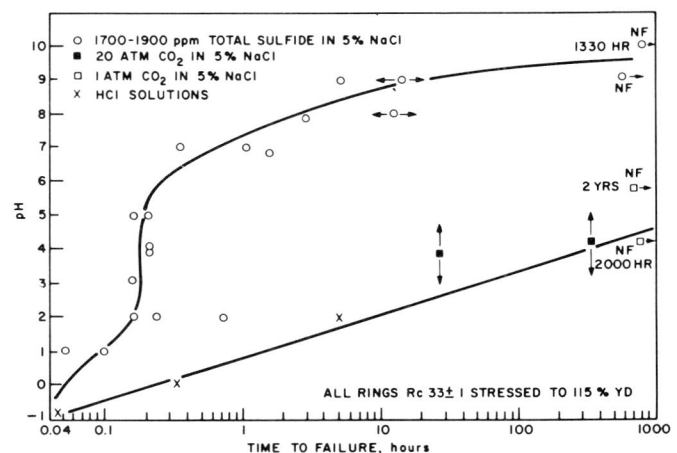

FIGURE 6 — Influence of pH on stress corrosion behavior of heat treated steel tubing. Hudgins, et al.[10]

standpoint of being capable of causing slow crack propagation in precracked specimens. Such steels are also susceptible to crack initiation and propagation in a variety of corrosive environments. Factors such as pH which influence general corrosivity also have pronounced influence on stress corrosion susceptibility. Lower strength steels (with yield strengths below 180,000 to 210,000 psi but above about 80,000 psi) are susceptible to cracking in environments that contain sulfides (or other promoters of hydrogen entry) or which have pH values low enough so that hydrogen evolution is the cathodic reaction. Sulfide content has an important influence on behavior but the general level of corrosivity does not appear to be a controlling factor.

## Microstructural Aspects

### Path of Cracking

For cracking in hydrogen sulfide environments, most investigators[10,15,37] have found that the path of cracking is transgranular with respect to the prior austenite grain boundaries. Phelps and Mears[12] found that cracking of 12MoV stainless was transgranular in water containing acetic acid and saturated with hydrogen sulfide but that the path could not be clearly distinguished in water saturated with hydrogen sulfide. Other investigators have also pointed out that identification of the path of cracking is difficult because failure in sulfide environments is usually associated with a single, large crack; small secondary cracks are the exception rather than the rule.

Cracking in sulfide solutions is not solely transgranular, however. Prange[38] found intergranular cracking in 9 percent nickel tubing steel which failed in a sour condensate well. Scheutz and Robertson[12] also found that sulfide cracking was intergranular in steels containing 10 and 30 percent nickel.

The opposite situation prevails in stress corrosion of the very high strength steels in environments not containing hydrogen sulfide in that intergranular corrosion along the prior austenite grain boundaries is the rule rather than the exception. Phelps and Loginow,[1] Davis,[2] and Dean and Copson[5] all report that cracking was predominantly intergranular. Davis, et al[3] found mixed inter- and transgranular cracking in 4340M steel and 4330 steel, but only intergranular cracking was found in semi austenitic precipitation-hardenable steels. In his work with the latter type of steel, Tiner[39] found that cracking progressed along prior austenite boundaries and also along delta ferrite boundaries. Setterlund[4] found that cracks in maraging steels caused by aqueous environments or various natural atmospheres were intergranular and branching but that those caused by trichloroethylene were wide and straight with blunt tips.

Electron fractography has developed into a powerful tool for the examination of stress corrosion fracture surfaces.[40] Phillips, et al[41] have described in detail the differences in fracture appearance between stress corrosion and hydrogen embrittlement in AISI 4340 steel. Stress corrosion fracture surfaces were characterized as surface nucleated, intergranular fractures with pronounced secondary cracking or deep crevices. More evidence of corrosion attack was present in areas where slow crack growth had occurred than in areas of fast crack growth. Hydrogen embrittlement fracture surfaces were also characterized as being intergranular, with it being noted that nucleation occurred below the surface. The grain boundary surfaces showed evidence of partial dimple formation with pronounced hairline (crack) indications. The amount of corrosion attack in the crack nucleus area was about the same as in areas of rapid fracture. The fracture appearance suggests, according to the authors, a large degree of mechanical separation in the case of hydrogen embrittlement and a higher degree of nonmechanical separation in the case of stress corrosion.

Sullivan[40] points out that hydrogen-embrittlement cracks may be transgranular as well as intergranular. As an example of the former, he documents the occurrence of quasi-cleavage facets on the fracture surface of hydrogen embrittled 18 percent nickel maraging steel with a yield strength of 230,000 psi. This mode of failure is characteristically transgranular.

It is apparent from the above discussion that environmentally induced cracking in the higher strength steels may be intergranular or transgranular and that the occurrence of either mode of failure does not establish the mechanism as "true" stress corrosion or hydrogen embrittlement.

### Effect of Microstructure on Crack Initiation

Fontana[42] conducted studies on the initial stages of stress corrosion cracking of AISI Type 403 stainless steel exposed to a 1:1 solution of hydrochloric acid in water containing 1 percent selenium dioxide. He found that cracks emanated from pits which appeared to originate at manganese sulfide inclusions. Metallographic examination showed that tempering temperature had a pronounced effect on the shape of the pits formed by the test solution. At tempering temperatures of 600 and 1000 F, the pits formed on stressed specimens were sharply notched at their bases, and with these tempering temperatures the steel was susceptible to stress corrosion cracking. These pits propagated in a direction normal to the tensile stresses and gradually became intergranular cracks along favorably oriented grain boundaries. At tempering temperatures of 1050 and 1100 F the pits were relatively smooth and rounded at their bases, and with these tempering temperatures the steel was resistant to stress corrosion cracking.

In alternate immersion tests in 3-1/2 percent sodium chloride solution, Davis[2] found that localized pitting served as the nucleus for stress corrosion cracking in AISI 4330M and 4340 steels and that the pits usually occurred at nonmetallic inclusions. Tiner and Gilpin[43] studied the behavior of AISI 4340 steel in 3 percent sodium chloride solution. These investigators found that pits leading to stress corrosion cracking were practically always formed at the sites of inclusions. The inclusion particles dropped out as a result of continued corrosion attack of the surrounding steel, which was attributed to variations in composition and stress in the micro regions around the inclusion. The growth of the pits during the incubation period for stress corrosion cracking was followed by metallographic sectioning and fractographic analysis. It was concluded that pits grew by slow chemical attack along prior austenite grain boundaries. After the pits obtained sufficient depth, a rapid but stable stress corrosion crack propagation occurred with gas evolution. In this growth region the fracture face exhibited a mixture of intergranular and transgranular areas.

It is evident from these studies that the initial step in the stress corrosion process is the formation of pits. The pits are prone to form at inclusion sites. Pit morphology is strongly dependent on stress and the metallurgy of the steel.

*Effect of Microstructure on Crack Propagation*

Lillys and Nehrenberg[44] studied the behavior of several martensitic stainless steels exposed to 5 percent sodium chloride spray and also exposed as cathodes in a cell containing 0.1 N sulfuric acid plus 3 mg arsenic per liter as the electrolyte. The former condition was considered to induce stress corrosion cracking whereas the latter induced hydrogen embrittlement. It was found that the tendency for stress corrosion cracking was minimized when 5 to 10 percent delta ferrite was present in the structure. It was noted that the cracks tended to go around delta ferrite rather than through this phase, thus interfering with crack propagation. These investigators did not find a clear association between microstructural changes on tempering and mode of cracking by either stress corrosion or hydrogen embrittlement. Even though precipitates could be detected in the grain boundaries after a temper at 850 F, exclusively intergranular crack propagation was not observed until after a 950 F temper for specimens subjected to stress corrosion conditions and after 1000 F for specimens exposed to hydrogen embrittlement. It is furthermore considered to be an open question as to whether susceptibility to intergranular cracking is the result of localized strains associated with the formation of a coherent chromium carbide or chromium impoverishment adjacent to the prior austenite boundaries.

Trozzo and McCartney[45] used electron microscopy and diffraction techniques to investigate three heats of AISI Type 410 stainless steel that exhibited different degrees of susceptibility to stress corrosion cracking in a high temperature water environment. Two heats which were susceptible to intergranular cracking were examined in the as-quenched condition and found to contain a continuous constituent in the prior austenite boundaries consisting of enriched austenite and martensite. Upon tempering at 650 F, the retained austenite transformed to martensite, thus creating a grain boundary network of essentially untempered martensite. Such a path would, according to these authors, provide an "easy" path for propagation of a crack. The grain boundary network was not as evident in the resistant heat, and in addition this heat had a smaller grain size and contained delta ferrite.

Tiner and Gilpin[43] made interesting observations on the microstructural aspects of crack propagation in AISI

4340 steel exposed to 3 percent salt solution. Tritiated water solutions were used in experiments to study the microsegregation of hydrogen during stress corrosion. A carbon replica and sensitive emulsion were used to detect the location of tritium on the fracture face. No tritium was found in the initial intergranular region of cracking or in the terminal, abrupt failure region. Tritium was concentrated in bands and clusters in quasi-cleavage areas in the region of stable crack growth, and it therefore appears that hydrogen plays a part in the formation of these areas. Experiments were also conducted in which thin foils of AISI 4340 steel were dipped into 3 percent sodium chloride solution acidified to pH 1.5 prior to examination by transmission electron microscopy. Areas adjacent to epsilon carbide precipitates were found to be preferentially attacked. This attack was attributed to microstrains and/or depletion of alloying elements from the area adjacent to the carbide.

Tiner and Gilpin conclude from their work that stress corrosion susceptibility in martensitic alloy steels is related to the presence of epsilon carbide in the microstructure. The susceptibility arises from the "metastability of epsilon carbide and composition variations...in the epsilon carbide or in the adjacent areas." This view does not appear to have general applicability because Phelps and Loginow[1] found that USS Airsteel X200 and 12MoV stainless steel were susceptible to stress corrosion cracking in marine atmosphere exposure tests in the untempered condition and also when tempered at 900 and 1000 F. Little, if any, epsilon carbide would be expected to be present under these conditions.[46]

Although some progress has been made in establishing the microstructural aspects in the steel which control stress corrosion crack propagation, more research in this area would be very desirable. This represents a very challenging area for future research.

## Effect of Stress

For both sulfide free and sulfide containing environments, the general effect of increased stress is to shorten the cracking time. Furthermore, for many steel-environment combinations, a threshold stress level is observed below which cracking does not occur in the maximum time of test evaluated. The results obtained by Snape[17] for unnotched beam specimens of N-80 steel heat treated to different hardness levels and exposed to 3-1/2 percent sodium chloride, 1/2 percent acetic acid solution saturated with hydrogen sulfide are typical, Figure 7. It is important to recognize that threshold values of the type shown can be changed by changing the environment, and thus they do not have general significance. Kihara, et al[18] present threshold stress level data for a number of heat treated constructional alloy steels in several different laboratory and field test environments containing sulfides.

For higher strength steels exposed to marine atmosphere, Phelps and Loginow[1] showed that failure time generally decreased as stress level increased. Although an apparent threshold stress level was found for some steels

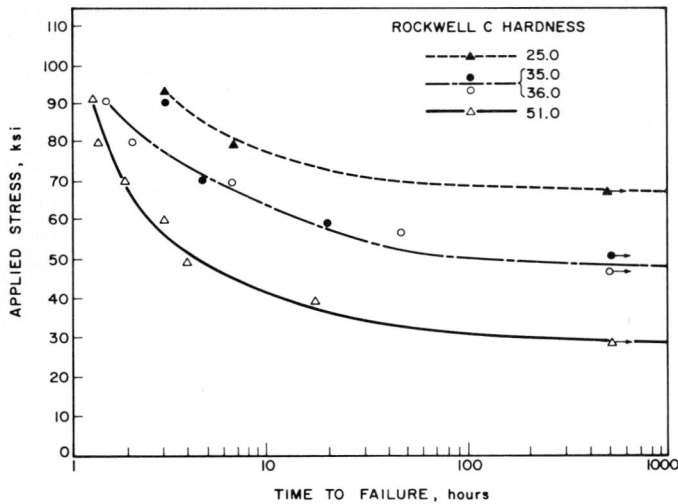

FIGURE 7 — Stress corrosion behavior of API N-80 type steel heat treated to different hardness levels and exposed to 3-1/2 percent sodium chloride, 1/2 percent acetic acid solution saturated with hydrogen sulfide. Snape.[17]

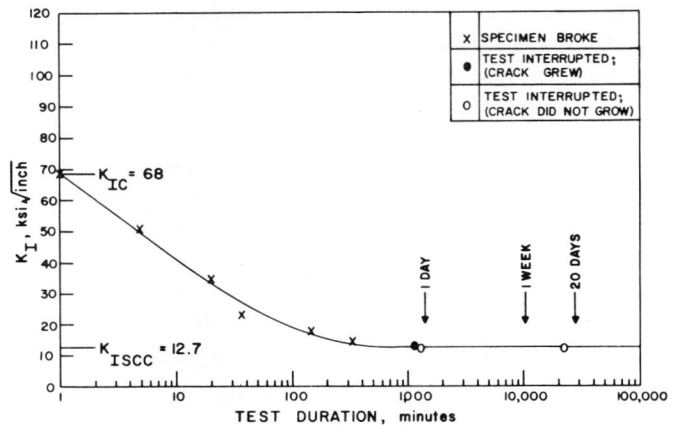

FIGURE 8 — Stress corrosion behavior of precracked cantilever beam specimens of AISI 4340 steel (tempered at 400 F) in 3-1/2 percent sodium chloride solution. Beachem and Brown.[44]

(between stress levels of 50 and 75% of the yield strength), most of the steels tested failed at all three stress levels evaluated (50, 75, and 90%). Similar results were found by Davis, et al.[3]

Tests with smooth specimens to determine the influence of stress on time to failure measure the time required for two different processes—crack initiation and crack propagation. Brown and his coworkers[47-50] contend that the initiation stage is "irrelevant and highly variable" because it involves the time necessary for the development of a pit (or pits) of sufficient depth and acuity to initiate the stress corrosion cracking process. They propose that the waiting period for the development of pits of suitable geometry can be avoided by the incorporation of a stress raiser in the specimen in the form of a fatigue crack. By this procedure, the test time is not only shortened but the state of stress for initiation of stress corrosion cracking can be described in a quantitative manner with the equations of fracture mechanics.

A considerable body of experimental data has been generated on the high strength steels utilizing fatigue cracked specimens.[47-51] The data show that the stress corrosion cracking process in high strength steels can, in fact, be caused to initiate immediately on the application of sufficient stress to the precracked specimen. The results obtained by Beachem and Brown[49] with AISI 4340 steel tempered at 400 F and exposed in 3-1/2 percent sodium chloride solution are typical, Figure 8. It may be noted that environment induced slow crack propagation occurred at stress intensity factors well below that ($K_{IC}$) required for fracture in air. As the crack grows by stress corrosion, the stress intensity at the root of the crack gradually increases until it reaches the value required for rapid mechanical fracture in air, at which time the specimen fails. Brown and Beachem[48] show experimentally that the stress intensity for rapid fracture of AISI 4340 steel is the same under stress corrosion conditions in 3–1/2 percent sodium

chloride as it is in air. Thus, as pointed out by Brown and coworkers, the environment has not decreased the inherent fracture toughness of the steel.

Rolfe and coworkers[51] utilized the cantilever beam technique effectively in a study of the stress corrosion susceptibility of high toughness steels in synthetic sea water. These investigators found that HY-80 steel with a yield strength at 89,000 psi and 5N-Cr-Mo-V steel with a yield strength of 135,000 psi completely resisted subcritical crack growth and fractured by tensile tearing at the same stress in synthetic sea water as in air. The data obtained with these and other steels evaluated are shown in Table 3. There appears to be no simple relationship between either yield strength or fracture toughness ($K_{IC}$) and the stress corrosion stress intensity threshold level ($K_{ISCC}$) for these steels.

On the basis of the experimental data available it seems well established that the use of precracked specimens does effectively eliminate the crack initiation step in the high strength steels and in this respect the test has a very definite advantage. It also appears to be established for the conditions evaluated that the environment causes slow, subcritical crack growth but it does not alter the inherent fracture toughness of the steel. For other conditions in which the basic mechanism of failure is hydrogen embrittlement, the environment may have a significant effect on fracture toughness, however. Another area of uncertainty is the specific influence of the "state of stress" at the crack tip on the corrosion process causing crack propagation.

## Summary

A large amount of information has been developed in recent years on stress corrosion cracking of steels with high yield strength. Although it has been shown that a number of factors associated both with the metal and the environment are of critical importance with respect to cracking

TABLE 3—Properties of Steels Evaluated with Fatigue-Cracked
Specimens Exposed to Synthetic Sea Water, Rolfe, et al[46]

| Steel and Melting Practice | Heat No. | Yield Strength (0.2% Offset), ksi | Tensile Strength, ksi | Charpy V-Notch Energy Absorption at +80 F, ft-lb | $K_{IC}$ ksi $\sqrt{}$ inch | $K_{ISCC}$ ksi $\sqrt{}$ inch |
|---|---|---|---|---|---|---|
| 18Ni (250) Electric-Furnace Air-Melted | X53674 | 252 | 259 | 12 | 72.6 | 49 |
| HY-80 Electric-Furnace Air-Melted | N54060 | 88.9 | 105 | 106 | NA[1] | [2] |
| 5Ni-Cr-Mo-V Electric-Furnace Air-Melted | X53957 | 135 | 142 | 112 | NA | [2] |
| 18Ni (180) Electric-Furnace Air-Melted | X53014 | 178 | 186 | 35 | 118 | 108 |
| 12Ni Electric-Furnace Air-Melted | X14689 | 176 | 183 | 36 | 130 | 40 |
| 12Ni Low Residual Vacuum-Induction-Melted | 50169 | 183 | 191 | 60 | 169 | 108 |

[1]Not applicable.
[2]No failures.

behavior, the specific mechanism(s) by which cracks propagate through steels have not been delineated except in the general sense.

This survey has shown that the strength level of the steel is the most important single factor determining sensitivity to environment induced cracking. Steels with yield strength of about 200,000 psi or over are susceptible to cracking in a number of environments including various natural atmospheres, salt solutions, organic solvents, various gases containing relatively small amounts of water vapor, and hydrogen gas. Steels with hardness values over Rockwell C22 (corresponding to a yield strength on the order of 80,000 psi) exhibit a general susceptibility in sulfide as well as other environments which cause hydrogen to enter the steel. For sulfide cracking there appears to be a general agreement that the mechanism is hydrogen embrittlement with the corrosion process serving as a source of hydrogen. For other aqueous environments, electrochemical polarization measurements have shown that cracking may occur by an active path corrosion mechanism or by hydrogen embrittlement, depending on the specific conditions. The microstructural and environmental factors controlling crack initiation and propagation by either of these mechanisms

have not, however, been defined. A surface adsorption mechanism may be involved in the cracking caused by gaseous hydrogen and organic solvents such as benzene, which do not corrode steel.

The path of cracking in the higher strength steels may be intergranular or transgranular with respect to the prior austenite grain boundaries. The occurrence of either mode of failure does not establish the mechanism as active path corrosion or hydrogen embrittlement. The initial step in the stress corrosion process is the formation of pits which are likely to form at inclusions. Crack propagation by either an active path corrosion or a hydrogen embrittlement mechanism is thought to be related to microstructural features within the metal but the specific details of such relationships have not been established. The effect of increased stress is to shorten the cracking time and for many steel-environment combinations, a threshold stress is observed below which cracking does not occur. It has been shown that the initiation stage for crack formation can be avoided by the utilization of precracked specimens for stress corrosion testing. An aggressive environment causes slow crack propagation in such specimens but it does not affect the inherent fracture toughness of the material.

## References

1. E. H. Phelps and A. L. Loginow. Stress Corrosion of Steels for Aircraft and Missiles. *Corrosion,* 16, 325t-335t (1960).
2. R. A. Davis. Stress Corrosion Investigation of Two Low Alloy High Strength Steels. *Corrosion,* 19, 45t-54t (1963).
3. R. A. Davis, G. A. Dreyer, and W. C. Gallaugher. Stress Corrosion Cracking Study of Several High Strength Steels.

*Corrosion,* 20, 93t-103t (1964).
4. R. B. Setterlund. Stress Corrosion Cracking of Maraging Steel. *Materials Protection,* 4, 27 (1965).
5. S. W. Dean and H. R. Copson. Stress Corrosion Behavior of Maraging Nickel Steels in Natural Environments. *Corrosion,* 21, 95-103 (1965).

6. C. J. Slunder. Stress Corrosion Cracking of High Strength Steels in Atmospheric Environments. Defense Metals Information Center, Battelle Memorial Institute, Columbus, Ohio, DMIC Report 158, September 15, 1961.

7. B. F. Brown. Stress Corrosion Cracking and Corrosion Fatigue of High Strength Steels. Defense Metals Information Center, Battelle Memorial Institute, Columbus, Ohio, DMIC Report 210, p. 91, October 26-28, 1964.

8. E. H. Phelps. Stress Corrosion Behavior of High Yield Strength Steels. Panel Discussion 27, Problems, Prevention, and Theories of Corrosion, 7th World Petroleum Congress Proceedings, Elsevier Publishing Company.

9. NACE Committee T-1B Report. *Materials Protection,* 3, 89-96 (1963).

10. C. M. Hudgins, R. L. McGlasson, P. Mehdizadeh, and W. M. Rosborough. Hydrogen Sulfide Cracking of Carbon and Alloy Steels. *Corrosion,* 22, 238-251 (1966).

11. Field Experience with Cracking of High Strength Steels in Sour Gas and Oil Wells. Report of Technical Practices Committee 1-G. *Corrosion,* 8, 351-354 (1952).

12. A. E. Schuetz and W. D. Robertson. Hydrogen Absorption, Embrittlement, and Fracture of Steel. *Corrosion,* 13, 437t-458t (1957).

13. J. P. Fraser, G. G. Eldredge, and R. S. Treseder. Laboratory and Field Methods for Quantitative Study of Sulfide Corrosion Cracking. *Corrosion,* 14, 517t-523t (1958).

14. J. P. Fraser and G. G. Eldredge. Influence of Metallurgical Variables on Resistance of Steels to Sulfide Corrosion Cracking. *Corrosion,* 14, 524t-530t (1958).

15. M. F. Baldy and R. C. Bowden. The Effect of Martensite of Sulfide Corrosion Cracking. *Corrosion,* 11, 417t-422t (1955).

16. R. S. Treseder and T. M. Swanson. Factors in Sulfide Corrosion Cracking of High Strength Steels. Presented at the 1967 Annual Meeting of the National Association of Corrosion Engineers. To

17. E. Snape. Sulfide Stress Corrosion of Some Medium and Low Alloy Steels. *Corrosion,* 23, 154-172 (1967).

18. H. Kihara, M. Watanabe, K. Horikawa, and M. Inagaki. Studies on the Sulfide Corrosion Cracking of High Strength Steels Caused by $H_2S$. Panel Discussion 27, Problems, Prevention, and Theories of Corrosion, 7th World Petroleum Congress Proceedings, Elsevier Publishing Company (in press).

19. E. H. Phelps and R. B. Mears. The Effect of Composition and Structure of Stainless Steels Upon Resistance to Stress Corrosion Cracking. Proceedings of the First International Congress on Metallic Corrosion, p. 319-327, Butterworths, 1961.

20. H. H. Uhlig. Action of Corrosion and Stress on 13% Cr Stainless Steel. *Metal Progress,* 57, 486-487 (1950).

21. B. F. Brown. Cracking of Martensitic Type 410 Stainless Steel in Corrosive Environments. Report of NRL Progress, p. 40-42, May, 1958.

22. B. F. Brown. Stress Corrosion Cracking and Related Phenomena in High Strength Steels. NRL Report 6041, November 6, 1963.

23. H. J. Bhatt and E. H. Phelps. Effect of Solution pH on the Mechanism of Stress Corrosion Cracking of a Martensitic Stainless Steel *Corrosion,* 17, 430t-434t (1961).

24. H. J. Bhatt and E. H. Phelps. The Effect of Electrochemical Polarization on the Stress Corrosion Behavior of Steels with High Yield Strength. To be published in the Proceedings of the Third International Congress on Metallic Corrosion, Moscow, USSR, May 16-26, 1966.

25. J. E. Truman, R. Perry, and G. N. Chapman. Stress Corrosion Cracking of Martensitic Stainless Steels. *Journal of the Iron and Steel Institute,* 745-756 (1964).

26. P. C. Hughes, I. R. Lamborn, and B. B. Leibert. Delayed Fracture of a Low Alloy High Strength Steel at Controlled Corrosion Rates. *Journal of the Iron and Steel Institute,* 728-731 (1965).

27. H. P. Leckie. Effect of Environment on Stress Induced Failure of High Strength Maraging Steels. This conference.

28. J. A. S. Green and E. G. Haney. Relationships Between Electrochemical Measurements and Stress Corrosion Cracking of Maraging Steel. *Corrosion,* 23, 5-15 (1967).

29. J. A. S. Green and E. G. Haney. A Stress Corrosion Test for Foil and Strip. To be published in ASTM Special Technical

30. F. K. Bloom. Stress Corrosion Cracking of Hardenable Stainless Steels. *Corrosion,* 11, 351t-361t (1955).

31. E. A. Steigerwald. Delayed Failure of High Strength Steel in Liquid Environments. *Proceedings of the ASTM,* 60, 750 (1960).

32. G. L. Hanna, A. R. Troiano, and E. A. Steigerwald. A Mechanism for the Embrittlement of High Strength Steels by Aqueous Environments. *Transactions ASM,* 57, 658-671 (1964).

33. H. H. Johnson and A. M. Willner. Moisture and Stable Crack Growth in a High Strength Steel. *Applied Materials Research,* 4, 34-40 (1965) January.

34. W. Hoffmann and W. Rauls. Ductility of Steel Under the Influence of External High Pressure Hydrogen. *Welding Journal Research Supplement,* 44, 225s-230s (1965).

35. J. B. Steinman, H. C. Van Ness, and G. S. Ansell. The Effect of High Pressure Hydrogen Upon the Notch Tensile Strength and Fracture Mode of 4140 Steel. *Welding Journal Research Supplement,* 44, 221s-224s (1965).

36. G. G. Hancock and H. H. Johnson. Hydrogen, Oxygen, and Subcritical Crack Growth in a High Strength Steel. *Trans. Met. Soc. AIME,* 236, 513-516 (1966).

37. J. P. Fraser and R. S. Treseder. Cracking of High Strength Steels in Hydrogen Sulfide Solutions. *Corrosion,* 8, 342-350 (1952).

38. F. A. Prange. Hydrogen Embrittlement Tests on Various Steels. *Corrosion,* 8, 355-357 (1958).

39. N. A. Tiner. Electron Microscopy of Stress Corrosion Cracking in ASM 350 Steel for a Supersonic Transport. *ASTM Special Technical Publication* No. 372, 10-23 (1964).

40. C. P. Sullivan. A Review of Some Microstructural Aspects of Fracture in Crystalline Materials. *Welding Research Council Bulletin* 122, (1967) May.

41. A. Phillips, V. Kerlins, and B. V. Whiteson. Electron Fractography Handbook Supplement. Air Force Materials Laboratory, Wright-Patterson Air Force Base, Ohio, 1966.

42. M. G. Fontana. Stress Corrosion Cracking in Type 403 Stainless Steel. WADC Technical Report, 56-242, ASTIA Document No. AD 97215, August, 1965.

43. N. A. Tiner and C. B. Gilpin. Microprocesses in Stress Corrosion of Martensitic Steels. *Corrosion,* 22, 271-279 (1966).

44. P. Lillys and A. E. Nehrenberg. Effect of Tempering Temperature on Stress Corrosion Cracking and Hydrogen Embrittlement of Martensitic Stainless Steels. *Trans. ASM,* 48, 327-355 (1956).

45. P. S. Trozzo and R. F. McCartney. Relationship of Microstructure and Stress Corrosion Cracking of Type 410 Stainless Steel. *Corrosion,* 16, No. 3, 26-30 (1960).

46. B. G. Reisdorf. The Tempering Characteristics of Some 0.4 Percent Carbon Ultra-High Strength Steels. *Trans. Met. Soc. AIME,* 227, 1334-1341 (1963).

47. B. F. Brown. A New Stress Corrosion Cracking Test for High Strength Alloys. *Materials Research and Standards,* 6, 129-133 (1966).

48. B. F. Brown and C. D. Beachem. A Study of the Stress Factor in Corrosion Cracking by Use of the Precracked Cantilever Beam Specimens. *Corrosion Science,* 5, 745-750 (1965).

49. C. D. Beachem and B. F. Brown. A Comparison of Three Specimens for Evaluating the Susceptibility of High Strength Steel to Stress Corrosion Cracking. Presented at the June, 1966 Annual Meeting of ASTM, Atlantic City, New Jersey.

50. M. H. Peterson, B. F. Brown, R. L. Newbegin, and R. E. Groover. Stress Corrosion Cracking of High Strength Steels and Titanium Alloys in Chloride Solutions at Ambient Temperature. *Corrosion,* 23, 142-148 (1967).

51. S. T. Rolfe, S. R. Novak, and J. H. Gross. Stress Corrosion Testing of Ultraservice Steels Using Fatigue Cracked Specimens. Presented at the June, 1966 Annual Meeting of the ASTM, Atlantic City, New Jersey.

# EFFECT OF ENVIRONMENT ON STRESS INDUCED FAILURE
## OF HIGH STRENGTH MARAGING STEELS

H. P. Leckie
U. S. Steel Corporation

## Abstract

The stress corrosion characteristics of a 12Ni and an 18Ni maraging steel have been evaluated using the cantilever-beam testing procedure. Results obtained for both steels show that short times to failure may be induced by the application of active potentials giving failure by hydrogen embrittlement; the data would indicate a failure mode consistent with a stress-sorption mechanism. Tests carried out only on the 18Ni steel showed that a high rate of crack propagation could be induced in this steel at potentials only slightly more active than the equilibrium potential for hydrogen ion discharge. Hydroxyl ion in high enough concentration strongly inhibits stress corrosion cracking of these steels; insufficient hydroxyl for complete inhibition may stimulate the process. The use of the cantilever-beam testing procedure in understanding mechanisms of stress corrosion and stress hydrogen failure is discussed.

## Introduction

The present study was undertaken as part of an overall program to evaluate the stress corrosion characteristics of various high yield strength steels for possible use in hydrospace applications. The failure of stressed high strength steels in aqueous solutions, unlike either structural carbon steel or the austenitic stainless steels, is not confined to solutions containing specific anions. In the majority of cases, it appears that the presence of water or water vapor is the controlling factor in the environmentally induced failure of high strength steels. Furthermore, increased susceptibility of these steels to both active path stress corrosion and hydrogen embrittlement cracking is found with increase in yield strength. A continuing emphasis on the need for high strength materials for use in aerospace, hydrospace, and chemical applications has resulted in increased efforts directed towards an understanding of the stress corrosion characteristics of such materials.

In its simplest terms, the stress corrosion cracking process may be considered to incorporate a crack initiation and a crack propagation stage. The time required for the initiation of a crack is often dependent on corrosion processes, the rate of which may vary considerably on two apparently identical materials. In addition, the time required for crack initiation is often some large percentage ($>90$ percent) of the total time to failure. Thus an evaluation of the susceptibility of a material to stress corrosion cracking by measurement of the total time to failure of a smooth, stressed specimen may, in fact, only measure the time required for the development of a corrosion pit, and bear no relationship to susceptibility to stress corrosion crack propagation.

Thus, Brown[1] has shown that although some materials, such as titanium and its alloys, may be resistant to stress corrosion cracking when tested as smooth unnotched specimens, they may readily fail in the presence of a sharp notch. Loading a notched specimen is intended to by-pass the crack initiation stage in the stress corrosion process and thus in the case of titanium nullifies, in part, the resistance which the highly protective oxide film offers to crack initiation.

The present work includes a study of some environmental effects governing the environmentally induced cracking of a 12Ni maraging steel, evaluated by the cantilever-beam testing procedure. The second part of this paper deals with the effect of applied potentials on the crack propagation characteristics of an 18Ni maraging steel. In addition, the present study is intended to furnish some further insight into the validity of the cantilever-beam testing method developed by Brown[1] as a technique for the evaluation of the resistance of high strength steels to a combination of stress and environment.

411

| Steel | C | Mn | P | S | Si | Ni | Cr | Mo | Ti | Al | Co |
|---|---|---|---|---|---|---|---|---|---|---|---|
| | | | | | Composition, Percent | | | | | | |
| 12Ni | 0.015 | 0.033 | 0.001 | 0.014 | 0.056 | 11.6 | 5.01 | 3.18 | 0.27 | 0.22 | ND |
| 18Ni | 0.003 | <0.02 | 0.001 | 0.004 | 0.003 | 17.1 | ND | 4.65 | 0.50 | 0.052 | 7.6 |

ND - Not determined

**Mechanical Properties**

| | Strength, ksi | | Elongation in 2 in., percent | Reduction of Area, percent | $K_{Ic}$ ksi $\sqrt{inch}$ |
|---|---|---|---|---|---|
| | Yield | Tensile | | | |
| 12Ni (1) | 187 | 191 | 12.7 | 54.3 | 105 |
| 12Ni (2) | 159 | 167 | 13.5 | 52.5 | 106 |
| 18Ni | 244 | 258 | 12.0 | 60.3 | 78 |

**Heat Treatments**

**12Ni Maraging Steel**

| No. 1 | No. 2 |
|---|---|
| 1 hour at 1500 F, water quench | 1 hour at 1500 F, water quench |
| 15 hours at 900 F, water quench | 30 hours at 1000 F, water quench |
| | 15 hours at 900 F, water quench |

**18Ni Maraging Steel**

1-1/4 hours at 1650 F - water quench
1-1/4 hours at 1525 F - water quench
3 hours at 900 F - air cool

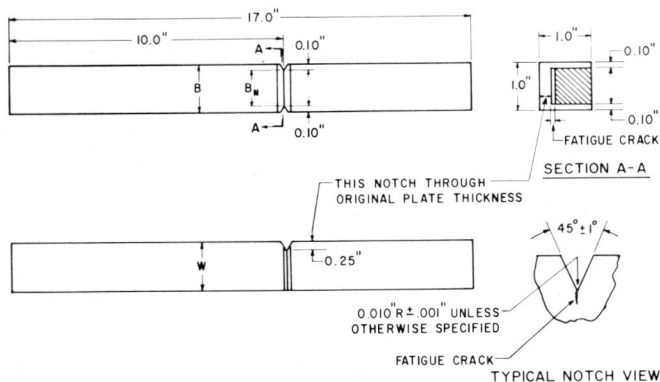

FIGURE 1 — $K_{IC}$ stress corrosion specimen.

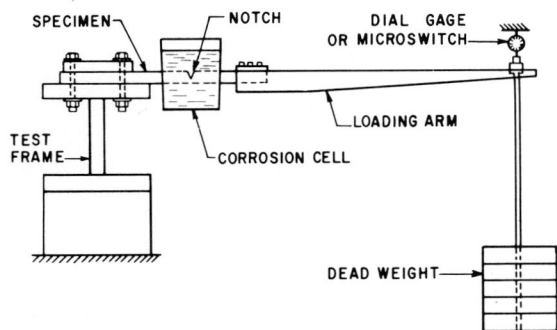

FIGURE 2 — Schematic drawing of $K_{IC}$ stress corrosion test specimen and fixtures.

## Materials and Experimental Work

Two maraging steels (a 12Ni and an 18Ni) were used having yield strengths of approximately 170 and 250 ksi. The chemical compositions and some pertinent physical properties of these steels are listed in Table 1.

Notched specimens were machined from plate to give the nominal geometry shown in Figure 1. A crack was induced at the base of the notch by fatigue in air and was such that the ratio of the total flaw depth (notch and fatigue crack) to the total specimen depth was 0.3 to 0.35. The specimens were stressed in bending in a fixture shown schematically in Figure 2.

The medium used for the stress corrosion tests was a 3 percent sodium chloride solution in distilled water and was contained in a polyethylene cell having provision for a platinum gauze counter electrode and a saturated calomel reference electrode. In this study all potential measurements are reported with respect to the saturated calomel reference electrode (SCE). In some experiments the solution pH was varied over the range 2 to 14 by the addition of either hydrochloric acid or sodium hydroxide.

Potentials either cathodic or anodic with respect to the open circuit potential were controlled with P.E.M. Voltamatic controllers accurate to within ± 5 mv. A microswitch was used to interrupt a timer on failure of the specimen. Observations on crack propagation were made with a Leeds-Northrup linear displacement transducer mounted at the end of the cantilever beam. Deflection of the end of the beam could be measured to within 0.001 inch.

Specimens were dead-weight-loaded while immersed in the environment; as the fatigue crack opened, capillary action presumably forced the solution to be drawn into the crack and resulted in a complete interface between metal and solution.

The critical stress-intensity factor required for failure in air, under plane strain conditions, was calculated from the following equation developed by Beuchner and later modified by Paris and Sih[2] and Irwin.[3]

$$K_{IC} = \frac{6M}{\sqrt{BB_N}\ (W-a)^{3/2}} \cdot f \frac{a}{W}$$

where $K_{IC}$ = critical stress intensity for plane-strain fracture

$M$ = bending moment

$B$ = specimen width

$B_N$ = net width for face-notch specimen

$W$ = specimen depth

$a$ = crack length (notch and fatigue crack)

| $f \dfrac{a}{W}$ = | 0.39 for $\underline{a}$ = | 0.04 |
|---|---|---|
| | 0.49 | 0.10 |
| | 0.60 | 0.20 |
| | 0.66 | 0.30 |
| | 0.69 | 0.40 |
| | 0.72 | 0.50 |
| | 0.73 | 0.60 (and larger) |

For specimens loaded to a stress intensity $K_i$, in the environment, (such that $K_i$ is less than $K_{IC}$), the occurrence of stress corrosion results in growth of the fatigue crack until the flaw depth reaches a stage where $K_i = K_{IC}$. Failure then occurs by sudden fracturing of the remaining cross section. The stress corrosion evaluation of materials tested in this manner is often based on the time required for failure in the environment for given initial values of $K_i/K_{IC}$. In the present work, however, the applied stress is calculated in terms of the nominal net section stress, $\sigma_N$, expressed as a percentage of the yield strength. The nominal net section stress may be calculated from the following equation:[4]

$$\sigma_N = \frac{6M}{B_N\ (W-a)^2}$$

where $M$, $B_N$, $W$ and $a$ are as listed above. As this paper is more concerned with the effect of environmental rather than materials parameters as stress corrosion, it was considered more suitable to express stress in terms of $\sigma$ rather than K values.

For hydrogen embrittlement susceptibility testing, the specimens had the same nominal geometry as those used for the stress corrosion studies (Figure 1).

## Results and Discussion

### 12Ni Maraging Steel

The stress corrosion characteristics of the 12Ni maraging steel was evaluated in two heat treatment conditions (No. 1 and No. 2), which are listed in Table 1. It should be emphasized that heat treatment No. 2 represents an intentionally overaged condition. The effect of these heat treatments on the time to failure at different applied stresses is shown in Figure 3. For the times shown on the curve, the plots of applied stress versus log time are linear functions. For very long times, this relationship does not hold and the curves tend to flatten out along the time axis and approach a limiting value of applied stress below which cracking will not occur in any reasonable length of testing period.

This limiting value of stress intensity or "stress corrosion limit" has been ascribed the designation $K_{ISCC}$ or $\sigma_{NSCC}$ depending on how the applied stress is calculated. The value of $\sigma_{NSCC}$ is not an absolute, however, as it will tend to lower with time. Thus although $\sigma_{NSCC}$ values may be used in ranking steels as to their resistance to stress corrosion, there is as yet no foundation for their use in the actual design of structures.

Figure 3 shows that the resistance to stress corrosion cracking of the steel given heat treatment No. 1 is considerably greater than that of the steel given heat treatment No. 2. The fracture toughness ($K_{IC}$) values of the two steels are 105 and 106 ksi $\sqrt{\text{inch}}$ for heat treatments No. 1 and 2, respectively; this difference is insignificant and would not account for such major differences in stress corrosion behavior. It has been reported[4] that within a given alloy-steel system (for example 12Ni or 18Ni maraging steels), the stress corrosion susceptibility is a function of $K_{IC}$, with resistance to stress corrosion

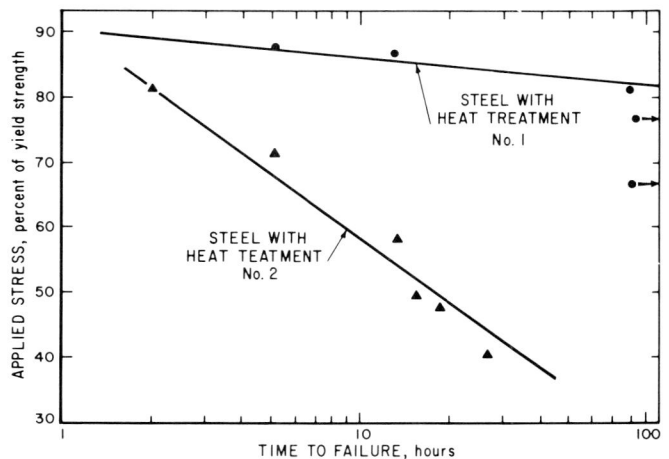

FIGURE 3 – Stress corrosion behavior of 12Ni-5Cr-3Mo steel in 3% NaCl solution.

increasing with increase in toughness. This effect was not noted with the two differently heat treated 12Ni maraging steels evaluated in the present study. According to the above-mentioned criterion, the susceptibility to stress corrosion of the two steels should have been similar as both had almost the same $K_{IC}$ value. It is thought that the large difference in metallurgical structure, caused by the different heat treatments, controlled the stress corrosion behavior and masked any relationship between stress corrosion and notch toughness.

Times to failure as a function of applied potential for both steels are shown in Figure 4. The measured "bulk" open-circuit potential in both cases was about -520 millivolts. The fact that hydrogen gas could be seen coming from the crack opening during long-term tests was indicative of acid conditions within the crack. It should be noted that although the apparent applied potential to the bulk specimens may be accurately controlled, the potential at the base of the crack is probably quite different because of changes in the environment at this location. Because of the crack geometry, corrosion products are partially prevented from diffusion out into the bulk solution and thus with time the environment within the crack may become strongly acidic (owing to hydrolysis of ferrous ions).

The use of applied anodic or cathodic currents to a metal or alloy under stress in order to distinguish between active path stress corrosion and hydrogen embrittlement as possible failure mechanisms in a particular environment has been described by Brown[5] and by Bhatt and Phelps.[6] These authors suggest that where the application of small cathodic currents, for example, increases the time to failure, the operating reaction at open circuit is stifled and therefore the cracking mechanism occurring in the absence of applied currents is active path stress corrosion. A converse argument holds true for increases in time to failure under the application of small anodic currents. In this event, the cracking mechanism would be classified as hydrogen embrittlement.

More meaningful information concerning the failure mechanism may be gathered, however, by controlling the specimen potential rather than by the use of impressed currents. Although it is the passage of current which gives rise to the potential, it is the electrode potential which controls an electrochemical reaction. Thus, the application of a constant current may give rise to a continually varying potential due to changes in the concentration of the environment or the possible precipitation of solid corrosion products; in the case of cathodic currents, the masking effect of hydrogen gas bubbles may also result in erratic potential-time behavior. As active dissolution and hydrogen evolution are potential dependent, it is not inconceivable to visualize a situation where erratic potential-time behavior might result in the reaction at the crack tip alternating between anodic dissolution and hydrogen ion discharge. It should be recognized, however, that for prenotched specimens, the as-measured bulk potential may be quite different from that at the base of the crack due to changes in environment within the crack and IR drop through the

length of the crack. In spite of this, applied potential versus time-to-failure curves for a steel at a constant stress level may nevertheless provide information concerning the failure mechanism under natural corrosion conditions. In a more practical sense, these curves may also be used to predict whether cathodic protection may be applied to a steel in a given environment without causing failure by hydrogen embrittlement. Thus, it is possible that with time a transition may occur in this type of test, whereby environmental conditions may change so as to be more conducive to hydrogen embrittlement than "active path" stress corrosion.

To study the effect of hydroxyl ion, which is known to inhibit corrosion in the presence of chlorides, a series of tests were carried out with solutions of varying pH. Figure 5 shows the time to failure for the 12Ni maraging steel at a constant stress level as a function of pH in the range pH 2 to 14. The minimum in time to failure at pH 10 to 12 has also been observed by others for 18Ni maraging steel.[7] This phenomenon may be explained in terms of sodium hydroxide acting as a "dangerous" inhibitor. Many inhibitors act in this manner; that is, the addition of less inhibitor than that required to give complete inhibition results in an increase in the intensity of corrosion. Only part of the metal surface is covered and this results in the small anodic areas having a high corrosion rate. Furthermore, the passivated portion of the metal surface acts as an efficient cathode that may control the total reaction rate and result in a stimulated anodic reaction.

As the pH approached 14, sufficient hydroxyl was present for complete passivation of the metal surface and resulted in considerable reduction in corrosion rate. Thus the stress corrosion susceptibility was also reduced. At pH 2, hydrogen was spontaneously evolved from the steel surface and the short times to failure may probably be attributed to both increased general corrosion together with some effect of hydrogen embrittlement.

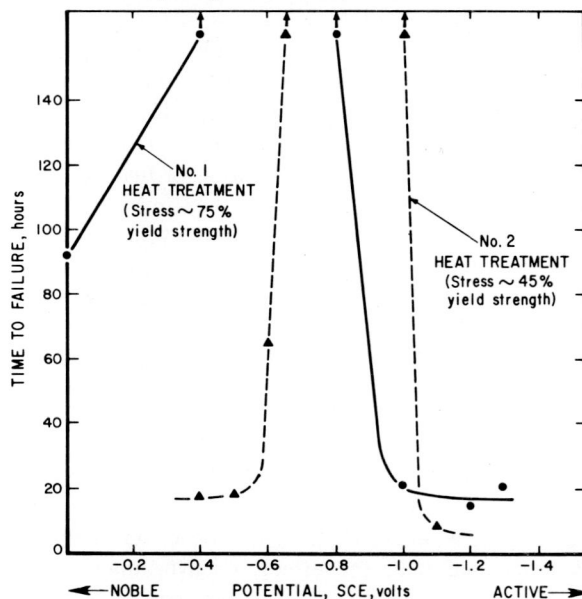

FIGURE 4 — Effect of applied potential on time to failure of 12Ni-5Cr-3Mo steel in 3% NaCl solution (applied stress as shown).

414

In a manner analogous to the determination of $\sigma_{NSCC}$, experiments were conducted to determine if there existed a lower stress limit below which failure by hydrogen embrittlement would not occur. Figure 6 shows applied stress versus time to failure for the 12Ni maraging steel at two charging potentials. At both potentials there was a very distinct lower stress limit below which no failure occurred in a 300-hour period. It was of interest to observe that the more active control potential (-1.5 volts), though discharging more hydrogen ions on the metal surface, was less severe in inducing hydrogen embrittlement failure than the -1.2 volts control potential. This effect may possibly be qualitatively explained from the increased hydrogen coverage on the metal surface at the more active potential resulting in an increased tendency for combination of hydrogen atoms to the molecular state. The rate of entry of

hydrogen atoms into the steel is also a function of the surface coverage; however, as hydrogen surface diffusion rates on metals are much greater than bulk diffusion rates, the increased coverage at the more active potential would be expected to have a greater effect on promoting the hydrogen combination reaction than hydrogen entry. Although this is a complex kinetics problem, it is not inconceivable that the hydrogen entry rate may be decreased at the expense of the hydrogen atom combination reaction.

### 18Ni Maraging Steel

Figure 7 shows the applied stress versus time to failure for the 18Ni maraging steel in 3 percent sodium chloride at -1.2 V. A well-defined critical stress limit exists at an applied stress of 25 percent of yield strength below which failure did not occur during the test period.

Crack propagation measurements were conducted on the 18Ni maraging steel, using a linear displacement transducer mounted at the end of the cantilever beam. Because of the very high yield strength of this steel and low applied stresses, deflection measurements made at the end of the beam are qualitatively representative of crack propagation. For low yield strength steels, on the other hand, deflection measurements of the beam made in this manner would probably represent both local yielding and propagation at the crack tip.

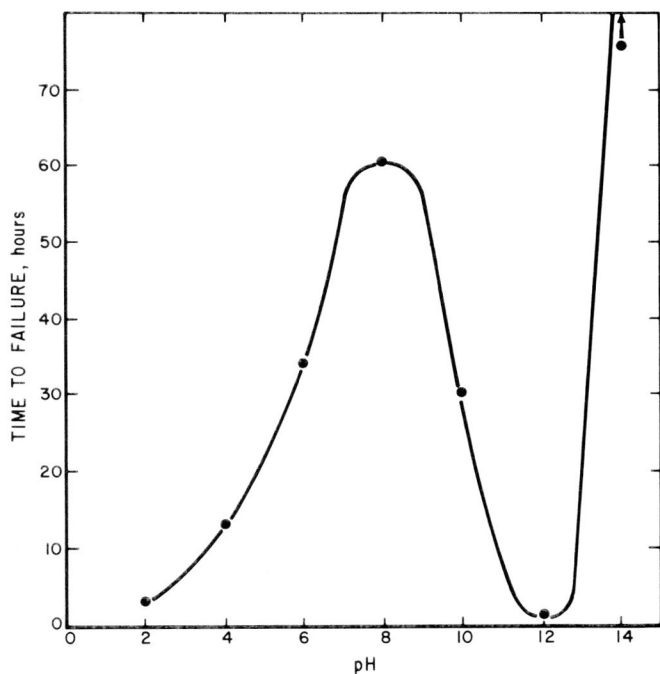

FIGURE 5 – Effect of pH on time to failure of 12Ni-5Cr-3Mo steel in 3% NaCl at applied stress of 80 percent of yield strength.

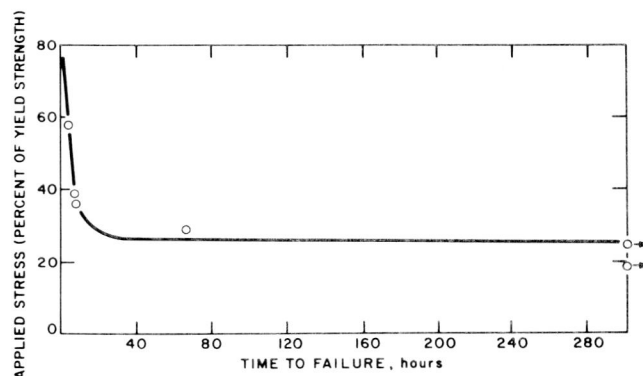

FIGURE 7 – Hydrogen susceptibility of 18Ni (250) steel in 3% NaCl at -1.2 V SCE.

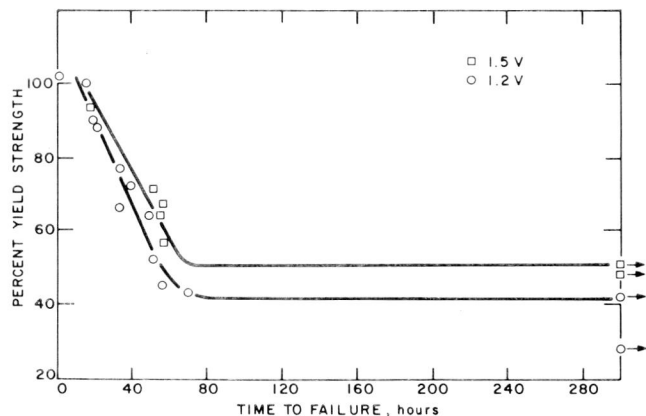

FIGURE 6 – Effect of applied potentials on resistance to hydrogen-stress cracking of 12Ni-5Cr-3Mo steel in 3% NaCl solution.

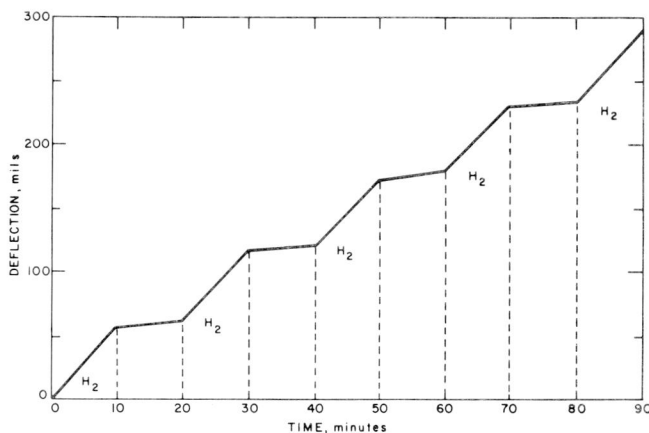

FIGURE 8 – Effect of hydrogen charging (at -1.2 volt) on crack propagation in 18Ni steel. Applied stress = 40% of yield stress.

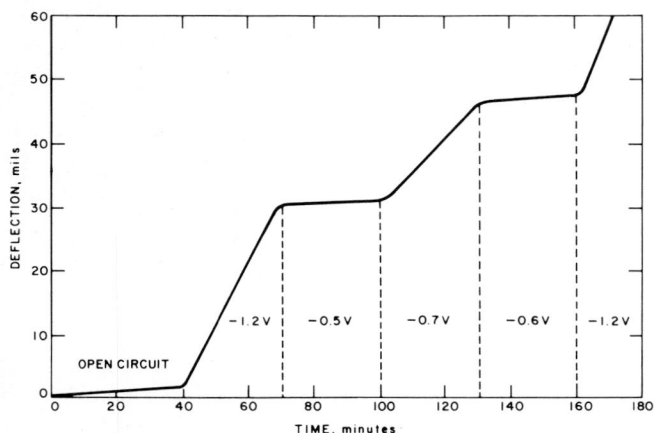

FIGURE 9 — Effect of applied potential on crack propagation rate for 18Ni maraging steel in 3% NaCl solution. Applied stress = 50% of yield stress.

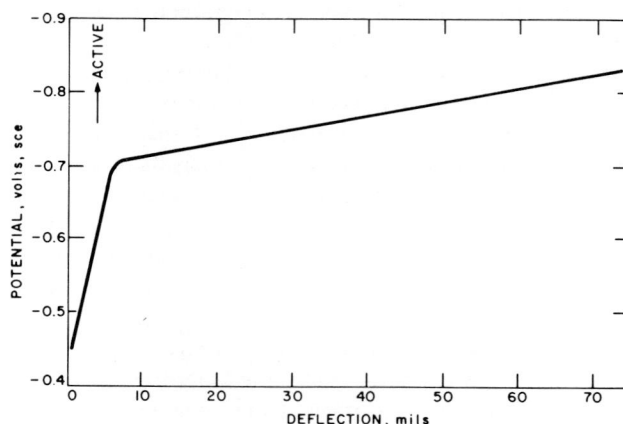

FIGURE 10 — Continuous crack propagation versus potential for 18Ni maraging steel in 3% NaCl solution. Applied stress = 50% of yield stress. Scan rate = 0.5 volt/hour.

The effect of intermittent applications of an applied potential of -1.2 V to the steel on crack propagation rate is shown in Figure 8. Other than the initially applied stress, no mechanical stimulus was used to induce crack propagation. Furthermore, the fact that no induction period was found for propagation after the application of the active potential might indicate a surface mechanism for crack growth. In such a mechanism, hydrogen adsorbed at the apex of the crack would reduce the surface energy of metal atoms according to the mechanism proposed by Petch and Stables.[8] Uhlig[9] has used the expression "stress sorption cracking" to characterize mechanisms of crack propagation involving reduction of surface energy due to adsorption.

The equilibrium discharge potential for hydrogen ions in this sodium chloride solution (pH 6.3) may be calculated to be approximately -0.62 V. Crack propagation rates were therefore examined at controlled potentials between open circuit (-0.45 V) and -1.2 V. These data are shown in Figure 9. Slight crack propagation was observed at the open circuit potential, possibly due to "active path" stress corrosion. The rate of crack propagation was the same at open circuit, -0.5 V and -0.6 V. At -0.7 V, however, the rate of crack propagation increased considerably and without any induction period. At -1.2 V, the crack propagation rate was even higher. It would therefore appear that the susceptibility of this steel to hydrogen embrittlement was manifested at -0.7 V, but not at -0.6 V. This is in agreement with the calculated potential value for hydrogen discharge, and this behavior is consistent with a hydrogen mechanism for crack propagation.

A continuous plot of applied potential versus crack propagation is shown in Figure 10. This was achieved by programming the applied potential at a scan rate of 0.1 volt per hour and plotting potential versus deflection using an X-Y recorder. The rate of crack propagation increases quite suddenly in the region of -0.7 V applied potential. This is in agreement with the data described in Figure 9. The difference of some 80 millivolts between the potential at which the propagation rate increased and the theoretical potential for discharge of hydrogen ions from the test

solution, may correspond to that energy required to activate hydrogen atoms to an energy level at which they may enter the steel. However inhomogeneities in the metal surface having a high over-voltage for hydrogen ion discharge, may also contribute to the above-mentioned potential difference.

The hydrolysis of anodic reaction products, particularly ferrous ions results in an increase in acidity within the crack. Furthermore, the crack geometry considerably reduces the outward diffusion of the resulting acidic environment. This change in pH within the crack may result in the spontaneous discharge of hydrogen ions being the major cathodic reaction in this region. A transition from oxygen to hydrogen reduction will normally result in decreased polarization at local cathodic sites within the crack which in turn increases the rate of anodic dissolution at the crack tip. This process may be autocatalytic resulting in increasing acidity, more rapid rates of hydrogen evolution and a possible change from cathodic to mixed potential control of the galvanic cell within the crack. Any contribution to the overall cathodic process resulting from oxygen reduction at the surface of the metal in the bulk electrolyte should be sufficiently minor that the anodic reaction at the crack tip should be essentially controlled by the rate of the hydrogen ion reduction reaction within the crack. Furthermore, as a result of the low hydrogen overpotential required to induce rapid crack propagation in the 18Ni maraging steel, it is believed that the acid conditions produced within the crack during natural corrosion will spontaneously cause the discharge of sufficient hydrogen ions to produce crack propagation by a hydrogen embrittlement mechanism. For the 18Ni maraging steel, the overall environmental and electrochemical changes leading to stress induced failure in a neutral corrosive environment may thus be summarized as follows:

1. Crack initiation occurs due to some localized corrosion process or film breakdown.

2. Crack growth occurs by an active path mechanism due to local stress concentration and anodic dissolution at the crack tip. Reduction of oxygen is the major cathodic reaction at this stage and the corrosion potential is more

noble than the equilibrium discharge potential for hydrogen ions.

3. Ferrous ions produced by the anodic dissolution process hydrolyze, resulting in increased acidity within the growing crack; crack geometry precludes the outward diffusion of these anodic reaction products. The equilibrium potential for hydrogen ion discharge shifts in the noble direction, according to the Nernst Equation, until this potential becomes more noble than the corrosion potential.

4. Spontaneous discharge of hydrogen ions occurs as the main cathodic reaction within the crack; hydrogen adsorption takes place at the crack tip and accelerated crack propagation occurs due to a stress-sorption mechanism.

The measurement of crack propagation rate as a function of potential might thus be used as a means of categorizing failure by hydrogen embrittlement and active path mechanisms for various steels under conditions of natural corrosion.

## Summary

The cantilever beam stress corrosion test method lends itself to a study of the effect of environmental factors on failure of high strength steels. The experimental data obtained by using this technique, however, can only be analyzed on a qualitative basis as environmental conditions at the base of the notch may be considerably different from those in the bulk solution. Furthermore, the change in environment at the base of the notch will normally provide an increased stimulus for both anodic dissolution and hydrogen ion discharge in this area; this condition, however, does simulate conditions in a natural stress corrosion crack and, as such, the cantilever-beam testing procedure may be a valid method for the evaluation of materials for service.

The effect of bulk solution pH on time to failure of the 12Ni maraging steel was complicated. At pH 2, failure was rapidly induced, probably due to the combination of high corrosion rate and hydrogen embrittlement. At pH 14, passivation was observed and specimens remained uncorroded and showed considerable resistance to stress corrosion; at pH 12, however, the presence of insufficient hydroxyl as an inhibitor resulted in stimulated corrosion and very short times to failure.

Crack propagation studies, conducted on 18Ni maraging steel during hydrogen charging, indicated that advancement of the crack tip occurred by a stress-sorption mechanism. From controlled potential studies, it was found that rapid crack propagation occurred only at potentials more active than the thermodynamic equilibrium hydrogen discharge potential.

## References

1. B. F. Brown. *Materials Research and Standards,* **6,** 129 (1966).
2. P. Paris and G. Sih. Stress Analysis of Cracks. *Fracture Toughness Testing and Its Applications,* ASTM STP 381 (1965) April.
3. G. R. Irwin. Assumptions Basic to $K_I$ Calculations when G is Provided by a Compliance Calibration. Notes for February 10, 1965, meeting of ASTM Committee for Fracture Testing.
4. S. T. Rolfe, S. R. Novak, and J. H. Gross. Stress Corrosion Testing of Ultraservice Steels Using Fatigue-Cracked Specimens. Paper presented at ASTM Meeting, Atlantic City, June, 1966.
5. B. F. Brown. Cracking of Martensite, Type 410, Stainless Steel in Corrosive Environments. Report of NRL Progress, (1958) May.
6. H. J. Bhatt and E. H. Phelps. *Corrosion,* **17,** 430t (1961).
7. J. A. Green and E. G. Haney. Paper presented at the Sixty-Ninth Annual Meeting of the ASTM, Atlantic City, New Jersey, June 27 to July 1, 1966.
8. N. Petch and P. Stables. *Nature,* **169,** 842 (1952).
9. H. H. Uhlig. *Corrosion and Corrosion Control.* John Wiley and Sons, Inc., New York, London, 1963.

## Discussion

**R. N. Parkins,** University of Newcastle-upon-Tyme and **E. G. Haney,** Carnegie Mellon University:

We would like to mention some results that we obtained some time ago at Mellon Institute on the stress corrosion cracking of an 18% Ni maraging steel immersed in an acid chloride solution (pH 2.2) and which appear to confirm the general characteristics of the results shown in Figures 8 and 9 of the paper by Dr. Leckie. The experiment to which we refer was performed in a hard beam testing machine with the crossheads locked and crack propagation was detectable by load relaxation. The experiment was performed galvanostatically and switching of the current from +10 to -10 m.amps/sq.in. produced sharp changes in the rate of load relaxation, as is apparent from Figure 1. Our interpretation of these results was that with applied anodic currents, and indeed at the free corrosion potential without applied current, the crack propagation rates were indicative of an active path corrosion mechanism, but that with applied cathodic currents crack propagation was by hydrogen embrittlement. Such a deduction was based upon the observation that small cathodic currents delayed cracking but higher cathodic currents ($>2$ m.amps/sq.in.) dramatically reduced the cracking time, results indicative of a material susceptible to active path stress corrosion and also to hydrogen embrittlement. In all of this, we appear to agree with the interpretation of Dr. Leckie.

What is less clear to us, however, is the justification for the statement that, after an initial stress corrosion crack forms by active path corrosion, the mechanism changes to one in which '...accelerated crack propagation occurs due to a stress-sorption mechanism' involving hydrogen. We put two specific questions: (1) Are the results shown in Figure 4, that applied potentials in the range -0.6 to -1.0 V markedly increase failure times, consistent with the idea of accelerated crack propagation due to hydrogen embrittle-

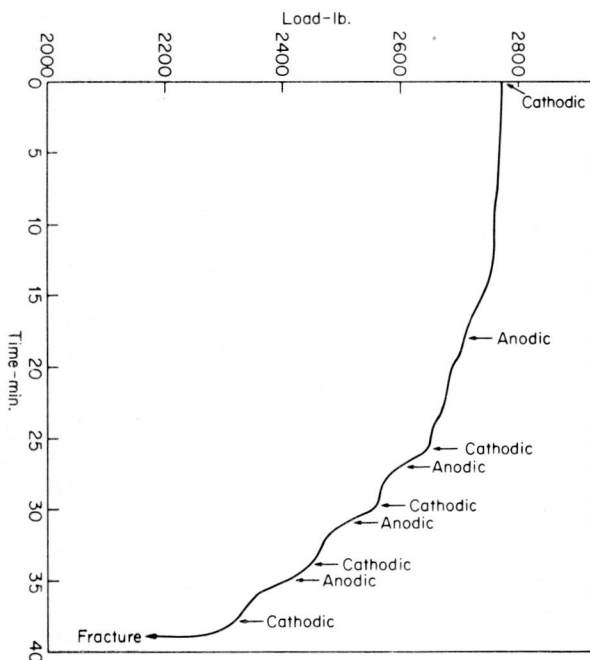

FIGURE 1 — Load vs time curve for 18% Ni maraging steel immersed in acid (pH 2.2) chloride solution and subjected to alternate galvanostatic currents of +10 and -10 in A/in².

ment at the free corrosion potential? (2) How is the result shown in Figure 10, indicating susceptibility to hydrogen embrittlement at -0.7 V, consistent with the pH of the solution within the crack being very appreciably less than 6.3?

**H. Leckie:**

I would like to thank Drs. Parkins and Haney for their valuable comments and questions. Before answering their two specific questions I would, however, like to make one point clear.

Any characterization of failure mechanisms based on measurements of crack propagation rate with alternating applied anodic and cathodic currents is inherently dangerous. We have found that crack propagation rates observed during the passage of cathodic currents are markedly affected by any prior dissolution at the crack tip resulting from the passage of anodic currents. The action of anodic currents at the crack tip will serve to cause crack blunting by dissolution and thus change the inherent state of applied stress. For this reason it is recommended that in all studies where crack propagation rates are measured as a function of applied potential those experiments requiring measurements under cathodic charging conditions be conducted first. In this way, changes in applied stress due to corrosion by anodic dissolution may be kept to a minimum.

To answer the specific questions asked by Drs. Parkins and Haney:

1. The incidence of failure due to hydrogen embrittlement at the free corrosion potential in "neutral" solutions is time-dependent. Under natural corrosion conditions, sufficient dissolution of iron must take place such that the

subsequent hydrolysis of ferrous ions within the crack produces acid conditions thermodynamically conducive to spontaneous hydrogen ion reduction. From the data shown in Figure 4, it must be concluded that insufficient time had elapsed to permit the development of an acid environment within the crack. Furthermore, the sensitivity of the lower strength 12Ni maraging steel to hydrogen induced failure is considerably less than that of 18Ni (250) maraging steel, where rapid crack propagation was observed (Figure 10) at potentials very close to the equilibrium discharge potential for hydrogen ions.

2. The experiment leading to the data shown in Figure 10, involved the continuous scanning of the specimen potential from the open circuit potential at a rate of 0.5 volt per hour in the active direction. Thus only a minimal amount of corrosion was allowed to take place and the environment within the crack remained essentially the same as that of the bulk solution.

**J. A. S. Green, RIAS:**

It is interesting to see that, using 12Ni maraging steel, you have produced results similar to those of myself and Haney[1] for the stress corrosion of 18Ni maraging steel in aqueous chloride environments; results which showed a minimum in the curve of time to failure as a function of pH in the range 10-12 pH.

At these values of pH our polarization studies suggested that stress corrosion was due to an anodic dissolution process. From your results you suggest a transition from an anodic dissolution mechanism to a hydrogen embrittlement mechanism with time or with increasing crack propagation. As you know our experiments were carried out on foil specimens, about two thousandths of an inch thick and in this case one might expect to observe mostly an initiation process rather than a propagation process. Hence in our case we would expect to observe the anodic dissolution process and probably not the hydrogen embrittlement mechanism. Therefore there is probably no conflict between your results and those of myself and Haney.

1. J. A. S. Green and E. G. Haney. *Corrosion*, p. 5 (1967) January.

**H. P. Leckie:**

In the region of pH 12 where very short times-to-failure were observed, I would consider insufficient time to have passed to permit sufficient change in the environment for the spontaneous discharge of hydrogen ions. I would therefore hesitate to attribute the minimum in time-to-failure to any hydrogen embrittlement mechanism, but would rather attribute the observed rapid failures to a local high intensity of anodic dissolution due to incomplete passivation by hydroxyl ions.

**R. A. Oriani, U. S. Steel Corp.:**

Since you deduce crack propagation velocity from the measured rate of deflection of a beam, it is conceivable that there were in your experiments contributions to the observed deflection other than from the crack propagation. One such contribution might be that arising from production of internal voids due to hydrogen charging. Therefore it is relevant to ask whether or not you used other independent means of measuring the crack propagation in addition to the deflection method.

**H. P. Leckie:**

I have no hesitation in agreeing with Dr. Oriani that measurement of beam deflection shows only an approximate correlation with crack propagation velocity. Beam deflection serves only as a qualitative guide to crack growth and in the present study I was more concerned with the relative rates of crack propagation with and without hydrogen charging. The fact that the crack propagation process showed a high state of "reversibility" as evidenced by its sensitivity to the intermittent application of applied anodic potentials (see Figure 8), would indicate to me that any role played by internal voids on crack propagation rate would be at most very minor.

**R. P. Wei, Lehigh University:**

In reference to these discussions on the conditions at the crack tip, I think it is fair to say that if you are looking to fracture mechanics to tell you what is the state of affairs at the very tip of the crack, you will be disappointed. The fracture mechanics approach is a continuum approach and does not incorporate detailed structural features of the material. I don't think you should dump the responsibility on me to explain what is going on precisely at the crack tip. The point that we are trying to emphasize is that if the plastically deformed zone at the crack tip is small in comparison with the size of the crack and other planar dimensions of the specimen or structure, the behavior of the material in this region would be governed by the surrounding elastic material and thus be characterized by the crack tip stress intensity factor, $K_I$, (for opening mode) based on linear elasticity. Within this limitation, fracture mechanics provides a useful quantitative basis for treating problems in crack growth and fracture. The crack driving force is defined in terms of the crack tip stress intensity factor which is a function of the applied load, the size of the crack and the geometry of the body.

In view of these comments and your apparent familiarity with fracture mechanics, I wonder why you chose to present your data in terms of the nominal bending stress which really has very little physical significance.

**H. P. Leckie:**

In a conference of this type, concerned primarily with *mechanisms* of stress corrosion cracking and where absolute materials parameters are of no great significance, I preferred to express stress in terms of a parameter meaningful to the majority of the audience. However, as a point of information, let me state that for the specimen size used in the present study (1 in. x 1 in.), the applied nominal bending stress $\sigma_N$ is related to the stress intensity factor $K_I$ by the relationship $\sigma_N$ (ksi) $\cong 2 K_I$ ($\sqrt{}$ ksi).

# MONITORING CRACK GROWTH OF HYDROGEN EMBRITTLEMENT AND STRESS CORROSION CRACKING BY ACOUSTIC EMISSION

W. W. Gerberich
University of California

and

C. E. Hartbower
Aerojet-General Corporation

## Abstract

A detailed investigation was made of the slow crack growth process for D6aC high strength steel tested in the hydrogenated condition, in distilled water and in combination. The experimental technique involved a combination of stress wave monitoring to determine the number of and time intervals between crack steps; a crack opening displacement gauge to incrementally measure the crack growth rate; and electron fractography to interpret the morphological nature of the growth process.

It was found that crack growth occurred as discontinuous steps for all test conditions. Also, the fractographic evidence showed all test conditions to result in similar failure modes with both intergranular and cleavage areas prominent. From the stress wave analysis, it was determined that the crack growth process could be approximated by an average jump being related to the theoretical crack tip displacement, $2\nu_c$, by

$$\ell* \sim \frac{2\nu_c}{\pi\epsilon_f} \sim \frac{K^2}{2\,\sigma_{ys}\,E\,\pi\epsilon_f}$$

where $\epsilon_f$ is the fracture ductility, K is the stress intensity factor, $\sigma_{ys}$ is the tensile strength and E is the modulus of elasticity. The time intervals between these steps could be approximately related to hydrogen diffusion as the controlling mechanism.

Phenomenological analyses of the diffusion-controlling mechanisms for both hydrogen embrittlement and delayed failure in distilled water were made. These indicated that a difference in the boundary conditions for hydrogen diffusion could account for the observed differences in the time-dependent cracking. The experimental data exhibited a synergistic effect when the steel was both hydrogenated and subjected to the distilled water environment. The fact that superposition of the individual theoretical treatments also indicated a synergistic effect gives added significance to the hypothesis that hydrogen diffusion is the controlling mechanism in both types of embrittlement.

## Introduction

Historically, two schools of thought have evolved concerning stress corrosion cracking—one leaning toward electrochemical dissolution concepts and the other toward brittle-crack-step concepts. It is suggested that there is no categorical answer to this question since the mechanism appears to vary as a function of the material-environment combination. For example, there has been some question as to whether cracking in high strength steels exposed to an aqueous environment more closely resembles hydrogen embrittlement rather than stress corrosion cracking. Therefore, an integrated investigation of hydrogen embrittlement and distilled water induced cracking was performed on one high strength steel. A number of questions on both types of cracking were under consideration; e.g., in cathodically charged steels, where is the hydrogen located? Is hydrogen movement induced by a stress or concentration gradient?

How does the crack growth process occur? Is delayed failure in an aqueous environment mainly a stress corrosion mechanism or is it more similar to hydrogen embrittlement? What controls final separation of the specimen? Some of these questions were easily answered. Others can only be speculated about at this time. To obtain as many answers as possible, several experimental techniques were utilized which provided considerable detail about crack incubation and propagation.

First of all, an accelerometer technique was utilized to monitor the stress waves given off by discontinuous crack extension. Not only did this allow an estimate of the amount of crack growth in each discontinuous movement, but it also gave information about the time-dependent mechanism involved between crack steps. Secondly, a crack opening displacement gauge was used to determine the instantaneous crack length at a given time which enabled crack growth rates and stress intensity factors to be described during the test. Finally, electron fractography was utilized to assist in analyzing the details of the microfracture growth process.

The experimental approach was to evaluate slow crack growth phenomena in D6aC steel by (1) testing in the hydrogenated condition, (2) testing nonhydrogenated samples in aqueous environments, and (3) testing hydrogenated samples in aqueous environments. This approach was considered to yield considerable information as to whether one or more mechanism was operative and if crack growth mechanisms would be simply additive or reinforcing.

## Materials

D6aC steel which was known to be susceptible to delayed failure[1] was evaluated in two heat treatment conditions. This high strength, martensitic steel had the following chemistry (weight percent) for the 0.130-inch thick sheet used in this investigation: C, 0.48; Mn, 0.67; P, 0.004; S, 0.004; Si, 0.19; Ni, 0.56; Cr, 1.07; Mo, 0.99; and V, 0.10.

The heat treatments were chosen to give a high strength, high toughness material and a relatively low strength, low toughness material. High toughness was achieved by austenitizing at 950 C for 30 minutes and tempering at 600 C for two hours; low toughness was achieved by austenitizing at 850 C for 15 minutes and tempering at 200 C for two hours. These two heat treatment conditions will be subsequently identified as 950/600 and 850/200. Since a lower austenitizing temperature and short solution time (i.e., the 850/200 condition) did not dissolve all of the prime carbides, both low toughness and low strength resulted.

The mechanical properties of the two conditions are compared in Table 1. The $M_s$ temperatures were determined by a thermal arrest technique to be 305 C for the 950/600 condition and 410 C for the 850/200 condition. This reflects the lower amount of carbon in solid solution for the latter condition which resulted from undissolved prime carbides.

## Experimental Techniques and Procedures

### Stress Wave Instrumentation

If a crack moves in a discontinuous fashion, it gives off an elastic wave similar to that resulting from shock loading.

The stress wave is transient in nature and involves vibratory motion with random frequencies. For very small movements of the crack front, the amount of elastic energy released is small and, thus, the amplitude of the stress wave is small. The stress wave was detected by means of a piezoelectric transducer with a flat frequency response to 7000 cps, a mechanical resonance at approximately 30,000 cps, and a charge sensitivity of 50 pico-coulomb/g. The signal from the transducer was amplified with a low noise charge amplifier and recorded on an instrumentation tape recorder (IRIG track dimensions) with a frequency response of 20,000 cps at 7-1/2 in/sec tape speed. Data were analyzed by tape playback into either an oscilloscope or a recording oscillograph.

### Stress Intensity and Crack Growth Determinations

The basic test philosophy was to start with pre-existing flaws and analyze the crack growth process. For this purpose a 1/8-in by 3-in by 12-in single edge notch specimen was prefatigue cracked until the total notch-plus-fatigue crack was about 0.6 in long. The parameter used as a basis for comparing crack growth rates was the stress intensity factor since Brown[2] and Johnson[3] have shown this to be a valid approach for stress corrosion cracking and hydrogen embrittlement. For calculation of the stress intensity factor, a collocation solution by Gross, Brown, and Srawley[4] for single edge notch specimens was utilized. A series approximation is involved; viz.,

$$K = Y P (a)^{1/2}/BW \qquad (1)$$

where P is the applied load, a the notch-plus-crack depth, B the thickness, W the width, and Y a parametric factor given by

$$Y = 1.99 - 0.4124(a/W) + 18.70(a/W)^2 - \\ 38.49(a/W)^3 + 53.85(a/W)^4 \qquad (1a)$$

Since the specimens were held under sustained load, the only unknown was crack length. This was determined from crack-opening-displacement (COD) measurements, a technique which has been utilized elsewhere[4] for determining crack length. All that is necessary for COD measurements of crack length is a predetermined calibration curve of $\nu BE/P$ versus a/W where $\nu$ is the crack opening displacement and E is the modulus. The calibration was the same as that used in another investigation[5] and was such that crack lengths to the nearest 0.01 in could be evaluated and

TABLE 1.

| Material Condition | 0.2% Yield Strength (ksi) | Ultimate Strength (ksi) | Elongation 2-in (%) | Precracked Charpy Impact, W/A (in-lb/in$^2$) |
|---|---|---|---|---|
| 950/600 | 210 | 230 | 9.0 | 1040 |
| 850/200 | 134 | 190 | 5.1 | 120 |

421

## Hydrogenation

To obtain hydrogenated material for evaluation, a standard procedure was utilized.[6] This consisted of cathodically charging for 5 minutes at 10 ma/in² in a 4% by weight solution of $H_2SO_4$ with 5 drops/liter of poison. The poison was 2 grams of phosphorous dissolved in 40 ml of carbon disulfide. The evolution of hydrogen at room temperature was prevented by cadmium plating the test specimens within 5 minutes after hydrogenation. The plating bath was 4 oz/gal of CdO and 16 oz/gal of NaCN with one percent brightner by volume. The pH was adjusted to 13 by the addition of NaOH. A current density of about 70 ma/in² was utilized for the 30-minute plating period. Subsequent to the hydrogenation and plating, the specimens were baked at 150 C to distribute the hydrogen through the specimen. Baking times of 1/2 hr and 3 hr were utilized to obtain a variation in hydrogen content since a previous investigation[7] had shown these to represent a severe and medium degree of embrittlement.

## Test Procedure

Specimens were loaded at 150 lb/sec to a sustained load of approximately 10 kips for the 850/200 condition and 30 kips for the 950/600 condition. The specimens were held for four hours, after which the load either was increased to a new sustained load level or produced failure. Table 2 gives the number of specimens evaluated for each test condition.

From the displacement chart, crack lengths were determined at several time intervals throughout the test. Using these crack lengths, stress intensity factors were calculated at the beginning, at several intermittent stages of slow crack growth, and at failure. Thus, for specific time intervals, the established crack lengths allowed average crack growth rates to be calculated. These were subsequently compared at specific stress intensity levels for the various environmental and hydrogenated conditions. For similar time intervals, tape recorded data of the stress waves associated with the crack growth were analyzed as to the number of stress waves per unit time. Thus, a three-fold comparison of stress intensity factor, crack growth rate and stress waves per second was accomplished with a single specimen in a specific environmental condition. Further comparison was made by electron fractographs at about 10,000X utilizing two-stage, plastic-carbon replicas shadowed with chromium.

## Results and Discussion

Since a relatively new technique has been utilized in this investigation, it is first necessary to establish the relevance of stress wave emission as a measure of stress corrosion and hydrogen induced slow crack growth. Following this, observations on crack initiation, crack propagation and crack instability will be made.

FIGURE 1 — SEN tension specimen cup and crack-opening-displacement gauge.

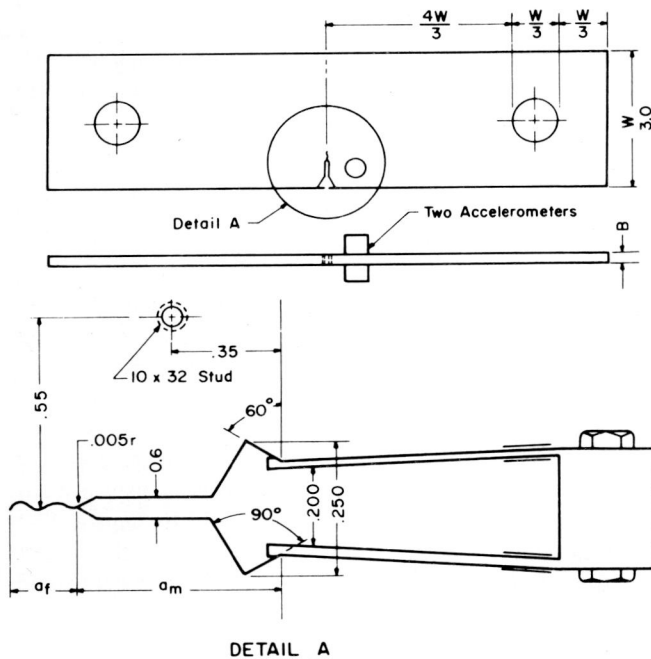

DETAIL A

FIGURE 2 — Single-edge-notch tensile specimen and crack opening displacement gauge.

incremental crack growths on the order of 0.003 in could be detected. The COD gauge intact with a single edge notch specimen is shown in Figure 1. The specimen and gauge details are presented in Figure 2.

TABLE 2.

| Environment | 950/600 Condition | | | 850/200 Condition | | |
| | | Hydrogenated | | | Hydrogenated | |
| | As-Rec. | 1/2-Hr Bake | 3-Hr Bake | As-Rec. | 1/2-Hr Bake | 3-Hr Bake |
|---|---|---|---|---|---|---|
| Air | (2) | (1) | (1) | (3) | (1) | (1) |
| I.W.[1] | (1) | (1) | (1) | (1) | — | (1) |
| D.W.[2] | (2) | (1) | (1) | (1) | — | (1) |

[1] Water inhibited by the addition of sodium dichromate to a neutral pH.
[2] Distilled water with a pH of 5.7.

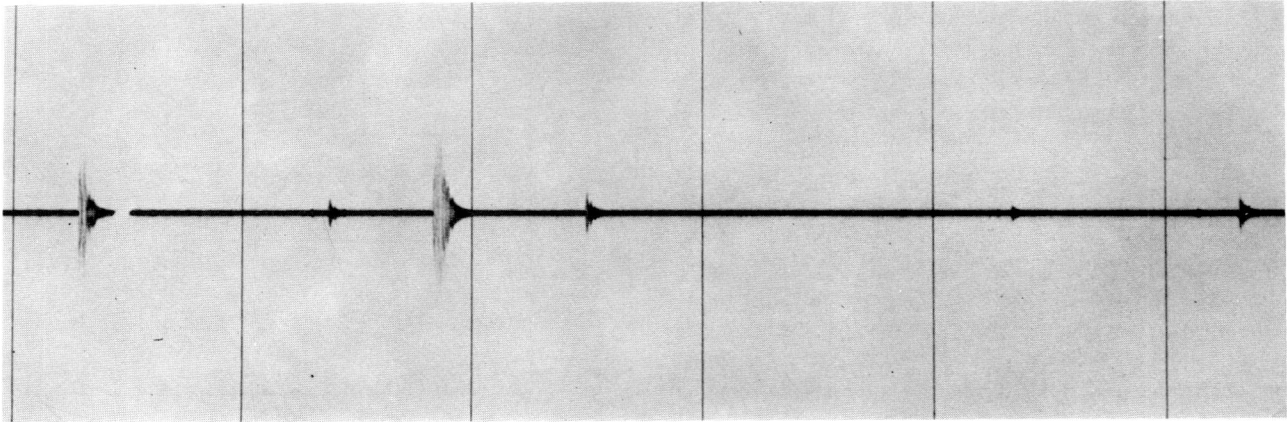

FIGURE 3 — Burst of stress waves associated with stress corrosion cracking of D6aC steel (950/600) in distilled water.

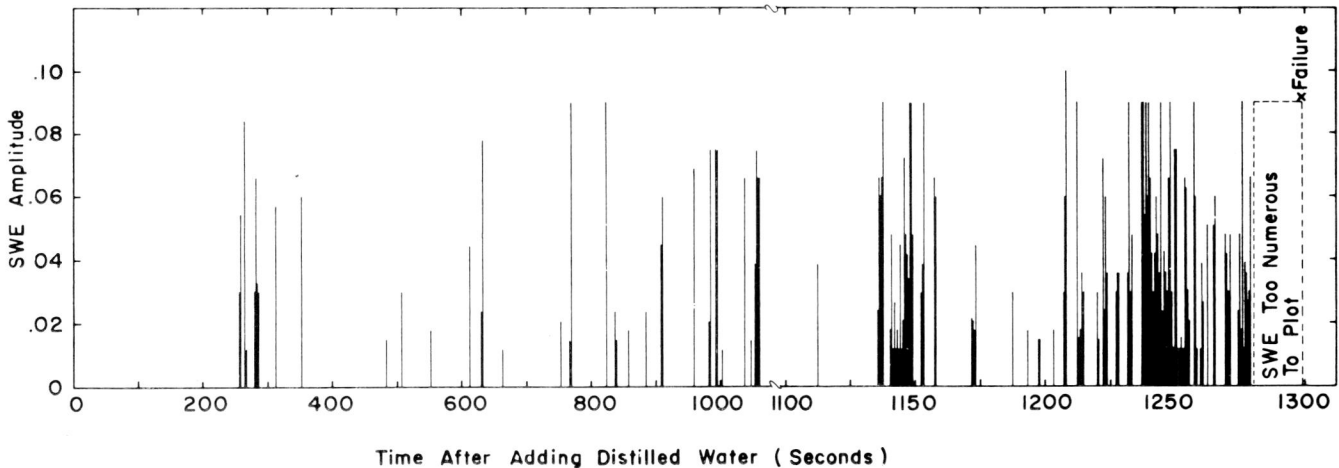

FIGURE 4 — Distribution and amplitude of stress waves at sustained load in D6aC steel specimen X-11 (austenitized at 900 C, tempered at 600 C, and tested in distilled water).

*Stress Wave Emission as a Measure of*
*Stress Corrosion Cracking*

It was important to establish that monitoring of stress waves did indeed reflect slow crack growth in this high strength steel. Swann and Embury[8] have shown that stress corrosion cracking by dissolution in a copper alloy resulted in no significant increase in acoustic emission when compared to the nonenvironmental test. On the other hand, Elsea[6] observed through acoustic emission studies that crack propagation in hydrogen embrittled steels was a discontinuous process. Thus, if stress wave emission (SWE) is going to give information concerning stress corrosion cracking, the mechanism must at least partially involve a brittle-crack-step process rather than purely a dissolution mechanism.

A burst of stress wave emission (SWE) associated with stress corrosion cracking in distilled water for the 950/600 condition is shown in Figure 3. The crack growth rate at this point was approximately 100 $\mu$-in/sec. Note the transient nature of the waves and the clearly defined time interval between occurrences. Actually, this is not typical

423

SWE in that it constitutes a burst with relatively short intervals between stress waves as compared to the average time interval for this crack growth rate. Further indication of the discontinuous nature of slow crack growth is shown in Figure 4. Here, a schematic showing SWE amplitude and time of occurrence is given for the 950/600 condition tested in distilled water. It is seen that the time between SWE becomes shorter as failure is approached. If stress corrosion in this high strength steel is a diffusion controlled mechanism, then the time between stress waves can be taken as the secondary incubation time, $\Delta t_s$. Thus, $\Delta t_s$ decreases as failure is approached. Another way of interpreting the data is that the number of SWE occurring per unit time increases as failure is approached. Both $\Delta t_s$ and number of SWE per second ($1/\Delta t_s$) will be utilized in discussing the results.

In the tests subjected to aqueous environments, it was observed from the COD data that the crack growth rate (da/dt) also increased as failure was approached. Thus, both SWE/second and da/dt increased as failure was approached. As the crack grew during the time at sustained load, the stress intensity factor also increased as failure was approached. It follows that both SWE/second and da/dt increased with increasing stress intensity. At several stages of the slow crack growth process, SWE/second and da/dt were determined. These trends are illustrated for the 950/600 condition in Figure 5. It is significant that this curve contains all data for the 950/600 condition including both baking times for the hydrogenated samples and tests

in distilled water, inhibited water and air. Although there may be a slight separation in the data for the various test conditions, it is not sufficient to warrant more than one curve. It would appear that the nature of the slow crack

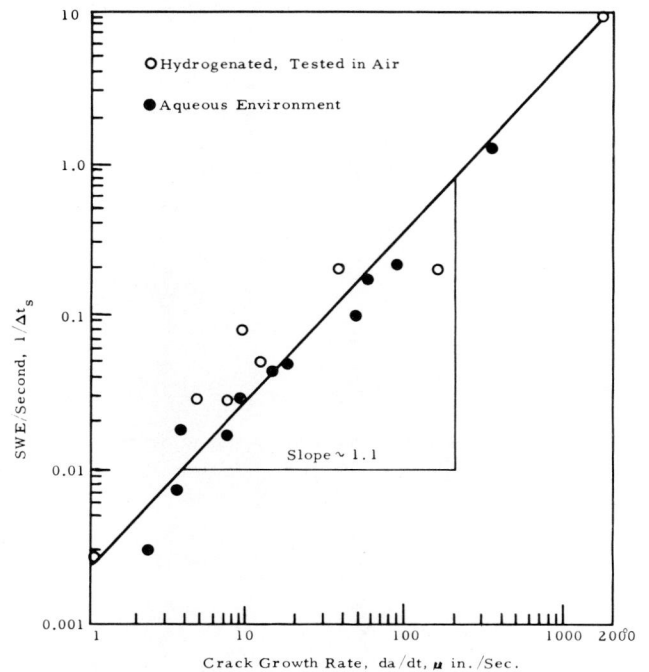

FIGURE 5 — Slow crack growth—stress wave relationship for 950/600 condition of D6aC steel.

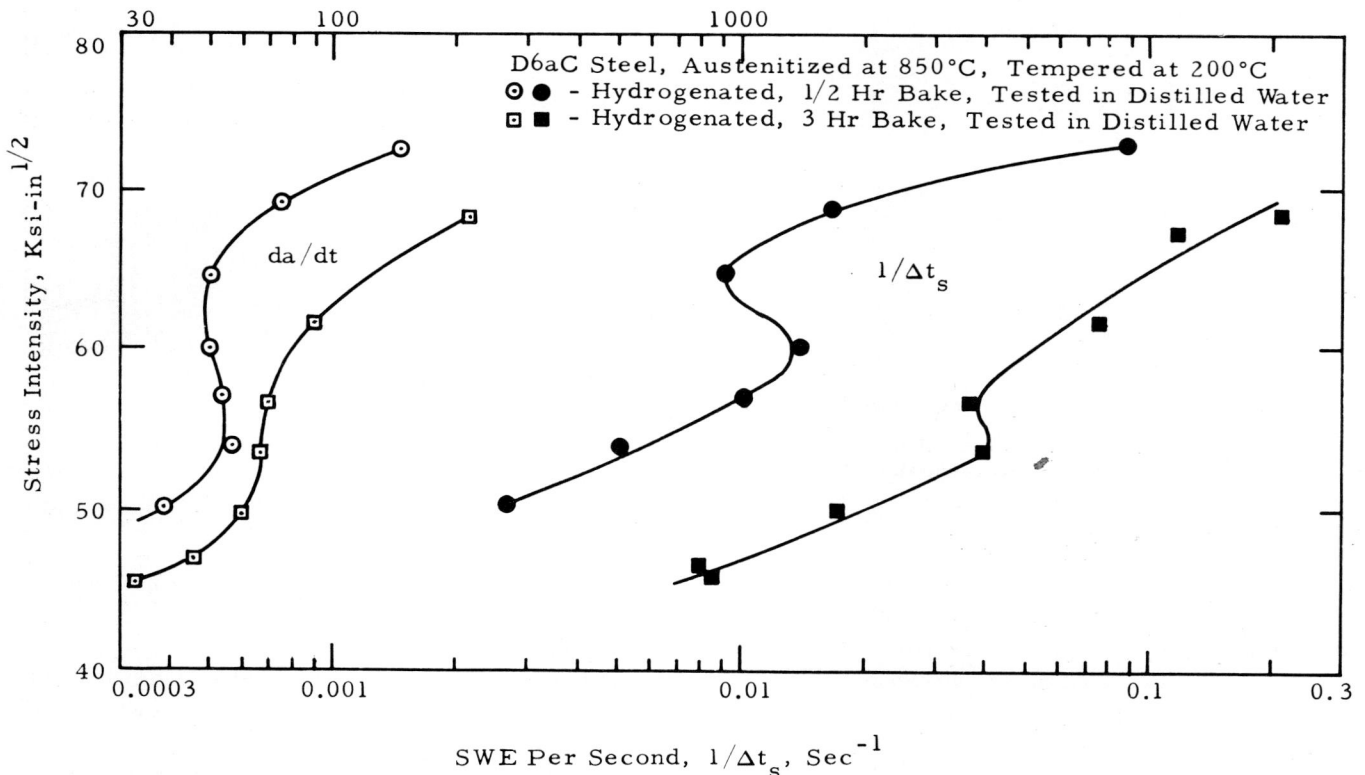

FIGURE 6 — Comparison of crack growth rate and stress wave emission data as a function of stress intensity level for D6aC steel (850/200).

growth process is not significantly different from hydrogen embrittlement versus stress corrosion in distilled water. If hydrogen embrittlement had involved brittle crack steps and stress corrosion cracking was largely by dissolution, one would expect a significant separation in the data.

Further indication that the SWE data are a sensitive indicator of the slow crack growth process is shown in Figure 6. The effect of increasing stress intensity factor on the crack growth rate and the SWE per second $(1/\Delta t_s)$ is shown for the 850/200 condition. The crack growth rate first increased, reached a steady-state level, then increased again with approaching failure. A similar behavior is exhibited by $1/\Delta t_s$ with increasing stress intensity. It is also shown that 3-hr baking gave larger values of da/dt than 1/2-hr baking at equivalent stress intensity levels. Similarly, the $1/\Delta t_s$ values for the 3-hr bake were greater than those for the 1/2-hr bake.

Thus, for both hydrogen embrittlement and stress corrosion cracking in aqueous environments, the SWE data can be utilized in describing the slow crack growth process in the two D6aC steel conditions investigated.

In the following sections, most of the analysis is based on data from the 850/200 condition. This is done because (1) the large amount of information obtained precludes dealing with both conditions within the space limitations of this paper, and (2) the 850/200 condition exhibited the classic quasi-brittle delayed failure, whereas the 950/600 condition failed in a ductile shear mode. Details on both conditions may be found elsewhere.[9]

*Observations on Crack Initiation*

It might be argued that with fatigue precracking, there is little point in belaboring crack initiation. However, there is no *a priori* reason why environmental or hydrogen induced cracking should immediately begin just because of the presence of a precrack. For stress corrosion cracking, one might consider that some time is required for corrosion products and/or adsorbed gases to form. Or, for hydrogen embrittlement, there might be a primary incubation time for a critical hydrogen level to develop near the crack tip, as suggested by Troiano.[10]

First, consider the SWE observations on rising load. At the loading rate of 100 lb/sec, it took about 100 seconds to arrive at the sustained load near 10 kips. In this time, the rising-load observations in Table 3 were made for the 850/200 condition. It is seen that, whether tested in air or distilled water, the nonhydrogenated samples behaved

**TABLE 3.**

| Condition | Environment | Number of Stress Waves |
|---|---|---|
| No Hydrogenation | Air | 93 |
| Hydrog. 1/2-hr bake | Air | 0 |
| Hydrog. 3-hr bake | Air | 4 |
| No Hydrogenation | Distilled Water | >50 |
| Hydrog. 1/2-hr bake | Distilled Water | 1 |
| Hydrog. 3-hr bake | Distilled Water | 5 |

similarly on rising load in that there were numerous stress waves. The hydrogenated samples indicated practically no crack movement on rising load whether tested in air or water. These observations suggest that hydrogenation delays the initial cracking on rising load.

As to why hydrogenation would initially inhibit crack initiation can only be conjecture at this time. Since dislocation movement is involved in the crack growth process, if dislocation pinning is sufficient, the stress required for crack initiation could be much greater. Hydrogen in interstitial solid solution could provide this pinning. The critical strain rate at which dislocations could leave their atmospheres is given by:[11]

$$\dot{\epsilon}_c \sim 4D\rho b/\ell \qquad (2)$$

where $\ell$ is the radius of the atmosphere, $\rho$ is the dislocation density, b is the Burger's vector, and D is the diffusivity. If it is assumed that the radius of the hydrogen atmosphere is about 4b,[12] the critical strain rate would be

$$\dot{\epsilon}_c \sim D\rho \qquad (3)$$

At a minimum, the dislocation density in this steel would be $10^{10}/cm^2$. Using this and a value of $2 \times 10^{-7}$ $cm^2/sec$ for the diffusivity of hydrogen at room temperature would necessitate a strain rate of $2 \times 10^3$ $sec^{-1}$ for breakaway.

The strain rate at the crack tip is readily determined since the crack is initially static. For a typical strain distribution,[13] the strain, $\epsilon$, at a distance, r, from the crack tip would be

$$\epsilon = \frac{\sigma_{ys} R_p}{Er} \qquad (4)$$

where $\sigma_{ys}$ is the yield strength, E is the modulus of elasticity, and $R_p$ is the plastic-zone diameter. In terms of the stress intensity parameter, K,

$$\epsilon \simeq \frac{K^2}{\pi E \sigma_{ys} r} \qquad (5)$$

and the strain rate can be described in terms of the stress intensity rate by

$$\dot{\epsilon} \simeq \frac{2K \dot{K}}{\pi E \sigma_{ys} r} \qquad (6)$$

The stress intensity rate for these tests was 420 psi-in$^{1/2}$/sec and the maximum stress intensity on rising load was 42,000 psi-in$^{1/2}$. These values lead to a value of about $0.3 \times 10^{-6}$ $r^{-1}$ in/sec for the strain rate. Thus, as the crack tip is approached, the strain rate becomes larger. However, even as close as one Burger's vector from the crack front, the strain rate would only be $0.3 \times 10^2$ $sec^{-1}$ which is still below critical. Thus, dislocations would not be expected to escape from their atmospheres. This does not mean that the crack cannot move. If some failure criterion is exceeded, for example a stress (and/or hydrogen pressure) sufficient to invoke the Griffith criterion, brittle crack extension will occur. The discussion herein i

425

intended only to illustrate that interstitial locking might inhibit crack motion at lower stresses.

Let us now consider crack "initiation" at sustained load. For the two conditions investigated, there were no significantly long primary incubation times before the crack growth process ensued. Although there were several instances where a time delay existed prior to the first SWE at hold, this incubation time was no longer than the time between the first and second SWE, or between the second and third SWE. For six tests of varying hydrogen level and environment, the primary incubation time ranged from 0.1 to 2.3 minutes with the average being about one minute. The secondary incubation time ranged from 0.4 to 9.0 minutes with the average being about three minutes. In three out of the six tests, however, the primary and secondary incubation times were the same within experimental error. Furthermore, those instances where the primary incubation times ranged down to 0.1 minutes appear anomalous in that if there were a true primary incubation time, it would be expected to be greater than the secondary incubation time. From these observations, it was concluded that the primary and secondary incubation times for this material were essentially the same.

Regardless of environment or hydrogenation, the incubation times were similar and very short. This suggests that hydrogen, which can diffuse rapidly at room temperature, might be the cause for both types of cracking in this steel. If this hypothesis is accepted, the question as to the origin and location of the hydrogen needs to be explored. For the distilled water tests, the hydrogen may form at the liquid-metal interface due to the reaction[14]

$$Fe + H_2O \rightarrow FeO + 2H \qquad (7)$$

The distilled water used in this investigation had a pH of 5.7. As to the hydrogenated samples, it is well established that large amounts of hydrogen are introduced during cathodic charging. However, there has been some question as to the location of the hydrogen since the equilibrium concentration at room temperature[15] is only $5 \times 10^{-4}$ ppm while the severity of hydrogen embrittlement increases progressively up to 10 ppm. At these high concentration levels it is obvious that the interstitial hydrogen must precipitate as molecular hydrogen in hydrogen traps. One such trap in the steel of this investigation was the interface between the matrix and the $M_3C$ type carbides that precipitated during the 200 C tempering treatment. A fractograph of the fracture surface of an 850/200 sample subjected to cathodic charging and baked for three hours is shown in Figure 7. The failure mode was partially intergranular and an $M_3C$ type particle is shown in one of these facets. Note that there is a rectangular impression inside a somewhat larger rectangle. The shape of the inner rectangle can be characterized by a length to width ratio of 0.15. It is significant that many of the $M_3C$ type carbides observed on the fracture faces of nonhydrogenated samples had a typical length to width ratio of 0.23 and some had values as low as 0.09. It was surmised that the inner impression represented the outline of the $M_3C$ carbide in the heat treated condition. Upon cathodic charging, it is hypothesized that the atomic hydrogen precipitated as molecular hydrogen at the carbide-matrix interface until sufficient pressures expanded the cavity to the dimensions of the outer rectangle. As pressures in the range of 200,000[16] to 1,500,000[17] psi have been calculated for trapped molecular hydrogen in steel, this is not an unreasonable speculation. A number of these expanded cavities were observed on the fracture surfaces of the hydrogen-embrittled steels, and it is suggested that these served as an effective trap for molecular hydrogen in this material. A similar observation in iron-silicon single crystals has been made by Gell, et al.[18]

It has been suggested that hydrogen may be the source of embrittlement for stress corrosion cracking in distilled water as well as for hydrogen embrittlement in this steel. Further evaluation of this hypothesis was made through observations of the characteristics of crack propagation.

*Observations on Crack Propagation*

Both crack-growth rate, da/dt, and SWE observations for the 850/200 condition are given in Table 4 as a function of stress intensity factor. The crack-growth-rate data as given in Figure 8, show the tendency for da/dt to increase with K. As to the environmental effects, the tabulation as shown in Table 5 for a stress intensity value of 50 ksi-in$^{1/2}$ indicates hydrogenation to be somewhat more severe than distilled water, and the combination of distilled water and hydrogenation to be most conducive to slow crack growth. It is interesting that the 1/2-hr baked material consistently cracked at a slower rate than that baked 3 hours. One might expect a higher concentration of hydrogen for a shorter baking time which should lead to the opposite trend in the data. However, if the baking time were not sufficient to homogenize the hydrogen distribution, the hydrogen might

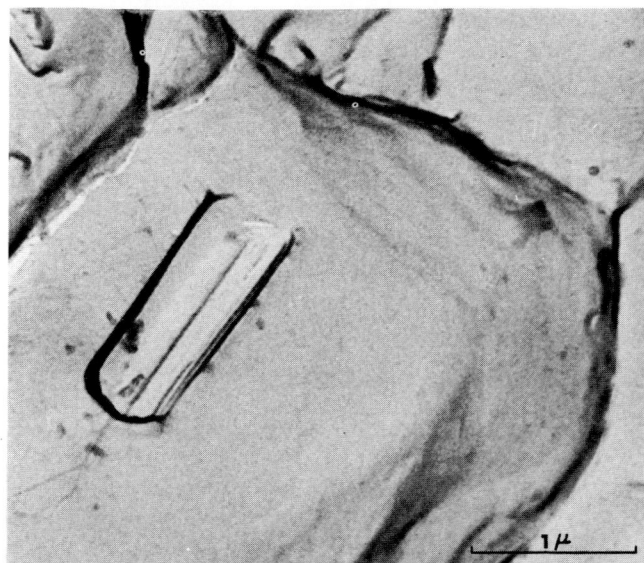

FIGURE 7 – Fractograph of an expanded cavity around a $M_3C$ type carbide in an intergranular fracture area.

TABLE 4.

| Spec. No. | Material Condition | Test Condition | Stress Intensity K,Ksi-in$^{1/2}$ | Crack Increm. $\Delta a$, in | Crack Growth Rate Interval from COD Chart, Minutes | Time Increm. $\Delta t$, min | da/dt $\mu$-in/sec | Stress Wave Emission Interval from Tape. Minutes | No. of SWE | Time Between SWE $\Delta_{ts}$, sec |
|---|---|---|---|---|---|---|---|---|---|---|
| W-19 | 1550/400 | Held in Air at 10.8 Kips | 51.5 | 0.060 | 0-242 | 242 | 4.1 | 45.5[1] | 4 | 680 |
| W-7 | 1550/400 | Held in Air at 12 Kips | 54.9 | 0.061 | 0-195 | 195 | 5.2 | 90-180 | 10 | 540 |
| W-8 | 1550/400 | Held in Distilled Water at 10.5 & 12 Kips | 43.6 | 0.066 | 0-256 | 256 | 4.3 | – | – | – |
|  |  |  | 57.5 | 0.045 | 257-300 | 43 | 17.5 | 257-300 | 23 | 112 |
|  |  |  | 61.7 | 0.036 | 300-322.7 | 22.7 | 26.3 | 300-322.7 | 15 | 90 |
|  |  |  | 64.0 | 0.021 | 322.7-331.55 | 8.85 | 39.5 | 322.7-331.55 | 13 | 41 |
|  |  |  | 66.8 | 0.021 | 331.85-339[2] | 7.15 | 49 | 331.85-339 | 9 | 48 |
|  |  |  | 68.6 | 0.024 | 339-343.5 | 4.5 | 89 | 339-343.5 | 9 | 30 |
|  |  |  | 70.8 | 0.027 | 343.5-346.7 | 3.2 | 140 | 343.5-346.7 | 22 | 8.7 |
| W-2 | 1550/400 Hydrog. 1/2-hr Bake | Held in Air at 10 Kips | 44.6 | 0.021 | 0-31.2 | 31.2 | 11.5 |  |  |  |
|  |  |  | 45.9 | 0.021 | 31.2-59.7 | 28.5 | 12.4 |  |  |  |
|  |  |  | 47.9 | 0.036 | 59.7-103 | 43.3 | 13.8 | 0-148 | 25 | 355 |
|  |  |  | 50.4 | 0.036 | 103-147.6 | 44.6 | 13.5 |  |  |  |
|  |  |  | 52.3 | 0.021 | 147.6-176.9 | 29.3 | 12.0 |  |  |  |
| W-6 | 1550/400 Hydrog. 1/2-hr Bake | Held in Distilled Water at 10 Kips | 50.3 | 0.057 | 0-25 | 25 | 38 | 0-23.3 | 4 | 375 |
|  |  |  | 54.0 | 0.045 | 25-38.33 | 13.33 | 56 | 23.3-40 | 5 | 200 |
|  |  |  | 57.1 | 0.042 | 38.33-51.66 | 13.33 | 52.5 | 40-54.7 | 9 | 98 |
|  |  |  | 60.3 | 0.039 | 51.66-65.00 | 13.34 | 49 | 54.7-66.6 | 10 | 72 |
|  |  |  | 64.7 | 0.066 | 65.0-87.3 | 22.3 | 49.5 | 66.6-89 | 12 | 112 |
|  |  |  | 69.2 | 0.036 | 87.3-96.63 | 9.33 | 64 | 89-98 | 9 | 60 |
|  |  |  | 72.8 | 0.039 | 96.63-101.16 | 4.53 | 143 | 98-101.2 | 17 | 11.2 |
| W-1 | 1550/400 Hydrog. 3-hr Bake | Held in Air at 10 Kips | 44.5 | 0.027 | 0-23.4 | 23.4 | 19.2 | 0-22.2 | 38 | 35 |
|  |  |  | 46.5 | 0.036 | 23.4-50.1 | 26.7 | 22.5 | 22.2-80 | 12 | 290 |
|  |  |  | 49.2 | 0.042 | 50.1-76.8 | 26.7 | 26.2 |  |  |  |
|  |  |  | 52.8 | 0.057 | 76.8-103.5 | 26.7 | 35.7 | 80-107 | 7 | 232 |
|  |  |  | 57.1 | 0.057 | 103.5-130.2 | 26.7 | 35.7 | 107-138 | 19 | 98 |
|  |  |  | 61.4 | 0.054 | 130.2-156.9 | 26.7 | 33.9 | 138-165 | 11 | 148 |
|  |  |  | 66.7 | 0.066 | 156.9-186.2 | 29.3 | 37.5 | 165-186 | 15 | 84 |
|  |  |  | 67.7 | 0.045 | 170.5-186.2 | 15.7 | 47.8 | 170-186 | 10 | 96 |
| W-3 | 1550/400 Hydrog. 3-hr Bake | Held in Distilled Water at 10 Kips | 45.4 | 0.015 | 0-7.9 | 7.9 | 32 | 0-11.5 | 6 | 115 |
|  |  |  | 47.0 | 0.036 | 7.9-21.23 | 13.33 | 45 | 11.5-26.5 | 7 | 129 |
|  |  |  | 49.9 | 0.048 | 21.23-34.56 | 13.33 | 60 | 26.5-39.0 | 13 | 58 |
|  |  |  | 53.5 | 0.0525 | 34.56-47.90 | 13.34 | 65.5 | 39.0-44.6 | 13 | 26 |
|  |  |  | 56.8 | 0.0375 | 47.90-57.15 | 9.25 | 67.5 | 44.6-59.1 | 31 | 28 |
|  |  |  | 61.6 | 0.078 | 57.15-71.65 | 14.50 | 90 | 59.1-70.0 | 49 | 13.4 |
|  |  |  | 67.2 | 0.051 | 71.65-76.58 | 4.93 | 172 | 70.0-75.1 | 36 | 8.5 |
|  |  |  | 68.2 | 0.026 | 74.58-76.58 | 2.00 | 217 | 75.1-77.2 | 27 | 4.7 |

[1]Random samplings of 242 minutes of data totaling 45.5 minutes.
[2]Note the interval 331.55-331.85 minutes is missing. An unusually large SWE and crack opening displacement was observed at this point corresponding to a crack step of 0.012 inches.

TABLE 5.

| Material Condition | Environment | da/dt, $\mu$-in/sec |
|---|---|---|
| No hydrogenation | Air | 3 |
| No hydrogenation | Distilled Water | 8 |
| Hydrog. 1/2-hr bake | Air | 13 |
| Hydrog. 3-hr bake | Air | 29 |
| Hydrog. 1/2-hr bake | Distilled Water | 40 |
| Hydrog. 3-hr bake | Distilled Water | 60 |

not be in locations conducive to embrittlement. Referring to Figure 8, it is significant that, at the higher stress intensity levels, the 1/2-hr baked samples tested in air tend to approach the crack growth rate of the nonhydrogenated sample tested in air. Similarly, the 1/2-hr baked sample tested in distilled water tends to approach the crack growth rate of the nonhydrogenated sample tested in distilled water. Recognizing that each data plot comes from one specimen, these data suggest that the embrittling effect of incomplete hydrogen homogenization becomes insignificant as the crack grows longer.

Another important observation was the individual effects of hydrogenation and distilled water versus the combined effects. If one or the other cracking mechanism were controlling, then the combined effect would be expected to be less than the sum of the individual crack growth rates. On the other hand, if the cracking mechanisms reinforced each other, one might expect the combined effects to be greater than the sum of the individual crack growth rates. As indicated in Table 5, the latter is the case which is commonly termed a synergistic effect. For example, the sum of the crack growth rates for the specimen tested in distilled water and for the 3-hr baked specimen tested in air was $37\,\mu$ in/sec, while the da/dt of the sample tested in combination was $60\,\mu$ in/sec. Another way of interpreting the synergistic effect is the ratio of the crack growth rate of a hydrogenated sample tested in water to the sum of the individual crack growth rates:

$$\frac{da/dt_{(H + W)}}{da/dt_{(H)} + da/dt_{(W)}} > 1 \qquad (8)$$

To have a synergistic effect, this ratio must be greater than unity. For the sample baked 3 hours, where hydrogen embrittlement was occurring throughout the test, this ratio ranged from 1.26 to 1.65 with the average being 1.41. The fact that the two crack growth mechanisms reinforced each other could be explained if hydrogen diffusion were a contributing factor in both types of embrittlement.

One final observation from Figure 8 was that the crack growth rate increased by more than an order of magnitude for the sample tested in distilled water; whereas, the hydrogenated samples exhibited fairly uniform crack growth rates. This observation was reinforced with the SWE data in Table 4. Considering the secondary incubation time, in the first half of the distilled water test, the value was 101 sec while in the last half it was 32 sec. In contrast to this, in the hydrogenated sample baked for 3 hours, $\Delta t_s$ was 112 sec in the first half and 106 sec in the second half of the test. From these trends, it must be concluded that the time-dependent mechanism governing crack growth was nearly *constant* in the hydrogen embrittlement tests but *varied* considerably in distilled water tests without prior hydrogenation.

The above observations give some information on the time between crack steps but do not indicate in what manner the crack moves. In an investigation[9] of spontaneous-strain-aging embrittlement, it was observed that the crack moved in jumps nearly equal to the theoretical crack tip displacement, $2\nu_c$. In terms of the stress intensity factor, this value is given by

$$2\nu_c = \frac{K^2}{m\,\sigma_{ys}E} \qquad (9)$$

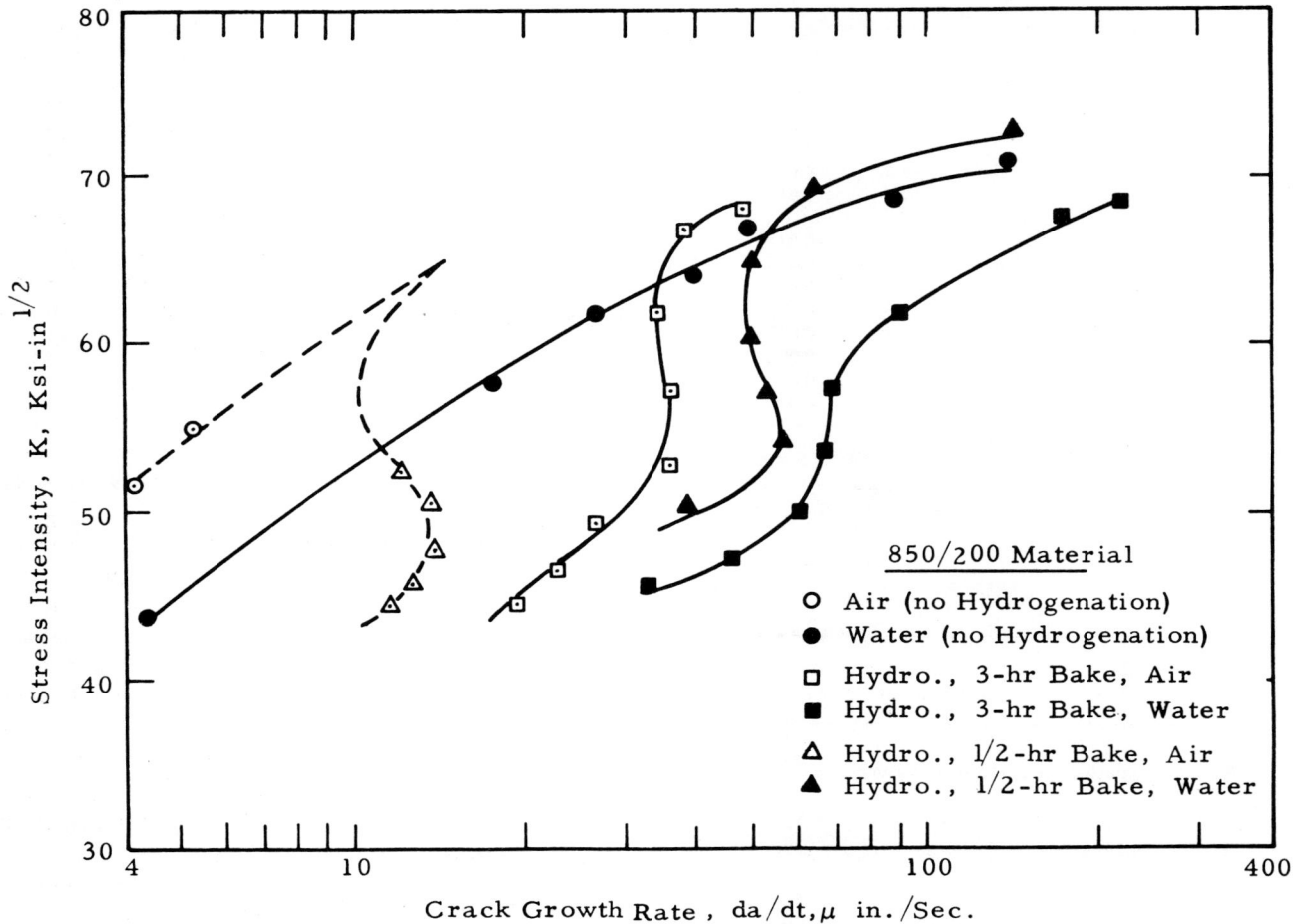

FIGURE 8 — Effect of environment and/or hydrogenation on crack growth rate in Dbac steel (850/200).

where m is about one for plane-stress and two for plane-strain situations. In terms of a fracture criterion, the crack may become unstable when the fracture ductility, $\epsilon_f$, is exceeded at some distance ahead of the crack. Wells[19] has postulated this distance, $\ell^*$, in front of the crack to be related to the crack tip displacement by

$$\ell^* = \frac{2v_c}{\pi \, \epsilon_f} \qquad (10)$$

For a specific stress intensity interval, i.e., $K_i$ to $K_f$, the average value of $\ell^*$ as determined from Equations (9) and (10) and the mean value theorem would be

$$\ell^*_{avg} = \frac{K_f^3 - K_i^3}{3m \, \sigma_{ys} \, E \, \pi \, \epsilon_f \, (K_f - K_i)} \qquad (11)$$

An average value of the experimentally observed crack-jump distance, $\ell_{obs}$, may be made by taking the crack increment and dividing it by the corresponding number of SWE. Thus,

$$\ell_{obs} = \Delta a / N_{SWE} \qquad (12)$$

From the data in Table 4 and Equations (11) and (12), a comparison between $\ell_{obs}$ and $\ell^*_{avg}$ is possible. This comparison is shown in Table 6 for a hydrogenated sample, a sample without hydrogenation tested in distilled water, and a hydrogenated sample tested in water. For the calculations, $\epsilon_f$ was determined to be 0.16 from uniaxial tensile data, E was taken as $30 \times 10^6$ psi, and two values of m were utilized.[1] Considering experimental errors, it appears that the crack is growing in a similar fashion

---

[1] According to Hahn and Rosenfield[20] there is a shift from plane strain to plane stress at $(K/\sigma_{ys})^2 \, t^{-1}$ equal to 1.3 where t is the specimen thickness. For the range of K values encountered in these tests, this parameter is on both sides of 1.3, and so it is arbitrary as to what value of m in Equation (11) is appropriate. Therefore, both the plane strain value of two and the plane stress value of one was used.

regardless of whether it is induced by hydrogenation or by a distilled water environment. Furthermore, it appears that the value of $\ell^*$ as a first approximation is a reasonable estimate of the crack-step size involved in the crack growth process.

Additional information on the crack growth process was obtained fractographically. As indicated in Figure 9, the fracture mode involved both intergranular and cleavage fracture. Both fracture modes were about equally predominant regardless of the hydrogenation or environment. The only difference between the intergranular fracture in hydrogenated samples and samples without hydrogenation tested in distilled water was that there was a slight pitting in the case of the distilled water. As to the cleavage mode, the river markings were somewhat obliterated by the corrosive environment, but the size of the cleavage facets were generally the same. The size of the facets observed in Figure 9 are about 0.0004 in while the average size from 20 observations was 0.00035 in. This average facet size was about a factor of four or five less than $\ell^*$ or $\ell_{obs}$. Thus, it is probable that the larger crack jumps involved the crack moving over several cleavage facets in one step. It is quite possible that intergranular fracture proceeds slowly along preferred sites until a critical point at which time the crack jumps through •the remaining material, this latter step involving cleavage. If this were the case, then the observed stress waves are probably associated with the larger cleavage steps. These fractographic and SWE observations suggest that the mode in which the crack moves is nearly identical in hydrogen embrittlement or distilled water cracking for this steel.

*Observations on Crack Instability*

It has been hypothesized[21] that the controlling factor for final failure in a stress corrosion test is the critical-stress-intensity factor, $K_c$, commonly termed fracture toughness. This has been shown to be the case for failure times ranging over three orders of magnitude in the case of

---

**TABLE 6.**

| Condition | $K_i$ (ksi-in$^{1/2}$) | $K_f$ (ksi-in$^{1/2}$) | $\Delta a$ (in) | $N_{SWE}$ | $\ell_{obs}$ (in) | $\ell^*_{avg}$ (in) |
|---|---|---|---|---|---|---|
| Nonhydrogenated Tested in Distilled Water | 55.5 | 72.2 | 0.174 | 91 | 0.0019 | 0.0010-0.0020 |
| Hydrogenated, Baked 3 hr, Tested in Air | 43.8 | 69.8 | 0.339 | 102 | 0.0033 | 0.0008-0.0016 |
| Hydrogenated, Baked 3 hr, Tested in Distilled Water | 45.0 | 69.5 | 0.318 | 182 | 0.00175 | 0.00082-0.00164 |

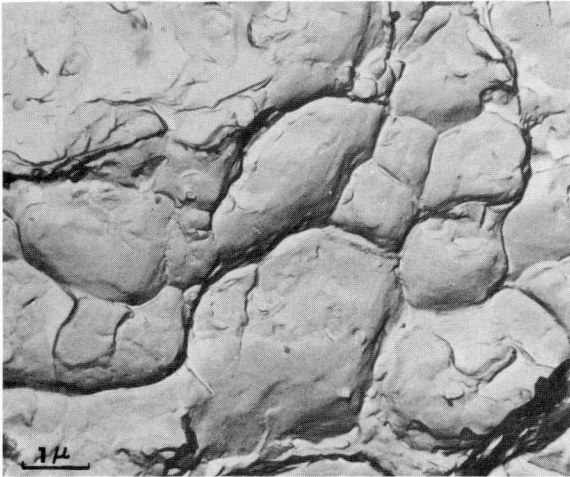

(a) Intergranular Fracture-Hydrogen

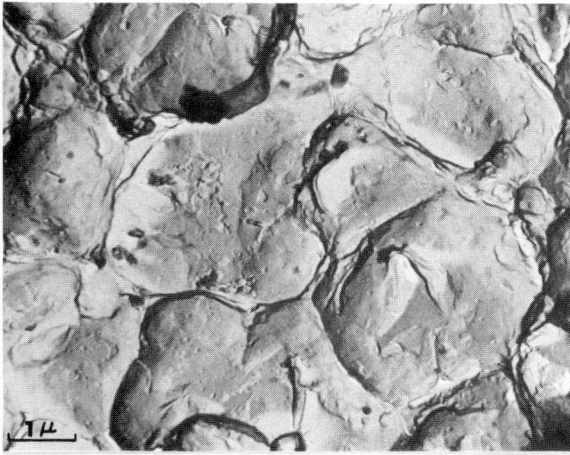

(b) Intergranular Fracture-Distilled Water

(c) Cleavage-Hydrogen + Distilled Water

(d) Cleavage Facet-Hydrogen

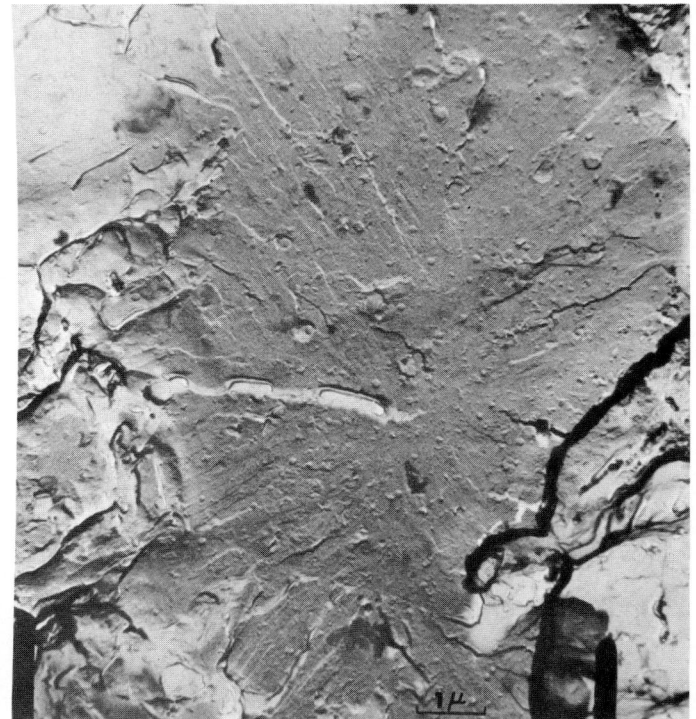

(e) Cleavage Facet-Distilled Water

FIGURE 9 — Electron fractographs of D6aC steel tested in the hydrogenated condition, in distilled water or in combinations.

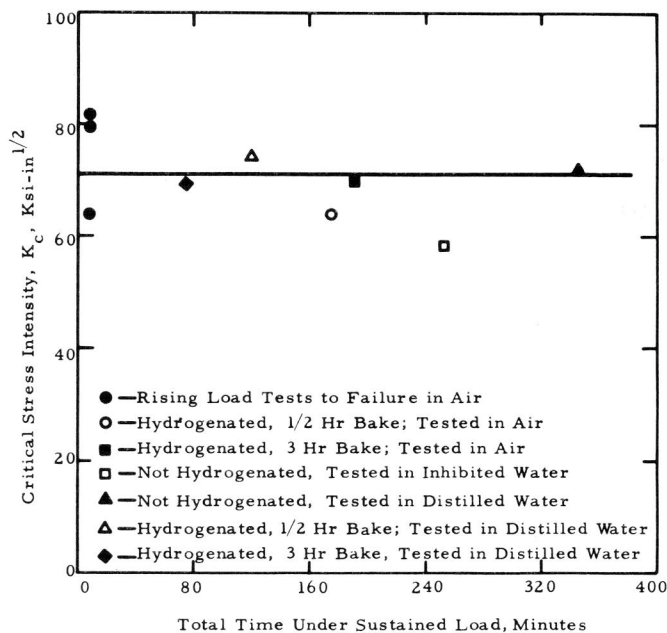

**FIGURE 10 – Critical stress intensity factors for (850/200) D6aC steel subjected to various environments.**

salt water corrosion in 18% nickel maraging steel.[22] It is also the case for the D6aC steel of this investigation regardless of hydrogenation or environment. All critical-stress-intensity factors for the 850/200 condition are shown in Figure 10 as a function of time at sustained load. Obviously, neither the imposed environment nor the time to failure affected $K_c$. Thus, even though the crack growth rate may have varied, at the point where the combined crack length and applied stress exceeds the modified Griffith criterion, failure ensues.

This is an important observation since, if the average crack growth rate can be described, then the time to failure may be described. For example, in terms of an infinite-plane solution, the critical-crack size, $a_{cr}$, is given by

$$a_{cr} = K_c^2 / \sigma_o^2 \pi \qquad (13)$$

where $\sigma_o$ is the applied stress. If an initial-defect size, $a_o$, is stipulated, in a time, $t_f$, to failure, the crack length would grow to a size given by

$$a_{cr} = a_o + t_f \, da/dt \qquad (14)$$

From Equations (13) and (14), the time to failure in terms of the average crack growth rate is

$$t_f = \left( \frac{K_c^2}{\sigma_o^2 \pi} - a_o \right) \left( \frac{da}{dt} \right)^{-1} \qquad (15)$$

Knowing that $K_c$ is independent of the time to failure, allows a calculation of $t_f$ for any applied stress level if $da/dt$ is known.

In summary, it has been hypothesized that hydrogen formation at the distilled water crack tip interface or cathodically introduced hydrogen at second phase "traps"

are contributing to the time-dependent failure mechanisms. Furthermore, both stress wave and fractographic evidence indicate that the step-by-step crack growth process is similar for the two failure mechanisms. The rate determining factor is the time-dependent phenomenon occurring between crack steps which leads to different crack growth rates for hydrogen embrittlement and stress corrosion cracking. Total failure instability is only encountered when the critical-stress-intensity factor is reached since the fracture toughness is unaffected by either hydrogenation or testing in distilled water.

## Phenomenological Models for Crack Growth

Based partially on the experimental observations of this investigation and partially on some observations from the literature, the following models are derived assuming hydrogen diffusion to lead to embrittlement.

### Hydrogen Induced Cracking

Troiano[10] was one of the first to study hydrogen embrittlement in detail and demonstrated that the crack was nucleated at some distance ahead of a notch. He also proposed that it was the stress-induced hydrogen diffusion to this region of high triaxiality which resulted in cracking. However, no failure criterion in itself was postulated. More recently, Tetelman[23] and Gell, et al[18] have shown the importance of the pressure from molecular hydrogen in combination with the applied stress as a criterion for fracture in iron-silicon single crystals. However, this model does not describe the time-dependency of the mechanism or the manner in which the crack growth proceeds. The following is a crude attempt to explain most features of hydrogen embrittlement. Although many will undoubtedly take exception to what is proposed, as a thought-provoking exercise for more detailed analysis, the following theoretical treatment is considered to be justified.

In polycrystalline steels similar to the material of this investigation,[6] hydrogen analysis has indicated little embrittlement when the hydrogen level is near one ppm but increasing amounts of embrittlement to about 10 ppm. Of course, these levels of hydrogen cannot be in interstitial solid solution and, thus, must be entrapped in cavities such as is shown in Figure 7. It is possible that once the pressure in these traps builds up to a critical amount, this in conjunction with the applied stress, triggers fracture and the crack moves one jump. This would require hydrogen diffusion against a back-pressure of molecular hydrogen. Although, it has been demonstrated that hydrogen can diffuse against large back-pressures,[24] it is not clear what the driving force would be. For the steel of this investigation, it has been demonstrated that the time between crack jumps for the hydrogenated samples stayed approximately the same over the entire test. In that the stress intensity was increasing during the test, it appears that $\Delta t_s$ is independent of stress intensity factor as well as time at sustained load.

From these observations, it is hypothesized that the diffusion of hydrogen from the surrounding area to a

431

distance S* in front of the crack nucleates fracture. Since $\Delta t_s$ was constant, it is also hypothesized that S* is constant during the crack extension process in a particular test sample. As a crude approximation, assume that as the hydrogen is drawn from the surrounding area, the depleted areas do not build up in concentration. Then, in order to build up an initial concentration, $C_o$, to a critical concentration, $C_{cr}$, at S*, the approximate equation would be

$$\frac{C_{cr} - C_o}{C_o} \cdot S^{*2} = 4D\Delta t_s \qquad (16)$$

It is obvious from the literature[6,7] that the hydrogen concentration level affects the time to failure (in this case the secondary incubation time) much more than is suggested by Equation (16). It is probable that S* is affected by the hydrogen concentration level. For example, at a low concentration level, the stress required to initiate failure is large and thus the distance from the crack tip at which the fracture strain could be approached would be large. This would allow S* to be large and hence the secondary incubation times to be large. Conversely, at high concentration levels, very low stresses may initiate failure and hence S* and $\Delta t_s$ could be very small. It is convenient to describe S* in terms of some physical parameter. The average facet size, d, as observed in the electron fractographs was picked as a reasonable first choice. From the observations above concerning the possible concentration effects on S*, an estimate of S* is

$$S^* \sim \frac{C_{cr}}{C_o} d \qquad (17)$$

This approximation in combination with Equation (16) leads to

$$\Delta t_s \simeq \frac{(C_{cr} - C_o) C_{cr}^2 d^2}{4C_o^3 D} \qquad (18)$$

For the cathodic charging and baking procedure of this investigation, it was surmised that the hydrogen content was about 3 ppm. Since hydrogen levels up to 10 ppm give increasing degrees of embrittlement, 10 ppm was taken to be the critical level. In conjunction with a value of $2 \times 10^{-7}$ cm$^2$/sec for the diffusivity and a value of d equal to 0.00089 cm, the value of $\Delta t_s$ calculated from Equation (18) is 25.6 sec.

The analysis to this point infers that no matter what stress is applied, cracking will occur. This is experimentally not true. For example, Troiano[10] has shown that, for each hydrogen level, a threshold stress exists below which cracking will not occur. This threshold is possibly connected to the minimum distance in front of the crack over which the fracture ductility can be exceeded. If this distance is less than one grain diameter, then fracture will probably not proceed. This has been suggested by Tetelman, et al[25] concerning a critical cleavage stress criterion in steel. A similar criterion in terms of the critical crack tip displacement is

$$\ell^* > \frac{1}{3} \frac{C_{cr}}{C_o} d \qquad (19)$$

At the highest effect concentration possible, i.e., $C_o = C_{cr}$, $\ell^*$ would still have to be greater than 1/3 an average grain diameter. A value less than d was chosen since some of the smaller cleavage facets were smaller than the average value, d. Also, the intergranular facets were about 1/3 the size of the cleavage facets and if enough of these failed in front of the crack, the remaining area might fracture abruptly in cleavage. If this were the case, Equation (19) would be quite reasonable.

It is now possible to combine these observations to describe the time-dependent phenomenon. If the crack is growing mainly by jumps, then the crack growth rate is simply the average jump distance divided by the time between jumps. Recalling that $\ell^*$ was the approximate jump distance, it follows that the crack growth rate may be described by

$$da/dt \sim \ell^*/\Delta t_s \qquad (20)$$

It was emphasized above that for a particular test temperature and hydrogen concentration level that $\Delta t_s$ is constant. Thus, the only parameter that affects the crack growth rate is $\ell^*$. Since $\ell^*$ is proportional to $K^2$, then for the 52% increase in K observed in Table 4, one would expect a 130% increase in da/dt. The fact that a 150% increase was observed encourages one to use $\ell^*$ as a reasonable crack growth parameter. Since the fracture mode was intergranular and cleavage with almost no microscopic shear lip, the plane-strain estimate of $\ell^*$ is utilized. From Equations (9), (10), (18) and (20), it follows that

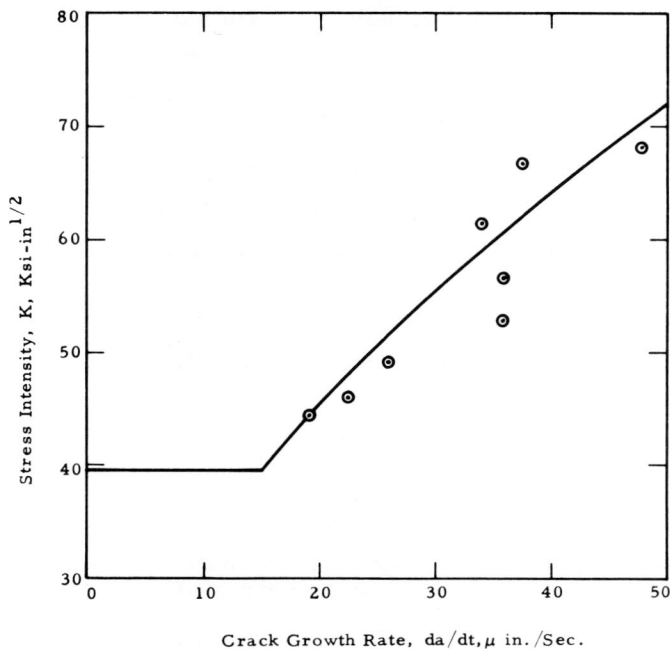

FIGURE 11 — Comparison of actual and predicted crack growth rates for hydrogenated D6aC steel.

432

$$da/dt \sim 2K^2 C_o^3 D/\sigma_{ys} E \pi \epsilon_f (C_{cr} - C_o) C_{cr}^2 d^2 \quad (21)$$

Using the same values for all parameters as given in the previous sections, calculations of $da/dt$ were made as a function of stress intensity. As shown in Figure 11, the agreement between the solid curve from Equation (21) and the experimental data is good. Note that the horizontal break off near $15 \mu$ in/sec is due to the criterion of Equation (19). Admittedly, considerable license was taken with a number of approximations and some of the assumptions may not be totally realistic. For example, there is no reason to expect a single critical hydrogen concentration level to trigger fracture for all initial hydrogen concentration levels and all applied stress levels. Gell, et al[18] have deduced that the pressure in microcracks just prior to crack propagation varies between 0.2 and 0.6 of the yield stress in silicon-iron. Of course, this was in the absence of a superimposed applied stress and the pressure variations were partially due to differences in microcrack size and test temperature. However, if the criterion they propose can be translated to the somewhat different case presented here, then one would expect a different critical pressure for each stress intensity level. The fact remains that the time between cracks jumps did *not* change with stress intensity. If a stress-plus-pressure criterion were controlling, then one might expect that, as the stress intensity increased, the critical pressure would decrease. The time required to build up this decreased pressure would be less. Thus, if this criterion were accepted, $\Delta t_s$ should decrease with increasing stress intensity. The fact that $\Delta t_s$ did not should stimulate further investigation.

To check some of the proposed features of the model, a comparison to the classic hydrogen embrittlement data of Johnson, et al[7] was made. Unfortunately, their data were reported in applied notch tensile stress and time to failure. For ease of comparison, Johnson's data was converted to stress intensity factors and the theoretical crack growth rate model was utilized to predict time to failure. The details of the conversion are given in the Appendix. The theoretical result in terms of applied to critical stress intensity is given in Figure 12 for various initial hydrogen concentration levels. Johnson's data are shown for comparison in Figure 13. Although the data are in terms of different baking time at 150 C, based upon the literature, it is probable that the hydrogen levels varied similar to those shown in Figure 12. It is significant that the range in time to failure and the threshold stress intensity are similar for the analysis and the experimental data.

*Distilled Water Induced Cracking*

For the case of hydrogen embrittlement described above, hydrogen is distributed throughout the specimen. It is obvious that even if distilled water induced cracking involved hydrogen diffusion, that the situation is completely different. First, the hydrogen must evolve at the liquid crack tip interface and secondly, it must diffuse from the crack front to the distance $S^*$ where fracture is nucleated. The diffusion model for this latter situation can be described by an error-function equation[26] where the hydrogen is diffusing "downhill" from the crack tip to $S^*$. In terms of the critical hydrogen level to promote embrittlement, $C_{cr}$, and the concentration level at the liquid crack tip interface, $C_o$, this would be

$$C_{cr} = C_o \left[ 1 - \text{erf} \, \frac{S^*}{2 \sqrt{D \Delta t_s}} \right] \quad (22)$$

If it is assumed as above that $C_{cr}$ is 10 ppm hydrogen, a description of $S^*$ and $C_o$ must still be made to calculate $\Delta t_s$. In the case of distilled water, the estimate of Equation (17) for $S^*$ has no bearing since hydrogen is not initially present throughout the specimen. However, for lack of a better choice, $S^*$ is chosen to be about the same as for the specimen examined in the section above of $S^* \sim 3d$. This value is still somewhat smaller than the experimentally observed value of the jump distance, $\ell_{obs}$.

As to the value of the hydrogen concentration at the liquid crack tip interface, this can only be speculation. From observations of plastic deformation effects on metal catalysis, it might be expected that surface dislocations and/or slip steps would act as preferred sites for the formation of atomic hydrogen. This would be in line with the observation of Chaudron and Moreau[27] who found that plastic deformation accelerated the permeation of hydrogen during pickling. It is hypothesized that a percentage of the emerging dislocations at the crack tip act as sites for atomic hydrogen to form. The crack tip can be described[28] as n dislocations of Burger's vector, b, which gives the height, h, of the crack to be

$$h = nb \quad (23)$$

It is recognized that this for an elastic crack and so this is a rough approximation at best. Since it is hypothesized that $C_o$ is proportional to n and the height of the crack is the crack tip displacement, it follows that

$$C_o \propto n = \frac{2 v_c}{b} \quad (24)$$

In terms of the stress intensity factor, Equations (9), (24) and a proportionality constant, A, give

$$C_o = A \frac{K^2}{2 \sigma_{ys} Eb} \quad (25)$$

It is presumed that the constant A is dependent upon the electrolyte, pH of the solution, activity of the metal, etc. The significance of Equation (25) is that the hydrogen concentration at the crack tip would be strongly dependent upon the stress intensity factor. That is, as the crack opening widened with increasing stress intensity, more hydrogen could evolve since more active sites would be exposed to the aqueous environment. Combining Equations (22) and (25) gives

433

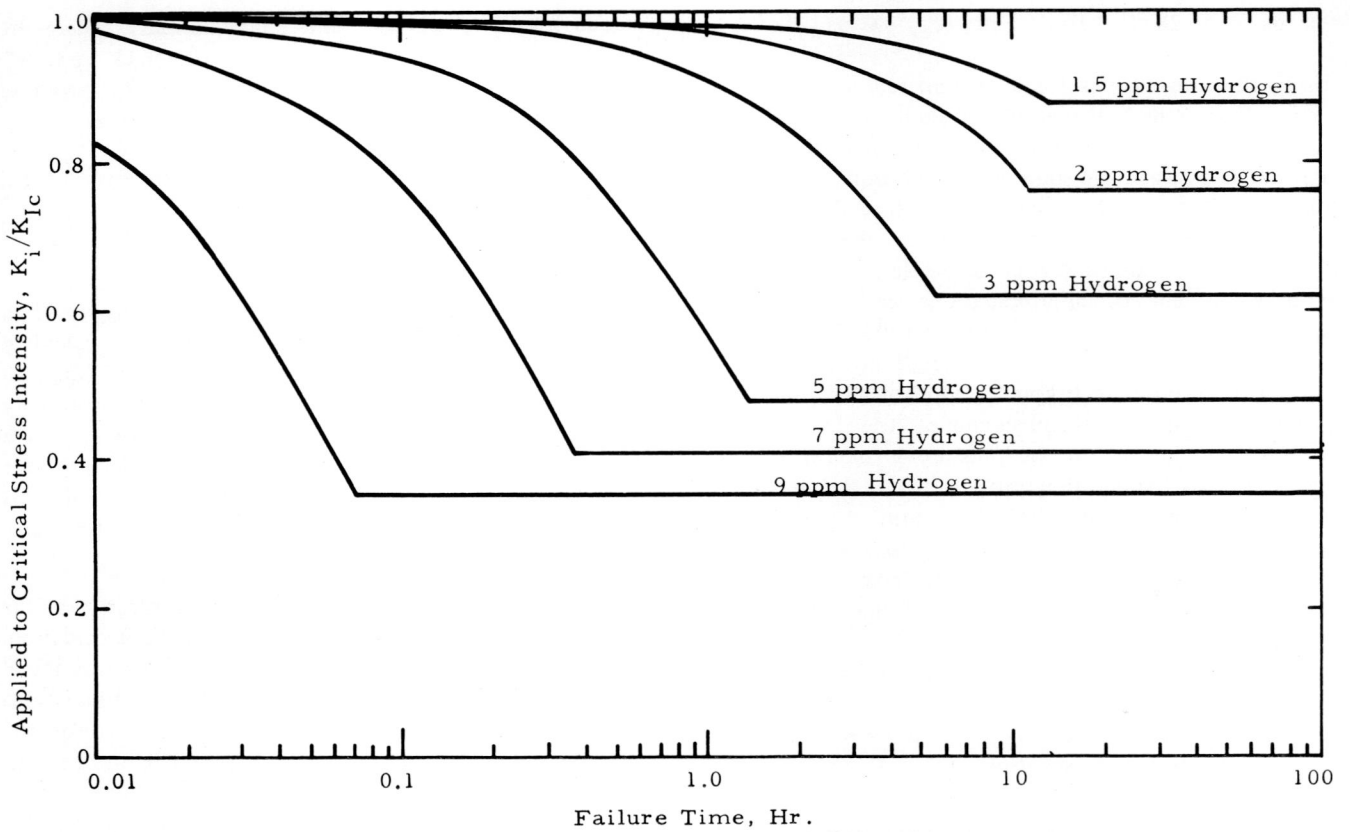

FIGURE 12 — Theoretical determination of failure time for various levels of hydrogenation as a function of applied stress intensity.

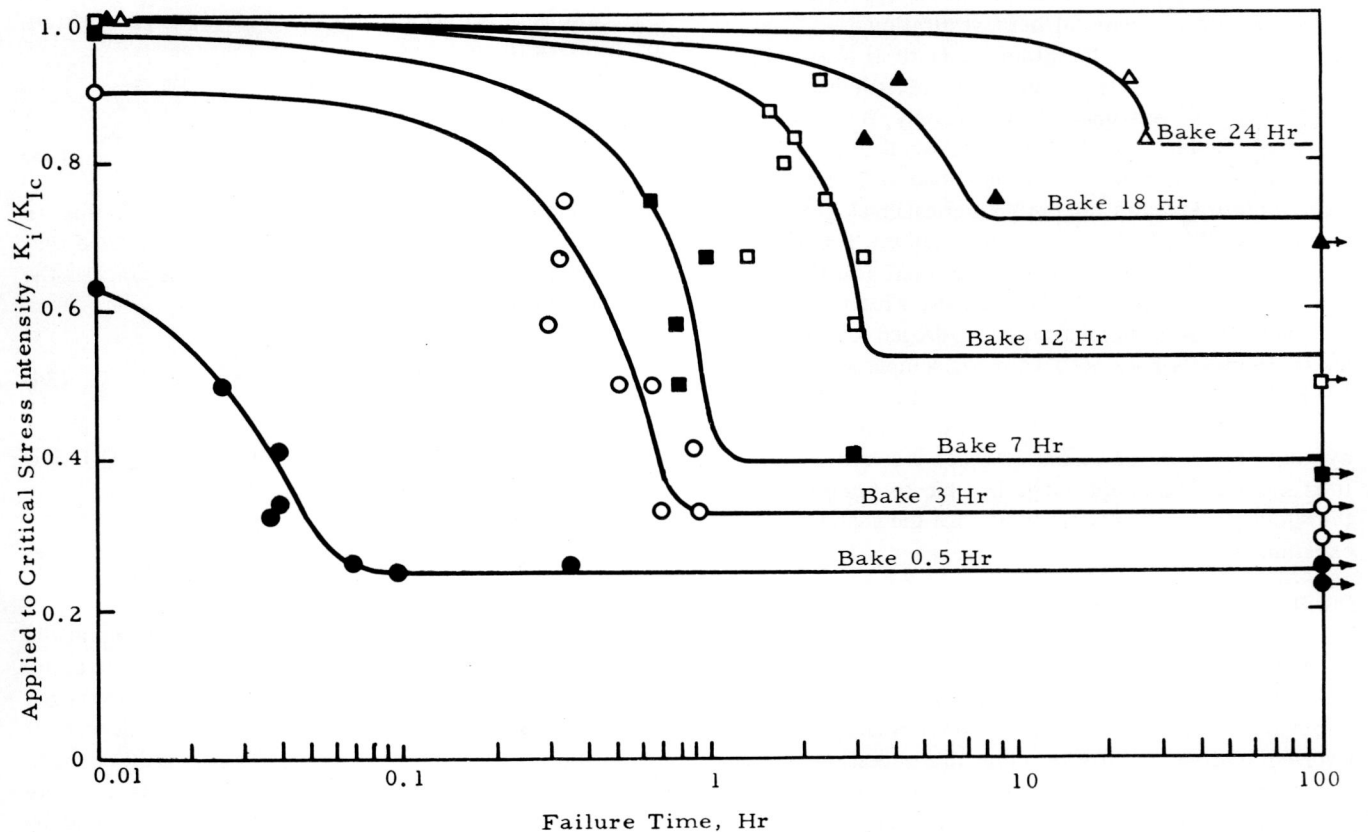

FIGURE 13 — Experimental determination of failure time in 4340 steel as a function of hydrogen level and applied stress intensity (Ref. 10).

$$C_{cr} = A \frac{K^2}{2\sigma_{ys} Eb} \left[ 1 - \text{erf} \left( \frac{3d}{2\sqrt{D\Delta t_s}} \right) \right] \quad (26)$$

which has all known quantities except A and $\Delta t_s$. Since there was no way to estimate A, it was derived from the lowest experimental data point giving A equal to $6 \times 10^{-10}$. Using this constant and the same method for determining da/dt, i.e., Equation (20), the theoretical curve was calculated as a function of stress intensity factor. This is compared to the experimental data points in Figure 14. It is interesting that the asymptote, where da/dt → 0, is just below the lower limit for hydrogen embrittlement shown in Figure 11. Referring again to Figure 14, the major difference between the model and the experimental data seems to be that the data indicate a slightly different trend with K. This difference is not always the case, however, as some more recent data in this laboratory on a slightly different heat treatment of the same material show a trend similar to the model. The important consideration is that the strong dependency of $\Delta t_s$ on stress intensity, as may be inferred from Equation (26) and the data in Table 4, is predicted. Thus, even though the constant A was taken from one data point, the model predicts the other data points reasonably well and gives a realistic threshold value for $K_{Iscc}$.

*Hydrogen Plus Distilled Water*

If hydrogen is diffusing toward S* from two sources, it might be expected that the critical hydrogen content would be achieved in a shorter time. Thus, $\Delta t_s$ would be less which would make da/dt greater as was indicated by the data. To demonstrate this phenomenologically, a superposition of the two previous treatments was made. From the hydrogen embrittlement model, Equation (18) gives

$$C_{cr} = \left[ \frac{4D\Delta t_s C_o^3}{d^2} + C_{cr}^2 C_o \right]^{1/3} \quad (27)$$

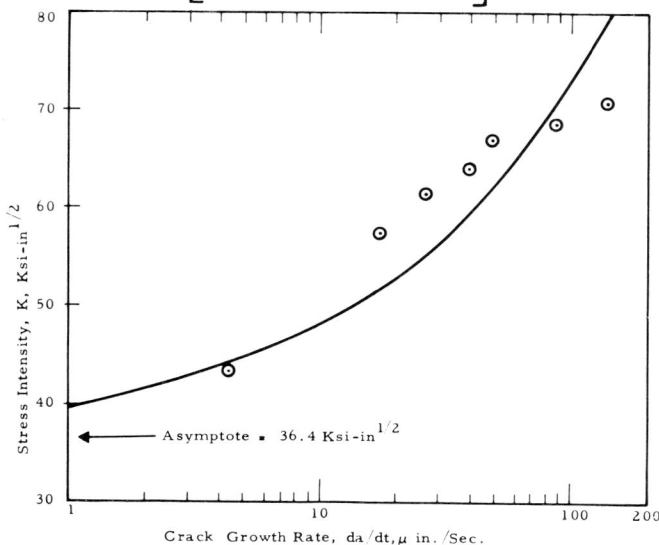

FIGURE 14 — Comparison of actual and predicted crack growth rates for D6aC steel in distilled water.

From the distilled water model, Equation (26) gives

$$C_{cr} = 6 \times 10^{-10} \frac{K^2}{2\sigma_{ys} Eb} \left[ 1 - \text{erf} \left( \frac{3d}{2\sqrt{D\Delta t_s}} \right) \right] \quad (28)$$

Assuming a simple superposition of the two models to give a crude estimate of the time for the hydrogen level to reach critical,

$$C_{cr} = \left[ \frac{4D\Delta t_s C_o^3}{d^2} + C_{cr}^2 C_o \right] + 6 \times 10^{-10} \quad (29)$$

$$\frac{K^2}{2\sigma_{ys} Eb} \left[ 1 - \text{erf} \left( \frac{3d}{2\sqrt{D\Delta t_s}} \right) \right]$$

Using the same values for all parameters as were utilized above, $\Delta t_s$ may be calculated for a given stress intensity factor. Then, from Equations (9), (10), and (20), da/dt may be calculated. This was accomplished as a function of stress intensity factor, and as noted in Figure 15, the predicted crack growth rates are in reasonable agreement with the experimental data. The difference is less than a factor of two in all cases. It would not be realistic to expect a superposition technique to give exact results since interaction of the two sources of hydrogen would produce gradient effects that are not taken into account. Thus, the agreement between the data and the superposition model is probably as good as could be expected

It is interesting that a synergistic effect similar to what was observed for the experimental data is also produced by the superposition of the two models. That is, if da/dt for the hydrogenation model and da/dt for the distilled water model are added and compared to da/dt for the superposition model, a strong synergistic effect is apparent. (Compare the solid curves in Figures 11, 14, and 15.) Using the synergistic ratio in Equation (8), the theoretical values

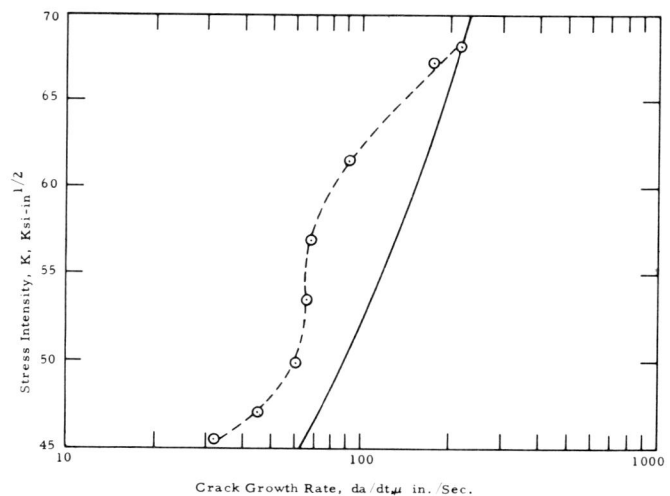

FIGURE 15 — Comparison of actual and predicted crack growth rates for hydrogenated D6aC steel tested in distilled water.

range from 1.75 to 2.55 with the average being 2.10. This strong synergistic effect indicates that hydrogen diffusion inward from two sources might accelerate crack growth over and above what might be expected if the cracking mechanisms were independent.

## Conclusions

1. In D6aC steel, the crack growth process, under hydrogenated or distilled water conditions, was discontinuous with the time between crack steps being the major rate-determining factor.

2. Crack growth rate, stress wave emission and fractographic studies indicate that hydrogen induced and distilled water induced failure involve essentially the same slow crack growth process.

3. In this steel, the crack growth rate can be approximated by

$$da/dt \simeq \ell^*/\Delta t_s$$

where $\ell^*$ is the average crack step size and $\Delta t_s$ is the time between crack steps.

4. The following observations were made concerning crack incubation:

a. Cathodic charging produces excess hydrogen, some of which precipitates at the $M_3C$-type carbide, particle-matrix interfaces.

b. Under rising load, hydrogenation inhibits initial crack growth until a threshold stress intensity is achieved.

c. The crack incubation time for a particular environmental combination was found to be essentially the same as the time between the first and second jumps or the second and third jumps indicating no uniqueness to primary incubation.

5. The following observations were made concerning crack propagation:

a. Both hydrogen and distilled water induced crack growth is accelerated with increasing stress intensity at the crack tip.

b. Stress waves as indicative of discontinuous crack motion were found to describe the crack growth rate in this investigation, the number/second being proportional to da/dt.

c. The time between stress waves, as indicative of a secondary incubation time, $\Delta t_s$, was found to remain nearly *constant* in the case of hydrogen induced crack growth, but was found to *decrease* in a distilled water environment.

d. For each discontinuous crack step, the average step size could be related to the crack tip displacement, $2v_c$, by

$$\ell^* \sim \frac{2v_c}{\pi \epsilon_f} \sim \frac{K^2}{2\sigma_{ys} E \pi \epsilon_f}$$

where $\epsilon_f$ is the fracture strain, K is the stress intensity factor, $\sigma_{ys}$ is the tensile yield stress and E is the modulus of elasticity.

e. Fractography demonstrated that hydrogenated samples, nonhydrogenated samples in distilled water and hydrogenated samples in distilled water all had the same characteristic fracture surface; i.e., intergranular areas between large cleavage facets.

f. Crack growth rate determinations showed a synergistic effect when a hydrogenated sample was tested in distilled water.

6. Phenomenological models for the crack growth rates under hydrogenated or distilled water conditions were derived assuming hydrogen diffusion to be the rate-controlling factor.

a. For hydrogen embrittlement, an initially uniform hydrogen concentration diffusing to a constant distance in front of the crack tip produces localized failure in a time, $\Delta t_s$, which is constant throughout the test. However, the crack growth rate does increase with increasing stress intensity since the localized crack step, $\ell^*$, increases with stress intensity.

b. For distilled water induced cracking, a varying hydrogen-concentration level at the crack tip produces a change in the time between crack steps, $\Delta t_s$. As the stress intensity increases, both $\ell^*$ and $1/\Delta t_s$ increase such that da/dt is a rapidly increasing function of stress intensity.

c. Superposition of the theoretical models gives a synergistic effect similar to what was observed for the experimental data.

## Added Note

In reviewing the paper for publication, the authors noted a serious error considering the compatibility of the crack nucleation and crack propagation hypotheses. In the hydrogen embrittlement model, it was stated that $S^*$, the crack nucleation point, was about $(C_{cr}/C_o)d$ whereas $\ell^*$, the crack growth step, must be greater than about $1/3(C_{cr}/C_o)d$. Thus, at the lower stress intensity levels, $S^*$ could be greater than $\ell^*$. This immediately raises the question, "How is it possible for the crack to jump a distance short of where it is nucleated?"

The above approximations were chosen so as to give a reasonable fit to the data. The fact that this leads to $S^*$ being greater than $\ell^*$ in some instances requires a re-assessment of the assumptions. There are three alternatives:

(1) It could be that the diffusion model is in error conceptually. This, however, awaits better evidence.

(2) It could be that $S^*$ is actually greater than $\ell^*$. This possibility arises since the problem was considered as a plane problem whereas it is a three-dimensional situation. Say that at a number of sites along the crack profile, the crack is initiated at $S^*$. At a certain point, the crack jumps forward to these points of initiation but remains fixed along the rest of its profile. This would require the crack front to be a series of hills and valleys. If this were possible, then the crack jump distance could be much larger locally than what is obtained by averaging through the thickness. Thus, even though $\ell^*$ may be locally as great as $S^*$, over the entire thickness, $\ell^*_{Avg}$ could be less than $S^*$.

(3) Although this latter situation is possible, it would be conceptually better and mathematically desirable to have $S^* \leqslant \ell^*$. This could be possible while still retaining the original diffusion model if one of the chosen constants were

436

in error. It is significant that in the initial analysis, the hydrogen diffusivity was taken as $2 \times 10^{-7}$ cm$^2$/sec. This value, although reasonable for a relatively homogeneous steel with low dislocation density, may be in error when severe hydrogen trapping is involved. In a recent British Welding Research Association report,[30] the effect of hydrogen traps on diffusivity is discussed. Depending upon the number of traps (as related to both deformation and inclusions), the diffusivity could be reduced by one or two orders of magnitude. In the present study, carbides were shown to act as hydrogen traps. If an order of magnitude decrease in D resulted from trapping, then in order to maintain the experimental fit to the data, S* in Equation (17) would have to be about $1/3(C_{cr}/C_o)d$. This would conveniently result in $S^* \leqslant \ell^*$ even at the lower bound of Equation (19).

Of the three alternatives, the latter is the most attractive since it not only makes better sense from a diffusion standpoint but also provides internal consistency between the crack initiation and propagation concepts.

## Acknowledgments

The research upon which this paper was based was sponsored under Contract AF 33(615)-2788 by the Air Force Materials Laboratory, Research and Technology Division, W-PAFB, with Mr. R. T. Ault as Project Engineer. Appreciation is also extended to Dr. G. S. Baker for his many helpful comments and suggestions.

## References

1. G. A. Dreyer and W. C. Gallaugher. *Investigation of the Effects of Stress Corrosion on High Strength Steels,* AFML-TDR-64-3, (1964) February.
2. B. F. Brown. A New Stress Corrosion Cracking Test Procedure for High Strength Alloys. *ASTM Materials Res. and Stds.,* **66**, No. 3, 129 (1966).
3. H. H. Johnson and A. M. Willner. Moisture and Stable Crack Growth in a High Strength Steel. *Applied Materials Res.,* **4**, 34 (1965) January.
4. W. F. Brown, Jr. and J. E. Srawley. *Plane Strain Crack Toughness Testing of High Strength Metallic Materials,* ASTM Special Tech. Pub., No. 410, 12 (1966).
5. C. E. Hartbower, W. W. Gerberich and H. Liebowitz. Investigation of Crack Growth Stress Wave Relationships. Presented at the National Symposium on Fracture Mechanics, Lehigh, 1967. To be published, *Journal of Applied Fracture Mechanics,* **1**, (1968).
6. A. R. Elsea and E. E. Fletcher. *Hydrogen-Induced Delayed, Brittle Failures of High Strength Steels.* DMIC Report 196 (1964) January.
7. H. H. Johnson, J. G. Morlet, and A. R. Troiano. Hydrogen, Crack Initiation, and Delayed Failure in Steel. *Trans. AIME,* **212**, No. 4, 528 (1958).
8. P. R. Swann and J. D. Embury. Microstructural Aspects of Stress Corrosion Failure. *High Strength Materials,* ed. V. F. Zackay, John Wiley and Sons, New York, p. 351 (1965).
9. C. E. Hartbower, W. W. Gerberich, and P. P. Crimmins. *Mechanisms of Slow Crack Growth in High Strength Steels,* AFML TR-67-26 (1967) February.
10. A. R. Troiano. The Role of Hydrogen and Other Interstitials in the Mechanical Behavior of Metals. *Trans. ASM,* **52**, 54 (1960).
11. A. H. Cottrell. *Dislocations and Plastic Flow in Crystals,* Oxford University Press, London (1953).
12. T. Bonizewski and G. C. Smith. *Acta Met.,* **11**, 166 (1963).
13. J. Hult and F. McClintock. *Ninth International Cong. Appl. Mech., Brussels,* **8**, 51 (1956).
14. E. E. Fletcher and A. R. Elsea. DMIC Report 219, Battelle Memorial Institute (1965).
15. W. Geller and T. Sun. *Arch. Eisenkuttenw.,* **21**, 437 (1950).
16. D. J. Carney, J. Chipman and N. Grant. *AIME Elec. Furn. Steel Proc.,* **6**, 34 (1948).
17. M. Smialowski. *Hydrogen in Steel,* Pergamon Press, Oxford, p. 154 (1962).
18. M. Gell, J. P. Briant and W. D. Robertson. *Trans. AIME,* **239**, 813 (1967).
19. A. A. Wells. *British Weld J.,* **10**, 573 (1963).
20. G. T. Hahn and A. R. Rosenfield. Sources of Fracture Toughness: The Relation Between $K_{Ic}$ and the Ordinary Tensile Properties of Metals. Presented ASTM Symposium on Applications Related Phenomena in Titanium and Its Alloys, Los Angeles, April, 1967.
21. B. F. Brown and C. D. Beachem. *Corrosion Science,* **5**, 745 (1965).
22. W. W. Gerberich, C. E. Hartbower, and P. P. Crimmins. A Fracture Mechanics Concept for Time to Failure in a Stress Corrosion Test. Presented at ASM Metals Forum on Stress Corrosion, Chicago, November, 1966.
23. A. S. Tetelman. *Fracture of Solids,* ed. D. C. Drucker and J. J. Gilman, Interscience, John Wiley and Sons, New York, p. 671 (1963).
24. P. Bardenheurer and G. Thanheiser. *Mitt. Kaiser Wilhem Inst. fur Eisenforschung,* **10**, 323 (1928).
25. A. S. Tetelman, T. R. Wilshaw, and C. A. Rau, Jr. The Critical Tensile Stress Criterion for Cleavage. Presented International Symposium on Fracture Mechanics, Stockholm, August, 1967.
26. P. G. Shewmon. *Diffusion in Solids.* McGraw-Hill, New York, p. 14 (1963).
27. G. Chaudron and L. Moreau. *Arch. Metall.,* **2**, 308 (1948).
28. A. S. Tetelman. *Fracture of Solids.* ed. D. C. Drucker and J. J. Gilman, Interscience, John Wiley and Sons, New York, p. 463 (1963).
29. P. C. Paris and G. C. Sih. *Fracture Toughness Testing and Its Applications,* ASTM Special Tech. Pub. No. 381, p. 30 (1965).
30. F. R. Coe and J. Moreton. Estimation of Diffusivity Coefficients for Hydrogen in Ferrous Materials. *British Welding Journal,* 43 (1967) June.

## Appendix

A detailed comparison was made between the hydrogen embrittlement model and data[7] on 4340 steel heat treated to the 230,000 psi tensile strength level. To accomplish this, it was necessary (1) to convert Johnson's[7] data into stress intensity factors and (2) to determine the time to failure in terms of initial and final stress intensities and the average crack growth rate.

In the conversion of net-section-stress data to stress intensity factors, it was first necessary to describe the stress intensity for the notch-round samples used by Johnson. From Paris and Sih,[29]

$$K_I = \sigma_{NET} (\hbar D_N)^{1/2} F (d_N/D_N) \qquad \text{(A-1)}$$

where $\sigma_{NET}$ is the net-section stress, $D_N$ is the outer diameter of the test bar and $d_N$ is the diameter of the notch root. The values of $d_N$ and $D_N$ were 0.175 and 0.250 in, respectively. During hydrogen-induced slow crack growth, $d_N$ would decrease and thus $d_N/D_N$ would decrease. For $d_N/D_N$ values ranging from 0.40 to 0.70, $F(d_N/D_N)$ ranges from 0.21 to 0.24.[29] As this was the expected range for these tests, a useful approximation for this set of data is

$$K_I \simeq 0.40\, \sigma_{NET}\, (D_N)^{1/2} \qquad \text{(A-2)}$$

For the 300,000 psi notch strength observed in 4340 steel with no hydrogenation, Equation (A-2) indicates an apparent $K_{Ic}$ of 64 ksi-in$^{1/2}$ ("apparent" since the size of the bars tested by Johnson, et al[7] were not quite large enough to give valid $K_{Ic}$ estimates). This, however, does not invalidate the present approach since apparent $K_{Ic}$ may serve as a failure condition for specimens of a similar diameter. Using Equation (A-2), the initial stress intensity factors were calculated for Johnson's data and put into the form of $K_i/K_{Ic}$. These values plotted against experimentally observed failure times are given in Figure 13.

It was next necessary to calculate the time to failure based upon the proposed model. Using an approach similar to what was used in Equations (13), (14), and (15), it may be shown that in terms of the initial, $K_i$, and critical, $K_{Ic}$, stress intensity factors, that the time to failure is

$$t_f = d_N \left[ 1 - \frac{K_i}{K_{Ic}} \right] \left[ da/dt \right]^{-1} \qquad \text{(A-3)}$$

The next step is to describe $da/dt$ from the hydrogen diffusion model. First, it will be recalled from Equation (20) that $da/dt$ may be described by $\ell^*$ and $\Delta t_s$. Since $\ell^*$ is varying throughout the test due to increased stress intensity, when one is considering the total time to failure, the average value of $\ell^*$ or Equation (11) must be utilized. This, in conjunction with Equations (A-3), (18) and (20) leads to

$$t_f = d_N \left[ 1 - \frac{K_i}{K_c} \right] \left[ \frac{6\sigma_{ys}\, E\pi\epsilon_f\, (K_{Ic} - K_i)(C_{cr} - C_o)}{(K_{Ic}^3 - K_i^3)(4DC_o)} \left( \frac{C_{cr}d}{C_o} \right)^2 \right] \qquad \text{(A-4)}$$

The unknown parameters are $d$ and $\epsilon_f$. Since 4340 steel is similar in composition to D6aC steel; since the two steels were heat treated to similar fracture toughness levels; and since they were both about equally susceptible to hydrogen embrittlement, the parameters of $d$ and $\epsilon_f$ from the present investigation were utilized. Thus, for any initial stress intensity level, $K_i$, the time to failure may be calculated from Equation (A-4). The threshold value of Equation (19) was also invoked, which, in terms of initial stress intensity, would be

$$K_i^2 > \frac{2}{3} \frac{C_{cr}}{C_o} d\sigma_{ys}\, E\pi\epsilon_f \qquad \text{(A-5)}$$

For an assumed critical hydrogen content of 10 ppm and several initial concentration levels, $C_o$, Equations (A-4) and (A-5) give the solid curves in Figure 12.

# ON HYDROGEN BRITTLENESS IN HIGH STRENGTH STEELS

H. H. Johnson
Cornell University

## Abstract

Recent experiments on hydrogen and slow crack growth in high strength steels are discussed and interpreted in terms of current concepts of hydrogen brittleness. Crack growth activation energies for internal and external hydrogen environments are in agreement with the measured activation energy for hydrogen diffusion in a high strength steel.

Molecular hydrogen at atmospheric pressure induces a more severe brittleness than either water or the usual electrolytic charging conditions. It is concluded that the pressure mechanism of hydrogen embrittlement is not operative in high strength steels.

## I. Introduction

The brittleness induced in steel by hydrogen is a problem of continuing theoretical and practical interest. In recent years more attention has been directed to high strength steels, no doubt because they are of interest in weight saving applications and may be susceptible to both brittle[1-6] and delayed[1-4] fracture at astonishingly low hydrogen concentrations. With damaging hydrogen concentrations well under one part per million, delayed failures have been observed[2] at applied stresses less than one-tenth of the yield strength in sharply notched and cathodically charged specimens of high strength steel. Hydrogen contents of this magnitude may be acquired from diverse and often unexpected sources.

With the lower strength quenched and tempered steels substantially greater hydrogen concentrations are necessary to induce brittleness. These higher hydrogen contents are unlikely to occur adventitiously. An unusually complete picture is contained in Figure 1 from Farrell and Quarrell,[6] which presents the smooth tensile fracture ductility as a function of both total hydrogen content and strength level. It is evident that damaging hydrogen concentrations of less than one-half part per million cause a severe brittleness at the highest strength level, as measured by reduction in area at fracture. It should also be recalled that sharply notched or precracked steel is more sensitive than smooth sections to hydrogen embrittlement; indeed, hydrogen-induced crack growth has been observed[2] at hydrogen levels which did not lower the reduction in area at fracture.

It is generally agreed that brittleness does not arise from hydrogen uniformly distributed in solution, for the average damaging hydrogen concentration is just too low to account for the observed effects. Several well-documented observations suggest that hydrogen diffuses to characteristic sites during deformation, and that the segregated hydrogen

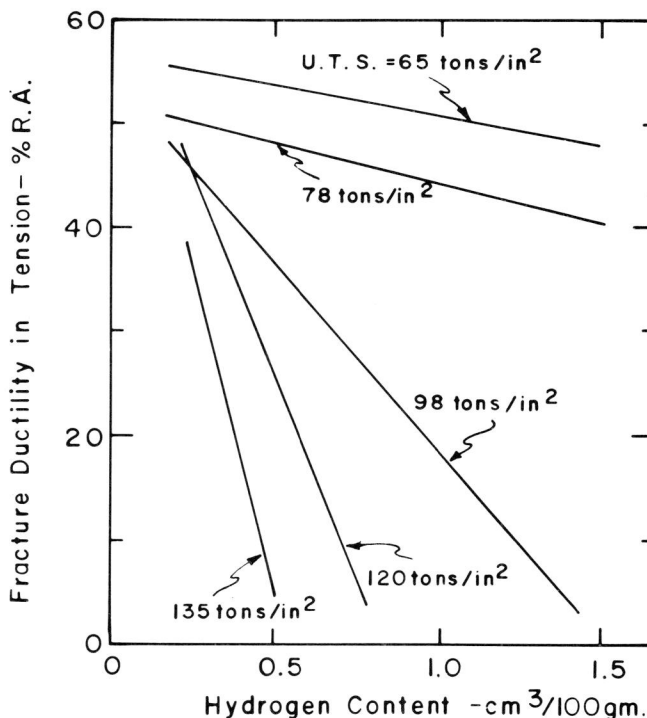

FIGURE 1 – Hydrogen concentration and fracture ductility of steel at different strength levels.[6]

439

is responsible for the brittle behavior. These observations include:

1. the very low average damaging hydrogen concentrations. Figure 1, for one part per million corresponds to only one hydrogen atom for about twenty thousand iron atoms,

2. the very high diffusivity[7] of hydrogen in iron and steel,

3. the unusual strain rate and temperature[8] dependence of hydrogen embrittlement,

4. the insensitivity of the true fracture stress to hydrogen level,[2] even when hydrogen-induced crack growth occurs at very low applied stresses, and

5. the lack of any significant effect of hydrogen upon the level of the stress-strain curve prior to fracture.

This last observation suggests strongly that hydrogen does not hinder the motion of dislocations, and that hydrogen simply allows or forces the normal fracture processes to become operative at unusually low macroscopic strains. In this sense hydrogen may be described as a catalyst for fracture.

Although general agreement exists on the segregation of hydrogen during deformation, there is considerable divergence of opinion as to the succeeding stages in the embrittlement process. Both the site of segregation and the embrittlement mechanism are controversial. Complete reviews[9-11] of the suggested mechanisms and the relevant experimental evidence are available, so attention here will be restricted to the basic physical concepts that have been invoked.

In one school of thought[12-14] the brittleness is associated with the development of high hydrogen pressures in internal voids. Atomic hydrogen in supersaturated solid solution is presumed to precipitate into voids or fissures developed during deformation, recombine to the molecular form, and build up a very substantial interior pressure. The driving force for the process is the supersaturated solution, and the interior pressure is then considered simply additive to the applied stress. This concept has the real and undeniable virtue of simplicity, but as will be evident later, it cannot be reconciled with the observed facts for high strength steels.

In the spirit of the Griffith analysis of fracture it has been suggested[15] that hydrogen lowers the fracture stress via adsorption on interior surfaces. Adsorption is presumed to lower the surface energy and therefore the fracture stress. This concept is considerably more difficult to test experimentally. In addition there is a conceptual uncertainty; since adsorption must of necessity follow in time an increment of crack extension, the kinetic mechanism whereby the increment of clean crack forms prior to adsorption is far from clear.

As the outcome of an exhaustive investigation of crack growth in hydrogenated high strength steels, Troiano et al[2-4,9,16] suggested that hydrogen diffused to regions of high triaxial stress and then acted to reduce the theoretical cohesive or fracture strength of the material. With these concepts a diverse set of experimental observations, such as the existence of reversible incubation periods for crack

initiation, the variation of crack initiation site with notch sharpness, and the effect of post-hydrogenation plastic strain upon ductility, were brought together in a self-consistent framework. Independent experimental support for the concept of hydrogen segregation in triaxially stressed regions has been provided by the recent electron microautoradiographic investigation of Gilpin et al.[17] With tritium as the isotope and a fine-grain nuclear emulsion, these investigators report that hydrogen migrates to a region near the notch root when a cathodically charged specimen is loaded in tension. However, a direct demonstration that hydrogen reduces the theoretical cohesive strength is admittedly difficult.

In this paper more recent experiments on hydrogen-induced brittleness and crack propagation are discussed. In II the role of water and water vapor as embrittling agents is considered, while III is directed to gas environments, especially hydrogen and oxygen. In IV the discussion turns again to mechanism.

## II. Slow Crack Growth, Water and Water Vapor

As a result of several recent investigations,[18-20] it is clear that water and water vapor can induce slow crack growth and delayed fracture in precracked specimens of high strength steel at applied stresses far below the net section yield strength. This effect displays many phenomenological similarities to hydrogen-induced slow crack growth and delayed fracture:

1. Water-induced brittleness, as measured by threshold stress intensity or crack growth rate, is comparable in magnitude to that observed with electrolytically-introduced hydrogen contents of less than one part per million.

2. Reversible incubation periods have been reported for both water[19] and hydrogen[12]-induced crack initiation.

3. In both cases a definite critical stress intensity, or applied stress, exists below which delayed fracture is not observed.

4. In both cases brittle behavior is more evident at high strength levels.

These similarities suggest that hydrogen is the causative agent in water-induced slow crack propagation and delayed fracture. This suggestion is further supported by a consideration of the temperature dependence of the crack growth rate.

A thermally-activated mechanism for crack growth in water and saturated water vapor is indicated[20] by Figure 2. Center precracked specimens of H-11 steel were tested at a constant stress intensity factor, and an apparent activation energy for crack growth of about 9000 cal/g.-atom was measured. In unsaturated water vapor the crack growth behavior is quite different; for a constant water vapor content, the crack growth rate actually decreases with increasing temperature. The activation energy of 9000 cal/g.-atom in water is in good agreement with a more recent study.[21]

A comparison of activation energies for water[20,21] and hydrogen[3]-induced crack growth suggests that hydrogen is the damaging agent in water-induced slow crack growth. A

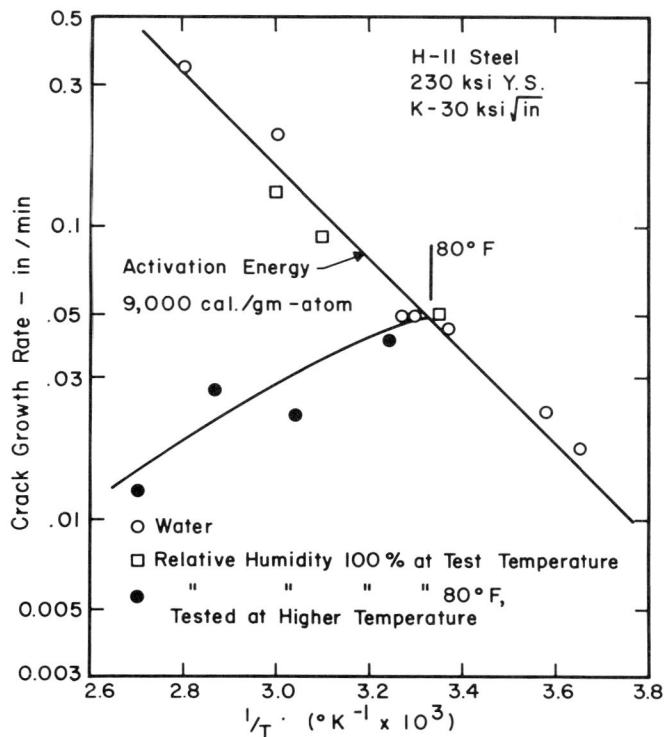

FIGURE 2 – Temperature dependence of crack growth in water and water vapor, H-11 steel.[20]

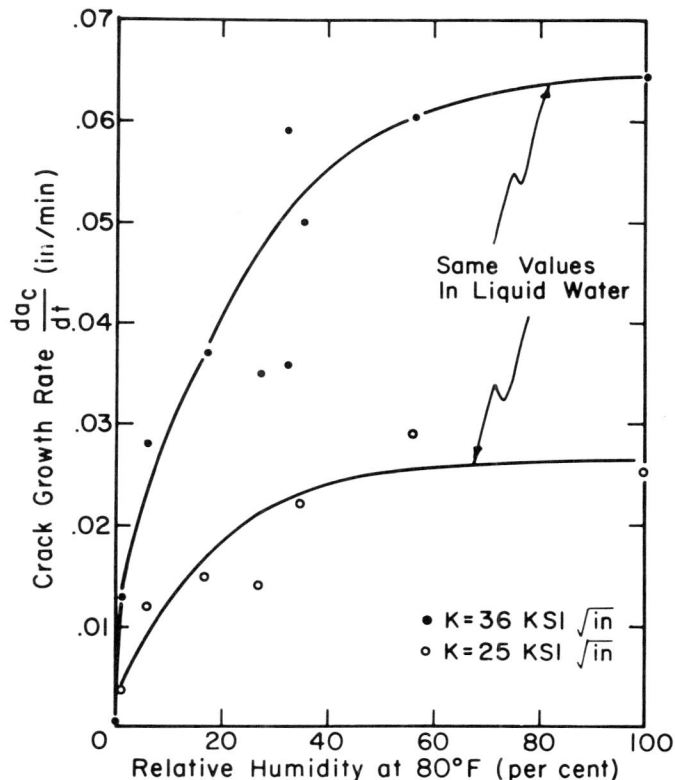

FIGURE 3 – Saturation of crack growth rates at relative humidities in excess of about sixty percent, H-11 steel.[20]

TABLE 1 – Activation Energies for Hydrogen-Induced Crack Growth, Brittleness, Recovery from Brittleness, and Diffusion in High Strength Steels

| Investigator | Experimental Description | Activation Energy |
|---|---|---|
| Beck, Bockris, McBreen, Nanis[7] | diffusion of electrolytic hydrogen through AISI 4340 | 9220 cal/g-atom |
| Johnson and Willner[20] | crack growth in water and saturated water vapor, center-cracked plates (H-11) | 9000 cal/g-atom |
| Van Der Sluys[21] | precracked double cantilever beam in water (4340) | 8500 cal/g-atom |
| Steigerwald, Schaller, and Troiano[3] | incubation period for crack initiation in cathodically charged notched rounds (4340) | 9120 cal/g-atom |
| Farrell and Quarrell[6] | time for 50% recovery of fracture stress, cathodic charging | 9800 cal/g-atom |
| Morlet, Johnson, and Troiano[16] | time for 50% of maximum brittleness, R.A., cathodic charging (4340) | 9600 cal/g-atom |
| Morlet, Johnson, and Troiano[16] | time for 50% recovery of R.A., cathodic charging (4340) | 8500 cal/g-atom |

441

compilation of these values is given in Table 1, along with activation energies for the onset[16] and recovery of hydrogen[6,16] brittleness and for hydrogen diffusion.[7] In view of the diversity of experimental methods and the scatter normally encountered in fracture testing, the agreement among the various crack growth and brittleness investigations is impressive. The water and hydrogen-induced slow crack growth activation energies are seen to be essentially identical, and this of course suggests a common mechanism. Further, the close agreement with the diffusion activation energy suggests that volume hydrogen diffusion is the rate-limiting factor in the embrittlement mechanism.

It should be noted that both internal (electrolytic hydrogen) and external (water) environments are represented in Table 1. Thus, the agreement of activation energies supports the concept of hydrogen migration under stress and further suggests that the embrittlement mechanism is independent of the source of hydrogen, and of the distribution of hydrogen at the time of stress application. In addition, volume diffusion is indicated to be the rate-limiting factor for both the onset and recovery of hydrogen brittleness.

The agreement between crack growth rates measured in water and saturated water vapor is striking, and has been interpreted[20] to result from water vapor condensation at the crack tip in highly humid environments. In room temperature experiments it appears that condensation occurs at about sixty percent relative humidity, Figure 3. The data are again for center-cracked H-11 steel specimens in argon-water vapor mixtures, with oxygen excluded. Saturation behavior is evident at both levels of stress intensity factor. Therefore, in highly humid environments the crack is effectively propagating in a little pool of bulk liquid. A similar saturation behavior is observed for moisture-enhanced fatigue crack growth in high strength steels.[22] It must be emphasized, however, that capillary condensation at the crack tip has not been demonstrated directly, but only inferred from an equivalence of crack growth rates.

The crack propagation mechanism is not thermally activated in an unsaturated water vapor environment, Figure 2; rather, for a constant water vapor content, the crack growth rate decreases with increasing temperature. This behavior suggests a surface-controlled process connected with water vapor adsorption. For a constant water vapor concentration the driving force for adsorption will decrease with increasing temperature, and adsorption isotherms are qualitatively similar to the curves of Figure 3.

It has been tacitly assumed in this section that both water and water vapor can supply hydrogen to the surface of steel, and that the hydrogen will then diffuse into the interior. For clean surfaces and water this was apparently first shown experimentally by Norton,[23] and has been confirmed by more recent investigations.[24] The diffusing hydrogen presumably results from the following reaction at the steel-water interface,

$$Fe + H_2O = FeO + H_2$$

Less extensive experimental results[25,26] also indicate that water vapor in contact with a clean surface can act as a source of hydrogen. This conclusion was inferred from measured hydrogen permeation rates when the entry surface was continually abraded while exposed to air. The measured permeation rate decreased markedly with a relative humidity of less than about 0.8 percent. With the clean surface provided by abrasion, the permeation rates were much higher than the values associated with normal atmospheric corrosion. The permeation rates were also decreased by the addition of oxidizing agents to the entry environment.

In the crack growth experiments summarized here the stressed crack tip undoubtedly is a clean surface.

### III. Hydrogen and Oxygen Environments

A striking brittleness associated with an external environment of molecular hydrogen at atmospheric pressure is demonstrated[27] in Table 2 and Figure 4 for center-cracked specimens of H-11 steel. Subcritical cracks initiate in hydrogen at lower stress field intensities and propagate at higher rates than in wet argon. The embrittlement potential of the hydrogen gas is remarkable, and appears to exceed the effective potential of both water and the electrolytic charging conditions normally employed.[2]

It is generally accepted that hydrogen can enter solid steel only in the atomic (or perhaps ionic) form; further, at room temperature hydrogen gas is quite completely molecular. However, hydrogen does disassociate upon chemisorption on iron,[28] and it may reasonably be assumed that the source of brittleness is the adsorbed

TABLE 2—Crack Initiation ($K_i$) and Unstable Fracture ($K_{Ic}$) Stress Field Intensities

|  | Hydrogen | Wet Argon | Dry Argon |
|---|---|---|---|
| $K_i$ (ksi $\sqrt{in}$) | 11 | 18 | 40 |
| $K_{Ic}$ (ksi $\sqrt{in}$) | $-^{(1)}$ | 40 | 40 |

$^{(1)}$Because of the long subcritical crack, $K_{Ic}$ could not be measured.

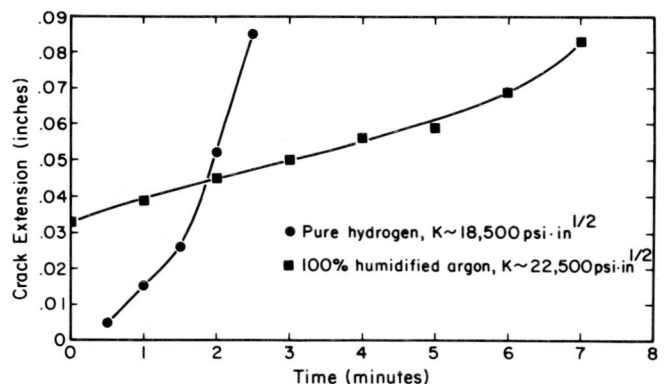

FIGURE 4 — Sub-critical crack growth in molecular hydrogen at atmospheric pressure and humidified Argon, H-11 steel.[27]

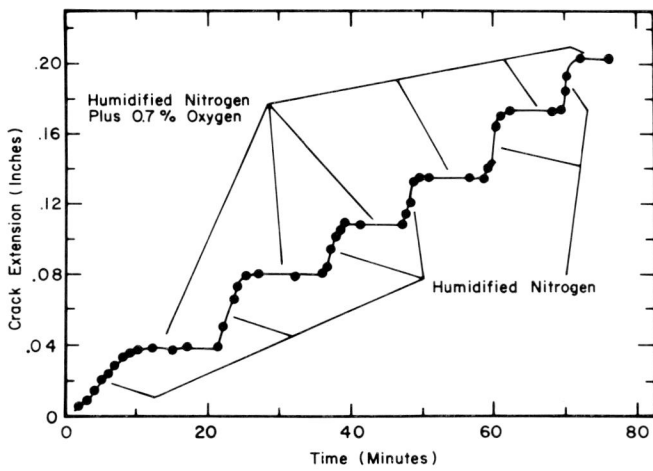

FIGURE 5 — Oxygen and sub-critical crack growth in humidified nitrogen, H-11 steel.[27]

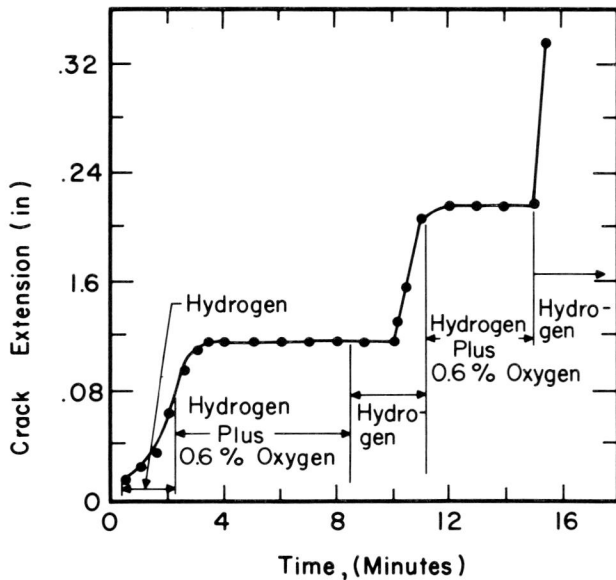

FIGURE 6 — Hydrogen-oxygen mixtures and sub-critical crack growth, H-11 steel.[27]

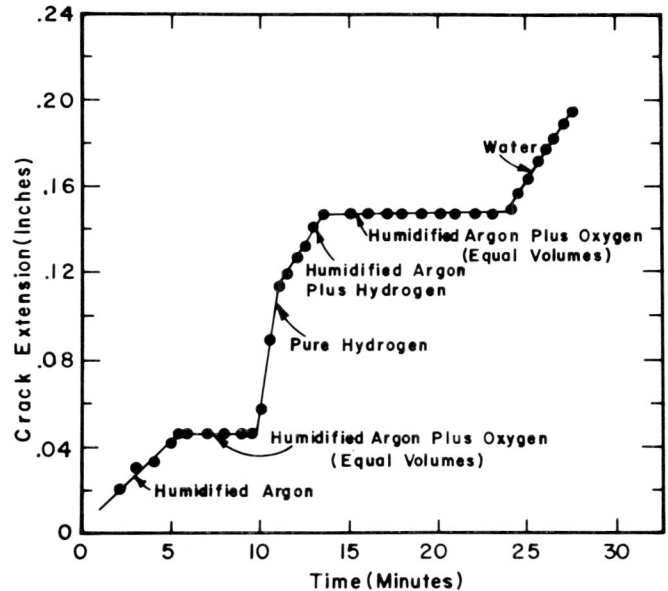

FIGURE 7 — Sub-critical crack growth in different water, water vapor, hydrogen, and oxygen environments, H-11 steel.[27]

hydrogen. Adsorption of hydrogen upon iron is virtually instantaneous[29] and this is consistent with the lack of an incubation period for crack initiation.

The influence of oxygen in vapor environments upon subcritical crack growth is equally striking, but in the opposite direction, for oxygen prevents initiation from a subcritical crack, and will even stop an already propagating crack. This effect is displayed in Figures 5-7 from Hancock and Johnson[27] for crack growth in environments containing varying proportions of argon, water, nitrogen, water vapor, hydrogen, and oxygen. It is evident that as little as 0.6 percent oxygen was sufficient to terminate subcritical crack growth in vapor environments essentially instantaneously. It is also evident from Figure 7 that moisture is the dominant component in a moisture-hydrogen environment, which is consistent with the condensation interpretation.

An oxygen-stopped crack may be restarted only when oxygen is removed from the gas environment. This suggests that the crack tip surface must adsorb oxygen in preference to hydrogen and water vapor. This is consistent with the well-known affinity of iron for oxygen, as reflected by a very high heat of adsorption and as multilayer coverage of iron by oxygen.[30] It has been suggested that this multilayer is essentially an oxide, and the logical interpretation is that this oxide provides an effective barrier to the passage of hydrogen. Presumably, when the oxygen supply is removed, hydrogen may reduce the oxide, while water and water vapor may either supply hydrogen or perhaps dissolve the oxide. Dissolution seems more probable with water.

The hydrogen-reduction hypothesis is consistent with a low energy electron-diffraction investigation[31] of the interaction between nickel and hydrogen and oxygen, which showed both preferential adsorption of oxygen and displacement of the oxygen by hydrogen when the oxygen supply was removed.

Further indirect confirmation is provided by the permeation experiments of Ewing and Ubbelohde.[32] They studied the permeation of electrolytic hydrogen through a decarburized steel membrane at rather high current densities, and also explored the effect upon hydrogen permeation of supplying different gases, principally nitrogen and oxygen, to the exit surface of the membrane. The experimental conditions are therefore not exactly equivalent to those of hydrogen embrittlement in high strength steels, but the results are nonetheless of considerable interest.

The permeation of hydrogen was substantially reduced when oxygen was supplied to the exit surface of the membrane from the gas phase, but the permeation activation energy was unaffected. The phenomenon may be described as "oxygen blocking" since no interaction was evident between the adsorbed oxygen and the hydrogen coming from the interior of the membrane except at very high current densities. It was established that the blocking process was reversible, i.e., upon evacuation of oxygen the normal permeation rate was quickly attained. Thus, these results are in qualitative accord with the observation that oxygen eliminates subcritical crack growth in vapor environments.

In further crack growth experiments[20,27] it was established that hydrogen entered from the external environment only when the specimen was under stress. In one experiment prior exposure to hydrogen gas for three hours at room temperature did not affect the subsequent crack initiation and growth behavior under stress. Evidently, hydrogen can enter only at a clean and oxygen-free surface, and this is provided at the stressed crack tip.

## IV. Comments on Mechanism

The experimental results just summarized indicate clearly that high strength steels are embrittled to about the same degree by water and the usual electrolytic charging conditions, and to a greater degree by molecular hydrogen at atmospheric pressure. This conclusion is evident from a comparison of threshold stress intensities and crack growth rates, and suggests that the "embrittlement potential" of low pressure hydrogen gas exceeds that of either water or electrolytic hydrogen. Furthermore, the correspondence of the activation energies reported in Table 1 suggests that the embrittlement mechanism is the same for external and internal sources of hydrogen. This in turn is in agreement with the usual concept that hydrogen migrates under stress or deformation, presumably to regions of high triaxial stress.

The pressure theory of hydrogen embrittlement cannot be reconciled with the substantial brittleness observed in molecular hydrogen at atmospheric pressure. The dissolved hydrogen concentration in the crack tip vicinity should not, from a thermodynamic point of view, exceed the value associated with an external hydrogen pressure of one atmosphere. Consequently, the development of substantial pressures in internal voids or microcracks is improbable. This reasoning should be equally valid for any hydrogen source, internal or external, which causes brittleness comparable to that of molecular hydrogen at atmospheric pressure. Therefore, it may also be concluded that the pressure concept cannot account for the slow crack growth and delayed fracture in high strength steels caused by water or electrolytically-introduced hydrogen.

## Acknowledgments

The author wishes to acknowledge the financial support of the Advanced Research Projects Agency through the Materials Science Center at Cornell University.

## References

1. R. P. Frohmberg, W. J. Barnett, and A. R. Troiano. *Trans. ASM*, **47**, 892 (1955).
2. H. H. Johnson, J. G. Morlet, and A. R. Troiano. *Trans. Met. Soc. AIME*, **212**, 526 (1958).
3. E. A. Steigerwald, F. W. Schaller, and A. R. Troiano. *Trans. Met. Soc. AIME*, **215**, 1048 (1959).
4. E. A. Steigerwald, F. W. Schaller, and A. R. Troiano. *Trans. Met. Soc. AIME*, **218**, 832 (1960).
5. J. G. Morlet, H. H. Johnson, and A. R. Troiano. *J.I.S.I.*, **189**, 37 (1958).
6. K. Farrell and A. G. Quarrell. *J.I.S.I.*, **202**, 1002 (1964).
7. W. Beck, J. O'M. Bockris, J. McBreen, and L. Nanis. *Proc. Roy. Soc., (London)*, A290, 221 (1966).
8. J. T. Brown and W. M. Baldwin, Jr. *Trans. Met. Soc. AIME*, **200**, 298 (1954).
9. A. R. Troiano. *Trans. ASM*, **52**, 54 (1960).
10. A. S. Tetelman. *Fracture of Solids*, (D. C. Drucker and J. J. Gilman, eds.) pp. 671-708, Interscience, New York (1963).
11. A. R. Elsea and E. E. Fletcher. Hydrogen-Induced, Delayed, Brittle Failures of High Strength Steels. Defense Metals Information Center Report 196, Battelle Memorial Institute (1964).
12. C. Zappfe and C. Sims. *Trans. AIME*, **145**, 225 (1941).
13. A. S. Tetelman and W. D. Robertson. *Trans. Met. Soc. AIME*, **224**, 775 (1962).
14. A. S. Tetelman and W. D. Robertson. *Acta Met.*, **11**, 415 (1963).
15. N. J. Petch and P. Stables. *Nature*, **169**, 842 (1952).
16. J. G. Morlet, H. H. Johnson, and A. R. Troiano. *J.I.S.I.*, **188**, 37 (1958).
17. C. B. Gilpin, D. H. Paul, S. K. Asunmaa, and N. A. Tiner. *Advances in Electron Metallography*, pp. 7-20, American Society for Testing and Materials Special Technical Publication 396 (1966).
18. E. A. Steigerwald. *Proc. ASTM*, **60**, 750 (1960).
19. G. L. Hanna, A. R. Troiano, and E. A. Steigerwald. *Trans. ASM*, **57**, 658 (1964).
20. H. H. Johnson and A. M. Willner. *Appl. Mat. Res.*, **4**, 34 (1965).
21. W. A. Van Der Sluys. Mechanisms of Environment-Induced Subcritical Flaw Growth in AISI 4340 Steel. Presented at First National Symposium on Fracture Mechanics, Lehigh University (1967).
22. C. Y. Li, P. M. Talda, and R. P. Wei. To be published in the *International Journal of Fracture Mechanics*.
23. F. J. Norton. *J. Appl. Phys.*, **11**, 262 (1940).
24. R. C. Frank, D. E. Swets, and D. L. Fry. *J. Appl. Phys.*, **29**, 892 (1958).
25. R. C. Frank and D. E. Swets. *J. Appl. Phys.*, **28**, 380 (1957).
26. D. E. Swets, R. C. Frank, and D. L. Fry. *Trans. Met. Soc. AIME*, **212**, 219 (1958).
27. G. G. Hancock and H. H. Johnson. *Trans. Met. Soc. AIME*, **236**, 513 (1966).
28. D. O. Hayward and B. M. W. Trapnell. *Chemisorption*, pp. 236-237, Butterworths, Washington (1964).
29. A. S. Porter and F. S. Tompkins. *Proc. Roy. Soc., (London)* A217, 544 (1953).
30. D. Brennan, D. O. Hayward, and B. M. W. Trapnell. *Proc. Roy. Soc., (London)* A256, 81 (1960).
31. L. H. Germer and A. U. MacRae. *J. Appl. Phys.*, **37**, 1382 (1962).
32. V. C. Ewing and A. R. Ubbelohde. *Proc. Roy. Soc., (London)* A230, 301 (1955).

# Discussion

**H. H. Uhlig, MIT:**

I would conclude that cracking in presence of one atmosphere hydrogen supports an adsorption mechanism. Perhaps Bill Robertson also concurs that adsorption can in part enter the formation of cracks in his experiments where a decrease in solubility of hydrogen resulting from quenching gives rise to high internal pressures. Hydrogen blisters in steel suggest that some pressure must have caused them. But I think that in the experiment that has just been described, one is almost forced to the conclusion that hydrogen adsorption alone enters the underlying mechanism of crack growth. I do not know how else it can be explained.

I have one comment on the effect of humidity. You found that an environment of one hundred percent relative humidity behaved the same with respect to crack propagation as did liquid water, but as you proceeded to very low relative humidities, the crack propagation rate fell off. Is that right?

I would surmise that at room temperature there is probably no reaction of iron with water vapor in contrast to liquid water with which a finite reaction occurs.

**W. D. Robertson, Yale University:**

When we take an iron silicon single crystal and heat it up to 900 C or so in one atmosphere hydrogen, quench it to room temperature, we observe that it is full of cracks which we see as cracks surrounded by arrays of decorated dislocations.[1] When we repeat the experiment in argon just to prove that something strange isn't going on, we don't find any cracks. Clearly there is a substantial pressure operating inside the crystal and clearly it is associated with the hydrogen.

1. A. S. Tetelman and W. D. Robertson. *Acta. Met.,* 11, 415 (1963).

**Dr. Oriani, U. S. Steel Corp.:**

It appears to me that the activation energy for crack propagation of 9000 calories per mole really applies to trapped diffusion rather than diffusion through a simple homogeneous matrix. Therefore, I question the correlation between activation energies for diffusion through pure iron and through a complicated structure like that of high strength steel. Presumably the distance, through which hydrogen diffuses, will contain traps.

**A. R. C. Westwood, RIAS:**

Have you obtained any evidence for discontinuous crack propagation from your studies, perhaps fractographic evidence?

**H. H. Johnson:**

It is possible that hydrogen can embrittle steel by more than one mechanism, with the operative mechanism depending upon the metallurgical circumstances of microstructure and strength level. As Dr. Uhlig points out, the occurrence of hydrogen blisters is presumptive evidence for substantial internal hydrogen pressures. However, hydrogen blisters are found only in lower strength steels and rarely, to my knowledge, in quenched and tempered high strength steels. Here Dr. Uhlig agrees that a mechanism not involving pressure must be operative.

Professor Robertson alludes to an elegant series of experiments on hydrogen and cracking in iron silicon single crystals. The results do indeed provide strong evidence for internal pressures associated with hydrogen. However, it does not follow necessarily that this is the only effect of the hydrogen. In this connection, it would be of interest to examine crack growth in precracked iron silicon subjected to an external hydrogen environment of known pressure. From a metallurgical point of view, iron silicon and high strength steels are quite different; the former has a lower strength level and a simpler microstructure, and requires higher hydrogen concentrations before displaying embrittlement.

Dr. Oriani questions a correlation which I have been unable to locate in the paper. The diffusion activation energy quoted in Table 1 is not for a pure iron, but rather, as is clearly indicated,[7] for an AISI 4340 membrane quenched and tempered to a strength level of 260,000 psi. The reported diffusion[7] activation energy of 9220 cal/mol is about four times the value normally obtained with pure iron. This difference may well be due to "traps", but the use of this term is of little value until the physical nature of the traps is elucidated.

In reply to Dr. Westwood, we have not undertaken a systematic fractographic investigation. However, it would not be surprising to find discontinuous crack growth with a size scale smaller than can be resolved by the electric potential method.

# THE MECHANISM OF HYDROGEN
# EMBRITTLEMENT IN STEEL

A. S. Tetelman*
Stanford University

## Abstract

The process of brittle fracture in structural materials can be separated into three stages: (1) crack nucleation, (2) slow crack growth, and (3) rapid, unstable fracture. Hydrogen embrittles steel by affecting the first two of these stages. In corroded, electrolytically charged or thermally charged specimens, excess hydrogen precipitates at inclusions or carbides in molecular form, causing the initiation of voids or microcracks. The hydrogen pressure in these defects causes them to grow either by plastic deformation or by cleavage, depending on the intrinsic toughness of the particular steel and the shape of the nucleating particle. It is shown that the size of the defects is determined by the spacing of the nucleating particles. Consequently, small voids or cracks will exist when a given volume of second phase is finely distributed. In hot rolled materials, alignment of inclusions can be used to minimize hydrogen embrittlement.

Microcrack or void coalescence, to form a macrocrack, occurs when a stress is applied to a hydrogenated structure. The effect of hydrogen concentration, applied stress, notch geometry, strength level, temperature, and microstructure on the incubation time for slow crack growth, the rate of slow crack growth, and the time to fail in a static test or the tensile ductility are considered. Finally, crack growth in external environments, such as hydrogen gas, is also discussed briefly.

## I. Introduction

During the corrosion process electrons are freed at anodic sites on the metal surface, flow through the metal, and cause a reduction of charged ions at cathodic sites on the surface. While the oxidation processes that occur at the local anode are of great importance in the stress corrosion cracking process, the cathodic reactions are of little importance, provided that the cathode does not become polarized. However, when high strength ferritic or martensitic steels corrode in strongly acidic (pH < 4) or strongly alkaline (pH > 10) solutions, hydrogen ions are reduced to hydrogen atoms at the local cathode. These atoms are able to diffuse into the metal and, in the presence of a sufficiently high stress, cause cracking and even total failure of the structure. This phenomena is known as hydrogen embrittlement. Some of the most spectacular instances of hydrogen embrittlement have occurred in oil well casing and tubing, particularly in natural gas wells that contain $H_2S$.[1]

In addition to the hydrogen embrittlement that can accompany stress corrosion cracking, numerous failures of cadmium plated high strength steel parts, where the hydrogen was introduced during electroplating, have also been reported.[2-5] Hydrogen cracking has also been observed in cast structures when a substantial amount of hydrogen was retained during solidification, particularly in massive castings[6] and in rapidly cooled weld metal.[7-9] More recently, two additional types of hydrogen embrittlement have been noted. First, there is the embrittlement of high strength steel in the presence of water vapor[10-14] or pure hydrogen at one atmosphere pressure. Secondly, there is the embrittlement that occurs in the presence of high pressure hydrogen gas.[15-19]

Since hydrogen embrittlement is one of the most serious forms of time-dependent fracture, a considerable effort has been made to understand the mechanism of cracking. Most of the interpretable research has been performed on plain or notched tensile specimens that were electrolytically (cathodically) charged with hydrogen and consequently the major portion of this review will be concerned with cathodically charged specimens.

In laboratory testing, the embrittlement appears as a decreased tensile ductility (reduction in area) in a tensile test (Figure 1), a decrease in notch tensile strength, and as a delayed failure in a static loading test (Figure 2). The yield strength is relatively unaffected by the presence of hydrogen. As shown in Figure 1, the effect of hydrogen

*Now Professor of Engineering, UCLA, Los Angeles, Calif.

becomes more severe as the strength level of the steel increases.

Several theories have been proposed to explain the mechanism of embrittlement. These theories, as well as most of the significant experimental work, have been reviewed in several extensive treatments during the past decade.[20-26] Basically, the theories fall into two groups. First, there is the "pressure theory" originally proposed by Zapffe,[27] subsequently modified by de Kazinsky,[28] Garofalo et al,[29] Bilby and Hewitt,[30] and Tetelman and Robertson.[31,32] This theory proposes that hydrogen embrittlement results from the precipitation of hydrogen gas at defects such as inclusions, and the expansion of microcracks and voids due to the gas pressure. In this model, the internal pressure, P, lowers the applied stress, $\sigma_F$, necessary to cause crack growth. Thus, below the yield strength $\sigma_Y$, unstable fracture occurs from the tip of a stopped crack[26] when

$$\sigma_F = P = \sqrt{\frac{2 E \gamma_p^*}{\pi c}} \qquad (1)$$

$$(\sigma \ll \sigma_Y)$$

where 2c is the crack length, E is the elastic modulus and $\gamma_p^*$ is the work done in initiating unstable fracture at the crack tip. Alternatively, when hydrogen is present inside a microcrack formed by dislocation pile-ups, the pressure P reduces the stress $\sigma_G$ required for microcrack growth[26,29,30]

$$\sigma_G = \frac{2 \gamma_m}{n b} - P \qquad (2)$$

where n is the number of dislocations in the pile-up having Burgers' vector b and $\gamma_m$ is the work done in microcrack propagation. $\gamma_m$ is directly proportional to the true surface energy, $\gamma_s$.

Secondly, there is the "decreasing strength theory" of Petch and Staples,[33] Bastien[20] and Troiano.[21] This theory proposes that the presence of dissolved hydrogen lowers the cohesive strength of the iron lattice, in a manner similar to that which occurs in liquid metal embrittlement. In this model, the decrease in cohesive strength results in a decrease in the surface energy of fracture and hence in a lowering of the applied stress necessary for crack propagation. Thus for pre-existing cracks

$$\sigma_F = \sqrt{\frac{2 E \gamma_p^*(H)}{\pi c}} \qquad (3)$$

$$(\sigma \ll \sigma_Y)$$

and for microcracks formed by plastic deformation

$$\sigma_G n b = 2 \gamma_m (H) \qquad (4)$$

where $\gamma_p^*(H)$ and $\gamma_m(H)$ signify a lowering of the work expended in crack propagation and microcrack growth in the presence of hydrogen.

Since both models predict a lowering in the stress necessary for crack propagation it is very difficult to separate them experimentally. It is well known, however, that microcracks can be formed in the absence of applied stress, simply by the presence of hydrogen concentrations in excess of the solubility limit[23,24,26-32] (Figure 3). It is difficult to see how these cracks could have been formed if there were no gas expansion to provide the work required to open the crack. Thus, while it is possible that dissolved hydrogen can affect the strength of atomic bonds, there is no evidence that it does so and some evidence from X-ray[34] and diffusion,[35] low temperature fracture,[36] and surface conductance[71] studies that it does not.

Troiano and his coworkers[21,37-39] have presented several valid objections to the original pressure theory; principally, that hydrogen induced crack growth occurs slowly and discontinuously and that the diffusion of hydrogen to regions of tri-axial stress in front of a growing crack is a significant factor in the embrittlement process. The original pressure theory, based on the rapid propagation of a crack when Equation (1) is satisfied, or the formation of an unstable microcrack when Equation (2) is satisfied, cannot account for these objections. However, a modified form of the pressure theory need not be inconsistent with the fact that hydrogen induced crack propagation occurs slowly and discontinuously, as will be shown below. In Section II some of the mechanisms of crack propagation in metals are discussed. The significant experi-

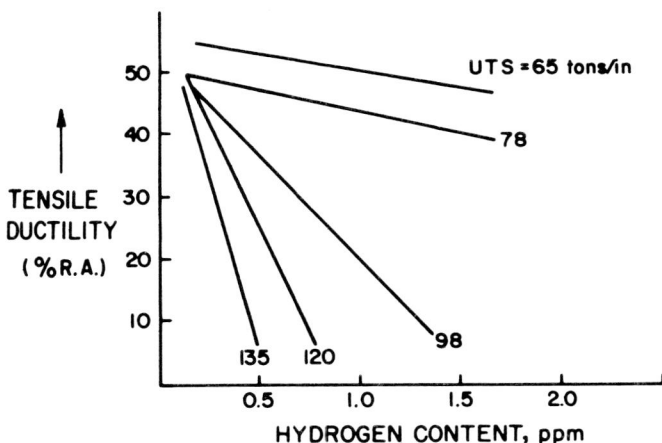

FIGURE 1 — The effect of hydrogen content on the tensile ductility of high strength steel.[24]

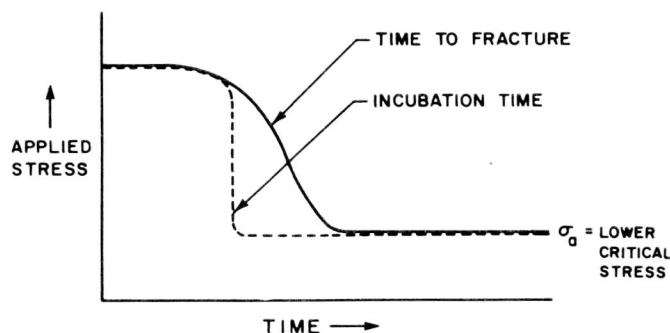

FIGURE 2 — Schematic diagram of the effect of applied stress on the incubation time for slow crack growth and the time to fracture for notched tensile specimens of hydrogenated high strength steel.[21]

447

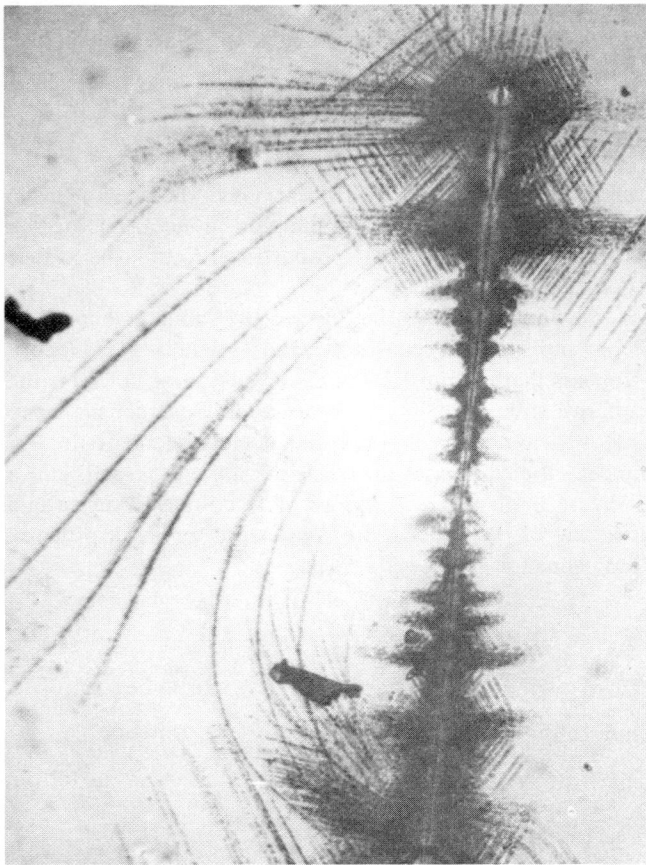

**FIGURE 3** — Microcrack produced in iron-3% silicon by the cathodic charging of hydrogen, in the absence of applied stress. Strain pattern around crack revealed by dislocation etch pitting.[31]

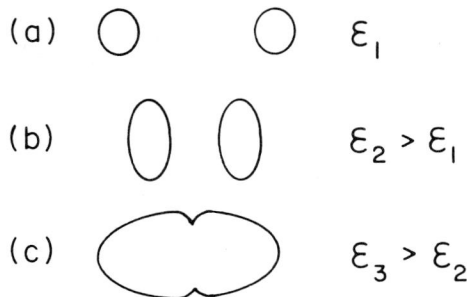

**FIGURE 4** — (a) Void formation at strain $\epsilon = \epsilon_1$, (b) elongation of voids at $\epsilon_2 > \epsilon_1$, and (c) coalescence of voids to form a crack at $\epsilon_3 > \epsilon_2$.

mental observations of hydrogen embrittlement in charged specimens are then reviewed in Sections III and IV and these observations are used to develop a self consistent mechanism for hydrogen embrittlement. Finally in Section V, some discussion of hydrogen embrittlement in an external environment (e.g., stress corrosion cracking) is presented.

## II. The Mechanics of Crack Propagation and Fracture

The process of brittle fracture in structural materials can be separated into three stages; crack nucleation, slow crack growth, and rapid, unstable fracture.

### A. Crack Nucleation

In flaw free materials, the first stage in the fracture process is the nucleation of a microcleavage crack or void. These defects are formed by the piling up and coalescence of dislocation groups in the vicinity of grain boundaries or hard particles such as inclusions.[25,40] As the applied stress (in a tensile test) or strain increases, increasing numbers of microcracks and voids are formed.[41-43] These act as strain concentrators which cause the material between them to fail in shear at low nominal strains (Figure 4).[44] Eventually, a sufficient number of voids and/or microcracks have formed and coalesced to lead to the development of a macrocrack (crack) about five grain diameters in length.

### B. Slow Crack Growth

Crack growth initially occurs discontinuously.[44] Increasing numbers of voids form ahead of its tip and join to it (coalesce). Crack propagation occurs by short, rapid advances (coalescence) followed by waiting periods in which the plastic strain ahead of the crack builds up sufficiently to cause void formation and local instability.[26,44]

### C. Rapid Fracture

As the crack grows longer, its ability to concentrate strain at its tip increases. Eventually, the crack is long enough to satisfy the criteria for unstable fracture (see below) and propagate rapidly, causing the structure to fail. The critical crack length at which this occurs is labeled $(2c_F)$ in subsequent discussion.

There are certain cases under which only one or two of these processes is observed. For example, at temperatures well below the ductile-brittle transition in BCC metals, the first microcrack that forms is able to spread unstably both through the grain in which it was nucleated and the boundary surrounding this grain, causing an unstable fracture without any detectable slow crack growth.[40,42] Stage B is then not detected (Figure 5a). The criterion for this to occur is then the same as the criterion for the initial growth of microcrack; namely that the applied tensile stress reach a value $\sigma_G$, given by Equation (2) with P = 0.

Most structural materials contain flaws that have been introduced by machining, improper welding, fabrication defects, etc. In this case, Stage A is absent and fracture involves the slow growth of the flaw of length $c = c_o$ at a stress $\sigma = \sigma_1$ until $c = c_F$ and rapid fracture can occur. This process of discontinuous, slow crack growth occurs under increasing stress (Figure 5b) in a tensile test or over a period of increasing time in a static test (Figure 5c).

The *microscopic aspects* of crack propagation depend on the type of material, the test temperature, and the yield strength level of the material. In BCC metals such as steel, fracture at low temperatures involves the nucleation and fast propagation, or nucleation, coalescence and fast propagation of microcleavage cracks. As the temperature increases, the yield strength $\sigma_Y$ decreases. Since the stress

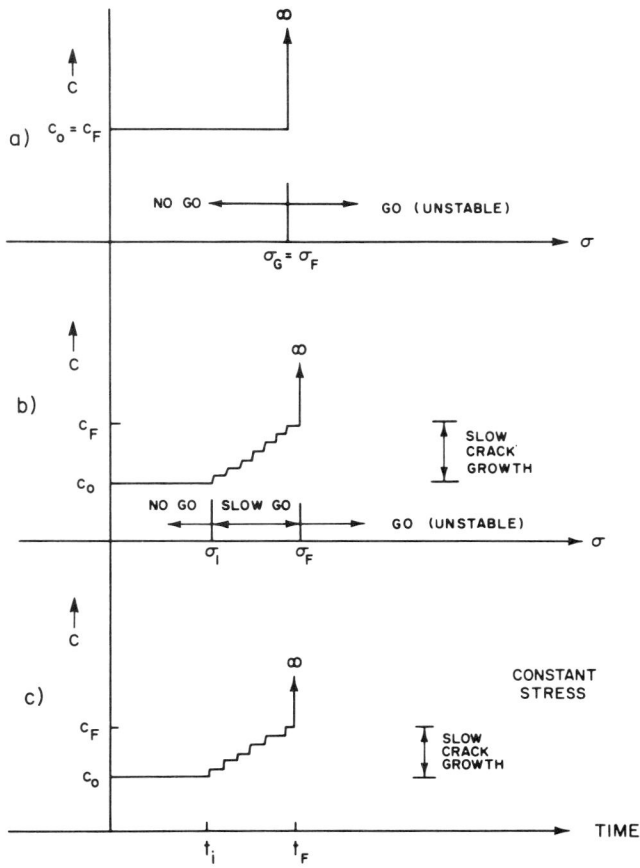

FIGURE 5 — The variation of crack length with applied stress. (a) Unstable fracture initiated at a stress $\sigma = \sigma_F$, without prior slow growth of crack of length $2c_0 = 2c_F$. (b) Slow crack growth from $c_0$ to $c_F$ occurs before unstable fracture at $\sigma = \sigma_F$. (c) Slow crack growth begins at time $t = t_i$ under constant stress; unstable fracture occurs when $c = c_F$ at time $t = t_F$.[26]

level ahead of an advancing crack $\sigma_{yy}$ can be no higher than about 2.5 $\sigma_Y$ assuming full triaxiality, the stress level at the crack tip decreases with increasing temperature. At some critical temperature the stresses are too low to cause microcleavage crack formation, and fracture occurs by the formation of voids at inclusions and the coalescence of these voids by plastic strain concentration.[26,40,45] Since void formation and coalescence involve larger local strains and hence absorb more energy than cleavage, the toughness or impact energy increases with increasing temperature (Figure 6). In low yield strength materials ($\sigma_Y < E/300$) the process of void formation and coalescence absorbs so much energy that the transition from cleavage to shear is a brittle-ductile transition. However, in high strength materials ($\sigma_Y > E/150$) the tensile stress level in the plastic zone ahead of the advancing crack is so high that a high density of voids form at temperatures where cleavage cannot occur. Consequently, smaller strains are involved in void coalescence (Figure 7) and the toughness is low. In this case, the cleavage to shear transition is *not* a brittle-ductile transition (Figure 6).

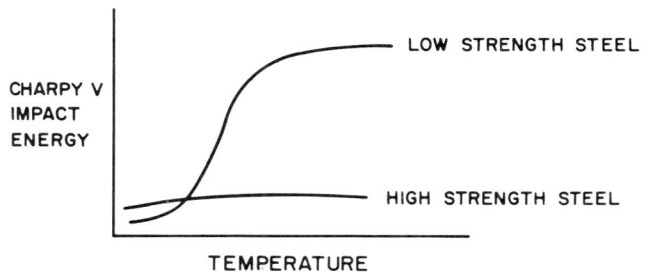

FIGURE 6 — Effect of temperature on the Charpy V notch impact energy for low strength ($\sigma_Y < E/300$) and high strength ($\sigma_Y > E/150$) steels.

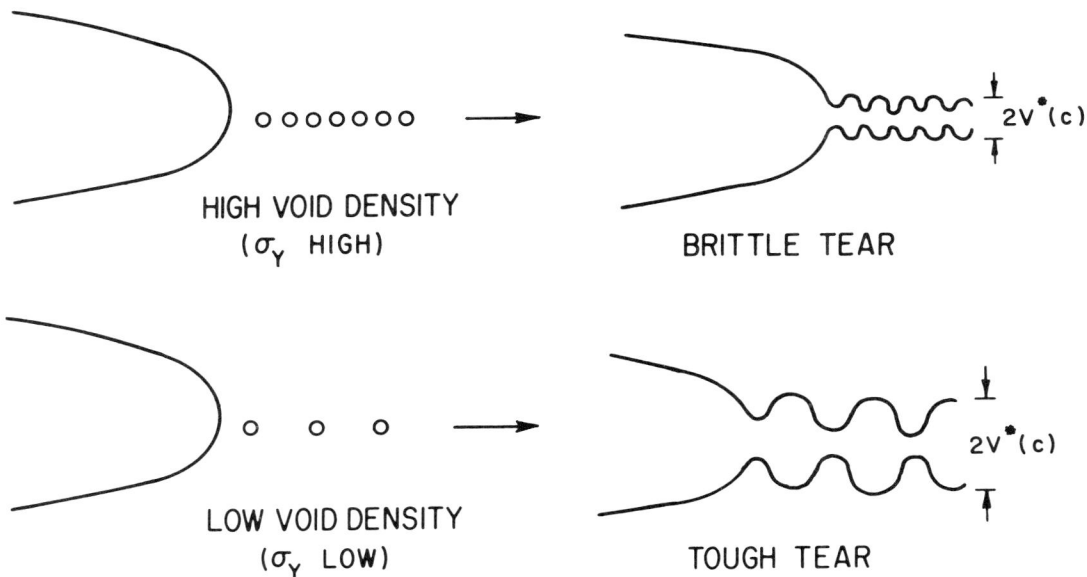

FIGURE 7 — Profile of fracture surface due to rupture. A high void density leads to a brittle rupture (small crack opening displacement) whereas a low void density leads to a tough rupture (large crack opening displacement).

449

The principles of *fracture mechanics* have been used to determine the macroscopic criteria for the unstable propagation of a crack (Stage C). It has been shown[46,51] that unstable fracture occurs when the crack opening displacement at the crack tip, $2V(c)$, reaches a critical value, $2V^*(c)$. Thus the fracture criterion becomes

$$V(c) = V^*(c) \qquad (5)$$

Since the tensile stress level in the plastic zone is of the order of the yield strength, the amount of work done at the crack tip is

$$G \cong 2\sigma_Y V(c) \qquad (6)$$

and consequently the critical amount of work done in unstable fracture is

$$G_c \cong 2\sigma_Y V^*(c) \qquad (7)$$

The methods of linear elastic fracture mechanics[50,52] indicate that unstable fracture can occur before general yield ($\sigma_F < \sigma_Y$) when

$$K^2 = EG_c = K_c^2 \qquad (8)$$

where K is known as the stress intensity factor

$$K = \sigma \sqrt{\alpha \pi c} \qquad (9)$$

and $K_c$, the critical value of K at which instability occurs, is known as the fracture toughness:

$$K_c = \sigma_F \sqrt{\alpha \pi c_F} \qquad (10)$$

$\alpha$ is an orientation factor that accounts for notch and structure geometry.[26,53] At low stress levels ($\sigma_F \ll \sigma_Y$) $\alpha \cong 1$ so that

$$\sigma_F = \sqrt{\frac{EG_c}{\pi c}} \qquad (11)$$
$$(\sigma_F \ll \sigma_Y)$$

Note that this is the same form as Equation (1) with $G_c = 2\gamma_p^*$ and P = 0. Introducing (7) gives

$$\sigma_F = \sqrt{\frac{2 E \sigma_Y V^*(c)}{\pi c}} \qquad (12)$$
$$(\sigma_F < \sigma_Y)$$

It is apparent from Equation (12) that once the critical displacement $2V^*(c)$ has been achieved, the crack will spread rapidly at $\sigma = \sigma_F$, since an increase in c decreases the stress required for propagation and the process is instable.

At the present time there are no general analytic expressions that can be used to describe fracture behavior after general yielding has occurred (i.e., when $\sigma_F > \sigma_Y$). Assuming that a critical displacement criteria is applicable, one can treat the crack as a strain concentrator so that the

ductility $\epsilon_F$ is that nominal strain which is required to produce the critical displacement $2V^*(c)$ at the crack tip; $\sigma_F$ is then the nominal stress required to achieve a given $\epsilon_F$, due to strain hardening.[26]

The physical meaning of a critical displacement criterion for unstable fracture has been the subject of much discussion.[46-51] A simple interpretation[47,48] is that the volume element of material at the crack tip behaves as a miniature tensile specimen whose gauge length, under local plane strain deformation, is of the order of twice the tip radius $\rho$ of the advancing crack. Consequently, a crack tip strain $\epsilon(c)$ produces a crack opening displacement

$$2V(c) = 2 \rho \epsilon(c). \qquad (13)$$

Unstable fracture occurs when the crack tip strain builds up to a critical value $\epsilon_f(c)$[44] which is proportional to, but not necessarily equal to, the ductility of a plane tensile specimen $\epsilon_f$, measured under identical conditions. Consequently, from Equation (5)

$$V^*(c) = \rho \epsilon_f(c) \qquad (14)$$

and thus the plane strain toughness $G_{Ic}$ is

$$G_{Ic} \cong 2 \sigma_Y \rho \epsilon_f(c). \qquad (15)$$

Under certain conditions, particularly in the presence of reactive environments or under alternating loading (fatigue), stable (slow) crack propagation can occur when the crack tip strain is less than $\epsilon_f(c)$ and the crack tip displacement is less than $V^*(c)$.[26,44] As the crack grows, its stress intensity factor K and hence its tip displacement $V(c)$ increase. Eventually, $V(c)$ equals $V^*(c)$ and the propagation becomes unstable; this marks the transition from Stage B to Stage C described above.

Suppose that a crack of length $2c_0$ exists in a structure subjected to a tensile stress $\sigma$ that is less than $\sigma_Y$. If the rate of slow crack growth ($dc/dt$) is known, then the time $t_F$ at which the structure will fail is determined by the condition that $c = c_F$ at $t = t_F$. For example, when ($dc/dt$) = A is a constant, failure will occur when

$$c_0 + A t_F = c_F = \frac{EG_c}{\alpha \pi \sigma^2} \qquad (16)$$

and hence

$$t_F = \left[ \frac{EG_c}{\alpha \pi \sigma^2} - c_0 \right] \frac{1}{A} \qquad (17)$$

Thus, a decrease in fracture toughness or an increase in applied stress leads to a decrease in lifetime, even if the rate of slow crack growth is unchanged.

In certain instances, particularly in the stress corrosion cracking of alpha brass in ammonium sulfate[54] or the embrittlement of high strength steel in the presence of water vapor,[12] the rate of slow crack growth increases with stress intensity factor (Figure 8) and hence as the crack

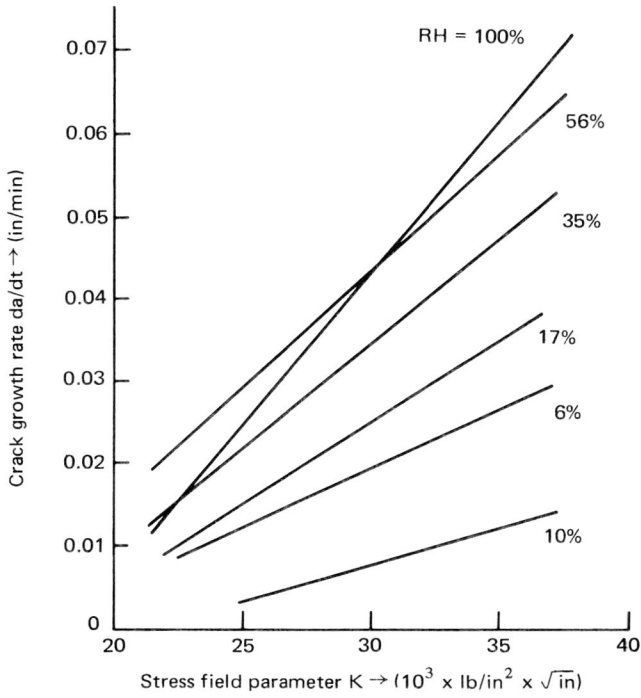

FIGURE 8 — Effect of stress intensity factor K and humidity level on the rate of slow crack growth in H-11 steel in humidified argon.[12]

length increases under a constant applied stress. For those cases where ($dc/dt$) is linearly proportional to K (Figure 8), we have

$$\frac{dc}{dt} = A' K \cong A' \sigma \sqrt{\alpha \pi c} \qquad (18)$$

and hence

$$\int_{c_o}^{c_F} \frac{dc}{c^{1/2}} = A' \sigma \sqrt{\alpha \pi} \int_0^{t_F} dt \qquad (19)$$

$$\tfrac{1}{2} (c_F^{1/2} - c_o^{1/2}) = A' \sigma \sqrt{\alpha \pi} \; t_F \qquad (20)$$

so that

$$t_F = \frac{1}{2A' \sqrt{\alpha \pi} \sigma} \left[ \left\{ \frac{EG_c}{\alpha \pi \sigma^2} \right\}^{1/2} - c_o^{1/2} \right] \qquad (21)$$

Consequently, an increase in applied stress $\sigma$ or growth constant $A'$ and/or a decrease in fracture toughness $G_c$ produces a decrease in the lifetime of the structure. The parameter $A'$ can be strongly dependent upon environment (Figure 8). Finally, for those cases such as fatigue[54] where the rate of crack propagation is proportional to the square of the stress intensity factor

$$\frac{dc}{dt} = A'' K^2 = A'' \sigma^2 \alpha \pi c \qquad (22)$$

$$\int_{c_o}^{c_F} \frac{dc}{c} = A'' \sigma^2 \alpha \pi \int_0^{t_F} dt \qquad (23)$$

$$\ln \left( \frac{c_F}{c_o} \right) = A'' \sigma^2 \alpha \; t_F \qquad (24)$$

$$t_F = \frac{1}{A'' \sigma^2 \alpha \pi} \ln \left[ \frac{EG_c}{\alpha \pi \sigma^2 c_o} \right] \qquad (25)$$

and again $t_F$ decreases with increasing $A''$ and $\sigma$ and/or decreasing $G_c$.

The preceding analyses have shown how the lifetime may be determined when a flaw of length $2c_o$ is present at the time t = 0 that a stress $\sigma$ is applied. In certain cases, particularly when hydrogen is introduced into a structure, the flaws do not exist initially but form after an *incubation time*, $t_i$.[21] If $2c_o$ is the flaw length at t = $t_i$, then Equations (17), (21), and (25) must be modified to read:

$$t_F = \left[ \frac{EG_c}{\alpha \pi \sigma^2} - c_o \right] \frac{1}{A} + t_i \qquad (26)$$
$$\left( \frac{dc}{dt} = A \right)$$

$$t_F = \frac{1}{2A' \sqrt{\alpha \pi} \sigma} \left[ \left\{ \frac{EG_c}{\alpha \pi \sigma^2} \right\}^{1/2} - c_o^{1/2} \right] + t_1 \qquad (27)$$
$$\left( \frac{dc}{dt} = A' K \right)$$

$$t_F = \frac{1}{A'' \sigma^2 \alpha \pi} \ln \left( \frac{EG_c}{\alpha \pi \sigma^2 c_o} \right) + t_i \; . \qquad (28)$$
$$\left( \frac{dc}{dt} = A'' K^2 \right)$$

Having developed equations which can predict the lifetime of a structure in terms of measurable parameters such as $t_i$, A, etc., it is possible to treat the problem of hydrogen embrittlement in terms of the effect of hydrogen on these parameters. In the following section we consider the problem of hydrogen induced crack nucleation, and the incubation time for crack formation under static loading (Stage A) in cathodically charged specimens. We then discuss the effect of hydrogen on the slow crack growth process (Stage B) and the conditions for final fracture. Finally, we consider the effect of an external hydrogen environment on the growth of cracks, as in the case of stress corrosion cracking.

451

## III. The Mechanism of Hydrogen Induced Crack Formation in the Absence of Applied Stress

The equilibrium solubility $C_H$ (in ppm) of hydrogen located in interstitial sites in the iron lattice varies with temperature T (K) and external hydrogen pressure $P_e$ (in atmospheres) as[55]

$$C_H = 42.7 \, P_e^{\frac{1}{2}} \exp\left(-\frac{6500}{RT}\right) \qquad (29)$$

Above 150 C, the diffusivity $D_H$ (cm² per sec) of hydrogen in iron also increases exponentially with temperature[35] according to the relation

$$D_H = 1.4 \times 10^{-3} \exp\left(-\frac{3200}{RT}\right) \qquad (30)$$
$$(T > 423 \, °K)$$

Measurements of the diffusivity by the gas effusion technique have shown that below 150 C the diffusivity decreases sharply, and varies with temperature as

$$D_H = 0.12 \exp\left(-\frac{7820}{RT}\right) . \qquad (31)$$
$$(T < 423 \, °K)$$

These observations suggest that the excess (above the solubility limit) hydrogen resides in "traps" and that below 150 C the diffusivity, as measured by gas effusion, is dependent upon the rate of release of hydrogen from these traps. Recent work[31,32] has shown that large voids or cracks are created by the expansion of hydrogen gas that has precipitated out of the iron lattice (Figure 3), and it is reasonable to associate these voids with the traps that cause the anomalous diffusion behavior.

Consider an iron specimen heated at a high temperature $T_1$ in the presence of 1 atmosphere of hydrogen gas (thermally charged) and then rapidly cooled (quenched) to room temperature $T_2$. Immediately after quenching the hydrogen content of the specimen $C_H(T_1) = C_H$ will be greater than the equilibrium content $C_H(T_2) = C_{eq}$ at T = $T_2$. Since there is no evidence for hydride formation in iron base alloys,[34] equilibrium can be achieved only when the excess hydrogen $(C_H-C_{eq})$ diffuses out of the iron lattice. Hydrogen atoms quenched into regions near to the specimen surface will be able to diffuse out to the surface, recombine with other atoms to form molecular hydrogen, and escape into the atmosphere. However, excess hydrogen atoms in the interior of the specimen are closer to *internal surfaces*, such as the interfaces between inclusions (or carbides) and the lattice; they will diffuse to these surfaces, recombine with other hydrogen atoms to form $H_2$ gas, and precipitate *inside the specimen* as molecular hydrogen.

Similarly, during cathodic charging (e.g., an electro-plating operation) or during certain corrosion reactions, hydrogen ions are reduced to hydrogen atoms at the metal surface. Most of these atoms recombine with others and are evolved as $H_2$ gas molecules. The remainder can be driven into the metal by the very high effective pressure (fugacity) and precipitate internally in the form of voids or cracks. The total hydrogen content will be determined by the current density, the charging time and the surface condition, since the latter determines the rate of surface recombination to form the $H_2$ molecule and hence the driving force for H atoms to enter the steel. The presence of "poisons" such as sulfides and arsenic are particularly effective in preventing surface recombination and when present they increase the amount of absorbed hydrogen.

The pressure of the hydrogen that has precipitated internally will be determined by the activity of the hydrogen atoms remaining in the lattice near the precipitation site, and by the constraints imposed by the mechanical properties of the material. Hydrogen atoms immediately adjacent to the inclusion precipitate out of the lattice until $C = C_{eq}$. This sets up a concentration gradient $[C_H-C_{eq}]$ which provides a driving force for diffusion to the interface. As increasing amounts of hydrogen precipitate at the interface, the pressure $P_H$ acting across the interface increases.

Although this local increase in pressure raises the equilibrium lattice concentration in the vicinity of the inclusion above $C_{eq}$, and the concentration of hydrogen away from the inclusion is decreased somewhat below $C_H$ (Figure 9), there is still a large driving force for (1) subsequent diffusion of hydrogen to the interface, (2) further increases in the amount of $H_2$ gas that has precipitated and hence (3) further increases in the pressure set up across the interface.

Initially, the pressure produced in the interface region can be extremely high. For example, if a specimen at one atmosphere pressure is quenched from 1000 C to room temperature, $C_H$ = 3.33 ppm, according to Equation (29). The interface pressure that could exist in equilibrium with this lattice concentration at room temperature is 89,000 atm = $1.3 \times 10^6$ psi. Since this pressure is of the order of the theoretical cohesive strength, the interface between hard particles and the matrix will almost certainly be broken during the initial precipitation of the hydrogen,

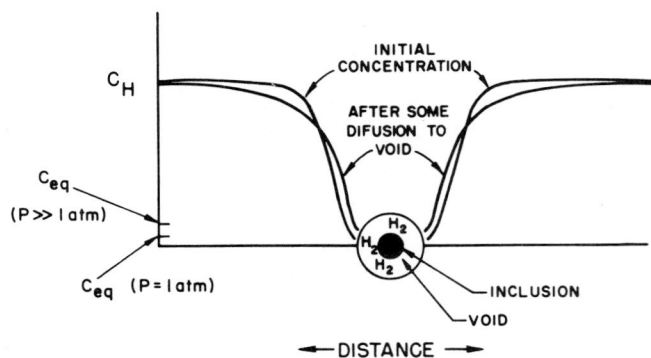

FIGURE 9 — Schematic diagram of the lattice hydrogen concentration immediately after excess hydrogen has been introduced (initial condition) and after some diffusion has occurred to the growing void. $C_{eq}$ is the equilibrium concentration, according to Equation (29).

forming a void. Once the void has expanded (see below), the pressure inside it decreases and additional diffusion of hydrogen to the interface and precipitation of hydrogen gas at the void surface will occur. The number of moles that enter a circular void or radius r per unit time is

$$\frac{dn}{dt} = 4 \pi r_o^2 J \qquad (32)$$

where at short times the flux J is given by[5 6]

$$J = D [C_H - C_{eq}] \left[ \frac{1}{r_o} + \frac{1}{\sqrt{\pi Dt}} \right] . \qquad (33)$$

For $r_o \cong 10^{-4}$ cm and $D = 5 \times 10^{-6}$ cm$^2$/sec (for untrapped hydrogen),

$$\frac{1}{r_o} >> \frac{1}{\sqrt{\pi Dt}}$$

at t = 1 sec so that

$$\frac{dn}{dt} \cong D [C_H - C_{eq}] 4 \pi r_o . \qquad (34)$$

Since the pressure inside the void is given by

$$P_H V = n RT \qquad (35)$$

the rate of pressure build up is

$$\frac{dP_H}{dt} = \frac{RT}{V} \frac{dn}{dt} = \frac{3 D}{r_o^2} RT [C_H - C_{eq}] \qquad (36)$$

Assuming spherical voids or volume V and

$$V = \frac{4 \pi r_o^3}{3}$$

neglecting the volume of the inclusion when the radius of the voids is greater than about twice that of the inclusion. Taking $C_H = 3.33$ ppm and $C_{eq} = 0.114$ ppm (for a pressure of 50,000 psi inside the void, after the interface has broken and the void has expanded slightly), gives $dP_H/dt = 500$ atm/sec for $r_o^= 10^{-4}$ cm, when R = 82.06 atm cm$^3$/mole, °K and the hydrogen concentration is expressed in units of moles/cm$^3$ (1 ppm of hydrogen = $3.85 \times 10^{-6}$ moles of H$_2$ that can precipitate out of a cubic centimeter of iron). This is very similar to the elastic loading rate that occurs in a conventional tensile test performed at an applied strain rate of 0.02 per minute, i.e., 670 atm per second.

## A. Void Expansion by Plastic Deformation

Under conditions where the iron lattice is inherently ductile and tough (e.g., pure iron at ambient temperature), the voids expand by plastic deformation and appear as spherical bubbles.[5 7] This condition is also favored if the precipitation site is spherical rather than pointed, since the stress concentration factor of the growing void will then be too low to allow the void to transform into a brittle crack. The total pressure required for the growth of a void of radius r by plastic deformation is approximately[5 8]

$$P \cong \sigma_Y + \frac{2\gamma}{r} \qquad (37)$$

where $\sigma_Y$ is the yield strength and $(2\gamma/r)$ is the force due to the surface tension of the void. Since $\gamma \cong 10^3$ ergs/cm$^2$, this term is negligibly small compared with $\sigma_Y$ for voids larger than about $10^{-4}$ cm. Consequently, the void growth occurs when $P_H \approx \sigma_Y$, and consequently the number of moles of hydrogen required to produce a void of radius r is

$$n = \frac{\sigma_Y}{RT} \frac{4 \pi r^3}{3} \qquad (38)$$

again neglecting the volume of the inclusion inside the void. Suppose that hydrogen atoms enter the void from a spherical volume V* that surrounds it (Figure 10), and that $(C_H V^*)$ is the maximum number of moles that can enter the void.[1] V* is determined by the condition that beyond a distance r* for the particular void the hydrogen will diffuse to another void of the same size (Figure 10). Thus 2r* is approximately the inter void spacing and thus the maximum radius of the void, $r_{max}$, is determined by the condition

$$\frac{4}{3} \pi (r^*)^3 C_H = \frac{\sigma_Y}{RT} \frac{4}{3} \pi r^3_{max} \qquad (39)$$

or

$$r_{max} = 1.2 r^* \left( \frac{C_H}{\sigma_Y} \right)^{1/3} \qquad (40)$$

for $C_H$ in convenient units of ppm and $\sigma_Y$ in units of psi, at room temperature. Thus for $C_H = 3$ ppm, $\sigma_Y = 60,000$ psi, $r_{max} = 0.04$ r* = $4 \times 10^{-4}$ cm for an average void spacing r* of $10^{-2}$ cm. It should be pointed out that the voids will not form at *every* second-phase particle (1) because of statistical considerations, and (2) because once a void forms at a given particle, and the hydrogen pressure decreases, there will be a local driving force set up for diffusion to that particular void rather than to an adjacent one. Furthermore, the kinetics of hydrogen recombination and pressure build-up will vary from one void to another, because of variations in the structure of the interface. Thus we should expect that r* will be proportional to, but not equal to, the inter-particle spacing. Consequently, the maximum void size is limited by the spacing of the inclusions or other particles that serve as precipitation sites. *When a given volume of second phase is finely distributed (r* small), the size of the voids will also be small.* We should therefore expect that the degree of hydrogen embrittlement could be altered by variations in processing conditions, since the latter affect the size, shape and distribution of second phase particles. Similarly, the void size decreases as the amount of excess hydrogen decreases and as the yield strength increases.

---

[1]Neglecting the equilibrium concentration $C_{eq}$ as being small compared to $C_H$.

Many aspects of this problem have been discussed previously[23,31,32,59,60] and need not be repeated here. This type of expansion occurs in inherently brittle materials (such as monocrystalline iron-3% silicon at room temperature), and when the particles and inclusions that serve as precipitation sites are sharp rather than round. Brittle crack propagation usually begins in a discontinuous manner by the formation of a microcrack nucleus ahead of the advancing crack, due to dislocation pile-ups, and the coalescence of this crack nucleus with the advancing crack tip[59] (Figure 11). When the crack is sufficiently long and sharp, large scale, rapid elastic propagation can occur. However, since essentially no hydrogen has time to enter the crack when it is moving, the pressure inside the crack decreases as the crack grows. Consequently, crack growth occurs until the pressure inside the crack drops below the Griffith value, Equation (41); the crack then remains at rest until diffusion of hydrogen to it causes the pressure to build up sufficiently to re-start it, at which point elastic propagation can again take place. The pressure required for crack propagation is given by Equation (1) with $\sigma = 0$.

$$P = \sqrt{\frac{2E \gamma^*_p}{\pi c}} \qquad (41)$$

Since the volume of the crack V is

$$V \cong \frac{8 P c^3}{3E} \qquad (42)$$

the number of moles of hydrogen required to spread the crack is

$$n = \frac{8 P^2 c^3}{3E\ RT} = \frac{16}{3\pi}\ \frac{\gamma^*_p c^2}{RT} = 6.8 \times 10^{-11}\ \gamma^*_p c^2 \qquad (43)$$

for $\gamma^*_p$ in ergs/cm$^2$, T = 300 °K and c in cm. Taking $\gamma^*_p = 10^4$ ergs/cm$^2$ as a typical value for the work required to propagate a sharp, stopped microcrack gives

$$n = 6.9 \times 10^{-7} c^2 \qquad (44)$$

As in the case of void growth by plastic deformation, the maximum size to which the crack will grow can be estimated by assuming that the hydrogen enters the crack from a cylinder of length 2c and radius r*, where 2 r* is the spacing between parallel cracks. Thus

$$2c_{max}\ \pi(r^*)^2\ C_H\ = 6.9 \times 10^{-7} c^2$$

$$c_{max}\ = 35\ (r^*)\ 2\ C_H \qquad (45)$$

when $C_H$ is again in convenient units of ppm. Thus, for $C_H$ = 3 ppm, r* = $10^{-2}$ cm, $c_{max}$ = 6 x $10^{-3}$ cm. As in the case of void growth by plastic flow, the growth of a brittle crack will be limited by the number of crack nuclei and the hydrogen concentration. Large scale crack propagation is possible in single crystals, where r* is large (say 1 cm), but

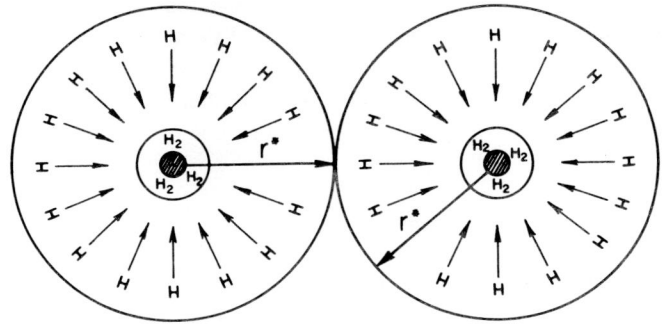

FIGURE 10 — Diffusion of excess hydrogen to growing void. Essentially all hydrogen atoms within a distance r* from a growing void will go to that particular void rather than to another.

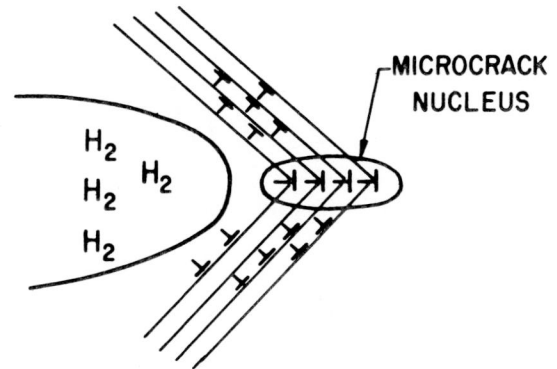

FIGURE 11 — Microcrack nucleus formed by dislocation pile up ahead of an advancing crack. Crack grows by joining with nucleus.[59]

in polycrystals, where r* is of the order of the grain size, $c_{max}$ small.

The fact that hydrogen induced crack growth occurs along the interface between long, sharp inclusions and the matrix may have practical significance. In structures that are loaded uniaxially (e.g., drill pipe or casing), prior hot rolling will align the inclusions parallel to the tensile axis. Any hydrogen cracks that form along these "fibers" will then be parallel to the tensile axis and coalescence by plastic strain concentration will be more difficult than if the cracks had lain perpendicular to the tensile axis.

## IV. The Mechanism of Delayed Failure in Hydrogenated Steels

*A. The Incubation Time Required for the Start of Slow Crack Growth in the Presence of an Applied Stress*

The preceding calculations have shown that in the absence of applied stress, excess hydrogen precipitates in small voids and cracks and causes these defects to grow out to a size that is dependent upon defect spacing and hydrogen concentration. We shall now examine the process of crack formation that occurs by the coalescence of these defects when a stress is applied to a hydrogenated material. It is most convenient to consider this process in terms of the delayed failure characteristics of notched tensile specimens of high strength steel. Troiano and his co-workers[21,37-39,61,62] have made electrical resistance measurements as a function of time during static loading, and obtained curves such as those shown in Figure 12. Immediately after application of the stress, the electrical resistance increases, a phenomenon associated with the elastic and plastic deformation that occurs at the notch tip. Following this rise, the resistance remains constant for a certain period of time (the *incubation time*) after which it again increases incrementally as slow crack growth begins.

Although elastic and plastic deformation contribute to the increased resistance following the application of load, some of this increase is almost certainly associated with void coalescence, and hence in crack formation in regions of high triaxial stress beneath the notch root.[61] The formation of a crack by void coalescence causes the hydrogen pressure inside it to decrease below that which exists in voids that have not coalesced. This provides a driving force for diffusion of hydrogen from adjacent voids until the pressure in the crack has built up sufficiently to allow it to begin growing slowly. It has been shown[62] that the logarithm of the reciprocal of the incubation time $t_i$ is proportional to the reciprocal of the absolute test temperature, indicating that the processes involved are thermally activated. The activation energy obtained from the data is 8900 cal/gm mole, consistent with the value for the diffusivity of trapped hydrogen at this temperature, 7800 cal/gm mole. Using the relation $x^2 = Dt$, it appears that hydrogen diffuses into the crack from a spherical volume whose radius is about $10^{-2}$ cm.

Figure 13 indicates that $t_i$ is relatively independent of applied stress but strongly dependent upon hydrogen concentration, which was varied by varying the degree of

--------

(2)Note: To prevent outgassing during testing at room temperature static loading tests are either performed in an electrolytic bath, with hydrogen continually introduced during testing, or on specimens that have been cadmium plated after charging.

outgassing by baking after cathodic charging.[2] This is consistent with the fact that increasing hydrogen concentrations imply larger voids prior to application of stress (and perhaps more of them), and hence a larger crack after the application of stress. Consequently, a smaller amount of hydrogen needs to diffuse to the crack to cause it to grow slowly, in the presence of the high longitudinal stresses that exist beneath the notch root. In addition, a higher initial hydrogen concentration provides a higher flux of hydrogen to the crack and thereby shortens the amount of time required for the introduction of a given amount of hydrogen.

Figure 13 indicates that there is a lower limiting value of applied stress beneath which crack incubation does not occur. This stress level is the same as the lower critical stress beneath which delayed failure does not occur (Figure 2). This lower critical stress $\sigma_a$ depends both on hydrogen concentration and root radius. In elastic-plastic deformation such as exists in the static loading tests on notched specimens, the longitudinal stress at the notch tip $\sigma_{yy}$ is given by[26]

$$\sigma_{yy} = K_{\sigma(p)} \sigma_Y \qquad (46)$$

where $K_{\sigma(p)}$ is the plastic stress concentration factor, and $\sigma_Y$ is the tensile yield strength. Prior to cracking, $K_{\sigma(p)}$ increases with increasing plastic zone size,[63] and hence with decreasing root radius $\rho$ and increasing applied stress, $\sigma$, until it achieves a maximum value (2.57 for parallel sided cracks) that is dependent upon the included flank angle of the notch. Although general solutions of the variation of $K_{\sigma(p)}$ with $\sigma$ are available only for bend loading,[64] some particular notch tension geometries have been worked out. Steigerwald et al[39] have used the solutions of Hendrickson et al[65] for a hyperbolic notch to show that for a particular hydrogen concentration the lower critical applied stress $\sigma_a$ is that the stress at which the longitudinal stress below the notch $\sigma_{yy}$ reaches a critical value $\sigma_c$, where $\sigma_c$ = 355 ksi for

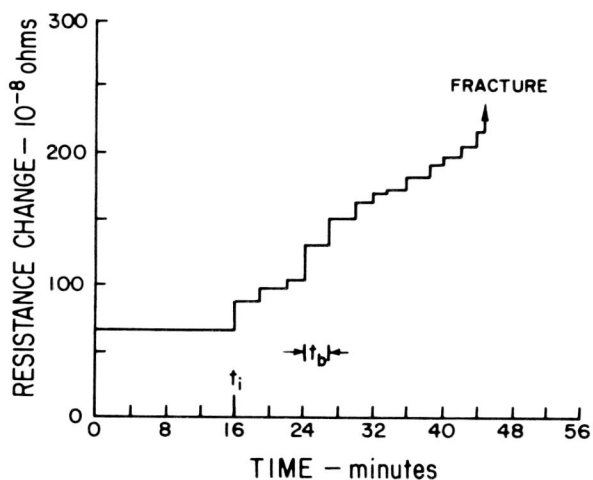

FIGURE 12 — The electrical resistance increase as a function of time for hydrogenated notched tensile specimen of 4340 steel, tested at an applied stress of 180 ksi at 0 F.[62]

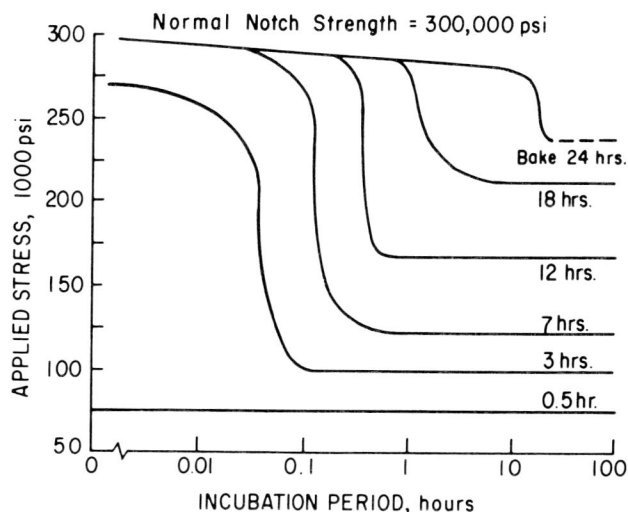

FIGURE 13 — Variation of incubation time with applied stress and hydrogen concentration; the latter was varied by baking for different times at 300 F after charging.[38]

455

specimens baked 3 hours at 300 F. This gives a value of $K_{\sigma(p)} = 1.69$ for $\sigma_Y = 210$ ksi, and $K_{\sigma(p)} = 1.48$ for $\sigma_Y = 240$ ksi. Consequently, the lower critical stress $\sigma_a$ decreases as the yield strength is raised (e.g., by tempering at a lower temperature or by testing at a lower temperature) or as the root radius is decreased, since this allows $K_{\sigma(p)}$ to build up more rapidly with applied stress. They also noted that for a given geometry and value of $\sigma_Y$, $\sigma_c$ and hence $\sigma_a$, decreased with increasing hydrogen concentration.

The existence of a critical local tensile stress for crack formation is consistent with recent theories of void growth,[45] which emphasize the importance of hydrostatic components in the process. Increasing hydrogen concentrations imply increasing hydrogen pressure inside the voids (or larger voids) and consequently lower longitudinal stresses at which they can coalesce to form a crack.

## B. Slow Crack Growth in Hydrogenated Steels and Final Failure

Figure 12 indicates that slow crack growth occurs in discontinuous bursts once the incubation time has been exceeded. The time between bursts, $t_b$, is considerably smaller than the incubation time, $t_i$, indicating that the distance over which diffusion is occurring is smaller than that required for the diffusion of hydrogen to the crack before it began to grow. The microscopic processes leading to slow crack growth have been the subject of much conjecture. Troiano et al[21,37-39] postulate that hydrogen atoms diffuse from the crack to positions in the iron lattice ahead of it which are subjected to high triaxial stress, and that embrittlement then results from the weakening of atomic bonds due to the presence of dissolved hydrogen. However, as stated previously, there is no evidence that hydrogen significantly affects the intrinsic strength of the iron crystal. Instead, it appears that the function of the hydrogen is to precipitate internally in microcrack and void nuclei (e.g., dislocation pile-ups at particle interfaces) that are forming ahead of the advancing crack in regions of high triaxiality, building up pressure inside them. Since the nuclei are small, only a small amount of hydrogen needs to diffuse into them before the pressure inside them is a relatively large fraction of the pressure inside the crack, $P_H$. This diffusion raises the local stress available for void formation from ($\sigma_{yy} = K_{\sigma(p)} \sigma_Y$) to ($\sigma_{yy} = K_{\sigma(p)} \sigma_Y + P_n$). The stress required to form a void $\sigma_G$ will vary statistically (Figure 14), since the particles responsible for void formation have varying sizes, shapes, interface strengths, etc.[26] However, for any distribution of values of $\sigma_G$, an increasing density of voids will be formed when hydrogen is present (Figure 14). These voids (Figure 15a) coalesce with each other, forming a microcrack (Figure 15b) which in turn coalesces with the advancing crack (Figure 15c) causing a burst of crack growth $\Delta c$. The process then repeats itself until the crack is sufficiently long to propagate unstably; this critical length depends on the applied stress and the value of $G_c$ (Equation 11).

The rate of slow crack growth is limited by the diffusivity of hydrogen since the hydrogen must diffuse

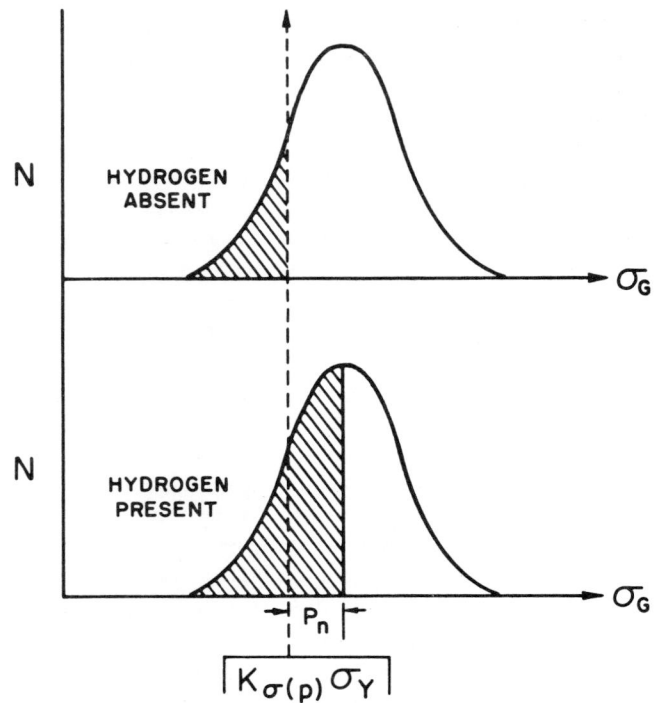

FIGURE 14 — The fraction of grains that crack, or voids that form, at a particular tensile stress level $\sigma_G$; shaded area is the total fraction of voids that form, or grains that crack, when $\sigma = \sigma_G$. The presence of a hydrogen pressure $P_n$ increases the density of voids and/or fractured grains ahead of an advancing crack, by increasing the local tensile stress level.[26]

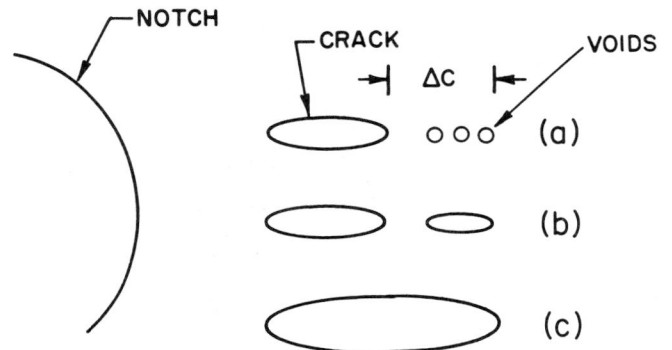

FIGURE 15 — Process of slow crack growth in notched tensile specimens. (a) Void formation ahead of crack, (b) void coalescence, (c) coalescence of large void with crack, causing crack tip to advance a distance $\Delta c$.

into a void nucleus a distance $\Delta c$ from the crack tip. Suppose that all of the hydrogen which enters these voids comes from the advancing crack. Then in a time $t_b$, the maximum value of $\Delta c$ is approximately $\sqrt{Dt_b}$. At room temperature, Steigerwald et al[62] noted bursts of crack growth at intervals, $t_b$, of about one minute. Taking $D \equiv 10^{-7}$ cm$^2$/sec for the diffusion of trapped hydrogen out of the crack into the nuclei gives $\Delta c \equiv 2.5 \times 10^{-3}$ cm. This is of the order of the size ($10^{-3}$ cm) of the individual microcracks that coalesce with the advancing crack, as shown in Figure 4 of Reference 21. The *rate of slow crack growth* is $(\Delta c/t_b) = 4 \times 10^{-5}$ cm/sec. This is in good agreement with reported values of the average rate of slow crack growth measured from the fracture surface of broken specimens, namely $1.4 \times 10^{-5}$ cm/sec. As the temperature decreases, the time between bursts increases. From the data of Steigerwald et al it is possible to obtain approximate (because of the scatter) values of $t_b$ at different temperatures and thereby determine the activation energy for the rate of slow crack growth. The value obtained in this manner, 7500 cal/gm mole, is in good agreement with the value of 7800 cal/gm mole for the diffusivity of trapped hydrogen (Equation 13).

While it has been established that the average rate of slow crack growth decreases with decreasing hydrogen concentration,[21] there is no definite indication as to the dependence of growth rate on stress intensity factor. Except for the last burst that preceeds instability, it appears from the data shown in Figure 12 that the resistance increment that accompanies each burst is independent of time, hence independent of crack length and hence independent of K. On this basis, the failure time of charged specimens is given by Equation (26), with A increasing and $t_i$ decreasing as the hydrogen content increases. Likewise, we would expect that A would increase as the yield strength increases (since this favors void formation[26]) and as the strain hardening rate decreases (since this favors void coalescence[45]), but these relations have not yet been established. However, it has been shown that for a given applied stress the time to failure does decrease as $\sigma_Y$ increases.[70] While part of this decrease undoubtedly is due to a decrease in $G_c$ with increasing $\sigma_Y$, some of it probably is due to increases in A and decreases in $t_i$.

The mode of hydrogen induced crack propagation in charged specimens is similar under uniaxial tensile loading. In unnotched specimens, fracture occurs well after general yield and, consequently, it is not possible to use the methods of linear elastic fracture mechanics to predict the failure stress or critical crack length. However, it is still apparent that the degree of hydrogen embrittlement will depend on the extent of hydrogen induced slow crack growth prior to instability. At very high strain rates, for example, hydrogen induced crack growth will not have time to occur before the material fails by the usual mode consistent with yield strength, temperature, etc. Hence the effect of hydrogen is minimal. Similarly, at very low temperatures the diffusivity of the hydrogen is too low to allow significant crack growth before failure. Again, therefore, hydrogen has little effect on ductility. The ductility of hydrogenated specimens of mild steel exhibits a minimum value somewhere below room temperature (depending on strain rate).[66] This results[26] from two competing effects. As the temperature increases, the increased rate of pressure build up in void nuclei ahead of the advancing crack more than compensates for the decrease in $\sigma_Y$ so that $\sigma_{yy}$ increases and a larger number of voids and/or microcracks can be formed (Figure 14). However, the maximum hydrogen pressure in the void nuclei is limited by the pressure in the advancing crack and thus by the hydrogen content of the specimen. Consequently, as the temperature

increases and $\sigma_Y$ decreases, $\sigma_{yy}$ will again decrease, fewer voids will form and coalesce, and the ductility will again increase.

These considerations indicate that since hydrogen causes embrittlement by producing an increase in the local stress field ahead of an advancing crack, as well as by helping to open the crack because of the pressure inside it, the same microstructural variables that increase ductility in the absence of hydrogen (e.g., fine grain size, spheroidal particles, and low inclusion content) will cause a smaller degree of embrittlement when hydrogen is present.[20,67]

Alloy composition has little direct effect on a steel's susceptibility to hydrogen embrittlement, in the sense that there is no one element that strongly increases or decreases susceptibility. However, it has been shown[25] that additions of silicon and chromium reduce the diffusivity of hydrogen in steel, and consequently their presence would be expected to reduce the rate of slow crack growth. The yield strength of the steel is an important factor and, as in the case of brittle fracture in the absence of hydrogen, the severity of embrittlement increases with strength (Figure 1). Since changes in strength can be achieved by changes in alloy composition as well as by variations in heat treatment, alloy composition can have an indirect effect on the degree of hydrogen embrittlement.

## V. Hydrogen Embrittlement in an External Hydrogen Environment

In addition to the hydrogen embrittlement that occurs when a large concentration of excess hydrogen is initially present *inside* the metal (e.g., in electroplated or rapidly solidified structures), there is also the embrittlement that can occur when hydrogen from an external environment is present during all stages of crack initiation and growth. Hydrogen embrittlement during corrosion is one example of this type of embrittlement. From a microscopic point of view, the embrittlement mechanism should be similar to that described in Sections III and IV, since the fugacity of the liberated hydrogen will be high enough to cause void formation and coalescence ahead of the advancing crack tip. One difference should be noted; namely, that since the faces of the growing crack are directly exposed to the external environment, there is a ready and constant supply of hydrogen available for crack growth. This could lead to a smaller value of the incubation time, $t_i$, and a faster rate of slow crack growth as compared with cathodically charged specimens.

It is extremely difficult to determine whether fracture in some corrosive environments is the result of hydrogen embrittlement or stress corrosion cracking, since the fracture surfaces exhibit many similar features, even when observed by electron microscopy. In high strength steels, both modes of failure are predominantly intergranular.[71] Careful examination by electron microscopy has revealed that stress corrosion cracking nucleates at the surface, whereas hydrogen corrosion embrittlement nucleates beneath the surface. Furthermore, the fracture surfaces resulting from stress corrosion cracking tend to be smoother and exhibit fewer hairline cracks, than those resulting from hydrogen embrittlement. Since corrosion products tend to obscure the detail in both cases, the exact analysis in all situations would be extremely difficult.

One simpler method of separating the two forms of embrittlement in testing is to note the effect of small impressed currents on the time to fail in a static test[10] or

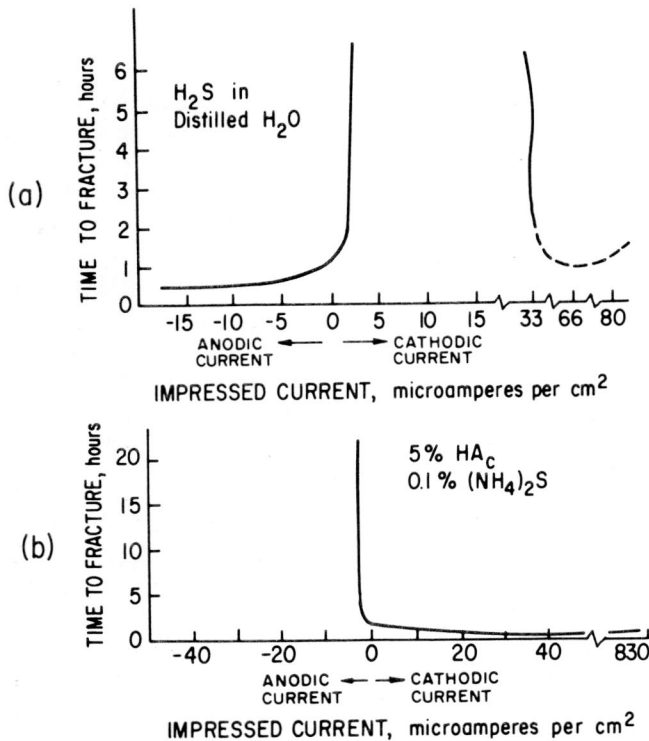

(a)

(b)

FIGURE 16 — Effect of impressed currents on time to fail of martensitic steel in (a) $H_2S$ solution and (b) acetic acid solution containing a sulfide poison.[10]

upon the rate of crack growth.[14] If the presence of a *small* cathodic current reduces embrittlement (Figure 16a) the fracture process in the absence of the imposed current is due to stress corrosion cracking. However, when anodic currents reduce the embrittlement (Figure 16b) the normal fracture process in the particular environment is hydrogen embrittlement. While large impressed anodic currents are also able to reduce the degree of hydrogen embrittlement, they may in turn cause stress corrosion cracking and vice-versa. Therefore, the degree of cathodic or anodic protection given to a particular structure operating in a particular environment must be carefully controlled.

Recent investigations[12,14] indicate that the rate of slow crack growth in high strength steel immersed in distilled water or water vapor increases with increasing temperature and increasing stress intensity factor. However, conflicting data on the kinetics of growth have been reported. Vanden Sluys[14] found that the rate of slow crack growth in 4340 steel ($\sigma_Y = 215$ ksi) is given by

$$\frac{dc}{dt} = \lambda \, e^{-\Delta H/RT} \qquad (47)$$

where the activation energy $\Delta H$ decreases with increasing stress intensity factor. His data show that

$$\Delta H = \Delta H_o - BK \qquad (48)$$

so that

$$\frac{dc}{dt} = \lambda \, e^{-\Delta H_o/RT} \, e^{BK/RT} \qquad (49)$$

where $\lambda = 7.5 \times 10^4$ in/min., $\Delta H_o = 9150$ cal/gm mole and $B = 30$ cal/l ksi in $^{1/2}$. The dependence of dc/dt upon K is shown in Figure 17, where it is noted that the rate of crack growth is finite at $K = 0$ (i.e., crack growth could occur in the absence of applied stress). When BK is small compared

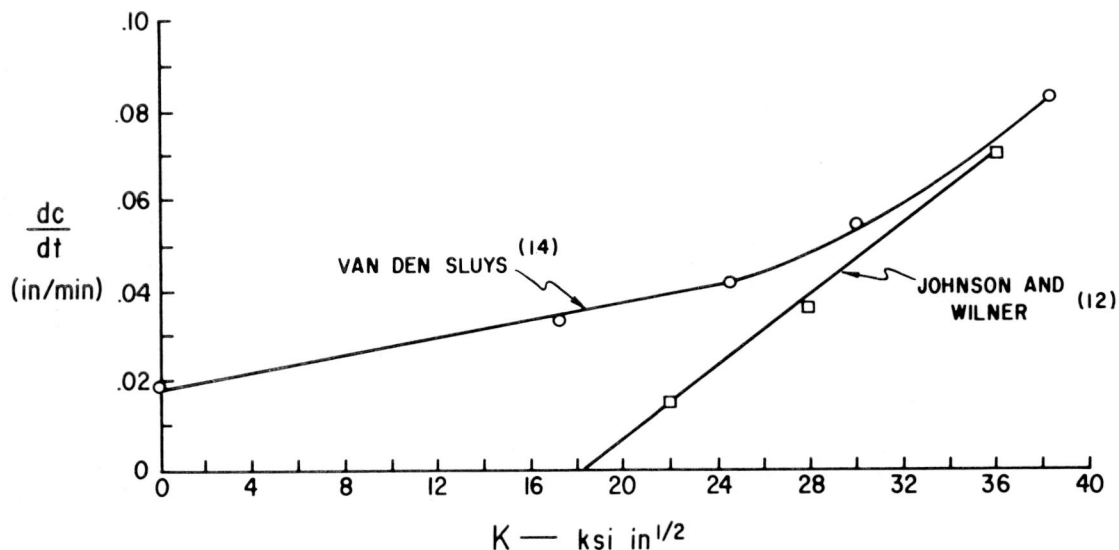

FIGURE 17 — Effect of stress intensity factor K on the rate of slow crack growth of 4340 steel in water[14] and H-11 steel in 100% humidified argon[12] at 80 F.

458

to RT the exponential can be expanded as $e^x \cong 1 + x$ so that

$$\frac{dc}{dt} = \lambda e^{-\Delta H_0/RT} \left[ 1 + \frac{BK}{RT} \right] \qquad (50)$$

and a linear dependence of $(dc/dt)$ upon K is found.

Johnson and Wilner[12] also noted that $dc/dt$ was linearly proportional to K, and that crack growth was thermally activated with $\Delta H \approx 9000$ cal/gm mole in H-11 steel ($\sigma_Y = 230$ ksi). Their data, however, indicate a much stronger dependence on K, Figure 17, and furthermore that $dc/dt = 0$ at a limiting value of $K = K^*_I$. At ambient temperature, 100% relative humidity, $K^*_I = 18$ ksi in $^{1/2}$. $K^*_I$ is then the analog of the parameter $K_{ISCC}$, below which stress corrosion cracking will not take place. The linear dependence of $(dc/dt)$ upon K means that Equation (27) can be used to predict the failure time under static loading, with $t_i = 0$ and K replaced by $(K-K^*_I)$. These workers also observed that in humidified argon the rate of slow crack growth decreased, and $K^*_I$ increased as the relative humidity of the atmosphere decreased (Figure 8). They were not able to conclude from their results whether hydrogen embrittlement or stress corrosion cracking was responsible for the slow crack growth, since a value of $\Delta H = 9$ kcal/mole is consistent with either the diffusion of hydrogen in iron or, in their opinion, the diffusion of oxygen in water. This suggests the need for measurements of the temperature sensitivity of stress corrosion cracking to determine the activation energy for the process, and thereby to compare it with values obtained in ambiguous situations such as described here.

In addition to the embrittlement which occurs in corrosive liquids and in the presence of a cathodic "protection" system, it has also been shown that embrittlement in high strength steels can occur in the presence of hydrogen gas.[13,15-19] Slow crack growth has been noted at hydrogen pressures as low as one atmosphere,[13] provided that oxygen is absent but in general the embrittlement is more pronounced at higher pressures (2000-10,000 psi). Also the embrittlement is more pronounced as the strength level of the steel increases. Since the maximum pressure that can build up inside a void is of the order of the external pressure, it is unlikely that the embrittlement is due to pressure build up inside the voids, as in the case of cathodically charged or corroded specimens. Instead, it appears that the primary function of the hydrogen is to absorb preferentially in place of oxygen[13] and promote embrittlement by removing the oxide layer.[3]

The effect of small oxygen additions on retarding the rate of slow crack growth in an H-11 steel is shown in Figure 18. Similarly, it has been suggested[13] that embrittlement in water and water vapor described above may result from the dissolution of protective oxide coatings in the presence of $H_2O$.

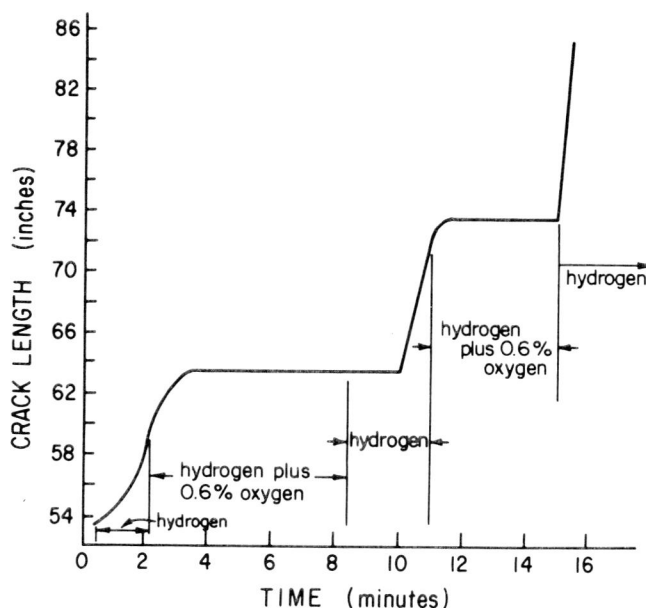

FIGURE 18 – Slow crack growth in H-11 steel in hydrogen and a hydrogen-oxygen mixture.[13]

The importance of an oxide film in retarding slow crack growth, and hence the importance of hydrogen in preventing film formation, is open to speculation. Since crack growth involves the coalescence of a void with the crack tip, the plastic processes taking place in the vicinity of the tip would be expected to play a large role in determining the crack opening displacement required for incremented growth. It is known, for example, that oxide layers, even on laboratory size tensile specimens, can increase the rate of strain hardening,[68,69] probably by blocking the exit of dislocations and causing the formation of piled up dislocation groups. These layers would probably produce even larger effects on the volume element that is necking down at the crack tip. If removal of the layer results in a decreased local rate of strain hardening, the local plastic flow becomes much more inhomogeneous and coalescence would occur at smaller crack tip displacements.

## VI. Summary

The process of brittle fracture in structural materials can be separated into three stages: (1) crack nucleation, (2) slow crack growth, and (3) rapid, unstable fracture. Hydrogen embrittles steel by affecting the first two of these stages. In corroded, electrolytically charged, or thermally charged specimens, excess hydrogen precipitates at inclusions or carbides in molecular form, causing the initiation of voids or microcracks. The hydrogen pressure in these defects causes them to grow either by plastic deformation or by cleavage, depending on the intrinsic toughness of the particular steel and the shape of the nucleating particle. It is shown that the size of the defects is determined by the spacing of the nucleating particles. Consequently, small voids or cracks will exist when a given volume of second phase is finely distributed. In hot rolled

---

[3] Based on its high heat of adsorption, oxygen would be expected to adsorb in place of hydrogen at equivalent partial pressures of the two gases, forming an oxide, provided reduction of the oxide did not occur.

459

materials, alignment of inclusions can be used to minimize hydrogen embrittlement.

Microcrack or void coalescence, to form a macrocrack, occurs when a stress is applied to a hydrogenated structure. The effect of hydrogen concentration, applied stress, notch geometry, strength level, temperature, and microstructure on the incubation time for slow crack growth, the rate of slow crack growth, and the time to fail in a static test or the tensile ductility are considered. Finally, crack growth in external environments, such as hydrogen gas is also discussed briefly.

## Acknowledgments

The author wishes to thank Professor G. M. Pound for helpful discussions during the preparation of this report and the National Aeronautics and Space Agency for support on Grant NSG-622.

## References

1. A. E. Scheutz and W. D. Robertson. *Corrosion,* **13,** 437 (1957).
2. G. Sachs. WADC Report TR53-254 (1954).
3. P. N. Vlannes, S. W. Strauss and B. F. Brown. NRL Rept 4906 (1957).
4. N. M. Geyer, G. W. Lawless and B. Cohen. *Hydrogen Embrittlement in Metal Finishing,* p. 109, Reinhold, New York (1961).
5. A. H. Sully and W. A. Bell. *J. Iron Steel Inst.,* **178,** 15 (1954).
6. J. H. Andrew, H. Lee, A. K. Malik and A. G. Quarrell. *J. Iron and Steel Inst.,* **153,** 67 (1946).
7. W. D. Biggs. *Brittle Fracture of Steel,* p. 333, MacDonald and Evans, London (1960).
8. M. Smialowski. *Hydrogen in Steel,* Addison-Wesley, Reading, Mass. (1962).
9. R. G. Baker and F. Watkinson. *Hydrogen in Steel,* BISRA Rept. 73, p. 123 (1962).
10. B. F. Brown. NRL Rept. 6041 (1963) November.
11. G. L. Hanna, A. R. Troiano and E. A. Steigerwald. *Trans ASM,* **57,** 658 (1961).
12. H. H. Johnson and A. M. Wilner. *App. Matls Res.,* p. 34 (1965) January.
13. G. G. Hancock and H. H. Johnson. *Trans AIME,* **236,** 513 (1966).
14. W. A. Van Der Sluys. University of Illinois, TAM Rept. 292 (1966).
15. W. Hofmann and W. Rauls. *Weld. J. Res. Supp.,* **255A** (1965).
16. R. A. Cavett and H. C. Van Ness. *Weld. J. Res. Supp.,* p. 316 (1963).
17. D. Williams and H. Nelson. To be published.
18. R. J. Walter and W. T. Chandler. Rocketdyne Research Rept. No. R6851 (1967) January.
19. J. B. Steinman, H. C. Van Ness and G. S. Ansell. *Weld. J.,* **44,** 221s (1965).
20. P. Bastien. *Physical Metallurgy of Stress Corrosion Fracture,* p. 311, Interscience, New York (1959).
21. A. Troiano. *Trans ASM,* **52,** 54 (1960).
22. P. P. Cottrell. *Prog. in Mat. Sci.,* 9, 4, 201 (1961).
23. A. S. Tetelman. *Fracture of Solids,* p. 671, Interscience, New York (1963).
24. K. Farrell and A. G. Quarrell. *J. Iron Steel Inst.,* **202,** 1002 (1964).
25. E. E. Fletcher, W. E. Berry and G. A. Elsea. DMIC Report No. 232 (1966).
26. A. S. Tetelman and A. J. McEvily. *Fracture of Structural Materials,* Wiley, New York (1967).
27. C. Zapffe and C. Sims. *Trans. AIME,* **145,** 225 (1941).
28. F. J. de Kazinsky. *J. Iron Steel Inst.,* **177,** 85 (1954).
29. F. Garafolo, Y. Chow and R. Ambegaokar. *Acta Met.,* **8,** 504 (1960).
30. B. A. Bilby and J. Hewitt. *Acta Met.,* **10,** 587 (1962).
31. A. S. Tetelman and W. D. Robertson. *Trans AIME,* **224,** 775 (1962).
32. A. S. Tetelman and W. D. Robertson. *Acta Met.,* **11,** 415 (1963).
33. N. J. Petch and Staples. *Nature,* **169,** 842 (1952).
34. A. S. Tetelman, C. N. J. Wagner and W. D. Robertson. *Acta Met.,* **9,** 205 (1961).
35. M. L. Hill and E. W. Johnson. *Trans. AIME,* **215,** 717 (1959).
36. A. Fayet. M.S. Thesis, Stanford University (1966).
37. J. G. Morlet, H. H. Johnson and A. R. Troiano. *JISI,* **189,** 37 (1958).
38. H. H. Johnson, J. G. Morlet and A. R. Troiano. *Trans. AIME,* **212,** 526 (1958).
39. E. A. Steigerwald, F. W. Schaller and A. R. Troiano. *Trans. AIME,* **212,** 832 (1960).
40. A. H. Cottrell. *Fracture,* p. 1, Wiley, New York (1959).
41. G. T. Hahn, B. L. Averbach, W. S. Owen and Morris Cohen. *Fracture,* p. 91, Wiley, New York (1959).
42. C. J. McMahon. Ship. Struc. Comm. Rept. SCC-161 (1964).
43. L. Kaechle and A. S. Tetelman. To be published in *Acta. Met.*
44. F. A. McClintock. *J. Appl. Mech.,* **25,** 282 (1958).
45. F. A. McClintock. *J. Appl. Mech.* (1968).
46. A. A. Wells. *Brit. Weld. Journ.,* p. 855 (1963).
47. G. T. Hahn and A. Rosenfield. *Acta Met.,* **13,** 293 (1965).
48. A. H. Cottrell. *Proc. Roy. Soc.,* **285,** 10 (1965).
49. B. A. Bilby, A. H. Cottrell and K. H. Swinden. *Proc. Roy. Soc.,* **272,** 304 (1963).
50. F. A. McClintock and G. R. Irwin. *Fracture Toughness Testing,* ASTM, Philadelphia, STP No. 381, p. 84 (1965).
51. J. F. Knott. *J. Iron Steel Inst.,* **204,** 1014 (1966).
52. G. R. Irwin. *Encl of Physics,* **Vol. VI,** Springer, Heidelberg (1958).
53. P. C. Paris and G. C. M. Sih. *Fracture Toughness Testing,* ASTM, Philadelphia, STP. No. 381, p. 30 (1965).
54. A. J. McEvily and A. P. Bond. *J. Electrochem. Soc.,* **112,** 131 (1956).
55. W. Geller and T. Sun. *Arch. Eisenhutt.,* **21,** 437 (1950).
56. H. S. Carslaw and J. C. Jaeger. *Conduction of Heat in Solids,* Oxford (1959).
57. A. S. Tetelman. D. Eng. Thesis, Yale University (1961).
58. A. T. Churchman, R. S. Barnes and A. H. Cottrell. *J. Nuc. Eng.,* 2, 88 (1961).
59. A. S. Tetelman and T. L. Johnston. *Phil. Mag.,* **11,** 389 (1965).
60. M. Gell, J. P. Briant and W. D. Robertson. *Trans. AIME,* **239,** 813 (1967).
61. W. J. Barnett and A. R. Troiano. *Trans. AIME,* **209,** 486 (1957).
62. E. A. Steigerwald, F. Schaller and A. Troiano. *Trans. AIME,* **215,** 1048 (1959).
63. T. R. Wilshaw and P. L. Pratt. *J. Mech. Phys. Solids,* **14,** 7 (1966).
64. T. R. Wilshaw, C. A. Rau and A. S. Tetelman. *Engineering Fracture Mechanics,* 1, 191 (1968).
65. J. A. Hendrickson, D. S. Wood and D. S. Clark. *Trans. ASM,* 50, 656 (1958).
66. T. Toh and W. M. Baldwin. *Stress Corrosion Cracking and Embrittlement,* p. 176, Wiley, New York (1956).
67. N. J. Petch. *Phil. Mag.,* 1, 331 (1956).
68. I. R. Kramer. *Trans. AIME,* **227,** 1003 (1963).
69. H. Nelson and D. Williams. *Evn. Sens. Mech. Behavior of Materials,* p. 107, Gordon and Breach (1967).
70. R. P. Frohmberg, W. J. Barnett and A. R. Troiano. *Trans. ASM,* 47, 892 (1955).
71. E. Geuss. *Surface Science,* 2, 48 (1964).

# Discussion

**J. McBreen, Yardney Electric Corp.:**

You mentioned in your paper that impurities in the metal are a necessary condition for precipitation of hydrogen gas to generate cracks in the metal. However, Flis and Janko[1] found that hydrogen generates blisters in polycrystalline Armco iron, zone-refined iron and single crystals of iron. On the other hand, they found that hydrogen does not generate blisters in iron whiskers. This result indicates that the initiation site, for hydrogen gas precipitation in the metal, is a dislocation or a group of dislocations and is not an occluded impurity.

1. J. Flis and A. Janko. *Bull. Acad. Polon. Sci. (Ser. sci. chim.),* **12,** 15 (1964).

**A. S. Tetelman:**

I did not say that impurity atoms were required for the precipitation of hydrogen gas. Rather, it is nonmetallic inclusions that are responsible for the cracking, since their surfaces provide sites for the precipitation of hydrogen molecules. I doubt that inclusions are present in iron whiskers, and consequently blisters are not observed in charged whiskers. To check this point further, it might be worthwhile to strain a whisker (to introduce dislocations) and subsequently to charge it with hydrogen. If blisters are not formed, it would prove that dislocation groups alone cannot generate hydrogen cracks. Alternatively, if blisters are formed, it would indicate that dislocation groups, like inclusions, can serve as sites for hydrogen precipitation.

**Dr. Oriani, U. S. Steel Corp.:**

Are you suggesting that a small amount of hydrogen dissolved in the lattice may, in fact, increase the yield strength of the metal by by some kind of cohesive energy effect, or is it a matter of pinning down dislocations?

**A. S. Tetelman:**

I am not sure which of these two processes would be taking place, and further experimentation along these lines would be required. For example, if aging experiments indicate that the process is thermally activated, with an activation energy comparable to that of hydrogen in iron, then there would be a strong indication that hydrogen pinning was important. Of course, it is first necessary to carry out careful experiments to determine the magnitude of any yield stress elevation near a crack tip.

**H. H. Uhlig, MIT:**

With respect to Dr. Oriani's remark, hydrogen may pin dislocations, but oxygen does so even better yet does not cause embrittlement.

**A. S. Tetelman:**

To my knowledge, there is no evidence that oxygen pins dislocations in iron.

**N. A. Tiner, McDonnell Douglas Corp.:**

I think Dr. Tetelman's theory on hydrogen embrittle-

ment may explain many phenomena. I do not like to use the expression, "junk," as the only source of void formation. We have found evidence that epsilon carbide particles may initiate cracks in steels. The epsilon carbide is able to absorb a considerable amount of hydrogen.

Electron fractographic analysis of fractured surfaces in 4340 steel clearly exhibits both cleavage zones and the presence of epsilon carbide in these cleavage zones.[1] Using the electron autoradiography technique, we have demonstrated that hydrogen (or tritium) can be adsorbed preferentially in these cleavage zones.

In general, a crack is initiated at several local sites by pit formation. Pits grow very slowly for a certain period; eventually they attain sufficient depth and acuity, and a rapid but stable crack propagation begins with moderate gas evolution. It has been observed that the stable crack growth areas contain a complex structure consisting of cleavage zones, intergranular zones where chemical anodic reaction occurred, and mechanically failed zones. At the beginning of the stable crack growth areas, intergranular zones are prominent, and towards the end the mechanically failed dimpled zones become prominent. By controlling the composition of 4340 steel and by modifying the amount of epsilon carbide present by heat treatment, one can control the amount of cleavage regions and crack growth process under stress in moist atmosphere or salt water.

Application of cathodic or anodic potential to 4340 steel can modify the total area occupied by cleavage zones and thus, to some extent, control the crack growth process.

1. N. A. Tiner and C. B. Gilpin. Microprocesses in Stress Corrosion of Martensitic Steels. *Corrosion,* **22,** 10 (1966) October.

**E. E. Denhard, Armco Steel Corp.:**

I thought this was a very interesting talk and I enjoyed it. Earlier in the program we heard a comment that fracture mechanics did not necessarily tie in with stress corrosion cracking or hydrogen embrittlement. I tend to think that it does.

The basis of the contention that fracture mechanics and stress corrosion cracking are not related probably resides in the fact that alloy systems have been observed too generally. We find in our development of specific families of alloys that a strong correlation exists. As an example, I would like to refer to the evolution of the precipitation hardening stainless steels. In the case of 17-7 PH, PH 15-7 Mo and most recently PH 14-8 Mo, there have been alloying changes and melting and processing changes that have resulted in improved, useful engineering properties. Although each of these materials is structurally similar and responds in the same manner to heat treatment, we find that the fracture toughness and stress corrosion resistance have improved, as some of the points made by Dr. Tetelman were incorporated.

Specifically, I would like to cite that the virtual elimination of all elements except those necessary for the performance of the alloy produced remarkable changes in the properties that we have been discussing. These gains are further enhanced when vacuum melting and consumable electrode vacuum remelting were employed. This we attributed to the elimination of harmful, dissolved gasses and the distribution of particles in the remelting cycle.

I believe that practical use can be made of the principles that Dr. Tetelman has expounded and the alloy systems described above substantiate, in a practical way, the importance of the control of impurities and the distribution of stress raising secondary constituents.

## The Three Kinds of Embrittlement Effects Produced in Iron and Steels by Hydrogenation

M. Smialowski
Institute of Physical Chemistry

Dependent upon the composition and structure of the given ferrous metal or alloy and mode of its charging with hydrogen the latter may produce different effects. Three kinds of these effects will be discussed here.

### 1. The Case of "Pure" Iron and Annealed Mild Steel

As is known, under ordinary conditions the solubility of hydrogen in[1] iron is very low. It increases with increasing temperature. Hence, the passage of hydrogen from the gaseous form into that dissolved in iron is an endothermic process. Small amounts of hydrogen, e.g., up to about 1 cm$^3$/100 g Fe, may be introduced into iron and annealed low-carbon steel specimens without any noticeable effects. On the contrary, when larger amounts of hydrogen are forced into iron and mild steel specimens by intense electrolytic charging,[1] elastic and plastic deformation may be observed. This is due to the precipitation of hydrogen from the solid solution, and accumulation of gaseous $H_2$ in vacancies and voids within the metal matrix. The total volume of hydrogen which can be accumulated inside of the given specimen by electrolytic charging decreases with increasing temperature.[1] Hence, this process is exothermic, as the whole. There occurs a striking similarity to the behavior of nickel which absorbs small amounts of hydrogen in an endothermic process (formation of the "alpha-phase", i.e., interstitial solid solution of H atoms in Ni), but binds larger volumes of hydrogen exothermically[2] (formation of the "beta-phase", i.e., nickel hydride[3]).

---

[1] By "intense electrolytic charging" one understands prolonged, e.g., lasting 0.5 hr or more, cathodic polarization of the given sample with a current density of several mA/cm$^2$ at room temperature in a "poisoned" acid solution, e.g., 0.5 molar sulfuric acid with 1 mg/l $As_2O_3$.

Basing on the analogy between the Ni-H and Fe-H systems one might assume that after saturation of the "alpha" solid solution characterized by random distribution of H atoms within the metal matrix, a further intense hydrogenation causes building up of the "beta-phase" characterized by a much more pronounced metal-hydrogen interaction and ordering tendency. But unlike the Ni-H system, in which the existence of the hydride phase was confirmed by X-ray[4] and neutron[5] diffraction studies, in the case of iron, probably due to its less dense b.c.c. crystal lattice and easiness of dislocation movements, the hydride phase disintegrates before being formed over ranges large enough to affect considerably the X-ray diffraction pattern. The disintegration of the hydride causes liberation of gaseous hydrogen within the metal matrix. Since $H_2$ is unable to diffuse through the crystal lattice, it accumulates under a very high pressure at some internal defects of the metal structure.

As shown by Flis and Janko,[6] single crystals of iron obtained by the strain-annealing method show after electrolytic charging with hydrogen a pronounced broadening of X-ray diffraction spots. Microscopic examination of single crystals and polycrystalline samples of zone refined iron or annealed mild steel after electrolytic charging reveals the presence of blowholes, blisters and cracks. These are evidently due to the damaging effect of the hydrogen accumulation. On the contrary, iron whiskers obtained by reduction of ferrous chloride with hydrogen do not undergo any destructive action of electrolytic charging detectable by the X-ray diffraction method or by microscopic observation, although mass-spectrometric analysis reveals the presence of hydrogen in electrolytically charged whiskers. Suggestion can be made that the resistance of iron whiskers toward the destructive action of electrolytic hydrogenation is due to the absence of large voids and movable dislocations. Presumably, the nucleation of the gas phase can occur only in voids large enough in comparison with the volume of the lattice unit cell and the $H_2$ molecule. Nonmetallic inclusions with incoherent interfaces are probably the main sources of such voids in iron.

Accumulation of hydrogen in these voids under a pressure of some 13,000 atmospheres[1] produces elastic and plastic strain in the surrounding metal, and this involves changes in the electrical, magnetic and mechanical properties of the sample: increase in electrical resistance, coercive force and hardness, and decrease in ductility.

It follows from this that the embrittlement of iron and annealed mild steel by hydrogen is chiefly due to secondary effects. The phenomenon of delayed failure, which is characteristic for high strength steels, does not occur in iron and annealed mild steel, since the loss in ductility is compensated by the gain in strength.

The major part of effects produced in iron and annealed mild steel by intense electrolytic charging is irreversible, i.e., does not disappear after the extraction of hydrogen. Stresses due to the plastic deformation may, of course, be released by heating, but internal rifts and surface cracks remain even after annealing at elevated temperatures.

A very simple and sensitive method for studying the

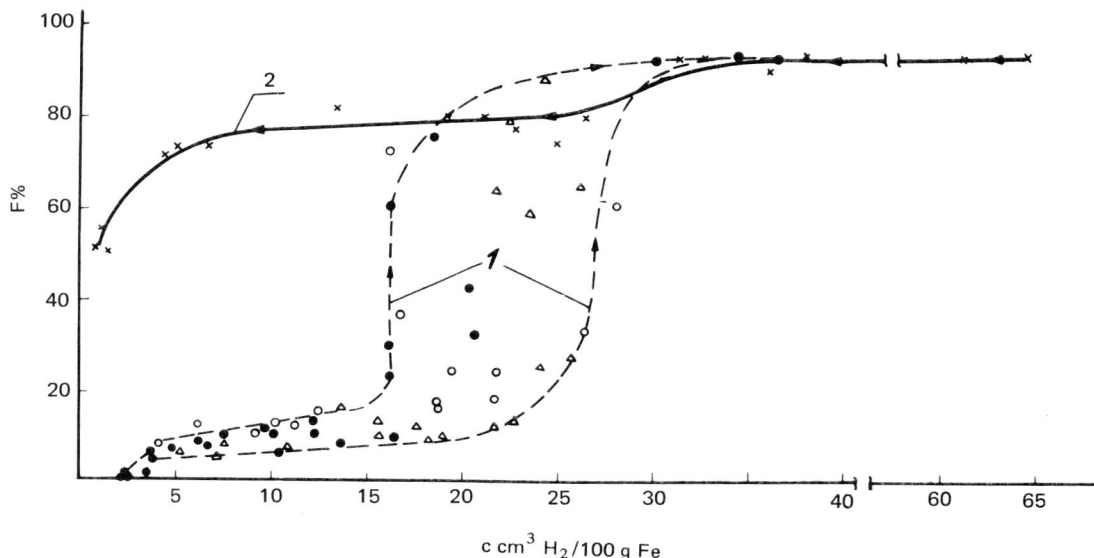

FIGURE 1 — Effect of the hydrogen content (c) in low-carbon iron wires on the change in number of twists to fracture (F). Curve 1—specimens charged electrolytically under various conditions. Curve 2—specimens charged electrolytically 1 hour at 2.5 mA/cm$^2$ and aged at room temperature in a vacuum.[7]

hydrogen embrittlement in iron and annealed steel consists in measuring the number of twists necessary to fracture a thin wire. Figure 1 shows the relationship between the concentration of hydrogen[2] introduced by electrolytic charging of a 0.5 mm thick iron wire and the loss in ductility related to the uncharged wire

$$F = \frac{n_o - n_H}{n_o} \cdot 100$$

where $n_o$ = number of twists for uncharged wire, and $n_H$ = number of twists for the wire specimen measured 3 minutes after interruption of the electrolytic charging.

The chemical analysis of the wire was as follows: 0.033% C, 0.064% Mn, 0.005% P, 0.011% S, 0.06% Cu, 0.11% Ni. The wires were charged from 4 to 1800 minutes in a 0.5 molar sulfuric acid solution with 10 mg As$_2$O$_3$ per liter. The differently marked points between two branches of the curve 1 were obtained at various current densities from 0.15 to 0.5 mA/cm$^2$. Curve 2 shows the results for wires charged to about 65 cm$^3$ H$_2$/100 g Fe and aged for various time periods under low pressure at room temperature.[7]

As may be seen, a hydrogen content less than about 2 cm$^3$ H$_2$/100 g Fe does not affect the ductility of the wire being studied. Between some 2 and 16 cm$^3$ H$_2$/100 g Fe the embrittlement F increases slowly with c. From 16 to 27 cm$^3$ H$_2$/100 g Fe there occurs the main part of plastic strain due to the accumulation of hydrogen in voids and F

considerably increases, but the experimental results scatter very irregularly. Suggestion can be made that this is due to the tendency of the Fe-H system to form two different crystal phases (alpha and beta). Higher concentrations than some 30 cm$^3$ H$_2$/100 g Fe do not change the F value any more.

Curve 2 shows that the extraction of hydrogen at room temperature from heavily hydrogenated specimens involves only a slight regeneration of the initial ductility. The same is true for both backing at 400 C and annealing at 700 C.

It is interesting to note that the susceptibility of iron to the embrittling effect of electrolytic charging greatly increases with the carbon content. Thus, a wire with 0.08% C showed from the beginning a much steeper course of the F against c curve than that shown in Figure 1, curve 1. A

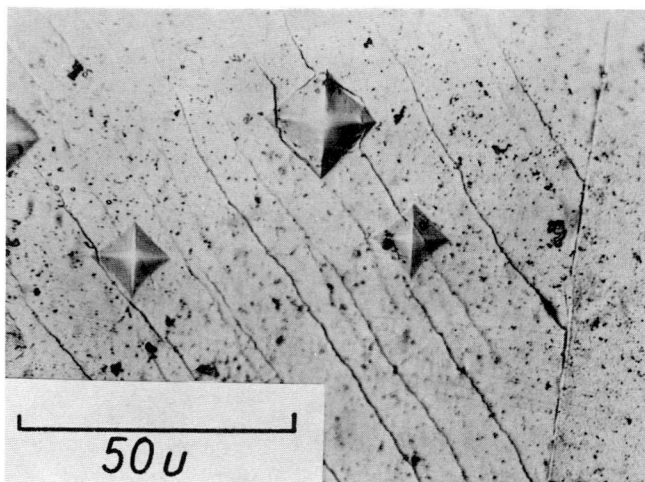

FIGURE 2 — Microcracks on the surface of a hydrogen-charged stainless steel sample.[11] Microhardness indentations made before and after charging are visible.

[2]The concentration of hydrogen was determined by vacuum extraction at 400 C. As is known, in electrolytically charged specimens the majority of hydrogen is accumulated near the surface.[8] during the torsion, these external layers of the wire are particularly active. Owing to the complexity of phenomena involved, the curves shown in Figure 1 do not necessarily correspond to the true relationship between hydrogen content and embrittlement.

noticeable loss in ductility occurred already at about 1 cm³ $H_2$/100 g Fe. An iron wire with 0.06% C gave intermediate results between those observed for wires containing 0.033 and 0.08% C.[7]

## 2. The Case of High Strength Steels

As shown by Troiano et al,[9] and others, the embrittlement of high strength steels is chiefly due to the "diffusive" form of the interstitially dissolved hydrogen. In contrast to the low carbon iron, concentrations much lower than 1 cm³ $H_2$/100 g Fe may bring about in these steels a heavy embrittlement and delayed failure. The stress-induced diffusion of hydrogen seems to play an essential role in these phenomena, but the exact process by which the diffusive hydrogen embrittles steel is unknown, as yet.

## 3. The Case of f.c.c. Nickel-Iron Alloys and Stainless Chromium-Nickel Steels

Both nickel-rich alloys with iron[10] and austenitic chromium-nickel steel[11] show the ability to form hydride phases in the surface layer of electrolytically charged samples. High compression stresses result, since the lattice spacings of the hydride phases are some 2% (case of austenitic Cr-Ni steel) to 6% (case of pure nickel) larger than those of the hydrogen-free metals and alloys. Thus, under the influence of intense electrolytic charging, the surface layer of a 22% Cr-21% Ni stainless steel attains compression stresses of the order of 115 kg/mm², and the

**TABLE 1**

| Metal or Alloy | $D_{20}$ (cm²/sec) | Reference |
|---|---|---|
| Low-carbon iron | $8.3 \times 10^{-5}$ | 12 |
| Nickel | $2.95 \times 10^{-10}$ | 13 |
| 22% Cr-21% Ni stainless steel | $2.7 \times 10^{-12}$ | 11 |

microhardness changes from 220 to almost 1000 Vickers units.[11] The hydride phases are unstable under ordinary conditions and begin to disintegrate immediately after interruption of the electrolytic charging. During this process the stresses are released, hardness decreases and many cracks are formed in the surface layer; see Figure 2. For nickel, their path is parallel to the {100} crystal face, whereas for austenitic chromium-nickel steel they are parallel to the {111} crystal face. The reason for this strange difference in the behavior of these two f.c.c. materials is unknown.

The hydrogen diffusion coefficient at room temperature is several orders of magnitude lower in f.c.c. metals and alloys than in b.c.c. iron, see Table 1.

Due to high compression stresses resulting from intense electrolytic charging, and to low values of the hydrogen diffusion coefficient, the effect of hydrogenation in f.c.c. metals and alloys is limited chiefly to thin surface layers. Under these conditions the embrittlement is slight and reversible, in a major part.

# References

1. W. Raczynski. *Bull. Acad. Pol. Sci., Ser. Sci. Chim.*, **15**, 25 (1967).
2. I. Czarnota and B. Baranowski. *Naturwissenschaften*, **51**, 262 (1964).
3. B. Baranowski and M. Smialowski. *J. Phys. Chem. Solids*, **12**, 206 (1959).
4. A. Janko. *Bull. Acad. Pol. Sci., Ser. Sci. Chim.*, **8**, 131 (1960).
5. E. O. Wollan, J. W. Cable and W. C. Koehler. *J. Phys. Chem. Solids*, **24**, 1141 (1963).
6. J. Flis and A. Janko. *Bull. Acad. Pol. Sci., Ser. Sci. Chim.*, **12**, 51 (1964).
7. W. Raczynski. Private Communication (1967).
8. M. Smialowski. *Hydrogen in Steel*, Pergamon Press, Oxford, p. 177 (1962).
9. H. H. Johnson, J. G. Morlet and A. R. Troiano. *Trans. Met. Soc. AIME*, **212**, 528 (1958); J. G. Morlet, H. H. Johnson and A. R. Troiano. *J. Iron Steel Inst.*, **189**, 37 (1958).
10. M. Smialowski, Z. Szklarska-Smialowska and A. Janko. *Omagiu R. Ripan, Acad. Rept. Romania*, Bucharest, p. 541 (1966).
11. M. Smialowski and A. Szummer. *Metallurgia Italiana*, **57**, 144, 155 (1965).
12. M. A. V. Devanathan, Z. Stachurski and W. Beck. *J. Electrochem. Soc.*, **110**, 886 (1963).
13. A. G. Edwards. *Brit. J. Appl. Phys.*, **8**, 406 (1957).

# PART VI

# ALUMINUM ALLOYS

# EVALUATION OF THE SESSION ON ALUMINUM ALLOYS

M. J. Pryor and M. R. Bothwell

The Aluminum Session of the symposium on "Fundamental Aspects of Stress Corrosion Cracking" was asked to address itself to the resolution or otherwise of the following five points.

1. Is the classic electrochemical mechanism of stress corrosion cracking consistent with recent advances in the detailed clarification of grain boundary structures in susceptible aluminum base alloys?

2. What is the detailed mechanism of crack propagation in depleted zones in susceptible aluminum alloys?

3. What is the role of film rupture in explaining crack propagation in susceptible aluminum alloys?

4. Is strain induced depolarization a factor in aluminum alloy stress corrosion cracking?

5. Does hydrogen play a significant role in aluminum stress corrosion cracking?

In the Chairman and Vice Chairman's opinion the meeting threw some considerable light on Items 3-5. It transpires that there is no strong evidence to support the contention that hydrogen entering the metal plays a significant role in stress corrosion cracking of susceptible aluminum alloys. There is further no available experimental evidence which suggests that strain induced depolarization is an operative mechanism in aluminum alloy stress corrosion cracking, although it is believed that some experiments should be conducted to resolve this question. Whereas it would certainly appear that aluminum oxide films must crack during the propagation of active stress corrosion cracks, there was likewise no strong feeling by the majority of those attending that film rupture constitutes a primary factor in cracking as in the well documented case of $\alpha$ brass cracking in ammoniacal solutions.

The classical electrochemical mechanism of Dix et al, still appears to attract large number of proponents. Information was presented at the meeting that some modification of the electrochemical mechanism is required in the case of aluminum-magnesium alloys and possibly in the case of aluminum-copper and aluminum-copper-magnesium alloys on account of better typification of grain boundary structures. These however are modifications in detail which do not detract from the major contention of the Dix theory. The situation appears to be considerably different in the aluminum-zinc-magnesium and aluminum-zinc-magnesium-copper alloys. Here it is considered that the identification of grain boundary paths susceptible to preferential corrosion is relatively weak and the information presented at the meeting did little to modify this conclusion. Considerable metallurgical studies were presented at the meeting which suggested novel means of building up stress concentrations at grain boundaries in this type of alloy. However, in the absence of identifying suitable localized means of grain boundary corrosion in susceptible alloys a reasonably satisfying mechanism for these two classes of alloys can hardly be said to exist at the present time.

Perhaps the most difficult area to resolve at the Conference was a satisfactory understanding of the crack propagation mechanism in alloys containing depleted zones adjacent to the grain boundary. Such depleted zones could be quite well described in terms of chemical composition and morphology. Ductile crack propagation in these low strength zones has been frequently proposed to account for SCC. Fractographic evidence appears, on balance, to be opposed to ductile crack propagation in low strength depleted zones on account of the absence of dimpling. This emerges as being an area of major importance which requires resolution in future work. If this point can be satisfactorily resolved in future work then there would appear to be a good chance that mechanisms involving local attack at grain boundaries and those relating more closely to the dislocation structure of the bulk metal can be resolved into a more satisfactory working mechanism.

# STRESS CORROSION MECHANISMS
# FOR ALUMINUM ALLOYS

D. O. Sprowls and R. H. Brown
Alcoa Research Laboratories

## I. Introduction

Aluminum alloys in tempers that are susceptible to stress corrosion cracking are characterized by microstructures wherein there has been a localized decomposition of solid solution at the grain boundaries, and, in most instances, identifiable precipitation in the grain boundaries can be established. Stress corrosion cracking typically occurs along the grain boundaries in contrast to the transgranular cracking generally associated with mechanical fractures resulting from fatigue, creep rupture, tensile overload, etc. (Figures 1 and 2). Anistropy of the grain structure, influenced by the composition and by the conditions under which an aluminum alloy product is worked from the cast ingot has a marked influence upon stress corrosion performance, as illustrated in Figure 3. Therefore, any alloying addition or metallurgical treatment that affects the precipitation of alloy constituents or the shape of the metal grains can markedly influence the resistance of an alloy to stress corrosion cracking.

It cannot be over-emphasized that the stress corrosion cracking process requires not only a susceptible alloy but the combination of a certain internal alloy structure, a sustained tensile stress, and exposure to particular types of environment. Both the internal structure and external environment are inseparably involved in the stress corrosion process.

Stress corrosion cracking has not been reported in the use of pure or commercially pure aluminum or in commercial alloys of the Al-Mn, Al-Si, Al-Mg with $< 3\%$ Mg, $Al-Mg_2$ Si and Al-Si-Mg types. The highly specialized metallurgical conditions that can render alloys of the latter two types susceptible in laboratory tests can easily be avoided in commercial practice. Stress corrosion resistant tempers have been developed for stronger alloys in the Al-Mg system containing more than 3% Mg, and high strength alloys of the Al-Cu and Al-Zn-Mg-Cu systems. Other tempers of these alloys can be susceptible to stress corrosion cracking, especially when stressed in the short transverse direction relative to the grain structure. The copper-free Al-Zn-Mg alloys differ from the latter group of alloys in that they are not as amenable to tempering to a stress corrosion resistant

condition, and they display a susceptibility to stress corrosion cracking in a much wider range of environments. The nominal compositions and typical tensile properties of the various alloys to be discussed are given in Table 1.

Stress corrosion studies of aluminum alloys were initiated in the Alcoa Research Laboratories approximately forty years ago with emphasis at that time on Al-Mg and Al-Cu types of alloys. Interest soon focused on the higher strength alloys of the Al-Zn-Mg and Al-Zn-Mg-Cu types. Stress corrosion evaluation has and should remain an important phase of alloy development.

## II. General Mechanism

The first general picture of the mechanism of stress corrosion of Al-Mg and Al-Cu alloys was presented by E. H. Dix, Jr.[2] in the 1940 Institute of Metals Division Lecture of the AIME and later in more detail for alloys in general by Mears, Brown and Dix.[3] Although others, notably Gilbert and Hadden,[4] Champion,[5] Farmery and Evans,[6] Thomas and Nutting,[7] Parkins,[8] and Haynie and Boyd,[9] have subsequently elaborated upon the electrochemical or the mechanical aspects of the mechanism and have sought to describe the processes in modern scientific terms, the original concept of the mechanism still remains largely unchanged, at least for aluminum alloys.

The generalized theory of the stress corrosion of alloys described by Mears, Brown and Dix[3] is as follows: Corrosion occurs along localized paths, producing fissures, components of tensile stress normal to the path create a stress concentration at the base of the localized fissures. These preferentially corroded paths may represent strata of relatively low inherent resistance to corrosion or they may be (as is usually the case) anodic to the contiguous metal. In aluminum-base alloys such pre-existent paths generally are associated with grain boundaries. The deeper the attack and the smaller the radius at the base of the fissure, the greater is the stress concentration. At sufficient concentration of stress, the fissures open further, thus exposing fresh unfilmed metal to the corrosion attack. Because this freshly exposed metal is more anodic, an increase in current

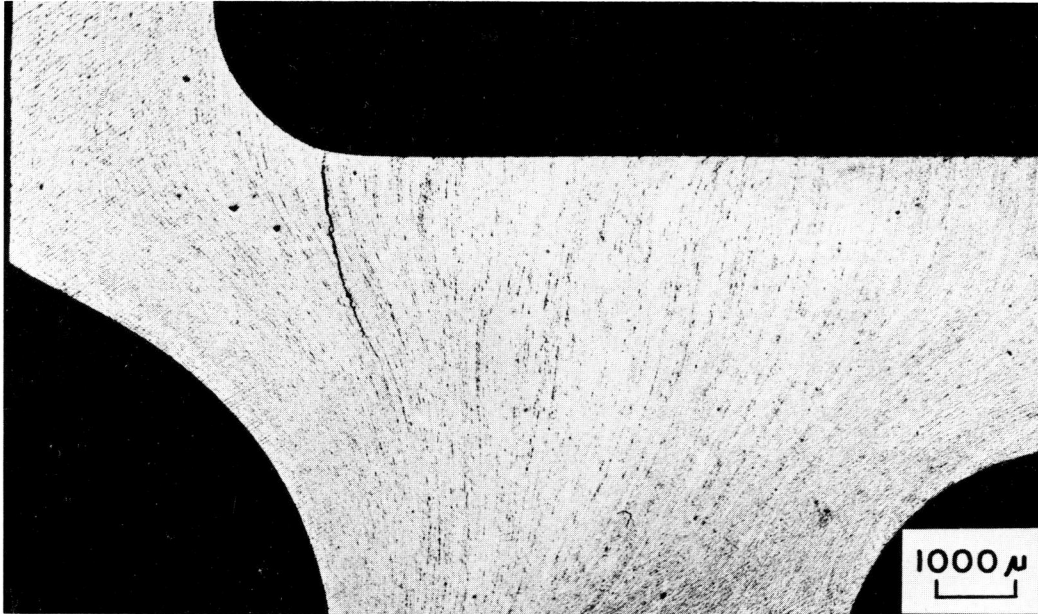

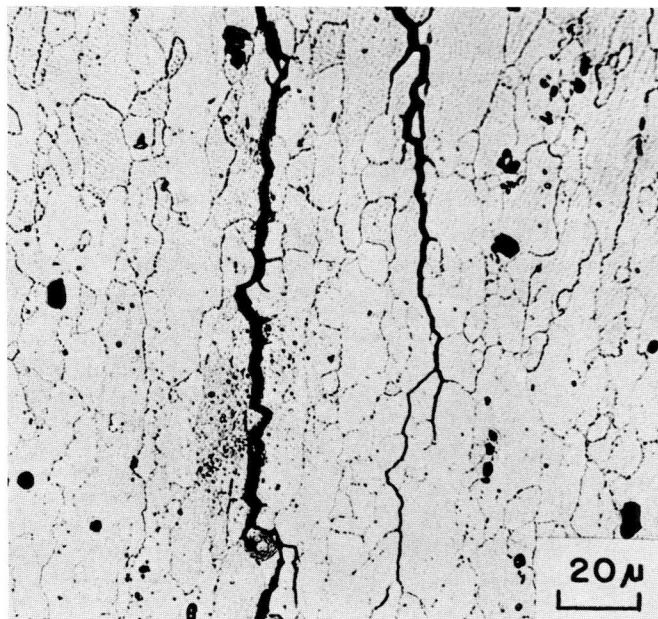

FIGURE 1 — Longitudinal section (top) through a corner of an impact-extruded and machined cylinder showing a stress corrosion crack following directional grain structure in a 7XXX series high strength aluminum alloy (Al-Zn-Mg-Cu-Cr). The enlarged section (bottom) illustrates the characteristic intergranular or inter-fragmentary nature of stress corrosion cracks in aluminum alloys. Keller's Etch.

467

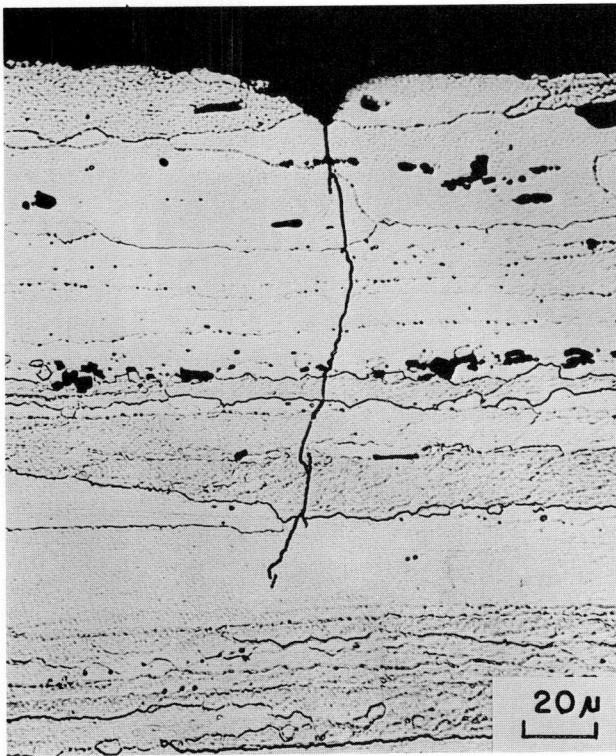

FIGURE 2 — Characteristic transgranular fatigue crack originating at a scratch in the surface of a 7XXX series alloy (Al-Zn-Mg-Cu-Cr) extrusion. Keller's Etch.

flow from the crack tip would be expected, and hence there is an acceleration of corrosion until protective films are reformed. Continued corrosion results in further separation of the metal, and as a result, an increased rate of penetration occurs because of the mutually accelerating effects of tensile stress and corrosion.

The exact location of the localized corrosion path and the specific roles of grain boundary precipitates and the solid solutions in the grains margins depend upon the alloy type and its metallurgical condition and upon the chemical nature of the environment. A discussion of the pertinent metallurgical and electrochemical factors that affect the performance of specific alloy-temper combinations that are susceptible to stress corrosion cracking is given below. Finally there is a recapitulation and appraisal of the general aspects of the mechanism of stress corrosion cracking of aluminum alloys.

Before getting into the details of the behavior of specific alloys, it seems important to consider the meanings of the terms stress corrosion and stress corrosion cracking as they are used in this paper. Stress corrosion is highly selective corrosion markedly accelerated by tensile stress; it may or may not lead to stress corrosion cracking.[3] Under some conditions the metallurgical state of the metal permits stress corrosion, but if a large number of nearly equal fissures are developed in close proximity, there will be no effective concentration of stress in any fissure, and cracking of the stressed member may not occur. On the other hand, metal in the same metallurgical state may stress corrosion

crack under other conditions of loading or corrosive environment that lead to the development of a small number of more localized fissures. Stress corrosion cracking, then, is the limiting case of stress corrosion, and it is favored by the occurrence of relatively localized fissures of stress corrosion.

Because stress corrosion in susceptible aluminum alloys is invariably intergranular, it is easy to confuse the occurrence of intergranular attack with stress corrosion. However, for the attack to be described as stress corrosion an accelerating effect of stress must be demonstrated. Therefore it is good testing practice to expose unstressed specimens simultaneously with stressed specimens. Under some conditions of stress corrosion testing, specimen failures can be simply the result of cross section area reduction by corrosion rather than the result of stress corrosion cracking. These distinctly different types of failure are illustrated in Figure 4. Serious errors in the interpretation of stress corrosion tests can result from the investigator not taking into proper account the limitation of his test procedure.

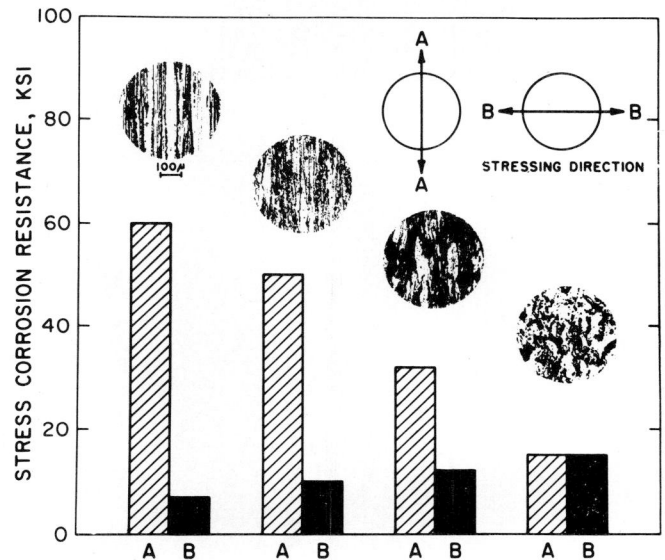

FIGURE 3 — Effect of grain geometry and stressing direction on resistance to stress corrosion cracking. The stress corrosion resistance was determined in two directions for extruded shapes of 7075-T6 alloy displaying various grain structures: parallel (A) and perpendicular (B) to the principal grain axis. Stress corrosion resistance was defined as the highest initially applied tension stress that did not cause stress corrosion cracking in 84 days of exposure in the 3.5% NaCl alternate immersion test. The resistance to stress corrosion cracking was highest when the most highly oriented grain structure was stressed parallel to the principal grain axis and lowest when the stressing direction was perpendicular to the principal grain axes. This same trend is applicable to other manufactured forms of 7075-T6 and also to other high strength aluminum alloys in a susceptible temper. Sprowls and Brown.[1]

468

## III. Factors Affecting the Mechanism of Stress Corrosion Cracking of Various Types of Aluminum Alloys

### A. Aluminum-Magnesium Alloys (5XXX Series)

*1. Physical Metallurgy*

**a. Natural Aging.** The binary Al-Mg alloys are the basis for an important class of non-heat treatable wrought alloys, as well as a few casting alloys whose characteristics can be altered by heat treatments. Although magnesium has substantial solubility in solid aluminum, the binary alloys do not show appreciable precipitation-hardening characteristics except when the magnesium content is greater than about 9%. Magnesium, however, does provide substantial strengthening and intensifies work-hardening characteristics.

Although these alloys are classified as non-heat treatable, the amount of magnesium soluble at the annealing temperature for the higher strength alloys such as 5086, 5083 and 5456 is considerably higher than can be retained in solid solution at room temperature. Thus, the fabricated products represent supersaturated solid solutions, and the

TABLE 1 – Nominal Composition and Typical Tensile Properties of Several Wrought Aluminum Alloys

| Alloy and Temper | Cu | Si | Mn | Mg | Zn | Cr | Other | Tensile Strength, ksi | Yield Strength, 0.2%, ksi | Elongation, % in 2 in. |
|---|---|---|---|---|---|---|---|---|---|---|
| | | | | Nominal Composition, % | | | | | | |
| | | | | | | | | | | |
| **Al-Cu Alloys (2XXX Series)** | | | | | | | | | | |
| 2014-T6 | 4.4 | 0.8 | 0.8 | 0.4 | – | – | – | 70 | 60 | 13 |
| 2024-T3 | 4.5 | – | 0.6 | 1.5 | – | – | – | 70 | 50 | 18 |
| 2024-T81 | 4.5 | – | 0.6 | 1.5 | – | – | – | 70 | 65 | 6 |
| 2219-T37 | 6.3 | – | 0.30 | – | – | – | 0.15 Zr, 0.1 V | 57 | 46 | 11 |
| 2219-T851 | 6.3 | – | 0.30 | – | – | – | 0.15 Zr, 0.1 V | 66 | 51 | 10 |
| 2219-T87 | 6.3 | – | 0.30 | – | – | – | 0.15 Zr, 0.1 V | 69 | 59 | 10 |
| 2020-T6 | 4.5 | – | 0.5 | – | – | – | 0.2 Cd, 1.1 Li | 84 | 77 | 7 |
| **Al-Mg Alloys (5XXX Series)** | | | | | | | | | | |
| 5454-O | – | – | 0.8 | 2.75 | – | 0.10 | – | 36 | 17 | 22 |
| 5454-H34 | – | – | 0.8 | 2.75 | – | 0.10 | – | 44 | 35 | 10 |
| 5086-O | – | – | 0.45 | 4.0 | – | 0.10 | – | 38 | 17 | 22 |
| 5086-H34 | – | – | 0.45 | 4.0 | – | 0.10 | – | 47 | 37 | 10 |
| 5083-O | – | – | 0.8 | 4.45 | – | 0.10 | – | 42 | 21 | 22 |
| 5083-H321 | – | – | 0.8 | 4.45 | – | 0.10 | – | 46 | 33 | 16 |
| 5456-O | – | – | 0.8 | 5.25 | – | 0.10 | – | 45 | 23 | 24 |
| 5456-H321 | – | – | 0.8 | 5.25 | – | 0.10 | – | 51 | 37 | 16 |
| 5456-H343 | – | – | 0.8 | 5.25 | – | 0.10 | – | 56 | 43 | 8 |
| **Al-Mg-Si Alloys (6XXX Series)** | | | | | | | | | | |
| 6061-O | 0.25 | 0.6 | – | 1.0 | – | 0.25 | – | 18 | 8 | 25 |
| 6061-T4 | 0.25 | 0.6 | – | 1.0 | – | 0.25 | – | 35 | 21 | 22 |
| 6061-T6 | 0.25 | 0.6 | – | 1.0 | – | 0.25 | – | 45 | 40 | 12 |
| 6066-T6 | 0.9 | 1.3 | 0.9 | 1.1 | – | – | – | 57 | 52 | 12 |
| 6070-T6 | 0.25 | 1.3 | 0.7 | 0.8 | – | – | – | 57 | 52 | 10 |
| **Al-Zn-Mg Alloys (7XXX Series)** | | | | | | | | | | |
| 7005-T53 | – | – | 0.45 | 1.4 | 4.6 | 0.12 | 0.15 Zr | 60 | 53 | 15 |
| 7039-T61 | – | – | 0.25 | 2.7 | 4.0 | 0.20 | – | 60 | 50 | 13 |
| 7039-T63 | – | – | 0.25 | 2.7 | 4.0 | 0.20 | – | 65 | 55 | 13 |
| **Al-Zn-Mg-Cu Alloys (7XXX Series)** | | | | | | | | | | |
| 7075-T6 | 1.6 | – | – | 2.5 | 5.6 | 0.30 | – | 83 | 73 | 11 |
| 7075-T73 | 1.6 | – | – | 2.5 | 5.6 | 0.30 | – | 73 | 63 | 13 |
| 7178-T6 | 2.0 | – | – | 2.7 | 6.8 | 0.30 | – | 88 | 78 | 10 |
| 7178-T76 | 2.0 | – | – | 2.7 | 6.8 | 0.30 | – | 81 | 71 | 11 |
| 7079-T6 | 0.6 | – | 0.20 | 3.3 | 4.3 | 0.20 | – | 78 | 68 | 14 |
| 7001-T6 | 2.1 | – | – | 3.0 | 7.4 | 0.25 | – | 98 | 91 | 9 |
| 7001-T75 | 2.1 | – | – | 3.0 | 7.4 | 0.25 | – | 84 | 72 | 12 |

Sources: Standards for Aluminum Mill Products, Ninth Edition, 1967 and *Aluminum,* (Kent R. Van Horn, ed.) **Vol. I,** Chapter 9, American Society for Metals (1967).

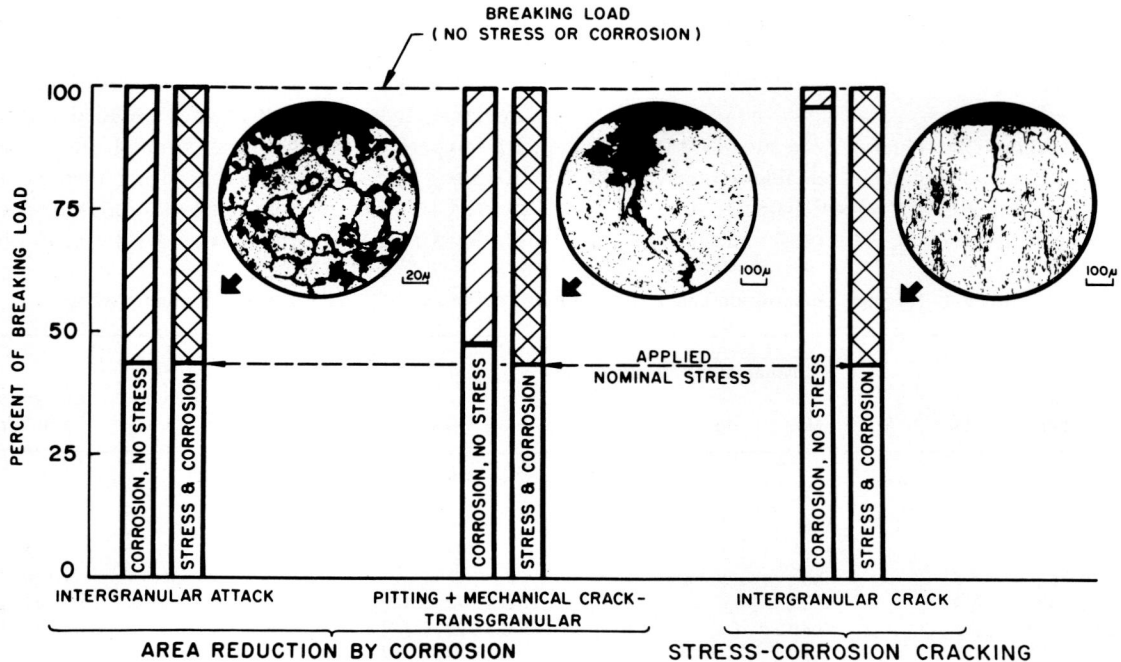

FIGURE 4 — Schematic comparison of specimen failures resulting from stress corrosion cracking and failures resulting from area reduction by corrosion. At the left and middle are examples of forms of corrosion that can result in failure of test specimens of certain aluminum alloys that are not susceptible to stress corrosion cracking. The particular forms of intergranular attack and pitting attack shown in the photomicrographs are not accelerated by stress. They can, however, especially the pits, cause stress concentration leading to transgranular mechanical failure. On the right is a characteristic intergranular stress corrosion crack. Brown and Sprowls.[10]

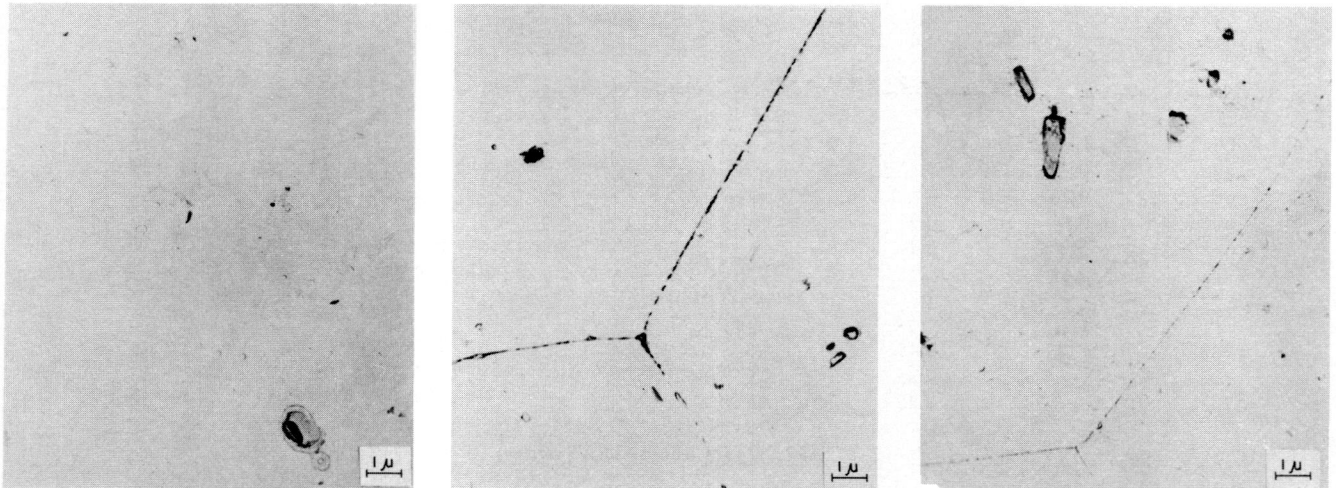

(a) As Fabricated

(b) Naturally Aged
24 Years

(c) Heated 7 Days
at 212 F

FIGURE 5 — Electron micrographs of anodic oxide replicas of Al-6% Mg-H12 (20% reduction by cold rolling) alloy. Note the indications of microstructural change produced by prolonged natural aging (b) and the similar effect produced by heating (c). Composition: 6.10% Mg, 0.02% Cu, 0.15% Fe, 0.11% Si. All samples were etched 5 seconds in 40% phosphoric acid. Dix, Anderson and Shumaker.[11]

470

excess magnesium tends to precipitate as an Al-Mg constituent. The precipitation is sluggish at room temperature but is stimulated by cold work (deformation) and by exposure to elevated temperatures up to the solid solution saturation temperature for the given alloy. As would be expected, precipitates nucleate preferentially in grain boundaries, then in dislocations produced by deformation and finally in the solid solution matrix. The structural changes accompanying such precipitation are illustrated in Figure 5. As shown, no indication of precipitate was found in a cold worked 6% Mg alloy when examined soon after fabrication. When examined after 24 years' aging at room temperature, however, the grain boundaries of such an alloy were outlined clearly. As shown in Figure 5c, the same type of structure can be produced in a much shorter time by heating the freshly prepared alloy at an elevated temperature such as 212 F.

**b. Nature of the Precipitate.** Fink and Smith[12] investigated the age hardening of Al-Mg alloys using high purity Al-10.3% Mg alloy sheet heat treated at 842 F, quenched in cold water and aged at 212 F, 392 and 572 F for various periods. They observed that etching effects caused by precipitation at grain boundaries could be observed microscopically before the aging had progressed far enough to change the lattice parameter or the tensile properties measurably. During aging at 212 F the tensile properties began to change before precipitation within the grains was indicated, whereas at the higher temperatures the tensile

properties did not begin to change until after general precipitation became evident. In all cases the lattice parameter began to change after the tensile properties changed. Debye-Scherrer X-ray patterns revealed that the matrix precipitating phase in specimens aged at 572 F was the equilibrium beta phase, generally referred to as $Mg_2 Al_3$, while in specimens aged at 392 F, the precipitation phase did not have the equilibrium beta crystal structure, and was designated as a transition phase (beta'). It seems reasonable, therefore, that it would be the beta or beta' phase that would have been precipitated in the grain boundaries long before it could be seen in the grains. Perryman and Brook,[13] using both a high purity Al-10% Mg alloy and a commercial purity Al-7% Mg alloy, confirmed the observations of Fink and Smith.

Edeleanu[14] suggested that inasmuch as the susceptibility to stress corrosion is at a maximum at an early stage in the aging process, the easily corrodible material in the grain boundary may not be the beta' or the beta phase, but only a high concentration of magnesium atoms segregated in the grain boundary as a first stage in the aging process. Edeleanu discounted evidence of grain boundary precipitation put forward by some investigators on the basis of microscopic examination of etched specimens because preferential grain boundary etching time and the relative orientation of adjacent grains, and could just as well be the result of selective attack of the magnesium-rich grain boundaries. Perryman[15] dismissed the argument as

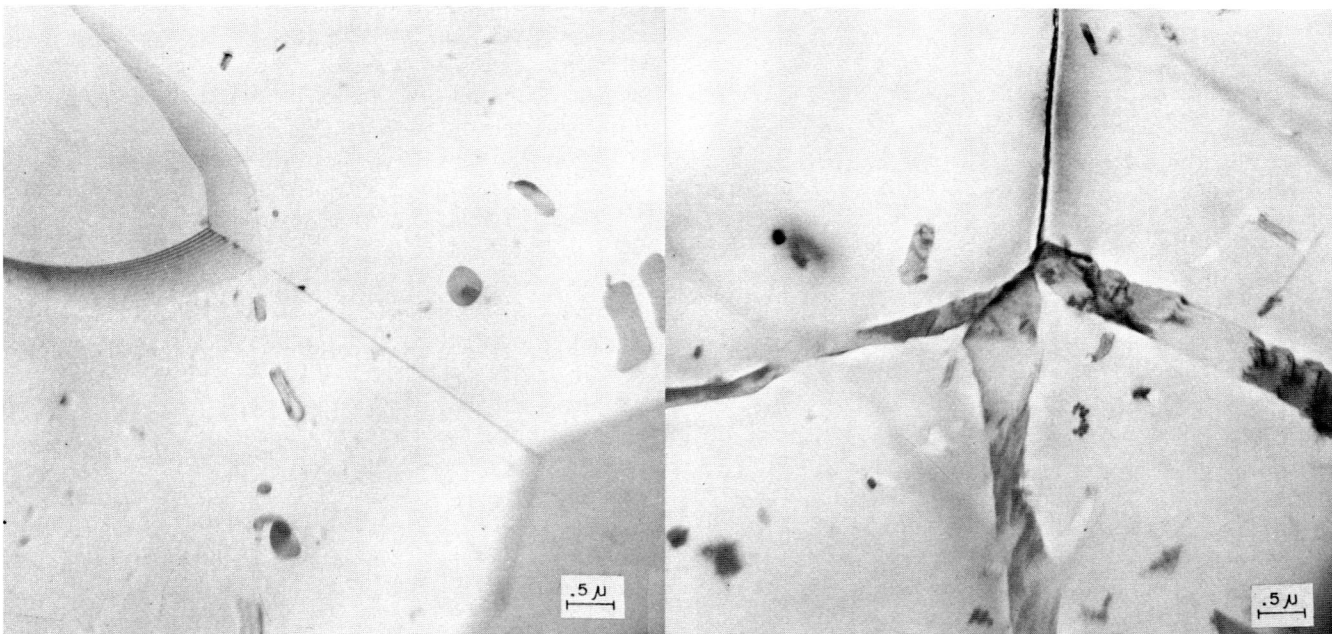

(a) As Fabricated

(b) Heated 30 Days at 300 F

FIGURE 6 — Electron transmission micrographs of thin foils prepared from 0.064 in thick sheet of X5356-0. The strong contrast shown by both the low-angle and high-angle grain boundaries in sample (b) indicate the presence of almost continuous grain boundary precipitate. A few particles of precipitate also are shown in the grain bodies of sample (b). The dark particles in sample (a) indicate constituents of relatively insoluble manganese or iron compounds. Composition: 5.15% Mg, 0.03% Cu, 0.22% Fe, 0.11% Si, 0.11% Mn, 0.10% Cr, 0.10% Ti. Robinson and Hunter.[18]

471

relatively unimportant, for, whether the etching effects are due to magnesium segregation or particles of the beta phase, the grain boundary will still be the anodic or "easily corrodible" path.

In recent years, however, electron microscopic studies of thin films by electron transmission have produced evidence that grain boundary precipitation is, in fact, present in stress corrosion susceptible materials. Eikum and Thomas[16] in studies of thin foils prepared from bulk Al-5% Mg alloy sheet after quenching followed by aging two days at 302 F observed discrete particles of precipitation in the grain boundaries (only). The precipitate particles were not identified, but were assumed to be beta or beta' phase.

Robinson[17] in recent electron transmission examinations of thin foils also prepared from annealed bulk Al-5% Mg alloy (X5356) sheet sensitized by aging 30 days at 300 F observed what appeared to be a continuous film of grain boundary precipitate (Figure 6). The precipitation in this sample would, of course, be considerably more advanced than that in the sample examined by Eikum and Thomas. Electron diffraction patterns of selected areas in the grain boundaries established the presence of $Mg_2Al_3$. These electron microscopic examinations therefore show Edeleanu's suggestion to be untenable.

Robinson's electron micrographs lend support to Mencarelli's[19] interpretation of electron micro-fractographs of a service stress corrosion failure in Al-7% Mg alloy. Mencarelli noted that the failure was intergranular and that the surfaces of the grain boundaries were smooth, showing no precipitate particles, thus indicating an advanced degree of grain boundary precipitation in the form of a uniform film.

## 2. Relationship of Stress Corrosion Cracking to the Microstructure

In general, the resistance to corrosion and stress corrosion of as-fabricated Al-Mg alloys is very high. Small amounts of grain boundary precipitate generally have negligible effect on resistance to corrosion or stress corrosion, so that for some period, natural aging is not particularly harmful. With longer aging times, particularly for cold worked alloys containing more than about 3.5% Mg, precipitation in the grain boundaries results in a continuous beta phase ($Mg_2Al_3$). This precipitate is strongly anodic to the Al-Mg solid solution matrix (Table 2) and in the presence of many electrolytes the $Mg_2Al_3$ corrodes selectively at a high rate because of the very narrow path of anodic phase present in the grain boundaries. A continuous anodic boundary precipitate thus produces, in particular environments, a susceptibility to intergranular attack and, in the presence of sustained tensile stress, to stress corrosion cracking.

A good correlation between the microstructures of the Al-Mg alloys and their resistance to stress corrosion cracking was noted in early studies at Alcoa Research Laboratories by Craighead[21] and by various other investigators, including Seibel,[22] Brenner and Roth,[23] Gilbert and Hadden,[4] and others. The examples shown in Figure 7

**TABLE 2—Electrode Potentials of Aluminum Solid Solutions and Constituents[20]**

| Phase | Potential, volts |
| --- | --- |
| Mg | -1.73 |
| Zn | -1.10 |
| $Mg_2Al_3$ | -1.24 |
| Al + 4 $MgZn_2$ | -1.07 |
| Al + 4 Zn | -1.05 |
| $MgZn_2$ | -1.05 |
| $CuMgAl_2$ | -1.00 |
| Al + 1 Zn | -0.96 |
| Al + 7 Mg | -0.89 |
| Al + 5 Mg | -0.88 |
| Al + 3 Mg | -0.87 |
| $MnAl_6$ | -0.85 |
| 99.95 Al | -0.85 |
| Al + 1 $Mg_2Si$ | -0.83 |
| Al + 1 Si | -0.81 |
| Al + 2 Cu | -0.75 |
| $CuAl_2$ | -0.73 |
| Al + 4 Cu | -0.69 |
| $FeAl_3$ | -0.56 |
| $NiAl_3$ | -0.52 |
| Si | -0.26 |
| Cu | -0.20 |

Note: 0.1 N calomel scale, measured in an aqueous solution of 53 g per liter NaCl + 3 g per liter $H_2O_2$ at 25 C.

for an Al-5% Mg alloy (X5356) were obtained by Dix, Anderson and Shumaker.[24] Alloys showing little or no grain boundary precipitation (Figure 7a) invariably have excellent resistance to stress corrosion cracking. Those showing extensive grain boundary precipitation, such as is shown in Figure 7b, are highly susceptible to stress corrosion cracking. Alloys having extensive general precipitation as well as wide bands of grain boundary precipitate (Figure 7c) have intermediate resistance to stress corrosion cracking. It is believed that the improved resistance to stress corrosion cracking obtained in the latter case can be attributed to the reduced current density for the anodic $Mg_2Al_3$ precipitate as a result of the increase in anode/cathode ratio.

The precipitate formed by heating at relatively high temperatures is coarse and generally does not form a continuous phase at the grain boundaries, and such structures (Figure 7d) have shown excellent resistance to stress corrosion cracking. However, the appearance of this latter structure can be misleading as shown by Perryman and Hadden[25] for an Al-7% Mg alloy that was cold worked 10% and aged one week at 482 F; although the microstructure showed discrete coarse particles of precipitate in the grain boundaries and in the grains, the material was highly susceptible to stress corrosion cracking. It seems probable that during the heating of this relatively high magnesium alloy, sufficient magnesium was retained in solid solution so that during or subsequent to air cooling additional precipitation occurred in the grain boundaries. This precipitate would be relatively fine and, in the

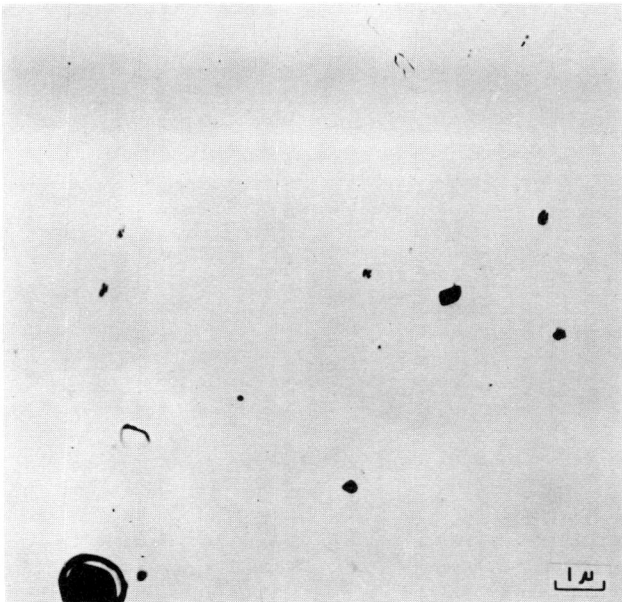

(a) As Fabricated
(Highly Resistant)

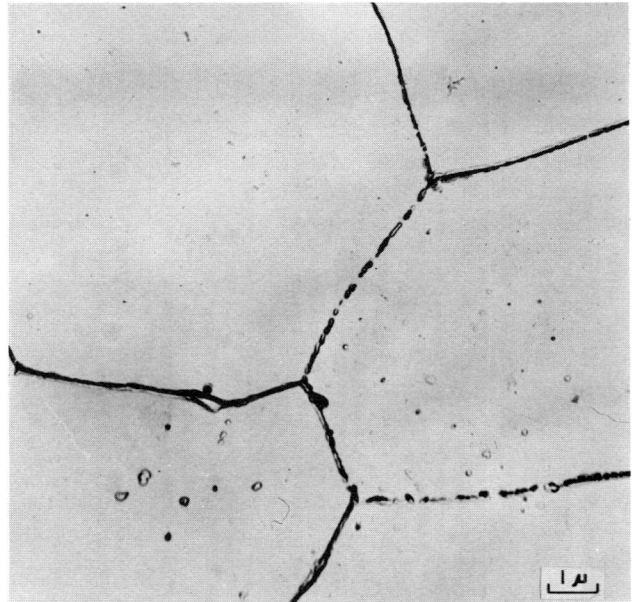

(b) Heated One Year
at 212 F
(Highly Susceptible)

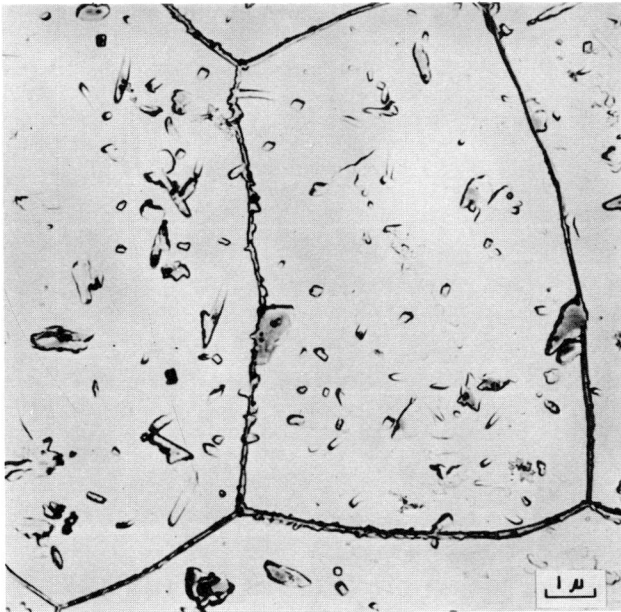

(c) Heated One Year
at 300 F
(Slightly Susceptible)

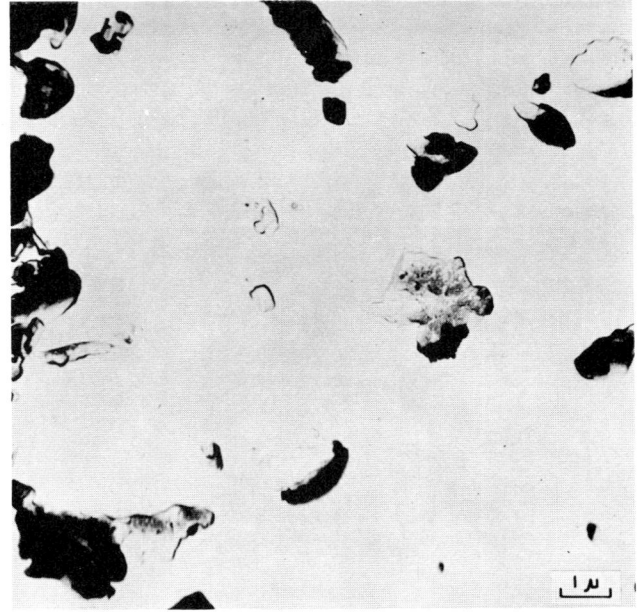

(d) Heated One Year
at 400 F
(Highly Resistant)

FIGURE 7 — Electron micrographs of anodic oxide replicas of X5356-H12 (20% reduction by the cold rolling) alloy. All samples were etched one second in Keller's Etch (HCl-$HNO_3$-HF) to reveal indications of precipitate location. The relative resistance to stress corrosion cracking as derived from Figure 11 is also noted above. Composition: 5.15% Mg, 0.03% Cu, 0.22% Fe, 0.11% Si, 0.11% Mn, 0.10% Cr, 0.10% Ti. Dix, Anderson and Shumaker.[24]

473

presence of the large particles of $Mg_2Al_3$, might not be revealed by the usual etchant.

Through the use of carefully controlled heating and cold rolling techniques, Anderson[26] has developed special stress corrosion resistant tempers (H323, H343) for the commercial Al-5% Mg alloys 5083 and 5456. Anderson[26] has developed similar tempers also for experimental alloys having still higher magnesium contents.

Because of the attempts of some investigators[27] to relate the stress corrosion susceptibility of other alloys to the presence of dislocations, samples of X5356-H12 heated for various periods at 300 F to different degrees of susceptibility to stress corrosion cracking, were examined with the electron microscope. As shown in the three micrographs in Figure 8, the presence of dislocation tangles in the vicinity of the grain boundaries did not affect the stress corrosion behavior, whereas the presence of the continuous grain boundary precipitate was directly relatable to the stress corrosion performance.

## 3. Factors Affecting the Precipitation

Factors that affect precipitation of the $Mg_2Al_3$, in addition to the time and temperature of heating include magnesium content and work hardening. Studies of the effects of alloy content have indicated that annealed material with up to 7% Mg is essentially free from susceptibility to stress corrosion cracking. Above this level, susceptibility increases progressively with increasing magnesium. The safe levels of magnesium are lowered drastically by cold working. This is illustrated by the stress corrosion data in Table 3. As shown, a 6% Mg alloy with as little as 10% cold reduction (by rolling) became highly susceptible to stress corrosion cracking after 20 years of aging at room temperature. A 4% Mg alloy required 30 to 40% cold

TABLE 3—Resistance to Stress Corrosion Cracking of Al-Mg Alloy Sheet[1] After 20 Years of Natural Aging at Room Temperature[11]

| Temper | F/N[2] | Days to Failure[3] |
|---|---|---|
| **Al-4.04% Mg Alloy** | | |
| Annealed | 0/2 | OK 180 |
| 5% cold reduction | 0/2 | OK 180 |
| 10% cold reduction | 0/2 | OK 180 |
| 20% cold reduction | 0/2 | OK 180 |
| 40% cold reduction | 3/3 | 13, 105, 135 |
| 60% cold reduction | 3/3 | 42, 42, 56 |
| 75% cold reduction | 1/3 | 62 days, OK 180 |
| **Al-6.01% Mg Alloy** | | |
| Annealed | 0/2 | OK 180 |
| 10% cold reduction | 2/2 | 17, 17 |
| 20% cold reduction | 2/2 | 2, 48 |
| 30% cold reduction | 2/2 | 2, 2 |
| **Al-6.15% Mg Alloy** | | |
| 75% cold reduction | 3/3 | 12, 13, 13 |
| **Al-5.99% Mg Alloy (Aged 15.3 Years)** | | |
| 75% cold reduction | 3/3 | 10, 10, 20 |

[1] Chemical composition: Cu, 0.01-0.05; Fe, 0.13-0.19; and Si, 0.06-0.08.
[2] F/N denotes number of specimens failed over number of specimens exposed.
[3] Test conditions: exposure, 3-1/2% NaCl alternate immersion; specimen, sheet tensile (X-grain) specimen stressed to 75% yield strength by dead weight loading as a simple beam.

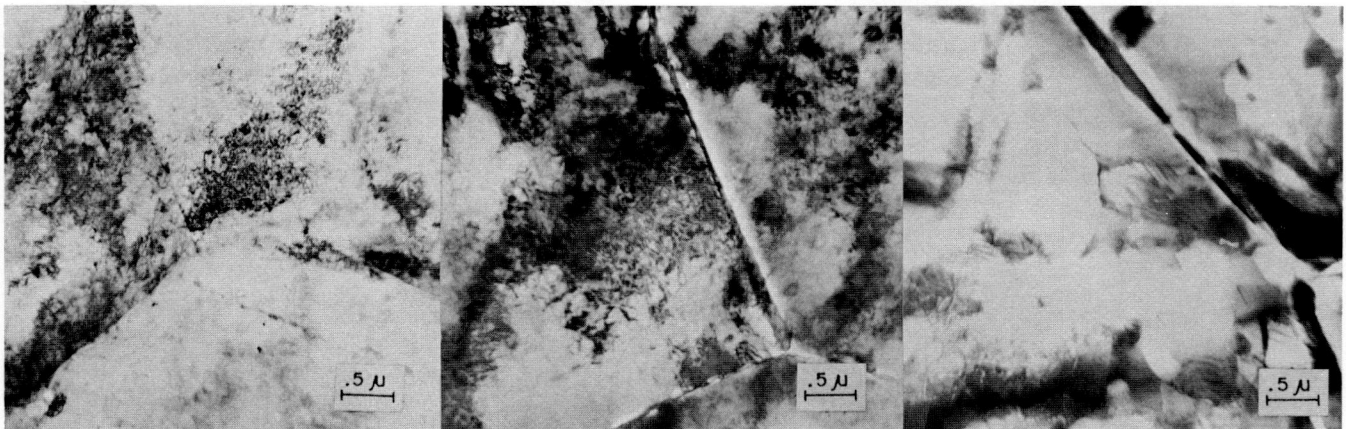

(a) As Fabricated          (b) Heated One Day at 300 F          (c) Heated 830 Days at 200 F

FIGURE 8 — Electron transmission micrographs of thin foils prepared from 0.064 in thick sheet of X5356-H12 (20% reduction by cold rolling) alloy. A relatively high density of dislocation tangles was present in all three samples although only the sample heated for one day at 300 F (b) was susceptible to stress corrosion cracking. Note also the indications of continuous precipitate in the grain boundaries of the two heated samples and the large particles of matrix precipitate in the grain boundaries of the two heated samples and the large particles of matrix precipitate in the sample heated for 830 days (c). Composition: 5.15% Mg, 0.03% Cu, 0.22% Fe, 0.11% Si, 0.11% Mn, 0.10% Cr, 0.10% Ti. Robinson and Hunter.[18]

reduction to become susceptible to stress corrosion cracking after 20 years' aging. A 5% Mg alloy given various amounts of cold reduction and heated one week at 212 F to simulate prolonged room temperature aging was susceptible to stress corrosion cracking with 20% or more cold reduction (Figure 9). It appeared that the threshold stress for this alloy when cold reduced 40% or more was between 25% and 50% of the yield strength.

On the other hand, Brenner and Metcalfe,[28] working with Al-5% Mg alloys containing 0-1% zinc, reported that small amounts of cold work (30% reduction) followed by heating at 158 F markedly reduced the resistance to stress corrosion cracking; and that large amounts of cold working (50% reduction) restored the high resistance of unworked material. Niederberger et al,[29] in tests of various Al-Mg and Al-Mg-Mn alloys in a seacoast atmosphere, observed that with magnesium contents of 5, 6 and 7% the H12 and H32 tempers (20% cold reduction) were more susceptible to stress corrosion cracking than the more highly cold worked H16 and H36 tempers (60% cold reduction). Although plausible explanations for an inverse effect of cold work can be advanced (e.g., large amounts of cold work produce a more highly directional grain structure and increase the number of lattice discontinuities for nucleation of general precipitation), additional studies that include metallographic and electron microscopic examinations are needed to resolve the apparently conflicting data.

The data obtained by Niederberger et al[29] also showed that additions of manganese and chromium to aluminum alloys with 6 and 7% Mg seemed to improve the resistance to stress corrosion. Manganese and chromium, however, have no known effect upon the pattern of $Mg_2Al_3$ precipitation pattern other than that of inhibiting formation of equi-axed grains and promoting the formation of elongated grains. An elongated grain structure, of course, would tend to be beneficial. Considerable Alcoa experience,[11] however, has shown that the main role of manganese is to enable a given yield strength to be obtained with a lower magnesium content. It has been found that for the control of stress corrosion cracking of commercial alloys and products the regulation of metallurgical treatments and fabricating practices is far more important than the addition of minor alloying elements such as manganese, chromium, zinc, copper, silver, etc. This thesis is confirmed by the data of Niederberger, et al which showed that the H24 (strain hardened and partially annealed) and H321 (hot rolled) tempers are difficult to sensitize. Properly manufactured tempers, such as H24, H321 and H343, should be stress corrosion resistant and difficult to sensitize at ambient climatic conditions; as a matter of fact, H24 and H343 temper products can only be sensitized by very long periods of heating at temperatures in the range of 200-250 F.

The safe level of magnesium also is decreased by exposures to elevated temperatures. The data in Figure 10 show the effect of heating at 200 F on the resistance to stress corrosion cracking of Al-Mg-Mn alloy sheet with three different Mg contents. The time required to sensitize the plastically deformed O temper sheet increased with decreasing magnesium content.

The effects of temperature and time of heating have been studied by various investigators,[24,31,32] but direct comparisons of the data are complicated by different metallurgical conditions of the alloys and by different stress corrosion test methods. The most extensive of the published data is that of Dix, Anderson and Shumaker[24] using an Al-5% Mg (X5356) alloy. In the unstabilized cold worked tempers, this alloy becomes susceptible to stress corrosion cracking on prolonged aging at room temperature; therefore in the USA these tempers are not generally recommended for use. The behavior of X5356 is similar to that of other high magnesium alloys, however, and illustrates the need for careful selection of alloys and tempers for use at elevated temperature. The specimens represented in Figure 11 were aged at room temperature or heated for various periods at temperatures to 400 F. The numbers adjacent to each data point give the length of exposure or days to failure for X5356-H12 (20% cold reduction) sheet in a laboratory corrosion test. As shown by this corrosion test, the strain hardened sheet became susceptible to stress corrosion cracking after four years of aging at room temperature. In the case of specimens heated at elevated temperatures, susceptibility to stress corrosion cracking developed after heating for approximately 6 months at 150 F, one week at 212 F or one day at 300 F. At temperatures approaching 400 F, however, no susceptibility to stress corrosion cracking was observed with heating times as long as two years and as short as one minute. The substantially better resistance of the annealed temper is shown by the dashed line, and the actual test data are given in Reference 24. Similar curves could be developed for other alloys and tempers, and they would be translated to the right or the left depending upon the alloy content and the amount of cold work. The position of the curve for any one alloy would also be influenced by the stress corrosion test procedure.

It has been observed by several investigators that additions of 1-2% zinc to Al-6% Mg,[33] Al-7.5% Mg[24] and Al-5% Mg[28] improved the resistance to stress corrosion cracking. The Alcoa Laboratories experience indicates that zinc accelerates the formation of precipitate in the grain bodies, as well as in the grain boundaries. Under these conditions longer aging times are required to sensitize the alloys containing zinc.

### 4. Electrochemical Factors

Mears, Brown and Dix[3] described a convincing experiment that illustrates the electrochemical aspects of the stress corrosion of Al-Mg alloys. It was reasoned that if an electrolyte were found in which the potential relationships of the precipitate and the Al-Mg solid solutions described above were reversed, stress corrosion cracking of an alloy containing "continuous" grain boundary precipitate should not occur if the mechanism were electrochemical. Figure 12 shows such a reversal in the potential difference between the $Mg_2Al_3$ and Al-Mg solid solutions. In an electrolyte

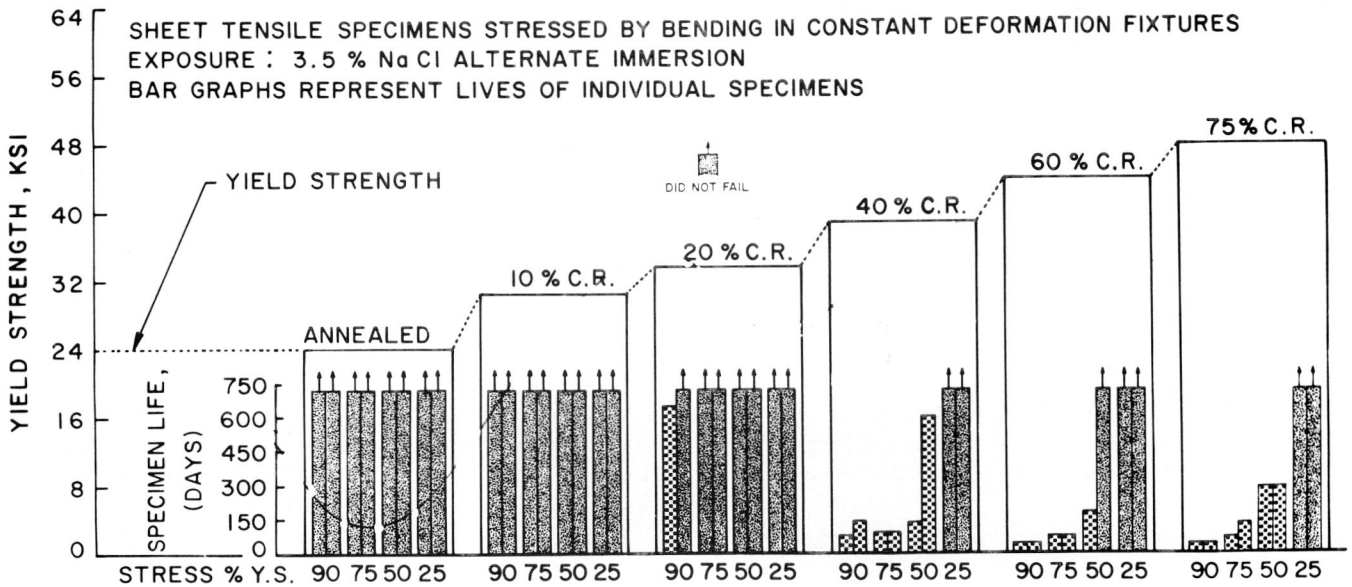

FIGURE 9 – Effect of amount of cold reduction on the yield strength and the resistance to stress corrosion cracking of Al-Mg-Mn alloy sheet (0.064 in) heated one week at 212 F. Composition: 5.16% Mg, 0.11% Mn, 0.11% Cr, 0.09% Cu. Dix, Anderson and Shumaker.[11]

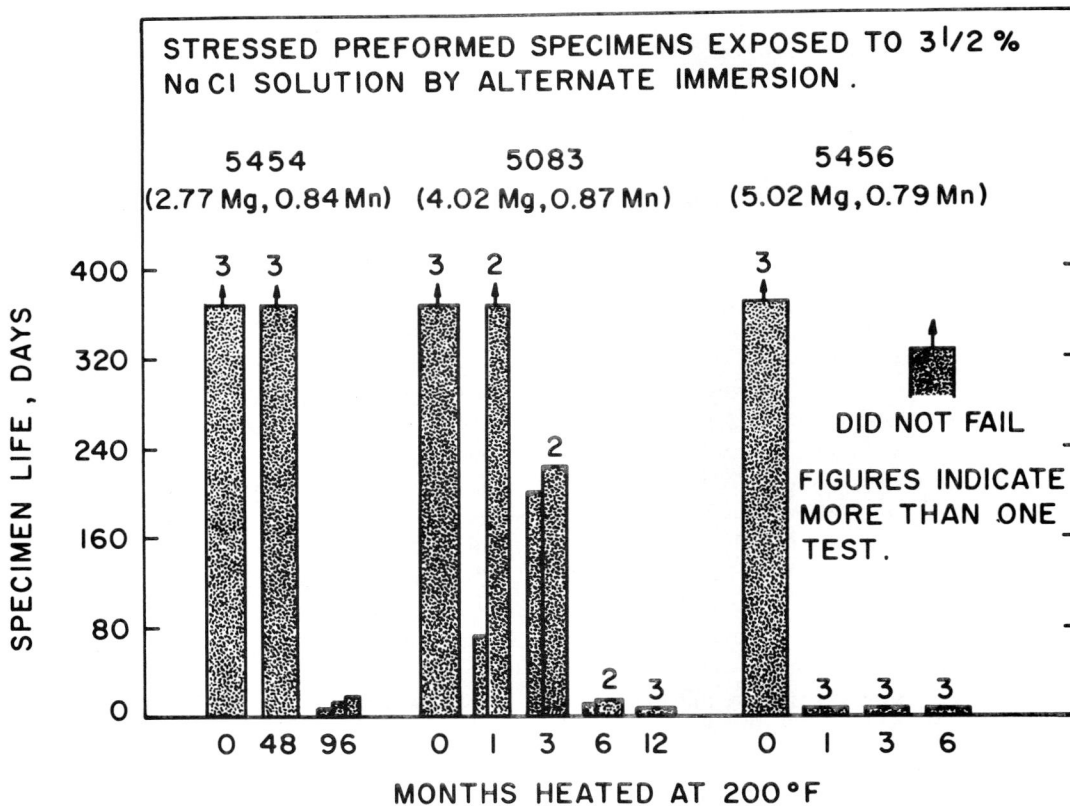

FIGURE 10 – Effect of heating on resistance to stress corrosion cracking of Al-Mg-Mn alloy sheet. Strip specimens of 0 temper sheet 0.064 in thick were plastically deformed at room temperature, then heated for various periods at 200 F and stressed by bending in constant deformation fixtures. Note the marked superiority of the lower magnesium alloy 5454 in resisting stress corrosion cracking after prolonged heating at 200 F. Rutemiller and Sprowls.[30]

containing 53 g NaCl and 3 g $H_2O_2$ per liter, the $Mg_2Al_3$ was about 200 mv anodic to the solid solutions; hence, a specimen of sensitized Al-10% Mg alloy sheet stress corrosion cracked within 15 minutes when stressed to 75% yield strength and immersed in this solution. When 10 g/l NaOH was added to the solution, however, $Mg_2Al_3$ became about 340 mv cathodic to the solid solutions. Thus, a similar stressed specimen exposed to the modified solution did not fail, and was removed from test after 125 hours of exposure.

General precipitation produced within the grain bodies by aging at relatively high temperatures would be expected from electrochemical considerations to have a beneficial effect because it increases the ratio of the area of the anodic phase to that of the cathodic solid solution; this should greatly reduce the intensity of the electrochemical attack on the grain boundary precipitate.

The effectiveness of Al-Mg constituent precipitated throughout the grain bodies in rendering an Al-5 alloy highly stress corrosion resistant was strongly suggested in an experiment performed by Cook.[34] A tensile specimen machined from 0.064 in sheet of X5456-H14,[1] heated for 30 days at 200 F, was stressed in bending to 75% of the tensile yield strength and immersed in aerated 3.5% NaCl solution (Figure 13). The sensitized X5456-H14[1] specimen failed between the second and third day of exposure. The experiment was repeated except that a piece of $Mg_2Al_3$ constituent was coupled to the sensitized and stressed specimen. The specimen was removed uncracked after an 11-day exposure, indicating that the presence of the constituent reduced the anodic current from the grain boundaries to a vanishingly small quantity. In a similar manner, the presence of general precipitation produced throughout the grains by appropriate metallurgical treat-

---

[1]The H14 temper is not a standard temper for 5456 alloy sheet.

ments could provide sufficient anodic area to minimize the anodic reaction at the grain boundaries.

## 5. Environmental Factors

Gilbert and Hadden[4] performed a number of experiments to investigate environmental factors in relationship to the general mechanism of stress corrosion cracking outlined above. Using a sensitized Al-7% Mg alloy they observed that stress corrosion cracking in a 3% sodium chloride solution did not begin in the absence of oxygen, and the admission of oxygen to uncracked or partially cracked specimens immersed in deaerated solution resulted in rapid cracking. They also observed that if oxygen were removed during the period of active cracking, the process was arrested.

During active stress corrosion cracking of Al-7% Mg alloy a stream of fine gas bubbles arose from the crack. Samples of the gas were analyzed by Gilbert and Hadden and found to consist essentially of hydrogen. The time at which bubbles began to appear was correlated with the potential-time graph for a cracking specimen, Figure 14. The potential of the stressed specimen was relatively unsteady compared to that of an unstressed specimen, but during the period of active cracking it shifted in the anodic direction slightly and remained fairly constant (Van Rooyen[35] observed that during this period of active cracking of a sensitized Al-7% Mg alloy stressed and immersed in $NaCl-NaHCO_3$ solution, there were a number of anodic jumps of the order of 5 to 39 mv). After the crack had proceeded completely across the specimen, evolution of hydrogen ceased and the potential became more cathodic again.

The effect of variations in pH of a 3% sodium chloride solution upon the time for cracking of Al-Mg alloys is shown in Figure 15. In general, the time for cracking increased as the curves differed somewhat above a pH of

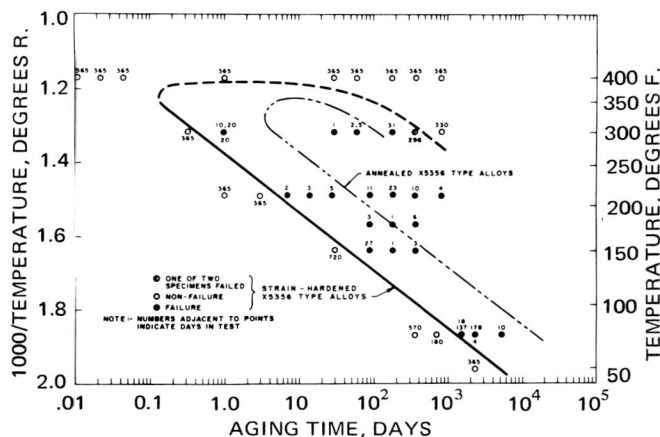

FIGURE 11 — Approximate time required to sensitize strain hardened X5356 type alloys to stress corrosion cracking. Composition: 5.15% Mg, 0.03% Cu, 0.22% Fe, 0.11% Si, 0.11% Mn, 0.10% Cr and 0.10% Ti. Dix, Anderson and Shumaker.[24]

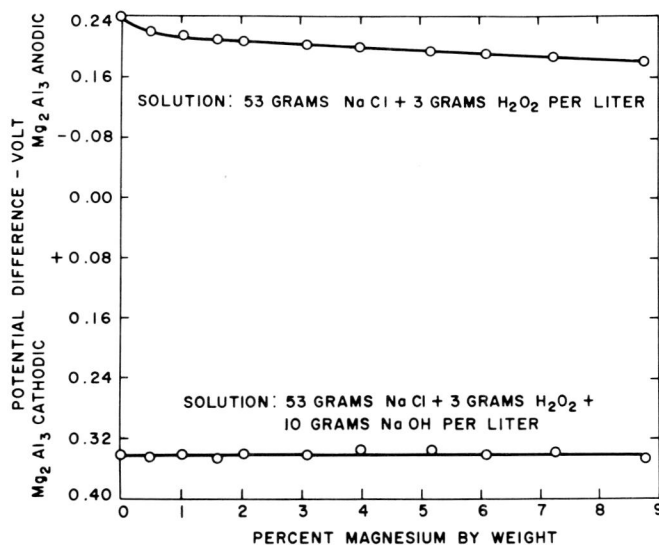

FIGURE 12 — Effect of electrolyte composition on potential difference between Al-Mg solid solutions and constituent $Mg_2Al_3$. Mears, Brown and Dix.[3]

477

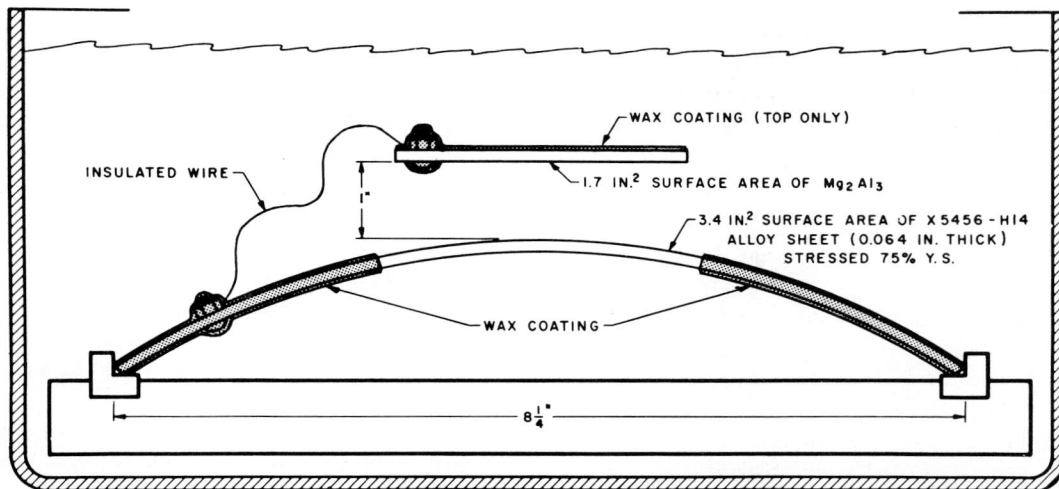

FIGURE 13 — Sketch of assembly used to demonstrate the electrolytic protection by $Mg_2Al_3$ constituent of a stressed specimen of sensitized X5456-H14 aluminum alloy. Cook.[34]

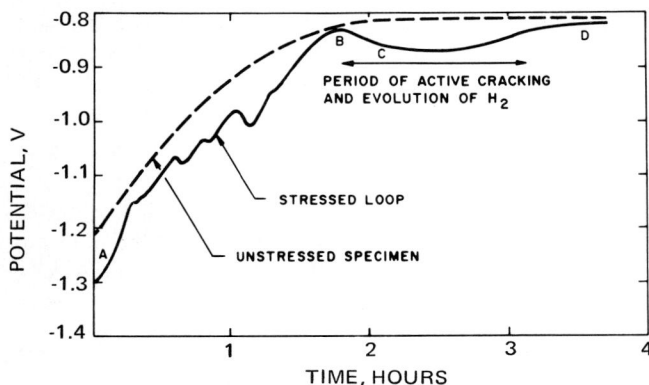

FIGURE 14 — Typical potential/time curve for stressed aluminum-5% magnesium alloy loop in 3% sodium chloride solution. Gilbert and Hadden.[4]

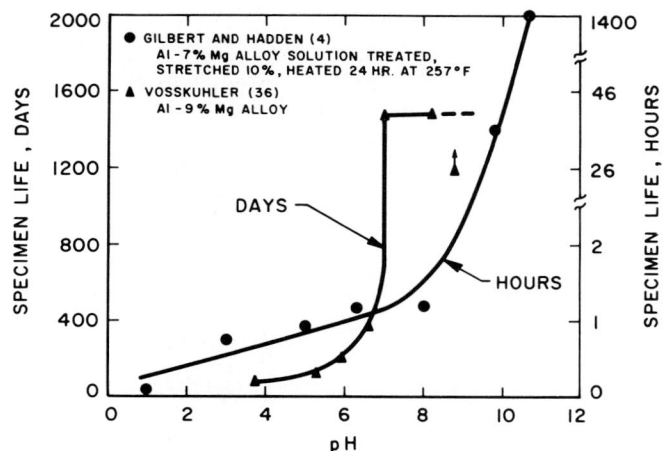

FIGURE 15 — Effect of pH of 3% sodium chloride solution upon the time for stress corrosion cracking of Al-Mg alloys. Loop specimens of 0.062 in thick sheet stressed about elastic limit by bending in constant deformation fixtures.

about 6.5. Presumably if these experiments had been extended to still higher pH solutions, cracking would have been prevented completely, as described previously in the experiment of Mears et al.[3]

The effect of varying concentration of sodium chloride upon the time for stress corrosion cracking of sensitized Al-Mg and Al-Mg-Mn sheet is shown in Figure 16. In a continuous immersion test of an Al-7% Mg alloy, Perryman and Hadden[25] observed that the time for cracking decreased sharply as the concentration of sodium chloride was increased from 1.5% to about 5% and then more gradually from 5% to 9%, after which the time was constant up to 25% sodium chloride. Cook[34] investigated the effect of decreasing the concentrations of sodium chloride from 3.5% to 0.005% in an alternate immersion test of sensitized

X5456-H14 (reduced 40% by cold rolling). As shown, the time to cracking increased steadily as the concentration was decreased. It is noteworthy that the sensitized alloy would stress corrosion crack in a sodium chloride solution as dilute as 0.005% (50 ppm) and possibly less.

## B. Aluminum-Copper Alloys (2XXX Series)

### 1. Physical Metallurgy

Copper is one of the most important alloying additions for aluminum because of its appreciable solubility in aluminum and its strengthening effects. Both cast and wrought Al-Cu alloys respond to solution heat treatment and subsequent aging with an increase in strength and

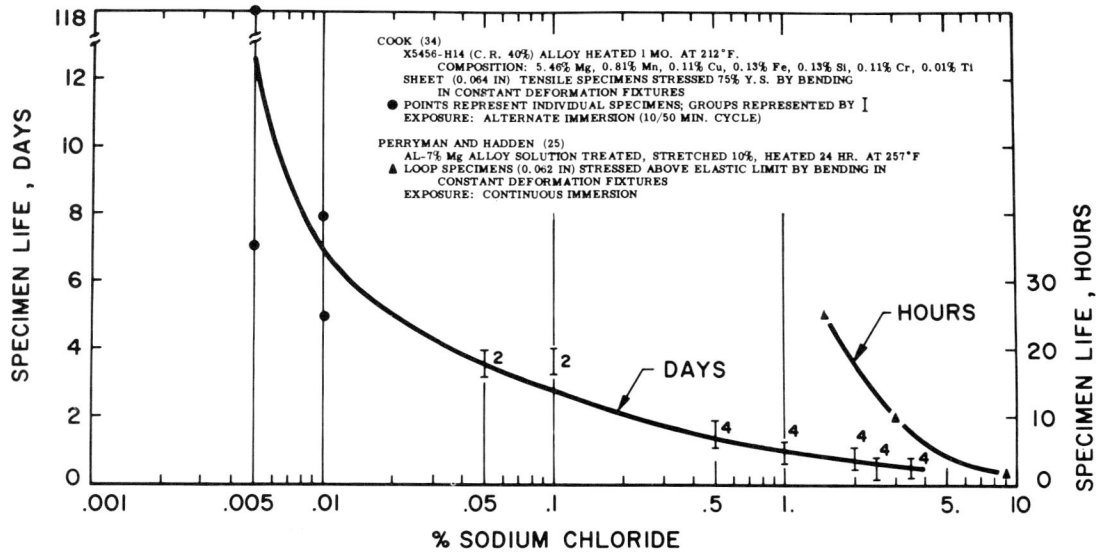

FIGURE 16 — Effect of concentration of sodium chloride upon time for stress corrosion cracking of sensitized Al-Mg or Al-Mg-Mn alloy sheet.

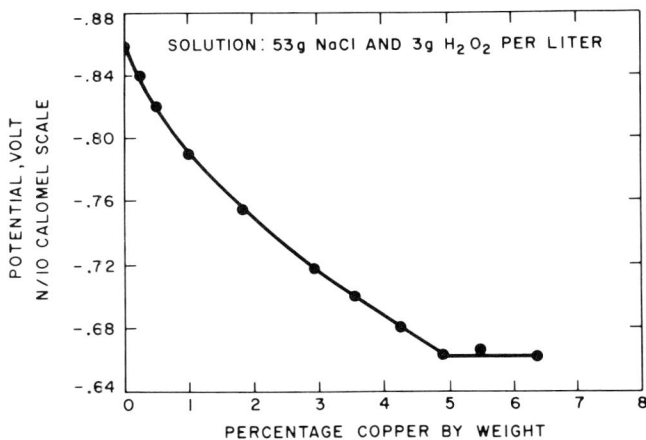

FIGURE 17 — Various Al-Cu binary alloys were solution heat treated for a long period of time at 977 F and then quenched rapidly into cold water. As increasing amounts of copper are thus placed in solid solution the potential is made less anodic as shown by the sloping curve. The break in the curve followed by the horizontal section indicates the maximum amount of copper soluble at the temperature of 977 F. Brown, Fink and Hunter.[39]

A-ANODE

C-CATHODE

R-REFERENCE ELECTRODE

M-MILLIAMETER

P-POTENTIOMETER

FIGURE 18 — Apparatus for measuring potential and current flow between grain boundaries and grains. Dix.[2]

hardness and a decrease in elongation. Maximum strengthening is obtained when the Cu content is between 4% and 6%, depending upon the influence of other alloying elements present. The addition of other alloying elements such as magnesium, silicon, manganese, nickel, lithium and cadmium, to basic Al-Cu alloys has led to the development of an important family of high strength heat treatable aluminum alloys. Adjustments of the total alloying additions produce quite different metallurgical responses

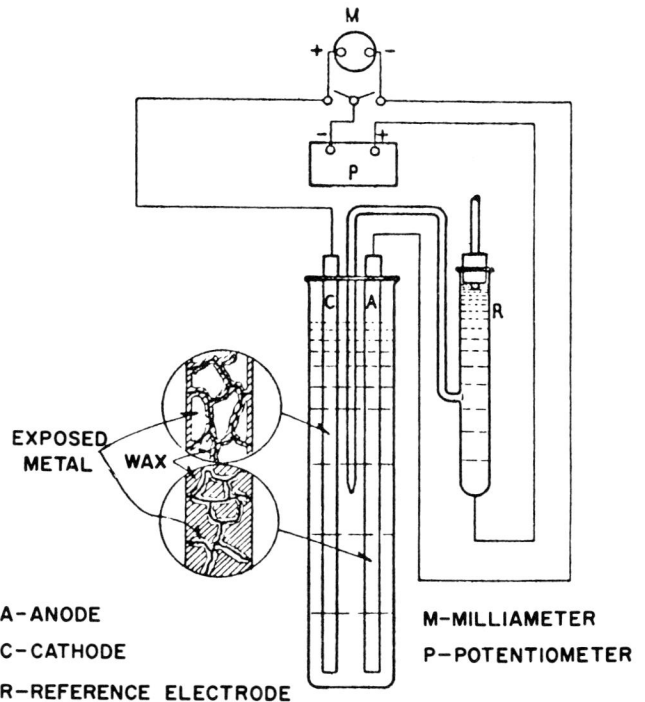

and mechanical properties, but the resistance to stress corrosion cracking of these alloys is influenced primarily by copper concentration gradients in the Al-Cu solid solution in the grain boundary regions.

The binary Al-Cu alloys and certain of the more complex Al-Cu-Si, Al-Cu-Mg and Al-Cu-Mn alloys are age

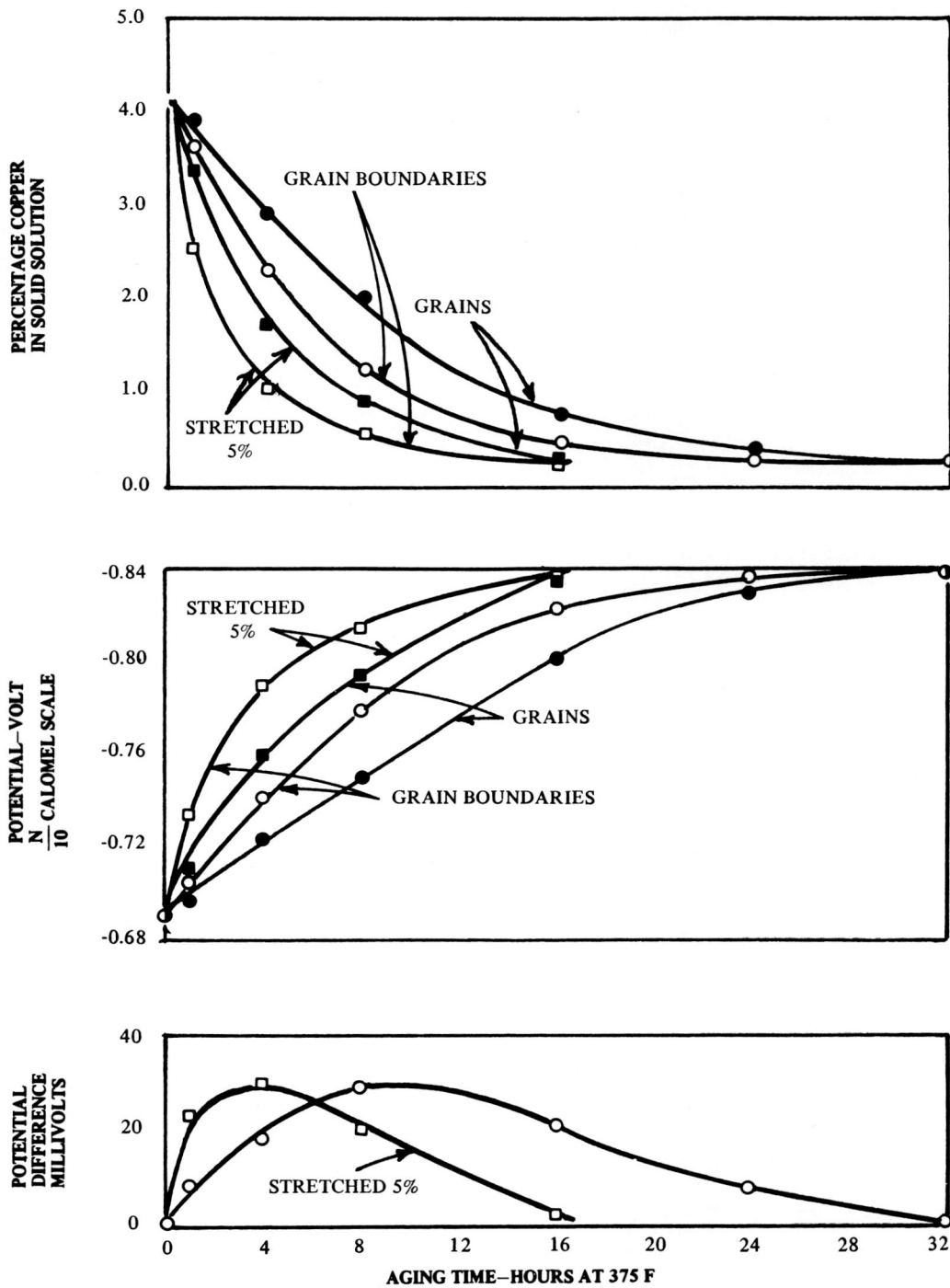

FIGURE 19 — The potentials of the grains and grain boundaries of an aluminum alloy containing 4 percent copper which was heat-treated at 930 F, quenched in cold water and aged at 375 F. Mears, Brown and Dix.[3]

480

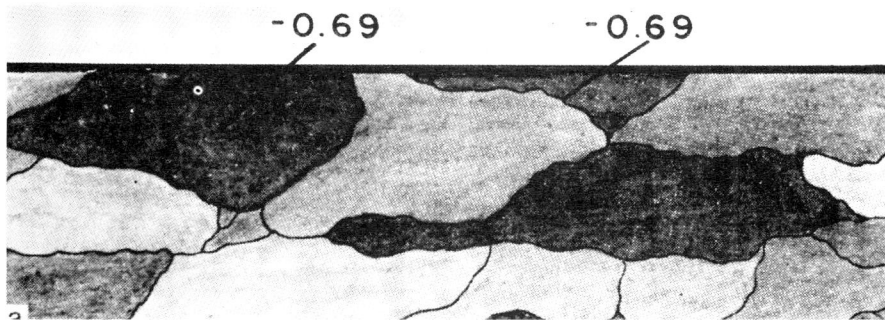

a. A uniform solid solution has been retained after rapid quenching from the temperature of solution heat treatment. The electrode potentials of grains and grain boundaries are equal.

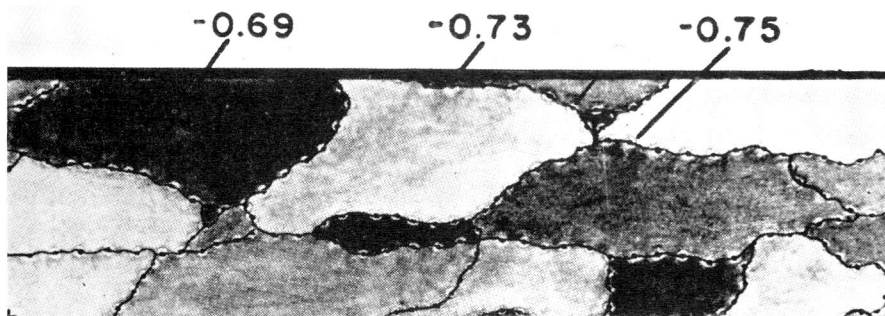

b. After a short period of reheating, precipitation along grain boundaries has commenced. Surrounding each particle of the precipitate is a volume of solid solution that has been depleted in copper content and is anodic to the rest of the structure.

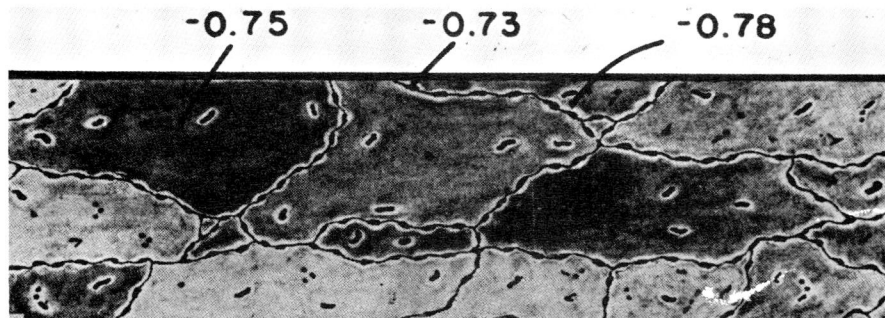

c. Further reheating has caused the copper-depleted solid solution along the grain boundaries to form an almost continuous anodic network. In this condition the alloy is markedly susceptible to intergranular corrosion.

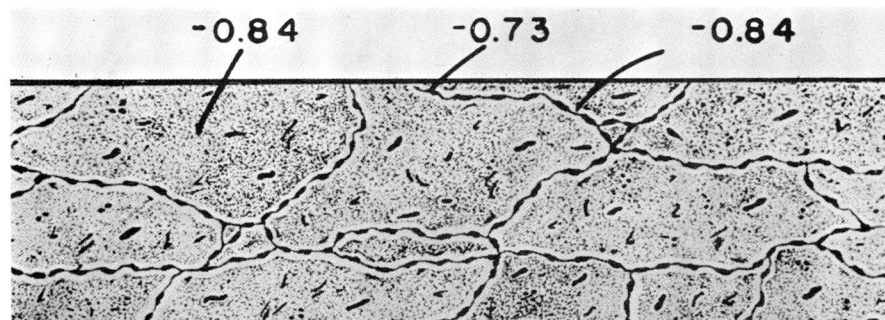

d. Extended reheating has caused nearly complete precipitation. The centers of grains and the volumes of solid solution at the grain boundaries have equal electrode potentials; both are anodic to the particles of precipitate.

FIGURE 20 — Schematic illustration of the microstructure of a wrought Al-4 Cu alloy showing the electrode potential relationship of the alloy phases. Dix, Brown and Binger.[40]

hardened by the precipitation of an Al-Cu phase, developing through several intermediate stages that have been described in the literature.[37]

**Al-Cu Solid Solution → GP1 Zones → GP2 Zones → $\theta'$ → $\theta$ (CuAl$_2$)**

In the Al-Cu-Mg type alloys with magnesium over about 1% the hardening constituent is an Al-Cu-Mg phase that progresses through the following stages.[38]

**Al-Cu-Mg Solid Solution → GP Zones → S$'$ → S (Al$_2$CuMg)**

The precipitate responsible for strengthening, of course, forms in the grain bodies, but it is likely that in the grain boundaries the equilibrium or the transition phase forms directly.

*2. Electrochemical Relationship in the Microstructure*

As shown in Figure 17, increasing amounts of copper in an aluminum solid solution changes the electrode potential markedly in the electropositive direction. Precipitation of aluminum-copper and aluminum-copper-magnesium phases thus alters the potential of the alloy in the anodic direction because of the formation of depleted solid solution regions low in copper. The initial precipitation usually occurs along grain boundaries and hence the depleted solid solution regions will first develop along these boundaries. In a corrosive medium such as sodium chloride solution, the anodic depleted regions corrode preferentially by an electrochemical process, producing fissures that serve as stress raisers.

By a technique illustrated in Figure 18 it is possible to measure the potential at the grain boundaries and at the grain centers. Figure 19 shows the change in potential at the grain boundaries and grain centers with time of aging at 375 F. It is shown that precipitation occurred more rapidly at the grain boundaries than within the grains, with the boundaries becoming anodic to the grain centers. The maximum difference in potential between the grain boundaries and grain centers, as shown by the lower curves occurred after aging for about 4 to 8 hours at this temperature. With more extended heating, the precipitation within the grain centers begins to catch up with that at the grain boundaries until virtually complete precipitation has occurred both at the grain boundaries and within the grains. Thus the difference in potential between the two has been reduced to almost zero. It is also shown in Figure 19 that the precipitation, both in the grains and the grain boundaries, is accelerated by plastic deformation (5% stretch).

The microstructural changes that bring about these differences in electrode potential are illustrated schematically in Figure 20. Figure 20a illustrates the uniform solid solution of copper in aluminum produced by rapid quenching following a solution treatment. The potentials of grains and grain boundaries are equal. Figure 20b illustrates the beginning of precipitation along the grain boundaries caused by a short period of reheating at 375 F. The

potential of the grain bodies has not changed, but that of the grain margins has started to shift in the anodic direction. Figure 20c illustrates the condition that exists when the copper-depleted solid solution along the grain boundaries forms an almost continuous network that is strongly anodic to the grain bodies and to the particles of precipitate. In this condition, the alloy is markedly susceptible to intergranular corrosion.

As aging is continued, precipitation within the grain increases and the potential of the grains becomes more anodic. Figure 20d illustrates the structure after precipitation is nearly complete. There is no longer a measurable difference in electrode potential between the grain boundaries and the grains, so this cause of selective corrosion has been eliminated. In a corrosive environment, electrochemical corrosion occurs between the particles of constituent and the matrix, but the attack is spread fairly uniformly, since the whole mass of metal, rather than just the grain boundaries, is anodic to the precipitate.

Hunter et al[41] using specimens thinned to 1000 Å for transmission electron microscopy succeeded in relating the path of intergranular attack to microstructural features of Al-Cu-Mg alloy 2024. Figure 21 shows an electron transmission micrograph illustrating the severe intergranular attack corresponding to the condition described in Figure 20c. Susceptibility to pitting attack resulting from a high degree of precipitation (Figure 20d) is shown in Figure 22. This alignment of pits along grain boundaries would probably appear as intergranular attack at light microscope magnifications and may be the type of corrosion existing in material which appears to corrode intergranularly but is not susceptible to stress corrosion cracking.

*3. Factors Affecting Precipitation and Resistance to Stress Corrosion Cracking*

The principal factors affecting precipitation in the Al-Cu class of alloys are total alloy content, rate of quench after solution heat treatment, plastic deformation after quenching and exposure to elevated temperatures. Although solution treated and quenched Al-Cu alloys are harder at room temperature, this phenomenon, in contrast to the behavior of the Al-Mg alloys, involves the formation of GP (Guinier-Preston) zones in the grain bodies, with no detectable precipitate formation in the grain boundaries. Artificial aging by heating the metal at a suitable temperature (usually in the 300 to 400 F range) nucleates precipitation in the grain boundaries and stimulates the precipitation in the grain bodies as described above. Slow cooling during quenching through a critical temperature range (750-600 F) determined by Willey[42] also can result in intergranular precipitation.

**a. Quenching Rate.** The effect of variations in cooling rate during quenching upon the resistance to intergranular corrosion and to stress corrosion cracking has been studied by Dix,[42] Ketcham[43,44] and Lifka.[45] In Figure 23 is shown the relationship between the type of attack and stress corrosion cracking of a binary Al-4.5% Cu alloy, a ternary Al-4.3% Cu-1.25% Mg alloy and a commercial Al-4.5% Cu-1.5% Mg-0.6% Mn alloy (2024).

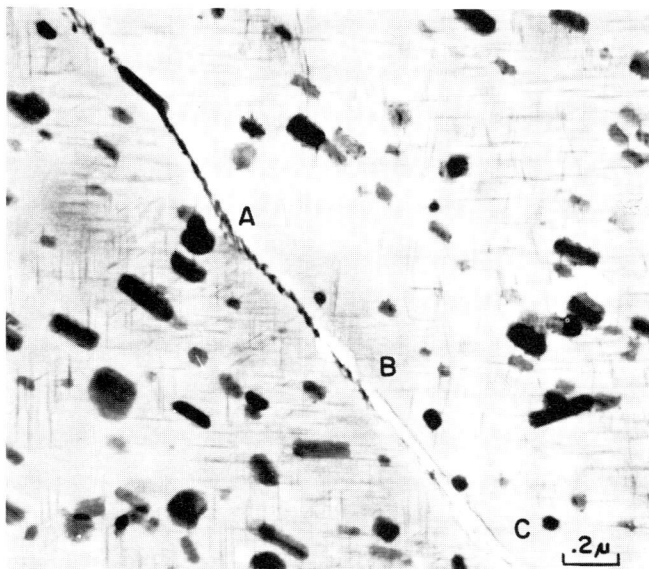

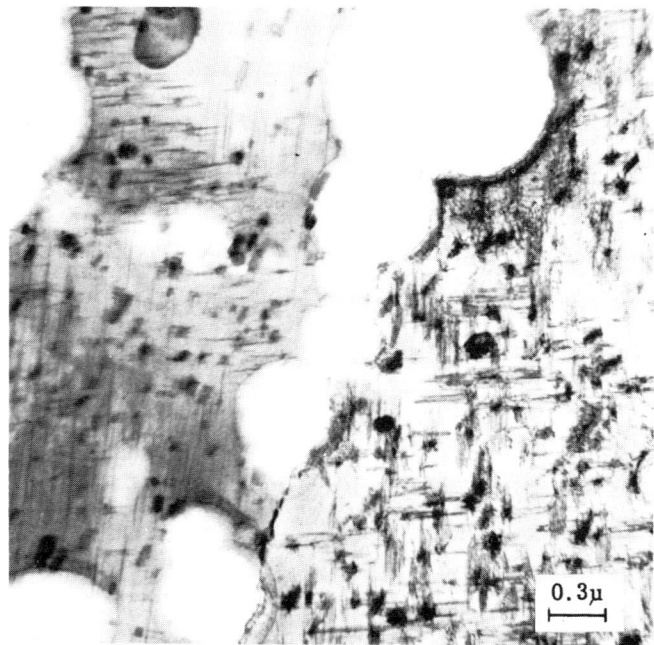

FIGURE 21 — Electron transmission micrograph of a thin metal specimen of an Al-Cu-Mg alloy (2024) corroded in NaCl-H$_2$O$_2$ solution. The metal had been solution heat treated, quenched in cold water and aged 4 hours at 375 F; this condition corresponds to that sketched in Figure 20c. Intergranular attack between points B and C followed the Cu-depleted grain margins visible between B and A. Particles of grain boundary precipitate are visible extending from B (surrounded by corrosion) to the top of the print. A Widmanstatten pattern of S' precipitate has formed in the grains. The large dark particles scattered through the grains are relatively insoluble constituents of Al-Mn and Al-Fe-Si compounds. In this condition 2024 alloy is highly susceptible to stress corrosion cracking. Hunter, Frank and Robinson.[41]

FIGURE 22 — Similar to Figure 21 except that the metal was aged 16 hours at 375 F, and in this condition would correspond to that shown in Figure 20d. Shows rounded pits in the grain body and along a grain boundary. Note also the advanced degree of precipitation in the grain bodies. In this condition 2024 alloy is highly resistant to stress corrosion cracking. Hunter, Frank and Robinson.[41]

In the first two alloys, Ketcham[44] contended that the range of cooling rates that caused susceptibility to stress corrosion cracking is greater than that causing susceptibility to intergranular attack. However, on a somewhat more complex alloy, Lifka[45] showed that in the entire range for which stress corrosion cracking is encountered there is some susceptibility to intergranular attack. As a matter of fact, the higher cooling rates that result in less extensive intergranular attack (because only the most anodic grain boundaries are attacked) may cause an increase in susceptibility to stress corrosion cracking. This might be anticipated because with a fewer number of grain boundaries attacked, there will be greater stress concentration than in the situation where all of the grain boundaries are equally attacked.

Lifka's data was confirmed by a program[46] wherein sections of 3/4 in diameter rolled rod of 2024 alloy were solution heat treated at 920 F and quenched in water at various temperatures to achieve increasing susceptibility to intergranular attack. C-ring specimens machined from these rods were stressed at 75% and 50% of the yield strength and exposed to 3.5% NaCl by alternate immersion. The results of these tests demonstrated that when a complete network of intergranular attack developed, as in the sample

quenched in water at 212 F. Stress corrosion cracking was unlikely to occur (Figure 24). However, with a lesser susceptibility to intergranular attack, specimens stress corrosion cracked even at 50% of the yield strength. With further decrease in amount of intergranular attack, then the percent of failures also decreased. These results were obtained in a relatively aggressive corrosion medium. However, in mildly corrosive environments even the more slowly quenched samples may not develop a complete intergranular network, and in such an instance stress corrosion cracking would occur. These considerations serve to again emphasize that stress corrosion susceptibility is determined not only by the internal structure of the metal but also by the nature of the environment and the method of stressing.

**b. Artificial Aging.** The beneficial effect of an adequate artificial aging treatment on the resistance to intergranular attack and to stress corrosion cracking is shown in Figures 19-22. Because it is essential to age the metal for a sufficient period, it is of interest to determine whether the desired metallurgical condition can be identified by metallographic examination. Samples of 2024 alloy aged for various periods have been examined by Frank and Robinson[47] with the electron microscope. Some electron micrographs illustrating various degrees of precipitation are shown in Figure 25. The as-quenched sheet is represented in Figure 25a, which reveals many helical dislocations frequently associated with dispersoid particles (Al-Mn constituent). Figure 25b is the same material after

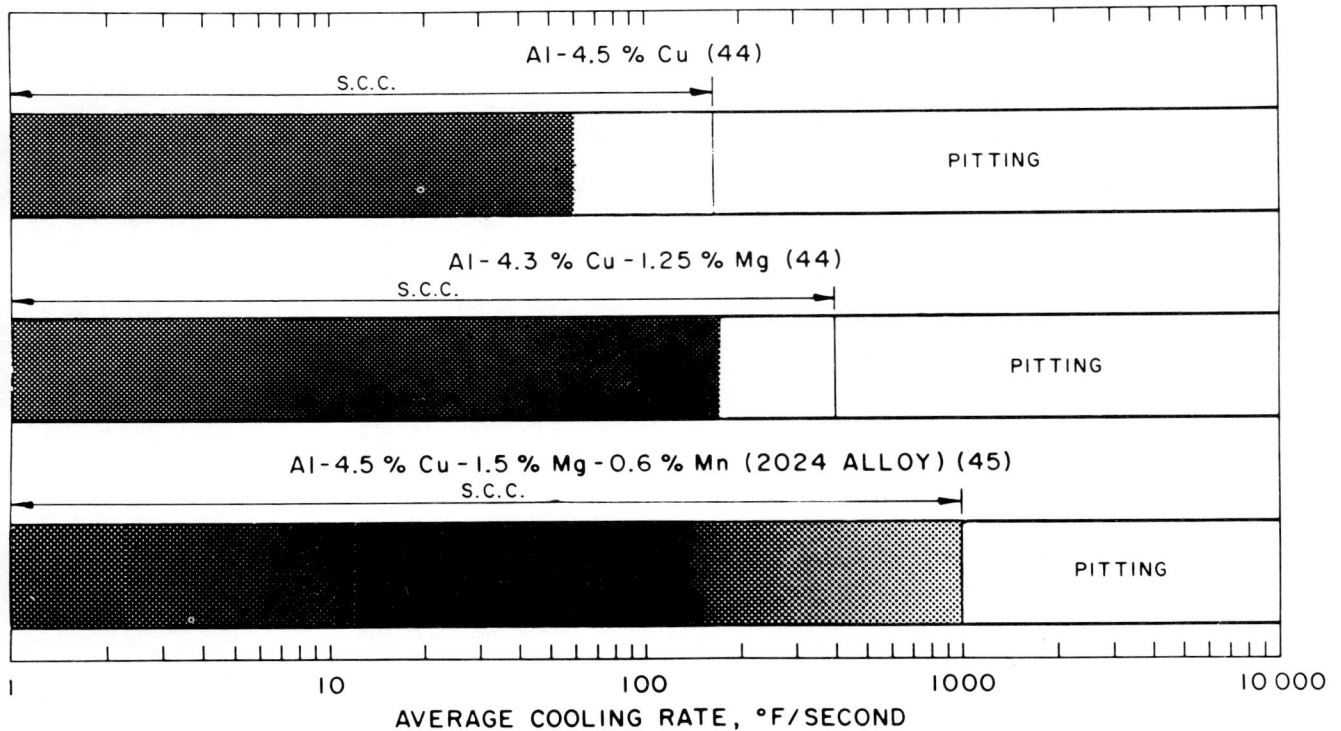

FIGURE 23 — Effect of cooling rate during quenching between 750-600 F on susceptibility to intergranular corrosion and stress corrosion cracking.

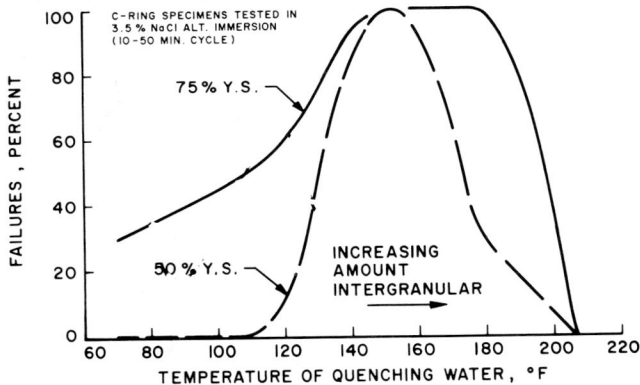

FIGURE 24 — Effect of degree of intergranular attack upon stress corrosion cracking of Al-Cu-Mg-Mn alloy (2024-T42) rod. Increasing susceptibility to intergranular attack was produced by solution heat treating a number of samples of 3/4 in diameter rolled rod for one hour at 920 F and quenching in water at various temperatures. Walsh.[46]

aging 0.5 hour at 375 F. The helical dislocations have changed into loop dislocations which appear serrated, indicating probably solute segregation or zone formation on the loops. Stumpf,[48] by X-ray analysis, detected zone formation at this stage and observed the definite formation of S′ after aging periods longer than two hours. In Figure 25c the development of the S′ phase is shown as numerous long, thin precipitate particles aligned in crystallographic directions and clearly associated with the residuals of the loop dislocations. Figure 25d shows the long, thin precipitated plates on crystallographic planes in a typical Widmanstatten structure. After four hours there was little, if any, evidence of residual dislocation loops, and there was no difference in degree of coherency after 0.5 to 16 hours. The equilibrium S phase was not detected by Stumpf until after 64 hours.

Because 2024 when rapidly quenched or aged 16 hours at 375 F is resistant to stress corrosion cracking, the structures represented in Figures 25a and 25d might be called stress corrosion resistant. The structures shown in 25b and 25c represent susceptible materials. Although it is easy to make broad distinctions, it is difficult to define the borderline aging conditions that separate the as-quenched material or the adequately aged material from the intermediately aged material with low resistance to stress corrosion cracking. The importance of relating the behavior of a given macro-, micro- and submicrostructure to specific corrosion environments cannot be over-emphasized. If it is a "stress corrosion cracking susceptible structure," it must be related to a type of environment and perhaps even to the magnitude of applied stress.

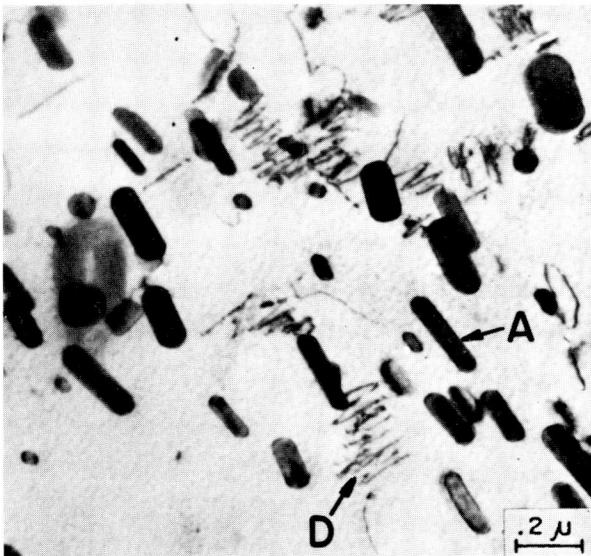

(a) as Quenched
Al-Mn dispersoid particles (A) and associated helical dislocations (D).

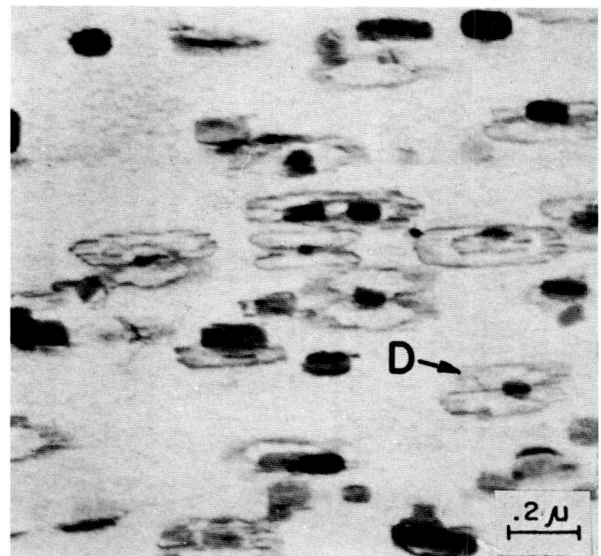

(b) Heated 0.5 hr at 375 F
Helical dislocations have dissociated into loop dislocations (D).

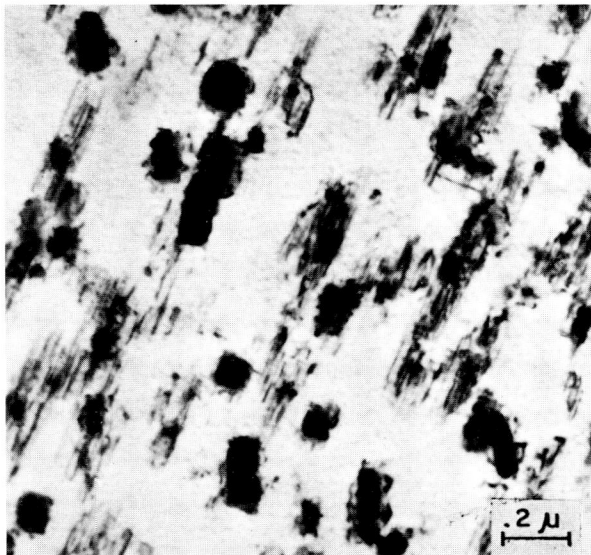

(c) Heated 4 hr at 375 F
Crystallographically oriented S′ precipitate associated with residual loops.

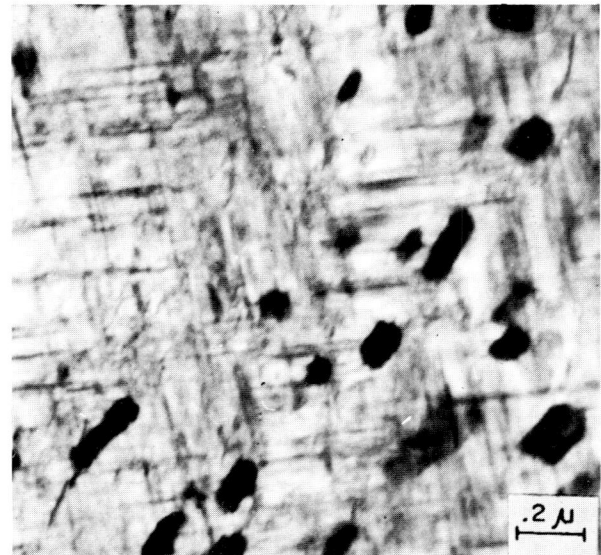

(d) Heated 16 hr at 375 F
Widmanstatten pattern of S′ precipitate.

FIGURE 25 — Electron transmission micrographs of thin foils prepared from 0.064 in thick sheet of 2024-T42 alloy solution treated at 920 F and quenched in water at 70 F (6000 F/sec). Frank and Robinson.[47]

The effect of introducing cold work between the quenching and aging operations accelerates the formation of the structure shown in Figure 25d. The precipitate pattern generally is finer because the plastic deformation increases the number of dislocations which can nucleate precipitate. Regardless of the microstructure or submicrostructure within the grains, however, it is essential that the solid solution in the body of the grain have essentially the same potential as that of the grain margins. Comparison of Figure 26 with Figure 19 shows that the minimum loss in tensile strength of 2024-T3 (stretched 1.5% after quench-

ing) exposed to a corrosive environment occurred at 16 hours aging, the same as the aging time required to minimize the potential difference between grains and grain boundaries of the stretched Al-4% Cu alloy.

It should be noted from Figure 26 that it is fortunate that the longer times of aging required to restore good resistance to stress corrosion also enables the cold worked 2024 to attain the highest tensile and yield strengths. These observations have been confirmed further by the work of Robertson[49] and Nock.[50]

485

### 4. Significance of Susceptibility to Intergranular Attack

Although the susceptibility to a mild degree of intergranular attack can result in maximum susceptibility to stress corrosion cracking of the as-quenched tempers (T3, T4) of Al-Cu alloys, it does not follow that the same is true for the artificially aged tempers (T6, T8). It may be seen from Figure 19 that if the aging treatment is not quite extended to the optimum period there will be a small difference in potential between grains and grain boundaries. Metal in this condition may be susceptible to a mixture of relatively wide ragged intergranular and pitting attack but not necessarily to stress corrosion cracking. A comparison of the various types of corrosive attack representative of different tempers of rolled bar stock of 2024 alloy is shown in Figure 27. The mill quenched T351 temper (about 1.0-1.5% minimum stretch) may be susceptible to scattered sites of fine, sharply delineated intergranular attack, as shown, and be susceptible to stress corrosion cracking in some chloride-containing environments when stressed across the grain. When artificially aged for 12 hours at 375 F to the T851 temper, or when reheat treated to the T42 temper, or when artificially aged from the T42 to the T62 temper, the resistance to stress corrosion cracking is very high. Compare the fine, penetrating intergranular attack in the T351 temper rod and the broad, less distinct network in the T62 and T851 tempers. The latter type of attack at higher magnifications probably would resemble that shown in Figure 22.

## C. Aluminum-Magnesium-Silicon Alloys (6XXX Series)

### 1. Physical Metallurgy

Al-Mg-Si structural alloys utilize magnesium and silicon in the form of the intermetallic compound $Mg_2Si$,[51] to secure a significant response to solution heat treatment and precipitation treatment. These elements may be present in stoichiometric amounts to combine as $Mg_2Si$, although silicon or magnesium in excess of that required for $Mg_2Si$ also may be employed. An excess of silicon provides an appreciable increase in strength over that secured from a specific quantity of $Mg_2Si$, but tends to lower the resistance to intergranular attack. Although the excess silicon also tends to lower slightly the resistance to stress corrosion, the resistance is still of a relatively high order. Most alloys in this class contain either manganese or chromium for increased strength and control of grain size. Copper is also an effective strengthening addition, but it, too, reduces the resistance to corrosion and stress corrosion. Alloys of the 6XXX series are used very extensively in applications requiring an intermediate strength and a high resistance to corrosion and to stress corrosion cracking.

The normal precipitation sequence in alloys with the balanced $Mg_2Si$ ratio may be diagrammed as follows:

$$\text{Solid Solution} \rightarrow \text{GP Zones} \rightarrow B' (Mg_2Si) \rightarrow B (Mg_2Si)$$

In addition, Thomas[52] has tentatively identified pure silicon particles adjacent to grain boundaries in an Al-1.53% $Mg_2Si$-0.04% Si alloy that had been heat treated and given a slight amount of aging (5 minutes at 400 F).

### 2. Effect of Heat Treating Variables Upon Resistance to Stress Corrosion Cracking

The Al-Mg-Si alloys in the commonly used products and tempers are highly resistant to corrosion and to stress corrosion cracking. In fact, we do not know of any authenticated record of a service failure caused by stress corrosion cracking of an Al-Mg-Si type alloy. This is especially significant in view of the fact that the solution heat treated, quenched and artificially aged T6 type tempers of these alloys are susceptible to intergranular corrosion in chloride environments. The susceptibility to intergranular attack is developed during an early stage of the artificial aging treatment, although it also can be

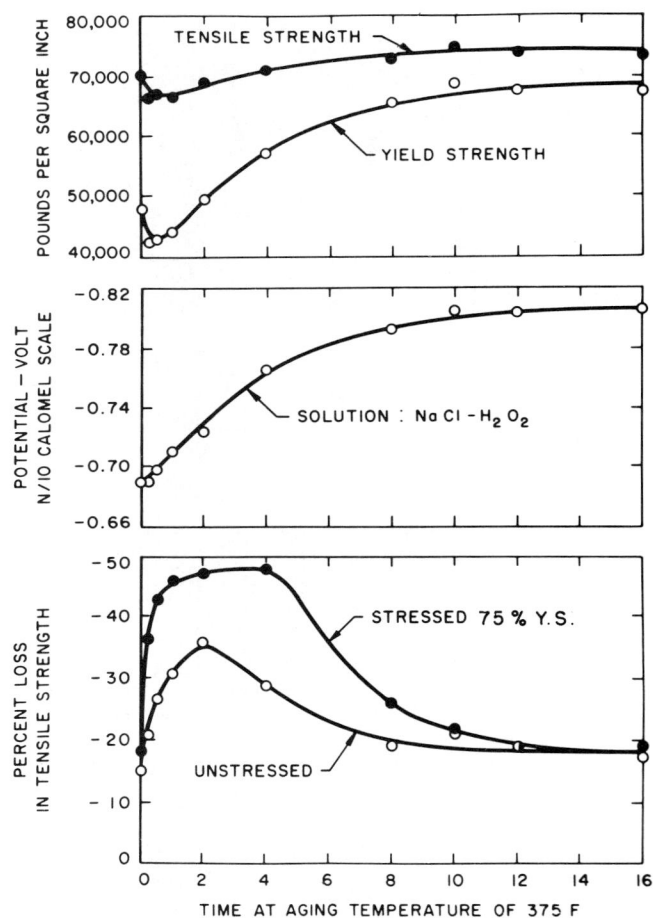

FIGURE 26 — The effect of aging on the tensile strength, yield strength, solution potential and resistance to corrosion and stress corrosion of a commercial Al-Cu-Mg-Mn alloy 2024-T3 (stretched 1.5% after quenching). Corrosion and stress corrosion resistance were evaluated by 48 hours of exposure to NaCl-$H_2O_2$ solution by alternate immersion (1.5/1.5 min cycle). Mears, Brown and Dix.[3]

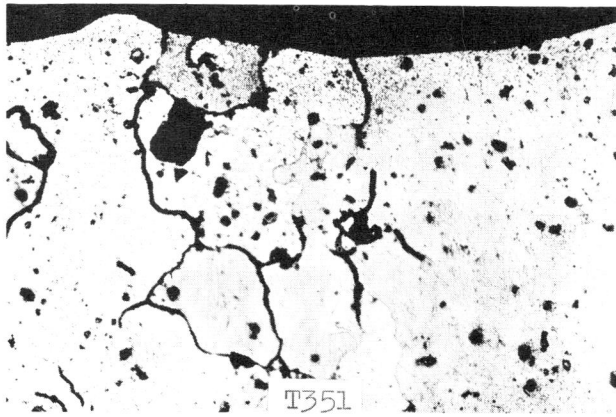

Re-solution heat treatment,
rapid quench

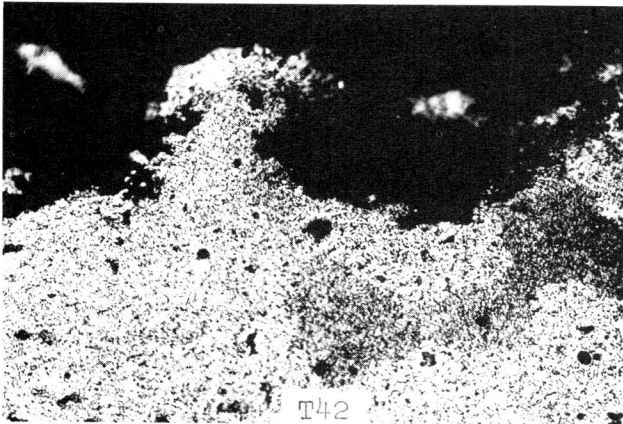

Precipitation treatment,
12 hours at 375 F

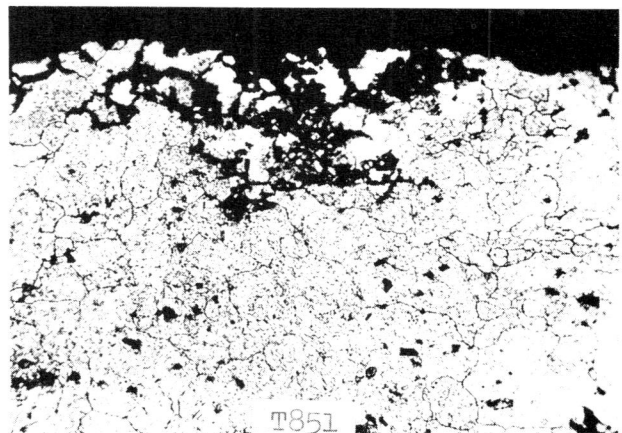

Precipitation treatment,
16 hours at 375 F

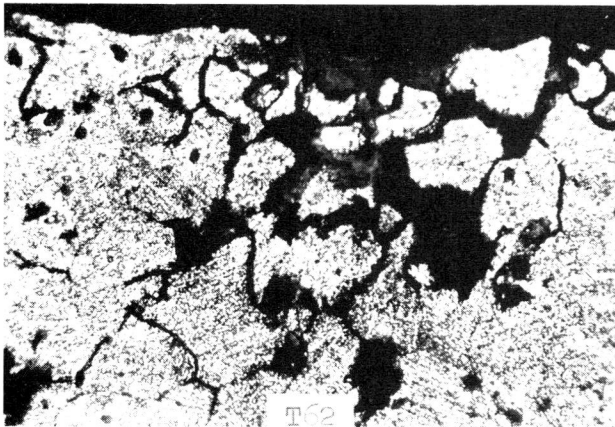

FIGURE 27 — Corrosion attack representative of various tempers of rolled bar stock of 2024 alloy. Samples were immersed for 6 hours in 53 g per liter NaCl plus 3 g per liter $H_2O_2$. Keller's Etch. 250X. Binger, Hollingsworth and Sprowls.[20]

487

developed in the as-quenched temper by a low cooling rate during quenching after the solution heat treatment.

Tests conducted at the Alcoa Research Laboratories on a balanced Al-Mg₂Si alloy (6061) have shown that with certain abnormal thermal treatments this type of alloy can be susceptible to stress corrosion cracking.[40] These conditions are developed when both a high degree of supersaturation of $Mg_2Si$ is obtained by using a relatively high solution heat treating temperature and a low cooling rate occurs during quenching. Examples are shown in Table 4. When 6061 alloy was quenched rapidly from the solution temperature of 970 or 1050 F, it was susceptible principally to pitting attack, and was not susceptible to stress corrosion cracking. Quenching into boiling water, however, caused susceptibility to predominantly intergranular attack, markedly increased losses in strength caused by corrosion and susceptibility to stress corrosion cracking. It should be noted that stress corrosion cracking occurred only with the highly stressed preformed specimens and not with the tensile specimens stressed to 75% of the yield strength. Aging the slowly quenched material to the T6 temper reduced the corrosion losses and eliminated the stress corrosion cracking tendency. Chadwick et al[53] reported that tensile stresses up to 90% of the proof stress had no effect upon the rate of corrosion in sodium chloride solution of Al-0.7% Mg-1.0% Si in either the as-quenched (rapidly cooled) or the artificially aged temper.

It is noteworthy, also, that welded and brazed assemblies of alloys in this class have demonstrated freedom from stress corrosion cracking even though widely varying thermal effects are produced in the parent metal in and adjacent to the fusion zones.

### 3. Proposed Mechanisms of Intergranular Attack

Two mechanisms for the intergranular attack in Al-Si-Mg and Al-Mg₂Si alloys are proposed.

a. If the initial grain boundary precipitate produced by slow quenching or an early stage of artificial aging is beta′ or beta $Mg_2Si$, these particles could serve as anodic sites resulting in lined-up pits along the grain boundaries. Akimow and Oleschko[54] reported $Mg_2Si$ to be about 750 mv more anodic than aluminum in 3% sodium chloride solution, but after 5 to 25 hours, the potential of the $Mg_2Si$ shifted to a potential equal to that of aluminum. Thus, as the particles of $Mg_2Si$ are chemically or electrochemically attacked, the potential shifts in the cathodic direction, thereby diminishing the driving force for the intergranular attack. Continued aging resulting in general precipitation of beta′ or beta $Mg_2Si$ distributes additional anodic centers throughout the grain bodies, thereby further minimizing the intensity of attack at the grain boundaries.

b. If silicon is the initial grain boundary precipitate that is produced by slow quenching or an early stage of artificial aging, the particles of elemental silicon could function as minute cathodes to stimulate electrochemical attack in the form of lined-up pits or continuous pitting along the grain boundaries. As shown in Table 2, not only is silicon strongly cathodic to Al-Mg₂Si solid solutions, but the Si depleted grain margins would tend to be slightly anodic to the grain centers. Consequently more intensive intergranular attack would be expected with alloys containing larger amounts of silicon, and this has been found to be true for both Al-Mg₂Si and binary Al-Si alloys.[55] Extending the time of aging to that used

TABLE 4—Effect of Heat Treating Variables Upon the Resistance to Corrosion and to Stress Corrosion Cracking of Al-Mg-Si Alloy 6061[1]

| Solution Heat Treatment Temp., °F | Temperature of Quench Water, °F | Aging Treatment | Tensile Properties | | | | Exposed to 3.5% NaCl Alternate Immersion (10/50 min Cycle) | | |
| | | | Tensile Strength ksi | Yield Strength ksi | Elongation % in 2 in. | Type of Attack | % Loss in T.S. After 1 Year[2] | | SCC of Preforms Time to Failure, Days [3] |
| | | | | | | | No Stress | Stressed 75% Y.S. | |
| 970 | 70 | None | 37.4 | 23.3 | 23 | I + P | 5 | 5 | 2 OK 730 |
| | 212 | None | 34.4 | 23.0 | 21 | I | 10 | 16 | 174, 425 |
| 1050 | 70 | None | 40.8 | 29.2 | 19 | P | 3 | 3 | 2 OK 730 |
| | 212 | None | 36.7 | 24.5 | 20 | I | 11 | 27 | 107, 153 |
| 970 | 70 | 18 hrs at 320 F | 48.8 | 42.6 | 14 | I | 4 | 6 | 2 OK 730 |
| | 212 | 18 hrs at 320 F | 46.0 | 40.5 | 13 | I | 7 | 9 | 2 OK 730 |
| 1050 | 70 | 18 hrs at 320 F | 54.0 | 47.0 | 13 | P | 4 | 5 | 2 OK 730 |
| | 212 | 18 hrs at 320 F | 47.6 | 41.2 | 12 | I | 5 | 7 | 2 OK 730 |

[1]All tests were made on x-grain specimens machined from 0.064 in thick commercial sheet of the composition: 0.26% Cu, 0.25% Fe, 0.53% Si, 0.01% Mn, 0.95% Mg, 0.24% Cr.
[2]Tensile specimens stressed in tension by bending and holding in constant deformation stressing frames.
[3]Tensile specimen blanks 0.75 in wide x 9 in long plastically deformed at room temperature (preformed specimen) and sprung into constant deformation stressing frames.

commercially to develop maximum strengths distributes anodic particles of $Mg_2Si$ throughout the grains, and tends to equalize the composition of the solid solution in the grain margins and grain centers, but does nothing to the Si particles already at the grain boundaries. Thus, aging treatments would have a stronger tendency to minimize the susceptibility to intergranular corrosion of alloys with balanced $Mg_2Si$ composition than those containing excess silicon. This mechanism is consistent with observations that short transverse specimens from rolled plate or transverse specimens from rolled plate or transverse specimens from rod of excess-silicon alloys, such as 6070-T6 and 6066-T6, are susceptible to stress corrosion cracking whereas similar specimens of 6061-T6 are not susceptible.

Both of these mechanisms appear consistent with observations that the susceptibility to intergranular attack in Al-Mg-Si alloys is not as deleterious as that encountered in other heat treatable aluminum alloys. The latter mechanism, however, better accounts for the lower resistance to intergranular corrosion and to stress corrosion cracking of the $Al-Mg_2Si$-Si type of alloy compared to the balanced $Al-Mg_2Si$ alloy.

### D. Aluminum-Zinc-Magnesium and Aluminum-Zinc-Magnesium-Copper Alloys (7XXX Series)

#### 1. Historical Development

As early as 1901, Ernst Murrman of Vienna was granted a U.S. Patent[56] in which he described ternary Al-Zn-Mg alloys encompassing the composition ranges of commercially available alloys. Of course, in his time the heat treatment of aluminum alloys was unknown. The exceptionally high strength obtainable by heat treatment of certain of the wrought Al-Zn-Mg alloys was first disclosed by Sander and Meissner[57] and Guertler and Sander.[58] Despite their attractive tensile properties and good fabricating characteristics, these alloys were not used commercially because of their unsatisfactory resistance to stress corrosion cracking. L. J. Weber[59] developed an alloy in 1932 with an improved resistance to stress corrosion cracking by additions of copper and manganese, but because of poor formability in the artificially aged condition and a still undesirable degree of susceptibility to stress corrosion cracking, there was little interest in the use of the alloy. The Weber alloy contained 10% Zn-2% Mg-2% Cu-1% Mn.

Continuing research by the Alcoa Research Laboratories led to the development of 7075 alloy[60-67] which was introduced commercially in 1943. Alloy 7075, originally, was produced in the form of sheet and has a very satisfactory resistance to stress corrosion cracking in this form resulting from combined effects of copper and chromium.[67] A higher strength modification, 7178, was introduced in 1951. Alloy 7079, with high elongation in the short transverse direction, followed in 1954, initially as a forging alloy for large sections and later for other products. The highest strength alloy in commercial use, 7001, was introduced in 1960; it was used initially for extrusions and later for several other products. A new alloy, AZ74, containing silver in addition to chromium and copper for further improvement in resistance to stress corrosion cracking is currently under development by a German manufacturer.[68,69] Nominal compositions and typical tensile properties are shown in Table 1.

Another recent advance in the Al-Zn-Mg-Cu alloy system was the development of thermal treatments that virtually eliminate stress corrosion cracking. Although these alloys when heat treated and aged to maximum strength (T6 type tempers) have a relatively high resistance to stress corrosion cracking in the form of sheet and other products when stressed in the longitudinal and long transverse directions relative to the grain structure, their resistance is relatively low when stressed in the transverse or short transverse direction (Figure 3). Hence, careful engineering, fabrication and assembly procedures are required for their successful application. Failure to apply these precautions, particularly with the increasing use of large thick sections that are extensively machined to make complex integral structural components, has resulted in a number of commercial stress corrosion cracking problems. With attention focused on this characteristic, precipitation treatments were developed to produce virtual immunity to stress corrosion cracking, with resultant sacrifices in strength from the T6 levels. The outstanding example is 7075-T73.[1,70,71]

Within the past few years Al-Zn-Mg alloys with intermediate strength compared to the high strength Al-Zn-Mg-Cu alloys, have received much attention. These alloys, such as 7039 and X7005, contain small amounts of manganese, chromium, titanium or zirconium. Copper is generally eliminated or limited to a very low amount to improve weldability. The copper-free Al-Zn-Mg alloys have been artificially aged to have a high resistance to stress corrosion cracking in the longitudinal and long transverse directions but not in the short transverse direction. Furthermore, they display a susceptibility to stress corrosion cracking in the short transverse direction in a much wider range of environments than most other types of aluminum alloys.

#### 2. Physical Metallurgy

The aging of Al-Zn-Mg alloys from room temperature to about 260 F is accompanied by the generation of Guinier Preston (GP) zones having an approximately spherical shape. Aging periods and temperatures that develop the highest strengths, characteristic of the T6 temper, produce zones having an average diameter of 20 to 35 Å. Very small amounts of a transition precipitate M' which is partially coherent on $(111)_{Al}$ planes, also can be detected in the T6 temper. The strengthening effects of the zones are believed to be predominantly the result of the increased resistance to dislocation movement arising from the stronger atomic bonds existing within the zones.[72] Aging at only slightly higher temperatures than those that produce maximum strength causes growth of the zones and an increase in the amount of M'. The strength of these alloys is very sensitive to zone size and M' is considerably less effective in developing strength.

The transition phase M' forms over a considerable range of alloy compositions that are in the Al + T ($Mg_3Zn_3Al_2$) field, as well as those in the Al + M field under equilibrium conditions. With increased time or higher temperature, the M' converts to M ($MgZn_2$) or, in cases where T is the equilibrium phase, is replaced by T ($Mg_3Zn_3Al_2$). Phases M' and M are frequently present immediately after quenching in grain boundaries of thick-section products. The precipitation sequence depends upon composition, but may be represented as:

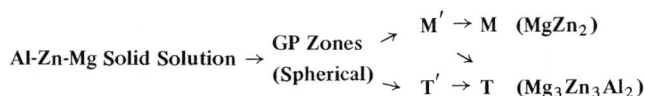

$$\text{Al-Zn-Mg Solid Solution} \rightarrow \begin{array}{c} \text{GP Zones} \\ \text{(Spherical)} \end{array} \begin{array}{c} \nearrow \\ \searrow \end{array} \begin{array}{c} M' \rightarrow M \quad (MgZn_2) \\ \\ T' \rightarrow T \quad (Mg_3Zn_3Al_2) \end{array}$$

An addition of up to 1% Cu to Al-Zn-Mg alloys does not appear to alter the basic precipitation mechanism. Higher copper contents afford greater precipitation hardening, with some contribution of copper atoms to zone formation, as indicated by an increased temperature range of zone stability.[73] Although the composition of M phase in the Al-Zn-Mg-Cu system can vary widely, the actual composition of M phase in Al rich alloys has never been established because precipitated particles are too small for analysis. H. C. Stumpf[74] has found that in 7075 alloy heat treated to approach equilibrium, the M-phase increases in copper and aluminum content with temperature. M-phase precipitated during a slow quench is similar to that in equilibrium at about 650 F.

Neither chromium nor manganese, according to Polmear and Scott-Young[73] seem to alter the basic precipitation mechanism outlined above for the simpler ternary Al-Zn-Mg alloys. They found that chromium increases the rate of aging of 7075 alloy at elevated temperature, but that it decreases rate of aging at room temperature and below. From these results, they concluded that chromium does not modify the lattice structure of the precipitating phase; rather, small sized chromium-rich particles that form during solution heat treatment serve as sites for the nucleation of precipitate. Manganese was found to have a negligible effect upon the aging process.

Transmission electron microscope studies performed at the Alcoa Research Laboratories by Robinson and Hunter[75] do not support the conclusions of Polmear and Scott-Young. Robinson and Hunter found that neither zones or the subsequently formed precipitate are directly associated with the chromium and manganese containing constituents but form with a random distribution in the matrix. Although zone growth is accelerated by chromium, this effect is believed to be associated with chromium atoms that remain in solid solution and increase retention of vacancies during quenching.

The presence of small amounts of silver is believed by Polmear[76] to stimulate nucleation of the M' phase that forms in the medium temperature range (250-450 F) through its interaction both with magnesium atoms and vacancies. Vietz et al[77] showed that the addition of the proper amount of silver to high purity Al-Zn-Mg and Al-Zn-Mg-Cu alloys produced a uniform dispersion of precipitate throughout the grains, including the grain margins. The silver had comparatively little effect on the precipitates in the boundaries.

Until the electrochemical potentials and the chemical analysis of the individual phases that are developed within complex polynary alloys can be separately determined, the interpretation of microstructures in relation to stress corrosion cracking will be extremely hazardous, if not meaningless. Hence, any of the mechanisms of precipitation discussed in the previous paragraphs, even if entirely correct, will not permit the establishment of a stress corrosion resistant structure from X-ray or electron diffraction and microscopic studies.

## 3. Relationship of Stress Corrosion Cracking to Composition

Special alloying additions to improve the resistance to stress corrosion cracking of Al-Zn-Mg alloys have been sought for many years and are still being investigated. Some of these developments were mentioned above.

One of the significant improvements was the use of chromium in combination with copper. Using several types of composite specimens Dix[67] demonstrated the beneficial effect of chromium in the 7075 alloy composition. These experiments demonstrated some interesting facts regarding the mechanism of stress corrosion crack initiation and propagation. Stress corrosion tests were made on specimens machined from composite sheet consisting of a core of 7075 alloy covered by metallurgically bonded surface layers of 7075 alloy without chromium. Interliners of Al-1% Zn alloy, each 1.5% of the total thickness, were used to bond the 7075 alloy without chromium to the standard 7075 alloy core. The sheet was aged for 24 hours at 250 F subsequent to a solution heat treatment and rapid quench. When the specimens were stressed by flexure and immersed in a boiling 6% NaCl solution, cracks developed in the tension surface of the alloy without chromium but not in the compression surface.

The upper photograph in Figure 28 shows the parallel cracks in the tension surface and the lower photograph shows the absence of cracks in the compression surface. Sections through the cracks in the tension surface are shown in the upper photomicrograph in Figure 29. The cracks were intergranular and did not extend beyond the surface layer of the chromium free alloy. Shallow pitting was present in the compression surface shown in the lower photomicrograph, but no stress corrosion cracks were found, thus illustrating that a tensile stress is required to initiate stress corrosion cracking.

This experiment is highly enlightening because it presented several facts related to the mechanism of stress corrosion cracking:

1. The high stress (75% Y.S.) caused stress corrosion cracking of the surface layer alloy (7075 without chromium) on the tension side but not on the compression side.

2. Each of the localized cracks produced a high stress concentration at the base of the narrow crevice.

490

FIGURE 28 — Sheet tensile specimens consisting of an alloy 7075-T6 core and surface layers, each 20% the thickness of the sheet, of alloy 7075 without chromium (T6) were stressed by flexure and immersed in a boiling 6% NaCl solution: (a) shows cracks which developed in the surface stressed to 75% of the yield strength in tension of the alloy without chromium and (b) the surface in compression of the alloy without chromium showed no cracks. Dix.[67]

FIGURE 29 — Photomicrographs of longitudinal sections through the surface layers of the specimens shown in Figure 28: (a) intergranular stress corrosion crack extending down through the tension surface layer to the interliner where it has started to proceed along the interface and (b) the compression surface showing small corrosion pits, but no cracks developed. Dix.[67]

3. The outer layers of the core alloy (7075) were in a high stress state, maintaining a high stress in the Al + 1% Zn alloy interliner.

4. Despite these severe conditions of stress, the crack did not penetrate into the relatively weak Al + 1% Zn alloy interliner.

5. The crevice produced in the surface layer could be considered a pre-stress corrosion crack analogous to pre-fatigue cracking.

6. Failure of the crack in surface layer alloy (7075 without chromium) to propagate into the relatively soft, low strength and anodic interliner demonstrated an inadequacy in the film rupture and mechanical mechanism theories.

Independent stress corrosion studies of Al-Zn-Mg alloys by various investigators have shown the beneficial effects of alloying additions, such as copper, chromium and manganese. Most of the work has been done on specimens of sheet and thin extrusions. The relative effectiveness of such additions is illustrated in Figure 30 with data obtained by Chadwick et al[78] using high purity sheet alloys with a base composition of 7% Zn-2.25% Mg. Using the criterion of specimen life, it is evident that individual additions of 0.25% or 1.25% Cu, 0.25% Mn or 0.25% Cr were not effective. Likewise the combination of 1.25% Cu and 0.25% Mn appeared to offer only slight improvement. The greatest benefit was derived from the combined additions of 1.25% Cu plus 0.25% Cr or 1.25% Cu plus 0.25% Cr and 0.25% Mn. These results are in line with the work of Dix.[67] Although the addition of chromium does alter the grain shape, as Dix has shown, this factor alone does not account for the other metallurgical effects of chromium in Al-Zn-Mg-Cu alloys. For example, chromium under certain conditions stimulates the precipitation in 7075 alloy and increases the quench sensitivity (as measured by the mechanical properties). The latter characteristic is disadvantageous but does demonstrate that this element can

491

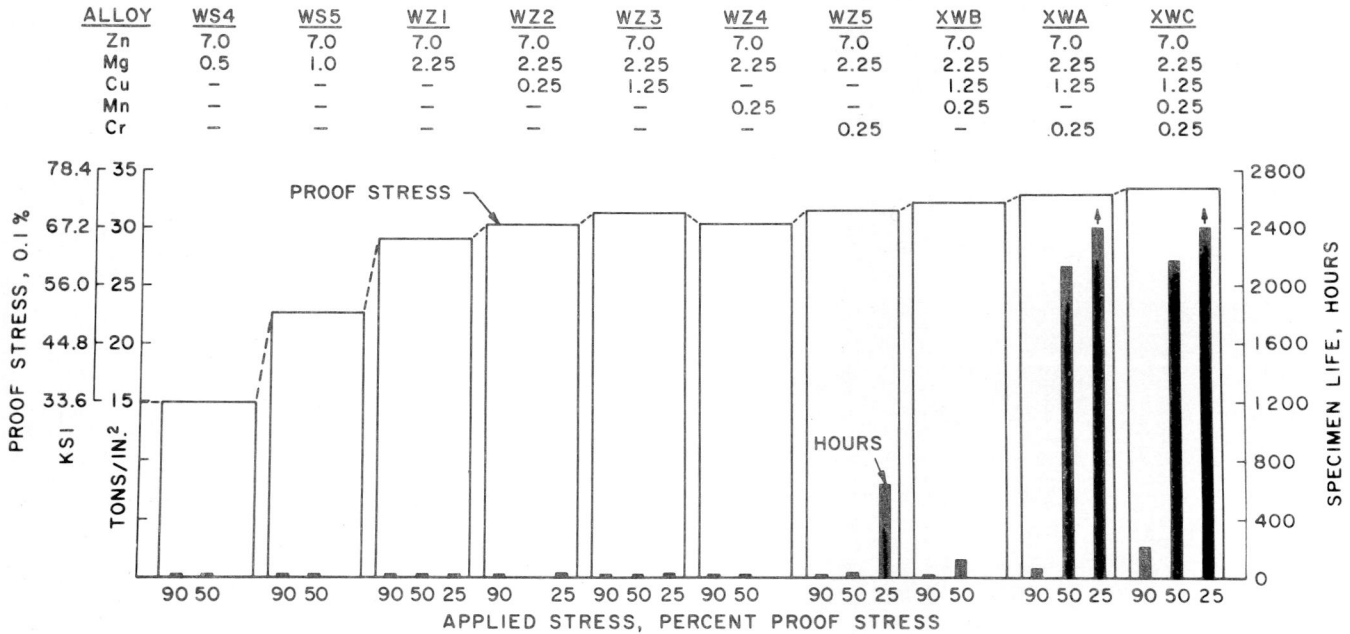

SHEET TENSILE SPECIMENS SPRING LOADED IN TENSION
EXPOSURE: 3 % NaCl INTERMITTENT SPRAY (THRICE DAILY)
BAR GRAPHS REPRESENT LIVES OF INDIVIDUAL SPECIMENS
OR THE MEAN SPECIMEN LIFE OF MULTIPLE SPECIMENS

| ALLOY | WS4 | WS5 | WZI | WZ2 | WZ3 | WZ4 | WZ5 | XWB | XWA | XWC |
|---|---|---|---|---|---|---|---|---|---|---|
| Zn | 7.0 | 7.0 | 7.0 | 7.0 | 7.0 | 7.0 | 7.0 | 7.0 | 7.0 | 7.0 |
| Mg | 0.5 | 1.0 | 2.25 | 2.25 | 2.25 | 2.25 | 2.25 | 2.25 | 2.25 | 2.25 |
| Cu | – | – | – | 0.25 | 1.25 | – | – | 1.25 | 1.25 | 1.25 |
| Mn | – | – | – | – | – | 0.25 | – | 0.25 | – | 0.25 |
| Cr | – | – | – | – | – | – | 0.25 | 0.25 | .0.25 | 0.25 |

FIGURE 30 — Effect of minor alloying additions on the proof stress and the resistance to stress corrosion cracking of high purity base Al-Zn-Mg alloy sheet (0.050 in) aged 18 hr at 257 F. Chadwick, Muir and Grainger.[78]

affect the metallurgical behavior of Al-Zn-Mg-Cu solid solutions.

Doyle,[79] however, citing results of transverse tests of large forged blocks, pointed out that although chromium additions may be useful for sheet, such additions to forgings do not necessarily give an improvement in stress corrosion resistance. Atmospheric stress corrosion tests at the Royal Aircraft Establishment (Farnborough) by Meikle[80] of forgings of different British and American alloys showed that variations in composition within limits do not have an outstanding effect especially in the short transverse direction. Heat treating and aging conditions have been shown to be of greater effect in producing better resistance to stress corrosion cracking.

Although several investigators[68,69,76,81] have reached the conclusion that additions of silver from 0.3-0.5% have improved the resistance to stress corrosion cracking of Al-Zn-Mg-Cu alloys, a number of investigations during the past ten years at the Alcoa Research Laboratories have failed to confirm this result using short transverse tests of thick sections. An extensive recent investigation[82] on 2 in thick plate of 7075 and 7075 type alloys, with and without 0.3% Ag, showed the same threshold stress for a given alloy type when thermally treated to develop equal strength.

### 4. Relationship of Stress Corrosion Cracking to Thermal Treatments and Microstructure

As helpful as the electron microscope has been in revealing previously unseen structures in alloys and in promoting the understanding of many phenomena of solid state metallurgy, the observation of these structures, unfortunately, does not always explain the stress corrosion behavior of an alloy. A discussion of some attempts to identify "stress corrosion resistant" or "stress corrosion susceptible" structures with alloy performance follows.

Thomas and Nutting[7] observed that intercrystalline mechanical fractures of Al-Zn-Mg and Al-Zn-Mg-Cu alloys at or near maximum hardness was associated with preferential slip in the precipitate-free layers adjacent to the grain boundaries. They concluded that the absence of precipitates in the grain margins was the result of vacancies escaping into the grain boundaries during quenching and thus not being available to nucleate precipitation in the matrix. Because stress concentration effects usually occur at the grain boundaries, dislocation movement may take place in the precipitate free regions under applied stresses considerably smaller than the macroscopic yield stress. If the metal is strained in a corrosive environment after aging to peak hardness, preferential flow will begin in the grain margins and preferential corrosive attack will occur along these regions where plastic flow has taken place. Thus, under a sustained tensile stress, intercrystalline stress corrosion cracking can then occur. Thomas[83] suggested that a solution to this problem is to eliminate the precipitate-free regions adjacent to the grain boundaries, while retaining a high mechanical strength. He proposed to heat treat, quench at such a rate as to produce precipitate-free grain margins, start the aging treatment and then interrupt it to deform the metal so as to introduce plastic flow near the grain boundaries. This deformation was to produce vacancies in the grain margins so that precipitation in these regions would result upon further aging.

Haney, Milton and Robinson[84] applied the suggestion of Thomas to Al-Zn-Mg-Cu alloys of the compositions listed in Table 5 using various thermal treatments. Specimens were tested of 0.064 in thick sheet that had been quenched in water at 80 and 176 F, cold rolled 0, 10 and 20%, aged various times at 250 and 302 F with and without preaging. The stress corrosion performance of tensile specimens stressed to 75% of the yield strength and exposed 26 weeks to 3.5% NaCl by alternate immersion (10/50 min cycle) was not affected by the preaging and deformation treatments. The major influence on the resistance to stress corrosion cracking was the aging temperature, although some change in microstructure was affected by the cold reduction. For example, Figure 31a shows the structure of alloy DTD 687 that was quenched in water at 176 F, preaged 1/2 hour at 302 F and then reheated 23-1/2 hours at 302 F. For comparison in Figure 31b is the structure of a similar specimen except that a 10% cold reduction step was introduced after the preage. Although the cold deformation did achieve an appreciable change in both the grain margins and the grains, both treatments resulted in sheet with equally good resistance to stress corrosion cracking. Lower temperature aging, on the other hand, with or without the cold reduction, resulted in decreased stress corrosion performance.

Gruhl[85] hypothesized that the stress corrosion crack sensitivity of an Al-5 Zn-3 Mg-0.3 Mn-0.15 Cr alloy is not to be correlated with the heterogeneous precipitates at the grain boundaries but with the zones which are related to single phase segregation in the matrix. Gruhl and Cordier[86] concluded from their reversion and re-hardening experiments on that alloy that stress corrosion is caused mainly by metastable redissolvable precipitates, and that precipitation of stable phases lead to a high specimen life in sodium chloride solution. They concluded also that the best practical measure would be a step-wise aging after quenching, especially for copper-containing alloys. Other developments at the Alcoa Research Laboratories led to similar conclusions regarding Al-Zn-Mg-Cu alloys.[70,71]

On the other hand, artificial aging treatments (isothermal or step-wise) have not been found for copper-free alloys that increase substantially the resistance to stress

TABLE 5 — Alloy Compositions Used for Experiments to Eliminate the Precipitate-Free Grain Boundary Region

| Alloy | Cu | Fe | Si | Mn | Mg | Zn | Cr |
|---|---|---|---|---|---|---|---|
| A[1] | 2.09 | 0.14 | 0.08 | nil | 2.73 | 6.65 | 0.23 |
| B | 1.51 | 0.12 | 0.08 | 0.51 | 2.74 | 6.79 | nil |
| C[2] | 0.55 | 0.12 | 0.11 | 0.21 | 2.92 | 5.83 | nil |

[1] Aluminum Association Alloy 7178.
[2] British Aircraft Specification DTD 687.

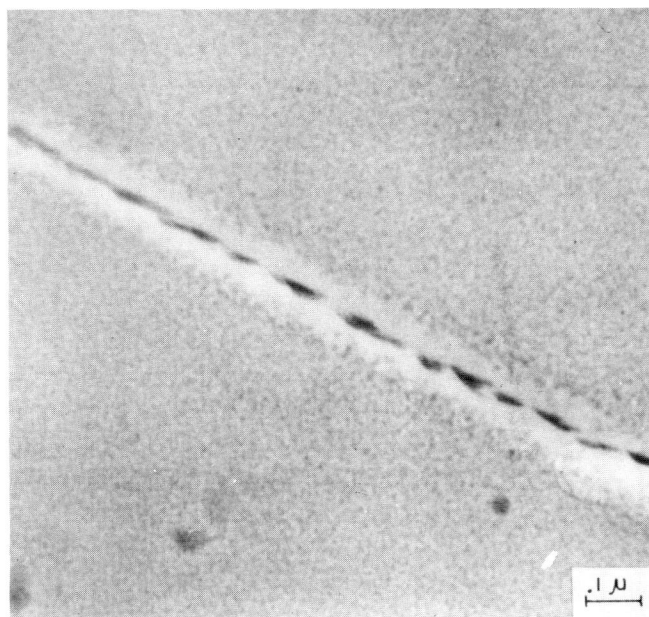

(a) Aged 24 hrs at 302 F (1/2 hr + 23 1/2 hrs)

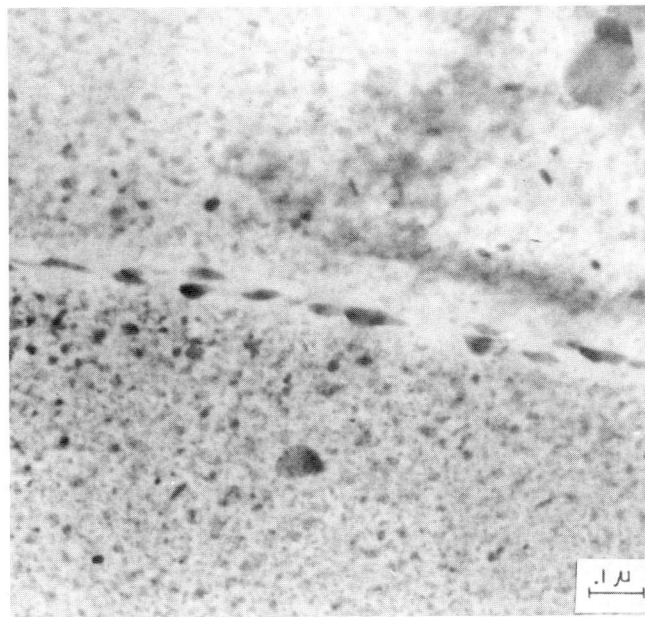

(b) Preaged 1/2 hr at 302 F, cold rolled 10%, aged 23-1/2 hrs at 302 F.

FIGURE 31 — Electron transmission micrographs of thin foils prepared from 0.064 in thick sheet of DTD687 alloy solution heat treated, quenched in water at 176 F and aged. Note that the wide precipitate-free regions adjacent to the grain boundary in (a) have been almost completely filled by precipitate caused by the preage and cold reduction treatment used for (b). Both samples, however, had a similar high resistance to stress corrosion cracking when stressed to 75% Y.S. Haney, Milton and Robinson.[84]

corrosion cracking in the short transverse direction and at the same time achieve mechanical strengths higher than the quenched and naturally aged alloy. For example, Vernam and Shumaker[87] obtained the following results with short transverse tests of commercially produced 2 inch thick plate of 7039 alloy. The as-quenched temper (naturally aged 19 months) which had a yield strength of 39.8 ksi failed by stress corrosion cracking at a stress of 20 ksi within 12 days in an industrial atmosphere. Items aged by various treatments, including one that actually reduced the yield strength to 35.7 ksi, were also susceptible: a stress of 20 ksi applied to the specimen with a yield strength of 56.6 ksi caused failure in 42-44 days and a stress of 30 ksi applied to the specimen with 35.7 ksi yield strength caused failure in 33-35 days.

In an effort to explain the difference in the stress corrosion behavior of 7075-T6 and 7075-T73, Jacobs[27] hypothesized that the quench induced dislocation structure observed in the T6 temper was vital to the initiation of a stress corrosion crack: "Because pitting proceeds identically in the T6 and T73, viz., by the dissolution of large $MgZn_2$ precipitate particles in the grain boundaries and grains, it is concluded that the critical role of dislocations is to assist in the nucleation of cracks of appropriate geometry for propagation." In more recent work Jacobs noted[88] that "dislocations appear to be harmful only when they are strongly pinned, or immobile, and[89] that "the stress corrosion resistance of 7075 aluminum is lowered more by an increase in precipitate-particle density than by an increase in dislocation density." He also suggested the interesting prospect of a quantitative forecast of the stress corrosion resistance of 7075 alloy and other precipitation-hardening alloys from a simple microstructural examination.

Holl,[90] on the other hand, after performing electron microscopic examinations of the deformation behavior of an Al-Zn-Mg-Cu alloy in various states of susceptibility to stress corrosion cracking rejected the views of both Thomas and Jocobs. Holl performed stress corrosion tests on short transverse specimens machined from commercially produced 3 in thick plate of an alloy containing 5.7% Zn-2.7% Mg-0.5% Cu-0.3% (Si + Fe) and heat treated to the five different conditions given in Table 6. Materials aged at 248 F to the maximum strength condition after either cold water quenching or air cooling from the solution heat treating temperature were both highly susceptible to stress corrosion cracking even though the residual dislocation contents were different, due to different quenching rates. However, marked changes in susceptibility were produced by aging treatments that did not involve any alteration to the grain boundary precipitate-free regions, indicating that the presence of such regions is not of primary importance to the cracking process. Holl concluded that the stress corrosion cracking behavior of an Al-Zn-Mg-Cu alloy is "essentially controlled by the mode of deformation of the alloy, which in turn is a function of the structural condition of the matrix." "In particular the best resistance to cracking will be found in material containing non-coherent precipitates. . .(which) normally are developed in the over-aged condition with its associated low mechanical strength."

Experience at the Alcoa Research Laboratories supports Holl's contention that neither the presence per se of a precipitate-free grain boundary region or a quench induced dislocation structure governs the resistance to stress corrosion cracking of Al-Zn-Mg-Cu alloys. Various alloy development studies have shown, however, that it is difficult to be sure of even a qualitative forecast of the

TABLE 6–Stress Corrosion Resistance of an Al-Zn-Mg-Cu Alloy[1] Heat Treated and Aged to Two Different Levels of Yield Strength[90]

| Quench | Aging Treatment | Tensile Properties[2] | | | Stress Corrosion Test Specimen Life, Hrs [3,4] |
| | | Tensile Strength, ksi | Proof Stress, 0.1% Offset, ksi | % Elongation | |
| --- | --- | --- | --- | --- | --- |
| Cold Water | 24 hrs at 248 F | 73.4 | 66.1 | 3 | 18.5 ± 8 |
| Air Cool | 24 hrs at 248 F | 73.2 | 65.7 | 3 | 22 ± 4 |
| Cold Water | 14 days at R.T. + 6 hrs at 329 F | 68.1 | 63.7 | 4 | 430 ± 46 |
| Cold Water | 40 hrs at 194 F | 66.8 | 52.1 | 7 | 12 ± 3 |
| Cold Water | 24 hrs at 248 F + 16 hrs at 329 F + 8 hrs at 347 F | 65.0 | 53.6 | 6 | 2000 Unbroken |

[1] Composition: 5.7% Zn-2.7% Mg-0.5% Cu-0.3% (Si + Fe).
[2] Short transverse tensile specimens machined from 3 in thick plate and solution heat treated 4 hrs at 869 F and quenched and aged as indicated.
[3] Specimens stressed to 85% of the proof stress as dead weight loaded cantilever beams (quadruplicates).
[4] Exposed to 0.5 N NaCl + 0.005 $NaHCO_3$ solution dripped onto each specimen.

stress corrosion resistance of an alloy simply by examining the microstructure.

Figures 32 through 36 show electron micrographs from the work of Robinson, Lifka and Shumaker[91] illustrating the difficulty of trying to correlate structures with stress corrosion resistance. The structures shown are for commercially fabricated 1 to 2 inch thick plate or forgings, and the stress corrosion data are for short transverse tests. Structures of 7075 alloy in the W, T6 and T73 tempers are shown in Figures 32, 33 and 34, respectively. The structure representative of the maximum strength T6 temper differed from that of the W temper principally by the high density of zone formation in the T6. The T73 temper overaged in comparison with the T6, exhibited zones of larger size with greater interparticle spacing and some platelets of M′ or M precipitate. A few residual quenched in dislocations also are present. The T73 temper is virtually immune to stress corrosion cracking in chloride environments whereas parts in the T6 and W tempers are susceptible at low stresses when tested in the short transverse direction. Thus the type of structure shown in Figure 34 might be judged to be representative of a stress corrosion resistant metallurgical condition. However, Figure 35 shows alloy 7079 in an experimental temper with a similar structure yet it was quite susceptible to stress corrosion cracking. Likewise, Figure 36 shows a similar structure in a Cu-free alloy, 7039,

which is susceptible to stress corrosion cracking at low stresses in the short transverse direction.

The rate of cooling of Al-Zn-Mg alloy products following solution heat treatment can have a marked effect upon their resistance to stress corrosion cracking after subsequent precipitation treatment, depending upon whether copper is present in the alloy and upon the direction of stressing relative to the grain structure. In copper-free alloys, resistance to stress corrosion in sodium chloride solutions is favored by a low cooling rate, as by cooling in air,[92,93] but with copper-containing alloys, this behavior generally is the opposite.

Fink and Willey[66] and Lifka[94] showed that rapid cooling of 7075-T6 alloy (Al-Zn-Mg-Cu-Cr) sheet through a critical temperature range (750-550 F) produced immunity to intergranular corrosion and to stress corrosion cracking in sodium chloride solutions; cooling rates greater than about 200 F/sec produced not only the maximum resistance to stress corrosion but also the maximum tensile properties. Decreasing the cooling rate to about 40 F/sec resulted in the formation of coarse precipitates of M′ or M phase in the matrix and in the grain boundaries. The results were a marked reduction in strength and a high degree of susceptibility to intergranular attack and stress corrosion cracking. A further decrease in cooling rate to about 4 F/sec, however, practically eliminated the susceptibility to

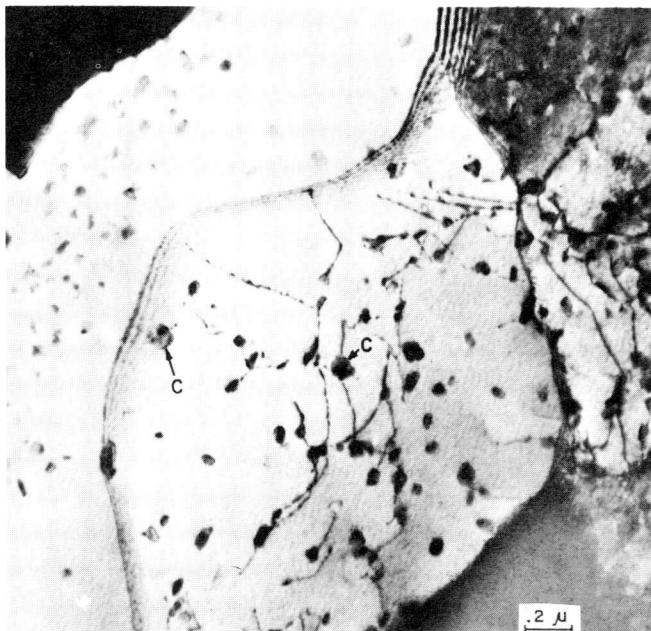

FIGURE 32 — Electron transmission micrograph of a thin foil prepared from rolled plate of 7075-W heat treated in the laboratory and quenched in cold water. Particles of chromium rich constituent (C) are present with dislocations pinned to some of them. There is no visible evidence of zones in the matrix or of M′ phase precipitate in the grain boundaries. Short transverse specimens susceptible to stress corrosion cracking at 25% Y.S. Robinson, Lifka and Shumaker.[91]

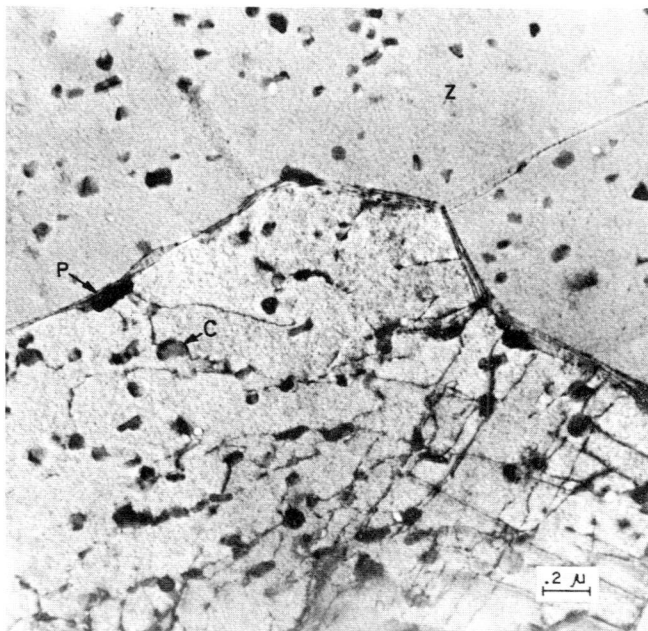

FIGURE 33 — Thin foil of 7075-T6 aged from the 7075-W plate shown in Figure 32. Microstructure of the T6 is similar to that of the W temper except that minute zones are visible in the grains (black specks Z) and numerous precipitate particles (P) are present in the grain boundaries. Dislocations are pinned to chromium rich constituent (c) and to particles of grain boundary precipitate (P). Short transverse specimens susceptible to stress corrosion cracking at 25% Y.S. Robinson, Lifka and Shumaker.[91]

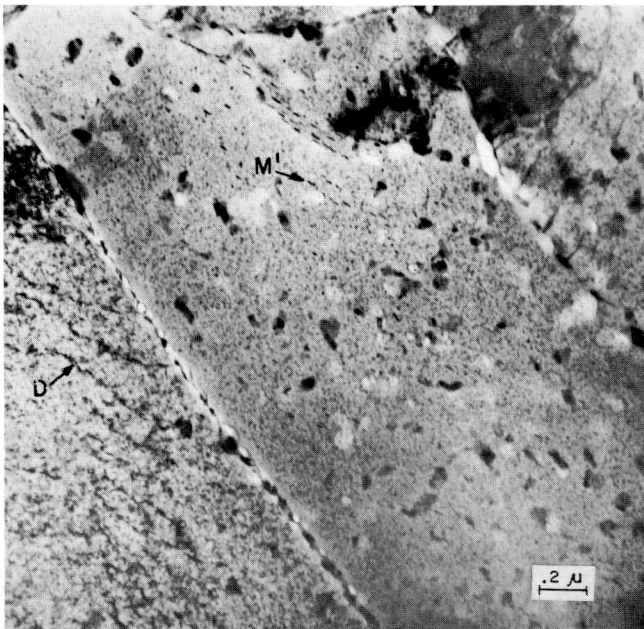

FIGURE 34 — Thin foil of 7075-T73 aged from the 7075-W plate shown in Figure 32. Compared to the 7075-T6 (Figure 33) the zones are larger and the spacing between them greater. Tiny platelets of M' precipitate (M') also are present. Residual quenching dislocations (D) are still visible. The density of the grain boundary precipitate has increased and there is a very narrow region devoid of zones immediately adjacent to the boundary precipitate. Short transverse specimens resistant to stress corrosion cracking at 75% Y.S. Robinson, Lifka and Shumaker.[91]

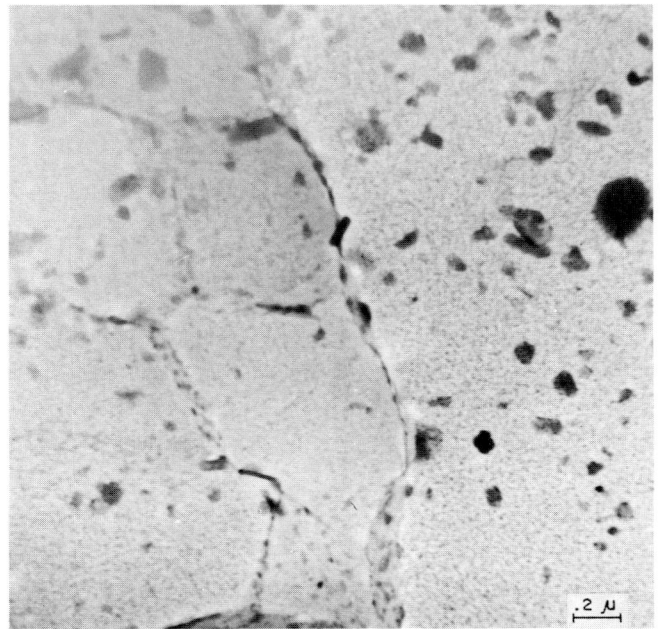

FIGURE 35 — Thin foil prepared from a forging of 7075 alloy in an experimental T7 type temper. Microstructure is similar to that of the 7075-T73 in Figure 34, yet short transverse specimens are susceptible to stress corrosion cracking at 50% Y.S. Robinson, Lifka and Shumaker.[91]

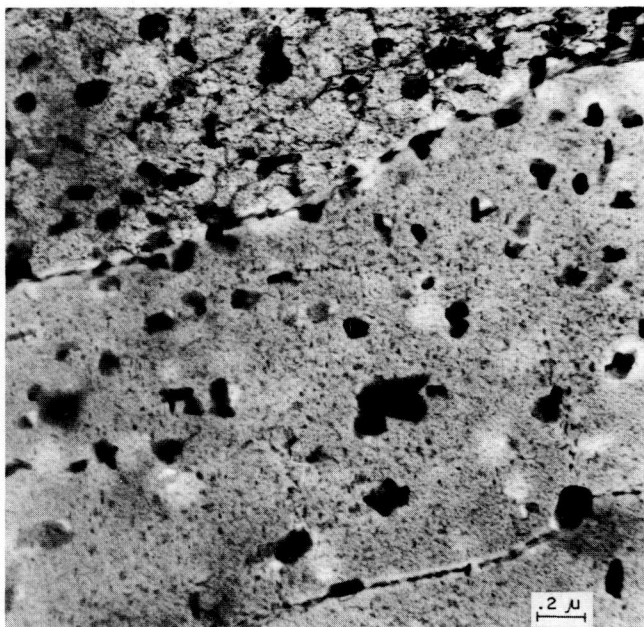

FIGURE 36 — Thin foil prepared from a rolled plate of 7039 alloy in a T6 type temper. Microstructure is similar to that of the 7075-T73 in Figure 34, yet short traNsverse specimens are susceptible to stress corrosion cracking at 25% Y.S. Robinson, Shumaker and Lifka.[91]

intergranular attack and to stress corrosion cracking but also resulted in a drastic loss of strength.

While the above trends furnish valuable guides for controlling the resistance to stress corrosion cracking of sheet and other products of similar thickness, they are relatively insignificant for plate and other products with an anistrophic grain structure that are also thick enough to permit stressing in the short transverse direction relative to the grains. Short transverse stresses are far more critical than tension stress acting parallel to one of the principal axes of the grains (refer to Figure 3) as in the case of sheet. Thus, drastically quenched ($>$ 1000 F/sec) short transverse specimens of 7075-T6 machined from rolled 2 in thick plate stress corrosion crack in sodium chloride solution at a sustained tensile stress as low as 11 ksi even though they are not susceptible to intergranular attack in the absence of applied stress. They are, in fact, not appreciably more resistant than similar specimens quenched at a relatively low rate so that they are susceptible to intergranular attack in the absence of applied stress.

Discussions regarding "resistant microstructures" and "susceptible microstructures" overlook the equally vital role of the electrochemical relationships of the different phases with the environment. If structure alone governs the stress corrosion resistance of an alloy, then specimens representing a susceptible structure should fail under sustained load in a dry inert atmosphere such as argon and helium gases. It is necessary to explain also the fact that specimens with an identifiable structure fail in some aqueous electrolytes and not in others.

496

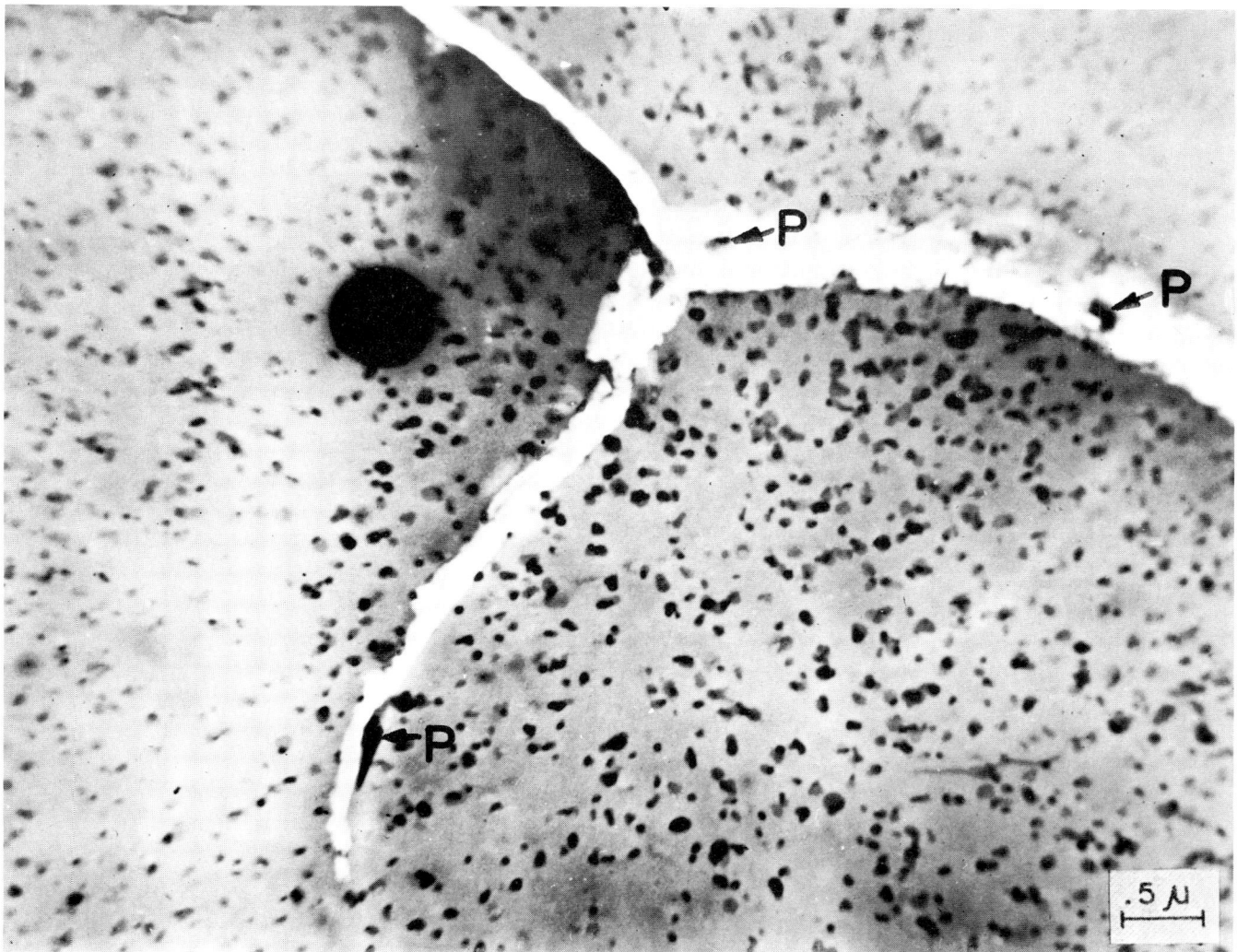

FIGURE 37 — Electron transmission micrograph of a thin metal specimen of Al-Zn-Mg-Cu-Cr alloy (7075-W) corroded in $NaCl-H_2O_2$ solution. The bulk metal was solution heat treated and then quenched in boiling water to cause a susceptibility to intergranular corrosion. This micrograph shows selective corrosion that has proceeded along the edges of three adjacent grains. The upper left and the lower boundaries lie at about $90°$ to the surface and the corrosion has followed a comparatively narrow path. The upper right boundary, on the other hand, lies at a relatively low angle to the specimen surface and the corrosion path appears to be wide. Particles marked P are grain boundary precipitates left intact and uncorroded. The small dark particles scattered through the grains are the relatively insoluble chromium-rich constituents. In this condition (7075-W) or when artificially aged to the T6 temper, 7075 alloy sheet is susceptible to stress corrosion cracking. Hunter, Frank and Robinson.[95]

## 5. Electrochemical Considerations

Hunter, Frank and Robinson[95] using specimens thinned to 1000 Å for transmission electron microscopy by the same technique used for 2024 alloy[41] studied the corrosion in $NaCl-H_2O_2$ solution of thin films of slowly quenched (45 F/sec) 7075-W alloy sheet. They observed extremely selective corrosion which extended along grain margins leaving particles of grain boundary precipitate unattacked, as shown in Figure 37. This observation is compatible with the previous suggestion of Fink and Willey[66] that the partial depletion of copper (along with zinc and magnesium) from the solid solution at the grain boundary regions of slowly quenched sheet causes the grain margins to become anodic to both the grain bodies and the $Mg(Al,Cu,Zn)_2$ phase precipitated in the grain boundaries.

These observations also are in accord with investigations of the effect of artificial aging on the electrochemical potential[(2)] of rapidly quenched 7075-W sheet.[96] Aging at 250 F caused the potential of the 7075-W to shift about 75 mv in the cathodic direction after 24 to 36 hours and to remain unchanged after 48 hours of total aging. If, after aging for 24 hours at 250 F, the alloy is aged for 8 hours at 350 F, the potential shifts about 35 mv in the anodic direction. The first change of potential with aging indicates

---

[(2)]Potentials measured in an electrolyte containing 53 g NaCl + 3 g $H_2O_2$ per liter.

497

the precipitation of zinc from solid solution at the lower temperature. The second aging step reduces the copper as well as zinc in solid solution in the grain bodies with the result that the grains and the grain boundaries attain the same potential. Such a series of events probably accounts for the superior resistance to intergranular attack and to stress corrosion cracking of short transverse specimens machined from thick sections of 7075-T73 compared to 7075-T6.

It has been noted in aging tests of rapidly quenched sheet of 7075 type alloy at temperatures in the range of 140 to 265 F[97] and of T6 temper sheet reheated at relatively high temperatures in the range of 320-420 F,[98] that for each temperature, there is a period of heating that causes a high susceptibility to intergranular attack, which can be eliminated by extended heating. Adenis et al,[98] however, concluded that although a partial depletion of solute elements obviously occurs in the immediate vicinity of the boundaries, the greater part of the precipitate-free region is still more highly supersaturated with solute elements than the grain bodies and hence anodic to them. They also concluded that continued heating causes the precipitate-free grain margins to lose their supersaturation and thus become less anodic and attain the same potential as the grain bodies. Doubt is cast upon this explanation, however, by the fact that susceptibility to intergranular corrosion is not developed in copper from Al-Zn-Mg alloys by any of these thermal treatments.[99,100] Therefore, it would appear that the electrochemical mechanism for intergranular susceptibility in Al-Zn-Mg-Cu alloys is markedly influenced by the extent of removal of copper from solid solution, rather than by a concentration of solute elements in the precipitate-free region.

It is not essential for the many aluminum alloy-temper combinations that are highly resistant to stress corrosion cracking to be immune to intergranular attack, although this is generally the case. Conversely, however, alloys and tempers that are susceptible to intergranular attack in the absence of applied stress, and specific anodic and cathodic phases often can be identified. Thus, it has been possible to develop stress corrosion resistant tempers for most types of aluminum alloys from the metallurgical and electrochemical knowledge available for the particular alloy system.

The Al-Zn-Mg-Cu alloys under some conditions follow this pattern and under other conditions do not: when slowly quenched and aged to maximum strength they are susceptible both to stress corrosion cracking and to intergranular attack; when rapidly quenched and aged to maximum strength they may be immune to intergranular corrosion in the absence of stress and still susceptible to stress corrosion cracking, particularly when stressed in the short transverse direction. However, the Al-Zn-Mg (copper-free) alloys seem to be a complete exception to the general pattern of behavior. Certain alloys of this type have about the highest susceptibility to stress corrosion cracking of any aluminum alloy, yet they do not corrode intergranularly in the absence of stress. The determination of an electrochemical model for these alloys is most difficult, and the situation is controversial. The two models given most consideration involve anodic components of: (a) grain boundary precipitates such as $MgZn_2$, or (b) plastically strained precipitate free grain boundary regions.

Cathodic protection of amphoteric metals such as aluminum presents difficulties because it leads to the generation of alkalinity. Corrosion resulting from the reaction of aluminum and hydroxyl ions is likely to occur before the potential required for protection against stress corrosion is reached. The possibility of such "over protection" in the cathodic protection of aluminum structures is well known by corrosion engineers and precautions are taken to prevent it. In general, the occurrence of stress corrosion cracking of aluminum alloys in chloride solution is markedly reduced as the solution is made increasingly alkaline. Consequently, there is the possibility that the alkalinity is the cause of the prevention of cracking and not the electrochemical retardation of the reaction because of a reduced potential difference between the anodic fissures and cathodic regions.

English and McHardy[101,102] have shown that the stress corrosion cracking of alloy 7075-T6 that occurred within one hour in an acidified chloride solution could, by cathodic protection, be prevented for at least several hundred hours in this aggressive solution (Figure 38). Of particular importance, they further demonstrated that, although increasing the pH of the solution of 12 in the absence of cathodic protection increased the time to failure, stress corrosion cracking still occurred (Figure 39). This confirms that the significant role of cathodic protection in this instance was to retard or prevent anodic dissolution.

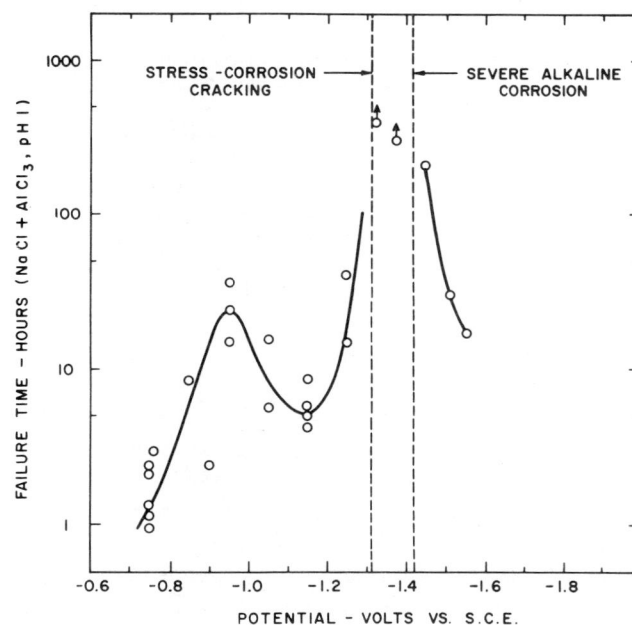

FIGURE 38 — Prevention of stress corrosion cracking of 7075-T6 alloy plate by cathodic protection. Short transverse 0.125 in diameter tensile specimens stressed 75% Y.S. English, McHardy and Hollingsworth.[101,102]

Gruhl and Cordier,[103] however, stated that the stress corrosion cracking of aluminum alloys is not caused by an electrochemical process. Additions to sodium chloride solutions that cause severe intergranular corrosion have no more effect on the time to failure of Al-5 Zn-3 Mg-0.3 Mn-0.15 Cr alloy than the addition of inhibitors.[104] Also fractures may be produced in the mildly corrosive air of the laboratory, in oil-water emulsions and in pure oils. Thus, Gruhl divided the stress corrosion process into two steps, the first being a preparatory period during which chemical or electrochemical corrosion mechanisms only accelerate the penetration of the surface layer but do not contribute to the actual stress corrosion cracking itself. Cracking starts in the second step by a metal-physical process that will be discussed in more detail in the next section.

## 6. Relationship of Stress Corrosion Cracking to Environment

Not enough attention has been given by some investigators to the selection of suitable corrosion test media. Sager, Brown and Mears[105] indicated the hazard of accelerated stress corrosion tests and emphasiz ed that appropriate laboratory tests for one alloy may differ from those for another alloy. Rosenkranz[68,106] also emphasized this point particularly when comparisons are to be made between Al-Zn-Mg alloys and Al-Cu type alloys. Lifka and Sprowls[107] reported the discrepancy between an industrial atmospheric exposure and the 3.5% NaCl alternate immersion test for certain Al-Zn-Mg-Cu alloys, and noted that the discrepancy of the alloy increased with decreasing copper

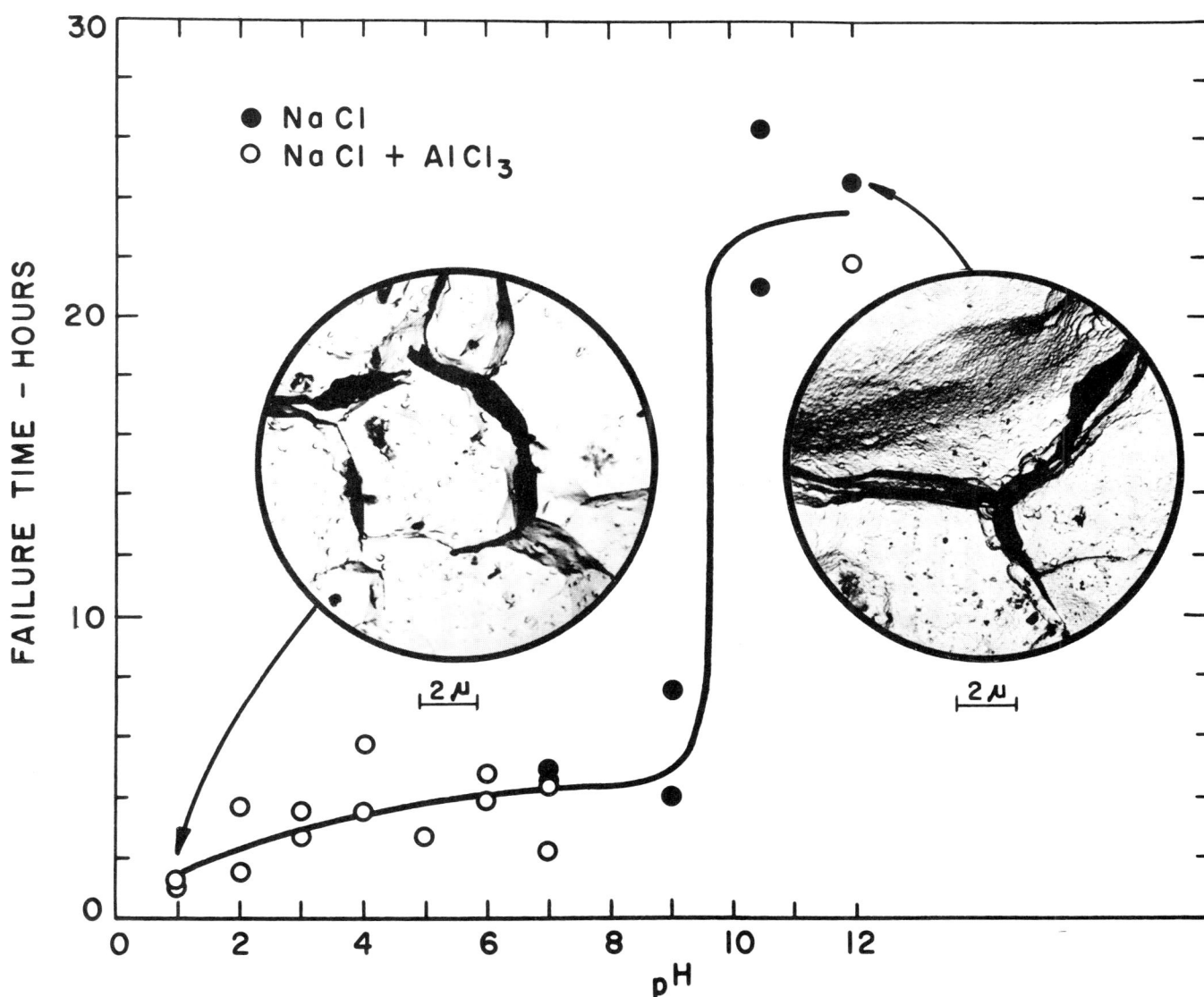

FIGURE 39 — Effect of pH upon stress corrosion failure time of short transverse specimens of 7075-T6 alloy plate stressed 75% Y.S. Electron micrographs of oxide replicas of fracture surfaces show relatively smooth, faceted characteristics of stress corrosion cracks in aluminum alloys. Dark lines or bands indicate intergranular branches from the fracture surface. The fracture surface also shows evidence of superficial pitting. McHardy and Hollingsworth.[102]

content. Helfrich[108] in a current investigation to develop an accelerated stress corrosion test for all types of high strength aluminum alloys again noted the variations in behavior of different alloy types with variables such as chloride concentration, solution pH and temperature.

Experience at Alcoa Research Laboratories has shown that, the copper-free Al-Zn-Mg alloys are more susceptible to stress corrosion cracking in a mildly corrosive inland industrial atmosphere than in room temperature alternate or continuous immersion exposures to neutral sodium chloride solution. An example is shown in Figure 40 with data that Shumaker[109] obtained in short transverse tests of 7039 alloy commercially produced plates of different thickness. In a 180-day exposure to 3.5% NaCl by alternate immersion the T63 temper[93] gave a much better performance than the T6 temper, whereas in a 36-month exposure to the atmosphere at New Kensington, Pa., the difference between the two tempers was negligible. Additional tests at lower applied stresses would be required to draw a fine distinction between the two tempers.

The importance of temperature on the rate of stress corrosion cracking of Al-Zn-Mg alloys has been reported by Gruhl,[110] Helfrich[111] and Romans and Craig.[112] Gruhl[110] found in tests of Al-5 Zn-3 Mg-0.3 Mn-0.15 Cr alloy sheet heat treated and aged (5 days at 194 F) to develop maximum susceptibility to stress corrosion cracking that a straight line resulted when he plotted applied stress against log of specimen life. This was true for elastic stresses down to about 12 kp/mm² (8.5 ksi) for various temperatures of NaCl solution ranging from 77 to 158 F. The effect of increasing temperature was to shorten the specimen life (approximately 5% for each 1.8 F). Essentially the same results were obtained with sheet that had been stretched to 5% permanent elongation after artificial

aging except that the slopes for the stress-log specimen life curves were slightly less.

Gruhl concluded that if the activation energy figures estimated from these data were accurate, then the activation energy involved in the stress corrosion process was slightly higher for undeformed materials than for deformed materials. He also stated that such activation values were not too far from those involved for the diffusion of vacancies, but pointed out that this was rationalization of data and had not been established. Gruhl did not attempt to associate the activation energy or the effect of temperature with any particular microstructure or constituent specie.

Stress-log specimen life curves obtained by Helfrich[111] with short transverse tests of 7039-T64 alloy plate are shown in Figure 41. He obtained many of the same experimental results as did Gruhl, and on the basis of calculated activation energy and an activation volume, concluded that the intergranular stress corrosion of 7039 alloy is a stress-activated and thermally activated process involving anodic dissolution of $MgZn_2$ at the grain boundaries. It should be remembered, however, that the mere establishment of an apparent activation energy relationship does not define the reactants involved in creating this energy relationship unless they have been previously established by other methods and techniques.

## IV. Discussion of Proposed General Theories

Many facts regarding the mechanism of the stress corrosion cracking of the 2XXX series and 5XXX series have been established and present a logical series of phenomena with regard to electrochemical potential of phases and distribution of these phases as revealed by microscopic studies. However, the case is not so obvious for the 7XXX series alloys, especially those not containing copper. In this sense, these alloys are examples that would support views expressed by Champion[5] that a single satisfactorily detailed theory cannot be developed for the

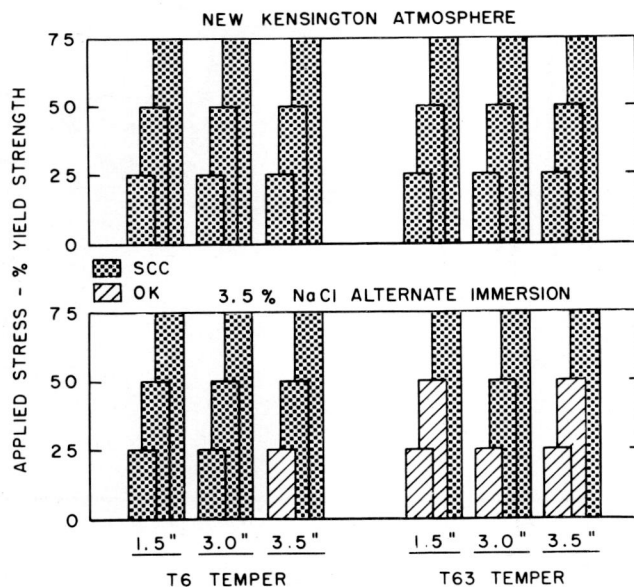

FIGURE 40 — Influence of corrosive environment on the stress corrosion performance of 7039-T6 and T63 alloy plate—short transverse stress. Shumaker.[109]

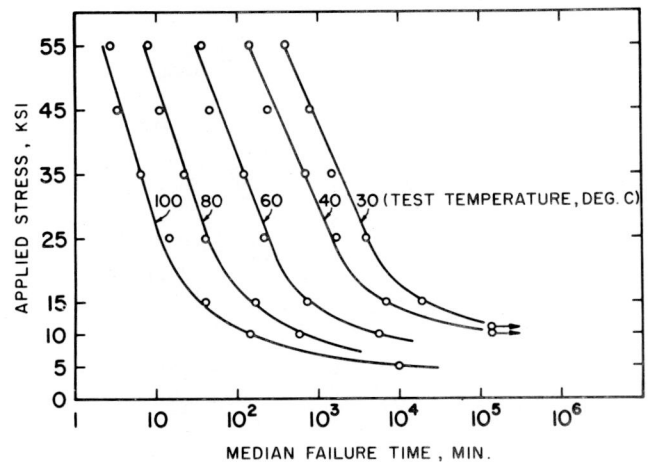

FIGURE 41 — Effect of test temperature on stress corrosion cracking of 7039-T64—short transverse stress. Helfrich.[108]

500

mechanism of all stress corrosion. On the other hand, Robertson and Tetelman[113] say that the intergranular stress corrosion of face centered cubic alloys seems to have some common requirements:

1. The existence of an anodic path in the material along the plane of the grain boundary;

2. Grain boundaries normal to the applied stress.

To this, we believe, should be added the possibility of having strata or paths more susceptible to corrosion than the adjoining metal. The marked influence of the anisotropy of the grain structure, particularly of hot worked products in thick sections upon the stress corrosion performance of an alloy was mentioned earlier (Figure 3). An obvious possible explanation lies in the shape of the grain as it influences the directness and the length of an intergranular path that is perpendicular to the direction of the applied stress.

## A. Mechanical and Film-Rupture Mechanisms

Robertson and Tetelman[113] have added to the postulates of Mears, Brown and Dix[3] the consideration that the normal stress across the boundary is produced by dislocation pile ups. Pugh and Jones[114] suggest that stress corrosion cracking will occur, or at least will be greatly enhanced, only when there is weakened metal in the grain boundaries or the grain margins, the weakening probably occurring as the result of precipitation in the grain boundaries. Hoar[115,116] and Hines[117,118] believe that plastic straining of the metal is required to have stress corrosion cracking continue. This concept has much in common with that of Logan[119] that the oxide film must be ruptured by the plastic deformation. It can be readily agreed that the oxide film must either be penetrated or broken in order for corrosive attack to proceed. However, reasons for the excellent stress corrosion resistance of many ductile aluminum alloys, even when the oxide film is ruptured, must be advanced. For the film-rupture theory to be valid there must be included an explanation for the anodic attack being limited to pitting in some alloys and forming fissures in other alloys. If plastic deformation plays an important role in the initiation by breaking the oxide film, much doubt remains as to the reason for fissure development along grain boundaries rather than pit development since the latter also requires breaks in the oxide film. Pugh, Hoar and Hines feel that the tip of the crevice is the anode of an electrolytic cell, but again our lack of understanding of such a mechanism is emphasized by the fact that the interior of a pit is also anodic to the surrounding metal. Moreover, the results of Dix' unique tests with composite sheets[67] would not be satisfied by the above theories.

Evans[120] raises a further objection to a film-rupture mechanism, based upon the experiments of Farmery.[6] Farmery observed that if a stress corrosion crack were allowed to propagate part of the way through a specimen of a susceptible Al-7% Mg alloy and then the crack arrested by the application of a cathodic current for 30 minutes, the crack did not advance again when the current was stopped,

although 15 hours later fresh cracks appeared elsewhere. A similar specimen was allowed to develop a crack through one-third of the cross-section before arrest by an impressed current; when the current was discontinued after 30 minutes the specimen was subjected to an additional load, and yet remained unbroken after 48 hours. As Evans stated: "It seems certain that if mechanical film rupture at the tip of the crack was the determining factor for propagation, the advance of the cracks would have been resumed after the discontinuation of the protective current at least when the load was increased." The alkali produced by the applied current if retained in the crack could have increased the radius of the "notch." However, if the alkali were removed from the "notch" the crack could be reinitiated. Since the alkali could be more easily diffused from the external surfaces it is not surprising that additional cracks developed.

In later papers Gruhl[104,121] would seem to amend his concept in a previous paper[110] of the mechanism of stress corrosion cracking. It appears that most of his concept is rationalized from studies on the AlZnMg3 alloy (Al-5 Zn-3 Mg-0.3 Mn-0.15 Cr). He describes stress corrosion cracking as a two-stage process. The first stage is largely chemical or electrochemical, whereas the true crack formation is determined in the second stage by a metal-physical (metall-physikalische) process. If this concept is correct, prevention of the chemical or electrochemical reaction in the preliminary period would also prevent the second step. Consequently, a remedial measure would be to eliminate the first stage and thereby prevent failure by not allowing the second stage ever to be initiated. Contrary to Gruhl's opinion, therefore, the chemical or electrochemical stage would be most important. His concept has some interesting aspects in that some alloys in some tempers, such as 2024-T81, 2219-T87 and 6061-T6, can tolerate initiation of intergranular fissures in some environments and still possess excellent resistance to stress corrosion cracking. On the other hand, numerous aluminum alloys may suffer electrochemical attack that results in pitting even when under stress. It is obvious that a theory must permit an explanation of the initiation by electrochemistry of the intergranular attack of such a nature that it results in cracking. Furthermore, metal-physical cracking should be initiated by high tensile stress in an inert environment with the same path of mechanical failure as if it had been initiated by electrochemical reaction at some lower initial stress. Thus far no evidence has been presented to justify such an observation. As a matter of fact, alloy 7039-T63 has an extremely long life, possibly infinite, when exposed under a short transverse stress of 75% Y.S. in a dry, purified mineral oil.[109] Gruhl's theory would still indicate that prevention of the oxidation-reduction first stage would prevent the development of cracking.

Another point that conflicts with Gruhl's theory is that there appears to be no correlation between stress corrosion resistance and fracture toughness. For example, alloys such as 2024-T851 and 2020-T651 have relatively low fracture toughness and yet have very high resistance to stress corrosion cracking. Conversely, 2024-T351, which has a relatively high fracture toughness, has a relatively low resistance to stress corrosion cracking when stressed in the short transverse direction. It would seem if "metal-physical" fracture resistance is so important, the improvement of fracture toughness would increase the stress corrosion performance. Consequently, if Gruhl's theory is to be helpful, some indication of means of increasing the metal-physical fracture resistance must be devised.

## B. Environmental Considerations

There would appear to be little doubt that some of the above steps, if not all, are operative to varying degrees in the stress corrosion cracking of Al-base alloys. The data shown in Figure 42 emphasize this possibility. These data were obtained on 2 in thick plates of Al-Cu alloy 2219-T37 and T87,[122] Al-Zn-Mg-Cu alloy 7075-T6 and T73[70] and Al-Zn-Mg alloy 7039-T63.[93] Experience has demonstrated that stress corrosion cracking of short transverse specimens of 2219-T37, 7075-T6 and 7039-T63 stressed to 75% of the yield strength might be anticipated. It is further anticipated that stress corrosion cracking probably would not occur in the case of 2219-T87 and 7075-T73. This graph (Figure 42) emphasizes the role of the environment in promoting stress-corrosion cracking and indicates, at least, that different steps in an overall mechanism can become controlling, depending upon the nature of the alloy and its temper.[123] It is important to note from Figure 42 that 2219-T37 when stressed to 75% of its yield strength was susceptible to stress corrosion cracking only in sodium chloride; 7075-T6 was susceptible in only sodium chloride,

sodium bromide and sodium iodide, while 7039-T63 was susceptible in sodium chloride, sodium bromide, sodium iodide, sodium fluoride, sodium nitrate and sodium chromate solutions. As a matter of fact, it would seem questionable that the latter alloy could survive in any aqueous solution. In contrast to the behavior of 7039-T63, 2219-T87 and 7075-T73 failed in only a few environments. This type of information alone serves to demonstrate not only the difference in performance, but most probably a difference in mechanism of the Cu-free 7XXX series alloy from either 2XXX or the Cu-bearing 7XXX series.

Another striking illustration of the significance of the relationship of the alloy and temper and the environment is shown in Figure 43 by the data obtained[124] in inhibited red fuming nitric acid (IRFNA). Although we[1] have found that the 3.5% NaCl alternate immersion test provides a reliable prediction of the stress corrosion performance of the alloys shown in Figure 43 when exposed in outdoor atmospheric environments, it is very apparent that this sodium chloride exposure test should not be depended upon to predict the behavior of alloys in unique environments such as hot (165 F) IRFNA. Not only did the 2024-T351 specimens that failed in the 3.5% NaCl alternate immersion test not fail in the IRFNA, but the highly stressed 7075-T7351 alloy specimens that were resistant in the 3.5% NaCl test, did fail in the hot IRFNA. It is gratifying that alloys 6061-T6, 2024-T851 and 2219-T87 were resistant to stress corrosion cracking in the IRFNA as well as in many other environments and in the alternate immersion test.

Haynie et al[9,125] on the basis of a relatively few experiments with a high purity ternary Al-Zn-Mg alloy have

SHORT TRANSVERSE TENSILE SPECIMENS, STRESSED 75% YIELD STRENGTH
EXPOSED BY CONTINUOUS IMMERSION AT 85° F
↟ SPECIMEN DID NOT FAIL

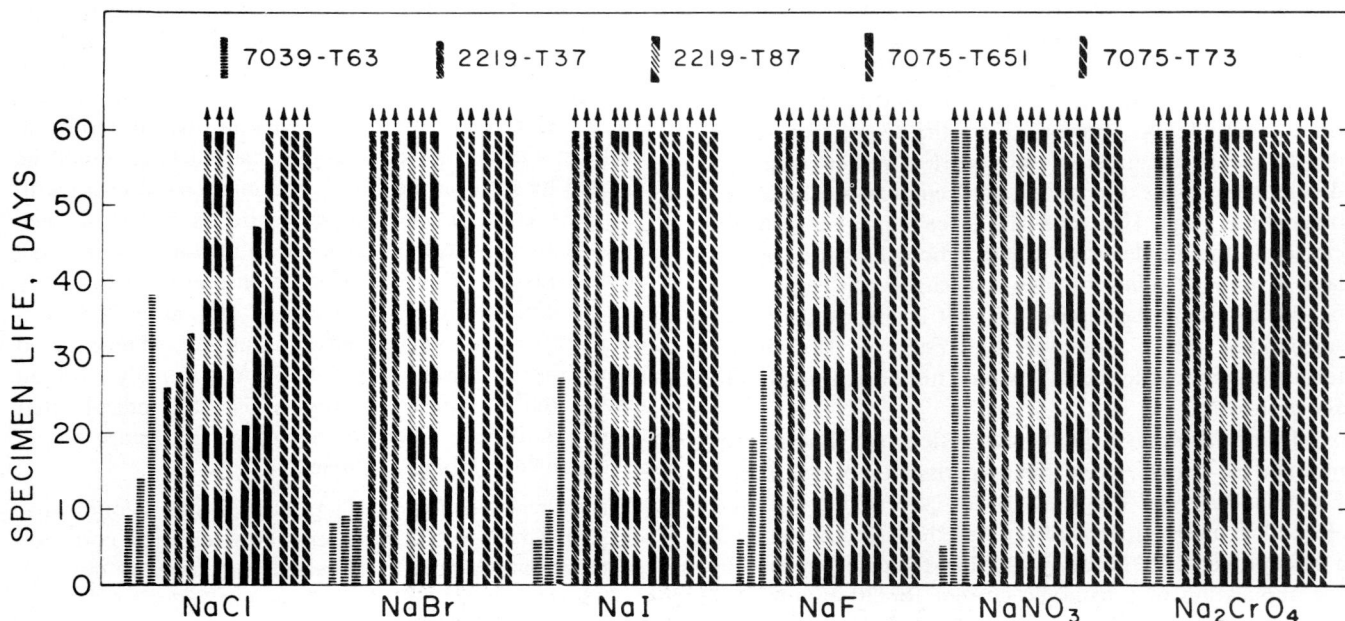

FIGURE 42 — Stress corrosion cracking of aluminum alloys in neutral aqueous solutions. Hunter and Sprowls.[122]

proposed a mechanism for the initiation of stress corrosion cracks in these alloys. This mechanism involves the absorption of cathodically produced hydrogen into strained mechanically weak (alloy depleted) grain margins. The hydrogen acts to reduce the activation energy for anodic dissolution of the metal and thus accelerates the localized corrosion at the grain boundaries perpendicular to the applied tensile stresses. Evans[126] previously suggested the possibility of atomic hydrogen becoming introduced into the grain boundaries of aluminum alloys but indicated the difficulty in devising definite experiments to substantiate the idea. This is still the situation today; further experimental evidence demonstrating the possible role of hydrogen in aluminum is needed. In any event, if hydrogen is involved in the cracking process, the actual mechanism will have to be reconciled with the well established cases of the prevention of stress corrosion cracking of various aluminum alloys by cathodic protection even when hydrogen is evolved as a cathodic reaction product.

## V. Summary

1. Most investigators agree that fissures are initiated by oxidation of the metal most generally by an electrochemical process influenced by the presence of a tensile stress.

2. Stress corrosion cracking is to be expected only when three requisites are simultaneously present: (a) Enduring tensile stress at the surface, (b) a microstructure or sub-microstructure identifiable in some instances, (c) a corrosive environment usually of specific nature, and (d) Requisites (b) and (c) are interdependent.

3. A stress corrosion susceptible structure can be defined only in relation to a specific corrosive environment.

4. The chemical, electrochemical, metallurgical and microstructural conditions required for stress corrosion cracking of the Al-Cu (2XXX) alloys have been reasonably well established. Also the measures to be taken to produce stress corrosion resistant tempers for normal environments or remedial steps to prevent stress corrosion cracking have been well documented.

5. The understanding of the mechanism of stress corrosion cracking of the Al-Mg (5XXX) alloys is probably more complete than for Al-Cu alloys. As is the situation for the Al-Cu alloys stress corrosion resistant tempers have been developed.

6. Although the Al-Zn-Mg alloys have excellent resistance to stress corrosion cracking in longitudinal and long transverse directions, relative to the grain structure, precautions must be taken to prevent the exposure of the short transverse direction stressed in tension. The alloys crack in a greater variety of electrolytes than either 7XXX series containing copper and chromium or the 2XXX series alloys. At the moment the mechanism is the subject of much controversy.

7. The Al-Zn-Mg-Cu-Cr alloys such as 7075-T6 have excellent stress corrosion resistance stressed in longitudinal and long transverse directions relative to the grain structure but precautions must be taken to prevent the exposure of the short transverse direction stressed in tension. The alloy 7075-T73 has a high resistance to stress corrosion cracking in all three directions in normal environments. The alloy X7178-T76 has excellent resistance in the longitudinal and long transverse and much improved resistance in short transverse as compared with 7075-T6 in normal environments.

8. The chemical, electrochemical, metallurgical and microstructural conditions required for stress corrosion cracking of the Al-Zn-Mg-Cu-Cr are not as well established as for the Al-Mg (5XXX) alloys or the Al-Cu (2XXX) alloys but considerably more is known than concerning the copper-free 7XXX alloys. In most instances grain boundary constituent of 7075-T6 is not attacked but the margin along the grain boundary is. This margin would appear to be at least partially depleted of copper as compared with copper content of the grain body. It would appear that more drastic aging causes reduction of copper in the grain

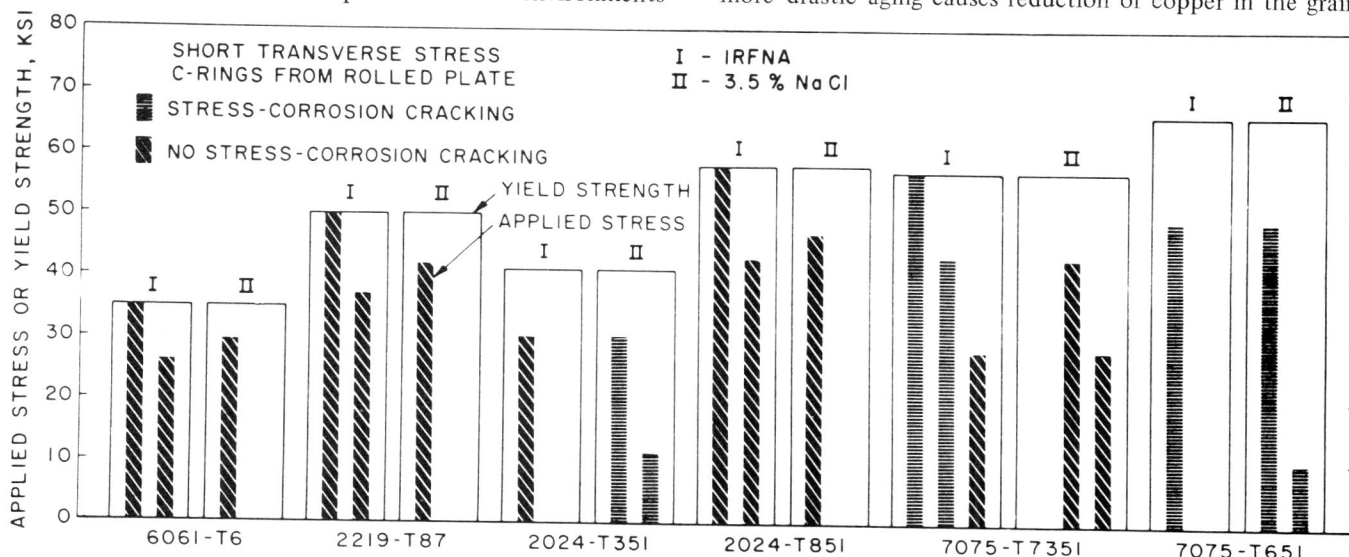

FIGURE 43 — Comparison of resistance to stress corrosion cracking of various alloys in inhibited red fuming nitric acid at 165 F and in 3.5% NaCl alternate immersion. Lifka[123]

body and grain margins to the same low value thereby minimizing anodic electrochemical action of the grain margin and hence contributing to excellent stress corrosion resistance of 7075-T73 in most environments.

# References

1. D. O. Sprowls and R. H. Brown. What Every Engineer Should Know About Stress Corrosion of Aluminum. *Metal Progress*, **81**, 4, 79-85 (1962) and **81**, 5, 77-83 (1962).

2. E. H. Dix, Jr. Acceleration of the Rate of Corrosion by High Constant Stresses. *Trans. AIME*, **137**, 11 (1940).

3. R. B. Mears, R. H. Brown and E. H. Dix, Jr. A Generalized Theory of Stress Corrosion of Alloys. *Symposium on Stress Corrosion Cracking of Metals*, 1944, p. 329, published jointly by ASTM and AIME.

4. P. T. Gilbert and S. E. Hadden. A Theory of the Mechanism of Stress Corrosion in Aluminum-7% Magnesium Alloy. *J. Inst. of Metals*, **77**, 237 (1950).

5. F. A. Champion. The Interaction of Static Stress and Corrosion of Certain Aluminum Alloys. *J. Inst. of Metals*, **83**, 385 (1954-55).

6. H. K. Farmery and U. R. Evans. The Stress Corrosion of Certain Aluminum Alloys. *J. Inst. of Metals*, **84**, 413 (1955-56).

7. G. Thomas and J. Nutting. The Aging Characteristics of Aluminum Alloys—Electron Microscopic Studies of Alloys Based on the Aluminum-Zinc-Magnesium System. *J. Inst. of Metals*, **88**, 81 (1959-60).

8. R. N. Parkins. Stress Corrosion Cracking. *Metallurgical Reviews*, **9**, 35, 201 (1964).

9. F. H. Haynie and W. K. Boyd. Stress Corrosion Cracking of Aluminum Alloys, DMIC Report No. 228, July 1, 1966, Defense Metals Information Center, Battelle Memorial Institute, Columbus, Ohio.

10. R. H. Brown and D. O. Sprowls. Electrochemical Aspects of the Mechanism of Stress Corrosion Cracking, Liberty Bell Corrosion Course II (1966) sponsored by Drexel Institute of Technology and the Philadelphia Section of NACE.

11. E. H. Dix, Jr., W. A. Anderson and M. B. Shumaker. Development of Wrought Aluminum-Magnesium Alloys, Alcoa Research Laboratories Technical Paper No. 14 (1958).

12. W. L. Fink and D. W. Smith. Age Hardening of Aluminum Alloys II—Aluminum-Magnesium Alloy. AIME Tech. Pub. 760, *Metals Technology*, (1936) December.

13. E. C. W. Perryman and G. B. Brook. Mechanism of Precipitation in Aluminum-Magnesium Alloys. *J. Inst. of Metals*, **79**, Part I, 19 (1951).

14. C. Edeleanu. A Mechanism of Stress Corrosion of Aluminum-Magnesium Alloys. *J. Inst. of Metals*, **80**, 187 (1951-52).

15. E. C. W. Perryman. Metallurgical Aspects of Stress Corrosion Cracking in Aluminum Alloys. *Stress Corrosion Cracking and Embrittlement*, John Wiley and Sons, p. 61 (1956).

16. A. Eikum and G. Thomas. Precipitation and Dislocation Nucleation in Quench-Aged Al-Mg Alloys. *Acta Metallurgica*, **12**, 537 (1964).

17. D. L. Robinson. Unpublished data at Alcoa Research Laboratories (1966).

18. D. L. Robinson and M. S. Hunter. Electron Micrographs by Transmission Techniques of Aluminum-Magnesium Alloys. Unpublished data, Alcoa Research Laboratories (1966).

19. E. Mencarelli. Micro-Fractrographic Characteristics of the Corrosion Under Tension in an Al-Mg Alloy Containing 7% Mg. *Acta Metallurgica*, **9**, 904 (1961).

20. W. W. Binger, E. H. Hollingsworth and D. O. Sprowls. *Aluminum*, (Kent R. Van Horn, ed.), **1**, 209-276 American Society for Metals (1967).

21. C. M. Craighead. Unpublished work at Alcoa Research Laboratories (1935).

22. G. Siebel. Corrosion Resistance of Hydronalium Particularly Toward Sea Water. *Aluminum*, **17**, 562 (1935).

23. P. Brenner and W. Roth. Recent Developments in Corrosion-Resistant Aluminum-Magnesium Alloys. *J. Inst. of Metals*, **74**, 159 (1948).

24. E. H. Dix, Jr., W. A. Anderson and M. B. Shumaker. Influence of Service Temperature on the Resistance of Wrought Aluminum-Magnesium Alloys to Corrosion. *Corrosion*, **15**, 2, 55t (1959).

25. E. C. W. Perryman and S. E. Hadden. Stress Corrosion of Al-7% Mg Alloy. *J. Inst. of Metals*, **77**, 207 (1950).

26. W. A. Anderson. Treatment of Aluminum-Magnesium Alloy, U.S. Patent No. 3,232,796, February 1, 1966 (Filed March 21, 1962).

27. A. J. Jacobs. The Role of Dislocations in the Stress Corrosion Cracking of 7075 Aluminum Alloy. *Transactions ASM*, **58**, 4, 579 (1965).

28. P. Brenner and G. J. Metcalfe. The Effect of Cold Work on the Microstructure and Corrosion Resistance of Al-5% Mg Alloys Containing 0-1% Zinc. *J. Inst. of Metals*, **81**, 261 (1952).

29. R. B. Niederberger, J. L. Basil and G. T. Bedford. Corrosion and Stress Corrosion of 5000 Series Aluminum Alloys in Marine Environments. *Corrosion*, **22**, 3, 68 (1966).

30. H. C. Rutemiller and D. O. Sprowls. Susceptibility of Aluminum Alloys to Stress Corrosion. *Materials Protection*, **2**, 63 (1963).

31. P. Brenner. Stress Corrosion in Aluminum Alloys. *Z. Metallkunde*, **44**, 85 (1953).

32. H. B. Romans and H. L. Craig, Jr. Atmospheric Stress Corrosion Testing of Aluminum Alloys. Presented at the Annual Meeting of the ASTM, June, 1967.

33. R. H. Brown. Unpublished work at Alcoa Research Laboratories (1935).

34. E. H. Cook. Unpublished data at Alcoa Research Laboratories (1959).

35. D. Van Rooyen. Qualitative Mechanism of Stress Corrosion Cracking of Austenitic Stainless Steel. *Corrosion*, **16**, 9, 421t (1960) September.

36. H. Vosskuhler. Influence of pH Values and Type of Corroding Solution on the Intercrystalline and Stress Corrosion of Aluminum-Magnesium Alloys. *Arch. Metallkunde*, **3**, 28 (1949).

37. J. M. Silcock, H. K. Hardy and T. J. Heal. Structural Aging Characteristics of Binary Aluminum-Copper Alloys. *J. Inst. of Metals*, **82**, 239 (1953).

38. W. A. Anderson. *Precipitation from Solid Solution*, American Society for Metals (1960).

39. R. H. Brown, W. L. Fink and M. S. Hunter. Measurement of Irreversible Potentials as a Metallurgical Research Tool. *Trans. AIME*, **143**, 115 (1940).

40. E. H. Dix, Jr., R. H. Brown and W. W. Binger. *ASM Metals Handbook*, 8th Ed., **1**, 916.

41. M. S. Hunter, G. R. Frank and D. L. Robinson. Mechanism of Corrosion of 2024 Alloy as Revealed by Electron Microscopy. *Proceedings of the Second International Congress on Metallic Corrosion*, National Association of Corrosion Engineers, p. 102 (1963).

42. E. H. Dix, Jr. Thermal Treatment of Aluminum Alloys. *Physical Metallurgy of Aluminum Alloys*, published in 1949 by the American Society for Metals, p. 200.

43. Sara J. Ketcham and F. H. Haynie. Electrochemical Behavior of Aluminum Alloys Susceptible to Intergranular Corrosion I—Effect of Cooling Rate on Structure and Electrochemical Behavior in 2024 Aluminum Alloy. *Corrosion*, **19**, 7, 242t (1963).

44. Sara J. Ketcham. Polarization and Stress Corrosion Studies of

an Al-Cu-Mg Alloy. *Corrosion Science*, 7, 6, 305 (1967).

45. B. W. Lifka. Unpublished work at Alcoa Research Laboratories (1961).

46. J. D. Walsh. Unpublished work at Alcoa Research Laboratories (1959).

47. G. R. Frank, Jr. and D. L. Robinson. Unpublished work at Alcoa Research Laboratories (1961).

48. H. C. Stumpf. Unpublished work at Alcoa Research Laboratories (1961).

49. W. D. Robertson. Correlation of Mechanical Properties and Corrosion Resistance of 24S-Type Aluminum Alloys as Affected by High Temperature Precipitation. *Trans. AIME*, 166, 216 (1945).

50. J. A. Nock, Jr. Reheating of 24S and 75S Aluminum Sheet. *Iron Age*, (1947) December.

51. E. H. Dix, Jr., F. Keller and R. W. Graham. Equilibrium Relations in Aluminum-Magnesium-Silicide Alloy of High Purity. *Trans. AIME*, 93, 404 (1931).

52. G. Thomas. The Aging Characteristics of Aluminum Alloys, Electron Transmission Studies of Al-Mg-Si Alloys. *J. Inst. of Metals*, 90, 57 (1961-62).

53. R. Chadwick, N. B. Muir and H. B. Grainger. The Effect of Iron, Manganese and Chromium on the Properties in Sheet Form of Aluminum Alloys Containing 0.7% Mg and 1.0% Si. *J. Inst. of Metals*, 82, 75 (1953-54).

54. *Gmelins Handbuch der anorganischen Chemie*, 8. Auflage, 393 (1942).

55. F. Booth. The Corrosion Resistance of Aluminum-Magnesium-Silicon Alloys. *Aluminum*, 38, 213 (1962).

56. Ernst Murrmann. U. S. Patent 684,707, October 15, 1901.

57. W. Sander and K. L. Meissner. Der Einfluss der Verbindung MgZn$_2$ und die Vergutbarkeit von Aluminum Legierungen. *Z. Anorg. Chem.*, 154, 144 (1926).

58. William Guertler and Wilhelm Sander. U.S. Patent 1,629,699, May 24, 1929.

59. L. J. Weber. U.S. Patent 1,924,729, August 29, 1933 (Alcoa).

60. W. L. Fink and L. A. Willey. Equilibrium Relations in Al-Mg-Zn Alloys of High Purity. *Trans, AIME*, 124, 78 (1937).

61. J. A. Nock, Jr. U.S. Patent 2,240,940, May 6, 1941 (Alcoa).

62. J. A. Nock, Jr. Alcoa's New High Strength Aluminum Alloy. *Metals and Alloys*, 20, 922 (1944).

63. F. Keller. Metallography of Alcoa 75S Alloy. *Iron Age*, (1945) October 4.

64. W. L. Fink, J. A. Nock, Jr. and M. A. Hobbs. Aging of 75S Aluminum Alloy. *Iron Age* (1945) November 1.

65. E. H. Dix, Jr. New Developments in High Strength Aluminum Alloy Products. *Trans. ASM*, 35, 130 (1945).

66. W. L. Fink and L. A. Willey. Quenching of 75S Aluminum Alloy. *Metals Technology*, American Institute of Mining and Metallurgical Engineers, 14, 5, (1947) August.

67. E. H. Dix, Jr. Aluminum-Zinc-Magnesium Alloys, Their Development and Commercial Production. (1949 Edward de Mille Compbell Memorial Lecture). *Trans. ASM*, 42, 1057 (1950).

68. Wilhelm Rosenkranz. U.S. Patent 2,823,994, February 18, 1958 (Otto Fuchs).

69. D. James. The Use of High Strength Aluminum Alloys. *J. Royal Aeronautical Society*, 70, 763 (1966).

70. D. O. Sprowls and J. A. Nock, Jr. U.S. Patent 3,198,676, August 3, 1965 (Alcoa).

71. P. L. Mehr, E. H. Spuhler and L. W. Mayer. Alcoa Alloy 7075-T73. *Alcoa Green Letter No. 206*, Revised August, 1965.

72. H. Y. Hunsicker. *Aluminum*. (Kent R. Van Horn, ed.) 1, 125, American Society for Metals (1967).

73. I. J. Polmear and P. S. Young. The Aging Characteristics of Two Commercial Alloys Based on the Al-Zn-Mg System. *J. Inst. of Metals*, 87, 65 (1958-59).

74. H. C. Stumpf. Unpublished work at Alcoa Research Laboratories (1963).

75. D. L. Robinson and M. S. Hunter. Unpublished work at Alcoa Research Laboratories (1962).

76. I. J. Polmear. The Properties of Commercial Al-Zn-Mg Alloys—Practical Implications of Trace Additions of Silver. *J. Inst. of Metals*, 89, 193 (1960-61).

77. J. T. Vietz, K. R. Sargent and I. J. Polmear. The Influence of Small Additions of Silver on the Aging of Aluminum Alloys: Further Observations on Al-Zn-Mg Alloys. *J. Inst. of Metals*, 92, 327 (1963-64).

78. R. Chadwick, N. B. Muir and H. B. Grainger. Stress Corrosion of Wrought Ternary and Complex Alloys of the Al-Zn-Mg System. *J. Inst. of Metals*, 85, 161 (1956-57).

79. W. M. Doyle and R. G. Jones. The Atmospheric Stress Corrosion Resistance of Some Forged High Strength Aluminum Alloys and an Assessment of the Effects of a Step Quench into Molten Salt. *The Aeronautical Quarterly*, Vol. X, 297 (1959).

80. G. Meikle. Further Experiments on the Atmospheric Stress Corrosion of Aluminum Alloys. Unpublished Ministry of Aviation Report No. Met-Phys 96 (1960) June.

81. E. DiRusso. Resistance to Stress Corrosion and Structural Characteristics of Al-Zn-Mg-Cu Alloys with Controlled Amounts of Chromium, Zirconium and Silver. *Aluminio*, Neuva Metallurgia, Vol. XXXIV, 331 (1965).

82. J. T. Staley and J. P. Lyle, Jr. Unpublished work at Alcoa Research Laboratories (1967).

83. G. Thomas. The Improvement in Stress Corrosion Resistance of Aluminum DTD 687 Alloys. *J. Inst. of Metals*, 89, 287 (1960-61).

84. E. G. Haney, R. V. Milton and D. L. Robinson. Unpublished work at Alcoa Research Laboratories (1960).

85. W. Gruhl. Electron Fractrographic Studies on Stress Corrosion Cracking Samples of AlZnMg3. *Aluminum*, 38, 775 (1962).

86. Wolfgang Gruhl and Hildegard Cordier. The Aging State and Stress Corrosion Cracking Behavior of AlZnMg3. *Z. Metallkunde*, 55, 10, 577 (1964).

87. W. D. Vernam and M. B. Shumaker. Unpublished work at Alcoa Research Laboratories (1967).

88. A. J. Jacobs. The Effect of Explosive Deformation on the Stress Corrosion and Mechanical Properties of 7075 Aluminum Alloy. AIAA/ASME Seventh Structures and Materials Conference, Cocoa Beach, Florida, April 18-20, 1966 (Contract NAS 7-162).

89. A. J. Jacobs. Study of Stress Corrosion Cracking of Aluminum Alloys. Final Report, May, 1967, prepared under Contract NOw 66-0390d for the Naval Air Systems Command, Department of the Navy.

90. H. A. Holl. Deformation Substructure and Susceptibility to Intergranular Stress Corrosion Cracking in an Aluminum Alloy. *Corrosion*, 23, 6, 173 (1967).

91. D. L. Robinson, B. W. Lifka and M. B. Shumaker. Unpublished work at Alcoa Research Laboratories (1966).

92. M. B. Shumaker, W. D. Vernam. Unpublished work at Alcoa Research Laboratories (1962). Effect of Quenching on Al-Zn-Mg Alloys.

93. W. D. Vernam and W. A. Anderson. U.S. Patent 3,171,760, March 2, 1965 (Alcoa).

94. B. W. Lifka and D. O. Sprowls. *Aluminum*, (Kent R. Van Horn, ed.) 1, 141, American Society for Metals (1967).

95. M. S. Hunter, G. R. Frank and D. L. Robinson. Unpublished work at Alcoa Research Laboratories (1963).

96. R. H. Brown. Unpublished work at Alcoa Research Laboratories (1938).

97. A. J. Martin. Stress Corrosion of an Aluminum Alloy. *Metal Industry*, 21, 511-515 (1956) December; 28, 531, 532, 540 (1956) December.

98. D. Adenis, R. Develay and A. Guilhaudis. Effect of a Stage-Treatment Tempering Process on the Mechanical Properties, the Structure and the Corrosion Resistance of A-Z5GU.

Unpublished Report by the Pechiney Co., Research Laboratory of Voreppe, April 3, 1967.

99. M. S. Hunter and R. H. Brown. Unpublished work at Alcoa Research Laboratories (1938).

100. G. R. Frank and M. S. Hunter. Unpublished work at Alcoa Research Laboratories (1965).

101. G. C. English and E. H. Hollingsworth. Investigation of the Mechanism of Stress Corrosion of Aluminum Alloys. U.S. Navy, Bureau of Naval Weapons Contract NOw 64-0170c, Final Report (1965).

102. J. McHardy and E. H. Hollingsworth. Investigation of the Mechanism of Stress Corrosion of Aluminum Alloys, U.S. Navy, Bureau of Naval Weapons Contract NOw 65-0327f, Final Report (1966).

103. W. Gruhl and H. Cordier, Written Discussion. *Trans. ASM*, **56**, 951 (1963).

104. W. Gruhl. Der Einfluss der Korrosionsbedingungen auf das SpanungriBKorrosionsberhalten von Al-Zn-Mg3. *Metall*, **17**, 197 (1963).

105. G. F. Sager, R. H. Brown and R. B. Mears. Tests for Determining Susceptibility to Stress Corrosion Cracking. *Symposium on Stress Corrosion Cracking of Metals,* Published jointly by ASTM and AIME, p. 255 (1944).

106. W. Rosenkranz. The Development of a High Strength Stress Corrosion Resistant Alloy of the Al-Zn-Mg Type. *Aluminum,* **39**, 290, Part I, 12, 741 (Part II) and 10, 630 (Part III) (1963).

107. B. W. Lifka and D. O. Sprowls. Stress Corrosion Testing of Aluminum Alloy 7079-T6 in Various Environments. *STP 425, Symposium on Stress Corrosion Testing,* published by ASTM (1967).

108. W. Helfrich. Development of a Rapid Stress Corrosion Test for Aluminum Alloys. Annual Summary Report, March 15, 1967, for Contract NAS 8-20286, sponsored by NASA, George C. Marshall Space Flight Center, Huntsville, Alabama.

109. M. B. Shumaker. Unpublished work at Alcoa Research Laboratories (1967).

110. W. Gruhl. The Temperature Dependence of the Stress Corrosion Cracking of AlZnMg3. *Z. Metallkunde,* **53**, 670 (1962).

111. W. Helfrich. Influence of Stress and Temperature on Short Transverse Stress Corrosion Cracking of Al-4.2% Zn-2.5% Mg Alloy. *STP 425, Symposium on Stress Corrosion Testing,* published by ASTM (1967).

112. H. B. Romans and H. L. Craig. Factors Affecting the Rate of Stress Corrosion Cracking in an Al-Zn-Mg Alloy. *STP 425, Symposium on Stress Corrosion Testing,* published by ASTM (1967).

113. W. D. Robertson and A. S. Tetelman. A Unified Mechanism for Intergranular and Transgranular Corrosion Cracking. *Strengthening Mechanisms in Solids,* published by the American Society for Metals, p. 217 (1962).

114. E. N. Pugh and W. R. D. Jones. The Mechanism of Stress Corrosion in a High Purity Al-Zn-Mg Alloy. *Metallurgia,* **63**, 3 (1961).

115. T. P. Hoar. Stress Corrosion Cracking, Plenary Lecture. *Proceedings Second International Congress on Metallic Corrosion, 1963.* National Association of Corrosion Engineers, Houston, Texas, p. 14.

116. T. P. Hoar. Stress Corrosion Cracking of Austenitic Stainless Steels in Aqueous Chloride Solutions. *Stress Corrosion Cracking and Embrittlement,* John Wiley and Sons, p. 107 (1956).

117. J. G. Hines. Development of Stress Corrosion Cracking in Austenitic Cr-Ni Steels. *Corrosion Science,* **1**, 1, 2 (1961).

118. J. G. Hines. On the Propagating of Stress Corrosion Cracks in Metals. *Corrosion Science,* **1**, 1, 21 (1961).

119. H. L. Logan. Film-Rupture Mechanism of Stress Corrosion. *Journal of Research of the National Bureau of Standards,* **48**, 2, 99 (1952).

120. U. R. Evans. *The Corrosion and Oxidation of Metals,* Edward Arnold, London, p. 691 (1960).

121. W. Gruhl. The Stress Corrosion Behavior of High Strength Aluminum Alloys. *Metall,* **19**, 3, 206 (1965).

122. C. B. Criner. U.S. Patent 3,253,965, May, 1966 (Alcoa).

123. M. S. Hunter. Study of Crack Initiation Phenomena Associated with Stress Corrosion of Aluminum Alloys. One Year Summary Report (1967), for Contract NAS 8-20396, sponsored by NASA, George C. Marshall Space Flight Center, Huntsville, Alabama.

124. B. W. Lifka. Unpublished work at Alcoa Research Laboratories (1967).

125. F. H. Haynie, D. A. Vaughan, D. I. Phalen, W. K. Boyd and P. D. Frost. A Fundamental Investigation of the Nature of Stress Corrosion Cracking in Aluminum Alloys. Technical Report AFML-TR-66-267, January, 1967, Contract AF 33(6150-171), sponsored by the U.S. Air Force Materials Laboratory, Wright-Patterson Air Force Base, Ohio.

126. U. R. Evans. On the Mechanism of Chemical Cracking. *Stress Corrosion Cracking and Embrittlement,* John Wiley and Sons, p. 158 (1956).

# Discussion

**H. H. Uhlig, MIT:**

With respect to adsorption, you mentioned that you found no specific ion which will cause cracking. I remember the data of Wassermann[1] who indicated that water alone can specifically cause stress cracking of the aluminum-zinc alloys. When stressed in presence of water vapor, they cracked very quickly. If they were stressed in vacuum, they also cracked, but in this case he showed it was a small amount of water in the oxide film which caused the failure. If the alloys were carefully dried to remove surface moisture and then placed in vacuum, the alloys did not crack but remained ductile. I would submit, therefore, that water is a specific substance in this case, probably adsorbing along certain active slip planes or perhaps grain boundaries causing cracking. I might also add that it is difficult to see how the action of a trace of water produces cracking by an electrochemical mechanism. Perhaps you can comment on this.

1. G. Wassermann. *Z. Metallkunde,* **34**, 297 (1942). See also E. Perryman. *Stress Corrosion Cracking and Embrittlement.* W. Robertson, Ed., p. 76, John Wiley & Sons, Inc., New York (1956).

**D. O. Sprowls and R. H. Brown:**

In addition to Wasserman's experiment with an Al-Zn alloy stress corrosion cracking in water vapor, Dix earlier reported[1] a somewhat similar experiment performed with a sensitized Al-10% Mg alloy. Indeed, we have never doubted that water might be an essential component of an environment that causes stress corrosion cracking of aluminum alloys and we do not know of any exception. In Dix's experiment and in other instances of specimens of Al-Zn-Mg alloys that have stress corrosion cracked in indoor atmospheric environments, there seems to be no visible evidence of corrosion associated with the failure. It is important to recognize that with the minute distances between sites of anodic (oxidation) and cathodic (reduction) reactions (of the order of 0.01 micron), the oxidation-reduction processes can occur as a result of classical electrochemical reactions. The fact that altering the potential of the metal surface by some means can materially affect the rates of these anodic and cathodic reactions in liquids of low electrical conductivity, indicates that electrochemical mechanisms are operative.

1. E. H. Dix, Jr. Acceleration of the Rate of Corrosion by High Constant Stresses. *Trans. AIME*, **137**, 11 (1940).

### T. P. Hoar, University of Cambridge:

An important consideration in attempting to devise a unifying theory for stress corrosion cracking is the fact that both aluminum and magnesium are very base materials. Once the protective film has been broken the metal atoms will certainly go into solution. While adsorption processes unquestionably occur, the penetration from this rapid dissolution would seem to be so rapid as to make bond breaking due to adsorption an insignificant process.

### D. O. Sprowls and R. H. Brown:

**Even though a unifying theory seems desirable, it is most important to recognize a basic theory which is specific enough that detailed mechanisms can be established for individual alloy systems. A generalized theory can be so broad that it is of little help in solving stress corrosion problems or in creating stress corrosion resistant alloys. Indeed, several of the proposals that can be found in the literature appear to be rationalizations of particular mechanisms and have not been of much help even in pointing the way to solving problems with stress corrosion cracking.**

### D. S. Thompson, Reynolds Metals Co.:

Little is still known of the distribution of Cu within the matrix and grain boundary regions. Could not the electrochemistry of 7075-T6 and T73 be governed by the distribution of Cu? How much do we know about the Cu content of grain boundary precipitates and the precipitate free zone?

### D. O. Sprowls and R. H. Brown:

**We believe that the electrochemistry of 7075-T6 and T73 is very definitely governed by the distribution of copper in the grain boundary precipitates, the precipitate-free region in the grain margins and the matrix in general. Unfortunately, there seems to be no quantitative information available to date. However, useful information regarding the composition of solid solutions can be obtained by potential measurements, as discussed briefly in the paper.**

**H. C. Stumpf recently presented**[1] **the results of some of his research at the Alcoa Research Laboratories on the composition of precipitate phases in Al-Zn-Mg-Cu alloys. The composition of the M and T phases can vary as a result of the substitution of copper and aluminum atoms of zinc, and the formulas for these phases therefore might best be designated as** $Mg(Al,Cu,Zn)_2$ **and** $Mg_3(Al,Cu,Zn)_5$,

respectively. The electrochemical potentials of the phases also will vary with composition changes.

Stumpf suggests that zones and coherent precipitates in Al-Zn-Mg-Cu alloys such as 7075 probably are close to $MgZn_2$ with some Cu substituting for Zn. The first M-phase with a measurable diffraction pattern that appears upon aging 7075 alloy at 350 F beyond the maximum strength at that temperature has parameters indicating very low Al-content, and is apparently $MgZn_2$ with Cu substituting for some of the Zn. On the other hand, M-phase precipitating in 7075 alloy during a slow quench has much higher Al and Cu content, and has parameters, and hence composition, approximating that of M-phase in equilibrium with the matrix at about 650 F.

1. H. C. Stumpf. Precipitate Phases in Al-Zn-Mg-Cu Alloys, presented at the Annual Meeting of AIME in Cleveland, Ohio, October 16, 1967.

### H. L. Craig, Jr., Reynolds Metals Co.:

I would like to compliment Sprowls and Brown on their paper, which in my opinion is a fair, thoroughly competent and comprehensive coverage of the state-of-the-art as it exists today. In support of the data they offered in regard to electrochemical factors, we would like to present the results of a similar series of experiments.[1] The usefulness of our experiments is that they were performed on a copper-free aluminum-zinc-magnesium alloy (7039). Thus this demonstrates directly the electrochemical nature of the process in the alloy system studied by Gruhl (Sprowls and Brown, Reference 103) in which he suggests the electrochemical mechanism does not operate. Using C-ring specimens and the boiling 1 N sodium chloride solution described in Reference 100, essentially the same curve was obtained for 7039-T63 alloy as English and McHardy (Reference 101 and 102) obtained for 7075-T6. A protected region from -1.52 to -1.65 volts (SCE) where no stress corrosion cracking occurred was found. This region was the same width (0.13 volts) but displaced 0.2 volts more negative than was found for 7075. This displacement can be attributed to many things, among them, the alloy, temperature, and environmental differences.

One important phenomenon was observed, which is unexplained to us, as yet. At potential values more negative than the protected potential, stress corrosion cracking was found to occur. The exposure times were too short (1 hour) to cause loss of cross sectional area by alkaline attack (cathodic corrosion) and the failure was found to be intergranular, by metallographic examination.

Two ancillary measurements were made. First, the surviving protected samples were continued on test after the protective potential was shut off. The corrosion potential was monitored. This potential fell from the set potential, by an exponential decay. These specimens failed at roughly -1.1 to -1.3 volts (the normal corrosion potential) in about the same elapsed time (100 to 700

---

[1] Performed by D. R. Geisler, Reynolds Metals Company.

seconds) as unprotected specimens. However, the more negative the set potential was, the more negative was the corrosion potential at the time of failure.

The second set of measurements was the pH of the bulk solution (the boiling provides good stirring and mixing during the test) at the end of the test. The solution was initially at a pH of 7.6 but this value increased to a maximum of 10.4 for a sample held at -1.6 V and fell to 8.1 for a sample held at -1.9 V. This behavior suggests a change in electrode reaction in the range of -1.5 to -1.65, and another reaction taking over from -1.65 to -1.9. These observations support Sprowls and Brown's generalization that the tendency of aluminum alloys toward stress corrosion cracking is reduced in alkaline solution. However, we suggest that this alkalinity is beneficial *because* it reduces the potential differences between local anodic and cathodic regions on the metal surface, and at the expense of an increased corrosion rate overall. We disagree with the interpretation of the results shown in Figure 40. Our tests indicate that unless the pH is maintained by vigorous stirring, or else by electrochemical reaction at the metal surface, then the reaction of the metal with the alkaline solution reduces the pH of the diffusion layer immediately adjacent to the metal surface to a range where stress corrosion cracking can occur.

With aluminum, the only way cathodic protection can prevent anodic dissolution is to maintain the local pH in the range from about 4 to 9, by an appropriate electrochemical reaction, so that the protective oxide film is chemically unattacked and practically insoluble.

### D. O. Sprowls and R. H. Brown:

**We thank Dr. Craig for his kind remarks and for mentioning the results of their very interesting cathodic protection experiment using still another type of alloy (Al-Zn-Mg). We concur with the suggestion that the formation of films of aluminum alloys corroding in alkaline solutions can give rise to variable local surface pH effects depending upon specific conditions of test.**

**Unfortunately it is often only at the beginning of a test that the potential measured of a corroding specimen has significance. For instance, if the corrosion results in the formation of localized fissures, the difficulty in placing the tip of the reference electrode sufficiently far down into the crevice to obtain the true potential of the corroding anode at the base of the fissure can lead to false interpretations of the potential measurements.**

### H. L. Logan, National Bureau of Standards:

I wish to point out the fact that it is necessary to cool the 2024 aluminum alloy very rapidly from the solution heat treating temperature to some temperature below 250 C to make it immune to intercrystalline corrosion whether or not it is stressed.

The solution heat treating temperature was 493 ± 5 C. We reported[1] that it was necessary to quench the material through the range of 400 C to approximately 125 C at a rate of 260 to 395 C per second (depending upon the copper content of the alloy) to make it resistant to severe

intercrystalline corrosion. Much higher quenching rates were necessary to make it immune to all intercrystalline corrosion. These data were obtained with 0.040 inch sheet. It is, of course, not possible to obtain such quenching rates with thick sheet or plate.

1. Journal of Research of the NBS, **26**, p. 321, R.P. 1378 (1941).

### D. O. Sprowls and R. H. Brown:

**We thank Dr. Logan for calling attention to this early work done at the National Bureau of Standards on the effect of quenching rate on the susceptibility of 2024 alloy to intercrystalline corrosion. The results obtained by Dr. Logan are in substantial agreement with results obtained at the Alcoa Research Laboratories by Dix and Willey at about that same time.**

### S. B. Brummer, Tyco Laboratories, Inc.:

As I understand it you are saying that the variation in stress corrosion susceptibility of the Al-Cu system with heat treatment results from the presence or otherwise of a depleted zone along the grain boundary. The implication is that this depleted zone is less noble than the matrix and provides a continuous path in some alloys where corrosive attack can occur—this being the path of the stress corrosion failure.

We[1] have found that for Al-4 Cu aged at 200 C and rapidly quenched (these are thin foils for use in transmission microscopy and they are cold water quenched) the depleted zone is present virtually from the beginning of the age-hardening process. The only difference, as the aging continues, in the grain boundaries is some growth of the precipitate particles lodged there and some widening of the depleted zone. Crucially, we find that in all circumstances for this material in sodium chloride solutions there is continuous intergranular attack.[2] This is true of the solutionized material and continues through the over aged condition. The only differences with respect to aging appear to be the rates of grain boundary attack. These appear to become more and more rapid as we increase the aging time.

It seems to me that such observations tend to rule out the Dix theory of stress corrosion for these materials. It may be that susceptibility to intergranular attack is necessary, but our results seem to indicate that it is not sufficient.

1. F. H. Cocks and S. B. Brummer. *Third Quarterly Report by Tyco Laboratories, Inc.* to NASA, Huntsville, Alabama on Contract NAS 8-20297, March (1967).
2. F. H. Cocks and S. B. Brummer. *Fourth Quarterly Report by Tyco Laboratories, Inc.* to NASA, Huntsville, Alabama on Contract NAS 8-20297, September (1967).

### D. O. Sprowls and R. H. Brown:

**The well established electrochemical mechanism of intergranular corrosion in an Al-4 Cu alloy (and other similar alloys) is described in detail in Figure 20. This schematic arrangement was drawn prior to the general use of the electron microscope on the basis of very early work**

of Brown and Dix from which Figures 17 and 19 were obtained. The relatively recent electron microscopic examination of corroded thin metal specimens by Hunter et al (Figure 21) and by Dr. Brummer et al has beautifully demonstrated the operation of the mechanism.

The effect of artificial aging of a high purity Al-4 Cu alloy upon the grain boundary condition is shown in Figure 19. The effect of initial aging is to produce a difference in potential between grain margins and grain bodies. Further aging increases this difference to a maximum after which more extended aging reduces the difference to insignificance. For a high purity Al-4 Cu alloy it takes about 30-32 hr heating at 375 F (Figure 19) to eliminate this potential difference. If Dr. Brummer had carried his aging experiment at 392 F (200 C) beyond an 8 hr period, he would have been able to observe a change in type of attack from intergranular to pitting, just as Hunter did (Figure 22) with alloy 2024.

**M. J. Pryor, Olin Mathieson Chemical Corp.:**

Before closing this discussion I would like to make one comment on Dr. Sprowls review paper. Several years ago we determined the corrosion rate of massive $\beta$ phase in sodium chloride solutions adjusted to different pH values. In nearly neutral sodium chloride solution the $\beta$ phase corroded at a high rate with vigorous hydrogen evolution whereas in strongly alkaline solution the $\beta$ phase was passive. We then coupled $\beta$ phase to a very large area of aluminum-5% magnesium solid solution, (approximately 500 times larger than the estimated area of the $\beta$ phase) measured the galvanic current and redetermined the weight loss of the $\beta$ phase. Although the $\beta$ phase certainly was quite strongly anodic to the aluminum-magnesium solid solution, the flow of galvanic current accounted for somewhat less than 5% of the total corrosion of the $\beta$ phase anode. The remaining and more important corrosion of the $\beta$ phase was clearly due to direct dissolution in the nearly neutral sodium chloride electrolyte. It appeared to us that the *primary* method by which the $\beta$ phase corroded was direct solution in the nearly neutral electrolyte with the galvanic effects being second order in nature. Experiments in which susceptible aluminum-magnesium alloys have been cathodically protected in sodium chloride solution can be equally well explained by a local rise in pH in an unbuffered solution combined with the very high pH sensitivity of the direct dissolution rate of the $\beta$ phase.

**D. O. Sprowls and R. H. Brown:**

The importance of high alkalinity in changing the difference in potential between an Al-Mg solid solution and $Mg_2 Al_3$, of course, is well known (Figure 12). Cook's experiment demonstrating prevention of stress corrosion cracking of a sensitized Al-5.25 Mg-0.8 Mn-0.1 Cr alloy (X5456-H14) by cathodic protection with an anode of $Mg_2 Al_3$ (Figure 13), however, was carefully controlled to avoid creating high alkalinity. The specimens were exposed in a continuously stirred solution into which oxygen was constantly being diffused, and the pH was maintained at

5.8-6.0 throughout the experiment with an automatic titrator. The possibility of a local rise in pH on the specimen surface was checked by periodic measurement of the potential of the couple and the open circuit potential of the stressed specimen. Moreover, when a piece of $Mg_2 Al_3$ was exposed in the solution with an uncoupled specimen with the same spatial arrangement as with the coupled specimen, the uncoupled specimen failed within a 2 to 3 day exposure.

In a preliminary experiment, a relatively large piece of $Mg_2 Al_3$ was placed only 2 to 7 mm from an uncoupled specimen but the pH of the oxygenated solution was not controlled. The open circuit potential of the uncoupled specimen shifted about 350 mv in the anodic direction to the same potential as that of the corroding $Mg_2 Al_3$ and the specimen did not fail. The anodic shift in potential and the survival of the specimen after 19 days was attributed to high local alkalinity produced by the corroding $Mg_2 Al_3$; the bulk pH of the solution increased from 5.5 to 6.5-6.9 where it remained. However, when saturated ammonium chloride solution with a pH of 4.6 was substituted for 3.5% sodium chloride, and the other conditions kept the same, an uncoupled specimen failed in 1.5 hours. The open circuit potential of a coupled specimen had not changed appreciably when the specimen was removed from test unbroken after 14 days, indicating no appreciable local rise in alkalinity although the bulk pH had increased to about 6.

The open circuit potential of the coupled specimen mentioned in the paper showed an anodic shift of only 100 mv from the potential of the uncoupled specimen compared to the 300 mv shift from the uncoupled specimen to the couple potential. Therefore, it was concluded that: (1) there was no large increase in local alkalinity on the surface of the specimen because of the flow of galvanic current, and that (2) the coupled specimen was protected because it was polarized to a potential where the difference in potential between the continuous precipitate in the grain boundaries and the grain bodies became insignificant.

## The Stress Corrosion Cracking of 7075-T6 Aluminum Alloy in Organic Liquids

H. W. Paxton and R. P. M. Procter
Carnegie-Mellon University

In yesterdays session Phelps[1] mentioned some results of Steigerwald demonstrating stress corrosion of a high-strength steel in various organic environments; tomorrow Pugh et al[2] and Brown and Sandoz[3] will discuss the stress corrosion of titanium alloys in organic liquids. In view of this it seems timely and relevant to this session to present some results showing stress corrosion cracking of an aluminum alloy in a number of organic media.

The stress corrosion of drawn bar-flats of commercial 7075-T6 aluminum alloy in various organic liquids has been studied, using fatigue-precracked specimens. Two specimen configurations were employed, a longitudinal specimen stressed in cantilever-bending with an RW-type crack (for an explanation of this nomenclature, see Reference 4) and a long-transverse specimen of double-cantilever-beam design with a WR-type crack. The specimen dimensions were large enough to ensure that the stress state was predominantly plane strain and in all cases the specimens were loaded initially to 60-90% of the dry-air plane-strain fracture-toughness, $K_{Ic}$, as calculated from the standard formulae.

The longitudinal specimens were exposed to fresh, reagent grade, methanol, ethanol, isopropanol and ethylene glycol. In all cases, essentially similar results were obtained, as illustrated in Figure 1; Region A is the initial fatigue-precrack, Region B shows some limited transgranular subcritical crack growth and Region C shows the final lateral spreading of intergranular stress corrosion cracks. Presumably the sequence of events resulting in this crack morphology is slow transgranular crack growth under the relatively high stress intensity until a suitable grain boundary is reached when the lateral intergranular crack growth occurs; this effectively blunts the original RW crack while the crack-opening-load on the lateral stress corrosion cracks decreases as crack growth occurs. The specimens were typically exposed for periods of about $2 \times 10^4$ minutes but it is estimated from the time/deflection curve of the loading-arm that the above sequence of events occurs in the first 4000 minutes. Figure 2 is high magnification

micrograph of the fatigue-precrack while Figure 3, by comparison, shows the transgranular stress corrosion crack at high magnification. There appears to be little doubt that some "stress corrosion" mechanism is involved; specimens exposed to ethanol without stress and specimens stressed in dry air for periods of $10^4$ mins. showed no evidence of any subcritical crack growth. Further, in the former case there were no signs of any general corrosion and the fatigue-precrack was indistinguishable from those observed in unexposed specimens.

The long-transverse specimens were exposed to reagent grade methanol, ethanol, isopropanol, acetone, carbon tetrachloride and benzene. In all cases, intergranular stress corrosion crack growth was observed but there were marked differences in the crack growth rates, ethanol and carbon tetrachloride being the most aggressive (with crack growth rates of the order of $10^{-6}$ cms/sec) and benzene the least (with a crack growth rate of the order of $10^{-7}$ cms/sec). A typical specimen fractured by overloading after being stressed for $2 \times 10^4$ minutes in methanol is shown in Figure 4; the four distinguishable regions, reading from bottom to top are the initial saw-cut, the fatigue-precrack, the region of stress corrosion crack growth and the final rapid fracture. Figure 5 shows the tip of an intergranular crack produced by the combined action of acetone and stress.

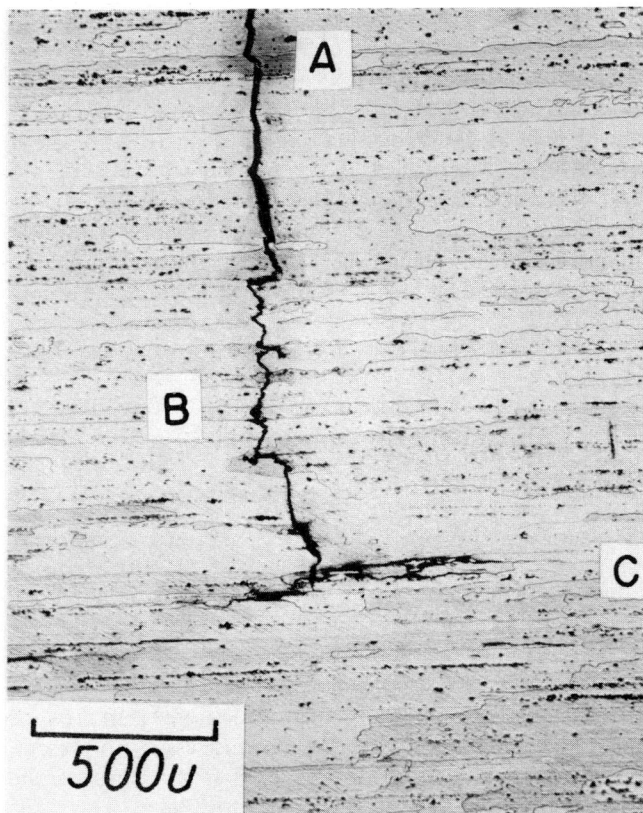

FIGURE 1 – Cracks in a longitudinal specimen of 7075-T6 stressed in cantilever bending at an initial plane strain intensity of approximately 90% of $K_{Ic}$ in reagent grade ethanol for 19,906 minutes.

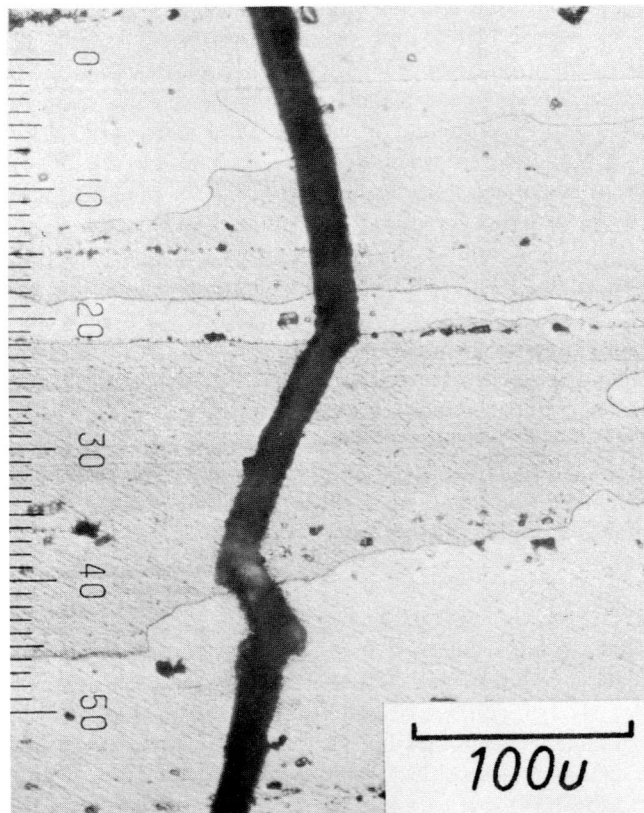

FIGURE 2 – Section of fatigue-precrack in specimen shown in Figure 1.

510

Finally we would present some evidence to show that the cracking may not be due to traces of water in the environments:

(a) Fresh, reagent grade ethanol was shaken with excess calcium oxide and then immediately sealed in the environment chamber around a longitudinal specimen; stressing produced the crack growth described above.

(b) Carbon tetrachloride, one of the most aggressive environments, has the lowest affinity for water, a maximum solubility of 0.0078 w/w% at 15 C.[5]

(c) The time/deflection curve of the loading-arm of a long-transverse specimen exposed to fresh reagent grade ethanol indicated that crack growth commenced immediately the stress was applied; no significant induction period could be detected. Further, although it was estimated (from conductivity measurements) that this environment absorbed up to 2% water from the atmosphere over the test period (about 3 weeks), no significant acceleration of the crack growth rate was observed.

(d) The time/deflection curves of the loading-arm of long-transverse specimens stressed in environments of sodium-dried benzene and water-saturated benzene (0.051 w/w% at 15 C[5]) were identical for periods of up to $2 \times 10^4$ minutes.

It is considered that these results may have some commercial significance; as yet, however, it is doubtful whether they throw any further light on the mechanism of stress corrosion of aluminum alloys, as already discussed in some detail this morning.

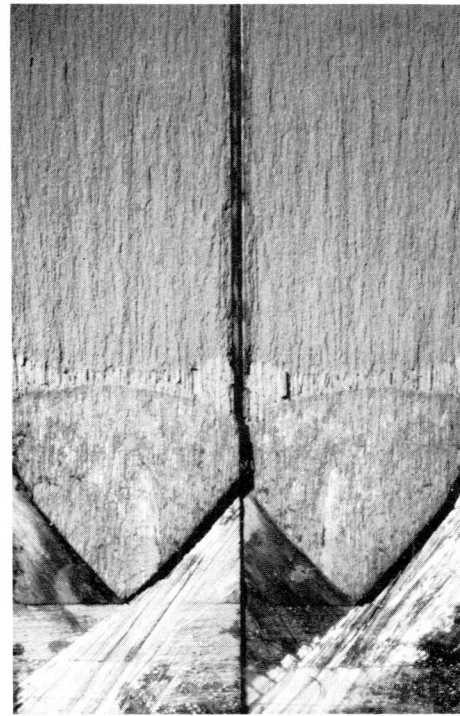

FIGURE 4 — Fracture surface of a long-transverse specimen of 7075-T6; specimen fractured by overloading after exposure to reagent methanol for 27,176 minutes at an initial plane strain stress intensity of approximately 75% of $K_{Ic}$; x 1:1 approx.

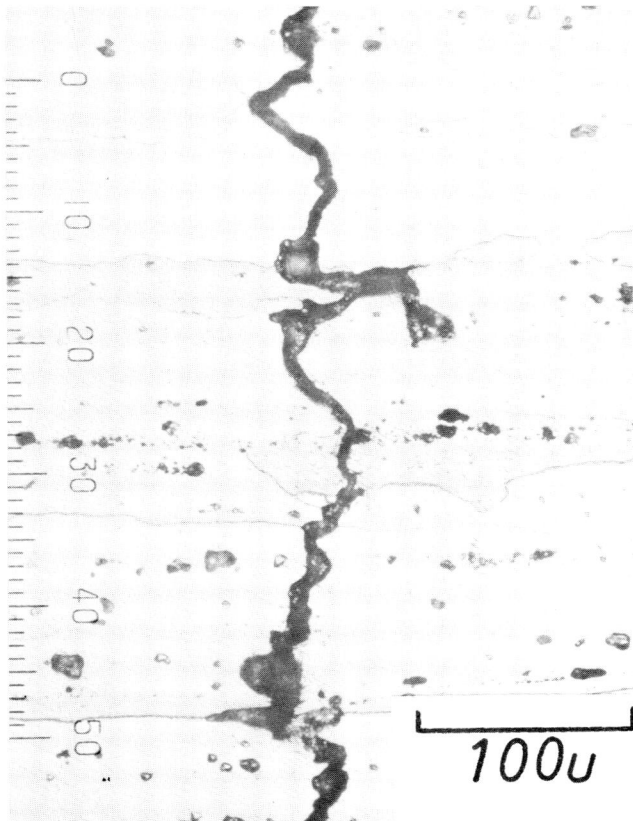

FIGURE 3 — Section of transgranular stress corrosion crack in specimen shown in Figure 1, for comparison with Figure 2

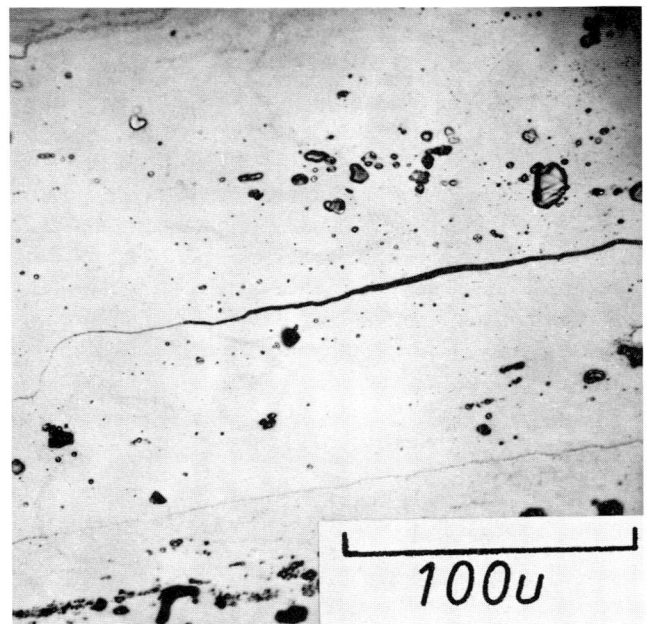

FIGURE 5 — Intergranular stress corrosion crack in a long-transverse specimen of 7075-T6 stressed in double-cantilever-bending to approximately 60% of $K_{Ic}$ in reagent acetone for 9747 minutes.

We would like to thank Sprowls and Brown for their interesting comments; the points they raise are discussed in detail in the paper "Stress-Corrosion of the Aluminum Alloy 7075-T651 in Organic Liquids" by R. P. M. Procter and H. W. Paxton, presented to the 1968 A.S.T.M. Fall Meeting held in Atlanta, Ga., and subsequently submitted to A.S.T.M. for publication.

# References

1. E. H. Phelps. A Review of the Stress Corrosion Behavior of Steels with High Yield Strength; paper presented at the Conference on Fundamental Aspects of Stress Corrosion Cracking, The Ohio State University, September, 1967.
2. A. J. Sedriks, P. W. Slattery and E. N. Pugh. Stress Corrosion Cracking of Alpha Titanium in Non-Aqueous Environments; paper presented at the Conference on Fundamental Aspects of Stress Corrosion Cracking, The Ohio State University, September, 1967.
3. B. F. Brown and G. Sandoz. Crack Propagation in High Strength Titanium Alloys in Organic Media; paper presented at the Conference on Fundamental Aspects of Stress Corrosion Cracking, The Ohio State University, September, 1967.
4. Second Report of the Special ASTM Committee on Fracture Testing of High Strength Metallic Materials. *Mat. Res. and Standards*, 1, 389 (1961).
5. C. K. Rosenbaum and J. H. Walton. The Use of Calcium Hydride for the Determination of the Solubility of Water in Benzene, Carbon Tetrachloride and Toluene. *J. Amer. Chem. Soc.*, 52, 3568 (1930).

**D. O. Sprowls and R. H. Brown:**

The results of the tests of fatigue-precracked specimens of 7075-T6 alloy bar in organic liquids, described by Dr. Procter, appear to be unprecedented, and further investigation will be required to explain them. The intergranular WR-type cracks developed in double-cantilever-beam specimens resemble typical intergranular stress corrosion cracks; however, the 0.1 to 1 mil per hour growth rates observed are markedly lower than typical growth rates for stress corrosion cracks in aqueous environments. Growth rates of about 10 to 100 mils per hour are quoted in the literature for intergranular (Al-Zn-Mg and Al-Zn-Mg-Cu alloys) and transgranular (18-8 type stainless steel) stress corrosion cracking in aqueous chloride solutions. The fact that crack growth was noted immediately in fresh ethanol may be an indication that the trace of water required to initiate a stress corrosion crack in 7075-T6 was present in the fatigue-precrack when the stress corrosion test was started. The presence of adsorbed water in the precrack could also explain the failure to show a difference in the sodium-dried and water-saturated benzene tests.

The transgranular extensions of RW-type fatigue-precracks in the longitudinal specimens are especially surprising. Stress corrosion cracks in 7075-T6 and other susceptible aluminum alloys characteristically are intergranular, and tend to follow a directional grain structure (Figures 1 and 3). Also Mulherin[1] was unable to propagate a WR-type transgranular fatigue-precrack in long transverse centilever beam of 7075-T6 and 7178-T6 immersed in 3.5% sodium chloride solution.

The meandering course and the nodular appearance of the transgranular fissure (Figure 3 of Procter) suggests a corrosion fissure rather than a crack. A possible explanation is that the strained film-free tip of the precrack corroded slowly to form directional fissures in the highly stressed (60-90% $K_{Ic}$) metal in the plane strain stress state at the crack tip. As the corrosion proceeded under the dead weight load, small concentrations of aluminum ions built up in the advancing fissure, increasing the local conductivity of the liquid. When a favorably oriented grain boundary was reached, preferential electrochemical corrosion in the grain boundaries caused lateral intergranular crack growth.

It would be interesting to determine whether the transgranular stress corrosion, and especially the lateral intergranular stress corrosion cracking in the longitudinal specimen could be prevented by cathodic protection or whether cracks could be propagated in an inert environment such as dry argon. Fractrographic examinations also might give additional clues regarding the actual mechanism of the observed phenomena.

1. J. H. Mulherin. Influence of Environment on Crack Propagation Characteristics of High Strength Aluminum Alloys. *Stress Corrosion Testing,* ASTM STP 425, Am. Society Testing Mats., p. 66 (1967).

# THE RELATIONSHIP BETWEEN STRUCTURE AND SUSCEPTIBILITY
# TO STRESS CORROSION IN ALUMINUM-MAGNESIUM ALLOYS

A. F. Beck and P. R. Sperry
Olin Mathieson Chemical Corporation

## Abstract

A detailed mechanism for the stress corrosion cracking of aluminum base alloys containing magnesium is proposed. Important features of the aging kinetics are presented and indirect evidence that there is a continuous solute depleted zone at the grain boundaries is offered. This is confirmed directly from electron metallographic examinations of the grain boundaries by means of a special technique for determining the composition of depleted zones. Concentration gradients in the solute-depleted zone are assessed. The mechanism for cracking is considered to relate to the softness of the denuded zone which in turn permits cooperative moevement of dislocations at crack tips. Removal of the second phase particles at the grain boundary by dissolution permits extension of the crack by a combined process of plastic flow and dissolution.

## I. Introduction

The non-heat-treatable wrought aluminum alloys containing magnesium as the principal alloying element form a commercially important class of alloys because of their combination of good strength, formability, weldability and corrosion resistance. However, much of the engineering potential in this alloy system cannot be realized because of increasing susceptibility to stress corrosion cracking experienced at higher magnesium contents. Alloys with less than 3% magnesium have no restrictions on their use from this standpoint.[1] Alloys with 3 to 5% magnesium can be used in the annealed condition or in some temper rolled conditions provided that the service temperature is maintained below about 90 C. Alloys with more than 5.5% magnesium can only be used in the annealed condition or with such severe restrictions that their use is hardly practical. Considerable effort has been devoted toward defining the limits of use of aluminum-magnesium alloys and toward extending the useful range of composition. Consequently, this alloy system has been the object of much research into the mechanism of stress corrosion failure and the contributing microstructural and electrochemical factors.[2-7] This paper deals primarily with one critical aspect of the microstructure which has not, heretofore, been possible to reveal, and which is believed to be essential in creating susceptibility.

The susceptibility to stress corrosion failure in Al-Mg alloys is unquestionably related to the decomposition of the supersaturated solid solution. The equilibrium solid solubility at room temperature in the pure binary alloy is less than 2% magnesium. Nevertheless, the supersaturated solid solution may remain stable for years and it is only when the magnesium content exceeds 3.5% that appreciable amounts of the second phase may become visible by microscopic examination. Alloys with substantially more than 7% Mg can easily retain nearly all magnesium in supersaturated solid solution simply by air cooling from the normal annealing temperature range. Whereas microscopically visible precipitate may take years to form at the grain boundaries of annealed material, cold working greatly accelerates the process.[1,3] The amount of cold reduction has to be quite severe before precipitate begins to appear extensively at the grain interiors. It has been shown that deformation bands, which are characterized by severe lattice reorientations analogous to those at large angle grain boundaries, are the most preferred sites for precipitation within the grains[8] and it is only when cold reduction by rolling is well in excess of 30% that more general precipitation is observed. It must be concluded, therefore, that nucleation near room temperature is very difficult to achieve[9,10] and that it occurs only where considerable three dimensional disregistry of the lattice exists. This probably follows from the unusually large unit cell of the stable $\beta$ ($Mg_2Al_3$) phase;[11] it is assumed also to relate to the metastable $\beta'$ which precipitates at or below 200 C and about which little is known.[12,13]

The growth of the precipitate is diffusion controlled but there is considerable evidence to suggest that activation energy at low temperatures is lower than that for high temperature diffusion because excess vacancies are easily trapped during cooling by coupling with the large magnesium atom.[5,14-18] The accelerating effect of cold working may be due to the creation of additional vacancies[16,19] which will promote growth in the grain boundaries, even though deformation may not be severe enough to have created new sites for nucleation within the grains.

Many attempts have been made to relate various stages of the decomposition process in alloys with up to 10% magnesium to changes detectable by X-ray diffraction, and to changes in mechanical properties.[10,12,13,20,21] These investigations were made on solution annealed material. We have attempted to apply these methods to the earliest stages of decomposition of an aluminum-7% magnesium alloy with various amounts of prior cold working. However, it was found to be completely insensitive to these bulk measurements, presumably because most of the decomposition process occurs in such a small fraction of the total volume, i.e., the grain boundary surface area multiplied by some small but finite thickness. However, some valuable clues were offered by metallographic observations and X-ray diffraction measurements which enabled us to hypothesize the existence of a continuous depleted zone of solid solution along the grain boundaries. Subsequently, a unique method was devised for proving the existence of this zone.

It is the purpose of this paper to present those data which are pertinent to the decomposition processes in aluminum-magnesium alloys with more than 4% Mg and to present evidence for the existence of a critical structural condition which leads to a high degree of stress corrosion susceptibility. Any proposed mechanism for stress corrosion cracking in Al-Mg alloys must take this into account.

## II. Experimental Procedure

The principal material used for this investigation was a high purity binary alloy of aluminum with a nominal addition of 7% by weight magnesium. Some complementary work was also carried out on a pure aluminum-4% magnesium alloy and on a commercial purity 7% Mg composition. The actual chemical analyses are given in Table 1.

The above alloys were cast by a semi-continuous direct chill process into rectangular ingots for subsequent rolling

TABLE 1–Chemical Composition of Al-Mg Alloys

| Nominal Composition | Weight % | | | |
| --- | --- | --- | --- | --- |
| | Mg | Fe | Si | Cu |
| 7% Mg – high purity | 6.99 | 0.005 | 0.001 | 0.002 |
| 4% Mg – high purity | 4.02 | 0.004 | 0.002 | 0.001 |
| 7% Mg – normal purity | 6.93 | 0.11 | 0.09 | <0.01 |

to sheet. The initial thickness and width dimensions were 2.6 and 6 inches. The rolling schedule was designed so that the material arrived at its final temper condition in the form of sheet, 0.060 inches thick and 8 inches wide. The details of processing are summarized in Table 2. Considerable care was taken to assure a high degree of homogeneity in composition and structure and to assure that individual fabricating variables could be easily isolated. The temperature of the last complete anneal, 355 C, was high enough to assure that all magnesium was dissolved. The air cooling did not produce any appreciable precipitation. Some of the cold worked samples were given a brief partial anneal of 230 C for 5 minutes to stabilize the mechanical properties against spontaneous recovery to which cold worked Al-Mg alloys are susceptible.[1,14,22]

The changes in properties associated with the decomposition process and with recovery from cold working were followed in a temperature range of 30 to 82 C, using thermostatically controlled oil baths capable of maintaining ± 0.2 C over long periods of time. Measurements were started within a few hours after cold working. Electrical resistivity measurements were made without removing specimens from the baths. Other measurements and observations were made on material periodically removed and cooled to room temperature. The samples for hardness testing were removed only long enough to make the measurement and then were replaced for further aging. Samples for metallographic and electronoptical examination and for X-ray diffraction were not returned for continued aging.

The purpose in limiting the aging temperature to a maximum of 82 C was to avoid overlapping with higher temperature kinetics believed to be associated with different activation energy. Aging periods in excess of 1-1/2 years have been studied.

The property measurements which were made in most detail were electrical resistivity and hardness but these were supplemented with periodic metallographic examination,

TABLE 2–Summary of Fabrication Procedure

| Step No. | Description |
| --- | --- |
| 1 | Blocks for rolling, approximately 9 x 6 x 2.63 inches, homogenized 16 hours at 445 C, then 4 hours at 500 C, cooled to 370 C for hot rolling. |
| 2 | Hot roll breakdown from 2.63 to 1.50 inches at 370 C. |
| 3 | Continued hot rolling from 1.50 to 0.250 inches at 425 C. |
| 4 | Alternate cold rolling (restricted to 40% reduction to avoid preferred orientation) and intermediate annealing at 425 C for 30 minutes. |
| 5 | Last full anneal, 4 hours at 355 C, air cool. |
| 6 | Last cold rolling, 15, 30, or 60% reduction in thickness, carried out within 24 hours after Step No. 5. |

electron microscope examination and lattice parameter measurement by X-ray diffraction.

Resistivity measurements were made with a precision Kelvin bridge on strips machined to a uniform width. Because the absolute resistance was fairly small and errors could creep in because of nonuniformity in cross-section and temperature fluctuations, the calculated resistivity values were reproducible to about ± 0.02 $\mu$ ohm-cm.

A variable load Brinell type hardness test was used in an attempt to detect changes in work hardening characteristics. The best mode of expression of hardness values, one which correlated fairly well with yield strength, was the logarithm of the load required to produce a Brinell impression of 1 mm diameter when using a 2.5 mm ball.

Metallographic examination was made on electrolytically polished samples and care was taken to avoid any heating of the specimens during preparation. A light etching in 10% $H_3PO_4$ enhanced the contrast between magnesium rich precipitate and the matrix, without disturbing the levelness of the electropolished surface. Consequently, phase contrast microscopy could be used for revealing fine details of structure.

X-ray diffraction was obtained from solid disc shaped sheet samples which were spun in a diffractometer. Peaks were traced for $CuK_{\alpha1}$ and $CuK_{\alpha2}$ of (422) and (333) (511) planes on annealed material. The $CuK_{\alpha1}$ and $CuK_{\alpha2}$ peaks could not always be resolved on cold worked and partially recovered material. In those cases, attention was given to the half-breadth of the combined peak and to changes in half-breadth and peak resolution during aging.

When it became obvious that there were concentration gradients in partially decomposed Al-Mg solid solutions which were confined to very small dimensions, it became necessary to develop a technique by which these gradients could be resolved by electron microscopy. It was reasoned that an anodically formed oxide replica which had an electron opacity proportional to the magnesium content of the substrate alloy would produce the required result, because the high electrical field under which the film was formed would tend to give a faithful rendering of the true breadth of adjoining zones of differing composition. The basis for such a method was described for an application to Al-Cu alloys[23] in an earlier publication by one of the authors. Details of the present method for Al-Mg alloys are given in Appendix A. The method was mainly sensitive to magnesium concentrations between 0 and 3 weight percent, which was of greatest usefulness.

## III. Results

### A. Solution Annealed Alloys

High purity or commercial purity samples that were originally in the solution annealed condition failed to show any changes in electrical resistivity or hardness for periods up to a year and a half. Furthermore, no microscopically visible precipitate appeared in any of the high purity alloys aged at 62.5 C or lower, but some grain boundary precipitate did become evident upon aging at 82 C for about 2000 hours. (See Figures 1a and 1b). The normal purity Al-7% Mg alloy showed an earlier onset and growth of visible precipitate at 82 C and 62.5 C, but otherwise it produced no effects which differed greatly from those in the high purity alloy. In agreement with other investigations,[10,12,13] the decomposition process, when confined to the grain boundaries only, did not affect a sufficient volume of the alloy to be detected by changes in hardness or conductivity. Similarly, there was no detectable decrease of lattice parameter, which might be expected to accompany a general precipitation of magnesium. On the contrary, there was strong evidence that Al-7% Mg alloy aged at 62.5 and 82 C for at least 10,000 hours had a more expanded lattice than the initial material. This was confirmed by re-annealing a sample previously aged at 82 C for 10,630 hours as shown in Table 3, whereupon the lattice parameter decreased again slightly and approached its original value. Simultaneously, symmetry and sharpness of the peak shape were restored.

### B. Cold Worked Alloys

Changes in resistivity and hardness were evident from the start of aging in cold worked materials, but in a manner which necessitated distinguishing between recovery following cold working and solid solution decomposition. There was an initial drop in resistivity of 0.04 to 0.05 $\mu$ ohm-cm for 15% cold work and of 0.09 to 0.10 $\mu$ ohm-cm for 30 and 60% cold work, regardless of aging temperature. This change was terminated within less than 400 hours and was unrelated to the appearance of grain boundary precipitate which could occur either sooner or later, depending upon degree of cold work and aging temperature. Therefore, the resistivity drop must be attributed to a stage in the recovery process. Along with this stage of recovery, there was a decrease in hardness, which differed from the resistivity in that the rate and the amount of softening were temperature dependent. Examples of these changes in high purity Al-7% Mg are given in Figures 2, 3, and 4. The scatter in data points precludes any meaningful kinetic analysis. Similar changes in resistivity and hardness have been reported by Perryman[12] on alloys with lesser magnesium contents.

One further evidence for role of recovery in these early property changes is the sharpening up of the X-ray diffraction peaks. Cold working causes the peaks to smear out with resulting lack of resolution of the $K_{\alpha1}$ and $K_{\alpha2}$ doublets. With increasing aging, the breadth at half the peak height, designated as B in Figures 2, 3, and 4 diminishes. At the aging temperature of 82 C, the doublets become resolvable again and the breadth at half height of $K_{\alpha1}$ can be measured, as indicated by the symbol, $B_{\alpha1}$. The absence of this effect in 60% cold worked material, Figure 4, is attributable to a decomposition effect as discussed below.

The initial instabilities in resistivity and hardness upon aging at 30 to 82 C were entirely absent when a stabilizing heat treatment of 230 C for 5 minutes was first applied. Again this points to recovery from cold working, although

515

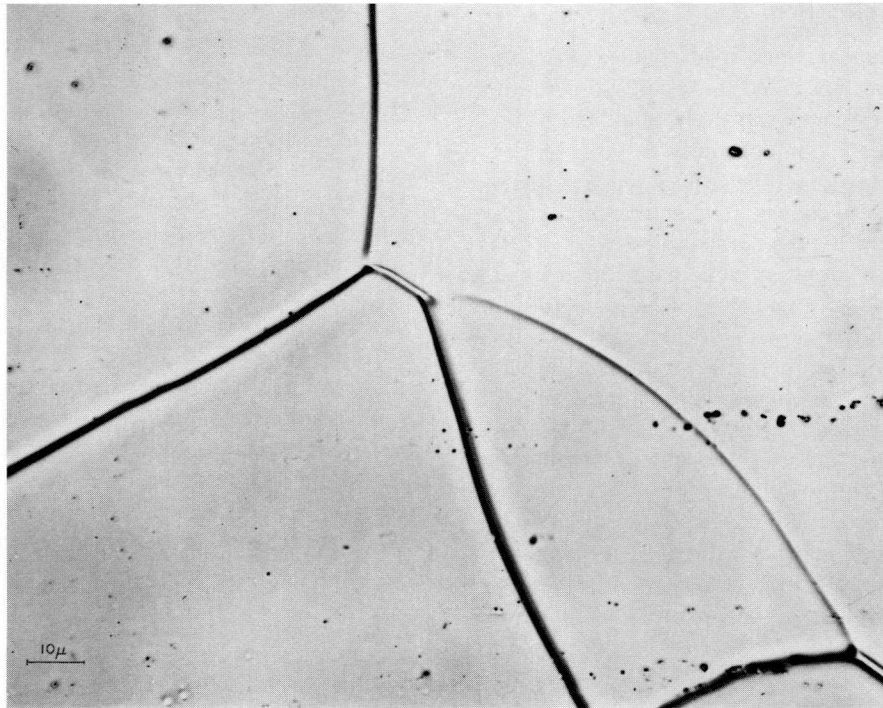

(a)

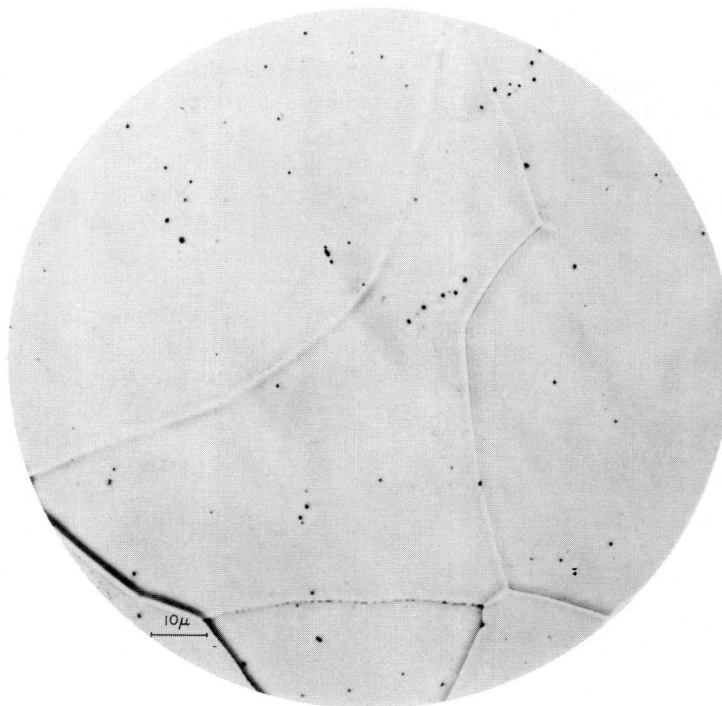

(b)

FIGURE 1 — High purity Al-7% Mg alloy, solution annealed: electropolished; etched with 10% orthophosphoric acid for 1 minute; viewed with phase contrast illumination; original magnification 750 X. (Note: dark or light spots within the grains are insoluble impurities or electropolishing defects.) (a) Aged at 62.5 C for 9600 hours, showing no change from unaged condition. (b) Aged at 82 C for 9600 hours, showing grain boundary precipitate and contrast effects which became apparent by about 2000 hours.

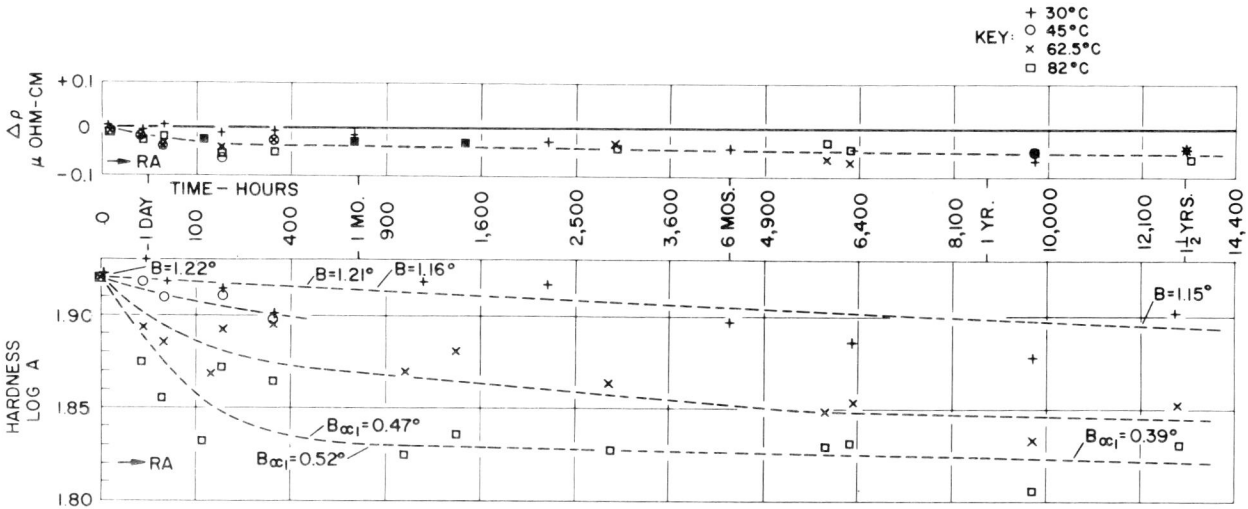

FIGURE 2 — High purity Al-7% Mg alloy, cold worked 15%, showing changes in resistivity, hardness, and X-ray diffraction line broadening during aging. "RA" denotes the level to which a recovery anneal of 230 C for 5 minutes reduced resistivity and hardness.

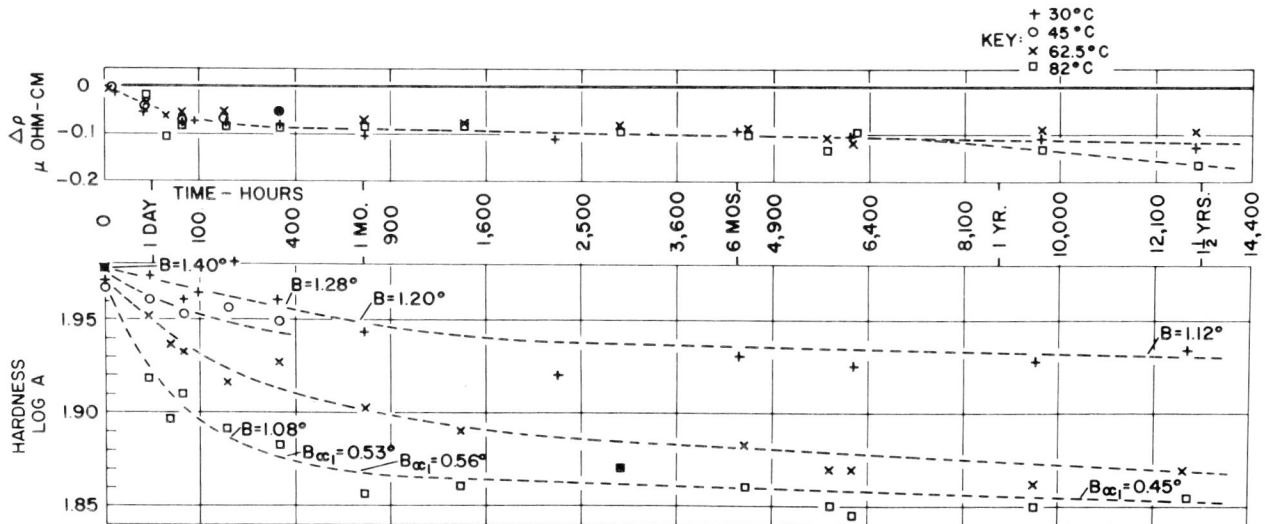

FIGURE 3 — High purity Al-7% Mg alloy, cold worked 30%, showing changes in resistivity, hardness, and X-ray diffraction line broadening during aging.

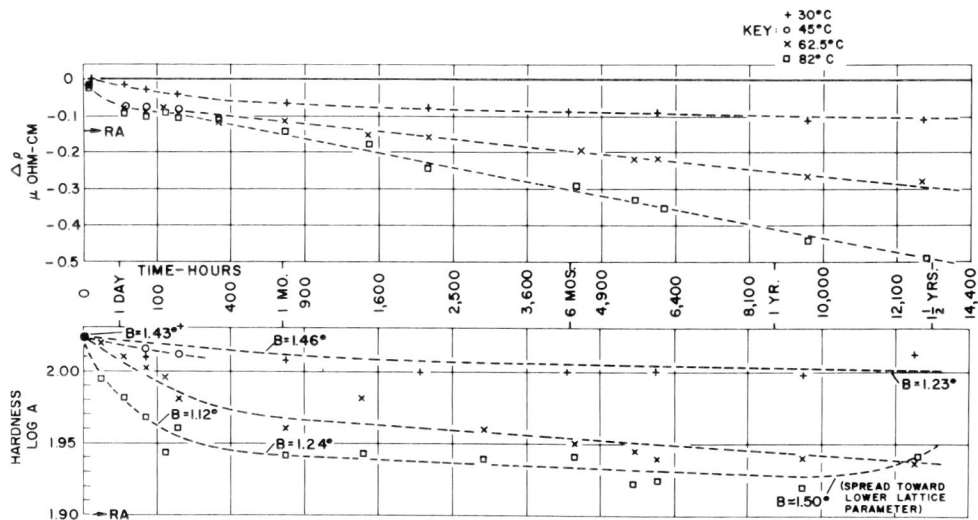

FIGURE 4 — High purity Al-7% Mg alloy, cold worked 60%, showing changes in resistivity, hardness, and X-ray diffraction line broadening during aging. "RA" has the same meaning as in Figure 2.

not without ambiguity because this treatment also initiates some visible precipitate.

Cold work definitely accelerated the decomposition of the solid solution, but initially this was only evident from metallographic examination. As little as 15% cold work caused a greater intensity of precipitate in the grain boundaries in 2200 hours at 82 C than was evident in annealed material in 9600 hours. As the amount of deformation increased to 30%, deformation or kink bands also became sites for nucleation of precipitate. With 60% cold work, slip planes were also decorated by the precipitate. Typical microstructures after extended aging at 82 C are shown in Figures 5a, 5b, and 5c. Thus, cold working not only accelerated the rate of decomposition at the most active nucleation sites, but it provided additional nucleation sites which multiplied the total volume of precipitate. Precipitate also appeared correspondingly sooner at 62.5 C. Metallographic evidence for acceleration of precipitation at 30 C was not conclusive. It should be noted that the short stabilizing heat treatment of 230 C for 5 minutes produced enough grain boundary precipitate (15% cold work) and general precipitate (60% cold work) to render these materials equivalent to aging for thousands of hours at 82 C. It should also be recorded that the magnitude of the resistivity and hardness decreases for a high purity Al-4% Mg alloy, cold worked 15%, were identical to those for the Al-7% Mg alloy, in spite of the fact that considerably less grain boundary precipitate appeared in the more dilute alloy during extended aging at 82 C. Therefore, that portion of the decomposition process which was confined mainly to grain boundaries can be stated to have no measurable effect on bulk resistivity or hardness of cold worked as well as annealed material.

## C. Observations Pertaining to Decomposition

Referring again to Figure 4, it is obvious that prominent departures from the effects previously noted and ascribed to recovery do occur in the Al-7% Mg alloy, cold worked 60%. The resistivity decrease at the two higher aging temperatures, 62.5 and 82 C, becomes proportional to the square root of time. This change correlates well with the qualitative metallographic observation of a highly intensified general precipitation within the grains. There is some indication from the hardness curves that the degree of softening at 82 C is not as great as would be predicted for the relative amount of cold working. This may be due to arrest of softening due to recovery by the onset of dispersion hardening. The rise in hardness beyond 10,000 hours at 82 C appears to be a real effect.

The most striking observation pertaining to extensive decomposition in heavily cold worked material was obtained by X-ray diffraction. Whereas the recovery process produces a sharpening and improved resolution in the diffraction peak, this process has been arrested and then reversed in material aged at 82 C, as indicated by the notation for line broadening in Figure 4. The manner in which this proceeds is best compared by superimposing three diffractometer traces, as shown in Figure 6. The solid

**TABLE 3—X-Ray Diffraction Lattice Parameter and Line Breadth Measurements on Annealed High Purity Al-7% Mg Alloy**

| Aging Treatment | Lattice Parameter ($a_o$), Å | | $a_o$ of Al Std. Å | | Difference $a_o$ Alloy and $a_o$ Al Std. Å | Alloy Half Breadth $B_{\alpha 1}$ (422)-Degrees |
|---|---|---|---|---|---|---|
| | Mean[1] | Std. Deviation | Mean[2] | Std. Diviation | | |
| None | 4.0843 | $0.0000_9$ | 4.0500 | 0 | 0.0343 | 0.18 |
| 62.5 C-11, 424 hr | 4.0856 | $0.0000_9$ | $4.0504_5$ | $0.0001_5$ | $0.0351_5$ | 0.19[3] |
| 82 C-864 hr | 4.0843 | $0.0004_1$ | 4.0498 | 0.0001 | 0.0345 | 0.21 |
| (A) 82 C-10, 630 hr | 4.0857 | $0.0004_6$ | 4.0500 | 0.0001 | 0.0357 | 0.32[3] |
| 82 C-11, 420 hr | $4.0857_5$ | $0.0000_9$ | $4.0504_5$ | $0.0001_5$ | 0.0353 | 0.22[3] |
| Same as (A) but re-annealed at 355 C, 1 hr, air cooled. | $4.0849_5$ | $0.0000_5$ | 4.0504 | 0.0001 | $0.0345_5$ | 0.16 |

[1]Each mean value is the average obtained from the four peaks, $CuK_{\alpha 1}$ and $CuK_{\alpha 2}$ of the (422) and (333) (511) planes.

[2]For the high purity aluminum standard, only two measurements could be made, $CuK_{\alpha 1}$ and $CuK_{\alpha 2}$ of the (422) planes. The mean of all the aluminum standard determinations was $4.0501_7$ with standard deviation 0.00028 Å at 24 ± 1 C. No extrapolation function was used.

[3]Distortion of the peak shape occurred such that it was spread in the direction of higher lattice parameter.

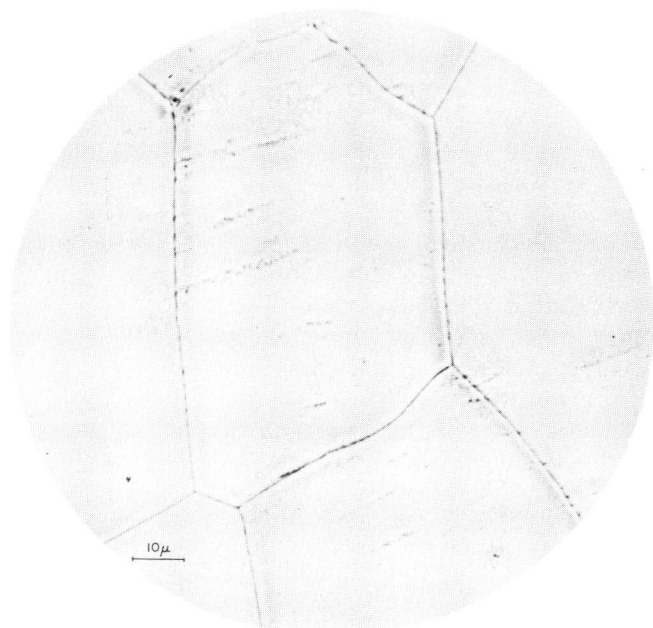

(a)

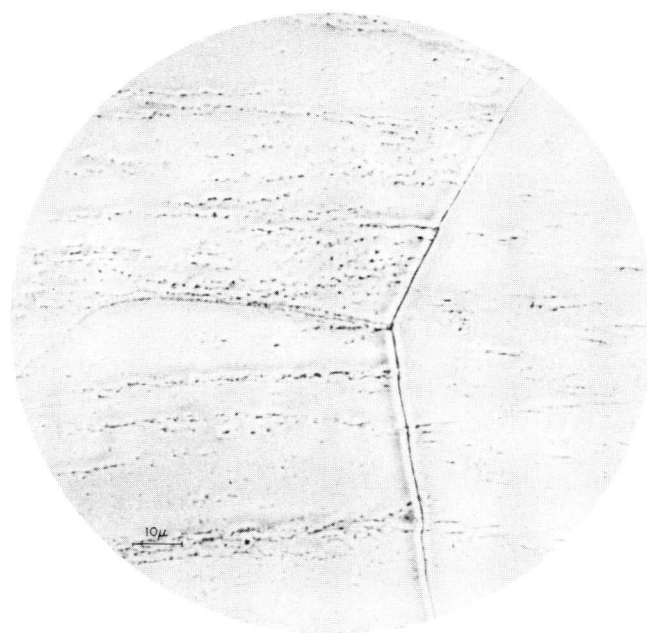

(b)

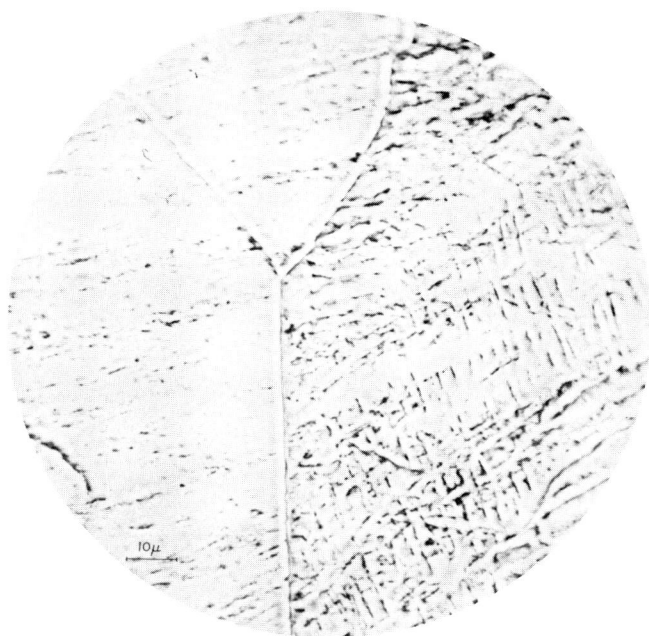

(c)

FIGURE 5 — Effects of aging on cold worked high purity Al-7% Mg alloy: electropolished; etched with 10% orthophosphoric acid for 1 minute; viewed with phase contrast illumination; original magnification 750 X. (a) Cold worked 15%, aged at 82 C for 9550 hrs. (b) Cold worked 30%, aged at 82 C for 9550 hrs. (c) Cold worked 60%, aged at 82 C for 9500 hrs.

line shows the unaged cold worked material with the smeared peak. The long dashed line shows an early recovery stage where narrowing from both low and high angle sides of the peak has occurred and some resolution of $CuK_{\alpha1}$ and $CuK_{\alpha2}$ is beginning to show. This is typical of recovery. The short dashed line, however, does not show the type of broadening which was associated with cold work. Rather, it clearly indicates that a spectrum of lattice parameters is present in the material, ranging from that associated with the 7% Mg level to one with a much lower value. The largest proportion of the volume of solid solution retains the supersaturated level of 7% Mg. Thus, the broadening is caused by the integrated effect of all solid solution gradients existing at various locations in the matrix. This indicates that the decomposition of the saturated solid solution is still highly localized in terms of relative volume and that steep gradients in composition and lattice parameter must yet exist at this advanced stage of bulk decomposition.

The use of phase contrast microscopy as a metallographic method was fortuitous in that it gave a very strong suggestion of a solute depleted zone surrounding all regions of precipitate, whether in grain boundaries or within the grains. Examples are shown in Figure 1b and in Figures 5a, 5b, and 5c. It must be emphasized that the metallographic evidence for depleted zones surrounding regions of precipitate is not entirely reliable because the chemical reactivity of the matrix during electropolishing and etching may have been altered by the mere proximity of second phase particles. However, the X-ray diffraction evidence strongly suggests that the phase contrast effect is associated with a solute depleted region around the precipitate and this, in turn, provides a valuable clue as to the state of the grain boundaries at earlier or less general stages of decomposition where electrical resistivity and lattice parameter measurements were not sufficiently sensitive to detect any changes. The general observation was made that the appearance of precipitate particles along grain boundaries in earlier stages of decomposition was accompanied by metallographic evidence of a depleted zone.

The morphology of the precipitate, especially at earlier stages of decomposition where the alloys are known to be susceptible to stress corrosion failure, is a significant consideration. Figures 7a and b show photomicrographs made with conventional bright field illumination, showing that the bulk of the particles are unconnected and, therefore, do not form a continuous film around the boundary, in accord with observations made by others.[4,24,25] Only at much more extended aging at 82 C does the precipitate give the appearance of being continuous. These observations suggest that the critical structural condition at which corrosion sensitivity is initiated is when sufficient precipitation has occurred at the grain boundaries to provide a continuous depleted zone in a high proportion of the boundaries. The electron microscope examination was aimed at obtaining a resolution of this problem.

## D. Electron Microscope Examination

The proportional thickness anodic film replica technique described in Appendix A was specifically developed for this alloy system. It was shown that, within the range of 0 to 3 weight percent magnesium, a film could be grown and its thickness calibrated against magnesium content. Beyond 3% magnesium, the films were so thin that further discrimination was not sufficiently sensitive. This method was applied to the Al-7% Mg alloy and a study was made at various stages of decomposition.

Figure 8 shows an electron micrograph of Al-7% Mg in the fully annealed condition, aged at room temperature for 2-1/2 years. Occasional grain boundary particles are noted. The light center represents a high magnesium concentration and, therefore, corresponds to the $\beta'$ precipitate alone. The black region surrounding the particle can very well be interpreted as being caused by thicker anodic film formation in the aluminum solid solution immediately adjacent to the particle. This is not the full extent of depletion since the method loses sensitivity above 3% magnesium.

A further and more convincing application of the technique is illustrated in Figure 9 for the alloy cold worked 30% and aged at 82 C for 9550 hours. Two grain boundaries are shown, one of which (A) appears to emerge nearly normal to the polished surface while another (B) emerges at an inclined angle. The interpretation of these replica contrasts is given schematically in Figure 10. It can be seen that the sequence of contrasts is reasonable for the concept of a highly depleted zone of solid solution immediately adjacent to the precipitate particles.

Examinations have been carried out on samples at intermediate stages of composition between the two extremes illustrated here and representations of both types of grain boundaries—continuously and intermittently depleted—can be found in varying proportions. It can be stated with certainty from this evidence that the condition of high stress corrosion susceptibility can be associated with

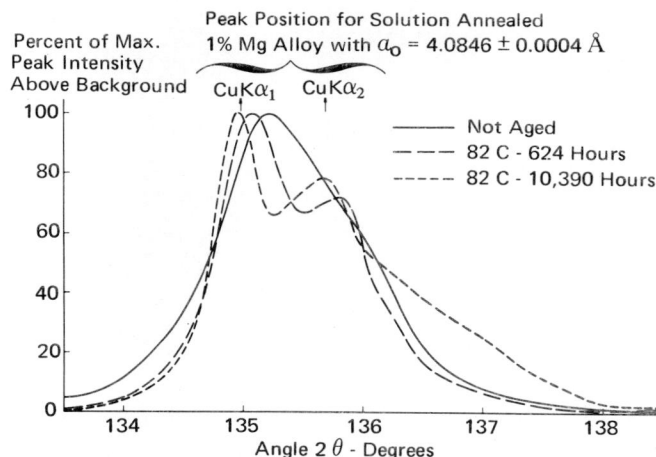

FIGURE 6 — X-ray diffraction scan of (422) $CuK_\alpha$ for high purity Al-7% Mg alloy, cold worked 60% and aged at 82 C, showing initial recovery from cold work and subsequent broadening due to solid solution decomposition.

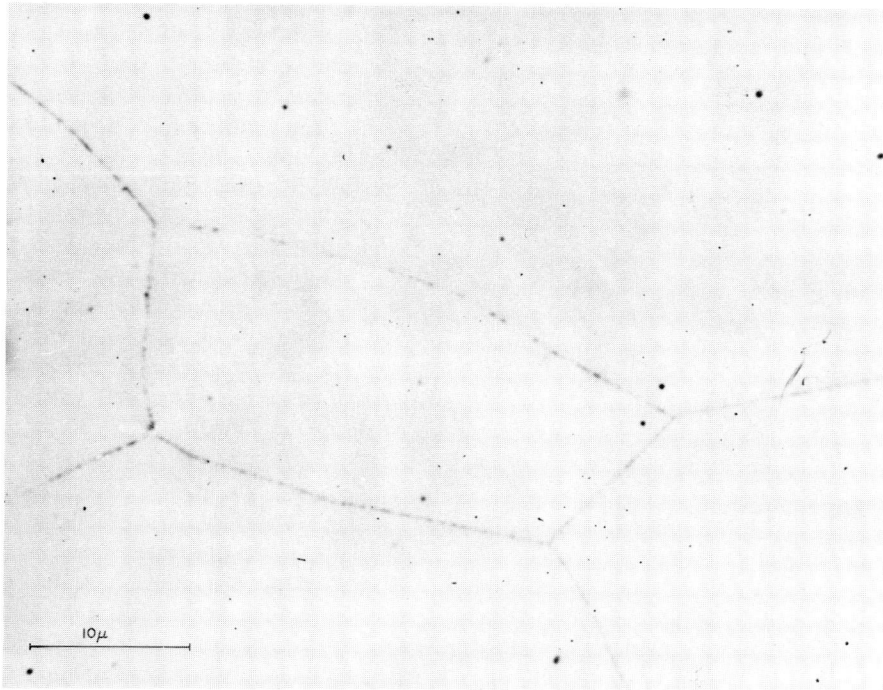

(a)

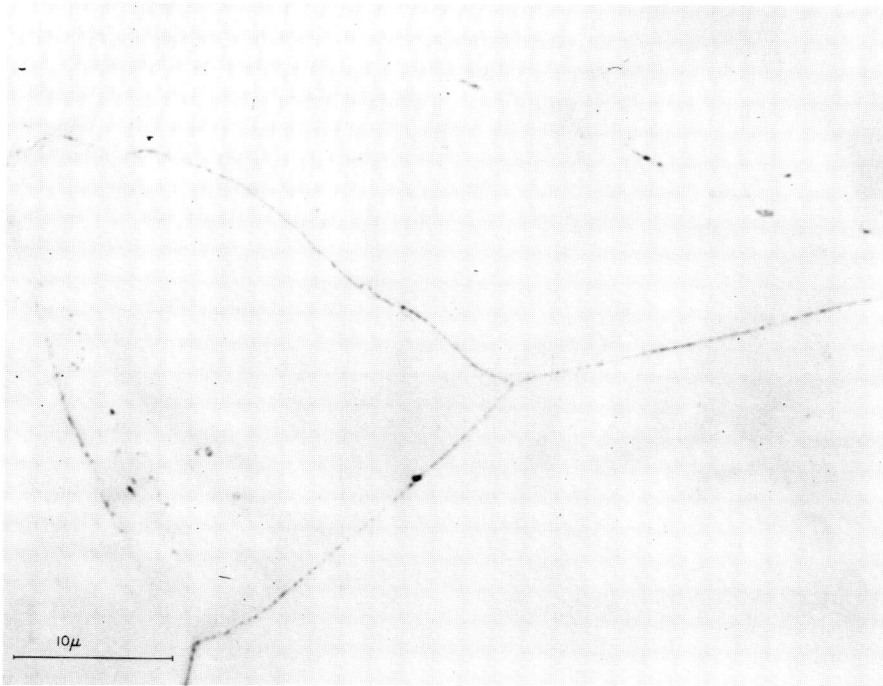

(b)

FIGURE 7 — Grain boundary precipitates in cold worked and aged high purity Al-7% Mg alloy which are known to have poor stress corrosion resistance: electropolished; etched with 10% orthophosphoric acid for 1 minute; bright field illumination; original magnification 1000 X. (a) Cold worked 15%, aged at 150 C for 4 hours. (b) Cold worked 30%, aged at 82 C for 360 hours.

521

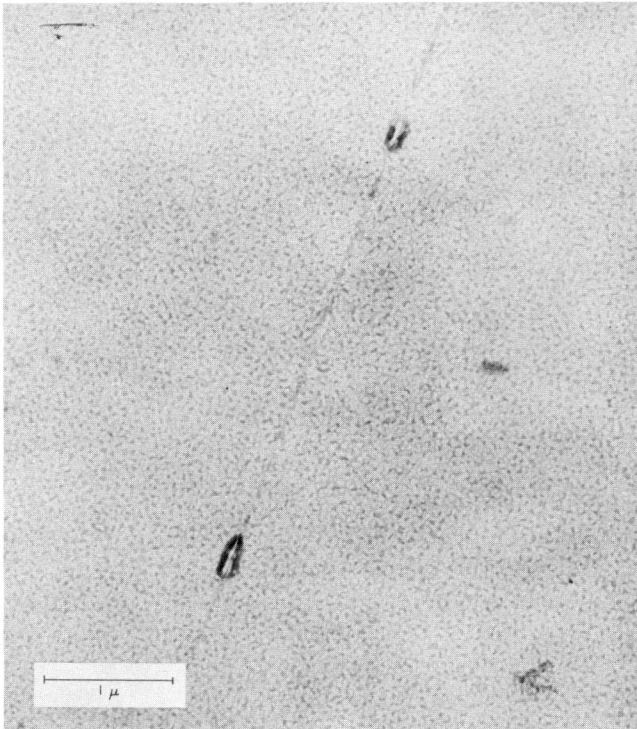

FIGURE 8 — Electron micrograph of proportional thickness anodic film replica of solution annealed high purity Al-7% Mg alloy, aged at room temperature for 2-1/2 years. Original magnification

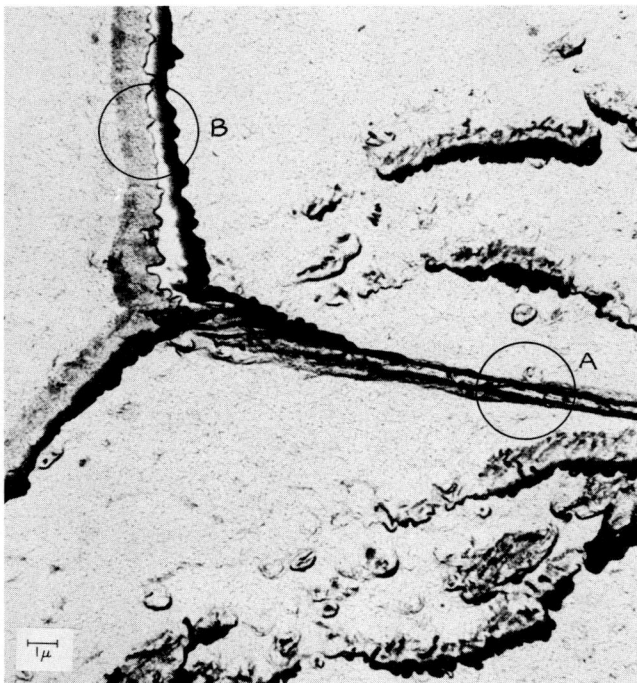

FIGURE 9 — Electron micrograph of proportional thickness anodic film replica of high purity Al-7% Mg alloy, cold worked 30% and aged at 82 C for 9550 hours. The intensity variations for the encircled grain boundary areas, A and B, are interpreted in Figure 10. Original magnification

a continuously depleted grain boundary region in a substantial proportion of the boundaries.

Other considerations give support to the preceding hypothesis. Consider, for example, the minimum volume of solid solution required to furnish enough of a magnesium concentration to form the magnesium rich precipitated phase. A calculation is given in Appendix B which relates to that portion required to be depleted to the level between the equilibrium value (assumed at 2%) and the 3% level of detectability. It turns out to be about 2.5 times the volume of the precipitate phase itself. The total volume of depleted zone may be anywhere up to seven times that of the actual second phase formed. Therefore, it is reasonable to predict that the continuous depleted zone will be formed quite early in the precipitation process and may well be the critical condition associated with low resistance to stress corrosion cracking.

## IV. Discussion

The aluminum-magnesium binary alloys and their commercial modifications have many unique characteristics which pose innumerable problems for research investigation. Many pieces belonging to the puzzle of stress

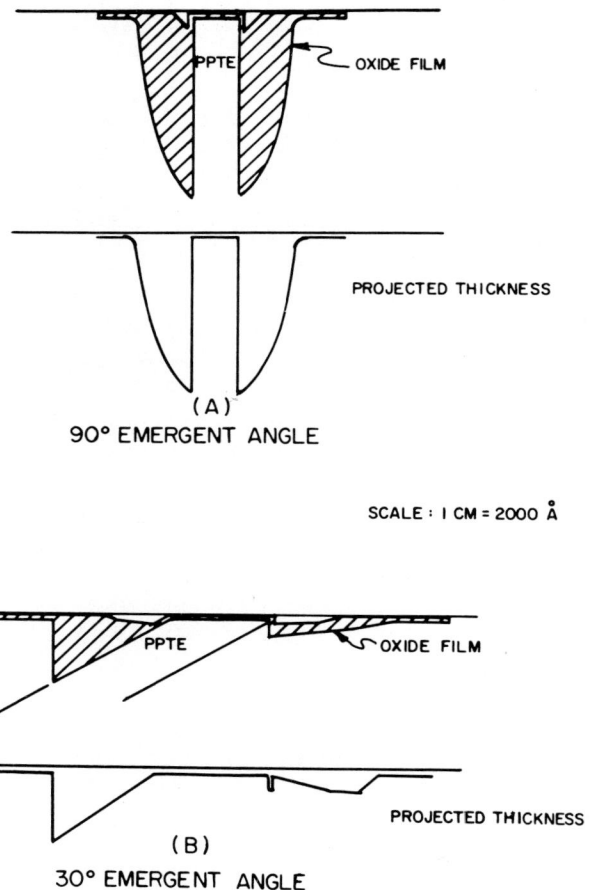

SCALE : 1 CM = 2000 Å

FIGURE 10 — Schematic representation of anodic oxide film formation about in grain boundary region for two emerging angles relating to encircled areas A and B in Figure 9.

corrosion cracking are being fitted together from widely diverse studies which have entirely different objectives. Comments on a few generalities are in order before proceeding to a discussion of the new observations reported herein.

One striking feature of aluminum-magnesium alloys is the high degree of supersaturation of the solid solution which can be readily retained near room temperature. This is surprising on two counts: (1) the high degree of lattice strain associated with the large magnesium atom should provide a strong driving force for precipitation and, (2) the relatively low activation energy for diffusion and the relatively rapid diffusion rates displayed at elevated temperatures belie the slow rate of · decomposition compared with other aluminum solid solution systems. The explanation which is provided for the first count would seem to make the second count even more surprising. It has previously been noted that Al-Mg alloys are prone to retain many quenched-in vacancies.[14,18] This is attributed to coupling of large magnesium atoms with vacancies, thus partially offsetting the increased strain caused by the lattice expanding element and simultaneously inhibiting the migration of vacancies to normal sinks. However, the availability of extra vacancies at or near room temperature should promote diffusion. Indeed, there is evidence that the migration rate of magnesium atoms below about 200 C is characterized by an activation energy about half that for normal elevated temperature diffusion.[5,18] Furthermore, it has been suggested that the accelerating effect of cold working on the decomposition comes partly from the excess vacancies created by the deformation.[16,19] Thus it is odd that the decomposition process is as sluggish as it is.

In the present work, some additional evidence was generated to substantiate that many quenched-in vacancies remain in the Al-7% Mg alloy, even after cooling in air from the annealing temperature of 355 C. It was shown in Table 3 that solution annealed material, aged for more than 10,000 hours, showed evidence of a slight lattice distortion in the direction of higher lattice parameter. Since many of these measurements were made at different periods over a span of time, there was the possibility that the effect may have been due to instrumental variations, even though the same pure aluminum standard was carried along each time. However, two measurements, one on a sample aged at 82 C for 10,630 hours and another on the same sample solution annealed anew, were made concurrently and showed that the effect must be real because the aged material was restored to its original condition by re-annealing. This effect could be explained by the very gradual migration of excess vacancies to normal sinks, during long term aging, leaving a higher net lattice expansion. Alternatively, there may be some form of clustering in the solid solution accompanied by annihilation of vacancies as suggested by Detert and Thomas.[18]

The initial resistivity decrease in cold worked material can also be associated with the migration of vacancies created by cold working to natural sinks or, alternatively, with the coupling of vacancies with solute atoms and consequent loss of some electron scattering propen-

sity.[16,19] This recovery mechanism is independent of softening and X-ray diffraction peak sharpening, which depend instead upon dislocation re-arrangement and formation of a regular sub-grain or cell structure.[14] These extra vacancies speed the rate of decomposition at large angle grain boundaries where nucleating sites already exist. However, small amounts of cold working, in the order of 15% or less, do not provide a large number of new nucleating sites. Therefore, the evidence of more rapid decomposition is confined mainly to the grain boundaries. It is only when deformation becomes severe enough to form deformation bands by extensive cross slip that the number of nucleating sites are multiplied and extensive decomposition within the grain occurs.[8] Beyond this stage pileups of dislocations on slip planes may also serve as nucleating sites.

Very little is known about the precipitating phase which comes out of solid solution below 200 C, designated as $\beta'$.[12,13] Therefore, one must speculate about it on the basis of what is known about the stable phase, $\beta$ or $Mg_2 Al_3$. Perlitz[11] has determined that $\beta$ has an extremely large face centered cubic unit cell, consisting of approximately 1200 atoms. $\beta'$ is a metastable transition phase which most probably has a simpler structure and possibly a different composition ratio. Nevertheless, it can be assumed from its nucleating behavior that it must require a large critical nucleus size in order to remain stable and grow.[9,10] This nucleus can only form rapidly where there is substantial lattice disregistry, such as at large angle grain boundaries or in the region of lattice rotations at kink or deformation bands.[8] The view that nucleation rate is the limiting factor in decomposition resolves the apparent anomalies associated with the large driving force and high rates of diffusional growth expected for precipitation from supersaturated Al-Mg solid solution. The fact that growth is diffusion controlled and proceeds at a sensible rate can be deduced from the course of the resistivity vs time curves in Figure 4 for heavily cold worked Al-7% Mg alloy aged at 62.5 and 82 C. Here the incubation time required for producing a large number of stable nuclei was sufficiently short that the growth rate alone was sensed beyond 100 hours of aging. The proportionality to square root of time is normal for diffusional growth.

The driving force for diffusional growth is the concentration gradient set up between the supersaturated matrix and the equilibrium solid solution composition at the interface between $\beta$ and $\beta'$ phase. This equilibrium composition is temperature dependent and can only be determined for low temperatures by extrapolation from high temperature data. It is judged to be less than 2% by weight at room temperature. A certain minimum volume of solid solution matrix is required to furnish the required magnesium concentration to form a unit volume of $\beta$ precipitate and this has been calculated as about seven times the precipitate volume. Therefore, each precipitate particle should have associated with it a surrounding volume at least seven times its own in which a concentration gradient exists. Upon very extended growth this volume would increase and the gradient would decrease. However, where precipitation is confined to planes or surfaces, such as high angle grain boundaries, and where it is made up of individual but closely spaced particles spread out over those surfaces, there must eventually come a point where the solute depleted zone is continuous and fairly uniform in the direction normal to the grain boundary. In the absence of precipitation within the grains, this then becomes a unique feature of the grain boundaries. This argument is opposite to that of Edeleanu[6] and Taylor[24] who supposed a higher concentration of magnesium in the solid solution adjacent to grain boundaries.

The present work leaves no doubt that such a solute depleted zone with a marked gradient can and does exist. It should be noted that it has already been demonstrated that a similar occurrence on a larger scale exists for precipitation of $\beta$ or $\beta'$ phase at higher temperatures and in alloys with higher magnesium contents.[12,13,20,21] Here large quantities of both supersaturated and equilibrium solid solution were shown to exist in the same alloy. It has been concluded that the precipitation process was "discontinuous" although there was no evidence of side-by-side growth of precipitation phase and recrystallizing matrix, as is found in some alloy systems. Saulnier[26] has shown metallographic evidence of two solid solutions. The present work has demonstrated that, in all probability, a transition situation exists at temperatures within the range at which high sensitivity to stress corrosion failure can develop. In this case, a gradient of lattice parameter exists adjacent to second phase particles and there is no indication that new aluminum grains are formed in the process. Any proposed stress corrosion cracking mechanism for these alloys should take into account the existence of a continuous depleted zone along crack-sensitive paths, namely, the grain boundaries.

First one must consider whether the depleted zone makes any contribution to the electrochemical aspects of stress corrosion in Al-Mg alloys. Its composition is such that its electrochemical potential in saline solutions would be much more noble than the $\beta$ phase and very slightly more noble than the supersaturated matrix.[1] It is hard to believe that this would create a substantially different galvanic situation than that which presupposes that the cathodic area is the 7% Mg solid solution rather than the denuded zone. The magnesium-rich $\beta$ phase will corrode rapidly in the presence of sodium chloride solution, even when it is not coupled to and driven by a cathodic phase. Therefore, the rate of localized attack on the intergranular $\beta$ phase should not be significantly influenced by contact with a slightly more cathodic phase than that represented by the grain centers. It has been pointed out by Farmery and Evans[4] that the bright fracture surface on Al-Mg alloys failed by stress corrosion is indicative of very little matter destroyed by corrosion and the retarding or stopping of corrosion failure by cathodic protection means that the discontinuous $\beta'$ phase is the corroding species. It must be concluded, therefore, that the solute depleted zone contributes to the mechanical aspects of stress corrosion failure, rather than the electrochemical aspects.

Of the mechanical effects, two possibilities are suggested. One of these is possible existence of a severe strain gradient which accompanies the composition and lattice parameter gradient through the denuded zone. The other possibility is the lower yield strength and greater ease of dislocation movement through the zone. Regarding the first possibility, attempts to calculate the strain gradient under the most severe conditions have shown that it cannot be any greater than about $10^{-5}$ (maximum lattice parameter difference divided by probable zone thickness at the stage where grain boundary precipitate becomes barely resolvable microscopically). Even though the removal of constraint at the precipitate interface by corrosion of the precipitate would be expected to produce some relaxation of this strained configuration, perhaps by creation of new surface in the form of a crack, the magnitude of the effect would not seem to be great enough to properly account for stress corrosion cracking. Furthermore, the role of the applied or residual tensile stress would not be explainable. A further objection to the strain gradient concept is that it is not as applicable to many of the precipitation hardening aluminum alloy systems which also fail by intergranular cracking, and it is not satisfying to conceive of entirely different mechanisms for the two classes of alloy.

A more satisfying explanation is that based upon the greater ease of the movement of dislocations through the denuded zone, when any of the three dimensional constraints imposed upon it are removed. Experimental support for such a mechanism is being developed by F. P. Ford of Olin's Metal Research Laboratories. This work is still in progress and will form the basis for later publications. However, it is sufficient to summarize the mechanism as follows:

1. Corrosion initiates at a few grain boundaries which are favorably oriented to have the highest resolved tensile stress normal to the grain boundary and may have a greater than average concentration of precipitate phase. It is not necessary to invoke galvanically controlled corrosion of the magnesium-rich phase although it appears that cathodic protection can slow down or prevent failure.[4]

2. Release of the constraints imposed by the interface between second phase and the denuded zone initiates a sudden localized flow of dislocations through the softer zone to emerge at the freshly created surface.

3. Dislocations converging from both sides upon the tip of the crevices created by removal of $\beta$ phase would be forced to pile up against each other unless the strain can be removed by creation of additional new surface in the form of a crack. The crack then exposes additional second phase and the process is repeated. However, the dimensional scale at which this stop-start mechanism occurs is such that no resolution of individual steps by physical or electrochemical measurements is postulated.

4. The stress concentrations produced at the ends of the favorably oriented grain boundaries, initially affected, result in transfer of this reaction to less favorably oriented exposed grain boundaries until a continuity is established which enables the crack to grow inward by the same mechanism.

The function of the applied or residual tensile stress is to initiate the movement of dislocation piled up in the stronger matrix into the denuded zone once the second phase particle has been removed. Furthermore, it helps to prevent relief of stresses by rounding off of the crack tip. The above mechanism presupposes a source of piled up dislocations within the grain matrix. This is conceivable in a precipitation hardened alloy where the hardening particles are very apparent obstacles to dislocation movement within the matrix. In the case of Ai-Mg alloys, where there is no appreciable precipitation hardening, one must take into account instead the unique strengthening effects of magnesium in solid solution, perhaps, abetted by some pre-precipitation clustering.[10,18,19] In particular, Mitra and Dorn[27] have shown that increasing magnesium raises the density of dislocations for a given strain and the rate of strain hardening is due to this increase in dislocation density which, in turn, results in long-range back stresses. These high dislocation densities and back stresses would be supportable in the solute depleted zone, as long as there exists a constraint imposed by the presence of second phase particles in the grain boundary. However, the removal of nearby particles by corrosion and the presence of an applied or residual tensile stress initiate the sudden release of dislocations to the common grain boundary causing a crack to form and exposing the next deeper particle.

Another possible matrix effect has been noted by Swann and Pickering[28] who have pointed to a relationship between alloys susceptible to transgranular stress corrosion failure and those which display the Portevin-Le Chatelier effect in the stress strain curve. The Al-Mg alloys display the Portevin-Le Chatelier effect very prominently, although they stress corrode intergranularly. Swann and Pickering suggest that there is a segregation of solute atoms to moving dislocations, a possibility which has also been mentioned by one of the present authors[29] as applicable to the deformation of Al-Mg alloys. However, it does not seem possible to make use of this effect in conjunction with the concept of the solute depleted zone to explain intergranular failure.

## V. Acknowledgments

A preliminary investigation which preceded the main part of the investigation presented herein was supported by the Department of the Army, Frankford Arsenal, under Contract No. DA-30-069-507-ORD-2652, under whose auspices, earlier publications were made.[8,29]

The authors are grateful to Olin Mathieson Chemical Corporation for granting permission to publish the results of the subsequent investigation. They also wish to acknowledge the specific assistance of many co-workers in contributing to the experimental results, and the many helpful discussions with their co-workers and supervisors at the Metals Research Laboratories. Much of the experimental data were garnered by Mr. Henry Smith and the metallographic work was carried out by Mrs. K. Fraenza. The X-ray diffraction measurements were made by Mr. R. S. Herman. Auxiliary stress corrosion testing, although not specifically described herein, was carried out under the supervision of Dr. W. Wolfe, Jr. Early guidance was obtained from I. Broverman, formerly with Olin, and was continued by Dr. J. Winter.

We are grateful for the encouragement and support given by Dr. M. J. Pryor, Associate Manager, Metallurgy and Corrosion Department, and Mr. J. B. Seastone, Manager of the Metals Research Laboratories.

## References

1. E. H. Dix, Jr., W. A. Anderson, and M. Byron Shumaker. *Corrosion,* **15,** 55t (1958).
2. P. Brenner and W. Roth. *J. Inst. Metals,* **74,** 159 (1948).
3. E. Lloyd Jones. *J. Appl. Chem.,* **4,** 1 (1954).
4. H. K. Farmery and U. R. Evans. *J. Inst. Metals,* **84,** 413 (1955-56).
5. E. C. W. Perryman and S. E. Hadden. *J. Inst. Metals,* **77,** 207 (1950).
6. C. Edeleanu. *J. Inst. Metals,* **80,** 187 (1951-52).
7. P. T. Gilbert and S. E. Hadden. *J. Inst. Metals,* **77,** 237 (1950).
8. P. R. Sperry. *Trans. AIME,* **224,** 191 (1962).
9. A. Eikum and G. Thomas. *Acta Met.,* **12,** 537 (1964).
10. O. Dahl and K. Detert. *Z. Metallkde.,* **36,** 94 (1955).
11. H. Perlitz. *Nature,* **154,** 606 (1944).
12. William L. Fink and Dana W. Smith. *Trans. AIME,* **124,** 162 (1937).
13. E. C. W. Perryman and G. B. Brook. *J. Inst. Metals,* **79,** 19 (1951).
14. E. C. W. Perryman. *Trans. AIME,* **206,** 1247 (1956).
15. C. Panseri, T. Federighi, and S. Ceresara. *Trans. AIME,* **227,** 1122 (1963).
16. C. Panseri, F. Gatto, and T. Federighi. *Acta Met.,* **6,** 198 (1958).
17. G. Thomas. *Phil. Mag.,* Ser. 8, **4,** 1213 (1959).
18. K. Detert and L. Thomas. *Acta Met.,* **12,** 43 (1964).
19. A. R. C. Westwood and T. Broom. *Acta Met.,* **5,** 249 (1957).
20. (Mme) A. R. Weill. *Rev. de Metallurgie,* **49,** 364 (1952).
21. Shigeru Matsuo. *Trans. Nat. Res. Inst. for Metals,* (Tokyo) **2,** 22 (1960).
22. P. Brenner. *Aluminium,* **36,** 589 (1960).
23. A. F. Beck. *J. Appl. Phys.,* **36,** 2944 (1965).
24. B. Taylor. *Can. Metall. Quarterly,* **3,** 313 (1964).
25. A. T. Thomas. *J. Inst. Metals,* **94,** 37 (1966).
26. A. Saulnier. *Rev. de Metallurgie,* **53,** 285 (1956).
27. Sandip K. Mitra and John E. Dorn. *Trans. AIME,* **227,** 1015 (1963).
28. P. R. Swann and H. W. Pickering. *Corrosion,* **11,** 369t (1963).
29. P. R. Sperry. *Acta Met.,* **11,** 153 (1963).

## Appendix A

The following describes the basis upon which a proportional thickness anodic replica technique was developed for Al-Mg alloys.

Pure aluminum will electropolish in an electrolyte comprised of 10% by weight NaOH, 64% $H_2O$ and 26% methanol, provided that a large area is exposed to the electrolyte (2 cm$^2$). However, when smaller areas are anodically treated, a thick, uniform, structureless and rigid film is formed on pure aluminum, accompanied by depression of the exposed area, and a very thin flexible and structureless film is formed on an aluminum-7% magnesium alloy, with no depression of the exposed area. Both films are transparent and even the thick film formed on pure aluminum does not exhibit the haze or the vertical pore structure normally found in films formed in sulfuric acid, which they otherwise resemble in that thickness is time dependent.

Using these observations, a standardized procedure was established so that film thicknesses formed on a series of aluminum-magnesium alloys could be considered on a comparative basis. The alloys contained 0.50, 1.0, 2.1, 3.0, 3.9, and 7.0 weight percent Mg and they were all solution heat treated and quenched. After the specimens were electropolished in perchloric acid solution and masked to expose the desired area (0.1 cm$^2$), they were lightly etched in the anodizing electrolyte for four seconds to dissolve any surface film left by electropolishing. Without removing the specimen from the electrolyte an initial forming voltage of 20 volts was applied. The voltage was then brought up to the final forming voltage of 40 volts in increments of 5 volts every 10.8 seconds. After holding the potential at the final value for the desired time, the specimens were washed thoroughly in distilled water and allowed to dry in a desiccator for at least a half hour.

Each specimen was held at the final forming voltage for periods of 36, 60, or 360 seconds. Since the anodic films formed on alloys containing 2.1% magnesium and less were obviously quite thick, they were stripped in mercuric chloride solution and mounted on glass slides for cross sectional thickness measurements by optical microscopy. The films formed on the alloys with higher magnesium content were thinner, almost certainly of the barrier layer type, and had to be examined by higher resolution measurement techniques. Therefore, the film thickness of one of the 7% magnesium specimens was first measured by an ellipsometer to provide an accurate thickness figure. This film then served as a standard against which the thicknesses of other films formed on alloys with 3.1% or more of magnesium could be quickly compared by shadow electron microscopy. The results of these thickness determinations are plotted as a function of magnesium content in Figure A-1. The thickness of the films formed on alloys containing less than 3% magnesium was strongly time dependent and decreased in a linear fashion with increasing magnesium content. At more than 3% magnesium, the film thickness was practically independent of time and decreased at a

much less rapid rate with increasing magnesium content.

The preliminary experiments had indicated that the anodizing of pure aluminum was accompanied by a depression of the exposed area. This is probably due to a substantial rate of direct dissolution of the anodic film by the alkaline electrolyte and would be expected to be also sensitive to the magnesium concentration. Accordingly, another set of specimens was prepared in identical fashion to that used in obtaining anodic film thicknesses, anodizing for 360 seconds at 40 volts. The specimens were sectioned across the anodized areas and the trench depth (defined as the distance between the outer surface of the oxide film and the original metal surface) was measured with the metallographic microscope. Figure A-2 shows the relation between the depth of the trench and magnesium concentration of the alloy. The curve within the range of 0-2.2% magnesium concentration is basically similar in form to the curve relating anodic film thickness to magnesium concentration. No trenching could be detected on the higher concentration alloys by this method.

These observations imply that in alloys containing less than 3% magnesium, the anodic film thickness is time dependent and comprises the difference between the rate of film formation and the rate of film dissolution, each of

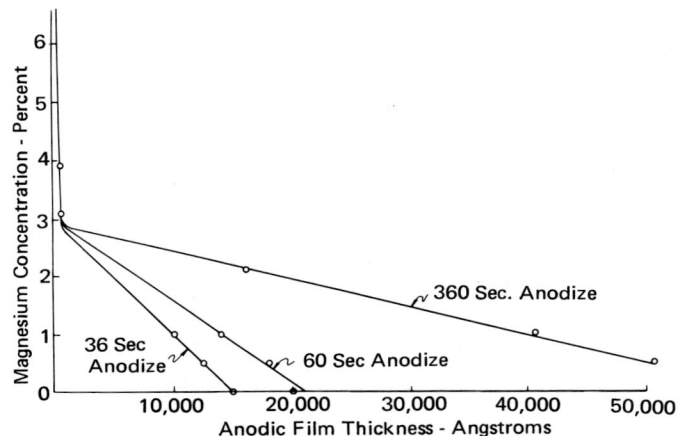

**FIGURE A-1 — Thickness of anodic films formed on binary Al-Mg alloys in sodium hydroxide electrolyte at 40 volts.**

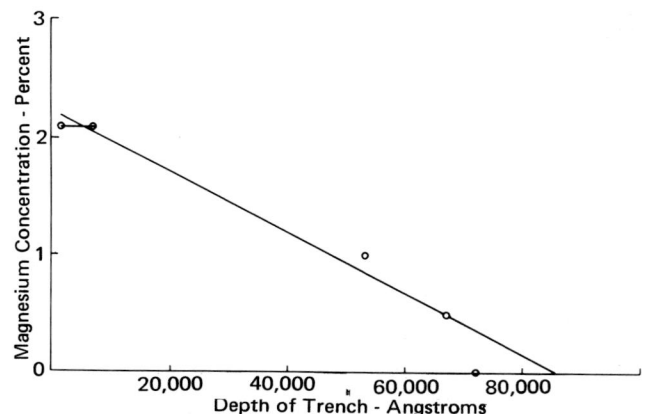

**FIGURE A-2 — Trenching in Al-Mg alloys caused by anodizing in sodium hydroxide electrolyte for 6 minutes at 40 volts.**

which in turn is sensitive to the magnesium concentration. This provides the information necessary for the interpretation of the contrast effects in anodic film replicas formed by this electrolyte on aluminum-magnesium alloys in various stages of solid solution decomposition, as illustrated by Figures 9 and 10 of this paper. It is assumed that the replica grows only perpendicularly to the surface. This assumption is considered valid since cationic movement must certainly be highly directional in the presence of a high applied field such as was used for anodizing this work.

## Appendix B

### Ratio of Widths of Depleted Zone and Precipitate

Consider a sheet of precipitate in a grain boundary[1] of finite width, but large length and breadth such that incremental volume changes will be reflected almost totally in width change. Assume a magnesium concentration gradient of a parabolic nature about the faces of the sheet. Then,

$$\frac{W_p}{W_z} = \frac{V_p}{V_z}$$

when, $W_p$ = width of the precipitate, $W_z$ = width of depleted zone, $V_p$ = volume of precipitate, and, $V_z$ = volume of depleted zone. To form a unit volume or "width" of precipitate, and neglecting density variations, $W_p (C_p - C_o)$ of magnesium are required and must be supplied by the adjacent volume of solid solution, where $C_p$ = conc. of Mg in precipitate as gms/cc and $C_o$ = conc. of Mg in original solid solution as gms/cc.

The magnesium concentration gradient may be expressed as:

$$C = aW^2 + C_i$$

where C = magnesium concentration as gms/cc, W = width of depleted zone at concentration C, and $C_i$ = magnesium concentration in solid solution in equilibrium with the precipitate as gms/cc.

Then:  $d[W_p(C_p - C_o)] = W \, dC = \left(\frac{C - C_i}{a}\right)^{1/2} dC$

Integrating between the equilibrium concentration and the original solid solution concentration

$$W_p(C_p - C_o) = \frac{1}{a^{1/2}} \int_{C_i}^{C_o} (C - C)^{1/2} \, dC$$

$$= \frac{2}{3a^{1/2}} (C_o - C_i)^{3/2}$$

and since  $a = \frac{C_o - C_i}{W_o^2}$

$$W_p(C_p - C_o) = \frac{2 W_o}{3 (C_o - C_i)^{1/2}} (C_o - C_i)^{3/2}$$

$$= \frac{2}{3} W_o (C_o - C_i)$$

$$W_o = \frac{3}{2} \frac{(C_p - C_o)}{(C_o - C_i)}$$

This expression provides the ratio between the total depleted zone and the width of the precipitate. Since this replica method cannot show the 7% magnesium boundary, but only about 3%, the expression must be modified to provide the ratio of distance from the precipitate to any solid solution of concentration C to the width of the precipitate. By substituting $\frac{C - C_i}{W^2}$ for the constant after the integration,

$$W_p(C_p - C_o) = \frac{2}{3} \frac{W}{(C - C_i)^{1/2}} (C_o - C_i)^{3/2}$$

where $C < C_o$
and re-arranging,

$$\frac{W}{W_p} = \frac{3}{2} \frac{(C_p - C_o)(C - C_i)^{1/2}}{(C_o - C_i)^{3/2}}$$

Setting $C_o$ = 0.184 gms/cc = 7% w/w Magnesium
$C_i$ = 0.053 gms/cc = 2% w/w Magnesium
$C$ = 0.079 gms/cc = 3% w/w Magnesium
$C_p$ = 0.669 gms/cc = 30% w/w Magnesium

$$\frac{W}{W_p} = \frac{3}{2} \frac{(0.669 - 0.184)(0.079 - 0.053)^{1/2}}{(0.184 - 0.053)^{3/2}} = 2.5$$

---

[1]The precipitate initially consists of chains of individual particles which may eventually grow together to form the assumed sheet. However, as long as the volume (hence, thickness) of the depleted zone is large compared with that of the precipitate and the spacing between precipitate particles is small, the assumption is valid.

This represents the ratio of the width of the 2% to 3% magnesium concentration portion of the denuded zone to the width of the precipitate, subject to the precipitate shape conditions mentioned earlier in the Appendix.

## Discussion

**E. N. Pugh, RIAS:**

Your model is similar to that proposed by Jones and myself for Al-Zn-Mg alloys [E. N. Pugh and W. R. D. Jones, *Metallurgia*, **63**, 3 (1961)] in that both suggest that cracking is mechanical, occurring in the precipitate-free zones at grain boundaries. One point which worries me is that we would expect that failure through the soft precipitate-free zones would be ductile and hence one would expect the resulting fracture surface to show the characteristic dimpled structure typical of ductile failure. Fractographic studies in the Al-Zn-Mg system have not revealed dimples. Do you find them in the Al-Mg system?

**A. F. Beck and P. R. Sperry:**

Unfortunately, we have not had the opportunity to do any fractographic studies of stress corrosion failures in the Al-7% Mg alloys. The interpretation of the picture offered by the fracture surface would have to be carefully considered in the light of several influencing factors. First of all, the three-dimensional morphology of the second phase precipitate in the grain boundary should be accounted for since we must assume that it is completely corroded out in the stress corrosion process. Secondly, we must be assured that the crack walls are not modified by secondary corrosion effects which may occur before the test is completed. Thirdly, there is no real guarantee that the relative softness of the denuded zone would produce a failure characteristic of a ductile material because of the constraints imposed upon this zone by the proximity of the harder grain matrix.

**T. P. Hoar, University of Cambridge:**

The possible ductile processes at the crack tip would, of course, disrupt any oxide film and it is possible that some strain–assisted dissolution would occur. In this case one would expect to see dissolution ledges rather than dimpling.

**W. J. Helfrich, Kaiser Aluminum & Chemical Corp.:**

Since paths for continuous electrochemical activity apparently do not exist in susceptible aluminum-magnesium alloys, it is tempting to assume that mechanical fracture processes must contribute to the propagation of stress corrosion cracks. A pile-up model for microcracking during intergranular stress corrosion is attractive in that grain boundaries and grain boundary precipitates should offer effective barriers to dislocation motion. And, the model should be equally applicable to both strain-hardenable and precipitation-hardenable alloys—whether they exhibit solute depletion or precipitate denudation at the grain boundaries. Unfortunately, the pile-up model contains no time dependent terms and, therefore, it cannot explain the influence of decreasing stress on longer times to failure. Moreover, the process by which dislocation pile-ups occur in an elastically strained metal prior to the first increment of crack extension is far from clear. Must we assume that dislocation pile-ups exist at grain boundaries prior to stress corrosion testing?

**A. F. Beck and P. R. Sperry:**

In answer to the question about dislocation pile-ups at the grain boundaries, it is quite certain that the strain hardened tempers of the Al-Mg alloys would exhibit such pile-ups because they would be necessary to insure propagation of slip from one grain to the next. However, it is to be noted that decomposition of the solid solution at the grain boundaries, which ultimately leads to stress corrosion susceptibility, sets in *after* the cold working and that there may be something analogous to a recovery process occurring as the denuded zones are formed. It is quite likely, therefore, that the dislocation density in the denuded zone will be lower than that in the adjoining matrix in the case of both strain hardened alloys and heat treatable alloys, or alternatively there will be a more orderly sub-grain arrangement in the denuded zone. The dislocation pile-ups in a solid solution and work hardened or a precipitation hardened grain matrix are restrained from moving into or through the denuded zone by the absence of any stress relieving mechanism. It is the disturbance of this balance by the corroding out of the second phase particles which is assumed to promote an avalanche of dislocation movement advancing simultaneously from both sides of the grain boundary which leads to a fracture.

It is true that there is no time dependent factor for the mechanical portion of such a stress corrosion mechanism, and, therefore, the time dependence of propagation may rest with the corrosion portion of the process. In any stress corrosion test, the time-to-failure may be made up of up to three components, one of which could consist of further metallurgical changes during exposure of the alloy which lead to greater susceptibility, another being initiation of a crack, and a third being the crack propagation or growth. The first component may be relevant over long periods of service exposure but is usually not a factor in laboratory tests. Generally, the initiation step consumes the greatest proportion of the total time-to-failure and it would have to include initial corrosion reactions causing breakdown of protective films in such a manner that a stress concentration along a nearly continuous path is introduced.

**A. J. Jacobs, Rocketdyne:**

Have you obtained a correlation between the presence or absence or the extent of the denuded zone and stress corrosion susceptibility?

**A. R. C. Westwood, RIAS:**

Do you have any evidence for a correlation between width of the denuded zone and susceptibility to stress corrosion cracking, and if so, what is it?

A. F. Beck and P. R. Sperry:

These two questions may be partially answered by some of the work currently being done by Mr. F. P. Ford of our laboratories. We have determined that the activation energy associated with the growth of precipitate in Al-Mg alloys at temperatures up to about 200 C is about 14 Kcal/g-atom which is about half that for the normal diffusion of magnesium in aluminum. By sensitizing alloys which have been cold worked either 60 or 80 percent, using single or duplex heatings at temperatures within a range of 65 to 150 C and for times between 1/2 and 168 hours, then subjecting these materials to an accelerated stress corrosion test, we can obtain a plot of stress corrosion life versus relative width of the denuded zone as shown in Figure 1. Before cold working, these samples were solution annealed and then cooled at 28 C per hour in order to precipitate some magnesium from solid solution. Otherwise, if they had been rapidly cooled, they would have failed so quickly that measurements of time-to-failure would have been meaningless. Figure 2 shows an electron micrograph of an anodic replica of a similar starting material, cold rolled 30 percent and without any sensitizing treatment. There is no evidence of any composition gradient in the matrix of this material even though there are numerous second phase particles both in the grain boundaries and in the grain matrix. Figure 3 shows the same material sensitized by heating at 150 C for 24 hours. A definite denuded zone appears after the thermal treatment and it seems to be continuous in many of the grain boundaries. The thickness of this zone on each side of the boundary is in the order of 0.1 microns. However, it must be recalled that this zone is revealed only if the magnesium content is no more than 3% (see Figure A-1 of the Appendix to the original paper). Therefore, the entire zone in which a concentration gradient exists may be considerably wider than this. It must also be remembered that the precipitate volume is increasing at the same time that the zone is thickening, so that zone width cannot be treated as an isolated variable.

It is certain that the stress corrosion life will not continue to decrease as the zone width increases infinitely, as eventually a point is reached where the zones surrounding the precipitate particles in the matrix and those in the grain boundaries will join up and the gradient becomes so small that the grain boundaries no longer offer a unique continuous path for fracture.

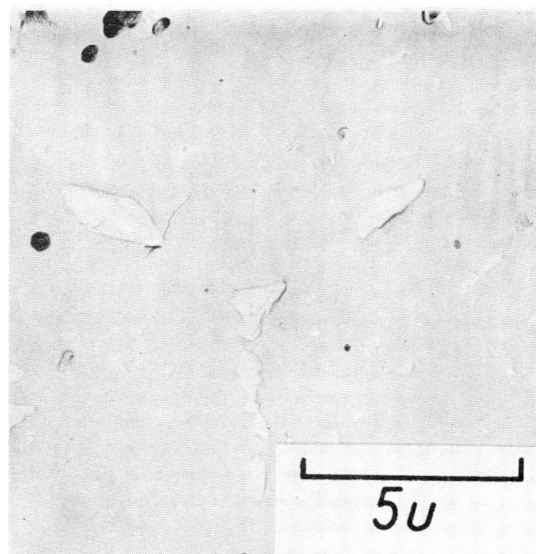

FIGURE 2 — Electron micrograph of quantitative anodic replica from commercial purity Al-7% Mg alloy, cold worked 30% after furnace cooling from 427 C. White areas are due to $\beta$ precipitate.

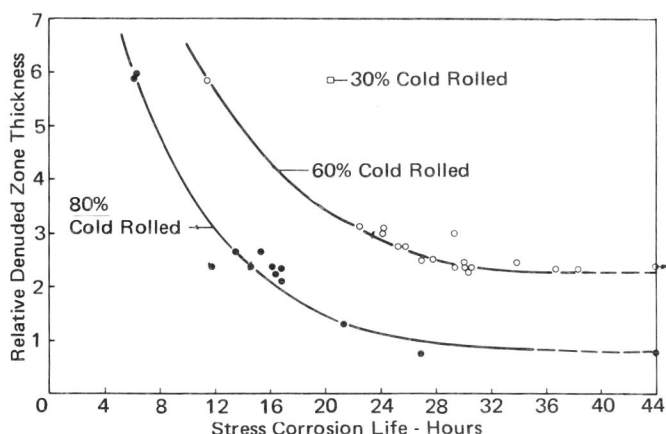

FIGURE 1 — Relationship between relative width of denuded zone and stress corrosion life. (Applied stress: 0.8 Y.S.; electrolyte: 6% NaCl + 0.005 M NaHCO$_3$; applied anodic current: 11 mA/sq in.)

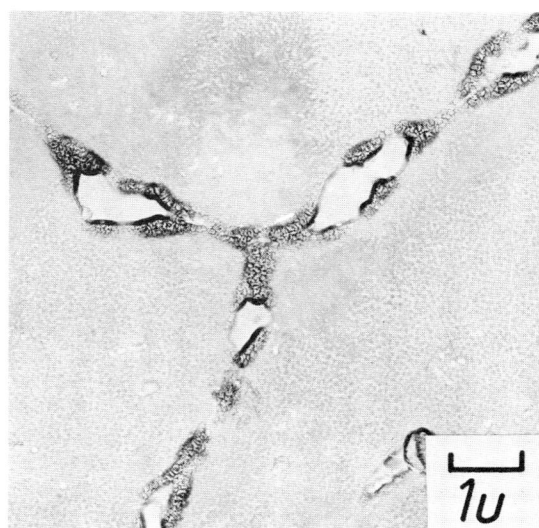

FIGURE 3 — Similar to Figure B, but specimen heated at 150 C for 24 hours after cold working. The stress corrosion life under test conditions of Figure 1 is about 20 hours.

# THE MECHANISM OF STRESS CORROSION
# CRACKING IN 7075 ALUMINUM

Alvin J. Jacobs
Rocketdyne

## I. Abstract

A new model is proposed in this paper for the stress corrosion cracking of 7075 aluminum. This model is similar in its broader aspects to the early model of Dix, which requires corrosion along a continuous anodic path combined with mechanical tearing of the metal at the tip of a corrosion crevice. As a result of calculations of the stress field around an edge dislocation situated near a grain boundary precipitate, it appears that the initiation of a stress corrosion crack can take place at the interface between the pitted precipitate particle and the aluminum matrix. These calculations indicate that a tensile stress in the order of 250,000 psi can act normal to the precipitate-matrix interface. The crack initiating at this interface or at the base of a pit propagates intergranularly via a series of chemical-mechanical (i.e., corrosion-mechanical fracture) steps. The mechanical fracture is a consequence of the fact that the advancing crack cannot easily be blunted by plastic flow, thus relieving the high stress concentrations at the crack tip. Any factor that leads to the immobilization of dislocations, or to the inactivation of dislocation sources, will contribute to the stress corrosion cracking of 7075 aluminum. For example, plastic deformation, wherein the dislocation density and, hence, the extent of dislocation-dislocation interactions are enhanced, will increase the susceptibility of 7075 to stress corrosion cracking. The nucleation of precipitates at dislocations is an even more important factor because small particles can exert a strong pinning effect on the dislocations. The first or stress corrosion stage of crack propagation is followed by a tensile stage, as soon as the remaining cross section is reduced sufficiently and the critical resolved shear stress is exceeded over a critical volume of material. The tensile stage is characterized by a predominantly transgranular-type fracture which occurs across the most favorably oriented slip planes. Fractographic evidence obtained in this and other studies substantiates a two-stage model.

Most of the current models for the stress corrosion cracking of high strength 7075 and related aluminum alloys invoke preferential plastic deformation in the ductile denuded zones adjacent to the grain boundaries. The results presented in this paper are not in harmony with such models. Thin-film electron microscopy has revealed that denuded zones are much less common in the susceptible -T6 temper than in the commercial D.T.D. 687 alloy or in ternary Al-Zn-Mg alloys, for example. A replica study of the slip characteristics of 7075-T6 and the resistant -T73 temper has shown that a regular tensile failure in these tempers features transgranular slip, and that plastic flow is not restricted to the denuded zones, as it is in D.T.D. 687. It is apparent from high- (explosive shock loading) and low-energy rate deformation (tension) studies of -T6 and -T73 that work hardening of the denuded zones, and not the maintenance of these zones in their ductile state, contributes to the susceptibility to stress corrosion cracking. When the capacity for plastic flow was reduced by notching the stress corrosion specimens, rapid failures could be induced even in -T73.

A correlation has been obtained between the macroscopic yield stress and the stress corrosion time to failure of 7075. Since the yield stress of a precipitation hardenable alloy such as 7075 can be expressed as a function of particle density and/or spacing, the above correlation may serve as a basis for predicting time to failure in terms of simple microstructural parameters.

## II. Introduction

Most of the current theories for the stress corrosion cracking of aluminum regard plastic flow as an essential step in the process. Indirect evidence for the involvement of plastic flow was obtained by Thomas and Nutting,[1] who observed that slip lines in susceptible D.T.D. 687[1] were restricted to the precipitate-free (denuded) zones along the grain boundaries. These investigators concluded that the preferential slip in the denuded zones caused anodic depolarization and enhanced corrosive attack and ultimately stress corrosion failure.

The mechanochemical theory of Hoar[2] and the film-rupture mechanism of Logan[3] have been extrapolated from studies on iron- and copper-base alloys to studies on aluminum alloys. According to the mechanochemical

---

[1]D.T.D. 687 is a commercial alloy similar to 7075 (Al-5.5% Zn-2.5% Mg-1.5% Cu- < 1% total Si, Fe, Mn, Cr, Ti) except for somewhat lower Cu and Cr contents and a higher Mn content.

theory of Hoar[2] stress corrosion cracks propagate by rapid dissolution of their mechanically yielding advancing edges, while their static sides dissolve extremely slowly. Rapid dissolution is thought to be favored by arrival at the dissolving surface of dislocation pileups and/or brittle fracture of protective oxide films caused by ductile yielding of the metal beneath (film-rupture mechanism). In both the mechanochemical and film-rupture models, dissolution at the crack tip leads to further stress concentration and hence to further localized plastic deformation. The repeated cycles of deformation and dissolution cause eventual failure.

Pugh and Jones[4] have espoused the film-rupture model to explain stress corrosion cracking in a high-purity aluminum alloy containing 5.5% Zn and 2.5% magnesium. Stress concentrations set up at the extremities of corrosion crevices were relieved by plastic deformation within the precipitate-free zones. The preferential deformation in turn ruptured protective (oxide) films in the grain boundary region, leading to further localized corrosive attack. The repeated cycles of corrosion and preferential deformation resulted in hardening and eventual crack initiation. No cracks were observed along the deformed paths before final fracture.

In their study of a 5.5% Zn-2.5% Mg aluminum alloy, McEvily, et al[5] also associated the soft grain boundary regions with stress corrosion cracking. This process was thought to be largely the result of a repetitive process of film rupture and mechanical advance (a phrase which was left undefined). When plastic flow was confined to the denuded zones, a crack propagated at a lower stress than when the deformation was not confined, as in the case of material cold rolled prior to aging. The authors concluded from their data that cold work prior to aging had a major beneficial effect on resistance to stress corrosion cracking. A surprising feature of the results is that unworked specimens, oriented in the transverse direction, tended to fail in approximately the same time as longitudinal specimens.

Thomas[6] was successful in improving the stress corrosion resistance of D.T.D. 687 alloy by interrupting the aging process, deforming, and then aging again. The principle of his technique was to introduce preferential plastic flow in the denuded zones, and, as a result of the dislocation interactions, excess vacancies and further precipitation upon re-aging.

A significant departure from the aforementioned theories is found in the work of Holl.[7] Holl studied an Al-Zn-Mg alloy that was the same compositionally as Pugh's[4] and McEvily's[5] except for small additions of copper (0.5%), silicon and iron (0.3% total). These small compositional differences may in fact account for the presence or absence of denuded zones. Using the same heat treatments as Pugh and McEvily, Holl did not obtain these zones. The dislocation arrangements in deformed material aged to various degrees of susceptibility to stress corrosion cracking were correlated with the degree of susceptibility. Dislocations in highly susceptible material tended to remain on their original slip planes and slip was concentrated in

well-defined bands. In material of low susceptibility, the dislocations formed uniformly distributed tangles, i.e., restricted slip did not occur. Thus, according to Holl, dislocation pile-ups can exist in susceptible conditions, and by exerting a high stress concentration over a short length of grain boundary can transform a simple corrosion fissure into a propagating brittle crack. This process is repeated whenever the crack becomes arrested. Holl concludes that the overall distribution and nature of precipitates within the matrix, through their control over deformation behavior, are the important factors in determining stress corrosion cracking susceptibility. The most susceptible condition is that containing G.P. zones or coherent precipitates; the most resistant condition contains noncoherent precipitates. It is significant that the two susceptible conditions studied by Holl, containing G.P. zones, were free of denuded zones, whereas his two resistant conditions containing noncoherent precipitates did show very narrow ($\sim 500$ Å) denuded zones. This is some of the most direct evidence that has been obtained against the denuded zone theories.

Gruhl and Cordier[8] had earlier reached the same conclusion as Holl, concerning the important role of precipitates in stress corrosion cracking. These investigators conducted reversion and rehardening experiments on an aluminum alloy containing 5% Zn-3% Mg (plus $\sim 1\%$ other elements). Their results indicated that stress corrosion was caused mainly by metastable, redissolvable precipitates (similar to the coherent $\eta$-phase reported by Schmalzried and Gerold).[9] When these precipitates were replaced by the stable T-phase upon aging at a higher temperature, the stress corrosion resistance underwent a marked improvement.

Extensive study of the 7075 alloy at Rocketdyne has failed to disclose the same prevalence of denuded zones, which investigators have found in D.T.D. 687 and Al-5.5% Zn-2.5% Mg. Furthermore, the morphology of the grain boundary precipitate was different from that observed in D.T.D. 687.[1] In the susceptible condition of D.T.D. 687, the grain boundary precipitates formed a continuous film, thereby preventing slip transfer from grain to grain; all the slip was confined to the precipitate-free boundary zones. The thin-film examination of 7075 showed a small probability of occurrence of film-type precipitates in both the -T6 (susceptible, maximum strength) and -T73 (resistant, lower strength) tempers. Thus, the detailed microstructures of 7075 and D.T.D. 687 differ, perhaps owing to the small differences in composition. Chromium[1] and copper[5,7] in particular, are known to promote uniform precipitation in Al-base alloys. As a result of the differences in microstructure, the detailed stress corrosion mechanisms may or may not be the same in the various alloys.

The model being proposed for stress corrosion cracking of 7075 is similar in some respects to Dix's electrochemical model.[10,11] The latter requires a continuous anodic path into the material. In the presence of a corrodent and a tensile stress, this path is preferentially attacked, and a stress concentration is set up at the tip of the resulting crevice. The stress concentration was thought to "tear the metal apart by mechanical action." The tearing action exposes fresh metal, which corrodes rapidly, thus leading to further stress concentration and further tearing of the metal. In the proposed model, the anodic path is continuous, but instead of consisting of a single phase, it consists of two phases ($MgZn_2$ and Al matrix) which alternate as anodes. The stress concentrations with which we are dealing also cause mechanical fracture. Crack propagation occurs by a cyclic repetition of corrosion and mechanical fracture, as in Dix's model.

The experimental program consisted of four major parts: (1) explosive shock loading of various heat treated conditions; (2) tensile deformation of 7075-T6 and -T73; (3) stress corrosion tests on notched 7075-T6 and -T73; and (4) a replica study of the slip characteristics of 7075-T6 and -T73. Parts 1 and 2 were designed to alter the dislocation density to determine whether there was a relationship between this parameter and stress corrosion resistance, as indicated in earlier work.[12] The primary objective of Part 3 was to compare the stress corrosion properties of 7075-T6 and -T73 having restricted capacity for plastic flow. In Part 4 the purpose was to follow the progressive development of slip lines with increasing deformation in -T6 and -T73. As a supplement to the foregoing experiments, a theoretical study of the elastic interactions between a grain boundary precipitate and a neighboring edge dislocation was undertaken; and finally a model was postulated for stress corrosion cracking in 7075 aluminum.

## III. Experimental Procedure

The first manifestation of a possibly important interaction between particles and dislocations appeared during the examination of thin films of 7075-T6.[12] It was observed in these films that dislocations often occurred next to large grain boundary precipitates (see Figure 22 in section entitled, "Postulated Mechanism") which were known to pit in a saline medium.[12] Similar observations were rarely, if ever, made in the case of -T73 thin films. Because stress corrosion cracks form readily at the base of pits in -T6 but not in -T73, the dislocation/grain boundary precipitate interactions were considered significant from the standpoint of stress corrosion crack initiation. Consequently explosive shock loading and tensile deformation experiments were conducted to ascertain the effect of increasing the dislocation density on the stress corrosion resistance. A theoretical study, which will be discussed in a subsequent section (see "Dislocation-Precipitate Interactions"), has yielded information concerning the magnitude of the interaction between a single edge dislocation and a single grain boundary precipitate.

### A. Explosive Shock Loading

The explosive shock loading was carried out using a plane-wave generator with driver and spall plates. Details concerning the experimental setup can be found in a previous paper.[13]

A total of 17 variously heat-treated conditions were shock loaded at 204 Kb. Ten of the specimens received no further treatment after being shocked; the other seven underwent further aging following the shocking. One of the specimens in the latter group was a shocked -T6 specimen which overaged after the shocking because of insufficient precooling. All the heat treatments are listed in the tables of results (Tables 4, 5, and 6 in the "Results" section). The 17 shocked specimens and their unshocked controls were machined from transverse sections of three forged billets.

The shock-induced changes in microstructure were studied by means of light and electron microscopy. Thin-film preparation for the Hitachi HU-11 electron microscope used is discussed in detail elsewhere.[12] Changes were measured in the mechanical (Knoop hardness, tensile yield and ultimate tensile strengths, and elongation) and stress corrosion properties. The tensile specimens were machined with their tensile axes parallel to the short-transverse direction of the billet. A strain rate of 0.005 inch/inch/min was employed in all tests. Stress corrosion tests were of the alternate immersion type and were conducted in a 3-1/2% aqueous NaCl solution. The specimens of these tests were identical to the tensile specimens in design and in orientation. A typical specimen is shown being mounted in a testing frame in Figure 1. All the stress corrosion specimens tested in this part of the investigation were loaded to 75% of their yield strength.

### B. Tensile Deformation

Four 7075-T6 and four -T73 specimens were subjected to stress corrosion tests after being plastically deformed in a tensile machine. The -T6 specimens were loaded in their stress corrosion frames to 50% of their post deformation yield strength, and the -T73 specimens to 75% of their post deformation yield strength. The post deformation yield strengths were measured on a second group of -T6 and -T73 specimens, which received the same deformations as the stress corrosion specimens. There was one important difference between the pre- and post deformation stress/strain curves for the -T6 and those for the -T73 specimens: the -T6 curves were discontinuous with respect to each other (the post deformation curves were higher than expected), while the -T73 post deformation curves merged continuously into the predeformation curves as expected (Figure 2). Part of the increase in yield strength of the -T6 specimens can be attributed to additional precipitation stimulated by the increased density of dislocations. The -T6 tensile and. stress corrosion specimens were of the type shown in Figure 1; the -T73 specimens were 1/8-inch rounds (Figure 3). The deformation stresses and the post deformation yield strengths are given in Table 1.

### C. Stress Corrosion Tests on Notched Specimens

As will be seen in the "Results" section, the shock loading and tensile deformation experiments suggested that the most important difference between the -T6 and -T73 tempers involves the mobility of dislocations and hence the

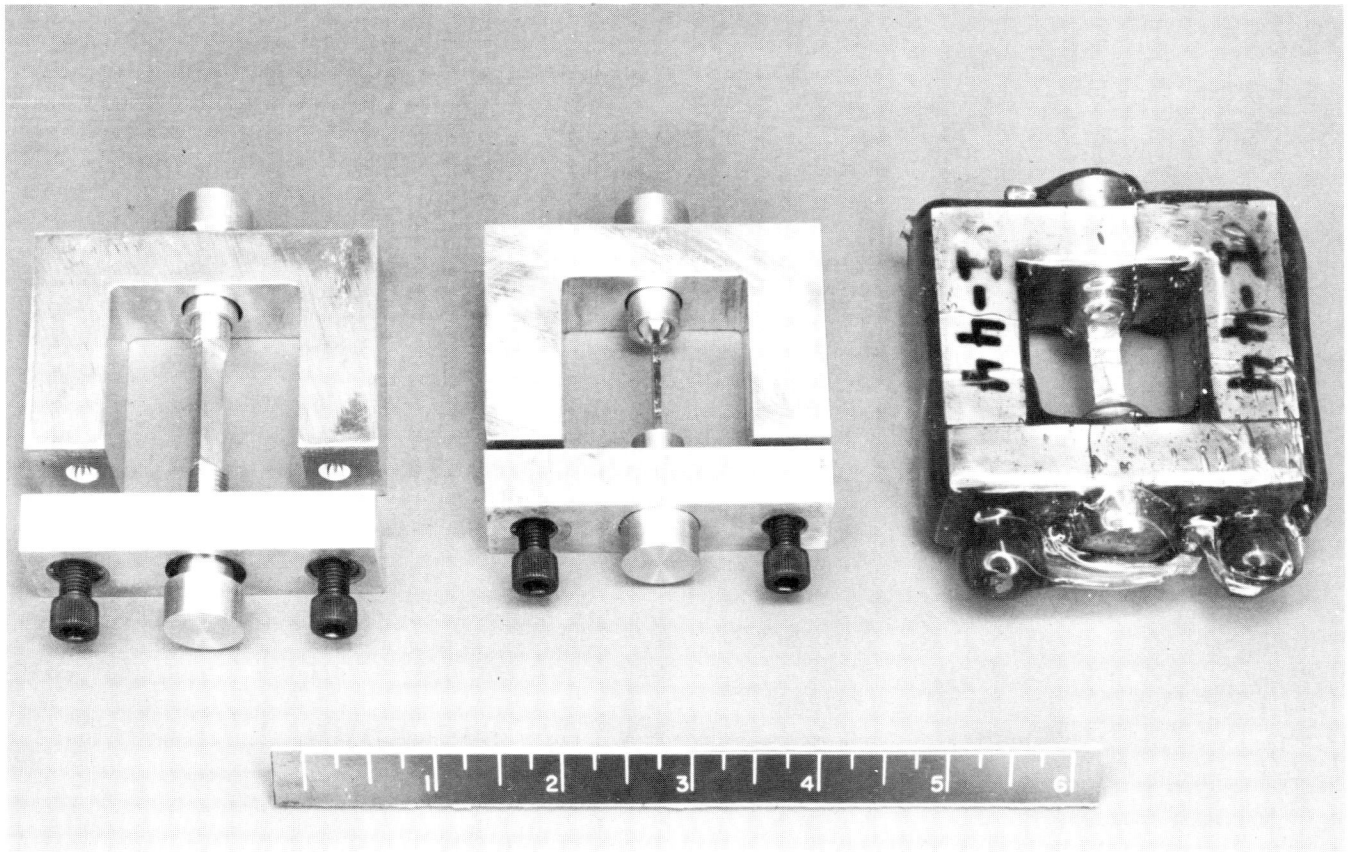

FIGURE 1 — Assembly of stress corrosion specimen in testing frame.

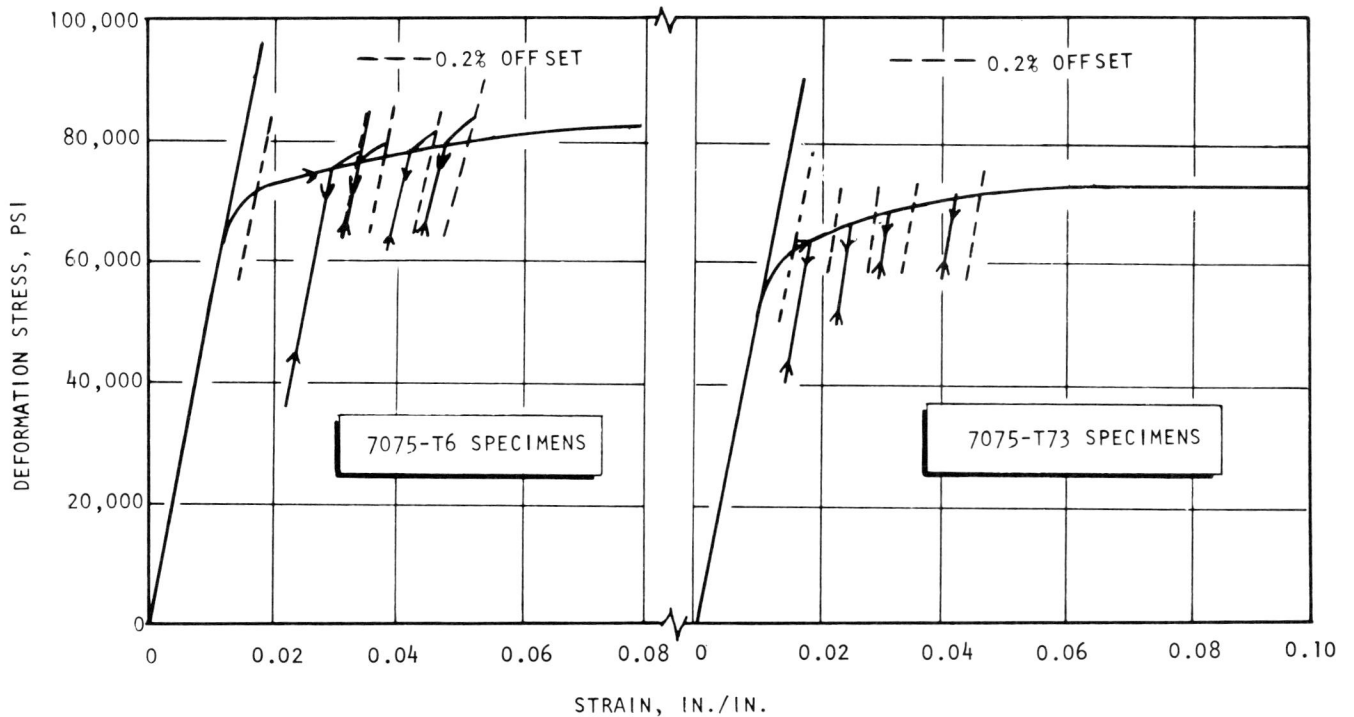

FIGURE 2 — Pre- and post-deformation stress/strain curves for 7075-T6 and -T73 specimens.

533

ease with which plastic flow takes place. The fine dispersion of G.P. zones in 7075-T6 reduces dislocation mobility and renders plastic flow at the tip of a crack very difficult. Dislocations in -T73 are more mobile because of the coarser particle dispersion, and plastic flow can occur more easily thus preventing high stress concentrations. It was decided to test these ideas by running stress corrosion tests on

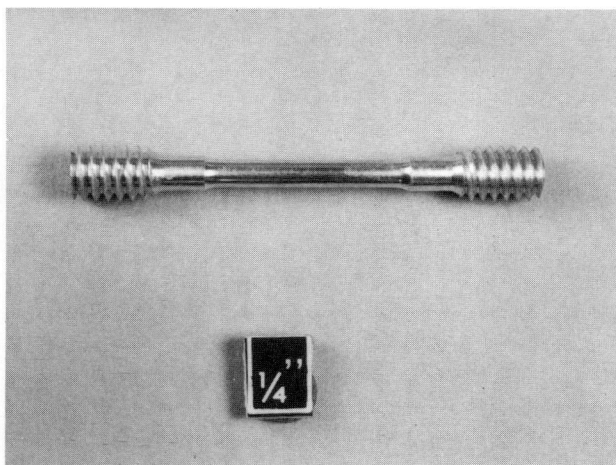

**FIGURE 3 — One-eighth-inch round stress corrosion specimen.**

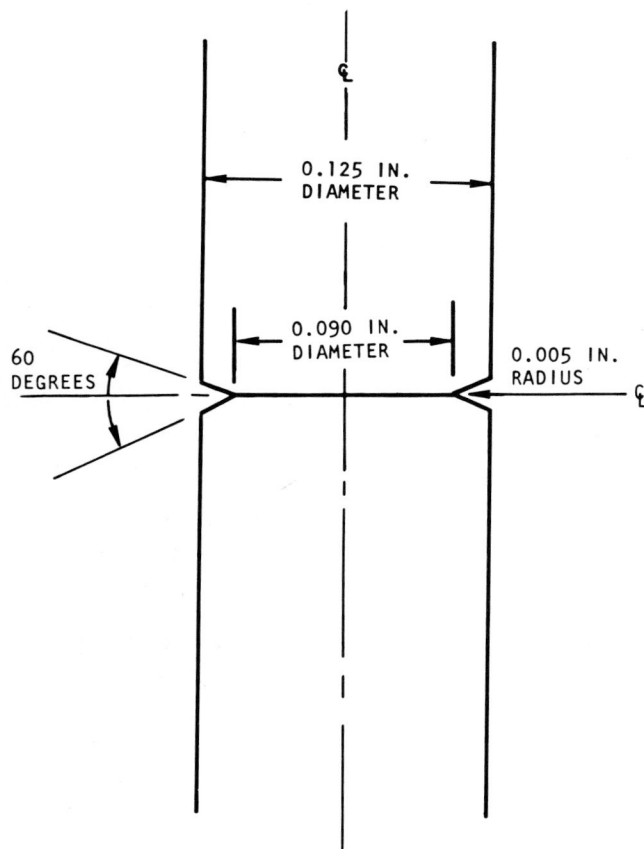

**FIGURE 4 — Notched 1/8-inch round stress corrosion specimen.**

**TABLE 1—Prior Deformations Received by 7075-T6 and -T73 Stress Corrosion Specimens and Resultant Yield Strengths**

| Specimen No. | Deformation Stress, psi | Post Deformation Yield Strength (0.2% Offset), psi |
|---|---|---|
| 7075-T6 | | |
| 134 | 75,500 | 78,100 |
| 136 | 76,800 | 79,100 |
| 139 | 78,100 | 81,000 |
| 141 | 79,100 | 84,300 |
| 143 (control) | Undeformed | 71,900 (Undeformed) |
| 7075-T73 | | |
| 8-1 | 63,000 | 65,040 |
| 5 | 65,540 | 67,600 |
| 6 | 67,480 | 69,550 |
| 7-1 | 69,590 | 71,700 |
| 15,16,15-1,15-2, 15-3,15-4,16-1 (Controls) | Undeformed | 62,500 (Undeformed) |

notched -T73 specimens. Plastic flow in a notched specimen is localized to the material immediately at the root of the notch. Thus, a notched -T73 specimen should approach in its behavior normal -T6, in which high stress concentrations can develop at the root of a crack because of restricted plastic flow. In the experiment described below, stress corrosion tests were also conducted on notched -T6 and unnotched -T6 and -T73.

Four 7075-T73 and four -T6 1/8-inch-round stress corrosion specimens were notched, as shown in Figure 4, prior to testing. The stress concentration at the root of such a notch is approximately 3.2.[14] Eleven unnotched -T73 and five unnotched -T6 specimens served as controls.

The specimens were loaded in stress corrosion frames to various fractions of the ultimate load. The ultimate loads were determined in tensile tests on separate specimens of the same dimensions and from the same billet as the stress corrosion specimens. Two tensile tests were conducted for each condition (notched -T73, etc.); typical load-strain curves obtained in these tests are shown in Figure 5. Each stress corrosion specimen was strained a preselected amount. The strain was measured by a 1/2-inch extensometer and read on the strain recorder of a Riehle tensile testing machine. The two loads corresponding to this strain in the corresponding pair of tensile tests were averaged, and the average load was divided by the average ultimate load obtained in the same pair of tensile tests. The fractions of ultimate load so computed appear in Table 2; the region of the load-strain curve (elastic or plastic), to which the load applies, is also indicated.

Electron fractographs were prepared from representative fracture surfaces. The replicas were of the two-stage, plastic-carbon variety and were shadowed with uranium oxide. The replicated specimens are noted in Table 2. Fractured tensile specimens 11-1 (unnotched -T73), 14 (notched -T73), 21 (unnotched -T6), and 23 (notched -T6) were also replicated for control purposes.

534

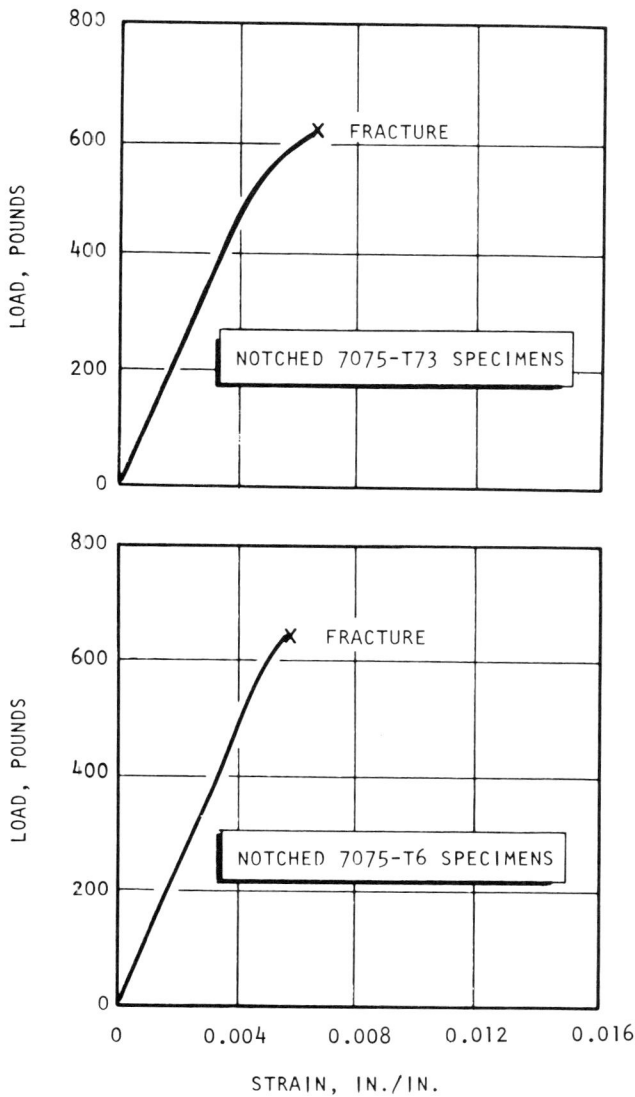

FIGURE 5 — Typical load vs strain curves for notched 7075-T6 and -T73 specimens.

## D. Slip Characteristics of 7075-T6 and -T73

This study was undertaken primarily to determine if slip occurs preferentially along grain boundaries, as in D.T.D. 687 where denuded zones are known to pervade the structure.[1] The study sought also to uncover similarities and differences in the slip behavior of 7075-T6 and -T73.

One series of 7075-T6 and another series of -T73 tensile specimens were deformed in an Instron machine, so the slip characteristics of these tempers could be studied by means of a replica technique. The specimens were of the type shown in Figure 1. Prior to deformation, they were electropolished according to a procedure described elsewhere.[12]

The elongation was measured by a deflectometer attached to the moving crosshead of the Instron. This quantity varied between 0.020 and 0.045 inch, the latter value being obtained at fracture. The crosshead speed was 0.05 inch/min. Typical load-elongation curves for -T6 and

TABLE 2–Fractions of Ultimate Load at Which Notched and Unnotched 7075-T73 and -T6 Stress Corrosion Specimens were Tested

| Condition | Specimen No. | Applicable Region of Load-Strain Curve | Fraction of Ultimate Load | Fractograph |
|---|---|---|---|---|
| 7075-T73 | | | | |
| Notched | 17 | Plastic | 0.79 | — |
| | 18 | Plastic | 0.89 | Yes |
| | 19 | Plastic | 0.95 | Yes |
| | 20 | Plastic | 0.99 | Yes |
| Unnotched | 16 | Elastic | 0.65 | — |
| | 15-1 | Elastic | 0.65 | — |
| | 16-1 | Elastic | 0.65 | Yes |
| | 15-2 | Elastic | 0.65 | — |
| | 15-3 | Elastic | 0.65 | — |
| | 15-4 | Elastic | 0.65 | — |
| | 9-1 | Plastic | 0.79 | — |
| | 10-1 | Plastic | 0.89 | — |
| | 11 | Plastic | 0.91 | — |
| | 12 | Plastic | 0.98 | — |
| 7075-T6 | | | | |
| Notched | 27 | Elastic | 0.27 | — |
| | 28 | Elastic | 0.55 | — |
| | 29 | Plastic | 0.91 | Yes |
| | 30 | Plastic | 0.95 | Yes |
| Unnotched | 25 | Elastic | 0.22 | — |
| | 31 | Plastic | 0.76 | — |
| | 32 | Plastic | 0.84 | — |
| | 33 | Plastic | 0.91 | — |
| | 34 | Plastic | 0.95 | Yes |

-T73 are shown for comparison in Figure 6. The deformations received by the two sets of specimens were approximately the same and are listed in Table 3.

A two-stage, plastic-carbon replica technique was employed. The shadowing material was uranium oxide deposited at an angle of 9.5°.

## IV. Results

### A. Explosive Shock Loading

1. **Tensile Tests.** The tensile results obtained from nine shocked specimens and four unshocked controls are summarized in Table 4. The table shows that -T6 Specimens IIIA and II have overaged compared to their respective controls. One of the reasons for the overaging lies in the accelerated aging kinetics of shocked, age-hardenable materials.[15] Furthermore, owing to insufficient precooling, both specimens overheated as a result of the shock loading. The average yield strengths of IIIA and II are approximately the same, indicating that they have overaged to the same extent.

The 350 F aging curves for shocked 7075-T6 (Specimens IIIB1 to IIIB5 and XI) are shown in Figures 7a and 7b. Aging time at 350 F is plotted against Knoop hardness in Figure 7a, and against yield strength in Figure 7b. Both curves are observed to fall off very steeply during the first hour of aging. The yield strength and hardness values of Specimens II and IIIA indicate that they have overaged the equivalent of about one hour at 350 F.

Shock loading is observed to have increased the yield strength of 7075-T73 by approximately 7250 psi (Table 4).

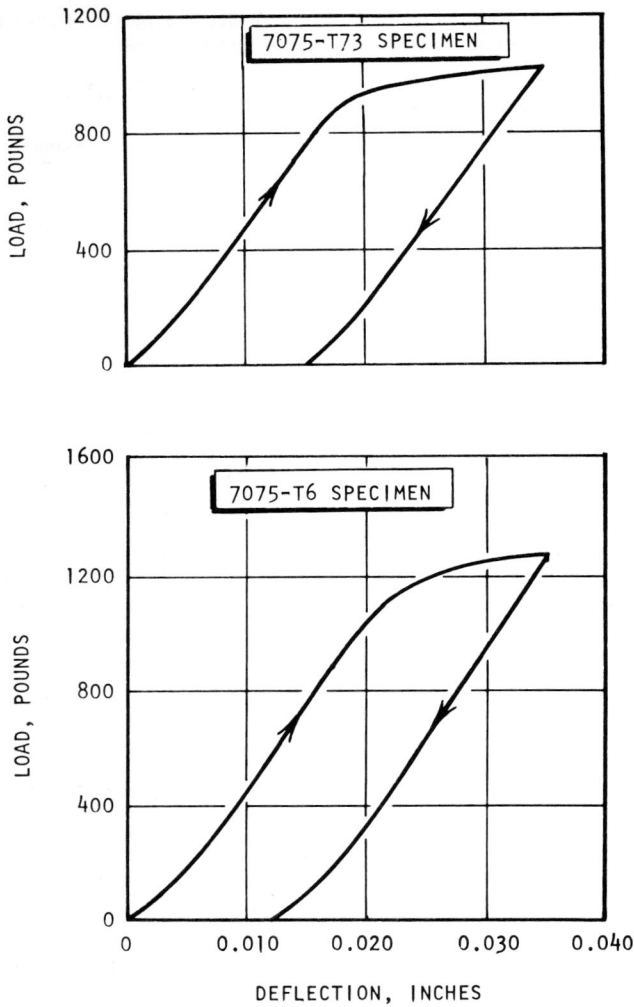

FIGURE 6 — Typical load vs deflection curves for 7075-T6 and -T73 specimens deformed in Instron Testing Machine.

### TABLE 4—Tensile Results Obtained from Shocked 7075 Aluminum and Unshocked Control Specimens

| Specimen | Heat-Treated Condition | Number of Tests | Yield Strength (0.2% Offset), psi | UTS, psi | % Elongation (1/2-in Gauge Length) |
|---|---|---|---|---|---|
| I | Unshocked 7075-T6 (control for IIIA) | 4 | 71,890 | 80,880 | 10.0 |
| IIIA | Solution-treated, -T6 age, shocked | 2 | 67,050 | 70,190 | 6.0 |
| V | Unshocked 7075-T6 (control for II) | 3 | 71,910 | 80,990 | 6.0 |
| II | Solution-treated, shocked, -T6 age | 4 | 67,240 | 70,320 | 3.0 |
| IVA | Unshocked 7075-T73 (control for IVB) | 4 | 61,860 | 72,110 | 10.0 |
| IVB | Solution-treated, -T73 age, shocked | 4 | 69,100 | 74,180 | 7.0 |
| XIC | Unshocked 7075-T6 (control for XI) | 4 | 72,440 | 82,760 | 12.0 |
| XI | Solution-treated, -T6 age, shocked | 4 | 82,960 | 88,840 | 7.0 |
| IIIB1 | Solution-treated, -T6 age, shocked, 1 hr age at 350 F | 4 | 72,100 | 78,910 | 6.0 |
| IIIB2 | As above, except 2 hr age at 350 F | 3 | 58,790 | 61,140 | 4.0 |
| IIIB3 | As above, except 3 hr age at 350 F | 4 | 55,890 | 57,640 | 4.0 |
| IIIB4 | As above, except 4 hr age at 350 F | 1 | 59,760 | 63,260 | 4.0 |
| IIIB5 | As above, except 5 hr age at 350 F | 3 | 51,080 | 54,770 | 3.0 |

### TABLE 3—Elongations of 7075-T6 and -T73 Tensile Specimens Deformed in Instron Machine

| Temper | Specimen No. | Elongation, inch |
|---|---|---|
| 7075-T6 | 6 | 0.023 |
| | 2 | 0.025 |
| | 3 | 0.030 |
| | 4 | 0.035 |
| | 5 | 0.040 |
| | 1 | 0.043 (Fracture) |
| 7075-T73 | 6 | 0.020 |
| | 2 | 0.024 |
| | 3 | 0.030 |
| | 4 | 0.035 |
| | 5 | 0.040 |
| | 1 | 0.046 (Fracture) |

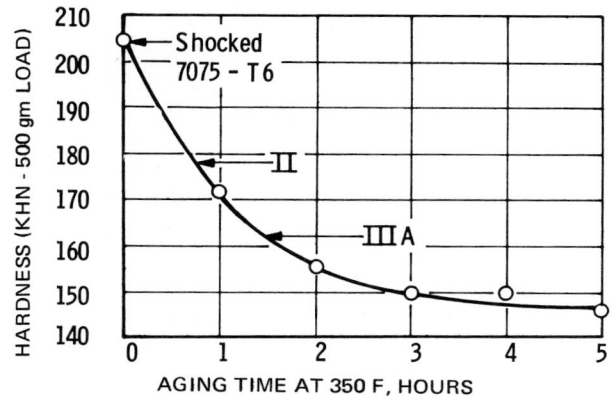

(a) HARDNESS VS AGING TIME AT 350 F

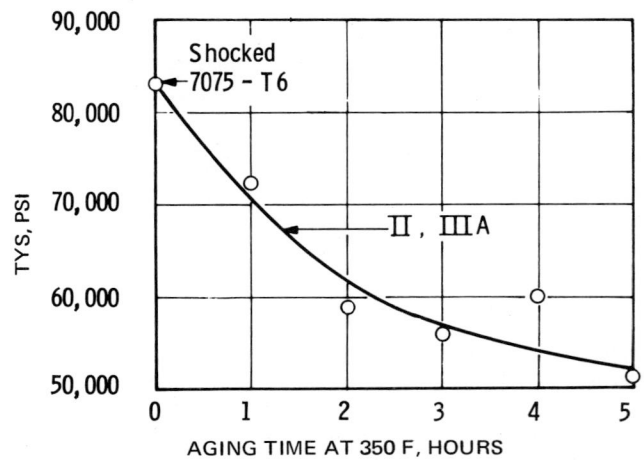

(b) TENSILE YIELD STRENGTH VS AGING TIME AT 350 F

FIGURE 7 — Aging curves obtained for shocked 7075-T6. (a) Hardness vs aging time at 350 F. (b) Tensile yield strength vs aging time at 350 F.

TABLE 5–Stress Corrosion Test Results Showing
the Effect of Altering the
Shock-Loading/Aging Sequence

| Specimen | Heat-Treated Condition | Time to Failure ($t_f$), days |
|---|---|---|
| V | Unshocked 7075-T6 (control for II) | 1.5 (4)[1] |
| II | Solution-treated, shocked, -T6 age | 1.5 (4) |
| I | Unshocked 7075-T6 (control for IIIA) | 2 (4) |
| IIIA | Solution-treated, -T6 age, shocked | 52 (4) |

[1]Number of tests in parentheses, $t_f$ is average value.

**2. Stress Corrosion Tests.** The results of alternate immersion tests are presented in Tables 5 and 6. The critical effect that the shock loading/aging sequence has on stress corrosion resistance is shown in Table 5. As already noted, Specimens II and IIIA were overaged to the same extent. Specimen II, which was shocked in the solution-treated condition and then aged, has a very low resistance to stress corrosion cracking. Specimen IIIA, which was shocked after being aged, has a high resistance. The radically different responses of these specimens to a stress corrosion environment are obviously the result of the subtle difference in their thermal-mechanical treatment.

It is interesting that a critical overaging time at 350 F is required for high stress corrosion resistance (Figure 8). This time is between one and two hours. Thus, Specimen IIIB1, which was overaged for one hour, has low resistance while Specimen IIIB2, which was overaged for two hours, has high resistance. The high resistance of Specimen IIIA, which was overaged the equivalent of 1-1/4 hours at 350 F, confirms the findings for the IIIB group of specimens. After the critical overaging time has been exceeded, the stress corrosion resistance of IIIB increases steadily with further overaging. Reference to Figure 7b shows that the yield strength of IIIB4, which seems to have too low a stress corrosion resistance according to Figure 8, is anomalously high. The deviations are in opposite directions, as expected.

Table 6 shows the effect of explosive shock loading on the stress corrosion resistance of 7075-T6 and -T73, as well as variously underaged and overaged (compared to maximum strength -T6) 7075 specimens. Note the longer lifetime of the unshocked specimens in every case except two where the $t_f$'s are the same. This result was found not only for those specimens with very high resistance ($t_f \geqslant 30$ days), but also for those with less resistance.

**3. Light and Electron Microscopy.** The shock-loaded grain structures had the same appearance as the unshocked structures in the light microscope.

The examination of thin films showed that all the shocked specimens had similar dislocation structures. Thus, 7075-T6 and -T73, e.g., were indistinguishable in this respect after shock loading. The pre-shock structure of 7075-T6 (Figure 9) underwent marked changes. The dis-

TABLE 6–Stress Corrosion Test Results Showing the Effect of Shock Loading on the Time to Failure of Variously Aged Specimens

| Specimen | Billet | Heat-Treated Condition | Time to Failure ($t_f$), days Unshocked | Time to Failure ($t_f$), days Shocked |
|---|---|---|---|---|
| VIIC-1, VIIA-B | 2 | Solution-treated, 4 hr age at 250 F | 10 (2)[1] | 2 (4)[1] |
| XIC, XI | 3 | 7075-T6 | 3 (4) | 2 (4) |
| XIIC, XII | 3 | 7075-T6, overaged 1/2 hr at 350 F | 4 (4) | 4 (4) |
| XIIIC, XIII | 3 | 7075-T6, overaged 1 hr at 350 F | 3 (4) | 3 (4) |
| XIVC, XIV | 3 | 7075-T6, overaged 1-1/2 hr at 350 F | 6 (4) | 3 (4) |
| XVC, XV | 3 | 7075-T6, overaged 2-1/4 hr at 350 F | 14 (4) | 5 (3) |
| VIIC-2, VIIIA-B | 2 | 7075-T6, overaged 3 hr at 350 F | 47 (1) | 35 (1) |
| IXC-1, IXA-B | 2 | 7075-T6, overaged 5-1/2 hr at 350 F | 71 (2) | 32 (3) |
| IXC-2, XA-B | 2 | 7075-T6, overaged 8-3/4 hr at 350 F | 63 (2) | 55 (2) |
| IVA, IVB | 1 | 7075-T73 | 51 (3) | 40 (4) |

[1]Number of tests in parentheses, $t_f$ is average value.

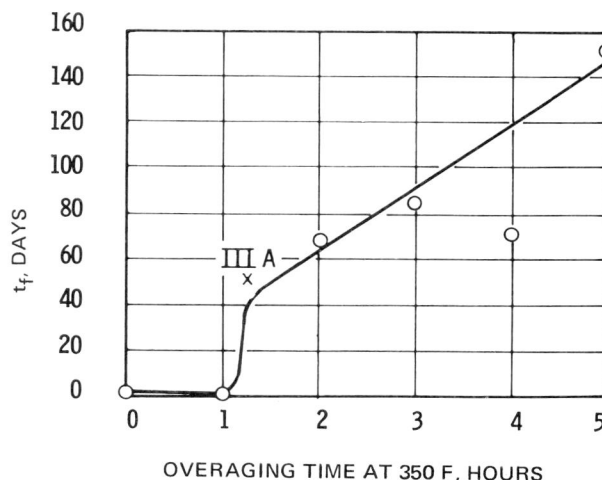

FIGURE 8 – Time to failure ($t_f$) vs overaging time at 350 F.

location density increased markedly and the long dislocations became shorter (Figure 10). Far more loops appeared, and the dislocations were uniformly distributed.

Particle-size counts were not made. The G.P. zones in shocked 7075-T6, which did not overage after shocking (Specimen IX) are not resolved in Figure 10. The largest precipitates were found in shocked and overaged Specimens IIIB1 to B5, as might be expected (Figure 11). No shearing of precipitates was detected, and no evidence for twin formation was found.

*B. Tensile Deformation*

The stress corrosion results obtained from the four plastically deformed 7075-T6 specimens are plotted in Figure 12. The curve shows that as the deformation stress is raised from 75,500 to 79,100 psi, the stress corrosion test life of -T6 is lowered by more than two-thirds. (The $t_f$ of the undeformed control specimen was 7 days.)

537

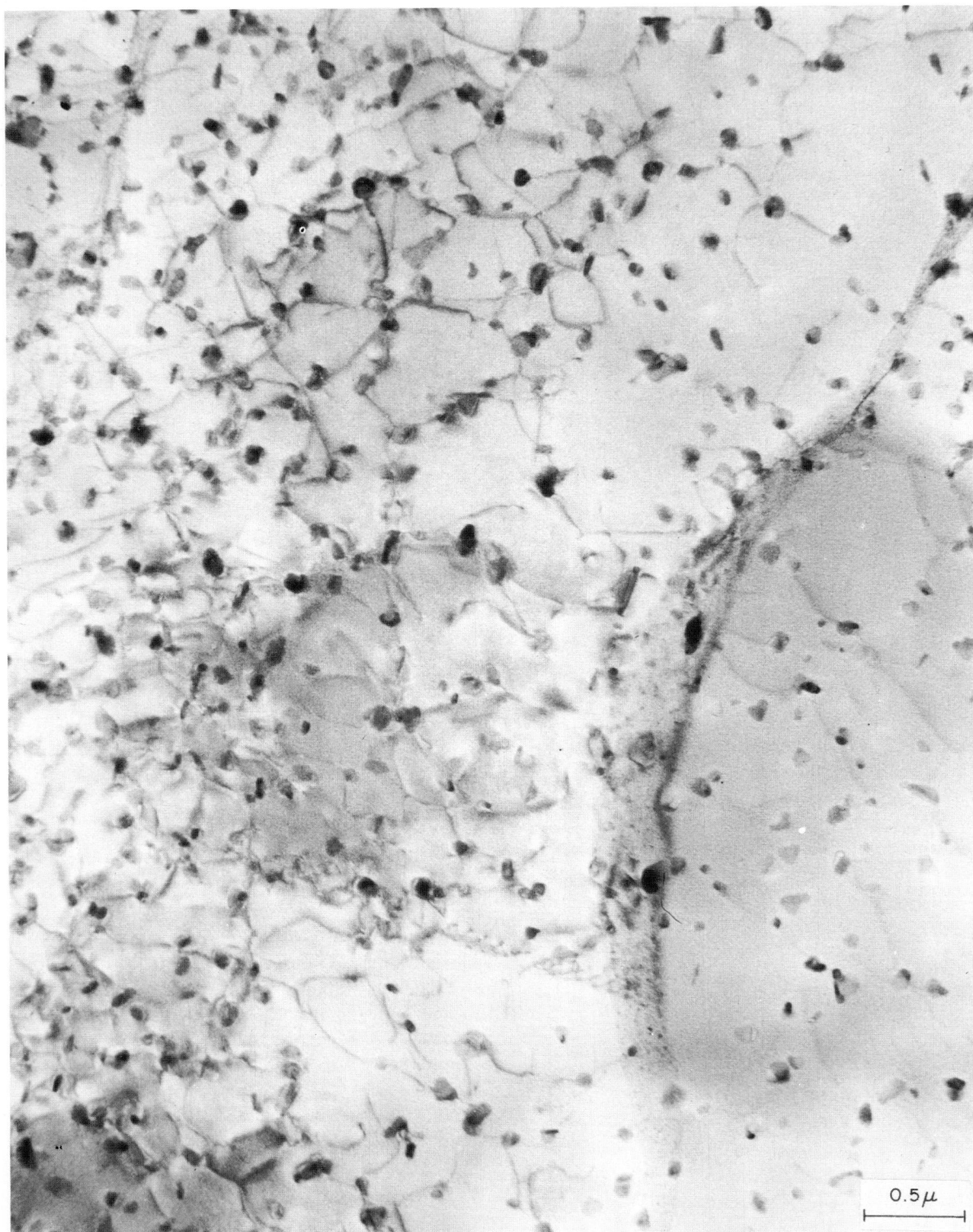

FIGURE 9 — Typical thin-film microstructure of 7075-T6 specimen (note fine dispersion of GP zones in background, dislocations, and large precipitate particles).

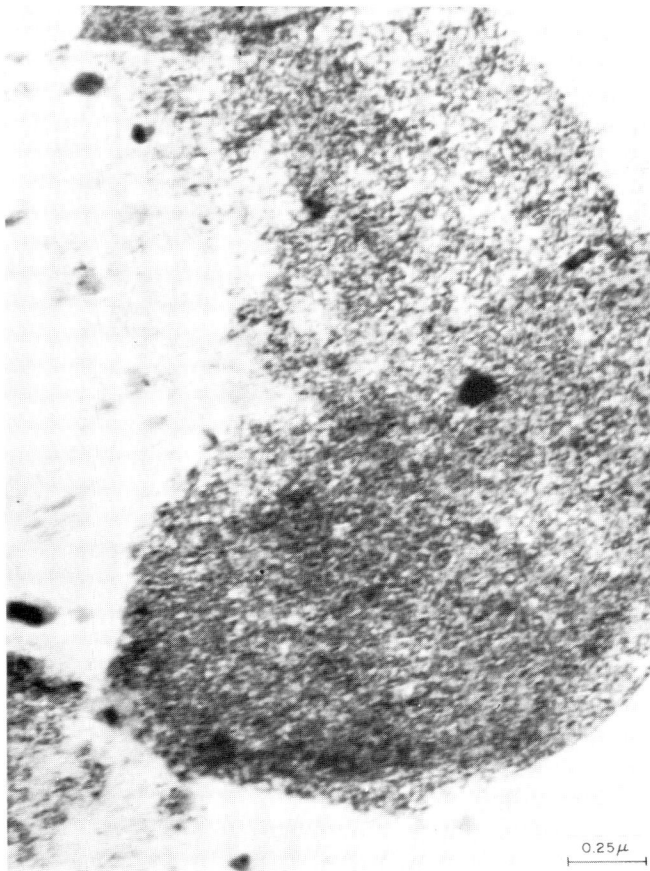

FIGURE 10 — Explosively shock loaded 7075-T6 (high-contrast area contains numerous dislocation loops).

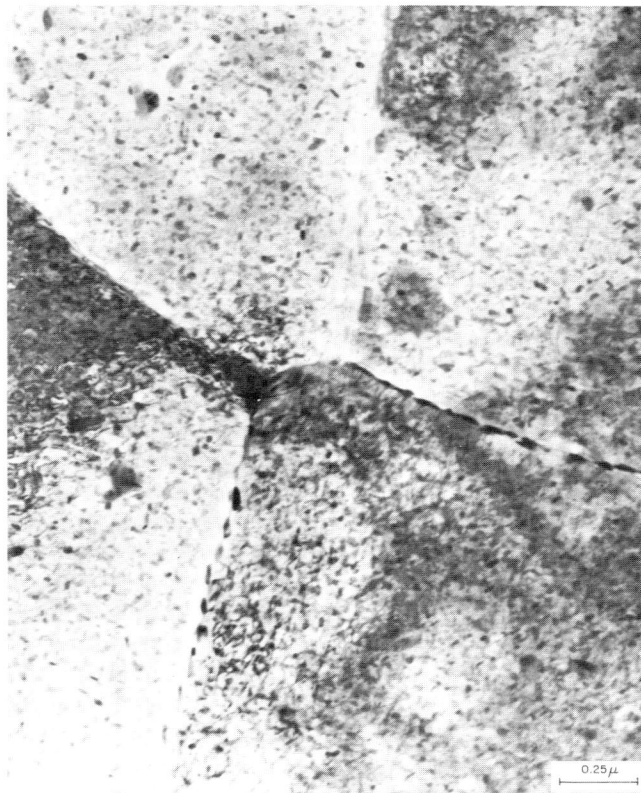

FIGURE 11 — Transmission micrograph of 7075, shocked in -T6 condition and aged at 350 F for 5 hours.

The -T73 specimens, on the other hand, were not adversely affected by the prior deformation (Figure 12). The $t_f$'s varied irregularly between a low value of 24 days at a prestress level of 63,000 psi, and a high value of 65 days at a prestress of 69,590 psi. On the average, these $t_f$ values were greater than the average $t_f$ of seven undeformed controls (26 days, Figure 13).

The results of the tensile deformation experiment can be explained in terms of dislocation-precipitate interactions. As seen above, the effect of the cold work was not the same in the -T6 and -T73. In the -T6, two factors contributed to the increase in yield strength: (1) The increase in dislocation density, and (2) the increase in particle density resulting from the increase in dislocation density. In the -T73, however, only the first of these factors was present. Assuming that the increase in dislocation density was not exactly the same in the two tempers, the small difference would easily be overwhelmed by even a small difference in particle density, which is now known to be a more important variable than the dislocation density in determining stress corrosion life. The increase in particle density with increasing prior deformation of -T6 resulted in the progressively shorter time to failure. The accompanying increase in dislocation density in -T6, or the increase in dislocation density alone in -T73, had a negligible effect on $t_f$.

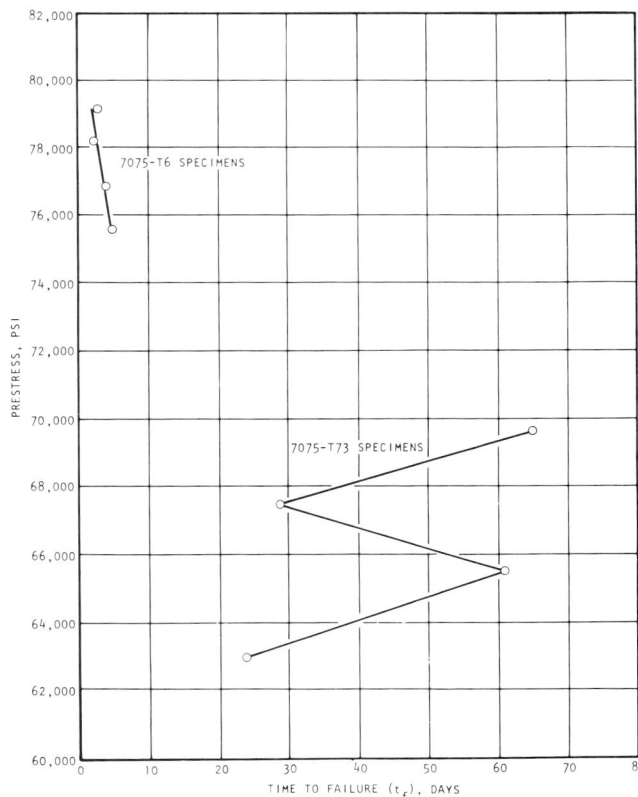

FIGURE 12 — Deformation prestress vs time to failure ($t_f$) of 7075-T6 and -T73 specimens.

539

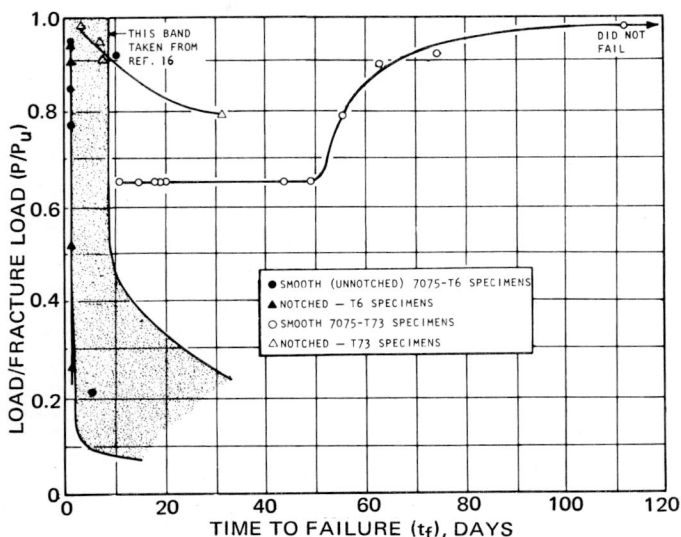

FIGURE 13 — Fraction of load to fracture (P/P$_u$) vs time to failure (t$_f$) of notched and unnotched 7075-T6 and -T73 specimens.

## C. Stress Corrosion Tests on Notched Specimens

A comparison of the results from notched and unnotched -T6 and -T73 stress corrosion specimens is shown in Figure 13, where the fraction of ultimate load (P/P$_u$) applied in the tests is plotted against time to failure (t$_f$). The results indicate that notched -T73 approaches the -T6 condition (notched or unnotched) in susceptibility, particularly at high values of P/P$_u$ ($> 0.9$). In fact, the t$_f$'s of the three most highly stressed notched T73 specimens fall well within the scatter band taken from Reference 16 for unnotched -T6. A critical P/P$_u$ is suggested for notched -T73, which is akin to the critical stress for unnotched -T6 (the stress below which stress corrosion failure will not occur).

The lifetimes of notched -T6, unlike those of notched -T73, are independent of load. All the notched -T6 specimens failed in one day or less as the load varied from 0.27 to 0.95 of the load at fracture. Since unnotched -T6 specimens are known to show a marked dependence on stress,[16] the effect of the notch is the same in -T6 as it is in -T73, viz, to enhance the susceptibility to cracking. However, this enhancement is less dramatic in the case of the -T6.

The results concerning the unnotched -T73 are rather surprising. The time to failure (t$_f$) actually increases with increasing stress level. Although the particular billet from which the specimens were prepared met tensile and conductivity specifications for -T73 material, t$_f$ varied from 10 to 49 days for seven specimens stressed at 65% of their ultimate tensile strength (UTS). Specimens stressed at 79, 89, and 91% of their UTS failed in 55, 63, and 74 days, respectively. The specimen stressed at the highest level (98% of UTS) did not fail in 112 days of testing.

It could be argued that the notch serves to concentrate anodic activity because of the high stresses developed at its root. Such an "area" effect has been observed by Farmery and Evans[17] and by Colner and Francis.[18] Farmery and Evans showed that the stress corrosion life of a partially coated Al-7% Mg specimen increased as the exposed (uncoated) area was reduced. However, when a stressed specimen having a small exposed area was electrically coupled to an unstressed specimen having a large exposed area, the life of the stressed specimen decreased. This is an electrochemical effect in which the stressed specimen acts as the anode and the unstressed specimen as the cathode, and the magnitude of the current flowing in the differential stress cell increases with increasing stress. Colner and Francis[18] have shown that a similar effect operates in the cracking of Al-4% Cu alloys. In the present investigation, however, evidence against an area effect was obtained from the notched -T6 specimen (Specimen No. 29) which broke at some distance from the notch. Since the minimum stress requirement for propagation of the crack was obviously met along the crack path followed, this path must have been more favorable from a chemical or electrochemical standpoint than any alternative path emerging from the notch.

The different stress dependence of t$_f$ for unnotched -T6 and -T73 specimens (Figure 13) emphasizes the basic difference between these two tempers concerning their ability to plastically deform. The difference between the t$_f$'s of -T6 and -T73 is accentuated as the stress level increases, which suggests that the ratio of maximum stresses present at the root of an advancing fissure (tensile stress)$_{max}$/(shear stress)$_{max}$ is increasing with applied stress in the case of -T6 and decreasing in the case of -T73. Thus, at the root of the fissure, the stress state is approaching balanced triaxiality in -T6 but deviating more and more from such a condition in -T73. Any corrosion fissures in -T73 are repeatedly blunted because of the high capacity for localized plastic flow of this temper.

**1. Fractography.** The fracture surfaces of the tested stress corrosion specimens disclosed a dark crescent-like area around the outside and a light area occupying the remainder of the surface. In the notched specimens where the failure was in the notch, the light area was larger; in the single notched specimen (Specimen 29) where the failure was away from the notch and in the unnotched specimens, the dark area was larger. From all indications, the dark area represents a slow, stress corrosion phase of failure, and the light area a more rapid, tensile-type fracture. The fact that the light area was larger in those specimens where failure was in the notch, as compared to the remainder of the specimens, is indicative of a much smaller stress absorbing capacity in the former group of specimens before rapid tensile failure.

The fractographs showed that the fracture surfaces in the dark (stress corrosion) areas were almost entirely intergranular in nature (Figure 14a), while those in the light (tensile overload) areas were predominantly transgranular (Figure 14b). Quite severe corrosion had taken place in the dark areas (Figure 14a), and the products of the corrosion reaction were considerably more abundant in these areas

540

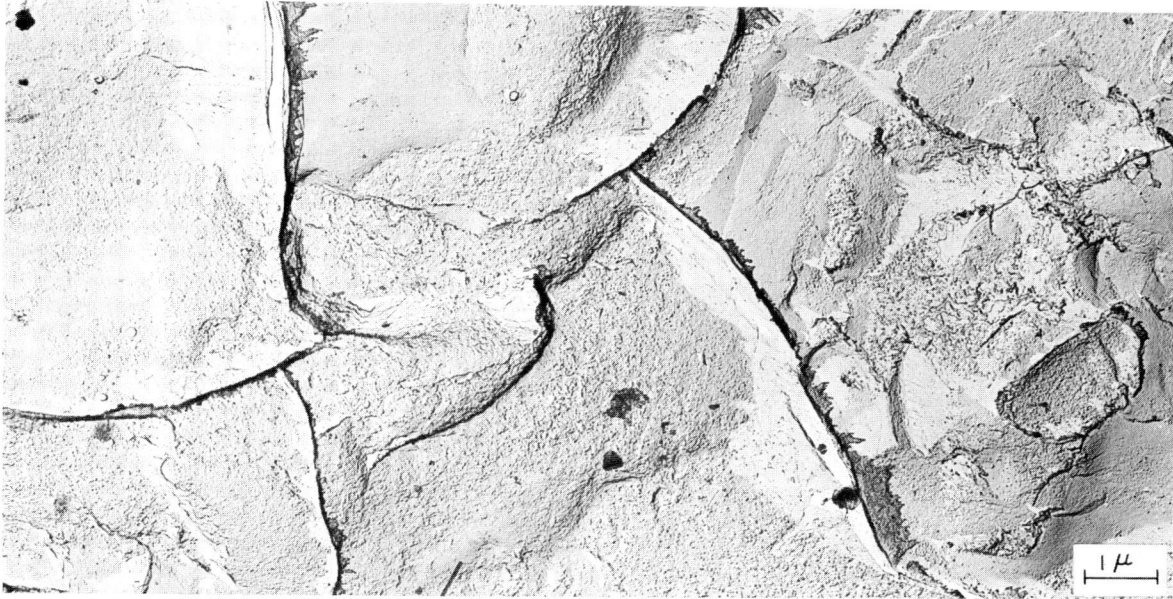

(a)

(b)

FIGURE 14 — (a) Intergranular fracture typical of stress corrosion phase of failure in a notched 7075-T73 specimen. Note corrosion product in rough-textured area. (b) Fractograph of a notched 7075-T6 specimen that failed away from the notch. Note transgranular fracture typical of tensile phase of failure.

541

than in the light, as might be expected from the relative times that these areas were exposed to the corrodent.

Although such signs of brittle fracture as cleavage steps were observed in the dark areas but not in the light, there were still numerous signs of ductility in the dark areas. A dimpled structure was frequently observed in the stress corrosion areas, as shown in Figure 15. Dimples were also observed frequently in the light areas (Figure 14b).

The fractographs obtained from the tested tensile specimens revealed more or less what was expected: a predominantly dimpled, transgranular appearance with the extent of dimpling being smaller in the notched than in the unnotched specimens. Occasionally, the fracture was observed to be intergranular (Figure 16).

In a microscope study of stress corroded D.T.D. 683 Al-Zn-Mg alloy, Forsyth and Ryder[19] found two types of fracture surface, the first a brightly reflecting zone, and the second a dull zone. Fractographs of the brightly reflecting zones showed that they were the result of intercrystalline fracture with little accompanying plastic deformation. The dull zones, which were apparently produced by more rapid fracture than the light zones, were characterized by a

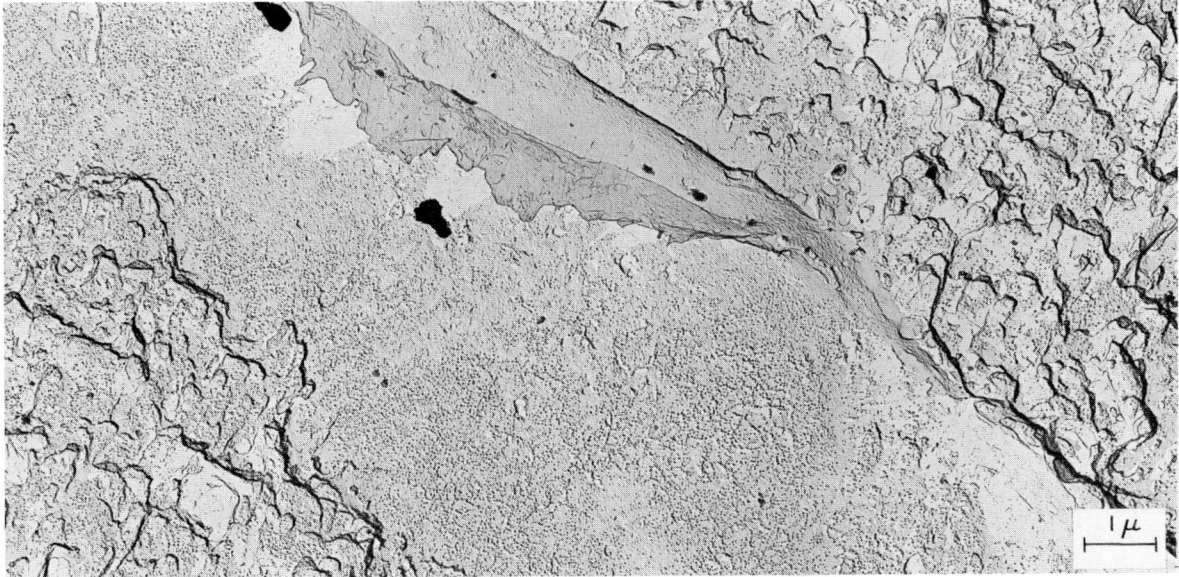

FIGURE 15 — Dimples indicating ductility in the stress corrosion area of an unnotched 7075-T6 specimen. Note widespread occurrence of corrosion product.

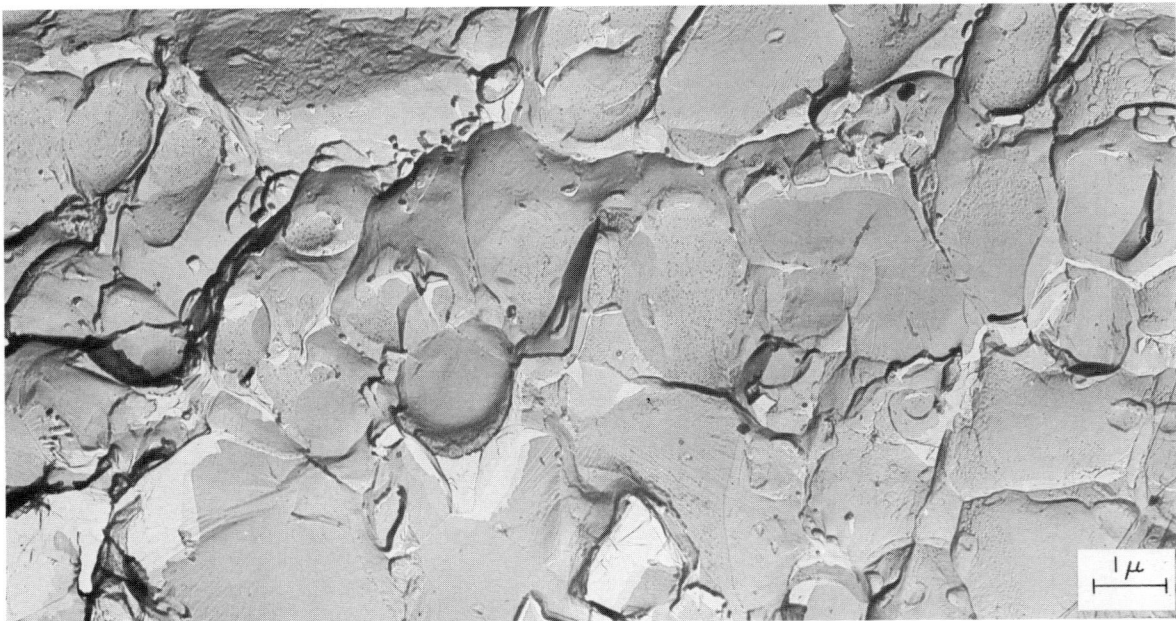

FIGURE 16 — Intergranular fracture in an unnotched 7075-T6 tensile specimen.

542

dimpled pattern. Such a pattern was also observed in a number of tensile specimens, thus suggesting that the dull areas of stress corrosion fractures were produced by normal tensile fracture.

English[20] confirmed the results of Forsyth and Ryder in a study of 7075-T6. All the fracture surfaces of tested stress corrosion specimens appeared dull with the exception of a semi-circular region extending in from the outside, which appeared much brighter. The dull region was transgranular, typical of tensile failures of 7075-T6, while the bright region was intergranular. The dull region was also more dimpled in appearance than the bright region.

Continuing English's work, McHardy[21] found that the intergranular cracking was associated with a slower process than the transgranular cracking. Intergranular cracks were shown by resistance measurements to grow linearly with time; the transgranular cracks developed at an exponential rate.

The fractographic findings made in this study complicate the picture presented above. The main point of difference concerns the ductility shown during stress corrosion cracking of 7075-T6 (ductility was also shown in stress corrosion failures of notched -T6 and -T73). Much more stress relaxation occurs by plastic flow than indicated by the results of Forsyth and Ryder[19] and English.[20] The ductility evidenced during the tensile portion of failure was in agreement with the findings of the others.

A less significant departure in the present results concerns the intergranular type of fracture observed occasionally in the light areas of stress corrosion specimens. The fracture surfaces of the tensile specimens also followed an intergranular path on occasion (Figure 16). Considerable dimpling was observed in the tensile specimens, confirming English's results for 7075-T6. The fracture surfaces were light, i.e., similar in appearance to the light areas in the stress corrosion specimens.

### D. Slip Characteristics of 7075-T6 and -T73

In general, the results obtained for the two series of specimens were similar. The slip lines in -T73 did tend to be finer and could not be detected as easily as those in -T6. This difference may indicate a larger number of active dislocation sources in -T73 than in -T6, so that in -T6 a given amount of slip would have to be accommodated by a greater displacement on any single slip plane than in -T73. The slip characteristics of -T6 and -T73 are summarized below.

1. The deformation (at a given level of strain) is nonuniform along the length of the specimens, from grain to grain, and within a given grain. Most of the deformation does not necessarily occur at the center of the reduced section.

2. Slip is transgranular. There are no indications that initial slip takes place along the grain boundaries.

3. With increasing deformation, slip bands, i.e., clusters of slip lines, appear and cross slip occurs.

4. With increasing deformation, the number of slip lines and bands increases, and the spacing between them decreases.

5. The slip lines and bands tend to become wavy at higher deformations.

Because the deformation was so heterogeneous from grain to grain in a given specimen, a heavily deformed grain could be found in a lightly deformed specimen, and vice versa; this is illustrated in Figure 17. Hence, the progressive stages in the development of slip lines in -T6 and -T73, which are portrayed in Figure 18, do not necessarily correspond with the deformation stages of the specimens themselves.

## V. Dislocation—Precipitate Interactions

The elastic interaction between an inclusion and the matrix containing dislocations, and thus the forces and stress fields between them, depend to a large extent on the elastic properties of these materials and the geometry and location of the dislocations. Exact elasticity solutions for the case of a circular inclusion and an edge dislocation have been treated by Dundurs and Mura[22] who showed that for certain combinations of material constants the dislocation has a stable equilibrium position in the matrix near the interface and that the interaction is very much affected by the orientation of the Burgers vector with respect to the inclusion.

If we imagine that we are looking along a grain boundary in 7075, then we might see a particle of $MgZn_2$ presenting a circular cross section, as shown in Figure 19. Let us consider one specific example, the case in which an edge dislocation has a Burgers vector in the negative y direction. The stress acting normal to the particle-matrix interface is then a special case of the following function:

$$
\sigma_{xx} = \frac{G_1 b_y}{\pi(K_1 + 1)} \left\{ -2 \left[ 1 - \frac{2x_1^2}{r_1^2} \right] \frac{x_1}{r_1^2} \right.
$$

$$
+ \left[ A + B - \frac{4Ax_2^2}{r_2^2} \right] \frac{x_2}{r_2^2}
$$

$$
+ \frac{2A(\beta^2 - 1)}{\beta^3} \left[ -\beta^2 + 2 \left( \beta^2 - 3 + \frac{4x_2^2}{r_2^2} \right) \frac{x_2^2}{r_2^2} + \frac{(\beta^2 - 1)}{\beta} \right.
$$

$$
\left. \left( 3 - \frac{4x_2^2}{r_2^2} \frac{ax_2}{r_2^2} \right) \frac{a}{r_2^2} \right] - \left[ A + B - \frac{4Ax^2}{r^2} \right] \frac{x}{r^2}
$$

$$
+ \frac{[A(2\beta^2 - 1) + M(K_2 + 1) - 1]}{\beta} \left[ \frac{1 - 2x^2}{r^2} \right] \frac{a}{r^2}
$$

$$
+ 2A \left[ 3 - \frac{4x^2}{r^2} \right] \frac{a^2 x}{r^4} \right\}
$$

where

$G$ = shear modulus

$\Gamma$ = $G_2/G_1$ ('2' refers to particle and '1' to the matrix)

$\beta$ = $\dfrac{c}{a} \geqslant 1$

$\gamma$ = Poisson's ratio

$K$ = $3 - 4\gamma$ (for plane strain)

$A$ = $\dfrac{1 - \Gamma}{1 + \Gamma K_1}$

$B$ = $\dfrac{K_2 - \Gamma K_1}{K_2 + \Gamma}$

$M$ = $\dfrac{\Gamma (K_1 + 1)}{(K_2 + \Gamma)(K_2 - 1 + 2\Gamma)}$

$x_1$ = $x - c$

$x_2$ = $x - \dfrac{a^2}{c}$

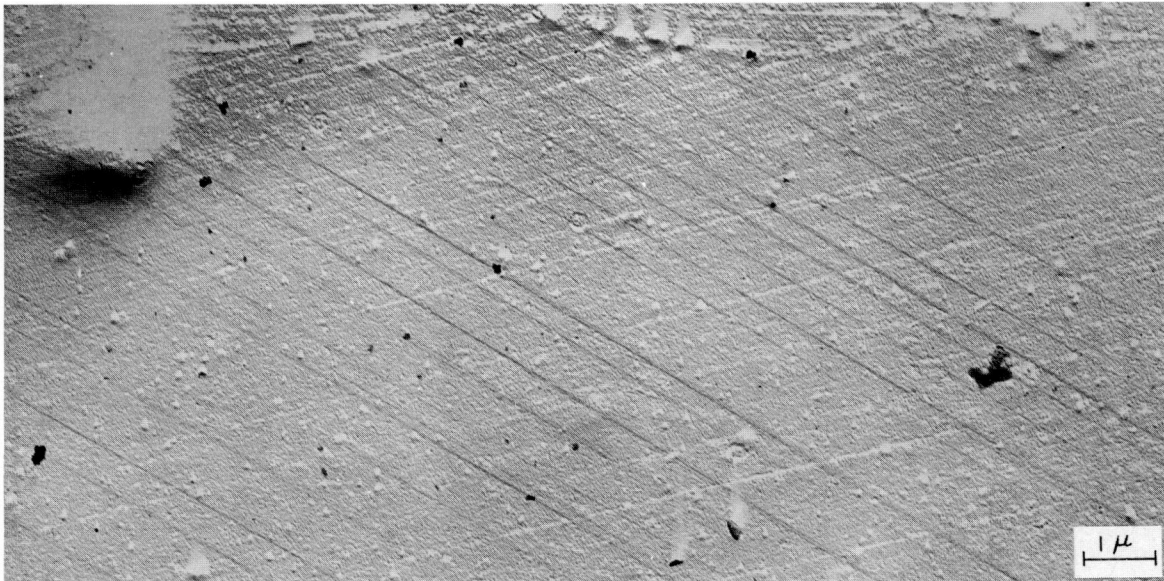

FIGURE 17 — Replicas depicting heavily and lightly deformed regions in lightly and heavily deformed 7075-T6 specimens, respectively. (a) Heavily deformed region in a lightly deformed specimen (elongation 0.025 inch). (b) Lightly deformed region in a heavily deformed specimen (elongation 0.040 inch).

544

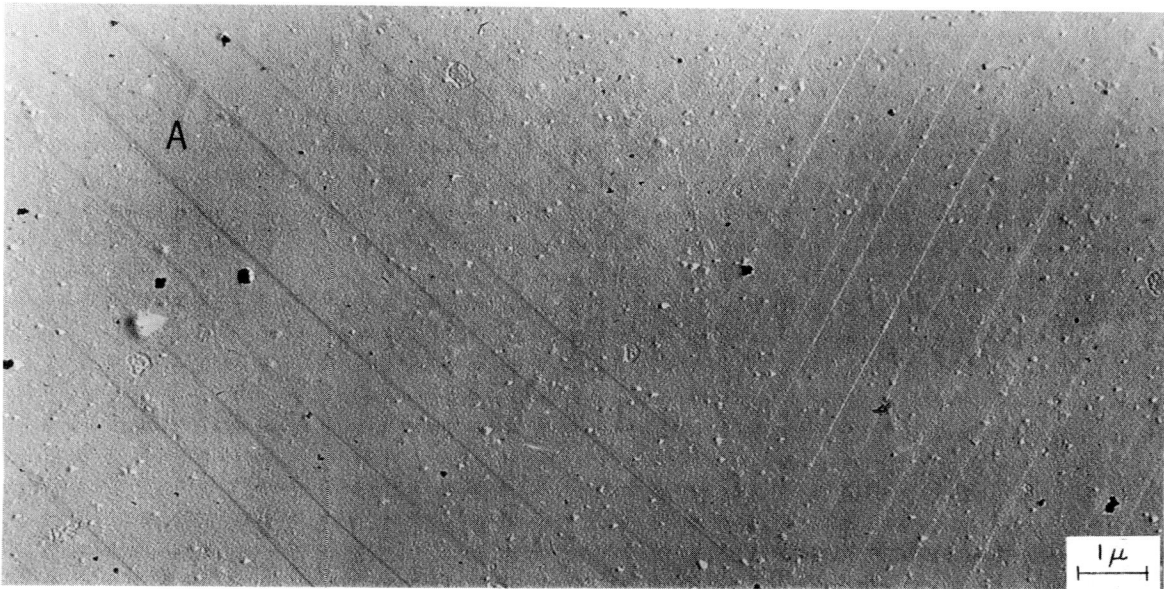

a. 7075-T6 specimen; elongation 0.030 inch (note widely spaced slip lines and bands at A).

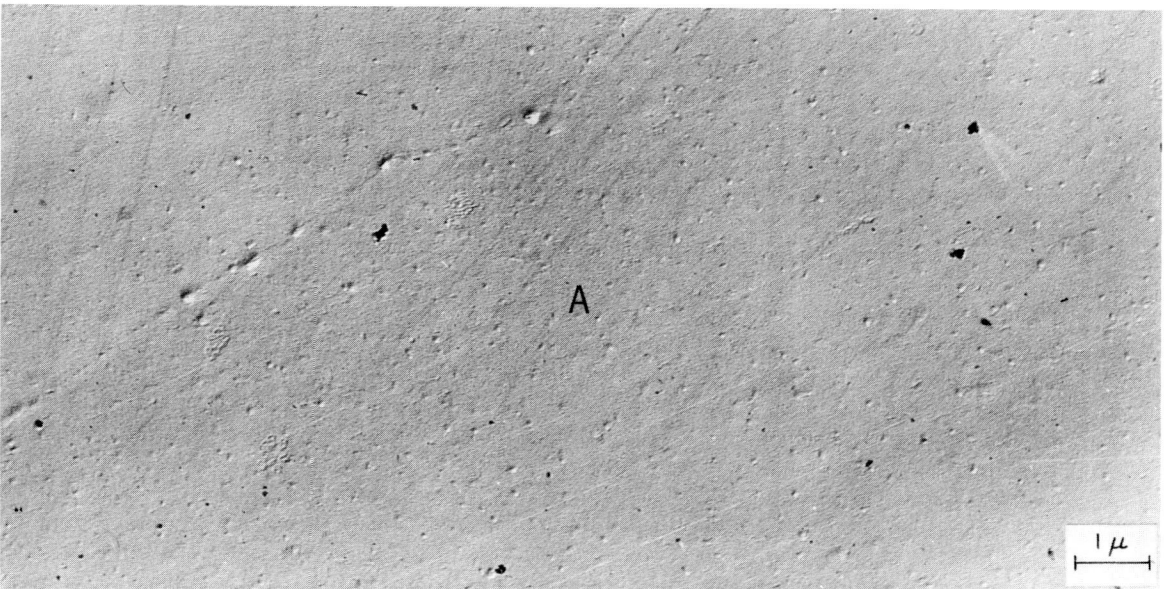

b. 7075-T6 specimen; elongation 0.030 inch (note widely spaced slip lines and bands; cross slip at A).

FIGURE 18 — Progressive stages in the development of slip lines in 7075 aluminum.

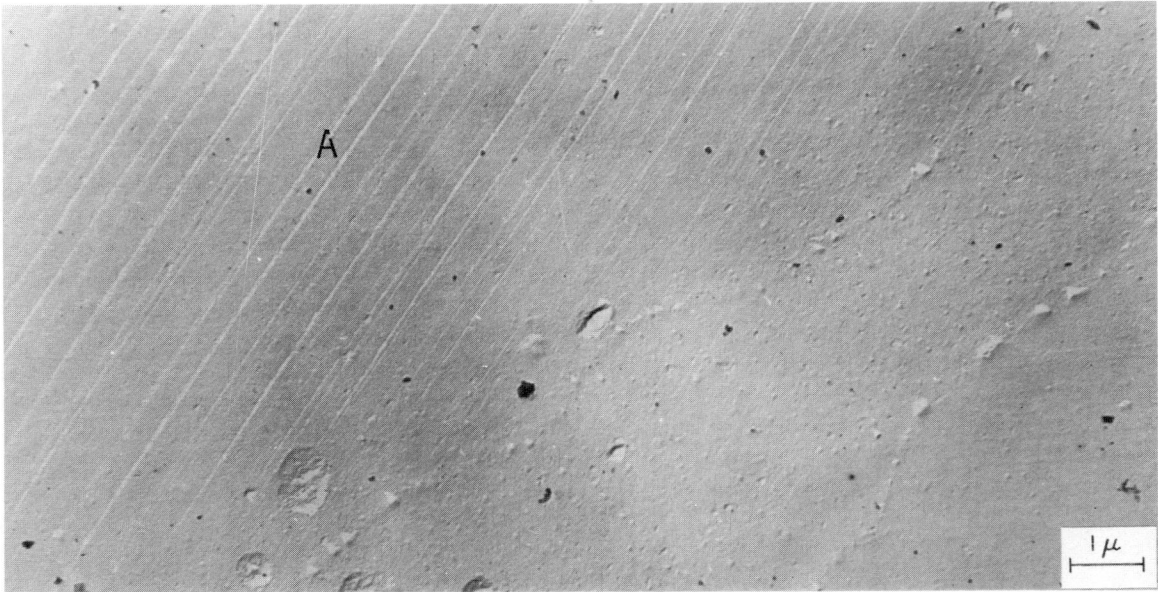

c. 7075-T6 specimen; elongation 0.040 inch (note closer spacing of slip lines and bands; cross slip at A).

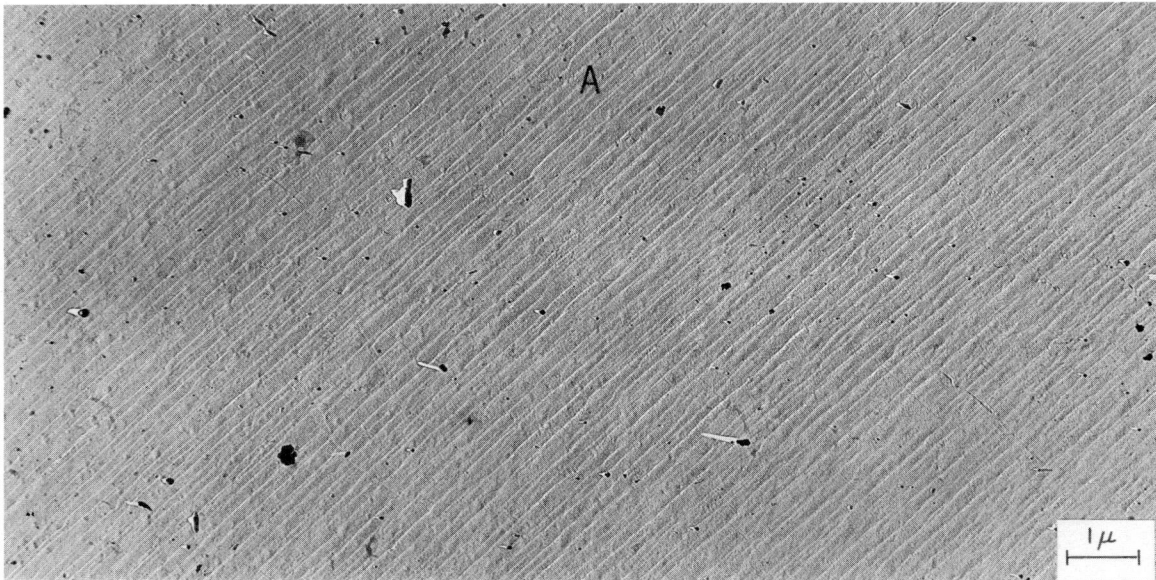

d. 7075-T6 specimen; elongation 0.23 inch (note very close spacing and fragmentation of slip lines and bands; cross slip at A).

FIGURE 18 — Progressive stages in the development of slip lines in 7075 aluminum. (continued)

546

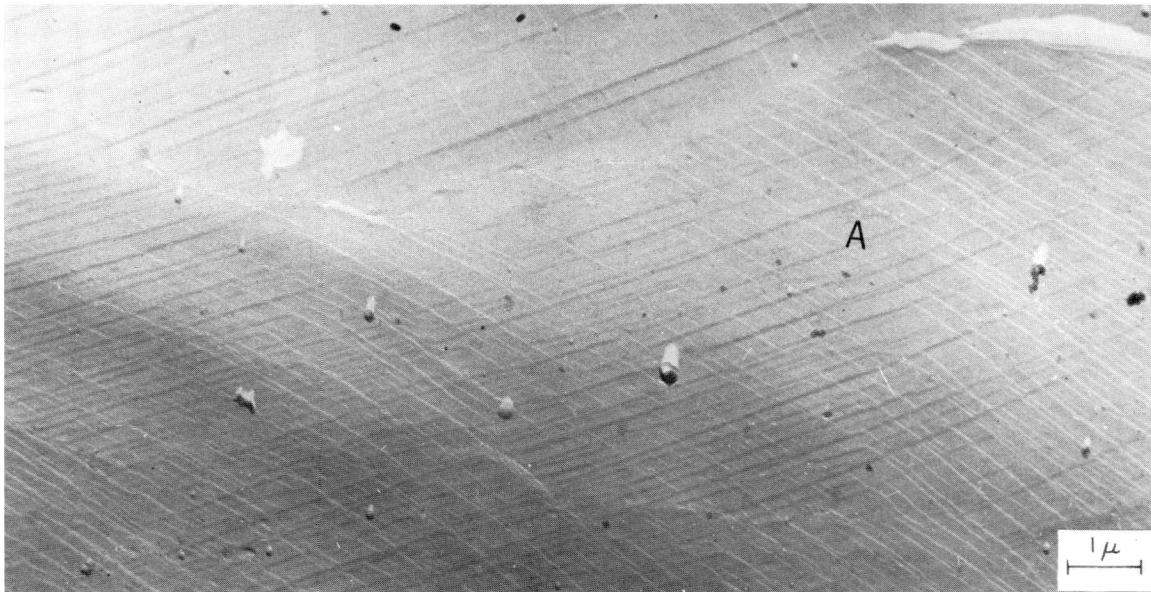

e. 7075-T6 specimen; elongation 0.043 inch (note fragmentation and waviness of slip lines and bands; large amount of cross slip at A).

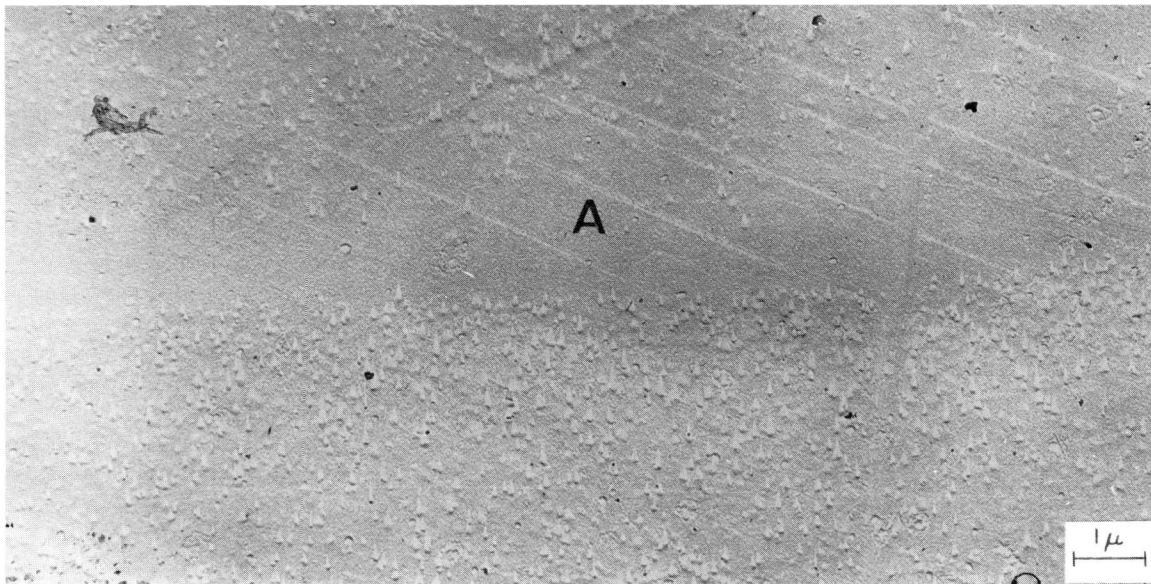

f. 7075-T73 specimen; elongation 0.030 inch (note widely spaced slip lines and bands at A).

FIGURE 18 — Progressive stages in the development of slip lines in 7075 aluminum. (continued)

g. 7075-T73 specimen; elongation 0.030 inch (note closer spacing of slip lines and bands).

h. 7075-T73 specimen; elongation 0.040 inch (note very close spacing and fragmentation of slip lines and bands; cross slip at A).

FIGURE 18 — Progressive stages in the development of slip lines in 7075 aluminum. (continued)

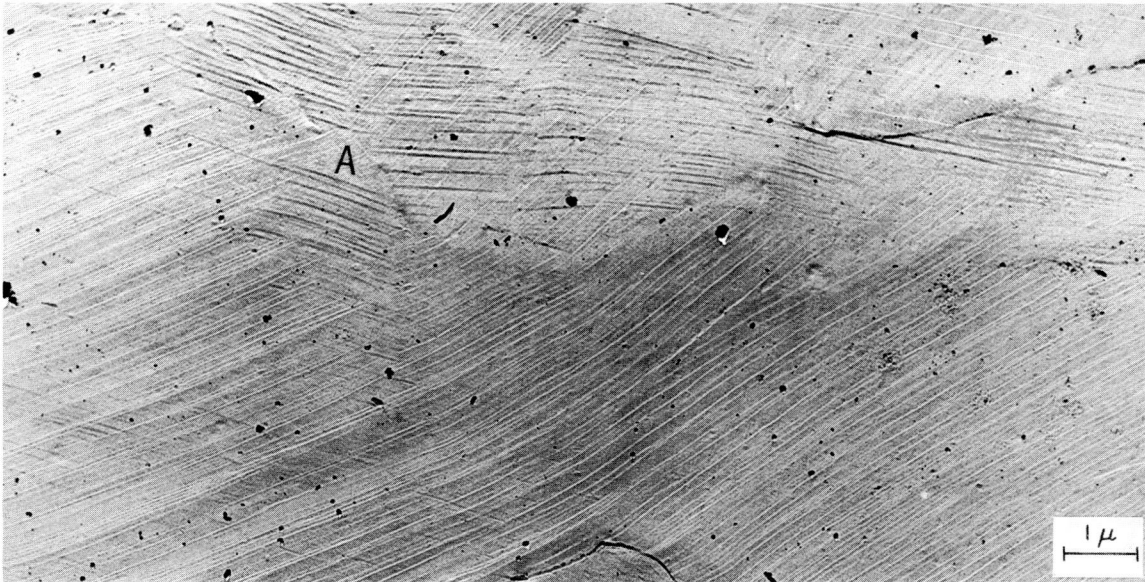

i. 7075-T73 specimen; elongation 0.040 inch (note large amount of cross slip at A).

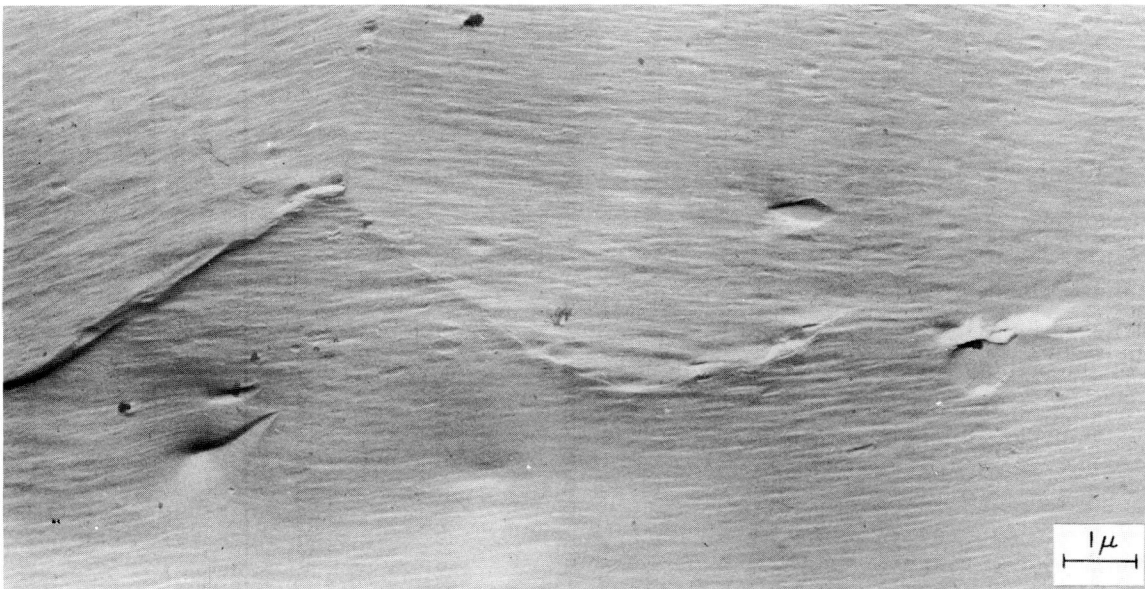

j. 7075-T73 specimen; elongation 0.046 inch (note extensive waviness and fragmentation of slip lines and bands).

FIGURE 18 — Progressive stages in the development of slip lines in 7075 aluminum. (continued)

An IBM 7094 computer was used to plot the isostress contours around the given edge dislocation. The particular plot for the case where $G_2/G_1 = 1.2$, $\gamma_1 = \gamma_2 = 0.33$, $a = 100$ b, and c - a = 10 b is shown in Figure 20. This and similar plots were then used to derive the four curves shown in Figure 21. The latter curves indicate the variation of $\sigma_{xx}$ at the particle-matrix interface, with the ratio $G_2/G_1$, for various distances between the dislocation and the interface.

Preliminary density and dynamic measurements involving the resonant frequency of a cylindrical specimen in torsion have yielded a $G_2/G_1$ ratio of 2. Referring to Figure 21, it is seen that for this ratio, $\sigma_{xx}$ may vary from 12,000 to 250,000 psi as the dislocation-interface distance decreases from 100 to 5 b. These stress values, of course, are based on an elastic model and preclude plastic flow in the particle or matrix.

## VI. Postulated Mechanism

It has been shown[12] that the two main microstructural differences between the susceptible -T6 and the resistant -T73 tempers of 7075 are: (1) The presence of numerous quenched-in dislocations in -T6 and a negligible (observable) density in -T73, and (2) a finer precipitate size and a larger number of precipitate particles in -T6 than in -T73. (Both of these differences can contribute to the 22% greater yield strength of -T6 compared to -T73.)[2] A typical thin-film micrograph of 7075-T6 was shown in Figure 9.

Thin-film microscopy disclosed no differences between the grain boundaries in -T6 and -T73, other than the close association of dislocations with precipitates in -T6 (Figure 22), which was not in evidence in -T73.[12] The composition of the grain boundary precipitates in the two tempers was shown to be the same, viz, $MgZn_2$, through the use of selected area diffraction and dark field techniques, and the precipitate morphologies and sizes were also similar. A

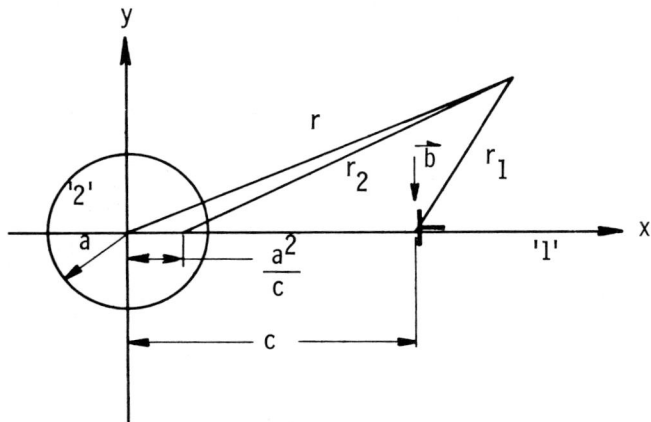

FIGURE 19 — Edge dislocation in the neighborhood of a precipitate having a circular cross section.

[2]Nominal yield and tensile strengths of 7075-T6 are 73,000 and 83,000 psi, respectively. For 7075-T73, these values are 60,000 and 71,000 psi, respectively.

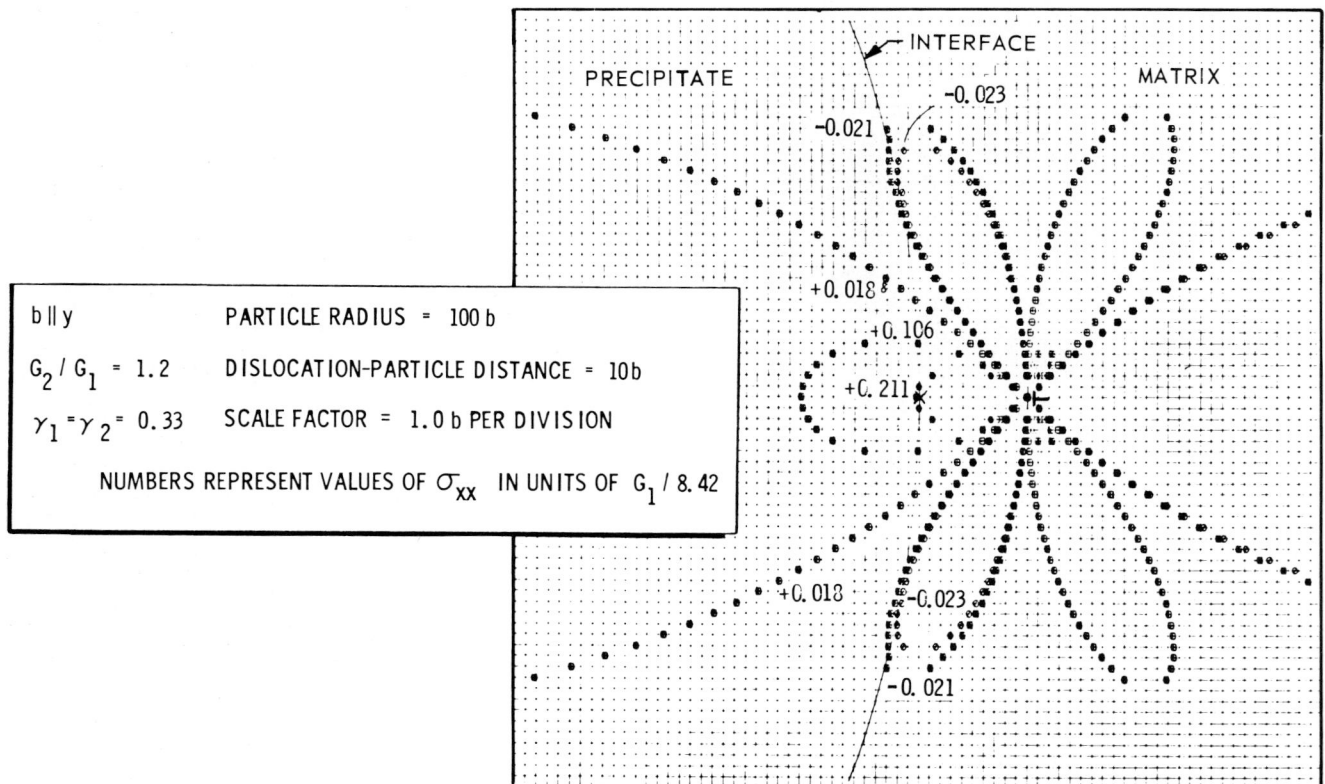

b ∥ y     PARTICLE RADIUS = 100 b

$G_2/G_1$ = 1.2     DISLOCATION-PARTICLE DISTANCE = 10 b

$\gamma_1 = \gamma_2$ = 0.33     SCALE FACTOR = 1.0 b PER DIVISION

NUMBERS REPRESENT VALUES OF $\sigma_{xx}$ IN UNITS OF $G_1/8.42$

FIGURE 20 — Isostress ($\sigma_{xx}$) contours for an edge dislocation situated near a precipitate.

corrosion study of unstressed -T6 and -T73 specimens in an aqueous 3-1/2% NaCl solution indicated that the main corrosion process is the same in the two conditions. This process consists of the dissolution of the grain boundary precipitates,[3] which thus act as anodes.[12]

A schematic drawing of a grain boundary in a 7075-T6 stress corrosion specimen is shown in Figures 23 and 24. This specimen is subjected to a uniaxial tensile stress amounting to 75% of yield in the short transverse[4] direction of the original forged billet. A single grain boundary is shown for simplification.

It is proposed that the initiation and propagation of a stress corrosion crack in 7075 occur as follows (Figures 23 and 24):

1. An $MgZn_2$ particle present in a grain boundary at the surface is anodic to the aluminum oxide on the surface. Thus it dissolves in the aqueous NaCl solution to form an elliptically shaped pit (Figures 23a and 24a).

2. There is a stress concentration at the base of the pit, which falls off rapidly with distance from the pit (Figure 23a). The stress at the base can be approximated by

$$\sigma_{max} = 2\sigma \left(\frac{c}{r}\right)^{1/2}$$

where

$\sigma$ = applied stress (plus any internal contributions)
c = length of the pit
r = radius of curvature at the base.[23]

In the case of -T6, a large stress also may act normal to the precipitate-matrix interface shown in Figure 24a. This stress is a resultant of the applied stress and the dislocation stress field, and, as seen in the last section, can be theoretically in the order of 250,000 psi. A stress corrosion crack will thus initiate at the base of the pit (Figure 23b) or at the precipitate-matrix interface (Figure 24b), depending on such factors as maximum tensile stress and the tensile strength of the boundary or precipitate-matrix interface. There is not enough experimental evidence at present to favor one initiation site or the other.

3. In either case (Figures 23b or 24b), the stress corrosion crack is observed to be accessible to the corrodent. The assumption is made that the freshly exposed aluminum is anodic to the pitted $MgZn_2$ particle as well as to the surface oxide of aluminum; thus the initial crack will acquire a configuration in which there is a high stress concentration at the tip (Figures 23c and 24c). This stress concentration can be reduced by plastic deformation ahead of the crack or by mechanical fracture. Fractographic evidence (see section entitled, "Stress Corrosion Tests on Notched Specimens," under "Results") indicates that both

---

[3] The large $MgZn_2$ particles in the grains also are attacked. However, their dissolution can be discounted in considering the model, because they do not form a continuous path into the metal.

[4] The short transverse direction is the shorter of the two mutually perpendicular directions defining the transverse section of the billet. A tensile stress applied in this direction leads to the most rapid stress corrosion failure.

processes can operate in 7075. Propagation of the crack between particles (Figures 23d and 24d) will take place by a combination of corrosion and mechanical fracture. The larger the role of slip in reducing the stress concentration at the crack tip, the longer the corrosion phase of the propagation, and the longer the time to failure (as in -T73, e.g.). The larger the role of mechanical fracture, the smaller is the amount of corrosion, and the shorter the time to failure (-T6, e.g.). If the propagating crack is to grow longer by corrosion, the crack tip must remain film-free and thus anodic to the oxide on the walls of the crack. This is easy to envisage where there is at least some dislocation motion ahead of the crack.

4. After the propagating crack has been halted by the next $MgZn_2$ particle, it will become completely covered with oxide, thus transforming the $MgZn_2$ particle into an anode. This particle will now pit, and the cycle comprising Steps (1) to (3) will be repeated.

5. As the total crack length increases, $\sigma_{max}$ also increases. Finally, when the critical resolved shear stress is exceeded over a critical volume of material, the second stage of failure is nucleated. A tensile-type fracture now ensues across the most favorably oriented slip plane(s). Whereas the first stage was predominantly intergranular in nature, the second stage is mainly transgranular.

## VII. Discussion

A consistent picture has emerged from the different experiments, which suggests an important role for mechanical fracture in the propagation of a stress corrosion crack. An equally important role, however, may be played by corrosion. Both processes seem to take place in any given condition of the alloy, with one of them predomi-

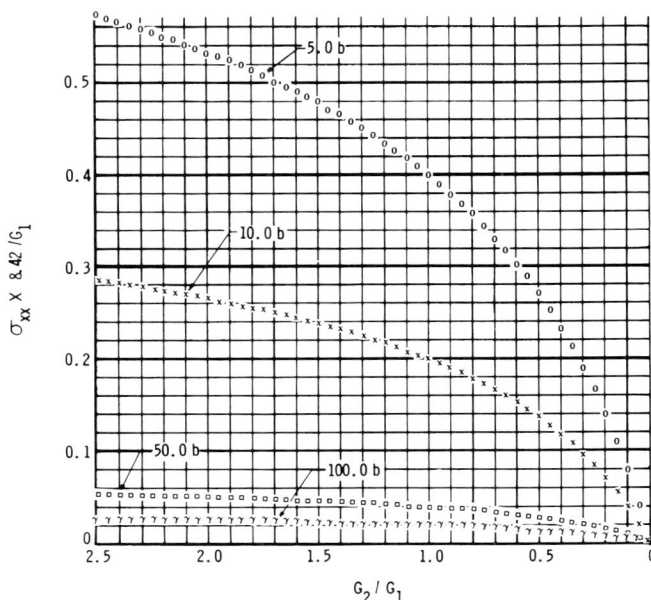

FIGURE 21 — Variation of tensile stress at precipitate-matrix interface ($\sigma_{XX}$) with shear-modulus ratio ($G_2/G_1$).

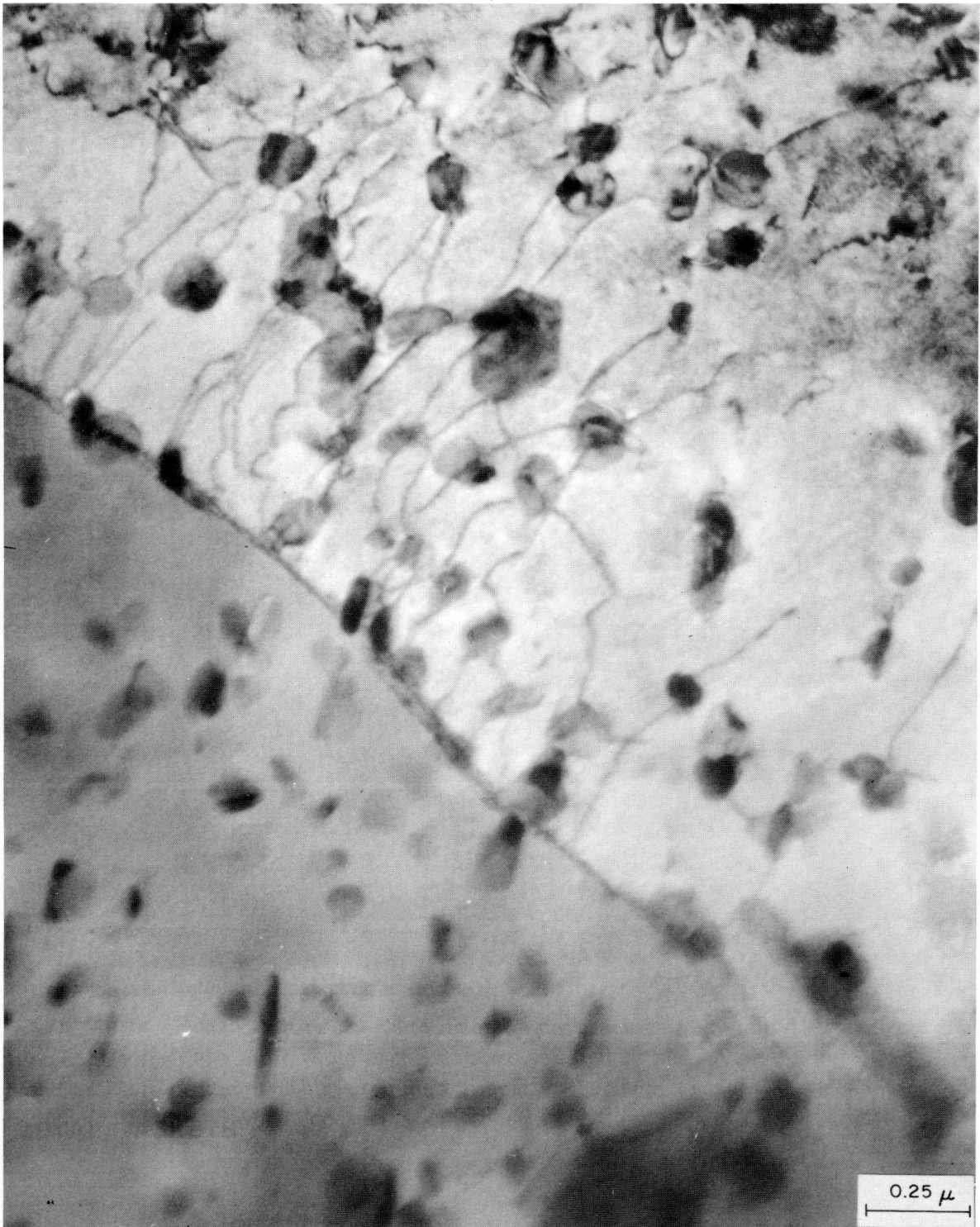

**FIGURE 22** — Transmission electron micrograph of 7075-T6 specimen showing close association of dislocations and grain boundary precipitates.

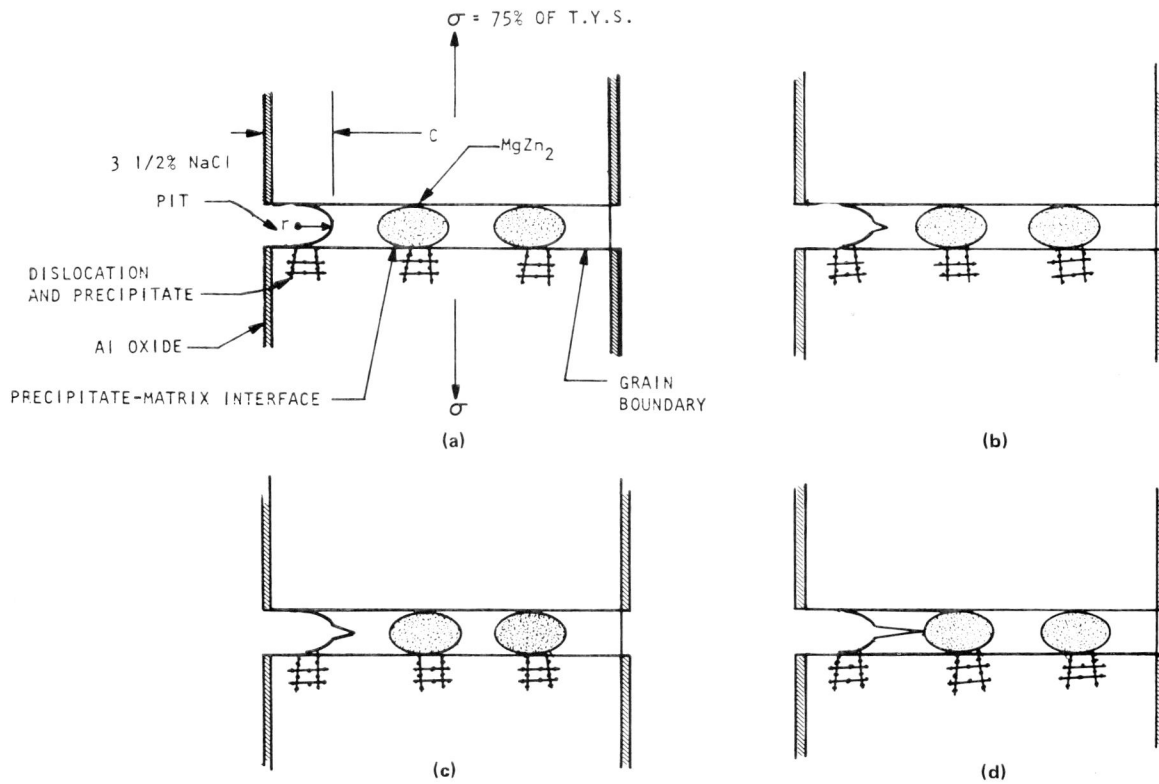

FIGURE 23 — Simplified schematic representation of the stress corrosion of 7075-T6 alloy loaded to 75% of its yield strength (short-transverse orientation) alternate A.

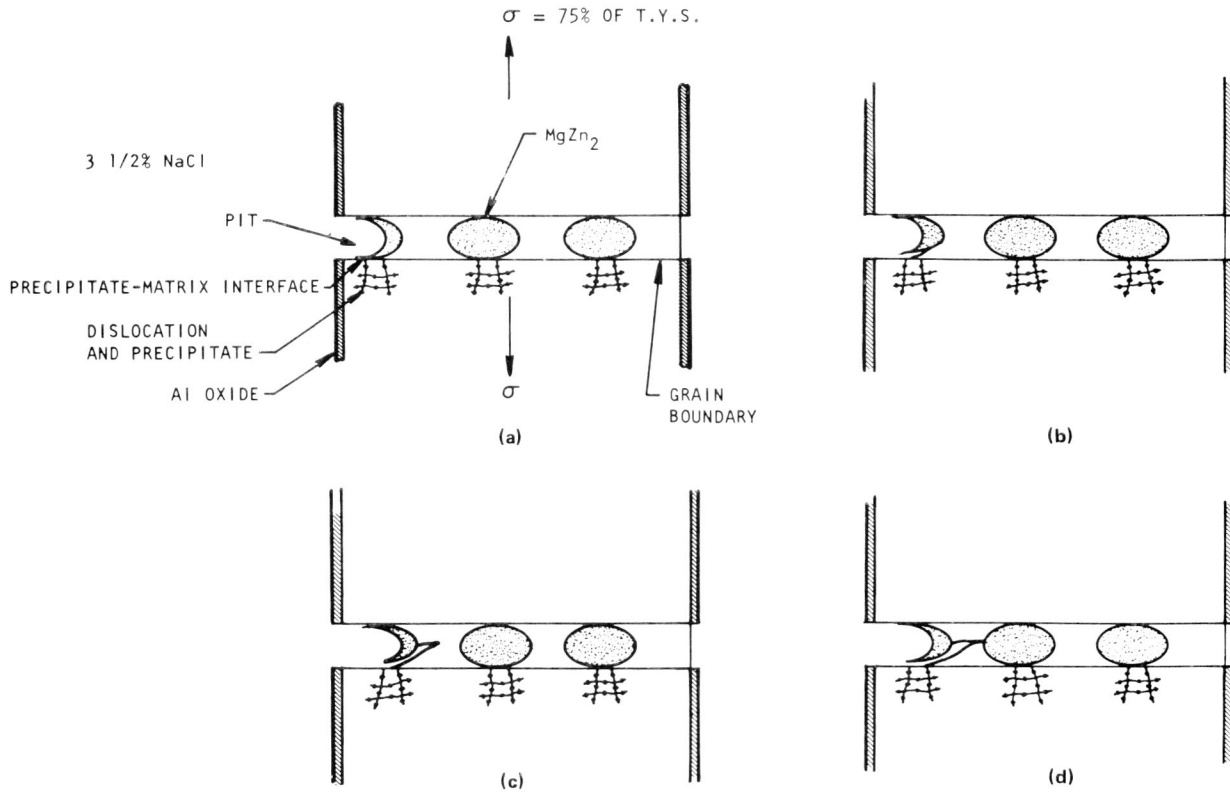

FIGURE 24 — Simplified schematic representation of the stress corrosion of 7075-T6 alloy loaded to 75% of its yield strength (short-transverse orientation) alternate B.

nating. In 7075-T6, the predominant process is mechanical fracture; in an "off-heat" -T73, such as the one used in the experiment on notched specimens, or in some susceptible condition intermediate between -T6 and -T73, the main process may be corrosion. Because corrosion is a much slower process than mechanical fracture, the time to failure of 7075-T73 is considerably longer than that of 7075-T6. Basically, the failure mechanism is believed to be similar in any condition of 7075; only the proportions of corrosion and mechanical fracture differ.

Whether the stress concentration at the tip of a crack will be relieved by plastic deformation or by mechanical fracture will depend on the ease of activating dislocation sources and the number of these sources. If dislocations can be generated readily, plastic deformation will dominate; otherwise, mechanical fracture will be the main process. The importance of corrosion as a propagation mode will increase as the extent of plastic deformation increases.

The results of this study have led to a better understanding of the role of dislocations and precipitate particles in the stress corrosion cracking of 7075 alloy. An increase in the density of either dislocations or particles is now known to enhance the susceptibility of this alloy. Such an increase will, of course, render dislocation generation and/or motion (i.e., plastic flow) more difficult, thus promoting mechanical fracture and rapid stress corrosion failures.

### A. Quantitative Prediction of Stress Corrosion Lifetime

Theoretical[24] and experimental studies[25] of stress-rupture, fatigue, and other fracture phenomena have disclosed a linear relationship between time to failure, $t_f$ (plotted logarithmically), and the applied stress. A similar relationship will now be developed using stress corrosion cracking data for the 7075 alloy. Hopefully, this relationship will lay a foundation for the eventual prediction of $t_f$ in terms of fine microstructure.

The stress corrosion data in this study have been obtained for a variety of microstructures, yield stresses, and applied stresses. In general, the applied stresses varied because the microstructure, and hence the yield stress varied (the applied stress was usually 75% of the yield stress). The time to failure was obtained as a function of applied stress, at constant yield stress, only in the experiments on notched and unnotched -T6 and -T73.

Thus, since the independent variable was usually the yield stress, and not the applied stress, a plot has been made of (log) time to failure vs the yield stress of the shock loaded specimens and their unshocked controls. A least-squares fit of the data to a straight line produces the equation,

$$\tau = -9950 \log_{10} t_f + 78,700 \quad (1)$$

where $\tau$ is the yield stress. As shown in Figure 25, this straight line has a very small slope, which reflects the observation that two specimens with the same yield strength can have widely different lifetimes, depending on

whether the main source of strengthening was work hardening or age hardening.

The present investigation has disclosed a correlation between dislocation and particle density on one hand, and stress corrosion life on the other. The latter decreases with an increase in the density of either dislocations or particles. Besides, it is known that the yield stress varies as

$$\tau = \tau_1 + \tau_2 + \ldots \ldots \quad (2)$$

where $\tau_1$ is a long-range stress contribution due to dislocations ($\tau_1 \sim \sqrt{\text{dislocation density}}$ and $\tau_2$ is a short-range contribution due to pinning by precipitates ($\tau_2 \sim \sqrt{\text{particle density}}$ or $\frac{1}{\text{interparticle spacing}}$, etc.).[5] Thus, in view of these considerations, the existence of a relationship such as Equation (1) is not too surprising.

It is apparent from the shock loading and tensile deformation experiments that $t_f$ is more sensitive to changes in particle density (or spacing) than to changes in dislocation density. For example, Table 6 shows that a several-orders-of-magnitude increase in dislocation density will cause a five-fold decrease in $t_f$ at most (cf. Specimens VIIC-1 and VIIA-B); whereas a 2000-fold decrease in particle density accompanying the transformation of -T6 to -T73[6] will effect a 100-fold increase in $t_f$. Also, it is seen in Figure 8 that the increase in $t_f$ is very rapid after a critical overaging time has been reached. This critical overaging time may correspond to the transformation from G.P. zones to a more stable precipitate phase with an accompanying decrease in particle density. In the tensile

---

[5] $\tau_2$ can be described by other functions of the particle density or the interparticle spacing.[26] Such factors as particle shape and coherency between particle and matrix may also contribute to the yield strength.

[6] Estimated from thin-film micrographs of 7075-T6 and -T73. The change in dislocation density is negligible compared to the change induced by shock loading.

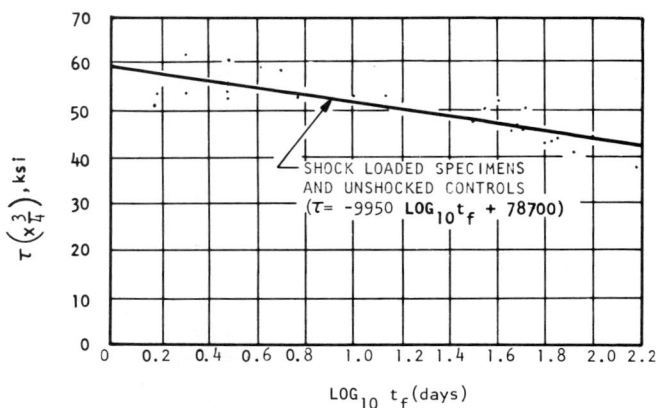

FIGURE 25 — Plot of yield stress vs log of time to failure for shock loaded 7075 and unshocked control specimens. Also shown are results for 7075-T6 and -T73 deformed in tension prior to stress corrosion testing.

554

deformation experiments, prestressing 7075-T6 in the plastic region of the stress-strain curve was observed to shorten the time to failure, while prestressing -T73 had virtually no effect. Presumably the difference in response of -T6 and -T73 was due to the additional precipitation in the -T6 but not in the -T73.

Considering the stronger dependence of $t_f$ on the particle parameter ($\tau_2$) than on the dislocation parameter ($\tau_1$), a fruitful approach to the quantitative prediction of $t_f$ might be as follows: We can write that

$$\tau = -k_1 \log_{10} t_f + k_2 \qquad (1')$$

and that

$$\tau = \tau_p + \tau_o \qquad (3)$$

where $\tau_p$ is the contribution to the yield stress due to precipitation hardening and $\tau_o$ is the contribution due to all other strengthening mechanisms. Treating $\tau_o$ as constant and combining Equation ($1'$) and (3), we obtain

$$\tau_p = -k_1 \log_{10} t_f + k_2 \qquad (4)$$

Thus, if $\tau_p$ can now be determined as a function of particle density, $f(V)$, or interparticle spacing, $F(\lambda)$, $t_f$ becomes predictable from an examination of the microstructure:

$$f(V) \text{ or } F(\lambda) = k_1 \log_{10} t_f + k_2 \qquad (5)$$

A test of this hypothesis is planned using specimens where only the particle size and size distribution vary.

### B. The Role of Denuded Zones

Because the precipitate-free (denuded) zone has been central to most current theories of stress corrosion in aluminum, a discussion of the recent nucleation studies conducted by Embury and Nicholson[27] and Lorimer and Nicholson[28] on Al-5.9% Zn-2.9% Mg has particular relevancy. These investigators have shown that the width of a denuded zone is determined by a number of factors: the quenching rate between the temperature of the G.P. zone solvus and the quench bath temperature, the holding time and temperature (before aging), the rate of heating to the aging temperature, and by the initial vacancy concentration. All these factors control the size distribution of G.P. zones, which, in turn, determines the width of the denuded zones.

The aging behavior of Al-Zn-Mg alloys is divided into three classes which are defined by the temperature ranges involved:

1. Alloys quenched and aged above the G.P. zone solvus ($\sim 155$ C in Al-5.9% Zn-2.9% Mg).
2. Alloys quenched and aged below the G.P. zone solvus.
3. Alloys quenched below and aged above the G.P. zone solvus.

In Class 1 no G.P. zones are formed; there is a very coarse dispersion of precipitates with nucleation principally on dislocations. In Class 2, G.P. zones form continuously and grow to a size whereat they are able to transform to precipitates. No denuded zone is formed other than a very small ($\sim 300$ Å) solute denuded zone due to precipitation in the grain boundary. In Class 3, the denuded zone width is controlled by the nucleation treatment below the G.P. zone solvus where the G.P. zone size distribution is determined. A long nucleation treatment gives a narrow denuded zone.

The well-known effect of trace additions of Ag on the Al-Zn-Mg system[29,30] is attributed by Lorimer and Nicholson to a raising of the G.P. zone solvus. (The Ag-containing alloy exhibits a very even dispersion of fine precipitate, i.e., there is no denuded zone). The Ag-free alloy is in Class 3 above, while the alloy containing Ag is in Class 2. Small additions of Cr[1] and Cu[5,7] to Al alloys are known to cause the same type of dispersion as Ag. The mechanism may also be the same.

The complexity of factors involved in denuded zone formation underscores the difficulty of predicting whether denuded zones should or should not be found in a given alloy, or even in a given temper of the same alloy. Considering only the minor variations in heat treatment from one laboratory to another, it becomes impossible to expect 7075-T6, e.g., to possess a characteristic denuded zone width. Added to the variations in heat treatment are the slight variations in composition from one lot of material to another and the inevitable heterogeneities in any single lot of material. Thus, the characterization of a given alloy or temper as a function of denuded zone width is reduced at best to a statistical evaluation.

The 7075-T6 heat treatment is such (24 hours at 250 F) that this temper probably falls in Class 2 of Lorimer and Nicholoson's classification. A very narrow ($\sim 300$ Å) denuded zone, due to precipitation in the grain boundary, is predicted for members of this class; when denuded zones were observed in -T6 in the present study, their width was usually not too different from the 300 Å value. Wider denuded zones are predicted for -T73[27] which is produced by aging at a higher temperature than -T6. A heat treated condition in Class 2 may show no evidence at all of denuded zones. For example, the two susceptible conditions studied by Holl fell in Class 2 but seemed to be completely devoid of denuded zones.

The present study provides substantial evidence against, and no evidence for, a denuded-zone mechanism in 7075. In the first place, the zones are not frequently observed in susceptible 7075. It can be reasonably assumed, that whatever zones were present would be preferentially cold worked upon the application of explosive shock loading or tensile deformation, e.g., thus negating their possible role in stress corrosion. In fact, the opposite has been observed: cold working decreased the resistance to stress corrosion. Finally the slip-line study has shown, that even in the earliest stages of deformation the slip lines traverse a given grain rather freely and are not concentrated in narrow regions surrounding the grain boundaries. The predominant

555

mode of tensile failure in 7075 is likewise transgranular.

Although Holl's model for stress corrosion cracking in Al-5.7% Zn-2.7% Mg-0.5% Cu[7] cannot be expected to apply in detail to 7075, because of obvious differences in composition, processing, and microstructure, this model and the author's model both assign no importance to the role of ductile denuded zones in the mechanism, contrary to most other current models. Besides, the two models possess other features in common. For example, both maintain that a high stress concentration can trigger a mechanical crack from a corrosion crevice and that crack propagation is a discontinuous process. Also both recognize the extreme importance of precipitate particles in influencing deformation and thus stress corrosion susceptibility. Gruhl and Cordier[8] were perhaps the first to associate an early precipitate phase with stress corrosion susceptibility, but they did not propose any mechanism, and they seemed to imply that the intrinsic properties of the precipitate were more important than an extrinsic property such as density, which can be so critical in determining deformation behavior.

*C. Preferential Corrosion at Dislocations*

No evidence has been found in the present studies for selective corrosion at dislocation sites. A number of investigators working with other alloy systems have reported such preferential dissolution. Tromans and Nutting[31] found that pits occurred at dislocations within the grains or at grain boundaries in copper alloys exposed to an ammonia environment. In the first case, the eventual extension of the pits into cracks proceeded transgranularly, while in the latter case the failure was intergranular. The pits, or sites of crack initiation, corresponded to high concentrations of solute atoms. Other investigators have observed corrosion tunnels in stainless steels, which they assumed formed along Lomer-Cottrell dislocations;[32] or chemically active sites on the surface of the metal which could be correlated numerically with the amount of cold work;[32] or corrosive attack at dislocation pileups.[33]

# VIII. Conclusions

The following conclusions are drawn from this investigation:

1. The stress corrosion resistance of 7075 aluminum is lowered by any factor that leads to the immobilization of dislocations, or to the inactivation of dislocation sources. Two such factors are plastic deformation and strain aging. Precipitate-dislocation interactions are much more important than dislocation-dislocation interactions in lowering the resistance.

2. The preceding findings provide a basis for optimizing the combination of yield strength and stress corrosion resistance of 7075. The optimum combination can be achieved by work hardening an overaged temper. A 69,000-psi yield combined with a 40-day stress corrosion lifetime has been obtained by explosively shock loading 7075-T73 at 204 Kb; however, this combination is not necessarily the optimum that is obtainable.

3. Calculation of the stress field around an edge dislocation neighboring a grain boundary precipitate indicates that the tensile stress which acts normal to the precipitate-matrix interface can be theoretically on the order of 250,000 psi. An interfacial stress corrosion crack in 7075-T6 could conceivably initiate under a stress of this order.

4. The basic difference between a susceptible temper such as -T6 and a resistant temper such as -T73 resides in their respective capacities for plastic deformation at the tip of a crevice. The -T6 is limited in its ability to deform, primarily because of its high density of G.P. zones, while the -T73 can deform more easily because of its lower density of precipitate particles. A high stress concentration in -T6 is more likely to be relieved by mechanical fracture than plastic flow, whereas in -T73 plastic flow is a more likely mechanism.

5. A rapid intergranular stress corrosion failure can be induced in a 7075-T73 specimen through the introduction of a notch. With its capacity for plastic flow thus limited, the -T73 behaves in a manner similar to -T6.

6. A stress corrosion failure in 7075-T6, or in notched -T73, involves at least some plastic flow, as evidenced by the dimpling observed in fractographs.

7. The slip characteristics of 7075-T6 and -T73 are in general similar. Slip is transgranular and there are no indications that initial slip takes place along the grain boundaries. With increasing deformation, slip bands, i.e., clusters of slip lines, appear and cross slip occurs.

8. The evidence obtained in this investigation suggests that ductile denuded zones do not play an important role in the stress corrosion cracking of 7075.

9. The effect of increasing stress is to prolong the time to failure of unnotched -T73 stress corrosion specimens.

10. Thin-film examinations have not disclosed any selective corrosion at dislocation sites.

11. A correlation has been obtained between the yield strength of 7075 and the stress corrosion lifetime. A basis may exist for the quantitative prediction of time to failure from mechanical-property measurements or from a microstructural examination of 7075.

# Acknowledgment

Helpful discussions have been held with Professor G. Thomas of the University of California, at Berkeley, and with Dr. R. Chang of the North American Aviation Science Center. Dr. W. T. Chandler and Mr. E. D. Weisert of Rocketdyne have offered constructive comments on the manuscript.

The elasticity computations were initiated and performed by Drs. R. Chang and L. J. Graham, respectively, of the Science Center, and the experimental measurements which supplemented these computations were conducted by Mr. N. J. Hoffman of Rocketdyne. Miss A. Palyo, of

Rocketdyne, prepared the thin films and the replicas which are shown herein.

Financial support for this study was received from the National Aeronautics and Space Administration, Marshall Space Flight Center, Huntsville, Alabama, under Contract No. NAS7-162; and from the Naval Air Systems Command, Department of the Navy, Washington, D.C., under Contract No. NOw 66-0309d.

## References

1. G. Thomas and J. Nutting. *J. Inst. Metals,* **88,** 81 (1956-60).
2. T. P. Hoar. *Corrosion,* **19,** 331t (1963).
3. H. L. Logan. *J. of Research Nat. Bureau of Standards,* **48,** 99 (1952).
4. E. N. Pugh and W. R. D. Jones. *Metallurgia,* **63,** 3 (1961).
5. A. J. McEvily, Jr., J. B. Clark, and A. P. Bond. *Effect of Thermal-Mechanical Processing on the Fatigue and Stress Corrosion Properties of an Al-Zn-Mg Alloy.* Publication preprint from Scientific Laboratory, Ford Motor Company (1966) November 3.
6. G. Thomas. *J. Inst. Metals,* **89,** 287 (1960-61).
7. H. A. Holl. *Corrosion,* **25,** 173 (1967) June.
8. W. Gruhl and H. Cordier. *Z. Metallkde.,* **55,** 577 (1964).
9. M. Schmalzried and V. Gerold. *Z. Metallkde.,* **49,** 291 (1958).
10. R. B. Mears, R. H. Brown, and E. H. Dix, Jr. *Symposium on Stress Corrosion Cracking of Metals.* ASTM-AIME, Philadelphia, 323 (1944).
11. E. H. Dix, Jr. *AIME Trans.,* **137,** 11 (1940).
12. A. J. Jacobs. *ASM Trans. Quart.,* **58,** 579 (1965).
13. A. J. Jacobs. The Effect of Explosive Deformation on the Stress Corrosion and Mechanical Properties of 7075 Aluminum Alloy. Paper presented at the AIAA Seventh Structures and Materials Conference, Cocoa Beach, Florida (1966) April 18-20.
14. M. Gensamer. *Strength of Metals Under Combined Stress.* American Society for Metals, Cleveland, Ohio, 22 (1941).
15. L. I. Van Torne and H. M. Otte. *Met. Eng. Quart.,* **6,** 43 (1966).
16. D. O. Sprowls and R. H. Brown. Technical Paper No. 17, Aluminum Company of America, Pittsburgh, Pennsylvania (1962).
17. H. K. Farmery and U. R. Evans. *J. Inst. Metals,* **84,** 413 (1955-56).
18. W. H. Colner and H. T. Francis. *J. Electrochem. Soc.,* **105,** 377 (1958).
19. P. J. E. Forsyth and D. A. Ryder. *Metallurgia,* **63,** 117 (1961).
20. G. C. English. Investigation of the Mechanism of Stress Corrosion of Aluminum Alloys, Bureau of Naval Weapons, Contract NOw 64-0170-c, Final Report, December 6, 1963 to February 6, 1965.
21. J. McHardy. Investigation of the Mechanism of Stress Corrosion of Aluminum Alloys, Bureau of Naval Weapons, Contract NOw 64-0170-c, Final Report, February 16, 1965 to February 16, 1966.
22. J. Dundurs and T. Mura. *J. Mech. Phys. Solids,* **12,** 177 (1964).
23. C. E. Inglis. *Trans. Inst. Naval Architects,* **55,** 219 (1913).
24. C. C. Hsiao. *Physics Today,* **19,** 49 (1966).
25. S. N. Zhurkov. *Int. J. Fracture Mech.,* **1,** 311 (1965).
26. R. F. Bunshah and C. G. Goetzel. A Survey of Dispersion Strengthening of Metals and Alloys, WADC Technical Report 59-414 (1959) July.
27. J. D. Embury and R. B. Nicholson. *Acta Met.,* **13,** 403 (1965).
28. G. W. Lorimer and R. B. Nicholson. *Acta Met.,* **14,** 1009 (1966).
29. I. J. Polmear. *J. Inst. Metals,* **87,** 24 (1958-59).
30. I. J. Polmear. *J. Inst. Metals,* **89,** 193 (1960-61).
31. D. Tromans and J. Nutting. *Fracture of Solids.* (D. C. Drucker and J. J. Gilman, ed.) p. 637, Interscience, New York, N. Y. (1963).
32. N. A. Nielsen. *Corrosion,* **20,** 104 (1964).
33. D. L. Douglass. Second International Congress on Metallic Corrosion, New York, N. Y. (1963).

## Discussion

**H. L. Craig and D. S. Thompson, Reynolds Metals Co.:**

Dr. Jacobs' stress corrosion results for 7075-T73 alloy are indeed surprising. The wording of his paper indicates that at stress levels above 65% of the ultimate tensile strength, only single specimens were tested. It is surprising that such provocative unsupported data should be published. Again, in the work on the effects of prestressing on time to failure, single specimens were used. It is common experience that at best, time to failure is a doubtful parameter to evaluate stress corrosion cracking, unless many specimens are used and differences are only considered significant if they involve a factor of 3 or 4 or better an order of magnitude. Have these results been reproduced? Not only is the data in Figure 13 for 7075-T73 suspect, due to failure to replicate these results, but the specimen holder shown in Figure 1 appears to be unsuitable for such high stress levels due to the torsional method of the loading. In the case of the notched specimens, it is normally difficult to determine the stress state at the root of the notch without the added complication of adding a shear stress to the applied tensile load. Further, the exact stress state of specimens loaded beyond the notch yield strength necessarily is ill defined.

It is difficult to see the usefulness of the calculation of the stress field in the vicinity of an edge dislocation with or without an interface (depicted in Jacobs' paper in the unlikely condition of complete coherency) between regions of differing shear modulus. On the basis of published lattice parameters and crystal structures, such an interface between $MgZn_2$ and an aluminum solid solution cannot be coherent. Hence, Jacobs' calculations, which are based on linear elasticity theory, are not applicable. One might just as well say that at the position $x = -b$ $y = 0$ (to use Jacobs' axes) that the stress $\sigma_{xx}$ would be approximately 800,000 psi which is three times Jacobs' stress! Such a calculation has no meaning in the core of a dislocation and neither does Jacobs' unless he is in fact dealing with a truly coherent interface.

Dr. Jacobs makes a somewhat unconventional use of electrochemical terminology when he talks of either $MgZn_2$ or freshly fractured aluminum surfaces being anodic with respect to aluminum oxide. In a way, he is correct in so much as the freshly exposed surface is more active chemically. However, the regions covered with an oxide film are usually regarded as passivated and strictly take no actual part in an electrochemical process other than acting as a barrier through which participating ions must diffuse.

ED NOTE: There is a combined discussion of the Jacobs and Speidel papers given by Sprowls at the end of the discussion on Speidel's paper.

**A. J. Jacobs:**

The 7075-T73 specimens tested in the tensile deformation and notched-bar studies originated from the same forging. Unfortunately, there was not enough material to conduct more tests than I have reported. The reproducibility of results should be established with another starting material. I should like to point out, with reference to the curve for smooth 7075-T73 specimens in Figure 13, the following. Suppose the four points at $P/P_u$ = 0.79, 0.89, 0.91, and 0.98 truly fall in the right-hand tails of probability distributions for $t_f$. The probability of such a compound event is infinitesimally small because the probability of each independent event is very small. In fact, let us allow eleven points to fall randomly on a line. The probability that four specified points out of the eleven (the four at higher $P/P_u$ levels) will lie to the right of the other seven is 1/330. If one also requires a specified order for the four points, then the probability is 1/7920.

As regards the stressing frame shown in Figure 1, a tensile, not a torsional, method of loading was used. The specimen was positioned by hand-tightening the threaded bushings on each end. The two spherically seated screws, on either side of the specimen, were tightened successively in increments of $\sim$ 0.0003 inch or less until the desired tensile strain was reached. A 1/2-inch extensometer was used to measure strain which was read on the strain recorder of a tensile testing machine. This procedure was described in Reference 13 in my paper.

The calculation of the elastic stress field between an edge dislocation and an $MgZn_2$ particle present in the grain boundary was intended to provide an order-of-magnitude result, which is indeed accurate to the extent that the particle-matrix interface is coherent. Published data might indicate that there is little or no coherency between an $MgZn_2$ particle and good 7075 aluminum lattice. An $MgZn_2$ particle located in a grain boundary is not surrounded by good lattice, and hence measured lattice parameters no longer constitute an adequate guide to the degree of coherency. Furthermore, the fact that Al forms compounds with both Mg and Zn suggests an affinity between Al atoms in the matrix and Mg and Zn atoms in $MgZn_2$ and, consequently, some coherency across an interface. The interface cannot be fully coherent but neither can it be completely noncoherent. The application of elasticity theory to a polycrystalline material is objectionable because a grain boundary is not a coherent interface; still the application proves useful. In the absence of exact knowledge concerning the coherency of the $MgZn_2$-matrix interface, the best possible estimate was made of stresses acting upon this interface.

**F. H. Cocks, Tyco Laboratories, Inc.:**

I would like to make a comment concerning the conclusion that the immobilization of dislocations or the inactivation of dislocation sources will contribute to stress corrosion cracking in 7075 aluminum. We have observed[1]

that for strains less than 1% and strain rates between 4.4 x $10^{-3}$ and 4.4 x $10^{-2}$ $(min)^{-1}$ the activation volume for 7075-T73 was greater than that for 7075-T651. Similar results have recently been obtained in the low strain, low strain rate region by others for 7075-T651 and 7075-0.[2] This result may be significant because while the activation volume can be calculated from macroscopic measurements of the change in flow stress with change in strain rate,[3] it may be interpreted microscopically as the average volume swept out as a dislocation loop advances from one pinning point to another. Hence it gives a direct measure of the extent to which dislocations are entangled or immobilized. Thus, this data supports your conclusion. However, we also found for 7075-T651 that the work hardening rate was higher in the short transverse direction than in the rolling direction. As is well known, the susceptibility in the short transverse direction is much higher than that in the rolling direction. Furthermore, the degree to which dislocations are entangled in aluminum alloys is also complicated by the fact that for many alloys, including 7075-T651, strain aging does occur;[4,5] and this can lead to negative strain rate effects[6] (negative activation volumes) depending upon the strain rate range chosen. Nevertheless, from the data now available, it does appear certain that dislocation arrangements play a critical part in the basic mechanism of cracking in high strength aluminum alloys.

1. NASA, G. C. Marshall Space Flight Center, Huntsville, Alabama, Contract No. NAS 8-20297, Annual Summary Report, June 1, 1967.
2. D. L. Holt, S. G. Babcock, S. J. Green and C. J. Maiden. *Trans. ASM,* **60,** 152 (1967).
3. R. M. Rose, D. P. Ferris and J. Wolff. *Trans. AIME,* **224,** 981 (1962).
4. D. V. Wilson and B. Russell. *Acta. Met.,* **8,** 468 (1960).
5. D. J. Bailey, W. F. Flanagan and G. E. Miller. *Acta. Met.,* **13,** 436 (1965).
6. P. P. Gillis. AIME, Fall 1967 Meeting, Cleveland, Ohio.

**A. J. Jacobs:**

Measurements of activation volume and related parameters provide a welcome addition to the stress corrosion literature on aluminum. Such measurements might help to explain not only why one temper is susceptible and another is not but also the orientation dependence of stress corrosion susceptibility, which has perplexed investigators for so many years. It is apparent that other factors, such as the proportion of grain boundaries oriented perpendicular to the tensile stresses must be considered also in the final analysis of orientation dependence.

**J. C. Williams, The Boeing Co.:**

I am troubled by the apparent lack of fractographic evidence to support your model. In your paper you state that in the less-ductile -T6 material the crack can propagate between $MgZn_2$ particles by mechanical means. This distance is 0.5 to 1.0 microns, based on micrographs from your own paper. Such a distance is easily resolvable fractographically, yet no such fractographic evidence has been reported. I think this point is rather critical and until cleared up represents a serious objection to your model.

**E. N. Pugh, RIAS:**

Apart from the absence of supporting fractographic evidence, I find the concept of brittle fracture between grain boundary precipitate particles difficult to accept in a FCC material. You argue that locking of dislocations by precipitates favors such behavior. However, it seems to me that the grain boundaries themselves would act as sources of dislocations, so that stress-concentrations would be relieved by the generation of dislocations rather than by brittle fracture. If one advocates a stage of mechanical fracture, I think it is more realistic to consider that a ductile process is involved. For example, I suggested that fracture occurs by void initiation at grain boundary precipitate particles followed by their coalescence to form a macrocrack [E. N. Pugh, Liberty Bell Corrosion Course II, 1966, p. 73]. Of course, such a model is again open to the criticism that it is not supported by fractographic evidence.

**W. J. Helfrich, Kaiser Aluminum & Chemical Corp.:**

The applicability of an electrochemical-mechanical model[1] for intergranular stress corrosion cracking of aluminum alloys would, in this instance, depend upon whether or not the grain boundary precipitates are attacked. You admitted to the difficulty of knowing whether pits in stress corroded foils of 7075-T6 were, in fact, former sites of grain boundary precipitation.[2] The evidence for this attack is questionable considering Mr. Sprowls' reference to the unpublished work of Hunter et al,[3] wherein it was reported that foils of 7075-T6 were attacked at the grain margins, leaving the grain boundary precipitates unattacked. Notwithstanding the possible non-correspondence between the corrosion behavior of thin foils and that of bulk alloys, it would seem necessary that the question of where electrochemical attack starts must be answered. Do you have additional evidence supporting the contention that grain boundary $MgZn_2$ precipitates are sites for initial attack during stress corrosion cracking of 7075-T6?

If precipitate particles do initiate intergranular cracking of alloy 7075, then we must explain how the incipient cracks join to form a macroscopic stress corrosion crack. Considering that grain boundary precipitates are frequently less than one micron apart, it isn't necessary that the incipient cracks propagate very far—either in the grain boundary or through a more ductile zone adjacent to the grain boundary. It may be sufficient merely to rupture the ligaments separating the sites of initial attack.[4] Of course, the question remains—is this step in the cracking process a result of brittle or ductile rupture? If it is brittle, I would think that little plastic deformation should accompany cracking.

1. J. J. Harwood. The Phenomena and Mechanism of Stress Corrosion Cracking. *Stress Corrosion Cracking and Embrittlement,* John Wiley, New York, p. 1 (1956).
2. A. J. Jacobs. The Role of Dislocations in the Stress Corrosion Cracking of 7075 Aluminum Alloy. *ASM Trans. Quart.,* 58, 579 (1965) December.
3. M. S. Hunter, G. R. Frank and D. L. Robinson. Unpublished work. (See D. O. Sprowls and R. H. Brown. Stress Corrosion

Mechanisms for Aluminum Alloys. *Symposium on Fundamental Aspects of S tress Corrosion Cracking,* Ref. 114).
4. W. J. Helfrich. Influence of Stress and Temperature on Short-Transverse Stress Corrosion Cracking of an Al-4.2% Zn-2.5% Mg Alloy. ASTM STP 425, 1967, in press.

**A. J. Jacobs:**

That crack propagation in 7075 is at least partly mechanical in nature was shown by the dimpled microstructure in Figure 15. Figure 1 shows how extremely brittle the stress corrosion area often appears. Second-phase particles (A) and sites formerly occupied by particles (B) are seen also in this intergranular fracture, with no evidence of microvoid coalescence. A reasonable speculation is that the ductile component of mechanical fracture increases as the crack grows, while the brittle component decreases. Especially interesting in the photograph are the heavily

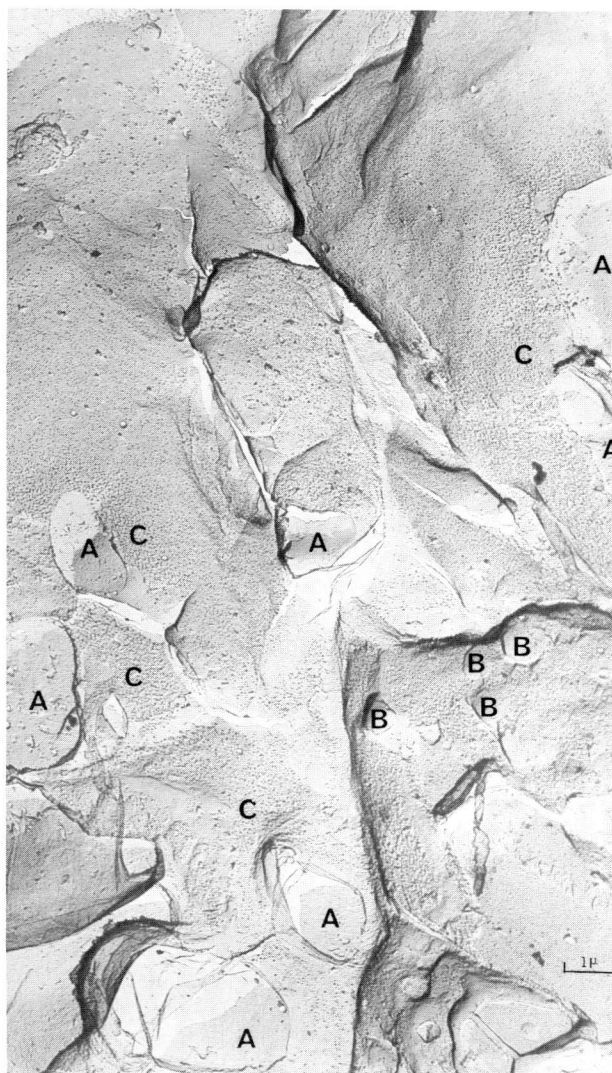

FIGURE 1 — Fractograph of the stress corrosion area in a notched 7075-T73 specimen.

corroded regions (C) surrounding the second-phase particles. These regions bear considerable resemblance to the surface structure resulting from cathodic treatment of a ternary Al-Zn-Mg alloy (nominally 4.3%Zn-3.3%Mg) in 3.5% NaCl solution.[1] Electrochemical as well as mechanical processes, therefore, were operative over the area shown in the fractograph. Unpublished data obtained by ultrasonically monitoring a growing stress corrosion crack in 7075-T6 have not only supported the findings of others (Reference 21 in my paper) regarding a two-stage growth process, but they have also indicated that the slow-growth (stress corrosion) stage is stepwise in nature.[2] Such stepwise growth argues strongly for an electrochemical-mechanical mechanism. My evidence for initial electrochemical attack of $MgZn_2$ particles present in the grain boundaries is still based largely on the microscopy that I carried out on corroded 7075-T6 and -T73 (Reference 12 in my paper).

1. D. A. Vaughan, et al. Fifth Progress Report on USAF Contract No. AF33(615)-1710, Wright-Patterson Air Force Base, Dayton, Ohio, May 15, 1965.
2. NASA Contract No. NAS8-20471, Marshall Space Flight Center, Huntsville, Alabama.

# INTERACTION OF DISLOCATIONS WITH PRECIPITATES IN HIGH STRENGTH ALUMINUM ALLOYS AND SUSCEPTIBILITY TO STRESS CORROSION CRACKING

M. O. Speidel
Boeing Scientific Research Laboratories

## Abstract

The influence of precipitation hardening, microstructure and dislocation arrangement on the susceptibility to intergranular stress corrosion cracking of high strength aluminum alloys has been examined by transmission electron microscopy. A high purity ternary aluminum-zinc-magnesium alloy and the commercial alloys 7075 and 2024 exhibit characteristic dislocation arrangements after deformation. In material of high susceptibility to stress corrosion cracking, long, straight, narrow bands of high dislocation density extend across the grains. Dislocations in the bands are piled up against the grain boundaries. In material aged to a reduced susceptibility, the slip bands contain dislocations of irregular curvature and many dislocation loops.

It is concluded that susceptibility to stress corrosion cracking in high strength aluminum alloys is enhanced by precipitates which are sheared during plastic deformation. Particles which are bypassed by moving dislocations, reduce the susceptibility to stress corrosion cracking.

Important structural parameters, which influence the susceptibility to SCC of precipitation hardening aluminum alloys, are the coherency of precipitates, as well as their size, volume fraction, misfit parameter and antiphase boundary energy.

## I. Introduction

The susceptibility to intergranular stress corrosion cracking of aluminum base alloys depends strongly on alloy composition and heat treatment. Although this complex phenomenon has been studied over more than four decades, the fundamental factors that render an alloy susceptible are still far from being understood.

It was the purpose of the present work to investigate the influence of the microstructure of precipitation hardened high strength aluminum alloys on the susceptibility to intergranular stress corrosion cracking. High strength aluminum alloys are based on the ternary alloy systems Al-Zn-Mg and Al-Cu-Mg or on the quaternary system Al-Zn-Mg-Cu. Commercial alloys contain also smaller additions of other elements.[1] Such alloys can reach a very high strength when they are solution heat treated, quenched and subsequently aged to precipitate small particles of other phases.[1-3] However, in this condition, the alloys are often found to be susceptible to intergranular stress corrosion cracking, the degree of susceptibility strongly depending on the heat treatment and thus on the microstructure of the alloys.[4-6]

Earlier attempts to explain the influence of the microstructure on the susceptibility to intergranular stress corrosion cracking of high strength aluminum alloys

concentrated on the grain boundary precipitates and the precipitation free zone along the grain boundaries. It was assumed that in susceptible alloys of the Al-Zn-Mg and Al-Zn-Mg-Cu type preferential flow would take place in the precipitation free zones and preferential corrosive attack would occur along the regions where plastic flow had taken place.[7] This view is still widely accepted[8,9] and attempts are being undertaken to control the susceptibility by controlling the width and the strength of the supposedly weak precipitation free grain boundary zone.[10]

More recent work however has shown that even in Al-Zn-Mg and Al-Zn-Mg-Cu alloys, which are most susceptible to intergranular stress corrosion cracking, slip is not concentrated in precipitation free zones but is concentrated in narrow bands across the grains.[11-15] These observations indicate that the important factors in determining the susceptibility to stress corrosion cracking are the overall distribution and nature of the precipitates within the matrix because of their interaction with dislocations during plastic deformation.

It was the objective of the present work to identify the more important structural parameters which control the susceptibility to stress corrosion cracking of high strength aluminum alloys. In the first section, available experimental data are collected which describe the susceptibility as a function of aging temperature and aging time. These data are then related to the microstructure and the observed deformation substructure. Finally, the observations are discussed in terms of precipitation hardening theories and the results compared with the assumptions made by some of the existing models for intergranular stress corrosion cracking of high strength aluminum alloys.

## II. Precipitation, Hardening and Susceptibility

In this section, we review briefly some facts known about the influence of aging time and aging temperature on the susceptibility to intergranular stress corrosion cracking (SCC) of high strength aluminum alloys. As a result, a simple diagram emerges, which will be used as a quick and convenient reference in the later sections of the present work.

Until very recently, the susceptibility to SCC of high strength aluminum alloys has been measured almost exclusively either as the time to failure of unnotched samples under stress in a corrosive environment, or as the highest sustained tension stress level that did not cause failure in some finite period of time (threshold stress level). Using the concepts of fracture mechanics, a more meaningful measure for the susceptibility to SCC would be either the growth rate of a stress corrosion crack as a function of the stress intensity factor, or $K_{Iscc}$, the limiting stress intensity at which a stress corrosion crack can propagate. Unfortunately, in the overwhelming majority of the available experimental papers, either time to failure or the threshold stress level have been used to describe the susceptibility to SCC. Thus, until more experimental data are available, the correlation described in this section is based on measurements of the threshold stress level and the time to failure.

Generally, the term "resistance to SCC" is used as to describe the inverse of the term "susceptibility to SCC".

### A. Al-Zn-Mg and Al-Zn-Mg-Cu

Precipitation hardening, aging sequence and susceptibility to SCC of these alloys have been studied extensively before.

The probable aging sequence of the ternary alloy is:[2,7,17-19]

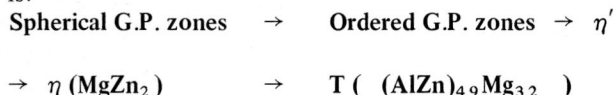

**Spherical G.P. zones** $\rightarrow$ **Ordered G.P. zones** $\rightarrow$ $\eta'$

$\rightarrow$ $\eta$ (MgZn$_2$) $\rightarrow$ T ( (AlZn)$_{49}$Mg$_{32}$ )

The first two phases of the sequence are coherent, and the nuclei of the transition phase $\eta'$ are thought to be semicoherent.[17-19] $\eta$ and T are incoherent. The sequence has been reported to be unaffected by the presence of small additions of other elements such as copper, which are thought to dissolve in the G.P. zones and the $\eta'$ phase.[7,15] The formation of the first three phases of the sequence is favored by low aging temperatures (e.g., room temperature) and short aging times. The formation of the intermetallic

phases $\eta$ and T is favored by long aging times and high aging temperatures.

Precipitation hardening at room temperature ("natural aging") is mainly due to G.P. zones.[16-18] The hardness maximum which is observed during aging at temperatures above 100 C[(1)] has been attributed to a mixture of G.P. zones, $\eta'$ and $\eta$.[7,16,18] The T phase occurs mainly in heavily overaged alloys, e.g., after aging at temperatures between 200 C and 300 C.[17-19]

The resistance to intergranular SCC of high strength Al-Mg-Zn alloys (measured as the time to failure) decreases monotonically during aging at room temperature[20,21] while the first three phases of the aging sequence precipitate[2,17,18] and the strength increases continuously.[6,16,20,21] Thus, the alloys which are fairly resistant immediately after quenching[20,21] become extremely susceptible to SCC after a long aging time at room temperature.[6,20,21] In this stage they also have a very low threshold stress level.[6]

Isothermal aging at temperatures between 70 and 180 C also causes an initial decrease of the time to failure by SCC in a wide variety of ternary, quaternary and commercial alloys.[16,20-26] However, after reaching a minimum value, the time to failure increases again progressively.[16,20-26] The experiments indicate, that the minimum time to failure is passed when the $\eta'$ particles grow and the $\eta$ and T phase begin to form.[6,16,25] It has been claimed that minimum time to failure occurs at maximum hardness, because the difference in hardness between the grains and the precipitate free zone was thought to be greatest a this stage.[7,9] However, studies of high purity ternary alloys as well as alloys with small additions of copper and other elements have indicated that minimum life occurs considerably earlier in the aging process than peak hardness and peak strength.[16,23-26]

The typical relationship between precipitation hardening and resistance to SCC of high strength aluminum alloys is illustrated schematically in Figure 1. For quick reference, the aging process is divided into three stages. In Stage I the strength of the alloy increases and the resistance

[(1)] "Artificial aging"; typical heat treatment one day at 130 C for alloys such as 7075 or AlZn$_6$Mg$_3$, see Table 1.

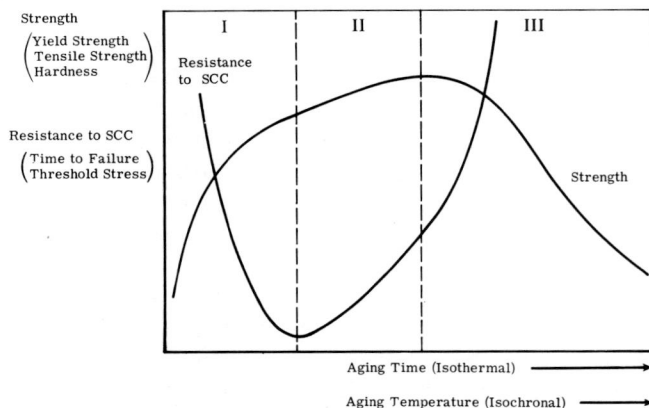

**FIGURE 1** — **Typical relationship between precipitation hardening and resistance to stress corrosion cracking of high strength aluminum alloys.**

to SCC decreases to a minimum as aging proceeds. In Stage II the resistance to SCC increases again while the alloy hardens further until peak strength is reached. In Stage III the alloy is overaged, the strength drops during further aging while the resistance to SCC increases markedly.

The outlined relationship (Figure 1) between precipitation hardening and resistance to SCC of high strength aluminum alloys is consistent not only with isothermal aging experiments[16,20-26] but also with observations during isochronal aging.[4-6,15,20,21,26-33] Earlier work has shown that aging temperatures intermediate between room temperature and 100 C are particularly unfavorable to the stress corrosion behavior,[26] and $\approx$ 120 C was quoted as the minimum aging temperature for commercial alloys.[5,27] In recent developments aging temperatures up to 180 C are proposed to assure long times to failure.[28-33] Figure 1, Stage III reflects the fact that an increase in resistance to SCC which is achieved by very high aging temperatures, requires some sacrifice in strength.

It has recently been shown that not only the time to failure but also the threshold stress level increases during isochronal aging in Stage II (Figure 1), long before the maximum yield stress is reached.[6] The threshold stress level increases further in Stage III where the alloys are overaged. The latter result is well known since it has led to the introduction of the T73 heat treatment which imparts significant resistance to the commercial 7075 alloy,[29] although it lowers the strength of the alloy by about 20% from the T6 condition.[4,28]

The relationship between precipitation hardening and resistance to SCC (or its inverse, the susceptibility to SCC) which is illustrated in Figure 1 holds for typical high strength aluminum alloys of the Al-Zn-Mg and Al-Zn-Mg-Cu type. It is not claimed that this correlation holds also for all other precipitation hardening aluminum base alloys. However, many examples of other (binary, ternary and commercial) aluminum base alloy systems are known where a high susceptibility to SCC coincides with a high volume fraction of small coherent precipitates. Conversely, as the volume fraction of incoherent particles increases, the resistance to SCC generally increases too. An example is given in the next section.

*B. Al-Cu-Mg*

High strength alloys based on this system contain about 4.5 wt% Cu and 1.5 wt% Mg. Commercial alloys, e.g., 2024, contain also small amounts of other elements.[1] Quite analogous to Al-Zn-Mg alloys, very small ordered coherent particles are reported to precipitate at room temperature after quenching from the solution temperature.[2,18,34] At the same time, G.P. zones like those in binary Al-Cu alloys are observed.[2,18,34] Upon further aging, a sequence of complicated phases has been observed which have not yet been thoroughly studied.

Alloys of this class, e.g., the commercial alloy 2024, are highly susceptible to SCC when solution heat treated, quenched and aged at room temperature (T3, T4 temper).[4,35,36] The resistance to SCC of these alloys

decreases rapidly during the first stages of reheating until a minimum resistance is obtained. Additional heating then increases the resistance and the resistance becomes very high, even in the case of short-transverse specimens.[4,35,36] Thus, quite a similar relationship as in Figure 1 seems to be valid: when the alloy is aged to contain a high volume fraction of coherent particles, it is highly susceptible; when it is aged at higher temperatures, ($\approx$ 190 C), the resistance passes a minimum, then increases again until the alloy is highly resistant near the hardness maximum, where it contains a high volume fraction of incoherent particles.

Thus the commercial alloy 2024 is another example of the fact that maximum susceptibility to SCC occurs long before maximum hardness in the aging process of precipitation hardened high strength aluminum alloys. After aging at room temperature ("natural aging", T3, T4, temper), 2024 exhibits a lower threshold stress level and a shorter time to failure and a lower yield strength than after aging for 12 hours at 190 C ("artificially aging", T6, T8 temper).[1,4,35,36]

It was the main purpose of the present work to explain the variations of the susceptibility with aging temperature and aging time as shown in Figure 1 in terms of the known microstructure and the resulting dislocation arrangement.

## III. Materials and Experimental Details

Transmission electron microscopy was used to study microstructure and dislocation arrangements in a high purity aluminum base alloy of the Al-Zn-Mg type and in the commercial 2024 (Al-Cu-Mg) and 7075 (Al-Zn-Mg-Cu) alloys.

The high purity alloy was melted from elements of 99.999% purity. Table 1 gives the composition determined by chemical analysis after homogenization at 480 C. The specimens were rolled to 0.4 mm thickness and solution heat treated at 480 C for one hour before quenching. After various aging treatments, the specimens were deformed $\approx$ 2% in a tensile test. Thin foils for transmission electron microscopy were prepared electrolytically using a standard 2/3 methanol + 1/3 nitric acid electrolyte operated at -20 C.

## IV. Experimental Results

In this section, the observed microstructure and deformation substructure of the alloys investigated are briefly described and related to the various stages of Figure 1.

*A. Aluminum-Zinc-Magnesium*

Figures 2 to 7 show typical dislocation arrangements which develop in the high purity ternary alloy Al-6%Zn-3%Mg when it is deformed after quenching into water and aging at different temperatures. Figure 2 corresponds to the beginning of Stage I where the alloy is fairly resistant to SCC. Some dislocations are straight and parallel (arrows). They seem either to come out of the grain boundary or to

TABLE 1—Alloy Compositions

| Designation | Zn | Mg | Cu | Fe | Si | Mn | Cr | Ti | Balance |
|---|---|---|---|---|---|---|---|---|---|
| Al-6%Zn-3%Mg | 6.18 | 3.00 | — | — | — | — | — | — | Al |
| 7075 | 5.57 | 2.52 | 1.39 | 0.16 | 0.17 | 0.03 | 0.19 | 0.03 | Al |
| 2024 | 0.25 | 2.0 | 4.5 | 0.5 | 0.5 | 0.6 | 0.1 | — | Al |

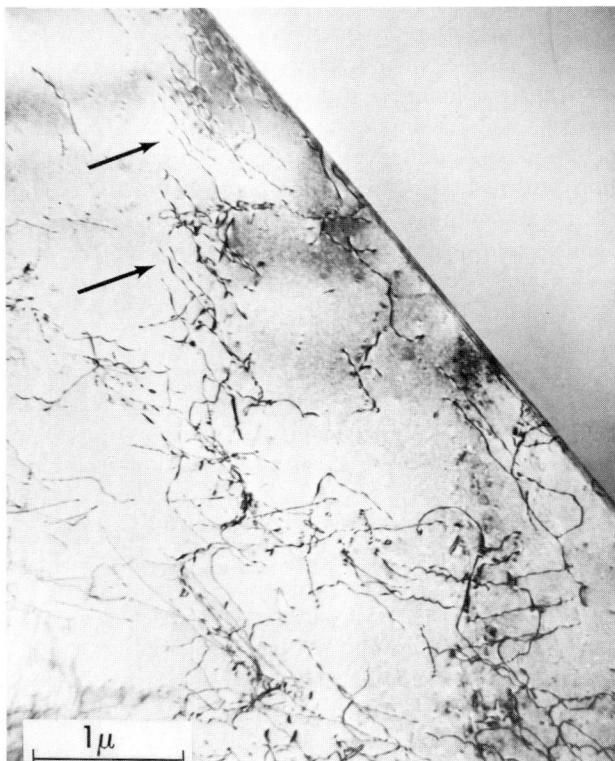

FIGURE 2 — Al-6%Zn-3%Mg, aged for 5 hours at 20 C. Grain boundary and dislocations.

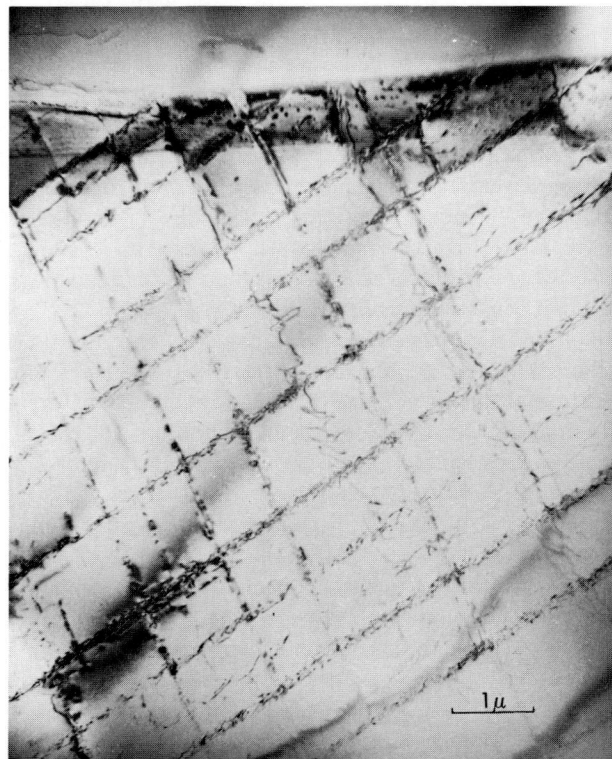

FIGURE 3 — Al-6%Zn-3%Mg, aged for 70 hours at 90 C. Grain boundary and dislocations, grain boundary precipitates.

be piled up against it. However, the dislocations are not as strictly confined to their original slip planes as in later stages of the aging process, that is, they leave their original slip planes relatively easily either during deformation or during the preparation of the thin foil.

Figure 3 corresponds to the middle of Stage II where the alloy is highly susceptible to SCC. The dislocations in the grain are confined to straight narrow slip bands which extend across the grain right up to the grain boundary. The spacing between the slip lines is roughly $1\mu$. As in Figure 2, the small coherent precipitates in the interior of the grain are not resolved. Larger precipitates are visible in the grain boundary near the top of Figure 3. No continuous film like grain boundary precipitation has been observed in an investigation of a large number of grain boundaries. There was also no evidence of preferential slip near the grain boundaries.

Figures 4 to 6 correspond to the end of Stage II, near maximum hardness, where the alloy is still very susceptible to SCC. Similarly to Figure 3, slip is concentrated in narrow

bands with a very high dislocation density (Figure 4). These slip bands extend across the entire grains. Within the bands, the dislocations are piled up against the grain boundaries (Figures 5 and 6). However, the dislocations in the pileups are neither straight nor parallel; they exhibit a rather irregular curvature and form many loops. Slip transfer across the grain boundary was frequently observed, an example being shown in the upper right corner of Figure 6. The precipitates in the interior of the grains are not resolved, they are however clearly visible at higher magnifications.

Figure 7 corresponds to the beginning of Stage III where the alloy is slightly overaged and the susceptibility is reduced. It is interesting to note that in this condition too, slip is planar and the dislocation distribution is highly inhomogeneous, that is, dislocations are concentrated in slip bands. However, these bands of high dislocation density consist almost exclusively of small dislocation loops which have nearly the same size as the small precipitates in the grains. Larger precipitates are observed along the grain

FIGURE 4 — Al-6%Zn-3%Mg, aged for 25 hours at 130 C.
Slip bands of high dislocation density.

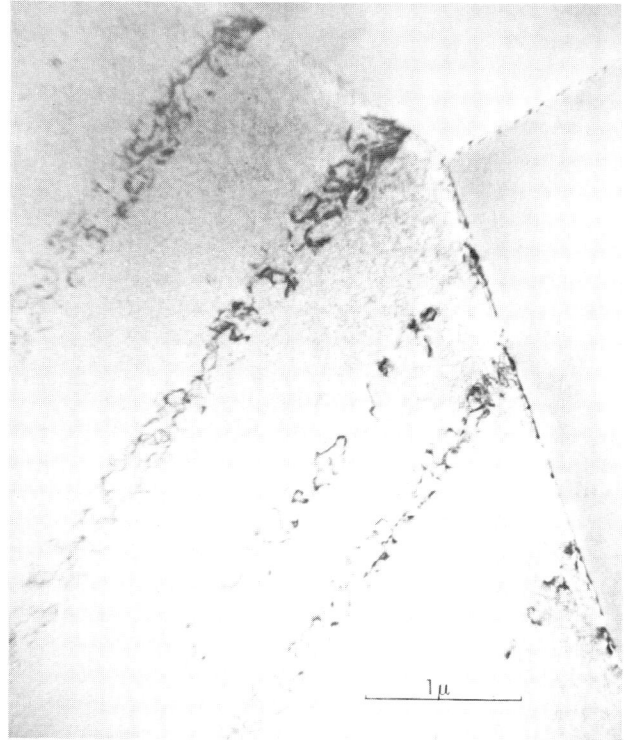

FIGURE 5 — Al-6%Zn-3%Mg, aged for 25 hours at 130 C.
Dislocation pileups at grain boundaries.

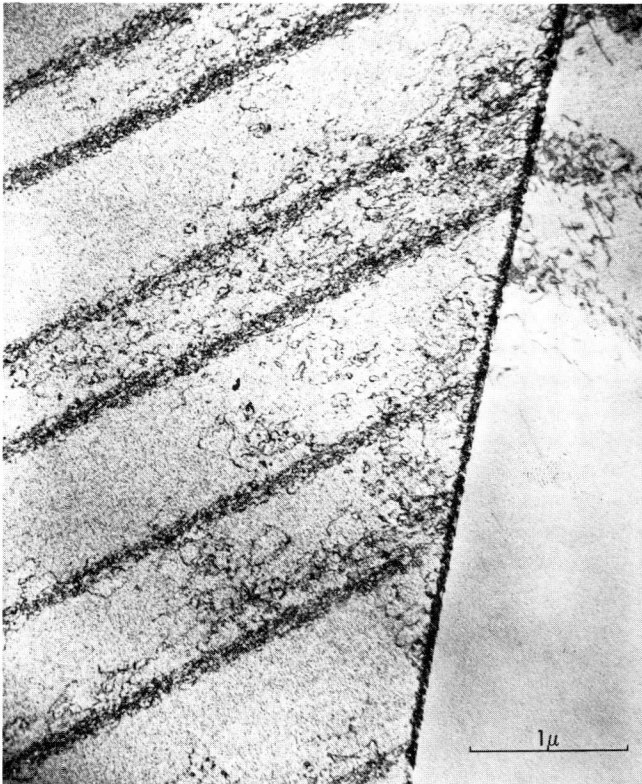

FIGURE 6 — Al-6%Zn-3%Mg, aged for 25 hours at 130 C.
Dislocation pileups and slip transfer across the
grain boundary.

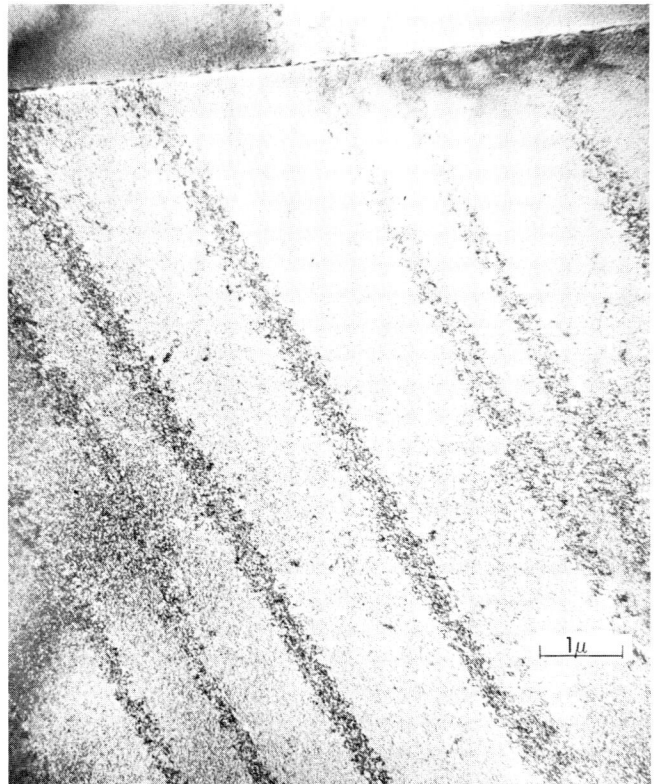

FIGURE 7 — Al-6%Zn-3%Mg, aged for 8 hours at 175 C.
Grain boundary and slip bands of high dislocation loop density.

565

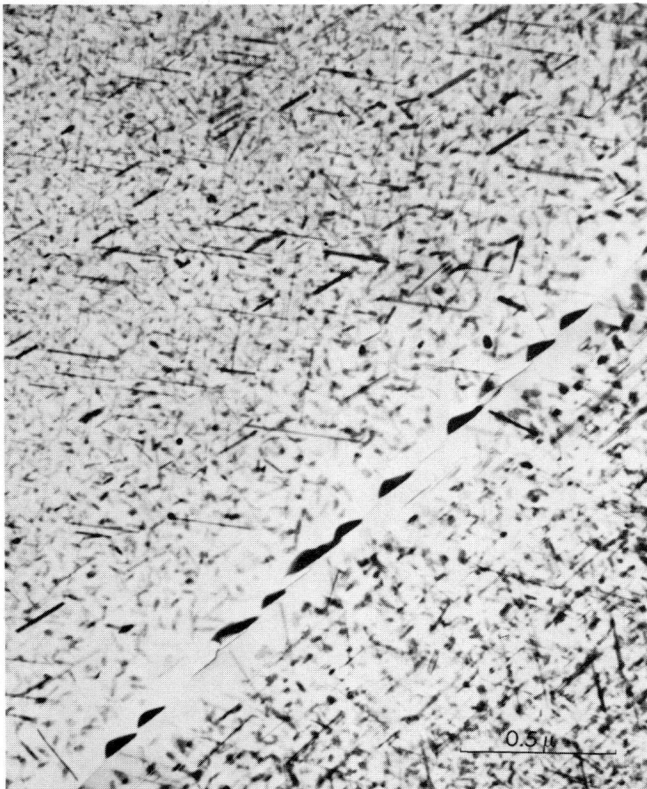

FIGURE 8 — Al-6%Zn-3%Mg, directly quenched from 500 to 150 C and aged for 15 hours. Overaged, large $\eta$ precipitates.

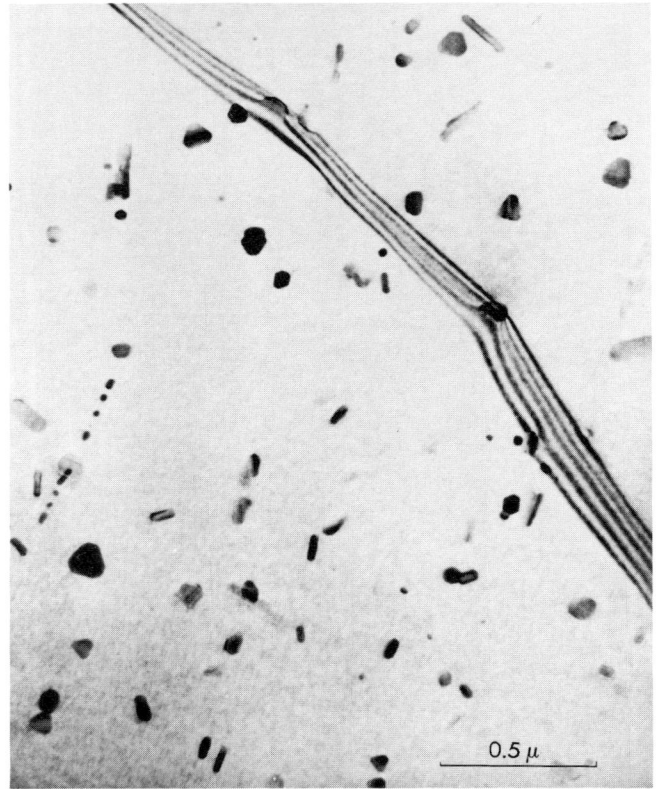

FIGURE 9 — 7075, aged for 10 days at 20 C. Grain boundary and particles of intermetallic phases.

boundaries. A close examination of a number of grain boundaries reveals that the precipitates are not film-like but discrete and occupy only about 20% of the grain boundary area. Along the grain boundary, a precipitation free zone of about 200 Å width has been observed. There was no sign of preferential slip in this zone. The width of the precipitation free grain boundary zone was about twice the interparticle distance of the precipitates in the matrix.

Figure 8 corresponds to the middle of Stage III. The alloy is heavily overaged and "immune" to SCC. Grain boundary precipitates now occupy about 90% of the grain boundary area. In the interior of the grain, large, incoherent particles of the $\eta$ phase are seen, which will not be sheared by moving dislocations.

## B. Aluminum-Zinc-Magnesium-Copper (7075)

Microstructure and properties of this group of alloys differ little from Al-Zn-Mg.

Figures 9 to 12 are taken from the commercial alloy 7075. The microstructure of a susceptible alloy near the end of Stage I is represented by Figure 9. The large dark particles in Figure 9 consist of insoluble[2] intermetallic phases, which are mainly due to the presence of small

amounts of Cr and Mn. These particles persist invariably throughout the aging process and thus constitute the main difference in the microstructure between high purity (ternary and quaternary) and commercial alloys. Moreover, these particles reduce the grain growth by pinning the grain boundary. This is evident from Figure 9.

Figure 10 shows the dislocation arrangement at the beginning of Stage I, where the alloy is even more resistant to SCC than similar treated Al-Zn-Mg. Some of the dislocations are straight, others are tangled or bow out between the particles of the intermetallic phases. The dislocation distribution is fairly homogeneous, which might partly be due to the fact that moving dislocations have to bypass the large insoluble particles.

Figure 11 corresponds to the middle of Stage II where the alloy is highly susceptible to SCC. Significantly, the dislocations are concentrated in bands of high dislocation density with a distance of roughly 1 $\mu$. The irregular curvature of the dislocations could partly be due to the bypassing of the insoluble particles. Figure 12, also corresponding to the middle of Stage II, shows an area of the same alloy, where the density of the insoluble particles is low. Evidently, dislocations coming out from one grain boundary, pile up against the opposite grain boundary. It is thought that the slip bands of Figure 11 form part of similar dislocation pileups.

As the aging process proceeds to Stage III, the deformation substructure resembles very much the one

---

[2] An unpublished investigation by the author has shown that these particles are insoluble during the usual solution heat treatment of the 7075 alloy; the particles are in no case the first precipitates formed after quench, as has been claimed.[37]

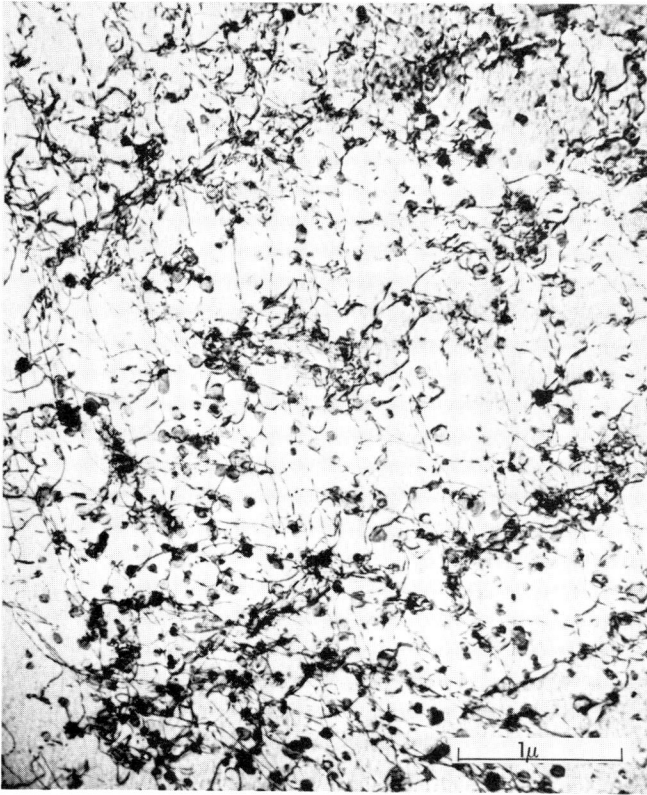

FIGURE 10 – 7075, aged 14 hours at 20 C. Dislocations and intermetallic phases.

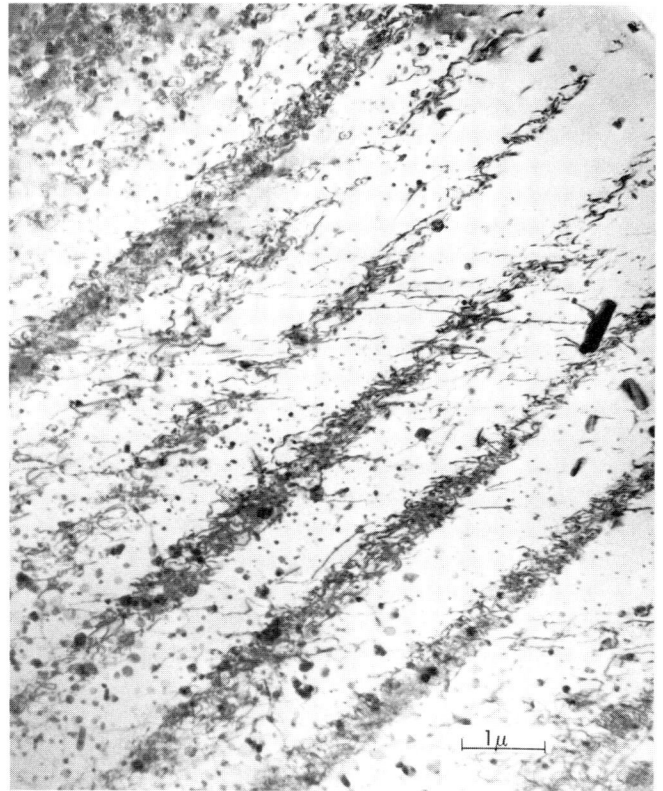

FIGURE 11 – 7075, aged 24 hours at 100 C. Dislocations in slip bands.

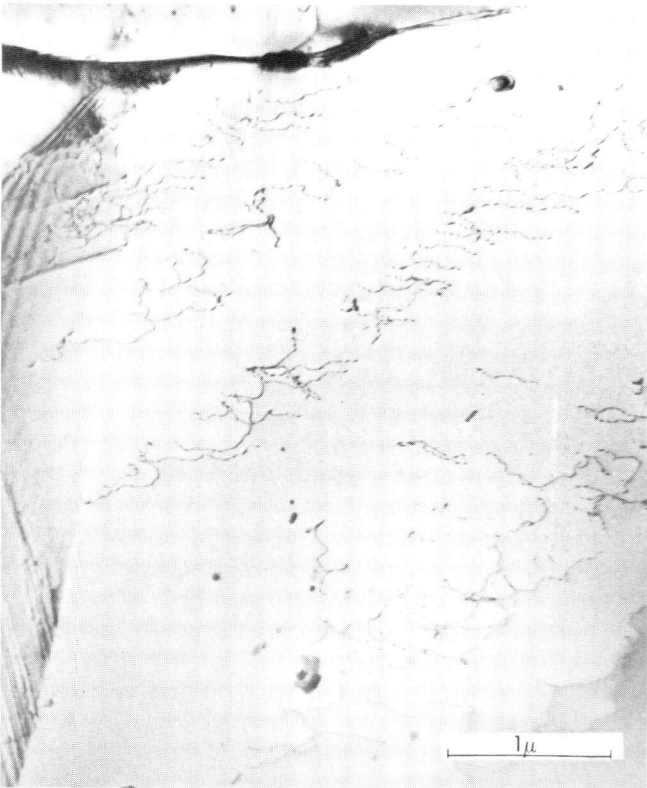

FIGURE 12 – 7075, aged 24 hours at 100 C. Dislocation pileups between grain boundaries.

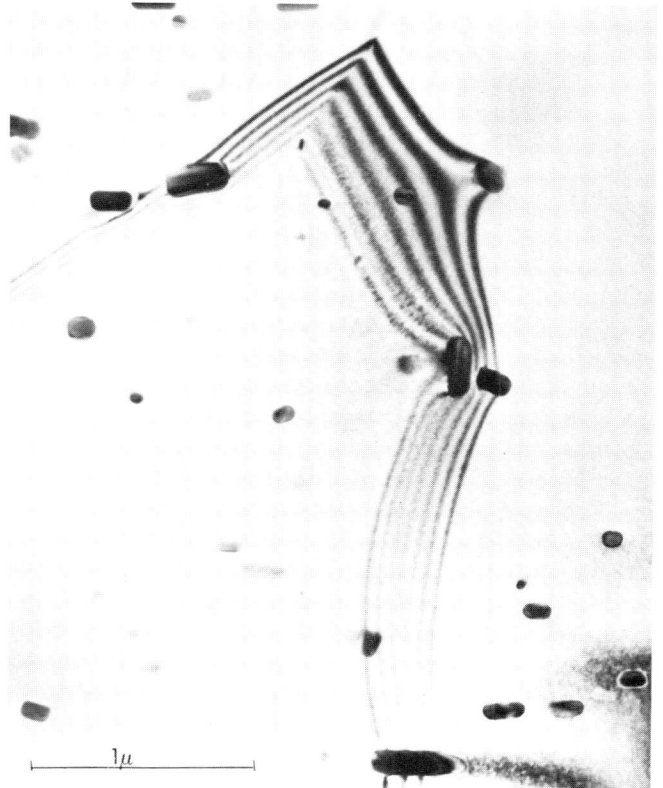

FIGURE 13 – 2024, aged 4 hours at 20 C. Grain boundary and particles of intermetallic phases.

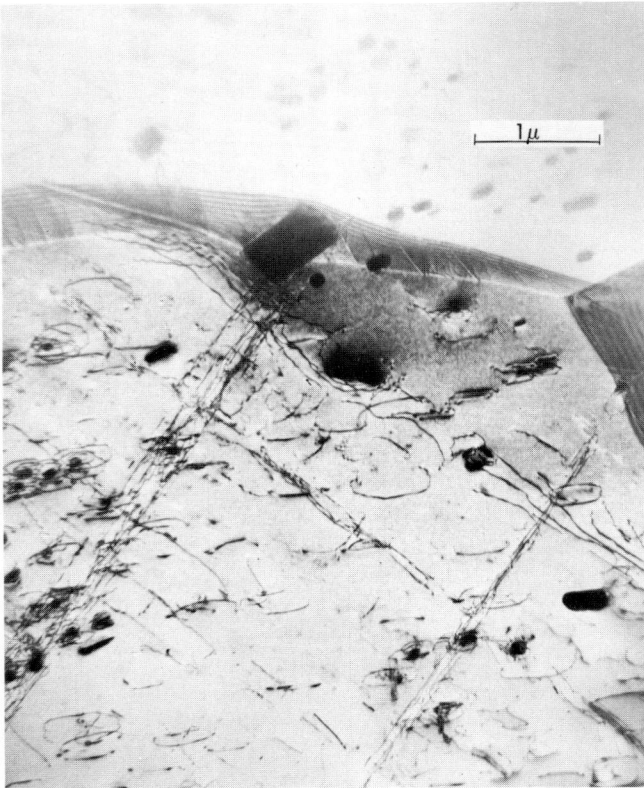

**FIGURE 14 — 2024, aged 24 hours at 100 C. Grain boundaries and dislocations.**

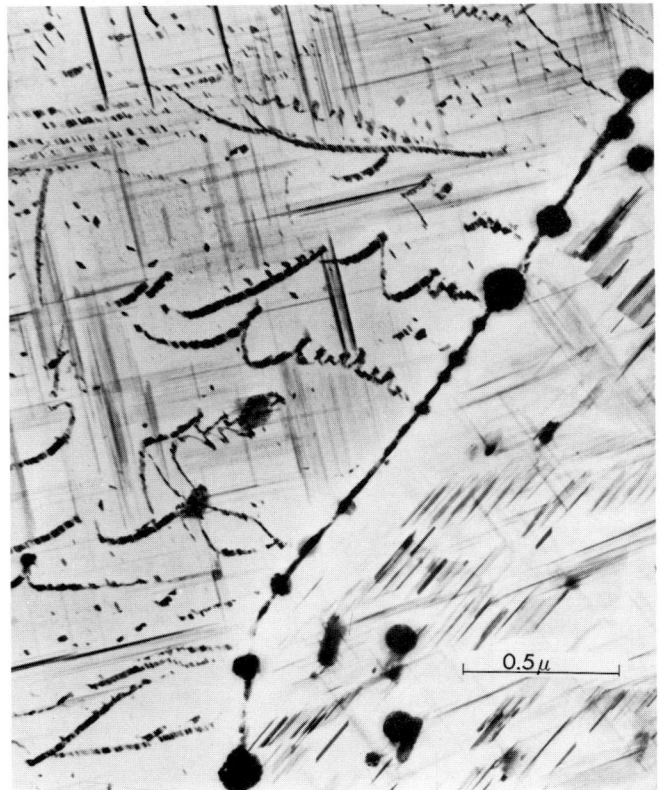

**FIGURE 15 — 2024, aged 22 hours at 200 C. Nucleation at helical dislocations, at the grain boundary, and in the grain.**

observed in Al-Zn-Mg. The slip bands contain a high number of very small dislocation loops.

### C. Aluminum-Copper-Magnesium (2024)

The microstructure of the commercial alloy 2024 at the beginning of Stage I (immediately after quenching) is shown in Figure 13. It looks very similar to Figure 9 of the 7075 alloy. While small coherent precipitates are not resolved, large particles of the intermetallic phases are seen as they have impeded the movement of the grain boundary during the recrystallization at the solution temperature. The deformation substructure of the alloy 2024 at the beginning of Stage I looks almost exactly as the one of 7075 (Figure 10).

Figure 14 shows the dislocation arrangement at the beginning of Stage II, where the alloy is very susceptible to SCC. Straight and parallel dislocations are concentrated in bundles. The precipitates in the grain are still very small and not resolved. The grain boundaries are almost free from incoherent precipitates.

Figure 15 represents the microstructure in the middle of Stage III where the alloy is overaged and highly resistant to SCC. In addition to the large plate shaped precipitates inside the grains, nearly continuous precipitation along the grain boundary is observed. Moreover, incoherent precipitates have formed and grown at helical dislocations. In practice, the alloy is cold worked before aging, and aged for a shorter time than the specimen corresponding to Figure 15 (T8 temper). In this condition, it has somewhat smaller and many more incoherent precipitates, nucleated at dislocation lines. Such precipitates are bypassed by moving dislocations, which then leave a high loop density in their wake, and the dislocation distribution will be similar to Figure 7.

### V. Discussion

#### A. The PFZ Hypothesis

The hypothesis of preferential flow in the grain boundary zone (PFZ) has been used to explain the influence of the aging process on the susceptibility to SCC of high strength aluminum alloys.[7] The following assumptions are then made:[7]

a. Maximum susceptibility occurs at or near maximum hardness.

b. At maximum susceptibility, slip occurs only (or at least preferentially) in the PFZ.

c. At maximum susceptibility, grain boundary precipitates form a continuous film or interconnected rows, thus preventing slip across the boundaries.

d. At maximum susceptibility, large areas near the grain boundaries are free from precipitates.

e. Preferential corrosive attack occurs along the regions where preferential plastic flow has taken place.

The experimental results presented in Sections 2 and 4 do not support the assumptions of the PFZ hypothesis:

a. As seen from Figure 1, maximum susceptibility occurs much earlier in the aging process than maximum hardness.

b. At maximum susceptibility as well as at maximum hardness, slip definitely occurs across the grains. No preferential slip near the grain boundary has been observed. See Figures 3, 5, 7, 12, and 14. This observation is consistent with earlier work.[11-15]

c. No continuous grain boundary precipitates have been observed at maximum susceptibility or at maximum hardness; slip transfer across the grain boundary however was observed. See Figures 3, 12, and 14; Figure 6.

d. Maximum susceptibility occurs when coherent precipitates predominate. During the early stages of the aging process, coherent precipitates form throughout the matrix with no PFZ at grain boundaries, since G.P. zones do not need lattice defects as nucleation site. As aging proceeds, some might be dissolved near grain boundaries, in favor of the grain boundary precipitates. However, near maximum susceptibility, only few grain boundary precipitates have been formed (Figures 3, 12, and 14) and thus, a PFZ, if any, must be very small.

A PFZ forms in overaged alloys, which are fairly resistant to SCC; moreover PFZ is pronounced in alloys which are not susceptible to SCC because of their low Zn + Mg content.[11]

e. If preferential corrosive attack would occur along the regions where preferential flow has taken place, one would expect SCC to be of the *transgranular* type in high strength aluminum alloys, since slip is concentrated in narrow bands across the grain. However, there is abundant evidence that SCC is of the *intergranular* type in high strength aluminum alloys.

Thus, our observations, consistent with other recent work,[11-15] do not indicate that the precipitation free grain boundary zone exerts a controlling influence on the susceptibility to stress corrosion cracking of high strength aluminum alloys, as has been claimed earlier[7] and is still widely accepted.[8-10,38,39]

## B. Dislocations in Pileups

The dominating feature in the deformation substructure of high strength aluminum alloys, susceptible to SCC, are dislocations concentrated in narrow straight slip bands and pileups against grain boundaries. As will be discussed in Section 5.3, dislocation pileups could affect the susceptibility to SCC either by their associated stress concentration at the grain boundary, or by controlling the slip step height. In the present section, we discuss the influence of the microstructure on the stress concentration and on the slip step height.

**Stage I.** As outlined in Section II, precipitation hardening of high strength aluminum alloys in Stage I is mainly due to coherent ordered precipitates. After short aging times, such particles are still small enough to be sheared by dislocations during plastic deforma-

tion.[2,12-14,40] The shear stress at which a dislocation can shear particles, depends on the cross section of the particles in the slip plane.[12,40] As the dislocation shears an obstacle (coherent particle, G.P. zone), it reduces the cross section of the obstacle in the slip plane. This is illustrated in Figure 16. Now, since the flow stress in such an activated slip plane is reduced, the following dislocations tend to remain and to move in the same plane, thus reducing the cross section of the particles even more, and further slip in the same plane is facilitated. This is the reason for the concentration of dislocations in narrow straight slip bands shown in Figures 3 to 6 and Figures 11, 12, and 14. Slip in activated slip planes continues until the dislocations are piled up (against obstacles such as grain boundaries) and the mutual repulsion between the dislocations equals the local reduction of the shear stress.[12,40]

Figure 17 shows the final dislocation arrangement. Dislocations have sheared coherent precipitates and are piled up against a grain boundary. In the interior of the grain, the particles are completely sheared. (This is a realistic assumption, since the typical diameter of the G.P. zones is 16 Å - 50 Å,[17,18,34] and thus only 6 - 20 dislocations are needed to shear them completely.)

When the particles are small and/or the pileups are long (due to a large grain size), almost all particles on a slip plane will be completely sheared off. In this case, the local reduction of the flow stress on active slip planes is proportional to $\tau_{Prec}$, the precipitation hardening. Therefore, in Stage I of the aging process, the concentration of dislocations in active slip planes and the slip step height[40] increase as precipitation hardening increases.

Dislocations have been observed to be piled up against grain boundaries, Figures 3, 5, 6, and 12. The effective shear stress $\tau_e$ which pushes the dislocations against the grain boundaries is thought to be equal to the externally

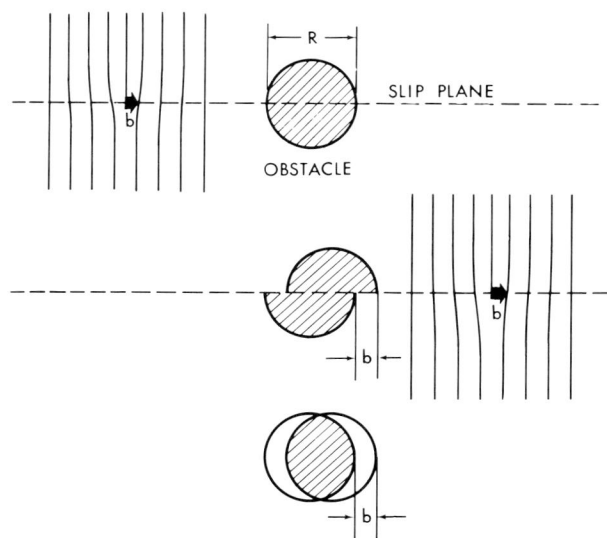

FIGURE 16 — Dislocation shearing a coherent precipitate, and associated reduction of the cross section.

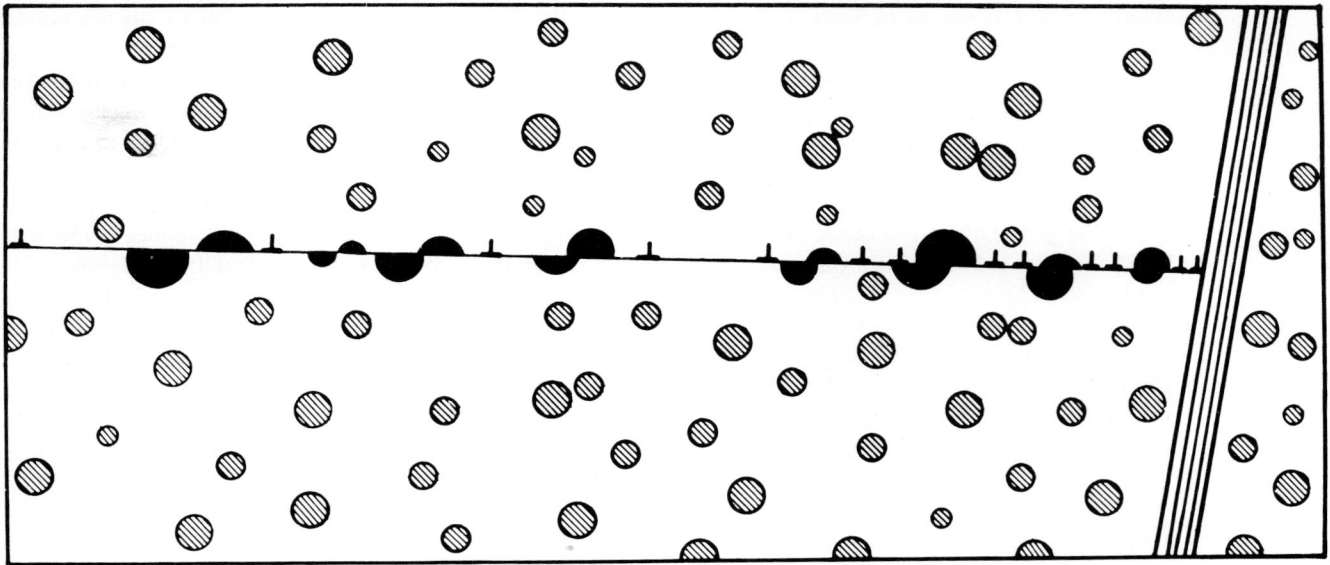

**FIGURE 17 — Dislocations, which shear precipitates pile up against a grain boundary.**

applied shear stress $\tau_a$ minus the friction stress $\tau_o$ a moving dislocation has to overcome.[41,42]

$$\tau_e = \tau_a - \tau_o \qquad (1)$$

We consider the friction stress to consist mainly of four terms:

$$\tau_e = \tau_a - (\tau_G + \tau_S + \tau_{SS} + \tau_{Prec}) \qquad (2)$$

Where: $\tau_G$ = shear stress due to elastic interactions with other dislocations;[43,44] $\tau_S$ = shear stress due to intersection of dislocations;[43,44] $\tau_{SS}$ = shear stress due to solid solution hardening; and $\tau_{Prec}$ = shear stress due to precipitation hardening.

As explained above, shearing dislocations reduce $\tau_{Prec}$ locally in active slip planes and give rise to a high number n of dislocations in the slip plane. Moreover, it follows from Equation (2) that a local reduction of $\tau_{Prec}$ in active slip planes also increases the shear stress $\tau_e$ under which the dislocations are piled up against the grain boundary. Thus, the stress concentration $n.\tau_e$ near the tip of a dislocation pileup at a grain boundary, increases rapidly as the alloys are aged in Stage I.

Moreover, plastic relaxation of stress concentrations becomes increasingly difficult as aging proceeds through Stage I. Plastic relaxation could occur by secondary slip[42,44] dipole formation[45] or cross slip. In any of these cases, the activation of new slip planes would be required. This becomes more difficult as aging proceeds, since full sized particles would have to be sheared. Thus, plastic relaxation, (which could reduce the slip step height as well as the stress concentration at the grain boundary) is the more difficult, the larger the increase of the critical shear stress due to particles which can be sheared during deformation.

Thus we are led to the general conclusion that in Stage I slip step height and stress concentration at the grain

boundary increase as the overall precipitation hardening of the grain ($\tau_{Prec}$) increases, due to precipitates which can be sheared during plastic deformation. $\tau_{Prec}$ in turn is controlled by the size, the volume fraction, the antiphase boundary energy and the misfit parameter of the precipitates.[40,46]

**Stage II**: If coherent particles grow very large in Stage II, or if the dislocation pileups are very short, a significant fraction of the particles will be sheared only partially. In this case, the stress concentration becomes a complicated function not only of $\tau_{Prec}$, but also of $d\tau_{Prec}/dR$, where R is the particle radius.[13,14] It is however quite probable that coherent or semicoherent precipitates in high strength aluminum alloys are bypassed while they are still very small.[17,18,34,49]

According to Sections II and IV, aging in Stage II creates an increasing volume fraction of precipitates which cannot be sheared by dislocations during plastic deformation. Dislocations bypass such particles either because they are incoherent or because they have too high a coherency stress field.[47-49] Thus, the irregular curvature of dislocations observed in Stage II can be attributed to the bowing out between large or incoherent particles and also to the formation of loops around them. (See Figures 3-6 and Figure 11).

Bypassing dislocations leave loops in their wake, which interact with mobile dislocations.[50] In terms of Equation (2), this process increases $\tau_G$ and $\tau_S$, but does not reduce $\tau_{Prec}$. Therefore, the trend described for Stage I is reversed in Stage II of the aging process. The stress concentration at the grain boundary is reduced and the slip step height is reduced too, as aging proceeds through Stage II.

The Effectiveness of the bypassing mechanism depends on the size and volume fraction of particles which are bypassed.

As far as susceptibility to SCC is concerned, Stage III is a mere continuation of Stage II. The volume fraction of particles which are bypassed increases further at the expense of particles which are sheared during plastic deformation. The observation of a high density of small loops in the slip planes at the beginning of Stage III is consistent with precipitation hardening theories which have shown that in this stage, hardening is mainly due to particles which are bypassed.[51] The effect of the particle shearing mechanism (concentration of slip in a few active slip planes) should vanish. The high density of loops in active slip planes is attributed to the high density of bypassed particles and could be brought about by a single dislocation moving across the slip plane. Bands of high dislocation (loop) density are therefore expected even in heavily overaged alloys which are very resistant to SCC. This indeed has been observed (Figure 11 in Reference 13). The stress concentration at the tip of such bands and the associated slip step will be very small by the same reasons as explained for Stage II.

## C. Susceptibility, Stress Concentration and Slip Step Height

In Section V.B., it has been shown how stress concentrations at the grain boundaries and the slip step height are influenced by the various aging stages. In this section, we try to describe how stress concentrations and slip steps in turn could influence the susceptibility to intergranular SCC.

Two groups of hypotheses of intergranular SCC are compatible with the present observations. The first group comprises hypotheses which require localized stress concentrations. The second group requires a concentration of dislocations in active slip planes, that is, a high slip step. In the following, we give examples of both groups of hypotheses. However, it should be noted that some of the hypotheses cited below are subject to serious criticism. Others could be inter-related. All the hypotheses are somewhat speculative and more direct evidence for one or another is highly desirable.

**Stress Concentration Hypotheses:**
a. Near the crack tip, stress concentrations form due to dislocation pileups and limited plastic relaxation.[13,14,52] The adsorption of the corrosive environment or its constituents lowers the strength of the strained atomic bonds at the crack tip[53] (stress sorption cracking).[54] The stress concentration needed to form a crack can be described as follows:

$$n \tau_e \geqq \left( \frac{E_o \gamma_o}{a} \right)^{1/2} \qquad (3)$$

$E_o$ is the elastic modulus of the atomic bond at the crack tip, $\gamma_o$ is the surface energy of the crack face, and a is the equilibrium interatomic distance. $E_o$ and $\gamma_o$ are both thought to be reduced by the presence of SCC-active species of the environment at the crack tip.[53] Thus, the presence of the environment reduces the fracture stress. The velocity of the crack would be limited by the rate with which the active species of the environment can be fed into the crack tip region.

b. Hydrogen reportedly concentrates at grain boundaries under localized high stresses.[39,55] These hydrogen rich areas are then assumed to become anodic with respect to the surrounding grains and thus create susceptible paths.

c. The elastic interaction between an intergranular precipitate and a dislocation is assumed to result in microcracks.[37,56] The crack is then assumed to propagate via a series of chemical-mechanical steps. Localized stress concentrations due to pileups might enhance this process.

**Slip Step Height Hypotheses:**
d. Preferential attack has been observed to occur by chemical dissolution at regions of high local dislocation density, e.g., dislocation pileups at grain boundaries.[57,58] Stress corrosion cracks are thought to propagate primarily by a single-stage mechanism involving a rapid rate of chemical attack at dislocation sites and linking of these corrosion sites to form a macrocrack.[57,58]

e. Stress corrosion crack growth has been assumed to be based on repeated formation and rupture of a protective oxide film at the tip of the advancing crack front.[59,60] A high slip step (planar slip) is thought to facilitate rupture of the film and thus should increase the susceptibility to SCC.[10]

f. The density of anodically active surface sites at the root of a yielding corrosion fissure is thought to be higher in materials exhibiting coarse slip, which therefore should be more susceptible to SCC[61] than alloys exhibiting fine slip.

To the author, hypothesis (a) seems to be the most logical one[13,14] and experiments are under way to determine to what extent it actually describes the real cracking process.

The interesting point however is, that all the hypotheses mentioned (and many more too) lead to the conclusion that susceptibility to intergranular SCC is controlled either by the stress concentration at the grain boundary or by the slip step height. Thus, regardless of special assumptions of the cracking process and free from associated speculation, we can determine the parameters which control the susceptibility to SCC through their control of stress concentration and slip step height. As outlined in Section V.B., such parameters are size, the volume fraction, the antiphase boundary energy, and the coherency stress field of particles which are sheared during plastic deformation. Other important parameters controlling the susceptibility to intergranular SCC of high strength aluminum alloys are the pileup length and the density of particles which are bypassed by dislocations during plastic deformation.

Oversimplifying, one could state: susceptibility to intergranular SCC is enhanced by precipitation hardening due to precipitates which are sheared during plastic deformation. Susceptibility to intergranular SCC is reduced by particles which are bypassed by dislocations.

## D. Examples

In the foregoing section, we have identified some of the structural parameters which will be essential for the quantitative prediction of susceptibility to SCC. Such a prediction is not yet possible because we do not know enough about the cracking process itself. However, our results enable us to explain in a qualitative way many observations some of which are listed below:

a. A reduction of the magnesium and zinc concentration reduces the susceptibility to intergranular SCC of Al-Zn-Mg and Al-Zn-Mg-Cu alloys.[3,62,63] We attribute this to the reduced volume fraction of coherent precipitates which can be sheared.[13,14]

b. A delayed or interrupted quenching process can effectively reduce the susceptibility to SCC of Al-Zn-Mg and Al-Zn-Mg-Cu alloys.[3,63,64] We attribute this to an increase of the volume fraction of particles which are bypassed and to a reduction of the volume fraction of particles which are sheared.[13]

c. Cold work prior to "artificial" aging reduces markedly the susceptibility to SCC of an Al-Zn-Mg-Cu alloy.[65] A recent careful investigation of an Al-Zn-Mg alloy has shown that cold working prior to aging reduces the growth rate of a stress corrosion crack by an order of magnitude.[10] These observations definitely invalidate a recently proposed model for intergranular SCC which attributed susceptibility to the existence of dislocations which were "pinned" by particles precipitated out during aging.[37,56,66] In contrast, our results indicate that the increased resistance to SCC, due to cold work prior to aging[10,65] is caused by an increased density of precipitates which are bypassed during subsequent plastic deformation. The formation of such particles is favored by cold work prior to aging (heterogeneous nucleation).

d. Our results indicate that susceptibility to SCC is strongly influenced by small coherent precipitates. If so, reversion should reduce the high susceptibility of "naturally" aged material. This has indeed been observed[20] for an Al-Zn-Mg alloy.

e. Our results indicate that susceptibility to intergranular SCC is reduced by particles which are bypassed by moving dislocations. This conclusion should not be limited to precipitates only. Powder metallurgy permits a fine distribution of small insoluble particles, which cause dispersion hardening. A combination of dispersion hardening with precipitation hardening results in very high strengths.[67] It is remarkable that such a combination also results in much better resistance to SCC than one could expect from the basic precipitation hardening high strength aluminum alloy.[67]

f. It has been reported that small additions of silver to high strength aluminum alloys reduce the susceptibility to SCC markedly.[30,33,68] On the other hand, it is well known that such silver additions facilitate the nucleation of the intermediate phase $\eta'$ at the expense of G.P. zones.[69-71] According to Section V., this reduces the susceptibility, since particles of the intermediate phase are more difficult to shear than G.P. zones.

Moreover, the easy nucleation leads to a fine distribution of $\eta'$ in silver bearing alloys and thus retards overaging. Therefore, one can increase the aging temperature without sacrifice of strength. Such a heat treatment definitely leads to an increased volume fraction of particles which are bypassed, at the expense of particles which are sheared, and this results in a reduction of the susceptibility to SCC, as outlined in Section V.

g. High strength aluminum alloys of the 7000 series (Al-Zn-Mg-Cu) can be susceptible to SCC when aged near peak hardness. (T6 temper.)[4,28] An additional aging treatment at higher temperatures imparts significant resistance to SCC to these alloys. (Duplex aging, T73 temper.)[4,28] According to our analysis, this is due to an increase of the volume fraction of particles which are bypassed and to a corresponding decrease of the volume fraction of particles which can be sheared.

The examples just mentioned substantiate the conclusions reached in the foregoing section: Susceptibility to SCC is enhanced by precipitates which are sheared during plastic deformation. The effectiveness of the particle shearing mechanism is determined by the size, the volume fraction, the antiphase boundary energy and the coherency stress field of the particles. Particles which are bypassed, reduce the susceptibility. The effectiveness of the bypassing mechanism is determined by the size and volume fraction of the bypassed particles.

Although these conclusions do not yet allow a quantitative prediction of the susceptibility to SCC, they allow at least a qualitative one and could be used to improve existing alloys.

## VI. References

1. Standards for Aluminum Mill Products, The Aluminum Association, New York (1965).
2. A. Kelly and R. B. Nicholson. *Progr. Mat. Sci.,* **10,** 149 (1963).
3. P. Brenner. *Aluminium,* **38,** 2 (1962).
4. D. O. Sprowls and R. H. Brown. *Metal Progress,* **81** April; **79** and **81,** May; **77** (1962).
5. R. Chadwick, N. B. Muir, and H. B. Grainger. *J. Inst. Met.,* **85,** 161 (1956-57).
6. W. Gruhl and H. Cordier. *Z. Metallkunde,* **55,** 577 (1964).
7. G. Thomas and J. Nutting. *J. Inst. Met.,* **88,** 81 (1959-60); G. Thomas. *Electron Microscopy and Strength of Crystals,* (G. Thomas and J. Washburn, ed.) p. 849, John Wiley, New York (1963).
8. H. L. Logan. *The Stress Corrosion of Metals,* John Wiley, New York (1966).
9. R. N. Parkins. *Metallurgical Rev.,* 9, 201 (1964).
10. A. J. McEvily, J. B. Clark, and A. P. Bond. *Trans. ASM,* **60,** 661 (1967).
11. R. Ryum, B. Haegland, and T. Lindtveit. *Z. Metallkunde,* **58,** 28 (1967).
12. E. Hornbogen. *Z. Metallkunde,* **58,** 31 (1967).
13. M. O. Speidel. Proceedings of the Air Force Materials Laboratory 50th Anniversary Technical Conference on Corrosion of Military and Aerospace Equipment, Denver, Colorado, 23-25 May 1967. (F. H. Meyer, ed.), AFML-TR-67-329 (1967).
14. M. O. Speidel. *phys. stat. sol.,* **22,** K71 (1967).
15. H. A. Holl. *Corrosion,* **23,** 173 (1967).
16. W. Koster. *Aluminium,* **34,** 694 (1958).
17. H. Schmalzried and V. Gerold. *Z. Metallkunde,* **49,** 291 (1958).
18. V. Gerold. *Aluminium und Aluminiumlegierungen,* (D. Alten-

pohl, ed.) Springer-Verlag, New York (1965).

19. J. D. Embury and R. B. Nicholson. *Acta Met.*, **13**, 403 (1965).
20. H. Vosskuhler. *Werkstoffe und Korrosion*, **1**, 179 (1950).
21. H. Vosskuhler. *Werkstoffe und Korrosion*, **8**, 463 (1957).
22. G. Meikle. *J. Inst. Met.*, **85**, 540 (1956-57).
23. E. N. Pugh. *RIAS Technical Report 65-7* (1965).
24. E. N. Pugh. Ph.D. Thesis, University of Wales (1959).
25. H. Klatte. *Werkstoffe und Korrosion*, **7**, 545; **7**, 708 (1956).
26. A. J. Martin. *Metal Ind.*, **21**, 511; **21**, 531 (1956).
27. E. H. Dix. *Trans. ASM*, **42**, 1057 (1950).
28. W. C. Rotsell and J. R. Long. *Metal Progr.*, **91**, 106 (1967).
29. U. S. Patent No. 319,867,6.
30. German Patent 1,198,570 (1966).
31. W. Rosenkranz. *Aluminium*, **39**, 290 (1963).
32. W. Rosenkranz. *Aluminium*, **39**, 741 (1963).
33. W. Rosenkranz. *Aluminium*, **43**, 105 (1967).
34. V. Gerold and H. Haberkorn. *Z. Metallkunde*, **50**, 568 (1959).
35. R. B. Mears, R. H. Brown, and E. H. Dix. *Symposium on Stress Corrosion Cracking of Metals*, ASTM and AIME, p. 323 (1944).
36. H. C. Rutemiller and D. O. Sprowls. *Stress Corrosion of Aluminum—Where to Look for It, How to Prevent It.* ALCOA (1962).
37. A. J. Jacobs. *Trans. ASM*, **58**, 579 (1965).
38. F. F. Booth. *Corrosion*, (L. L. Shreir, ed.) J. Wiley, New York (1963).
39. W. K. Boyd. *Battelle Technical Review*, 5 (1965).
40. H. Gleiter and E. Hornbogen. *phys. stat. sol.*, **12**, 235, 251 (1965).
41. E. Smith and J. T. Barnby. *Metal Sci. J.*, **1**, 56 (1967).
42. J. Friedel. *Dislocations*, Pergamon Press, New York (1964).
43. H. Kronmuller. *Moderne Probleme der Metallphysik*, (A. Seeger, ed.) Springer Verlag, New York (1965).
44. H. Kronmuller. *Canadian J. Physics*, **45**, 631 (1967).
45. P. R. Swann and J. D. Embury. *High-Strength Materials*, (V. F. Zackay, ed.) J. Wiley, New York, p. 327 (1964).
46. H. Gleiter. *Z. Metallkunde*, **58**, 99 (1967).
47. H. Gleiter and E. Hornbogen. *Z. Metallkunde*, **58**, 101 (1967).
48. H. Gleiter. *Acta Met.*, **15**, 1213, 1223 (1967).

49. V. Gerold and H. Haberkorn. *phys. stat. sol.*, **16**, 675 (1966).
50. H. Gleiter. *Z. Metallkunde*, **58**, 236 (1967).
51. H. Gleiter. *Z. Metallkunde*, **58**, 306 (1967).
52. W. D. Robertson and A. S. Tetelman. *Strengthening Mechanisms in Solids*, ASM Seminar, 1960, Metals Park, Ohio, p. 217 (1962).
53. N. S. Stoloff and T. L. Johnston. *Acta Met.*, **11**, 251 (1963).
54. H. H. Uhlig. *Treatise on Fracture*, (H. Liebowitz, ed.) Academic Press, New York (in press).
55. F. H. Haynie, D. A. Vaughan, D. I. Phalen, W. K. Boyd, and P. D. Frost. Technical Report AFML-TR-66-267 (1967).
56. A. J. Jacobs and N. J. Hoffman. *A New Model for Stress Corrosion Cracking in the 7075 Aluminum Alloy*, Preprint (1967).
57. D. Tromans and J. Nutting. *Corrosion*, **21**, 143 (1965).
58. D. Tromans and J. Nutting. *Fracture of Solids*, (D. C. Drucker and J. J. Gilman, ed.) John Wiley, New York, p. 637 (1963).
59. A. J. McEvily and A. P. Bond. *J. Electrochemical Soc.*, **112**, 131 (1965).
60. A. J. McEvily and A. P. Bond. *Environment-Sensitive Mechanical Behavior* (A. R. C. Westwood and N. S. Stoloff, ed.) Gordon and Breach, New York (1966).
61. J. G. Hines. *Corrosion Sci.*, **1**, 21 (1961).
62. H. Hug. *Aluminium und Aluminiumlegierungen*, (D. Altenpohl, ed.) Springer Verlag, New York (1965).
63. H. G. Petri, G. Siebel and H. Vosskuhler. *Aluminium*, **26**, 2 (1944).
64. P. Brenner. *Z. Metallkunde*, **44**, 85 (1953).
65. G. Thomas. *J. Inst. Met.*, **89**, 287 (1960-61).
66. A. J. Jacobs, AIAA Seventh Structures and Materials Conference Volume, p. 243 (1966).
67. A. P. Haarr. ALCOA Research Laboratories, Contract No. DA-36-034-ORD-3559RD (1966).
68. U. S. Patent 2,823,994, February 18 (1958).
69. Y. Baba. *Trans. JIM*, **7**, 224 (1966).
70. I. J. Polmear. *J. Inst. Met.*, **89**, 51, 193 (1960-61).
71. J. T. Vietz, K. R. Sargant, and I. J. Polmear. *J. Inst. Met.*, **92**, 327 (1963-64).

## Discussion

**P. R. Swann, Imperial College, London, England:**

I would like to suggest that the best way to study the distribution of slip is not to look at the distribution of dislocations in thin films, but to look at surface replicas of the deformed material. This technique is much more quantitative than the thin film technique since we can measure the height of slip steps and we can also see the distribution of the slip within a single slip band. The thin film technique shows the dislocation distribution existing within the material after the deformation is completed. Unlike the surface replica method it does not give a record of the preceding deformation.

**M. O. Speidel:**

I agree that the investigation of surface replica of deformed material is a particularly suitable way to study the distribution of slip. Such experiments have been carried out with a limited number of precipitation hardening aluminum base alloys[1-5] as well as other precipitation hardening alloys.[6-8] The results support our view that particles which are sheared by dislocations cause coarse slip and high slip steps, and that particles which are bypassed can considerably reduce the height of the slip steps.

A well documented example is the alloy Al-4 wt% Cu. GP I and GP II zones are sheared[1,2,4,9] by dislocations and thus cause coarse slip and high slip steps.[1,2,4,5] In contrast, $\Theta'$ and $\Theta$ particles, most of which are bypassed[1,3,4,10] render the slip steps extremely small.[1,3-5] In fact, slip steps can become so small that slip lines do not show up at the surface of the crystals, even after considerable deformation.

This latter effect can be misleading: Only very faint or no slip lines will be seen on replicas of the surface of a deformed polycrystal which contains a high density of small particles that are bypassed by dislocations. Thus, the associated deformation in the grain boundary is exaggerated and seems to be predominant just because the slip in the grain interior is hard to detect or does not show up at all at the surface. The best way to study the distribution of slip is therefore a combination of both, the replica technique and transmission electron microscopy, since both methods complement each other.

**E. N. Pugh, RIAS:**

I noticed in several of your transmission electron micrographs that well-defined precipitate-free zones were present at grain boundaries. Earlier work using optical microscopy[1] and electron microscopy using replica techniques,[2] has indicated that preferential plastic deformation can occur in these precipitate-free zones. It is surprising therefore that your micrographs of deformed materials do not appear to show evidence for a large density of dislocations in the grain boundary regions. Have you seen evidence of preferential grain boundary deformation in thin foils and, if not, how do you reconcile your observations with those using the other methods?

1. E. N. Pugh and W. R. D. Jones. *Metallurgia,* **63**, 3 (1961).
2. G. Thomas and J. Nutting. *J. Inst. Metals,* **86**, 7 (1957-58); **88**, 81 (1959-60).

## M. O. Speidel:

We have seen no evidence for a large density of dislocations in the precipitation free grain boundary zones of deformed susceptible alloys.

Some slip within the grain boundary itself could be due to the movement of grain boundary dislocations which have been discovered recently by Gleiter and Baro.[11] These grain boundary dislocations have been observed to emit lattice dislocations at triple points. This could provide an explanation for the apparent growth of grain boundaries into adjoining grains at triple points, as described in the first reference you quote.

As already indicated in the reply to P. R. Swann's comments, seemingly preferential grain boundary deformation can in some cases be attributed to a lack of slip lines to show up at the surface of deformed grains. This is to be expected when the alloy contains a fine distribution of precipitates which are bypassed by dislocations. In this respect it is interesting to note that the replica work you mention was done with definitely overaged alloys, which presumably contain precipitates that are bypassed.

High aging temperatures, long aging times or a low Mg + Zn content could cause the formation of precipitation free grain boundary zones which are wide enough to give rise to preferential deformation. However, these are the conditions which render the alloys resistant to stress corrosion cracking.

## A. J. Jacobs, Rocketdyne:

I wish to cite some results obtained in my slip-line and explosive shock loading studies as evidence against Dr. Speidel's slip-step and stress-concentration hypotheses, respectively. Reference to Figures 17 and 18 in my paper, which show slip lines in deformed 7075-T6 and -T73 tensile specimens, will disclose that the slip-step heights in the two tempers differ little if at all. I did not find an order-of-magnitude greater step height in 7075-T6 such as Dr. Speidel's hypothesis would predict. The only restriction on the orientation of the replicated surfaces was a consequence of the tensile axes being aligned in the short transverse direction of the original forging. The slip planes must intersect the replicated surfaces in a nearly random fashion, thus excluding any appreciable effect of preferred orientation on slip-step height.

Figure 1 shows a thin-film electron micrograph taken of an explosively shock loaded 7075-T6 specimen after it was overaged for 5 hours at 350 F. The shock loading has produced the dense arrays of dislocations, which are observed to be piled up at a grain boundary. Let us assume that the shock-induced dislocations have sheared G.P. zones in the 7075-T6, thus developing a high stress concentration at the head of each pileup. I have observed experimentally (Reference 13 in my paper) that aging of the shocked 7075-T6 at 350 F for 5 hours or less has little if any effect on the dislocation structure, and hence the stress concentration at the head of a pileup; and that only the interparticle spacing is increased. Thus, using Dr. Speidel's argument, we should expect the high susceptibility of shocked 7075-T6 to be undiminished by overaging at 350 F for 5 hours since the initial stress concentrations are not relieved. Such a shocked and overaged specimen, however, survived 5 months of alternate-immersion testing under an applied stress of 75% of yield.

## M. O. Speidel:

You mention that the slip step heights in the T6 and T73 temper of the alloy 7075 differ little if at all. In contrast to this, A. J. Jacobs[12,13] concluded from his surface studies on deformed samples of the same alloy that "the slip lines in -T73 did tend to be finer and could not be detected as easily as those in -T6."

You show that plastic deformation prior to an aging treatment for 5 hours at 350 F results in a high resistance to stress corrosion cracking. This is by no means contrary

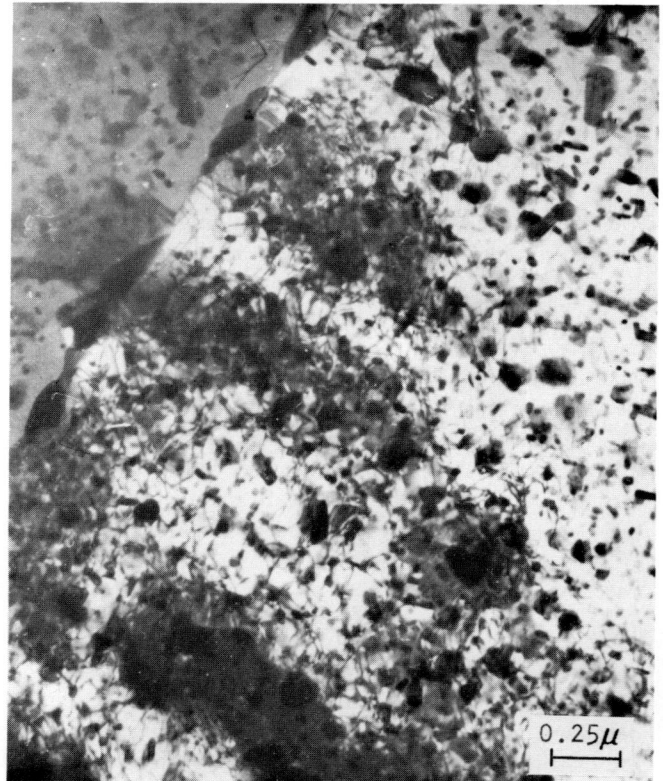

0.25μ

FIGURE 1 — Thin-film micrograph of explosively shock loaded and overaged (5 hours at 350 F) 7075-T6 showing dislocation pileups at a grain boundary. This condition is highly resistant to stress corrosion cracking.

to our analysis which is confirmed by your observation: In Section V.D.c. of our paper, we pointed out that plastic deformation prior to "artificial" aging can enhance the formation of precipitates which are bypassed by moving dislocations. Thus, shock loading prior to aging at the fairly high temperature of 350 F should increase the resistance to stress corrosion cracking. Your results appear to confirm this once more. (A much more reliable confirmation of this prediction has since been given by McEvily, Clark, and Bond[14] who used the fracture mechanics approach.)

Your assumption that the shock-induced dislocations have sheared G.P. zones in the 7075-T6 is questionable, since a temperature increase of several hundred degrees C is supposedly[15] associated with your type of shock loading. This could as well cause the dislocations to bypass the precipitates. Even if G.P. zones had been sheared, overaging of the deformed structure for 5 hours at 350 F would have caused new and different precipitates to form.

It has been reported[15] that shock loading causes overaging of a 7075 alloy, even without additional heat treatment. Moreover, it has been reported[12] that aging for 5 hours at 350 F causes a 40% reduction of the yield strength of a shock loaded 7075 T6 alloy. These two observations indicate the high mobility of point defects and solute atoms during shock loading and overaging. Thus it is safe to assume that your thermo-mechanical treatment resulted in rearranged and pinned dislocation arrays. Only *mobile* dislocations of unrelaxed pileups cause stress concentrations. Therefore, in contrast to your assumption, the defect structure introduced by shock loading and aging for 5 hours at 350 F will not cause stress concentrations. Thus your results cannot be regarded as evidence against the stress concentration hypothesis.

Although we do not agree with your conclusions; your experimental results are quite useful when interpreted in the following way:

You present an electron micrograph of a 7075 alloy which contains a fairly high density of dislocations. The alloy has been overaged for 5 hours at 350 F *after* the dislocations were introduced. There is little doubt that the dislocations were pinned, considering the high mobility of point defects and solute atoms during shock loading and subsequent aging at 350 F. In other words, the alloy contains a fairly high density of pinned dislocations. Your experiment shows that in this condition the alloy survived 5 months of alternate immersion testing under an applied stress of 75% of the yield stress. This is a valuable result since it gives direct and unbiased evidence against a hypothesis[12,15-17] which holds that in 7075, a short time to failure by stress corrosion cracking is related to the existence of pinned dislocations next to grain boundary precipitates, and that resistance to stress corrosion cracking is related to the absence of pinned dislocations.

## W. D. Sylwestrowicz, Bell Telephone Laboratories:

Dislocations piled against grain boundaries play a fundamental role in the proposed mechanism of stress corrosion cracking (SCC). According to this model, large stress concentrations produced by pileups of dislocations are responsible for the high susceptibility of the materials to SCC. It is claimed that the photomicrographs, Figures 3 to 7, show these pileups, but with the exception of Figure 5, a close examination of them does not disclose the existence of large pileups against grain boundaries. On the contrary, in Figure 6, the density of dislocations in slip bands is larger in the middle of the grain than at the grain boundary. This photomicrograph is of the material which is very susceptible to SCC. The fact that distinct slip bands are present (Figure 7) even at the beginning of Stage III of aging where large incoherent precipitates are formed, is in disagreement with the proposed mechanism for formation of slip bands. It should also be kept in mind that distinct slip bands were observed in high purity single crystals of aluminum where precipitates could not be responsible for the formation of these slip bands. The assumption that, in the local area, through which dislocations passed after shearing coherent precipitates, the flow stress is smaller than in the surrounding material might be correct, but this smaller stress is still larger than in the crystal prior to precipitation of the coherent phase. With the increasing size of incoherent precipitates during Stage III aging, the distance between precipitates increases linearly with the radius of precipitates, therefore the stress, $\tau$, to expand dislocations between them decreases, according to the Orowan equation.

$$\tau \approx \frac{\mu b}{d} ,$$

where $\mu$ is the shear modulus, b is the Burgers vector and d is the distance between precipitates. This should lead to a larger number of dislocations reaching grain boundaries in Stage III than in the Stage II (where distance between precipitates is smaller) and according to the proposed mechanism to larger susceptibility to SCC, in contradiction to the observed decreasing susceptibility of the material in this stage of aging.

## M. O. Speidel:

It was one of our objectives to show that (in contrast to a widely held belief) planar dislocation arrangements and dislocation pileups at grain boundaries really do occur in precipitation hardened aluminum base alloys which are susceptible to stress corrosion cracking. If you admit this for Figure 5, we have reached that objective.

We have never claimed that Figure 7 shows pileups which produce large stress concentrations. The dark bands in that photomicrograph are areas of high density of dislocation loops. As pointed out in Section V.B., very few dislocations need to move across the matrix to create a dislocation loop distribution similar to that in Figure 7. This is because prismatic cross slip gives rise to a number of dislocation loops near each particle. For details see References 18-20. The observation of bands of high dislocation loop density is therefore by no means in disagreement with the idea that precipitates which are sheared cause coarse slip (high slip steps), and that particles which are bypassed, reduce the slip step height. There is abundant evidence for this in the published literature.[1-7] No doubt, slip bands can be observed in pure aluminum. We have never claimed that only precipitates were responsible for their formation. However, stress concentrations due to slip bands in pure aluminum are thought to be readily reduced by plastic relaxation.[21]

We are glad you agree that in the local area, through which dislocations passed after shearing particles, the flow stress is smaller than in the surrounding material. We have never claimed that this smaller shear stress is as small or even smaller than the critical resolved shear stress of the supersaturated solid solution.

You base your final argument on the Orowan equation, assuming a smaller distance between precipitates in Stage II (underaged) than in Stage III (overaged). However, the Orowan equation is applicable only to particles which are bypassed; it is not valid for particles which are sheared.[20] Using the Orowan equation for Stage II is to tacitly assume that precipitation hardening in the underaged condition is due to precipitates which are bypassed. Experimental results however suggest that in Stage II (underaged) precipitation hardening is mainly due to precipitates which are sheared, and that in contrast to your assumption the distance between the bypassed precipitates is larger in Stage II than in Stage III: The radii of curvature of dislocations in Stage II are larger than in Stage III, as shown by a comparison of Figures 5 and 12 to Figure 7. This leaves your argument and your conclusions without basis.

### P. R. Sperry, Olin Mathieson Chemical Corp.:

You refer to deformation mechanisms which operate throughout the entire alloy matrix and which are induced by stresses above the nominal yield stress of the alloy. I object to this approach in studying stress corrosion mechanisms on the basis that it does not relate to the conditions of stress corrosion cracking where the applied or residual stresses can be substantially below the nominal yield stress. Indeed, stress corrosion failure can occur at stress levels as low as twenty-five percent of the yield.[1] I do not question that some dislocation movement and consequent plastic deformation may occur well below the yield stress, but I do question the magnitude of it compared with your observations. Furthermore, it is difficult to rationalize the large changes in degree of susceptibility with the orientation of the test specimen with respect to principal working directions in wrought alloys. These differences in susceptibility are not accompanied by the same degree of difference in yield strength.

I believe that more attention needs to be paid to the deformation characteristics of the localized volumes of the alloy which actually form the path for the stress corrosion failure—namely, the grain boundaries and the associated denuded zone. It is most likely that the difference in flow characteristics between these zones and the grain matrix is of more significance than the flow characteristics of the matrix itself.

1. E. H. Dix, Jr. Aluminum-Zinc-Magnesium Alloys—Their Development and Commercial Production, Campbell Memorial Lecture, *Transactions ASM,* **62**, 1057-1127 (1950).

### M. O. Speidel:

You admit that "some dislocation movement and consequent plastic deformation may occur well below the yield stress". This might have some influence on the initiation of stress corrosion cracks. The plastic deformation near the tip of an already existing crack however is determined by the stress intensity at the crack tip (and the yield strength of the material) rather than by the applied net cross section stress. For details see the paper R. P. Wei presented at this conference.

We should like to mention that stress corrosion cracking has been observed at applied stresses which are even lower fractions of the macroscopic yield stress than you indicate: There is a significant probability of failure by stress corrosion cracking for 2014-T6, 2024-T4, and 7075-T6 in the standard 3.5% NaCl alternate immersion test and for 7079-T6 in sea coast atmosphere if tested in short transverse direction under an applied stress of 15% of the yield.[22] The lower limit of the fraction the yield stress at which stress corrosion cracking in high strength aluminum alloys can be observed, seems to be near 10%.

Changes in susceptibility with specimen orientation and grain shape have been described elsewhere[23] to a limited degree.

We share your belief that more attention needs to be paid to the deformation at and near grain boundaries, especially since there is as yet no conclusive experimental evidence for the often reiterated statement that a difference in flow characteristics between the denuded zones and the grain matrix is of significance in stress corrosion cracking.

### D. A. Thompson, Reynolds Metals Company:

I wish to make a comment and ask one question. My comment is that although Dr. Speidel's mechanism is attractive, it cannot be considered an essential portion of a stress corrosion cracking mechanism. At least not for 7075 which is one of the alloys he considers. Dr. Speidel himself has pointed out that his work is based on generalizations of stress corrosion behavior as a function of aging practice and not upon specific results. The aging conditions he chose to produce susceptible materials consisted of low temperatures for short times, while immune materials were aged at much higher temperatures for relatively long times. It is not surprising, therefore, that considerable differences in precipitate size and distribution were produced and hence differences in the mode of deformation were observed. It is our experience that both susceptible and immune materials can be obtained by aging at the same temperature. The structures of such materials can be readily compared. Figure 1 shows a typical aging curve for 7075 plate at the final aging temperature (177 C) of a two step practice. In a stress corrosion test (constant strain short transverse subsize tensiles stressed to 75% of the yield and exposed in alternate immersion to a 3½% NaCl environment) material aged to Condition A failed by stress corrosion cracking within 5 days, while material aged to Condition B failed eventually due to severe pitting, but showed no evidence of stress corrosion cracking. The microstructures (typical of commercial alloys) of these two conditions are demon-

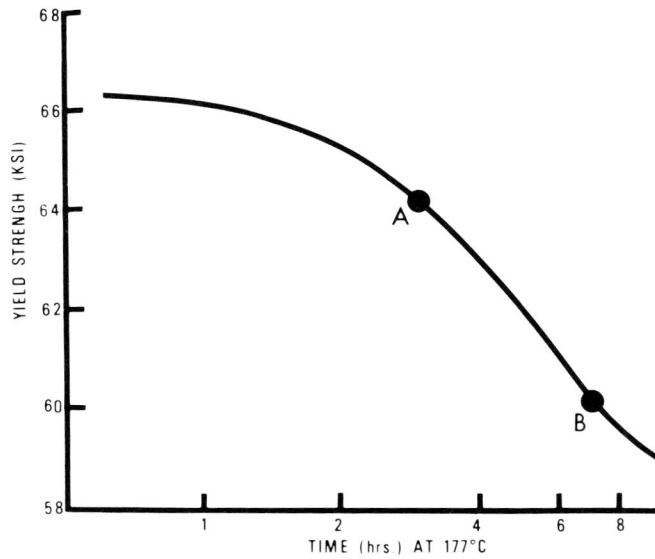

(a)

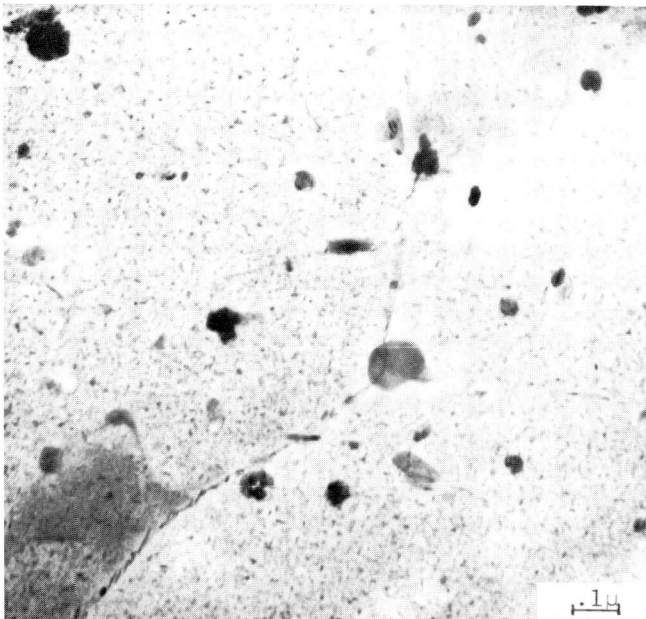

(b)

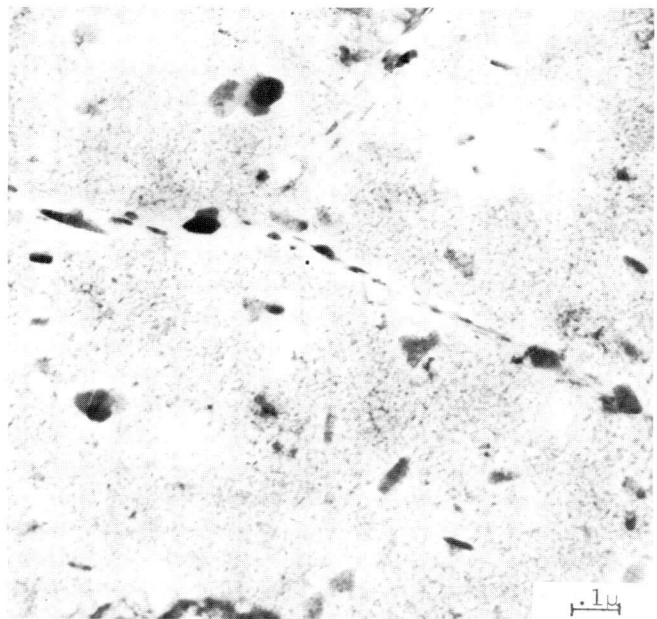

(c)

FIGURE 1 — (a)Typical aging curve for 2 inch thick for 7075 aluminum alloy plate at the final aging temperature (177 C) of a two step practice. Solution heat treated at 468 C for 2 hours—cold water quenched. Aged: 5 days at room temperature, then heated at 14 C/hr to 10.7 C held for 7 hours and heated at 14 C/hr to 177 C. (b, c) Electron micrographs at times designated on the curve of (a).

strated in the corresponding micrographs. Note the similarity of the shape and size of the precipitates which indicates no obvious phase change: indeed it is difficult to actually identify these particles. The degree of coherency cannot be estimated since no strain fields are associated with these particles. Unfortunately, work on plastically deformed specimens has still to be carried out, yet it is difficult to imagine material A deforming in a completely different mode from B, as I feel sure Dr. Speidel will suggest.

I would like to ask Dr. Speidel if he has examined materials aged in the manner I have described?

Has he made any estimate of the numbers and sizes or volume fraction of incoherent precipitates necessary to stop the formation of planar arrays of dislocations?

**M. O. Speidel:**

It was an objective of our paper to show that in high strength aluminum alloys a high susceptibility to stress corrosion cracking correlates well with the presence of precipitates which are sheared during plastic deformation. Precipitates (or other particles) which are bypassed, correlate with a reduced susceptibility. Although you do not disagree with that, you question the importance of changes in the dislocation-precipitate interaction in Stage III, alluding to electrochemical changes or "fracture mode variations".

In our paper we have by no means excluded the possible influence of other parameters such as changes in the electrochemistry or cohesive strength. The experimental material you present is insufficient to support your statement that changes in the dislocation-precipitate interaction, as described in our paper, exert no influence on the rate of crack propagation under conditions where immunity is being approached.

We do not anticipate that there is just one size and one kind of precipitates in Al-Mg-Zn-Cu alloys at maximum hardness. Thus, during the process of overaging, there will be a *gradual* change of the ratio of the number of precipitates which are sheared to the number of those which are bypassed. Therefore the stress and strain concentration at grain boundaries will change gradually as does the deformation mode and the susceptibility to stress corrosion cracking. A comparison of your two electron micrographs does not yield enough information to exclude such a gradual difference in the dislocation-precipitate interaction of the specimens A and B.

Your Figure 1 and the results of the associated stress corrosion tests confirm once more the first part of Stage III of Figure 1 in our paper. Your experience that both susceptible and immune materials can be obtained by aging at the same temperature is not new and has been published quite often in the past, as we have pointed out in our paper. This general experience is part of the experimental basis of our Figure 1 where resistance to SCC is plotted versus time of *isothermal* aging processes, too.

Commercial precipitation hardening high strength aluminum base alloys, aged near maximum hardness, contain a variety of coherent, semicoherent and incoherent second-phase particles, each kind of a certain size distribution. In view of this complex structure it seems neither meaningful nor possible at this time to quantitatively calculate dislocation-precipitate interactions. Besides, neither coherency of precipitates nor planarity of dislocation arrangements are useful single parameters to describe the influence of the microstructure on stress and strain distribution at grain boundaries. A more important question is, whether the precipitates responsible for the high strength are sheared or bypassed, and to what extent this affects the stress and strain concentration where a slip band impinges on the grain boundary.

**D. O. Sprowls, Alcoa:**

The family of Al-Zn-Mg-Cu alloys, with variations in composition and thermal treatment, furnishes a variety of microstructures and and degrees of susceptibility to stress corrosion cracking. Consequently, a variety of stress corrosion mechanisms can be visualized and have been proposed by various investigators. Details of specific mechanisms that appear to explain the behavior of a particular composition and microstructure, however, do not seem adequate for others. The situation can be either oversimplified or be made to seem hopelessly baffling when one attempts to apply the same specific details to the exclusion of all other considerations.

At Alcoa Research Laboratories, we have found that even a single alloy, such as 7075, is so complex that in different metallurgical conditions it appears that some aspects of the mechanism differ. Therefore, it seems unlikely that the behavior of alloy 7075 can be explained solely by the consideration of a particular mechanical property such as a high capacity for plastic deformation, or a microstructural feature such as the size and spacing of matrix precipitate particles, types of dislocations, etc. Metallurgical characteristics such as these must be considered together with environmental factors to attempt an explanation of the behaviors of various tempers.

Two examples are offered to illustrate characteristics of certain tempers of 7075 alloy to stimulate further consideration of the mechanisms proposed by Messrs. Jacobs and Speidel. Consider, for example, the following compari-

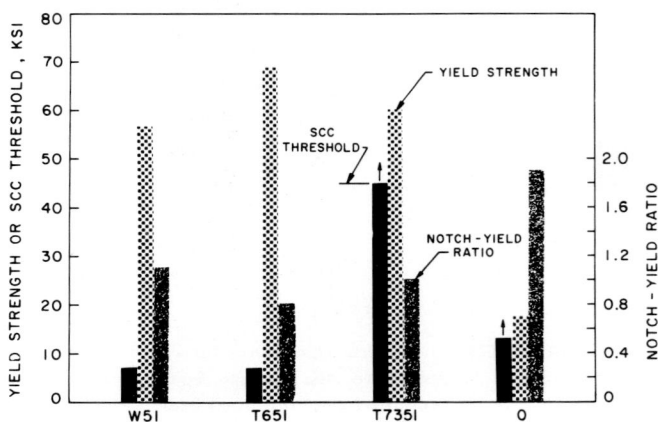

FIGURE 1 — Short transverse tests of two inch thick 7075 alloy plate.

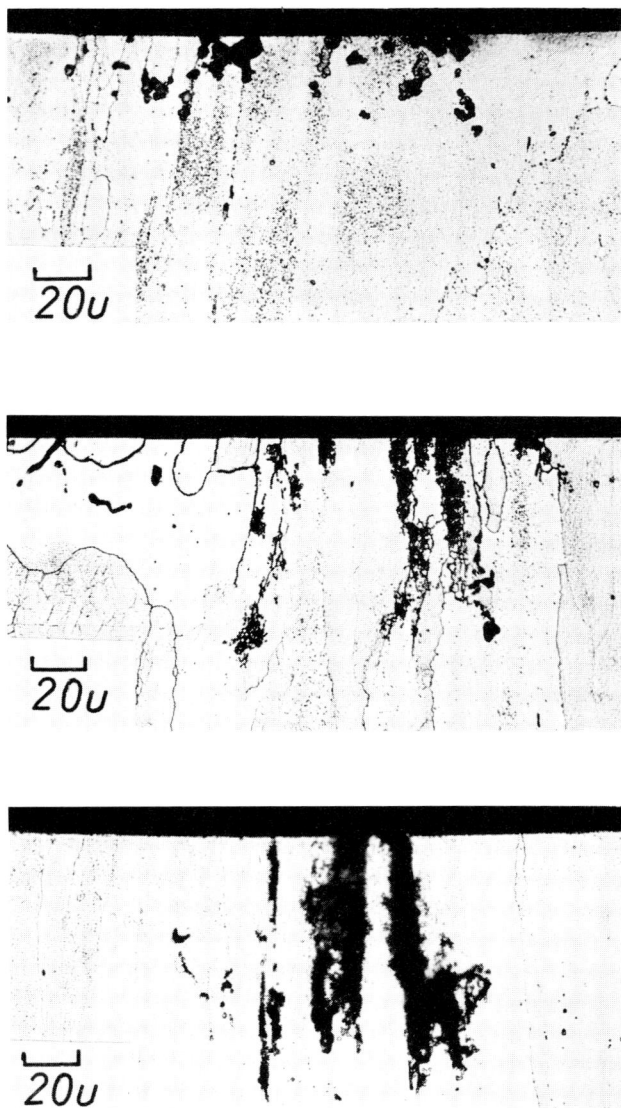

FIGURE 2 — Variations of the form of end-grain attack of 7075 alloy plate in audified NaCl-AlCl₃ solution. Top—T7351; Middle—T651; Bottom—T6 rapidly quenched.

sons of yield strength and notch toughness with the resistance to stress corrosion cracking of several different tempers of 7075 alloy plate (Figure 1). First, the W51 temper has a notch-yield ratio (a measure of the capacity to deform plastically in the presence of a stress raiser) similar to that of the T73 temper, yet the W51 temper is susceptible to stress corrosion cracking at stresses far below its yield strength. In Section IV of our paper is a more general discussion of the lack of correlation of stress corrosion resistance with toughness. Secondly, the large difference in yield strength between the W51 and T651 tempers indicates a significant difference in precipitate size and spacing (see Figures 32 and 33 in our paper), yet the susceptibility of the two tempers to stress corrosion cracking is similar. The significance of these characteristics, however, is· indicated by the high resistance to stress corrosion cracking of the O temper which represents an extreme degree of these proposed "good" characteristics, namely a high notch toughness, low density of precipitate dispersion and very few dislocations. Yet the yield strength is too low to be acceptable. The T7351 temper provides a practical compromise of desired properties.

There is, however, another favorable characteristic that both the T73 and the O tempers have, and that is an electrochemical homogeneity in the grain boundary regions. This is indicated by their freedom from susceptibility to intergranular attack in chloride solutions in the absence of applied stress. Whereas commercial products such as forgings and thick plate of 7075-T651 may be susceptible to intergranular attack in chloride solutions, similar items of 7075-T7351 are susceptible to random pitting attack (Figure 2). But neither is this criterion of type of attack alone sufficient to predict susceptibility to stress corrosion cracking of 7075 alloy. For example, reheat treated and rapidly quenched 7075-T6 short transverse tensile specimen blanks that are not susceptible to intergranular attack in the absence of applied stress are susceptible to stress corrosion cracking at low applied stress. Particularly in this latter case, additional research is needed to clarify the mechanism of the synergistic effects of the sustained tension stress and the chemical or electrochemical reaction of the alloy with the environment.

## References

1. R. J. Price and A. Kelly. *Acta Met.,* 12, 159 (1964).
2. R. J. Price and A. Kelly. *Acta Met.,* 12, 979 (1964).
3. D. Dew-Hughes and W. D. Robertson. *Acta Met.,* 8, 147 (1960).
4. D. Dew-Hughes and W. D. Robertson. *Acta Met.,* 8, 156 (1960).
5. J. M. Silcock. *Acta Met.,* 8, 589 (1960).
6. G. Lutjering and E. Hornbogen. *Z. Metallkunde,* 59, 29 (1968).
7. R. W. Guard. *Strengthening Mechanisms in Solids,* ASM Seminar, 1960, Metals Park, Ohio, p. 253 (1962).
8. M. O. Speidel. Unpublished work on Cu-Ni-Si alloys.
9. K. Matsuura and S. Koda. *J. Phys. Soc. Japan,* 18, Supl. I, 50 (1963).
10. S. Koda, K. Matsuura and S. Takahashi. *J. Inst. Met.,* 91, 229 (1962-63).
11. H. Gleiter and G. Baro. *Mater. Sci. Eng.,* 2, 224 (1967).
12. A. J. Jacobs. Paper presented at this conference.
13. A. J. Jacobs. Contract NOw 66-0309d, prepared for Naval Air Systems Command, Department of the Navy, Final Report, May, 1967.
14. A. J. McEvily, J. B. Clark, and A. P. Bond. *Trans. ASM,* 60, 661 (1967).
15. A. J. Jacobs. *AIAA Seventh Structures and Materials Conference Volume,* April 18-20, 1966, Cocoa Beach, Florida, p. 243.
16. A. J. Jacobs. *Metal Progress,* 89, 80 (1966).
17. A. J. Jacobs. *Trans. ASM,* 58, 579 (1965).
18. H. Gleiter and E. Hornbogen. *Z. Metallkunde,* 58, 101 (1967).
19. H. Gleiter. *Z. Metallkunde,* 58, 236 (1967).
20. H. Gleiter. *Acta Met.,* 15, 1213 and 1223 (1967).
21. J. Friedel. *Dislocations,* Pergamon Press, New York (1964).
22. D. O. Sprowls and R. H. Brown. *Metal Progress,* 81, No. 4, 79-85 (1962) and 81, No. 5, 77-83 (1962).
23. M. O. Speidel. *Proceedings of the Air Force Materials Laboratory Fiftieth Anniversary Technical Conference on Corrosion of Military and Aerospace Equipment,* Denver, Colorado 23-25 (1967), AFML-TR-67-329, p. 1915.

# AN ELECTROCHEMICAL STUDY OF THE MECHANISM OF STRESS CORROSION CRACKING IN AN ALUMINUM-ZINC-MAGNESIUM ALLOY

F. H. Haynie and W. K. Boyd
Battelle Memorial Institute

## Abstract

The objective of this study was to develop a reasonable basis for the stress corrosion cracking in an Al-Zn-Mg alloy. A variety of qualitative mechanisms have been proposed but most ignore the role of the oxide film at the grain boundary as a rate controlling factor. Experimental evidence suggests that the rate of oxide film growth is enhanced at the grain boundaries. This increased growth rate permits more rapid oxidation of the grain boundaries.

## Introduction

It is well documented that stress corrosion cracking involves an interaction between tensile stress and a corrosive environment and a susceptible material. It follows that this interaction mechanism may be studied by observing the change in electrode kinetics as a function of applied tensile stress. However, most of the alloy systems, which are susceptible to stress corrosion cracking, form a natural, protective oxide on the surface when exposed to air or water, which complicates the electrode kinetics of these alloys. Even when reproducible data are obtained, they are difficult to interpret because the behavior of the oxide film at any one time may be dependent on its entire prior history. For this reason, a study of the transient behavior of metal electrodes when stress, overpotential, or both are applied, should yield additional information about the mechanism of stress corrosion cracking.

## Theoretical Discussion

Stress corrosion cracking is generally associated with alloys that form passive films and environments that cause pitting of these alloys. This association has led some investigators to believe that the initiation stage is the process of breaking down the passive film.[1,2] Whether these initiation sites propagate as cracks is dependent on counteracting rates of anodic dissolution of the metal and oxide-film repair.[3]

In aluminum alloys, the time for initiation of stress corrosion cracks is stress dependent. Also, cracks are restricted to intergranular paths. Therefore, the breakdown of the passive film by pitting cannot fully explain the initiation of stress corrosion cracks in these alloys. Initiation and propagation of a stress corrosion crack could be preceded by localized plastic flow of the metal.[4] The stress-dependent "incubation" period could be explained

by the movement of dislocations to grain boundaries where slip occurs when the localized internal stress exceeds the flow stress of the material. The slip in the metal ruptures the oxide and exposes the active metal. The propagation of the crack becomes a function of the continuing exposure of active metal by localized plastic flow.

An alternative mechanism by which grain boundaries are selectively attacked when stress is applied has been postulated.[5] The theory is based on the absorption of hydrogen into grain boundary regions. Depleted zones in precipitation-hardening alloys should be mechanically weaker than the main part of the grains. These zones are expected to plastically deform at relatively low stresses; however, their extremely small volume restricts the total amount of flow that may occur. Thus, small notches should form at grain boundaries. The material at the root of a notch is in a triaxial state of stress and has a higher hydrostatic-stress component than the grain that is subjected only to a uniaxial tensile stress. If we assume that the change in notch geometry in the mechanically weak zones is such that the flow stress is maintained but not exceeded, the hydrostatic-stress component will equal the applied stress less two-thirds of the flow stress for the weak material. The hydrostatic-stress component on the grains is one-third of the applied stress. The ratio is

$$\frac{3\sigma - 2K}{\sigma} = \text{hydrostatic-stress component ratio,}$$

where $\sigma$ is the applied stress and $K$ is the flow stress of the weak-zone material. It is postulated that the hydrostatic-stress component causes preferential absorption of hydrogen, which in turn causes an increase in the activation energy for dissolution of the grain boundary material.

None of these theories consider the possibility that an

580

oxide film may always be present on the corroding surface and that the kinetics may be controlled by the rate of diffusion of cations through the oxide. Hunter and Fowle have shown that when aluminum is anodized, a duplex corrosion-product film is formed.[6] The film consists of a protective barrier layer adjacent to the aluminum and a more permeable outer bulk layer. The maximum thickness of the barrier layer is a function of the applied potential. Dignam suggests that the rate-controlling process for the corrosion of aluminum is the site-to-site diffusion of the metal ions caused by a strong field across the oxide film.[7]

Recently, the passive nature of certain oxides on iron has been attributed to a proton-rich outer layer.[8] This layer would be expected to be more poorly conducting than a more stoichiometric oxide and would thus be able to support a large field.[9] The occupation of cation vacancy sites in $Al_2O_3$ by protons should reduce the diffusivity of aluminum ions by a vacancy-diffusion mechanism.[10] The applied potential, stress, and proton concentration could be the factors that determine the number of available vacancies into which aluminum ions may jump, and thus control the rate of corrosion of aluminum.

The object of this study is to determine which of the above theories of stress corrosion cracking are applicable to the aluminum-zinc-magnesium alloy.

## Experimental Procedure and Results

A high-purity aluminum-4.05 weight percent zinc-3.01 weight percent magnesium alloy was selected for this study. The concentration of any particular residual element such as iron was less than 0.01 weight percent. The material in 0.06-inch thick sheet was solution heat treated at 880 F for 1/4 hour and cold-water quenched. After at least 5 days at room temperature, the alloy was aged at 240 F for 48 hours. The nominal tensile properties of the alloy are: Proportional limit—35 ksi; 0.2 percent offset yield stress—52 ksi; ultimate strength—60 ksi; and modulus of elasticity—$10.3 \times 10^3$ ksi.

Because of the lack of grain-growth inhibitors, the heat treatment produced a microstructure of large, equiaxed grains having an average diameter of 0.015 inch. This feature is desirable in this study because stress corrosion cracking in this alloy follows an intergranular path.

## Electrochemical Studies

Sheet tensile specimens were prepared from the material. One face of each 1.5 x 2.5-inch reduced section was ground down to leave a thickness of less than 0.02 inch. Both sides of the reduced section were electropolished in a chromic-phosphoric-sulfuric acid solution.

The equipment used in this study consisted of a potentiostat, an x-y recorder, a strip-chart strain recorder, and a specially constructed electrode-straining device. A picture of the latter and schematic that shows how it may be used are shown in Figure 1. A strain-gage-instrumented specimen was used to calibrate strain gages mounted on the straining device. In this manner, the load applied to a

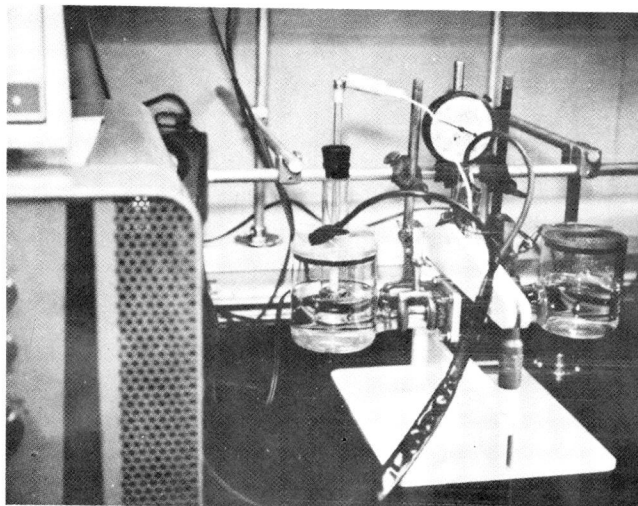

(a)

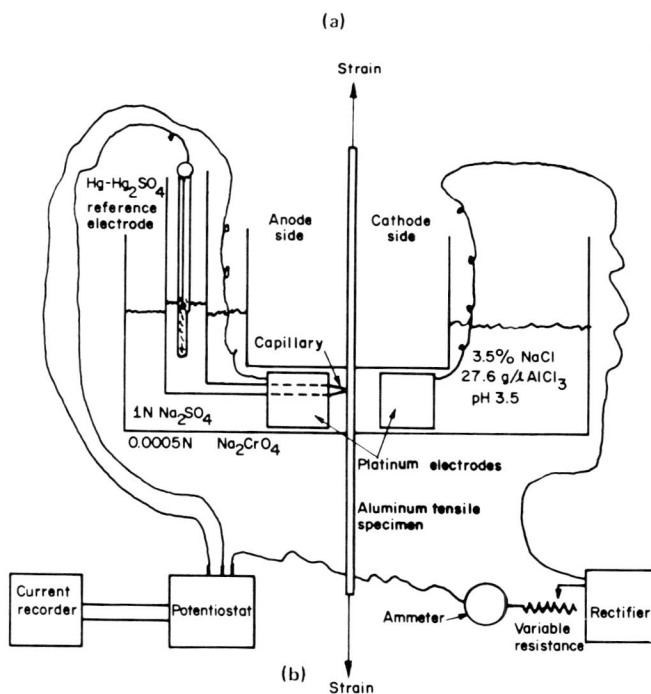

FIGURE 1 — (a) Electrochemical measurement apparatus. (b) Schematic diagram of electrochemical measurement apparatus.

specimen can be monitored by recording the strain on the straining device.

The tensile specimen acts as the working electrode for two separate but identical three-electrode cell systems. The counter electrodes are platinum, and the reference electrodes are mercury-mercurous sulfate. This arrangement allows the sides of the specimen to be polarized at different potentials and also allows the specimen to be exposed to different solutions at the same time. The area of the specimen exposed to solution on either side is $8.2 \text{ cm}^2$.

Two series of experiments were performed. The initial series provided preliminary information for performing the second series. In the first series, two basically different types of solutions were used. A 1 N $Na_2SO_4$ solution inhibited with 0.0005 N $Na_2CrO_4$ was selected as a solution that does not cause noticeable pitting in this alloy.

581

A 3.5 percent NaCl solution containing 27.6 g/l $AlCl_3$ adjusted to a pH of 3.5 was selected as a solution that normally causes rapid stress corrosion cracking and pitting.

One side of an unstressed specimen was exposed to the $Na_2SO_4$ solution and anodically polarized for 3 hours at -0.500 V with respect to a $Hg-Hg_2SO_4$ reference electrode

### TABLE 1–Results of Electrochemical Studies

| Anodic Charging | Cathodic Charging | Tensile Stress Applied | Tensile Stress Not Applied |
|---|---|---|---|
| Yes | Yes | Failed | No failure |
|  | No | No failure | No failure |
| No | Yes | No failure | No failure |
|  | No | Not tested; no failure expected | Not tested; no failure expected |

or +0.09 V versus the normal hydrogen electrode until the current was steady at 1.16 $\mu a/cm^2$. The corrosive NaCl solution was then placed on the opposite side of the specimen and a constant 116 $\mu a/cm^2$ of cathodic current was applied to this exposed surface. After 13 hours, the anodic current on the side exposed to the sodium sulfate had increased to 3.48 $\mu a/cm^2$. The specimen was then stressed in tension to approximately 30 ksi. Within 5 minutes the specimen started to crack.

A second specimen was exposed to anodic polarization in the $Na_2SO_4$ solution and stressed in tension to approximately 50 ksi. The opposite side was not exposed to the corrosive salt solution nor to the cathodic charging. The specimen did not stress corrosion crack within 11 hours.

A third specimen was cathodically charged for 17 hours on the side exposed to the corrosive NaCl solution. The specimen was then stressed to approximately 30 ksi. There

### TABLE 2–Results of Various Stress-Corrosion Cracking Experiments

| Test | Solution | Stress, ksi | History | Time to Crack Initiation, hr | Remarks |
|---|---|---|---|---|---|
| 1 | 1 N $Na_2SO_4$ (pH 4-4.8) | 40 | The specimen was stressed momentarily at different levels in cycles before applying the 40 ksi, the specimen was polarized at +0.09 V versus NHE (anodic) after the stress was applied. | 12.1 | The varying stress cycles were used to study the effect of stress on the corrosion potential. |
| 2 | 1 N $Na_2SO_4$ (pH 4-4.8) | 40 | Polarized at +0.09 V until steady current was observed prior to applying stress | 2.0 | |
| 3 | 1 N $Na_2SO_4$ (pH 4-4.8) | 40 | Polarized for 18 hours at 0.09 V, then cycled to various stress levels before applying stress | 1.0 | Cycles were used to study the effect of stress on the applied current. Failure was accompanied by an audible pop. |
| 4 | 1 N $3Na_2SO_4$ $10^{-3}$ N $Na_2CrO_4$ (pH 4-4.8) | 40 | Polarized at +0.09 V before applying stress | 0.167 | A ten-fold erratic increase in current accompanied the application of stress. Audible pop at failure. Crack appeared to initiate under an O-ring seal near the specimen edge. |
| 5 | 1 N $3Na_2SO_4$ $10^{-3}$ N $Na_2CrO_4$ (pH 4-4.8) | 20.8 | Polarized at +0.09 V before applying stress | 35.3 | |
| 6 | 1 N $3Na_2SO_4$ $10^{-3}$ N $Na_2CrO_4$ (pH 4-4.8) | 22.8 | One side polarized at +0.09 V while the other side was polarized at -0.71 V (cathodic) before applying stress | 16.5 | |

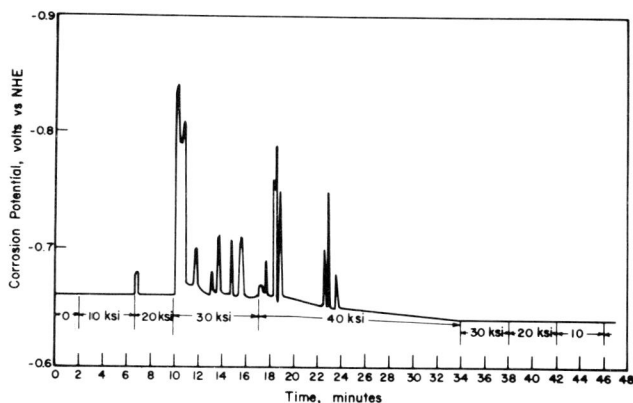

FIGURE 2 — Effect of tensile stress on corrosion potential.

was no cracking for 23 hours. The Na₂SO₄ was placed in the opposite cell and that side was polarized anodically. Almost immediately there was an indication of crack initiation. Table 1 summarizes the combinations of conditions that were tested and the results that were obtained.

The only failure in this series occurred when stress, anodic charging, and cathodic charging were all present.

A second series of specimens was subjected to various conditions of solution, stress level, and applied potential. Both the strain on the load fixture and the current were recorded. Descriptions of these tests and the results are given in Table 2.

Figure 2 shows the effect of stress on the corrosion potential of a specimen immediately after it was exposed to the 1 N Na₂SO₄ solution. Peaks in the potential were probably caused by gross slip, which ruptured the air-formed protective oxide and exposed fresh metal. No change in potential was noted as the stress was removed. However, the initiation of stress corrosion cracks was not necessarily associated with gross slip in this alloy. For example, in Figure 3a, which is a micrograph of a cracked specimen, it will be seen that the part of the crack perpendicular to the applied stress, where it is believed to have initiated, is free of gross slip, while slip is associated with boundaries parallel to the applied stress and with areas where the crack stopped. It may also be noted that although the specimen retained its polished appearance, the solution was sufficiently corrosive to etch the grain boundaries. Figure 3b is a micrograph of the unexposed opposite side of the same crack area. The reduction in cross section caused by the "cracking" from the exposed side has increased the stress on the unexposed side beyond the yield strength of the material, and a large amount of gross slip has occurred.

A specimen polarized at 0.09 V versus NHE immediately upon exposure to the solution and then stressed gave a current-time plot similar to Figure 2, with one important exception. There was some reduction in the current when the stress was removed. This suggests that a portion of the current change as a function of stress is reversible and is not associated with the breakdown and buildup of the oxide film. In addition, when a steady current value is obtained before stress is applied, the

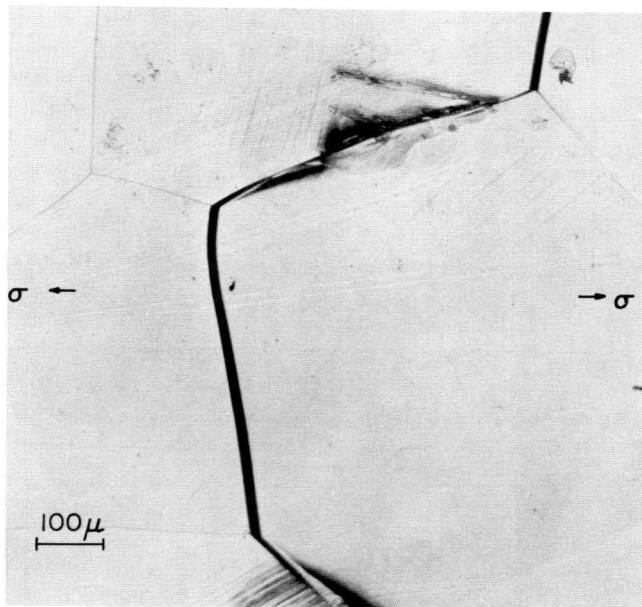

(a)

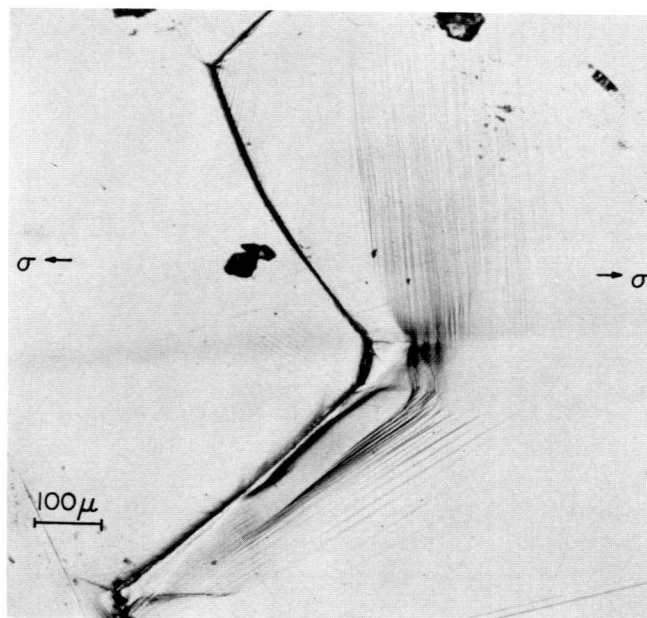

(b)

FIGURE 3 — Stress corrosion crack. (a) Exposed side in 1 N Na₂SO₄, pH 4-4.8. (b) Unexposed side.

irreversible current peaks, similar to the potential peaks in Figure 2, are not observed, and only the reversible change in current is noted.

Three different time ranges for polarization transients on unstressed specimens were observed. The shortest time range was observed in a potential decay curve shown in Figure 4. The initial slope at less than 10 seconds is probably associated with the re-establishment of the solution double layer. The hump and second slope may be the result of changes occurring within the oxide film. The current transients in Figure 5, which occur when the level of the applied potential is changed, suggest that ion concentrations within the oxide film may be changing. The

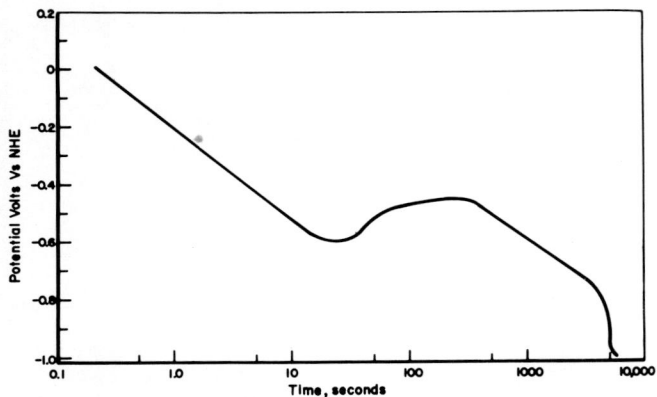

FIGURE 4 — Potential decay curve from +0.09 V vs NHE.

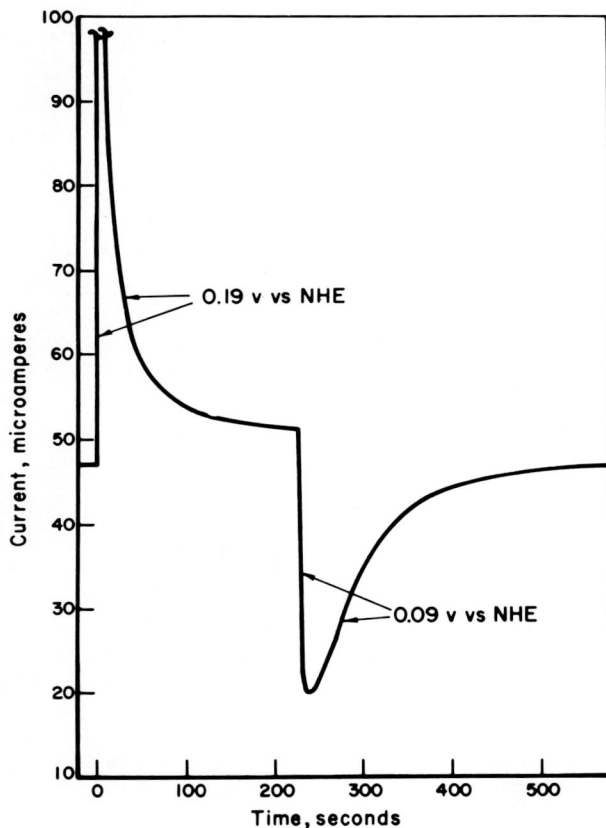

FIGURE 6 — Long-term transient when 0.090 V vs NHE is applied after steady state corrosion potential is reached.

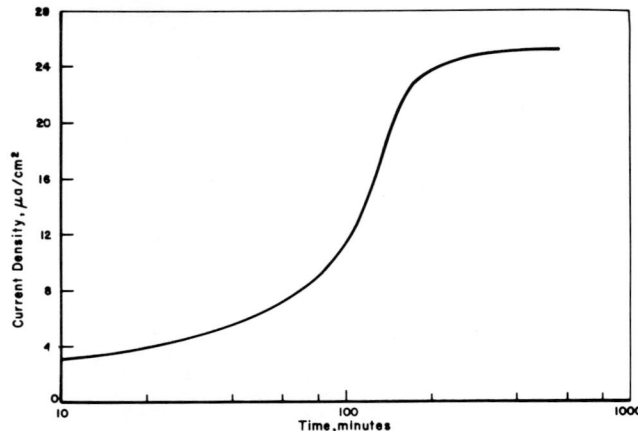

FIGURE 5 — Short-term transients when potential is switched.

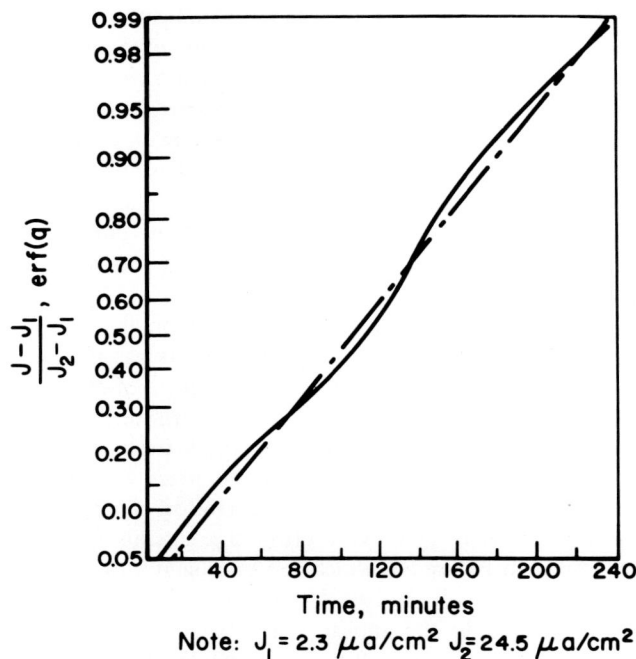

Note: $J_1 = 2.3 \ \mu a/cm^2$ $J_2 = 24.5 \ \mu a/cm^2$

FIGURE 7 — Long-term current transient initiated by applying +0.09 vs NHE.

observed current behavior is consistent with a change in the gradient of the cation concentration at the metal-oxide interface. For example, an instantaneous increase in the anodic potential should result in an infinite gradient, which should rapidly lessen as diffusion into the oxide occurs until a steady-state gradient is established. On the other hand, an instantaneous decrease in the anodic potential should lower the equilibrium concentration of cations at the metal-oxide interface, which in turn should reduce the local concentration gradient. The local concentration gradient should then increase as the excess cations throughout the oxide diffuse away to re-establish a new, lower, steady-state gradient.

A third long-term transient is shown in Figure 6. If the

transient behavior observed in Figure 6 is the result of the establishment of steady-state cation gradients within the oxide film, then it follows that the transient in Figure 6 can be related to either an increase in the diffusivity or a decrease in the film thickness, or to both. The shape of the curve is similar to that of an error function. The degree to which the data fit an error function is shown in Figure 7, where the current-density values are normalized between the two steady-state limits and plotted on a normal probability scale versus time. Data from the best-fit line are replotted in Figure 8, with the error function coordinate converted to the square root of the term in the exponent.

When stress is applied, there is first an immediate, reversible increase in current, which is followed by a transient, irreversible increase in current similar to the transient that is observed when the anodic potential is first applied. An example of this behavior is given in Figure 9.

584

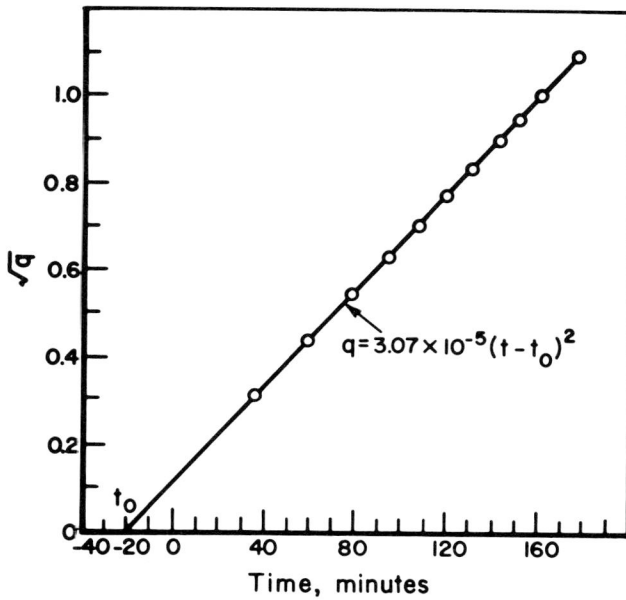

FIGURE 8 – Exponential term in transient initiated by over potential.

$$q = 3.07 \times 10^{-5}(t - t_0)^2$$

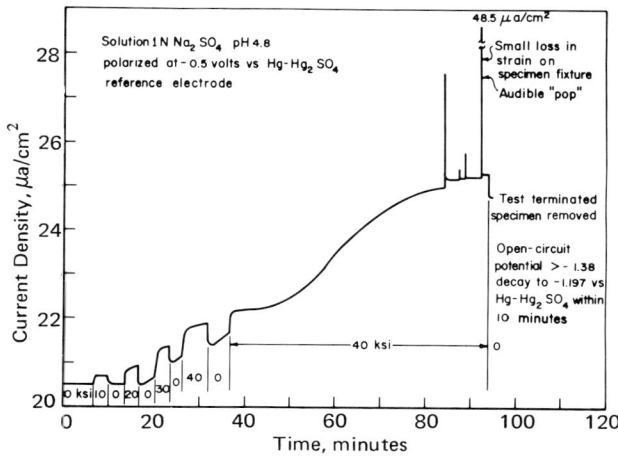

FIGURE 9 – Effect of stress on current density.

Solution 1 N Na$_2$SO$_4$ pH 4.8 polarized at -0.5 volts vs Hg-Hg$_2$SO$_4$ reference electrode

48.5 $\mu$a/cm$^2$

Small loss in strain on specimen fixture

Audible "pop"

Test terminated specimen removed

Open-circuit potential > -1.38 decay to -1.197 vs Hg-Hg$_2$SO$_4$ within 10 minutes

40 ksi

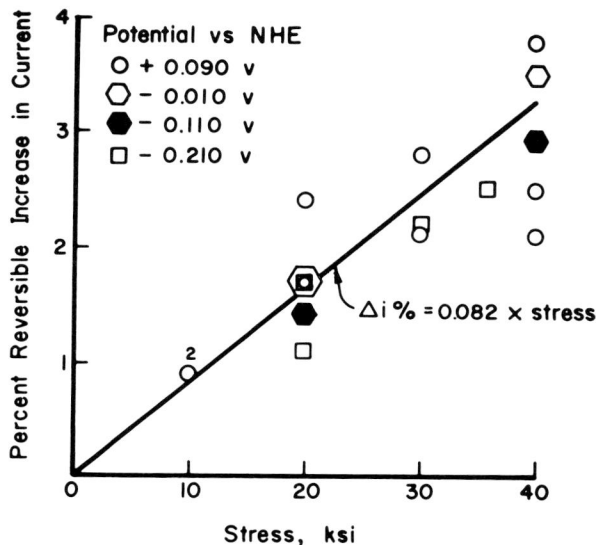

FIGURE 10 – Effect of applied tensile stress on percent change in current density.

Potential vs NHE
O + 0.090 v
⬡ - 0.010 v
⬢ - 0.110 v
□ - 0.210 v

$$\Delta i\,\% = 0.082 \times \text{stress}$$

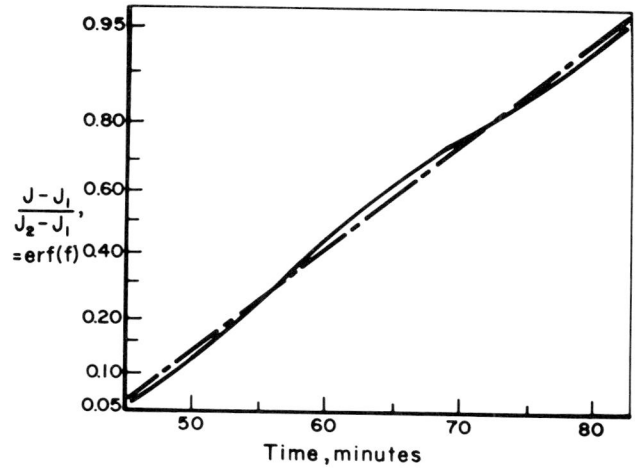

FIGURE 11 – Long-term current transient initiated by stress.

$$\frac{J - J_1}{J_2 - J_1}, = \text{erf}(f)$$

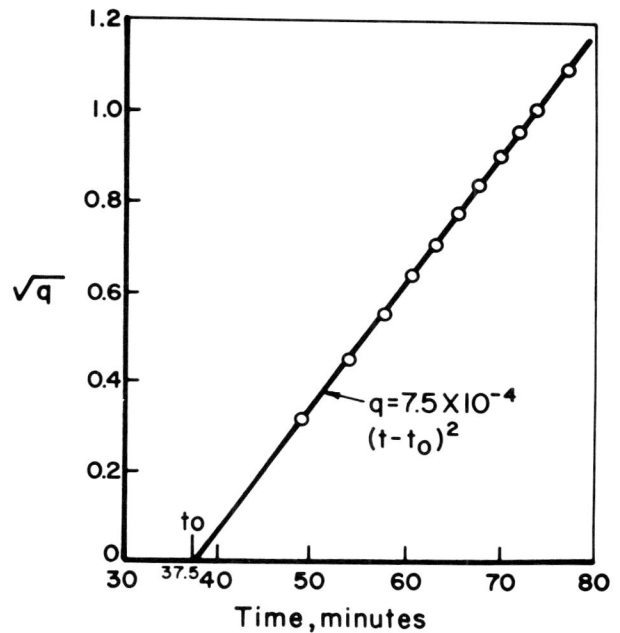

FIGURE 12 – Exponential term transient initiated by stress.

$$q = 7.5 \times 10^{-4}(t - t_0)^2$$

The percent increase in the current, which is reversible, appears to be directly proportional to the applied stress, as is shown in Figure 10. Figures 11 and 12, which are similar to Figures 7 and 8, are based on the data from the transient portion of the curve in Figure 9, where the stress was held at 40 ksi. For this reason, it is believed that the same type of change in the oxide film occurs when either stress or anodic potential is applied.

## Autoradiographic Studies to Detect the Presence of Hydrogen

If hydrogen in some form is involved in the mechanism of stress corrosion cracking in this alloy, it would be helpful to know whether it concentrates at grain boundaries. The following preliminary experiments were conducted in order to make this determination.

Several bent-beam specimens were electropolished in a

585

**TABLE 3—Data for Different Conditions in Autoradiographic Studies**

| Condition | Current, ma | Current Density, $\mu a/cm^2$ | Duration of Electrolysis, hr | Length of Film Exposure, hr |
|---|---|---|---|---|
| Stressed (40 ksi) | 1.50 | 120 | 4.5 | 16 |
| Unstressed | 1.50 | 150 | 4.5 | 16 |
| Stressed (40 ksi) | 1.25 | 100 | 4.5 | 16 |
| Unstressed | 1.00 | 100 | 4.5 | 16 |
| Stressed (40 ksi) | 0.65 | 50 | 3.5 | 2, 60 |
| Unstressed | 0.50 | 50 | 3.5 | 2, 60 |
| Stressed (40 ksi) | 0.65 | 50 | 6.0 | 3, 60 |
| Unstressed | 0.50 | 50 | 6.0 | 3, 60 |
| Lighter (20 ksi), stressed | 0.65 | 50 | 6.0 | 3, 60 |
| Unstressed | 0.50 | 50 | 6.0 | 3, 60 |
| No $H^3$, unstressed | 0.50 | 50 | 6.0 | 2, 60 |
| No $H^3$, stressed (40 ksi) | 0.65 | 50 | 6.0 | 3, 60 |

phosphoric-chromic-sulfuric acid solution. Some specimens were stressed by constant deflection in four-point-loading jigs. Others were not stressed. These specimens were subjected to different exposure conditions. Some specimens were cathodically charged while others were not. Tritiated water was added to some electrolytes.

The electrolyte consisted of 125 ml of 1 N $Na_2SO_4$. In addition, the radio-active solution contained 100 millicuries (5 ml) of tritiated water.

A summary of the different exposure conditions is given in Table 3. The higher current densities caused caustic attack of the aluminum. Thus, the lower current densities for longer exposure were more satisfactory.

After exposure to the solution under the various conditions of charging, each specimen was cleaned. A 1-micron film of VYNS (a Bakelite Company trade designation for a polyvinyl polymer applied in a solution) followed by a 1-micron film of collodion was applied to each specimen to prevent the possibility of the aluminum reacting with the halides in the autoradiographic film. A Kodak Autoradiographic Stripping Plate AR. 10 was then applied to the specimens and exposed for the times indicated in Table 3. The film was developed for 3 minutes in D-19 and fixed for 3 minutes in a Kodak acid fixer.

Figure 13 is typical of the autoradiographs obtained by this method. The four pictures represent four different types of environmental exposure. Figures 13a and 13b show the difference between stressed and unstressed specimens cathodically charged in the tritiated solution. The dark line in Figure 13b is caused by heavy exposure of the film above a stress corrosion crack. The small black spots along the grain boundary at the top of the picture are also caused by exposure of the film. Neither of these phenomena is present in the unstressed specimen. Figures 13c and 13d represent controls which were not exposed to tritiated water. A crack is present in Figure 13d; however, heavy exposure of the film above the crack is not evident. The difference between Figures 13b and 13d is attributed to the presence of tritium in the grain boundaries of the specimen charged in the tritiated solution.

The cracking of the specimens was not desired. The cracking behavior was attributed to a decrease in pH of the small volume of solution caused by some cathodic dissolution of the metal. The cracking may have been avoided by using a larger volume of solution and lower current densities or by coating the tensile side of a bent specimen and charging only the compression side. Cracking should be avoided because, if the VYNS film separating the metal from the autoradiographic film is broken, then the metal will react with the halides in the film and give a false exposure picture similar to Figure 13b. For this reason, it is felt that the black dots along the uncracked grain boundaries are more indicative of the presence of hydrogen than is the dark, black line above the crack.

These experiments were few in number and were primarily concerned with the development of a technique. However, the results indicate that hydrogen is present in higher concentrations at grain boundaries of stressed materials that are susceptible to stress corrosion cracking than in the same material unstressed. Stress apparently preferentially increases the solubility for hydrogen at the grain boundaries.

## Discussion of Results

The shapes of the long-term current transients initiated either by stress or by applied anodic potential are similar. Although the corrosion process in each case is diffusion controlled, the empirically determined exponential term in the error function is not that normally associated with diffusion processes. The exponent that normally describes transient concentration gradients is $-L^2/4Dt$, where L is the layer thickness, D is the diffusivity, and t is time. The empirically determined exponent has the form of $-kt^4$, where k is some constant. Therefore, any changes in the shape of the concentration gradient are apparently overshadowed by either a decrease in film thickness or an increase in the diffusivity, or both. An increase in the anodic potential on aluminum alloys in nonpitting solutions usually causes an increase in the film thickness rather than a decrease. Also, stress should not appreciably alter the solubility of the oxide. Therefore, the observed long-term transients are very likely the result of increases in diffusivity.

A possible explanation for the observed behavior is that protons are being "pumped" out by the anodic potential. The potential is well above the equilibrium potential between hydrogen and hydrogen ions in this solution. Therefore, hydrogen atoms or molecules should not be present. However, protons may be adsorbed into the oxide from the solution and occupy cation vacancy sites. Removing some of these protons by applying a strong charge should leave unoccupied vacancies into which aluminum ions can jump. Thus, the diffusivity of aluminum ions through the oxide should increase.

The reversible change in current, as a function of stress,

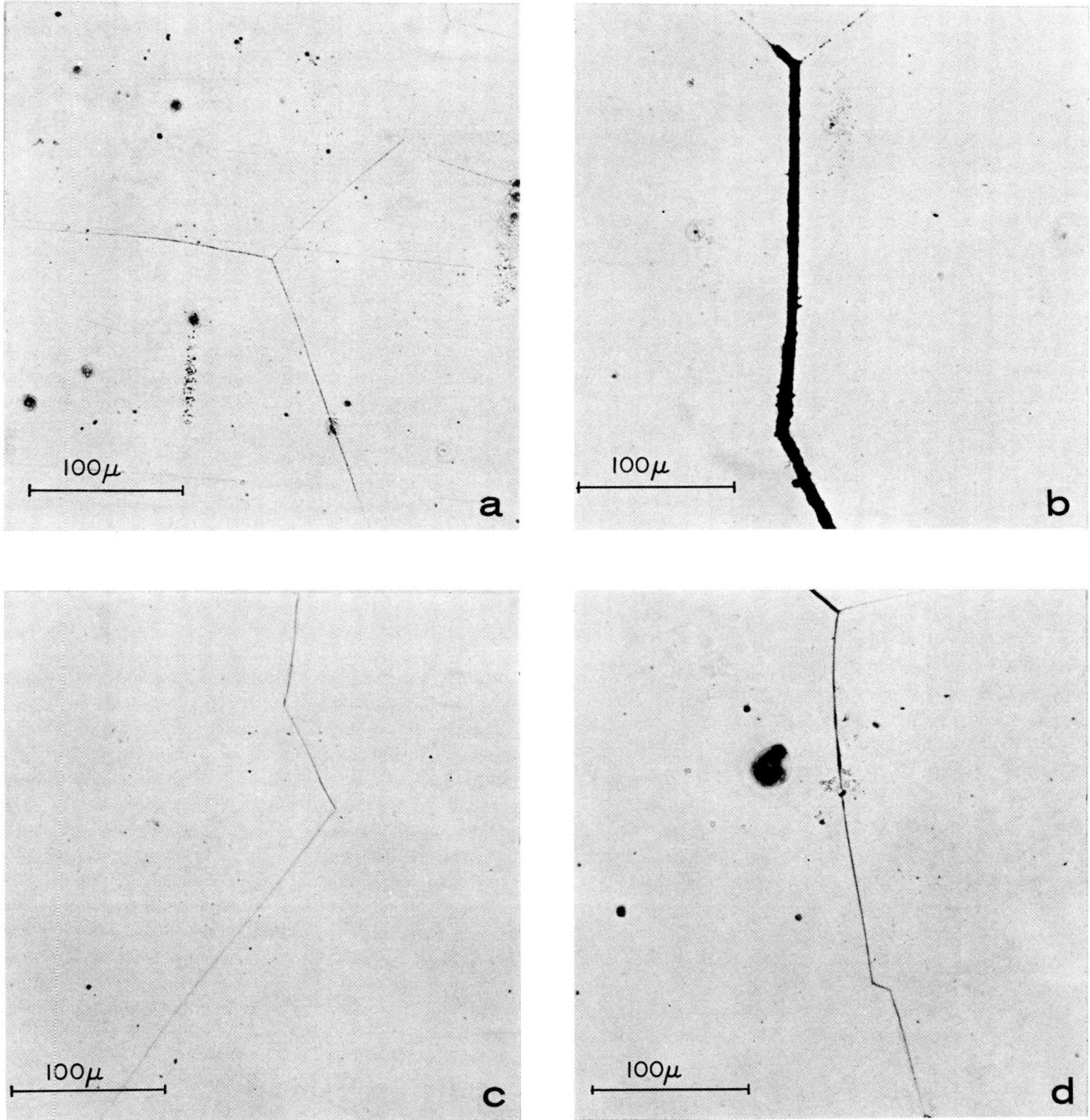

FIGURE 13 — Photomicrographs of different exposure conditions. (a) Unstressed—charged in tritiated solution for 6 hours at 50 $\mu a/cm^2$—60-hour film exposure. (b) Stressed 20 ksi—charged in tritiated solution for 6 hours at 50 $\mu a/cm^2$—60-hour film exposure. (c) Unstressed—not charged—60-hour film exposure. (d) Stressed 40 ksi—charged 6 hours in nontritiated solution at 50 $\mu a/cm^2$—60-hour film exposure.

is probably associated with the creation and annihilation of vacancies caused by the change in volume resulting from the hydrostatic-stress component. If this is true, the diffusivity should be highest at points on the surface where the oxide is subjected to triaxial stress states (at the roots of cracks and at notches created by submicroscopic plastic flow at mechanically weak grain boundaries). The strain on the oxide lattice apparently also "loosens" additional protons to be "pumped" out by the charge.

The percent change in current initiated by the applied potential is 960, while the percent change initiated by a stress of 40 ksi is only 13.5. The reversible change in current is 3.3 percent. However, these latter two changes may be the only ones involved in the intergranular stress corrosion cracking of this alloy because the former is expected to occur uniformly over the surfaces.

If it is assumed that the stress effect is a function of the hydrostatic-stress component rather than of the applied stress and that the flow stress of the grain boundary material is around 5000 psi, at an applied tensile stress of 40,000 psi, according to Equation (1), the current at the grain boundaries should be 2.75 times higher than it is on the grains. This mechanism can account for a preferential attack at grain boundaries caused by stress without altering either the thermodynamic potential or the exchange current of the grain boundary material.

To properly evaluate the results presented in Table 2, it is necessary to have some knowledge of the expected variance in this type of data. In a separate experiment, the statistical distribution of the times for initiation of stress corrosion cracks was determined for this alloy in a 1 N $Na_2SO_4$ solution.[11] The data fit equally as well to either a log-normal or a log-maximum value distribution. The variance was relatively constant between applied tensile stresses of 15,000 and 45,000 psi but increased at both higher and lower stresses. For the log-normal distribution, four standard deviations may be expressed by multiplying or dividing the median by 2. This value will be used to judge the observed differences in the results given in Table 2. If any two single values are separated by more than 4 standard deviations, there is less than a 5 percent probability that the two values belong to the same sample.

The first four specimens were stressed above the bulk-flow stress of the material. The fact that the specimens that were stressed to 40 ksi after the anodic potential was applied failed in less than one-sixth of the time required for the specimen to which the stress was applied before the potential indicates that the mechanical rupture of the oxide film does accelerate stress corrosion cracking. However, this process is much less likely to occur when the material is stressed below the bulk-flow stress. The last two specimens, which were used to determine the effect of introducing atomic hydrogen into the metal, were stressed in this range. The difference between the times to failure of these two experiments is only marginally significant because the difference in stress can account for a difference of 4 hours. However, these results, in conjunction with the results of the autoradiography, suggest that hydrogen at the grain boundaries does contribute to stress corrosion cracking.

Hydrogen atoms that are introduced into the strained metal on the cathodic side of the specimen are expected to diffuse along grain boundaries because of the concentration gradient. When they reach the anodic side of the specimen they are ionized. The addition of protons at the metal-oxide interface, where there is already an excess of cations, should accelerate the diffusion of aluminum ions through the oxide film. Although some competition between aluminum ions and protons for cation vacancy sites might be expected, there may not be any tendency for protons to be retained in a highly strained lattice to which a strong field is applied. It thus follows that the corrosion of the grain boundaries should be accelerated.

## Conclusions Leading to a Possible Mechanism for Intergranular Stress Corrosion Cracking

When this alloy is stressed above the bulk-flow stress, the mechanical rupture of the oxide film contributes to the initiation of stress corrosion cracks. However, this mechanism is much less likely to occur below the bulk-flow stress of the material and, therefore, does not entirely account for the observed stress corrosion cracking behavior.

Hydrogen may be involved in the mechanism of stress corrosion cracking in two ways. First, hydrogen absorbed into grain boundaries may accelerate localized attack by increasing the cation gradient through the strained oxide film. Second, the relative distribution of protons in the oxide at grains and grain boundaries may cause preferential grain boundary attack.

Both applied anodic potential and applied tensile stress increase the diffusivity of aluminum ions through a film of its oxide. The change in diffusivity may be attributed to an increase in the number of cation vacancies available for a vacancy-diffusion mechanism. If protons that normally occupy such sites are removed, the diffusivity should increase. Additional vacancies can be created by the application of tensile stresses. The number of such vacancies should be a function of the hydrostatic-stress component rather than of the applied stress. Therefore, it may be expected that more vacancies will be formed at submicroscopically notched grain boundaries. A more rapid diffusion of aluminum ions through the oxide above grain boundaries should contribute to the preferential attack of grain boundaries when stresses above the flow stress of the weak grain boundary material are applied. This mechanism does not require a change in either the thermodynamic potential or the exchange current of the material when stress is applied.

## References

1. F. A. Champion. The Interaction of Static Stress and Corrosion with Aluminum Alloys. *J. Inst. Metals*, 83, 385 (1955).

2. H. L. Logan. Film-Rupture Mechanism of Stress Corrosion. *J. of Res., National Bureau of Standards*, 48, 99 (1952) February.

3. T. P. Hoar. Influence of Strain and Straining on Anodic Activity. Paper presented at the Electrochemical Society Meeting, Pittsburgh, Pennsylvania (1963) April.

4. E. N. Pugh and W. R. D. Jones. The Mechanism of Stress Corrosion in a High-Purity Aluminum-Zinc-Magnesium Alloys. *Metallurgia*, **63**, 3 (1961) January.

5. F. H. Haynie and W. K. Boyd. Stress Corrosion Cracking of Aluminum Alloys, Defense Metals Information Center Report 228, Battelle Memorial Institute, Columbus, Ohio (1966) July 1.

6. M. S. Hunter and P. Fowle. Naturally and Thermally Formed Oxide Films on Aluminum. *J. Electrochemical Society*, **103**, 482 (1956) September.

7. M. J. Dignam. Oxide Films on Aluminum, I. Ionic Conduction and Structure, II. Kinetics of Formation in Oxygen. *J. Electrochemical Soc.*, **109**, 184, 192 (1962) March.

8. M. C. Bloom and L. Goldenberg. $\gamma Fe_2O_3$ and the Passivity of Iron. *Corrosion Sciences*, **5**, 623 (1965).

9. J. Kruger and J. P. Calvert. Ellipsometric-Potentiostatic Studies of Iron Passivity. *J. Electrochemical Soc.*, **114**, 43 (1967).

10. P. G. Shewmon. *Diffusion in Solids*, McGraw-Hill Book Co., New York, pp. 137-155 (1963).

11. F. H. Haynie. The Statistical Distribution of the Times for Initiation of Stress Corrosion Cracks in an Aluminum-Zinc-Magnesium Alloy. To be submitted as a thesis to The Ohio State University, Columbus, Ohio.

## Discussion

**G. Martin, North American Rockwell, Inc.:**

You suggest in your paper that the current changes observed as shown in Figure 9 are due to protons arriving from the outside of a passive film. If that were the case, the mechanism should be completely reversible in loading and unloading and one should obtain symmetric current pulses on loading and unloading. However, such reversibility is not indicated by your test. Let us assume that these protons arise from charges travelling within the metal to the surface during the loading cycle. If those charges are associated with dislocation movement, for instance, no changes would occur on unloading. This could explain the fact that reversibility of the current effect is not observed.

**F. H. Haynie:**

The effect of stress on anodic current density at an applied potential is shown in Figure 9. There appears to be two contributing effects, a small effect which is reversible and a large effect which is irreversible. The irreversible effect is believed to be caused by the removal of protons from cation vacancy sites within the oxide film. I did not wish to give the impression that these protons were absorbed during the test. This process is assumed to have taken place prior to the time at which a potential producing an anodic current was applied. Bloom and Goldenberg[8] have suggested a similar mechanism for passivity of iron in that absorbed protons inhibit the diffusion of the metal ions through the oxide film. These protons may be partially removed by applying a potential which produces an anodic current. The application of tensile stresses enhances the removal of the protons. The irreversible effect of stress in Figure 9 is explained by the fact that the current was still being applied when the stress was removed. The direction of the current flow opposes any re-absorption of protons.

# PART VII

# TITANIUM ALLOYS

# EVALUATION OF SESSION ON TITANIUM ALLOYS

S. P. Rideout and J. C. Scully

## Introduction

With respect to the general objective of the conference "to identify factors which will serve as a basis for the quantitative prediction of stress corrosion cracking phenomena", this session appears to have succeeded to about the same degree as the sessions on other alloy systems. The state of our knowledge has been advanced by these sessions, but mechanism studies should be continued to bring further advancements towards the goal of quantitative predictability of stress corrosion behavior.

The papers and discussions presented during this session have dealt with stress corrosion cracking of titanium alloys in a variety of environments ranging from elevated temperature exposures to halide salts to ambient temperature exposures to aqueous and nonaqueous solutions. In evaluating the session it is obvious that there is no single mechanism that is generally accepted as an explanation for all cases of cracking. In the review paper by Boyd and the paper by Sedriks, et al, the view is expressed that in various environments cracking occurs by different mechanisms. It may be naive to expect a single mechanism to explain a phenomenon which, by title, involves both stress and corrosion, especially when one considers the possible degrees of interaction of these two factors. Actually, it is difficult to establish general agreement on a given mechanism for any specific case of cracking.

## Status of Mechanistic Aspects

From the optimistic point of view, it appears that our understanding of stress corrosion cracking of "teen-age" titanium alloys is about as far advanced as our understanding of cracking in more mature alloy systems that have been studied for much longer times. This is because most of the mechanistic concepts that have been developed can be applied to any alloy system in which susceptibility to stress corrosion occurs. It is not surprising that many of the same uncertainties and controversies are also applicable.

There are several aspects of stress corrosion of titanium alloys on which there is fairly good agreement (although some dissention on any given point is inevitable). It has been well established that the cracking process involves two distinct stages, e.g., initiation and propagation. Corrosion seems to be the dominant factor in crack initiation, and in a few cases such as methanol and hot-salt cracking, there seems to be a consensus that crack initiation occurs due to embrittlement caused by corrosion-produced hydrogen. However, in most environments, the corrosion processes involved in crack initiation are not clearly understood and are open to speculation. The rate of crack propagation varies over a wide range depending on the nature of the environment and the level of stress in the material. In general, stress appears to be the dominant factor in crack propagation. The extreme example of this is the propagation of pre-existing fatigue cracks in specimens statically loaded in any one of a variety of aqueous and nonaqueous environments in which the initiation of stress corrosion cracks may not occur. Additional evidence of the dominant role of stress is provided by fractographic studies. The surfaces of cracks produced in a variety of environments appear similar, showing characteristics of brittle rupture ("quasi-cleavage") and very little evidence of corrosive attack except in cases where the fracture was exposed to the environment for a fairly long time following the crack formation.

Among the metallurgical factors, it has been well established that alloy chemistry and heat treatment influence susceptibility to stress corrosion cracking. In the Ti-Al system, susceptibility increases with increasing aluminum content and the ordering transformation in the alpha phase is deleterious. In general, however, much more study of titanium alloys is needed to fully understand the mechanism(s) by which alloying or trace elements and heat treatment alter the stress corrosion susceptibility.

## Unsolved Questions and Controversies

The major questions and controversies associated with stress corrosion of titanium alloys are, for the most part, the same questions and controversies that have arisen in other alloy systems. Because these questions are generally well known and have been discussed many times over, they can be summarized without detailed elaboration as follows:

1. Is hydrogen involved in stress corrosion cracking of titanium alloys?

There are powerful arguments both for and against the involvement of hydrogen, and this controversy is likely to continue for some time. Titanium alloys are known to be susceptible to two forms of hydrogen embrittlement; that which is due to hydride precipitation in metal containing relatively high concentrations of hydrogen, and that which is due to hydrogen in solution (low strain rate embrittlement).

Some investigators believe that stress corrosion cracking in some environments is due to embrittlement caused by corrosion-produced hydrogen. It has also been suggested that nascent hydrogen may be the active species involved in a stress sorption mechanism of cracking, in which case neither hydride formation nor solution of hydrogen in the metal would be required to cause cracking.

The controversy over hydrogen is a good example of the fundamental problems which frustrate attempts to resolve specific aspects of stress corrosion mechanisms. It is difficult, if not impossible, to conceive and perform definitive experiments which yield unambiguous and irrefutable evidence to prove a hypothesis. Regarding the hydrogen question as an example, even when hydrogen is shown to be present both in the corrosion products and in cracked specimens, this cannot be unanimously accepted as proof that hydrogen caused the cracking.

2. Can all of the observed phenomena be explained by a single mechanism, such as stress sorption or electrochemical dissolution along an active path, or should we allow for several different mechanisms depending on the system?

Problems of semantics are bound to arise in discussions of these questions. For example, is lowered resistance to propagation of pre-existing cracks really a stress corrosion phenomenon? Does pre-cracking by fatigue actually eliminate the crack initiation stage, or merely intensify the effect of stress in the initiation of true stress corrosion cracking.

3. Can the apparent immunity of some alloys to stress corrosion be explained in terms of structural features (dislocations, etc.) and alloy chemistry, or will every alloy be susceptible to cracking in some specific environment?

## Areas for Future Research

These questions involve a myriad of related questions, and each question signals an area for additional study.

There are several areas of research on titanium alloy that seem to deserve immediate attention as follows:

1. Develop kinetic data to relate electrochemical reactions to the initiation and propagation of stress corrosion cracks in alloys which have been thoroughly characterized in terms of fine structure and mechanical properties.

The excellent work by Beck and by Blackburn and Williams of the Boeing Scientific Research Laboratories represent significant contributions in this area. More work of this type and caliber is needed to develop bases for quantitative prediction of stress corrosion phenomena. The use of fracture toughness testing techniques on notched specimens, with and without fatigue cracks, will continue to provide valuable data for rating the relative susceptibility of various alloys to stress corrosion and for studying the role of stress in the cracking mechanism.

2. Crack initiation in environments such as $N_2O_4$, sea water, and various organic solutions should be studied to determine if the incubation period is related to the extent of corrosion or to the stress level in the material.

3. Electron microscopy studies of the initial stages of corrosive attack on thin foils of susceptible alloys would be helpful in clarifying the role of corrosion in crack initiation.

4. Wherever possible radiotracers such as $^3H$ and $^{36}Cl$ should be employed to study the role of various chemical species in the corrosion reactions.

As a final note, the facts that stress corrosion cracking can occur and that controversies arise over the mechanism(s) have not seriously hindered the applications of metal alloys in general, and there should be no undue pessimism about broadening the practical applications of titanium alloys. Indeed, it is fortunate that susceptibility to stress corrosion of titanium alloys was first discovered in laboratory tests, and that research is progressing both in development of resistant alloys and in the definition of environmental conditions that should be avoided in practice to minimize the threat of stress corrosion cracking. As Dr. Staehle pointed out in his introduction to this conference, the circumstances were somewhat different during the early development and application of austenitic stainless steels, in which stress corrosion cracking was regarded as merely an interesting laboratory curiosity until stress corrosion damage of industrial equipment was recognized as a serious problem.

# STRESS CORROSION CRACKING
# OF TITANIUM AND ITS ALLOYS

W. K. Boyd
Battelle Memorial Institute

## Introduction

Two properties of titanium which have made it attractive for a variety of applications are its high strength-to-weight ratio and excellent corrosion resistance to many environments.

Titanium is an inherently active metal but forms a thin oxide film which is very protective. The apparent stability and integrity of this film in environments which caused stress corrosion cracking of more common structural metals and alloys suggested that titanium alloys might be quite resistant to stress corrosion cracking. For example, early investigators[1,2] were unable to crack titanium in either boiling 42% $MgCl_2$ or boiling 10% NaOH solutions which are commonly used to study stress corrosion cracking in stainless steels, using combinations of such active and passive agents as:

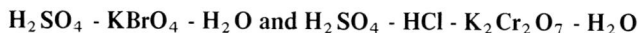

$H_2SO_4$ - $KBrO_4$ - $H_2O$ and $H_2SO_4$ - HCl - $K_2Cr_2O_7$ - $H_2O$

nonetheless, the susceptibility of titanium and its alloys to stress corrosion cracking has been demonstrated in a number of environments. A summary of environments known to initiate cracking and the susceptible alloys are shown in Table 1.

It is the purpose of this paper to indicate the present general position on the stress corrosion cracking of titanium by first reviewing some of the general features associated with some of these aggressive environments which have not been studied in much detail. This is followed by a discussion in some detail of the metallurgical and environmental factors which appear to play a role in the cracking mechanism, particularly as associated with the exposure of titanium and its alloys to hot salt, nitrogen tetroxide, methanol, and sea water.

## Fuming Nitric Acid

The first reported incident of stress corrosion cracking of titanium and its alloys occurred in dry red fuming nitric acid (RFNA) service.[3] The cracking for the most part followed an intergranular path. There is no indication that the cracking is related in any way with the pyrophoric deposits which may form on titanium as a result of exposure to red fuming nitric acid. It is however, interesting to note that both phenomena are limited to anhydrous RFNA. For some alloys $NO_2$ appears to be necessary for cracking while for others, namely the Ti-8Mn and the Ti-6Al-4V alloys, cracking has been encountered in RFNA containing no $NO_2$. In any event the addition of 1.5 to 2.0 percent water completely inhibits the reaction. This role of water is quite interesting and will be discussed in more detail in connection with cracking in other environments.

## Hot-Salt
## Stress Corrosion Cracking

The susceptibility of titanium alloys to hot-salt cracking has largely been demonstrated through the use of a variety of laboratory tests, no service failures from hot-salt cracking have been reported even though titanium alloys have been used in air frames and jet engines at operating temperatures as high as 900 F.[4]

All of the commercial alloys, but not unalloyed titanium, are susceptible to some degree to hot-salt stress corrosion cracking. The alpha-phase alloys, such as Ti-5Al-2.5Sn, Ti-7Al-12Zr, and Ti-5Al-5Sn-5Zr, are apparently most susceptible to attack.[5] The alpha-beta alloys are less susceptible, and the degree of susceptibility may increase with increases in aluminum content.[5] For example, the Ti-8Al-1Mo-1V alloy (both as mill annealed and duplex annealed) is very susceptible. However, the Ti-8Mn alloy, which contains no aluminum, is also susceptible.

Alloys with intermediate resistance are Ti-5Al-5Sn-5Zr-1Mo-1V, Ti-6Al-4V, Ti-6Al-6V-2Sn, Ti-5Al-2.75Cr-1.25Fe, and Ti-3Al-11Cr-13V. Among the most resistant alloys are Ti-4Al-3Mo-1V, Ti-2.25Al-1Mo-11Sn-5Zr-0.25Si, (IMI 679),[5] and an experimental Ti-2Al-4Mo-4Zr alloy.[6]

### Effect of Temperature, Stress, and Time

Hot-salt stress corrosion cracking of titanium alloys is a

| Environment | | |
|---|---|---|
| Medium | Temp., F | Susceptible Titanium Materials |
| Cadmium | >610 | Ti-4Al-4Mn |
| | 625-750 | Ti-8Mn |
| Mercury | RT | Ti-75A, Ti-6Al-4V |
| | 700 | Ti-13V-11Cr-3Al |
| Silver | | |
| Ag plate | 875 | Ti-7Al-4Mo, Ti-5Al-2.5Sn |
| AgCl | 700-900 | Ti-7Al-4Mo, Ti-5Al-2.5Sn |
| Ag-5Al-2.5Mn | 650 | Ti-6Al-4V, Ti-8Al-1Mo-1V |
| Chlorine | 550 | Ti-8Al-1Mo-1V |
| Hydrochloric Acid | | |
| 10% | RT | Ti-5Al |
| 10% | 95 | Ti-5Al-2.5Sn |
| - - | 650 | Ti-8Al-1Mo-1V |
| Nitric Acid | | |
| RFNA | RT | Ti, Ti-8Mn, Ti-6Al-4V, Ti-5Al-2.5Sn, Ti-2Fe-2Cr-2Mo |
| Sulfuric Acid | | |
| 7-60% | RT | Ti-5Al |
| Chloride Salts | | |
| various, residues | 550-800 | All commercial alloys |
| Nitrogen tetroxide | | |
| (no xs NO) | 85-165 | Ti-6Al-4V |
| Methyl alcohol | RT | Ti-6Al-4V |
| | | Ti-6Al-4V, Ti-8Al-1Mo-1V |
| | | Ti-75A, Ti-6Al-4V, Ti-8Al-1Mo-1V, Ti-5Al-2.5Sn, Ti-4Al-3Mo-1V |
| Methyl chloroform, inhibited | 700 | Ti-8Al-1Mo-1V, Ti-6Al-4V, Ti-5Al-2.5Sn, Ti-13V-11Cr-3Al |
| Ethyl alcohol | RT | Ti-8Al-1Mo-1V |
| | | Ti-8Al-1Mo-1V, Ti-5Al-2.5Sn |
| Ethylene glycol | RT | Ti-8Al-1Mo-1V |
| Trichloroethylene | 700 | Ti-8Al-1Mo-1V, Ti-5Al-2.5Sn |
| | 1150, 1500 | Ti-5Al-2.5Sn |
| Trichlorofluoro-ethane ("Freon PCA") | 1450 | Ti-8Al-1Mo-1V, Ti-5Al-2.5Sn, Ti-6Al-4V, Ti-13V-11Cr-3Al |
| Chlorinated diphenyl ("Aerochlor 1262") | 600-700 | Ti-5Al-2.5Sn |
| Sea Water | ambient | Unalloyed Ti (with high oxygen content, i.e., 0.317 percent) Ti-8Mn Ti-2.25Al-1Mo-11Sn-5Zr-0.2Sc (IMI-679) Ti-3Al-11Cr-13V Ti-4Al-4Mn Ti-5Al-2.5Sn Ti-6Al-2.5Sn Ti-6Al-4V Ti-6Al-3Cb-2Sn Ti-6Al-4V-1Sn Ti-6Al-4V-2Co Ti-6Al-6V-2.5Sn Ti-7Al-2Cb-1Ta Ti-7Al-3Cb (as received and beta annealed) Ti-7Al-3Mo Ti-7Al-3Cb-2Sn Ti-8Al-1Mo-1V Ti-8Al-3Cb-2Sn |

function of temperature, stress, and time of exposure. In very general terms, hot-salt stress corrosion cracking has not been observed below about 500 F. The temperature range of greatest susceptibility is 550 F to 800 F, and within this range, time to failure is decreased as either the temperature or stress level is increased. There also appears to be an upper temperature limit at which general corrosion is so rapid as to mask any stress corrosion cracking. These limits are about 800 F, 900 F, and 1000 F for the Ti-6Al-4V, Ti-8Al-1Mo-1V, and Ti-7Al-12Zr alloys, respectively.[7]

These general effects of temperature, stress, and time are illustrated for the Ti-8Al-1Mo-1V alloy in Figure 1. Some inconsistencies are apparent in this figure and probably arise from differences in heat treatment and/or the test conditions that were used by the various sources. Most recent information indicates, for example, that stress corrosion cracking, per se, of titanium alloys "does not occur at 500 F, at least within 8000 hours", although it does occur at 525 F "under high stresses and long times".[6] Figure 2 shows some 1000-hour exposure data for several alloys which agree with this premise.

The threshold stress, or stress above which hot-salt stress corrosion cracking can occur, has been reported for several alloys using various time periods. Longer times at temperature tend to reduce the threshold stress values. For example, the threshold stress of Ti-8Al-1Mo-1V is decreased by 50 percent at 850 F when the time increases from 100

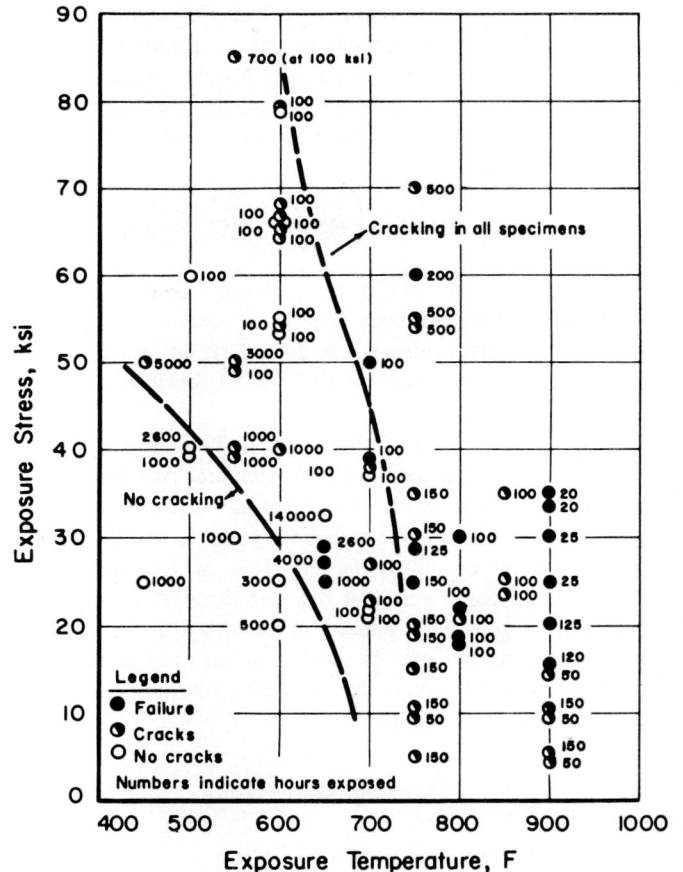

FIGURE 1 – Effect of exposure variables on the occurrence of visible salt stress corrosion in Ti-8Al-1Mo-1V.[7]

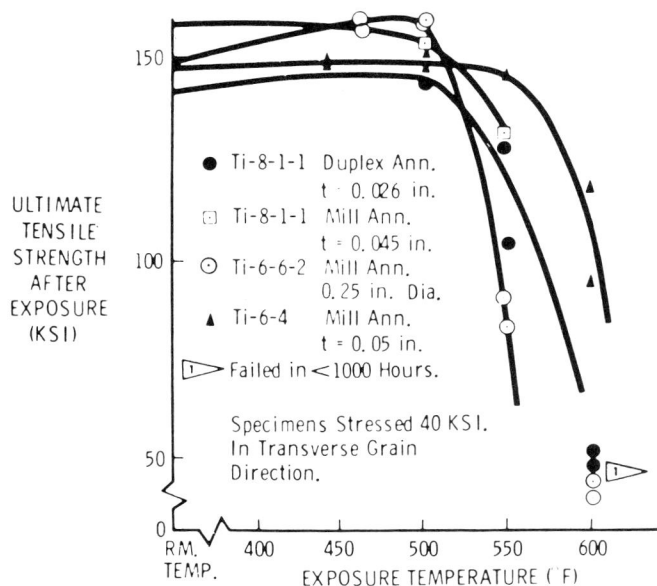

FIGURE 2 — Residual strength of titanium alloys after exposure to sodium chloride for 1000 hours.[8]

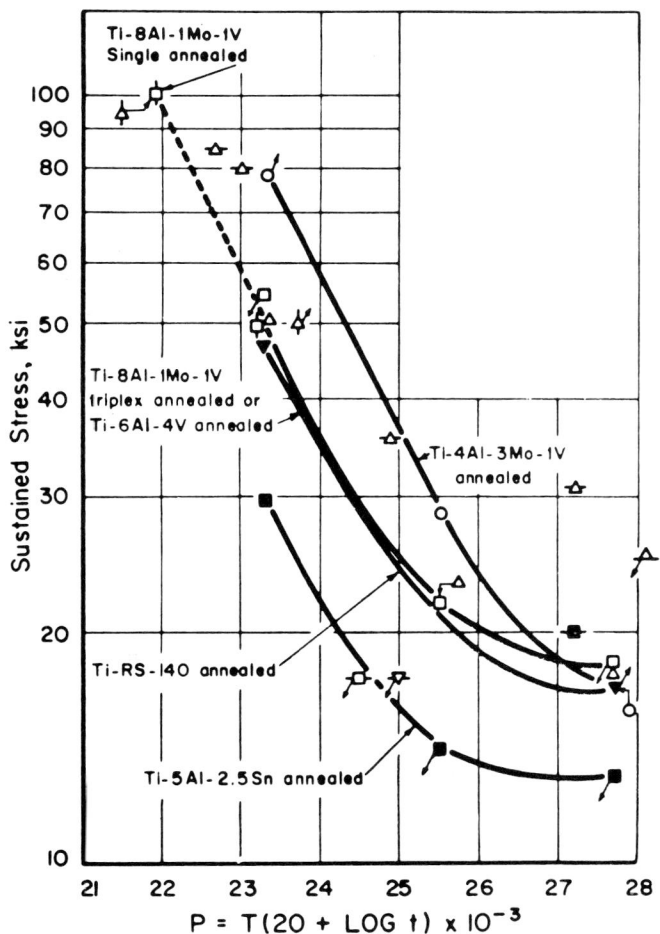

FIGURE 3 — Application of Larsen-Miller parameter for predicting stress corrosion cracking by hot salt of annealed titanium alloys.[9,10]

to 1000 hours.[5]

The combined effects of time, temperature, and stress for several titanium alloys are shown in Figure 3,[10,11] which represents data from many sources. These data suggest the stress corrosion cracking thresholds for the various alloys. This plot employs the empirical Larsen-Miller parameter, originally used for generalizing creep data in steel.[12] Excellent agreement is indicated for the data. From this plot, the estimated threshold stress for hot-salt cracking at 550 F and 30,000 hours is 45,000 psi for Ti-4Al-3Mo-1V (annealed), 30,000 psi for Ti-8Al-1Mo-1V (triplex annealed) and Ti-6Al-4V (annealed), 28,000 psi for Ti-5Al-2.75Cr-1.25Fe (annealed) and 18,000 psi for Ti-5Al-2.5Sn (annealed).

*Oxygen*

The necessity for oxygen in the hot-salt stress corrosion cracking of titanium alloys has been reported by several investigators. For example, hot-salt stress corrosion cracking of Ti-5Al-2.5Sn was readily observed at 800 and 900 F at an air pressure as low as 10 microns Hg. However, when the pressure was reduced to one micron Hg, no cracking was observed.[6]

The loss of ductility of stress titanium specimens exposed to hot salt is lessened as the oxygen content or air pressure is reduced.[13,14] At an air pressure equivalent to that at an altitude of 70,000 feet, 34 mm Hg, a decrease in susceptibility is indicated over that at atmospheric pressure for the Ti-8Al-1Mo-1V alloy at 550 F.

Oxygen present in the oxide film may also be sufficient to promote hot-salt cracking.[7,15] For example, two holes were drilled in a Ti-5Al-2.5Sn block. NaCl was placed in both holes. $TiO_2$ was also put in one hole. The holes were closed and welded shut in a vacuum arc furnace. The specimen was rolled at 1800 F and then held at 900 F for 100 hours. No reactivity was observed in the cavity containing NaCl alone, and white crystals remained. The other cavity, however, had reacted to form a black hygroscopic corrosion product.[7]

The necessity for oxygen probably accounts for the fact that cracking occurs at the edges of salt deposits, and is more severe for thin salt coatings.[7]

*Water*

The role of water in the hot-salt stress corrosion cracking of titanium alloys is not clearly known. The moisture content of air in the dewpoint range of -40 to 60 F appears to have little effect on the loss of ductility of the Ti-8Al-1Mo-1V alloy at 550 F using NaCl.[10,14] When extra-dry oxygen is used in baked out and evacuated equipment, no hot-salt cracking is reported after 2 hours at 800 F with NaCl ($<0.01$ percent $MgCl_2$).[6] A similar sample with humid air was severely cracked.

In the absence of oxygen, water by itself is not sufficient to promote cracking. For example, when ice was sublimed in an evacuated system free of oxygen, no stress corrosion was found after 2 hours at 800 F.[6]

595

In other experiments, moisture was reported to exert a strong influence.[15,16] In one study, the equipment used was nearly closed, and the flow of air could be regulated from an air compressor. Moist air was maintained at 1.8 to 2.8 percent water. Dry air was obtained by passing it at 20 to 40 ml/min through Drierite to give an estimated dewpoint of -100 F ($<$ 10 ppm). Cracking of the Ti-8Al-1Mo-1V alloy at 650 F and 50,000 psi stress when exposed to sea salt required 150 hours in dry air versus 10 hours for moist air. A similar result was obtained by others.[15]

In experiments using a mixed salt of NaCl and $MgCl_2 \cdot 6H_2O$, severe cracking was reported when using dry oxygen.[17] The water of hydration of the $MgCl_2$ is apparently sufficient to promote the cracking. However, when "a small amount of excess water" is added to the system, longer life was found. This apparently indicates a critical moisture level.

On the basis of these results, it appears that water is a necessary requirement, and must be considered in any mechanism study. When the amount of water present is very low, as with baked-out equipment or dry air, the severity of the test may vary with water content. This could cause the apparent variation in results with different salts in early work. At intermediate water levels, no variation in the severity of attack is noted. At high water levels, the reaction products might be diluted, causing a decline in severity of the attack.

### Hydrogen

In the state-of-the-art report on hot-salt cracking prepared for NASA in 1964,[4] it was pointed out that several reactions involving titanium and sodium chloride could result in the production of hydrogen, and that its role in the cracking mechanism should be studied. Since that time, data developed by Rideout et al[18] strongly suggest that absorption of corrosion-produced hydrogen promotes cracking. Using radioactive-tracer techniques, he finds high hydrogen concentration in the crack areas. He further observes in the hot stage microscope that although corrosion stains appear almost immediately around salt crystals, cracking does not initiate until about 1-1/2 hours later. The cracks appear abruptly, propagate rapidly for a short distance and then pause. The crack propagates by stepwise abrupt extensions. At various intervals after the first sign of a crack, additional cracks initiated at other sites. Rideout notes that in many instances, the crack sites were close together and cracks joined to form larger cracks. These same studies also confirmed the fact that no cracking could be initiated unless moisture was present. In view of these results, Rideout proposes that hot-salt cracking occurs as a result of hydrogen embrittlement.

Further evidence to support a hydrogen embrittlement mechanism is found in the work of Kirchner and Ripling.[19] They were able to accelerate cracking of a Ti-6Al-4V alloy by impressing a current of 20 $\mu a/in^2$ on the specimen. When made the cathode, the specimen failed in 4.9 hours at 650 F under an applied stress of 25,000 ksi. A similar specimen made the anode failed in 20 hours. In both cases the fracture followed an intergranular path.

### Chlorine

The fact that gaseous chlorine will cause cracking of titanium at elevated temperatures suggests that free chlorine or HCl produced by the reaction of titanium oxide and sodium chloride might be responsible for the cracking. Some investigators have reported that they detected chlorine as a product of the reaction. However, Logan et al,[20] using precision techniques and a mass spectrograph could not find chlorine in the gaseous products from their experiments. In addition, most of the evidence points to the fact that no cracking will occur unless the salt is in intimate contact with the titanium surface.

While the above observations do not eliminate the possibility of free chlorine being the cracking agent, they are strong support for an alternative mechanism.

### Postulated Mechanism

While extensive laboratory investigations of such factors as salt composition, type of reaction, and the effects of $O_2$, water, and other environmental factors have been conducted, the mechanism of the cracking is not completely understood. On the other hand, the roles of oxygen and water appear quite clear. Oxygen in an oxide (such as $TiO_2$) must be present before cracking will occur. Likewise, water also appears necessary although its critical concentration is low, say, of the order of 10 ppm.

The roles of hydrogen and chlorine, and whether the cracking species is liquid, gaseous or solid are uncertain. The fact that no cracking occurs below, say, 500 F is strong evidence to support the need of a liquid phase at some point in the cracking reaction. Theories involving chlorine of HCl gases and embrittlement by hydrogen are not completely consistent with observations. However, the hydrogen-embrittlement theory would seem to more nearly explain the observed incubation period to the initiation of a crack, the apparent stop-start stepwise propagation of the crack, and the need for water.

## Stress Corrosion Cracking in Nitrogen Tetroxide

Laboratory studies conducted in the early 1960's indicated that titanium and a number of titanium alloys were completely passive to nitrogen tetroxide. The first indication that titanium alloys would stress corrosion crack in $N_2O_4$ came early in 1965 when a Ti-6Al-4V tank filled with $N_2O_4$ ruptured during a pressure test at Bell Aerosystems Company. Failure occurred after about 40 hours of exposure at 105 F and a stress level of 90,000 psi.

### $N_2O_4$ Purity

Subsequent investigations have already demonstrated that titanium alloys will stress corrosion work in $N_2O_4$ containing dissolved oxygen (no excess of NO) but are immune to cracking $N_2O_4$ containing a small excess of NO. Oxygen and NO cannot exist at the same time since they combine to form $NO_2$ according to the following reaction:

$$1/2\,O_2 + NO \rightarrow NO_2.$$

Some indication of the possible roles of oxygen and NO is obtained from a consideration of thermodynamic data for reactions of water with $N_2O_4$.

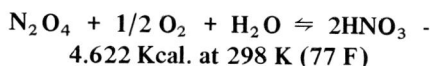

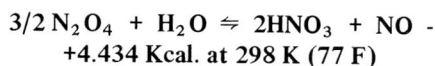

$$N_2O_4 + 1/2\,O_2 + H_2O \leftrightharpoons 2HNO_3 -$$
$$4.622\ Kcal.\ at\ 298\ K\ (77\ F)$$

$$3/2\,N_2O_4 + H_2O \leftrightharpoons 2HNO_3 + NO -$$
$$+4.434\ Kcal.\ at\ 298\ K\ (77\ F)$$

These data suggest that water does react spontaneously with $N_2O_4$ in the presence of oxygen, but does not react spontaneously with $N_2O_4$ to produce nitric acid if NO is present. Thus, from Reactions 1 and 2, it will be seen that at equilibrium red $N_2O_4$ should contain a different $HNO_3/H_2O$ ratio is the critical factor in the cracking of titanium in $N_2O_4$ and that the cracking mechanism is similar to that observed in red fuming nitric acid. The reaction of titanium with $HNO_3$ would also suggest that hydrogen ions from the nitric acid would produce embrittlement at the apex of the crack. Such a condition would be quite compatible with the mechanism of cracking in methanol and aqueous solutions where the hydrogen appears to play an important role in the cracking mechanism.

Much of the $N_2O_4$ is produced by oxidizing nitrosyl chloride (NOCl), producing nitryl chloride ($NO_2Cl$) which in turn is fractionally distilled into $Cl_2$ and $NO_2$. Nitrogen tetroxide produced by this method necessarily contains some NOCl. Even that material produced from the oxidation of ammonia may contain trace amounts of chlorides. This fact has led a number of investigators to postulate that an active chlorine atom is the species responsible for the cracking. They point out that titanium will react with an active chlorine atom to form titanium tetrachloride, which is a liquid and therefore nonprotective, and that cracking of titanium can be induced in dry chlorine gas. Further evidence in support of chlorides is found in the fact that electron-probe analyses of fractures show higher chloride concentrations in the interface than on the surface of the material.[21]

Perhaps the most damaging evidence against the role of chlorides is the fact that titanium has not been found to crack in NOCl or $NO_2Cl$, which are the species present in $N_2O_4$. Furthermore, mass spectrographic analyses have not revealed the existence of chlorine gas in equilibrium with $N_2O_4$. The proven existence of either chlorine gas or a titanium chloride salt would certainly lend strong support for the need of an active chlorine atom in the cracking mechanism.

*Stress*

Certainly one of the most dominant factors in the

stress corrosion cracking of titanium alloy in $N_2O_4$ is the applied stress. Cracking of Ti-6Al-4V has occurred over the stress range 40,000 to 90,000 psi. In general it appears that crack initiation occurs in about the same length of time at both the high and low stress levels. Of significance however is the fact that the frequency of the cracks (i.e., the number per square inch) is much less at the lower stress level than at the high stress level. Studies made at the Bell Aerosystems Company indicated that the crack density on the internal surface of some tanks stressed to 90,000 psi was of the order of 15,000 per square inch. This magnitude of crack density is significantly different than that normally observed in the case of stress corrosion cracks in other environments and in other alloy systems. It would appear that there is a direct relationship between crack density and coarse slip steps. The higher the stress, the greater is the number of slip steps and, correspondingly the greater is the number of cracks per given area.

*Suggested Mechanism of Cracking*

Even though $N_2O_4$ is a nonelectrolyte, the presence of water is evidence for an electrochemical step in the cracking mechanism. Likewise water would be a source of hydrogen so that one cannot rule out an embrittling mechanism involving hydrogen, which would be consistent with cracking mechanism suggested for titanium in other environments.

It would also appear that there is evidence to support an oxidation mechanism at the crack tip akin to the Ti-LOX-GOX (liquid-oxygen-gaseous oxygen reaction). The cracks appear to initiate at coarse slip steps. Such a condition would result in rupture of the protective oxide film, thus exposing a fresh surface that is rapidly oxidized through plastic deformation. The protective oxide would be continuously ruptured, exposing fresh metal at the apex of the crack.

It is also possible that preferential adsorption of contaminant ions such as $Cl^-$ at slip steps prevents the formation of protective films which otherwise normally form on titanium in oxidizing media. This would be consistent with the observation that higher chloride concentrations are found in the fracture area than on the surface.

## Stress Corrosion Cracking in Methanol

Tomashov[22] found that solutions of methyl alcohol with additions of bromine were extremely corrosive to titanium and titanium alloys. He also noted that some of the alloys exhibited a tendency toward intergranular attack. Later, several Japanese investigators[23] reported that titanium and zirconium would suffer stress corrosion cracking in methanol containing HCl or $H_2SO_4$. Cracking of U-bend-type specimens occurred within one hour in methanol containing 0.4% HCl and in about 24 hours in an environment containing one percent $H_2SO_4$.

These rather obscure references seemed of little importance until a Ti-6Al-4V alloy tank containing methanol failed catastrophically while under a sustained load test. The methanol was seemingly fairly pure. This failure and others which were identified as stress corrosion cracking have stimulated considerable research effort to elucidate the factors, both environmental and metallurgical which promote crack initiation and propagation in methanol.

*Nature of the Cracking Mechanism*

If one examines the chemistry of the reactions of metals with a series of alcohols it will be seen that they are most reactive with methyl alcohol, somewhat less reactive in ethyl alcohol, and so on down the line. The longer the chain, the less reactive the alcohol becomes. The data suggest that the behavior of titanium is consistent with that of other metals.

The free energy of formation of titanium methyl oxylate is favorable but it does require a high activation energy. Apparently, stressing of the titanium results in a significant lowering of the activation energy. This is borne out by the fact no titanium is found in methanol that has been in contact with unstressed titanium, while considerable dissolved titanium (12 ppm) was detected in methanol to which U-bend samples of titanium had been exposed.

Although there is little doubt that titanium will react with pure methanol to form a soluble methyl oxalate and liberate hydrogen, it does appear that small amounts of contaminants are necessary for the initiation and propagation of stress corrosion cracks. One of these contaminants is water. Using electrochemical techniques and time to failure measurements, Haney and co-workers[24] found a critical water content at which failure times are at a minimum. For example, in $CH_3OH$ + 0.0001 N NaCl, minimum cracking times were found to occur at 0.1 volume percent water. As the chloride level was raised, the minimum in the time-to-failure curve as a function of the water content in methanol was shifted towards higher percentages of water. It is interesting to note that additions of bromine and iodine ions to methanol displace the minimum toward lower water contents (as low as 0.01 volume percent for NaI additions). Susceptibility to stress corrosion cracking also increased markedly with increasing chloride content of the methanol.

It would appear that the water may act as an anodic inhibitor. In such cases it has been demonstrated that if sufficient inhibitor is not added, rapid localized attack such as pitting and/or stress corrosion cracking is more apt to occur than if no inhibitor were present. At much larger inhibitor additions, the metal becomes completely passive.

The influence of anodic and cathodic polarization on time to failure has been investigated for unalloyed titanium and a number of titanium alloys. In general, impressed anodic currents are found to decrease time to failure, whereas small cathodic currents markedly increase times to failure. This behavior is consistent with electrochemical attack along an active path and not with a mechanism involving hydrogen embrittlement. However, it is interesting to note that at the highest current densities

investigated by Haney, several failures which appeared to involve hydrogen occurred in a Ti-6Al-4V alloy.

There is increasing evidence to show that hydrogen also may be playing a role in the methanol cracking mechanism. The electron microautoradiography work of Tiner[25] shows that hydrogen in quantities of less than 50 ppm (as $H^3$) introduced into titanium alloys preferentially segregates to the beta phase in alpha-beta alloys and to grain boundaries in all alpha alloys but is dispersed quite uniformly in beta-type alloys.

Scully[26] using transmission electron microscopy has observed hydride formation along alpha-beta phase boundaries of a Ti-5Al-2.5Sn alloy specimen after cracking in methanol. He has also found that hydride formation occurred only in susceptible alloys and in those environments which cause corrosion cracking.

The adsorption of hydrogen and its segregation to the beta phase would seem to explain the brittle behavior of the beta regions observed in the examination of fracture faces. Alpha and alpha-beta type alloys exhibit mixtures of ductile dimple and brittle cleavage areas. In general, the stress corrosion cracks take transgranular paths through alpha grains, but follow by cleavage to the alpha-beta phase boundaries.

## Titanium Alloys Exposed to Sea Water

Titanium and its alloys exhibit excellent pitting resistance to sea water and other chloride solutions. On the basis of standard stress corrosion cracking evaluation techniques such as U-bend and four-point loaded specimens, titanium alloys were not believed to be susceptible to stress corrosion cracking in chloride salt solutions. However, Brown,[27] using specimens of a titanium alloy in the form of a prenotched fatigue cracked bar, found that with static load tests under plain strain conditions, the resistance to further crack propagation was drastically reduced in a 3 percent NaCl solution at room temperature. This is an important observation since it indicates that the stress corrosion cracking resistance of some titanium alloys is dependent on the integrity of the protective oxide film and not on the intrinsic resistance of the alloy lattice to the propagation of a stress corrosion crack.

Alloys which have shown some degree of susceptibility are listed below but not necessarily in order of susceptibility:

Unalloyed Ti (with high oxygen content, i.e., 0.317 percent).

Ti-8Mn
Ti-2.25Al-1Mo-11Sn-5Zr-0.2Si (IMI-679)
Ti-3Al-11Cr-13V
Ti-4Al-4Mn
Ti-5Al-2.5Sn
Ti-6Al-2.5Sn
Ti-6Al-4V
Ti-6Al-3Cb-2Sn

TABLE 2—Effect of Sea Water on Titanium Alloys[1][28]

| Titanium Alloy | Condition | In Air Slow-Notch Bend Test Nominal Bending Stress, ksi | In Air Static-Load Cantilever Test Nominal Bending Stress, ksi | Time, min | In Sea Water Static-Load Cantilever Test Nominal Bending Stress, ksi | Time, min | Fracture Appearance Sea Water Embrittled? |
|---|---|---|---|---|---|---|---|
| **Alpha Alloys** | | | | | | | |
| Ti Unalloyed (RS-70) | Alpha rolled | 182 | 157 | 45 | 64 | 3 | Yes |
| | Alpha rolled + 1400 F, 16-hr AC | – | – | – | 104 | 1 | Yes |
| 5Al-2.5Sn | Alpha-beta rolled | 170 | – | – | 65 | 3 | Yes |
| 6Al-2.5Sn | Beta rolled | 233 | 181 | 40 | 110 | 3 | Yes |
| | Alpha-beta rolled | 221 | 166 | 760 | 109 | 6 | Yes |
| **Near-Alpha Alloys** | | | | | | | |
| 8Al-2Cb-1Ta | Beta rolled | 186 | – | – | 129 | Immed | Yes |
| 7Al-3Cb (0.06 O$_2$) | Beta rolled | 232 | – | – | 110 | 10 | Yes |
| | Alpha-beta rolled | 193 | 166 | 70 | 125 | 3 | Yes |
| 7Al-3Cb (0.1 O$_2$) | Beta rolled | 235 | – | – | 144 | Immed | Yes |
| | Alpha-beta rolled | 256 | – | – | 131 | 4 | Yes |
| 7Al-3Cb-2.5Sn | Beta rolled | 200 | – | – | 111 | 1 | Yes |
| | Alpha-beta rolled | 213 | – | – | 114 | 9 | Yes |
| 6Al-3Cb-2Sn | Beta rolled | 220 | – | – | 120 | Immed | Yes |
| 7Al-3Cb-2Sn | Beta rolled | 233 | – | – | 158 | Immed | Yes |
| 8Al-3Cb-2Sn | Beta rolled | 110 | – | – | 126 | Immed | Yes |
| 6.5Al-5Zr-1V | Alpha-beta rolled | 222 | 186 | 180 | 186 | 200 | No |
| **Alpha-Beta Alloys** | | | | | | | |
| 6Al-2Sn-1Mo-1V | Alpha-beta rolled | 209 | 196 | 9 | 180 | 1430 | No |
| 6Al-4V (Low O$_2$) | Alpha-beta rolled | – | – | – | 180 | Immed | No |
| 6Al-4V (High O$_2$) | Alpha-beta rolled | 101 | 135 | 15 | 103 | 150 | No |
| 6Al-2Mo | Alpha-beta rolled | – | – | – | 165 | 180 | No |
| | Alpha-beta rolled + 1750 F, 1-hr AC + 1100 F, 2-hr AC | – | – | – | 191 | 1 | No |
| 7Al-2.5Mo | Alpha-beta rolled | 209 | 198 | 500 | 169 | Immed | No |
| | Alpha-beta rolled + 1735 F, 1-hr WQ | 216 | – | – | 192 | 150 | No |
| | Alpha-beta rolled + 1735 F, 1-hr WQ + 1100 F, 2-hr AC | 205 | 166 | 25 | 135 | 13 | No |
| 5Al-2Sn-2Mo-1V | Beta rolled | 242 | 190 | 6 | 177 | 105 | No |
| | Alpha-beta rolled | 185 | 171 | 1 | 143 | 110 | No |
| 6Al-2Sn-3V-1Mo | Beta rolled | 211 | 115 | 1845 | 120 | 342 | No |
| | Alpha-beta rolled | 192 | 106 | 1780 | 140 | 2 | No |

[1]All specimens were fatigue cracked to a total notch depth of 25 to 35 percent.
Immed. - Immediate.

Ti-6Al-4V-1Sn
Ti-6Al-4V-2Co
Ti-6Al-6V-2.5Sn
Ti-7Al-2Cb-1Ta
Ti-7Al-3Cb (as received and beta annealed)
Ti-7Al-3Mo
Ti-7Al-3Cb-2Sn
Ti-8Al-1Mo-1V
Ti-8Al-3Cb-2Sn.

Preliminary screening tests indicate the following alloys to be insensitive to sea water crack propagation for the conditions used:

Ti-2Al-4Mo-4Zr
Ti-4Al-3Mo-1V
Ti-5Al-2Sn-2Mo-2V
Ti-6Al-2Mo
Ti-6Al-2Sn-1Mo-1V
Ti-6Al-2Sn-1Mo-3V
Ti-6Al-2Cb-1Ta-0.8Mo
Ti-6.5Al-5Zr-1V
Ti-7Al-2.5Mo (as received and beta annealed + WQ + 1100 F, aged for 2 hr).

*Relationship Among Composition, Heat Treatment, Microstructure, and Susceptibility to Cracking*

The susceptibility of precracked titanium alloys to stress corrosion cracking appears to be adversly affected by aluminum, tin, manganese, cobalt, and/or oxygen content. On the other hand, the presence of isomorphous beta stabilizer such as molybdenum, columbium or vanadium reduces or eliminates susceptibility to cracking.[28,29] These effects are illustrated by the data developed by Lane[28] and are summarized in Table 2. Alloys containing more than 6 percent aluminum are particularly susceptible to stress corrosion cracking. This susceptibility of high-aluminum-bearing titanium alloys to rapid crack propagation in marine environments is believed to be the result of ordering of the microstructure. Such ordering could also explain the detrimental effects of oxygen and manganese. Crossley[30] has previously shown that additions of 6 to 10 percent aluminum in titanium can cause embrittlement by ordering when the binary alloys are aged in the range 900 to 1300 F. This coincides rather well with the stress corrosion cracking susceptibility observed for some high-aluminum-bearing alloys heat treated in this temperature range. In general, the behavior of a susceptible material can be improved by water quenching from a high temperature beta anneal.

Lane et al[28] have shown the existence of a correlation between microstructure and cracking behavior for several titanium alloys containing aluminum. They note that materials with a matrix of coarse, long platelets in the microstructure were most susceptible, whereas those containing fine platelets and alpha dispersions were not susceptible.

*Discussion of Mechanisms*

The available evidence strongly suggests that crack propagation in the case of the precracked specimens is electrochemical in nature. Studies at Battelle and elsewhere have shown that an actively propagating crack can be stopped by the application of a cathodic potential. However, contrary to most cases of stress corrosion cracking, the application of an anodic potential does not appear to significantly increase susceptibility to cracking.

Potential measurements made during step loading of susceptible Ti-8Al-1Mo-1V alloy specimens show potential peaks after each load is applied, which then return in a fairly short time to the potential measured before the load was applied.[31] When sufficient load is added, however, the potential becomes very active and there is no indication of repassivation. The nature of the anodic path at this point is not clear. Scully[32] suggests that when exposing a bare titanium surface under conditions of high strain, a hydride is produced, which overcomes the strong repassivation tendency.

## Liquid Metal Embrittlement

Although it is generally recognized that the mechanism of liquid metal embrittlement differs from that of stress corrosion cracking there are some interesting similarities which warrant discussion. Titanium has been found to crack under some solutions in contact with mercury, cadmium, and silver brazing alloys. Cesium also appears to degrade the physical properties of titanium. In the latter two cases, which occur only at high temperatures, it would appear that the embrittlement results from the diffusion of cesium or silver along grain boundaries and the formation of brittle phases which result in loss of ductility.

In the case of the cracking of titanium alloys when contacted by liquid mercury or liquid cadmium (610 F) it would appear that cracking will not occur unless the protective $TiO_2$ film is ruptured exposing a fresh titanium surface. For example, U-bend specimens of titanium alloys prepared in air and then exposed to liquid mercury do not fail. On the other hand, bending of the titanium while in contact with mercury, result in an almost instantaneous failure. These observations further indicate the need for the rupture of the protective $TiO_2$ film in initiating stress corrosion cracking in titanium and its alloys.

## Conclusions

A considerable amount of data for titanium alloys of both commercial and experimental types in a variety of shapes and metallurgical conditions has been accumulated over the past several years. To date, however, a completely satisfactory mechanism for stress corrosion cracking of titanium alloys has not yet been demonstrated. On the other hand, the data to indicate that a number of variables appear to play an important role in the initiation and propagation of stress corrosion cracks in all environments. These include both metallurgical and environmental factors and may be summarized as follows:

(1) For most, if not all environments, it would appear that an alloy can be classified as either susceptible or

600

immune to stress corrosion cracking on the basis of composition alone. For example, susceptibility to cracking increases with aluminum content. Tin and oxygen also appear to exert a similar detrimental effect as do eutectoid β-stabilizers such as manganese and cobalt. Susceptibility, on the other hand, decreases with increasing content of isomorphous β-stabilizers such as molybdenum, vanadium, columbium, and tantalum. Of these molybdenum is the most favorable.

While the addition of alloying elements can alter corrosion behavior by affecting the polarization of anodic and/or cathodic reactions it does not seem that alloy content significantly affects the corrosion reactions of titanium alloys. Rather, it would appear that the compositional dependence of stress corrosion cracking behavior of titanium alloys is related to the distribution of sites for localized attack or to the absorption and precipitation of embrittling or highly anodic species.

(2) With the exception of $N_2O_4$, the mechanism of cracking appears to involve at least in part an electrochemical step.

(3) It would appear that oxygen and water are required for cracking to occur. The data suggest that critical levels exist for both oxygen and water at which cracking times are at a minimum. The presence of an active chloride species also seems to increase susceptibility to cracking in all environments.

(4) There is strong evidence to suggest that a part of the cracking mechanism involves absorption of embrittling species from the environment. Hydrogen is the most likely embrittling species to be absorbed, particularly from aqueous environments.

Titanium alloys of the $\alpha + \beta$ type are known to be susceptible to slow-strain-rate hydrogen embrittlement when both phases are saturated with hydrogen. Embrittlement is found only at creep strain rates and is believed to be the result of strain-induced precipitation of hydride. The strain rates at which this has been observed appear to be consistent with those predicted in the vicinity of an advancing stress corrosion crack. This suggests that embrittlement could occur in the crack tip region at hydrogen levels below those necessary for general hydride precipitation. Crack propagation could result from failure of brittle hydride phases, or selective dissolution along slip planes due to the presence of hydride or hydrogen-rich areas.

An alternative role of hydrogen might be to prevent reformation of protective oxide films once they have been ruptured.

# References

1. H. H. Uhlig and J. R. Cobb, Jr. *Metal Progress,* **63,** 74 (1963).
2. M. G. Fontana. *Ind. and Eng. Chem.,* 48-49 (1956).
3. J. B. Rittenhouse. The Corrosion and Ignition of Titanium in Fuming Nitric Acid, Jet Propulsion Laboratory, California Institute of Technology, External Publication 338 (1956) May 21.
4. W. K. Boyd and F. W. Fink. Phenomenon of Hot-Salt Stress Corrosion Cracking of Titanium Alloys, Report No. Cr-117, NASA (1964) October.
5. M. J. Donachie, Jr., W. P. Danesi, and A. A. Pinkowrsh. Effects of Salt Atmosphere on Crack Sensitivity of Commercial Titanium Alloys at 600-900 F. Paper presented at the Fifth Pacific Area National Meeting of the American Society for Testing and Materials, Seattle, Washington, October 31-November 5, 1965.
6. A. J. Hatch, H. W. Rosenberg, and E. F. Erbin. Effects of Environment on Cracking in Titanium Alloys, Titanium Metals Corp. of America, Henderson, Nevada. Paper presented at 5th Pacific Area National Meeting of ASTM, Seattle, Washington, October 31-November 5, 1965.
7. V. C. Petersen and H. B. Bomberger. The Mechanism of Salt Attack on Titanium Alloys, Crucible Steel Company of America. Paper presented at Fifth Pacific Area National Meeting of the ASTM, Seattle, Washington, October 31-November 5, 1965.
8. R. A. Wood. The Ti-8Al-1Mo-1V Alloy, DMIC Report No. S-10 Defense Metals Information Center, Battelle Memorial Institute, Columbus, Ohio (1965) April 1.
9. D. E. Piper and D. N. Fager. The Relative Stress Corrosion Susceptibility of Titanium Alloys in the Presence of Hot Salt. Paper presented at the Fifth Pacific Area National Meeting of the ASTM, Seattle, Washington, October 31-November 5, 1965.
10. C. H. Avery and R. V. Turley. Chloride Stress Corrosion Susceptibility of High Strength Stainless Steel, Titanium Alloy, and Superalloy Sheet, Douglas Aircraft Co., Long Beach, California, ML-TDR-64-44, Vol. I (1964) March and Report No. ML-TDR-64-44, Vol. II, Stress Corrosion Data Summary (1964) May, under Air Force Contract AF 33(657)-8543.
11. R. V. Turley and C. H. Avery. Elevated-Temperature Static and Dynamic Sea-Salt Stress Cracking of Titanium Alloys. Paper presented at the Fifth Pacific Area National Meeting of the ASTM, Seattle, Washington, October 31-November 5, 1965.
12. F. R. Larson and J. Miller. A Time-Temperature Relationship for Rupture and Creep Stresses. *Trans ASME,* **52,** 765 (1952) July.
13. G. J. Heimerl, D. N. Braski, D. M. Royster, and H. B. Dexter. Salt Stress Corrosion of Ti-8Al-1Mo-1V Alloy Sheet at Elevated Temperatures, NASA Langley Research Center. Paper presented at the Fifth Pacific Area National Meeting of the ASTM, Seattle, Washington, October 31-November 5, 1965.
14. D. N. Braski. Preliminary Investigation of Effect of Environment Factors on Salt Stress Corrosion Cracking of Ti-8Al-1Mo-1V at Elevated Temperatures, NASA Technical Memorandum, TMX-1048, Langley Research Center, Langley Station, Hampton, Virginia (1964) December.
15. H. L. Logan, M. G. McBee, C. J. Bechtoldt, B. T. Sanderson, and G. M. Ugiansky. Chemical and Physical Mechanisms of Salt Stress Corrosion Cracking of the Titanium 8-1-1 Alloy. Paper presented at the Fifth Pacific Area National Meeting of the ASTM, Seattle, Washington, October 31-November 5, 1965.
16. R. L. Kirchner and E. J. Ripling. Diffusion of Corrosion Products in Hot Salt Stress Corrosion Cracking of Titanium, Materials Research Laboratory, Inc., Richton Park, Illinois (1965) October.
17. H. L. Logan, M. J. McBee, C. J. Bechtoldt, B. T. Sanderson, and G. M. Ugiansky. Mechanism of Stress Corrosion of Titanium Alloys Exposed to Sodium Chloride at Elevated Temperatures, NBS Report 8690, U. S. Department of Commerce, National Bureau of Standards, Washington, D. C. (1964) May 4.
18. S. P. Rideout, M. R. Louthan, and C. L. Selby. Basic Mechanisms of Stress Corrosion Cracking of Titanium. Paper presented at the Fifth Pacific Area National Meeting of the ASTM, Seattle, Washington, October 31-November 5, 1965.
19. R. L. Kirchner and E. J. Ripling. NASA TN-D-1798, p. 37 (1963) May.
20. H. L. Logan, M. J. McBee, G. M. Ugiansky, C. J. Bechtoldt, and

B. T. Sanderson. Stress Corrosion Cracking of Titanium. ASTM STP 397 (1966).

21. G. F. Kappelt and E. J. King. Observations on the Stress Corrosion of the 6Al-4V Titanium Alloy in Nitrogen Tetroxide, Bell Aerosystems Company. Paper presented at the AFML 50th Anniversary of Corrosion of Military and Aerospace Equipment Technical Conference, Denver, Colorado, May 23-25, 1967.

22. N. D. Tomashov, R. M. Al'tovskiy, and V. B. Vladimirov. Study of the Corrosion of Titanium and Its Alloys in Methyl Alcohol Solutions of Bromine, Translation FTD-TT-63-672/1+2, pp. 221-233a, Translation Division, Foreign Technology Division WPAFB, Ohio, from Korroziya i Zashchita Konstruktsionnykh Metallachoskikh Materialov, Moscow (1961) DMIC No. 57587.

23. K. Mori, A. Takamura, and T. Shimose. Stress Corrosion Cracking of Titanium and Zirconium in HCl-Methanol Solutions. *Corrosion,* **22,** 29-31 (1966) February.

24. E. G. Haney, G. Goldberg, R. E. Emsberger, and W. T. Brehm. Investigation of Stress Corrosion Cracking of Titanium Alloys. Second Progress Report, Mellon Institute, under NASA Grant N6R-39-008-014 (1967) May.

25. N. A. Tiner, T. L. Mackay, and C. B. Gilpin. Stress Corrosion Cracking of Titanium Alloys at Ambient Temperature in Aqueous Solutions, Douglas Astropower Lab Report SM-49105 Q3, March, 1967.

26. Private Communication.

27. B. F. Brown, T. J. Lennox, Jr., R. L. Newbegin, M. H. Peterson, J. A. Smith, and L. J. Waldron. Marine Corrosion Studies, NRL Memorandum Report 1574, Second Interim Report of Progress, U. S. Naval Research Lab., Washington, D. C. (1964) November.

28. I. R. Lane, J. L. Cavallero, and A. G. S. Morton. Fracture Behavior of Titanium in the Marine Environment, MEL R&D Phase Report 231/65, U. S. Navy Marine Engineering Laboratory, Annapolis, Maryland (1965) June; see also I. R. Lane, Jr., J. L. Cavallero, and A. G. S. Morton. Sea Water Embrittlement of Titanium. Paper presented at the Fifth Pacific Area National Meeting of the ASTM, Seattle, Washington, October 31-November 5, 1965.

29. A Study of the Stress Corrosion Cracking of Titanium Alloys in Sea Water with Emphasis on the Ti-6Al-4V and Ti-8Al-1Mo-1V Alloys, Research Report No. R471, Project No. 93002, Reactive Metals, Inc., Niles, Ohio (1965) October 18.

30. F. A. Crossley and W. F. Carew. Embrittlement of Ti-Al Alloys in the 6 to 10 Percent Aluminum Range. *J. Metals,* **209,** 43-46 (1957) January.

31. D. N. Williams, R. A. Wood, E. L. White, W. K. Boyd, and H. R. Ogden. Studies of the Mechanism of Crack Propagation in Salt Water Environments of Candidate Supersonic Transport Titanium Alloy Materials, Final Report SST-66-1, Battelle Memorial Institute, Columbus, Ohio, under Federal Aviation Agency Contract FA-SS-66-1 (1966) January.

32. J. C. Scully. Kinetic Features of Stress Corrosion Cracking. *Corrosion Science,* **7,** 197-207 (1967).

# Prepared Discussion

## Preferential Segregation of Hydrogen in Titanium Alloys

### N. A. Tiner
### McDonnell Douglas Corporation

I would like to comment on the reference made by W. K. Boyd on our work on the preferential segregation of hydrogen in titanium alloys and its possible role in stress corrosion cracking, which was sponsored by NASA Headquarters with R. H. Raring as Project Scientist. We have introduced hydrogen in amounts of less than 50 ppm in the radioactive isotope form—tritium—into the alloy samples by gas adsorption at elevated temperatures, and evaluated its distribution in the microstructure of the alloys by electron microautoradiography technique. Tritium is a beta emitter and its position in the metal is revealed by the development of silver filaments in the beta track sensitive emulsion replicas.

The microautoradiographs shown in Figures 1 and 2 clearly demonstrate the distribution of hydrogen in different titanium alloys. It was evenly distributed throughout the matrix of the all-beta alloy Ti-13V-11Cr-3Al (Figure 1a); in the all-alpha alloy Ti-5Al-2.5Sn hydrogen was segregated in the grain boundaries (Figure 1b); and in the alpha-beta alloys, Ti-8Al-1M-1V and Ti-6Al-4V, it was segregated in the beta phase (Figures 2a and 2b).

The recording efficiency of a microautoradiography, that is the ratio of the number of silver filaments to the tritium atoms, can be evaluated by determining the amount of silver filaments produced in a given emulsion exposed to a sample which contains known amounts of uniformly distributed tritium and by taking into account the energy

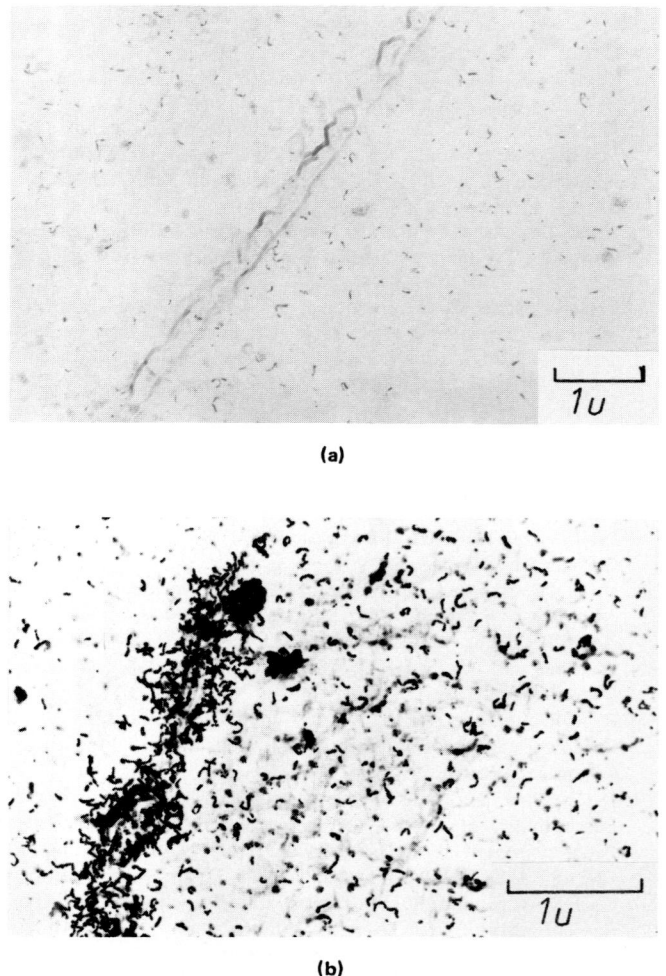

(a)

(b)

FIGURE 1 — Electron microautoradiographs illustrating distribution of tritium in (a) Ti-3Al-13V-11Cr and (b) Ti-5Al-2.5Sn alloys.

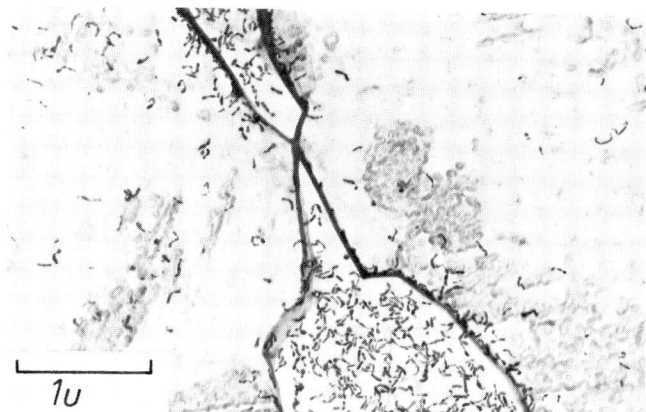

(a)

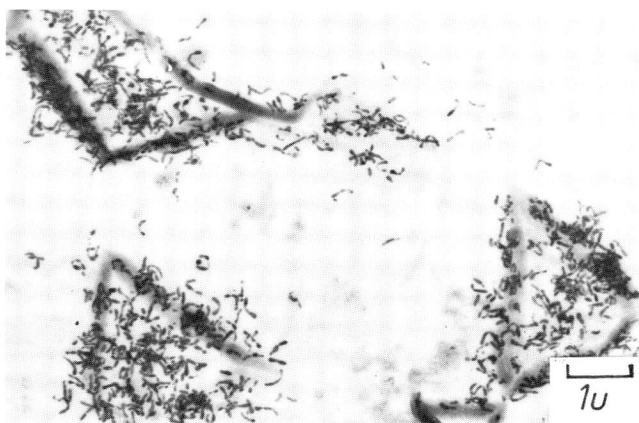

(b)

FIGURE 2 — Electron microautoradiographs illustrating concentration of tritium in the beta phase in alpha-beta alloys (a) Ti-8Al-1Mo-1V and (b) Ti-6Al-4V.

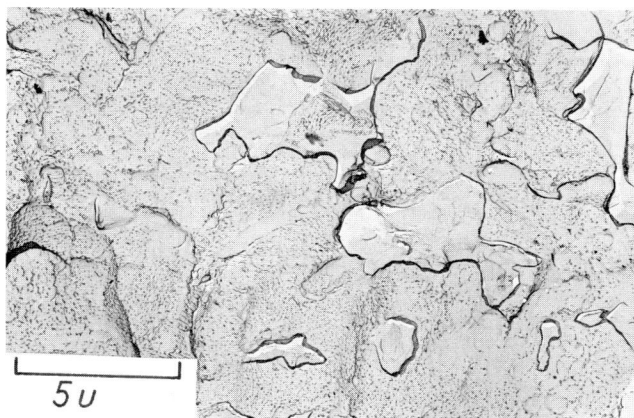

(a)

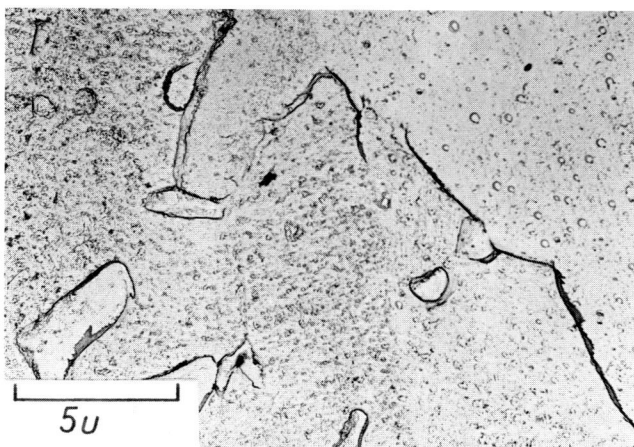

(b)

FIGURE 4 — Electron micrographs depicting the fracture behavior of beta particles in Ti-6Al-4V alloy fracture in aqueous salt solution. (a) Micro-fractograph of stress corrosion cracked face after etching in $HF-HNO_3-H_2O$ solution. (b) Fracture profile of stress corrosion cracking.

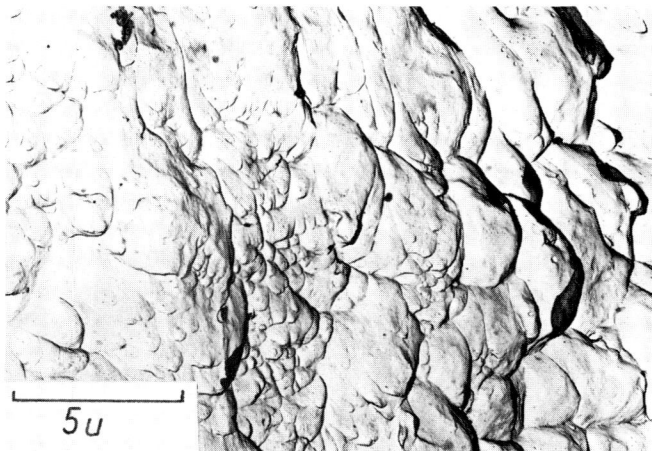

FIGURE 3 — Electron microfractograph of beta alloy Ti-13V-11Cr-3Al showing transgranular dimple rupture in air and aqueous salt solutions.

of the beta particles and the absorption coefficient of titanium. In the illustrated samples, it was found to be 18%. Using this value, it was estimated that the concentration of hydrogen in the segregated regions of the alloys examined was in the range of 300-500 ppm, relatively high.

We believe that the ability of beta particles to absorb and retain a high concentration of hydrogen in the alpha-beta or near-alpha alloys has a significant effect on the cracking behavior of these alloys under stress in air or in corrosive environments. An all beta phase with uniformly distributed low hydrogen content usually propagates cracks by microvoid coalescence or dimple formation (Figure 3). However, the concentration of hydrogen in the beta particles in alpha-beta alloys, causes these particles to fracture by cleavage as depicted by the cleavage markings noted in the beta particles on the etched fracture surface (Figure 4a), or by the manner the beta particles are oriented relative to the cracked surface profile (Figure 4b).

Preliminary studies made by electron microauto-radiography on alpha-beta alloys revealed no hydrogen segregation in the stress concentrated regions of a crack tip. Beta particles appeared to dissolve hydrogen and prevent its diffusion. We may, therefore, infer that any hydrogen, which may be produced by chemical or electrochemical process on a crack surface in an aqueous environment, is soaked up by the beta particles and if sufficient hydrogen concentration can be built up in these micro-regions, they become brittle. The crack tip does not blunt by slip, and the crack propagates by cleavage at an accelerated rate.

# ELECTROCHEMICAL ASPECTS OF TITANIUM STRESS CORROSION CRACKING

T. R. Beck
Boeing Scientific Research Laboratories

## Abstract

Notched tensile specimens of Ti:8%Al-1%Mo-1%V alloy were tested in air and in various electrolyte solutions under potentiostatic conditions. It was found that stress corrosion cracking of this alloy occurred only in the presence of three anions—chloride, bromide and iodide. The velocity of crack propagation was linearly related to the applied potential with an intercept at -900 mv versus SCE. The same line fit the data for chloride, bromide, and iodide solutions indicating that the same electrochemical mechanism controls the stress corrosion cracking velocity.

A quantitative model for the electrochemical kinetic and mass transport processes in a propagating stress corrosion crack has been developed. Kinetic data obtained for oxidation of and hydrogen ion reduction on newly generated Ti:8-1-1 surface were used in the model. Results of the calculations compared to experimental data for stress corrosion cracking of Ti:8-1-1 alloy indicate that there is a current of halide ions to the tip corresponding to the formation of a monolayer of adsorbed halide ions or titanium halide. The mechanism of propagation appears to be either a lowering of surface energy or electrochemical reaction at the crack tip with velocity controlled by mass transport.

## I. Introduction

In 1965 a research program to investigate the mechanism of stress corrosion cracking (SCC) of titanium alloys was initiated at the Boeing Scientific Research Laboratories. The pertinent electrochemical observations and theory developed to date will be summarized in this paper based on three previous papers.[1-3] M. J. Blackburn and J. C. Williams[4] describe the metallurgical aspects but it should be recognized that the respective processes are complimentary.

To set the stage for the discussion, Figure 1 shows an arbitrary conceptual division of regions, subject to study by the several disciplines involved, in and around a propagating stress corrosion crack. Linear elastic continuum mechanics can predict the stresses in the elastic region around a crack, and a considerable literature has been built up in this field.[5] Continuum plastic models can be applied to the plastic zone around the tip of a crack, but fewer analyses have appeared describing events in this field.[6] The analyses are further complicated by inhomogeneities in composition and structure at a scale larger than atomic which cause perturbations from the continuum approaches, such as stress concentrations at grain boundaries.[7] A continuum electrochemical model that appears to be consistent with our data will be described in this paper.

Events at the atomic scale are still in the realm of speculation. Because all observations on SCC are made at the macroscopic level, we believe that events at the macroscopic continuum level should be well understood before drawing firm conclusions on events at the atomic scale. There are, however, some interactions between the

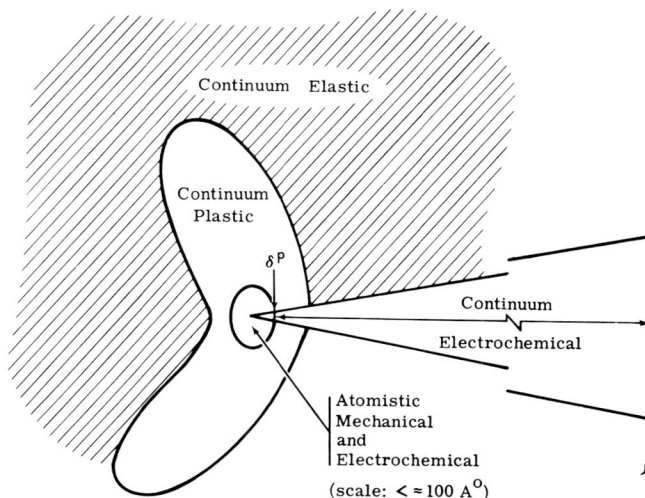

FIGURE 1 — Regions of study in and around a propagating SCC crack.

continuum electrochemical, elastic and plastic phenomena that can be explored.

The observations reported in this paper are based entirely on titanium: 8%Al-1%Mo-1%V alloy (Ti:8-1-1). The experiments were conducted in aqueous salt solutions using notched tensile specimens and potentiostatic control of potential. Stress corrosion cracking of Ti:8-1-1 is characterized by a very rapid transcrystalline cleavage type failure of the alpha phase.[4] The theoretical analysis is concerned with only quasi-steady-state crack propagation; initiation mechanisms are not considered here.

## II. Experimental

### A. SCC Tests

Titanium:8-1-1 in the mill annealed and duplex annealed condition was chosen as the alloy for initiating the program because it had been shown by prior investigators to be a commercially available titanium alloy very susceptible to SCC.[8]

Test specimens of this alloy were designed with small size and minimum cost so that large numbers of them could be used in evaluating environmental effects. They were 0.127 to 0.152 cm (50 to 60 mil) thick, 2.54 cm wide and 15 cm long. The specimens had one or two, 60-degree, 0.32 cm (1/8 in) deep 2.5 x 10$^{-3}$ cm (1 mil) root-radius notches. In the most recent tests, the single notched specimens were fatigue cracked. Some specimens were anodized to 70-80 volts in a one-normal sulfuric acid bath to minimize electrolytic reactions on the surface during testing. Specimens were tested in tension in a 10,000 kg Instron Model TT universal testing machine. Tests were conducted in air and in various electrolyte solutions at controlled potential in a Teflon cell equipped with a platinum counter electrode and salt bridge to a saturated calomel electrode. A Wenking Model 6379 TR potentiostat was used and electrical connection to the specimen was made through the wedge action jaws. Current flowing to the specimen was recorded versus time during the test using a Moseley x-y plotter. A window was provided in the cell for observing propagation of the crack on the surface of the specimens. Most of the tests were conducted in 0.6 molar salt solutions, corresponding to the total 3-1/2 percent salt content of sea water expressed as sodium chloride. All potentials are reported in millivolts with the saturated calomel electrode (SCE) as the zero standard of reference.

Velocity of crack propagation has been measured in two ways. First, an average velocity is available from many runs by dividing the measured SCC crack length by the time of SCC crack propagation, estimated from the SCC current versus time plots for the runs.[1] The second method was to differentiate the crack length versus time curve. The crack length versus time was determined by visually observing the progress of the crack tip as it passed ruled pencil lines on the surface of the specimens.

### B. Electrochemical Kinetics

Advantage was taken of rapid brittle failure of mill-annealed Ti:8-1-1 to obtain electrochemical kinetic data for newly generated surface as exists on the walls of a propagating stress corrosion crack.[2] Specimens were broken on the tensile machine under potentiostatic conditions in the same cell as used for the SCC tests. Current was plotted on a strip chart recorder. This technique was satisfactory for kinetics of formation of multi-layers of oxide, but not for the formation of the first layer of oxide because the current was too high for the potentiostat and the recorder response was too slow.

Kinetics of oxidation and of hydrogen ion reduction on new metal surface during the formation of the first monolayer of oxide were measured using a smaller Teflon cell of similar design. The double-notched mill-annealed Ti:8-1-1 specimens were 0.152 cm (0.060 in) thick and 0.32 cm (1/8 in) wide. A coating of epoxy resin was applied to the specimen to avoid reaction on the pre-existing surface. The resin was scored over the notch in the metal to localize the break in the resin and minimize adhesion failure and exposure of pre-existing titanium surface. A sudden break was caused by dropping a 100 lb weight connected through a lever arm to the specimen. Travel of the lever arm was limited so that the new fracture surfaces separated by about 2 mm. Movement of the lever arm closed a microswitch that triggered the sweep in the Tektronix type 545A oscilloscope. The Polaroid camera shutter was open on time exposure.

## III. Results

### A. Fracture Strength in Salt Solutions

Stress corrosion cracking of Ti:8-1-1 alloy in aqueous environments at room temperature has been found to be very specific to three anions; chloride, bromide and iodide, and to date no others. Other anions investigated were fluoride, hydroxide, sulfide, sulfate, nitrite, nitrate, perchlorate, cyanide and thiocyanate. Different alkali and alkaline earth cations had little effect on fracture strength or velocity within the limits of accuracy of the experiments. The SCC fracture load for notched and precracked specimens versus potential in neutral 0.6 M chloride, bromide and iodide solutions is given in Figure 2. The large number of experimental points is not shown for purpose of clarity. (The scatterband width is indicated in the left of Figure 2.) Precracked specimens give curves for strength versus potential of the same form as for notched specimens but the strength is considerably reduced in the region of susceptibility.

At potentials more negative than about -1000 mv, the specimens were cathodically protected in all solutions. Sodium fluoride solution and solutions of other non-SCC producing anions gave results at all potentials in the same scatterband as the air values. At potentials more positive than -1000 mv, SCC susceptibility in varying degrees occurs in chloride, bromide and iodide solutions. A region of anodic protection occurs in chloride and bromide solutions. It is possible to stop a propagating crack by switching the potential to either the anodic or cathodic protection zone.

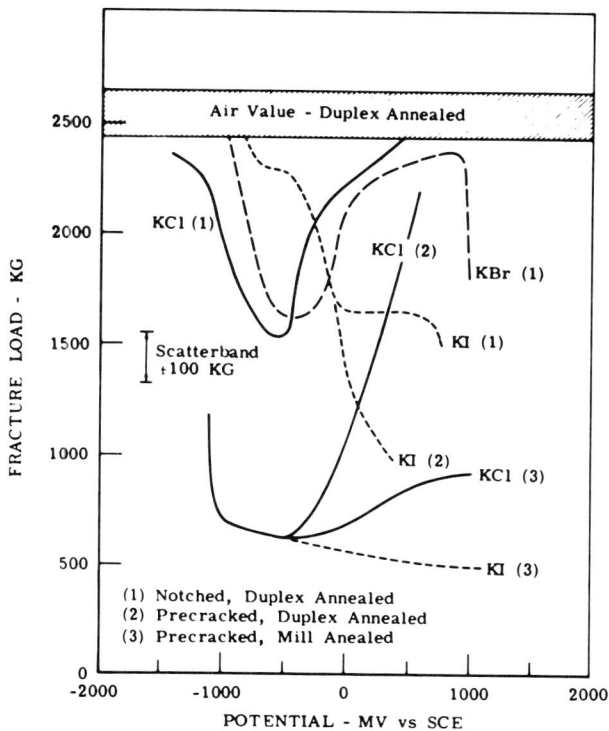

FIGURE 2 — Fracture load versus applied potential for Ti:8-1-1 in 0.6 M halide solutions.

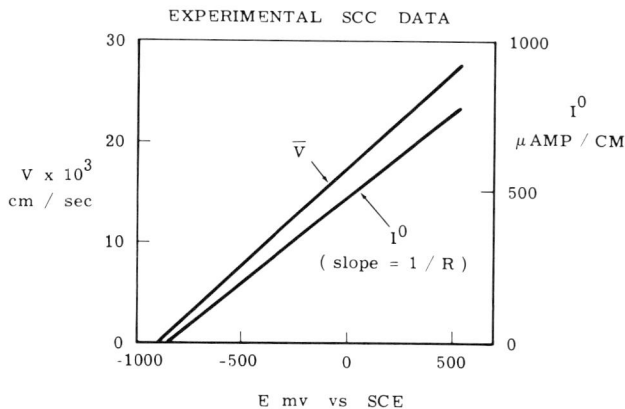

FIGURE 3 — Typical relation of velocity and initial SCC current to potential in 0.6 M halide solutions.

Pitting corrosion associated with a loss in strength was observed at +1000 mv in bromide solution and +2000 mv in chloride solution with the notched duplex-annealed specimens.

## B. Crack Propagation Velocity and Current

Crack propagation velocity was found to be linear with applied potential in 0.6 M chloride, bromide and iodide solutions. Typical data for those notched, duplex-annealed specimens represented in Figure 2 that failed below about 1800 kg load (i.e., where a significant amount of SCC occurred), are plotted in Figure 3.[1] The zero-velocity

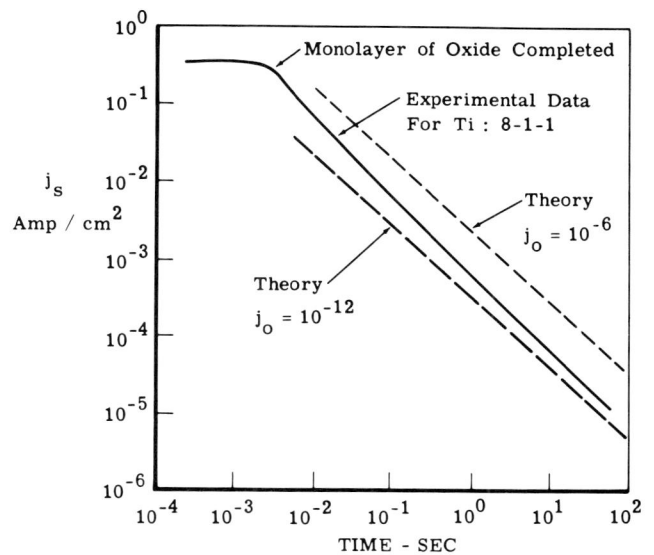

FIGURE 4 — Kinetic data for growth of oxide on Ti:8-1-1 alloy.

intercept of this line is at a potential of about -900 mv. Anodic current flowing into a propagating crack was also linearly related to potential with an intercept near -850 mv as shown. Further, the velocity could be changed at will or the crack stopped with a given specimen by adjusting the potential. This clearly demonstrated that the crack propagation velocity is controlled by electrochemistry.

## C. Electrochemical Kinetics

**1. Kinetics of Anodic Film Growth.** Results of the kinetic experiments using 2.54 cm wide, 0.152 cm thick, mill-annealed specimens are shown in Figure 4.[2] The curves were plotted from x-y records and oscilloscope data from the time of fracture. At a potential of zero volts to SCE applied to the titanium specimens, the 0.6 M chloride, bromide and iodide solutions gave essentially the same current versus time relationship. The initial, approximately horizontal, part of the curve corresponds to formation of about a monolayer of oxide ions. The charge density is $(3.5 \times 10^{-1}$ amp/cm$^2)(2.5 \times 10^{-3}$ sec$) = 880 \times 10^{-6}$ Cb/cm$^2$. Monolayer coverage of oxide ion gives about $425 \times 10^{-6}$ Cb/cm$^2$. The difference between these two values can be attributed to surface roughness and experimental error. Thereafter the current decays approximately with the reciprocal of time.

From the coincidence of the curves, the same oxidation mechanism appears to apply for the chloride, bromide, and iodide with the specimen at zero mv to SCE; the oxidation of titanium by water. The current versus time relation increases with increased positive potential in 0.6 M chloride as expected qualitatively from theory. Experiments with 0.6 M fluoride gave higher current densities, consistent with the known corrosiveness of fluoride to titanium.

The growth rate of an anodic oxide film starting from a

---

[1]Definitions of all symbols are given at the end of the paper.

607

molecular thickness is:[9]

$$\frac{dt}{d\tau} = A(j \cdot j_c) \quad (1)$$

and

$$j = j_o \exp\left(\frac{\beta \Delta \phi}{t}\right) \quad (2)$$

A solution of these equations may be obtained for a plane electrode under potentiostatic conditions ($\Delta\phi$ = constant) assuming that $j \gg j_c$ during the initial period of film growth:

$$d\tau = -\left(\frac{\beta \Delta \phi}{A j_o}\right) \frac{dI}{I^2 (\ln I)^2} \quad (3)$$

The solution to the right hand term containing I is tabled.[10] The bracketed constants on the right hand side can be estimated:

$$\beta \approx 6 \times 10^{-6} \text{ cm volt,}^{11} \quad A = M_o/zF\rho = 4.85$$
$$\text{cm}^3/\text{Cb for rutile, } j_o \approx 10^{-12} \text{ amp/cm}^2 \text{ for}$$
$$\text{titanium}^{11} \text{ and } \Delta\phi \approx \phi - \phi_e - \phi_f - \eta^9 \quad (4)$$

In neutral solution, $\phi_e$ for titanium oxidation is about -1.5 volts versus SCE.[12] Assuming the Flade potential is 0.5 volts[9] and neglecting the overpotential for the surface reaction, $\eta$, which becomes negligible as the film thickness increases, gives $\Delta\phi$ = 1.0 volt for an applied potential of 0 volts to SCE.

Equation (3) is plotted in Figure 4 using the above values. A second plot of Equation (3) using $j_o = 10^{-6}$ is also shown. The curves for the two values of $j_o$ bracket the experimental data for Ti:8-1-1.

**2. Kinetics of Oxidation and Hydrogen Ion Reduction on Newly Generated Bare Metal.** Preliminary kinetic experiments on newly generated surface with the small specimens were made in concentrated HCl because the electrochemical mass-transport-kinetic model (described in Section IV. A. 2.) indicated an increase in acid concentration in a propagating SCC crack. The experiments gave an anodic current at potentials more positive than about -900 to -800 mv and a cathodic current at more negative potentials. The anodic reaction was assumed to be formation of the first monolayer of oxide and the cathode reaction to be hydrogen ion discharge. Assuming Tafel slopes of 120 mv/decade(i.e., transfer coefficients of 0.5 and one-electron rate determining step) for each reaction the exchange current densities for the anodic and cathodic reactions would be on the order of $10^{-2}$ and $10^{-7}$ amp/cm$^2$, respectively. The anodic and cathodic current densities at the mixed potential for the new surface appeared to be on the order of $10^{-1}$ to 1 amp/cm$^2$. The results of these experiments suggested that the -850 mv intercept for the current in Figure 3 is the mixed potential for hydrogen ion discharge and formation of the first monolayer of oxide.

**3. Mixed Potential of New Surface.** Although the mixed potential for these two processes appeared to be about -900 to -800 mv in 12 M HCl solution, the IR drop in the electrolyte between the new surfaces and the Luggin

capillary tip at the high current densities observed threw some doubt into its precise value. To determine the mixed potential without IR drop, the potential just after fracture and exposure of new metal surface, was measured at open circuit with an oscilloscope. The input impedance was $10^6$ ohms so that the oscilloscope should have had little influence on an electrode with an initial current on the order of 5 ma ($10^{-1}$ amp/cm$^2$ current density) and a high conductivity electrolyte.

The initial potentials are plotted versus pH in Figure 5. The pH values were calculated assuming unit activity coefficient in all cases. A line with a slope of -59 mv per pH unit drawn through the experimental points appears to give a reasonable fit. This slope would be expected if the anodic and cathodic reactions have the same pH dependence for their reversible potentials and if the kinetic parameters are independent of pH. Oxidation of titanium by water (whatever the valence of the titanium in the oxide) and hydrogen ion reduction both have the same pH dependence for reversible potential. Kinetic parameters for hydrogen and oxygen formation are not usually significantly pH dependent.

## IV. Discussion

### A. Continuum Electrochemical Mass-Transport-Kinetic Model

**1. First Approximation: Constant Resistivity IR Drop Model.** The kinetic experiments suggested that the -850 mv current intercept in Figure 3 is the mixed potential for oxide formation and hydrogen ion reduction occurring near the tip of the crack. The difference between the applied potential and this mixed potential would then give the potential drop in the electrolyte in the crack. The rapid

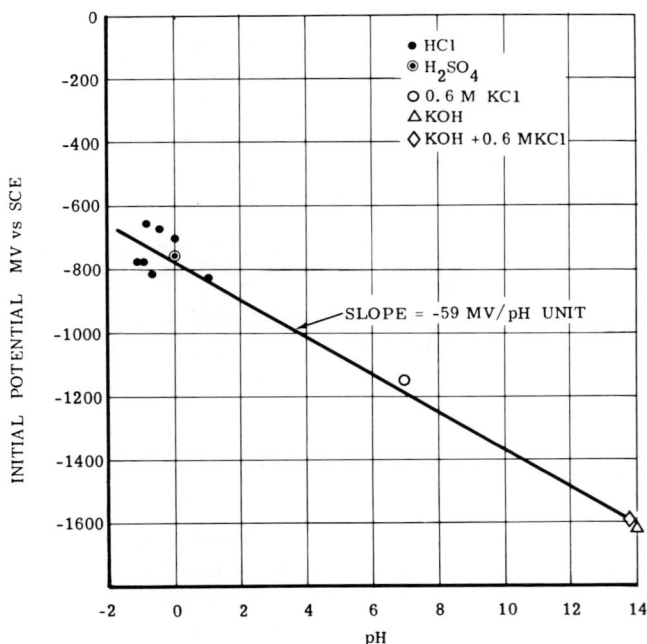

**FIGURE 5 – Initial open circuit potential versus pH.**

decay in current density with increased oxide thickness (Figure 4) further indicates that most of the current flows most of the way into the crack. The resistance of a constant-resistivity electrolyte in a uniform small-angle crack in a unit thickness specimen as pointed out by Hines[13] is:

$$R_e = \frac{\rho_e}{\gamma} \ln (\ell/\delta) \qquad (5)$$

The slope of the current versus potential curve in Figure 3 gives a resistance of about 2000 ohm for a unit thickness specimen. Assuming a bulk electrolyte resistivity of 20 ohm cm (for 0.6 M KCl solution) and a crack angle of 0.05 radians (3 degrees observed) requires that $\ln (\ell/\delta)$ be 5 or that $\ell/\delta$ be on the order of 100. This appeared to be a reasonable value assuming $\ell = 10^{-2}$ cm. i.e., about 1/10 the 0.12 cm (0.050 in) specimen thickness where appreciable current enters from the sides of the crack; and $\delta = 10^{-4}$ cm. The value of $\delta$ cannot be defined *a priori* with precision but it must certainly be larger than $10^{-6}$ to $10^{-5}$ cm from the geometric apex because this is the zone where the electrical double layers on the walls of the crack would intersect in a 3° crack. A finite time would be required for the first monolayer to form, so $\delta = 10^{-4}$ cm would appear to be the right order of magnitude.

The simple model also gave the right order of magnitude for total current. The current required to form the first monolayer on the two walls is:

$$I_M = 2 Q_o V_e . \qquad (6)$$

The current to build up multilayers of oxide is:

$$I_S = 2 \int_{\delta}^{\ell} j_s d_y . \qquad (7)$$

But from Figure 4:

$$j_s \approx \frac{K}{\tau} \qquad (8)$$

and the age of the surface at a point y distance from the geometric apex is:

$$\tau(y) = y/V_e \qquad (9)$$

Eliminating $j_s$ and $\tau$ from Equations (7), (8), and (9) gives

$$I_S = 2 K V_e \ln(\ell/\delta) \qquad (10)$$

The total current is therefore:

$$I = 2V_e [Q_o + K \ln (\ell/\delta)] \qquad (11)$$

Assuming $Q_o = 425 \times 10^{-6}$ Cb/cm² (one $O^=$ per titanium atom on the basal plane), $K \approx 10^{-3}$ Cb/cm² (experimental data, Figure 4), and $\ln (\ell/\delta) = 5$ (as from the calculation of resistance), gives $\Delta I/\Delta V \approx 10.8 \times 10^{-3}$ Cb/cm² compared to about $30 \times 10^{-3}$ Cb/cm² from Figure 3.

The simple model, although it gave order of magnitude agreement with experiment was deficient in several respects

such as it neglected the effect of potential gradient on kinetics of oxidation and the effects of changes in electrolyte concentration in the crack on resistance. It was also assumed that the velocity and current intercepts were at the same potential in Figure 3, whereas it was found that a cathodic current was required in experiments in order to stop a crack. Therefore a more rigorous analysis was formulated, which is described below.

**2. Mass-Transport-Kinetic (M-T-K) Model.** Figure 6 shows the more rigorous mass-transport-kinetic model of the propagating SCC and definitions of some of the terms.[3] There is a uniform small-angle crack with angle, $\gamma$, propagating at the velocity, $V_e$, through the material. A moving set of coordinates was chosen with the zero at the geometric apex of the crack. (Note: the actual crack tip is displaced from the geometric apex by the distance, $\delta^t$ due to its curvature.) This system has the advantage that the wedge of electrolyte can be considered to be in plug flow moving with the apex at a velocity $V_e$ and a quasi-steady-state approximation can be made. The convection term in the mass-transport equations was therefore neglected in the one-dimensional treatment employed.

The lower boundary of the continuum mass-transport model was assumed to be $\delta^P$ where the two electrical double layers on the walls intersect. From $\delta^P$ to $\delta$ there is a zone in which the first monolayer of oxide is formed on the walls. From $\delta$ to $\ell$ multilayers of oxide are formed. At point y from the geometric apex there is a surface current density for oxidation, $j_s$, and a potential in the electrolyte, $\Phi$. The potential was nondimensionalized by F/RT and referenced to the potential at $\delta^P$. There is a concentration in the electrolyte, C, and a current density in the cross section of the crack, i, which is related to the fluxes of the various ions, N. There are no gradients across the crack in this one-dimensional model.

There is one equation for $j_s$ in the region $\delta^P$ to $\delta$ where bare metal is oxidized, and another equation for $j_s$ in the region $\delta$ to $\ell$ where multilayers of oxide are forming. The boundary conditions are: at $\delta^P$, $\Phi = 0$ and $I^P$ equals the tip current; and at $y = \delta$, the oxide coverage, $\theta$, is unity. The problem is solved by the Runge-Cutta-Gill numerical integration procedure implemented on a digital computer, iterating until the concentration at $\ell$ converges to the bulk concentration. Calculations give the concentration at the tip and the potential and current density at $\ell$.

The system of equations used in the model is given in Table 1. It is beyond the scope of this paper to explain all

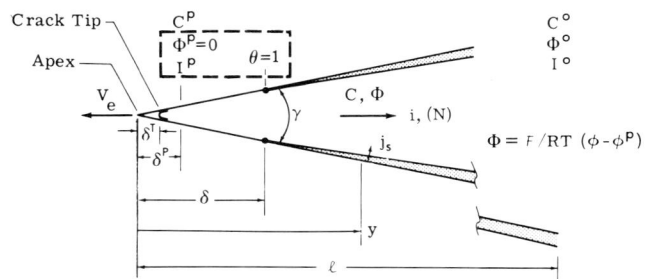

**FIGURE 6 — Mass-transport-kinetic model for SCC.**

**TABLE 1—System of Equations Used in Mass-Transport-Kinetic Model**

| | | |
|---|---|---|
| Flux Equations (14): | $N = -D \dfrac{dC}{dy} - z\,D\,C\,\dfrac{d\Phi}{dy}$ | Equation 12 |
| Electroneutrality: | $\Sigma\, z\,C = 0$ | Equation 13 |
| Relation of current density and fluxes: | $i = F\,\Sigma z\,N$ | Equation 14 |
| Relation of total current to current density: | $I = i\,\gamma\,y$ | Equation 15 |
| Mass Balance: | $dI = \gamma(i\,dy + y\,di) = 2\,j\,dy$ | Equation 16 |
| Kinetic Equations: | $j = j_s - j_H$ | Equation 17 |

$$@\ \delta \leqslant y \leqslant \ell,\ j_s = j_o \exp\left\{ \frac{B(\Phi - \Phi_e - \Phi_f - X)}{\dfrac{A}{V_e}\displaystyle\int_{\delta^p}^{y} j_s\,dy} \right\} \qquad \text{Equation 18}$$

$$j_H = 0$$

$$@\ \delta^p \leqslant y \leqslant \delta,\ j_s = i_m (1-\phi)\exp\left\{\frac{n}{2}(\Phi - \Phi_e)\right\} + j_o\,\phi\exp\left\{ \frac{B(\Phi - \Phi_e - \Phi_f - X)}{t_o} \right\}$$

$$\text{Equation 19}$$

$$j_H = j_H(i - \phi)\exp\left\{\tfrac{1}{2}(\Phi - \Phi_H)\right\} \qquad \text{Equation 20}$$

| | | |
|---|---|---|
| Definition of Surface Overpotential, X: | $j_s = i_o\,2\sinh\left\{\dfrac{n'}{2}\,X\right\}$ | Equation 21 |
| Definition of $\phi$: | $\phi = \dfrac{1}{Q_o V}\displaystyle\int_{\delta^p}^{y} j_s\,dy$ | Equation 22 |

of the equations (the model is described fully in Reference 3), but a few comments are required. It is assumed that the only wall reactions are oxidation of titanium by water and hydrogen ion reduction. Therefore the alkali metal cation from the bulk solution is not reacted and its current is zero at all positions in the crack. The halide was assumed to be not involved in the wall reactions but may be involved at the crack tip so its current is zero or a constant. The hydrogen ion current varies with position and depends on the rates of the wall reactions.

Values of the parameters used in the solution are given in Table 2. All of the parameters except $\gamma$, $\delta^p$ and $\ell$ came from sources independent of the SCC experiments. The diffusivities are approximate values. The angle, $\gamma$, is the approximate macroscopic value observed on the surface of specimens with propagating cracks. The exchange current densities are order of magnitude values estimated from the electrochemical kinetics experiments. The value of B in the high-field conduction equation came from Johansen et al.[11] The value of A was calculated from the density of bulk rutile. The reversible potentials for oxidation and hydrogen ion reduction were from Latimer,[12] converted to the SCE scale, and nondimensionalized. The charge density of a monolayer of oxide is based on one oxide ion per

titanium atom in the basal plane. The value of $\delta^p$ is based on the minimum double layer thickness of 2.5 Å on each wall and the angle of 0.05 radians. The value of $\ell$ is 1/10 of a unit thickness specimen.

The first calculations were made before the kinetic data for hydrogen ion reduction on bare metal were available and $i_H$ was assumed zero. The potential of the tip was assumed to be -900 mv or 35 in dimensionless form. The tip current, being unknown, was assumed to be zero. A typical velocity of $10^{-2}$ cm/sec was chosen for the initial calculation. The experimental values of current and potential from Figure 3 for this velocity are respectively about $200\ \mu A/cm$ and -400 mv or -20 in dimensionless form referenced to the tip potential.

Results of the initial calculation are given in Table 3. Of the kinetic parameters used in the calculations, $j_o$ had the dominant effect and the lower and upper bound levels of $10^{-12}$ and $10^{-6}$ amps/cm$^2$ from Figure 4 were used. A $10^6$ fold variation of $j_o$ gives only a four-fold change in the current and about a two-fold change in the potential. The reason for this is that the higher the value of $j_o$ the faster a resistive oxide layer is built up thus limiting the current. Also the faster the oxide layer is formed the greater the rate of generation of hydrogen ion and the higher the con-

**TABLE 2—Values of Parameters Used in Mass-Transport-Kinetic Model**

$D_+$ = 1 x $10^{-5}$ cm²/sec

$D_-$ = 1 x $10^{-5}$ cm²/sec

$D_H$ = 6 x $10^{-5}$ cm²/sec

$z_+$ = +1

$z_-$ = -1

$z_H$ = +1

$\gamma$ = 0.05 radians (3 degrees)

$i_H$ = 2 x $10^{-8}$ amp/cm² (or zero)

$i_m$ = 2 x $10^{-3}$ amp/cm²

$i_o$ = 2 x $10^{-3}$ amp/cm²

$j_o$ = $10^{-12}$ to $10^{-6}$ amp/cm²

$n$ = -1

$n'$ = 1

$B$ = (6 x $10^{-6}$ cm/volt)/(F/RT)

$A$ = 4.85 x $10^{-5}$ cm³/Cb

$\Phi_e$ = 40 (dimensionless equilibrium potential)

$\Phi_H$ = 7 (dimensionless equilibrium potential)

$Q_o$ = 425 x $10^{-6}$ Cb/cm²

$\delta^p$ = $10^{-6}$ cm

$\ell$ = $10^{-1}$ cm

**TABLE 3—Initial Results**

For $V_e$- $10^{-2}$ cm/sec, ($i_H$ = 0 and $I^P$ = 0 in calc.)

| | $j_o$-amp/cm² | $I^o$ – $\mu A/cm$ | $\Phi^o$ |
|---|---|---|---|
| Exp. | – | 200 | -20 |
| Calc. | $10^{-12}$ | 30 | -0.5 |
| | $10^{-6}$ | 120 | -1.0 |

**TABLE 4—Results with Inclusion of Hydrogen Ion Discharge Mechanism and Limiting Tip Current**

Conditions:

$V_e$ = $10^{-2}$ cm/sec
$i_H$ = 2 x $10^{-8}$ amp/cm²
$j_o$ = $10^{-8}$ amp/cm²

Results:

$I^o$ = 27 $\mu A/cm$
$I^p$ = 7.2 $\mu A/cm$
$\Phi^o$ = -4.6
$C_-^p/C_-^o$ = $10^{-3}$

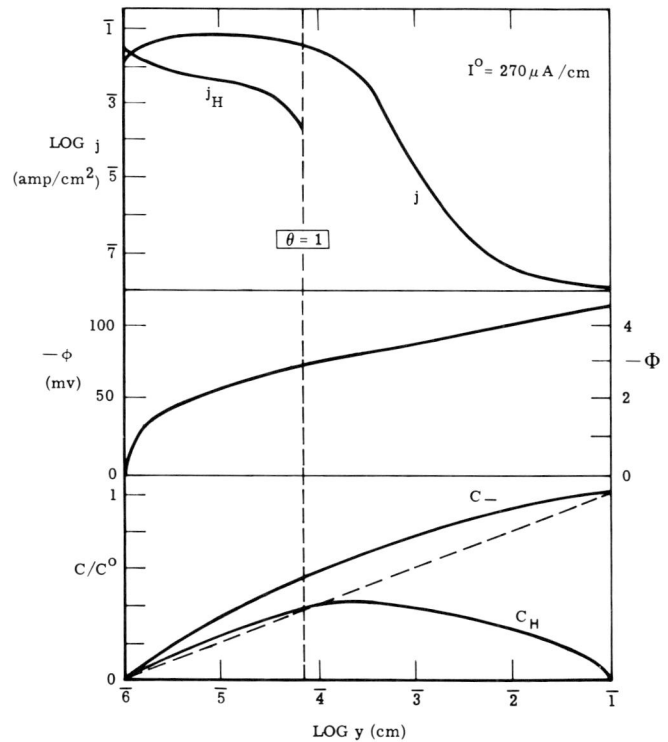

FIGURE 7 — Calculated current density, potential and concentration as a function of position in a propagating stress corrosion crack.

ductivity of the electrolyte and therefore the relatively smaller increase in potential. Calculated currents approach the same order of magnitude as obtained by experiment, but the potential is at least twenty-fold too low. The reason for this is that the hydrogen ion carries most of the current in the model and hydrogen ion concentration increases toward the tip. On the first iteration of the calculations using constant bulk solution resistivity the computer solution like the IR drop model gave about the same potential as the experiment, but where the concentration was allowed to build up and hydrogen ion carried the current the potential was too low.

At this point it became apparent that a lower conductivity must be obtained in the crack in order to obtain potentials compatible with experimental results. The only feasible way to accomplish this appeared to be to have a mass transport limiting current density at $\delta^p$ such that the concentration at $\delta^p$ would become small. By trial and error it was found that a tip current of 7.2 $\mu amp/cm$ was close to the value of the limiting current, as it gave a concentration of halide ion at $\delta^p$ one-thousandth that of the bulk solution. Results are shown in Table 4 and plots of flux, potential and concentration versus position in the crack are shown in Figure 7. The potential is approaching the right

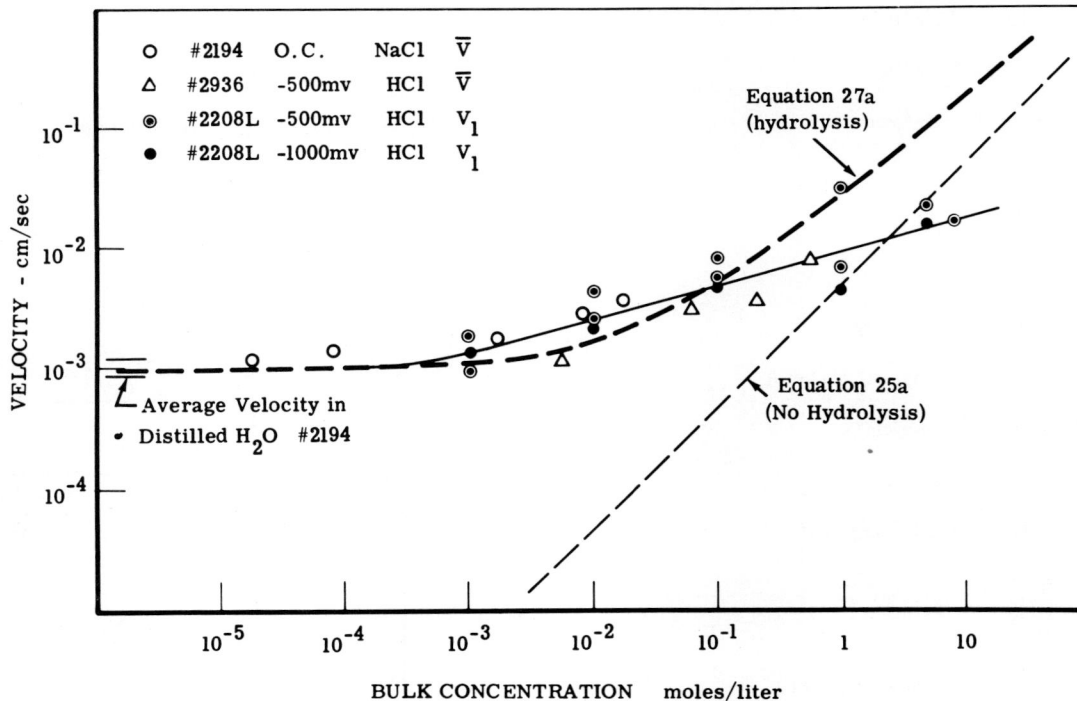

FIGURE 8 — Correlation of crack propagation velocity with halide ion concentration.

order of magnitude and can be increased further by approaching the limiting mass transport rate more closely thus giving a lower concentration at $\delta^p$.

Two further experimental facts might be mentioned that are consistent with the results of the M-T-K model. On suddenly changing to open-circuit conditions, the potential decays to the mixed potential over an interval of $10^{-2}$ to 10 seconds. This is consistent with a change in a mass transport process. SCC velocity experiments conducted over a range of temperatures from 0 C to 70 C gave an activation energy of about 3.5 Kcal, again consistent with a mass transport limited process.

**3. Simple Hydrolysis Model.** There are a number of reasons for suspecting that hydrolysis of the initially formed titanium halide occurs in the crack. In this section a simple mass transport model including hydrolysis of titanium halide is described.

It is instructive to first calculate velocity for the limiting case of a mass-transport-controlled velocity with no hydrolysis or wall reactions. This case is represented by the dashed line in the concentration plot in Figure 7. It can be readily shown that for a small, constant-angle crack in a unit-thickness specimen and for constant diffusivity that:

$$C_-^\circ = \frac{I_-}{z_- D_- \gamma} \ln\left(\frac{\ell}{\delta^p}\right) \qquad (23)$$

Assuming that a monolayer of titanium halide is formed on each wall, the tip current can be related to velocity by:

$$I_- = 2n\, Q_x V_e \qquad (24)$$

Eliminating $I_-$ gives:

$$V_e = \frac{z_- F D_- \gamma C_-^\circ}{2n\, Q_x \ln\left(\frac{\ell}{\delta^p}\right)} \qquad (25)$$

Equation (25) is plotted in Figure 8 and compared to a collection of experimental velocity versus concentration data. Values of the terms used in Equation (25) are given in Table 5. The data were taken on three different sheets, at three potentials and with NaCl and HCl electrolytes. Both initial and average velocities are included as sometimes one was more convenient than the other to measure. The data are somewhat scattered as expected from the variety of conditions but nevertheless show significant trends. The velocity is not linearly related to concentration as predicted from Equation (25), but varies approximately as the 0.27 power over about four decades of concentration. At low concentration, the velocity does not approach zero, but becomes asymptotic to the velocity observed in distilled water.

If it is accepted that a halide mechanism occurs at the crack tip to cause crack propagation, it is mandatory that the halide ion is conserved within the crack in distilled

612

TABLE 5–Constants Used in Equations 25 and 27
for Plots in Figure 8

| | |
|---|---|
| $z_-$ | $= 1$ equiv/mole |
| $F$ | $= 96,500$ Cb/equiv |
| $D_-$ | $= 1 \times 10^{-5}$ cm²/sec |
| $\gamma$ | $= 0.05$ |
| $n$ | $= 1$ |
| $Q_x$ | $= 425 \times 10^{-6}$ Cb/cm² |
| $\ell$ | $= 10^{-1}$ cm |
| $\delta^p$ | $= 10^{-6}$ cm |
| $V_e^s$ | $= 10^{-3}$ cm/sec |

| | | |
|---|---|---|
| $V_e = 5.0\, C_-^{\,\circ}$ cm/sec where $C_-^{\,\circ}$ is in mole/cm³ | | Equation 25a |
| $C_-^{\,\circ} = 1.18 \times 10^{-2}\, V_e \ell n\,(V_e \times 10^3)$ | | Equation 27a |

water because there is no source of comparable magnitude to the tip current. In other words, hydrolysis of titanium halide or displacement of adsorbed halide ions must occur. Chloride ion can be gathered from the content in the metal as new metal surface is exposed, but this amount is insufficient to cause cracking unless it is allowed to accumulate in the electrolyte in the tip zone. For example, it can be calculated that to accumulate a monolayer on both walls of the tip zone of $10^{-6}$ cm length would require exposing about $10^{-1}$ cm length of new surface if there were ten parts per million atomic of chloride in the metal and chloride were removed only from the surface layer.

Inclusion of titanium halide hydrolysis in the rigorous mass-transport-kinetic model entailed additional complexity and required hydrolysis rate constants with unknown value. It was therefore decided to test the hydrolysis concept in a much simplified model before altering the more rigorous model. The following assumptions were made:

(1) A uniform, small-angle crack propagates at a velocity, $V_e$, through a unit-thickness specimen.

(2) The environment is a hydrogen halide solution, i.e., only $H^+$ and $X^-$ ions are present and their diffusivities are constant.

(3) The reaction at the tip is: $Ti + 2X^- \rightarrow TiX_2 + 2e$ with a current $I = 2n\, Q_x V_e$.

(4) The $TiX_2$ remains adsorbed on the surface to the position, $\delta^h$, where hydrolysis occurs and goes to completion:

$$TiX_2 + 2H_2O \rightarrow TiO_2 + 2X^- + 4H^+ + 2e$$

(5) No further oxidation of titanium or hydrogen ion reduction occur in the crack. Therefore, from $\delta^h$ to $\delta^p$ there is a constant current of halide ions, $I_- = 2n\, Q_x V_e$ and from $\delta^h$ to $\ell$ there is a constant current of hydrogen ions, $I_H = 4n\, Q_x V_e$. This last assumption is probably the weakest

link but it is justified on the basis that it makes a simple analysis possible (continued oxidation with formation of multilayers of oxide generates considerably more $H^+$).

(6) A constant time for hydrolysis is assumed such that

$$\delta^h = \delta^{hs}\, \frac{V_e}{V_e^s} \qquad (26)$$

where the superscript, s, refers to the condition in pure water where the bulk concentration $C^\circ = 0$.

Using these assumptions and solving the mass transport equations gives:

$$C_-^{\,\circ} = \frac{2n\,(1 + \frac{D_H}{2D_-})Q_x}{F\,\gamma\,D_H}\, V_e \ln \frac{V_e}{V_e^s} \qquad (27)$$

It turned out that this relationship of velocity to concentration is independent of the values of $\delta^p$ and $\ell$ chosen.

Equation (27) is plotted in Figure 8 using the constants shown in Table 5. Equation (27) appears to have the right form as compared to the experimental data but it gives velocities too high in concentrated solutions. The fit is close enough, however, to warrant adding the hydrolysis step to the more rigorous mass-transport-kinetic model; currently underway.

### B. Implications of M-T-K Model

**1. Significance of Halide Ion Tip Current.** The halide ion tip current goes either to charge the electrical double layer or to an electrochemical reaction consuming halide ions within the tip zone (i.e., @ $y < \delta^p$). The limiting tip current corresponds to the order of magnitude for one monolayer of adsorbed halide ions or of titanium dihalide, the thermodynamically stable form at the tip potential.[12] The tip current can be defined as: $I^p = 2n\, Q_x V_e$. For $I^p = 7.2\ \mu$Amp/cm, $Q_x = 425\ \mu$Amp/cm² (for dihalide) and $V = 10^{-2}$ cm-sec; $n = 0.85$ of a monolayer.

In the SCC mechanism, the hydrolysis must occur on the walls of the crack. The hydrolyzable covalent tetrachloride would not form at the tip potential and if the dihalide were to go into solution it would ionize and titanium ions would conduct current from the tip zone. With complete ionization, there would be no flux of halide ions required. The concentration of titanium halide in solution would increase toward the crack tip and the high polarization could not be obtained with the mass-transport-kinetic model.

Further, if hydrolysis of titanium halides occurred in solution, there should be a considerable difference in velocity with the different halides. The SCC velocity, as a function of potential, appears to be relatively independent of whether the environment has chloride, bromide or iodide ions, again pointing to a wall reaction.

It is not certain, however, that a true compound is formed as the halide ion may be adsorbed, with the tip current of halide ions being the double-layer charging current. The regeneration of halide ions in solution would be by a displacement by oxide rather than a hydrolysis in this case. The rate of displacement by oxide could be less sensitive to the particular halide ion than the rate of surface hydrolysis of the dihalide. The mass-transport-kinetic model gives a value of 0.85 for n in Equation (24). The dihalide would give a value of one and halide ions adsorbed one-to-one on the surface titanium atoms would give a value of 0.5 for the value of $Q_x = 425 \, \mu\text{Amp/cm}^2$ used. A more careful analysis will be required to distinguish between dihalide and adsorbed halide ion.

**2. Exclusion of Hydride Mechanism.** The rate of hydrogen ion discharge within the zone $\delta^t < y < \delta^p$ is small because if the hydrogen ion current were of comparable value to the halide ion current there would be no potential gradient. This would appear to exclude the hydride mechanism.

It can also be demonstrated that the crack tip "outruns" diffusion through the metal of hydrogen from discharge in the zone, $\delta^p < y < \delta$. A simplified model for which results can be readily calculated will be used. Consider that the metal specimen is divided into thin sheets conductive to hydrogen separated by infinitesimally thin nonconducting membranes. The sheets, $\Delta y$ in thickness, are normal to the planes of the new surface and parallel to the crack front. Unsteady-state diffusion at a constant surface flux is assumed (ignoring the decrease due to increase in $\theta$ and potential) at the edge of each of these sheets, starting at time of formation of the fracture edge. The age of the fracture edge is; $\tau(y) = y/V$ (Equation 9). The concentration of hydrogen at the surface, y distance from the geometric apex for a constant surface flux, by analogy to heat transfer is:[15]

$$C_{x=0} = 1.13 \, \frac{N_{x=0}}{D_H} \, \sqrt{D_H \, \tau(y)} \qquad (28)$$

where x is the distance into the sheets from the fracture edge. Assuming the upper limit for current density of one amp/cm²:

$$N_{x=0} = \frac{i}{zF} \approx 10^{-5} \, \text{mole/cm}^2 \, \text{sec.}$$

The diffusivity of hydrogen in titanium at room temperature was not found, so a value recently determined for hydrogen in iron of about $10^{-5} \, \text{cm}^2/\text{sec}$[16] will be used. The age of the surface at a distance of $\delta^p = 10^{-6}$ cm and for a velocity of $10^{-2}$ cm/sec, is $\tau(\delta^p) = 10^{-4}$ sec. The age of the surface at $\delta = 10^{-4}$ cm (where $\phi = 1$ in Figure 7) for the same velocity is $\tau(\delta) = 10^{-2}$ sec. Putting these values of $\tau(y)$ in Equation (28) gives $C_{x=0}^{\delta^p} \approx 3 \times 10^{-5}$ mole/cm³ and $C_{x=0}^{\delta} \approx 3 \times 10^{-4}$ mole/cm³. Converting to mole fraction of hydrogen in titanium gives $M_H^{\delta^p} \approx (3 \times 10^{-5})/(4.5/47) \approx 3 \times 10^{-4}$ and $M_H^{\delta} \approx 3 \times 10^{-3}$.

The hydrogen concentration is maximum at the surface (x = 0) in this model and decreases rapidly going into the metal. Furthermore, a maximum and constant value of $j_H$ was chosen (a rapid decrease is shown in Figure 7) and a finite time for hydrogen ion discharge at $\delta^p$ (the M-T-K model indicates no H⁺ discharge at $y < \delta^p$, therefore $\tau(\delta^p) = 0$). In spite of using the most favorable conditions to

produce a maximum hydrogen concentration, the mole fraction appears to be at least two orders of magnitude too low on the surface at $10^{-6}$ to $10^{-4}$ cm from the apex and must decrease toward the tip. The hydride mechanism for SCC therefore appears very unlikely for Ti:8-1-1 under the conditions of our experiments.

**3. Exclusion of Oxide Wedging Mechanism.** Using the calculated current density distribution shown in Figure 7 it can readily be shown that the oxide thickness on the walls is always considerably less than the crack width of a uniform 3 degree crack. The oxide wedging mechanism would only be possible if there is a considerable deviation in the crack angle or error in the kinetic data. In other words, the crack width also "outruns" the oxide growth.

### C. Unresolved Electrochemical Questions

While the electrochemical mass-transport-kinetic model and the simple hydrolysis model appear to be consistent with experimental data, a number of questions remain to be resolved. Some of these questions can probably be answered at the continuum level; others may require understanding at the atomic level. A few of the outstanding questions will be briefly outlined here. Work is currently underway in our laboratory to resolve these.

**1. Why do Only Chloride, Bromide and Iodide Ions Cause SCC of Ti:8-1-1?** This may be because most anions can be readily incorporated in the oxide on the walls of the crack and never reach the crack tip. Chloride, bromide and iodide ions, being relatively large compared to the oxide ion (and containing no oxygen) may not be so readily incorporated in the titanium oxide lattice. On the other hand, the differences may be related to surface properties at the atomic scale.

**2. What Causes the Anodic Protection Zone in Chloride Solutions?** This may be directly related to the first question in that chloride may more readily be incorporated in titanium oxide at higher anodic potentials. Radiotracer experiments are presently underway to test this hypothesis.

**3. Could SCC in Distilled Water be Due to the Water Itself?** Although SCC in distilled water is consistent with the hydrolysis model, assuming that the initial chloride is extracted from the metal, it has not been definitely proven that water alone does not cause SCC. It is intended to obtain some chloride-free metal to resolve this question.

**4. What is the Mechanism of SCC Initiation?** Although a quantitative model has been developed for a quasi-steady-state crack propagation, a model for initiation has not been developed.

### V. Conclusions

1. Experiments thus far conducted indicate that chloride, bromide and iodide ions are the unique stress corrosion cracking agents for Ti:8-1-1 alloy in aqueous solution.

2. Fracture strength and velocity of crack propagation in these media are controlled by applied potential; there-

fore an electrochemical mechanism is involved in the rate determining step.

3. Electrochemical kinetic data have been obtained for oxidation of, and hydrogen ion reduction on, newly generated Ti:8-1-1 alloy surface.

4. A continuum electrochemical mass-transport-kinetic model has been formulated. Employing the independently determined electrochemical kinetics data together with the assumption of SCC velocity limited by halide ion mass transport, can give calculated potentials and currents consistent with experimental SCC data.

5. The magnitude of the calculated halide ion tip current corresponds to approximately a monolayer of titanium dihalide or adsorbed halide ions formed at the tip of a propagating stress corrosion crack. The hydride and oxide wedging mechanisms appear to be excluded in the SCC of Ti:8-1-1 alloy under the conditions of the experiments described herein.

6. Variation of SCC velocity with chloride concentration indicates hydrolysis of the initially formed titanium halide or displacement of adsorbed halide in the crack. An equation derived for a simple hydrolysis model approximately fits the concentration data.

## VI. Nomenclature

$A$ = $M_o/zF\rho$ cm$^3$/Cb for rutile

$B$ = constant in high field equation (nondimensionalized in respect to potential)

$C$ = concentration, mole/cm$^3$

$C^o$ = bulk concentration

$C^p$ = concentration at $\delta^p$

$D$ = diffusivity, cm$^2$/sec

$F$ = Faraday, 96,500 Cb/equiv, or 23,060 cal/volt equiv

$I$ = $j/j_o$ nondimensionalized current density

$I$ = current along axis of crack in unit width specimen, amp/cm

$i$ = current density in cross section of crack, amp/cm$^2$

$j$ = current density, amp/cm$^2$

$K$ = a constant

$\ell$ = crack length to position where current enters from sides, cm

$M$ = molecular weight, gm/mole

$M$ = mole fraction, dimensionless

$N$ = flux, mole/cm$^2$ sec

$n$ = number of electrons in rate determining step

$n$ = number of monolayers

$Q$ = charge density of surface species, Cb/cm$^2$, $Q_o$ for oxide, $Q_x$ for halide

$R$ = gas content, 1.987 cal/deg mole

$R_e$ = resistance, ohms

$T$ = temperature, °K

$t$ = thickness, cm

$t_o$ = thickness of first monolayer of oxide, cm

$V_e$ = electrochemically controlled crack propagation velocity, cm/sec

$X$ = overpotential, nondimensionalized

$x$ = distance into metal normal to fracture surface, cm

$y$ = distance from apex of crack, cm

$z$ = equiv/mole

$\beta$ = constant in high field equation, cm/volt

$\gamma$ = crack angle, radians

$\delta$ = distance from crack apex to position where monolayer of oxide is complete, cm

$\delta^p$ = distance from crack apex to position where electrical double layers intersect, cm

$\delta^t$ = distance from apex to crack tip, cm

$\eta$ = overpotential, volts or mv

$\phi$ = oxide coverage, dimensionless

$\rho$ = density, gm/mole

$\rho_e$ = resistivity, ohm cm

$\tau$ = time, sec

$\phi$ = potential, volts or mv

$\Phi$ = $F/RT\,\phi$, dimensionless potential

### Subscripts

$+$ = cation

$-$ = halide ion

$c$ = corrosion

$d$ = ductile

$e$ = equilibrium potential

$e$ = electrochemically controlled velocity

$f$ = Flade potential

$H$ = hydrogen ion

$M$ = monolayer of oxide

$m$ = metal (exchange current density for oxide on metal)

$o$ = oxide (exchange current density for oxide on oxide)

$o$ = exchange current density

$s$ = surface

$x$ = halide

### Superscripts

$h$ = position in crack where hydrolysis occurs

$o$ = bulk

$p$ = position in crack where double layers intersect

$s$ = pure solvent

$t$ = crack tip

## Acknowledgment

The author is indebted to Dr. M. J. Blackburn for considerable cooperation in the design, execution and analysis of the SCC experiments and to Professor E. A. Grens, II of Berkeley for his contributions to the rigorous development of the electrochemical mass-transport-kinetic model.

This effort was partially supported by NASA/ Headquarters contract NAS7-489.

# VII. References

1. T. R. Beck. Stress Corrosion Cracking of Titanium Alloys, I. Ti:8-1-1 Alloy in Aqueous Solutions. *Journal of the Electrochemical Society,* **114,** 551 (1967).
2. T. R. Beck. Stress Corrosion Cracking of Titanium Alloys, II. An Electrochemical Mechanism. *Journal of the Electrochemical Society,* **115,** 890 (1968).
3. T. R. Beck and E. A. Grens II. Analysis of Current Density Distribution in a Propagating Stress Corrosion Crack. Presented to The Electrochemical Society, Dallas, Texas, May, 1967.
4. M. J. Blackburn and J. C. Williams. Aspects of Metallurgical Structure in Cracking. This conference.
5. e.g., P. C. Paris and G. C. Sih. *Fracture Toughness Testing and Its Applications.* Special Technical Publication 381, ASTM, 1965.
6. e.g., F. A. McClintock and G. R. Irwin. *Fracture Toughness Testing and Its Applications.* Special Technical Publication 381, ASTM, 1965.
7. C. Zener. *Trans. ASM,* **A40,** 3 (1948).
8. B. F. Brown. ASTM Annual Meeting, Lafayette, Ind., June 13-18, 1965.
9. K. S. Vetter. *Electrochemical Kinetics.* (Translation) Academic Press, New York, 1967.
10. National Bureau of Standards. *Handbook of Mathematical Functions with Formulas, Graphs, and Mathematical Tables.* Ed.—M. Abramowitz and I. A. Stegun, pp. 245-248 (1964).
11. H. A. Johanson, G. B. Adams and P. Van Rysselberghe. *J. Electrochem. Soc.,* **104,** 339 (1957).
12. W. Latimer. *Oxidation Potentials.* 2nd Ed., Prentice-Hall, Englewood Cliffs, N. J. (1952).
13. J. G. Hines. *Corrosion Science,* **1,** 21 (1961).
14. V. Levich. *Physicochemical Hydrodynamics.* (Translation), Prentice-Hall, Englewood Cliffs, N. J. (1962).
15. H. S. Carslaw and J. C. Jaeger. *Conduction of Heat in Solids.* Oxford Press (1959).
16. W. Beck, J. O'M. Bockris, J. McBreen and L. Nanis. *Proceedings of the Royal Society,* **A290,** 220 (1966).

# Discussion

**T. P. Hoar, University of Cambridge:**

The model which has been proposed still does not give an explanation for the process by which the crack propagates. It is not at all clear to me that your model negates the view which we have held; namely, that the crack propagates by a high anodic current at the tip which flows to the crack walls.

**T. R. Beck:**

Within the present formulation of the model the number of crack propagating mechanisms is greatly restricted, however, e.g., it has been shown that the brittle hydride and oxide mechanisms and the oxide wedging mechanism are not likely. Further, results of the computations and the crack velocity experiments in high concentration chloride solutions (Figure 8) indicate that halide ions flow into the "tip zone" at a rate corresponding to the formation of a monolayer of adsorbed halide ions or titanium dihalide. I consider these results as a positive contribution to the understanding of stress corrosion cracking of titanium.

I agree that the mechanism of interaction of halide ions with the new titanium metal atoms within the "tip zone" is outside the scope of the present continuum model and this is an area requiring further experimental and theoretical development. That the tip current corresponds to formation of a monolayer of halide, however, indicates that there is no gross amount of corrosion within the "tip zone".

**H. H. Uhlig, MIT:**

I would like to support the point of view that has been expressed by Dr. Beck; his model of crack growth is intriguing. One hopes that perhaps he could vary the chloride ion activity to see how doing so modifies the rate of crack growth. With respect to effect of potential, differentiation might be made between the potential which is necessary to stop corrosion of titanium, which would have some bearing on Dr. Hoar's electrochemical model,

and the presumably different potential which would be necessary to desorb chloride ions, bearing on the model of stress sorption cracking. This is one approach that might be used to assess the validity of the two models.

**T. R. Beck:**

Regarding the effect of chloride ion activity on crack velocity, I presented data in Figure 8 in the text, although I omitted it from the oral presentation for lack of time. I repeat that the velocities in concentrated chloride solutions are in agreement with the mass transport model but the velocities at low chloride concentration deviate, suggesting chloride ion recycling within the crack.

Regarding the effect of potential, unfortunately the tip is "screened" from the externally applied potential by the wall reactions and transport phenomena in the crack. Therefore varying the potential applied to a specimen gives no definitive answers in respect to the tip. A question that has passed through my mind many times is that if it is shown that a current of halide ions equivalent to monolayer coverage flows into the "tip zone" and they presumably interact with the stressed metal atoms at the crack tip, will it ever be possible to say that the interaction is purely electrochemical (i.e., charge transfer) purely a sorption process (i.e., electrical double layer) or a mixture of the two? In respect to electrical double layer phenomena, we still do not know a very fundamental number, the point of zero charge of bare titanium metal surface.

**R. W. Staehle, Ohio State University:**

The model proposed omits consideration of the flux of oxidized ions moving away from the crack tip. Would you comment as to how this consideration would affect your model?

**T. R. Beck:**

The halide anion was considered to be mass transport limited because it is the only species that will give a low concentration in solution at the tip and a potential gradient in the right direction. Hydrogen ion transported toward the tip could give a low concentration but the potential gradient would be in the wrong direction. Soluble titanium ions produced at the tip and transported out would give a potential gradient in the right direction but the concentration would be high at the tip. Therefore if $Ti^{++}$ is formed at the tip it is assumed that it remains adsorbed on the walls, with halide ion to satisfy electroneutrality, and the resulting adsorbed salt carries no net charge out. If titanium surface atoms are not electrochemically oxidized in the tip zone, the halide ions that enter the "tip zone" are assumed to be carried out adsorbed on the walls with their positive image charges on the metal side of the interface, again with a zero net charge carried out of the tip zone on the walls.

**D. A. Vermilyea, General Electric Research Laboratory:**

I would like to ask how sensitive the whole model is to the precise geometry which you assume at the base of the tip. You have taken a three-degree crack; suppose you took instead a parallel sided crack, with a hemispherical tip. Would that make a substantial difference?

**T. R. Beck:**

Altering the crack shape will, of course, affect the potential drop in the crack but I believe that there is no reasonable shape that will give a sufficiently high potential drop within the scope of the present continuum model without having the limiting mass transport of halide ion to the "tip zone". We have not explored variations of crack angle in the computer computations but the effect can be illustrated in some simplified limiting cases.

With no wall reactions the electrolyte resistance in a small angle crack with straight walls simplifies to Equation (5) in the text. Although using the resistivity of bulk 0.6 M KCl outside of the crack gives about the right resistance as shown in the text, the electrolyte in the crack must become strongly acid due to the reaction $Ti + 2H_2O \rightarrow TiO_2 + 4H^+ + 4e$ on the walls, giving about an order of magnitude lower resistance. It is not likely that the crack angle is an order of magnitude smaller than three degrees used in the calculations in order to give the required resistance with acid electrolyte in the crack.

Now let us explore the consequences of a parallel-sided crack with a half-cylinder shaped tip. The electrolyte resistance in a unit thickness specimen would be:

$$R_e = \frac{\rho_e L}{W}$$

where L = length of the parallel-sided zone and W = its width. On the optical photomicrographs that we have made of cross sections of arrested cracks, the measured crack angles down to a distance of $10^{-3}$ cm from the crack tip were in the range of one to four degrees. Without using too much imagination the crack angle was observed to be uniform to within $10^{-4}$ cm of the apparent crack tip. Because there is a relaxation of stresses when the specimens

are removed from the tensile machine the crack angles during propagation are assumed to be larger than these. We therefore chose an angle of three degrees as a reasonable average value to use in the calculations. If it is assumed that the length of the parallel-sided zone is the same as the uniform-angle zone that it replaces, then $W = \gamma L$ and

$$R_e = \frac{\rho_e}{\gamma}$$

and

$$\Delta E = \frac{I \rho_e}{\gamma}$$

If it is further assumed that $L = 10^{-4}$ cm (i.e., that distance below resolution on optical photomicrographs), $I = 7 \times 10^{-4}$ amp/cm (monolayer coverage of oxide for $V = 10^{-2}$ cm/sec; see Figure 7), $\rho_e = 2$ $\Omega$cm (concentrated HCl), and $\gamma = 0.05$; then $\Delta E = 28$ millivolts in the straight-sided zone. This is again too small (as compared to an order of magnitude larger $\Delta E$ in Figure 3 for $V = 10^{-2}$ cm/sec) and we are forced to consider a means whereby the electrolyte conductivity can be decreased. A low concentration near the tip produced by limiting halide ion mass transport appears to be the most likely way to achieve a low electrolyte conductivity.

**A. J. Forty, University of Warwick:**

I should like to point out that the geometrical shape of crack used in Dr. Beck's model is not consistent with the idea that cracking occurs by cleavage. The wide angle of the crack tip (three degrees according to you) can only exist if very extensive plastic deformation is taking place. This must surely have a significant effect on your analysis.

Also, I should like to suggest that the value of $\delta^t$ should be considered more carefully. The apex might well be a great distance ahead of the apparent tip of the crack during cleavage. I wonder if Dr. Beck can comment on this?

**T. R. Beck:**

The angle of three degrees in the outer part of a crack is an experimentally measured macroscopic quantity that is determined by the elastic behavior of the specimens under tension. We also measured on optical photomicrographs of cross-sectioned cracks (@ 1000x) that this approximate angle was valid to within $10^{-3}$ cm from the apparent crack tip and estimating by eye it appeared valid to within $10^{-4}$ cm from the apparent crack tip. In formulating the model we chose the simplest assumption in respect to geometry, i.e., a uniform angle to the tip. If Professor Forty has a better approximation than this, we would be very appreciative of the information. We are aware that there is some plastic deformation around the crack tip region.

The critical question in the second comment, I think, relates to the relative values of $\delta^t$ and $\delta^p$. It is assumed in our model that $\delta^p > \delta^t$. We chose a limiting value of $10^{-6}$ cm for $\delta^p$ in our calculations, giving a crack width at $\delta^p$ of 5 Å, or about two adsorbed layers for a three degree crack. A value of $10^{-5}$ cm for $\delta^p$ would perhaps be more reasonable for our continuum model because interaction of the diffuse parts of the electrical double layers would probably become important at a width of 50 Å. Now, is it likely that $\delta^t$ is greater than $10^{-5}$ cm from the apex? We think that it is not likely based on fitting the Elliott cleavage crack tip profile[1] asymptotically into a three degree crack. If it turns out that $\delta^t > \delta^p$ then we have drawn wrong conclusions regarding a SCC crack but I don't believe that this is likely.

1. H. A. Elliott. *Proc. Phys. Soc.* (London), B, 59, 208 (1947).

### E. N. Pugh, RIAS:

I should like to make a comment which is relevant to Dr. Blackburn's paper and also to the previous paper by Dr. Beck. Both authors state that failure in titanium alloys in aqueous solutions occurs by cleavage which, by definition, is a brittle process occurring with high velocity. At the same time, evidence is presented which indicates that the overall rate of cracking is relatively slow. Therefore we must conclude that crack propagation is discontinuous. Is there any evidence to support this conclusion?

### T. R. Beck:

The only experimental evidence we have regarding a continuous or discontinuous mode of crack propagation is that acoustic emission studies revealed that SCC propagation is very quiet compared to fracture in air of specimens embrittled by heat treatment. This is certainly not definitive but it suggests that the SCC may occur by a continuous process. That brittle fracture is normally fast does not seem to me to preclude slow cleavage in a SCC susceptible material like Ti:8-1-1 which has restricted slip systems[1] that might allow local stresses greater than the yield stress and which could have considerably reduced tensile stress at the crack tip by halide ion interaction.

1. See M. J. Blackburn and J. C. Williams, this conference.

### J. C. Scully, University of Leeds:

I am certain that the tip of the crack does remain active. What disturbs me about the stress corrosion cracking of titanium and Dr. Beck's approach is that whereas in copper alloys or austenitic steels we discuss localized tunnel growth, etc., as it applies to slow cracking processes, in this system we are concerned to account for a cleavage process which on *average* occurs at velocities up to cm/min and which in an individual grain occurs at much higher velocities. When the tip of a crack reaches a grain boundary we must inhibit slip either by raising the local critical shear stress or by lowering the local cleavage stress or, of course, by doing both. I believe that hydrogen can play some role in both processes. I cannot see a mechanism involving halide ions alone operating in distilled water and a variety of organic environments. I think that the successful application of cathodic polarization does not necessarily eliminate the role of hydrogen since in our constant straining experiments cleavage occurs even at relatively high current densities. One never gets back to dimple fracture. I suspect that an explanation of this apparent contradiction

probably lies in the build up and stabilization of films. What I am concerned with is the evolution of hydrogen on *bare* metal surfaces at the tips of cracks.

### T. R. Beck:

Dr. Scully has many points and beliefs which I will try to separate and respond to individually.

1. Yes, the tip and walls remain active until passivated by many monolayers of oxide, and this is accounted for quantitatively in our model.

2. We have seen no evidence of tunneling in SCC of Ti:8-1-1.

3. We have no evidence yet that the velocity in individual grains is *much* higher than the average velocity. (See comment to E. N. Pugh.)

4. Slip is certainly inhibited in some manner at the crack tip (see comment to E. N. Pugh) but my calculations indicate that the amount of hydrogen ion reduction on the crack walls is small and the crack tip "out runs" the hydrogen.

5. I can visualize halogen ions being the SCC agent in distilled water and methanol if there is a source of halogen such as the metal itself which has been reported to contain on the order of 10 ppm of chloride,[1] and the chloride recycles. I cannot, however, completely exclude the possibility that water may be a SCC agent that gives a velocity of $10^{-3}$ cm/sec by itself (see Figure 8). We have not explored this possibility quantitatively yet because the halide hydrolysis or displacement mechanism appears to work quantitatively rather well in the model.

6. The fact that a stress corrosion crack in titanium can be stopped by application of a very negative potential does not in itself eliminate a hydride mechanism because at applied potentials more negative than the mixed potential (-800 mv to SCE) there would be a net consumption of hydrogen ion in the crack and the electrolyte in the crack would become alkaline. We have observed experimentally that a large molar ratio of hydroxyl to halide ion will inhibit SCC at all potentials. We have rejected the hydrogen mechanism in our model on the basis that, although hydrogen ion is reduced in the monolayer zone, our calculations indicate that the crack tip "out runs" the transport of hydrogen to the tip. Because the model, which is based on a rigorous formulation of electrochemical transport and kinetic equations and uses values of parameters obtained independently of SCC experiments, gives results in reasonable agreement with SCC experimental data, we have chosen to accept it as a working hypothesis and a reasonable approximation to the actual electrochemical events in a SCC crack in titanium until proved otherwise by ourselves or others.

7. I wonder where the data are that support Dr. Scully's statement regarding cleavage at high cathodic current densities. We observe a disappearance of cleavage of duplex annealed Ti:8-1-1 when the potential is switched to a cathodic protection potential.

8. I am also concerned with evolution of hydrogen near the tip of a crack and it is quantitatively accounted for in our model.

1. T. R. Beck and M. J. Blackburn. *AIAA Journal*, 6, 326 (1968).

## A. R. C. Westwood, RIAS:

I would like to comment on Dr. Scully's point about the need for some species to diffuse from the environment into the solid ahead of the crack tip, inhibiting plastic flow in this region, in order to allow cleavage to occur in an otherwise ductile metal. Such diffusion into the solid is not necessary if embrittlement occurs by means of adsorption, as in liquid-metal embrittlement. In this case, it is considered that the tensile strength of the atomic bonds constituting the crack tip is reduced so much by the adsorbing species that they fracture before the stress to activate sources ahead of the crack is reached. It is possible to induce cleavage in pure aluminum monocrystals in this way, using liquid gallium as the embrittling environment. Further discussion of this possibility may be found in Reference 1.

1. A. R. C. Westwood, C. M. Preece and M. H. Kamdar. *Trans. ASM*, 60, 723 (1967).

## R. S. Ondrejcin, Savannah River Laboratory:

In Section D-1, you propose that $Cl^-$, $Br^-$, and $I^-$ are less readily incorporated into the $TiO_2$ lattice than most other anions. In our paper, Table 1 showed that, without applied electric fields, $Cl^-$ adsorbed onto the surfaces of several metals. We showed the adsorption of large amounts of $Cl^-$ as $^{36}Cl^-$ on Ti alloys at ambient temperature, with only trace adsorption of $Na^+$ even though NaCl solutions were used. For reasons given in our paper, we came to the conclusion that $Cl^-$ was occupying oxygen vacancies in the titanium oxide lattice.

The fact that ions causing stress corrosion cracking are adsorbed into protective oxide lattices has been previously demonstrated. Overman[1] has shown that chlorides are adsorbed onto stainless steels and ascribed the result to anodic areas. In this work he also showed the desorption of corrosion inhibitors and replacement by chlorides. Others[2,3] have also shown the adsorption of chlorides in protective oxide lattices that eventually led to stress corrosion cracking.

Surface adsorption or reaction as a general phenomenon is quite common. Mattox[4] states that after cleaning a surface, contamination may remain in the form of adsorbed gases bound with 0.1-5 ev, chemisorbed gases bound with 1-10 ev or compound layers several lattice parameters thick in extent bound with 1-10 ev. The chemisorbed gases or compound layers are not stoichiometric in composition as shown by field ion microscopy studies. Since perfect lattices are not formed, halide ions could be incorporated easily.

1. R. F. Overman. Using Radioactive Tracers to Study Chloride Stress Corrosion Cracking of Stainless Steels. *Corrosion*, 22, 48 (1966) February.
2. C. R. Bergen. Initiation of Stress Corrosion Cracking, Migration of Chloride in Oxide Films on Austenitic Stainless Steels. *Corrosion*, 20, 269t (1964) September.
3. F. Bevlacqua and G. M. Brown. *Chloride Deposition from Steam Onto Superheater Fuel Clad Materials*, GNEC 295 (1963) October 18.
4. D. M. Mattox. *Interface Formation and the Adhesion of Deposited Thin Films*, SC-R-65-852 (1965) January.

## T. R. Beck:

Section D of my text lists some experimental results, the explanations of which appear to lie outside of the mass-transport-kinetic model as it is now formulated. Some speculative hypotheses were given as a guide for designing further critical experiments. One of these experiments, completed after the paper was written, consisted of anodizing Ti:8-1-1 surfaces freshly broken in neutral solutions of 0.004 M to 0.04 M sodium chloride solutions containing Cl-36 ion. The current densities varied from $10^{-4}$ to $10^{-1}$ amp/cm$^2$, covering the maximum values expected in a SCC crack and therefore the highest expected electric fields for driving the negative chloride ion into the oxide.

Results calculated from the counting rate on the new surface at the completion of the experiments and the total coulombic charge passed showed that the chloride absorption (or adsorption) accounted for only about 0.1% of the charge passed. In other words the anodic layer was 99.9% metallic oxides and 0.1% metallic chlorides assuming negligible dissolution of metal ions. Furthermore, the fraction of chloride was independent of current density in the above range, for the same coulombic charge passed.

These results indicate that chloride absorption in the walls of a SCC crack plays no significant role in stress corrosion cracking of titanium. It is also doubtful that anodic protection in chloride solutions can be attributed to chloride absorption as suggested in Section IV-C-2 and another hypothesis must be made for the passivation. The hypothesis given in IV-C-1, however, has not been disproved by the experiments just described.

Now the question is, how do these chloride absorption results relate to those of Mr. Ondrejcin? He shows in his Table 1 that Ti:8-1-1 dipped in a Cl-36 solution of pH 5-6 (and unspecified concentration) gave a count corresponding to about one $\mu$gm/cm$^2$ of chloride. This is equivalent to about 15 close packed monolayers of chloride ion. My results computed on this basis correspond to about one monolayer of chloride. But Mr. Ondrejcin further shows in his Figure 1 that the chloride count decreases by at least an order of magnitude in acid solutions. When titanium is anodized in a neutral solution an acid condition is developed next to the surface because hydrogen ion is a product of the oxidation. Therefore my absorption would be expected to be lower than his and there is no contradiction between his and my results. His experiments were conducted at open circuit with specimens that already had an air-formed film and therefore small pH change next to the surface. The mass-transport-kinetic model for SCC shows that a very acid condition is developed in a propagating crack and therefore chloride absorption on the walls would be small.

# METALLURGICAL ASPECTS OF THE STRESS CORROSION
# CRACKING OF TITANIUM ALLOYS

M. J. Blackburn and J. C. Williams
The Boeing Company

## Abstract

This paper should be read in conjunction with that of T. R. Beck,[1] which deals with the electrochemical factors influencing the stress corrosion cracking (SCC) of titanium alloys in aqueous solutions. The metallurgical and mechanical factors which obviously interact with the electrochemistry are considered here. The number of variables make generalization difficult unless these are qualified by specification of the test conditions. It is shown that failure of $\alpha$-phase in Ti:Al alloys and in the commercial alloy Ti:8Al:1Mo:1V under SCC condition occurs by cleavage on the $\{10\bar{1}8\}$ - $\{10\bar{1}7\}$ plane of the hexagonal phase. The general phase structure, of these alloys is described and it is shown that the $\alpha \rightarrow \alpha + \alpha_2$ (Ti$_3$Al) transformation is of considerable importance in determining susceptibility. In the commercial alloy presence of the $\beta$-phase and the martensitic phases reduce susceptibility. Results on the binary Ti:Al alloys indicate that the onset of susceptibility to SCC occurs between 4-5% aluminum which correlates with a change from homogeneous to planar dislocation arrangements. The influence of stress on the nucleation and propagation of a crack has been analyzed for precracked specimens, using the methods of linear elastic mechanics. From these results several factors which influence the nucleation stage are discussed. It is proposed that for a propagating crack, there are two components of fracture, i.e., electrochemical and mechanical. At low $\alpha$-phase strength levels or aluminum contents the electrochemical component predominates while at higher strength levels or aluminum content the mechanical component increases. Some qualitative correlations are made between mechanical properties, deformation structures, fracture mode, and susceptibility to SCC.

## I. Introduction

It is now well established that some titanium alloys show a drastic reduction in strength when tested in certain environments. T. R. Beck[1] in the previous paper will consider some of the many facets of the problem of embrittlement in aqueous solutions at room temperature, and in this paper we shall also deal with embrittlement under these conditions. We shall refer to this embrittlement as stress corrosion cracking (SCC) although an alternate theory regards the phenomena as due to hydrogen embrittlement (HE).[2] Let us briefly review the features of the phenomena that have been established to date.

**Environments:** The ions that can produce SCC have been listed by Beck,[1] as he has shown the influence of potential and concentration on susceptibility. It has been shown that organic solvents[3] can also produce embrittlement, but we shall not discuss this aspect of the problem.

**Alloys:** A very large number of alloys have been tested in a wide range of heat treatment conditions.[4,5] It has been shown both in this investigation and by other workers that alloy composition and heat treatment can vary susceptibility. In addition, it appears that rolling texture (preferred orientation) is an important variable which is less easily

controlled and about which less is known.

**Mechanics:** The initial discovery of SCC was made on notched specimens[6] and most subsequent testing, at least in the USA, has been performed on notched and in many cases, precracked specimens. The need for a stress concentration has been questioned by Scully,[7] but at present, the only well documented failures in the absence of a notch apply to tests conducted in organic solvents.

We have introduced in the above brief description of the phenomenon, a number of variables which can be altered independently of one another and, moreover, can sometimes be altered inadvertently. In addition to the need for controlled test conditions, there is another problem, that of defining an index of susceptibility. In many reports the ratio of the fracture load, stress or stress intensity in air and in environment is taken as the susceptibility index. Such testing is usually performed under dead weight or constant load conditions which leads to an increasing stress or stress intensity during the test. In this investigation we have measured the stress intensity for crack nucleation and its effect on subsequent crack propagation velocity under various loading (and unloading) conditions.

TABLE 1–Alloy Compositions (by weight)

TABLE 1–Alloy Compositions (by weight)

**(a) Ti:Al**

| Designation | Al | O | N | H | C |
|---|---|---|---|---|---|
| Ti:6 wt% Al | 6.11 | 0.110 | 0.013 | 0.004 | 0.016 |
| Ti:8 wt% Al | 8,04 | 0.105 | 0.012 | 0.004 | 0.020 |
| Ti:8.65 wt% Al | 8.62 | 0.100 | 0.006 | 0.0015 | 0.013 |
| Ti:10 wt% Al | 10.28 | 0.100 | 0.018 | 0.006 | 0.018 |

**(b) Ti:8-1-1**

| Designation | | Al | Mo | V | O | N | H | C |
|---|---|---|---|---|---|---|---|---|
| 0.060 in Sht No. | 2283 | 7.8 | 1.04 | 1.0 | 0.075 | 0.0012 | 0.003 | 0.040 |
| | 2194 | 7.6 | 1.05 | 0.98 | 0.109 | 0.008 | 0.004 | 0.040 |
| | 2208 | 7.8 | 1.0 | 1.0 | 0.090 | 0.015 | 0.003 | 0.023 |
| | 2279 | 7.7 | 1.1 | 1.1 | 0.090 | 0.009 | 0.004 | 0.025 |
| 0.500 in plate | | 7.8 | 1.0 | 1.0 | 0.080 | 0.010 | 0.009 | 0.010 |

The paper is divided into several sections in an attempt to isolate the various factors which influence susceptibility to SCC. It will become apparent that we consider only the α-phase susceptible to SCC in the alloys investigated. Thus we have used Ti:8Al:1Mo:1V (Ti:8-1-1) to generate much of the quantitative data and Ti:Al alloys to show general trends in mechanical behavior, for cleavage plane determinations, etc. However, the complexity of the phase structure and phase distribution and the small and invariable grain size in Ti:8-1-1 leads to some difficulty in comparisons.

## II. Experimental

### (i) Alloys

Tests were performed on several 0.060 in sheets and on 0.5 in plate of Ti:8-1-1. A series of Ti:Al alloys were also tested, the compositions of which are listed in Table 1.

### (ii) Specimens

The notched tensile specimens produced from the 0.060 in Ti:8-1-1 and the Ti-Al alloys have been described by Beck.[1] A small number of notched precracked specimens of the 0.500 in Ti:8-1-1 plate were tested in four point bending. The specimen configuration and dimensions for the bend test are described in Reference 8.

### (iii) Testing

The general testing procedure has been described by Beck.[1] Most specimens were loaded using a slow crosshead speed (0.005 cms/min) until the first indication of cracking,

which was usually the development of an anodic current. After initiation three methods of loading were employed, the crosshead motion was continued, stopped or reversed. In order to investigate the influence of higher initial loads, specimens were cathodically protected and on attainment of the required load, the potential was switched to the test potential. From such tests values of the initiation load (which can be converted to net area stress or stress intensity factor) and velocity of cracking were obtained. Also the stress intensity during a test can be computed from the record of the crack length and load. The variation of susceptibility to SCC with potential has been described by Beck,[1] the majority of the results presented here were conducted using 0.6 M KCl at a potential of -500 mV or in 0.6 M KI at various potentials.

### (iv) Crack Propagation Velocity

Velocity was measured by the observation of the movement of a crack past lines on the specimen surface. A typical distance-time plot for a static crosshead test is shown in Figure 1 from which it is seen that three velocities can be defined, $V_1$, $V_2$, and $V$.

### (v) Analysis of Data

The load-crack length data from these tests were analyzed using linear elastic mechanics; calculation of the stress intensity factor, K, was performed using the equations given by Srawley and Brown.[9] However, it was found that the conditions for plane strain fracture were usually violated during crack propagation in tests on the 0.060 in sheet. Thus some of the SCC crack propagation

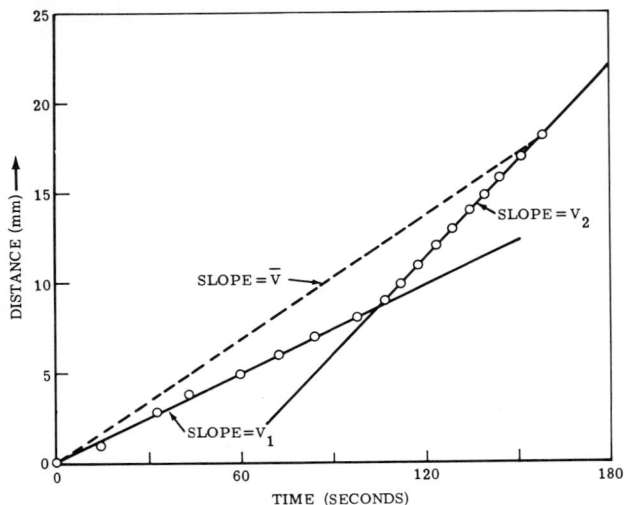

FIGURE 1 — Typical distance: time record showing definition of $V_1$, $V_2$, and $\bar{V}$.

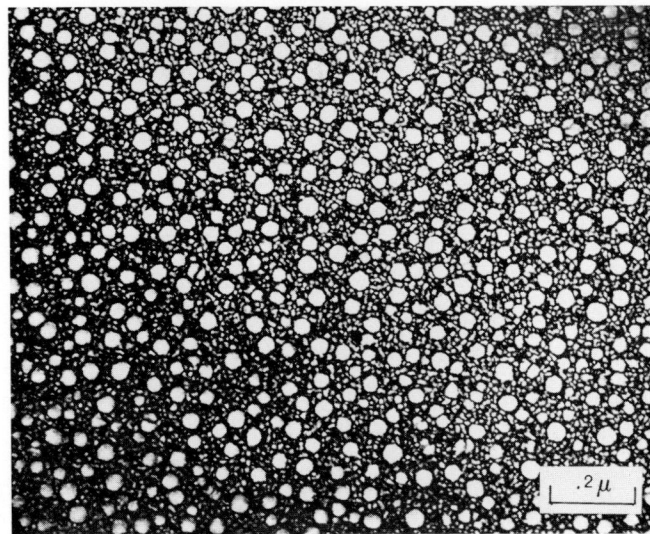

FIGURE 2 — $\alpha_2$ particles in step cooled Ti:8.65 wt% Al, showing two particle sizes. Dark field, $\bar{g}$ = (1120) $\alpha_2$, [0001]$_\alpha$ Zone Normal.

occurs under mixed plane strain and plane stress conditions. Direct comparison of fracture and velocity data for different conditions is complicated by this change in fracture type.

### (vi) Heat Treatment

Heat treatments were performed in argon atmosphere or vacuum furnaces, where necessary specimens were water quenched. In order to produce a dispersion of the $\alpha_2$-phase in the $\alpha$-phase, some specimens were step cooled from 700 C and other specimens were isothermally aged at 500 and 600 C.

### (vii) Reproducibility of Data

One of the most puzzling features of this work has been the irreproducibility of data from sheet to sheet (there are of course minor inconsistencies in the results from one sheet). Some of the variability can be traced to differences in heat treatment, grain size, distribution of phases and preferred orientation but it appears that other more nebulous factors are present. We can only suggest that some processing factor or impurity elements contribute in some way.

## III. Results

### A. Phase Structure

The phase structure of the Ti:Al alloys,[10] Ti:8-1-1[11,12] and other commercial alloys,[13] have been described in a series of papers. We shall show below that only the hexagonal $\alpha$-phases in these alloys are considered susceptible to SCC and thus the other phases, e.g., $\beta$-phase and $\alpha'$ martensite will not be discussed here. The marten-

sitic transformation $\beta \rightarrow \alpha''$, which has a hexagonal structure, is probably more relevant and it will be shown that there are differences in susceptibility for this phase in the Ti:Al alloys and in the commercial alloys. However, the morphology of the phase and its internal structure are similar in the Ti:8Al and Ti:8-1-1 alloys. In both Ti:8Al and Ti:8-1-1 low temperature aging produces a dispersion of the $\alpha_2$ (Ti$_3$Al) phase in the $\alpha$-phase. The morphology and distribution of the $\alpha_2$-phase in the $\alpha$-phase in step-cooled specimens is shown in Figure 2. One other aspect of transformation behavior relevant to SCC susceptibility in these alloys is decomposition of the $\beta$-phase during low temperature aging. It has been shown that the hexagonal $\omega$-phase is formed in the $\beta$-phase of Ti:8-1-1 on low temperature (260 C) aging.[13] A subsequent section will show that the presence of this phase makes the alloy more susceptible.

### B. Mechanical Properties and Dislocation Arrangements

Aluminum additions to titanium increase the modulus and yield strength and decrease ductility.[14,15] The yield stress-composition curve tends to be concave upwards and Figure 3 shows such a relationship. However, interstitial solute elements probably have the predominant effect on yield stress and it appears that the effect of aluminum is additive to the interstitial content in determining the absolute strength of an alloy. Thus, the yield stress composition curve is always concave upwards but the position of this curve on the stress axis is largely determined by interstitial content.

Yield strengths of the Ti:8.65 wt% Al alloy have been determined as a function of heat treatment and these results are plotted in Figure 4. Although at present insufficient data is available to determine the grain size dependence of the mechanical properties in this alloy,

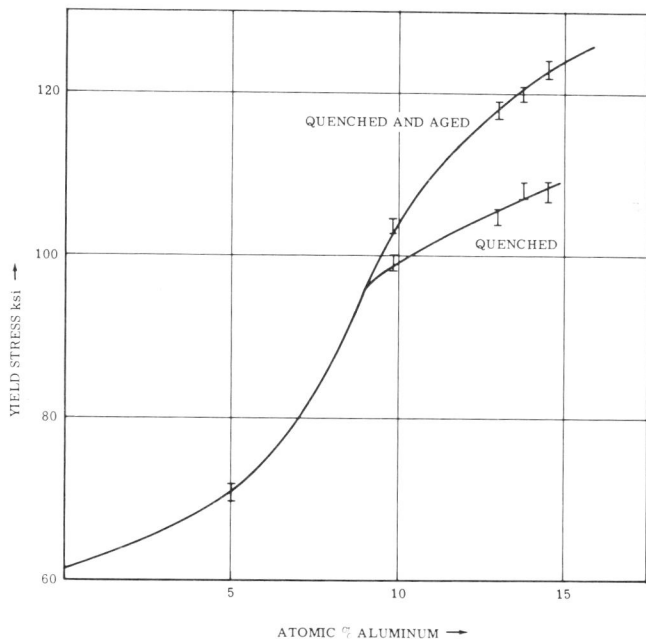

FIGURE 3 — Variation of yield stress with aluminum content.

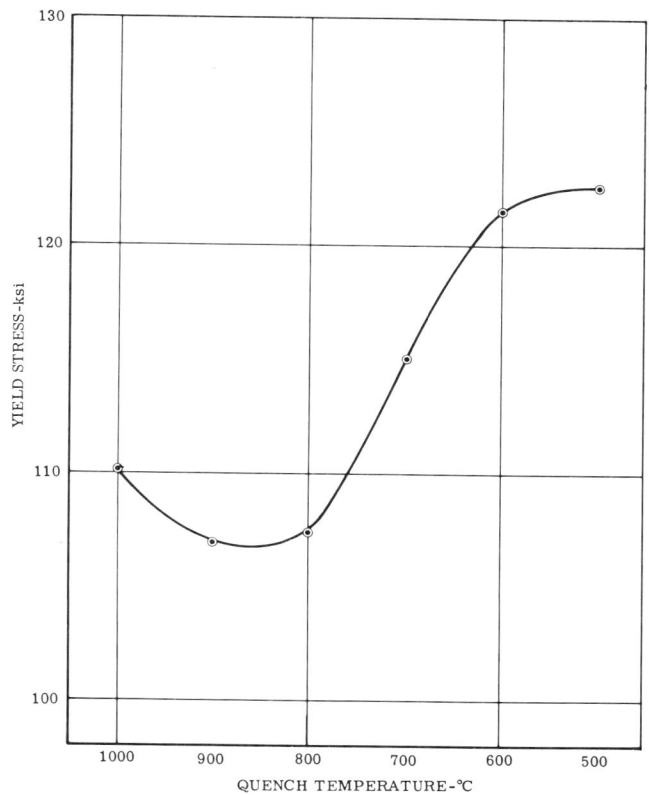

FIGURE 4 — Yield stress vs quench temperature for Ti:8.65 wt% Al.

(a)

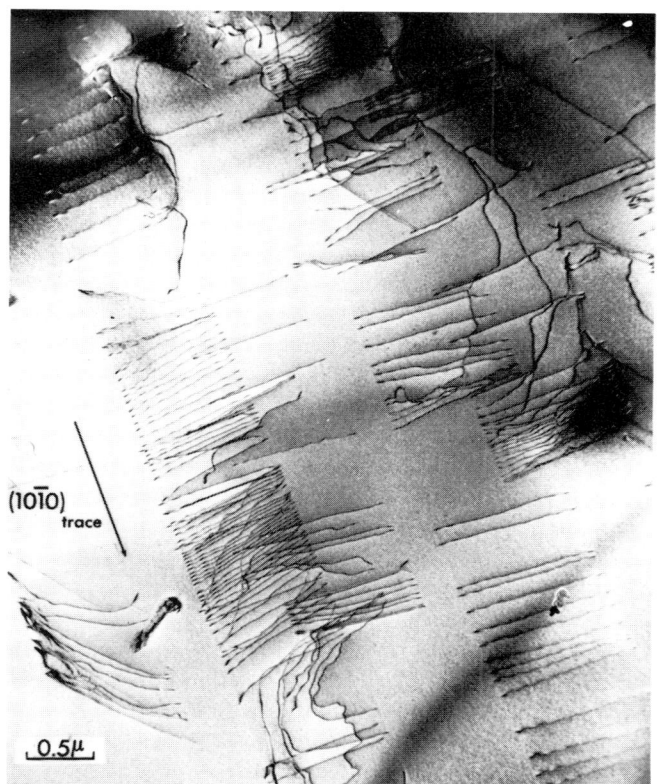

(b)

FIGURE 5 — Dislocation arrangements after ∼3% deformation. (a) Extensive tangling in commercially pure titanium (1500 ppm oxygen). (b) Coplanar arrays in quenched Ti:8.65 wt% Al.

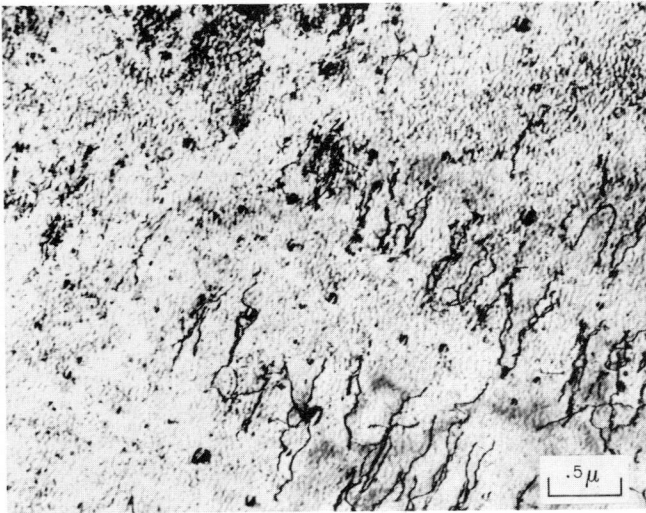

FIGURE 6 — $\{11\bar{2}2\}$ slip in commercially pure titanium (1500 ppm oxygen). $[11\bar{2}0]_\alpha$ Zone Normal, $\bar{g}$ = $(0002)_\alpha$.

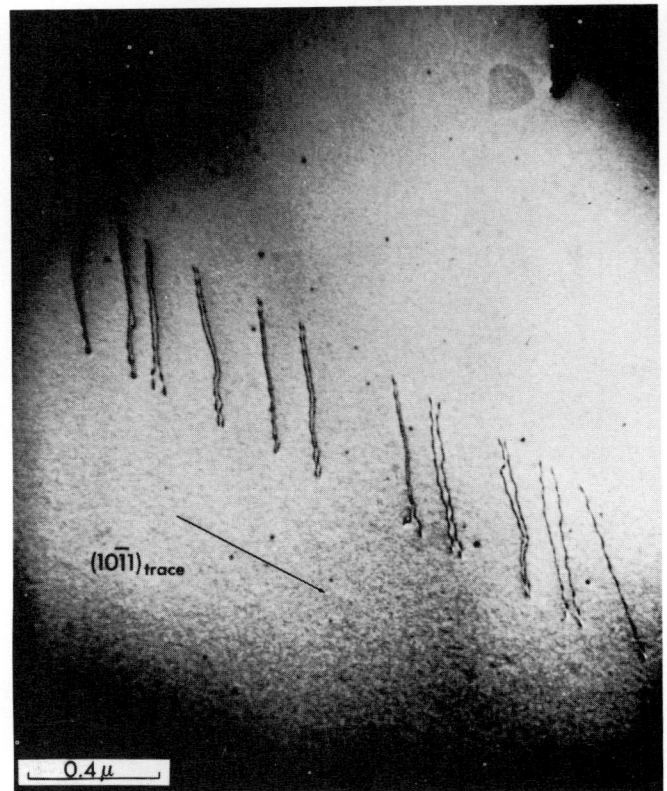

$(10\bar{1}1)_{trace}$

FIGURE 7 — Dislocation pairs in deformed Ti:8% Al aged at 500 C.

several coarse grained specimens have been tested. In all cases these specimens fractured by cleavage without macroscopic yielding.

Dislocation arrangements have been studied in deformed impure Ti, Ti:Al alloys and Ti:8-1-1 and the more important observations are summarized below:

(i) The dislocation arrangements vary from cellular arrays in unalloyed, low oxygen titanium to coplanar arrays in the Ti:8.65 wt% Al alloy as shown in Figures 5 (a) and (b). The transition from cellular to coplanar arrays occurs at an aluminum content of ~ 5 wt% Al.

(ii) Evidence for slip on or near $\{1122\}$ has been found in alloys containing 0, 4, 5, 6, and 8 wt% Al, but the extent of such slip appears to decrease with increasing Al concentration. The Burger's vector for this type of slip has not been determined, but it has been shown that it is not $<10\bar{1}0>$. Examples of such dislocations are shown in Figure 6.

(iii) Some dislocation tangling occurs in all alloys at higher strains, but the strain required to produce tangling increases with increasing Al content.

Several additional observations specific to alloys which exhibit coplanar slip, i.e., > 5 wt% Al, can also be listed.

(i) The thickness of the slip bands decreases with increasing aluminum content. The extent of basal slip at low strains decreases with increasing aluminum content, resulting in slip predominately on prism and pyramidal planes (especially at yield).

(ii) Intersection of two prism slip bands often results in blockage of one of the bands. In addition, contrast experiments show that when interpenetration of the slip bands occurs, the dislocation reaction

$$\frac{a}{3}\,[1\bar{2}10] + \frac{a}{3}\,[\bar{2}110] \rightarrow \frac{a}{3}\,[\bar{1}\bar{1}20]$$

seldom occurs.

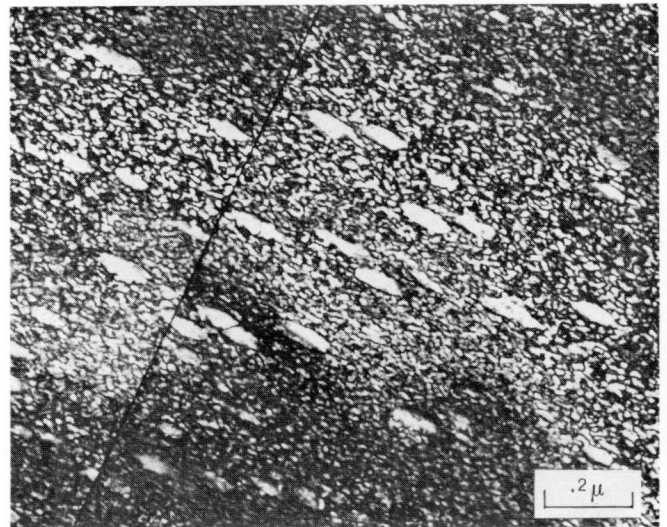

FIGURE 8 — $\alpha_2$ particles in step-cooled Ti:8.65 wt% Al which have been sheared during deformation. Dark field, $\bar{g}$ = $(10\bar{1}1)\alpha_2$ $[11\bar{2}0]$ Zone Normal.

624

FIGURE 9 – Dislocation arrangements in deformed, high oxygen commercially pure titanium ($\sim$3800 ppm oxygen) showing tendency toward coplanar slip. [$10\bar{1}2$] Zone Normal.

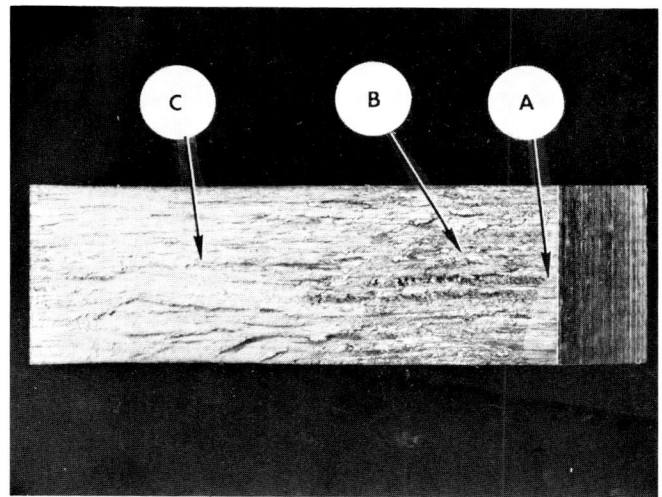

FIGURE 10 – Fracture surface of 0.500 in thick notch bend SCC specimen showing fatigue precrack (A), stress corrosion crack growth (B) and rapid fracture (C). Approx. 4x magnification.

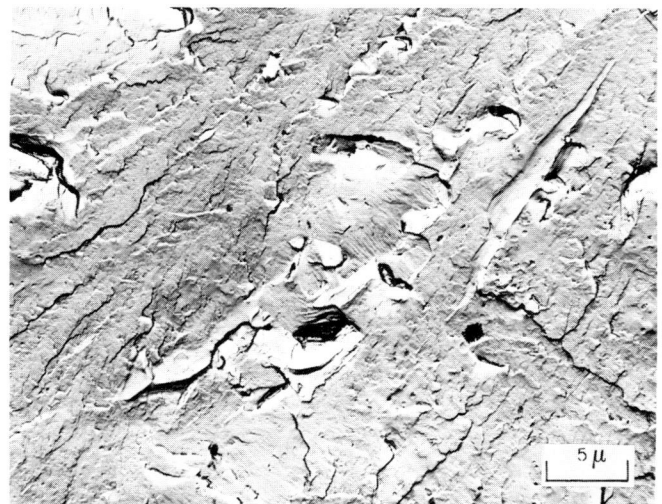

FIGURE 11 – Electron fractograph from SCC zone of a Ti:8-1-1 specimen showing cleavage of alpha phase.

(iii) Cross slip is infrequently observed.

(iv) In the Ti:8.65 wt% Al alloy dislocation pairs are frequently observed in the quenched (disordered) condition and are always present in the ordered condition as shown in Figure 7.

(v) Shearing of ordered ($Ti_3Al$) domains during deformation has been observed in the Ti:8.65 Al alloy; an example of which is shown in Figure 8.

Dislocation arrangements have also been studied in deformed commercially pure titanium containing high (0.38 wt%) oxygen. This material also exhibits a marked tendency toward coplanar slip as shown in Figure 9. The slip bands in this material are comparable in thickness to those found in a 6 wt% Al alloy.

## C. Fracture

The fracture surface of a SCC specimen is generally characterized by several macroscopically distinguishable zones as shown in Figure 10. The zone resulting from crack propagation by SCC is marked 'B' while the zone marked 'C' corresponds to rapid fracture after $K_{IC}$ has been reached.

In the type of tests reported here, we can vary the relative extent of these zones by varying the crosshead speed and its direction of motion after slow crack growth (SCC) begins.

Electron fractography has been used to study the fracture mode associated with SCC and several observations can be listed.

(i) The occurrence of cleavage fracture characterizes SCC in all susceptible alloys as shown at 'A' in Figure 11.

(ii) Regions of ductile fracture are observed in the Ti:8-1-1 alloy. It has been shown that ductile rupture of beta or martensitically transformed beta regions result in such regions and that the alpha phase fails by cleavage.

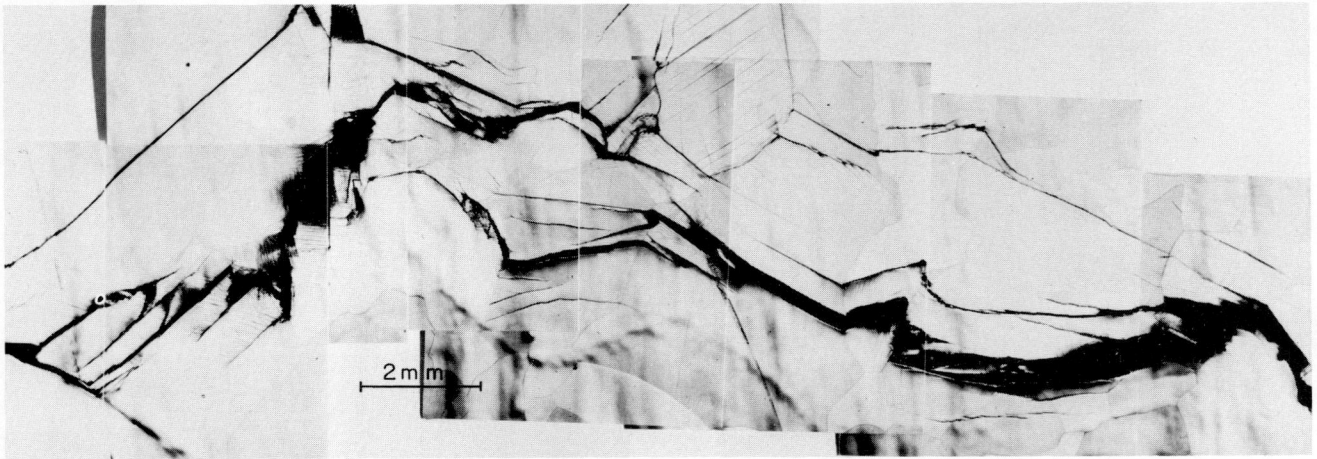

FIGURE 12 — SCC crack profile in Ti:8.65 wt% Al showing extensive branching of crack and limited extent of plastic deformation which accompanies cracking. Magnification: 9X.

(iii) The fracture mode of the $\alpha$-phase usually changes from cleavage in the SCC zone to ductile rupture in the rapid fracture zone.

(iv) As $K_I$ tends to $K_{IC}$ the areal percent of cleavage decreases although the transition zone is usually relatively narrow.

The crack path has also been observed optically on electropolished specimens of Ti:Al and Ti:8-1-1 alloys. As seen in Figure 12, the crack is branched and follows a transgranular path. Movies taken of the propagation of the surface crack in Ti:8 % Al indicates that propagation occurs discontinuously. However, the branched nature of the crack and the continuity of the current-time plots indicate that cracking is continuous but the macroscopic crack front advances discontinuously.

The cleavage plane has been determined, using standard back reflection x-ray techniques, in coarse grained specimens of the Ti:8% Al alloy fractured in air and by SCC. In both cases the cleavage plane can be described by a 12-14° rotation from the basal plane about $[1\bar{2}10]$ and thus is of the type $\{10\bar{1}7\}$ or $\{10\bar{1}8\}$. The physical significance of this plane is not clear at present.

### D. Effect of Heat Treatment

#### 1. Fracture Initiation in Ti:8-1-1

The effect of heat treatment on susceptibility to SCC has been studied in a 0.060 in sheet of Ti:8-1-1. Specimens were quenched from a series of solution treatment temperatures and tests performed in air and in 0.6 M KCl at -500 mV. The results are plotted in Figure 13. However, before analyzing these results several points must be made.

(i) The tests were performed on equiaxed structures excluding the transformed structures.

(ii) It should be emphasized that the comparisons are relative as changes in heat treatment produce changes in the

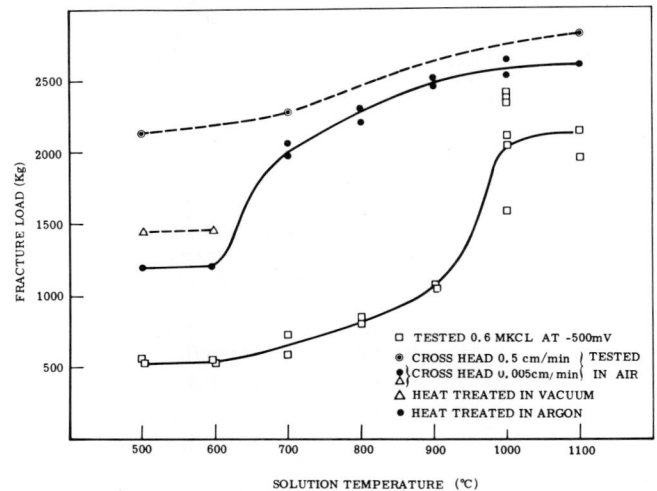

FIGURE 13 — Sheet 2283. Variation of fracture load with solution temperature for Ti:8% Al Al:1% Mo:1% V.

fracture mode. Thus, specimens tested in air failed under plane stress and some of the specimens tested in KCl failed under plane strain conditions. Larger specimens are required for an absolute comparison. (Such specimens have the drawback that different cooling rates are produced at the surface and mid section leading to differences in structure through the thickness.)

(iii) Recent work at NRL has shown that the environment of heat treatment produces changes in susceptibility.[16] We have encountered an apparently similar effect in this study. Crack initiation in air in specimens heat treated at 500 to 600 C was found to be dependent upon environment as can be seen in Figure 13. However, these differences were not so extreme in specimens tested at faster rates (see (iv) below) or in specimens tested in KCl.

626

**TABLE 2 – Summary of Results for Long Time,
Low-Temperature Aged Ti:8-1-1**

| Heat Treatment | Specimen Number | Fracture Load (kg) | Velocity X10³ cm/sec | | |
| --- | --- | --- | --- | --- | --- |
| | | | $V_1$ | $V_2$ | $\overline{V}$ |
| As Rec. Duplex Ann +10,000 hrs at 260 C | 1050 (L) | 710 | 0.2 | 6.25 | 4.7 |
| | 994 (L) | 713 | – | 14.1 | 8.85 |
| As Rec. Duplex Ann +10,000 hrs at 260 C | 1051 (T) | 779 | 3.38 | 8.39 | 6.85 |
| | 990 (T) | 750 | 5.21 | 28.3 | 13.3 |

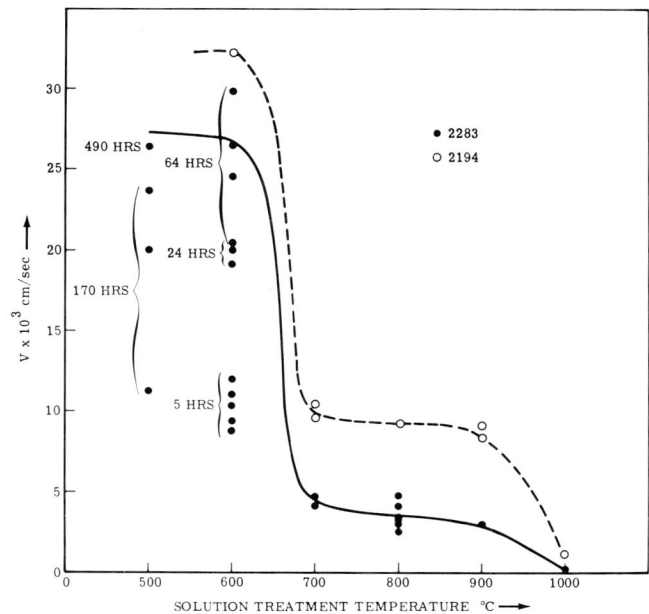

FIGURE 14 – Variation of velocity ($\overline{V}$) with solution treatment temperature.

(iv) Slow crack extension occurred in specimens heat treated at 500 and 600 C which leads to inaccurate air fracture load values. Slow crack growth could be eliminated by testing at faster rates as shown in Figure 13 when the obvious discontinuity between 700 and 600 C disappears for specimens tested in air.

(v) The phase change $\alpha \rightarrow \alpha + \alpha_2$ that occurs below 680 C[1] is rather sluggish and long aging times are required to approach equilibrium. The effect of this phase transformation is far more evident in the velocity changes discussed in the next section.

From Figure 13 the following points can be made. Increasing solution treatment temperature tends to increase the fracture load in both air and KCl. For specimens tested in KCl there is a discontinuity between 900 and 1000 C which corresponds to a rapid decrease in the volume fraction of primary $\alpha$-phase and to the production of the martensitic phases $\alpha'$ and $\alpha''$. Specimens quenched from 1100 C have a completely martensitic structure, $\alpha''$, which although it has a hexagonal structure, appears to be virtually immune to SCC. This behavior should be contrasted with that of the martensites in Ti:8% Al, discussed below, and in Ti:5Al:2.5Sn[17] which are susceptible to SCC. The fracture load decreases with solution treatment temperatures below 900 C. Although, as we shall show in the next section, there is a considerable change in velocity between 600 and 700 C, the fracture load does not show a discontinuity in this alloy. However, in material that is step cooled from 800 C a much larger change can be produced; the maximum difference that has been observed is $\sim$ 600 Kg which corresponds to a change in K of $\sim$ 24 ksi $\sqrt{}$ in.

The above results apply to specimens which are at equilibrium at the solution treatment temperature, quenched and given no subsequent heat treatment.[2] It has been shown that retained $\beta$-phase can decompose during low temperature aging, and this decomposition has been described in some detail elsehwere,[11,13] it was shown that

the $\omega$-phase forms after very long (10,000 hours) aging times at 260 C. Formation of this phase influences susceptibility of Ti:8-1-1 as shown in Table 2; producing approximately a twofold increase in velocity without large changes in the initiation loads. A similar effect has been observed in commercially pure titanium containing 0.30 wt% Fe and 0.38 wt% oxygen. In this alloy $\beta$-phase stabilized by the iron has also been shown to contain the $\omega$-phase, resulting in a very susceptible condition.

## 2. Effect on Velocity – Ti:8-1-1

The formation of ordered particles of $\alpha_2$ in the $\alpha$-phase although in many cases having a relatively small effect on initiation load has a much larger effect on crack velocity. Figure 14 illustrates the change of velocity with heat treatment for two sheets of Ti:8-1-1. It can be seen that the velocity changes by a factor $\sim$ 4 between 600 and 700 C. Figure 14 also illustrates the intrinsic differences observed between various sheets of Ti:8-1-1, i.e., sheet 2194 always has a higher velocity than sheet 2283, and it should be emphasized that more extreme differences have been encountered. However, the general shape of velocity: heat treatment curves are the same, i.e., differences being in the absolute velocity values. Velocity is not changed to a large extent by heat treatment in argon or vacuum.

## 3. Ti: 8% Aluminum

Much less testing has been performed on these alloys and only preliminary results are presented here. The same trends can be observed as in Ti:8-1-1. Thus, with increasing solution treatment temperature, the net area initiation

---

[1]This temperature depends on the aluminum content of the alloy.

[2]In this investigation we have not studied the influence of tempering the martensitic structures on susceptibility.

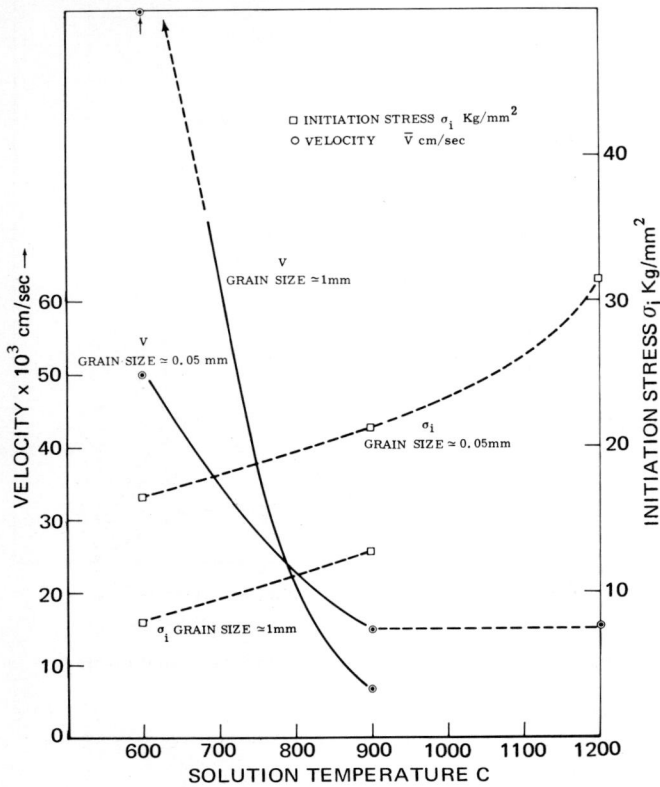

FIGURE 15 — Summary of fracture and velocity data obtained for Ti:8.65 wt% Al.

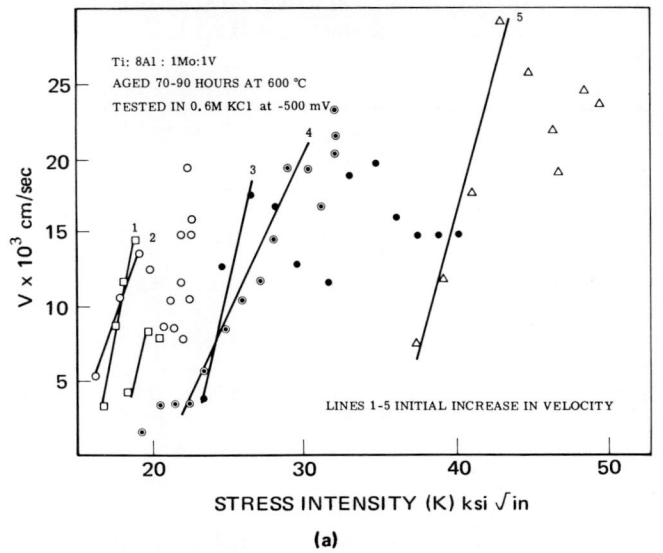

(a)

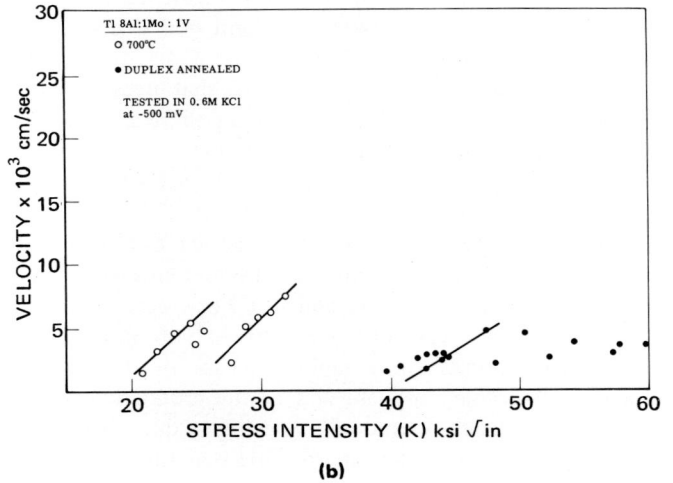

(b)

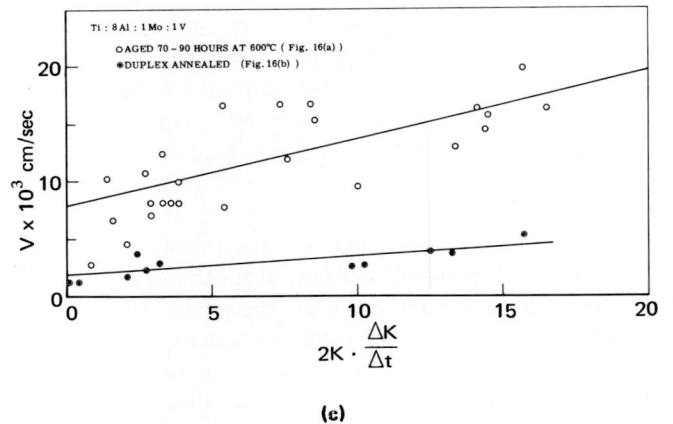

(c)

FIGURE 16 — 0.5 inch plate, four point bend specimens. (a) Variation of velocity with stress intensity factor (K). (b) Variation of velocity with stress intensity factor (K). (c) Variation of velocity with 2K · ΔK/Δt, data from Figure 16 (a).

stress $\sigma_I{}^{(3)}$ tends to increase and the velocity tends to decrease. As with Ti:8-1-1, the velocity shows a discontinuity between 700-800 C, the temperature range over which the $\alpha_2$ phase is precipitated. Grain size has a large effect on $\sigma_I$ as can be seen from Figure 15. In the large grained specimens step cooled to produce a dispersion of $\alpha_2$ phase particles the velocity was estimated at $> 0.1$ cms/sec and there the fracture may have contained a high proportion of mechanical cleavage. In the fracture of these large grained specimens the amount of plastic flow is very limited. (See Figure 12).

### E. Effect of Stress Intensity

Crack velocity usually changes during a test, (see Figure 1) and it can also be varied by heat treatment. In order to investigate the influence of stress on velocity we have used the methods of linear elastic mechanics to compute the stress intensity factor, $K_I$ at the crack tip. Calculations were made for plane strain conditions which are valid over a considerable range of K values in the 0.500 in plate specimen but are only valid for low temperature aged (500 and 600 C) material in the 0.060 in specimens. The data from the 0.060 in sheet however shows similar trends as that for the plate material and the results may be used to establish some general behavior patterns.

_____

(3)$\sigma_I$ is used rather than the initiation load as several different thicknesses were tested.

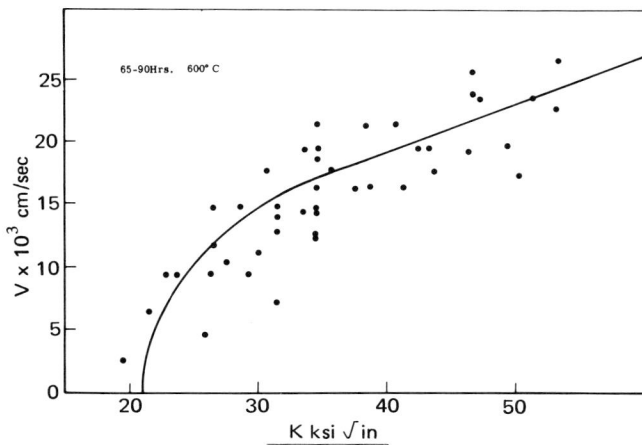

FIGURE 17 — Sheet 2283. Variation of velocity with K (static crosshead conditions).

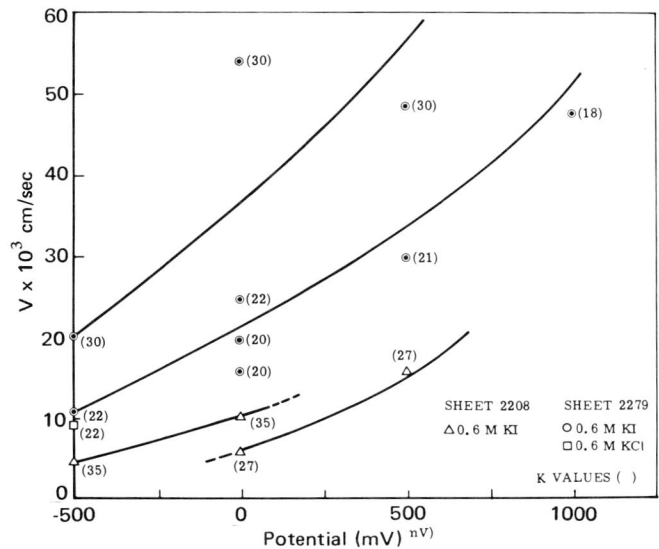

FIGURE 18 — Sheets 2279 and 2208. Velocity vs potential (K const. · $\Delta K/\Delta t \sim 0$).

The results for the 0.5 in plate were analyzed both for the variation of velocity with the K value and for the variation of velocity with the time dependent change of K; $\Delta K/\Delta t$. It was found that there was a considerable variation of behavior dependent upon the heat treatment of the specimens. Figures 16 (a), (b), and (c) illustrate the results for several heat treatment conditions of the 0.500 in plate and Figure 17 illustrates the results for the 0.060 in sheet aged at 600 C. The following general observations can be listed (at a fixed concentration and potential).

(i) The crack tends to accelerate after initiation. The rate of acceleration varies with heat treatment. Velocity (in cm/sec) varying as $3\text{-}4 \times 10^{-3}$ K (600 C), $1 \times 10^{-3}$ K (700 C) and $0.7 \times 10^{-3}$ K (800 C) (K in ksi $\sqrt{\text{in}}$).

(ii) In the 800 C specimens tested under static crosshead conditions the crack appears to reach a constant velocity which is relatively independent of the K level.[4]

(iii) In the 600 C aged specimens the acceleration is independent of initial K level.

(iv) There is a general upward trend of velocity with K level in the 600 C specimens. This is more evident in Figure 17 for the 0.060 in sheet, in which the tests were run under static crosshead conditions. The results shown in Figure 16 (a) include tests in which the crosshead was reversed and it was found that this influences the velocity.

As the velocity of the cracking appeared to change with the loading conditions, i.e., the rate of change of K, the data shown in Figures 16 (a) and (b) for the 600 C specimen was replotted as velocity versus $2K \, \Delta K/\Delta t$ for reasons outlined in the discussion. The resultant plot is shown in Figure 16 (c) from which it can be shown that although there is still considerable scatter, there appears to be a linear correlation. Further, the velocity was found to

be approximately constant if a reversed crosshead test was conducted in which K was held constant and thus $\Delta K/\Delta t \simeq 0$. Figure 18 shows the variation of velocity with potential in such tests. Figure 19 (a) illustrates the rather large scatter when velocity is plotted versus K value for tests at three different potentials. If the results of these three tests are replotted as velocity versus $2K \, dK/dt$ again approximately linear relationships result as shown in Figure 19 (b). It should also be noted that the intercepts of these curves on the velocity axis correlate reasonably well with Figure 18. The scatter at higher velocities, e.g., the +500 mV test, probably result from inaccuracies in the velocity measurements.

### F. General Susceptibility of Titanium-Aluminum-Alloys

The general variation of susceptibility of titanium-aluminum alloys tested in 0.6 M KCl at -500 mV is shown in Figures 20 (a) and (b) in which the K factor for initiation and crack velocity are plotted. K values for initiation were calculated for plain strain conditions and thickness of the 6% Al specimen was 0.2 in and that of the 8 to 10% alloys 0.06 in thick. Thus depending on the validity criterion accepted for plane strain conditions the values for intermediate K levels may be taken as valid or not. The low K values are almost certainly valid while the air values of the quenched specimens are invalid. However, the general trend of the results are significant and thus the decrease in K values for initiation and the increase in velocity with aluminum content indicate that the alloys containing $< \sim 5\%$ aluminum should be virtually immune.

### G. Effect of Potential on Velocity

The variation of velocity of crack propagation has been described by Beck[1] who showed that the relationship was approximately linear. This determination was for one sheet

---

[4]The velocity tends to increase again in the later stages of a test when $K \to K_{IC}$.

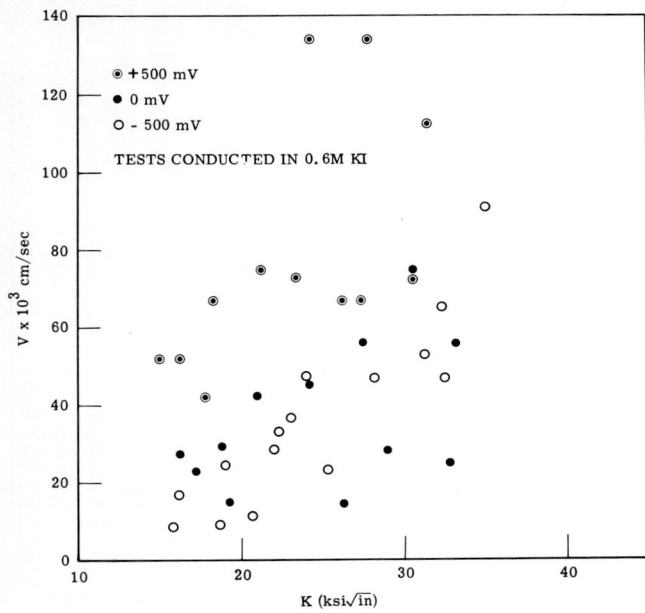

(a)

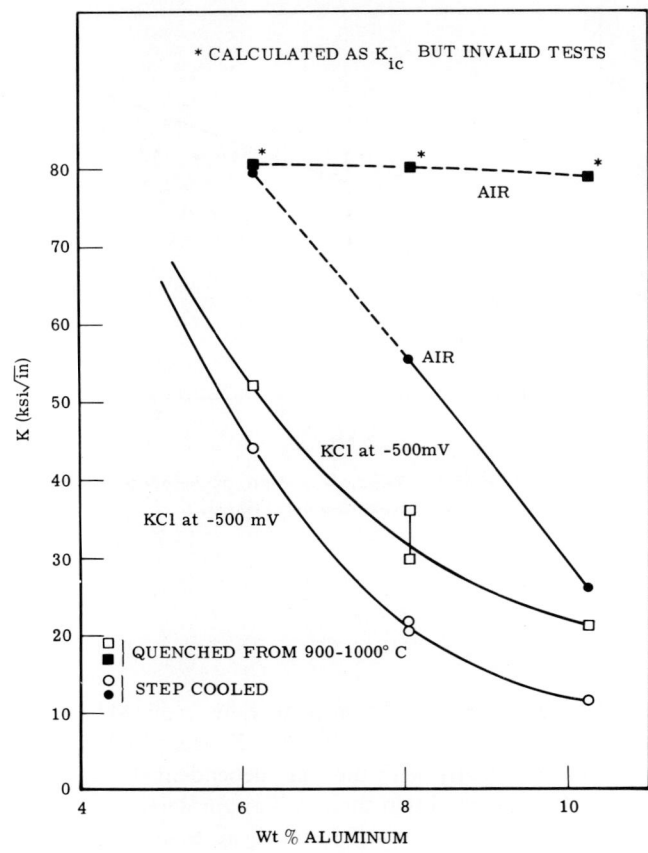

(a)

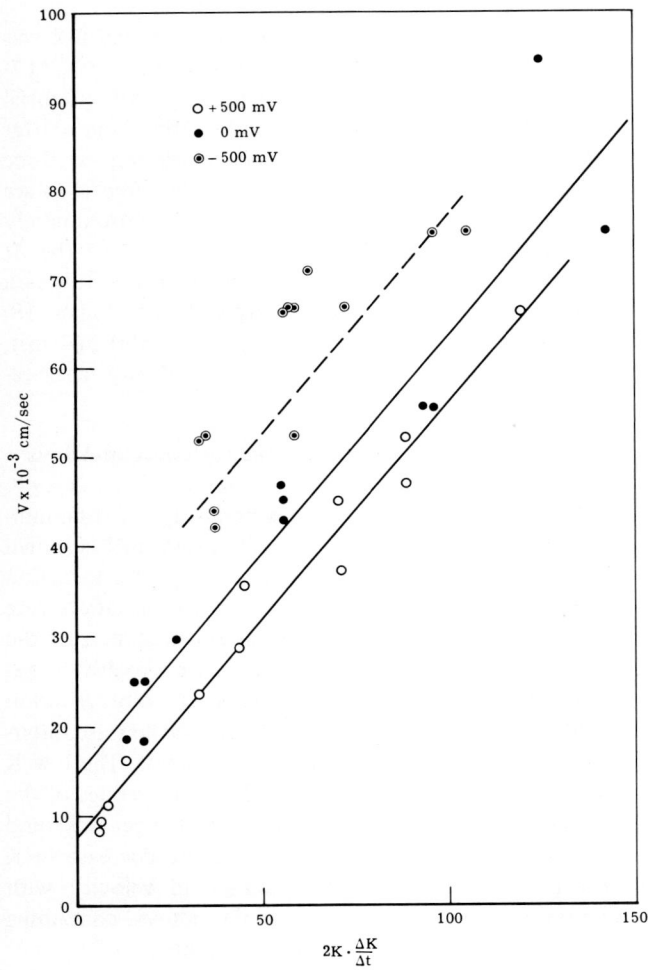

(b)

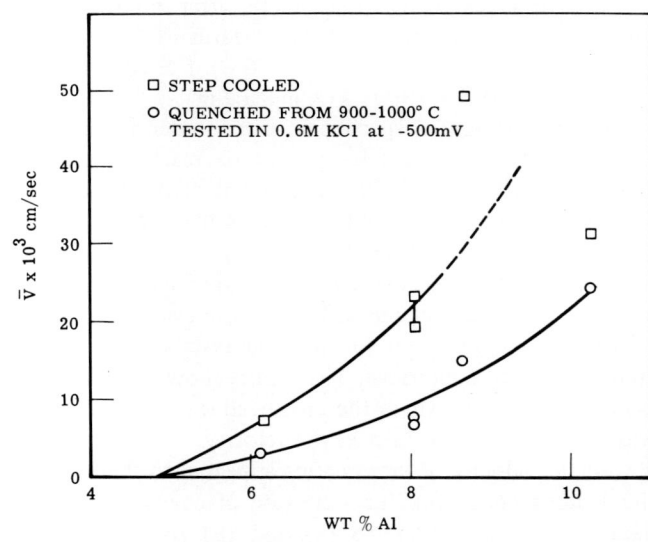

(b)

FIGURE 19 — (a) Sheet 2279. Variation of velocity with K at several potentials. (b) Sheet 2279. Variation of velocity with $2K \cdot \Delta K/\Delta t$ at several potentials.

FIGURE 20 — (a) Variation of K for initiation of cracking in a series of Ti:Al alloys. (b) Variation of velocity ($\overline{V}$) with Al content.

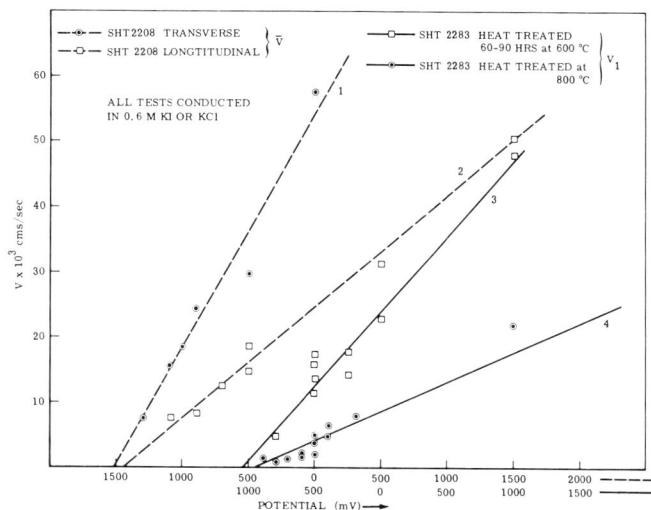

FIGURE 21 – Variation of velocity with potential showing the influence of specimen orientation and heat treatment.

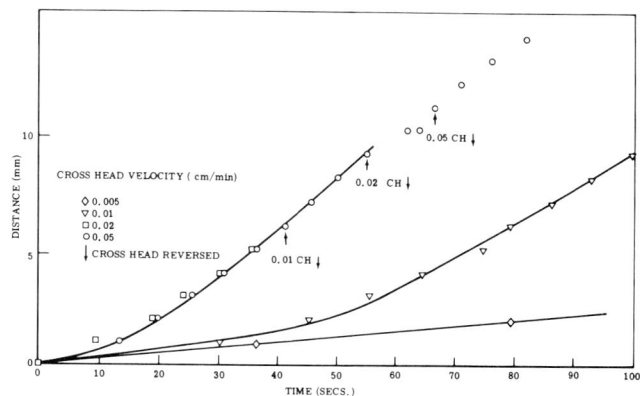

FIGURE 22 – Distance vs time for different initial crosshead velocity (crosshead stopped at crack initiation).

of material and although a linear relationship is usually found, a considerable variation in slope and the intercept for zero velocity has been found. Figure 21 illustrates two of the structural parameters that appear to influence such curves. Curves one and two show the variation for specimen orientation taken for one sheet, as can be seen when the crack propagates in the transverse direction the velocity is considerably faster than for a longitudinally propagating crack. Further a longitudinal crack often propagated at an angle 30° to the normal stress axis. A second factor is heat treatment, illustrated in Curves 3 and 4. From these it can be seen that specimens heat treated below 700 C have a more rapid propagation and are susceptible to lower potentials.

## H. Effect of Preferred Orientation

This effect has not been investigated systematically at present. However, it may be expected that as the cleavage plane is near the basal plane, its general orientation to the applied stress (see discussion) may affect susceptibility. The relationship between preferred orientation and susceptibility to SCC has been demonstrated by Fager and Spurr[17] for Ti:8-1-1. They showed that when the average cleavage plane is oriented parallel to the applied stress, the alloy was essentially immune to SCC. The differences observed in sheet 2208 tested in the transverse and longitudinal directions may have their origin in a preferred orientation effect.

## I. Effect of Loading and Unloading Rates

We have described in Sections A and E, the effect of unloading rates on the crack velocity. It is considered that the two stage curves, i.e., showing $V_1$ and $V_2$ sections are produced by a mechanical factor in the loading of

specimens, i.e., the rigid wedge type grips. If specimens are pin loaded or four point loaded, the crack still accelerates but the shape of the curve is generally concave upwards rather than divided into two distinct sections.

The second point of importance is whether the initiation of cracking is a dynamic or static process. For instance, it may be postulated that slip has to occur to produce fresh surface with which the environment can react. Two observations are relevant to this; firstly, the rate at which a crack accelerates is related to the initial loading rate as shown in Figure 22. Secondly, however, specimens loaded to the SCC initiation load in air and left for periods up to sixteen hours show exactly the same behavior, when the solution is added, as a dynamically loaded specimen, i.e., there appears to be no induction time before cracking is initiated.

## IV. Discussion

From the mass of rather confusing results we have to try to extract some of the salient points. It should be emphasized we are dealing with aqueous solutions and embrittlement in organic solvents, although showing similar trends, may occur by a different mechanism.

### 1. Fracture Initiation Criterion

We shall consider a crack initiating under plane strain conditions. As this appears to be a cleavage type process, we shall postulate that these conditions are necessary for SCC of a susceptible alloy.

(i) A critical normal stress.

(ii) The presence of an active environment.

(iii) Rupture of the oxide film (?)

The evidence for the first point is the well defined minimum stress intensity (all other conditions being

631

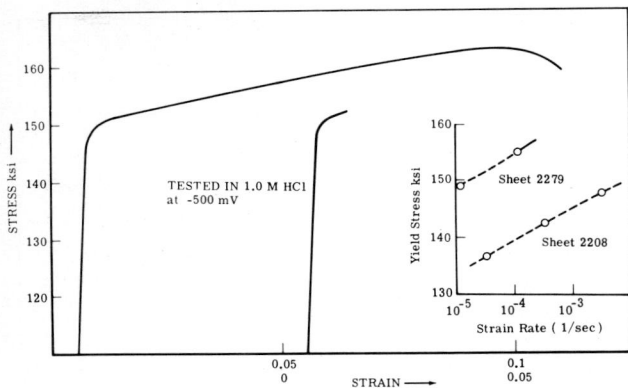

FIGURE 23 – Sheet 2279. Stress-strain curves for unnotched electropolished specimens tested in several environments.

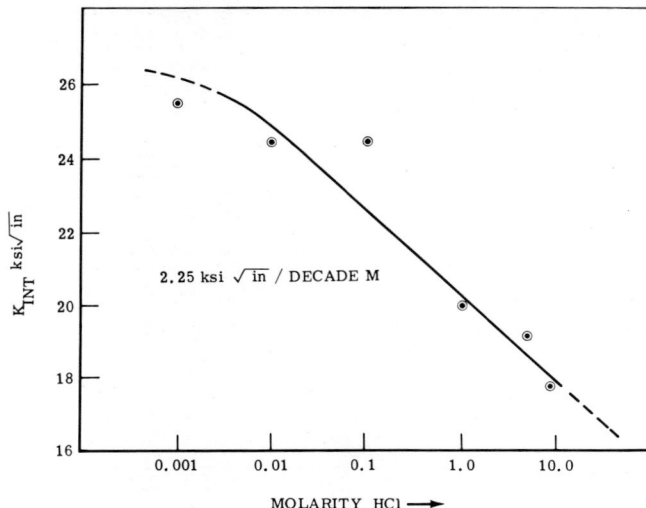

FIGURE 24 – Sheet 2208. Variation $K_{INT}$ with molarity of HCl at -500 mV.

specified) below which fracture will not initiate or propagate. The evidence for the second point is if the environment is removed or potential changed to a large cathodic value (-2000 mv) the cracking stops (under both plane strain and mixed conditions). The evidence for the third point is perhaps inconclusive (see Section I of Results) and not really essential to the argument.

We should next attempt to evaluate the normal stress condition for failure. Here the analysis of Hahn and Rosenfield[18] is of relevance as we are dealing with the onset of slow crack propagation and not the actual process of propagation. These workers show that the plastic constraint factor (pcf) in front of a sharp notch under plane strain conditions can be expressed for mild steel by pcf = 1 + 2 (K/Y), where K = stress intensity factor and Y = yield stress. This relation is in general agreement with the results of Barton and Hall.[19]

The minimum value of $K_{INT}$ that we have observed in Ti:8-1-1 is $\sim$ 10 Ksi $\sqrt{}$ in with a corresponding yield stress Y = 150 ksi which gives a value of $\sigma$ max = 1.13 Y. For duplex annealed material $K_{INT} \sim$ 40 Ksi $\sqrt{}$ in which for a yield stress of 120 Ksi give $\sigma$ max = 1.66 Y. Thus for duplex annealed material it is probable that SCC will occur only under plane strain conditions and thus there will be a limiting sheet thickness below which SCC will not occur. Such a thickness dependence is in fact observed. $K_{INT}$ tends to decrease as the Ti:8-1-1 is strengthened by precipitation of $\alpha_2$, i.e., as the yield stress increases. Thus at the highest yield strength (150 Ksi) it should become possible to produce SCC under plane stress condition or even in a uniaxial tension test. This is true in the case of Sheet 2279 as shown in Figure 23 which shows the drastic reduction in elongation produced by conducting a tension test in 1 M HCl at a potential of -500 mV. To obtain a complete analysis of fracture initiation, for one heat treatment, we must consider the following factors:

potential, concentration and preferred orientation. The first point is discussed in Beck's paper.[1] The variation of $K_{INT}$ with concentration (of HCl) is shown in Figure 24. Finally, to account for the effect of preferred orientation we resolve the applied stress on to the average cleavage plane. Thus we could write

$$K_{INT} = \frac{K'}{Cos^2 \phi} \pm (\text{potential term})$$

$$\pm (2.25 \text{ Ksi in/decade M}) [0.6 \text{ M} = 0]$$

(1)

where $K' = K$ when $\phi = 0$, $\phi$ is the angle between the applied stress axis and the average cleavage plane normal. The variation of $K_{INT}$ with heat treatment below 900 C appears to be approximately proportional to the uniaxial yield stress (Y) and can be expressed by

$$K_{INT} = (240 - 1.56 \text{ Y}) [\text{Y in ksi}]$$

(2)

which appears to fit the results for several but unfortunately not all sheets of Ti:8-1-1 that have been tested. This relationship could be taken as an indication of the variation $K'$, as most sheets have similar preferred orientations, but not as an absolute value. It is no doubt possible to construct such empirical equations for $K_{INT}$ for several titanium alloys but due to the number of variables, the amount of work involved is considerable.

### 2. Propagation

In this section we shall discuss the relative changes in velocity with heat treatment in Ti:8-1-1. In Section III.D.2 it was shown that velocity changed by a factor of $\sim$ 4 between solution treatment temperatures of 800-600 C. It is in this temperature range that the $\alpha_2$ phase is precipitated. Also it was shown in Section III.E. that the effect of

632

stress intensity on velocity was rather complex, there being a general increase in velocity with K level but that velocity also appeared to be related to the rate of loading or unloading which we have correlated with the rate of change of K in this time. Crack propagation is also influenced by the electrochemical factors of concentration and potential and by the preferred orientation of the specimen. We shall not discuss the effect of concentration or preferred orientation here. There are at least two explanations for these observations. Firstly, the electrochemical parameters may be changed by a dispersion of $\alpha_2$ phase, this possibility has not been investigated at this time. Secondly, there may be an increasing component of mechanical failure which would lead to faster velocities. This mechanical component must also occur by a cleavage mechanism as there is no evidence of a change in fracture mode, i.e., from flat cleavage facets to "dimples". Intuitively this seems a reasonable postulate as cleavage failures can be produced in air in material with a high yield strength ($\sim$ 150 ksi). For instance in the 2279 sheet about 50% of the failure occurs by cleavage when it is tested in air at a crosshead velocity of 0.5 cms/min. We assume therefore that the measured velocity is a combination of mechanical ($V_m$) and electrochemical ($V_e$) terms which are additive, i.e.,

$$V = V_e + V_m \qquad (3)$$

Considering first $V_e$, this increases with potential (see Figure 18) and also depends upon K level. Tests were conducted at -500, 0 and 500 mV in which range the potential variation can be expressed by

$$V_e \times 10^3 = 18 (1.100 + \chi) \qquad (4)$$

where $\chi$ is the potential in volts

The dependence of $V_e$ upon K can be approximately represented by

$$V_e \times 10^3 = (0.5 (K) + y) \qquad (5)$$

where y is a function of potential.
Thus we can compute $V_e$ for a test at a given potential and a known K level.

The next problem is to isolate the mechanical component of failure. It has been shown in fatigue crack propagation that the crack advance per cycle is related to crack tip opening displacement.[20] A similar correlation has been shown for slow crack propagation in steels;[21] in this latter case the rate of cracking is about two orders of magnitude less than in Ti:8-1-1 under the conditions reported here. Thus an attempt was made to correlate the crack velocity to the rate of crack opening displacement. (Tests are underway to directly measure such displacements but cannot be reported at this time.) Crack opening displacement, $\delta$ is related to the stress intensity factor K (for plane strain) by

$$\delta = \frac{K^2}{YE} \quad \text{where E is the elastic modulus} \qquad (6)$$

If we assume that crack velocity is proportional to the rate of change of displacement then

$$V \propto \frac{d\delta}{dt} = \frac{2K}{YE} \frac{dK}{dt} \qquad (7)$$

Thus the data in Figures 16 (a) and (b), and Figure 19 (a) was replotted as V vs 2K dK/dt and it can be seen from Figures 16 (c) and 19 (b) that reasonable straight line relationships result. If we try to isolate the mechanical component of cracking from Equation (3)

$$V - V_e = Vm \qquad (8)$$

Thus calculating $V_e$ at each point of a test from Equation (5) for the data in Figure 19 (a), subtracting this value from the observed velocity V, and plotting the resultant velocity versus 2K dK/dt results in Figure 25. This shows a roughly linear relationship which passes through the origin. For the alloy Ti:8-1-1 it is possible to write an expression for velocity as,

$$V = V_e + AK \frac{dK}{dt} \qquad (9)$$

where $V_e$ is a function of K and potential, and is dependent upon heat treatment and A is a constant also dependent upon heat treatment. It is found however that the slopes of the lines are two to three orders of magnitude greater than 1/YE. Most treatments of a relationship between crack tip opening displacement and crack extension specify a failure criterion in the form of a critical strain at a distance from the crack tip. As this appears to be a cleavage process the substitution of a critical strain may or may not be valid. However, if some length parameter $\ell$ is substituted in Equation (7), i.e.,

$$\frac{dS}{dt} = \frac{1}{YE\ell} \cdot \frac{dK}{dt} \qquad (10)$$

we obtain a type of strain rate equation. In fact the equation is equivalent to that of Hahn and Rosenfield for a *static* crack where $\ell$ was associated with the plastic zone size. It need only be noted that if a value for plastic zone size is substituted for $\ell$ the slope of the line in Figure 25 and for that calculated for mill annealed material is of the right order of magnitude.

In summary, several empirical relationships for crack propagation have been established. We have separated these into mechanical and electrochemical components and have correlated such a mechanical component with a strain rate type term although such a correlation may be fortuitous. Essentially, in the more brittle condition, Ti:8-1-1 may have an increasing mechanical component of failure which appears reasonable as the stress intensity for SCC approaches $K_{IC}$ at which level failure can occur by a mixture of cleavage and "ductile" failure. For an absolute correlation, the strain rate at the tip of propagating crack must be considered and the length parameter $\ell$ defined rigorously.

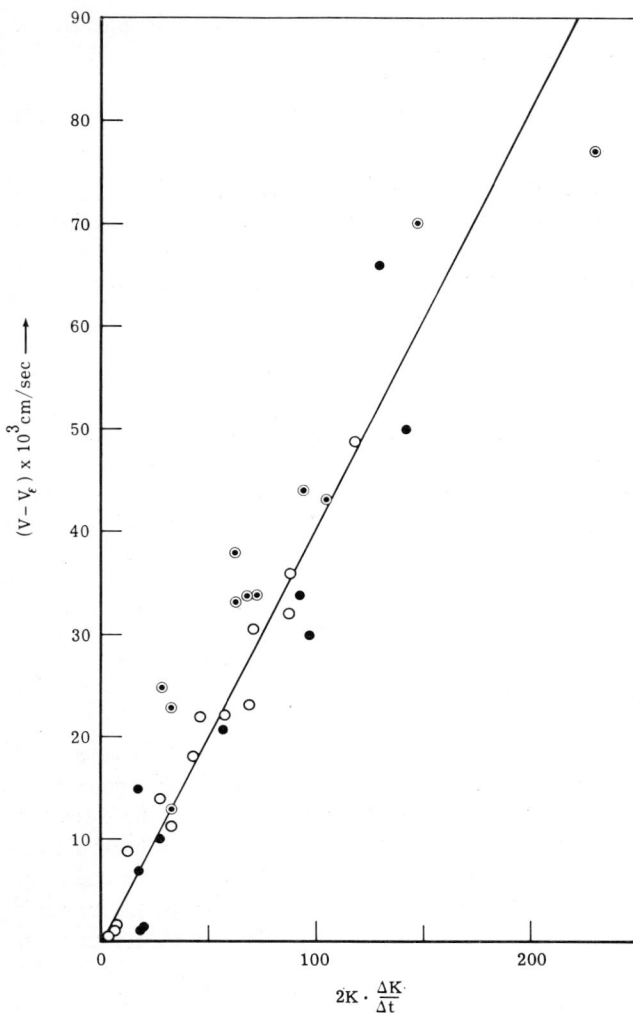

**FIGURE 25 — Sheet 2279. Data from Figure 19 replotted as $(V-V_e)$ vs $2K \cdot \Delta K/\Delta t$.**

Krafft[22] has formulated a quantitative model for SCC of titanium alloys based on a dissolution stage (electrochemical) superimposed on a mechanical failure stage. We have not applied Krafft's model to our results due to the lack of detailed mechanical property data. The fracture appearance of a SCC failure (cleavage like) does not appear to be consistent with the statement of the model. However, there is impressive agreement with Krafft's calculated and observed failure times. It should be noted that this agreement is for alloys with slower crack velocities than mill annealed Ti:8-1-1 and thus the constant A in Equation (9) is probably small. Detailed discussion of this model must be deferred until a direct application can be made to Ti:8-1-1 in order to correlate crack velocity with changes in mechanical properties produced by various heat treatment.

### 3. Susceptibility Criterion

We consider that the metallurgical factors control the susceptibility of titanium alloys to SCC. Essentially we have to explain (a) what determines the susceptibility of a given alloy and (b) how does heat treatment etc., affect susceptibility within this specified alloy.

Our general postulate is that aluminum content of the $\alpha$-phase has the predominant influence on susceptibility in $\alpha$ and super $\alpha$ alloys. This is illustrated by Figures 20 (a) and (b) which indicate that alloys containing $< \sim 5\%$ aluminum should be immune to SCC. However, it should be noted that at least four factors could shift this value to lower aluminum contents, viz:

(i) Larger grain size.

(ii) Higher oxygen content.

(iii) Higher electrolyte concentration (and possibly more unfavorable potentials).

(iv) A sheet texture in which the average cleavage plane lies normal to the applied stress.

Until more systematic work is performed on binary alloys the effect of other alloying elements remains unknown. One might expect that alloying elements which behave in a similar manner to aluminum may have the same effect, e.g., Sn, In, Ga, etc., and probably oxygen, as long as the electrochemical factors remain about the same.

It should be possible to relate the general metallurgical characteristics of the titanium-aluminum system to SCC susceptibility. Increasing aluminum content has been shown to promote (a) increased yield strength, (b) coplanar slip, and (c) decreased number of slip systems. These factors influence the ductility, plastic anisotropy and work hardening characteristics of the $\alpha$-phase. Possible origins of these effects will be described in a separate paper.[24] The influence of several of these factors on brittle fracture have been discussed by McEvily and Johnston[25] with special emphasis on slip character. The general results of the present investigation are in agreement with the behavior trends predicted by these workers. It should be noted however that there is still a gap between this approach and quantitative prediction of fracture.

It has been shown in many alloy systems that coplanar slip is associated with susceptibility to SCC, and this correlation has been found so frequently that it cannot be fortuitous. Coplanar slip is thus usually considered a necessary condition for susceptibility to SCC. Two, of several, arguments advanced to explain the correlation require either formation of a large slip step for crack nucleation[26] or a stress concentration at a piled up group to produce a brittle crack.[27] No direct evidence for either of these events has been obtained but we agree that both may occur. We suggest that possibly a more important factor may be the inability of the material to relax stress concentrations around a propagating crack. If this is a factor, then the mobility of dislocations would be an important parameter. Possible indirect evidence for this is the behavior of alloys containing the $\beta$-phase which has been embrittled by a dispersion of the $\omega$-phase. As the initiation load remains almost unchanged, fracture initiation is still controlled by the $\alpha$-phase but the velocity of crack propagation is increased. Thus the $\beta$-particles no longer act as ductile inclusions[5] and increase the ability of the material to sustain a sharp crack. It has been shown that the cleavage plane in these alloys is of the type

$10\bar{1}7$ - $10\bar{1}8$ and that the predominate slip vector is $\langle 11\bar{2}0\rangle$. As there is only a 12-15° misorientation between the slip vector and the cleavage plane, it is apparent that grains favorably oriented for cleavage will have a low resolved shear stress on the slip systems. Thus it will be difficult to relax any stress concentration by slip and this will accentuate preferred orientation effects. Essentially, we conclude that planar slip may influence nucleation of a crack but the factors listed above result in the ability of the material to sustain a sharp (and propagating) crack in the presence of an active environment.

In Ti:Al alloys containing $\geqslant 7\%$ Al low temperature aging produces a dispersion of the $\alpha_2$-phase and such a dispersion tends to accentuate the effects produced by aluminum additions to titanium listed above. The presence of this phase leads to both a lower initiation stress intensity and faster crack propagation. There appears to be a correlation of susceptibility to yield stress in both Ti:8-1-1 and Ti:Al alloys. Now the yield strength depends in part on the size and volume fraction of $\alpha_2$ particles, if such particles are sheared as has been shown in Figure 8. (A rather simple minded model for the increase in yield strength is included in Reference 11.) It has been shown in Figure 2 that step cooling leads to the formation of several sizes of $\alpha_2$ particles and would be expected to produce a large volume fraction of the phase, i.e., it is not possible to produce a large volume fraction of large particles by isothermal aging unless prohibitively long aging times are used. Thus it is not unexpected that step cooled specimens will have the highest yield strength and the highest susceptibility to SCC. A quantitative explanation of the reduction in initiation stress with both aluminum content and the presence of the $\alpha_2$-phase cannot be formulated at this time. Qualitatively the changes in mechanical properties, dislocation arrangements and slip modes are related to conditions for the onset of cleavage fracture. If the starting point is taken as the solid solution, cleavage failure occurs in a 12.5% aluminum alloy, and the onset of cleavage may be depressed to lower aluminum contents by metallurgical factors such as grain size and the precipitation of the $\alpha_2$-phase. In the presence of an active environment cleavage failure occurs at even lower aluminum contents and two further variables are introduced, concentration and potential. This behavior is represented diagrammatically in Figure 26. It should be remembered, however, that several of all of these effects can be present at one time. The faster velocities are due to a combination of, increases in the electrochemical velocity and an increased mechanical component in the fracture process. We postulate that high local strain rates, in these rate sensitive materials (see inset in Figure 23), locally raise the stress to that required for mechanical cleavage. The difference between the stresses for electrochemical and mechanical cleavage decrease with increasing aluminum content and the formation of the

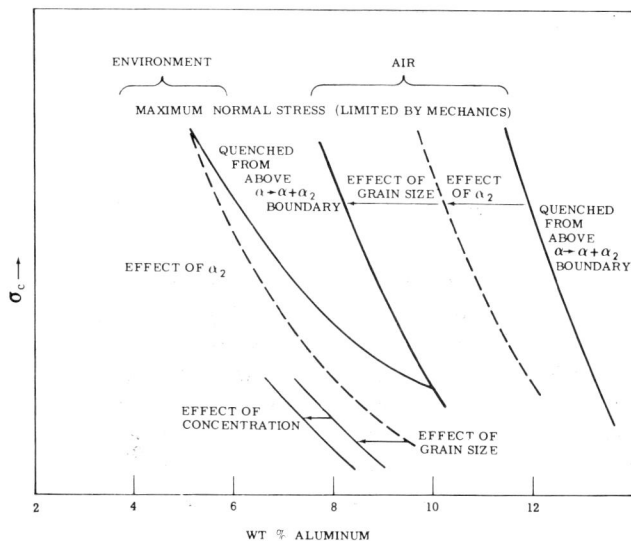

**FIGURE 26** – Schematic representation of influence of metallurgical and electrochemical variables on cleavage stress ($\sigma_c$) for Ti:Al alloys.

$\alpha_2$-phase. Thus it is to be expected that the mechanical component of fracture increases with both these factors.

Finally, considering the variation of susceptibility with solution treatment temperature ($> 900$ C) in the Ti:8-1-1. The reduction in susceptibility on quenching from high temperatures is associated with increasing volume fraction of the nonsusceptible phases $\beta$, $\alpha'$ and $\alpha''$ and to the corresponding reduction of volume fraction and mean path in the $\alpha$-phase. Some of the reasons for the nonsusceptibility of these phases are probably electrochemical in nature are discussed below.

## 4. Electrochemistry

Beck has considered many of the aspects of the phenomena which are included under this heading.[1] We will only comment on two factors, which are metallurgical in origin but which have an influence on the electrochemistry. Firstly, the $\beta$, $\alpha'$ and $\alpha''$ phases are not susceptible to SCC, while the $\beta$-phase in Ti:Mn and Ti:13-11-3 (B130VCA) and the $\alpha''$ phases in Ti:Al and Ti:5Al-2.5Sn are. The most obvious differences between the susceptible and non-susceptible phases are chemical, as structurally no marked differences have been detected, e.g., the $\alpha''$ in Ti:Al and Ti:8-1-1 appear microstructurally identical.[6] Thus we, as

---

[5] Preliminary work on a Ti:11.6% Mo alloy has shown that it is not susceptible to SCC in the $(\beta + \omega)$ condition. Thus the increased velocity is probably not due to the susceptibility of the $\beta$-phase.

[6] However, recent work has shown that the deformation characteristics of $\alpha''$ in Ti:5-2.5 differ from those of Ti:8-1-1 in the following ways:(i) The martensite plate boundaries in Ti:5-2.5 are basically low angle boundaries with small misorientation between adjacent plates. This allows relatively easy propagation of slip from one plate to the next. (ii) There are generally less variants of $\alpha''$ in a prior beta grain of Ti:5-2.5 than in Ti:8-1-1. This factor coupled with (i) above, results in a larger effective slip length (or grain size) in Ti:5-2.5 than in Ti:8-1-1. It is thus considered that the variations in susceptibility of $\alpha''$ result, at least in part, from these less obvious differences in slip character.

other workers, attribute nonsusceptibility to the Mo and possible V content of the nonsusceptible phases. Secondly, there appears to be electrochemical differences between the behavior of an $\alpha$-phase containing $\alpha_2$ particles and one that does not, e.g., in $V_e$ values and in the intercept of potential:velocity plots. We do not suggest explanations for either of these observations but they are obviously of practical importance.

In this study we have tried to separate the variables that contribute to SCC of titanium alloys. We consider that Beck has shown that the process is neither hydrogen embrittlement (HE) nor an oxide wedging process. However, in the above discussion we do not specify the mechanism of interaction of the environment with the metal. Until this is elucidated we consider it premature to attempt quantitative application of dislocation models to

the fracture process. Such models treat the cracking as essentially mechanical, the environment effects being included in the rather nebulous surface energy terms. The evaluation of such energy terms will involve a detailed knowledge of at least the shape of the crack tip, the structure of the electrolyte on this scale and its effect on the surface and possibly on dislocation mobility. Until this stage is reached, it is considered that the continuum and semi-empirical approach used here is the most realistic.

## Acknowledgments

The authors wish to express their appreciation for the experimental assistance of Mrs. H. Wallner, Mr. P. Olson, Mr. R. Lee and Mr. R. Boyer. This work was supported in part by ARPA Order No. 878 (JCW) and by NASA Contract NAS7-489 (MJB).

## References

1. T. R. Beck. Electrochemical Aspects of Titanium Stress Corrosion Cracking. This conference.
2. G. Sanderson and J. C. Scully. *Environment Sensitive Mechanical Properties of Materials*. A. R. C. Westwood and N. S. Stoloff, editors, Gordon and Breach, New York, 511 (1966).
3. G. Sandoz and R. L. Newbegin. *Report on NRL Progress*, p. 28 (1967) March.
4. D. E. Piper, S. H. Smith and R. V. Carter. *Boeing Document D6-60067*, p. 16 (1967) March.
5. W. F. Spurr. *Boeing Document D6-A10065-1* (1966) March.
6. B. F. Brown. *Materials Research and Standards*, 6, 219 (1966).
7. G. Sanderson and J. C. Scully. *Nature*, 211, 179 (1966).
8. W. F. Spurr. *op. cit.*, 18 (1966) March.
9. J. E. Srawley and W. F. Brown. *Fracture Toughness Testing and Its Applications*, ASTM, 133 (1965).
10. M. J. Blackburn. *Trans. AIME*, 329, 1200 (1967).
11. M. J. Blackburn. *Trans. ASM*, 59, 694 (1966).
12. M. J. Blackburn. *Trans. ASM*, 59, 876 (1966).
13. J. C. Williams and M. J. Blackburn. *Trans. ASM*, 60, 373 (1967).
14. R. I. Jaffee. *Progress in Metal Physics*, 7, 75, Pergamon Press
15. F. A. Crossley and W. F. Carew. *Trans. AIME*, 209, 43 (1957).
(1958).
16. D. G. Howe. *Report of NRL Progress*, 32 (1967) February.
17. D. N. Fager and W. F. Spurr. *Trans. ASM*, 61, 283 (1968).
18. G. Han and A. Rosenfield. *Trans. ASM*, 59, 909 (1966).
19. F. W. Barton and W. J. Hall. *Ship Structure Committee Report SSC-147* (1963).
20. F. A. McClintock. Discussion paper by C. Laird, Atlantic City ASTM Meeting (1967).
21. W. W. Gerberich and C. E. Hartbower. This conference.
22. J. M. Krafft. *Report of NRL Progress*, 6 (1966) March.
23. H. Logan. *The Stress Corrosion of Metals*, Chapter 1, Wylie (1966).
24. M. J. Blackburn and J. C. Williams. To be published.
25. A. J. McEvily and T. L. Johnston. *Proc. of First Internat. Conf. on Fracture*, p. 515, Japanese Society for Strength and Fracture of Materials, Japan (1966).
26. H. Pickering and P. Swann. *Corrosion*, 19, 373 (1963).
27. W. Robertson and A. Tetelman. *Strengthening Mechanisms in Solids*, p. 217, ASM (1962).

## Discussion

**E. N. Pugh, RIAS:**

I should like to make a comment which is relevant to Dr. Blackburn's paper and also to the previous paper by Dr. Beck. Both authors state that failure in titanium alloys in aqueous solutions occurs by cleavage which, by definition, is a brittle process occurring with high velocity. At the same time, evidence is presented which indicates that the overall rate of cracking is relatively slow. Therefore we must conclude that crack propagation is discontinuous. Is there any evidence to support this conclusion?

**M. J. Blackburn:**

Dr. Pugh states that a cleavage crack, by definition, propagates rapidly and in many cases of catastrophic cleavage failure of metallic materials this is indeed true. Such cracks propagate under conditions of limited plastic flow, which prevents blunting of the crack, and this sets a lower limit on crack velocity. Low[1] considers that "in the limit one would not expect to propagate a cleavage crack

slowly except in the exceptional cases where the cohesive strength of the cleavage plane is very low compared with the resistance to glide in the glide planes that are oblique to the cleavage plane". Such conditions may apply to the SCC of titanium alloys for it has been shown that the condition for cleavage are the most unfavorable for slip. Two examples of slow cleavage-like crack growth may be given. Firstly in a brittle substance such as glass cracks may propagate slowly, as anyone who has suffered a cracked windshield can attest. Secondly in liquid metal embrittlement the degradation of the cleavage or cohesive strength appears to override the inherent ductility of the material.

We list below some pertinent observations to crack propagation in $\alpha$-phase Ti alloys under SCC conditions:

(a) The crack follows a specific crystallographic plane and microscopically the fracture surface exhibits many of the features of cleavage failure. The fracture facets contain steps with a spacing $\sim 0.5 - 1\,\mu$, i.e., considerably smaller than the $\alpha$-grain size.

(b) The macroscopic fracture surface is very rough and crack branching is observed indicating that the fracture front is rather irregular.

(c) The current:time record during cracking indicates that fracture occurs continuously but the fine structure on such a record possibly indicates that the rate of surface production is not constant.

(d) Acoustic emission studies[2] during cracking show that cracking of duplex annealed Ti:8-1-1 is essentially "silent". This indicates that the cracking does not occur rapidly over a sufficiently large area to produce an emission event. In mill annealed Ti:8-1-1 emissions are produced during SCC.

From the above evidence we conclude that SCC failure exhibits several features of cleavage cracks which may propagate with a spectrum of velocities. It is considered that pre-existing slip bands and grain boundaries are regions in which a crack will propagate more slowly. Beck's[3] model proposes that the transport of halide ions to the crack tip zone is a controlling process and this transport rate sets an upper limit on crack velocity. In duplex annealed Ti:8-1-1, crack propagation appears to be only slightly dependent on stress (when $K < 0.6\ K_{IC}$), thus the limiting crack velocity does appear to be controlled by the electrochemical conditions, and no rapid cleavage events occur (i.e., $V \geqslant 10^3$ cm/sec). In mill annealed material the average velocity is higher and acoustic emissions are detected during cracking, thus in this condition some mechanical or rapid cleavage may occur, the velocity of such cracks are unknown.

1. J. R. Low. *Fracture,* Ed. B. L. Averback, D. K. Felbeck, G. T. Hahn and D. A. Thomas. The M.I.T. Press, Cambridge, Mass. p. 68 (1959).

2. A. Pollock. *Acoustic Emission Occurring During Stress Corrosion Cracking of Titanium Alloys.* Boeing Doc. D1-82-0658. To be published.

3. T. R. Beck. This volume.

# METALLOGRAPHIC STUDIES OF THE STRESS CORROSION CRACKING
# OF TITANIUM ALLOYS IN AQUEOUS CHLORIDE SOLUTIONS

G. Sanderson, D. T. Powell and J. C. Scully
The University of Leeds

## Abstract

Ti, Ti-5Al-2.5Sn, Ti-6Al-4V and a series of binary Ti-Al and Ti-Sn alloys have been studied in $MgCl_2$ solutions boiling at 154 C. The first three materials have also been studied in 3% NaCl solution at room temperature. At 154 C pitting occurs and under stress all the alloys suffer intergranular cracking and fissuring. Surface hydrides change the predominant mode to transgranular in the richer alloys. The mechanism is thought to be the result of slow dissolution. In 3% NaCl solutions the cracking takes place as an interrupted cleavage process as revealed by scanning electron microscopy. This occurs as a result of hydrogen pickup on freshly created metal surfaces at the tip of the propagating crack where plastic deformation aids the hydride formation mechanism which initiates the cleavage.

## Introduction

Titanium metal and its alloys normally exhibit excellent corrosion resistance to aqueous neutral chloride environments. In recent years, however, stress corrosion failures have been reported, firstly in laboratory investigations and, more recently, under service conditions. Some organic and inorganic liquids have also been found to cause failure. It is not known whether residual traces of chloride compounds are always responsible for this.

Several investigations of aqueous chloride cracking have been reported. In 1951 Uhlig and Cobb[1] found that an unspecified alloy was not susceptible to cracking in $MgCl_2$ solutions boiling at 154 C. In 1956 Fontana[2] reported the intergranular cracking of Ti-5Al-2.5Sn alloy under stress in 10% HCl solutions at 35 C but found that it was immune in the $MgCl_2$ environment. In 1965, however, Sanderson and Scully[3] reported that both the Ti-5Al-2.5Sn $\alpha$ alloy and the Ti-6Al-4V $\alpha + \beta$ alloy were susceptible in this environment. Cracking was mainly but not completely intergranular. Their experiments showed that very severe cold work was necessary for the pit initiation that preceded crack initiation. Titanium metal did not crack but it suffered pitting attack in the same environment. Henrikson[4] has also reported pitting in titanium specimens exposed to $CaCl_2$ solutions at 130 C in autoclaves.

Failures in aqueous chloride solutions at room temperature were found in 1964 when Brown[5] observed that specimens of Ti-8Al-1Mo-1V alloy exhibited a lowering of resistance to crack propagation when tested in the pre-cracked notch bar test while immersed in sea water. Lane et al[6] have characterized this type of failure as a time dependent reduction of strength producing a rapid failure (which has been reported[7] as propagating at ins/hour or ins/min) and a distinctive appearance of the fracture surface. Judy et al[8] have shown that the corrosion process produces 'quasi-cleavage' surfaces during the corrosion fatigue of Ti-7Al-2Cb-1Ta alloy.

Lane et al[6] concluded from their investigation that susceptibility to transgranular stress corrosion fracture can be eliminated in some alloys (a) by heat treatment in the $\beta$ range, (b) by the addition of isomorphous $\beta$ stabilizers, and (c) by lowering the aluminum content. Aluminum was considered to promote embrittlement by forming the ordered $Ti_3Al$ phase.

Treatments that produce a discontinuous network of the $\alpha$ phase lower and possibly even remove susceptibility. Thus the $\alpha + \beta$ Ti-6Al-4V alloy is not susceptible to low cycle fatigue[8] and has been reported[9] immune to stress corrosion although Brown[10] has reported that this alloy exhibits a lowering of resistance to crack propagation when tested in sea water. It must be added that it is not only the $\alpha$ phase alloys that are susceptible to sea water stress corrosion. Ti-8Mn and Ti-13V-11Cr-3Al alloys, for example, are susceptible. Lane et al[6] have therefore concluded that the eutectoid structure and omega phase may be additional factors in promoting embrittlement.

Feige and Murphy[9] have shown that the application of cathodic polarization raises the fracture stress of $\alpha$ alloys in sea water to the value for fracture in air whereas anodic polarization raises the sea water fracture stress but not so high. They also reported that the application of cathodic polarization arrests surface cracks but not deep tunnelling cracks, possibly because of the poor throwing power down the tunnels.

Transgranular fracture of Ti-5Al-2.5Sn alloy in 3% NaCl solutions acidified to pH 0.75 has been reported[11] in sheet specimens that were chemically polished and then strained while immersed in the electrolyte. The cracking was considered to be associated with the thin layer of hydride phase formed during chemical polishing. Experiments on thin foils have shown[12] that a γ-hydride precipitate is formed along the line of the bend if a thin foil of the same alloy is deformed in the same environment. Foils of titanium metal do not develop the second phase under similar conditions. Tomashov[13] has also reported cracking in stressed α phase titanium alloys arising from hydride formation. Cracking occurred after cathodic polarization in HCl and $H_2SO_4$ solutions. Titanium metal specimens treated similarly did not crack and suffered a normal ductile failure when subsequently broken.

In this paper simple U-bend tests and dynamic tensile tests are reported together with experiments employing thin foil transmission electron microscopy and scanning electron microscopy. Cracking in aqueous chloride environments at 154 C and at room temperature has been investigated. An attempt has been made to relate the electrochemical parameters, fracture characteristics and physical metallurgical factors together in order to discern the basic cracking mechanisms that are operative during the stress corrosion of α phase titanium alloys.

## Experimental Methods

The compositions of the materials used in this investigation are given in Table 1.

The commercially available metal and ternary alloys were in sheet form 0.06 cm thick in the annealed condition. The Ti-2Cu alloy was cold-rolled from 0.1 cm to 0.025 cm. Subsequently the alloy was heated at 798 C in an argon atmosphere for 2 hours and quenched into water. This treatment produced an equiaxed grain structure containing a minimum amount of the $Ti_2Cu$ phase. The binary Ti-Al alloys were in sheet form 0.06-0.08 cm thick in the annealed condition. The binary Ti-Sn alloys had been cold rolled to 0.025 cm thickness and were annealed at 850 C for 3 hours in an argon atmosphere followed by slow cooling.

The highest purity grade of chemicals commercially available was used. Solutions were made up with distilled water.

Qualitative stress corrosion tests were performed on simple U-bend specimens, prepared by shearing the specimen and the holder from the same sheet. Each specimen was 1.25 x 5 cm and it fitted into two acute notches cut along one edge of the holder. No attempt was made to calculate the amount of plastic deformation or the value of the stress imposed on specimens during the bending and clamping process. Optical examination of all specimens was undertaken before immersion in order to ensure that no cracks were created during the preparation. Before assembly both specimens and holders were thoroughly degreased in acetone or ethyl alcohol. In some experiments the assembly was made while specimens were immersed.

The aqueous magnesium chloride environment (b.pt. 154 C) was contained in a heated flask fitted with a reflux condenser to maintain the composition of the solution. U-bend specimens were completely immersed in the boiling solution and when taken out for examination were quenched in water and dried.

Standard flat specimens stamped from a die were used in experiments with an Instron tensile testing machine. These had a 5 cm gauge length and were 1 cm wide. For some experiments a single 90° notch was filed 0.2 mm deep in from the center of one edge. The specimens were passed through a slit in the bottom of a polyethylene beaker and cemented into place with an inert glue. After mounting this arrangement vertically into the testing machine the electrolyte was poured into the beaker to a depth of 1 cm. Specimens were then loaded to fracture at different strain rates and examined for indications of stress corrosion.

Thin foil specimens suitable for electron microscopy were prepared by a two-stage process.[14] The material was chemically thinned to a thickness of 0.017 cms in a solution of the following composition: 44 wt% HCl, 40 vol $H_2O_2$ and water in the volumetric proportions 1:6:3, and maintained below 30 C. The final stage of foil preparation, using the 'window' technique, was performed by electro-polishing at -30 C using a cell voltage of 40 V and the following solution: 295 cc methyl alcohol, 175 cc n-butyl alcohol and 30 cc perchloric acid.

All foils were subjected to an extremely thorough examination in the electron microscope before performing experiments because of the possibility of hydrogen contamination of specimens during preparation.

Chemical polishing was done with a solution containing 44% HF and 73% $HNO_3$ in the volumetric ratio 2:3 as previously described.[12]

#### TABLE 1–Fracture and Embrittlement Times
#### for the Commercial Alloys (hours)

| | | | Materials | | | |
|---|---|---|---|---|---|---|
| | Fe | H | Al | Sn | V | Cu |
| Ti | 0.08 | 30 ppm | – | – | – | – |
| Ti | 0.07 | 100 ppm | 5.14 | 2.54 | – | – |
| Ti | 0.14 | 80 ppm | 6.24 | – | 3.87 | – |
| Ti | | | – | – | – | 2.0[1] |
| Ti | | | 2.16 | – | – | – |
| Ti | | | 4.50 | – | – | – |
| Ti | | | 6.67 | – | – | – |
| Ti | | | 8.64 | – | – | – |
| Ti | | | – | 3.0[1] | – | – |
| Ti | | | – | 8.0[1] | – | – |

[1]Nominal Composition.

639

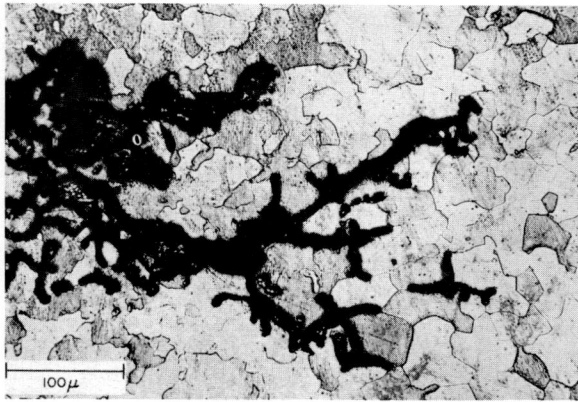

FIGURE 1 – Optical micrograph of a predominantly intergranular stress corrosion crack in Ti-5Al-2.5Sn
alloy after exposure to $MgCl_2$ solution. Specimen etched in 2% HF-2% $HNO_3$ solution.

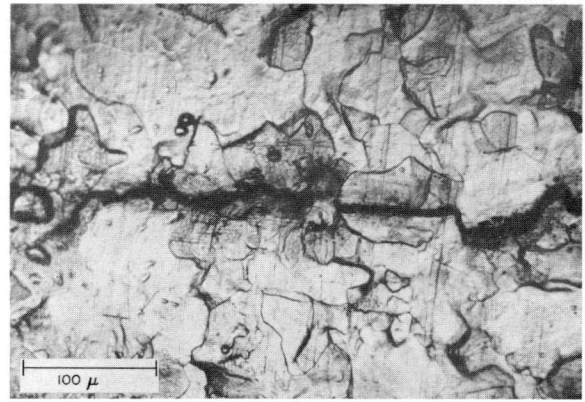

FIGURE 3 – Optical micrograph of a predominantly transgranular crack in a chemically polished
specimen of Ti-5Al-2.5Sn alloy after exposure
to an acidified $MgCl_2$ solution. Specimen
etched in 2% HF-2% $HNO_3$ solution.

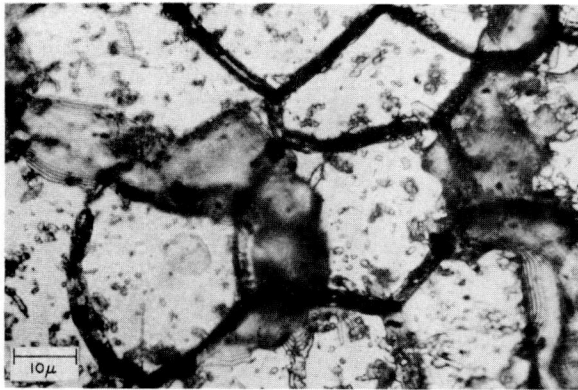

FIGURE 2 – Optical micrograph of intergranular grooving in
Ti-5Al-2.5Sn alloy after exposure to acidified
$MgCl_2$ solution. Unetched.

FIGURE 4 – Electron micrograph of a thin foil of Ti-5Al-
2.5Sn alloy prepared by chemical polishing.
The lath-like precipitate in $\gamma$-hydride.

## Experimental Results

### $MgCl_2$ Solutions at 154 C

All the alloys examined were susceptible to stress
corrosion cracking which was predominantly intergranular.
As reported earlier[3] all the materials developed an overall
bluish coloration after a few minutes immersion in the
unacidified solutions but not in solutions acidified by the
addition of hydrochloric acid. After a period of time all the
materials developed small pits which were preceded by
localized thickening of the surface film into the interference color range. In the alloys cracks developed from the
pits and propagated across the outer surface of the bent
specimen in the region of maximum curvature. Once this
had started further oxide thickening did not appear to be
necessary. If, however, a partially cracked specimen was
removed from the solution the process of film thickening
occurred again around the tip of the old crack before
further propagation of the crack continued. Crack propagation rates in all the susceptible materials appeared to be

similar: approximately 0.1-0.5 cm/hour. Titanium metal
suffered from pitting but not crack.

In acidified solutions crack initiation occurred more
rapidly than in unacidified solutions. Coupling specimens to
platinum also shortened the time to failure in either
solution.[3] Coupling to iron prevented crack initiation and
pitting.[3]

An example of the wide blunt cracks that developed in
Ti-5Al-2.5Sn alloy is shown in Figure 1. This alloy also
suffered severe and widespread grain boundary grooving in
acidified solutions, even if unstressed, as shown in Figure 2.
The effect of chemically polishing specimens of this alloy
before experiments was twofold: (a) it shortened the time
to failure, and (b) it changed the mode of cracking from
predominantly intergranular to predominantly transgranular. A stress corroded chemically polished specimen of
Ti-5Al-2.5Sn alloy is shown in Figure 3. Chemical polishing
of this alloy produces an intragranular network of small
$\gamma$-hydride precipitates as shown in Figure 4 and reported
previously.[12] The matrix/hydride interface is incoherent
and very reactive. Chemically polished foils immersed in

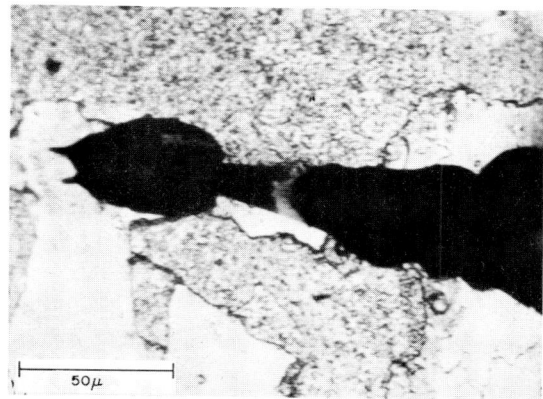

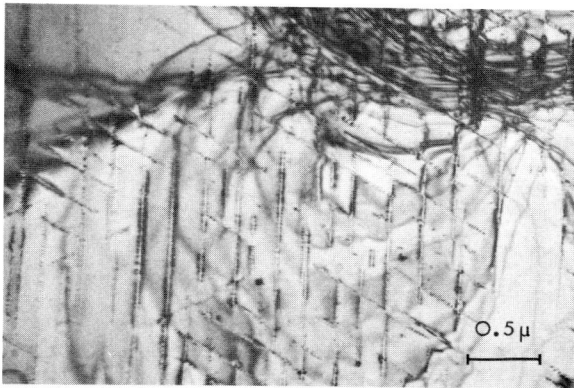

**FIGURE 5** — Electron micrograph of a thin foil of Ti-5Al-2.5Sn alloy prepared by chemical polishing which has been immersed in MgCl$_2$ solution containing 1% of a 10 wt% solution of chloroplatinic acid for one minute. Platinum has deposited galvanically at the hydride/matrix interfaces which are the first sites to be attacked.

**FIGURE 7** — Optical micrograph of a predominantly intergranular stress corrosion crack in a chemically polished specimen of Ti-2.16Al alloy after exposure to acidified MgCl$_2$ solution. Unetched.

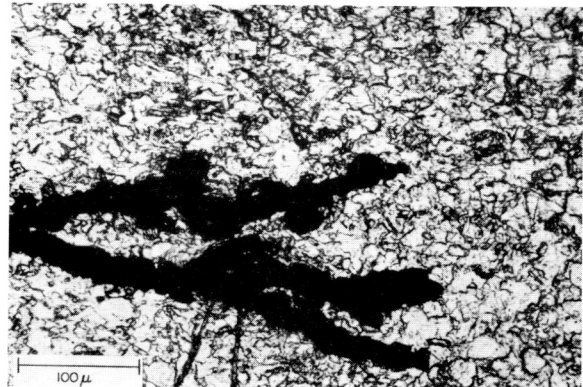

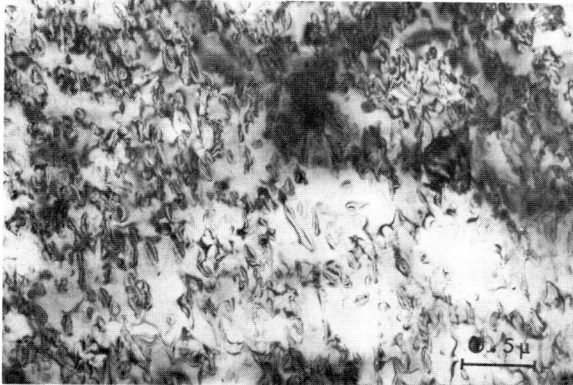

**FIGURE 6** — Electron micrograph of a thin foil of Ti-2Cu alloy, prepared by chemical polishing, exhibiting small hydride precipitates.

**FIGURE 8** — Optical micrograph of a predominantly intergranular stress corrosion crack in a specimen of Ti-4.5Al alloy after exposure to MgCl$_2$ solution. Specimen etched in 2% HF-2% HNO$_3$ solution.

MgCl$_2$ solutions are preferentially attacked at the interfaces. This is shown in Figure 5 which illustrates a specimen immersed for one minute in a solution to which chloroplatinic acid had been added. Platinum atoms have deposited galvanically along the interfaces. The change in the mode of cracking of Ti-5Al-2.5Sn alloy as a result of chemical polishing can therefore be attributed to the creation of the reactive transgranular interfaces.

The two-phase $\alpha + \beta$ alloy, Ti-6Al-4V, was the most susceptible of the commercial alloys studied as indicated by the times to failure. Stress corrosion cracks were intergranular although the small grain size of the material studied made observations difficult. By contrast with the Ti-5Al-2.5Sn alloy very little branching occurred in the Ti-6Al-4V alloy. Chemically polished specimens of the two-phase alloy were more susceptible than specimens tested with the as-received surface condition but it was not

possible to discern whether any transgranular cracking resulted from this treatment as in the Ti-5Al-2.5Sn alloy.

Specimens of the Ti-2Cu alloy exhibited pitting and oxide thickening but did not fracture unless they were chemically polished when they then suffered intergranular cracking. Chemical polishing produces very small hydrides in this alloy as shown in Figure 6 and they are more widely spaced than in the Ti-5Al-2.5Sn alloy. Thus the polishing treatment does not provide a continuous transgranular path.

The type of cracking observed in the Ti-Al binary alloys varied considerably. In the dilute alloys stress corrosion cracks consisted of pits that were joined together by short sections of wide intergranular fissures. Chemical polishing increased the susceptibility but did not alter the mode of cracking. A cracked specimen of chemically polished Ti-2.16Al alloy is shown in Figure 7. In the

641

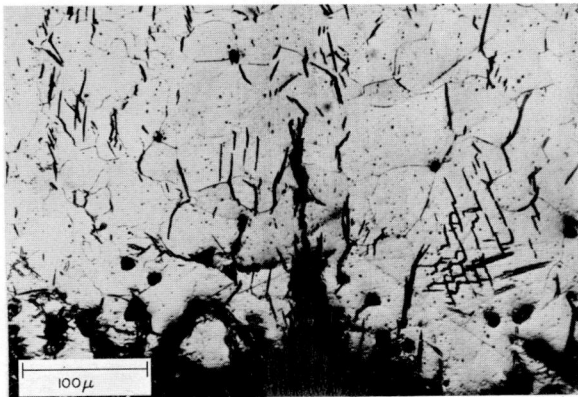

FIGURE 9 — Optical micrograph of predominantly trans-granular cracks produced in a chemically polished specimen of Ti-5Al-2.5Sn alloy by bending while immersed in acidified NaCl solution. Specimen etched in 2% HF-2% HNO₃ solution.

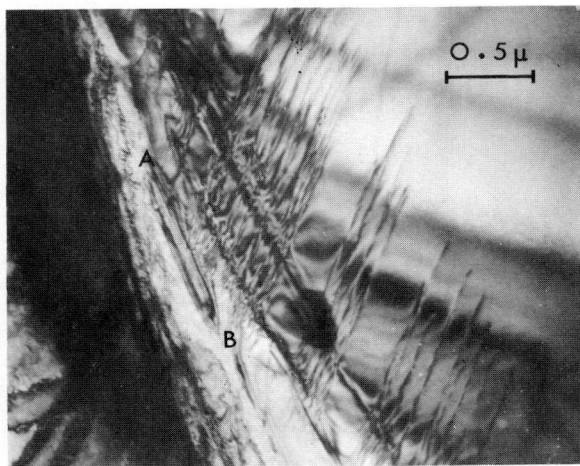

FIGURE 10 — Electron micrograph of a thin foil of Ti-5Al-2.5Sn alloy, produced by electropolishing, bent while immersed in acidified NaCl solution for 4 hours. A hydride precipitate (AB) has formed along the line of the bend.

Ti-4.5Al alloy the pits were smaller and more numerous at the onset of cracking than in the lower alloy while cracks were narrower as shown in Figure 8. Chemically polished specimens exhibited similar intergranular cracking characteristics although the cracks appeared to be somewhat narrower than in the as-received material. The Ti-6.67Al and Ti-8.64Al alloys failed by intergranular cracking; the general appearance of cracking was similar in both cases to that shown in Figure 1 for the Ti-5Al-2.5Sn alloy. Furthermore the same transition from predominantly intergranular to predominantly transgranular cracking was observed as a result of chemical polishing.

The Ti-Sn alloys both exhibited pitting in MgCl₂ solutions but they only suffered intergranular cracking when the solutions were acidified. Pits were more numerous

on Ti-Sn alloys than on Ti-Al alloys. Chemical polishing shortened the time to failure but did not alter the mode of cracking in either alloy. Cracks were narrow and showed very little branching.

### NaCl Solution at Room Temperature

The behavior of titanium, Ti-5Al-2.5Sn and Ti-6Al-4V alloys was examined in this environment.

U-bend specimens immersed for 200 days in neutral 3% NaCl solution and in the same solution acidified with HCl to pH 0.75 showed no signs of corrosion attack. This was also true for specimens assembled while immersed. From these results it appeared that the chloride ion did not cause breakdown of the protective film nor did it delay the repassivation of freshly exposed metal sufficiently to promote pit initiation when the film was mechanically ruptured. Chemically polished specimens assembled prior to immersion showed no attack but specimens of Ti-5Al-2.5Sn alloy assembled while immersed in the acidified environment developed transgranular cracks over 42 days as shown in Figure 9. The titanium and Ti-6Al-4V alloy showed no signs of attack over 200 days when tested under identical conditions. Some specimens of the susceptible alloy were examined daily after being dried. These developed cracks in about the same time as other specimens that were not disturbed during the test. It appeared therefore that the bending of specimens while immersed in the environment was of paramount importance but that whatever form of attack was initiated was not affected by intermittent drying.

The main effect of bending a chemically polished specimen is the rapid breaking of either some of the hydride precipitates lying in the surface or the matrix/hydride interfaces. Observations on foils containing hydrides suggests that it would be the interface that would break. The fresh surfaces produced on chemically polished specimens strained in air will rapidly oxidize and cracking does not therefore occur after immersion. When specimens are strained in the solution, however, the fresh surfaces within the micro-cracks form so rapidly that repassivation occurs only after some of the hydrogen discharging on the active surface has entered the alloy and has caused precipitation of the γ-hydride phase. This was illustrated, as reported briefly elsewhere,[12] by experiments on thin foils of Ti-5Al-2.5Sn alloy. When foils were bent while immersed in the acidified environment a precipitate of γ-hydride was formed along the bend in the foil as illustrated in Figure 10. Similar experiments in 3% Na₂SO₄ solution acidified with H₂SO₄ to the same pH did not result in hydride formation. Neither environment caused hydride formation in titanium metal foils. With such experiments it is not possible to measure the strain rate imposed on foils when they are bent nor is it possible to ensure it is always the same yet the experiments were done 5 times and the same qualitative results were obtained each time. Foils of the alloy and titanium metal immersed for 10 hours without bending exhibited no detectable change upon re-examination.

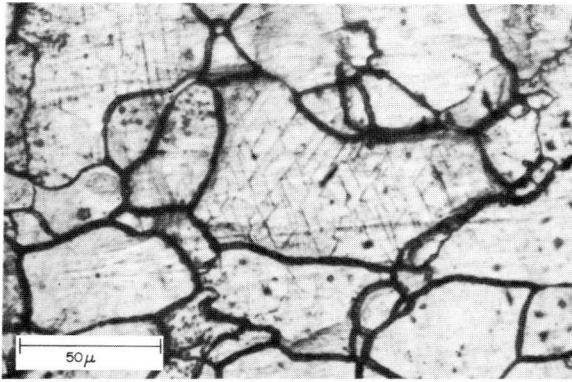

FIGURE 11 — Optical micrograph of a specimen of Ti-5Al-2.5Sn alloy etched in 2% HF-2% HNO₃ solution after being immersed in NaCl solution for 200 days. Grain boundary grooving and intragranular precipitates can be observed.

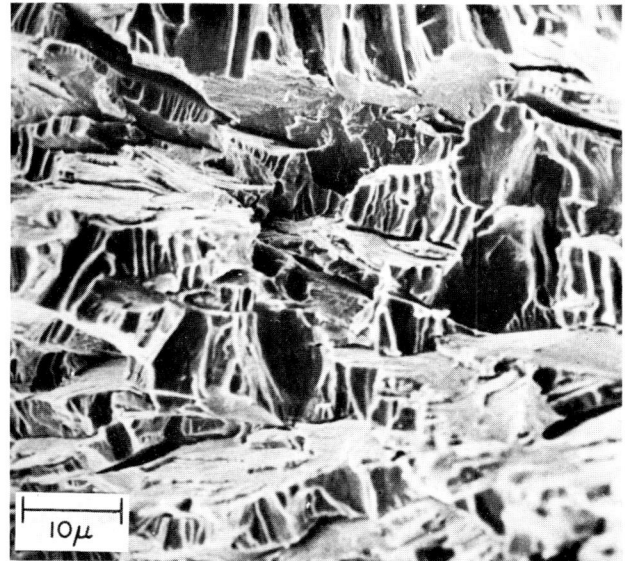

FIGURE 12 — Scanning electron micrograph of the fracture surface of a specimen of Ti-5Al-2.5Sn alloy formed in NaCl solution while strained to fracture at 0.005 cm/min. The main crack has clearly branched downwards into the surface at many points. Although the overall topography is comparatively rough the individual sections exhibit striations including 'river' pattern markings that are characteristic of brittle crack propagation (indicated by an arrow).

Although no change observable under the optical microscope occurred in bulk specimens immersed for 200 days, some reaction has occurred and was detected by changes in the etching characteristics of the materials. After etching in an aqueous solution of 2% HF and 2% HNO₃ for 60 seconds, exposed surfaces in the as-received condition of Ti-5Al-2.5Sn alloy exhibited pronounced intergranular grooving and transgranular precipitates as shown in Figure 11. These etching effects were most pronounced in the region of the bend of specimens. If the surface was lightly abraded after exposure but before etching then no etching effects were observed. Instead the specimen then had the same appearance as a specimen polished and etched without any immersion in the NaCl solution. This indicated that the environmental effects produced during the 200 days immersion was confined to the surface layers. Similar etching phenomena were observed on specimens of commercially pure titanium immersed for 200 days.

Although the nature of the contaminant introduced into the titanium and Ti-5Al-2.5Sn alloy was not ascertained, the appearance of the precipitates in Figure 11 was similar to the hydrides shown in Figure 4 with the obvious exception that the difference in size is over an order of magnitude. Hydrides in titanium however, can grow at room temperature to a size at least as great as that of the precipitates shown in Figure 11 over a period of a few days,[16] particularly if the nucleation rate is low.

Further evidence that the precipitates were hydrides was provided by the results of etching chemically polished specimens that had been immersed for 200 days. Specimens of the Ti-5Al-2.5Sn alloy exhibited only intergranular grooving. Since chemical polishing creates a high density of small hydride precipitates exposure to NaCl solutions could not result in any of them growing large enough to be seen in the optical microscope. Chemical polishing does not produce hydrides in titanium and it was found that chemically polished titanium specimens exhibited the same etching phenomena after 200 days exposure as specimens with surfaces in the as-received condition.

From these experiments two conclusions could be drawn. Firstly, the grain boundaries were sites for preferential attack, which was also observed in the experiments in acidified MgCl₂ experiments (Figure 2). Secondly, exposure to the corrodent promoted the formation of hydrides. It is unlikely that the etching treatment created the hydrides (a) because it did not create them on unexposed specimens, and (b) hydrides are unlikely to grow so large in one minute.[17] Growth during 'aging' after etching as reported elsewhere[16] could also be ruled out since the precipitates were seen immediately after the etching treatment.

The experiments in this section showed (a) that hydrides in the surface promoted transgranular failure in acidified NaCl solutions in Ti-5Al-2.5Sn alloy plastically deformed while immersed, (b) that hydrides were formed under the same conditions in hydride-free foils and (c) that slow hydride growth occurred in hydride-free bulk specimens plastically deformed in neutral solutions.

Additional experiments were performed in order to crack specimens in neutral sea water so that fractographic examination and comparisons could be made between failures in the environment and in air.

Tensile specimens of Ti-5Al-2.5Sn alloy in the as-received condition were pulled to fracture in both the neutral and acidified solutions at several strain rates (crosshead speeds 0.005-0.125 cm/min). Crack propagation occurred at crosshead speeds 0.05-0.2 cm/min for unnotched specimens and 0.005-0.05 cm/min for notched

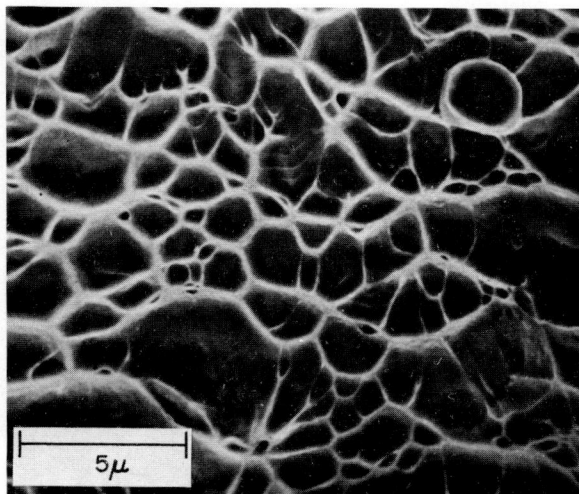

FIGURE 13 — Scanning electron micrograph of the fracture surface of a specimen of Ti-5Al-2.5Sn alloy strained to fracture at 0.005 cm/min in air. The specimen exhibits the 'dimple' surface commonly observed in ductile failure. The chevron markings seen in the center of some of the dimples were not identified.

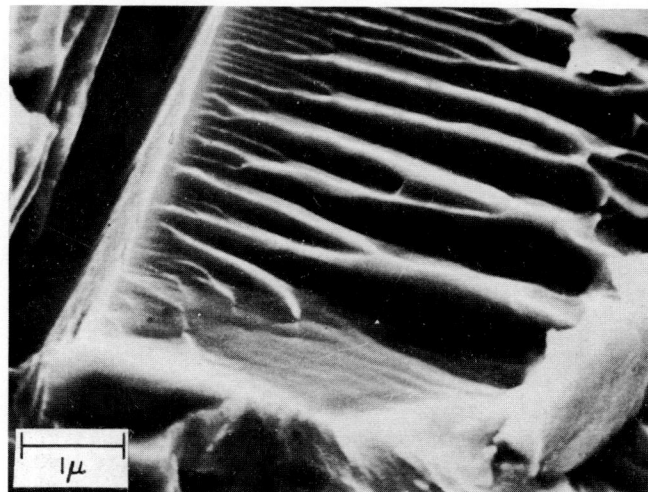

FIGURE 14 — Scanning electron micrograph of the fracture surface of a U-bend specimen of Ti-5Al-2.5Sn alloy which broke after 15 minutes exposure to a methanol/HCl mixture. The characteristic 'river' pattern of brittle fracture can be clearly seen, starting from the edge of an intersecting or branching crack.

specimens. Single cracks were initiated at the base of the notch and propagated right across the specimen perpendicularly to the direction of tensile stress. The progress of the crack could be followed since it took about 30 seconds to travel about 0.8 cms. In most specimens the crack was straight and unbranching. In a few specimens, however, the conditions for general yield were reached at the tip of the crack since ductile failure at 45° to the vertical occurred as the last part of the fracture.

Specimens of the Ti-5Al-2.5Sn alloy examined in the scanning electron microscopy exhibited flat facets and 'river pattern' surfaces characteristic of a brittle fracture together with deep fissures. An example is shown in Figure 12. Specimens broken in air exhibited the normal 'dimple' surface characteristic of ductile tearing as shown in Figure 13. The embrittled fracture surface was similar to that found in acidified NaCl solutions and also in MeOH/HCl solutions,[18] an example of which is shown in Figure 14. Notched specimens cathodically polarized at 1 and 10 mA/cm² in acidified solutions exhibited similar cracking behavior and identical fracture surfaces. Most significantly, hydride-containing specimens broken *in air* also showed similar "river pattern" surfaces.

## Discussion

From the results reported above and from the literature it is clear that titanium alloys can be susceptible to both intergranular and transgranular cracking in aqueous chloride solutions. While the cracking at 154 C and at room temperature have points in common it is important to discuss them separately.

*MgCl₂ Solutions at 154 C*

The intergranular cracking of the alloys in MgCl₂ solutions at 154 C is a slow propagation phenomenon resulting from grain boundary segregation as originally shown by Fontana.[2] Kirchener and Ripling[19] have also demonstrated the importance of grain boundary segregation in their investigation of hot salt cracking. The development of grain boundary grooving in the work above suggests that the grain boundaries are regions of enhanced solute and perhaps impurity segregation.

The initiation of pitting in regions that have been very severely cold worked is probably caused by faults in the repaired film. Cracking occurs only in the alloys where grain boundary segregation is found. The results on the Ti-Al binary alloys showed very clearly the relative transition from pitting to cracking as aluminum was added. The effect of chemical polishing upon the cracking process was to provide additional sites for the initiation of corrosion attack for two reasons: (a) because of faulting in the film over the heavily dislocated surface, and (b) because of segregation of solute atoms to the dislocations in the incoherent interfaces. The reactivity of dislocations in Ti-5Al-2.5Sn alloy for example has been illustrated by the preferential electropolishing of pileups in thin foils.[3] Chemically polished specimens of the richer binary alloys pitted more readily than as-received specimens and all the alloys cracked more readily. The failure of the small transgranular hydrides that formed in the more dilute binary alloys to alter the mode of cracking or to initiate transgranular pits may be due to the lesser chemical reactivity of interfacial dislocations in these alloys as a result of lower solute atom segregation. In the richer alloys, attack was initiated at the hydride/matrix interfaces and could continue along dislocation pileups. Whether the transgranular cracking continued into the alloy away from the surface or reverted to intergranular cracking was not determined. Chemical polishing produces hydrides to considerable depth,[17] however, so change would not necessarily occur once the crack had propagated inwards and first encountered a grain boundary. Whether a change occurred after it had penetrated more deeply than the depth of the hydrided layers is not known.

## NaCl Solutions at Room Temperature

Titanium and its alloys do not normally undergo pitting corrosion in NaCl solutions at room temperature. In order to initiate a stress corrosion crack there must be an unusual breakdown in the protective film. In fact the resistance of titanium alloys to stress corrosion lies mainly in the extreme protectiveness of this film, which in preventing pit initiation also prevents crack initiation. This resistance is well shown by the results reported above. Specimens of Ti-5Al-2.5Sn alloy plastically deformed while immersed in the acidified environment failed to develop cracks unless the cross-head speed was high. By comparison, other susceptible materials, e.g., 18 Cr-Ni steels[20] and magnesium alloys,[21] readily develop cracks when dynamically strained at low cross-head speeds in the appropriate cracking environments. In titanium alloys emergent slip steps are repassivated too rapidly for corrosion attack of any significance to occur.

The cracking of chemically polished Ti-5Al-2.5Sn alloys in the U-bend and unnotched tensile straining experiments can be attributed to the presence of hydride precipitated in the surface. The effect of plastic deformation is to produce a very sharp micro-notch very rapidly. The important factor in crack initiation is the production of a fresh surface very rapidly. The interaction of emergent slip steps and fresh surfaces with stress corrosion environments has been considered in detail.[22-5] It has been suggested that the sudden production of fresh surface area causes local depletion of dissolved passivating species and thereby delays repassivation. Water is thermodynamically unstable in the presence of bare titanium metal and also the passivated surface at the active end of the passive film potential range according to the Pourbaix diagram.[26] During the repassivation process, therefore, hydrogen is discharged on the metal surface at the tip of the crack, enters the metal and a hydride is nucleated. This is the critical step in sea water failures of titanium alloys. Under increasing stress and/or continuing hydrogen discharge, crack propagation proceeds. For a ductile fracture to change to a cleavage fracture the local shear stress must be raised and/or the local cleavage stress must be lowered. It is suggested that the entry of hydrogen into the lattice may produce both these effects. Firstly, the formation of the hydride on slip planes will inhibit local plastic flow and it is also possible that "hydrogen atmospheres" will exert a locking effect on dislocations. Secondly, the hydride phase is brittle and will initiate cleavage. Crack propagation proceeds either entirely as a result of corrosion processes or by the corrosion process initiating bursts of brittle crack propagation which may occur, for example, in alloys that exhibit high strength or low ductility associated with ordering processes.

In order to initiate cracking an area of fresh metal must be created rapidly. This is most easily done by straining a surface containing hydrides as described above but the presence of hydrides before exposure to the environment is not necessary. In hydride-free specimens cracking occurs if there is a stress-raising notch which can cause local rapid tearing at the apex. The presence of a fatigue crack, as used in the test of Brown,[5] apart from being a stress raiser, will also help to make the environment more aggressive because of the large area/volume ratio within it, tending to promote crevice attack, although cracking occurs in notched specimens without a fatigue crack.[6] The effect of the notch in causing local tearing will be greatest in thick specimens approximating to plane strain conditions. Feige and Murphy have shown, for example, that the fracture stress in sea water of susceptible alloys diminishes as the thickness is increased.[9] The size and shape of the hydride precipitate is probably important in this respect. In the thin sheet material used in the work reported above, the stress corroded specimens exhibited none of the ductile thinning as found in specimens broken in air and characteristic of plane stress conditions. Since the hydride forms a platelet phase approximately perpendicular to the applied stress, local lateral contraction is probably prevented, giving rise to displacements in only two orthogonal directions and resulting in local plane strain conditions.[27]

Hydride precipitation in $\alpha$-Ti alloys occurs primarily on $\{10\bar{1}0\}$ and $\{10\bar{1}1\}$ slip planes.[17] It is promoted by plastic deformation[28] and strain-aging experiments have shown[29] that hydrogen segregates very rapidly to dislocations in $\alpha$ phase alloys. Hydride formation occurs preferentially on planes perpendicular to the applied load in stressed, cooling alloys.[30] The formation of the $\gamma$-hydride phase is aided by dislocation movement since the atom rearrangements that occur in both processes are very similar. The addition of elements that raise the c/a ratio of the titanium lattice will aid the hydride formation movements which are similar to the forming of an FCC layer of stacking fault in a hexagonal lattice.[31]

The important electrochemical requirement for cracking is a delay in repassivation permitting the rapid formation of a hydride precipitate. In neutral solutions the alloy surface can be expected to repassivate more rapidly than in acidic solutions and the failure to crack chemically polished specimens of Ti-5Al-2.5Sn alloy deformed into a U-shape in neutral solutions contrasted with the cracking of the same alloy dynamically strained in the same environment is an indication of the critical conditions that are needed for failure. If repassivation can be delayed, however, then any $\alpha$ phase titanium alloy will fail in any aqueous environment since hydrogen will be discharged at all values of pH. Failures in $H_2SO_4$,[13] distilled water[6] and NaOH solutions[6] at pH 10 have been reported. In strongly oxidizing environments cracking will be more difficult. There is evidence, for example, that susceptible alloys do not crack in chromate solutions.[9] Environments that remove the protective film and generate hydrogen will also cause similar failures. Extremely rapid transgranular cracking of Ti-5Al-2.5Sn alloy occurs in methanol/HCl mixtures, for example, followed by a much slower process of intergranular embrittlement.[18]

Solute elements will affect susceptibility according to the effect that they have on the various factors that together form the complex cracking process. Aluminum, for example, promotes hydride formation,[17] promotes the formation of wide slip steps by altering the cellular dislocation tangles of titanium to the coplanar arrays observed in Ti-5Al-2.5Sn alloy[3] and the Ti-8Al alloy, delays repassivation by increasing the critical current density for passivation of titanium[32] and causes embrittlement by ordering processes which are governed by the selected heat treatment. Aluminum therefore increases the susceptibility of titanium which is itself susceptible if the impurity content is high.[6]

The formation of the hydride phase is usually under nucleation control[28] which in turn is dependent upon the attainment of a critical stress.[28] The diffusion of hydrogen is very rapid. Williams[28] has calculated that 0 C hydrogen diffuses ca. $1.5 \times 10^{-3}$ cm in one minute. Internal friction measurements have indicated that there is a stress-induced interstitial diffusion of hydrogen in titanium[33] and in alloys undergoing plastic deformation, therefore, this distance would be increased. The hydrogen overpotential on $\gamma$-hydride is very much lower than on the metal surface.[34] For a given potential drop down a crack hydrogen discharge will therefore concentrate on the hydride surface once it has formed. Significantly, it has been reported[9] that when fracture occurs the potential of a specimen falls into the hydrogen evolution range.

It appears, therefore, that the initiation of transgranular failure in $\alpha$ phase titanium alloys is a form of slow strain rate hydrogen embrittlement to which these alloys are prone when they contain intermediate amounts of hydrogen.[28] The propagation mechanism which has been outlined above will depend upon the physical metallurgical characteristics of the alloy. This is currently being examined and will be reported upon later in detail. In $\alpha + \beta$ alloys and in $\beta$ alloys the BCC $\beta$ phase probably suffers hydrogen embrittlement similar, perhaps, to that occurring in ferritic materials.

## Conclusion

In boiling $MgCl_2$ solutions slow intergranular stress corrosion cracking occurs in titanium alloys as a result of prior grain boundary segregation. In some $\alpha$ phase alloys the reactivity of dislocation pileups may cause transgranular cracking of a similar slow kind. Similar corrosion attack occurs at room temperature but it is extremely slow and unlikely to cause failure. Under conditions of increasing stress, however, the rapid formation of the hydride phase promotes local embrittlement and very rapid crack propagation. This occurs in titanium as well as titanium $\alpha$ alloys and in any environment in which hydrogen can rapidly enter the metal lattice.

## Acknowledgments

The authors wish to thank Imperial Metal Industries (Kynoch) Ltd., for financial support of this work. They are also grateful to Dr. J. Sikorski and Mr. T. Buckley of the Department of Textile Physics, University of Leeds, for generous assistance with the Scanning Electron Microscope in that Department.

## References

1. H. H. Uhlig and J. R. Cobb, Jr. *Metal Progr.*, **59**, 816 (1951).
2. M. G. Fontana. *Ind. and Eng. Chem.*, **48**, 9 (1956).
3. G. Sanderson and J. C. Scully. *Environment Sensitive Mechanical Properties of Materials*, ed. A. R. C. Westwood and N. S. Stoloff, Gordon and Breach, New York, p. 511 (1966).
4. S. Henrikson. *Current Corrosion Research in Scandinavia*, ed. J. Larinkari, Keskusliitto, Helsinki, p. 51 (1964).
5. B. F. Brown. *Materials Research and Standards*, No. 3, **6**, 129 (1966).
6. I. R. Lane, Jr., J. L. Cavallaro and A. G. Morton. *Stress Corrosion Cracking of Titanium*, ASTM, Philadelphia, p. 246 (1966).
7. W. S. Pellini, R. J. Goode, P. P. Puzak, E. A. Lange, and R. W. Huber. *US NRL Report 6300*, p. 62 (1965) June.
8. R. W. Judy, Jr., T. W. Crooker, R. W. Morey, A. A. Lange, and R. J. Goode. *Trans. ASM*, **59**, 195 (1966).
9. N. G. Feige and T. J. Murphy. WESTEC Conference, 1966, Los Angeles.
10. B. F. Brown, B. W. Forgeson, T. J. Lennox, Jr., T. C. Supton, R. L. Newbegin, M. H. Peterson, J. A. Smith, and L. J. Waldron. NRL Memo 1634 (1965) July.
11. G. Sanderson and J. C. Scully. *Nature*, **211**, 179 (1966).
12. G. Sanderson and J. C. Scully. *Corrosion Sci.*, **6**, 541 (1966).
13. N. D. Tomashov and V. N. Modestova. *Corrosion of Metals and Alloys*. Trans. A. D. Mercer, ed. C. J. L. Booker, National Lending Library for Science and Technology, Boston Spa, Yorkshire, p.216 (1964).
14. M. J. Blackburn. *Trans. ASM*, **59**, 694 (1966).
15. N. A. Neilsen. *Corrosion*, **20**, 104t (1964).
16. F. C. Holden and R. D. Buckert. *Trans. Met. Soc. AIME*, **218**, 383 (1960).
17. G. Sanderson and J. C. Scully. *Trans. Met. Soc. AIME*, **239**, 1883 (1967).
18. G. Sanderson and J. C. Scully. *Corrosion Sci.*, **8**, 541 (1968).
19. R. L. Kirchener and E. J. Ripling. First Interim Report on Elevated Temperature Stress Corrosion of High Strength Sheet Materials in the Presence of Stress Concentrates, Materials Research Laboratory, Inc., Chicago, 1964.
20. T. P. Hoar and J. M. West. *Proc. Roy. Soc.*, **A268**, 304 (1962).
21. E. G. Coleman, D. Weinstein and W. Rostoker. *Acta Met.*, **9**, 491 (1961).
22. J. C. Scully. *British Corrosion J.*, **1**, 355 (1966).
23. J. C. Scully. *The Physical Basis of Yield and Fracture*, The Institute of Physics, London, p. 119 (1966).
24. J. C. Scully. *Corrosion Sci.*, **7**, 197 (1967).
25. J. C. Scully. *Corrosion Sci.*, **8**, 513 (1968).
26. M. Pourbaix. Atlas d'Equilibres Electrochimiques a 25°C, Gauthiers-Villars, Paris (1963).
27. A. H. Cottrell. *The Mechanical Properties of Matter*, Wiley, New York, p. 135 (1964).

28. D. N. Williams. *J. Inst. Metals*, **91**, 147 (1962-3).
29. E. Smith. *Nature*, **181**, 902 (1958).
30. M. R. Louthan, Jr. *Trans. Met. Soc. AIME*, **227**, 1166 (1963).
31. A. T. Churchman. *Proc. Roy. Soc.*, A226, 216 (1954).
32. V. V. Andreeva and V. I. Kazasia. Third International Congress on Metallic Corrosion, May, 1966, Moscow, to be published.
33. W. Koster, L. Bangert and M. Evers. *Z. Metallk.*, **47**, 564 (1956).
34. R. Otuska. The Institute of Physical and Chemical Research, Tokyo, Private communication.

# Discussion

**T. P. Hoar, University of Cambridge:**

When titanium reacts with water it produces two products: an oxide and a hydride. The former is a passivating agent and the latter is an activating agent. The hydride may either activate brittle fracture or may activate anodic dissolution. In either case we have a system where virtually no reaction is occurring on the crack walls and passivating and activating processes are occurring at the crack tip. In terms of unifying principles we can agree that the crack walls and tips are in different states.

**J. C. Scully:**

This point is of critical importance and requires considerable study in itself. The hydride may have two opposite roles: it may initiate a brittle crack but it may also act as a passivator. Otsuka,[1] for example, has shown that the presence of hydride lowers the corrosion rate of titanium in acidic solutions. Our paper quotes his observation that the hydride has a low hydrogen overpotential, which means that it will promote the passivation of adjacent regions. Conceivably, too much hydride within a crack may even repassivate the new surfaces created by crack propagation too rapidly for sufficient hydrogen pickup to continue the process. We have indirect evidence that a process of this kind may explain the beneficial effect of cathodic polarization which is seemingly contradictory to our hydrogen embrittlement mechanism.

1. R. Otsuka. *Scientific Papers Inst. Phys. and Chem. Res.*, **54**, 97 (1960).

**T. R. Beck, Boeing Scientific Research Laboratory:**

One of the basic problems in the literature on stress corrosion cracking is that insufficient distinction has been made between initiation and propagation of a crack. Time to failure with a smooth specimen does not distinguish between these and I submit that the results of Dr. Scully reflect largely the initiation step rather than the propagation step. Dr. Scully is possibly correct that titanium hydrides may be involved in the initiation step in methanol but, I believe they are involved only indirectly during crack propagation.

**J. C. Scully:**

In our description of the experiments in $MgCl_2$ solutions we have not even mentioned the times to failures because they do reflect differences in the initiation process as Dr. Beck rightly points out. This not true for our experiments in NaCl solutions since specimens were dynamically strained to fracture. Crack initiation occurs when the plastic deformation prevents repassivation of freshly created surfaces and allows hydrogen pickup. During the period following this process the hydrogen must lower the cleavage stress of the lattice locally before void initiation and coalescence occur and the ductile dimple fracture stress is exceeded. In the fractographs shown in our paper we have indicated well developed cleavage patterns but we also have evidence of a mixed mode where cleavage has occurred during void formation producing what I call a "garden wall effect" which, regrettably, is a singularly English description. Where this occurs the hydride is initiating fracture which then proceeds a short distance for other reasons. Furthermore, if the alloy is not tough the initiated cleavage crack arising from hydrogen pickup may propagate as a cleavage crack for metallurgical reasons. For these reasons we can agree to a limited extent with Dr. Beck. Where we disagree is in explaining the mechanism of cleavage in aqueous NaCl and MeOH/HCl environments as a corrosion process in which hydrogen is the embrittling species. Unless this enters the lattice cleavage does not occur. Hydrogen is therefore directly involved.

**T. J. Murphy, Titanium Metals Corp. of America:**

There is another argument against the idea that hydrides are an essential part of the total operation, based on the trends of titanium-aluminum binary alloys. By "essential" I mean that the hydrides are central in a mechanistic description and will be involved in, for instance, descriptions of corrosion.

As aluminum content of a titanium-aluminum binary is increased, the susceptibility to this effect that we are talking about will increase; whereas the hydrogen solubility increases enormously.

On a simple hydride precipitation mechanism, one would assume that in order to produce a better alloy, the alloy content should be increased.

**J. C. Scully:**

This point is answered in detail in our paper[1] on hydride formation. As aluminum is added to titanium hydride formation becomes an easier process on an atomistic scale. Aluminum certainly does increase the solid solubility of hydrogen in titanium but much more important is that it promotes hydride formation under electrochemical conditions (a) for crystallographic reasons, (b) because it promotes the formation of coplanar arrays of dislocations which results in wide slip steps which are difficult to repassivate, and (c) because it delays the repassivation process for electrochemical reasons. It is also for these reasons that aluminum increases the stress corrosion susceptibility of single phase $\alpha$ titanium alloys.

1. G. Sanderson and J. C. Scully. *Trans. AIME Met. Soc.*, 239, 1883 (1967).

**N. A. Nielsen, Du Pont Company:**

It does appear that all stress corrosion fracture surfaces examined by electron fractography contain cleavage-like features and there are points of similarity between fracture morphology in titanium alloys and stainless steel. I would like to ask Dr. Scully, however, if the river patterns in his fractographs are directed in the normal fashion relative to the direction of classic brittle crack propagation, namely that the confluence of the markings points in the direction of crack propagation. Our experience with stress corrosion cracked stainless steel has been that the cleavage-like patterns tend to fan out in the opposite sense to this.

**J. C. Scully:**

As a result of studying the work of Mr. Nielsen we have examined all our fractographs and have also gone back to studying the original surfaces further. We are confident that in most examples that we can be certain about the river patterns corresponding to the expected configuration: the confluence of markings points in the direction of crack propagation. In Mr. Nielsen's case a reversed river pattern could be explained by the initiation occurring in front of the crack tip and running back to the advancing crack.

**A. J. Sedriks, RIAS:**

I would like to raise a point regarding Dr. Scully's observations relating to failures in methanol-hydrochloric acid solutions. At RIAS we have examined many failures of Ti-5Al-2.5Sn alloy in methanol-0.6% HCl-1.0% $H_2O$ solutions, and have also observed relatively rapid crack propagation in self-stressed specimens of the U-bend type and a more slow intergranular embrittlement in the unstressed specimens. However, we have found no evidence to suggest that the crack path changes from intergranular to transgranular in the presence of stress under these conditions of testing. A metallographic section of a typical stress corrosion crack is shown in Figure 1, where it is seen that although some transgranular sections and branching is

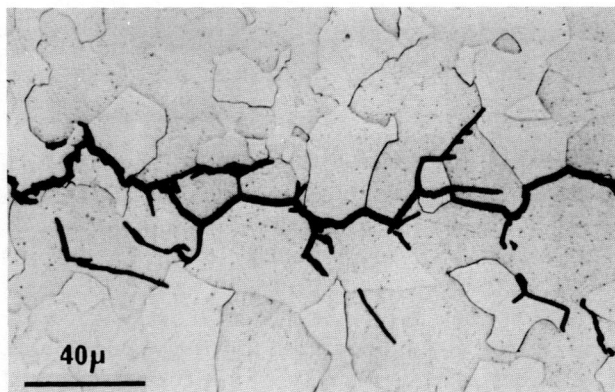

**FIGURE 1** — Stress corrosion crack in Ti-5Al-2.5Sn alloy exposed to methanol-0.6% HCl-1.0% $H_2O$ solution.

in evidence, the crack path is predominately intergranular.

I would like to add, also, that current understanding of hydrogen embrittlement is not sufficient to enable prediction of crack path. In fact intergranular failures of titanium occur in methanol vapor, where existing evidence favors an embrittlement process associated with the diffusion of hydrogen into the metal.[1]

1. A. J. Sedriks, P. W. Slattery, and E. N. Pugh. Stress Corrosion Cracking of Alpha Titanium in Non-Aqueous Environments, this volume.

**J. C. Scully:**

The answer to the two points made by Dr. Sedriks is covered in our summary and in the reference which it contains which should appear early in the new year. It contains, for example, a micrograph of a transgranular crack in Ti-5Al-2.5Sn alloy. The fractographs exhibit the characteristic river pattern cleavage (like that in Figure 14 of our paper at this conference) which is identical with those found in aqueous NaCl solution. This type of cleavage has been seen by Brown at ONR Laboratory and Blackburn at Boeing, both of whom have analyzed a predominant transgranular plane. The slow intergranular attack appears as a simple form of grain boundary separation. Furthermore the same appearance is found in U-bend specimens of Ti (which do not suffer transgranular cleavage) as in unstressed specimens of Ti-5Al-2.5Sn broken in air after exposure to MeOH/HCl. This is a critically important distinction. The simplest mechanism is one of grain boundary dissolution. It has been shown in England that hydrogen enters the grains although we have not seen this (a) after corroding foils in MeOH/HCl, or (b) after making thin foils from bulk specimens exposed to MeOH/HCl. Whenever titanium is active it is probable that hydrogen enters the lattice. In our extensive study of hydrogen in thin foils we never saw any evidence that foils heavily saturated with hydrogen were intergranularly weak. Finally, I think that there is no reason to distinguish between reactions in liquid and vapor phases.

## Written Contribution on Stress Corrosion Cracking of Titanium Alloys in Methanolic Environments

### J. C. Scully

In a recent paper[1] we have reported upon our work on the failure in methanolic environments of the alloys used in our investigation of aqueous cracking which is reported above. I wish to summarize our main observations here.

The methanol/hydrochloric acid mixture that we employed caused rapid removal of the protective film which could sometimes be seen to float away. U-bend specimens of the alloys suffered very rapid fracture as described in Table 1. The cleavage patterns observed on the fracture surfaces were similar to those observed in sea water failures and we attribute this to the same cause: the entry of hydrogen atoms along the slip plane at the tip of the crack, in this environment as a result of reaction between a

**TABLE 1—Fracture and Embrittlement Times
for the Commercial Alloys (hours)**

| | Fracture Time | | Embrittlement Times |
| | Methanol | Methanol/HCl | Methanol/HCl |
| --- | --- | --- | --- |
| Ti | 48 | 4 | 350 |
| Ti-5Al-2.5Sn | 24 | 0.1-0.5 | 70 |
| Ti-6Al-4V | 30 | 0.3-0.6 | not embrittled in 1000 hours |

'clean' titanium surface and methanol. The function of water in inhibiting cracking can be explained by its role in repassivating the freshly exposed surface before a deleterious amount of hydrogen can enter the lattice and in hydrolyzing (and preventing the formation of) the titanium-methoxy-chloro complexes that are formed.

We have also observed a second, different phenomenon in titanium and Ti-5Al-2.5Sn alloy but not in Ti-6Al-4V alloy: intergranular embrittlement. Upon exposure to the methanol/hydrochloric acid mixture the grain boundaries are preferentially attacked and specimens suffer a complete loss of strength after a period of time which is largely dependent upon the acidity and water content of the environment. Times for complete embrittlement compared with times for failure are shown in Table 1. After this time specimens that were 0.06 cms thick could be broken by hand. No stress is required for this phenomenon. If an external stress is applied as, for example, in a U-bend then the grain boundaries on the outside of the bend where the maximum tensile stress is exerted will be pulled apart. Under anodic polarization titanium dissolves in methanol at $Ti^{3+}$ and there is rapid penetration of the grain boundaries with adjacent regions exhibiting the hydride phase. This is also shown in the fracture surfaces obtained by breaking embrittled specimens in air. The formation of the hydride phase which has an extremely low hydrogen overpotential is probably an integral part of the grain boundary penetration mechanism since it provides a local cathodic depolarizer. In this respect it is of interest to note here the report made at the conference by Dr. J. Kruger (National Bureau of Standards) that chemically polished specimens do not exhibit this embrittlement. Since chemical polishing saturates the surface layers with hydrogen it would inhibit the pickup of hydrogen during the exposure to the methanolic environment. In $\alpha + \beta$ alloys hydrogen would dissolve preferentially in the $\beta$ phase and a depolarizing hydride may not be produced in the $\alpha$ phase. This may explain the failure of the $\alpha + \beta$ alloy to embrittle (it should be noted that it does suffer from transgranular cleavage) although in our paper the failure to embrittle was ascribed to some unknown factor 'poisoning' the grain boundary dissolution mechanism.

## Reference

1. G. Sanderson and J. C. Scully. *Corrosion Sci.*, 8, 541 (1968).

# THE ROLE OF MOISTURE AND HYDROGEN IN HOT-SALT
## CRACKING OF TITANIUM ALLOYS

S. P. Rideout, R. S. Ondrejcin,
M. R. Louthan, Jr. and D. E. Rawl
Savannah River Laboratory
E. I. du Pont de Nemours and Co.

## Abstract

The role of moisture and hydrogen in the stress corrosion cracking of Ti-8Al-1Mo-1V exposed to hot chloride salts was investigated. The adsorption and retention of moisture during the application of salt deposits and subsequent heating, and the extent of HCl and hydrogen generation during corrosion were studied using radiotracer techniques and mass spectrographic analyses of volatile corrosion products. Hot-stage microscopy and cinematography were used to study crack initiation and propagation, and the characteristics of fracture surfaces were examined by electron fractography. The effects of NaCl were compared to those of $SnCl_2 \cdot 2H_2O$, which not only retains much more moisture but also has a much lower melting point than NaCl. These studies revealed an obvious association between the occurrence of cracking and the amounts of HCl and hydrogen generated during hot-salt corrosion. This, combined with results of supplementary experiments using sodium iodide and bromide, indicates that hydrogen, rather than the halide, plays the key role in the cracking process. The observations are consistent with a stress-sorption mechanism for cracking, in which corrosion-produced nascent hydrogen is proposed to be the sorbed species responsible for cracking.

## I. Introduction

Information concerning the susceptibility of titanium alloys to stress corrosion cracking has accumulated rapidly during recent years as a result of extensive laboratory testing programs to evaluate high strength engineering materials for aircraft, space, and marine applications. The first cause for concern that susceptibility to stress corrosion might be a significant problem in the use of titanium alloys was the discovery that some alloys crack when stressed in contact with chloride salts at elevated temperatures.[1,2] This phenomenon, called hot-salt cracking, is a threat to many titanium alloy structural components operating at elevated temperature because sources of chloride contamination are so numerous. The list of other environments that can produce stress corrosion damage in titanium alloys has grown since 1964, when it was discovered that specimens with pre-existing fatigue cracks are susceptible to stress corrosion at room temperature in sea water.[3] Cracking can occur at ambient temperatures in a variety of aqueous and nonaqueous media. Many laboratories currently are investigating the mechanism of cracking in various environments. The Savannah River Laboratory, under sponsorship of the National Aeronautics and Space Administration, is conducting research to develop fundamental information on the phenomenon of hot-salt cracking.

Hot-salt cracking was first thought to be caused by dry salt deposits, and moisture was not considered to be important.[2] Chlorine gas, produced as an intermediate and regenerable product of salt-metal reactions in the presence of oxygen or a reducible oxide, was proposed to be the cause of stress corrosion. However, this proposal was based on observations of hot-salt corrosion effects at test temperatures from 900 to 1400 F[2] and on analytical evidence of small amounts of chlorine in volatile products of corrosion at 1200 F.[4]

In contrast, studies at SRL[5] on NaCl cracking of Ti-8Al-1Mo-1V at a lower temperature (650 F) indicated that moisture is important in the salt corrosion process, and that HCl gas is generated. Exposure of stressed specimens to hot HCl gas alone, with no salt deposit, caused cracking which occurred in a manner similar to the delayed failure phenomenon associated with hydrogen embrittlement. Several features of the hot-salt cracking phenomenon also indicated that corrosion-produced hydrogen might be involved in the mechanism of cracking. Through the use of radiotracer techniques,[5] hydrogen was shown to be retained in areas corroded at 650 F by salt initially deposited from a solution containing tritiated water, $^3H_2O$. Direct, hot-stage metallographic observations of hot-salt stress corrosion revealed that cracks initiated abruptly following an incubation period, the duration of which

650

depended on exposure temperature, salt composition, and alloy composition.[6] The effect of salt composition on the incubation period for cracking was also investigated, particularly with respect to the amounts of moisture retained in the salt deposit and the amounts of HCl gas and hydrogen generated during corrosion.[7] Those results were the basis for the proposal that corrosion-produced hydrogen rather than chlorine gas is responsible for hot-salt cracking.

The objective of this paper is to further define how moisture, HCl, and hydrogen are involved in hot-salt stress corrosion of titanium alloys.

## II. Experimental Procedure

### A. Specimens for Radiotracer Studies and Hot-Stage Microscopy

As described for previous studies[7] the test specimens were metallographically polished 3/4- x 3- x 0.050-inch strips of duplex-annealed Ti-8Al-1Mo-1V alloy. The strips were mounted in 4-point loading holders and stressed by bending to a surface-fiber stress of $10^5$ psi at room temperature, which caused them to yield slightly when heated to test temperatures.

Salt solutions used in studies of adsorption of moisture and chlorides (Tables 1-4) were made radioactive by adding either tritium as $^3H_2O$ (1 Ci per ml) $^{22}$NaCl (1 Ci per ml) or chloride as $Na^{36}Cl$ (0.03 mCi per ml). The presence of tritium on the specimens was determined by counting in a windowless, gas-flow proportional counter, and the chloride was counted with a GM beta counter. The absorption of hydrogen (as $^3H$) by the metal in salt-corroded areas was confirmed by first removing all salt, etching the surface to dissolve a small increment of metal, and then counting the etching solution in a beta liquid scintillation counter.

For experiments to determine the time to initiate cracking, (Table 5) deposits of salt were applied in the area of maximum stress by evaporating three drops of saturated aqueous solution on the specimens. This procedure produced a fairly dense deposit of coarse crystals covering a spot about 1/2 inch in diameter. Multiple specimens were then heated isothermally in stagnant air using a small electric oven. Specimens were removed at intervals, and after removing the salt deposits, the surfaces were microscopically examined for evidence of cracking.

In order to permit direct hot-stage metallographic observations of salt-metal reactions, droplets of dilute solutions were evaporated on the pre-polished surfaces.[6] The resultant salt crystals were small enough to be viewed with a conventional metallurgical microscope. The specimen loading fixture was positioned directly on the microscope stage, and heating was accomplished by placing a tiny, hand-made coil of resistance wire against the underside of the specimen and adjusting the current with a powerstat. Movies of the hot-salt stress corrosion process were made through the eyepiece of the microscope using a

TABLE 1 – Adsorption of $Na^+$ and $Cl^-$ on Selected Metals[1][7]

| Material | Surface Condition | Adsorption, $\mu g/10\ cm^2$ | |
| --- | --- | --- | --- |
| | | $Na^+$ | $Cl^-$ |
| Type 304 Stainless Steel | Polished | 0.00 | 12.0 |
| Titanium | Polished | 0.00 | 12.0 |
| Ti-8Al-1Mo-1V | Polished | 0.14 | 10.0 |
| Ti-8Al-1Mo-1V | Mill Oxide | 0.03 | 9.4 |
| Tantalum | Oxidized | 0.01 | 10.0 |
| Zircaloy-2 | Oxidized | 0.03 | 8.5 |
| Platinum | Oxidized | 0.00 | 4.5 |

[1]$Na^+$ as radiotracer $^{22}$Na
$Cl^-$ as radiotracer $^{36}$Cl

TABLE 2 – Effect of Immersion Time of Ti-8Al-1Mo-1V on Adsorption of $^3H_2O$ from NaCl Solution (pH 6.0)

| Specimen No. | Immersion Time, hr | Treatment After Immersion | Counts/10 Min (3.6 cm² Surface Area) | |
| --- | --- | --- | --- | --- |
| | | | Counter Reading | $2\sigma$ Error |
| 1 | 0.5 | Dried with absorbent tissue in air | 534 | ± 240 |
| 2 | 0.5 | (Same as above) Subsequently rinsed in flowing hot water | 725 190 | ± 240 ± 240 |
| 3 | 0.5 | Dried with absorbent tissue and rinsed immediately in flowing hot water | 31 | ± 240 |
| 4 | 26 | Dried with absorbent tissue | 1130 | ± 260 |
| 5 | 26 | (Same as above) Subsequently rinsed in flowing hot water | 862 699 | ± 260 ± 260 |
| 6 | 26 | Dried with absorbent tissue and rinsed immediately in flowing hot water | 519 | ± 260 |

651

16-mm camera equipped with a single frame attachment for speeds down to one frame per second.

The characteristics of stress corrosion fracture surfaces were studied by conventional replication and electron microscopy techniques.

### B. Mass Spectrometer Analyses of Volatile Corrosion Products

A Consolidated Engineering Corporation Model 21-103 mass spectrometer was used to analyze volatile corrosion products that were evolved when mixtures of Ti-8Al-1Mo-1V alloy and sodium chloride were heated in a closed, heated glass reaction vessel attached directly to the mass spectrometer.[7] Titanium alloy chips were wetted with salt solution and dried for one hour at 110 C. Chips were used to assure a high surface area/salt ratio. The pressure in the reaction vessel was reduced so that at temperature, without a reaction, the pressure would be one atmosphere. About 2% of the gas in the reaction vessel was removed each time a sample was taken. The stopcocks in the reaction vessel and on the mass spectrometer were greased with "Kel-F,"[1] a lubricant unattacked by $Cl_2$ and other strong oxidants.

### C. Electron Microprobe Analyses

The distribution of Na and Cl in cracks and adjacent regions was determined using a Materials Analysis Corporation Model 400 electron microprobe.[7] X-rays were diffracted with a potassium acid phthalate crystal for Na and a pentaerythritol crystal for Cl. Spectrometers were calibrated with carbon-coated sodium chloride crystals so that

[1]Trademark of Minnesota Mining and Manufacturing Company, St. Paul, Minnesota.

**TABLE 3—$^3H_2O$ Radiotracer Indication of Moisture in Salt Deposits**

| Type of Salt Deposit[1] | Counts per Minute |
|---|---|
| NaCl | 35,600 |
| $SnCl_2 \cdot 2H_2O$ | 149,400 |

[1]Produced by evaporation of 100 $\mu l$ of saturated salt solution of Ti-8Al-1Mo-1V specimen.

atomic concentrations of Na and Cl could be shown on equivalent scales in Figure 7.

## III. Results and Discussion

### A. Radiotracer Studies of Adsorption

Previous work[5] showed that some form of chloride other than NaCl is strongly adsorbed on titanium alloy surfaces that are wetted at room temperature with NaCl solution and subsequently rinsed in flowing hot water. Continuation of the adsorption studies[7] showed preferential adsorption of chlorides on a variety of metals, Table 1. The effect of solution pH on chloride adsorption by Ti-8Al-1Mo-1V at room temperature, Figure 1, indicates that the chloride is not present as HCl molecules, because the absorption was maximum in the pH 5-6 range and decreased as the pH was increased or decreased. If adsorbed chloride ions were accompanied by hydrogen ions, the amount adsorbed would be expected to increase in acidic solutions. Based on the results of these studies, it is proposed that chloride ions are absorbed into the metal oxide film, probably occupying oxygen vacancies in the lattice. The presence of chloride ions in the oxide film should contribute to the breakdown of passivity during exposure at elevated temperatures.

Because chloride absorption at room temperature was

**TABLE 5—Effects of Type of Halogen Salt and Initial Solution pH on Time to Initiate Cracking of Ti-8Al-1Mo-1V[7]**

| Salt | pH of Initial Solution | Exposure Temp, °F | Time to Initiate Cracking, Min |
|---|---|---|---|
| NaCl | 4.1 | 650 | 80 |
| | 0.5 | 650 | 40 |
| NaBr | 4.7 | 650 | 150 |
| | 0.5 | 650 | 75 |
| NaI | 8.9 | 750 | 150 |
| | 0.5 | 750 | 75 |
| $SnCl_2 \cdot 2H_2O$ | 4.1 | 650 | 30 |
| | 0.5 | 650 | 15 |
| | 0.2 | 650 | 10 |
| CuCl | 3.4 | 650 | 60 |

**TABLE 4—Hydrogen ($^3H$) Absorption by Ti-8Al-1Mo-1V in Salt-Corroded Area**

| Specimen No. | Specimen Treatment[1] | $\beta$ Counter Reading, Counts/10 Min | | | $2\sigma$ Error |
|---|---|---|---|---|---|
| | | A | B | C | |
| 1 | | 1461 | 430 | 0 | ± 245 |
| 2 | | 1069 | 352 | 325 | ± 245 |

[1]Specimen Treatment: Stressed specimens treated with hot NaCl for 75 hours at 650 F and rinsed in flowing hot water for one minute.

A - Counts made after two chemical etches that removed a total 0.2 mil.
B - Counts made after an additional 0.1 mil removed by grinding.
C - Counts made after an additional 0.1 mil removed by grinding.

not associated with hydrogen ions or HCl molecules, the HCl gas detected during hot-salt corrosion must be generated by reactions involving moisture. Various possible sources of moisture were investigated as described below.

Experiments with radiotracer $^3H$, (tritium) as $^3H_2O$, Figure 2, demonstrated that moisture is adsorbed on titanium alloy surfaces that appear to be dry at room temperature. In these tests, specimens with and without prior exposure to NaCl solution were wetted with $^3H_2O$ and allowed to dry at room temperature. In Figure 2 both specimens showed a gradual decrease in radioactivity during aging at room temperature, which would be expected due

to an exchange between atmospheric and adsorbed moisture. Prior exposure to NaCl solution had no significant effect on moisture adsorption; the slight difference shown in Figure 2 is within the range of reproducibility on duplicate specimens.

On specimens that were dried in air immediately after wetting, the $^3H_2O$ was easily removed by exchange with hot rinse water, indicating that the moisture was not tightly bound to the surface. On specimens immersed for extended times in tritiated salt solutions, the hot water rinse did not remove all of the radiotracer, Table 2. This retention may be due to absorption of some moisture into the oxide film.

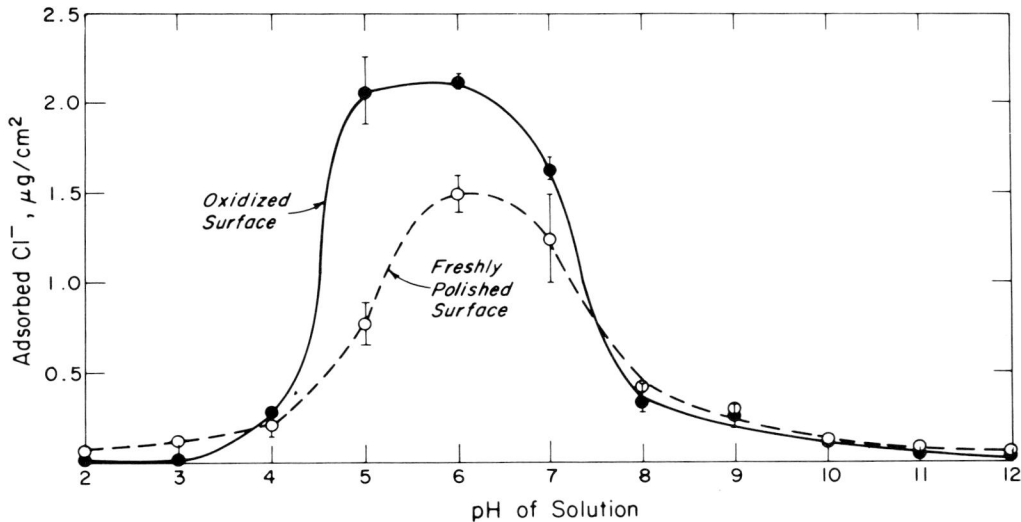

FIGURE 1 — Effect of pH on adsorption of Cl⁻ by Ti-8Al-1Mo-1V in NaCl solutions.[7]

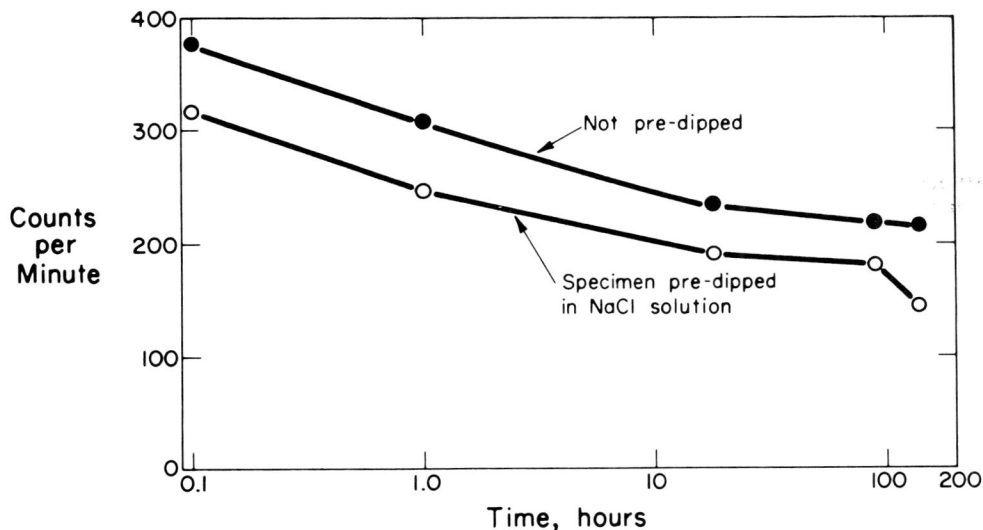

FIGURE 2 — Radiotracer evidence of adsorbed moisture (or $^3H_2O$) on Ti-8Al-1Mo-1V at room temperature.

Pre - dried NaCl Crystals

NaCl Deposited by Evaporation
of Saturated Solution

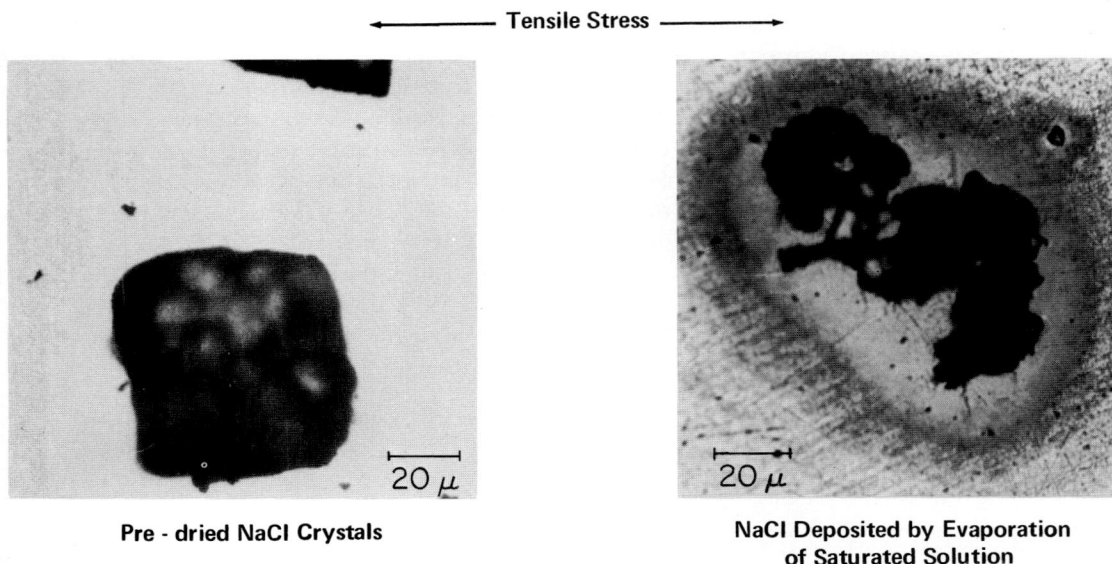

FIGURE 3 — Effect of moisture on NaCl cracking of Ti-8Al-
1Mo-1V at 650 F[7] (specimen was exposed 90
minutes).

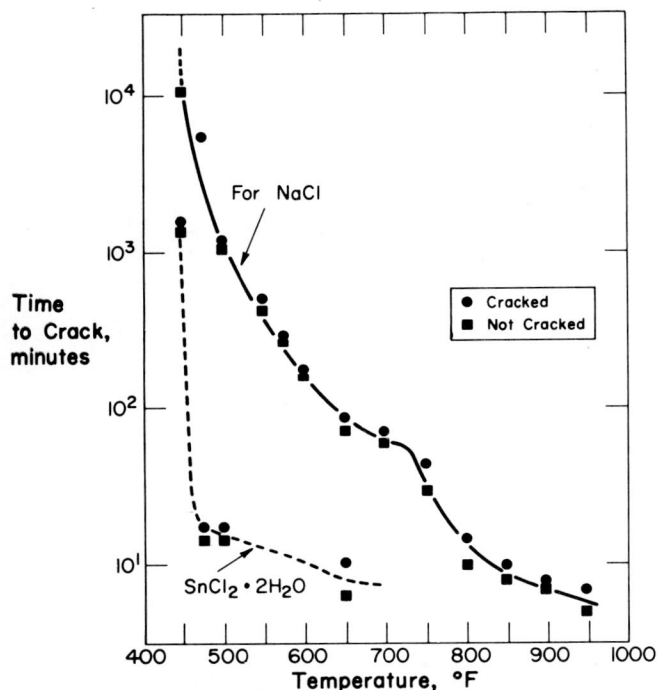

FIGURE 4 — Effects of salt composition and temperature on
time to initiate cracking of Ti-8Al-1Mo-1V.

In order to demonstrate that the most important source of moisture involved in hot-salt corrosion is that which is retained in salt deposited by evaporation of solutions, deposits of NaCl and $SnCl_2 \cdot 2H_2O$ containing tritium traces were studied (Table 3). The amount of moisture adsorbed in the salt deposit was significantly greater than the amount retained by the absorption in the protective oxide film (Figure 2).

The effect of retained moisture on stress corrosion cracking was compared on specimens with pre-dried salt crystals, Figure 3.[7] The Ti-8Al-1Mo-1V specimens were photographed directly through the hot-stage microscope after being heated at 650 F for 90 minutes. Corrosion staining and cracking occurred in the sequence reported previously[6] on the specimen with the "moist" salt; but there was no evidence of corrosion or cracking on the specimen exposed to the pre-dried salt crystals. Under these test conditions, neither moisture present in room air nor moisture adsorbed on the specimen surface were sufficient to initiate stress corrosion. The possibility remains, however, that atmospheric moisture might be sufficient to promote attack after much longer exposure times or after exposure at higher temperatures.

After heating a specimen at 650 F for 75 hours and subsequently cooling and removing all salt and corrosion products from the surface, the absorption of corrosion-produced hydrogen by the metal was shown by counting the $^3H$ activity, Table 4. The data substantiates the observation of $^3H$ in salt-corroded areas made previously[5] by autoradiographic techniques.

### B. Effect of Type of Salt and Moisture Content on Cracking

In previous studies,[6,7] the time to initiate hot-salt cracking was shown to be dependent on exposure temperature, salt composition, and alloy composition. In a continuation of these studies, the effect of moisture content of the salt on cracking of Ti-8Al-1Mo-1V was investigated by comparing the effects of NaCl with $SnCl_2 \cdot 2H_2O$. As shown in Figure 4, the time to initiate cracking was much shorter for $SnCl_2 \cdot 2H_2O$ than for NaCl, especially at temperatures above the melting point of $SnCl_2$, 475 F. Although the liquid salt greatly accelerates the stress corrosion phenomenon, it is important to note that cracking can occur at temperatures below the melting points of both $SnCl_2$ and NaCl. This indicates that the presence of a liquid phase is not an essential requirement for hot-salt cracking.

The electrochemical nature of hot-salt corrosion reactions was vividly revealed by the experiments performed at temperatures above the melting point of $SnCl_2$. During the initial attack by the fused salt, small globules of pure, molten tin appeared on the specimens. This tin metal, the identity of which was confirmed by chemical analysis, could only be produced by electrochemical oxidation of the titanium alloy specimen and reduction of the tin ions ($Sn^{++}$) of the salt to tin metal. The oxidation of the titanium alloy was obvious from the formation of corrosion pits. During continued exposure to the atmosphere, the tin metal oxidized. Cracking was initiated only after significant corrosion had occurred, which indicates that the cracking was not caused by the liquid tin, or by titanium corrosion products (such as titanium chlorides). This was confirmed by immersing stressed Ti-8Al-1Mo-1V in molten tin at 700 F, abrading the surface to break the oxide film, and exposing it for 90 minutes. No cracking occurred.

Evidence in support of a stress-sorption theory of cracking was found during the hot-stage microscopy experiments. Hot-stage microscopy revealed that, with both NaCl and $SnCl_2 \cdot 2H_2O$, the initial propagation of cracks was very rapid. However, cracks caused by NaCl were small, and further growth occurred very slowly, apparently by intermittent extensions. Cracking caused by $SnCl_2 \cdot 2H_2O$ was much more severe, and the initial extent of cracking was directly dependent on the amount of salt on the specimen. The addition of more $SnCl_2 \cdot 2H_2O$ to hot specimens caused immediate rapid extension of cracks. In some cases in which the specimens were cooled to room temperature after the initial cracks formed, the residual salt and corrosion products partially dissolved as a result of absorbing atmospheric moisture, and further rapid crack propagation (0.1 inch/min) was observed at room temperature. This behavior appears to be similar to the stress corrosion that has been reported[3] in titanium alloys precracked by fatigue and exposed to ambient temperature corrosion media. The rapid crack propagation at room temperature appear to be best explained on the basis of a stress-sorption mechanism of cracking.

Evidence of "tunneling," i.e., lateral extension of the crack beneath the specimen surface was observed, especially in the case of $SnCl_2$ cracking. An obvious example is illustrated in Figure 5, which shows the ends of cracks extending through to the edge of a specimen before they extended the full width of the specimen. Figure 5 also shows plastic deformation and "necking" ahead of the advancing cracks.

### C. Analyses of Volatile Corrosion Products

The difference in cracking severity caused by NaCl and

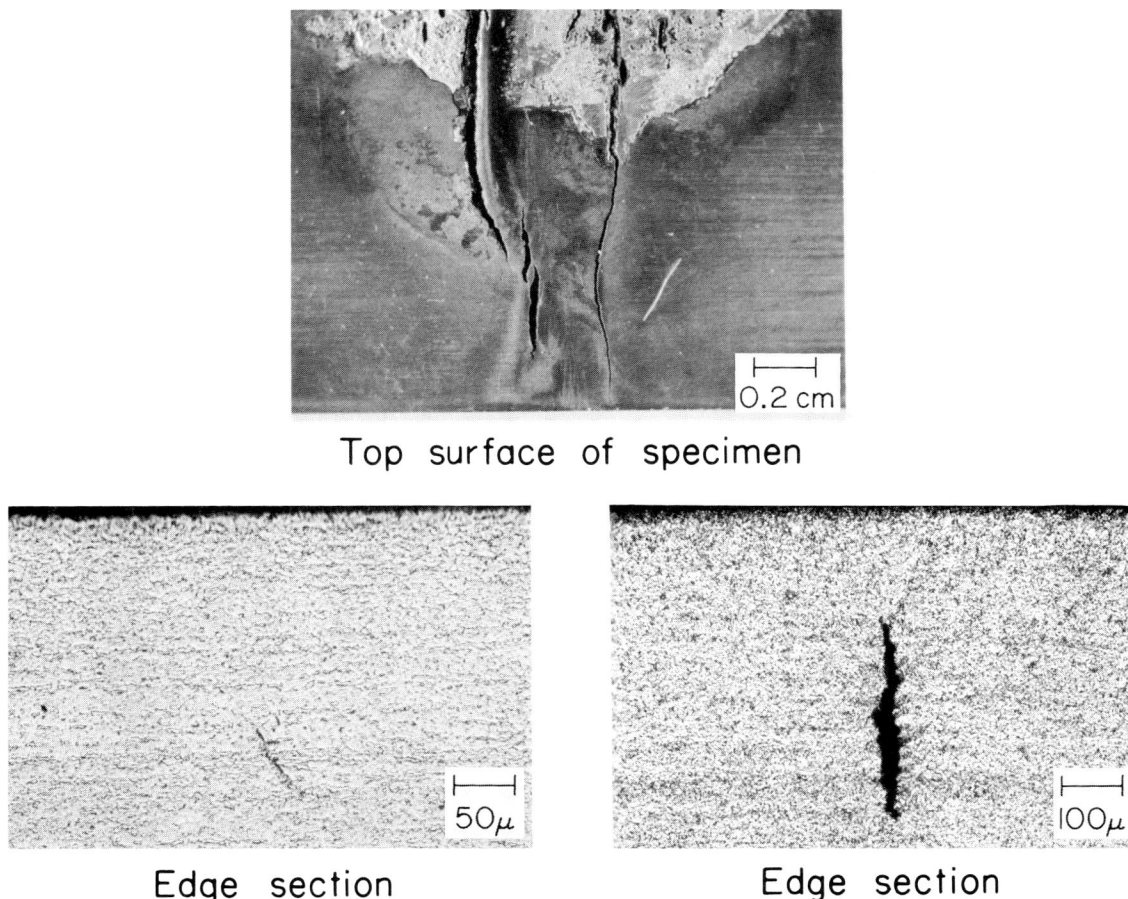

Top surface of specimen

Edge section

Edge section

FIGURE 5 — "Tunneling" of $SnCl_2$-induced cracks in Ti-8Al-1Mo-1V. (Specimen was exposed at 650 F for 10 minutes.)

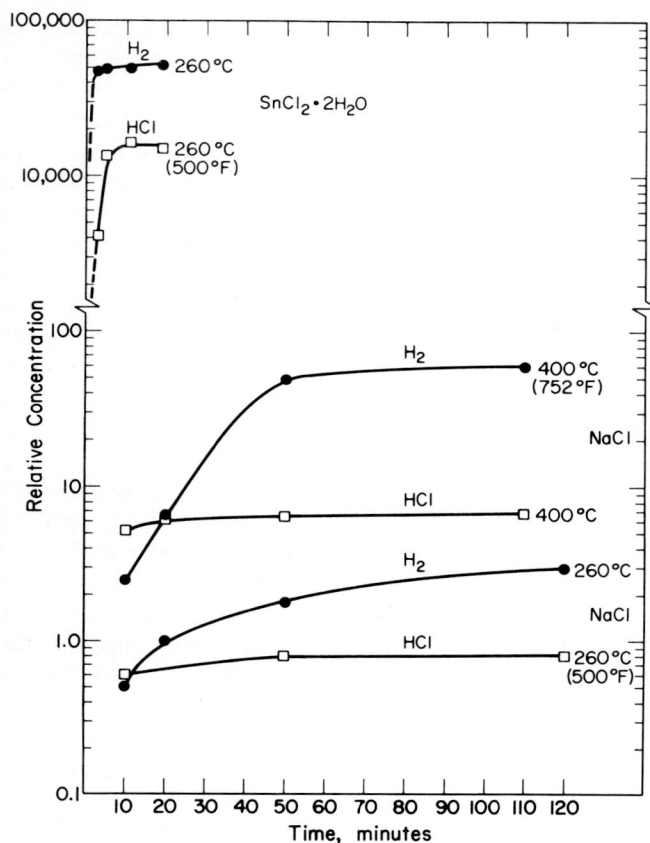

FIGURE 6 — Evolution of $H_2$ and HCl during hot salt corrosion of Ti-8Al-1Mo-1V.

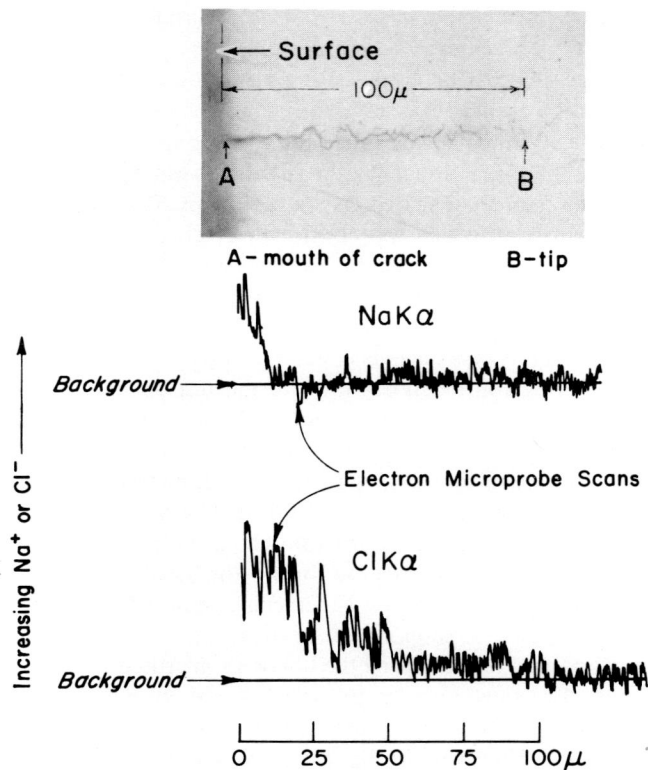

FIGURE 7 — Electron microprobe analyses of Na and Cl in hot-salt crack in Ti-8Al-1Mo-1V.[7]

$SnCl_2 \cdot 2H_2O$ appears to be due to the greater amount of moisture, and consequently the greater quantities of HCl and hydrogen generated during corrosion by $SnCl_2 \cdot 2H_2O$, as shown in Figure 6.

These mass spectrochemical analyses of volatile corrosion products generated during attack of Ti-8Al-1Mo-1V by the two different salts show an obvious association with the time to initiate cracking, Figure 4, and the relative amounts of HCl and hydrogen produced, Figure 6. At 500 F, more than 10,000 times as much HCl and hydrogen were generated by $SnCl_2 \cdot 2H_2O$ than by NaCl, and within much shorter times.

The marked increase in the concentration of hydrogen during the initial periods of corrosion, Figure 6, supports the hypothesis that corrosion-produced hydrogen promotes cracking. No chlorine gas was detected in the volatile corrosion products. Spectral data were collected to mass 170 to ensure that $TiCl_2$ or $TiCl_3$ would be detected if present. However, only $H_2O$, HCl, and $H_2$ were observed as volatile corrosion products. The metal chlorides were not expected because they should hydrolyze in air at the exposure temperature to produce oxides, HCl, and hydrogen.

The production of halogen acids by the reaction of water with a hydrolyzable halide salt at elevated temperature is termed pyrohydrolysis and is a common analytical technique for the analysis of halide salts.[8] Pyrohydrolysis requires a reaction of $H_2O$ with the halide salt to form a volatile species of the halogen (e.g., HCl, HBr). This

reaction is often accelerated by the addition of aluminum oxide or vanadium pentoxide when the salt is difficult to hydrolyze, as is the case with NaCl. Thus, previous reports[2,4] that metal oxides are involved in hot-salt cracking can be explained on the basis that the oxide accelerates pyrohydrolysis. In some cases, water of hydration in metal oxides would also contribute to the process.

All of the ingredients for pyrohydrolysis are present in the hot-salt stress corrosion of titanium alloys.[7] Both aluminum and vanadium are present in the oxide film on Ti-8Al-1Mo-1V alloy; HCl has been observed as a corrosion product, and water has been shown to be necessary for hot-salt cracking. Thus, the experimental evidence demonstrates that pyrohydrolysis initiates the corrosion process. HCl penetration of the oxide film, rendered less protective by the prior absorption of chloride, produces attack of the metal to form metal chlorides and hydrogen. More HCl and hydrogen are then generated by hydrolysis of the metal chlorides.

Evidence that HCl, rather than NaCl is the form of chloride present in cracks was obtained by electron microprobe analyses for Na and Cl along the length of cracks.[7] Specimens that were cracked during exposures to NaCl at 650 F were polished in nonaqueous lubricants so that the crack cross section could be scanned by an expanded, $8 \mu$ diameter electron beam. Care was taken to prevent sodium chloride from being forced into the crack during sample preparation. Seven cracks were examined. Crack depth ranged from $75 \mu$ to $320 \mu$. These analyses showed that sodium was concentrated at the mouth of the crack and that chloride was present in decreasing concentrations from the mouth toward the crack tip. A typical crack and the accompanying sodium and chloride concentration profiles are shown in Figure 7. The penetration of chloride but not sodium was also supported by autoradiographic studies[7] of samples cracked with $^{22}$NaCl and Na$^{36}$Cl. The chloride tracer but not sodium was found concentrated in the cracked regions.

## D. Electron Microscopy of Stress Corrosion Crack Surfaces

Examinations of the fracture surfaces of Ti-8Al-1Mo-1V alloy samples cracked by exposure to moist and dry HCl, SnCl$_2$ · 2H$_2$O, and NaCl revealed that cracking in all cases was predominately intergranular with limited regions of transgranular cleavage. Little evidence of ductile failure was noted. In general, the observations were consistent with a stress-sorption mechanism of fracture. Evidence of dislocation movement, and therefore plastic deformation accompanying fracture was also observed.

Some evidence of corrosion on fracture surfaces was observed but corrosion probably occurred after the fracture was formed.

Typical fractographs of samples cracked under five different conditions are shown in Figure 8. The fracture surfaces are quite similar and several features are common to most of the samples:

A. Intergranular cracking, shown by grain shapes is revealed on the fracture surface. There was little evidence of ductile failure.

B. Secondary cracking.

C. Rough grain surfaces with areas of more or less regular ripples, steps or folds (see arrows). These regions probably result from serpentine glide, glide plane decohesion and stretching, and are interpreted as evidence of dislocation movement during the formation of the fracture surfaces. Figure 9 shows such regions in more detail.

D. Pitting, probably resulting from corrosion after cracking was also observed in some samples (compare Figures 8a, b, and c with d and e). Severely pitted regions are shown in Figure 10 to emphasize the extent to which

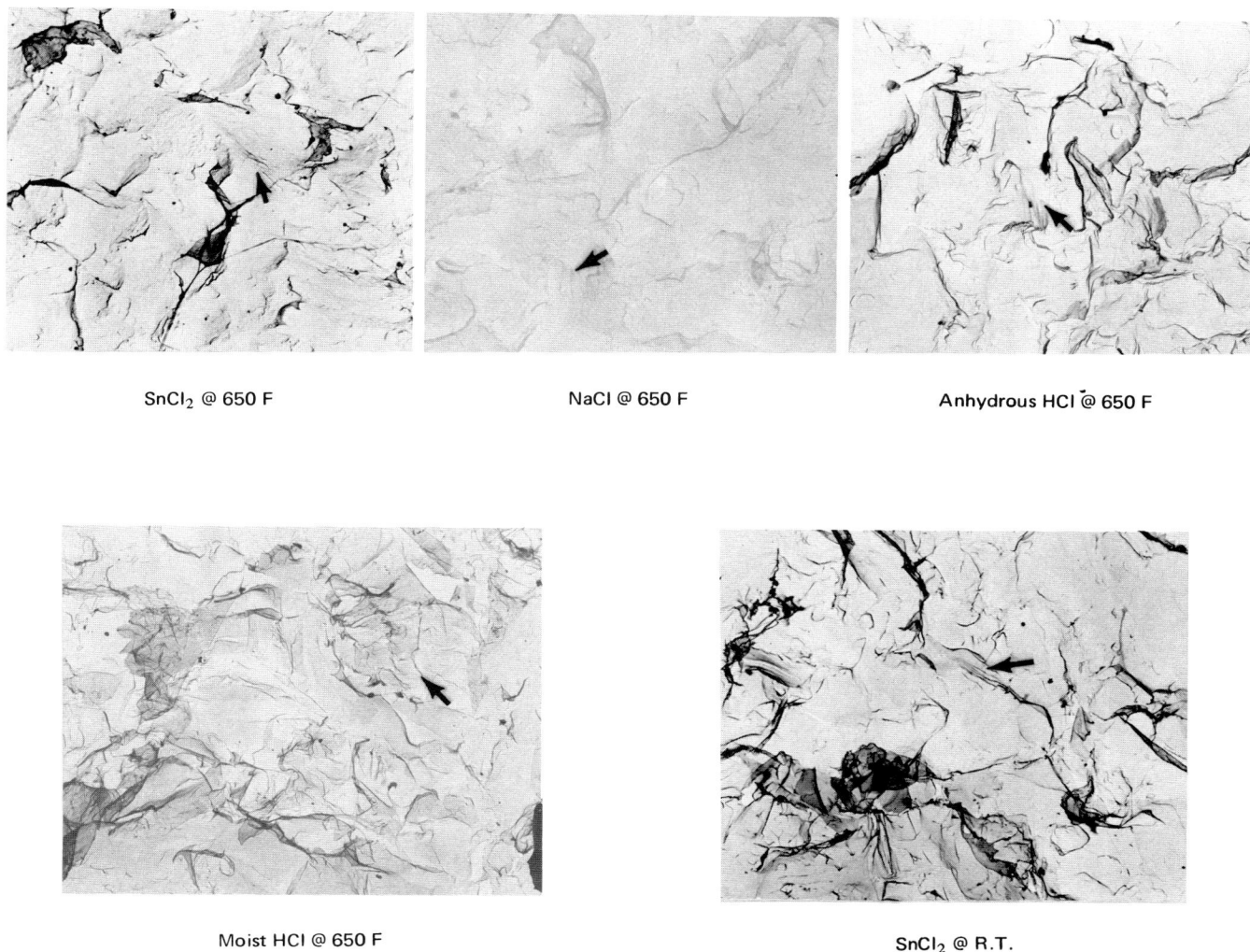

SnCl$_2$ @ 650 F

NaCl @ 650 F

Anhydrous HCl @ 650 F

Moist HCl @ 650 F

SnCl$_2$ @ R.T.

FIGURE 8 — Typical fractographs of hot-salt cracks in Ti-8Al-1Mo-1V.

corrosion can occur.

The river patterns, Figure 11, characteristic of transgranular cleavage were observed in limited regions of most of the samples. The relatively smooth grain surfaces, the topographic features, and the evidence of cleavage fracture indicate that failure must have been mechanical although electrochemical corrosion occurred at the surface. Thus, the most reasonable mechanism for hot-salt cracking appears to be the stress-sorption mechanism.

*E. Cracking in Various Halide Salts*

Previous work[5-7] demonstrated that various halide salts in addition to NaCl can cause hot-salt cracking of titanium alloys. The times required for crack initiation in Ti-8Al-1Mo-1V exposed to various halide salts deposited from saturated solutions are shown in Table 5. The effectiveness of the halide in promoting cracking increased as the size of the ion decreased (i.e., Cl > Br > I). The pH of the saturated salt solution initially applied to the specimen is also important; the time to initiate cracking decreased with decreasing pH, Table 5. This result indicates that the hydrogen ion is more important than the halide ion in promoting cracking.

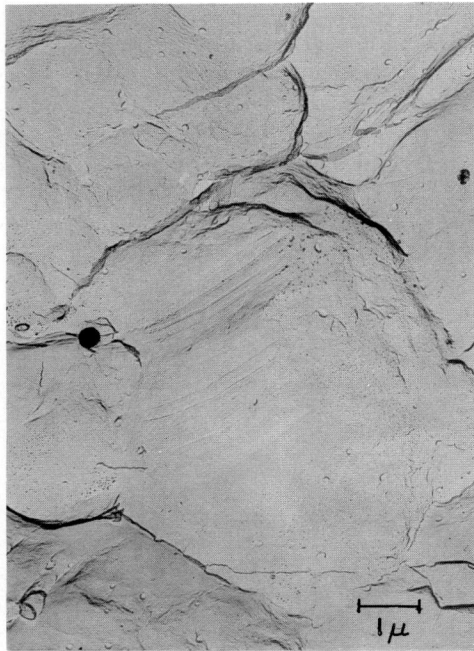

NaCl - 650 F

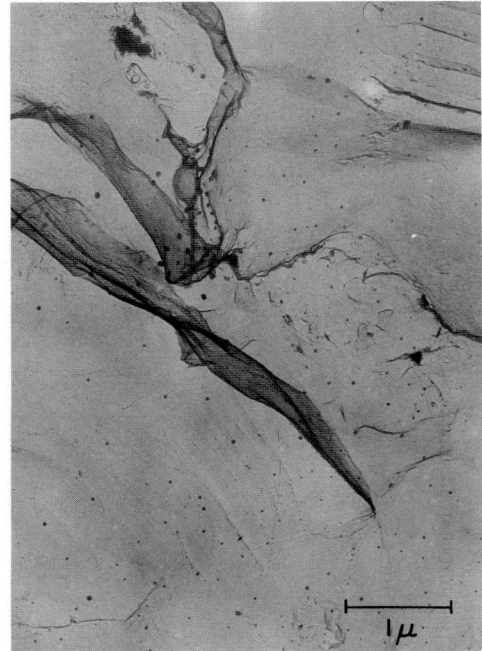

Anhydrous HCl - 650 F

FIGURE 9 — Fractographs showing evidence of dislocation movement accompanying fracture during hot-salt cracking.

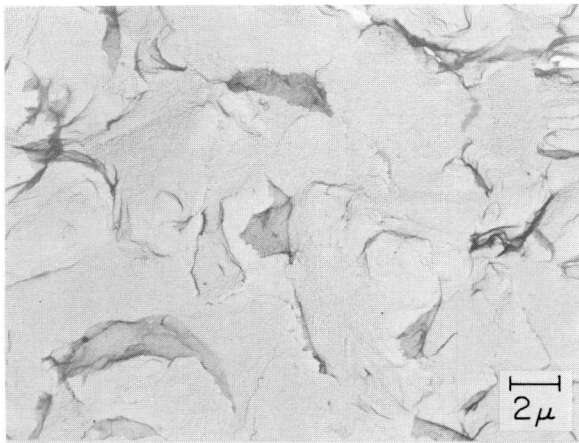

Anhydrous HCl at 650°F

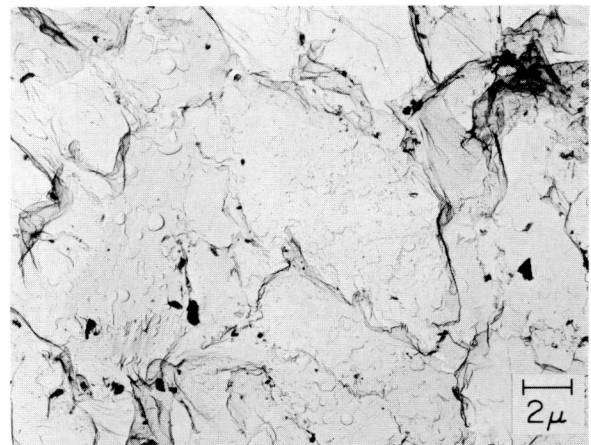

SnCl$_2$ at 650°F

FIGURE 10 — Fractographs showing evidence of corrosion of fracture faces.

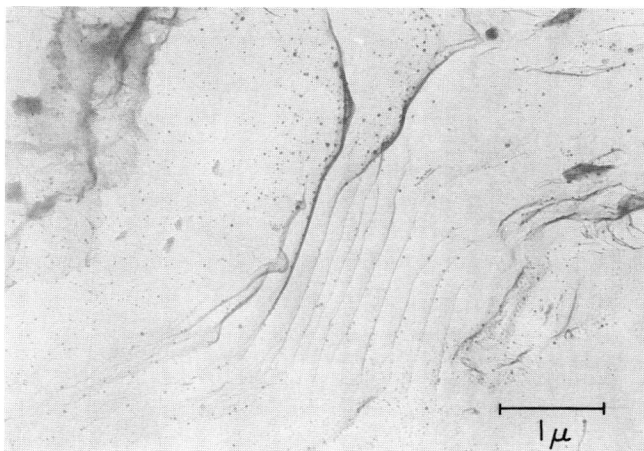

**FIGURE 11 –** Fractograph showing typical river patterns found in limited regions of both hot-salt and HCl cracks.

## IV. Conclusions

The principal experimental results to date that support a stress-sorption mechanism for hot-salt cracking of titanium alloys are:

- Surface corrosion products are generated prior to cracking.
- Cracking is due to mechanical fracture with corrosion after propagation.

After initiation, rapid crack propagation occurs, even at room temperature.

Of the two species, hydrogen chloride and hydrogen, that might be active in the stress sorption process, corrosion-produced nascent hydrogen is proposed to be the sorbed species responsible for cracking. The stress corrosion cracking process appears to occur by the following sequence:

a. Moisture retained in salt deposits is required to initiate pyrohydrolysis of the salt in contact with the metal oxide film.

b. Pyrohydrolysis generates a hydrogen halide, which penetrates the oxide film and reacts to form metal halides and hydrogen.

c. Hydrolysis of the metal halides reforms a hydrogen halide and generates hydrogen.

d. Hydrogen is sorbed by the metal surface, weakens the intermetallic bonds, and causes cracks to form because of the applied stress.

## Acknowledgments

The Savannah River Laboratory is operated by the E. I. du Pont de Nemours and Company for the U. S. Atomic Energy Commission, under Contract AT(07-2)-1. The work reported here was done for the National Aeronautical Space Administration, under Purchase Order R-124 issued to the USAEC.

## References

1. G. W. Bauer. Elevated Temperature Stability of Commercial Titanium Alloys. Paper presented at Physical Metallurgy Symposium, Watertown Arsenal (1955) September.
2. *Progress Report on the Salt Corrosion of Titanium Alloys at Elevated Temperature and Stress,* TML Report No. 88, (1957) November.
3. B. F. Brown. A New Stress Corrosion Cracking Test Procedure for High Strength Alloys. *Materials Research and Standards,* 6, No. 3 (1966) March.
4. V. C. Petersen and H. B. Bomberger. The Mechanism of Salt Attack on Titanium Alloys. *Stress Corrosion Cracking of Titanium,* ASTM STP 397, 80-94 (1966).
5. S. P. Rideout, M. R. Louthan, Jr., and C. L. Selby. Basic Mechanisms of Stress Corrosion Cracking of Titanium. *Stress Corrosion Cracking of Titanium,* ASTM STP 397, 137-151 (1966).
6. S. P. Rideout. The Initiation of Hot-Salt Stress Corrosion Cracking of Titanium Alloys. Paper presented at the *ASTM Symposium on Applications–Related Phenomena in Titanium Alloys,* Los Angeles, California (1967) April; to be published in an ASTM Special Technical Publication.
7. R. S. Ondrejcin, C. L. Selby, and S. P. Rideout. Role of Chloride in Hot-Salt Stress Corrosion Cracking of Titanium-Aluminum Alloys. USAEC Report DP(NASA)-1118 (1967) July.
8. C. J. Rodden. *Analytical Chemistry of the Manhattan Project,* McGraw-Hill Book Co., New York, p. 729 (1950).

## Discussion

**T. J. Murphy, Titanium Metals Corporation of America:**

The general intent of this paper appears to be to demonstrate that in a particular environment causing corrosion of titanium alloys, and also stress corrosion of most alloys, that hydrogen is a by-product of the corrosion reaction and that hence, hydrogen is somehow the main cause of the stress corrosion cracking.

However, the following generalizations can be made about the corrosion of titanium alloys:

1. In the presence of water, hydrogen will be found to be absorbed by the metal unless there is a very strong oxidizer present.

2. Stress corrosion of titanium alloys occurs only in a selective range of environments, including both strongly oxidizing and neutral environments.

It is, therefore, not valid to claim that the finding of hydrogen after corrosion by a neutral environment is a proof of the significance of hydrogen in a stress cracking phenomenon. The finding of hydrogen only proves that corrosion has occurred. The failure to find hydrogen after corrosion merely proves that the environment is highly oxidizing. As the two extremes of present stress corrosion theory suggest "corrosion as such" and "fracture as a result of corrosion by-products" as mechanisms, the mere finding of hydrogen does nothing to distinguish between these extremes.

It may be further noted that the susceptibility to stress corrosion cracking in both hot salt and aqueous environments is increased with increasing aluminum content, whereas the solubility of hydrogen increases. It is stated that the corrosion of aluminum bearing alloys produces more hydride precipitation than does the corrosion of pure titanium. This may be regarded merely as a demonstration that the total corrosion of the aluminum bearing alloys must be very many times that of the pure titanium, and supports a cracking-by-dissolution hypothesis equally with that of a hydrogen embrittlement type hypothesis.

**S. P. Rideout, et al:**

Our paper presents experimental evidence that moisture is necessary for hot-salt stress corrosion cracking in the temperature range investigated, and that HCl, which is produced by pyrohydrolysis of the salt, initiates corrosion and generates hydrogen.

We recognize that demonstrating the presence of hydrogen does not constitute direct proof that hydrogen is the main cause of stress corrosion cracking. On the other hand, when hydrogen is known to be present it should be included among corrosion by-products that may be suspected of causing stress corrosion cracking. On the basis of hot-stage metallographic observations of cracking and subsequent electron microscopy of fracture surfaces (fractography), we concluded that hot-salt cracking does not occur due to "corrosion as such". Corrosion of the metal surface occurred before the initiation of cracking was observed, but cracks appeared abruptly and propagation was often too rapid to be accounted for by localized corrosion. Also, the fracture surfaces showed little evidence of corrosion. We propose that a stress sorption mechanism provides the most satisfactory explanation for hot-salt cracking. **Our reasons for suggesting that corrosion-produced nascent hydrogen, rather than HCl or some other products, is the sorbed species that causes cracking are given in the paper and are discussed further in a later report.[1]**

With respect to your comments on stress corrosion cracking of aluminum-bearing titanium alloys, we agree that both the solubility of hydrogen and the susceptibility to cracking increase with increasing aluminum content. However, we see no connection between our paper and your comments about hydride precipitation in these alloys, because we made no mention of hydride precipitation. The role that we hypothesize for nascent hydrogen as a sorbed species is the lowering of the energy required to break the bonds between metal atoms and thus propagate a crack. The surface concentration of sorbed hydrogen could be less than that required to form a hydride. We do not reject the possibility that microscopic hydride particles, which could serve as crack nucleation sites, might be formed during an incubation period of corrosion in highly localized areas on the metal surface, but we have not observed this in our work.

1. R. S. Ondrejcin and M. R. Loughan, Jr. *Role of Hydrogen Chloride in Hot-Salt Stress Corrosion Cracking of Titanium-Aluminum Alloys.* USAEC Report DP(NASA)-1130, E. I. du Pont de Nemours and Co., Savannah River Laboratory, Aiken, S. C. (1967).

**S. B. Brummer, Tyco Laboratories, Inc.:**

Your Figure 1 shows a maximum absorption of $Cl^-$ of $2 \mu g/cm^2$ for an oxidized electrode. This is equivalent to $6 \times 10^{-8}$ g atoms/cm$^2$ or 30 monolayers. One guesses that some of this material must have diffused down grain boundaries, but it is still a large amount and one wonders how it could be taken up by the oxide which I believe is no more than a couple of hundred Angstroms thick. The absorption of other halides with different ion sizes would seem to be of particular interest here.

**S. P. Rideout, et al:**

Your assumption that the oxide layer is a couple of hundred Angstroms thick is correct; the estimated thickness was 200 Å. Thirty monolayers of $Cl^-$ would amount to 50-55 Å and it is agreed that this is a large amount. The distribution of $Cl^-$ within the oxide has not been investigated by us; in fact we have not definitely identified whether we are dealing with adsorption, absorption or both. We believe that the phenomenon is initially due to adsorption combined with partial incorporation, i.e., absorption, into the oxide lattice.

If a demonstrable effect of adsorption with ionic size exists, the best approach would be to compare $Cl^-$ (1.81 Å dia.) with $I^-$ (2.19 Å dia.) especially if the effect of size is small. A comparison with $F^-$ (1.33 Å dia.) would not be too pertinent since fluoride forms the extremely stable $TiF_6^=$ complex as it dissolves the titanium oxide. In addition $F^-$ salts do not cause hot-salt stress corrosion cracking of Ti-Al alloys but do cause severe corrosion.

**J. A. S. Green, RIAS:**

I wish to dispute the interpretation of Figure 1 which illustrates the effect of solution pH on chloride adsorption by Ti-8Al-1Mo-1V at room temperature. Your conclusion from this figure is that the chloride is not present as HCl molecules because adsorption was maximum in the neutral range and decreased as the pH was increased or decreased.

This figure illustrates a difference in chloride adsorption between a freshly polished and an oxidized surface. If the chloride were present as HCl molecules then the oxidized surface, having presumably a greater affinity for the adsorption of chloride ions, should show an adsorption maximum at a lower value of pH than the polished surface. Figure 1 shows that firstly neither adsorption maxima occur exactly at neutral pH values and secondly the maximum adsorption for the oxidized surface, which contains more chloride ions and possibly more hydrogen ions, occurs at about pH 5.5 compared with about 6.2 for the freshly polished surface. Since pH itself is a logarithmic scale I suggest this difference is significant and might indicate an increase in the concentration of hydrogen ions.

You also argue that if the adsorbed chloride ions were accompanied by hydrogen ions then the amount of chloride adsorbed would be expected to increase in acid solutions. This may not be the case if oxide dissolution occurs under these conditions.

S. P. Rideout, et al:

We cannot accept your interpretation of our Figure 1. We interpret the results to indicate that the Cl⁻ was not adsorbed as HCl.

As you pointed out, pH is a logarithmic scale. In Figure 1 the pH 5-7 range represents a molar hydrogen ion concentration decrease of a factor of 100. On the oxidized specimen the chloride decrease in the pH 5-7 range is not close to a factor of 100; in fact, it is less than a factor of 2 (2.1 to 1.7 $\mu g/cm^2$). On the freshly polished surface chloride adsorption increased while the hydrogen ion concentration decreased a factor of 10 (pH 5-6) then decreased as the hydrogen ion decreased another factor of 10 (pH 6-7). If the observed chloride adsorption changes were due only to H⁺ accompanying Cl⁻, then the Cl⁻ should have decreased by about a factor of 100 over the pH 5-7 range, and both the oxidized and polished specimens should have reacted in the same manner. We consider the difference in the adsorption maxima for the oxidized and freshly polished surfaces as being relatively insignificant. In both cases the specimens were initially polished in air and, therefore, had a very thin oxide film. The "freshly polished" specimens were immersed in the chloride solutions immediately, but the "oxidized" specimens were stored in a 50% relative humidity cabinet at room temperature for 18 hours.

Although it is known that titanium oxides are amphoteric, we do not believe that dissolution of the oxide had an appreciable effect on the results shown in Figure 1.

A. R. C. Westwood, RIAS:

You suggest that chloride ions can be absorbed into the metal oxide film, possibly occupying the position of oxygen vacancies in the lattice. This would appear to raise a problem of charge equalization, cf., $Cl^{1-}$ and $O^{2-}$. Would you care to comment on this?

S. P. Rideout, et al:

Assuming that there is no space charge developed in the oxide film, a change in the cation valence would be necessary to maintain charge neutrality if the Cl⁻ occupied an oxygen vacancy. We have not identified the position of the Cl ions.

J. E. LeSurf, Chalk River Nuclear Laboratories:

In your model, you say stannous chloride hydrolyzes at the temperature of test whereas sodium chloride requires catalysts such as aluminum or vanadium.

If this is correct, I would expect the stannous chloride to induce cracking in certain alloys which are immune to sodium chloride. Is there any evidence of this?

S. P. Rideout, et al:

We have not studied stannous chloride effects on alloys immune to sodium chloride cracking. In comparing the effects of various salts on a given alloy, we have always observed that stannous chloride produces more severe cracking at lower temperatures after shorter incubation times.

# STUDIES OF HOT SALT CRACKING
# OF THE TITANIUM 8%Al-1%Mo-1%V ALLOY

Hugh L. Logan
National Bureau of Standards

## Abstract

Two approaches to the problem of hot salt cracking of the titanium alloy are reported. In the first of these the susceptibility of the alloy to cracking in contact with a number of chlorides was studied. Only NaCl, LiCl and a molten eutectic mixture of LiCl and KCl were found to severely crack stressed specimens exposed in air at 800 F.

In the second phase of the program the effects of environments on the alloy in contact with NaCl were investigated. Data indicate that the oxide or series of oxides formed on the alloy surface were important in determining whether specimens developed stress corrosion cracks.

Data also indicate that little or no chlorine was produced in the corrosion reaction.

## I. Introduction

In an earlier paper[1] specimens and results obtained in an investigation of the hot salt stress corrosion cracking of the Ti-8-1-1 titanium alloy were described. In the present paper these earlier data pertinent to the present paper are summarized. More recent data and possible mechanisms of failure of the Ti-8-1-1 alloy in hot salt are discussed.

## II. Materials and Experimental Techniques

### A. Material Compositions

Two lots of the Ti-8-1-1 alloy were used in this investigation; sheet material 0.040 inch thick, and rod, 1 inch in diameter. The chemical compositions of these materials are given in Table 1.

### B. Sheet Metal Specimen Preparation

Sheet specimens were used for two purposes: to determine (1) whether the cation, combined with the chloride, had an effect on the stress corrosion cracking of the alloy and (2) whether the application of an applied current will affect the exposure period to failure of specimens subject to tensile stresses and exposed in a molten chloride.

The sheet material was used in the mill annealed condition. Two types of specimens were used: 1-inch by 6-inch beam specimens and conventional 1/2-inch reduced section tensile specimens. The sheared edges were milled off the beam specimens to eliminate possible residual stresses

from shearing. These specimens were stressed from 40,000 to 80,000 psi in the outer fibers by four point loading. In some cases the convex surface was wet with distilled water and a dry alkali or alkaline earth chloride sprinkled on the surface. In others, a 10% aqueous solution of sodium

TABLE 1—Composition of Ti-8-1-1 Alloy Used In This Investigation

| Element | Weight Percent | |
| | Rod | Sheet |
| --- | --- | --- |
| Aluminum | 7.7 | 8.2 |
| Molybdenum | 1.0 | 0.97 |
| Vanadium | 0.7 | 0.94 |
| Iron | 0.08 | 0.10 |
| Nitrogen | 0.0022 | ND[1] |
| Oxygen | 0.062 | ND |
| Hydrogen | 0.010 | ND |
| Carbon | 0.01 | ND |

**Results of Spectroscopic Examination[2]**

| Chromium | vw | vw |
| --- | --- | --- |
| Copper | vw | vw |
| Magnesium | t | vw |
| Manganese | vw | vw |
| Nickel | — | vw |
| Silicon | w | w |
| Tin | vw | — |

[1]ND – not determined.
[2]w, 0.01 to 0.1%; vw, 0.001 to 0.01%; t, <0.001%.
Analyses were performed by the Microchemical Analysis Section of NBS.

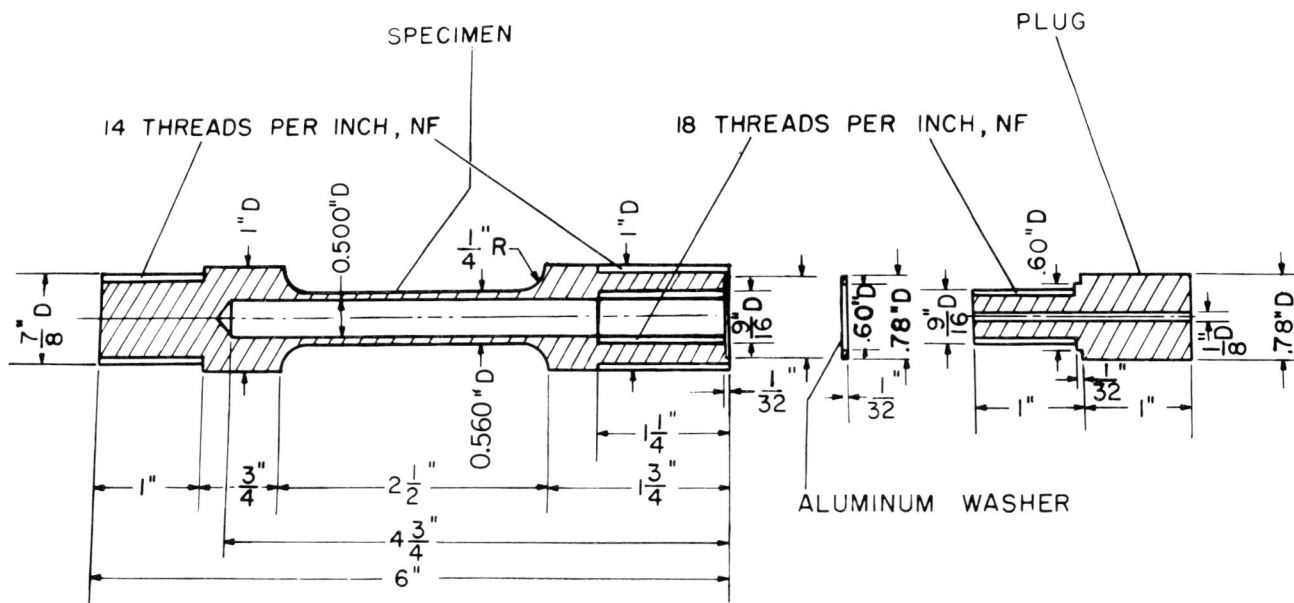

**FIGURE 1 – Drawing of hollow specimen used in this investigation.**

chloride was aspirated onto the surface which was then dried in a hot air stream. Specimens were exposed at 800 F in a circulating air furnace for 280 days unless visible cracks were detected earlier.

Tensile specimens were mounted in an insulated stainless steel cell wrapped with a heating coil, fitted with a chromel-alumel thermocouple, and filled with the dry-mixed KCl-LiCl eutectic (mp 670 F). The system was brought to temperature at 750 F, the specimen loaded in tension at 10,000 psi by means of a lever system, and exposed until failure occurred.

### C. Hollow Specimen Preparation

Hollow specimens were used to study the effect of oxygen and varying amounts of water vapor on the susceptibility of the alloy to stress corrosion cracking and in an effort to determine what gaseous corrosion products were formed by the corrosive process.

Blanks about 6 inches long were cut from the rod stock and given the following duplex anneal heat treatment: one hour at 1750 F, air cool, then 8 hours at 1050 F and air cool. After heat treatment the rod pieces were machined into hollow specimens as shown in the drawing, Figure 1. After the specimens had been degreased, a coating of salt was deposited on the inner surfaces in the following manner: Specimens were heated to about 250 F and were then filled with a 10% solution either of NaCl or a salt mixture containing seven parts of NaCl to one part of $MgCl_2$. Before the solution had reached the specimen temperature, it was pipetted out, leaving a thin layer of salt on the interior wall.[1] The specimens were then closed with a plug machined from the rod stock. There was a connection through the plug to the specimen interior so

that an atmosphere could be introduced (after the specimens were closed) into the cavity. This connection may also be used to obtain a sample of the gaseous environment in the interior of the specimen. The specimen and plug arrangement are the same as those used previously with stainless steel.[2] Thermocouples were attached to the shoulders of the specimens and to the centers of the reduced sections. Specimens were placed in conventional creep furnaces heated to 750 F and, after thermal equilibrium had been reached, stressed, using a lever system, through hollow pull rods attached to the ends of the specimens to 73,500 psi (90% of yield strength).[3] The specimens were exposed at temperature until failure occurred or for periods as long as 600 hours.

## III. Results and Discussion

### A. Role of Salt Composition

There was wide scatter in exposure periods to failure of the sheet specimens stressed by four point loading. Exposure periods to failure for specimens exposed to NaCl generally increased with decreasing stress and, in the early work, ranged from 64 days for specimens stressed to 80,000 psi to 91 days for specimens stressed to 40,000 psi in the outer fiber.

In a check run, specimens (from the same melt, but a different sheet) coated with NaCl and subjected to a tensile stress of 80,000 psi failed in approximately one week compared to the average of 60 days mentioned earlier. Contamination of the NaCl with LiCl was suspected and salt removed from one of the failed specimens was found to contain 1.6 ppm of lithium compared to less than 0.1 ppm of lithium in the stock NaCl.

The experiment was repeated at a lower stress level with known amounts (0, 100 and 1000 ppm) of LiCl being

---

[1]In one experiment, dry NaCl was sprinkled into the interior of a dry specimen.

added to the 10% spray solution of stock NaCl. Periodic inspection revealed cracks on one specimen coated with NaCl alone after 5 days exposure. All of the specimens showed cracks on microscopic examination after 9 days. Exact time to initiation of cracks on the different specimens could not be observed, but in general, the severity of cracking increased with increasing lithium additions and corrosion products gave a blacker appearance with the greatest addition. The data suggest that lithium must be present in appreciable amounts to affect the exposure period to failure by stress corrosion cracking.

In order to evaluate the effect of the cation on the exposure period to failure, sheet specimens were also coated with various alkali and alkaline earth chlorides, namely CsCl, KCl, LiCl, KCl + LiCl, BaCl$_2$, CaCl$_2$, MgCl$_2$ and SrCl$_2$, stressed to 80,000 psi in the outer fibers and heated at 800 F in the circulating air furnace. Specimens coated with solid LiCl or with a LiCl-KCl eutectic mixture (mp 670 F) failed in less than 20 hours. A cold U-bend specimen dipped into the molten eutectic mixture failed as soon as the surface was wetted.

Preliminary microscopic examinations of the remaining four-point loaded specimens removed from the furnace after 280 days exposure did not reveal any obvious cracking. However, after the specimens were cleaned by pickling in H$_2$O + 4% HNO$_3$ + 2% HF, varying crack patterns were observed on all specimens except the one coated with MgCl$_2$ and the uncoated control. The severity of cracking decreased in the order BaCl$_2$, KCl, CaCl$_2$, CsCl, SrCl$_2$ (see Figure 2). Cracks were associated with pits in specimens coated with KCl and SrCl$_2$. No trends that might be expected on the basis of chemical periodicity were found. Data are summarized in Table 2.

In work reported earlier,[1] we coated a specimen with a one-to-one mixture of NaCl and MgCl$_2 \cdot$ 6H$_2$O and determined the X-ray diffraction patterns of the mixture at various temperatures up to 900 F. The magnesium hexahydrate broke down successively to MgCl$_2 \cdot$ 4H$_2$O and MgCl$_2 \cdot$ 2H$_2$O at temperatures of 190 F and 260 F. Above 385 F, the MgCl$_2 \cdot$ 2H$_2$O slowly changed to an amorphous or glassy product that persisted to 680 F and then gradually changed to magnesium oxide.

We believe that the MgCl$_2$ did not crack the metal because the glassy character of the chloride served as a protective coating on the alloy until most of it was eliminated by the change to oxide at the temperature of the experiment. We have made no elevated temperature X-ray diffraction studies of the other hydrated chlorides that we used.

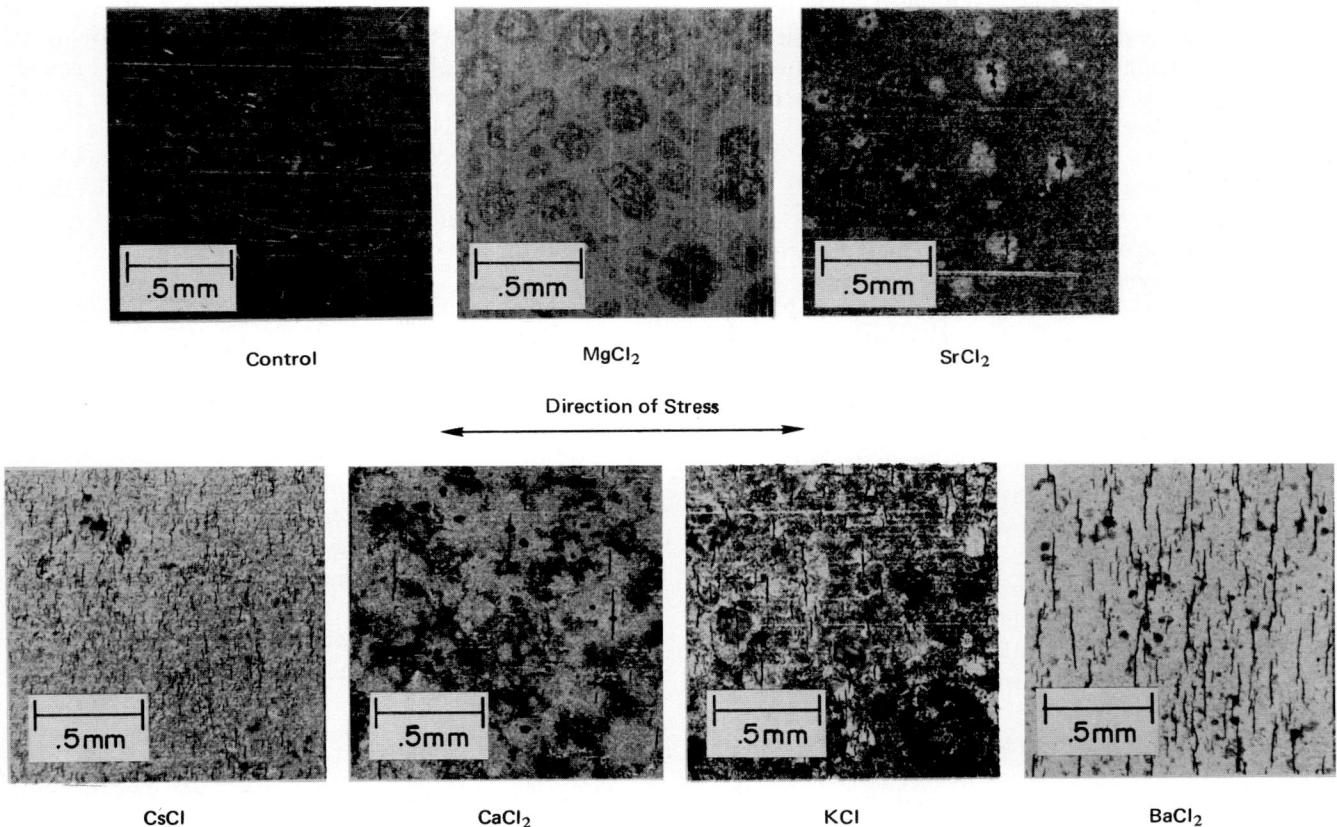

FIGURE 2 — Surfaces of four point loaded (80,000 psi) bend specimens which were coated with representative I and II group chlorides and exposed at 800 F for 280 days. Varying cracking severity is shown after surfaces were cleaned with an acid pickle.

TABLE 2–Exposure Periods to Failure of Sheet Specimens of the Ti-8-1-1
Titanium Alloy Stressed in Contact with Chlorides at Elevated Temperatures
(800 F Unless Otherwise Indicated)

| Type of Loading | Applied Stress | Corrodent | Exposure Period to Failure |
|---|---|---|---|
| 4-point | 80,000 psi | NaCl | 5-64 d |
| 4-point | 60,000 psi | NaCl | 5-70 |
| 4-point | 60,000 psi | NaCl[1] | 5-9 |
| 4-point | 40,000 psi | NaCl | ~91 |
| 4-point | 80,000 psi | BaCl$_2$ | <282 |
| 4-point | 80,000 psi | CaCl$_2$ | <282 |
| 4-point | 80,000 psi | CsCl | <282 |
| 4-point | 80,000 psi | KCl | <282 |
| 4-point | 80,000 psi | LiCl | <1 |
| 4-point | 80,000 psi | MgCl$_2 \cdot 6H_2O$ | >282 |
| 4-point | 80,000 psi | SrCl$_2$ | <282 |
| 4-point | 80,000 psi | –– | >282 |
| 4-point | 80,000 psi | LiCl + KCl | <1 |
| direct tension | 10 ksi | Molten[2] LiCl + KCl | 1 hr |
| direct tension | 10 ksi | LiCl + KCl[3] | 1 |
| direct tension | 10 ksi | LiCl + KCl[4] | 2 |

[1]NaCl + 100 or 1000 ppm LiCl.
[2]MP 670 F, specimens exposed at 750 F.
[3]Specimen made anode using externally applied current.
[4]Specimen made cathode using externally applied current.

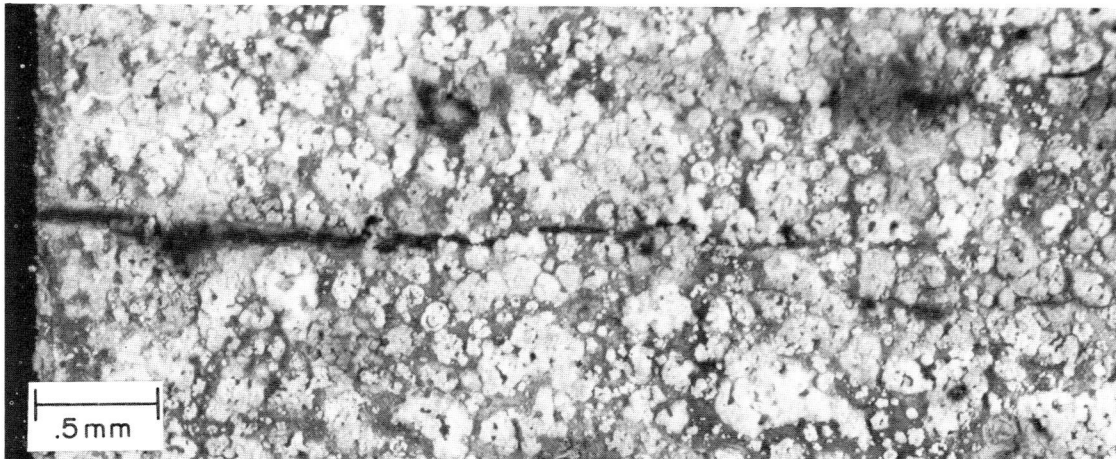

FIGURE 3 — Cracks in four-point loaded specimen coated with NaCl and heated for 64 days at 800 F. White translucent material contains NaCl and larger amounts of anatase, rutile and X phase. Light grey contains small amounts of NaCl and rutile and larger amounts of anatase and X phase. The dark grey is primarily rutile.

## B. Corrosion Products

Figure 3 shows a crack in a specimen coated with NaCl and heated for approximately 64 days at 800 F and the corrosion products on the surface of the specimen. As reported earlier,[1] X-ray diffraction patterns of these products indicated the presence of at least four phases, anatase, rutile, NaCl and at least one unidentified phase, designated X. Efforts made to separate these corrosion products as to color and other physical characteristics were not successful. The white translucent material, Figure 3, contained some NaCl and larger amounts of anatase, rutile and the unknown phase X. Three other corrosion products clearly distinguishable on the original specimens, but difficult to differentiate in a black and white photograph, were also studied. They all contained NaCl, anatase, rutile, and the unknown phase X, but the relative amounts differed in the different materials, possibly because of the incomplete separation.

Finally, a sheet specimen coated with NaCl was heated in oxygen at a pressure of one atmosphere for 30 days at 800 F. A subsequent microscopic examination showed it to be coated with light and dark whiskers, Figure 4. The light whiskers were NaCl, and the dark, rutile. We have no evidence that the NaCl whiskers are important in the cracking process. Kofstad[4] shows rutile whiskers formed by oxidation of titanium at 500 C (932 F) at an oxygen pressure of 0.1 torr. Hurlen[5] also reports that rutile whiskers are sometimes formed on top of a rutile film. Formation of these whiskers suggests the presence of stresses in the rutile.

## C. Effects of Applied Currents in Molten Salts

The tensile specimens exposed in the molten eutectic of LiCl and KCl, stressed in direct tension to 10,000 psi, failed in approximately one hour. Upon removal from the eutectic mixture the specimens were severely pitted and had a metallic rather than the characteristic oxide coated appearance. It is probable that the molten eutectic mixture simply acted as a flux in removing the oxide layers from the surface of the alloy. The specimens, however, appeared to fail by stress corrosion cracking rather than primarily from overload. In one experiment the specimen was made the anode by applying a potential difference of 3 volts between the specimen and cell wall. The exposure period increased slightly, but this may represent scatter in the data. The exposure periods to failure of other specimens exposed under the same conditions except that they were made the cathodes, were approximately doubled.

## D. Hollow Specimen Machined from Rod Material

**1. Effect of Water Vapor.** A drop or two of water was placed in the interiors of the first specimens coated with the 7 NaCl + 1 $MgCl_2 \cdot 6H_2O$ mixture (the specimen cavity being filled with air). These specimens failed in 226 to 600 hours. Specimens coated with the salt mixture with the cavity subsequently filled with oxygen at a pressure of 4 to 6 psi failed in less than 72 hours. Figure 5 shows cracks in the interior wall of a specimen that failed and was subsequently split so that the interior could be examined. Many cracks were usually found in addition to that one producing the failure. As was indicated in the discussion of sheet specimens, $MgCl_2 \cdot 6H_2O$ will break down to give off 2 and subsequently 4 molecules of water. Hence, conditions leading to the failures reported with the 7 NaCl, 1 $MgCl_2$ were the same as those in specimens containing NaCl + $H_2O$. The water probably reacts with the titanium to form $TiO_2$ as follows:

$$Ti + 2H_2O \rightarrow TiO_2 + 2H_2$$

and probably some lower oxides. At the temperature of exposure, approximately 750 F, it is expected that the hydrogen combines with the titanium to form a hydride.

Several specimens coated with NaCl, then filled with purified argon, moistened by bubbling through water before it entered the specimen cavity, failed after exposure periods ranging from 74 to 326 hours. Here again it is believed that the water reacted with the titanium to form oxides more complex in some areas, than those on a machined specimen not previously heated above 250 F.[6]

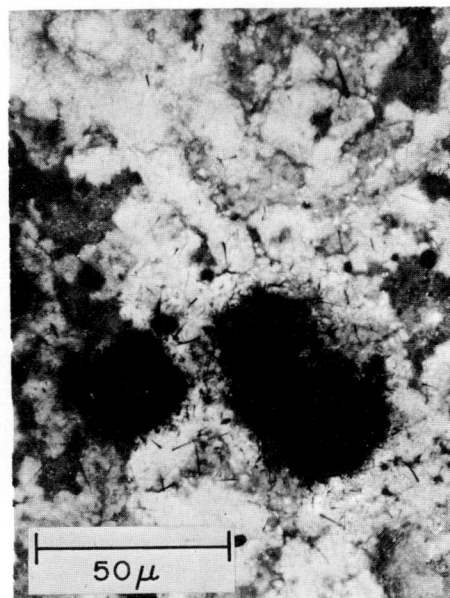

FIGURE 4 — Surface of sheet specimen coated with NaCl after exposure in oxygen atmosphere at 800 F for 30 days. Whiskers are either primarily NaCl (white) or rutile (black pyramids).

FIGURE 5 — Cracks extending into the interior wall of a hollow specimen adjacent to the main crack which caused the specimen to fail.

As was noted earlier, specimens coated with the 7 NaCl + 1 $MgCl_2 \cdot 6H_2O$ mixture with the specimen cavity filled with oxygen under pressure, failed in a relatively short time. On the other hand specimens coated with NaCl (no $MgCl_2 \cdot 6H_2O$ added) and filled with dry oxygen at reduced pressures ($\sim 0.2$ Torr) failed only after long exposure periods ($> 500$ hrs) and one did not fail before the experiment was terminated. These data indicate that a supply of available oxygen in the specimen cavity was important in producing cracking.

A group of specimens was preoxidized by heating them in tank oxygen at 800 F for 60 to 70 hours. These specimens were coated with NaCl in the usual manner, mounted in the stress corrosion racks, evacuated to a pressure of less than $10^{-3}$ Torr and, finally, filled with purified and dried argon.[2] Specimens failed after expo-

---

[2] The tank Argon flowed slowly over titanium chips heated to 1470 F and then through a dry ice-acetone trap.

sure periods ranging up to 250 hours. A specimen exposed under the same conditions except that it had not been preoxidized did not fail in 500 hours.

Just how these preformed oxide films function to produce cracking is not clear. They could, of course, occlude water. To investigate this possibility, attempts were made to remove such water. A preoxidized specimen was coated with NaCl crystals by withdrawing the solution, evacuated to $10^{-7}$ Torr, and heated at temperatures up to 750 F for approximately two days before it was filled with purified Argon. This specimen subsequently stressed to 73,500 psi at 750 F failed in about 22 hours. It has been recognized that hydrogen could be adsorbed on and diffuse interstitially[7] into rutile films from contact and reaction with a water solution, i.e., water entrained in the interior of a NaCl crystal. Therefore, instead of coating the interior of a specimen with NaCl from an aqueous solution finely ground dry NaCl was placed in the specimen cavity and scattered on the side walls. The preoxidized specimen was then evacuated using a mechanical fore pump and a liquid nitrogen cold trap and heated to 750 F for approximately two days prior to the introduction of ultrapure dry Argon to pressure of 5 psig, and stressing at temperature. The specimen failed in less than 24 hours as the result of a stress corrosion crack penetrating through the specimen wall. Other stress corrosion cracks were also found penetrating into the specimen wall from the interior cavity. Data on hollow specimens are summarized in Table 3.

The data obtained on hollow specimens indicate that apparently a necessary condition for failure to occur is that there must be appreciable oxidation of the interior metal surface. This may result from reduction of water at temperature of the experiment or from contact with sufficient oxygen again at an elevated temperature and usually also in the presence of water vapor. Too much water vapor, however, seems to have an inhibiting effect.

Kofstad[6] reports that the rutile modification of $TiO_2$ is the only oxide that has been detected in the oxide scale formed by the oxidation of titanium in oxygen below 1000 C. However, he also states that lower oxides have been observed on the oxidation of the metal in air in the presence of water vapor. This latter condition is expected in these experiments and we may assume that a series of oxides exist between the rutile at the exterior surface and the metal itself.

**2. Chlorine as a Corrosion Product.** Gas samples were taken from the interior cavities of specimens in which the pressure of oxygen had been reduced to 2 x $10^{-1}$ Torr prior to loading. Mass spectrographic analysis did not show the presence of HCl or $Cl_2$, suggested products in the chemical action leading to stress corrosion cracking of this alloy.[8] The sensitivity was one part in $10^4$, hence, if HCl or $Cl_2$ was produced in the reaction at all, it was produced only in very small amounts. In subsequent experiments, oxygen flowed over a sheet specimen coated with NaCl and heated to 750 F and was bubbled through a starch-potassium iodide solution. There was no detectable color change. This again indicated that if $Cl_2$ was produced, it was only in minute quantities.

TABLE 3—Exposure Periods to Failure of Hollow Ti-8-1-1 Alloy Specimens (In the Duplex Annealed Condition), Coated with One or More Chlorides, Stressed in Direct Tension to 90% of Their Yield Strength and Exposed at 750 F in Various Environments

| Corrodent | Environment | Exposure Period to Failure |
|---|---|---|
| **Specimens Without Preoxidation** | | |
| 7 NaCl + MgCl$_2$ · 6H$_2$O | Air | 226-600 hr |
| 7 NaCl + MgCl$_2$ · 6H$_2$O | Oxygen, 4 to 6 psig | $<$72 |
| 7 NaCl + MgCl$_2$ · 6H$_2$O + NaOH | Argon | 132 |
| 7 NaCl + MgCl$_2$ · 6H$_2$O + NaOH | Argon, 5 psig | $>$208 - 570 |
| NaCl | Wet Argon | 74 - 326 |
| NaCl | Dried Argon | $>$500 |
| NaCl | Dry oxygen $\sim$0.2 Torr | $>$500 |
| **Preoxidized at 800 F, $>$60 hr in Tank Oxygen** | | |
| NaCl | Dried Argon | $<$250 |
| NaCl[1] | Ultrapure dried Argon | $<$22 |
| NaCl[2] | Ultrapure dried Argon, 5 psig | $<$24 |

[1]Specimen evacuated to $10^{-7}$ Torr, heated 2 days at temperatures up to 750 F before adding Argon and stressing.

[2]Specimen coated with dried NaCl powder evacuated (fore pump and N$_2$ trap) and heated 2 days at 750 F.

**3. Sodium Hydroxide as a Corrosion Product.** Other workers[9,10] have suggested that NaOH is a product of the reaction that would lead to cracking. This reaction is:

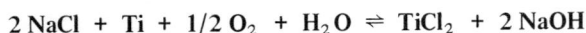

$$2\,NaCl + Ti + 1/2\,O_2 + H_2O \rightleftharpoons TiCl_2 + 2\,NaOH$$

We coated the interiors of three specimens with crystals from a solution containing 10% NaCl, $MgCl_2 \cdot 6H_2O$ and 10% NaOH. One specimen in which the Argon was at atmospheric pressure (and in which an air leak was a possibility) failed in 132 hours. Argon was introduced into the other systems at 5 psig. They were believed to be leak tight and showed no evidence of cracking when the experiments were terminated after 208 and 570 hours. The specimen exposed for 570 hours had elongated about 1 1/2 percent indicating that it had been subjected to plastic deformation. As was indicated above, the proposed reaction involving NaOH is reversible. Hence, the presence of NaOH would tend to make the reaction go to the left and cracking would not be expected. We have found no evidence of NaOH in X-ray diffraction patterns of corrosion products. However, the NaOH could be present in such minute quantities as not to be detected.

**4. Colored Corrosion Products.** There was a gray-blue film in the interior of some of the hollow specimens where NaCl crystals had been in contact with the metal at 750 F. We were able to strip some of this film from the interior of one specimen for examination in the electron microscope. A transmission micrograph is shown in Figure 6. The spike-like structures are believed to be the beginnings of whiskers found on sheet material after long exposure at temperatures (see Figure 4). Electron diffraction studies indicated that the film was composed of anatase and rutile, both nominally $TiO_2$.

The failed ends of hollow specimens showed two distinct areas. An irregular discolored area (usually blue) extending from the inner surface of the specimen into the metal, and a much brighter one, extending from the discolored area to the outer surface. The discolored area is believed to delineate the area of slow crack propagation and the bright one, that of the metal that failed by tensile fracture, after the load carrying capacity of the specimen had been reached.

Hurlen[5] states that rutile acquires a dark gray-blue color when kept in a reducing atmosphere at high temperatures. He suggests that the color may be due to oxygen vacancies, each with a trapped electron, $O_v^{..}e$, or to trivalent titanium ions.

Johnson[11] states that a blue coloration is produced if the rutile crystal is heated in a fore-pump vacuum or in a hydrogen atmosphere, or if it is doped with lithium. He suggests that the color may be due to hydrogen interstitials, but states that $Ti^{3+}$ interstitials appear to be the current favorites.

*E. Metallographic Studies*

Metallographic studies were made of specimens containing stress corrosion cracks. A typical crack is shown in Figure 7. The cracks tend to follow the grain boundaries or $\alpha$-$\beta$ boundaries. An electron probe study was made of the matrix and the precipitate ($\beta$ phase) of the annealed alloy.

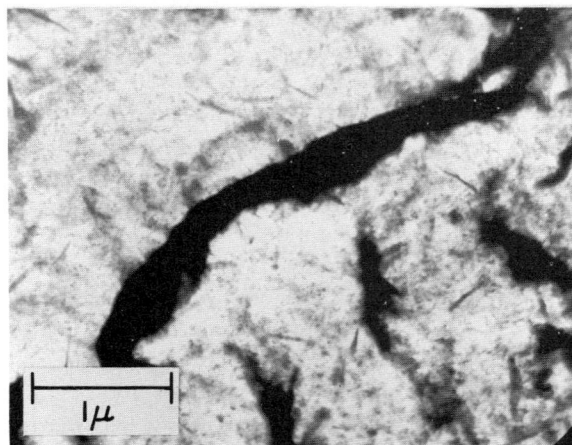

FIGURE 6 — Electron transmission micrograph of surface film stripped from interior surface of failed specimen. Note dark spike like structures, probably the beginning of whiskers. Dark diagonal band is structure too thick to be penetrated by electron beam.

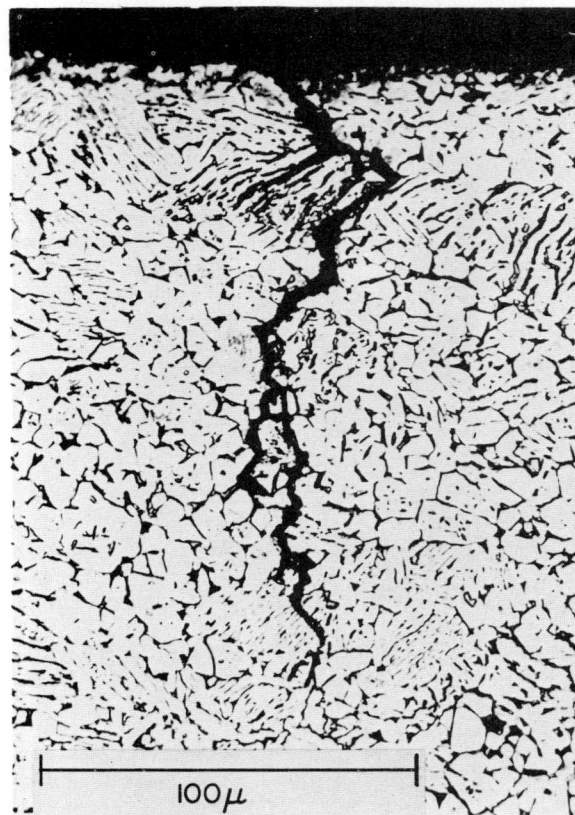

FIGURE 7 — Intercrystalline stress corrosion crack in specimen exposed at 750 F under stress of 73,500 psi. Interior of specimen coated with NaCl + $MgCl_2$ mixture. Specimen cavity filled with dry oxygen. Note textured structure near origin of crack and interior of specimen. Etched 100 ml $H_2O$, 3 ml HF, 3 ml $HNO_3$.

668

TABLE 4—Ratio of Metallic Content of α-Matrix to β-Phase (Precipitate)

| | |
|---|---|
| Ti-matrix/Ti-β phase | 1.04 |
| Al-matrix/Al-β phase | 1.36 |
| No-matrix/Mo-β phase | 0.11 |
| V-matrix/V-β phase | not determined |

Table 4 gives the relative ratios in the α-matrix and the β-phase of titanium, molybdenum and aluminum. Data indicated approximately nine times as much molybdenum in the β-phase as in the α-matrix. The probe analysis also indicates that the region immediately adjacent to the β-phase was depleted in molybdenum, i.e., the molybdenum content was lower than in the β-phase as a whole. Depletion of molybdenum adjacent to the β-phase may be a reason why stress corrosion cracks follow the β-phase. They also follow grain boundaries; it is to be expected that regions of enrichment and impoverishment at the grain boundaries would be too narrow to be detected by the probe in its present state of development.

*F. Mechanism of Cracking*

**1. Role of Preoxidation.** The fact that we obtained failures in specimens that were preoxidized or heated under conditions where oxides could readily form while we did not obtain failures in other specimens, suggests that there is something about the properties of these oxides that is important in specimen failure. Moisture could have been present during the oxidation of most of the failed specimens. Hence, we could expect trapped hydrogen interstitials in the oxides or hydrides in the metal. This would suggest that failures are due to hydrogen embrittlement. This idea is held by others[10] and we do not entirely discard it. The fact that excessive amounts of water appear to inhibit failures is, however, an argument against hydrogen embrittlement.

**2. Diffusion in Rutile.** We expect the oxide of the exposed surface to be rutile and anatase, both $TiO_2$. There have been several recent studies of diffusion of foreign atoms in rutile that are pertinent to our discussion.

Chester and Bradhurst[7] have shown that hydrogen has a very high mobility in rutile. Johnson[11] studied the diffusion of the lithium ion in rutile because he considered that the lithium ion was similar in dimensions to the hydrogen ion. He reported that diffusion of the lithium ion was strongly anisotropic being much greater in the c-direction than in any other.

Bogomolov[12] studied the diffusion of oxygen in rutile and reported that the diffusion coefficient was several orders of magnitude greater parallel to the c-axis than perpendicular to it.

The oxide which we stripped from the interior of a specimen was crystalline. Hence, we could expect hydrogen, lithium, oxygen or chloride ions to diffuse down the c-axes of those crystals that were oriented with their c-axes approximately normal to the oxide surface. Kofstad[13] suggests that above 761 F diffusion (presumably

oxygen) is probably lattice or volume diffusion, but points out that grain boundary diffusion "could also be important."

We have been considering that the oxide is $TiO_2$, but the basic alloy is only 90% titanium. We have no information as to how the cation composition of the oxide compares with that of the metal, but it is reasonable to suppose that the composition of the oxide above metal areas where there is either a depletion or concentration of one of the alloying metals will also be affected to some degree. Introduction of an oxide of aluminum or of that of the other alloying elements could affect the structure of the rutile and modify the paths for diffusion of the foreign ion or ions to the metal surface.

**3. Mechanisms.** We are suggesting two possible mechanisms for the hot salt cracking of the alloy. First, hydrogen in the metal from the decomposition of water may produce cracking by hydrogen embrittlement. However, we have earlier noted an objection to this idea. Second, we are suggesting that hydrogen, lithium ions, or chloride ions diffuse along the c-axes of suitably oriented oxide crystals or along high angle grain boundaries to the metal surface and at regions subjected to high states of stress cut the metallic bonds holding the metallic atoms together producing sharp notches, which in turn produce stress concentrations in the metal at their tips and that cracks penetrate into the alloy by cyclic chemical cutting and mechanical failures.

Cracks were found to be associated with salt crystals containing approximately $10^7$ times as much chloride as lithium and in most cases entraining some water. There were in most cases of failure, several orders of magnitude more of chlorine present as chloride, than hydrogen in contact with the alloy. However, only sodium and lithium chlorides and the eutectic produced complete failures of specimens in a reasonable time. These facts, together with the difference in behavior of the preoxidized specimens and those that had not been given this treatment pose many questions as to just what the mechanism is that produces failures. However, our data suggest that the chloride diffusing through the oxide or oxides formed on the metal surface in the presence of the water vapor is responsible for the cracking.

## IV. Summary

We have investigated the susceptibility of the Ti-8-1-1 titanium alloy to stress corrosion cracking on exposure to chlorides at temperatures of 750 to 800 F. Our results were:

1. There was a wide scatter in exposure periods to failure by stress corrosion cracking in four-point loaded bent beam specimens coated with NaCl or NaCl + < 1000 ppm of LiCl. Periods ranged from 5 to 64 days for specimens stressed to 80,000 psi in the outer fiber. Periods were less than one day for specimens coated with LiCl alone.

2. Cracking of the bent beam specimens was produced using a number of chlorides. In decreasing order of severity,

669

those investigated were: $BaCl_2$, KCl, $CaCl_2$, CsCl and $SrCl_2$.

3. A molten eutectic mixture of KCl and LiCl (mp 670 F) produced failures in U-bend specimens as soon as the specimen was wetted. This is believed to be due in part to the fluxing action of the eutectic.

4. Sheet tensile specimens subjected to a stress of approximately 10,000 psi in a molten eutectic mixture of KCl and LiCl at 750 F failed after approximately 60 minutes. Making the specimen the anode by applying an external potential of approximately 3 volts had no marked effect on the exposure period to failure. Making the specimen the cathode, with the same applied potential, approximately doubled the exposure period to failure.

5. Different colored corrosion products found on the surfaces of sheet specimens coated with NaCl were not readily separable and all contained anatase, rutile (both forms of $TiO_2$) and an unidentified phase. Whiskers of NaCl and rutile were also found on the surface of a sheet specimen, heated for a long period in a stream of oxygen.

6. Cracking could be produced in hollow specimens coated with NaCl + $MgCl_2 \cdot 6H_2O$ or NaCl heated to 750 F and stressed to 90% of their yield strength at temperature.

7. Hollow specimens coated with NaCl and exposed to dry oxygen were quite resistant to cracking, however, cracks developed in specimens exposed in a moist argon atmosphere. Specimens that had been preoxidized (heated 60 hours or more at 800 F in a stream of oxygen) prior to coating with NaCl, failed in less than 24 hours under stress at 750 F. Further, any water present in these experiments was in exceedingly minute amounts.

8. No $Cl_2$, HCl or NaOH reaction products were detected within the limits of the experiment techniques in the stress corrosion cracking of the alloy.

9. Stress corrosion cracking was intercrystalline or followed the $\alpha$-$\beta$ boundaries. An electron probe analysis of the $\alpha$-matrix and the $\beta$-phase indicated that there was approximately 1/9 as much molybdenum in the alpha as in the beta phase.

10. The data indicate that the type of oxide formed on the alloy surface may play an important part in determining whether cracks will develop in the alloy.

## Acknowledgments

This investigation was supported by NASA, Washington. Their permission to publish these data is appreciated. J. R. Ambrose, C. J. Bechtoldt, M. J. McBee, B. T. Sanderson and G. M. Ugiansky collaborated in various phases of the investigation.

## References

1. H. L. Logan, et al. ASTM STP 397, p. 215 (1966).
2. H. L. Logan. *Materials Research and Standards,* **2**, No. 2, 98 (1962).
3. W. D. Jenkins and W. A. Willard. *J. of Research of the NBS,* **70C**, 5 (1966).
4. P. Kofstad. *High Temperature Oxidation of Metals,* Wiley, New York, p. 172 (1966).
5. T. Hurlen. *Acta Chem. Scan.,* **13**, 365 (1959).
6. P. Kofstad. Ref. 4, p. 169.
7. P. Chester and D. Bradhurst. *Nature,* **199**, No. 4898 (1963) September 14.
8. V. C. Peterson and H. B. Bomberger. ASTM STP 397, p. 80 (1966).
9. G. Martin. ASTM STP 397, p. 95 (1966).
10. S. P. Rideout, et al. *ibid.,* p. 137.
11. O. W. Johnson. *Physical Review,* **136**, A284 (1964).
12. V. N. Bogomolov. *Soviet Phys. Solid State (English Translation),* **5**, 1468 (1964).
13. P. Kofstad. Ref. 4, p. 171.

## Discussion

**R. S. Ondrejcin and S. P. Rideout,**
**Savannah River Laboratory:**

All of the following comments deal with Part III—Results and Discussion.

In Section D-1, "Effect of Water Vapor," your proposed reaction

$$Ti + 2H_2O \rightarrow TiO_2 + 2H_2$$

implies that the protective oxide film is penetrated by water. Titanium metal does react with water, but the rate of reaction very quickly becomes negligible because the resulting oxide film is an effective barrier to further reaction. Thus, only a very small amount of hydrogen would be produced by this reaction. If this were not so, failures of titanium alloys due to corrosion would be common in heated water or steam systems. Actually, as you have noted in the next to the last paragraph, water has an inhibiting effect on stress corrosion cracking under certain circumstances. We propose that this occurs when the amount of water present is sufficient for the above reaction to proceed and reform and maintain a protective film. However, this does not mean that a hydrogen mechanism cannot be operative (F-1 Role of Preoxidation and F-3 Mechanisms) in hot-salt stress corrosion cracking if the source of hydrogen is the reaction between the metal and HCl.

The results in D-1 appear to be consistent with an explanation based on pyrohydrolysis of halide salts (Heat + Water + Halide Salt → Hydrogen Halide + Salt Oxide). In all cases where moisture was obviously present, whether from $MgCl_2 \cdot 6H_2$ or humidified Argon, cracking was rapid. We propose that in these cases HCl was formed by pyrohydrolysis, penetrated the protective film, and attacked the metal producing metal chloride plus hydrogen. The case of low pressure dry oxygen causing cracking after long periods of time could also be a case of reduced moisture, which reduced the amount of HCl formed by pyrohydrolysis.

670

In the cases of your tensile tube specimens with preformed oxide, the oxide probably contained water, and damage to the metal could have occurred during heating prior to filling with dry Argon. The preformed oxides on the specimens can and do occlude water as shown by us.[1] Normally, however, the water inclusions in NaCl from evaporated solutions are the most important source of water.

In Section D-2 you report that you did not detect $Cl_2$ by the starch-iodide test that has commonly been used in titanium stress corrosion cracking literature to "prove" the presence of chlorine gas. We have also tried this test and did not detect $Cl_2$. In connection with this, we would like to point out that this test is valid for chlorine only if the starch-iodide solution remains at pH 5 to 8 throughout the test. If the solution becomes acidic, as it could if the gaseous products being passed through it contained pyro-hydrolytically produced HCl, a false indication of $Cl_2$ would be obtained because of a color change due to air oxidation. Acidified iodide solutions are slowly oxidized to iodine by oxygen.[2] The degree to which the solution becomes acidified will obviously depend on the amount of HCl, and in cases where minute amounts of HCl are formed the pH would change very little. Other workers[3] who reported that the starch-iodide test gave a positive indication of $Cl_2$ from reactions at 1200 F may have actually detected the effects of HCl gas.

In Section D-3 you report that NaOH was not observed by X-ray diffraction of corrosion products and, that if present, it probably was formed only in minute quantities. You propose that the reaction

$$2NaCl + Ti + 1/2O_2 + H_2O \rightleftharpoons TiCl_2 + 2NaOH$$

is reversible, and that it would go to the left if NaOH were added. We doubt that this reaction is valid under the conditions described. Although $TiCl_2$ may be formed as an intermediate product, it should be converted to an oxide in the presence of moisture. The possibility of driving your proposed reaction to the left by addition of NaOH seems unlikely because, if Ti and $O_2$ or $H_2O$ are present, the following reactions will occur:

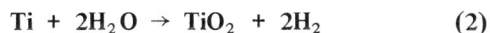

$$Ti + O_2 \rightarrow TiO_2, \text{ or} \qquad (1)$$

$$Ti + 2H_2O \rightarrow TiO_2 + 2H_2 \qquad (2)$$

These reactions are irreversible.

Similarly, the addition of NaOH cannot drive the reaction to the right because the NaOH will be consumed in the reactions:

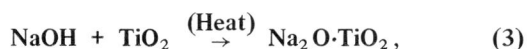

$$NaOH + TiO_2 \xrightarrow{\text{(Heat)}} Na_2O \cdot TiO_2, \qquad (3)$$

$$Na_2O \cdot 2TiO_2, \text{ or}$$

$$Na_2O \cdot 3TiO_2 + H_2$$

Once the titanium oxide has reacted, aluminum in the alloy can be attacked by

$$3NaOH + Al \rightarrow NaAlO_2 + Na_2O + 3/2 H_2 \qquad (4)$$

These reactions are also irreversible.

We propose that failure to detect NaOH by X-ray diffraction was either due to a small quantity being present or conversion of NaOH to other products.

In answer to Dr. Martin's question about the types of titanium oxides observed, you indicated that you detected rutile and anatase. We have observed the same oxides, and we agree with Dr. Martin's suggestion[4] that the presence of anatase is evidence that NaOH was generated during hot-salt corrosion reactions.

### References

1. S. P. Rideout, R. S. Ondrejcin, M. R. Louthan, Jr., and D. E. Rawl. The Role of Moisture and Hydrogen in Hot-Salt Cracking of Titanium Alloys. This Conference.
2. I. M. Kolthoff and E. B. Sandell. *Textbook of Quantitative Inorganic Analysis.* 3rd Ed., p. 587-8, The Macmillan Co., New York, N. Y. (1952).
3. V. C. Petersen and H. B. Bomberger. The Mechanism of Salt Attack on Titanium Alloy. *Stress Corrosion Cracking of Titanium,* STP 397, American Society for Testing Materials, Philadelphia, Pa., p. 80 (1966).
4. G. Martin. Investigation of Long-Term Exposure Effects Under Stress of Two Titanium Structural Alloys. *Stress Corrosion Cracking of Titanium,* ASTM STP 397, p. 95 (1966).

**H. L. Logan:**

We appreciate these comments and we agree with some of them. In areas where there is disagreement we should like to indicate on just what data our ideas are based.

Our data indicate that specimens that were preoxidized (heated in oxygen for 60 to 70 hours at 800 F) failed after reasonable short exposure periods when exposed under stress and in contact with NaCl at 750 F.

It is possible, but not probable under the conditions of our experiment, that water could have been present in sufficient quantity during preoxidation to damage the underlying metal. We appreciated the fact that water could be occluded in our NaCl crystals and for that reason, used finely ground and heated NaCl, which we scattered on the interior wall of one of our specimens. This specimen was subsequently filled with ultrapure Argon and failed in less than 24 hours. This was a much shorter exposure period than that we obtained with specimens containing either wet argon or $NaCl + MgCl_2 \cdot 6H_2O$.

The fact that we get failures in some nonpreoxidized specimens with a small amount of water available suggests that we most probably have the reaction suggested between the water and titanium, but that the oxygen build-up is slow compared with that occurring in pure oxygen. Why larger amounts of water appear to have an inhibiting action is unclear at this time.

Your suggestion that NaOH would react with $TiO_2$ to produce among other things $H_2$, is interesting since in two of three experiments in which we had added NaOH to the $NaCl + MgCl_2$ solution we obtained no failures.

We do not rule out hydrogen entirely as the cause of failures. However, we had no failures in specimens coated with NaCl (by evaporation, presumably with some entrained $H_2O$, but without preoxidation) when exposed in dry Argon. We did get an early failure in a preoxidized specimen where precautions were taken to eliminate $H_2O$. In view of these data, we consider that a considerable oxidation of the metal with diffusion of the chloride ion through the oxide is the more probable mechanism.

# STRESS CORROSION CRACKING OF ALPHA TITANIUM
## IN NONAQUEOUS ENVIRONMENTS

A. J. Sedriks, P. W. Slattery, and E. N. Pugh
Research Institute for Advanced Studies (RIAS)

## Abstract

A study has been made of stress corrosion cracking of alpha titanium in liquid nitrogen tetroxide and various methanol environments. On the basis of the observations, it does not appear that the failures in the different environments can be attributed to a single mechanism, but several mechanisms are operative. Failures in nitrogen tetroxide exhibit features which indicate that crack propagation occurs by the repeated formation and rupture of a brittle surface oxide film. On the other hand, failures in methanol vapor-air atmospheres are consistent with some form of hydrogen embrittlement, while those obtained in methanol-halogen-water solutions appear to be best described as arising from electrochemical dissolution.

## I. Introduction

The susceptibility of titanium alloys to stress corrosion cracking when exposed to red fuming nitric acid,[1] various aqueous solutions,[2-4] and sodium chloride at elevated temperatures,[5] has been recognized for some time. More recently, it has been observed that stress corrosion failures also occur in nonaqueous liquids, for example, in nitrogen tetroxide[6] and methanol-hydrochloric acid and methanol-sulfuric acid solutions.[7] Failures in nitrogen tetroxide, which is used as a rocket fuel oxidizer, have been prevented in practice by ensuring the presence of free nitric oxide in the tetroxide liquid.[8] Stress corrosion cracking in methanol environments has caused concern in the aerospace industry,[9] and also in the organic chemical industry, where titanium containers are being considered for use in organic synthesis. The mechanisms of the failures in nitrogen tetroxide and methanol environments are not understood.

The purpose of this paper is to describe and discuss data obtained from a current investigation of the mechanism of stress corrosion cracking of alpha titanium in nitrogen tetroxide and various methanol environments. Evidence is presented which suggests that stress corrosion cracking in nitrogen tetroxide and methanol environments does not occur by the same mechanism, and that in methanol environments alone the possibility of two distinct mechanisms being involved must be considered.

## II. Experimental

The studies were confined to alpha phase materials, namely, pure titanium, unalloyed (A55) titanium, Ti-5 Al binary alloy and a Ti-5 Al-2.5 Sn alloy of a low interstitial element content. All the test specimens were prepared from materials in the vacuum annealed condition. The composition and mechanical properties of these materials in the vacuum annealed condition are given in Table 1. Three types of un-notched specimens were prepared: (1) flat tensile specimens with a reduced section measuring 2 x 0.2 x 0.04 in, (2) U-bend specimens measuring 3 x 0.25 x 0.04 in with a bend diameter of 0.25 in, and fasteners of the same material as that being tested, and (3) 'double-bow' specimens of the type designed by Heimerl and Braski.[10] The 'double-bow' configuration, Figure 1, was found to be convenient for studies using nitrogen tetroxide. These specimens were prepared from strips measuring 4 x 0.25 x 0.04 in, following the procedures described by Lisagor et al,[11] with strip curvatures calculated to give an outer fiber stress equivalent to about 90% of the yield stress. The specimens were washed with soap and water, rinsed with distilled water, degreased with acetone, and dried with ethyl alcohol.

Nitrogen tetroxide of two compositions was used. The first, subsequently referred to as 'oxygenated', was prepared by bubbling oxygen for 30 minutes through liquid nitrogen tetroxide initially containing 99.5% $N_2O_4$, 0.1% $H_2O$ and 0.08% Cl. The second, subsequently referred to as 'inhibited' was of a similar composition with regard to $N_2O_4$, $H_2O$, and Cl content, but also contained approximately 0.5% NO. The presence of the nitric oxide ensures

TABLE 1–Composition and Mechanical Properties of Alloys

| | | Pure Titanium | Unalloyed (A55) Titanium | Ti-5 Al Alloy | Ti-5 Al-2.5 Sn Alloy |
|---|---|---|---|---|---|
| Composition (% wt) | Al | – | – | 5.10 | 5.20 |
| | Sn | – | – | – | 2.50 |
| | Fe | 0.028 | 0.15 | 0.034 | 0.16 |
| | N | 0.0055 | 0.0083 | 0.0051 | 0.0058 |
| | O | 0.038 | 0.113 | 0.038 | 0.059 |
| | C | 0.018 | 0.038 | 0.030 | 0.030 |
| | H | 0.0014 | 0.0018 | 0.0010 | 0.0015 |
| Hardness (HV20kg) | | 126 | 214 | 290 | 305 |
| U.T.S. (psi) | | 46,000 | 75,000 | 78,000 | 112,000 |
| 0.2% Proof Stress (psi) | | 28,500 | 56,000 | 69,000 | 102,000 |
| Tensile Elong. on 2 in. (%) | | 37 | 22 | 14 | 12 |

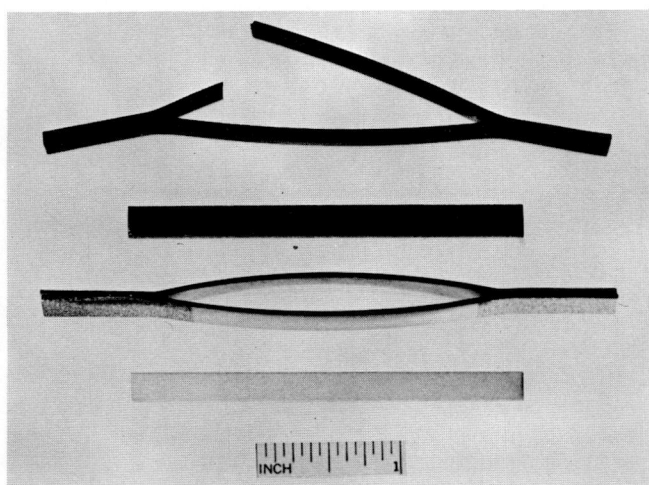

FIGURE 1 — Appearance of self-stressed (double-bow configuration) and unstressed (flat strip) specimens of Ti-5 Al-2.5 Sn alloy after exposure to $N_2O_4$. Top pair: exposed to oxygenated $N_2O_4$, showing stress corrosion failure in self-stressed specimen and presence of dark surface film on both specimens. Bottom pair: exposed to inhibited $N_2O_4$ showing no evidence of surface film and absence of stress corrosion cracking.

that the solution is free of dissolved oxygen.[8]

In the stress corrosion tests, the nitrogen tetroxide liquid was contained in stainless steel cylinders under a pressure of 250 psi. Oxygen and helium were used as the pressurizing gases for the oxygenated and inhibited liquids, respectively. The 'double-bow' specimens and unstressed alloy strips were immersed in each of the liquids for 96 hours at 49 C, and after exposure dried in air.

Three types of methanol environments were used: (1) methanol vapor-air atmospheres, (2) reagent grade methanol liquid, classified as 99.9% Mol. pure, and (3) methanol-bromine-water solutions containing various proportions of water. The solutions were prepared from 99.9% Mol. pure methanol liquid; reagent grade bromine liquid (99.5% Br, minimum) and distilled water.

Specimens of all three configurations (i.e., U-bend, 'double-bow' and unstressed tensile specimens) were exposed to methanol environments. Tests in the methanol vapor-air environment were carried out by placing the specimens in the vapor space in a closed dessicator (volume = 2000 cc) partially filled with reagent grade methanol. In tests using liquid methanol and methanol solutions, the environments were contained in sealed glass jars. All the tests in methanol environments were carried out at room temperature (22 C). The U-bend and 'double-bow' specimens were observed during testing by means of a low-power microscope (X 5), and the times noted at which a stress corrosion crack was first visible and at which the crack had propagated through the thickness of the specimen.

## III. Failures in Nitrogen Tetroxide

### A. Surface Studies

The general appearance of stressed and unstressed specimens of Ti-5 Al-2.5 Sn alloy exposed to inhibited and oxygenated nitrogen tetroxide is shown in Figure 1. Specimens exposed to inhibited nitrogen tetroxide revealed no evidence of stress corrosion cracking, and examination of specimen surfaces by X-ray and reflection electron diffraction revealed no change in the surface condition. On the other hand, all specimens exposed to oxygenated nitrogen tetroxide exhibited a black surface film, Figure 1, and the stressed specimens showed numerous stress corrosion cracks. Thus it is evident that correlation exists between the formation of the surface film and stress corrosion cracking.

The surface film on the stress corrosion fracture surfaces was removed by immersion in a methanol-5% bromine solution, and examined by selected area electron diffraction and transmission electron microscopy. Although much of the liberated film was of a thickness greater than that required for electron transparency (4000 Å), a number of thinner areas were present, and typical structures in these areas are shown in Figure 2. In some areas the film was continuous, Figure 2a, while in others it appeared to

| Measured by Selected Area Electron Diffraction Using Detached Film | Measured by Reflection Electron Diffraction "in situ" | ASTM Powder Data for $TiO_2$ (Rutile) |
|---|---|---|
| d (Å) | d (Å) | d (Å) |
| 3.242 | 3.265 | 3.245 |
| 2.483 | 2.485 | 2.489 |
| 2.321 | – | 2.297 |
| 2.185 | 2.195 | 2.188 |
| 2.054 | – | 2.054 |
| 1.682 | 1.686 | 1.687 |
| 1.621 | – | 1.624 |
| – | | 1.480 |
| 1.452 | – | 1.453 |
| 1.359 | – | 1.360 |
| 1.342 | – | 1.347 |

FIGURE 3 – Metallographic section of oxide layer formed on shot-peened surface of Ti-5 Al-2.5 Sn alloy during 96 hour exposure to oxygenated $N_2O_4$ at 49 C. Region above oxide is nickel plate. Unetched.

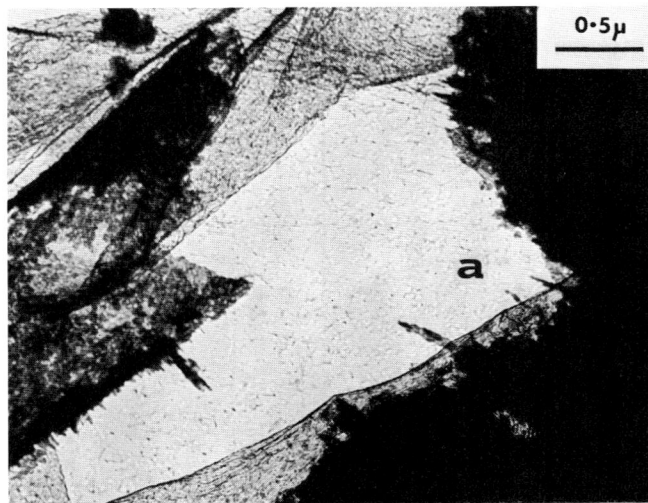

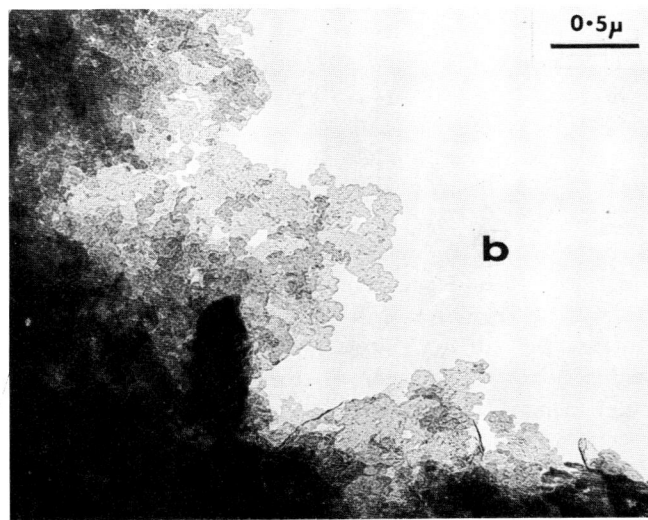

FIGURE 2 – Transmission electron micrographs of surface film removed from stress corrosion fracture surfaces.

consist of many individual platelets, Figure 2b. Selected area electron diffraction patterns taken from these areas exhibited diffraction spots typical of a monocrystal. The fact that the same monocrystal pattern was obtained from areas containing many individual platelets (e.g., Figure 2b) can be explained by assuming that the growth of the platelets is governed by the titanium substrate (i.e., their growth is epitaxial). In other areas, the oxide had folded over or become mechanically damaged, and these areas gave diffraction patterns consisting of "spotted" rings, enabling interplanar spacings of the lattice of the film to be determined. These spacings, measured using a polycrystalline gold foil as a standard, revealed that the film consisted of the rutile modification of titanium dioxide, Table 2. The possibility that the bromine solution had affected the structure of the surface film was also considered. To clarify this point, an "in situ" examination of the stress corrosion fracture surface was made using reflection electron diffraction. The patterns obtained by electron diffraction "in situ" confirmed the presence of rutile, with no evidence being found of the presence of any of the lower oxides of titanium, Table 2.

X-ray diffraction and reflection electron diffraction of the bulk specimen surfaces, as opposed to the stress corrosion fracture surfaces, indicated that the surface film on these external surfaces had a more complex structure. In addition to the rutile ($TiO_2$) phase, diffraction peaks corresponding to the more intense $Ti_2O_3$ and TiO reflections were also noted. This difference in surface oxide structures may arise from a difference in the surface condition of the metal in contact with the environment. Thus, while the external specimen surface has an air-formed film on it, and below this it may also contain a thin layer of alpha titanium-oxygen solid solution resulting from heat treatment, the newly formed fracture surface would be, initially, quite clean.

Metallographic examination of sections of specimens,

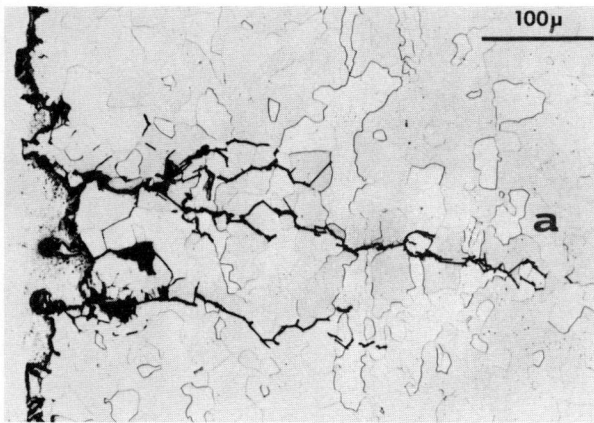

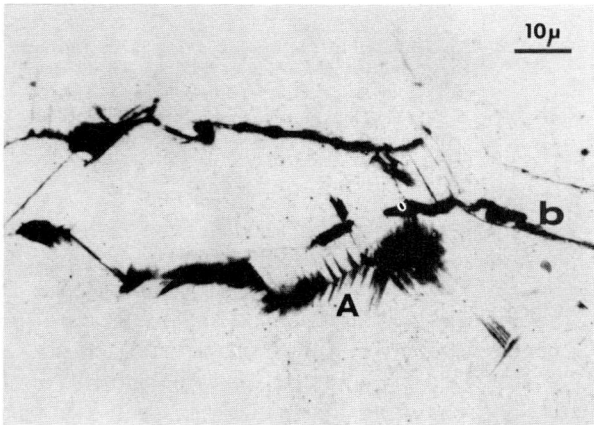

FIGURE 4 — Stress corrosion cracks formed in Ti-5 Al-2.5 Sn alloy during exposure to oxygenated $N_2O_4$. (a) Etched in Kroll's reagent, (b) unetched.

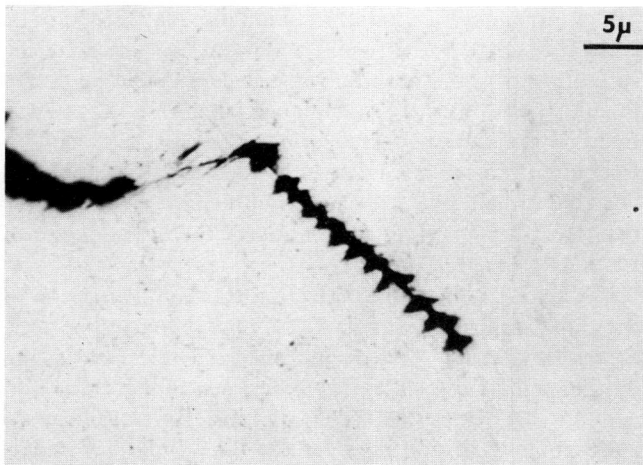

FIGURE 5 — Appearance of stress corrosion crack tip in Ti-5 Al-2.5 Sn alloy exposed to oxygenated $N_2O_4$. Unetched.

which had been nickel plated to protect the surface oxide from damage encountered in metallographic preparation, revealed that plastic deformation is necessary to cause extensive oxide formation. Surfaces of stressed specimens, that had been exposed to oxygenated nitrogen tetroxide,

exhibited oxide layers 2-5 $\mu$ in thickness, Figure 3, while the oxide was barely detectable, by metallographic sectioning, on surfaces of unstressed and undeformed specimens. Thick oxide was in evidence on surfaces stressed in both tension and compression, and also on surfaces stressed by shot peening. In the latter case, intergranular penetration of the oxide and cracking had occurred in the deformed surface regions, Figure 3. It was also noted that the growth of the oxide occurred more rapidly along certain crystallographic paths within the grains. Etching to reveal plastic deformation indicated that these crystallographic paths were parallel to slip traces showing that, within the grains, oxide forms preferentially along slip planes. Examination of many sections indicated that the growth of the surface oxide in plastically deformed areas involves oxide growth along slip planes and lateral merging of these leading to apparently continuous areas of oxide.

### B. Crack Morphology

Low power optical metallography of etched sections of specimens containing stress corrosion cracks revealed that cracking was predominantly intergranular, Figure 4a. The Kroll etch used to reveal the titanium microstructure also severely attacked the surface traces of the cracks, obliterating any detail. Consequently, further studies were carried out using unetched specimens. These revealed that oxide growth had occurred into the grains adjacent to the intergranular crack, Figure 4b, in a manner similar to that observed on stressed surfaces (i.e., by oxide penetration along slip planes and lateral merging). A significant observation was that oxide growth had occurred along slip plane clusters spaced at regular intervals along the intergranular crack (e.g., Figure 4b, A). This effect was more noticeable near the crack tips, where the environment had been in contact with the crack surface for the shortest time. A section of a crack tip is shown in Figure 5, where it is seen that oxide growth into the adjacent grains has occurred along groups of closely spaced slip planes, with a distinct separation between each group. This may be taken as evidence that periodic 'bursts' of plastic deformation occur during the propagation of the crack, and that cracking is discontinuous.

The stress corrosion fracture surfaces were examined by means of the scanning electron microscope,[1] optical microscopy (utilizing a fractographic goniometer stage), and by means of replicas using transmission electron microscopy. The regions of stress corrosion fracture surface near the crack source, which had been in contact with the environment for the longest time, revealed little detail. In the regions near the crack tip, however, well defined intergranular facets were in evidence. Two-stage replica electron micrograph of the faceted region is shown in Figure 6, where it is seen that some intergranular facets exhibit step-like markings which do not appear to follow the crystallography of the underlying grains (e.g., Figure 6, A). It has not yet been established whether these step-like

[1]By courtesy of JEOLCO (U.S.A.) Inc., Medford, Mass.

676

FIGURE 6 – Replica electron micrograph of stress corrosion fracture surface. Ti-5 Al-2.5 Sn alloy exposed to oxygenated $N_2O_4$.

markings coincide with the discontinuities that are evident in the metallographic sections of the cracks, Figure 5, but it should be noted that the separation between markings in the replica is about the same as that between the discontinuities visible in sections (i.e., about $2 \mu$).

## C. Discussion

The possibility that crack growth in Ti-5 Al-2.5 Sn alloy during exposure to oxygenated nitrogen tetroxide occurs by the repeated formation and fracture of a brittle oxide film has been suggested by one of the authors.[12] This suggestion was made after preliminary studies, and the present observations provide further support for this view. The observation that both stress corrosion cracking and surface oxide growth occur in oxygenated nitrogen tetroxide, and that no detectable oxide growth or cracking occurs in inhibited nitrogen tetroxide is fully in accord with the occurrence of the oxide-rupture mechanism.

Cracking by this mechanism was first proposed to account for the failure of $\alpha$-brass in "tarnishing" ammonia environments,[13-16] where the surface film consists of brittle cuprous oxide.[13] The essential features of the model proposed for brass are illustrated schematically in Figure 7, where the sequence (a) to (g) shows the formation and cracking of a brittle cuprous oxide film on a ductile brass substrate. Cracks formed in the oxide do not propagate into the metal substrate, becoming blunted by slip, and further propagation requires further formation and fracture of the oxide at the crack tip. Cracking thus proceeds in a discontinuous fashion. The expected appearance of a section of a crack formed in this manner is shown in Figure 7g.

A comparison of the features associated with stress corrosion cracking of $\alpha$-brass in certain ammonia environments and Ti-5 Al-2.5 Sn alloy in oxygenated nitrogen tetroxide indicates that several similarities exist. Forty and Humble[13] have shown that the tarnish found on the surfaces of $\alpha$-brass after exposure to ammoniacal environ-

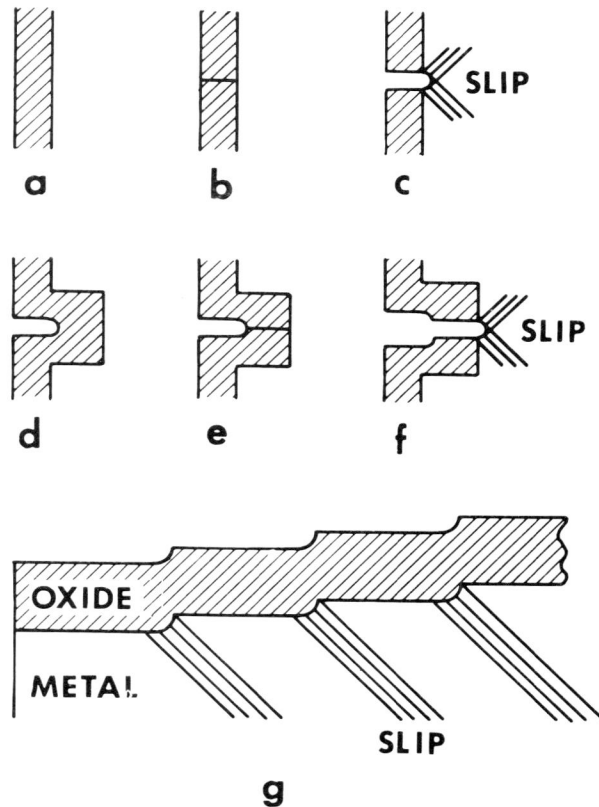

FIGURE 7 – Schematic representation of the tarnish formation and rupture sequence, (a) to (f), proposed for stress corrosion cracking of brass. The features of the resulting fracture surface are shown in (g).

ments consists of cuprous oxide, also in the form of individual platelets which give rise to monocrystal electron diffraction patterns. The formation of epitaxial monocrystalline oxides is therefore common to both the brass-ammonia and titanium-nitrogen tetroxide systems. Also, both oxides exhibit oxide to metal volume ratios well in excess of unity, namely 1.73 for rutile and 1.64 for cuprous oxide.[17] Such volume ratios indicate the presence of high lateral compressive stresses which give rise to compact and protective oxide layers. Both rutile[18] and cuprous oxide[19] are brittle at room temperature.

Evidence for discontinuous crack propagation has been found in the $\alpha$-brass-ammonia system by McEvily and Bond.[14] These investigators examined replicas of stress corrosion fracture surfaces by electron microscopy and found that markings or striations existed, analogous to those observed in fatigue fracture surfaces. These striations were considered to indicate positions of crack arrest. In the present instance, evidence for discontinuous crack propagation has also been obtained, primarily from metallographic examination of crack sections, Figure 5. The periodic occurrence of slip line clusters along the length of the intergranular crack is consistent with a discontinuous crack propagation model of the type shown in Figure 7. After the oxide has broken and the crack has been arrested by slip in the substrate metal, the environment comes into contact with a plastically deformed region at the crack tip. Oxide growth may then proceed both along the slip planes and along the grain boundaries, and it is the rapid penetration of the oxide along planes on which slip has occurred that makes the detection of the slip line clusters possible, Figure 5. It is considered that each slip line cluster may therefore be taken as indicating the approximate position of crack arrest. The observation that most of the crack path is intergranular, Figure 4a, indicates that the penetration of the oxide is more rapid along grain boundaries than along slip planes.

On the basis of this model, a stepped or striated fracture surface would be expected, Figure 7g, provided that the steps are not obliterated by further reaction with the environment (e.g., by dissolution or further oxide growth). Although markings were observed in micro-fractographs that could be interpreted as steps, Figure 6, the profusion of slip indications that are also evident in replicas of fracture surfaces has made unambiguous identification impossible. Further studies are in progress to establish the topography of the stress corrosion fracture surface.

It must be noted that a difference exists in the spacing of the discontinuous steps of cracking in the present instance, and those observed on stress corrosion fracture surfaces of brass by McEvily and Bond.[14] The inter-striation spacings observed in the latter are of the order of $0.1 \mu$,[14] while in the present case the distance between the slip line clusters, Figure 5, is clearly an order of magnitude greater. A question that must be asked is whether it is reasonable to assume that the oxide will grow to a thickness of about $2 \mu$ before it will crack, or whether other processes occur leading to the enlargement of the unit step of crack propagation (i.e., the step defined by the distance between slip clusters). The first possibility is that part of the unit step of propagation is formed by dissolution of the metal. However, Kammerer et al[6] claim that only minor surface metal dissolution occurs in nitrogen tetroxide, suggesting that the contribution of dissolution is not large. The second possibility is that the brittle crack that forms in the oxide does not stop at the oxide-metal interface but propagates for some distance into the metal. Such a possibility was considered by Edeleanu and Forty[20] in the stress corrosion cracking of α-brass. Essentially this requires that the crack

attains a critical velocity in the oxide enabling it to propagate into the metal. There is no evidence for such propagation in α-brass. However, in the present instance the substrate metal is a high strength alloy with a solid-solution-hardened hcp lattice, exhibiting considerably less ductility, Table 1, than the fcc α-brass. Thus it is possible that a high velocity crack, initiated in the epitaxially formed and therefore coherent brittle rutile, may propagate for some distance into the metal.

It is evident from the preceeding discussion that, although some of the details of the cracking process are not fully understood, the observed features of the stress corrosion failure are consistent with an oxide-rupture mechanism being operative.

## IV. Failures in Methanol Environments

It may be seen from Table 3 that (1) failures can occur in apparently pure methanol liquid and methanol vapor-air atmospheres, (2) times to failure are much shorter in the presence of halogens, particularly bromine, and (3) failures in methanol-bromine solutions can be inhibited by the additions of water to the environment. These observations are in general agreement with those of Mori et al,[7] Johnston et al,[9] and Haney[21] who have reported failures in alpha, alpha + beta, and beta titanium alloys in various methanol and methanol-chloride-water solutions.

It may be seen from Table 3 that stressed specimens of Ti-5 Al-2.5 Sn alloy failed both in reagent grade methanol liquid and methanol vapor-air atmospheres in comparable times. Unlike the failures in oxygenated nitrogen tetroxide, the fracture surfaces in these environments were not visibly tarnished, and the failures were characterized by the formation of very few cracks. The cracks formed in both liquid and vapor were essentially intergranular, and metallographic and microfractographic examination of crack profiles and fracture surfaces, respectively, revealed no evidence of discontinuous crack propagation. Although the failures in methanol liquid and methanol vapor-air atmospheres appear to be similar, significant differences were

**TABLE 3—Relationship Between Environment and Time to Failure of Ti-5 Al-2.5 Sn U-Bend Specimens**

| Environment | Time to Failure |
|---|---|
| $CH_3OH$ (Reagent Grade 99.9 Mol % Pure) | 8 days |
| $CH_3OH$ (Reagent Grade, dried with CaO powder) | 4 days |
| $CH_3OH$ (Reagent Grade, redistilled) | 2 days |
| $CH_3OH$ vapor-dry air mixture | 1-7 days |
| $CH_3OH$ + 0.012% $I_2$ | 2 days |
| $CH_3OH$ + 1.35% $I_2$ | 5 hours |
| $CH_3OH$ + 2.0% $Br_2$ | 10 min |
| $CH_3OH$ + 2.0% $Br_2$ + 2.5% $H_2O$ | 10 min |
| $CH_3OH$ + 2.0% $Br_2$ + 10.0% $H_2O$ | 13 min |
| $CH_3OH$ + 2.0% $Br_2$ + 45.0% $H_2O$ | 4 days |
| $CH_3OH$ + 2.0% $Br_2$ + 50.0% $H_2O$ | N.F. |

**TABLE 4—The Effect of Exposure to Methanol Environments on the Ductility of Alpha Titanium**

| Condition of Unstressed Specimen | Material | % Tensile Elongation on 2 in. |
|---|---|---|
| 1. Vacuum annealed | Ti-5 Al-2.5 Sn | |
| | Pure Ti | $12 \pm 1$ |
| | | $37 \pm 2$ |
| 2. Exposed to methanol vapor for 168 hours | Ti-5 Al-2.5 Sn | |
| | Pure Ti | $2 \pm 0.5$ |
| | | $10 \pm 4$ |
| 3. Exposed to methanol vapor for 24 hours | Pure Ti | |
| | | $18 \pm 6$ |
| 4. Exposed to methanol liquid for 168 hours | Ti-5 Al-2.5 Sn | |
| | Pure Ti | $12 \pm 1$ |
| | | $37 \pm 2$ |
| 5. Re-annealed in vacuum after exposure to methanol vapor for 168 hours | Ti-5 Al-2.5 Sn | |
| | Pure Ti | $12 \pm 1$ |
| | | $35 \pm 3$ |

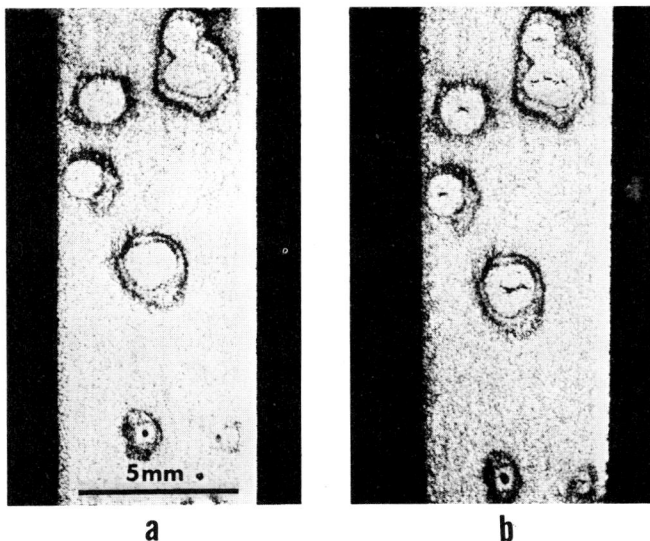

FIGURE 8 — Surface appearance of Ti-5 Al-2.5 Sn alloy exposed to methanol vapor-air atmosphere for 168 hours at 22 C. (a) Surface prior to stressing. (b) Surface after stressing to fracture in tension. Note association of cracks with stains.

observed, and these are discussed in the following sections.

## A. Failures in Methanol Vapor-Air Atmospheres

Although failures in methanol vapor occurred during the simultaneous application of stress and environment, embrittlement could be obtained also by exposing *unstressed* specimens to the environment and subsequently stressing them in the absence of the environment. No cracks were formed in the unstressed specimens during exposure to the vapor and cracking occurred only on subsequent application of stress. The extent of embrittlement observed after exposure to methanol vapor, as indicated by a decrease in tensile elongation (strain rate = 2 in/min), is shown in Table 4 for both Ti-5 Al-2.5 Sn alloy and pure titanium. A further significant observation was that embrittlement could be eliminated by re-annealing the exposed specimens in vacuum (4-1/2 hours at 830 C in $10^{-6}$ mm Hg), Table 4.

Exposure of specimens to methanol vapor resulted also in a change in the surface appearance. Unstressed specimens formed stains or discolored areas during exposure, Figure 8a, and in all instances the cracks that formed on subsequent stressing were associated with these surface stains, Figure 8b. Similar staining and association of cracks with the stains was observed during the failure of stressed specimens in methanol vapor-air atmospheres.

The fracture surfaces of the embrittled specimens were characterized by the presence of shiny intergranular facets at the surface of the specimen and ductile transgranular regions in the center of the specimen, Figure 9. The proportion of the fracture surface exhibiting intergranular facets increased with increasing time of exposure to the vapor, and in specimens exposed for 168 hours the faceted areas represented more than 50% of the total fracture surface.

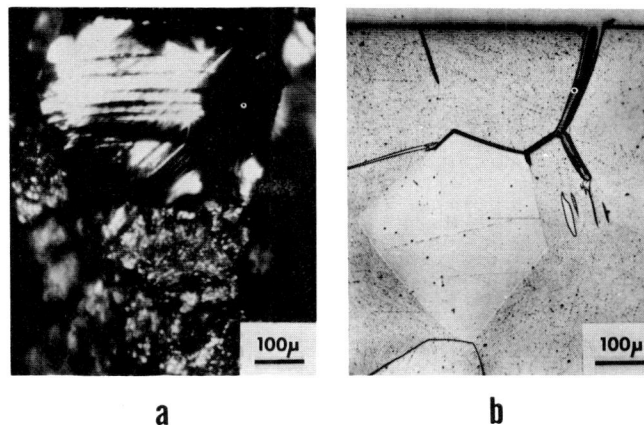

FIGURE 9 — Appearance of brittle cracks in pure titanium stressed after 24 hour exposure to methanol vapor-air atmosphere at 22 C. (a) Optical fractograph showing planar facet at specimen surface with adjoining ductile failure region. (b) Section through intergranular crack produced on bending; etched with Kroll reagent.

The fact that embrittlement can be eliminated by vacuum annealing, suggests that some form of hydrogen-induced embrittlement is involved. It is unlikely that any other atomic species, which could be generated by exposure to methanol vapor-air atmosphere, would have sufficient mobility at room temperature to diffuse through the metal to the observed extent. It may be suggested, therefore, that embrittlement results from the generation of hydrogen at the specimen surface followed by its diffusion along grain boundaries. There is considerable evidence that hydrogen causes embrittlement of titanium,[22] but it should be noted that the mechanism of the failure is not understood. In particular, it is not known whether failure results from hydride formation or from the presence of atomic or molecular hydrogen in the lattice. In the present case metallographic examination, at magnifications up to 2000 X, of 'sensitized' grain boundaries (i.e., boundaries directly below the stains that were subsequently found to crack on stressing) revealed no evidence of the presence of hydrides, although they appeared to be more readily attacked by etchants (e.g., Kroll etch) than 'nonsensitized' boundaries. The possibility is being examined that precipitation of hydrides occurs during stressing, but no unambiguous evidence for this has been found.

Hydrogen may be supplied by the reaction:

$$CH_3OH \rightleftharpoons HCHO + H_2 \qquad (1)$$

It is well known that this reaction occurs at elevated temperatures (300 C) when methanol vapor is passed over various metal and oxide catalysts, and recent work by Ambrose and Kruger[23] has indicated that the reaction occurs also at *room temperature* in the presence of titanium.

Many questions remain concerning the entry of hydrogen into the titanium metal. In particular, it is not known whether hydrogen generation occurs at the metal or the oxide surface. The generation of hydrogen at the metal surface requires the penetration of reactant species through pores in the oxide. Alternatively, the reaction may occur at the oxide surface and hydrogen may diffuse through the oxide to the metal. Chester and Bradhurst[24] have suggested that rapid diffusion of atomic hydrogen may occur in rutile at room temperature. The significance of the observed staining also remains to be explained. A possible explanation may be that staining is a manifestation of "blistering" (i.e., formation or collection of reaction products at the metal-oxide interface). Such a phenomenon has been observed in the anodic polarization of titanium in formic acid,[25,26] which may be formed by further oxidation of formaldehyde.

Further studies are also needed to provide an explanation of the reported[23] decrease in the time to failure of U-bend specimens with decreasing methanol vapor-air volume.

### B. Failures in Reagent Grade Methanol Liquid

Unlike the vapor case, failures in methanol liquid require the simultaneous application of stress and environment. Exposure of unstressed specimens to methanol liquid did not result in embrittlement, Table 4. Also the staining that was observed during exposure to methanol vapor was not observed on specimens exposed to methanol liquid. These observations question the role of hydrogen in failure induced by methanol liquid. The observation of Johnston et al[9] that cracking of Ti-6Al-4V alloys in reagent grade methanol liquid can be inhibited by cathodic protection and accelerated by anodic stimulation also casts doubt on the possibility that hydrogen embrittlement is occurring.

It is recognized that very small quantities of halogen together with water in the methanol liquid (e.g., 0.001 N NaCl + 0.3% $H_2O$)[27] will cause cracking in very short times. The question arises, therefore, whether reagent grade methanol liquid can be regarded as being entirely free from halogens and water. Furthermore the initial purity of the methanol liquid may be irrelevant if the source of contaminants is the titanium surface, which may contain adsorbed chlorides and water. The possibility exists that failures in reagent grade methanol may be the same as failures in methanol-halogen-water solutions. In an attempt to obtain a better understanding of the mechanism of failure in methanol-halogen-water solutions, a series of stress corrosion tests were conducted in methanol-2% bromine-water solutions, and these are described in the next section.

### C. Failures in Methanol-Bromine-Water Solutions

Methanol-2% bromine-water solutions were adopted in this study primarily because the studies of Tomashov et al[28] provide some insight into the corrosion of unstressed titanium and titanium alloys in these environments. Before discussing the behavior of stressed specimens, it is necessary to summarize briefly the observations of Tomashov et al[28] regarding the corrosion behavior of unstressed specimens of unalloyed titanium.

These investigators found that the air-formed oxide film is not soluble in methanol-bromine solutions, and suggested that corrosion commences only after the penetration of bromine molecules through weak zones or cracks in the film. Contact of bromine with the metal gives rise to a rapid reaction, and results in undermining and liberation of the oxide film. It may be noted here that this type of reaction with steels and other alloys forms the basis of the Mahla-Nielsen[29] technique to produce oxide replicas for use in electron microscopy studies. After the film is removed, more uniform surface corrosion takes place, although grain boundary regions containing impurities are more rapidly attacked. The introduction of water into a methanol-2% bromine solution lowers the corrosion rate as measured by weight loss, and this is attributed to the participation of water molecules in the formation of the protective film. It is not clear, however, whether the water provides oxygen or the water molecules are themselves incorporated in the surface film.

Although water additions reduce corrosion, as measured by weight loss, additions of up to 5% water actually increase the extent of intergranular attack. Tomashov et al[28] estimated the tendency for intergranular attack by means of the ratio of the increase in the ohmic resistance of the specimen to the relative reduction in weight after corrosion. This parameter can be seen, Figure 10 (Curve I), to increase with water contents up to 5%, and

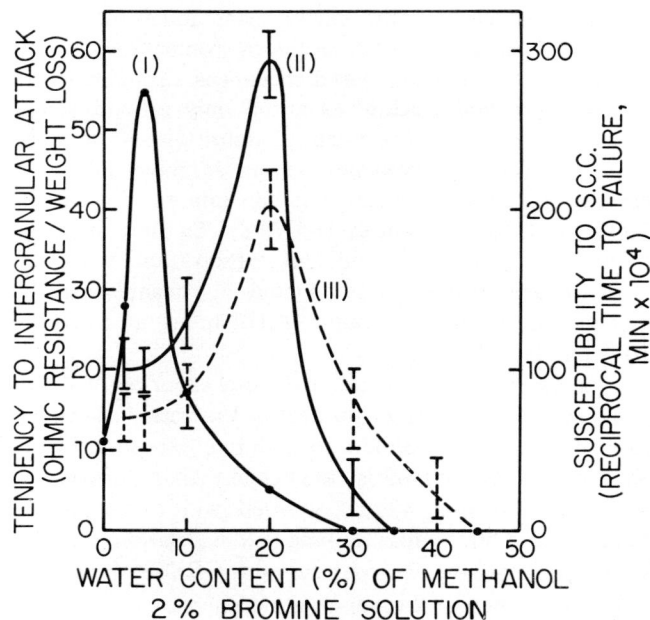

FIGURE 10 — Variation of tendency to intergranular corrosion and susceptibility to stress corrosion cracking with water content in a methanol-2% bromine solution. Curve I: Unalloyed titanium, tendency to intergranular corrosion as measured by Tomashov et al. Curve II: Unalloyed titanium, susceptibility to stress corrosion cracking. Curve III: Ti-5 Al alloy, susceptibility to stress corrosion cracking.

this increase is attributed to the difference between the water content required to passivate titanium grain surfaces and that required to passivate the impurity containing grain boundaries. For water contents greater than 5% both the tendency to intergranular corrosion and overall weight loss decrease, becoming immeasurable at 30% water.

The present investigation was concerned with determining how corrosion behavior in this system was related to susceptibility to stress corrosion cracking. U-bend specimens of unalloyed (A55) titanium and Ti-5 Al binary alloy were used, with susceptibility to stress corrosion cracking being taken as the reciprocal of the time required for a crack to penetrate through the thickness of the specimen. The results of this study, together with Tomashov's data on the tendency to intergranular corrosion of unalloyed titanium are shown in Figure 10. It is evident that the maximum susceptibility to stress corrosion cracking (Curve II) does not coincide with the maximum tendency to intergranular corrosion (Curve I). The data shows that the maximum susceptibility to stress corrosion cracking occurs at a water content at which the *grain boundaries* are almost passivated. The coincidence of maximum susceptibility and onset of surface passivation, as determined by electrochemical measurements, has also been observed by Haney[21] in a Ti-13V-11Cr-3Al alloy exposed to methanol-0.15 N NaCl solutions containing water. These observations suggest that the process by which cracks propagate involves electrochemical dissolution. As pointed out by Haney, the increasing passivation of the surface would be expected to cause corrosion currents generated at the remaining active sites to become more intense. In methanol-bromine-water solutions passivation refers specifically to the passivation of grain boundaries and the active sites may be equated with active grain boundary sites.

Accepting the proposal that failure is electrochemical in nature, consideration must be given to the exact contribution of stress in the failure process. A possible answer can be based on the film-rupture model discussed by Champion in 1948.[30] It was suggested that in metal-environment systems which exhibit both intergranular corrosion and stress corrosion cracking, the role of stress in the latter is to prevent passivation at the extremities of crevices or growing cracks. In unstressed specimens intergranular attack eventually ceases by the formation of passive films. In the presence of tensile stresses, however, stress concentrations at the tip of the crevice may attain sufficient magnitude to cause localized plastic deformation, leading to rupture of the surface film and thereby exposing a fresh metal surface to the corrosive environment. However, if passivation occurs before a sufficient stress concentration is produced to cause plastic yielding, then further crack propagation by dissolution will be prevented. Thus a competition was envisaged between localized dissolution and passivation.

The observation[28] that addition of water to the methanol-2% bromine solution increases the anodic polarization capacity of the titanium, and at 30% water this increase is very rapid, indicates that the actual time taken for the passive film to form on an exposed surface becomes very short at the higher water contents. This observation, together with the stress corrosion data of Figure 10, indicates that a correlation exists between the increased rate of passivation and the inhibition of stress corrosion cracking. These observations are, therefore, quite consistent with the model of Champion.[30]

In considering the behavior of titanium alloys, it should be noted that inhibition of stress corrosion cracking of the Ti-5% Al alloys occurs at 45% water, Figure 10 (Curve III), as opposed to at 30% water for the unalloyed titanium. In the Ti-5 Al-2.5 Sn alloy inhibition was achieved only at 50% water, Table 3. These observations may be taken to indicate that: (1) the surface film on the alloys is less protective, possibly as a result of incorporation of aluminum and other solute atoms, (2) kinetics of dissolution are altered, or (3) that differences in the deformation characteristics, arising from alloying, in some way alter the intergranular stress corrosion cracking behavior. A study of both the metallurgical and chemical aspects of stress corrosion failures in Ti-Al alloys is in progress.

It has been pointed out by Parkins[31] that the film-rupture model proposed by Champion[30] predicts a transcrystalline crack path. Even if the initial corrosion crevice is formed at a grain boundary site, the rupture of the protective film by slip-step emergence would be expected to re-direct subsequent corrosion and rupture cycles along the slip steps, leading to transgranular cracking. In the present case, however, the corrosion studies by Tomashov et al[28] have clearly demonstrated that in the methanol-2% bromine-water solutions grains are more readily passivated than grain boundaries. Thus, emergent slip steps at the crack tip in locations some distance away from the grain boundary plane will repassivate very quickly, while slip steps emerging at or near the boundary plane will repassivate less quickly, enabling some corrosion to occur. The net effect of this difference in repassivation kinetics will be to keep the corrosion and film rupture cycles near the plane of the grain boundary.

# V. Conclusions

The work reported in this paper suggests that failures of alpha titanium in nitrogen tetroxide and methanol environments arise as a result of basically different processes. The failures in nitrogen tetroxide exhibit features which indicate that crack propagation occurs by the repeated formation and rupture of an oxide film. On the other hand, failures in methanol vapor are consistent with some form of hydrogen embrittlement, while those obtained in methanol-halogen-water solutions can be best described as arising from electrochemical dissolution. The diversity of the possible reactions that can occur when titanium alloys are exposed simultaneously to tensile stress and various environments emphasizes the view that the term stress corrosion cracking can only be regarded as a generic term encompassing a number of specific mechanisms.

## Acknowledgments

The authors wish to thank Dr. A. R. C. Westwood for helpful and stimulating discussions, and Mr. R. D. Masteller (Martin Marietta Corp., Denver) for providing certain environmental testing facilities. The authors are also pleased to acknowledge financial support received from U. S. Army Materials and Mechanics Research Center, Watertown.

## References

1. G. C. Kiefer and W. W. Harple. *Metal Progress,* 63, 2, 74 (1953).
2. M. G. Fontana. *Ind. Eng. Chem.,* 48, 59A (1956).
3. B. F. Brown. Marine Corrosion Studies, Third Interim Report of Progress, NRL Memorandum Report 1634, July, 1965, pp. 1-29, U. S. Naval Research Laboratory, Washington, D. C.
4. G. Sanderson and J. C. Scully. *Environment-Sensitive Mechanical Behavior* (A. R. C. Westwood and N. S. Stoloff, ed.) pp. 511-540, Gordon and Breach, New York (1965).
5. S. P. Rideout, M. R. Louthan and C. L. Selby. *Stress Corrosion Cracking of Titanium,* ASTM Symposium, Seattle 1965, pp. 246-259, ASTM Technical Publication No. 397.
6. H. G. Kammerer, E. J. King, and G. P. Kappelt. *Trans. ASM,* 59, 586 (1966).
7. K. Mori, A. Takamura, and T. Shimose. *Corrosion,* 22, 29 (1966).
8. J. D. Jackson, W. K. Boyd, and R. W. Staehle. Stress Corrosion of Ti-6 Al-4V in Liquid Nitrogen Tetroxide, DMIC Technical Note, April, 1966, Battelle Memorial Institute, Columbus, Ohio.
9. R. L. Johnston, R. E. Johnson, G. M. Ecord, and W. L. Castner. Stress Corrosion Cracking of Ti-6 Al-4 V Alloy in Methanol, NASA Technical Note D-3868, February 1967, NASA, Washington, D. C.
10. G. J. Heimerl and D. N. Braski. *Materials Research and Standards,* 5, 18 (1965).
11. W. B. Lisagor, C. R. Manning, and T. T. Bales. Stress Corrosion Cracking of Ti-6 Al-4 V Alloy in Nitrogen Tetroxide. Langley Working Paper LWP-275, September, 1966, NASA Langley Research Center, Hampton, Va.
12. A. J. Sedriks. *Trans. AIME,* 239, 916 (1967).
13. A. J. Forty and P. Humble. *Phil. Mag.,* 8, 247 (1963).
14. A. J. McEvily and A. P. Bond. *J. Electrochem. Soc.,* 112, 131 (1965).
15. E. N. Pugh and A. R. C. Westwood. *Phil. Mag.,* 13, 167 (1966).
16. E. N. Pugh. *Environment-Sensitive Mechanical Behavior.* (A. R. C. Westwood and N. S. Stoloff, ed.) pp. 351-402, Gordon and Breach, New York (1965).
17. O. Kubaschewski and B. E. Hopkins. *Oxidation of Metals and Alloys,* pp. 8-11 and 61-67, Butterworths, London (1953).
18. K. H. G. Ashbee and R. E. Smallman. *Proc. Roy. Soc.,* 274A, 195 (1963).
19. J. A. Sartell, R. J. Stokes, S. H. Bendel, T. G. Johnson, and C. H. Li. *Trans. AIME,* 215, 420 (1959).
20. C. Edeleanu and A. J. Forty. *Phil. Mag.,* 5, 1029 (1960).
21. E. G. Haney. Investigation of Stress Corrosion Cracking of Titanium Alloys, Mellon Institute Progress Report No. 1 (NGR-39-008-041), November, 1966, Mellon Institute, Pittsburgh, Pa.
22. H. M. Burte. *Trans. ASM,* 51, 814 (1959).
23. J. R. Ambrose and J. Kruger. *Corrosion Science,* to be published.
24. P. F. Chester and D. H. Bradhurst. *Nature,* 199, 1056 (1963).
25. R. A. Piggott, H. Leckie and L. L. Shrier. *Proceedings of the Second International Congress on Metallic Corrosion,* pp. 953-965, New York (1963).
26. I. R. Lane, L. B. Golden, and W. L. Ackerman. *Ind. Eng. Chem.,* 45, 1067 (1957).
27. E. G. Haney, R. Goldberg, R. E. Ernsberger, and W. T. Brehm. Investigation of Stress Corrosion Cracking of Titanium Alloys, Mellon Institute Progress Report No. 2 (NGR-39-008-014), May, 1967, Mellon Institute, Pittsburgh, Pa.
28. N. D. Tomashov, R. M. Altovskiy, and V. B. Vladimirov. Study of the Corrosion of Titanium and Its Alloys in Methyl Alcohol Solutions of Bromine. Translation FTD-TT-63-672/1 + 2, pp. 221-233a, Translation Division, Foreign Technology Division WPAFB, Ohio.
29. E. M. Mahla and N. A. Nielsen. *J. Appl. Phys.,* 19, 378 (1947).
30. F. A. Champion. *Symposium on Internal Stresses in Metals and Alloys,* pp. 468-469, Inst. of Metals, London (1948).
31. R. N. Parkins. *Met. Reviews,* 9, 201 (1964).

## Discussion

**T. R. Beck, Boeing Scientific Research Laboratories:**

I have one question and one comment.

The question is: What was the velocity of the crack propagation in $N_2O_4$, in centimeters per second?

It must be orders of magnitude slower than the velocities we observed.

This perhaps shows that in one material there may be several different mechanisms, depending upon the environment. The possibility of a chloride mechanism cannot be ruled out, however, because commercial $N_2O_4$ contains appreciable chlorine in one form or another.

I tend to agree with your observations that there are two mechanisms involved in methanol.

One is possibly hydrogen embrittlement which is responsible for initiation as Dr. Scully described, and then there is the other type of propagation where the halide is apparently involved at the crack tip, whether by reaction or adsorption, I don't know.

**A. J. Sedriks:**

We have not measured the crack velocities. However, such measurements have been made, and it is reported[1] that cracking in $N_2O_4$ is 3 to 4 orders of magnitude slower than in salt water.

1. J. D. Jackson, W. K. Boyd and R. W. Staehle. Stress Corrosion of Ti-6 Al-4 V in Liquid Nitrogen Tetroxide, DMIC Technical Note, April 11, 1966.

**R. W. Staehle:**

I question the applicability of the film rupture concept (in the mode of its application to copper alloys) to cracking of titanium in $N_2O_4$. In copper a relatively thick film is successively broken and the total distance of the crack is the sum of the thicknesses of individual oxide growths which have been broken. If film rupture operates here, it appears doubtful that the thickness of the film is sufficient to be similar to the copper case.

**A. J. Sedriks:**

Our metallographic studies have shown that in $N_2O_4$ oxide layers of considerable thickness (e.g., ~ 7 $\mu$, Figure 3 of paper) can form on *deformed* grain surfaces, and the rate of oxide penetration along grain boundaries appears to be even more rapid.

**J. Kruger, National Bureau of Standards:**

We had believed that hydrogen embrittlement was involved in the cracking of Ti in methanol vapor, until we found that the time to failure was almost linearly dependent on the volume of the container in which one carried out the experiment. This indicated to us that apparently some sort of a species has to be formed in the vapor atmosphere and when a critical concentration of this species is reached, cracking occurs. Hydrogen embrittlement may still be involved, but there appears to be some other species that also takes part in the process. A description of these results by J. R. Ambrose and myself appears in *Corrosion Science,* 8, 119 (1968).

My second comment is that vacuum annealing does not necessarily show hydrogen is embrittling. Hydrides can also be present and these would decompose upon annealing at temperatures above 400 C.

**A. J. Sedriks:**

On the basis of our observations we suggest that failures in methanol vapor are associated with the *entry* of hydrogen into the metal. I agree that it remains to be established whether the actual cracking process requires presence of hydrides or hydrogen in the lattice. I also agree that the "volume effect" observed by you does not invalidate the idea that hydrogen in the metal is responsible for the embrittlement.

**A. R. C. Westwood, RIAS:**

I would like to comment on the relationship between time to failure, $t_F$, and testing volume—that is, the smaller the testing volume, the shorter $t_F$. A similar relationship has been noted in two other embrittlement systems, namely, α-brass in aqueous ammonia,[1] and polycrystalline silver chloride in aqueous chloride environments.[2] In both cases, such behavior could be correlated with the formation, by dissolution of the specimen, of the critical, active species, which subsequently was primarily responsible for failure of the specimens by stress corrosion cracking. This possibility can be examined for a new system by comparing $t_F$ for specimens tested in "fresh" or "used" solutions. If relevant, $t_F$ should be less in the "used" solutions.[3]

1. E. N. Pugh, W. G. Montague and A. R. C. Westwood. *Trans. ASM,* 58, 665 (1965).
2. A. R. C. Westwood, D. L. Goldheim and E. N. Pugh. *Discuss. Faraday Soc.,* No. 38, 147 (1964).
3. E. N. Pugh and A. R. C. Westwood. *Stress Corrosion Testing,* ASTM STP 425, 228 (1967).

# SUBCRITICAL CRACK PROPAGATION IN Ti-8Al-1Mo-1V ALLOY IN ORGANIC ENVIRONMENTS, SALT WATER, AND INERT ENVIRONMENTS

George Sandoz
Naval Research Laboratory

## Abstract

A comparative study of the stress corrosion susceptibility of a Ti-8Al-1Mo-1V alloy in salt water, alcohols, and alkanes was made utilizing precracked specimens and cantilever loading. All of these environments were found to cause crack propagation at values of stress intensity less than required to produce fracture in dry air. In dry air, however, the stress intensity required to produce crack growth and fracture was found to be time and section size dependent and lower than $K_{Ic}$.

The long-chain alcohols and the alkanes appear to cause crack propagation at about the same stress intensity level. Similarly, salt water, methanol, and ethylene glycol are of a class, but produce crack propagation at lower levels of stress intensity.

The environments studied, except for dry air, appear to cause crack propagation at about the same stress intensity level whether the specimens meet the requirements for plane strain conditions or not.

## Introduction

Some titanium alloys are known to be susceptible to stress corrosion cracking (SCC) in sea water,[1] certain alcohols,[2] and alkanes.[3] The work reported here was undertaken to provide a quantitative comparison of the effects of these environments on the SCC susceptibility of a single titanium alloy in the hope that clues on the mechanism or mechanisms would evolve.

## Material and Procedure

A Ti-8Al-1Mo-1V mill-annealed plate 1 inch thick was selected as the source of specimens. The alloy designated T-19 had a yield strength of 123 ksi and contained 48 ppm hydrogen. All specimens were of WT orientation, i.e., the specimens were cut with the long dimension perpendicular to the rolling direction and notched so as to cause crack growth and fracture during testing to take place through the plate thickness.

The cantilever beam test developed by Brown[4] was used to measure SCC susceptibility. In this test specimens containing a sharp flaw (fatigue crack) are loaded in bending. A flexible plastic bottle is attached to the specimen at the flaw to contain the desired liquid or gaseous environment.

Analysis of the stress system is done using fracture mechanics. A simple calculation yields the value of the stress intensity parameter, K. As described in Reference 4, all that is required is the measurement of the specimen

dimensions, the crack depth, and a knowledge of the moment applied. The crack depth (fatigue crack) is estimated before a test, then measured exactly after the specimen is broken. From the data collected, using several specimens, the time to fracture may be plotted as a function of initial stress intensity, $K_i$.

Simple expressions from fracture mechanics[5] also permit an estimate of the specimen dimensions required to assure plane strain conditions. Plane strain conditions are known to be the most severe in mechanical tests and are generally regarded to promote SCC also. Generally, the critical dimension in the cantilever beam type specimen is the specimen breadth B. In the present investigation, specimens of various breadth were used in order to test the effects of environment on specimens, both with and without plane strain conditions.

## Results

### Non-Environmental Effects

During the course of the investigation, it was observed that delayed fractures (probably following slow crack growth) took place even in "neutral" environments at stress intensity levels lower than the critical stress intensity level $K_{Ix}$ required to produce fracture on continuous rapid loading in air. ($K_{Ix}$ is the first approximation of $K_{Ic}$, the plane strain fracture toughness index.) Accordingly, some

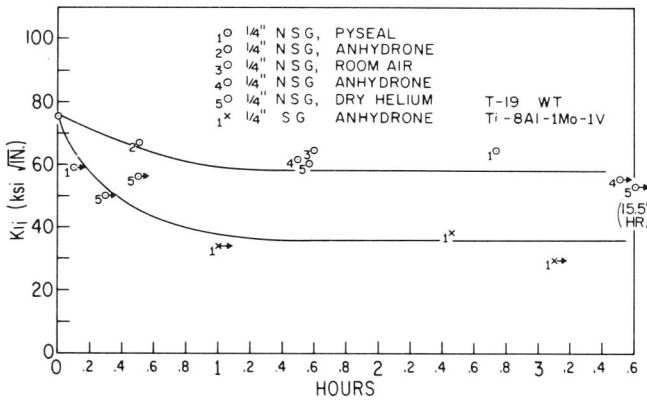

FIGURE 1 – Effect of stress intensity on the time to fracture of 1/4-in specimens in inert environments. Numbers identify single specimens. Arrows indicate no fracture in time shown.

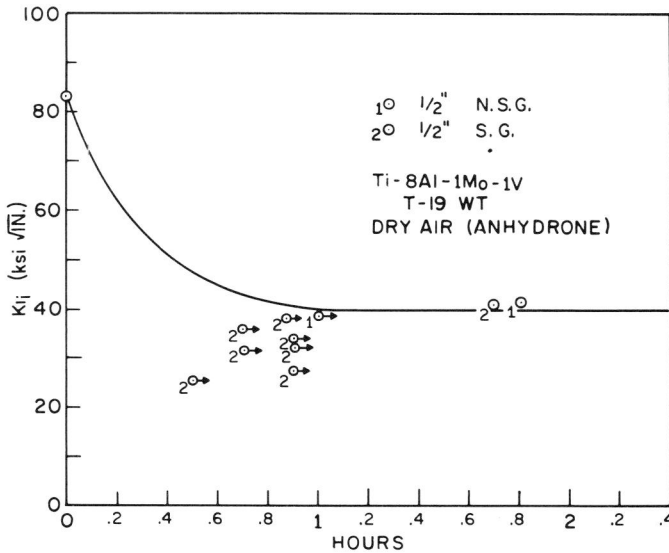

FIGURE 2 – Effect of stress intensity on the time to fracture of 1/2-in specimens in a dry air environment.

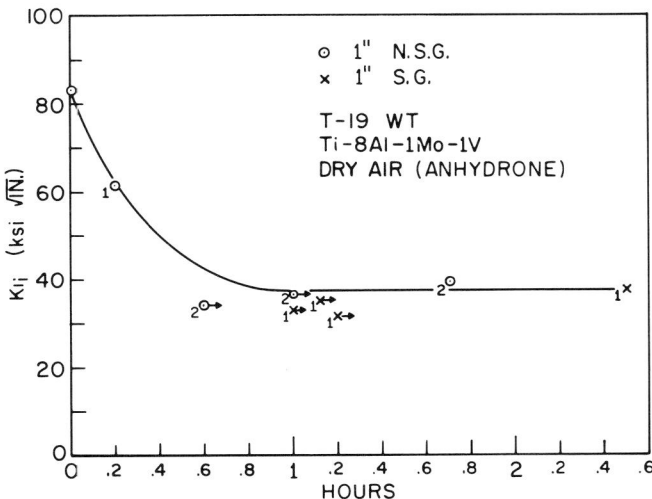

FIGURE 3 – Effect of stress intensity on the time to fracture of 1-in specimens in a dry air environment.

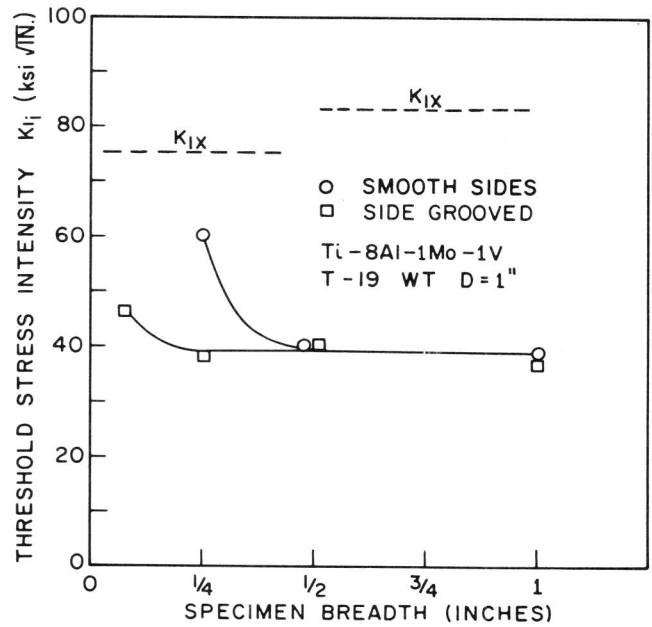

FIGURE 4 – Threshold stress intensity required for crack propagation in dry air as related to specimen breadth.

experiments were conducted to evaluate this characteristic of the alloy.

The results on specimens 1/4-in in breadth are shown in Figure 1, where values of critical stress intensity $K_{Ix}$ are plotted against fracture time. The specimens with no side grooves (NSG) result in a curve showing a threshold value at about 60 ksi√ in; this is the case whether the environment is room air, dry air, or dry helium. The same result was obtained on one specimen sealed from the atmosphere with a wax (pyseal) before test.

One specimen, 1/4-in in breadth, but side-grooved (SG), developed a lower threshold K value of about 40 ksi√ in in dry air. A side-grooved specimen only 0.075 in in breadth was found to propagate cracks at a threshold value of 45 ksi√ in, a value also considerably lower than the value of 60 ksi√ in required to propagate cracks in the 1/4-in specimens with no side grooves.

The results from specimens 1/2-in in breadth, Figure 2, show that a threshold value of about 40 ksi√ in is obtained with both smooth and side-grooved specimens. Similar results, Figure 3, were obtained with specimens 1-in in breadth.

These results are summarized in Figure 4, where the threshold stress intensity levels for non-environmental crack growth and delayed fracture are presented as a function of specimen breadth. For this particular alloy, threshold values obviously increase as specimen breadth is decreased to less than 1/2 in. There is also a rather abrupt change in the value of $K_{Ix}$ which occurs at the same thickness range. This range approximates the thickness limitation for plane strain conditions.

Because a threshold value in dry air appears for each specimen size class, such values are henceforth designated $K_{IH}$. This is apparently a safer index of long-term load carrying capability than $K_{Ic}$. Similar threshold values in other environments are designated $K_{Iscc}$, and the difference

685

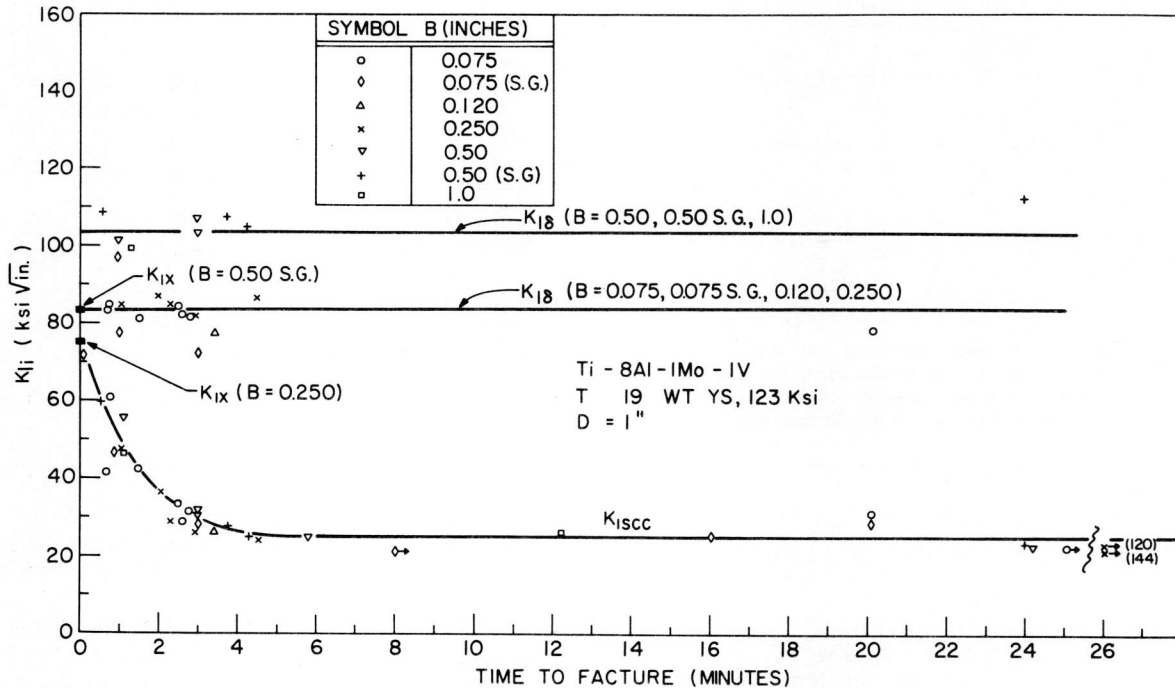

**FIGURE 5** — Effect of stress intensity on the time to fracture of specimens of various breadth in a 3-1/2 percent NaCl-water environment.

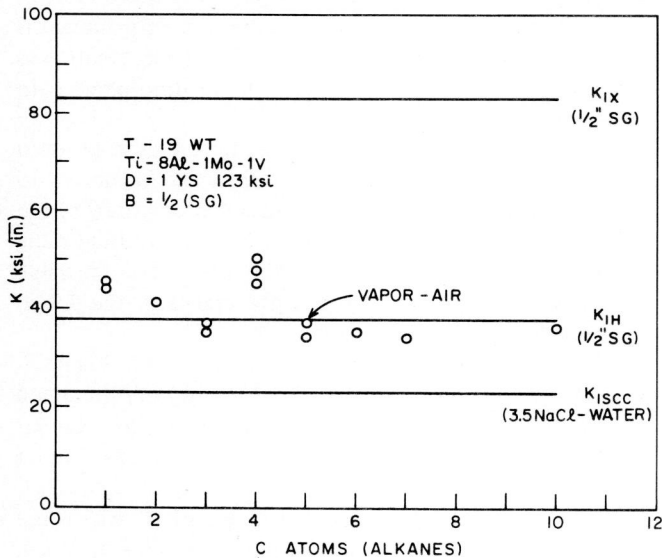

**FIGURE 6** —Threshold stress intensity for crack growth and fracture of side-grooved 1/2-in specimens in normal alkanes with increasing number of C atoms.

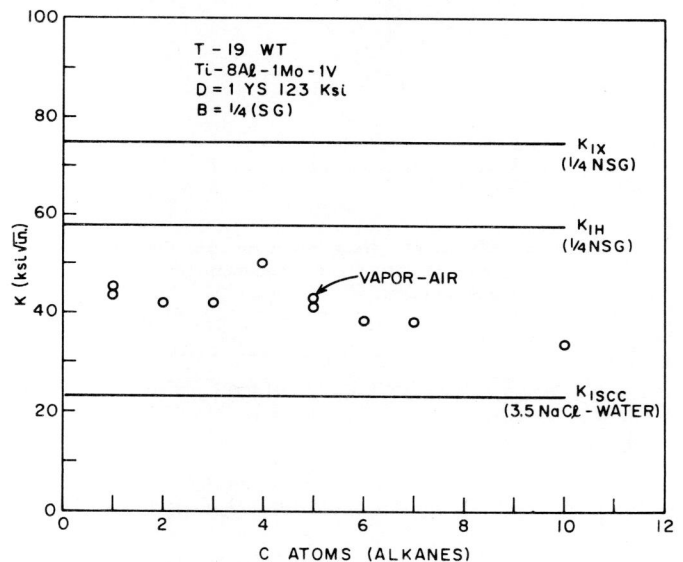

**FIGURE 7** — Threshold stress intensity for crack growth and fracture of non-side-grooved 1/4-in specimens in normal alkanes with increasing number of C atoms.

between $K_{IH}$ and $K_{Iscc}$ is a measure of the degradation caused by a given environment.

### Section Size Effect in Salt Water

The stress corrosion characteristics of the T-19 alloy in water containing a 3.5 percent NaCl are summarized in Figure 5. As indicated, a series of specimens ranging in breadth from 0.075 in to 1.0 in were tested. No significant differences in the values of $K_{Iscc}$ were observed with changes in specimen thickness; the value is about 24 ksi$\sqrt{}$ in. As indicated previously and in Figure 5, the dry fracture toughness $K_{Ix}$ of the thicker specimens (B ≥ 0.5-in) is about 83 ksi$\sqrt{}$ in, whereas the thin specimens (B ≤ 0.25-in) have a $K_{Ix}$ value of about 75 ksi$\sqrt{}$ in. In addition, there are two levels of $K_{I\sigma}$ indicated in Figure 5, with the transition

686

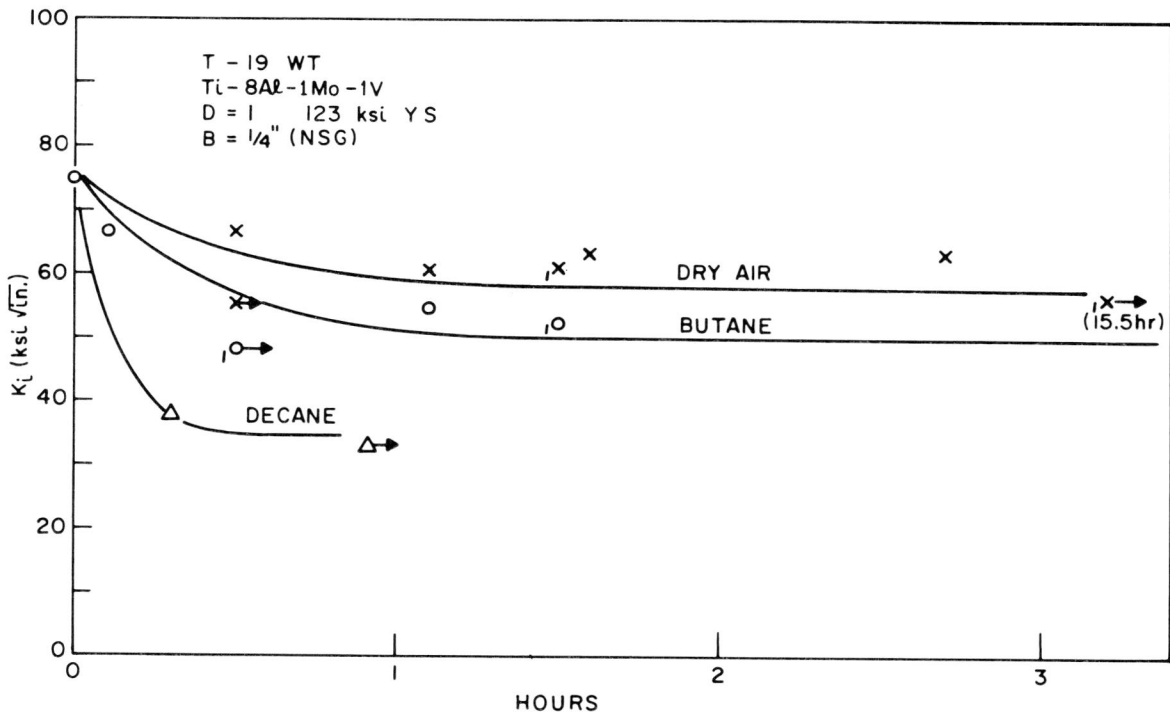

FIGURE 8 — Effect of stress intensity on time to fracture of non-side-grooved 1/4-in specimens tested in dry air, n-butane and n-decane.

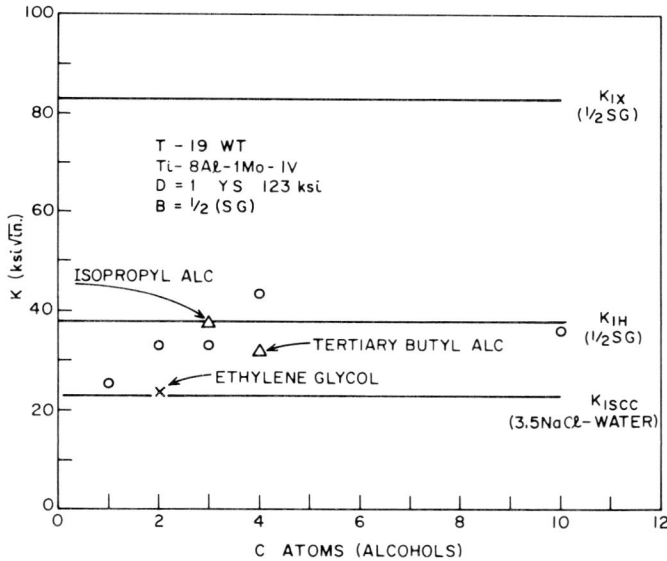

FIGURE 9 — Threshold stress intensity for crack growth and fracture of side-grooved 1/2-in specimens tested in normal alcohols containing increasing number of C atoms. Similar results with other alcohols and glycol as indicated.

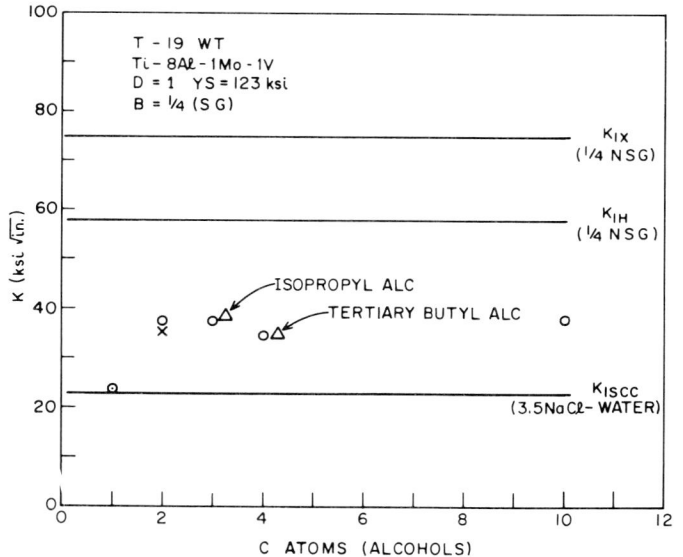

FIGURE 10 — Threshold stress intensity for crack growth and fracture of non-side-grooved 1/4-in speci- mens tested in normal alcohols with increasing number of C atoms. Similar results with other alcohols as indicated.

corresponding to the same thickness range. $K_{I_\sigma}$ is an estimate of the purely mechanical fracture toughness obtained by measuring the crack depth on broken specimens to the line of demarcation between corrosion and fast fracture; it corresponds generally to $K_{Ix}$ but varies with the extent of stress corrosion crack depth because of departure from the assumptions used in the equation for K.

The $K_{I_\sigma}$ data points in Figure 5 are represented by the upper symbols which match the $K_{Iscc}$ data points.

*Effects of Alkanes*

Figures 6 and 7 present the results of the $K_{Iscc}$ determinations in alkane environments for specimens 1/2 in

687

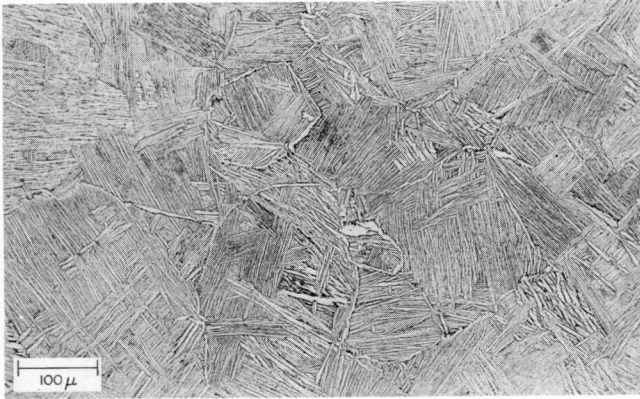

**FIGURE 11 — Microstructure of Ti-8Al-1Mo-1V T-19 alloy.**

and 1/4 in in breadth, respectively. No significant effect of specimen breadth could be detected nor did there appear to be any discontinuity in passing from the gaseous alkanes into the liquid alkanes. Moreover, gaseous pentane in air produced cracking as readily as liquid pentane, as indicated. There were observed differences in rates, however, as in Figure 8. The butane and decane curves show the extremes of $K_{Iscc}$ level observed with the alkanes.

On the basis of the 1/2-in specimens, Figure 6, no degradation by the alkanes can be shown, because the values of $K_{Iscc}$ of about 40 ksi√ in correspond closely to the values of $K_{IH}$ obtained for these specimens. Some degradation in the 1/4-in specimens is indicated because $K_{IH}$ is higher in these specimens, as in Figure 7.

*Effects of Alcohols*

The effects of alcohols are summarized in Figures 9 and 10. Again, there appears to be no significant effect of section size on the $K_{Iscc}$ values obtained. All of the alcohols with two or more carbon atoms produce $K_{Iscc}$ values that hover around the 40 ksi√ in level and thus these alcohols resemble the alkanes. Methanol and ethylene glycol, however, produce $K_{Iscc}$ values that correspond to the value of $K_{Iscc}$ in salt water. (These are the same two environments known to produce crack initiation in smooth specimens stressed in tension to near yield stress.[6]) No significant differences between the effects of primary and secondary or tertiary alcohols could be seen.

## Metallography

The microstructure of the T-19 alloy at 200X is seen in Figure 11. The structure is typical of the alloy cooled slowly from above the $\beta$ transus, and consists of an $\alpha$ and $\beta$ mixture with some of the former $\beta$ grains outlined by $\alpha$. Fractographs at 6000X showing surfaces formed during slow crack growth at stress intensity levels near $K_{Iscc}$ in various environments are shown in Figures 12-16. The fractographs are notably similar. Apparently crack propagation is by a cleavage mode regardless of the environment. It should be added that as the stress intensity increases, either because of crack propagation or by the application of initial loads (stress intensity) well above

$K_{Iscc}$, increasing areas of ductile mode rupture are observed.

## Discussion

The fact that $K_{IH}$ levels in the alloy occur well below the $K_{Ix}$ or $K_{Ic}$ level suggests the influence of hydrogen. The only other explanation that occurs is the possibility of a creep-rupture type of crack growth. However, preliminary experiments involving vacuum annealing of the alloy T-19 to remove hydrogen indicates that $K_{IH}$ varies inversely with hydrogen content. With the hydrogen content reduced from the original 48 ppm to 2 ppm, $K_{IH}$ rises essentially to the value of $K_{Ix}$. These vacuum annealing experiments, however, have produced essentially no changes in the values of $K_{Iscc}$ in environments other than dry air ($K_{IH}$).

It is also possible that a hydrogen type mechanism accounts for the observed stress corrosion cracking in salt water, the alkanes, and the alcohols. Perhaps the fresh titanium alloy surface reacts with water and some of the alcohols to yield the alkoxide and hydrogen. This could account for the lower $K_{Iscc}$ values found with water and methanol. The difficulty in starting a crack in a smooth specimen with water, relative to methanol, can be accounted for by the insolubility of the alkoxide formed with water, whereas it is soluble in alcohol.

The longer-chain alcohols and alkanes produce almost identical $K_{Iscc}$ values and may therefore produce cracking by a similar mechanism which may also involve hydrogen. At this stage, the nature of the reaction is not known. A petroleum-cracking type reaction to yield unsaturated hydrocarbons and hydrogen could account for the bulk of the observations, but the reactivity of the simplest alkane, methane, cannot readily be explained in this way.

The apparent insensitivity to section size of the alloy when tested in the corrosive environments may be partially explained by the lower values of initial stress intensity required. Lower values of initial stress intensity at least initially relax the requirements on specimen breadth for achieving plane strain conditions. In the salt water environments, however, specimens definitely too thin to be in plane strain cracked quite readily and at rates comparable to much thicker specimens. Thus, the expected decrease in susceptibility to stress corrosion cracking upon the loss of plane strain conditions did not materialize. This is probably not the general case and further work in this area is planned.

## Acknowledgments

The author is indebted to R. L. Newbegin for conducting the tests. The fractographic display was prepared by J. E. Flint. Dr. B. F. Brown and Dr. R. A. Meussner provided helpful counsel and discussion. A number of people in the Chemistry, Metallurgy, and Mechanics Divisions were helpful in giving advice and materials.

This research was supported by the Advanced Research Projects Agency of the Department of Defense as part of the ARPA Coupling Program on Stress Corrosion Cracking (ARPA Order 878).

688

FIGURE 12 — Fractograph of the slow crack growth surface in dry air.

FIGURE 14 — Fractograph of the slow crack growth surface in methanol.

FIGURE 13 — Fractograph of the slow crack growth surface in 3-1/2 percent NaCl-water.

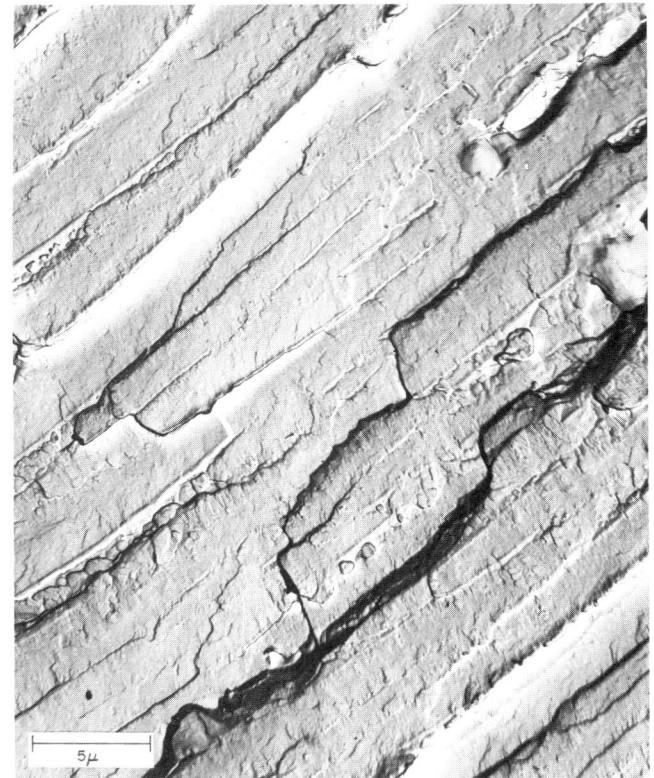

FIGURE 15 — Fractograph of the slow crack growth surface in n-butanol.

**FIGURE 16 — Fractograph of the slow crack growth surface
in n-pentane.**

## References

1. B. F. Brown. A New Stress Corrosion Cracking Test for High Strength Alloys. Materials Research and Standards, 6, No. 3, 129-133 (1966) March.
2. E. G. Haney. Investigation of Stress Corrosion Cracking in Titanium Alloys. Mellon Institute, NASA Research Grant NGR-39-008-014, Semi-Annual Progress Report No. 1 (1966) June through November.
3. G. Sandoz. Stress Corrosion Cracking Susceptibility of a Titanium Alloy in a Non-Electrolyte. *Nature*, 214, 166-167 (1967) April.
4. B. F. Brown and C. D. Beachem. A Study of the Stress Factor in Corrosion Cracking by Use of the Precracked Cantilever Beam Specimen. *Corrosion Science*, 5, 745-750 (1965) November.
5. W. F. Brown, Jr. and J. E. Srawley. Plane Strain Crack Toughness Testing of High Strength Materials. ASTM Spec. Tech. Publ. No. 410 (1966) December.
6. G. Sandoz. Effects of Some Organics on the Stress Corrosion Susceptibility of Some Titanium Alloys. Seminar on Accelerated Crack Propagation of Titanium by Methanol, Halogenated Hydrocarbons and Other Solutions, sponsored by DMIC, Battelle Memorial Institute (1967). DMIC Report 228, March 6, 1967.

## Discussion

**M. J. Blackburn, Boeing Scientific Research Laboratory:**

When you heat treat your specimens are you sure that you do not affect other factors which influence stress corrosion cracking? For instance the metallurgical structure, i.e., phases present, their morphology, grain size, the preferred orientation, etc., must remain constant in order to carry out a true comparative test. Did you check these other parameters which may vary during your heat treatments?

**G. Sandoz:**

The vacuum-annealing heat treatments referred to by Dr. Blackburn were preliminary experiments as stated in the paper. A parallel between the reduction of hydrogen content and an increase in the critical stress intensity parameter $K_{IH}$ for slow crack growth in air was shown, but no proof of a causal relationship was claimed.

It was recognized that metallurgical effects other than hydrogen removal would probably take place during vacuum annealing, as Dr. Blackburn suggests. In at least one case, however, no apparent changes in microstructure or hardness were apparent after a vacuum anneal. It was also noted that vacuum annealing produced no significant changes in the $K_{Iscc}$ values of the alloy in environments other than dry air ($K_{IH}$). Because metallurgical effects would be expected to produce changes in the $K_{Iscc}$ values in all the environments, and because hydrogen is known to produce slow crack growth in air in other metals, the presence of hydrogen is suspected to account for the observations.

690

# STUDY OF STRESS CORROSION CRACKING
## OF COMMERCIAL TITANIUM ALLOYS

R. E. Adams and E. von Tiesenhausen
Titanium Metals Corporation of America

## Abstract

Salt water and hot salt cracking phenomena have been studied at TMCA with emphasis on commercial alloys and applications. This study was aimed at determination of singular factors adversely affecting stress corrosion resistance in salt water and hot salt environments and elimination of these factors from alloy development programs. To keep experimental conditions as simple as possible, single phase alloys were sought which exhibited resistance and susceptibility to stress corrosion. Such alloys were found. The alpha alloy Ti-5Al-2.5Sn and the beta alloy Ti-13V-11Cr-3Al are susceptible to salt water cracking while the alpha alloy Ti-10Zr-4Sn and the beta alloy Ti-11Mo-5Zr-5Sn are resistant. In addition, studies were made of the alpha-beta alloy Ti-8Al-1Mo-1V, which is susceptible to salt water and hot salt cracking.

The susceptible single phase alloys and the Ti-8Al-1Mo-1V alloy have been studied by means of optical and electron metallography and transmission electron microscopy. Degree of salt water fracture susceptibility of Ti-8Al-1Mo-1V alloy was related to its fine microstructure. Optical metallography of Ti-8Al-1Mo-1V alloy indicated that hot salt cracks generally propagate along alpha-beta phase boundaries. Optical metallography of Ti-13V-11Cr-3Al revealed that salt water cracks propagate transgranularly while the cracks in Ti-5Al-2.5Sn seem mainly intergranular. Planar dislocation arrays have been observed in both the Ti-13V-11Cr-3Al alloy and the Ti-5Al-2.5Sn alloy but are more predominant in the former.

Studies of binary alloy systems have shown that concentrations of interstitial elements far greater than normally found in commercial alloys do not promote susceptibility to stress corrosion. Of the many substitutional alloying elements studied, Hf, Mo, Nb, Re, Ta, and Zr do not have adverse effects on hot salt cracking susceptibility of binary alloys unless present in exceptionally high concentrations. Data gathered on binary alloys indicate alloy additions resulting in a change of $\beta$ lattice parameter in excess of 0.5% contribute to stress corrosion susceptibility.

Salt water and hot salt stress corrosion of titanium alloys are being studied at TMCA in an attempt to design commercial alloys with minimum susceptibility to these phenomena. In the course of this work, somewhat random observations have been made which might serve as beginnings for basic research into the phenomena by those organizations so inclined. Two such observations, constitution and processing variables, are common to both phenomena and will form the subject of this paper.

Resistance to salt water corrosion is tested using a center fatigue cracked sheet specimen, Figure 1. Alloys to be studied are fabricated into specimens of this type and tested in static tension in both air and a 3.5% solution of NaCl. The net stress and time to failure are plotted as shown in Figure 2. The points plotted as runout data indicate the specimen sustained the applied load for 24 hours. Figure 2 shows data for the susceptible, commercial alpha alloy Ti-5Al-2.5Sn in the flash annealed condition; susceptibility is, of course, indicated by the much lower

stresses necessary for fracture in salt water.

Tests of this nature have revealed cph and bcc single phase alloys both immune and susceptible to low energy fracture in salt water. The cph single phase alloy Ti-5Al-2.5Sn is susceptible to salt water cracking in all conditions of heat treatment while the cph single phase alloy Ti-10Zr-4Sn, having an aged sheet structure, is not susceptible. Experience has shown that the aging should produce maximum susceptibility. In addition to the Ti-10Zr-4Sn alloy, other compositions in the Ti-Zr-Sn family up to the unordered Ti-18Zr and Ti-18Sn, where some degree of order is present,[1] appear to be immune in the aged condition. The single phase bcc alloy Ti-13V-11Cr-3Al in a solution annealed condition, expected to give minimum susceptibility, is susceptible to salt water cracking as shown in Figure 3, while the single phase bcc alloy Ti-11Mo-5Zr-5Sn is immune even in an aged condition. Table 1 summarizes this data and shows short-term tensile properties for these materials.

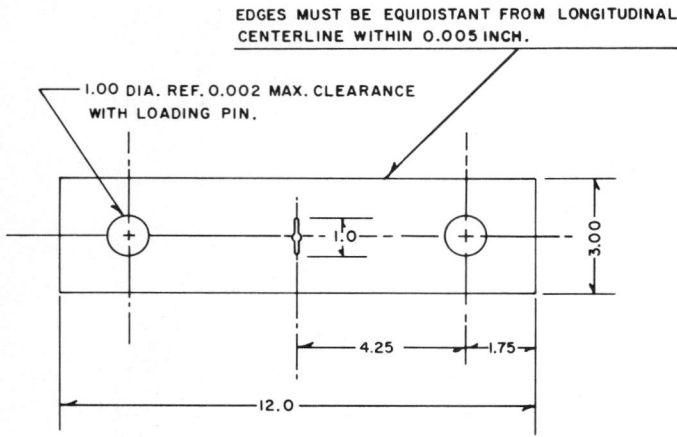

FIGURE 1 — Center cracked sheet specimen.

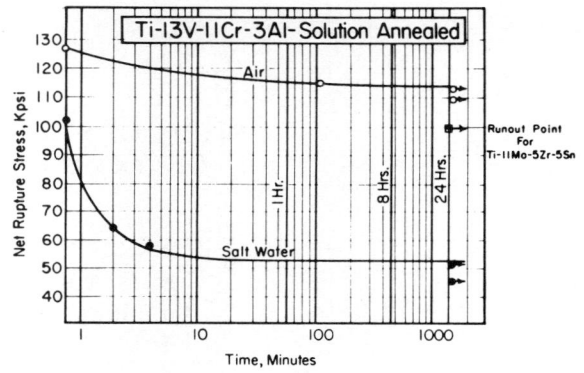

FIGURE 3 — Stress rupture curves in air and 3.5% salt water for center fatigue cracked specimen. Nominal 0.023-inch thick, longitudinal tests.

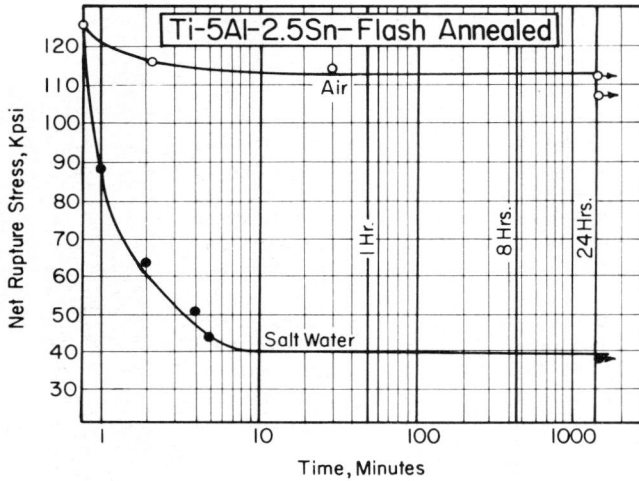

FIGURE 2 — Stress rupture curves in air and 3.5% salt water for center fatigue cracked specimen. Nominal 0.030-inch, longitudinal tests.

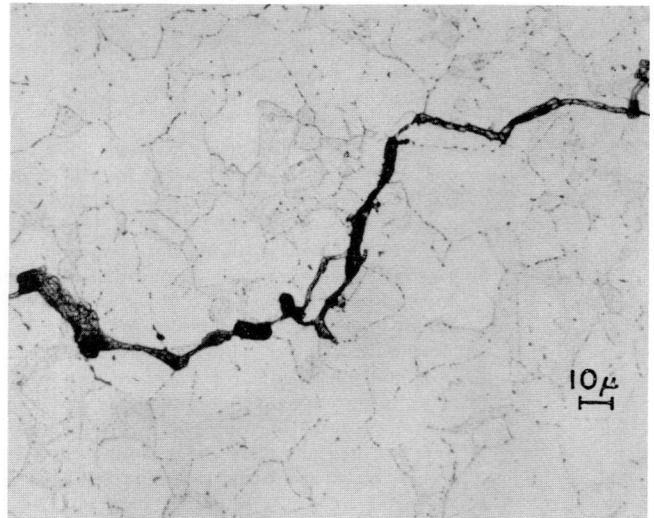

FIGURE 4 — Salt water crack in flash annealed Ti-5Al-2.5Sn alloy.

TABLE 1–Cph and bcc Single Phase Alloys Immune and Susceptible to Salt Water Cracking

| Alloy | Allotropic Form | Heat Treatment | Mechanical Properties | | | Stress Corrosion |
| | | | US Ksi | YS Ksi | % Elong. | |
| --- | --- | --- | --- | --- | --- | --- |
| Ti-5Al-2.5Sn | cph | Flash Anneal (746C-8hrs-FC+816C-1min-AC) | 138.3 | 126.0 | 16 | Susceptible |
| Ti-10Zr-4Sn | cph | 593C-24hrs-AC | 89.0 | 82.0 | 14 | Immune (Salt water test ran out at 80% of air value) |
| Ti-13V-11Cr-3Al | bcc | Solution Anneal (788C-10min-AC) | 141.8 | 137.2 | 19 | Susceptible |
| Ti-11Mo-5Zr-5Sn | bcc | 760C-5min-AC+538C-16hrs-AC | 167.0 | 154.0 | 12 | Immune |

692

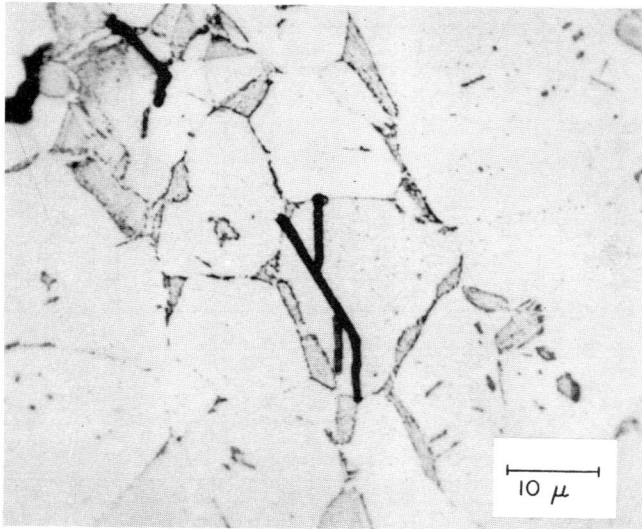

FIGURE 5 — Crystallographic secondary crack in flash annealed commercial Ti-5Al-2.5Sn alloy.

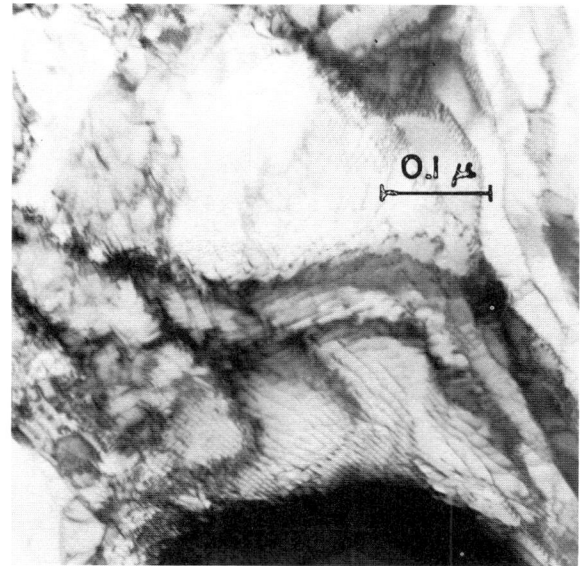

FIGURE 7 — Planar dislocation arrays in flash annealed Ti-5Al-2.5Sn-0.5Fe alloy.

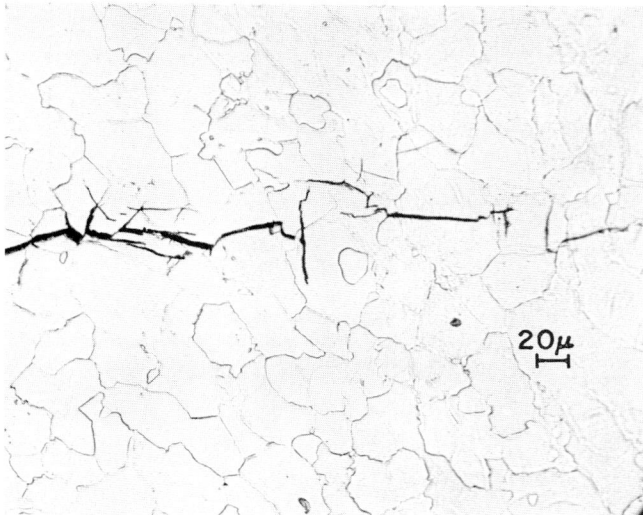

FIGURE 6 — Salt water crack in solution heat treated Ti-13V-11Cr-3Al alloy.

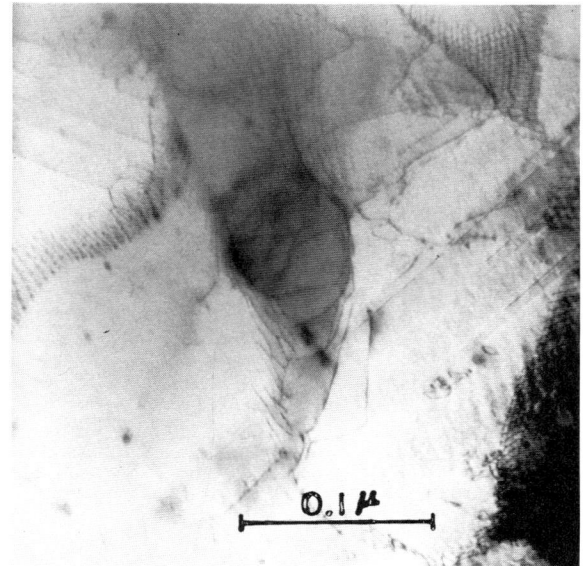

FIGURE 8 — Planar dislocation arrays in solution heat treated Ti-13V-11Cr-3Al alloy.

In an attempt to rationalize the difference in behavior of these alloys, crack paths were studied by optical metallography. In addition, these four alloys were viewed in transmission electron microscopy. Optical metallography of a Ti-5Al-2.5Sn specimen shows that salt water cracks in this alloy have a mixed mode, i.e., they show a mixed intergranular and a transgranular path, Figure 4. Some preference is shown for the intergranular path. The alloy in this photograph is the commercial Ti-5Al-2.5Sn formulation in which a small amount of iron accounts for the beta phase seen in the grain boundaries. An alloy formulated without the Fe exhibits the same salt water behavior and is entirely single phase. A distinctly crystallographic secondary crack has been observed in salt water cracked commercial Ti-5Al-2.5Sn alloy, Figure 5; but the fracture planes have not been indexed because of the small grain size. Salt water cracks in the beta Ti-13V-11Cr-3Al alloy are entirely transgranular, Figure 6.

Transmission electron microscopy of these four titanium alloys shows that the two susceptible alloys often exhibit planar dislocation arrays, Figures 7 and 8, while the nonsusceptible alloys have structures such as shown in Figures 9 and 10. The apparent correlation between planar dislocation arrays and salt water cracking susceptibility is interesting in light of similar correlations found in single phase alloys in other systems.[2-4] However, no definite cause and effect relationship has been shown. Indeed, the relationship between stress corrosion and planar dislocation

693

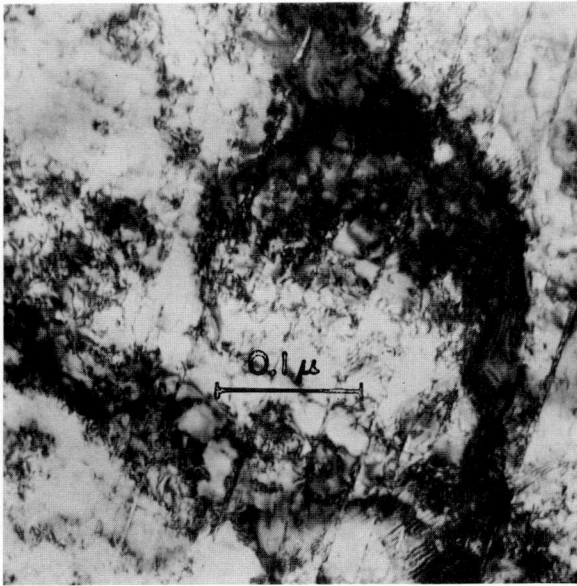

FIGURE 9 – Ti-10Zr-4Sn alloy after 2.6% deformation. Not susceptible.

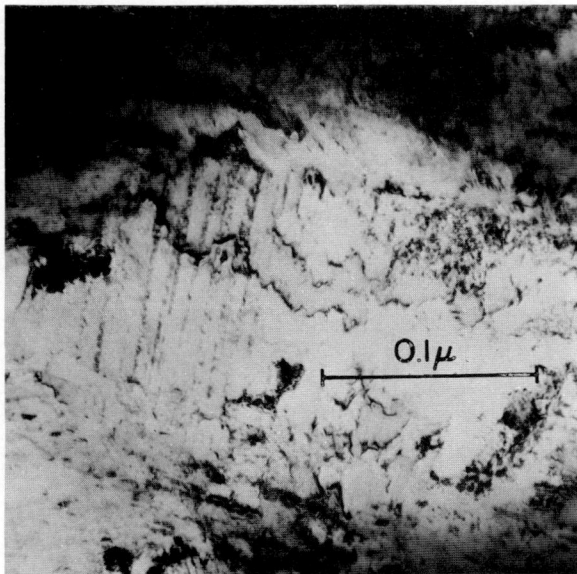

FIGURE 10 – Ti-11Mo-5Zr-5Sn alloy after 3.4% deformation.

FIGURE 11 – Stress rupture curves in air and 3.5% salt water for center fatigue cracked specimens. Nominal 0.025-inch, longitudinal tests.

arrays in other systems has been attributed to ordering effects. Here the immunity of an ordering alloy such as Ti-18Sn does present an anomaly.

Heat treatment appears to affect the degree of susceptibility of titanium alloys to salt water cracking in at least two ways. The first of these is an ordering effect. The multi-phase Ti-8Al-1Mo-1V alloy in the form of .025-inch gage sheet exhibits low energy failures in both air and salt water in the 760 C-8hrs-FC, or mill annealed condition, but exhibits much higher energy fractures in the 760C-8hrs-FC+788C-15min-AC, or duplex annealed con-

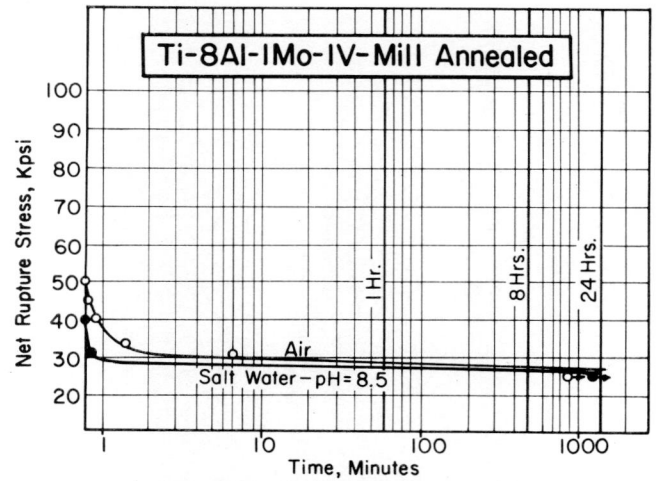

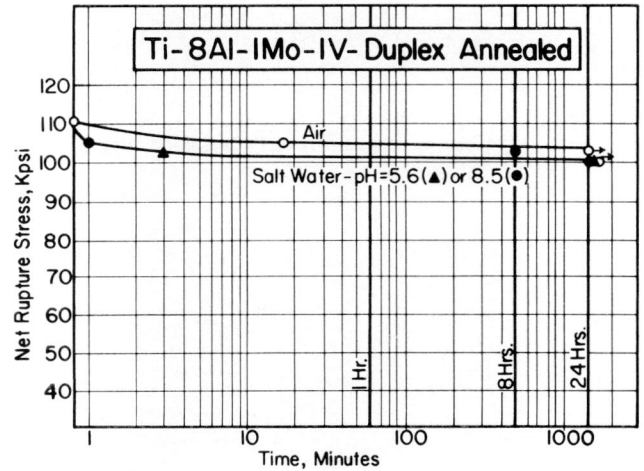

dition, as shown in Figure 11.[5] Even though fracture in air occurs at low stresses in the mill annealed condition, the rapid decline of time to fracture in salt water indicates salt water susceptibility. Blackburn has demonstrated that mill annealed Ti-8Al-1Mo-1V contains domains of long range order whereas the duplex annealed alloy does not.[6] Indeed, the low fracture strength of the mill annealed alloy in air is indicative of long range order.

In addition to the effects of ordering, heat treatments designed to eliminate the low fracture strengths inherent in ordered Ti-8Al-1Mo-1V by elimination of the long range order can cause changes in the degree of salt water cracking susceptibility.[7] Table 2 gives salt water data from both longitudinal and transverse specimens of Ti-8Al-1Mo-1V alloy in four states of heat treatment. The net runout stresses increase from top to bottom of the table. The mill anneal heat treatment promotes long range order but the remaining three heat treatments are designed to suppress long range order. Figures 12 through 15 are electron photomicrographs of chromium shadowed replicas of rolling plane and transverse Kroll-etched surfaces of the Ti-8Al-1Mo-1V alloy in the conditions of heat treatment shown in the table. The beta phase in the mill annealed and

TABLE 2—Effect of Heat Treatment on Net Runout Stress

| Rolling Temp. | Heat Treatment | Nomenclature | Gage (in) | Net Runout Stress (Kpsi) |
|---|---|---|---|---|
| From 982 C | 760C-8hrs-FC | Mill Anneal | .025 | L ~ 25<br>T ~ 25 |
| From 982 C | 760C-8hrs-FC+788C-15min-AC | Duplex Anneal | .050 | L   40.4<br>T ~ 40 |
| From 982 C | 760C-8hrs-FC+1010C-5min-AC+746C-15min-AC | Triplex Anneal | .050 | L   112.3<br>T   51.9 |
| From 1010 C | 1010C-5min-AC+746C-15min-AC | 2B2 | .045 | L   108.9<br>T   106.7 |

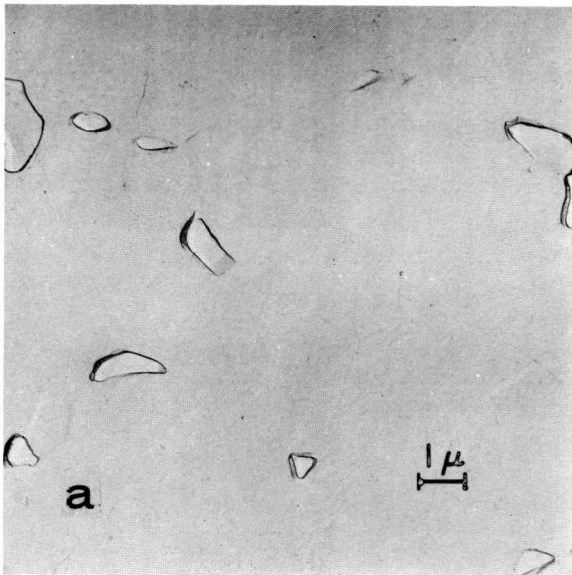

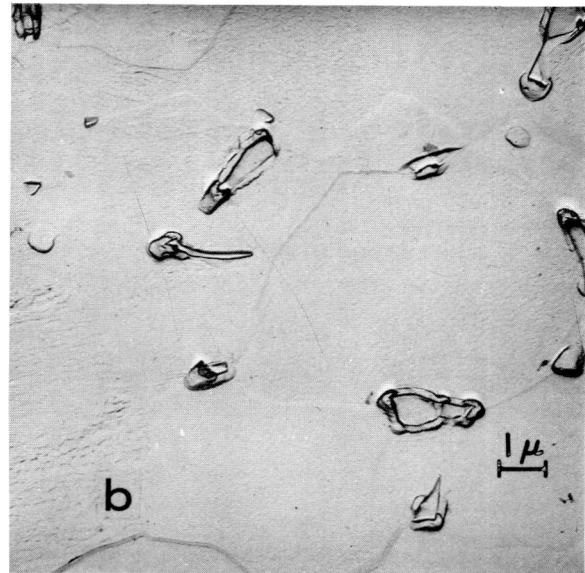

FIGURE 12 — Mill annealed Ti-8Al-1Mo-1V. (a) Plan view, (b) Transverse section.

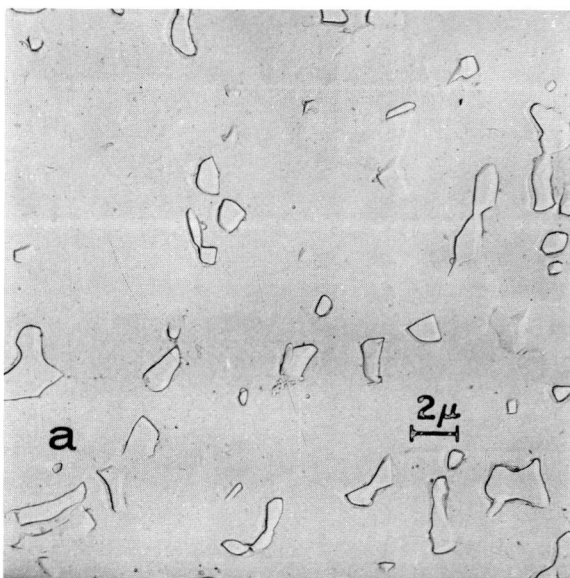

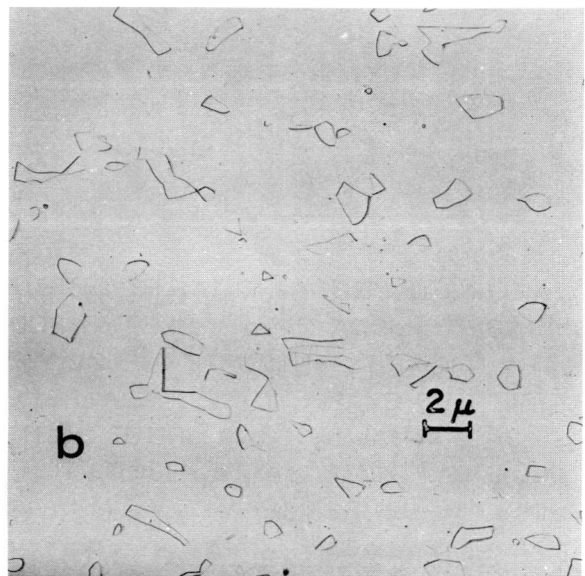

FIGURE 13 — Duplex annealed Ti-8Al-1Mo-1V. (a) Plan view, (b) Transverse section.

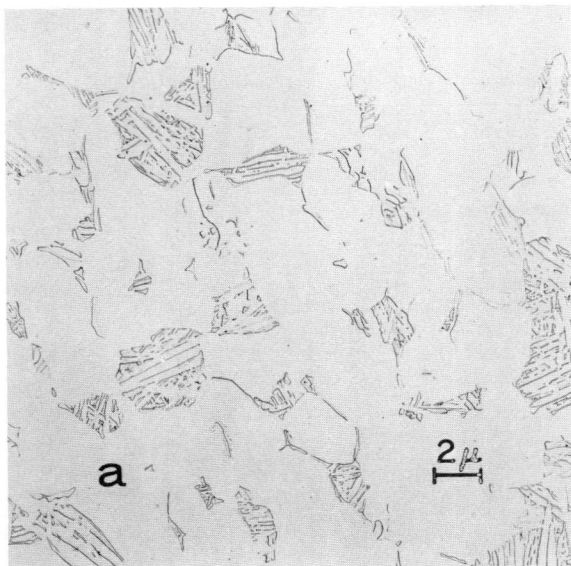

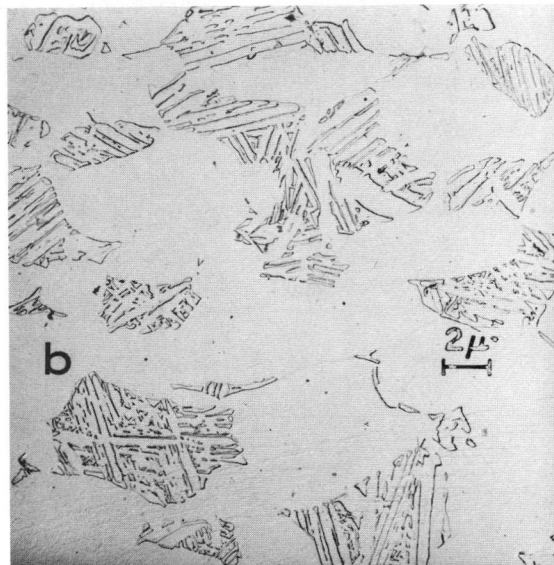

**FIGURE 14 — Triplex annealed Ti-8Al-1Mo-1V. (a) Longitudinal section, (b) Transverse section.**

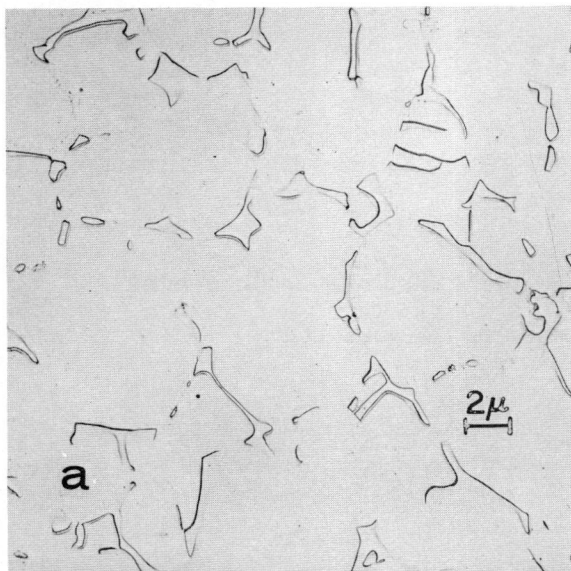

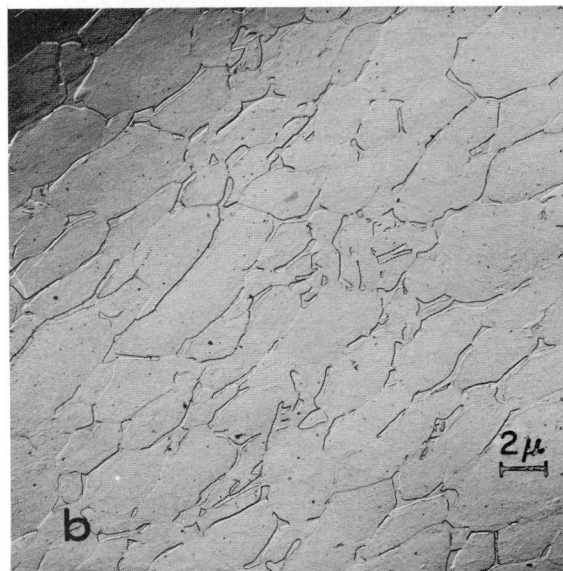

**FIGURE 15 — Ti-8Al-1Mo-1V in the 2B2 condition. (a) Plan view, (b) Transverse section.**

most susceptible material is massive and equiaxed, Figure 12. Duplex annealing, which decreases susceptibility slightly, retains the equiaxed beta configuration while eliminating ordering, Figure 13. Triplex annealing results in formation of a script-type beta structure, Figure 14. The 2B2 process, Figure 15, gives a structure in which regions of alpha are enclosed by nearly continuous beta and which seems to be immune to salt water cracking in both the longitudinal and transverse directions. These results indicate the length of mean free alpha path may be some index to salt water cracking susceptibility. Figure 16 seems to support this thesis by indicating that salt water cracks in Ti-8Al-1Mo-1V alloy tend to be reluctant to propagate

across the beta phase.

For high temperature and stress environments, hot salt cracking becomes as serious as salt water cracking in marine environments. The quantitative hot salt stress corrosion test at TMCA utilizes a sheet specimen having a gage length of variable cross section, Figure 17. This specimen is coated with sodium chloride by wetting both sides with a warm, aqueous slurry of NaCl followed by application of as much dry NaCl as will adhere to the specimen. Subsequent drying produces a thick continuous salt coat. The coated specimens are brought to temperature in muffle creep furnaces and are loaded in static tension. Results of exposure are evaluated by breaking the specimens into transverse strips

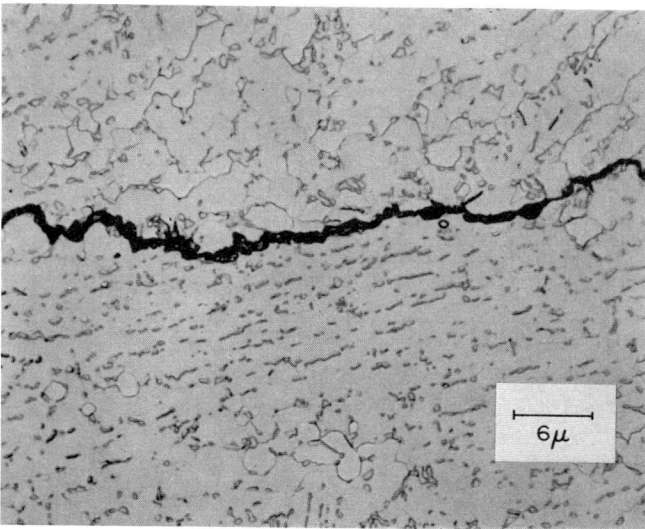

FIGURE 16 – Salt water crack in duplex annealed Ti-8Al-1Mo-1V.

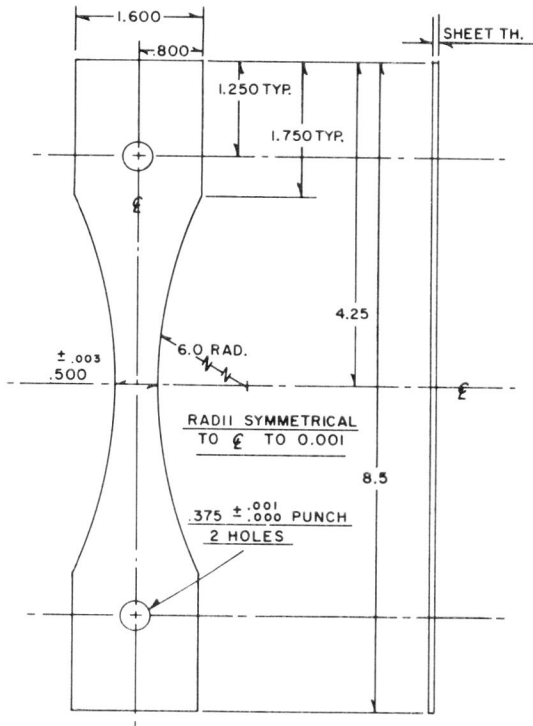

FIGURE 18 – Critical stress v time for Ti-8Al-1Mo-1V.

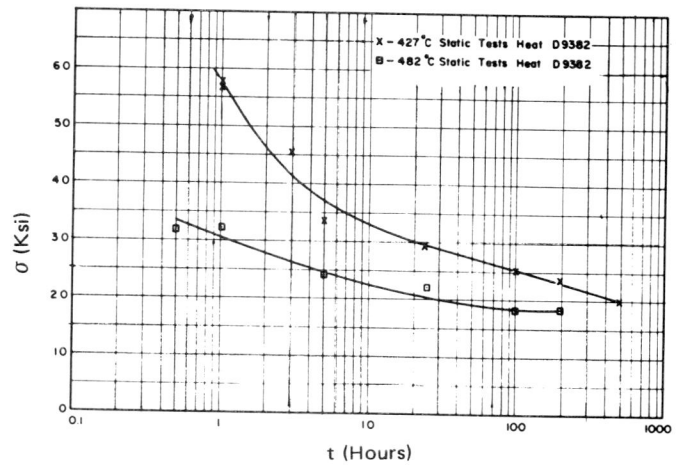

FIGURE 19 – Critical stress v time for two heats of Ti-8Al-1Mo-1V.

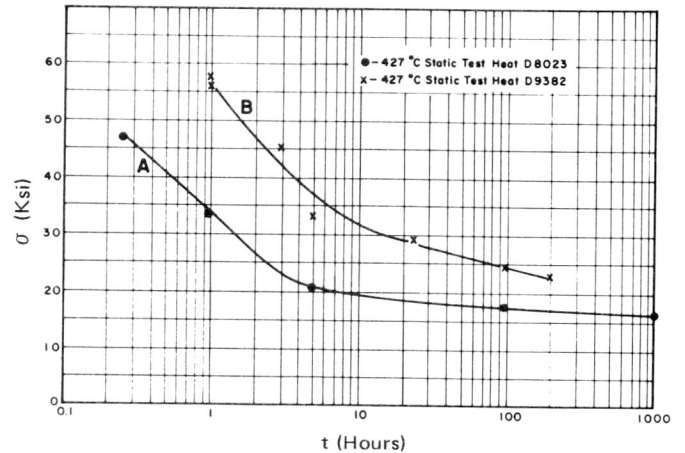

FIGURE 17 – Hot salt cracking specimen.

TABLE 3 – Analysis of Ti-8Al-1Mo-1V Sheet Materials "A" and "B"

| Element | A (%) | B (%) |
|---|---|---|
| Fe | .04 | .06 |
| Cr | .025 | .010 |
| Mo | 1.0 | 1.0 |
| Al | 7.8 | 7.7 |
| V | 1.1 | 1.2 |
| Sn | .023 | .023 |
| Mn | .002 | .002 |
| Mg | <.001 | .001 |
| Ni | <.001 | <.001 |
| Cu | .011 | .003 |
| Zr | <.001 | <.001 |
| B | <.001 | <.001 |

approximately 1/8-inch wide and examining the fractured surfaces at a magnification of 30X for discoloration due to stress corrosion. The maximum cross section at which discoloration is observed is used to calculate the threshold stress for hot salt cracking for the particular temperature and time of the test. Figure 18 shows results of such tests at 427 C and 482 C for the Ti-8Al-1Mo-1V alloy in the duplex annealed condition. As would be expected, the critical stress is less at higher temperatures.

Such tests have shown that final processing can also affect the degree of susceptibility to hot salt cracking.[8]

Figure 19 shows critical stress curves for two sheets of duplex annealed Ti-8Al-1Mo-1V rolled at different temperatures. Curve A is drawn from data on a sheet rolled high in the alpha-beta phase field while Curve B represents a sheet rolled at a lower temperature but still in the alpha-beta field. The results of analyses of these sheets are given in Table 3 and show that the sheet compositions are

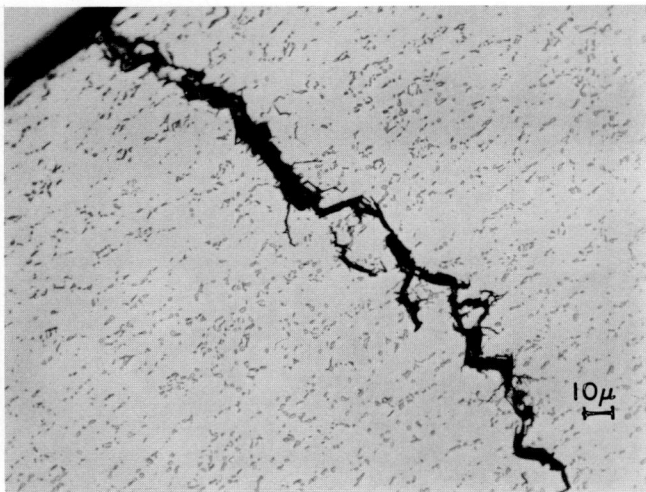

FIGURE 20 — Hot salt crack in Ti-8Al-1Mo-1V.

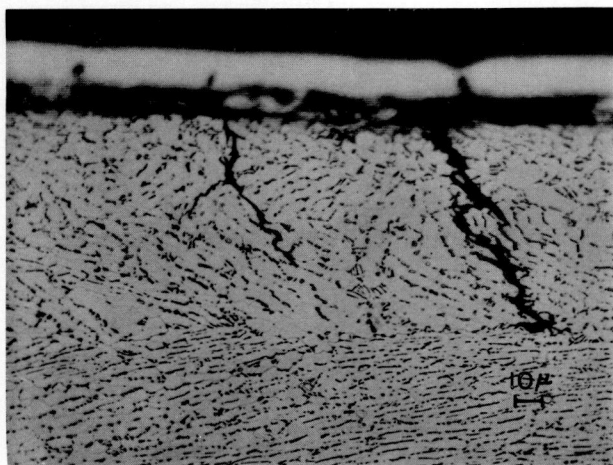

FIGURE 21 — Arrest of hot salt crack by beta phase in Ti-8Al-1Mo-1V.

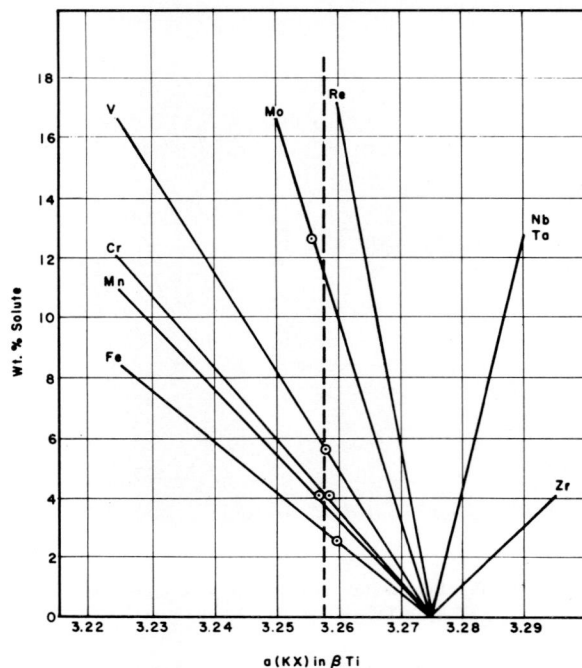

FIGURE 22 — β Ti solid solution lattice spacing.

TABLE 4—Stress Corrosion Limits for Binary Titanium Alloys

| Group | Element | Stress Corrosion Limit (% Element) | |
|-------|---------|:-----------:|:----------:|
| | | Greater Than | Less Than |
| II A | Beryllium | 1.0 | —- |
| III A | Boron | .5 | —- |
| | Aluminum | 3.0 | 4.0 |
| IV A | Carbon | 1.0 | — |
| | Silicon | 2.5 | 5.0 |
| | Tin | 3.0 | 5.0 |
| V A | Nitrogen | .2 | — |
| I B | Copper | —- | 1.0 |
| | Silver | — | 2.5 |
| IV B | Zirconium | 40.0 | 50.0 |
| | Hafnium | 10.0 | —- |
| V B | Vanadium | 4.0 | 5.0 |
| | Niobium | 10.0 | — |
| | Tantalum | 10.0 | —- |
| VI B | Chromium | 3.0 | 5.0 |
| | Molybdenum | 12.0 | 13.0 |
| | Tungsten | 2.5 | 5.0 |
| VII B | Manganese | —- | 5.0 |
| | Rhenium | 15.0 | — |
| VIII | Iron | 2.0 | 3.0 |
| | Cobalt | 5.0 | 7.5 |
| | Nickel | 2.5 | 5.0 |

very similar. Metallography of cracked specimens, however, revealed a difference in phase distribution as shown in Figures 20 and 21. Figure 20 shows a hot salt crack in sheet characterized by Curve A of Figure 19; this crack has propagated almost unimpeded. Figure 21 shows a crack in sheet characterized by Curve B. The beta phase, extended in the longitudinal sheet direction by rolling, is seen as lamellae parallel to the plane of the specimen and has blunted and stopped a hot salt crack propagating in the short transverse sheet direction. The impediment to crack propagation by these beta lamellae shown in Figure 21 could well account for the longer times necessary to form visible corrosion cracks in sheet material B.

Pure titanium is not susceptible to hot salt cracking. Susceptibility becomes a problem as the concentration of alloying elements exceeds critical limits. These limits have been determined using a very severe, qualitative stress corrosion test.[9] Various binary alloys were melted, broken down by hot rolling in the beta field and finished rolled in the alpha-beta field. The sheet was descaled by sandblasting and pickling and cut into specimens. The test specimen used was a 1/2-inch by 4-inch strip of alloy sheet restrained

## TABLE 5–Critical Concentrations for Ti-Zr Base Ternary Alloys

| Base | Critical Level, % Element More Than | Less Than | |
|------|------|------|------|
| Ti-5Zr | 2.5 | 5.0 | Co |
| Ti-5Zr | — | 0.5 | Cu |
| Ti-5Zr | 0.5 | 1.0 | Fe |
| Ti-2.5Zr | 2.5 | — | Si |
| Ti-5.0Zr | 2.5 | — | Si |
| Ti-10.0Zr | 0.5 | 1.0 | Si |
| Ti-2.5Zr | 2.5 | 5.0 | V |
| Ti-5.0Zr | 2.5 | 5.0 | W |

by a wire in a 180 degree 1/2-inch radius bend, such that the one edge was held in tension. These specimens were exposed at 427 C for 2 hours to free chlorine and air, each having a partial pressure of 1/3 atmosphere. The specimens were then examined for stress corrosion which was, in most cases, very apparent if it existed at all. The limits determined by these tests are shown in Table 4. Examination of this table shows that the critical limits vary widely for different elements. The absence of periodicity in these limits made the chemical nature of the solute an unlikely rationale. Consideration of the effect of solute addition on unit cell dimensions led to the most striking correlation. Figure 22 shows the expansion in beta lattice parameter[10] as a function of solute concentration for many of the elements studied. The circled points identify the concentrations at which each solute lends susceptibility to hot salt stress corrosion to the titanium base. These points fit well around a vertical line describing a lattice parameter of 3.258 kx. This would seem to indicate that a beta lattice contraction of about 0.5% is connected with susceptibility to hot salt cracking. It must be mentioned here that if the contraction correlation were universally valid, both silver and tin should produce alloys with high resistance to stress corrosion which is not the case. These anomalies are unexplained at this time.

The possibility of producing stress corrosion immune titanium alloys with large concentrations of zirconium as a solute made Ti-Zr bases attractive candidates for studying critical solute concentrations in ternary systems. Some of the concentration limits defined from testing of ternary alloys are shown in Table 5. Examination of this table with respect to binary limits defined in Table 4 shows that the effects are not additive but that complex interactions probably take place. These results on ternary alloys indicate that mapping of composition domains with respect to hot salt cracking susceptibility will be a tedious undertaking involving testing of each and every composition of possible interest.

## Summary

It is proposed that the observations discussed herein form bases for the following conclusions:

1. Susceptibility to low energy fracture in salt water varies widely with composition, and it is possible to find single phase cph and bcc alloys both susceptible and immune to this phenomenon.

2. In a given alloy, Ti-8Al-1Mo-1V, the degree of susceptibility to low energy fracture in salt water can be varied with heat treatment, either by changing long range order or by altering the physical distribution of the beta phase in a matrix devoid of long range order.

3. The propagation of hot salt cracks into Ti-8Al-1Mo-1V may be altered by the physical distribution of the beta phase.

4. The composition limits for hot salt stress corrosion immune binary alloys vary widely with solute and cannot be used to predict compositions for immune ternary or higher order alloys.

## References

1. Defense Metals Information Center, The Effects of Alloying Elements in Titanium, Report 136A, 106-109, September 5, 1960.
2. P. R. Swann. Corrosion, 19, 102t (1963).
3. D. Tromans and J. Nutting. Corrosion, 21, 143 (1965).
4. D. L. Douglas, G. Thomas, and W. R. Roser. Corrosion, 20, 15t.
5. A. J. Hatch, H. W. Rosenberg, and E. F. Erbin. Effects of Environment on Cracking in Titanium Alloys, ASTM STP 397, Stress Corrosion Cracking of Titanium.
6. M. J. Blackburn. Phase Transformations in the Alloy Ti-8Al-1Mo-1V, Boeing Scientific Research Laboratories, DI-82-0402, January, 1965.
7. E. V. Tiesenhausen. Electron Metallography of Ti-8Al-1Mo-1V in Various Conditions of Salt Water Susceptibility. Titanium Metals Corporation of America, Henderson Technical Laboratories, 48-22, No. 7.
8. R. E. Adams. Stress Corrosion in Commercial Alloys, Titanium Metals Corporation of America, Henderson Technical Laboratories, 48-20, No. 9.
9. H. D. Cox. Stress Corrosion Alloy Development, Titanium Metals Corporation of America, Henderson Technical Laboratories, 48-20, No. 4.
10. Defense Metals Information Center, The Effects of Alloying Elements in Titanium, Report 136A, September 16, 1960.

## Discussion

**G. Martin, North American Rockwell, Inc.:**

Some of our data on SCC cracking have shown the crack to be associated with micro-segregation, as revealed by electron microprobe studies. This has been reported in *Materials Protection,* 4, No. 8, p. 23 (1965). Have you made any similar studies or observations?

**R. E. Adams and E. von Tiesenhausen:**

We have attempted to use an electron microprobe to discover solute segregation which might account for the paths of observed cracks. To date we have not been successful. Our microprobe spot size is about 5 microns; we are aware that bands of segregation very much smaller than

5 microns in width would not be detected.

**M. J. Blackburn, Boeing Scientific Research Laboratory:**

I should like to make three comments:

1. Figures 7, 8, and 10 do not show planar groups of dislocations. Figure 8 appears to show sub-boundaries while Figures 8-10 contain regions of spontaneous transformations. Your conclusion is correct but you do not illustrate it.

2. Figure 11 is misleading as it does not take into account the thickness effect in duplex annealed Ti-8Al-1Mo-1V. Such material is susceptible in sheet $\sim$ 0.05 inch thick.

3. In designing for SCC resistance the conditions for hot salt SCC immunity are probably different than for aqueous SCC immunity. In the former one attempts to construct a structure in which the grain boundaries lie normal to the expected crack propagation direction. In the latter one attempts to produce a preferred orientation with the basal plane normal to the cracking direction. It may not prove possible to produce both structures at the same time.

**R. E. Adams and E. von Tiesenhausen:**

We will try to answer your comments in order. First, as pointed out in the text, Figure 10 is not supposed to show planar dislocation arrays. We agree that Figures 7 and 8 do show sub-grain boundaries. However, we think close inspection will also show planar dislocation arrays.

Secondly, we do not think Figure 11 is misleading. We do not contend that duplex annealed Ti-8Al-1Mo-1V alloys are resistant to salt water cracking in all thicknesses. We have merely stated that for 0.025 inch gage Ti-8Al-1Mo-1V sheet, a mill anneal results in very low energy fractures while a duplex anneal does not. This is certainly a change in degree of susceptibility to low energy fracture in salt water brought about by different heat treatments—while is all we intended to demonstrate.

We agree with your third and last comment. While the two quite separate phenomena of salt water and hot salt stress corrosion exhibit the similarities mentioned in this paper, they also exhibited many differences—one of which you have just mentioned.

**J. C. Williams, The Boeing Company:**

At first sight, your results on the high tin content alloy appear to conflict with general ideas regarding the influence of formation of ordered particles on susceptibility. It must be remembered, however, that the role of such ordered particles is to promote coplanar slip, and to do so, these particles must form homogeneously. Preliminary results from our laboratory show that the Ti:Sn system differs from the Ti:Al system in that $Ti_3Sn$ does not precipitate homogeneously. This may explain the differences between the influence of Sn and Al additions on scc susceptibility. It should also be noted, however, that an alloy containing roughly equal parts by weight of Sn and Al which total 12-13 atom percent can exhibit homogeneous precipitation of ordered particles, presumably $Ti_3(Al,Sn)$.

**R. E. Adams and E. von Tiesenhausen:**

We thank you for this comment. The inhomogeneous precipitation of $Ti_3Sn$ could possibly be the answer to the anomaly we mentioned earlier.

# PART VIII

# PANEL DISCUSSION

# PROCEEDINGS FROM PANEL DISCUSSION

Chairman
W. D. Robertson, Yale University

Members
T. P. Hoar, Cambridge University
P. Paris, Lehigh University
E. N. Pugh, Research Institute for Advanced Studies (Martin Company)
P. R. Swann, Imperial College
H. H. Uhlig, Massachusetts Institute of Technology

*A panel discussion was held Thursday evening September 14. Moderator of the session was Professor W. D. Robertson of Yale University. Members of the panel were Professor T. P. Hoar of Cambridge University in England, Dr. E. N. Pugh of the Research Institute for Advanced Studies, (Martin Company), Professor Paul Paris of Lehigh University, Dr. P. R. Swann of Imperial College in England and Professor H. H. Uhlig of The Massachusetts Institute of Technology.*

*The panel members were asked to consider three separate issues. Each member was given about three minutes to state his views on a particular issue and after each member had stated his views on this issue, the floor was open for discussion. The three issues considered were: (1) What can we say about our present capability for predicting the incidence of stress corrosion cracking? (2) What are the best kinds of experiments to evaluate susceptibility? (3) What directions should be taken in the future? The answers to these separate questions given by panel members will be noted by a superscript (1), (2), (3), respectively. Additional discussion by the panelists is not superscripted. Replies which were originally given orally have been edited by the various discussors and panel members. Most of the irrelevant material has been omitted.*

*In editing these discussions some attempt was made to preserve the informality of the presentations and subsequent discussion.*

**Chm. Robertson:**

These experts are here to answer your questions. They have already told me they will, however, not take any responsibility for the answers. As you know very well, you get exactly what you pay for.

It is appropriate to note the first law of corrosion which I have written on the blackboard which Dr. Hoar tells me is a law from Cambridge, "If material can get in the wrong environment, it will," and Dr. Hoar has a wonderful picture to prove this, which consists of a monstrous, great yellow brass fire hydrant, presumably in London, with a monstrous great corrosion crack down the side of it.

The agenda for the evening will be an attempt to turn the discussions of the last four days inside out. By inside out, I mean we have all been discussing the mechanism of corrosion, but somewhere along the line we are individually, and certainly all of us collectively, in the long run saddled with the responsibility to be able to tell a design engineer, "Look, you can do this. You mustn't do that." As a result of good judgement, hopefully, the thing will last the next twenty years. Depending on how old you are, you may or may not be dead at the time it blows up.

We will break discussions down into three parts. One will be predictability, and where this joins reliability is a little hard to say, but essentially we want to build a piece of apparatus today and we know only about ten percent of the answers to questions we should know to really do it properly. Nobody can wait until we get the other ninety percent of the answers, so we have to do the best we can today.

Secondly, we have to, after all, base our judgement on something or other. Therefore, we have to consider the significance of the tests we use to evaluate situations.

Finally, as a result of adding these two together, where do we go from here?

We will start with each of the five members of the panel giving very quickly (three minutes) his considered opinion, but that means considered between last night and this morning, on predictability.

In traditional fashion, I will start on my right with Professor Uhlig.

**H. H. Uhlig:**[1]

Predictability is a most desirable goal. We engage in a certain amount of prediction any time that we, for example, point out environments damaging to specific metals or alloys. Or when we recommend the use of a ferritic stainless steel over and above an austenitic stainless steel in a chloride environment. Or when we recommend avoiding brass where there is an obvious source of ammonia.

I recall a recent example of mistaken specification involving the use of brass bands around red cedar flower pots. Perhaps you have seen them for sale on the market. Of course, when someone adds an ammonia-containing fertilizer to the soil contained in such pots, the brass bands spring off by stress corrosion cracking.

I think predictability is going to improve only when we arrive at a better understanding of basic mechanisms. Otherwise I shall say right now that, in my opinion, there is very little we can do over and above what we are already doing.

**Chm. Robertson:**

Dr. Hoar, let us hear your considered opinion.

**T. P. Hoar:**[1]

I would say that predictability must be based on assessing the response to certain experiments. In particular, we have found in our studies of caustic cracking and nitrate cracking in mild steels, ammonia cracking of brass, and chloride cracking of stainless steels, that the straining electrode experiment is most revealing. Specifically, the specimen is allowed to reach the open circuit potential at which cracking occurs; that potential is then set on the potentiostat and the current recorded; the specimen is then pulled in traction at the constant potential and the current is measured again. If the ratio of straining to nonstraining current is less than 50, the alloy would be expected not to crack; if the ratio is greater than 50 it may be expected to crack with a fair degree of confidence. This procedure would enable one to assess a wide variety of alloy-environment systems.

**Chm. Robertson:**

Dr. Paris

**P. Paris:**[1]

I have tried to ask myself the question of why I am here because a little over a year ago I was certainly not in the field of stress corrosion, never had been, and I didn't have any idea that I ever would be. I think the reason is perhaps that there is something to be learned in the area of continuum mechanics which applies to stress corrosion cracking; when one has a crack, the stress conditions are changed. I think my comment on predictability would be that we have learned within the last two or three years a good deal about predictability for the case of pre-existing cracks and I think I will reserve my remarks for later when we discuss what should be done in the future.

**Chm. Robertson:**

Dr. Pugh

**E. N. Pugh:**[1]

In considering the question of predictability, I will assume that I have been asked if a given solid can be used safely in a certain environment. There is not sufficient time to carry out a test and there is no previous work in the literature on this system, so that I can be guided only by my existing knowledge of factors which promote stress corrosion susceptibility.

I would consider first the structure of the solid. On the basis of Dr. Graf's extensive studies, I would caution against the use of a homogeneous alloy containing a significant concentration of a more noble solute. From the literature on the cracking of Al alloys, notwithstanding the papers presented at this Conference, I would be hesitant to recommend an age-hardening system in which a precipitate-free zone is formed at the grain boundaries.

In considering the characteristics of the solid, I would *not* take dislocation structure into account. We have seen at this meeting that the presence of planar dislocation arrays is not necessary for cracking in either the brass-ammonia (E. N. Pugh, J. V. Craig and A. J. Sedriks, This Volume) or the austenitic stainless steel-aq. $MgCl_2$ systems (J. Bode and R. A. Dodd, This Volume). In the case of brass, the dislocation structure influenced the path of cracking in nontarnishing solutions; however in tarnishing solutions, the commercially important case, the path of failure was intercrystalline for alloys exhibiting cellular structures or planar dislocation configurations.

Further, from the discussion concerning the behavior of copper, I do not think it is safe to assume that pure metals are necessarily immune to stress corrosion cracking. The fact that some pure metals do not fail in certain environments, e.g., pure iron does not appear to fail in nitrate solutions (L. M. Long and H. H. Uhlig, *J. Electrochem. Soc., 112,* 964 1966), does not allow us to assume that all pure metals are immune. Such an assumption implies that a single generalized mechanism exists, which is by no means established.

Next consider the chemistry of the system. Being an advocate of the tarnish-rupture model, I would ask if thick oxide films form at the surface. If such films were formed then I would want to know whether they satisfy the conditions for the operation of the oxide-rupture model, namely that the oxide be epitaxed to the metal substrate, grows into the metal, and is brittle at the operating temperature. From our work at RIAS, I would be suspicious if stable complex ions are formed by dissolution of the solid in the environment. We have found that the formation of such ions is a prerequisite for cracking to occur in the brass-ammonia system [E. N. Pugh and A. R. C. Westwood, *Phil. Mag., 13,* 167 (1966); E. N. Pugh, W. G. Montague and A. R. C. Westwood, *Trans. ASM, 58,* 665 (1965)] and in the failure of the nonmetal silver chloride in various aqueous environments [A. R. C. Westwood, D. L. Goldheim and E. N. Pugh, *Phil. Mag., 15,* 105 (1967)]. At this meeting, Ronnquist has suggested that the adsorption of complex ions plays an important role in stress corrosion phenomena. Finally, if the solid were BCC or HCP, I would fear reactions which generate hydrogen; I do not at the present time feel cause for alarm if the material were FCC.

I should add that if all these danger signals were absent then I would still recommend that, at our present level of understanding, a stress corrosion test be carried out before the system is put into service.

**Chm. Robertson:**

Dr. Swann

**P. R. Swann:**[1]

Now I feel we should be honest and admit that none of us understands the mechanism of stress corrosion cracking and consequently we cannot predict how we should avoid it under all environmental conditions. However, on the basis of our present knowledge I would make a guess that we should seek an alloy whose protective surface film repairs itself so rapidly when ruptured by slip that corrosion tunnelling does not have time to develop.

**Chm. Robertson:**

The floor is now open for discussion, pot-shots at the panel, individually, collectively, however you like it.

**M. Garfinkle:**

I think one of the major problems is one of using proper terminology. For example, titanium-aluminum alloys are subject to so-called stress corrosion in methanol and in hot salt environments at 500 C and yet we give both phenomena the same name. It is like a physician or someone in the medical profession giving all the diseases that have a temperature rise the same name. Therefore, when you start looking for underlying principles, underlying data, unifying causes, you are pursuing folly. Corrosion under stress does not necessarily lead to stress corrosion. The reason will depend on different factors for different metal-environment systems.

**Chm. Robertson:**

Dr. Uhlig

**H. H. Uhlig:**

May I comment? These are the same sort of arguments that were bandied about when the electrochemical theory of corrosion was first proposed. Many comments ran along the lines: How can this possibly be true of all metals? How can differing metals be corroded by the same electrochemical mechanism? Some investigators suggested instead that corrosion must be a colloidal phenomenon. Others suggested that it must be a direct chemical reaction involving acids such as carbonic acid in rain water. But eventually it was agreed that the electrochemical mechanism underlies the corrosion of all metals, by and large. There are exceptions to the theory even today, but, essentially, the unifying principle it encompassed has proved to be correct.

Admittedly, titanium corrodes differently than does aluminum, and aluminum corrodes differently than does steel, but they all corrode nevertheless by the operation of galvanic cells.

What I tried to say in my lecture the other day is that I believe there is an underlying unifying mechanism (stress sorption cracking) by which all metals, and also nonmetals, are subject to environmental cracking. Compelling evidence for it exists, and it is well worth our while, in view of the practical consequences, to spend some time evaluating the evidence.

**T. P. Hoar:**

May I say a word?

**Chm. Robertson:**

Yes

**T. P. Hoar:**

I am not entirely in agreement with Professor Uhlig here.

I am rather inclined to think that there may be several important factors in the underlying mechanism of stress corrosion cracking, and some are important in certain systems and others are important in others. Also, I think the point Professor Uhlig takes that, after all, electrochemistry underlies all corrosion is possibly not quite right. There are certainly many forms of deterioration which are not electrochemical. In just the same way, I would think that there may be matters connected with stress corrosion cracking that have nothing to do with plastic yielding at the bottom of a crack, although I think many cases probably do have to deal with that.

Similarly, I think there may be many cases of stress corrosion cracking that are not electrochemical. For example, the crazing, as it is usually called, of certain plastic materials, when exposed to organic solvents is not electrochemical, but it is stress corrosion cracking.

**D. Sprowls:**

If one is interested seriously in improving the performance of material susceptibility to stress corrosion, then one has only one of two ways to go: modify the alloy so that it is immune from stress corrosion, or reduce the level of stress so that it is below this apparent threshold.

From a practical point of view, the vast bulk of stresses that persist are forming stresses. These stresses can be, for a modest effort, relieved by stress annealing treatment, just as 70-30 brass is relieved every day of the week and resists stress corrosion for a relatively modest price.

From the standpoint of predictability, it is only lack of attention to the literature on the part of the user that gets us into the stress corrosion problem.

I must also say that the mechanistic studies of stress corrosion cracking have been singularly sterile in leading into any concept which can be used to develop an alloy that can be used with high stresses. I think in part this is due to the fact that the factors which have been looked at, at least in part, are factors that cannot be controlled; only the factors of composition and structure can be controlled by the metallurgist.

**Chm. Robertson:**

Let me assume the prerogative of the Chairman and pose the problem in a way substantially similar to your own in this fashion:

The engineer does not ask what are the cohesive forces and the mechanism by which a material holds itself together. He asks us, or someone: What is the yield strength? What he really wants to know is what the maximum stress may be that it can safely—I emphasize safely and reliably—be applied to this material. It may be awful low. If this is the case, it is too bad. He has to design himself out of this in some other way.

What I am saying is that we should plot stress to failure against time and get endurance curves. Then we can say, "Okay, that is the best we can do at the moment," and begin to move this endurance limit up.

If I may add parenthetically, the first time I did a corrosion test, I found something that busted in ten seconds. I ran in to the director and said, "Look, it breaks." He said, "*&!! I don't want it to break. I want it not to."

**G. Martin:**

This conference has shown that almost all materials will stress corrode. Reducing the stress may be the simplest way out. A beautiful example in the Army recently occurred where cracking had begun because of erosion problems, they solved the erosion problem and now stress corrosion cracks are initiated by fatigue.

**T. P. Hoar:**

It seems to me that a lot of the pragmatic evidence is that most materials do not stress corrosion crack unless the operating stress at the bottom of the crack is very near to or just exceeds what we call the yield strength. I think if we are down to 90 percent of this yield strength (noting it is difficult to define in fcc metals) we shall usually not get stress corrosion cracking. This end can be achieved through design. This being so, then, it seems to me that we have a good chance of avoiding stress corrosion cracking if we can increase the Hooke's law portion of the stress strain curves.

**R. W. Staehle:**

We must be careful to note from Nielsen's and Pickering's work (see our literature review) that stresses from corrosion products can become significant and can add sufficiently to applied stresses to put the crack tip into the critical range of stress.

**E. H. Phelps:**

I would like to say we are somewhat naive to approach the problem of predictability as we have tonight. Frankly, a practical man doesn't approach practical problems with mechanistic studies. Sure, they give you a general background. They give you a feeling of the problem, but when it comes right down to brass tacks on a particular decision on this material, you do it on the basis, hopefully, of past experience and that is what a lot of you have just said. This is not really predictability. It is extrapolating past experience. If you don't have past experience, you try to work out some way to obtain the necessary engineering data. If it comes out in accord with the mechanistic ideas, this is fine, but sometimes it doesn't. Frankly, in my own personal experience, I think we are asking too much to say that we can, in the true sense of the word, take a new system and a new environment and predict what would happen.

**T. P. Hoar:**

I entirely agree.

**L. Graf:**

Concerning the specificity of the environment, I would like to emphasize that on alloys containing a noble metal component as solute all environments are "wrong." This means that all corrosive agents cause stress corrosion cracking unless the noble metal component dissolves as a complex ion. Here no specific corroding agents are required as has so far been widely assumed, because the cathodic areas on the crack walls, necessary for the marked electrochemical process in the cracks, are formed from the noble metal component remaining or redeposited on the alloy during the attack of the environment (see my paper).

On the other hand, in technical alloys without any noble component, a specificity of the environment does exist, because in these cases the cathodic areas on the crack walls must be formed from suitable corrosion products. Environments which do not yield appropriate corrosion product layers will not cause cracking: Thus, the basis for specificity of environments. I refer to brass where especially ammonia-containing corrodents cause stress corrosion cracking. In this case, during the proceeding of the corrosion process, $CuO/Cu_2O$ form and act as cathodes on the crack walls.

**M. Garfinkle:**

I want to point out that the problem of predictability is quite real. It is as simple as asking how we get ten years experience in five years. Thus, we must conduct mechanistic experiments.

**M. O. Speidel:**

If I were given a high strength alloy, no matter what it is based upon, and if I were asked whether this alloy might be susceptible to stress corrosion cracking, I would be worried if it contained precipitates which can be sheared by dislocations. And, if I were asked how to improve this alloy, I would say: "Change the precipitates so that they are by-passed by dislocations."

**Chm. Robertson:**

The next topic concerns test methods that we can employ to improve our knowledge of predictability.

**P. R. Swann:**[2]

I would like to discuss the role of dislocations in stress corrosion cracking. In particular, what can we determine about the cracking probability by looking at dislocation substructure?

Firstly, I would like to restrict my discussion to transgranular failure. Recent experimental work on such failures indicates that dislocations have a role not during their 'life' within the crystal but in their 'death' when they emerge at the surface to form slip steps. In this case two physical factors would seen to favor the nucleation of transgranular cracks, (a) coarse slip steps, (b) a high rate of growth of individual steps relative to the rate of film repair. The dislocation substructure can only give information about the former. In a crude way, the observed substructure gives an indication of the probable path of a stress corrosion crack but it does not give any information about the kinetics of crack propagation.

The progress of the crack is determined by an intimate mixture of physical and chemical processes and it is probable that the rate controlling process varies during crack propagation since both the physical and chemical conditions are also changing. With so many variables the task of predicting times to failure in susceptible alloys seems very formidable. On the other hand any information on the factors controlling the morphology of the corrosion reaction during crack propagation could give the vital clue needed to predict alloy-environment combinations which are immune to failure.

### E. N. Pugh:[2]

As I indicated earlier, I do not feel that our present knowledge permits us to predict susceptibility from the properties of the solid or the environment. Therefore the only means available to us is to carry out a stress corrosion test. In this regard, the test using precracked specimens seems to me to be the most reliable. The failure of titanium alloys in sea water clearly demonstrates this, for in that case tests using smooth test-pieces would not have indicated susceptibility. The degree to which this and other laboratory tests can be correlated with service behavior is another question and one which I am not qualified to discuss.

In mechanistic studies, the actual test method does not seem to me to be critical. The important thing is that we should understand our particular test method and the significance of what we are measuring. For example, constant load tests on smooth sheet specimens are useful in many respects, but tell us virtually nothing about the stress dependence of the stress corrosion process. The fracture mechanics approach is valuable in this respect since it permits us to define our stress conditions. However, I would like to add a note of caution concerning such tests. The use of precracked specimens does not necessarily eliminate the initiation period. For example, it does not eliminate the incubation period in those cases where the critical chemical species responsible for cracking are produced by dissolution of the test-piece. Thus it is evident that the fracture mechanics approach must be combined with a thorough knowledge of the chemistry of the system.

### Chm. Robertson:

Dr. Paris

### P. Paris:[2]

Rather than represent fracture mechanics, I think I would like to represent continuum mechanics of solids and comment that what one wishes to do when testing is to model something which is going to happen in the structure. Often structural failures which are supposedly unpredictable, are almost all caused by pre-existing flaws which make fracture mechanics important.

Now, in modeling, we pay very careful attention to factors such as electrochemical potential, pH, solution chemistry, and others which we control very carefully. When we say the stress in stress corrosion must have a role, someone would expect stress would be controlled carefully; and yet I find sitting and listening to papers at this conference and others that very often people pay little attention to stress and to its careful definition.

Now, I think when it does come down to predictability that if one looks at engineering problems across the board, one can argue on certain kinds of structures you can presume there is no crack and you have an initiation problem. However, I have been associated with high strength alloys in structures like aircraft where there are pre-existing cracks and they are going to grow under stress corrosion cracking. In order to assess this question, one must model that structure and fracture mechanics provides us with a tool for modeling pre-existing cracks. Making a reasonable mechanical model of the same stress conditions which exist in service, in one way or another enhances one's capability to predict.

### T. P. Hoar:[2]

I would agree very much that experiments in the laboratory in which fracture time is measured as the only indication of susceptibility are now a long way out of date. All of us who work in stress corrosion cracking have used time to fracture as a parameter, but we know that it consists at least of two parts: time of initiation and the time of propagation. The other parameter we have used, applied load, gives us no indication of the stress at the advancing edge of the crack.

Neither of these parameters (applied load and time) is really a parameter at all. It is a thing of no great interest from the point of view of fundamental mechanism or, I would suggest, from the point of view of practice for the engineer. For example, if I say the time to fracture of a particular alloy under my conditions in the laboratory is 32.5 hours, the engineer doesn't know whether the structure is going to last for three hours or 30,000 hours because the two situations are not related. Therefore, I think all the measurements of applied load and of consequent time to fracture gives us very little more than absolutely preliminary indication of whether the thing will crack or not. It doesn't give us any quantitative information at all, and people who have tried to make it quantitative have always fallen down. Consequently, I would like to make quantitative a simple sort of measurement which is not necessarily associated with the crack at all; the simplest and most accurate measurement I can make is one of current or current density which does seem to be associated with a number of cases of cracking as I have said earlier.

Consequently, any quantitative measurement I want to make will probably be an electrochemical one of current density, and the change of current density with time and the change of current density with stress. I would say, with reference to the fracture mechanics case, that an experiment done under constant strain rate without cracking is perhaps liable for a few seconds, at any rate, to be the measurement of something under a reasonably steady state condition.

### H. H. Uhlig:[2]

I believe there is something to be said for accelerated tests even though there are admitted hazards in using them.

The boiling 60 percent calcium nitrate, 3 percent ammonium nitrate solution is used as an accelerated test for the susceptibility of carbon steels. It was developed at the I. G. Farben-industrie on the basis that if a steel specimen subjected to this test lasted 200 hours, they could safely use the material for nitrate solutions in their plants without danger of cracking. I think that when one can get down to practical experience of this kind, the test has meaning. This is one example of an accelerated test that has proved useful to the chemical industry.

The magnesium chloride test, on the other hand, has proved useful in the evaluation of materials for chloride exposures. If a material withstands the magnesium chloride test for a reasonable number of hours (200-1000 hours), it will certainly withstand less severe conditions in practice for a longer period of time. Failure may be a matter of two years or three years, or perhaps five years, but at least one has an indication of whether the material can be used at all.

I would say with respect to stress level, that one should bear in mind that the precracked specimen is probably most useful for high strength materials, if I understand this test correctly. For low strength materials, if one uses a specimen stressed beyond the elastic limit and applies a constant flow stress by means of a spring load, the specimen surface is subject to all possible stress levels. If the specimen then withstands accelerated test conditions, one is justified, with some degree of confidence, in using that material in an engineering design under similar or related environmental conditions.

### Chm. Robertson:

The floor is now open for general discussion.

### A. R. C. Westwood:

I would like to comment on the need for doing experiments the results of which can be transferred directly across to the behavior of real structures in practical situations. Most of us in research laboratories are faced with a limited testing capacity, and therefore tend to use small specimens and endeavor to do short term tests. On the other hand, in a large structure, the crack tip may be a considerable (diffusion) distance away from the surfaces of the solid. Thus, because of differential diffusion rates, stagnation, etc., the "actual" chemical environment at the crack tip may be considerably different from its "apparent"

environment, namely the external environment. For this reason, the embrittlement behavior of a large structure containing a crack could be considerably different from that of a thin strip specimen, for which the environment has ready access to the crack tip. It follows that, where possible, parallel tests should be performed using specimens of considerably different dimensions, and explanations sought for any differences in behavior observed.

### T. P. Hoar:

I agree with that, but I say when Hines and I started work on this about fifteen years ago, we started on 26-gauge steel wires. Hines finally got up to three-eights inch cylinders. However, the results are substantially the same as for the wires.

### J. Kruger:

It seems to me that most stress corrosion experiments are interpreted without knowing the real conditions of the experiment. Are, for example, the potentials and pH's that are measured those at the base of the crack where the phenomenon is happening? Or do we know what are the real stresses at the base of the crack? Perhaps the application of the techniques used by those employing the concepts of fracture mechanics can answer this question in a more realistic way. Finally, the extrapolation of results obtained from the study of dislocation arrays in very thin foils may be not wholly warranted. Although we are usually not able to do better than we have done with the tools available, we should always bear in mind these limitations when interpreting results.

### N. A. Tiner:

We have been doing some work on the stress corrosion cracking of commercial beryllium metal by electron fractography techniques. If you fracture beryllium in air or in salt water, it fractures by cleavage. By producing etched pits on the fracture face and examining the shape of them, one can identify the direction of the cleavage planes. If a salt solution is applied on a metal surface, the chemical attack starts at certain nuclei, and progresses in the same direction as the cleavage takes place.

Now, if one conducts stress corrosion tests, first by exposing to salt solution for a certain period of time and letting the pits grow a certain amount, then applying a stress to break it, and second, by applying simultaneously the same stress and salt solution exposure, the fracture time is found to be the same in both cases.

These tests seem to indicate that commercial beryllium is not susceptible to stress corrosion cracking. I wonder if Dr. Hoar conducted tests with beryllium, and could verify these results by his potentiometric measurements technique?

### T. P. Hoar:

I think the only answer I can make is use the words of my famous countryman who was half American and who said, "Give us the tools and we will finish the job."

**M. J. Blackburn:**

I should like to ask two questions and then make an observation.

Firstly, has anyone tried to define the stress or strain criterion for stress corrosion cracking? This is apparently different in the various alloy systems that are susceptible. Little attention appears to be paid to this factor.

Secondly, is the velocity of cracking an important parameter in the analysis of SCC in a specific system? It is obviously an important design criterion in some applications, however, I suggest it is an important parameter in any model of SCC. For instance both Professor Uhlig and Dr. Hoar in their models are concerned with the mechanism of crack propagation. Surely they should try to explain quantitatively how fast a crack propagates yet there has been almost no kinetic data presented at this conference for them to explain.

Finally, I was impressed by the sharpness of a SCC crack when it propagates. In the films shown on Tuesday when the crack advances, which it appears to do discontinuously, it does so as a sharp crack. (Ed. Note: This was observed in the movie by Nielsen in cracking of stainless steel in boiling $MgCl_2$.) When it stops however, there is considerable plastic relaxation around it and the crack assumes a much blunter appearance. Thus it appears that the plastic flow process, i.e., movement of dislocation does not occur during a crack jump. This suggests that the decision to flow or crack is made very near the crack tip and there appear to be only two possible explanations: either the environment affects the production of dislocation at the crack surface, or something diffuses into the metal and inhibits dislocation production and/or motion. It is possible that at least some of the factors listed by Dr. Swann are indicative of this condition for the inhibition of dislocated motion.

**T. P. Hoar:**

The rate of propagation of most stress corrosion cracking is relatively rapid on the order of about a millimeter an hour, give or take a factor of ten, either way. In practice many failures occur after several thousand hours, certainly many hundred hours, and the major part of that time is the time to initiation. Therefore, I believe that we ought to study the initiation period before any cracking occurs at all, as well as study the much shorter period during crack propagation.

**P. Paris:**

Dr. Hoar has said that we should study initiation, and I would go back to my comment earlier that it depends on what sort of problem we are looking at. I think in the titanium alloys, as Dr. Blackburn has referred to, that the problem is very much one that the types of structures he would like to build out of the titanium alloys already will have cracks and he is very worried about how fast these cracks might grow. How can we create conditions so that the crack won't grow?

In fracture mechanics tests on stress corrosion cracking, we have found that in materials there are threshold levels not of stress itself, but of the combination of stress and crack sizes reflected by the stress intensity factor at the crack tip. Therefore, it is a combination of flaw size and stress level which we wish to avoid. Contrary to earlier comments which said we want to keep the stresses below a certain level, flaw size also is important here.

Now, I think there is another thing which Dr. Blackburn referred to, which is: What are the conditions for the crack to grow? Why in some cases does the crack get blunted and in other cases why does it grow rapidly from the tip? We have to consider both sides (from the metal as well as environment) of the picture. I think both Dr. Blackburn and I look inside the material most of all, he being a man who looks at structures and I like to look at the nice continuum. On the outside, we have the environment. There is an interaction between them. If one takes a simple-minded point of view that the environment destroys ability to carry stress in material which is highly stressed, one can say, "Then, the environment is degrading material all around the crack tip," and if it degrades it in such a way that it spreads the crack tip vertically, it makes another crack, or if it only attacks the very highly stressed material directly in front of the crack, then perhaps it makes the crack grow without being blunted.

I think studies of this nature are rather important. I would say that these fracture mechanics tests which have been run on titanium alloys by people at the Boeing Company are probably some of the most valuable things for quantitatively looking at the conditions themselves.

**J. C. Scully:**

I have a feeling that we are talking at cross purposes. There are two types of people who are interested in stress corrosion cracking. Firstly, there are engineers who want to build airplanes and submarines. They want to know the critical flaw or crack size that will propagate in a service environment. It is necessary to employ mathematical formulae to arrive at approximate answers but the basis of such calculations is not completely sound, since, for example $K_I$ and $K_{ISCC}$ are not related in titanium alloys [M. H. Peterson, B. F. Brown, R. L. Newbegin and R. E. Groover, *Corrosion,* **23**, 142 (1967)] and probably other structural materials as well. Secondly, there are laboratory scientists studying the fundamental mechanisms. They are concerned with the reactions between the metal at the tip of a crack and the environment there, including the timing [J. C. Scully, *Corrosion Sci.,* **7**, 197 (1967)] of such reactions. One function of this conference is to bring these two groups together for a useful exchange, because each can help the other. In this general context it is misleading to reject the U-bend test. It is very valuable in its limited way. The only objection, as with any test, is that more data should not be elicited from it than it can provide. We in Leeds University use it for a preliminary screening test and in order to obtain fractographic evidence. For these purposes it is perfectly adequate. Employing tests that are more elaborate does not, a priori, provide better data, particularly in the field of stress corrosion.

**Chm. Robertson:**

I think we are now on the topic of what we should be doing about improvement—what we can do to improve our predictability.

**H. H. Uhlig:**[3]

There are many things we could be doing, among which is to pay more attention to inhibitors. I think a great deal can be said for the use of a small amount of inhibitor in a damaging environment, as was practiced formerly, for example, by the American railroads. Small additions of nitrates to alkaline boiler waters effectively decreased the number of steam locomotives which failed by stress corrosion cracking. I think one could similarly use inhibitors in environments which otherwise cause cracking of titanium or stainless steels or aluminum alloys. There are many metal structures, of course, used under conditions where inhibitors are not feasible. You can't put an inhibitor in the ocean, for example, but you certainly can do so in chemical process solutions.

**T. P. Hoar:**[3]

I agree with what Professor Uhlig has said. I would be a bit more general. I think what is needed is good fundamental research in fundamental research laboratories, and it doesn't matter whether they are in universities or in large corporations. Very often in large corporations you find them being much more academic than the academies. Apart from that, this is absolutely necessary and we must get the money from somewhere.

We must obviously be much more cooperative and work together with the practical metallurgists and the practicing engineers. I am perfectly serious in saying there is not enough social contact between our various types of people who are interested in this subject.

**P. Paris:**[3]

I feel somewhat an outsider in this field. For that reason, I can look you all over and say, "These are stress corrosion cracking people," and say, "What really is the problem here?" One of the things which I see is that you all regard stress corrosion cracking as a very highly complex phenomenon, and all kinds of details here and there come out in the papers.

Now, I think from the point of view of what I would look for in research is to look for the simplest test, the overriding factors which allow us to generalize and categorize horizons and classify things. I think that there are different kinds of environmental cracking problems. Perhaps you would like to define stress corrosion cracking as something other than the hydrogen problem, and perhaps we can't mix the two; but I think in many cases there are similar features. They all have cracks. They all involve environmental factors. Let's look for the similarities in these things.

Now, one of the places where we discover great similarities are simply when we put a crack in something and then watch what happens when there is something as simple as water around it. I am quite surprised at the similarities in the cracking of glass and high strength steel in pure water.

I think we should look for more of that kind of research where we obtain carefully run data under a set of conditions where we can see those simplicities rather than making things more complicated than they really are.

**E. N. Pugh:**[3]

As you have probably gathered during this meeting, it is my opinion that there is no single, generalized theory of stress corrosion but that several mechanisms exist, each being operative in certain systems. Viewed in this light, it is difficult to make any general statement about the path of future research. Rather, let me discuss some of the specific systems which are of particular interest to me.

In the brass-ammonia system, the tarnish-rupture model in its current form [A. J. McEvily and A. P. Bond, *J. Electrochem. Soc.,* 112, 638 (1965); E. N. Pugh, J. V. Craig and A. J. Sedriks, This Volume] proposes that the rate of cracking is determined by the rate of growth of the tarnish. At the present time it is not possible to test this proposal, since there is no quantitative data available on the growth characteristics of the tarnish. This is clearly an area requiring attention. We at RIAS, in conjunction with Dr. Kruger of N.B.S., are approaching this by means of ellipsometry. It may also be necessary to use other techniques, e.g., cathodic reduction.

In the case of age-hardening aluminum alloys, a major point to be resolved concerns the role of the precipitate-free zones at grain boundaries. At this meeting, several authors [A. J. Jacobs; M. O. Spiedel] have suggested that the zones are unimportant in the failure of high strength alloys based on the Al-Zn-Mg system. However, the fact remains that the zones are present at grain boundaries in these alloys and stress corrosion cracking is intercrystalline. Frequently the fact that the zones are narrow in commercial alloys is considered to support the view that they play no role in stress corrosion failure. There is no basis for such a view, since it could be argued with equal justification that narrow zones promote stress corrosion susceptibility by confining preferential grain boundary deformation to a smaller volume. It seems to me that further work is necessary to correlate the width of the zone with susceptibility to stress corrosion cracking.

**P. R. Swann:**[3]

I agree with Dr. Hoar that there should be a lot more co-ordination between the various scientific approaches used to study stress corrosion cracking.

Stress corrosion has both physical and chemical aspects and we cannot hope to understand the phenomenon without pooling our knowledge from both these lines of investigation. For example, the physical studies indicate that the corrosion reaction at the crack tip may be confined to pores which are less than 200 atoms in diameter. This information should be considered in terms of the electrochemical reaction which must surely be influenced by this type of morphology. Similarly, one must ask what is the origin of corrosion tunnelling? Physical explanation such as

708

corrosion along grown-in dislocations are not supported by experimental observations. It is likely that there is a purely electrochemical explanation. We know that these corrosion tunnels can grow very rapidly—as fast as stress corrosion cracks in fact—yet only a few years ago we were saying that corrosion penetration would not proceed that rapidly and we incorporated stages of brittle failure into the stress corrosion mechanism in order to account for the cracking rate. Thus, in agreement with Roger Staehle I feel that a very useful area of research now would be firstly to reconsider the kinetics of corrosion reactions under conditions of restricted lateral dissolution and secondly to investigate the factors determining the formation of corrosion tunnels and crevices. This is the sort of fundamental information required to help us improve predictability.

From the practical standpoint it seems to me that predictability could also benefit from the introduction of a rapid stress corrosion test. It is possible that by studying the beginnings of stress corrosion crack propagation—by a replica technique for example—we may be able to decide in a short time whether or not a material will eventually crack. This test would allow us to study a much larger number of alloys under wider ranges of conditions and could enable us to recognize trends in stress corrosion behavior which would be easily missed in the more fundamental types of investigation.

### R. W. Staehle:

There are a number of very specific areas which should be investigated to illuminate processes occurring during stress corrosion cracking. These are as follows:

1. Electrochemical processes on heterogeneous materials. It is the essential nature of most engineering alloys to be heterogeneous. The situation at grain boundaries in aluminum alloys is a particularly good case. In close proximity are precipitates, denuded zones, and the metastable average bulk concentration. Data are needed for the kinetics of both the oxidation and reduction processes on each of these elements. Further, an analytical method for handling these heterogeneous processes is required.

2. Electrochemistry of crevice geometries. While there has been considerable talk of lowered pH inside advancing cracks, precipitation of corrosion products, and cathodic material on crack walls, we have yet to have satisfactory analytical solutions to handle electrochemical analysis within the restricted geometries of crevices and cracks. The best work in this area is currently being done by Ted Beck at Boeing and careful attention should be given to the outcome of this work.

3. Dissolution processes at solute enriched dislocations. There is great controversy in the literature concerning the role of dislocations in local dissolution which might be involved in crack initiation. The possibility of dissolution at dislocations will depend on the electrochemical potential and the chemical identity of the solute which is enriched.

4. Transient dissolution at emergent slip steps. When slip steps emerge, fresh metal is exposed and has been shown to dissolve rapidly. The amount of material which

dissolves will depend greatly on the nature of the environment.

5. Adsorption processes. Various ions appear to exert effects which suggest anodic inhibition due to adsorption blocking of dissolution sites. Much clearer descriptions of factors affecting dissolution processes are needed.

### A. R. C. Westwood:

On the basis of what is known at present, I do not believe that there is any one general and unifying mechanism for stress corrosion cracking. Nor do I believe that there are many mechanisms, but rather a limited number of principal mechanisms which will encompass the behavior of most important materials in a majority of environments. I also consider, with Professor Uhlig, that it is the responsibility of researchers not merely to study stress corrosion cracking, but also to devise ways of preventing this phenomenon. However, we are not going to be able to achieve the latter objective for any particular metal-environment system unless we have detailed information regarding the mechanism of cracking in that specific system. This brings us to the crux of the problem—that of knowing which system we are studying. It is most important that we make the effort to characterize the chemistry of the environment, and the chemical nature, structure and stress state of the material before beginning any experiments. With these reasonably under control, it should be possible to devise some critical experiment, or experiments, which will indicate which of the principal failure mechanisms is operative in the system under study.

It has become evident during this meeting, and is all too evident from the literature, that much of the stress corrosion work in progress at this time is insufficiently critical. The design of experiments is often poor, and many programs are begun without any working hypothesis in the hope that if sufficient data is gathered, the answer will become clear. Experience suggests that revelation does not occur in many instances.

I would suggest that, for the next few years at least, we stop investigating the behavior of complex industrial alloys, containing numerous elemental constituents, exposed to totally uncharacterized environments, if we expect to produce any useful understanding of the mechanisms of stress corrosion failure. What is required at this time are carefully designed experiments with well characterized systems which will allow discrimination between the several possible mechanisms of embrittlement for the system under study, and which will define (if relevant) the critical species in the environment which is causing premature failure. With such information at hand, it should then be possible to utilize well-established physical-chemical principles to choose appropriate inhibitors—either for addition to the solid or the environment—for the metal-environment system in question.

### M. Henthorne:

I think that this conference affords a good opportunity for discussing the merits of unified stress corrosion mechanisms as applied to specific systems. Some of the existing unified mechanisms are so different that it should not be too difficult (with the diverse scientific experience represented at this conference) to design critical experiments to prove or disprove some of them. With this in mind, I should like to consider one system—austenitic stainless steel in a chloride environment. Both the "Hoar Anodic Dissolution" and the "Uhlig Stress Sorption" mechanisms have been applied to this system. The former thrives on plastic deformation at the crack tip whereas the latter thrives on the lack of it. As a basis for discussing critical experiments, I should like to ask Dr. Hoar and Professor Uhlig whether they agree that one of these theories must be incorrect for a given system. The question does not concern which one (if either) is correct but merely whether one must be incorrect.

### T. P. Hoar

All I know is that I have found it possible to accelerate the rate of dissolution of straining material by a very significant factor. We have repeated this experiment many times and there is no doubt the effect occurs. Whether this is the critical factor in austenitic stainless steel cracking in chloride solution, I would hesitate to say. I think at the moment it probably is. On this particular aspects of stress sorption cracking, I don't understand it sufficiently well to pronounce on it.

### H. H. Uhlig:

With regard to the generalized adsorption mechanism of cracking, I can only say that as yet I have faith and hope in it rather than any conviction of its final demonstration. It promises to supply the underlying unifying mechanism that some of us are looking for, and for this reason I feel it deserves our further consideration.

Professor Paris hinted at this need and I support his remarks. I didn't coach him. I think we must always bear in mind that the fracture mechanism with which we are concerned occurs through environmental causes in non-metals as well as in metals.

There is good evidence for example that for austenitic stainless steels the stress sorption mechanism applies. Whether electrochemistry also enters is currently a relevant question. It may be that electrochemical reactions are necessary to produce metal complexes which then adsorb and induce subsequent fracture. As yet we don't know.

### Chm. Robertson:

Along those same lines, I would like to make this comment. I have been very much impressed during these four days with two things. The first three days I had the feeling the most sophisticated piece of apparatus that is being employed is the Instron testing machine. This proves not to be quite true. This problem divides itself into two parts. There is the engineering type of data that we need to get tomorrow morning to use tomorrow morning. It is not the last word. It won't answer all the questions. It will help the man who has to build that thing tomorrow.

On the other hand, we could make more use of the extremely sophisticated, extremely delicate, extremely sensitive apparatus and techniques being used and developed by the chemists, by the physicists and the electronics people. Almost anything we want to measure can be measured with pretty near any sensitivity you need today, if you know what you want to measure. I have a feeling that we are not using this kind of capability.

Of course, there is no point in taking sophisticated pieces of apparatus and asking them the wrong questions. They will give you the right answer if you ask the right question.

### R. C. Carlston:

Now for a word from our Sponsors. It is somewhat distressing to see the apparent lack of vision in providing research directions to solve the major corrosion problems. In the three years that I have been associated with the Metallurgy Branch of ONR my prime preoccupation has been on this very point: the present day contributors to corrosion science and engineering have not been able to keep ahead of the problems and provide a basis for confidence in their ability to adequately use the funds available for corrosion research. It is only due to the extreme need to get at least engineering solutions to the stress cracking problem in high strength alloys that funding is as high as it is. Since I am leaving the "Corridors of Power" spoken of by C. P. Snow, for the groves of academe, I can speak objectively and as one removed from the scene.

ONR contributes support to conferences such as this one in order to provide the extra additional burst of steam to get a field moving ahead. The Washington Corrosion Dialogue which we jointly sponsored with NBS and NRL was an attempt to spur good people into activity by pointing out the opportunities and shortcomings of the field. The shortcomings still seem to outweigh the opportunities. Since ONR's job is to bring Science to the Navy and Navy problems to the Scientific community, it implies some sort of dialogue. If the scientific value of a field is negligible, ONR is the wrong agency to be concerned with this dialogue, there are other organizations, such as the Naval Material Commands which should be concerned with dialogues in the engineering realm.

The competition for research funds is becoming more severe. Funds for corrosion can only be justified if there are obvious directions and personnel to use them. If funds for corrosion research dry up, researchers such as myself will research in other fields. Graduate students will select other professors or other departments. The fate of Schools of Mines in this country should be an object lesson to us.

Professor Staehle in his opening remarks provides considerable food for thought on the optimum direction of corrosion research. However these observations were generally directed towards steel.

What can we gather as fruitful directions in environmental fracture? Some thoughts that come to mind are:

1. Study of model systems with precipitation hardness and in which dislocation arrays are unchanging (no age hardening). Perhaps SAP aluminum alloys would be a good place to start.

2. Continued work on the ductility of metal oxides. This was discussed at the Washington Corrosion Dialogue and I feel represents a very fruitful area.

3. Role of alloy chemistry in controlling oxide properties. The data by Beck and Sperry presented here indicates major changes in oxide thickness near the precipitate-free zone. All the work on brass and titanium tarnish and on oxides on aluminum alloys that I am familiar with fails to indicate a direct role for the minor components.

4. Chemisorption on crack surfaces. In conventional surface chemistry studies powdered solids are required in order to measure the amount of adsorbed species. These measurements are valueless in quantitative SCC interpretations. Some of the work presented here is using radiographic techniques to look at adsorption should find wider application. The gas chromatograph should be used more to see if the hydrocarbons or alcohols crack on the fresh metal surface. The sensitivity should be high enough for this determination.

5. More attention to the physical chemistry of the electrolytes used in SCC tests. The new data by Streicher on the variations of boiling point of $MgCl_2$ solutions is amazing, as is the statement on the variations of pH's in commercial grades of $MgCl_2$. This is an intolerable situation if one wants to do research of some fundamental significance. The effect of the changing environment during a long SCC test should be clarified. More data on activity coefficients (which can be obtained from isopiestic measurements) should be available. If complex or ion pair species are important in SCC, then the observations of Westwood on the role of the cation should be taken into consideration. All in all our knowledge of the solution phase does not engender much confidence in the scientific basis of SCC tests.

One could go on, but these five areas are representative of key areas for attack.

**Chm. Robertson:**

Gentlemen, I think we have not beaten this subject to death by any means. I hope we have beaten it into some more life, but before we beat ourselves to death, I think we should get some lubrication and find out if this inhibitor, alcohol, has any value.

# AUTHOR'S INDEX
# SUBJECT INDEX

# AUTHORS INDEX

# DISCUSSION AUTHORS INDEX

# V

# W

## WATER

## WATER (Contd.)

# Y

# Y

# Z

## ZINC